C000128439

£95.00

Telecommunications Engineer's Reference Book

Edited by
Fraidoon Mazda
MPhil DFH DMS MIMgt CEng FIEE

With specialist contributions

Butterworth-Heinemann Ltd
Linacre House, Jordan Hill, Oxford OX2 8DP

 PART OF REED INTERNATIONAL BOOKS

OXFORD LONDON BOSTON
MUNICH NEW DELHI SINGAPORE SYDNEY
TOKYO TORONTO WELLINGTON

First published 1993

© Butterworth-Heinemann Ltd 1993

All rights reserved. No part of this publication
may be reproduced in any material form (including
photocopying or storing in any medium by electronic
means and whether or not transiently or incidentally
to some other use of this publication) without the
written permission of the copyright holder except in
accordance with the provisions of the Copyright,
Designs and Patents Act 1988 or under the terms of a
licence issued by the Copyright Licensing Agency Ltd,
90 Tottenham Court Road, London, England, W1P 9HE.
Applications for the copyright holder's written permission
to reproduce any part of this publication should be addressed
to the publishers

British Library Cataloguing in Publication Data
Mazda, Fraidoon F.
    Telecommunications engineer's reference book
    I. Title
    621.382

    ISBN 0 7506 1037 9

Library of Congress Cataloguing in Publication
Mazda, Fraidoon F.
    Telecommunications engineer's reference book/Fraidoon Mazda
    p. cm.
    Includes bibliographical references and index.
    ISBN 0 7506 1037 9
    1. Telecommunications. I. Title
    TK5101.M37 1993
    621.382–dc20   92–27846
                                                             CIP

Printed and bound in Great Britain

Contents

Contents

Contents

Foreword

Telecommunications is a prime industry, like electricity, water and gas and, like these industries, it impacts on every individual, organisation and country. Telecommunications is, however, much younger and as such it is more dynamic and vibrant. It is growing and changing at a phenomenal rate.

Politically, telecommunications is going through an exciting period. Old state owned monopolies are being privatised, and liberalisation has resulted in many new entrants. As organisations have become more multinational, so have these telecommunication operators.

Competition has quickened the pace of technology development. Copper is being rapidly replaced in the trunk network, including underseas, and is under threat in the local loop. The pace of fibre deployment is accelerating and wireless communications has provided personal mobility which was unpredictable two decades ago.

Telecommunications is an exciting business, so much so that it is easy to forget the most important consideration in every business; telecommunication only exists to serve the customer. What the customer desires is services which meet his requirements at prices which he considers to be good value.

Twenty years ago the services business was a niche industry on the edges of POTS. By 1990 the world market for value-added services was $17 billion, and by the year 2000 it will exceed $80 billion.

In Europe alone, the services market was $9 billion in 1991 and will exceed $30 billion by the year 2000 — almost 40% of the world market. In addition a European Commission paper estimates that by year 2000 over 60% of all EC employment will depend on telecoms based activity. However, a RACE study found that Europe's telecommunication operators currently gain only 5% of their revenues from specialised business services, compared with 20% in Japan and the US.

The aim of technology is to provide the customer with services. For example higher bandwidth, enabled by the use of synchronous transmission over optical fibre, will support a host of new applications, such as image and high speed data. Similarly intelligent networks will grow, the intelligence and functionality being moved closer and closer to the customer.

The trend in economics of networks will have a significant impact on customers as well as providers. So long as tariffs remain high, private networks will continue to grow. If, however, tariffs fall closer to costs, we will see increased demand for public network services. Here the experience of the US market is illustrative: of the 500+ US corporations that built private networks in the 1980s, 80–90% have since moved their voice traffic on to virtual networks, as the price of switched voice service has fallen.

The trends in customer needs, technology and regulation are combining to create an entirely new kind of network, with new controls and competitive forces to govern its operation. The characteristics of this network are fairly clear already.

First, in wideband access electronics will migrate much closer to the customer in the coming months and years, driven not only by technology but more importantly by demands for service responsiveness and lower operating costs. In many cases a fibre will terminate in the basement of the business building. Almost all large businesses and many medium and small locations will have direct access to a fibre based connection. This will lead to wideband access at up to 2 Mbits/s becoming widely available, with short provisioning times, in many markets by 1995. In addition, because fibre systems can easily transport tens of megabits of information, the network will be positioned to transmit at much higher speeds with marginal cost increases, as service demand arises.

Coupled with pan-European wireless networks, the economics of fibre access, for both narrowband and wideband, will shift dramatically, obsoleting today's tariff structures.

Access will become increasingly liberalised to give customers choice. A degree of regulation will remain, if only because of spectrum issues and because some national authorities believe it will guarantee future revenues.

Second, in the transport network, fibre systems are being installed that operate at speeds of up to 2.4 gigabits per second. This has dramatically lowered costs per bit of information carried. It has also changed network planning rules away from the traditional, point-to-point systems towards large, self-healing rings. These rings span many exchanges and are often interconnected, like the Olympic symbols, to cover complete cities. Rings not only dramatically increase the reliability of any service, but they also make it much easier to provision bandwidth services quickly, as any information entering a ring is immediately available to all other points in the ring.

The combination of low cost transport and easy access will enable a telecommunication operator to concentrate its switching at a smaller number of sites, leading to larger, more cost-effective switches. It will also make it easier to offer new services because a single service node, attached at one point on a ring, can provide service to anyone connected at any other point on the ring. This lowers the entry hurdles for new services by enabling ubiquitous access at a small incremental cost.

Some degree of control over the transport backbone will also persist, to avoid duplication of resources, to protect its integrity and to co-ordinate and set standards that allow us to move things across the total infrastructure.

But in the third area of services, the intelligent network we hear so much about today, the customer will demand and get totally unregulated competition.

How will this new technology platform evolve from today's network? We will see increased utilisation of wideband access.

Initially there will simply be more and smaller sites, but once connected experience has shown that data traffic, especially LAN to LAN interconnection, increases dramatically when all sites of a business can flexibly communicate with each other.

Next we will see interswitching of wideband service — once businesses can transparently connect at arbitrary rates, there will be an accelerated drive to switch data. Initially this will be between corporate locations, but soon after there will be a demand to connect with networks from other companies. These needs will be met by the addition of service nodes, for example a frame relay switch, as required at the most convenient points in the network.

Finally we will see the evolution to broadband. Since fibre will be used in both the access and transport networks, there will no longer be an inherent limitation to broadband service. Therefore, as the need surfaces, it will be possible to introduce broadband services,

in the form of B-ISDN, broadband video, or other services, by adding interfaces at the ends of the network and service nodes within the network.

Five hundred years ago a European voyage of discovery led to the opening of new markets and new worlds. Today the telecommunications world is embarking on a similar voyage, with even greater potentials. But on this voyage our pole star must be the needs of customers, for it is customers who create new wealth and prosperity. By doing so we will succeed in building a new economy — a networked economy — for the greater benefit of all.

Desmond F Hudson
President and Chief Executive
Northern Telecom Europe Ltd.

Preface

'Time and technology wait for no man.' So goes the old saying and this is certainly true in telecommunications where the past decade has seen technology advance at breakneck speed. Spurred on by international standardisation and the incentive of increased competition, changes have occurred which impact the environment of every individual both at home and in the work-place.

Against this background the task of producing a single volume which covers the whole field of telecommunications seems Herculean! How successful I have been in my particular labours only the reader can judge!

The book has been written by engineers for engineers. The prime readership is practising engineers within industry and research establishments. It will also be useful as a supplementary text for undergraduate courses in telecommunications.

The book aims to maintain a balance between new developments and established technology since, especially in telecommunications where investments are high, equipment installed in the network tends to have a relatively long life. The material is advanced, coverage under each topic being detailed.

The chapters are all self contained, in the format of a reference book, so the reader can be selective in the material he reads. A comprehensive contents list and index help in locating a particular topic. Overlap between chapters is kept to a minimum, although it has not been eliminated altogether in order to maintain continuity.

The book is structured into four parts. Part 1 introduces mathematical techniques which are required for the analysis of telecommunication systems, and which are used subsequently in other chapters of the book.

Part 2 deals with the physical environment of telecommunications. Basic principles are introduced, such as teletraffic theory; electromagnetic waves; optics and vision; sound, speech and hearing; the ionosphere and the troposphere; and signals and noise. Once again these principles are built on in subsequent chapters.

Part 3 covers fundamental telecommunication topics. Examples are the political and regulatory environment of the telecommunications industry; telecommunication standards; the open system interconnect reference model; multiple access techniques, which are used in a variety of telecommunication systems; network management; analogue and digital modulation; time division multiplexing; radio spectrum management; and digital transmission.

The final path describes telecommunication applications and represents the largest section of the book. The topics have been selected and grouped so as to cover all the major areas within telecommunications, spanning the field of transmission and switching, the transmission media being copper, fibre optic or wireless. Both the public and private networks are described. Some of the topics in this section are: synchronous digital hierarchy; asynchronous transfer mode; the integrated services digital network; switching systems; centrex; call management; voice processing; electronic data interchange; radio systems, such as paging, PMR, cellular, personal communication networks and microwaves; local and wide area networks; packet switching and fast packet switching; video transmission.

One of the problems of producing a book in a field which is changing rapidly is that the material can get out of date. In this I am grateful to the authors for working to a very tight schedule, to ensure that the time lag between the material being written and the publication of the book could be kept to a minimum.

The quality of the book is determined by the knowledge and presentation skills of its authors. The authors who have contributed to the Telecommunications Engineer's Reference book are all specialists in their fields, working in organisations that are in the forefront of the technology concerned. My thanks to them all for producing what, I am sure will be, a major reference book in telecommunications.

Fraidoon Mazda
Bishop's Stortford
February 1993

Acknowledgements

The production of this reference book would have been impossible without the good will, help and co-operation of the telecommunications industry, the users of telecommunication equipment and members of the academic profession. Bare acknowledgements are very inadequate but the editor wishes to thank the following firms and organisations which so readily made available information and illustrations and permitted members of their specialist staffs to write contributions:

AT&T EasyLink Services
Alcatel Bell Telephone
Anderson Consulting
Aston University
Bell Northern Research
British Aerospace
BT
Cellnet
Commission of the European Communities
Dowty Communications
ELMAC Services
Ericsson
Gandalf Digital Communications
GN Netcom
Hewlett-Packard

Hiltek
Hutchinson Microtel
IBA Engineering Division
ISICAD
Multitone Electronics
NEC
Newbridge Networks
Northern Telecom
Omincom Inc
Queen Mary and Westfield College
Radio Communications Agency
Reichle De Massari
Rockwell International
Rohde & Schwarz
Rutherford Appleton Laboratory
South Midlands Communications
Sprint International
TeleSciences Transmission Systems
Telindus
Trend Communications
University of Cambridge
University of Essex
Vodafone

List of Contributors

Malcolm Appleby, MA
Cellnet

Steve Berrisford
Northern Telecom

Paul W Bizzell
AT&T EasyLink Services

Richard A Boulter, BSc (Hons) CEng FIEE
BT

P A Bradley, BSc MSc CEng MIEE
Rutherford Appleton Laboratory

D G Bryan, DFH CEng FIEE
Telecommunications Consultant

J H Causebrook, BSC PhD CEng MIEE
Vodafone Ltd

Luc Ceuppens, Ind Ing
Telindus Ltd

G J Cook, BSc (Eng) CEng MIEE
BT plc

Ian Corbett, BSc CEng MIEE
BT Laboratories

Jim Costello
Telecommunications Consultant

David M Davidson
Northern Telecom

L M Davis
NEC (UK) Ltd

Paul Dyer
Northern Telecom

T J Egginton, BEng (Sheffield University)
Gandalf Digital Communications Ltd

Robert S Ferguson, BSc (Eng)
Independent Consultant

William J Fitzgerald
University of Cambridge

J E Flood, OBE DSc FInstP CEng FIEE
Aston University

Harold C Folts, BSEE MSSM
Omnicom Inc

J R Fox, MA (Cantab) MSc PhD MIEE CEng MSCTE
BT Laboratories

Jim Giacobazzi
TeleSciences Transmission Systems

R J Gibbens, MA, Dip Math Stat, PhD
University of Cambridge

Terry Goble
Northern Telecom Europe

R V Goodman, CEng MIEE
Broadcasting and Telecommunications Engineering Consultant

David Green
Rohde & Schwarz

Takis Hadjifotiou
Bell Northern Research

Fred Harrison, BSc CEng MIEE
Cellnet

Pat Hawker
Formerly IBA Engineering Division

D R Heath, BSc PhD CPhys MInstP
British Aerospace

Graham Hewitt
ISICAD (UK) Ltd

Mike Hillyard, BSc (Eng) CEng MIEE
BNR Europe Ltd

Mark Holker, CEng FIEE MBIM
Hiltek Ltd

J Hoolan
Dowty Communications Ltd

John Holdsworth
Newbridge Networks Ltd

P J Howard
Telecommunications Consultant

Fred Howett
Northern Telecom

Steve Hurst, BSc CEng
Bell Northern Research

David L Jeanes
Bell Northern Research

Edwin V Jones, BSc MSc PhD CEng MIEE
University of Essex

Kanagendra, BTec MBA CDipAF
Northern Telecom Europe

A C Keene, BSc CEng MIEE
Trend Communications Ltd

Derek Kingaby, BTech CEng
Reichle De Massari (UK) Ltd

J A Lane, DSc CEng FIEE FInstP
Radio Communications Agency

Gary Law, BSc PhD
Anderson Consulting

David Lockstone
Bell Northern Research

C Lorek, BSc (Hons) AMIEE
South Midlands Communications Ltd

M D Macleod, MA PhD MIEEE
University of Cambridge

P J Marnick, BSc (Hons) CEng MIEE
Hutchinson Microtel Ltd

Mark Matthews
Northern Telecom Europe

Fraidoon Mazda, MPhil DFH DMS MBIM CEng FIEE
Northern Telecom

John McFarlane
Northern Telecom

S A Mohamed, BSc MSc PhD CEng MIEE
BT Laboratories

K L Moran, BSc (Hons) CEng MIEE
Sprint International

D G Morrison, MA
BT Laboratories

Richard J Mumford, CEng MIEE
Multitone Electronics plc

Clive R Nightingale, Dip.EE CEng FIEE
Formerly Chief Power and Building Services Engineer (BT)

Malcolm A Nugent
GN Netcom (UK) Ltd

Jean R Oliphant
Rockwell International

Professor A D Olver, BSc PhD CEng FIEE FIEEE
Queen Mary and Westfield College

S C Pascall, BSc PhD CEng MIEE
Commission of the European Communities

K Jell Persson
Ericsson Ltd

M Smouts
Alcatel Bell Telephone

John Price
Northern Telecom Europe

J P Russell
Trend Communications Ltd

R G Russell, BSc (Hons) CEng MIEE
Hutchinson Microtel Ltd

Michael J Simmonds
Telindus Ltd

Eur Ing S F Smith, BSc (Eng) CEng FIEE
Northern Telecom Europe

Carolyn Story, BSc (Hons)
Bell Northern Research

R S Swain, CEng MIEE
BT Laboratories

Michael Talbot-Smith, BSc CPhys MInstP
Independent Consultant

Hugh Walker, BA (Cantab) MSc
Hewlett-Packard Ltd

Samuel Welch, OBE MSc (Eng) CEng FIEE
Telecommunications Consultant
Formerly Head of Signalling, BT

Phil Whiting
University of Cambridge

Hubert A J Whyte
Newbridge Networks Ltd

Tim Williams, BSc CEng MIEE
ELMAC Services

David J Withers, CEng FIEE
Telecommunications Consultant

1 Statistical analysis

Fraidoon Mazda
MPhil DFH DMS MBIM CEng FIEE
Northern Telecom

Contents

1.1 Introduction

Data are available in vast quantities in all areas of telecommunications. This chapter describes the more commonly used techniques for presenting and manipulating data to obtain meaningful results.

1.2 Data presentation

Probably the most common method used to present data is by tables and graphs. For impact, or to convey information quickly, pictograms and bar charts may be used. Pie charts are useful in showing the different proportions of a unit.

A strata graph shows how the total is split amongst its constituents. For example, Figure 1.1 shows that the total revenue ob-

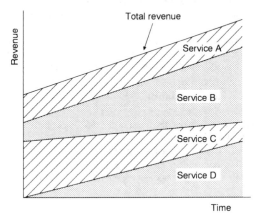

Figure 1.1   Illustration of a strata graph

tained by a PTO steadily increases with time, but that only services B and D have growth, whilst service C is reducing and may eventually become unprofitable.

Logarithmic or ratio graphs are used when one is more interested in the change in the ratios of numbers rather than their absolute value. In the logarithmic graph, equal ratios represent equal distances.

Frequency distributions are conveniently represented by a histogram as in Figure 1.2. This shows the number of people using a given service, banded according to age group. There are very few users below 20 years and above 55 years, the most popular ages being 35 to 40 years. This information will allow the service provider to target its advertising more effectively.

In a histogram, the areas of the rectangles represent the frequencies in the different groups. Ogives, illustrated in Figure 1.3, show the cumulative frequency occurrences above or below a given value. From this curve it is possible to read off the total number of users above or below a specific age.

1.3 Averages

1.3.1 Arithmetic mean

The arithmetic mean of n numbers x_1, x_2, x_3, ..., x_n is given by Equation 1.1 which is written as in Equation 1.2.

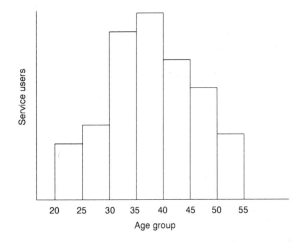

Figure 1.2   A histogram

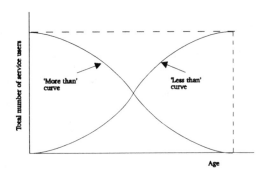

Figure 1.3   Illustration of ogives

$$\bar{x} = \frac{x_1 + x_2 + x_3 + ... + x_n}{n} \tag{1.1}$$

$$\bar{x} = \frac{\sum\limits_{r=1}^{n} x_r}{n} \tag{1.2}$$

The arithmetic mean is easy to calculate and it takes into account all the figures. Its disadvantages are that it is influenced unduly by extreme values and the final result may not be a whole number, which can be absurd at times, e.g. a mean of 2.5 men.

1.3.2 Median and mode

Median or 'middle one' is found by placing all the figures in order and choosing the one in the middle or, if there are an even number of items, the mean of the two central numbers. It is a useful technique for finding the average of items which cannot be expressed in figures, e.g. shades of a colour. It is also not influenced by extreme values. However, the median is not representative of all the figures.

The mode is the most 'fashionable' item, that is, the one which appears the most frequently.

1.3.3 Geometric mean

The geometric mean of n numbers x_1, x_2, x_3, ..., x_n is given by Equation 1.3.

$$x_g = \left(x_1 \times x_2 \times x_3 \times .... \times x_n \right)^{1/n} \qquad (1.3)$$

This technique is used to find the average of quantities which follow a geometric progression or exponential law, such as rates of changes. Its advantage is that it takes into account all the numbers, but is not unduly influenced by extreme values.

1.3.4 Harmonic mean

The harmonic mean of n numbers x_1, x_2, x_3, ..., x_n is given by Equation 1.4.

$$x_h = \frac{n}{\sum\limits_{r=1}^{n} \frac{1}{x_r}} \qquad (1.4)$$

This averaging method is used when dealing with rates or speeds or prices. As a rule when considering items such as A per B, if the figures are for equal As then the harmonic mean is used, but if they are for equal Bs then the arithmetic mean is used. So if a plane flies over three equal distances at speeds of 5m/s, 10m/s and 15m/s the mean speed is given by the harmonic mean as in expression 1.5.

$$\frac{3}{\frac{1}{5} + \frac{1}{10} + \frac{1}{15}} = 8.18 \text{m/s} \qquad (1.5)$$

If however, the plane were to fly for three equal times, of say, 20 seconds at speeds of 5m/s, 10m/s and 15m/s, then the mean speed would be given by the arithmetic mean as in expression 1.6.

$$\frac{5 + 10 + 15}{3} = 10 \text{m/s} \qquad (1.6)$$

1.4 Dispersion from the average

1.4.1 Range and quartiles

The average represents the central figure of a series of numbers or items. It does not give any indication of the spread of the figures in the series from the average. Therefore measurements of errors made on two circuits A and B may result in the curves shown in Figure 1.4. Both circuits have the same calculated average errors, but circuit B has a wider deviation from the average than circuit A and at the top end its errors may be unacceptably high.

There are several ways of stating by how much the individual numbers in the series differ from the average. The range is the difference between the smallest and largest values. The series can also be divided into four quartiles and the dispersion stated as the

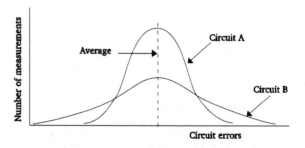

Figure 1.4 Illustration of deviation from the average

interquartile range, which is the difference between the first and third quartile numbers, or the quartile deviation which is half this value.

The quartile deviation is easy to use and is not influenced by extreme values. However, it gives no indication of distribution between quartiles and covers only half the values in a series.

1.4.2 Mean deviation

This is found by taking the mean of the differences between each individual number in the series and the arithmetic mean, or median, of the series. Negative signs are ignored.

For a series of n numbers x_1, x_2, x_3, ..., x_n having an arithmetic mean of $\bar{x}$ the mean deviation of the series is given by Equation 1.7.

$$\frac{\sum\limits_{r=1}^{n} |x_r - \bar{x}|}{n} \qquad (1.7)$$

The mean deviation takes into account all the items in the series but it is not very suitable since it ignores signs.

1.4.3 Standard deviation

This is the most common measure of dispersion. For this the arithmetic mean must be used and not the median. It is calculated by squaring deviations from the mean, so eliminating their sign, adding the numbers together, taking their mean and then the square root of the mean. Therefore, for the series of n numbers as above, the standard deviation is given by Equation 1.8.

$$\sigma = \left(\frac{\sum\limits_{r+1}^{n} (x_r - \bar{x})^2}{n} \right)^{1/2} \qquad (1.8)$$

The unit of the standard deviation is that of the original series. So if the tariff charged is in dollars for a given service, by different PTOs, then the mean and the standard deviation are in dollars.

To compare two series which have different units, such as the cost of a service and the quality of that service, the coefficient of variation is used, which is unitless, as in Equation 1.9.

$$Coefficient\ of\ variation = \frac{\sigma}{\bar{x}} \times 100 \qquad (1.9)$$

1.5 Skewness

The distribution shown in Figure 1.4 is symmetrical since the mean, median and mode all coincide. Figure 1.5 shows a skewed distribution with positive skewness. If the distribution bulges the other way, the skewness is said to be negative.

There are several mathematical ways for expressing skewness. They all give a measure of the deviation between the mean, median

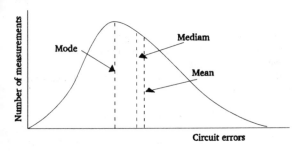

Figure 1.5 Illustration of skewness

and mode and they are usually stated in relative terms for ease of comparison between series of different units. The Pearson coefficient of skewness is given by Equation 1.10.

$$P_k = \frac{mean - mode}{standard\ deviation} \tag{1.10}$$

Since the mode is sometimes difficult to measure this can also be stated as in Equation 1.11.

$$P_k = \frac{3\ (mean - median)}{standard\ deviation} \tag{1.11}$$

1.6 Combinations and permutations

1.6.1 Combinations

Combinations are the number of ways in which a proportion can be chosen from a group. Therefore the number of ways in which two letters can be chosen from a group of four letters A, B, C, D is equal to 6 i.e. AB, AC, AD, BC, BD, CD. This is written as in expression 1.12.

$$^4C_2 = 6 \tag{1.12}$$

The factorial expansion is frequently used in combination calculations where factorial n is written as in expression 1.13.

$$n! = n \times (n - 1) \times (n - 2) \times .... \times 3 \times 2 \times 1 \tag{1.13}$$

Using this the number of combinations of r times from a group of n is given by Equation 1.14.

$$^nC_r = \frac{n!}{r!\ (n - r)!} \tag{1.14}$$

1.6.2 Permutations

Combinations do not indicate any sequencing. When sequencing within each combination is involved, the result is known as a permutation. Therefore the number of permutations of two letters out of four letters A, B, C, D is 12, i.e. AB, BA, AC, CA, AD, DA, BC, CB, BD, DB, CD, DC. The number of permutations of r items from a group of n is given by Equation 1.15.

$$^nP_r = \frac{n!}{(n - r)!} \tag{1.15}$$

1.7 Regression and correlation

1.7.1 Regression

Regression is a method for establishing a mathematical relationship between two variables. Several equations may be used to determine this relationship, the most common being that of a straight line. Figure 1.6 shows the number of defective public telephones which were reported at seven instances in time. This is called a scatter diagram. The points can be seen to lie approximately on the straight line AB.

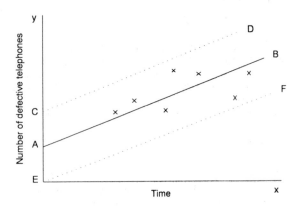

Figure 1.6 A scatter diagram

The equation of a straight line is given by Equation 1.16, where x is the independent variable, y the dependent variable, m the slope of the line and c its intercept on the y axis.

$$y = mx + c \tag{1.16}$$

c is negative if the line intercepts the y axis on its negative part and m is negative if the line slopes the other way to that shown in Figure 1.6.

The best straight line to fit a set of points is found by the method of least squares as in Equations 1.17 and 1.18, where n is the number of points. The line passes through the mean values of x and y, i.e. $\bar{x}$ and $\bar{y}$.

$$m = \frac{\sum xy - \frac{\sum x \sum y}{n}}{\sum x^2 - \frac{(\sum x)^2}{n}} \tag{1.17}$$

$$c = \frac{\sum x \sum xy - \sum y \sum x^2}{(\sum x)^2 - n \sum x^2} \tag{1.18}$$

1.7.2 Correlation

Correlation is a technique for establishing the strength of the relationship between variables. In Figure 1.6 the individual figures are scattered on either side of a straight line and although one can approximate them by a straight line it may be required to establish if there is correlation between the reading on the x and y axis.

Several correlation coefficients exist. The product moment correlation coefficient (r) is given by Equation 1.19 or 1.20.

$$r = \frac{\sum (x - \bar{x})(y - \bar{y})}{n \, \sigma_x \, \sigma_y} \tag{1.19}$$

$$r = \frac{\sum (x - \bar{x})(y - \bar{y})}{\left(\sum (x - \bar{x})^2 \sum (y - \bar{y})^2 \right)^{1/2}} \tag{1.20}$$

The value of r varies from +1, when all the points lie on a straight line and the number of defects increase with time to −1, when all the points lie on a straight line but defects decreases with time. When r = 0 the points are widely scattered and there is said to be no correlation between the x and y values.

The standard error of estimation in r is given by Equation 1.21.

$$S_y = \sigma_y (1 - r^2)^{1/2} \tag{1.21}$$

In about 95% of cases, the actual values will lie within plus or minus twice the standard error of estimated values given by the regression equation. This is shown by lines CD and EF in Figure 1.6. Almost all the values will be within plus or minus three times the standard error of estimated values.

It should be noted that σ_y is the variability of the y values, whereas S_y is a measure of the variability of the y values as they differ from the regression which exists between x and y. If there is no regression then r = 0 and $\sigma_y = S_y$.

It is often necessary to draw conclusions from the order in which items are ranked. For example, two customers may rank the styling of a telephone and we need to know if there is any correlation between their rankings. This may be done by using the Rank correlation coefficient (R) given by Equation 1.22, where d is the difference between the two ranks for each item and n is the number of items.

$$R = 1 - \frac{6 \sum d^2}{n^3 - n} \tag{1.22}$$

The value of R will vary from +1 when the two ranks are identical to −1 when they are exactly reversed.

1.8 Probability

If an event A occurs n times out of a total of m cases then the probability of occurrence is stated to be as in Equation 1.23.

$$P(A) = \frac{n}{m} \tag{1.23}$$

Probability varies between 0 and 1. If P(A) is the probability of occurrence then $1 - P(A)$ is the probability that event A will not occur and it can be written as $P(\bar{A})$.

If A and B are two events then the probability that either may occur is given by Equation 1.24.

$$P(A \, or \, B) = P(A) + P(B) - P(A \, and \, B) \tag{1.24}$$

A special case of this probability law is when events are mutually exclusive, i.e. the occurrence of one event prevents the other from happening. Then Equation 1.25 is obtained.

$$P(A \, or \, B) = P(A) + P(B) \tag{1.25}$$

If A and B are two events then the probability that they may occur together is given by Equation 1.26 or 1.27.

$$P(A \, and \, B) = P(A) \times P(B|A) \tag{1.26}$$

$$P(A \, and \, B) = P(B) \times P(A|B) \tag{1.27}$$

P(B|A) is the probability that event B will occur assuming that event A has already occurred and P(A|B) is the probability that event A will occur assuming that event B has already occurred. A special case of this probability law is when A and B are independent events, i.e. the occurrence of one event has no influence on the probability of the other event occurring. Then Equation 1.28 is obtained.

$$P(A \, and \, B) = P(A) \times P(B) \tag{1.28}$$

Bayes' theorem on probability may be stated as in Equation 1.29.

$$P(A|B) = \frac{P(A)P(B|A)}{P(A)P(B|A) + P(\bar{A})P(B|\bar{A})} \tag{1.29}$$

As an example of the use of Bayes' theorem suppose that a company discovers that 80% of those who bought its multiplexers in a year had been on the company's training course. 30% of those who bought a competitor's multiplexers had also been on the same training course. During that year the company had 20% of the multiplexer market share. The company wishes to know what percentage of buyers actually went on its training course, in order to discover the effectiveness of this course.

If B denotes that a person bought the company's product and T that he went on the training course then the problem is to find P(B|T). From the data P(B) = 0.2, $P(\bar{B})$ = 0.8. Then from Equation 1.29 expression 1.30 is obtained.

$$P(B|T) = \frac{0.2 \times 0.8}{0.2 \times 0.8 + 0.8 \times 0.3} = 0.4 \tag{1.30}$$

1.9 Probability distributions

There are several mathematical formulae with well defined characteristics and these are known as probability distributions. If a problem can be made to fit one of these distributions then its solution is simplified. Distributions can be discrete, when the characteristic can only take certain specific values, such as 0, 1, 2, etc., or they can be continuous, where the characteristic can take any value.

1.9.1 Binomial distribution

The binomial probability distribution is given by Equation 1.31.

$$(p+q)^n = q^n + {}^nC_1 p q^{n-1} + {}^nC_2 p^2 q^{n-2}$$
$$+ .... + {}^nC_x p^x q^{n-x} + ... + p^n \qquad (1.31)$$

p is the probability of an event occurring, q (=1 − p) is the probability of an event not occurring and n is the number of selections.

The probability of an event occurring m successive times is given by the binomial distribution as in Equation 1.32.

$$p(m) = {}^nC_m p^m q^{n-m} \qquad (1.32)$$

The binomial distribution is used for discrete events and is applicable if the probability of occurrence p of an event is constant on each trial. The mean of the distribution B(M) and the standard deviation B(S) are given by Equations 1.33 and 1.34.

$$B(M) = np \qquad (1.33)$$

$$B(S) = (npq)^{1/2} \qquad (1.34)$$

1.9.2 Poisson distribution

The Poisson distribution is used for discrete events and, like the binomial distribution, it applies to mutually independent events. It is used in cases where p and q cannot both be defined. For example, one can state the number of times a telephone circuit failed over a given period of time, but not the number of times when it did not fail.

The Poisson distribution may be considered to be the limiting case of the binomial when n is large and p is small. The probability of an event occurring m successive times is given by the Poisson distribution as in Equation 1.35.

$$p(m) = (np)^m \frac{e^{-np}}{m!} \qquad (1.35)$$

The mean P(M) and standard deviation P(S) of the Poisson distribution are given by Equations 1.36 and 1.37.

$$P(M) = np \qquad (1.36)$$

$$P(S) = (np)^{1/2} \qquad (1.37)$$

Poisson probability calculations can be done by the use of probability charts as shown in Figure 1.7. This shows the probability that

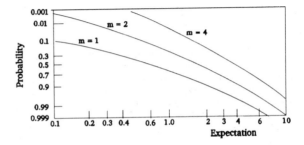

Figure 1.7 Poisson probability paper

an event will occur at least m times when the mean (or expected) value np is known.

1.9.3 Normal distribution

The normal distribution represents continuous events and is shown plotted in Figure 1.8. The x axis gives the event (for example telephone line failure) and the y axis the probability of the event occurring. The curve shows that most of the events occur close to the mean value and this is usually the case in nature. The normal curve is given by Equation 1.38, where $\bar{x}$ is the mean of the values making up the curve and σ is their standard deviation.

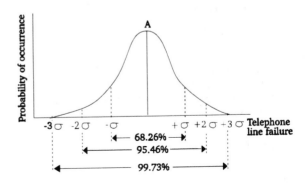

Figure 1.8 The normal curve

$$y = \frac{1}{\sigma (2\pi)^{1/2}} \exp\left(\frac{-(x-\bar{x})^2}{2\sigma^2} \right) \qquad (1.38)$$

Different distributions will have varying mean and standard deviations but if they are distributed normally their curves will all follow Equation 1.38. These distributions can be normalised to a standard form by moving the origin of their normal curve to their mean value, shown as B in Figure 1.8. The deviation from the mean is now represented on a new scale of units given by Equation 1.39.

$$\omega = \frac{x - \bar{x}}{\sigma} \qquad (1.39)$$

The standardised normal curve now becomes as in Equation 1.40.

$$y = \frac{1}{(2\pi)^{1/2}} \exp\left(\frac{-\omega^2}{2}\right) \qquad (1.40)$$

The total area under the standardised normal curve is unity and the area between any two values of ω is the probability of an item from the distribution falling between these values. The normal curve extends infinitely in either direction but 68.26% of its values (area) fall between $\pm\,\sigma$, 95.46% between $\pm\,2\sigma$, 99.73% between $\pm\,3\sigma$ and 99.994% between $\pm\,4\sigma$.

Table 1.1 gives the area under the normal curve for different values of ω. Since the normal curve is symmetrical, the area from $+\,\omega$ to $+\,\infty$ is the same as from $-\,\omega$ to $-\,\infty$. As an example of the use of this table, suppose that 5000 telephones have been installed in a city and that they have a mean life of 1000 weeks with a standard deviation of 100 weeks. How many telephones will fail in the first 800 weeks? From Equation 1.39, expression 1.41 is obtained.

$$\omega = \frac{(800 - 1000)}{100} = -2 \qquad (1.41)$$

Ignoring the negative sign, Table 1.1 gives the probability of telephones not failing as 0.977 so that the probability of failure is 1 − 0.977 or 0.023. Therefore 5000 x 0.023 or 115 telephones are expected to fail after 800 weeks.

1.9.4 Exponential distribution

The exponential probability distribution is a continuous distribution and is shown in Figure 1.9. It has the form given in Equation 1.42, where $\bar{x}$ is the mean of the distribution.

$$y = \frac{1}{x} \exp\left(\frac{-x}{\bar{x}}\right) \qquad (1.42)$$

Whereas in the normal distribution the mean value divides the population in half, for the exponential distribution 36.8% of the population is above the average and 63.2% below the average. Table 1.2 shows the area under the exponential curve for different values of the ratio $K = x/\bar{x}$, this area being shown shaded in Figure 1.9.

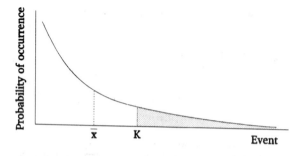

Figure 1.9 The exponential curve

As an example suppose that the time between failures of a piece of equipment is found to vary exponentially. If results indicate that the mean time between failures is 1000 weeks, then what is the probability that the equipment will work for 700 weeks or more without a failure? Calculating K as 700/1000 = 0.7 then from Table

Table 1.1 Area under the normal curve from $-\infty$ to ω

ω	0.00	0.02	0.04	0.06	0.08
0.0	0.500	0.508	0.516	0.524	0.532
0.1	0.540	0.548	0.556	0.564	0.571
0.2	0.579	0.587	0.595	0.603	0.610
0.3	0.618	0.626	0.633	0.640	0.648
0.4	0.655	0.663	0.670	0.677	0.684
0.5	0.692	0.700	0.705	0.712	0.719
0.6	0.726	0.732	0.739	0.745	0.752
0.7	0.758	0.764	0.770	0.776	0.782
0.8	0.788	0.794	0.800	0.805	0.811
0.9	0.816	0.821	0.826	0.832	0.837
1.0	0.841	0.846	0.851	0.855	0.860
1.1	0.864	0.869	0.873	0.877	0.881
1.2	0.885	0.889	0.893	0.896	0.900
1.3	0.903	0.907	0.910	0.913	0.916
1.4	0.919	0.922	0.925	0.928	0.931
1.5	0.933	0.936	0.938	0.941	0.943
1.6	0.945	0.947	0.950	0.952	0.954
1.7	0.955	0.957	0.959	0.961	0.963
1.8	0.964	0.966	0.967	0.969	0.970
1.9	0.971	0.973	0.974	0.975	0.976
2.0	0.977	0.978	0.979	0.980	0.981
2.1	0.982	0.983	0.984	0.985	0.985
2.2	0.986	0.987	0.988	0.988	0.989
2.3	0.989	0.990	0.990	0.991	0.991
2.4	0.992	0.992	0.993	0.993	0.993
2.5	0.994	0.994	0.995	0.995	0.995
2.6	0.995	0.996	0.996	0.996	0.996
2.7	0.997	0.997	0.997	0.997	0.997
2.8	0.997	0.998	0.998	0.998	0.998
2.9	0.998	0.998	0.998	0.998	0.999
3.0	0.999	0.999	0.999	0.999	0.999

1.2 the area beyond 0.7 is 0.497 which is the probability that the equipment will still be working after 700 weeks.

1.9.5 Weibull distribution

This is a continuous probability distribution and is given by Equation 1.43, where α is called the scale factor, β the shape factor and γ the location factor.

$$y = \alpha\beta(x - \gamma)^{\beta-1} \exp\left(-\alpha(x - \gamma)^{\beta}\right) \qquad (1.43)$$

Table 1.2   Area under the exponential curve from K to +∞

K	0.00	0.02	0.04	0.06	0.08
0.0	1.000	0.980	0.961	0.942	0.923
0.1	0.905	0.886	0.869	0.852	0.835
0.2	0.819	0.803	0.787	0.771	0.776
0.3	0.741	0.726	0.712	0.698	0.684
0.4	0.670	0.657	0.644	0.631	0.619
0.5	0.607	0.595	0.583	0.571	0.560
0.6	0.549	0.538	0.527	0.517	0.507
0.7	0.497	0.487	0.477	0.468	0.458
0.8	0.449	0.440	0.432	0.423	0.415
0.9	0.407	0.399	0.391	0.383	0.375

The shape of the Weibull curve varies depending on the value of its factors. β is the most important, as shown in Figure 1.10, and the Weibull curve varies from an exponential ($\beta = 1.0$) to a normal distribution ($\beta = 3.5$). In practice β varies from about $\frac{1}{3}$ to 5. Because the Weibull distribution can be made to fit a variety of different sets of data, it is popularly used for probability distributions.

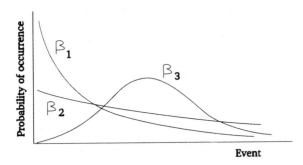

Figure 1.10   Weibull curves ($\alpha = 1$)

Analytical calculations using the Weibull distribution are cumbersome. Usually predictions are made using Weibull probability paper. The data are plotted on this paper and the probability predictions read from the graph.

1.10   Sampling

A sample consists of a relatively small number of items drawn from a much larger population. This sample is analysed for certain attributes and it is then assumed that these attributes apply to the total population, within a certain tolerance of error.

Sampling is usually associated with the normal probability distribution and, based on this distribution, the errors which arise due to sampling can be estimated. Suppose a sample of n_s items is taken from a population of n_p items which are distributed normally. If the sample is found to have a mean of μ_s with a standard deviation of

σ_s, then the mean μ_p of the population can be estimated to be within a certain tolerance of μ_s. It is given by Equation 1.44.

$$\mu_p = \mu_s \pm \frac{\gamma \, \sigma_s}{\sqrt{n_s}} \tag{1.44}$$

γ is found from the normal curve depending on the level of confidence we need in specifying μ_p. For $\gamma = 1$ this level is 68.26%, for $\gamma = 2$ it is 95.46% and for $\gamma = 3$ it is 99.73%.

The standard error of mean σ_c is often defined as in Equation 1.45.

$$\sigma_c = \frac{\sigma_s}{\sqrt{n_s}} \tag{1.45}$$

Therefore Equation 1.44 can be re-written as in Equation 1.46.

$$\mu_p = \mu_s \pm \gamma \sigma_c \tag{1.46}$$

As an example suppose that a sample of 100 items, selected at random from a much larger population, gives their mean weight as 20kg with a standard deviation of 100g. The standard error of the mean is therefore $100/(100)^{1/2} = 10$g and one can say with 99.73% confidence that the mean value of the population lies between 20 $\pm$ 3 × 0.01 or 20.03kg and 19.97kg.

If in a sample of n_s items the probability of occurrence of a particular attribute is p_s, then the standard error of probability p_e is defined as in Equation 1.47, where $q_s = 1 - p_s$.

$$p_c = \left(\frac{p_s q_s}{n_s} \right)^{1/2} \tag{1.47}$$

The probability of occurrence of the attribute in the population is then given by Equation 1.48, where γ is again chosen to cover a certain confidence level.

$$P_p = P_s \pm \gamma P_c \tag{1.48}$$

As an example suppose a sample of 500 items shows that 50 are defective. Then the probability of occurrence of the defect in the sample is 50/500 = 0.1. The standard error of probability is $(0.1 \times 0.9/500)^{1/2}$ or 0.0134. Therefore one can state with 95.46% confidence that the population from which the sample was drawn has a defect probability of 0.1 $\pm$ 2 × 0.0134, i.e. 0.0732 to 0.1268; or one can state with 99.73% confidence that this value will lie between 0.1 $\pm$3 × 0.0134, i.e. 0.0598 to 0.1402.

If two samples have been taken from the same population and these give standard deviations of σ_{s1} and σ_{s2} for sample sizes of n_{s1} and n_{s2} then Equation 1.45 can be modified to give the standard error of the difference between means as in Equation 1.49.

$$\sigma_{dc} = \left(\frac{\sigma_{s1}^2}{n_{s1}} + \frac{\sigma_{s2}^2}{n_{s2}} \right)^{1/2} \tag{1.49}$$

Similarly Equation 1.47 can be modified to give the standard error of the difference between probabilities of two samples from the same population as in Equation 1.50.

$$p_{dc} = \left(\frac{p_{s1} q_{s1}}{n_{s1}} + \frac{p_{s2} q_{s2}}{n_{s2}} \right)^{1/2} \qquad (1.50)$$

1.11 Tests of significance

In taking samples one often obtains results which deviate from the expected. Tests of significance are then used to determine if this deviation is real or if it could have arisen due to sampling error.

1.11.1 Hypothesis testing

In this system a hypothesis is set up and is then tested at a given confidence level. For example, suppose a coin is tossed 100 times and it comes up heads 60 times. Is the coin biased or is it likely that this falls within a reasonable sampling error? The hypothesis is set up that the coin is not biased. Therefore one would expect that the probability of heads is 0.5, i.e. $p_s = 0.5$. The probability of tails, q_s is also 0.5. Using Equation 1.47 the standard error of probability is given by Equation 1.51.

$$p_c = \left(\frac{0.5 \times 0.5}{100} \right)^{1/2} = 0.05 \qquad (1.51)$$

Therefore from Equation 1.48 the population probability at the 95.45% confidence level of getting heads is $0.5 + 2 \times 0.05 = 0.6$. Therefore it is highly likely that the coin is not biased and the results are due to sampling error.

The results of any significance test are not conclusive. For example, is 95.45% too high a confidence level to require? The higher the confidence level the greater the risk of rejecting a true hypothesis, and the lower the level the greater the risk of accepting a false hypothesis.

Suppose now that a sample of 100 items of production shows that five are defective. A second sample of 100 items is taken from the same production a few months later and gives two defectives. Does this show that the production quality is improving? Using Equation 1.50 the standard error of the difference between probabilities is given by expression 1.52.

$$\left(\frac{0.05 \times 0.95}{100} + \frac{0.02 \times 0.98}{100} \right)^{1/2} = 0.0259 \qquad (1.52)$$

This is less than twice the difference between the two probabilities, i.e. $0.05 - 0.02 = 0.03$, therefore the difference is very likely to have arisen due to sampling error and it does not necessarily indicate an improvement in quality.

1.11.2 Chi-square test

This is written as χ^2. If O is an observed result and E is the expected result then Equation 1.53 is obtained.

$$\chi^2 = \sum \frac{(O - E)^2}{E} \qquad (1.53)$$

The χ^2 distribution is given by tables such as Table 1.3, from which the probability can be determined. The number of degrees of freedom is the number of classes whose frequency can be assigned

independently. If the data are presented in the form of a table having V vertical columns and H horizontal rows then the degrees of freedom are usually found as in Equation 1.54.

$$\text{Degrees of freedom} = (V - 1)(H - 1) \qquad (1.54)$$

Returning to the earlier example, suppose a coin is tossed 100 times and it comes up heads 60 times and tails 40 times. Is the coin biased? The expected values for heads and tails are 50 each so that expression 1.55 is obtained.

$$\chi^2 = \frac{(60 - 50)^2}{50} + \frac{(40 - 50)^2}{50} = 4 \qquad (1.55)$$

The number of degrees of freedom is one since once we have fixed the frequency for heads that for tails is defined. Therefore entering Table 1.3 with one degree of freedom the probability level for $\chi^2 = 4$ is seen to be above 2.5% i.e. there is a strong probability that the difference in the two results arose by chance and the coin is not biased.

As a further example suppose that over a 24 hour period the average number of accidents which occur in a factory is seen to be

Table 1.3 The Chi-square distribution

Degrees of freedom	Probability level				
	0.100	0.050	0.025	0.010	0.005
1	2.71	3.84	5.02	6.63	7.88
2	4.61	5.99	7.38	9.21	10.60
3	6.25	7.81	9.35	11.34	12.84
4	7.78	9.49	11.14	13.28	14.86
5	9.24	11.07	12.83	15.09	16.75
6	10.64	12.59	14.45	16.81	18.55
7	12.02	14.07	16.01	18.48	20.28
8	13.36	15.51	17.53	20.09	21.96
9	14.68	16.92	19.02	21.67	23.59
10	15.99	18.31	20.48	23.21	25.19
12	18.55	21.03	23.34	26.22	28.30
14	21.06	23.68	26.12	29.14	31.32
16	23.54	26.30	28.85	32.00	34.27
18	25.99	28.87	31.53	34.81	37.16
20	28.41	31.41	34.17	37.57	40.00
30	40.26	43.77	46.98	50.89	53.67
40	51.81	55.76	59.34	63.69	66.77

as in Table 1.4. Does this indicate that most of the accidents occur during the late night and early morning periods? Applying the χ^2 tests the expected value, if there was no difference between the time periods, would be the mean of the number of accidents, i.e. 5. Therefore from Equation 1.53, expression 1.56 is obtained.

Table 1.4 The Chi-square distribution

Time (24 hour clock)	Number of accidents
0–6	9
6–12	3
12–18	2
18–24	6

$$\chi^2 = \frac{(9-5)^2}{5} + \frac{(3-5)^2}{5} + \frac{(2-5)^2}{5} + \frac{(6-5)^2}{5} = 6 \qquad (1.56)$$

There are three degrees of freedom, therefore from Table 1.3 the probability of occurrence of the result shown in Table 1.4 is seen to be greater than 10%. The conclusion would be that although there is a trend, as yet there are not enough data to show if this trend is significant or not. For example, if the number of accidents were each three times as large, i.e. 27, 9, 6, 18 respectively, then χ^2 would be calculated as 20.67 and from Table 1.3 it is seen that the results are highly significant since there is a very low probability, less than 0.5%, that it can arise by chance.

1.11.3 Significance of correlation

The significance of the product moment correlation coefficient of Equations 1.19 or 1.20 can be tested at any confidence level by means of the standard error of estimation given by Equation 1.21. An alternative method is to use the Student t test of significance. This is given by Equation 1.57, where r is the correlation coefficient and n the number of items.

$$t = \frac{r(n-2)^{1/2}}{(1-r^2)^{1/2}} \qquad (1.57)$$

Tables are then used, similar to Table 1.3, which give the probability level for $(n-2)$ degrees of freedom.

The Student t for the rank correlation coefficient is given by Equation 1.58, and the same Student t tables are used to check the significance of R.

$$t = R\left(\frac{n-2}{1-R^2}\right)^{1/2} \qquad (1.58)$$

1.12 Bibliography

Besterfield, D.H. (1979) *Quality control*, Prentice Hall.

Caplen, R.H. (1982) *A Practical approach to quality control*, Business Books.

Chalk, G.O. and Stick, A.W. (1975) *Statistics for the engineer*, Butterworths.

Cohen, S.S. (1988) *Practical statistics*, Edward Arnold.

David, H.A. (1981) *Order statistics*, Wiley.

Dudewicz, E.J. and Mishra, S.N. (1988) *Modern mathematical statistics*, Wiley.

Dunn, R.A. and Ramsing, K.D. (1981) *Management science, a practical approach to decision making*, Macmillan.

Fitzsimmons, J.A. (1982) *Service operations management*, McGraw-Hill.

Grant, E.I. and Leavenworth, R.S. (1980) *Statistical quality control*, McGraw-Hill.

Hahn, W.C. (1979) *Modern statistical methods*, Butterworths.

Jones, M.E.M. (1988) *Statistics*, Schofield & Sims.

Mazda, F.F. (1979) *Quantitative techniques in business*, Gee & Co.

Siegel, A.F. (1988) *Statistics and data analysis*, Wiley.

Taylor, W.J. and Watling T.F. (1985) *The basic arts of management*, Business Books.

2   Fourier analysis

William J Fitzgerald
University of Cambridge

Contents

2.1 Introduction

This chapter considers Fourier analysis and associated transform methods for both discrete-time and continuous-time signals and systems. Fourier methods are based on using real or complex sinusoids as basis functions, and they allow signals to be represented in terms of sums of sinusoidal components.

Euler and d'Alembert showed that the wave equation (Equation 2.1.) could be satisfied by any well-behaved function of the variable $x + ct$ or $x - ct$, i.e. Equation 2.2.

$$\frac{\partial^2 \Phi}{\partial x^2} = \frac{1}{c^2} \frac{\partial^2 \Phi}{\partial t^2} \qquad (2.1)$$

$$\Phi(x,t) = f(x + ct) + g(x - ct) \qquad (2.2)$$

Boundary conditions, of course, impose restrictions on the functions f and g, but apart from these restrictions the functions f and g are completely arbitrary. This result started a long controversy, since it had been shown by Daniel Bernoulli (1727), that the solution to the wave equation could also be represented as a superposition of sinusoidal components. If the solution obtained by Bernoulli was as general as that of Euler and d'Alembert, it follows that an arbitrary function can be represented as a superposition of sinusoidal components. Euler had difficulty accepting this, and it was Jean-Baptiste Fourier (1768-1830) whose work 'Memoire sur la Chaleur' expounded the method now known as Fourier analysis and eventually showed the above equivalence.

It is of fundamental importance in both linear systems theory, and signal processing in general, that the input and/or output signals of interest can be represented as linear combinations of simple basis functions, and the Fourier series representation is one such method that allows the signals of interest to be decomposed into harmonic components using a sinusoidal basis. This is clearly of interest if one is considering the spectral composition of signals, and in this area, Fourier analysis and the Fourier transform are used widely.

It should be realised that the Fourier representation is just one of many possible representations, and the choice of the signal representation will be determined by the particular nature of the problem under investigation.

Suppose that we have a function f(t) that we wish to represent on a finite interval (t_1, t_2), where t can obviously represent time, space or any other dimension relevant to our problem, in terms of a set of a basis functions $\psi_1(t), \psi_2(t), \dots \psi_n(t)$. We will assume that these functions are orthogonal on the region of support (t_1, t_2), i.e. Equation 2.3.

$$\int_{t_1}^{t_2} \psi_i(t) \psi_j(t) \, dt = 0 \qquad (2.3)$$

We will use the notation $< \psi_i | \psi_j >$ to denote the integral above. The idea of orthogonality expressed above, is the same as that applied to vectors and vector spaces, and our representation of f(t) in terms of the functions $\psi_i(t)$, $i = 1, 2, \dots, n$ is equivalent to representing a vector f in terms of an orthogonal set of vectors that span the space containing f.

We will assume that the representation of f(t) can be written as a linear combination of the basis functions $\psi_i(t)$ as in Equation 2.4.

$$f(t) = \sum_{i=1}^{n} c_i \psi_i(t) \qquad (2.4)$$

This will, in general, be in error since it is only a representation of the function f(t), and we will require that the representation should be as close as possible to f(t). Many measures of closeness exist, but a common measure is the mean squared error (MSE). We therefore require that the coefficients c_i, $i = 1, 2, \dots n$ are chosen to minimise its value in Equation 2.5.

$$MSE = \frac{1}{t_2 - t_1} \int_{t_1}^{t_2} \left[f(t) - \sum_{i=1}^{n} c_i \psi_i(t) \right]^2 dt \qquad (2.5)$$

This expression is the mean squared error averaged over the interval (t_1, t_2). Defining the functions in Equations 2.6 and 2.7, then the expression for the mean square error above can be written as in Equation 2.8.

$$\alpha_i = \int_{t_1}^{t_2} f(t) \psi_i(t) \, dt = <f | \psi_i> \qquad (2.6)$$

$$\beta_i = \int_{t_1}^{t_2} \psi_i^2 \, dt = <\psi_i | \psi_i> \qquad (2.7)$$

$$MSE = \frac{1}{t_2 - t_1} \left[\int_{t_1}^{t_2} f(t)^2 \, dt + c_1^2 \beta_1 + c_2^2 \beta_1 + \dots \right.$$
$$\left. + c_n^2 \beta_n - 2c_1 \alpha_1 - 2c_2 \alpha_2 - \dots - 2c_n \alpha_n \right] \qquad (2.8)$$

Using the identity of Equation 2.9 the expression for the mean squared error can be written as in Equation 2.10.

$$c_i^2 \beta_i - 2c_i \alpha_i = \left(c_i \sqrt{\beta_i} - \frac{\alpha_i}{\sqrt{\beta_i}} \right)^2 - \frac{\alpha_i^2}{\beta_i} \qquad (2.9)$$

$$MSE = \frac{1}{t_2 - t_1} \left[\int_{t_1}^{t_2} f(t)^2 \, dt \right.$$
$$\left. + \sum_{i=1}^{n} \left(c_i \sqrt{\beta_i} - \frac{\alpha_i}{\sqrt{\beta_i}} \right)^2 - \sum_{i=1}^{n} \frac{\alpha_i^2}{\beta_i} \right] \qquad (2.10)$$

From the form of this expression, it is clear that the MSE is always greater than or equal to zero, since it is the sum of squared terms, and that it achieves its least value when the middle term above is zero, i.e. as in Equation 2.11.

$$c_i = \frac{\alpha_i}{\beta_i} = \frac{<f | \psi_i>}{<\psi_i | \psi_i>} \qquad (2.11)$$

Therefore, the best approximation of an arbitrary signal or function f(t), in the mean squared error sense, over the region of support (t_1, t_2), that can be represented as a linear superposition of orthogonal basis functions, is achieved by choosing the coefficients c_i according to the above expression, which is the normalised projection of the function in the direction of the basis function ψ_i.

As is clear from above, when the coefficients c_i are chosen using the above criterion, the mean squared error is simply the averaged difference between two terms, and this difference can be made as small as one likes by including more and more terms in the summation term. Thus in the limit, the mean squared error is zero when Equation 2.12 is satisfied.

$$\int_{t_1}^{t_2} f(t)^2 \, dt = \sum_{i=1}^{\infty} c_i^2 \int_{t_1}^{t_2} \psi_i^2 \, dt \qquad (2.12)$$

If this relationship holds, then the infinite sum of the weighted basis functions is said to converge in the mean to f(t), an equality known as Parseval's relation, and if it holds for all f(t) of a certain class, then the set $\psi_i(t)$ is said to be complete for that class of functions.

If the basis functions are complex valued functions of a real argument t, orthogonality is defined as in Equation 2.13 where ψ_j^* is the complex conjugate of ψ_j and the generalised Fourier coefficients are given by Equation 2.14.

$$< \psi_i | \psi_j^* > = \int_{t_1}^{t_2} \psi_i \psi_j^* \, dt = 1 \; or \; 0 \qquad (2.13)$$

$$c_i = \frac{< f | \psi_i >}{< \psi_i | \psi_i >} \qquad (2.14)$$

If $< \psi_i | \psi_i > = 1$, the set ψ_i is called an orthonormal set of basis functions.

For example, the trigonometric system of functions with period 2π forms an orthogonal set over the region $(-\pi, \pi)$ and it can be shown that the following forms an orthonormal set over this region:

$$\frac{1}{\sqrt{2\pi}}, \frac{1}{\sqrt{\pi}} \sin(t), \frac{1}{\sqrt{\pi}} \cos(t), \ldots, \frac{1}{\sqrt{\pi}} \sin(nt), \frac{1}{\sqrt{\pi}} \cos(nt), \ldots$$

Clearly, other orthonormal sets or trigonometric functions can be defined over other intervals, e.g. for the interval $(0, \pi)$, the set

$$\left[\sqrt{\frac{2}{\pi}} \sin(nt) \right]_{n=1}^{\infty}$$

is orthonormal.

If ψ_i is an orthonormal set, the generalised Fourier coefficients for the representation of a function f, are given by Equation 2.15 and as an example, we can consider the orthonormal trigonometric system of period 2π for which Equation 2.16 to 2.20 are satisfied, for (k=2,3,...).

$$c_n = < f | \psi_n > \qquad (2.15)$$

$$c_o = \frac{1}{\sqrt{2\pi}} \int_{-\pi}^{\pi} f(t) \, dt \qquad (2.16)$$

$$c_1 = \frac{1}{\sqrt{\pi}} \int_{-\pi}^{\pi} f(t) \sin(t) \, dt \qquad (2.17)$$

$$c_2 = \frac{1}{\sqrt{\pi}} \int_{-\pi}^{\pi} f(t) \cos(t) \, dt \qquad (2.18)$$

$$c_{2k-1} = \frac{1}{\sqrt{\pi}} \int_{-\pi}^{\pi} f(t) \sin(kt) \, dt \qquad (2.19)$$

$$c_{2k} = \frac{1}{\sqrt{\pi}} \int_{-\pi}^{\pi} f(t) \cos(kt) \, dt \qquad (2.20)$$

Substituting these coefficients into the general expression for the expansion of f(t) in terms of these orthonormal basis functions, we find that the Fourier series for the signal, or function, f(t) can be expressed as in Equations 2.21 and 2.22, which may be written as in Equation 2.23, where A_o, A_n and B_n are appropriately defined.

$$f(t) = \left[\frac{1}{\sqrt{2\pi}} \int_{-\pi}^{\pi} f(t) \, dt \right] \frac{1}{\sqrt{2\pi}}$$
$$+ \sum_{n=1}^{\infty} \left(\left[\frac{1}{\sqrt{\pi}} \int_{-\pi}^{\pi} f(t) \sin(nt) \, dt \right] \frac{1}{\sqrt{\pi}} \sin(nt) \right.$$
$$+ \left. \left[\frac{1}{\sqrt{\pi}} \int_{-\pi}^{\pi} f(t) \cos(nt) \, dt \right] \frac{1}{\sqrt{\pi}} \cos(nt) \right) \qquad (2.21)$$

$$f(t) = \frac{1}{2} \left[\frac{1}{\pi} \int_{-\pi}^{\pi} f(t) \, dt \right]$$
$$+ \sum_{n=1}^{\infty} \left(\left[\frac{1}{\pi} \int_{-\pi}^{\pi} f(t) \sin(nt) \, dt \right] \sin(nt) \right.$$
$$+ \left. \left[\frac{1}{\pi} \int_{-\pi}^{\pi} f(t) \cos(nt) \, dt \right] \cos(nt) \right) \qquad (2.22)$$

$$f(t) = \frac{1}{2} A_o + \sum_{n=1}^{\infty} (A_n \cos(nt) + B_n \sin(nt)) \qquad (2.23)$$

What we have shown is that if a function f(t) can be represented by a Fourier expansion, then the coefficients of the expansion may be calculated by the methods described. However, the question of convergence of the expansion has not yet been addressed. The necessary and sufficient conditions for the convergence of a Fourier expansion are well known, but it is useful to state a sufficient condition, known as the Dirichlet condition, which states that if f(t) is bounded and of period T and if f(t) has at most a finite number of maxima and minima in one period and a finite number of discontinuities, then the Fourier series for f(t) converges to f(t) at all points where f(t) is continuous, and converges to the average of the right hand and left hand limits of f(t) at each point where f(t) is discontinuous.

In many applications, such as the design of filters, it may be necessary to use only a finite number of terms of the Fourier series to approximate a function f(t) over $(0, T_p)$, and it is therefore of much interest to inquire what effect the truncation of the series has (Banks, 1990). The error incurred obviously decreases as one takes into account more and more terms when the function f(t) is continuous. However, in the neighbourhood of discontinuities, ripples occur, the magnitude of which remain roughly the same even as more and more terms are included in the Fourier expansion. These ripples are referred to as Gibbs' oscillations.

2.2 Generalised Fourier expansion

As an example of using the generalised Fourier expansion, let us consider representing the function shown in Figure 2.1, in terms of the Legendre Polynominals, which form an orthogonal set on the interval (-1,1). The corresponding normalised basis functions are given by Equations 2.24 to 2.27, where the $P_n(t)$ are the Legendre polynominals, which may be generated by the expression of Equation 2.28, or by using the recurrence relation of Equation 2.29.

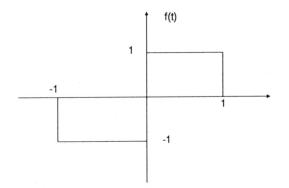

Figure 2.1 The function f(t)

$$\Phi_o(t) = \frac{1}{\sqrt{2}} \tag{2.24}$$

$$\Phi_1(t) = t\sqrt{\frac{3}{2}} \tag{2.25}$$

$$\Phi_2(t) = \sqrt{\frac{5}{2}}\left(\frac{3}{2}t^2 - \frac{1}{2}\right) \tag{2.26}$$

$$\Phi_n(t) = \left(\frac{2n+1}{2}\right)^{1/2} P_n(t) \tag{2.27}$$

$$P_n(t) = \frac{1}{2^n\,n!}\frac{d^n}{dt^n}(t^2 - 1)^n \tag{2.28}$$

$$nP_n(t) = (2n-1)\,t\,P_{n-1}(t) - (n-1)\,P_{n-2}(t) \tag{2.29}$$

The generalised Fourier coefficient is given by Equation 2.30, where n = 0, 1, 2...

$$c_n = <f\,|\,\Phi_n> = \int_{-1}^{1} f(t)\,\Phi_n(t)\,dt \tag{2.30}$$

Using the expressions for Φ_n given above, we obtain Equations 2.31 to 2.34.

$$c_o = \int_{-1}^{1} \frac{f(t)}{\sqrt{2}}\,dt = 0 \tag{2.31}$$

$$c_1 = \int_{-1}^{1} \sqrt{\frac{3}{2}}\,t f(t)\,dt = \sqrt{\frac{3}{2}} \tag{2.32}$$

$$c_2 = \int_{-1}^{1} \sqrt{\frac{5}{2}}\left(\frac{3}{2}t^2 - \frac{1}{2}\right) f(t)\,dt = 0 \tag{2.33}$$

$$c_3 = \int_{-1}^{1} \sqrt{\frac{7}{2}}\left(\frac{5}{2}t^3 - \frac{3}{2}t\right) f(t)\,dt = \sqrt{\frac{7}{16}} \tag{2.34}$$

In general, the coefficient c_n is zero when n is even, for this particular example. Hence the function f(t) in Figure 2.1 can be represented in terms of the Legendre polynominals as in Equation 2.35.

$$f(t) = \sum_{k=0}^{\infty} c_k\,\Phi_k(t)$$
$$= \frac{3}{2}t + \frac{7}{4\sqrt{2}}\left(\frac{5}{2}t^3 - \frac{3}{2}t\right) + \dots + c_n\,\Phi_n(t) + \dots \tag{2.35}$$

We have shown that an arbitrary function, f(t), can be expressed in terms of a superposition of orthogonal basis functions, and we have derived expressions for the generalised Fourier coefficients in terms of the projection of the given function onto the orthogonal basis functions.

If a signal, x(t), repeats itself exactly every T_p seconds, then x(t) may be represented as a linear combination of harmonically related-complex exponentials of the form given in Equation 2.36, where the fundamental frequency is given by Equation 2.37

$$x(t) = \sum_{k=-\infty}^{\infty} c_k\,e^{j2\pi k f_0 t} \tag{2.36}$$

$$f_o = \frac{1}{T_p} \tag{2.37}$$

Hence one can regard the exponential signals:

$$e^{j2\pi k f_o t} \qquad k = 0, 1, 2, \dots$$

as the building blocks from which we can construct periodic signals of various forms by properly choosing the fundamental frequency and the coefficients c_k.

Given a periodic signal x(t) with period T_p, we may represent it by a Fourier series where the fundamental frequency f_0 is selected to be the reciprocal of T_p. As before, the Fourier coefficients c_k are obtained by multiplication of the Fourier representation by the complex exponential $e^{-j2\pi l f_o t}$ where l is an integer, followed by integration over a single period, either 0 to T_p or more generally t_0 to $t_0 + T_p$ where t_0 is arbitrary. We thus obtain Equation 2.38.

$$\int_{t_o}^{t_o + T_p} x(t)\,e^{-j2\pi l f_o t}\,dt$$
$$= \int_{t_o}^{t_o + T_p} e^{-j2\pi l f_o t}\left(\sum_{k=-\infty}^{\infty} c_k\,e^{j2\pi k f_o t}\right) dt$$
$$= \sum_{k=-\infty}^{\infty} c_k \int_{t_o}^{t_o + T_p} e^{j2\pi f_o (k-l) t}\,dt \tag{2.38}$$

The integral on the r.h.s. is identically zero if k ≠ l and is equal to T_p if k = l, and therefore Equation 2.39 can be obtained.

$$c_k = \frac{1}{T_p}\int_{t_o}^{t_o + T_p} x(t)\,e^{-j2\pi i k f_o t}\,dt \tag{2.39}$$

It is now of interest to consider the average power, P, of a periodic signal x(t) which given by Equation 2.40.

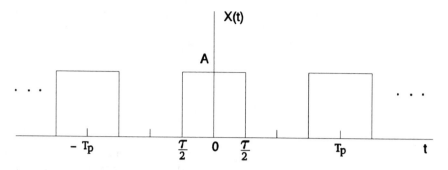

Figure 2.2 Continuous time periodic train of rectangular pulses

$$P = \frac{1}{T_p} \int |x(t)|^2 \, dt = \frac{1}{T_p} \int x(t) x^*(t) \, dt \tag{2.40}$$

Using the Fourier representation of x(t), and the expression found for the Fourier coefficients we can write Equation 2.41.

$$
\begin{aligned}
P &= \frac{1}{T_p} \int x(t) \left(\sum_{k=-\infty}^{\infty} c_k^* e^{-2j\pi k f_o t} \right) dt \\
&= \sum_{k=-\infty}^{\infty} c_k^* \left(\frac{1}{T_p} \int x(t) e^{-2j\pi k f_o t} \right) dt \\
&= \sum_{k=-\infty}^{\infty} c_k^* c_k = \sum_{k=-\infty}^{\infty} |c_k|^2
\end{aligned}
\tag{2.41}
$$

This relationship between the average power and the square of the Fourier coefficients is called Parseval's relation, as mentioned earlier in the context of function representation. The kth harmonic component of the signal has a power $|c_k|^2$ and hence the total average power in a periodic signal is just the sum of the average powers in all the harmonics. If $|c_k|^2$ is plotted as a function of kf_o, the resulting function is called the power density spectrum of the periodic signal x(t). Since the power in a periodic signal exists only at discrete values of frequencies i.e. Equation 2.42 is satisfied, the signal is said to have a line spectrum, and the frequency spacing between two adjacent spectral lines is equal to the reciprocal of the fundamental period T_p.

$$f = 0, \ \pm f_o, \ \pm 2f_o, \ \dots \tag{2.42}$$

The Fourier coefficients c_k are in general complex, and may be represented as in Equation 2.43 and hence an alternative to the power spectrum representation may be obtained by plotting the magnitude spectrum $|c_k|$ and phase spectrum Θ_k as a function of frequency.

$$c_k = |c_k| e^{j\Theta_k} \tag{2.43}$$

Phase information is therefore lost in using the power spectral density.

For a real valued periodic signal, the Fourier coefficients c_k can easily be shown to satisfy Equation 2.44, which implies that the power spectrum, and hence the magnitude spectrum, are symmetric functions of frequency. However, the phase spectrum is an odd function.

$$c_{-k} = c_k^* \tag{2.44}$$

As an example of this analysis, the Fourier series and power spectral density of the rectangular pulse train shown in Figure 2.2 will be given, and since the signal x(t) is even, we will select the integration interval from $\frac{-T_p}{2}$ to $\frac{T_p}{2}$, as in Equation 2.45 and 2.46, for $k = \pm 1, = \pm 2, \dots$, and the power spectral density is obtained by squaring these quantities.

$$c_o = \frac{1}{T_p} \int_{-\tau/2}^{\tau/2} x(t) \, dt = \frac{A\tau}{T_p} \tag{2.45}$$

$$
\begin{aligned}
c_k &= \frac{1}{T_p} \int_{-\tau/2}^{\tau/2} A \, e^{-j2\pi k f_o t} \, dt \\
&= \frac{A}{\pi f_o k T_p} \frac{e^{j\pi k f_o \tau} - e^{-j\pi k f_o \tau}}{2j} = \frac{A\tau}{T_p} \frac{\sin(\pi k f_o \tau)}{\pi k f_o \tau}
\end{aligned}
\tag{2.46}
$$

It is now important to introduce the concept of aperiodic signals and transform methods, before dealing with discrete data.

2.3 Fourier transforms

Consider an aperiodic signal x(t) which is of finite duration, Figure 2.3. A periodic signal $x_p(t)$ can be created from x(t) by translation by fixed amounts, T_p, as shown. This new periodic signal, $x_p(t)$, approaches x(t) in the limit as T_p approaches infinity, and the spectrum of $x_p(t)$ should be obtainable from the spectrum of x(t) in the same limit.

As before, we can obtain Equations 2.47 and 2.48, where $f_o = 1/T_p$.

$$x_p(t) = \sum_{k=-\infty}^{\infty} c_k \, e^{j2\pi k f_o t} \tag{2.47}$$

$$c_k = \frac{1}{T_p} \int_{-T_p/2}^{T_p/2} x_p(t) \, e^{-j2\pi k f_o t} \, dt \tag{2.48}$$

Between the limits $\pm \frac{T_p}{2}$, $x_p(t)$ can be replaced by x(t), and since x(t) is zero outside this range of integration, Equation 2.49 may be obtained.

$$c_k = \frac{1}{T_p} \int_{-\infty}^{\infty} x(t) e^{-j2\pi k f_o t} dt \tag{2.49}$$

A new function, X(f), can now be defined as the Fourier transform of x(t) as in Equation 2.50 and the Fourier coefficient c_k can be written as in Equation 2.51, which are samples of X(f) taken at multiples of f_o and also scaled by the factor $f_o(=1/T_p)$.

$$X(f) = \int_{-\infty}^{\infty} x(t) e^{-j2\pi f t} dt \tag{2.50}$$

$$c_k = \frac{1}{T_p} X(k f_0) \tag{2.51}$$

Therefore Equation 2.52 can be obtained.

$$x_p(t) = \frac{1}{T_p} \sum_{k=-\infty}^{\infty} X\left(\frac{k}{T_p}\right) e^{j2\pi k t / T_p} \tag{2.52}$$

As described above, we require to take the limit as T_p approaches infinity, and it is therefore convenient to define a frequency differential $\delta f = \frac{1}{T_p}$ such that in the limit δf approaches zero. We may therefore write Equation 2.53, and taking the limit as $\delta f \to \sim 0$ we obtain Equations 2.54 and 2.55

$$x_p(t) = \sum_{k=-\infty}^{\infty} X(k\delta f) e^{j2\pi k t \delta f} \delta f \tag{2.53}$$

$$\lim_{T_p \to \infty} x_p(t) = x(t) = \lim_{\delta_f \to 0} \sum_{k=-\infty}^{\infty} X(k\,\delta f) e^{j2\pi f t} df \tag{2.54}$$

$$x(t) = \int_{-\infty}^{\infty} X(f) e^{j2\pi f t} df \tag{2.55}$$

These equations show that x(t) and X(f) form a so-called Fourier Transform pair, and the Fourier Transform of x(t) exists if the signal has a finite energy, i.e. as in Equation 2.56.

$$\int_{-\infty}^{\infty} |x(t)|^2 dt < \infty \tag{2.56}$$

Earlier we defined the average power of a periodic signal. It is now possible to similarly define the energy of an aperiodic signal as in Equations 2.57 and 2.58.

$$\begin{aligned} E &= \int_{-\infty}^{\infty} |x(t)|^2 dt = \int_{-\infty}^{\infty} x(t) x^*(t) dt \\ &= \int_{-\infty}^{\infty} x(t) dt \left(\int_{-\infty}^{\infty} X^*(f) e^{-j2\pi f t} df \right) \end{aligned} \tag{2.57}$$

$$\begin{aligned} E &= \int_{-\infty}^{\infty} X^*(f) df \left(\int_{-\infty}^{\infty} x(t) e^{-j2\pi f t} dt \right) \\ &= \int_{-\infty}^{\infty} |X(f)|^2 df \end{aligned} \tag{2.58}$$

Hence the energy of an aperiodic signal can be written as in Equation 2.59 which is also known as Parseval's relation, (Wax, 1954).

$$E = \int_{-\infty}^{\infty} |x(t)|^2 dt = \int_{-\infty}^{\infty} |X(f)|^2 df \tag{2.59}$$

2.4 Discrete sequences

In order for a digital computer to manipulate a signal, the signal must be sampled at a chosen sampling rate, $1/T_s$, giving rise to a set of numbers called a sequence. If the continuous signal was x(t), the sampled sequence is represented by $x(nT_s)$, where n is an integer, and the independent variable, t, could represent time or a spatial co-ordinate for example. The analysis can, of course, be extended into higher dimensions.

In order to move between the continuous domain and the discrete domain, the idea of a sampling function must be introduced, and from the definition of the Dirac delta function ($\delta(t)$) as in Equation 2.60, it is clear that this function meets the requirement.

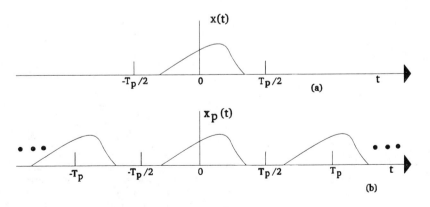

Figure 2.3 An aperiodic signal and a periodic signal constructed by repeating the periodic signal

$$\int_{-\infty}^{\infty} x(t)\,\delta(t-\tau)\,dt = x(\tau) \tag{2.60}$$

Consider an analog signal x(t) that is continuous in both time and amplitude, and assume that x(t) has infinite duration but finite energy. Let the sample values of the signal x(t) at times $t = 0,\ \pm T_s,\ \pm 2T_s,\ ...,$ be denoted by the series $x(nT_s),\ n = 0,\ \pm1,\ \pm2,\ ....,$ where T_s is the sampling period and $f_s = 1/T_s$ is the sampling rate. The discrete time signal $x_d(t)$ that is obtained by sampling the continuous signal x(t) can then be written as in Equation 2.61, where $\delta(t-nT_s)$ is a Dirac delta function located at time $t = nT_s$, and each delta function is weighted by the corresponding sample value of the input signal x(t).

$$x_d(t) = \sum_{n=-\infty}^{\infty} x(nT_s)\,\delta(t-nT_s) \tag{2.61}$$

For the case of discrete data, exactly analogous transform methods may be applied as for continuous signals, and we must now discuss the implementation issues for such methods.

2.5 The discrete Fourier transform

The DFT is used extensively in digital signal processing (Burrus, 1985), and is used routinely for the detection and estimation of periodic signals. The discrete Fourier transform (DFT) of a discrete-time signal x(n) is defined as in Equation 2.62, where $k = 0,\ 1,...,$ N-1 and $W_N^{nk} = e^{j2\pi nk/N}$ are the basis functions of the DFT.

$$X(k) = \frac{1}{N} \sum_{n=0}^{N-1} x(n)\,W_N^{nk} \tag{2.62}$$

These functions are sometimes known as 'twiddle factors'. The basis functions are periodic and define points on the unit circle in the complex plane. Figure 2.4 illustrates the cyclic property of the basis functions for an eight point DFT, and the basis functions are equally spaced around the unit circle at frequency increments of F/N, where F is the sampling rate of the input signal sequence. In this figure the cyclic character of the twiddle factors are illustrated as follows:

$$W_8^0 = W_8^8 = W_8^{16} = W_8^{24} = ...$$
$$W_8^1 = W_8^9 = W_8^{17} = W_8^{25} = ...$$
$$W_8^2 = W_8^{10} = W_8^{18} = W_8^{26} = ...$$
$$\cdot \qquad \cdot \qquad \cdot \qquad \cdot$$
$$\cdot \qquad \cdot \qquad \cdot \qquad \cdot$$
$$\cdot \qquad \cdot \qquad \cdot \qquad \cdot$$
$$W_8^7 = W_8^{15} = W_8^{23} = W_8^{31} = ...$$

The set of frequency samples which define the spectrum X(k), are given on a frequency axis whose discrete frequency locations are given by Equation 2.63 where k = 0, 1,...., N-1.

$$f_k = k\frac{F}{N} \tag{2.63}$$

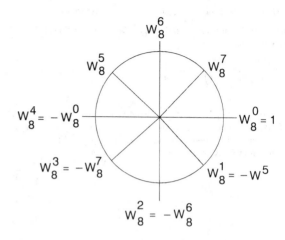

Figure 2.4 Cyclic properties of the basis functions for an eight point DFT

The frequency resolution of the DFT is equal to the frequency increment F/N and is referred to as the bin spacing of the DFT outputs. The frequency response of any DFT bin output is determined by applying a complex exponential input signal and evaluating the DFT bin output response as the frequency is varied.

Consider an input signal given by Equation 2.64, then the DFT of x(n) can be expressed as a function of the arbitrary frequency variable f by Equation 2.65.

$$x(n) = e^{j2\pi fn/F} \tag{2.64}$$

$$X(k) = \frac{1}{N} \sum_{n=0}^{N-1} x(n)\,W_N^{nk} = \frac{1}{N} \sum_{n=0}^{N-1} e^{j2\pi fn/F}\,W_N^{nk} \tag{2.65}$$

This summation can be evaluated using the geometric series summation to give Equation 2.66.

$$X(k) = \frac{1}{N}\frac{1 - e^{-j2\pi(k/N-f/F)N}}{1 - e^{-j2\pi(k/N-f/F)}} \tag{2.66}$$

Defining Ω by Equation 2.67, the DFT of x(n) can be written as in Equation 2.68.

$$\Omega = 2\pi\left(\frac{k}{N} - \frac{f}{F}\right) \tag{2.67}$$

$$X(k) = e^{-j\Omega(N-1)/2}\frac{\sin\dfrac{\Omega N}{2}}{N\sin\dfrac{\Omega}{2}} \tag{2.68}$$

The first term in this expression is the phase of the response, and the ratio of sines is the amplitude response. If k is an integer, then X(k) = 1, for these values of k, and zero elsewhere. If k is not an integer, then none of the DFT values are zero. This is called spectral leakage. Hence, an unit impulse at the kth frequency location is only obtained when Equation 2.69 is satisfied, where k is an integer.

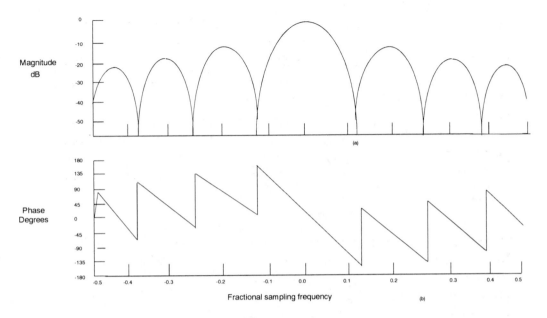

Figure 2.5 Frequency and phase response of a DFT bin output for an eight point FFT: (a) magnitude; (b) phase angle

$$f_k = \frac{kF}{N} \tag{2.69}$$

Figure 2.5 shows the frequency response of a DFT bin output for an eight point DFT, and the high sidelobe levels are a consequence of truncation.

2.6 The inverse discrete Fourier transform

Given the discrete Fourier transform X(k) of the input sequence x(n), the inverse discrete Fourier transform (IDFT) of X(k) is the original time sequence, and is given by Equation 2.70.

$$x(n) = \sum_{k=0}^{N-1} X(k) W_n^{-nk} \tag{2.70}$$

The proof is easily obtained by substitution and interchanging the order of summation. The form of the IDFT is the same as the DFT apart from the factor $\frac{1}{N}$ and the sign change in exponent of the basis functions, and consequently the DFT algorithm can be used to compute these transforms in either direction. It should be noted that the DFT is equal to the Z-transform of a sequence, x(n), evaluated at equally spaced inputs on the unit circle in the z-plane (see later).

2.7 The fast Fourier transform

Special analysis and many other applications often require DFT's to be performed on data sequences in real time and on contiguous sets of input samples. If the input sequence has N samples, the computation of the DFT requires N^2 complex multiplies and N^2-N complex additions.

The FFT is a fast algorithm for the efficient implementation of the DFT where the number of time samples of the input signal N are transformed into N frequency points, and the required number of arithmetic operations are reduced to the order of $\frac{N}{2} \log_2(N)$. Several approaches can be used to develop the FFT algorithm.

Starting with the DFT expression, consider factorising it into two DFT's of, length N/2 by splitting the input samples into even and odd samples, in Equations 2.71 and 2.72, where k = 0, 1, 2,..., N-1.

$$X(k) = \frac{1}{N} \sum_{n=0}^{N-1} x(n) W_N^{nk} \tag{2.71}$$

$$X(k) = \frac{1}{N} \sum_{m=0}^{N/2-1} x(2m) W_N^{2mk} \tag{2.72}$$
$$+ \frac{1}{N} \sum_{m=0}^{N/2-1} x(2m+1) W_N^{(2m+1)k}$$

Consider x_1 and x_2 to represent the normalised even and odd sample components respectively as in Equations 2.73 and 2.74, for m = 0, 1, 2, ... (N/2 - 1).

$$x_1(m) = \frac{x(2m)}{N} \tag{2.73}$$

$$x_2(m) = \frac{x(2m+1)}{N} \tag{2.74}$$

Therefore Equation 2.72 may be written as in Equation 2.75, where Equation 2.76 holds and each of the summation terms is reduced to an N/2 point DFT.

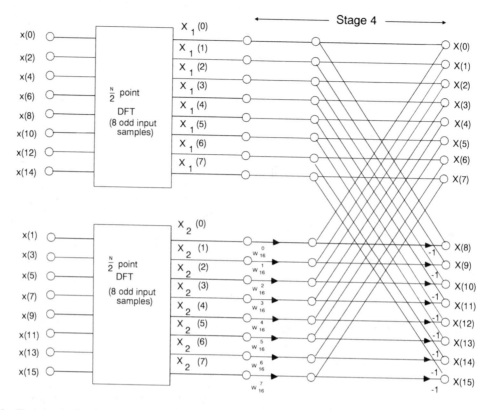

Figure 2.6 First step in developing a 16 point decimation in time FFT signal flow graph

$$X(k) = \sum_{m=0}^{N/2-1} x_1(m) W_{N/2}^{mk} + W_N^k \sum_{m=0}^{N/2-1} x(m) W_{N/2}^{mk} \qquad (2.75)$$

$$W_N^{2n} = W_{N/2}^n \qquad (2.76)$$

The general form of the algorithm may be written as in Equation 2.77 and 2.78, where Equations 2.79 and 2.80 hold.

$$X(k) = X_1(k) + W_N^k X_2(k) \qquad (2.77)$$

$$X\left(k + \frac{N}{2}\right) = X_1(k) + W_N^{k+N/2} X_2(k)$$
$$= X_1(k) - W_N^k X_2(k) \qquad (2.78)$$

$$W_N^{k+N/2} = -W_N^k \qquad (2.79)$$

$$W_{N/2}^{m(k+N/2)} = W_{N/2}^{mk} \qquad (2.80)$$

Since the DFT output is periodic Equations 2.81 and 2.82 can be obtained and the form of the algorithm given above is refered to as the decimation in time FFT butterfly, and an example for a sixteen point FFT is shown in Figures 2.6 and 2.7

$$X_1(k) = X_1\left(k + \frac{N}{2}\right) \qquad (2.81)$$

$$X_2(k) = X_2\left(k + \frac{N}{2}\right) \qquad (2.82)$$

The decomposition process is repeated until two-point DFT's are generated. Each decomposition is called a stage, and the total number of stages is given by Equation 2.83.

$$M(N) = \log_2 N \qquad (2.83)$$

Thus a 16 point DFT requires 4 stages, as shown in Figure 2.8. The algorithm is now re-applied to each of the N/2 sample DFT's. Assuming that $\left(\dfrac{N}{2}\right)$ is even, the same process can be carried out on each of the $\left(\dfrac{N}{2}\right)$ point DFT's to further reduce the computation. If $N = 2^M$ then the whole process can be repeated M times to reduce the computation to that of evaluating N single point DFT's.

2.8 Linear time-invariant digital systems

The theory of discrete-time, linear, time invariant systems forms the basis for digital signal processing, and a discrete-time system performs an operation on the input signal according to a defined criteria to produce a modified output signal. The input signal x(n), is the system excitation, and y(n) is the response of the system to the excitation, see Figure 2.9, (Kamen, 1990). The transformation operation can be represented by the operator R. Linear and time-invari-

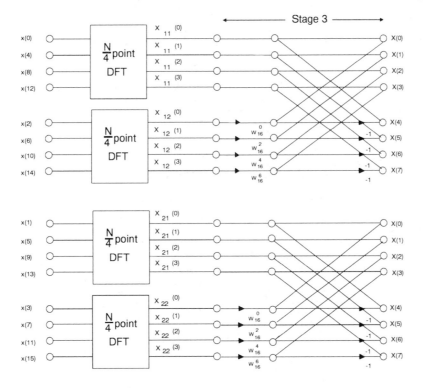

Figure 2.7 Second step in developing a 16 point decimation in time FFT signal flow graph

ant systems can be completely characterised by their impulse response, h(n), which is defined by Equation 2.84.

$$h(n) = R[\delta(n)] \qquad (2.84)$$

Once the impulse response is determined, the output of the system for any given input signal is obtained by convolving the input with the impulse response of the system as in Equation 2.85.

$$y(n) = R[x(n)] = \sum_{k=-\infty}^{\infty} x(k)h(n-k) \qquad (2.85)$$

A system is linear if and only if the system's response to the sum of two signals, each multiplied by arbitrary scalar constants, is equal to the sum of the system's responses to the two signals taken separately, as in Equation 2.86.

$$y(n) = R[a_1x_1(n) + a_2x_2(n)]$$
$$= a_1R[x_1(n)] + a_2R[x_2(n)] \qquad (2.86)$$

A system is time-invariant if the response to a shifted version of the input is identical to a shifted version of the response based on the unshifted input, and a system operator R is time-invariant if Equation 2.87 holds for all values of m.

$$R[x(n-m)] = z^{-m}R[x(n)] \qquad (2.87)$$

The operator z^{-m} represents a signal delay of m samples.

The z-transform provides a very powerful method for the analysis of linear time-invariant discrete systems, which can be represented in terms of difference equations, via the operator R, relating the input signal samples to the output signal samples.

In the following, we will define the properties of the z-transform and then we will apply the methods to the analysis of discrete time linear time-invariant systems.

The z-transform of any data sequence x(n), is defined as in Equation 2.88.

$$X(z) = \sum_{k=-\infty}^{\infty} x_k z^{-k} \qquad (2.88)$$

In this definition, z is a continuous complex variable and X(z) is referred to as the 'two-sided z-transform', since both positive and negative values of the index k are allowed.

As an example of a z-transform, let us consider x(n) to be samples of an exponential function such that $x_k = 0$ for $k < 0$, and $e^{-\alpha k}$ for $k \geq 0$ and $\alpha > 0$. The z-transform of this sampled signal is given by Equation 2.89, which is a simple rational function of α and z. Since the signal is zero for $k < 0$, we have a one sided transform in this case. Table 2.1 shows some common sampled sequences and their z-transforms.

$$X(z) = \sum_{k=0}^{\infty} e^{-\alpha k} z^{-k} = \frac{z}{z - e^{-\alpha}} \qquad (2.89)$$

In linear systems analysis, the concept of a transfer function is fundamental and is defined simply as the transform of the output of

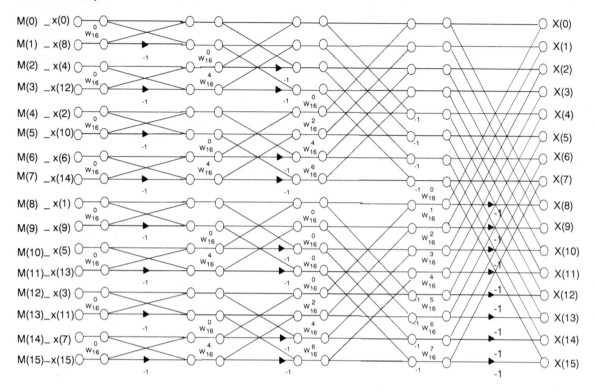

Figure 2.8 Flow graph of a 16 point DIT FFT

the system divided by the transform of the input. The Laplace transform is an important tool that is used in continuous systems theory, and for a continuous signal x(t), this transform is defined as in Equation 2.90.

$$X(s) = \int_0^\infty x(t) e^{-st} dt \qquad (2.90)$$

If, as before, we sample this continuous signal x(t), we obtain the sampled signal $x_s(t)$ given by Equation 2.91, with x(t) = 0 for t < 0.

$$x_s(t) = \sum_{n=0}^\infty x(t) \delta(t - nT) \qquad (2.91)$$

The Laplace transform of the sampled signal $x_s(t)$ is then as in Equation 2.92.

$$X_s(s) = \int_0^\infty \sum_{n=0}^\infty x(t) \delta(t - nT) e^{-st} dt$$
$$= \sum_{n=0}^\infty x(nT) e^{-snT} \qquad (2.92)$$

Making the substitution gives Equation 2.93.

$$z = e^{sT} \qquad (2.93)$$

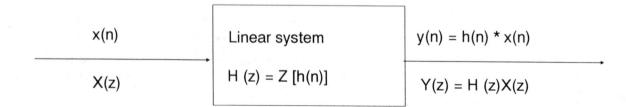

Figure 2.9 Transfer function relationship for linear systems

Table 2.1 Commonly used z-transform pairs

$x(n)$	$X(z)$	Region of convergence
$\delta(n)$	1	All z
$u(n)$	$\dfrac{z}{z-1}$	$\lvert z \rvert > 1$
$a^n u(n)$	$\dfrac{z}{z-a}$	$\lvert z \rvert > \lvert a \rvert$
$-a^n u(-n-1)$	$\dfrac{z}{z-a}$	$\lvert z \rvert < \lvert a \rvert$
$n a^n u(n)$	$\dfrac{az}{(z-a)^2}$	$\lvert z \rvert > \lvert a \rvert$
$-n a^n u(-n)$	$\dfrac{az}{(z-a)^2}$	$\lvert z \rvert < \lvert a \rvert$
$\dfrac{(n+k-1)!}{N!(k-1)} a^n u(n)$	$\dfrac{z^k}{(z-a)^k}$	$\lvert z \rvert > \lvert a \rvert$
$a^{\lvert n \rvert}$	$\dfrac{a^2-1}{a}\;\dfrac{z}{(z-a)(z-\frac{1}{a})}$	$\lvert a \rvert < \lvert z \rvert < \lvert a \rvert^{-1}$
$\sin(n\omega)u(n)$	$\dfrac{z\sin\omega}{z^2 - 2z\cos\omega + 1}$	$\lvert z \rvert > 1$
$\cos(n\omega)u(n)$	$\dfrac{z(z-\cos\omega)}{z^2 - 2z\cos\omega + 1}$	$\lvert z \rvert > 1$
$a^n \sin(n\omega)u(n)$	$\dfrac{az\sin\omega}{z^2 - 2az\cos\omega + a^2}$	$\lvert z \rvert > \lvert a \rvert$
$a^n \cos(n\omega)u(n)$	$\dfrac{z(z-a\cos\omega)}{z^2 - 2az\cos\omega + a^2}$	$\lvert z \rvert > \lvert a \rvert$

Using the definition of Equation 2.94 gives Equation 2.95 which is the z-transform of the sampled sequence, $x(nT)$ and is also the Laplace transform of the sampled signal $x_s(t)$.

$$X(z) = X_s(s) \tag{2.94}$$

$$X(z) = \sum_{n=0}^{\infty} x(nT)z^{-n} \tag{2.95}$$

Before deriving an expression for the transfer function and frequency response of a general linear system, a few of the properties of the z-transform need to be explained.

2.8.1 Linearity

The z-transform of the sum of two sequences multiplied by arbitrary constants is the sum of the z-transforms of the individual sequences, as in Equation 2.96, where Z represents the z-transform operator and $X(z)$ and $Y(z)$ are the z-transforms of the sequences $x(n)$ and $y(n)$ respectively.

$$Z[ax(n) + by(n)] = aX(z) + bY(z) \tag{2.96}$$

2.8.2 Delay property

Consider a sampled sequence that has been delayed by p samples, and define the delayed sequence to be $x'(nT)$, as in Equation 2.97.

$$x'(nT) = x(nT - pT) \tag{2.97}$$

The z-transform of this delayed sequence is then as in Equation 2.98.

$$\begin{aligned}X'(z) &= \sum_{n=0}^{\infty} x'(n)z^{-n} \\ &= \sum_{n=0}^{p-1} x'(n)z^{-n} + \sum_{n=p}^{\infty} x'(n)z^{-n}\end{aligned} \tag{2.98}$$

This may be written in terms of the undelayed sequence, and with a redefinition of the summation index in the second term, we obtain Equation 2.99.

$$X'(z) = \sum_{n=0}^{p-1} x(n-p)z^{-n} + \sum_{n=0}^{\infty} x(n)z^{-(n+p)} \tag{2.99}$$

Therefore, the z-transform of a delayed sequence is given by Equation 2.100.

$$X'(z) = \sum_{n=0}^{p-1} x(n-p)z^{-n} + z^{-p}X(z) \qquad (2.100)$$

The first term represents a contribution from any initial conditions, and if $x(n) = 0$ for $n < 0$, the z-transform of a delayed sequence is just $z^{-p}X(z)$, where p is the delay. This is of course, analogous to the shift theorem for the Laplace transform.

2.8.3   Convolution summation property

From the linear system theory point of view, this represents one of the most valuable properties. Consider the definition of the convolution of an input sequence x(n), with the impulse response h(k) of a linear system, to yield an output y(n), as in Equation 2.101.

$$y(n) = \sum_{k=-\infty}^{\infty} h(k)x(n-k) \qquad (2.101)$$

Taking the double sided z-transform of this equation gives Equation 2.102.

$$Y(z) = \sum_{n=-\infty}^{\infty} \left[\sum_{k=-\infty}^{\infty} h(k)x(n-k) \right] z^{-n} \qquad (2.102)$$

Again, changing the order of summation, and defining p = n-k, we obtain Equation 2.103.

$$Y(z) = \sum_{k=-\infty}^{\infty} h(k)z^{-k} \sum_{p=-\infty}^{\infty} x(p)z^{-p} \qquad (2.103)$$

This can therefore be written as the product of the z-transforms of h(k) and x(n) as in Equation 2.104.

$$Y(z) = H(z)X(z) \qquad (2.104)$$

Other important properties of the z-transform are shown in Table 2.2.

In both signal processing applications and linear systems theory, linear recursive operators are used extensively, examples in both areas being the design of recursive digital filters amd feedback systems in control, respectively, and the general input-output relationship for such a linear recursive system can be written in the form shown in Equation 2.105.

$$\sum_{k=0}^{p} a_k y(n-k) = \sum_{k=0}^{q} b_k x(n-k) \qquad (2.105)$$

Taking the z-transform of both sides of the expression, and interchanging the order of summation we obtain Equation 2.106.

$$\sum_{k=0}^{p} a_k \left[\sum_{n=-\infty}^{\infty} y(n-k)z^{-n} \right]$$
$$= \sum_{k=0}^{q} b_k \left[\sum_{n=-\infty}^{\infty} x(n-k)z^{-n} \right] \qquad (2.106)$$

Using the shift theorem, this expression can be written as in Equation 2.107.

Table 2.2   Properties of the z-transform

Property	Time series	z–transform	Region of convergence
	$x(n)$	$X(z)$	$r_{cx} < |z| < r_{ax}$
	$y(n)$	$Y(z)$	$r_{cy} < |z| < r_{ay}$
Linearity	$ax(n) + by(n)$	$aX(z) + bY(z)$	At least $\max(r_{cx}, r_{cy}) < |z| < \min(r_{ax}, r_{ay})$
Time shift	$x(n-m)$	$z^{-m}X(z)$	$r_{cx} < |z| < r_{ax}$
Convolution	$\sum_{k=-\infty}^{\infty} x(k)y(n-k)$	$X(z)Y(z)$	At least $\max(r_{cx}, r_{cy}) < |z| < \min(r_{ax}, r_{ay})$
Exponential multiplication	$a_n x(n)$	$X(a^{-1}z)$	$|a|r_{cx} < |z| < |a|r_{ax}$
Time multiplication	$nx(n)$	$-z \dfrac{dX(z)}{dz}$	$r_{cx} < |z| < r_{ax}$
Product	$x(n)y(n)$	$\dfrac{1}{2\pi j} \oint_C X(w)Y\left(\dfrac{z}{w}\right)w^{-1}\,dw$	$r_{xc}r_{cy} < |z| < r_{ax}r_{ay}$
Correlation	$\sum_{k=-\infty}^{\infty} x(k)y(n+k)$	$X(z^{-1})Y(z)$	$\max(r_{ax}^{-1}, r_{cy}) < |z| < \min(r_{cx}^{-1}, r_{ay})$

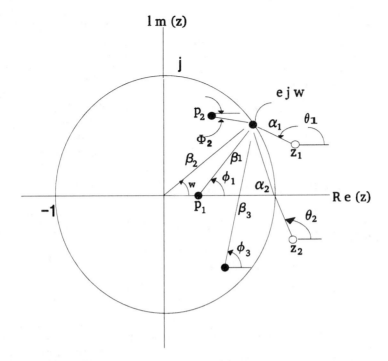

Figure 2.10 Geometrical construction of the frequency response for a linear system with three poles and two zeroes

$$\left[\sum_{k=0}^{p} a_k z^{-k}\right] Y(z) = \left[\sum_{k=0}^{q} b_k z^{-k}\right] X(z) \tag{2.107}$$

This is used to define the transfer function, H(z), of the system, which may be written as in Equation 2.108 where H(z) is given by Equation 2.109.

$$Y(z) = H(z)X(z) \tag{2.108}$$

$$H(z) = \frac{b_0 + b_1 z^{-1} + \dots + b_q z^{-q}}{a_0 + a_1 z^{-1} + \dots + a_p z^{-p}} \tag{2.109}$$

From the transfer function of a system, the frequency response is found by evaluating the transfer function at $z = e^{j\omega}$, where the angular frequency $\omega = 2\pi f$.

Factorising the above transfer function as in Equation 2.110, where the zeroes and poles, z_i and p_i, may be complex numbers, and evaluating this function at $z = e^{j\omega}$, we obtain the associated frequency response as in Equations 2.111 and 2.112.

$$H(z) = \frac{b(z - z_1)(z - z_2)\dots(z - z_q)}{(z - p_1)(z - p_2)\dots(z - p_p)} \tag{2.110}$$

$$H(e^{j\omega}) = \frac{b(e^{j\omega} - z_1)(e^{j\omega} - z_2)\dots(e^{j\omega} - z_q)}{(e^{j\omega} - p_1)(e^{j\omega} - p_2)\dots(e^{j\omega} - p_p)} \tag{2.111}$$

$$H(e^{j\omega}) = \frac{b\alpha_1(\omega)\alpha_2(\omega)\dots\alpha_q(\omega)}{\beta_1(\omega)\beta_2(\omega)\dots\beta_p(\omega)} \tag{2.112}$$

The complex functions $\alpha_i(\omega)$ and $\beta_i(\omega)$ are given by Equations 2.113 and 2.114.

$$\alpha_i(\omega) = e^{j\omega} - z_i \tag{2.113}$$

$$\beta_i(\omega) = e^{j\omega} - p_i \tag{2.114}$$

A vector interpretation of the frequency response for a linear zeros system with three poles and two zeros is shown in Figure 2.10 and Equations 2.115 and 2.116.

$$|H(e^{j\omega})| = \frac{|b||\alpha_1| * |\alpha_2|}{|\beta_1| * |\beta_2| * |\beta_3|} \tag{2.115}$$

$$\begin{aligned} angle\{H(e^{j\omega})\} = {} & \Theta_1 + \Theta_2 - \Phi_1 \\ & - \Phi_2 - \Phi_3 + angle\{b\} \end{aligned} \tag{2.116}$$

2.9 The inverse z-transform

In the section describing the Fourier transform, it was straightforward to relate x(n) to X(k) through the definition of the integral transform, and vice versa. In this section we will consider methods of obtaining the inverse z-transform, that is, to obtain x(nT) given X(z).

The formal method is derived using Cauchy's integral theorem. From the definition of the z-transform, multiplying both sides by z^{m-1} and integrating around a closed contour in the z-plane, gives Equation 2.117.

$$\oint_C X(z) z^{m-1} dz = \oint_C \sum_{n=0}^{\infty} x(nT) z^{m-n-1} dz \qquad (2.117)$$

If the path of integration encloses the origin, then from Cauchy's integral theorem, the right hand side is zero except when m = n, in which case it is $2\pi j$.

Therefore Equation 2.118 can be obtained, which may be evaluated using the residue theorem.

$$x(nT) = \frac{1}{2\pi j} \oint_C X(z) z^{n-1} dz \qquad (2.118)$$

The remaining methods involve partial fraction expansions and straightforward inversion by division.

2.10 Data truncation

As mentioned before, the Fourier transform of any signal satisfies the periodic relationship as in Equation 2.119.

$$X\left(e^{j(\omega+2\pi)}\right) = X\left(e^{j\omega}\right) \qquad (2.119)$$

Due to this periodicity, one can consider the frequency range $-\pi < \omega < \pi$ to be the fundamental set of frequencies.

As seen before, the Fourier transform is of fundamental importance in characterising the spectral content of signals, be they in the time domain, spatial domain, etc. However, the Fourier transform requires the entire set of the signal samples, and the question therefore arises concerning the applicability of transform techniques when the data is of finite support.

The procedure of filling in the "missing data" with zeros is a very common method of trying to account for the situation.

As before, the discrete Fourier transform of a finite data set can be written as, in Equation 2.120.

$$X_N\left(e^{j\omega}\right) = \sum_{n=0}^{N-1} x(n) e^{-j\omega n} \qquad (2.120)$$

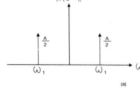

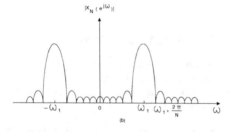

Figure 2.11 Magnitude of the Fourier transform associated with: (a) an untruncated sinusoid; (b) a truncated sinusoidal time series

Replacing x(n) by its inverse Fourier transform, gives Equation 2.121.

$$X_N\left(e^{j\omega}\right) = \sum_{n=0}^{N-1} \left[\frac{1}{2\pi} \int_{-\pi}^{\pi} X\left(e^{jv}\right) e^{jv} dv \right] e^{-j\omega n} \qquad (2.121)$$

Interchanging the order of the integral and the summation, and using the definition of Equation 2.122 gives Equation 2.123, where * means convolution of the non-truncated Fourier transform $X(e^{j\omega})$ with the rectangular window transform $W_r(e^{j\omega})$.

$$W_r\left(e^{j\omega}\right) = \sum_{n=0}^{N-1} e^{-j\omega n}$$

$$= e^{-j\omega(N-1)/2} \frac{\sin(\omega N/2)}{\sin(\omega/2)} \qquad (2.122)$$

$$X_n\left(e^{j\omega}\right) = \frac{1}{2\pi} \int_{-\pi}^{\pi} X\left(e^{jv}\right) W_r\left(e^{j(\omega-v)}\right) dv$$

$$= \frac{1}{2\pi} X\left(e^{j\omega}\right) * W_r\left(e^{j\omega}\right) \qquad (2.123)$$

When only a finite amount of data is present, the effect in trying to estimate the underlying Fourier transform manifests in terms of the convolution of the underlying transform with the transform of a rectangular window. This means that in the time domain, the data have been 'multiplied' by a window which is unity over the duration of the data, and zero outside. As the amount of data increases, the Dirichlet kernel, W_r, tends towards a Dirac delta function. The Dirichlet kernel is plotted as a function of frequency, ω, in Figure 2.11, and it can be seen to consist of many lobes centred at frequencies 0, and $\frac{k\pi}{N}$ for k = 3, 5, 7, ... The main lobe has a width of $\frac{4\pi}{N}$ and an amplitude of N, and the side lobes each have a width of $\frac{2\pi}{N}$.

To determine the effects of using only a finite amount of data, consider the example where the data consists of a pure sinusoid as in Equation 2.124.

$$x(n) = A \cos(n\omega_1) \qquad (2.124)$$

The corresponding Fourier transform is given by Equation 2.125 for $-\pi < \omega \le \pi$.

$$X\left(e^{j\omega}\right) = \pi A \left[\delta(\omega - \omega_1) + \delta(\omega + \omega_1) \right] \qquad (2.125)$$

The Fourier transform of the truncated sequence is therefore given by Equation 2.126.

$$X_N\left(e^{j\omega}\right) = A e^{-j(\omega-\omega_1)(N-1)/2} \frac{\sin\left[\frac{(\omega-\omega_1)N}{2}\right]}{\sin\left[\frac{(\omega-\omega_1)}{2}\right]}$$

$$+ A e^{j(\omega+\omega_1)(N-1)/2} \frac{\sin\left[\frac{(\omega+\omega_1)N}{2}\right]}{\sin\left[\frac{(\omega+\omega_1)}{2}\right]} \qquad (2.126)$$

Table 2.3 Commonly used data windows

Window	$w(n), 0 \leq n \leq (N-1)$	Main–lobe width (rad)	$20 \log \left(\dfrac{\text{Main–lobe amplitude}}{\text{Largest side–lobe amplitude}} \right)$
Rectangular	1	$\dfrac{4\pi}{N}$	- 13dB
Bartlett	$\dfrac{2n}{N-1} \quad 0 \leq n \leq \dfrac{N-1}{2}$ $2 - \dfrac{2n}{N-1} \quad \dfrac{N-1}{2} < n \; N-1$	$\dfrac{8\pi}{N}$	- 27dB
Hanning	$0.5 \left[1 - \cos\left(\dfrac{2\pi n}{N} \right) \right]$	$\dfrac{8\pi}{N}$	- 32dB
Hamming	$0.54 - 0.46 \cos\left(\dfrac{2\pi n}{N} \right)$	$\dfrac{8\pi}{N}$	- 43dB
Blackman	$0.42 - 0.5 \cos\left(\dfrac{2\pi n}{N} \right) + 0.8 \cos\left(\dfrac{4\pi n}{N} \right)$	$\dfrac{12\pi}{N}$	- 58dB

Thus the effect of using only a small data set is to smear out the original delta function spectrum. This effect is commonly known as spectral leakage.

In attempts to reduce this spectral leakage, a variety of so called data windows have been introduced in order to 'smooth out' the ripples introduced by the rectangular window. A few of the window types are, Triangular, Hanning (or raised cosine), Hamming, Blackman etc. For a good introduction to windowing see (Harris, 1978). The effects of various data windows are shown in Table 2.3.

Clearly there is a trade off between side lobe levels and width of the main peak, so caution has to be applied in applying data windows depending on the application at hand. One should also say that there is a school of thought that windowing the data by anything other than a rectangular window distorts the original data, and depending on the application, (spectral analysis for example), maybe model based signal processing is more appropriate than just calculating a window based FFT, but again, this will depend on the precise nature of the application (Jaynes, 1987).

2.11 Conclusions

In this chapter, we have introduced the concept of orthogonal basis functions and the methods of obtaining the generalised Fourier coefficients which can be used in order to expand a particular signal of interest in terms of 'elementary' basis functions, for example sines and cosines.

Consideration was given to the representation of continuous signals and functions, and the analysis then considered the case of discrete data sequences.

The Fourier transform was introduced and applied to aperiodic signals and the relationship between the power in a signal and the expansion coefficients was given. Ideas concerning spectral analysis were introduced.

Linear systems theory was briefly touched upon, the z-transform was introduced and the concepts of transfer function and frequency response were discussed.

Fast implementations of the Discrete Fourier transform, using the FFT were discussed, and the ideas of spectral leakage and windowing were mentioned.

There exists a vast literature concerned with function expansion and representation, some references for which are given below.

The subject of transform methods is similarly vast, and it must be appreciated that the Fourier and z-transforms are members of a transform family including Radon transforms, Wigner transforms, Wavelet transforms and Hartley transforms, (Bracewell,1986).

2.12 References

Banks, S. (1990) *Signal Processing, Image Processing and Pattern Recognition*, Prentice Hall.

Bracewell, R.N. (1986) *The Hartley Transform*, Oxford University Press.

Burrus, C.S., Parks, T.W. (1985) *DFT/FFT and Convolution Algorithms*, Wiley Interscience.

Harris, F.J. (1978) *Proc. 66, Number 1 On the use of windows for harmonic analysis with the discrete Fourier transform*, IEEE.

Jaynes, E.T. (1987) Bayesian spectrum and Chirp analysis. *In Maximum Entropy and Bayesian Spectral Analysis and Estimation Problems*, Kluwer.

Kamen, E.W. (1990) *Introduction to Signals and Systems*, Maxwell Macmillan.

Walker, J.S. (1988) *Fourier Analysis*, Oxford University Press.

Wax, N. (ed) (1954) *Noise and Stochastic Processes*, Dover.

3   Queuing theory

Phil Whiting
University of Strathclyde

Contents

3.1   Introduction

3.1.1   Some queuing problems

Queuing is a ubiquitous feature of electronic systems such as computers and communication networks. Queues will build up, even if the capacity of the system exceeds the load on it. This is an inevitable consequence of the fact that arrivals and services take place in a random fashion. Indeed the more random the services and the arrivals are, the more queues build up. Thus it is possible for long queues to develop at even quite light loads arising as a consequence of sheer variability in the pattern of arrivals and services.

If the queue length distribution does not depend on time the queue is said to be in equilibrium. This is only possible if the queue's capacity is not exceeded. In most queuing situations the equilibrium builds up rapidly. Even when the load itself is not constant the changes in it take place more slowly than in the queue so that the equilibrium is effectively 'tracked'. This means that equilibrium models can be used to determine all the usual key performance measures: delay, queue lengths etc. Based on this, the results here are confined to equilibrium models.

Typical delay performance for a single server queue in equilibrium with a single customer class is shown in the steadily increasing graph depicted in Figure 3.1. The horizontal axis is the

representative of system performance. A fast response is a strict requirement for many electronic systems and so modelling delays and finding strategies which make efficient use of the resources within these systems becomes an essential part of their design. For example if the graph represents the performance of a computer controlling a telephone exchange, one way to reduce the average delays would be to schedule the work so as to process shorter jobs, such as call set-ups and clear downs first. This procedure 'shares out' delay in a sensible fashion. Longer jobs, for example those associated with background routines are given lower priority and are held back. Telephone calls are connected as quickly as possible, whilst the longer jobs take on an increase in delay which is often small in comparison with the amount of time needed to process them.

It is not always quite so obvious what the capacity of a queuing system is as it was in the example depicted in Figure 3.1, where the queue remained stable provided the arrival rate is less than the service rate. A communication channel which allows a group of users to share it by means of random multiple access protocols, is a case in point. Such a channel will be occupied not only with the transmission of users' information but also with reservation periods where the users actually obtain rights to transmit. Some time is used in transmissions, some in reservation but how much time is spent in each task? This depends on the nature of the protocols themselves.

For example, consider the operation of slotted ALOHA depicted in Figure 3.2. Packets of information are all the same length and a

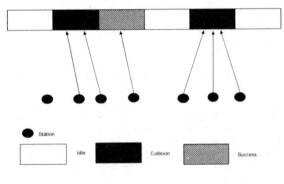

Figure 3.2   The slotted ALOHA protocol

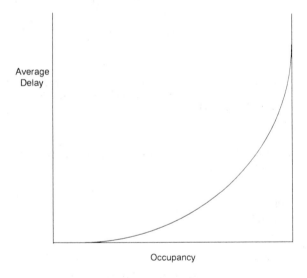

Figure 3.1   Delay performance of a single server queue

occupancy (arrival rate/service rate), which is the proportion of time the customers keep the server busy. The vertical axis is average delay. As the graph shows, there is an increasing delay penalty for using the system closer and closer to full capacity (occupancy =1). Also shown is the graph for a deterministic system (constant time between arrivals and constant service time). No queue builds up until the system is at full load. When the occupancy is less than 1 it is said that the queue is stable and an equilibrium will then exist, as already mentioned.

In most queuing situations arrivals and services do not take place in a deterministic fashion and so it is the former graph which is more

packet is received successfully if it is the only one to be transmitted in a particular slot. If two or more are transmitted there is a collision and none are successfully received, such packets are retransmitted at random in later slots. But there are many ways to choose a slot for retransmission at random and this choice is critical. It determines how successful the protocol is in avoiding collisions and how many packets can be eventually transmitted. A poor protocol choice may give very little useful throughput, or, worse still, cause the channel to jam. In this case it turns out that using fixed retransmission probabilities does not work very well. It makes no allowance for the variation in the backlog of packets awaiting retransmission. However, adjusting the retransmission probability according to an estimate of this backlog does perform adequately. Each packet is retransmitted with high probability when the backlog is estimated to be low and with low probability when the estimated backlog is high.

In queuing network problems there is more than one queue and customers make a series of visits from one queue to the next. In such networks there are interactions between the individual queues within it. For example the pattern of arrivals at one queue is determined by the departure patterns from the queues which have customers feeding into it (together with the new arrivals to the network). Since these departure patterns themselves depend on the arrivals to those queues analysis can prove very difficult.

It is interesting to learn, therefore, that for one very wide class of networks it is relatively easy to determine the equilibrium distribution of the customers within the network. Furthermore the form of this distribution is particularly striking. It is simply the product of the equilibrium distribution for each queue operating as if it were in isolation!

Such models have been used to analyse the performance of packet switched networks. In these networks, packets of information are transmitted from source to destination via a series of transmission links. These transmission links are interconnected by switching nodes which queue the packets in storage buffers until it is their turn to be transmitted. (Packet switched networks are sometimes referred to as store and forward networks.)

From these models it is known that the delays which packets experience and, indeed, the throughput of the network itself depends strongly on the routes which the packets take through it. But determining the best choice of routes using such models is not easy because the assignment of one particular route or set of routes to one group of packets has an effect on the delays which other packets experience. However effective routing algorithms have been proposed based on models such as the ones mentioned above (Gallager, 1977).

3.1.2 Little's law

There are very few completely general queuing results. However there is one, which is of considerable utility for the analysis of queues in equilibrium, Little's law. It even applies to systems which can hardly be thought of as queues at all. Suppose that customers arrive to the system (depicted as a black box in Figure 3.3) at a rate λ and that the average sojourn time for each customer is E[D], in equilibrium. Suppose further that the time average number of customers within the system is E[N]. Then Little's law gives Equation 3.1.

$$\lambda E[D] = E[N] \qquad (3.1)$$

Little's law is an accounting identity and can be understood as such. Suppose customers are charged at a rate of £1 per second they remain in the system. There are two equivalent ways in which the money can be collected. The first is to collect the appropriate amount from each customer as they leave. Since the average duration within the system is E[D] and the mean departure rate must be λ the rate at which money is being collected is λ E[D]. The other way to collect the money is for the customers to pay continuously as they remain in the system. Since the average number of customers within the system is E[N] the rate at which money is being collected is also E[N]. By altering the rates of payment one may obtain other similar identities.

3.1.3 Kendall Queuing Notation

As randomness plays such an important part in queuing performance queues are categorised accordingly. The notation A/B/m/S/P is in common use, as in Table 3.1.

Table 3.1 Notations in common use

Symbol	Item
A	Interarrival distribution
B	Service distribution
m	Number of servers
S	Storage capacity
P	Customer population

Omission of either the storage or the population entry means they are infinite. The most often used interarrival and service distributions are given in Table 3.2.

Table 3.2 Distribution symbols in use with Kendall queuing notation

Item	Symbol
Deterministic	D
Erlangian with k degrees of freedom	E_k
General	G
Hyperexponential with j degrees of freedom	H_j
Markovian	M

Markovian is equivalent to a Poisson process, if the customer population is infinite, and to exponential for the service distribution. The Erlangian distribution is just the sum of k independent, identically distributed exponential variates. Sometimes this is referred to as a server having k exponential service 'phases'. See Figure 3.4(a) illustrates E_3. (This distribution is also referred to as the gamma.) The hyperexponential is constructed from the exponential distribution as well but the customer undergoes a single service phase allocated at random from a number of possible phases, see Figure 3.4(b).

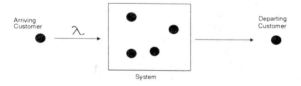

Figure 3.3 Illustration of Little's law

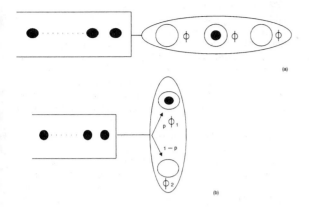

Figure 3.4 An Erlangian E_3 and a Hyperexponential H_2 server: (a) E_3; (b) H_2

Some examples of queues represented in Kendall queuing notation are:

1. D/G/1; single server queue with deterministic arrivals and an arbitrary service time.
2. M/M/3/10; a queue with Poisson arrivals, three exponential servers and room for 10 customers, including those in service.
3. M/M/1//20; a queue with exponential interarrival times with rate proportional to the number of customers not in queue, a single exponential server, and infinite waiting room. The customer population is 20.

In the case of queuing networks one may wish to specify the queue types whilst ignoring the nature of the arrival process to it altogether. In such cases it may be written, for example, that there is a network of ./M/1 queues meaning only that there is a single server at each of the nodes with exponentially distributed service times.

3.2   Models based on the exponential, Markov process and Markov chains

3.2.1   The memoryless property and the Poisson process

The exponential distribution is encountered frequently in queuing analysis. One reason is that the exponential can be used as a building block to construct other distributions as has been shown earlier. Indeed the distribution of virtually any positive random variable may be approximated using the exponential (Kelly, 1979). However, the following property is more significant reason for its importance in queuing theory.

The density of the exponential is $\varphi e^{-\varphi s}$ and integration of this gives the corresponding distribution function $1 - e^{-\varphi s}$. Suppose X is the random variable drawn from this distribution. Say that X, "completes" when the time corresponding to X is reached starting from 0). Suppose t seconds have elapsed and X has not completed. The memoryless property is this: that the distribution of remaining time until X completes in no way depends on t and is given by the same exponential distribution as X.

To see this must be the case, consider the following example. A random job from a class with exponential processing time requirements, with rate parameter φ, has been the sole task within a computer for t seconds. The total processing requirement is X. Let us compute the probability that the job will take at most a further s seconds to be completed. The proportion of random jobs whose processing times lie in the interval (t,t+s] is given by the area A under the graph in Figure 3.5, as marked. However this particular

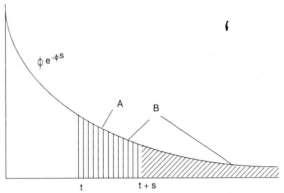

Figure 3.5   Conditional probability that the job is completed within s seconds

job is one which has taken t seconds already and it is the proportion of all such jobs which are completed within a further s seconds that is required. The probability a job takes at least t seconds is given by the tail region B. Thus the conditional distribution of the remaining time until the job is completed, given that t seconds have elapsed, is as in Equation 3.2.

$$Pr\left\{ X \leq t+s \mid t < X \right\} = \frac{Area\ A}{Area\ B}$$

$$= \frac{Pr\left\{ t < X \leq t+s \right\}}{Pr\left\{ t < X \right\}}$$

$$= \frac{e^{-\varphi t} - e^{-\varphi(t+s)}}{e^{-\varphi t}} = 1 - e^{-\varphi s} \tag{3.2}$$

This is seen to be independent of t. The conditional probability that the job is completed within a further s seconds is given by the very same exponential distribution as would be used to determine the probability of the job being completed in s seconds starting from time 0. Often it is said that the job is being processed at rate φ, meaning that the probability that the job is completed in the next infinitesimal time interval dt is $\varphi\ dt$, given it has not been completed already.

The Poisson process may be constructed from the exponential. Indeed, it is useful to regard the Poisson process as a sequence of customers arriving at a queue with mutually independent and identical exponential interarrival times. As such, the Poisson process 'inherits' the memoryless property from the exponential. This means that the probability an arrival takes place in any given interval is independent of the history of the queue prior to that interval and in particular of the state of the queue immediately before it arrives. The parameter of the Poisson process is the same rate parameter as the underlying exponential distribution.

In fact given a sequence of independent random variable, X_1, X_2, X_3, ... with common exponential distribution rate parameter λ, the sequence of arrival times is determined by expression 3.3, starting from time 0.

$$X_1, X_1 + X_2, X_1 + X_2 + X_3, ... \qquad (3.3)$$

Now that the construction follows, the Poisson distribution can be checked. To do this recall that the density of the sum of k independent exponential random variable with rate parameter λ is given by expression 3.4, which is the k-Erlangian distribution with parameter λ (Feller, 1970).

$$\lambda \frac{(\lambda t)^{k-1}}{(k-1)!} e^{-\lambda t} \qquad (3.4)$$

Denote the number of arrivals in time interval (0,t] by N_t, then Equation 3.5 may be obtained.

$$Pr\{N_t = k\} = Pr\{X_1 + ... + X_k \le t ; X_1 + ... + X_k + X_{k+1} > t\}$$

$$= \int_0^t \lambda \frac{(\lambda s)^{k-1}}{(k-1)!} e^{-\lambda s} e^{-\lambda(t-s)} ds$$

$$= \frac{(\lambda t)^k}{k!} e^{-\lambda t} \qquad (3.5)$$

3.2.2 Markov processes and Markov chains

Markov process models underlay a great deal of queuing analysis and a grasp of these models is essential to understanding analytical models of queues. A stochastic process X(s) defined on a countable state space K is said to be Markov if, given a finite sequence of n > 1 points (nearly always points in time) $s_1 < s_2$ .... $< s_n$, Equation 3.6 holds.

$$Pr\{X(s_n) = j_n | X(s_1) = j_1; ....; X(s_{n-1}) = j_{n-1}\}$$

$$= Pr\{X(s_n) = j_n | X(s_{n-1}) = j_{n-1}\}, j_1, ... j_n \ \varepsilon \ K \qquad (3.6)$$

The conditioning event must have positive probability. In words, the probability of finishing up in a particular state conditional on the process visiting given states at given times depends only on the most recent of those states stipulated. Thus to determine the probability of future events one need only take the current state into account. Notice that the above probability, the transition probability from j_{n-1} to j_n, may also depend on the time, but if it depends only on the difference $s_n - s_{n-1}$ the process is called time homogeneous. If, in addition, any state can be attained from any other state the process is said to be irreducible.

A discrete time Markov process is called a Markov chain. For simplicity it may be supposed that transitions take place at unit intervals. In Markov chains it is possible that certain states can be visited at intervals which are constant multiples of some given number v > 1. This is illustrated in Figure 3.6 which is for the absolute difference of heads to tails in a series of coin tossings. The even states are visited every other transition, so v = 2. Such a chain is called periodic. We shall not consider such chains here. All the chains considered will be aperiodic.

Time homogeneous Markov chains which are irreducible and aperiodic, may have an equilibrium probability distribution $\pi(j)$ given by Equation 3.7, where $p(k,j)$ is given by Equation 3.8.

$$\pi(j) = \sum_{k \in K} \pi(k) p(k,j) \qquad (3.7)$$

$$p(k,j) = Pr\{X(s+1) = j | X(s) = k\} \qquad (3.8)$$

If an equilibrium distribution exists the distribution of the process will always converge to it as in Equation 3.9, and, having this property, it must be unique. $\pi(j)$ can be regarded as the long run average proportion of time the process spends in state j.

$$\lim_{s \to \infty} Pr\{X(s) = j | X(0) = k\} = \pi(j) \qquad (3.9)$$

As far as the Markov processes here are concerned, they may be regarded as arising in the following way. The construction is based on the exponential which was discussed in the previous section. In each state j the rate at which transitions are made to state k is q(j,k). Thus the probability that the process enters state k in the next interval of length dt is q(j,k)dt. The probability that a transition out of state j will take place at all in the time interval dt is therefore given by Equation 3.10.

$$\sum_{k \ne j} q(j,k) dt = q(j) dt \qquad (3.10)$$

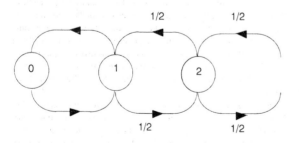

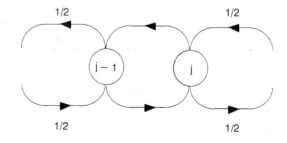

Figure 3.6   A coin tossing chain with period 2

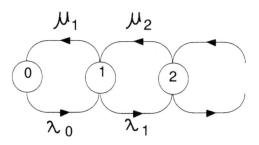

Figure 3.7 A linear birth-death model

Put another way, each visit to j has a duration which is exponential with rate parameter $q(j)$. The probability that the process then enters state k is given by Equation 3.11.

$$p(j,k) = \frac{q(j,k)}{q(j)} \tag{3.11}$$

The equilibrium distribution, if it exists, satisfies Equation 3.12, which are referred to as the global balance equations. $\pi(j) q(j,k)$ is called the probability flux out of j into state k in equilibrium.

$$\sum_{k \in K} \pi(j) q(j,k) = \sum_{k \in K} \pi(k) q(k,j) \tag{3.12}$$

3.2.3 Birth-Death models of queues

The underlying idea of this class of queuing models is to regard arriving customers as births and departures as deaths thus the queue alters by at most one. The most general form of linear birth-death process is depicted in Figure 3.7.

The global balance equations can be obtained by equating the probability flux out of each state with the probability flux into it as already described. (Equation 3.13.)

$$\lambda_0 \pi_0 = \mu_1 \pi_1 \, ;$$

$$(\lambda_k + \mu_k) \pi_k = \lambda_{k-1} \pi_{k-1} + \mu_{k+1} \pi_{k+1}, k \geq 1 \tag{3.13}$$

However these equations may be solved by using a simpler set of equations, known as the local (detailed) balance equations, as in Equation (3.14).

$$\lambda_k \pi_k = \mu_{k+1} \pi_{k+1}, k \geq 0 \tag{3.14}$$

From these equations the equilibrium solution is easily seen to be as in Equation 3.15, and π_0 is found from the fact that the probabilities must sum to 1.

$$\pi_k = \pi_0 \prod_{j=0}^{j=k} \frac{\lambda_j}{\mu_{j+1}}, k = \sim 1 \tag{3.15}$$

It can be seen that if a probability distribution which satisfies the detailed balance equations can be found then it must satisfy the global balance equations. This is so because each global balance equation is the sum of two detailed balance equations, excluding the first and the last, if there is a last. These two are just a single local balance equation. (Apart from the simplification provided, the sig-

nificance of the local balance equations is that they show that the linear birth death process is reversible in equilibrium. In crude terms, reversible Markov processes cannot be distinguished, statistically, going forwards in time from going backwards in time. From this it is clear that a Markov process must be in equilibrium to be reversible.)

By taking different birth and death rates one can obtain a wide range of queuing models, for example as in Table 3.3.

Note that in each case the mean sojourn time, $E[D]$, can be found by an application of Little's law. However in the case of M/M/K//L there is only a finite number of customers and in the case of M/M/1/S, customers are lost because there is only finite storage. In neither case is the arrival rate of customers entering queue λ.

For M/M/K//L Equation 3.16 may be obtained, where θ is the mean rate at which the customers complete a cycle of standing idle, queuing and service.

$$\theta \left(E[D] + \frac{1}{\lambda} \right) = L, E[Q] = \theta E[D] \, ; \tag{3.16}$$

Equation 3.16 follows from Little's law applied to all the customers, $\frac{1}{\lambda}$ is the mean time a customer stands idle before returning to queue for service. The second part comes from Little's law applied to the queuing and service stages, $\sum_k k Q_k = E[Q]$.

Substituting for θ gives Equations 3.17 and 3.18.

$$E[Q] = \frac{L E[D]}{\left(E[D] + \frac{1}{\lambda} \right)} \tag{3.17}$$

$$E[D] = \frac{E[Q]}{\lambda (L - E[Q])} \tag{3.18}$$

For M/M/1/S the mean arrival rate of customers entering queue is given by expression 3.19.

$$\frac{\lambda (1 - \rho^S)}{(1 - \rho^{S+1})} \tag{3.19}$$

Again from Little's law we have Equation 3.20.

$$E[D] = \left[\frac{\rho (1 - \rho^{S+1})}{(1 - \rho)(1 - \rho^S)} - \frac{(S+1) \rho^{S+1}}{(1 - \rho^S)} \right] \frac{1}{\lambda}$$

Table 3.3 Equilibrium queue distribution for some birth-death models

Queue type	Parameters	Equilibrium queue distribution
M/M/1	$\lambda_k = \lambda , k \geq 0$ $\mu_k = \mu , k \geq 1$	$Q_k = (1 - \rho) \rho^k , k \geq 0$ $E[Q] = \dfrac{\rho}{(1 - \rho)}$
M/M/K//L	$L > K , \lambda_k = (L - k) \lambda$ $\mu_k = k \mu , k \leq K$ $\mu_k = K \mu , k > K$	$Q_k = \begin{pmatrix} L \\ k \end{pmatrix} \left(\dfrac{\lambda}{\mu} \right)^k Q_0 , k \leq K$ $Q_k = \begin{pmatrix} L \\ k \end{pmatrix} \left(\dfrac{\lambda}{\mu} \right)^k \dfrac{k!}{K!} K^{K-k} Q_0 , K < k \leq L$
M/M/1/S	$\lambda_k = \lambda , k < S$ $\lambda_k = 0 , k \geq S$ $\mu_k = \mu , k > 0$	$Q_k = \dfrac{(1 - \rho)}{\left(1 - \rho^{S+1} \right)} \rho^k , k \leq S$ $E[Q] = \dfrac{\rho}{(1 - \rho)} - \dfrac{(S + 1) \rho^{S+1}}{1 - \rho^{S+1}}$
M/M/∞	$\lambda_k = \lambda ,$ $\mu_k = k \mu$	$Q_k = e^{-\rho} \dfrac{\rho^k}{k!} , k \geq 0$ $E[Q] = \rho$

$$= \left[\frac{(1 - \rho^{S+1})}{(1 - \rho)(1 - \rho^S)} - \frac{(S + 1) \rho^S}{(1 - \rho^S)} \right] \frac{1}{\mu} \qquad (3.20)$$

3.3 Transform methods

3.3.1 Customer arrival and departure distributions

It is possible to think of the distribution of the number of customers in a queue in three ways:

1. The distribution of the number of customers found in queue by an arriving customer.
2. The distribution of the number of customers left in queue by a departing customer.
3. The distribution of the number of customers in queue at a particular time.

Fortunately it is the case that, in equilibrium, the first two of these distributions coincide in very general circumstances. This will be demonstrated in a moment. It is even possible that all three of these distributions will coincide in equilibrium, this is the case when the arrival process is Poisson.

For the equality of the first two distributions in equilibrium it is sufficient that arrivals and departures should take place singly and that at least one of the two equilibrium distributions should exist. This latter condition holds for most queues, even Non-Markovian ones, provided that the queue is stable. To see this suppose, for simplicity, that the queue is initially empty. (The argument also works when there is an initial queue of customers but this minor complication is ignored.)

Figure 3.8 shows the kth departure leaving $j \leq m$ customers still in the system. This means that customer $k+m+1$ is yet to arrive and that when he does he will find m or less customers in the system. (Equation 3.21.)

$$Pr \left\{ d_k \leq m \right\} \geq Pr \left\{ a_{m+k+1} \leq m \right\} \qquad (3.21)$$

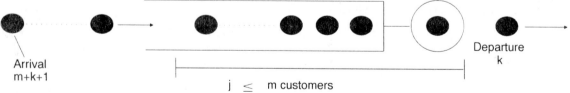

Arrival
m+k+1

$j \leq$ m customers

Departure
k

Figure 3.8 Customers 'seen' on arrival and departure

Now consider the arrival of customer m+k+1 and suppose that he too finds j ≤ m customers in the system. This means that the kth departure has already taken place and left behind at most m customers. (Equation 3.22.)

$$Pr\left\{a_{k+m+1} \le m\right\} \ge Pr\left\{d_k \le m\right\} \tag{3.22}$$

Hence Equation 3.23 can be obtained, and if we suppose that the equilibrium arrival distribution A(m) exists then Equation 3.24 follows.

$$Pr\left\{a_{k+m+1} \le m\right\} = Pr\left\{d_k \le m\right\} \tag{3.23}$$

$$A(m) = \lim_{k \to \infty} Pr\left\{a_{k+m+1} \le m\right\}$$

$$= \lim_{k \to \infty} Pr\left\{d_k \le m\right\} = D(m) \tag{3.24}$$

Similarly the equilibrium departure distribution can be shown to exist provided the equilibrium arrival distribution does and the two are once again equal.

3.3.2 Outline of the method

The approach is based on a transformation of the Markov equations which describe the queuing process and so obtaining algebraic equations for the transforms, and then solving these equations. This latter step usually involves finding zeros of functions. The method can be applied to both equilibrium and transient queues (Takacs, 1962).

The most commonly used transforms are the probability generating function (z-transform), for discrete random variables and the Laplace transform for non-negative continuous random variables. If N is a discrete random variable and T a non-negative continuous (or mixed) random variable, Equation 3.25 may be obtained, where p_k is given by Equation 3.26 and H(t) is the distribution of T.

$$f(z) = E[z^N] = \sum_{k=0}^{\infty} p_k z^k, H^*(s)$$

$$= E[e^{-sT}] = \int_0^{\infty} e^{-st} dH(t) \tag{3.25}$$

$$p_k = Pr\left\{N = k\right\} \tag{3.26}$$

A little care is needed in working with the Laplace transforms of queuing variables since mixed distributions can occur e.g. waiting times which are a mixture of an atom at the origin (no wait at all) and a continuous density (waiting time conditional on having to wait).

Moments can be obtained from these by taking derivatives at 1 and 0 respectively, as in Equation 3.27. The derivatives give factorial moments in the case of the probability generating functions and moments about the origin (to within a sign) in the case of the Laplace transform.

$$\frac{d^n f}{dz^n} = E[N(N-1)\dots(N-n+1)], \frac{d^k H^*}{ds^k}$$

$$= (-1)^k E[T^k] = (-1)^k h_k \tag{3.27}$$

3.3.3 The M/G/1 queue in equilibrium

In general the M/G/1 queue is not Markov unless one includes the time to complete the customer in service as well as the number of customers in the queue. However an analysis can be conducted by examining the queue at special instants. In fact the number of customers in queue between each departure is a Markov chain (referred to as the embedded Markov chain). This is so because the arrival process is Poisson.

Suppose the arrival rate of customers is v and the service distribution is H(x) with density h(x). The probability p_k that k customers arrive during a customer service is given by Equation 3.28.

$$p_k = \int_0^{\infty} e^{-vx} \frac{(vx)^k}{k!} h(x) dx \tag{3.28}$$

Transforming to get the generating function for the p_k's gives Equation 3.29.

$$\sum_{k=0}^{\infty} p_k z^k = \int_0^{\infty} e^{-vx} \frac{(vzx)^k}{k!} h(x) dx$$

$$= \int_0^{\infty} e^{-vx} \sum_{k=0}^{\infty} \frac{(vzx)^k}{k!} h(x) dx$$

$$= \int_0^{\infty} e^{-vx+vxz} h(x) dx = H^*(v - vz) \tag{3.29}$$

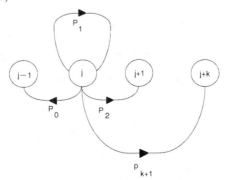

Figure 3.9 The embedded Markov chain of the M/G/1 queue

The interchange of summation and integral can readily be justified. Thus the transform of p is obtained through the Laplace transform of H. The embedded Markov chain of arrivals is determined through p but as the reader can see from Figure 3.9 the empty state is a special case. A customer departing and leaving the queue empty marks the start of an idle period.

The simplest way to analyse this chain is to work with the random variables directly. (Alternatively transform the equilibrium equations of the embedded Markov chain). Let Q_n denote queue length immediately following the nth departure, A_n the number of arrivals during the nth service then Equation 3.30 can be obtained, where I_n is 1 to allow for the departure of customer n-1 except if customer n-1 departs before customer n arrives, in which case I_n is 0, because $Q_{n-1} = 0$.

$$Q_{n+1} = Q_n + A_{n+1} - I_{n+1} \tag{3.30}$$

The probability generating function for Q_{n+1} is given by Equation 3.31.

$$Q_{n+1}(z) = E[z^{Q_{n+1}}] = E[z^{Q_n - I_{n+1}}]E[z^{A_{n+1}}]$$

$$= \left(\frac{E[z^{Q_n}] - q_{0,n}}{z} + q_{0,n} \right) H^*(\upsilon - \upsilon z)$$

$$= \left(\frac{Q_n(z) - q_{0,n}}{z} + q_{0,n} \right) H^*(\upsilon - \upsilon z) \tag{3.31}$$

Note that the number of arrivals during each service are independent of the current queue length, allowing this distribution to be factored out at the start of (Equation 3.31). By taking limits as $n \rightarrow \infty$, an equation for the equilibrium generating function, Q, for the number of customers left behind by one departing may be found from Equation 3.32.

$$Q(z) = \left(\frac{Q(z) - q_0}{z} + q_0 \right) H^*(\upsilon - \upsilon z)$$

$$= \frac{H^*(\upsilon - \upsilon z)(z - 1)q_0}{z - H^*(\upsilon - \upsilon z)} \tag{3.32}$$

Q exists whenever the queue is stable. However $-H^{*\prime}(0) = \frac{1}{\mu}$ is the mean service duration and so this condition is $\rho = -\upsilon H^{*\prime}(0) < 1$.

Setting $z = 0$ shows that q_0 is the equilibrium probability that a customer departs leaving the queue empty. Dividing by z - 1, taking limits as $z \rightarrow 1$ and applying L'Hopital's rule determines q_0 as in Equation 3.33 and hence Equation 3.34.

$$1 = Q(1) = \frac{q_0}{\lim_{z \to 1} \frac{z - H^*(\upsilon - \upsilon z)}{z - 1}} = \frac{q_0}{1 + \upsilon H^{*\prime}(0)} \tag{3.33}$$

$$q_0 = 1 - \rho, \quad Q(z) = \frac{(1 - \rho)H^*(\upsilon - \upsilon z)(z - 1)}{z - H^*(\upsilon - \upsilon z)} \tag{3.34}$$

$Q(z)$, as derived, is the generating function for the number of customers left behind in queue by a departing customer. However this is then the equilibrium distribution for the number of customers which the customer finds on arrival. This follows from the equality of equilibrium customer arrival distributions and customer departure distributions result described earlier. Note also that Q gives the time equilibrium of customers in queue as well because of Poisson arrivals.

Q can be used to obtain the equilibrium waiting time transform. Let S be the total time a customer spends in the system (queuing time plus service time) with equilibrium Laplace transform $T^*(s)$. By making an analogous argument to the one that we made for the distribution of the number of customers which arrive during a service, $Q(z)$ may be found. This is just the number of arrivals during the customers system time, so that Equation 3.35 may be obtained.

$$Q(z) = T^*(\upsilon - \upsilon z) \tag{3.35}$$

However the service time and waiting time are independent, giving Equation 3.36.

$$W^*(s)H^*(s) = T^*(s) \tag{3.36}$$

Putting these two together, and replacing $\upsilon - \upsilon z$ with s gives Equation 3.37 and Equation 3.38.

$$W^*(s)H^*(s) = T^*(s)$$

$$= \frac{(1 - \rho)H^*(s)\left[\left(1 - \frac{s}{\upsilon} \right) - 1 \right]}{\left(1 - \frac{s}{\upsilon} \right) - H^*(s)} \tag{3.37}$$

$$W^*(s) = \frac{(1 - \rho)s}{\upsilon H^*(s) + s - \upsilon} \tag{3.38}$$

This is the equilibrium transform for the waiting time.

3.3.4 The G/M/m queue in equilibrium

The analysis is very similar to the above but instead work with the queue immediately after each arrival. The waiting distribution follows immediately from this because the remaining time to complete the service of the customer at the front of the queue is exponential. (See the "memoryless" property of the exponential above.) Thus if r(z) is the generating function of customers in queue ahead of an arrival, the transform of the waiting distribution is then given by Equation 3.39 and Equation 3.40.

$$W^*(s) = r\left(\frac{\mu}{\mu + s} \right) \tag{3.39}$$

$$r(z) = \sum_{0}^{x} R_m z^m \tag{3.40}$$

The form of r is particularly simple for the G/M/m queue. Work the opposite way around from the M/G/1 queue and look at the number of departures between two arrivals. Suppose the interarrival density is given by f(x). Then assume that there are n > j customers in the queue. The probability that there are j departures before the next arrival is given by Equation 3.41 if n - j ≥ m so that all servers are busy during this period.

$$q_{n,j} = \int_0^\infty e^{-m\mu x} \frac{(m\mu x)^j}{j!} f(x)\, dx \tag{3.41}$$

For the R_n, n ≥ m-1, the equilibrium probability that an arrival finds n customers ahead of him in queue is given by Equation 3.42, where the equation includes all the possibilities: the preceding customer may find n -1, n, n + 1, ..., ... customers in queue and then that there are 0, 1, 2, ..., ... corresponding departures.

$$R_n = \sum_{k=0}^\infty R_{k+n-1} \int_0^\infty e^{-m\mu x} \frac{(m\mu x)^k}{k!} f(x)\, dx \,,\, n \geq m \tag{3.42}$$

These equations have the solution given by Equation 3.43 provided Equation 3.44 holds.

$$R_n = C \eta^n, n \geq m - 1 \tag{3.43}$$

$$\eta = F^*(m\mu - m\mu\eta) < 1 \tag{3.44}$$

Thus η is determined through the Laplace transform of F. A unique root exists if $m\mu\alpha < 1$ where α is the arrival rate. By setting n = m − 1 we obtain Equation 3.45. In the special case where m = 1 the normalisation of Equation 3.46 gives Equation 3.47 and the queue length distribution is geometric.

$$C = R_{m-1} \eta^{1-m} \tag{3.45}$$

$$\sum_0^\infty R_n = 1 \tag{3.46}$$

$$R_0 = 1 - \eta \tag{3.47}$$

To obtain the remaining probabilities, in the case when m > 1, R_{m-1}, R_{m-2}, ..., ..., R_0, compute the probability $q_{n,j}$ of there being j departures between two customer arrivals when there are n customers initially. This has been done already in the case n − j ≥ m. Suppose n ≤ m, then Equation 3.48 may be obtained, and if n > m ≥ n − j, then Equation 3.49 is obtained.

$$q_{n,j} = \int_0^\infty \binom{n}{j} (1 - e^{-\mu x})^j e^{-\mu(n-j)x} f(x)\, dx \tag{3.48}$$

$$q_{n,j} = \int_0^\infty \binom{m}{n-j} e^{-\mu(n-j)x} \int_0^x \frac{m\mu(m\mu t)^{n-m-1}}{(n-m-1)!}$$

$$\times \quad (e^{-\mu t} - e^{-\mu x})^{m-n+j}\, dt\, f(x)\, dx \tag{3.49}$$

The equilibrium probabilities that there are k customers found in queue on arrival for k = m − 1, m − 2, ..., ..., are given by a series of equations such as Equation 3.50, Equation 3.51, and so on.

$$R_{m-1} = \sum_{j=0}^\infty q_{m+j-1,j} R_{m+j-2}$$

$$= q_{m-1,0} R_{m-2} + R_{m-1} \sum_{j=1}^\infty \eta^{j-1} q_{m+j-1,j} \tag{3.50}$$

$$R_{m-2} = \sum_{j=0}^\infty q_{m+j-2,j} R_{m+j-3}$$

$$= q_{m-2,0} R_{m-3} + q_{m-1,1} R_{m-2} + R_{m-1} \sum_{j=2}^\infty \eta^{j-2} q_{m+j-2,j} \tag{3.51}$$

These equations can be solved recursively by setting $R_{m-1} = 1$ and then determining R_{m-2}, R_{m-3}, ..., ..., in turn. The solution is completed by renormalising the probabilities to sum to 1, as in Equation 3.52.

$$1 = \sum_0^{m-1} R_j + R_{m-1} \sum_{j=1}^\infty \eta^j = \sum_0^{m-1} R_j + R_{m-1} \frac{\eta}{(1-\eta)} \tag{3.52}$$

3.3.5 Results from the transforms

By differentiating Equation 3.38 and setting s to 0, the mean waiting time in a M/G/1 queue is obtained. This formula is known as the Pollazcek-Kinchine formula (Equation 3.53).

$$E[W] = \frac{\upsilon h_2}{2(1-\rho)} \tag{3.53}$$

Differentiating again the variance of the equilibrium wait may be determined, as in Equation 3.54.

$$Var[W] = \{E[W]\}^2 + \frac{\upsilon h_3}{3(1-\rho)} \tag{3.54}$$

In fact by a manipulation the waiting time transform can be inverted, as in Equation 3.55.

$$W^*(s) = \frac{(1-\rho)}{1 - \rho \frac{(1 - H^*(s))}{s/\mu}}$$

$$= (1-\rho) \sum_{k=0}^\infty \left[\rho \frac{(1 - H^*(s))}{s/\mu} \right]^k \tag{3.55}$$

However the Laplace transform of the residual service time density r(x) = μ(1 − H(x)) is given by expression 3.56, so that Equation 3.57 gives the equilibrium waiting time density (Benes, 1956) in an M/G/1 queue.

$$\frac{(1 - H^*(s))}{s/\mu} \tag{3.56}$$

$$w(x) = (1-\rho) \sum_{k=0}^{\infty} \rho^k r^{*k}(x) \tag{3.57}$$

For the G/M/1 queue the equilibrium distribution of queue length on arrival (and therefore on departure as well) is geometric, as in Equation 3.58.

$$Pr\{Q=k\} = (1-\eta)\eta^k \tag{3.58}$$

From this it follows immediately that the equilibrium G/M/1 waiting time distribution is exponential, as in Equation 3.59.

$$Pr\{W \le x\} = 1 - \eta\, e^{-\mu(1-\eta)x}, x \ge 0 \tag{3.59}$$

The probability of not waiting at all is given by setting x to be 0, $1 - \eta$. This will not be the probability that the server is idle in general with an exception for the case when the arrival process is Poisson. In fact the waiting time distribution of the G/M/m queue, is always exponential with a point probability of not having to wait at all as the reader may verify.

3.4   Queuing networks

3.4.1   With general customer routes

The results of this section can be applied to both open and closed queuing networks. In an open queuing network customers make a sequence of visits to various nodes within the network before departing from the network altogether. In closed networks on the other hand the customer population within the network remains fixed with no new customers entering the network nor ones within in it departing. Examples of these kinds of network with yet more general servers can be found in (Kelly, 1979).

The results are similar in both cases but begin by considering the open case. The network is supposed to have J nodes. The server, at each node j, applies service at a rate which depends on the total number of customers present $\varphi_j(n_j)$, taken to be zero if there are no customers present. Each customer within the queue receives a part of this effort according to the service allocation vector $\gamma(k, n_j), k \le n_j$. The amounts of service a customer requires at each queue are independent of one another and distributed exponential with unit mean. Some examples of how this vector might be set, along with the service rate, to obtain various kinds of server, are as follows:

1. ./M/1 queue with first come first served scheduling as in Equation 3.60.
2. ./M/m queue with first come first served scheduling as in Equation 3.61 and Equation 3.62.
3. Processor sharing as in Equation 3.63.

$$\varphi(n) = \varphi, \gamma(1,n) = 1, \gamma(j,n) = 0 \ otherwise \tag{3.60}$$

$$\varphi(n) = n\,\varphi\,\gamma(j,n) = \frac{1}{n}, j \le n \le m \tag{3.61}$$

$$\varphi(n) = m\,\varphi\ n > m,$$

$$\gamma(j,n) = \frac{1}{m}, j \le m, \gamma(j,n) = 0 \ otherwise \tag{3.62}$$

$$\varphi(n) = \varphi,\ n \ge 1, \gamma(j,n) = \frac{1}{n}, j \le n \tag{3.63}$$

The customers' routes through the network are determined by an ordered set of nodes, which may be regarded as the list of nodes which the customer will visit in the order in which he will visit them. A list is denoted r = (r(1),...,r(S(r))) where S(r) is the number of nodes visited. Repeat visits are permitted.

It is supposed that customers following route r arrive as a Poisson stream with rate υ_r, independently. Furthermore it will be supposed that the number of routes is finite although this is not a necessary assumption.

Apart from specifying which order the customers of a particular routing class visit a queue it is also necessary to specify how they enter each queue. This is determined by the random entrance vector, δ, which is independent of routing class. Given that there are n_j customers in the queue immediately prior to the entry of the new customer the position of the new customer is given by $\delta(k, n_j + 1)$. By choice of this vector it is possible to model queues with last come first served scheduling or service in random order.

It remains to specify the state of the network. It is not enough simply to stipulate the number of customers in each queue since this ignores which class of customers are in what positions. The state of node j is given by a vector $c_j(n_j)$ where the kth component of c_j is determined by the routing class of the customer in position k together with the stage which he has reached along his route. The state of the network consists of a vector whose components are the individual queue state vectors, C. Let q(C,D) be the transition rate from state C to state D.

There are three kinds of transition within the network, an arrival to the network, a customer moving between queues and a departure. The new state of the network immediately after the arrival of a customer, following route r, into position k of its initial queue is given by $A_k^r(C)$. The state of the network immediately after the

Table 3.4   Queuing network transition rates

Transition	Rate
Arrivals	$\upsilon_r\,\delta(k, n_j + 1)$
Departures	$\varphi_g(n_g)\gamma(k, n_g)$
Moving between queues	$\gamma(e, n_i)\varphi_i(n_i)\delta(k, n_h + 1)$

departure of a customer on route r from position k at its last queue is $L_k^r(C)$. The state of the queue immediately after a customer following route r moves from queue i position e to queue h position k is $M^r_{ie,hk}(C)$. Denote by j the first queue on route r and g the last queue on that route, then these transitions take place at the rates given in Table 3.4.

The equilibrium queue distribution is of product form, as in Equations 3.64 to 3.66, where G_j is a normalisation constant, a_j is the total traffic arriving at node j, and is given by Equation 3.67, and $\alpha_j(r)$ is the number of visits that customers on route r make to node j and (with a little abuse of notation) $\upsilon_{r(k)}$ is the arrival rate of the class of the customer who is currently in position k.

$$\pi (C) = \prod_{j} \pi_{j} (c_{j}) \tag{3.64}$$

$$\pi_{j} (c_{j}) = G_{j} \prod_{k=1}^{n_{j}} \frac{\upsilon_{r} (k)}{\varphi_{j} (k)} \tag{3.65}$$

$$G_{j}^{-1} = \sum_{n=0}^{\infty} \frac{a_{j}^{n}}{\prod_{k=1}^{n} \varphi_{j} (k)} \tag{3.66}$$

$$a_{j} = \sum_{r} \alpha_{j} (r) \upsilon_{r} \tag{3.67}$$

The following result makes it easy to verify that Equation 3.64 is indeed the equilibrium queue distribution.

Theorem 1

Suppose that numbers q'(C,D) > 0 for each pair of states C,D can be found so that Equation 3.68 is obtained.

$$\sum_{D \neq C} q' (C , D) = q' (C) = q (C) = \sum_{D \neq C} q (C , D) \tag{3.68}$$

Furthermore, suppose numbers $\pi (C) > 0$ for each state C can be found satisfying Equation 3.69 for each pair of states C,D. Then π is the equilibrium probability distribution for both Markov process whose transition rates are determined by q(C,D), q'(C,D) respectively.

$$\pi (C) q (C , D) = \pi (D) q' (D , C) \tag{3.69}$$

It is sufficient to obtain the equilibrium equations from Equation 3.68, as in Equation 3.70, but the left hand side is given by Equation 3.71.

$$\sum_{D \neq C} \pi (C) q' (C , D) = \sum_{D \neq C} \pi (D) q (D , C) \tag{3.70}$$

$$\pi (C) q' (C) = \pi (C) q (C)$$

Table 3.5 Transition rates for the reversed network

Transition	Rate
Arrivals	$\upsilon_{r} \gamma (k , n_{g} + 1)$
Departures	$\varphi_{j} (n_{j}) \delta (k , n_{j})$
Moving between queues	$\gamma (1 , n_{i} + 1) \varphi_{j} (n_{h}) \delta (k , n_{h})$

$$= \sum_{D \neq C} \pi (C) q (C , D) \tag{3.71}$$

In order to make use of this result we must find suitable transition rates q'(C,D). This is done by constructing the time reversed queuing network which has transition rates given by Table 3.5.

In the reversed network customers start from their last queue and follow their route backwards, and also the roles of γ and δ are swapped. Thus the first queue on route r is g, the last j and the queue transition is from queue h position k to queue i position e.

Consider the probability flux of arrivals of customers on route r to their first node j, r(1) = j, it is easily verified that Equation 3.72 holds and, by symmetry, a similar relationship holds for departures, as in Equation 3.73.

$$\upsilon_{r} \delta (k , n_{j} + 1) \pi (C) = \varphi_{j} (n_{j} + 1) \delta (k , n_{j} + 1) \pi (A_{k}^{r} (C)) \tag{3.72}$$

$$\varphi_{g} (n_{g} + 1) \gamma (k , n_{g} + 1) \pi (C) = \upsilon_{r} \gamma (k , n_{g} + 1) \pi (L_{k}^{r} (C)) \tag{3.73}$$

Similarly for transitions between queues from node i position e to node h position k following route r, Equation 3.74 is also easily verified.

$$\varphi_{i} (n_{i}) \gamma (e , n_{i}) \delta (k , n_{h} + 1) \pi (C) = \varphi_{h} (n_{h} + 1) \delta (k , n_{h} + 1) \gamma (e , n_{i}) \pi (M_{ iehk}^{r} (C)) \tag{3.74}$$

By adding Equations 3.72 to 3.74 and summing over all possible transitions out of state C, Equation 3.68 may be obtained.

The total rate out of state C in both networks is given by Equation 3.75.

$$q (C) = q' (C) = \sum_{j=1}^{J} \varphi_{j} (n_{j}) + \sum_{r} \upsilon_{r} \tag{3.75}$$

Thus the conditions of theorem 1 are verified and Equation 3.64 is indeed the equilibrium distribution of the network.

As described so far the customers have to call at each node in turn along their route. However it is possible to model customer classes in which each new customer is assigned one from a possible set of routes at random. This is achieved as follows. Let s be a route which can be followed. Suppose the probability that this route is followed is f_{s}. Each such route s is then offered traffic $\upsilon_{s} = \upsilon f_{s}$ where υ is the total traffic offered by the customer class using these random routes.

The approach to closed queuing networks is very similar. To begin with customers may be regarded as following a route given by a list of nodes in the order in which they are to be visited. However when a customer departs the final node in its list it returns to the first and cycles through the network again. For each route there is a population of customers which follow it, N_{r}. Let N denote the population vector giving the number of customers following each route r.

The above definitions resemble those for an open network but with no departures or arrivals from the network. A reasonable candidate for the equilibrium is to use the same form as the open network. However there are no arrivals and so a set of dummy arrival rates are assigned to each route υ_{r}. The precise values are not important as long as they are positive. The reason for this freedom in choice of arrival rates is mentioned in a moment.

Only certain states of the corresponding open network can be attained in the closed network. Thus, to obtain the candidate closed equilibrium distribution, the open distribution is renormalised to the total probability of all the possible states T in the closed queuing network, as in Equation 3.76 where π (C) is defined in Equation 3. 64 so that the equilibrium probability of being in state C is given by expression 3.77.

$$G^{-1}(N) = \sum_{C \varepsilon T} \pi(C) \tag{3.76}$$

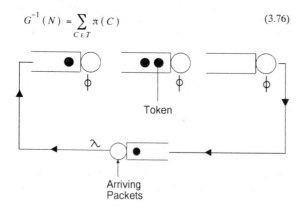

Figure 3.10 Window flow control over three consecutive transmission links

$$G(N)\pi(C) \tag{3.77}$$

That this is indeed the equilibrium may be verified using the same argument based on theorem 1. Since the system is closed the equilibrium distribution cannot depend on the dummy arrival rates. The normalisation constant cancels out the dependence of the equilibrium distribution on the dummy arrival rates.

As an example, consider a simple model of a series of transmission links access to which is regulated by window flow control, see Figure 3.10. As depicted, a packet gains access by obtaining one of the window flow control tokens. This token is carried with the packet over the three transmission links before the token is released. It is supposed to return immediately to be available for other packets to use. As Figure 3.10 shows this can be represented by a closed cyclic queuing network with the tokens as customers. These are 'served' by the arrivals which take place at rate λ and then by the transmission links. Arrivals which find no tokens are lost.

Suppose that there are N tokens and that the service rate at each of the transmission links is φ. The network state is represented by Equation 3.78.

$$n = (n_1, n_2, n_3, n_4), n_1 + n_2 + n_3 + n_4 = N \tag{3.78}$$

Using Equation 3.64, the equilibrium distribution is then given by Equation 3.79, where G is given by Equation 3.80.

$$\pi(n) = G^{-1} \frac{1}{\varphi^{n_1}} \frac{1}{\varphi^{n_2}} \frac{1}{\varphi^{n_3}} \frac{1}{\lambda^{n_4}} \tag{3.79}$$

$$G = \sum_{n:n_1+n_2+n_3+n_4=N} \frac{1}{\varphi^{n_1}} \frac{1}{\varphi^{n_2}} \frac{1}{\varphi^{n_3}} \frac{1}{\lambda^{n_4}} \tag{3.80}$$

The probability a packet is lost because there is no token available is given by expression 3.81.

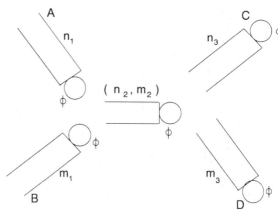

Figure 3.11 Communication network with two customer routes

$$G^{-1} \sum_{n:n_4=0} \frac{1}{\varphi^{n_1}} \frac{1}{\varphi^{n_2}} \frac{1}{\varphi^{n_3}} \tag{3.81}$$

As a second example consider the communication network shown in Figure 3.11. Customers move from A to C via the central queue or from B to D via the central queue with arrival rates υ and λ respectively. The service rate at each queue is φ.

Let n_i denote the number of customers going from A to D at each stage i and m_i the number at each stage going from B to C then, again using Equation 3.64, the equilibrium distribution is as in Equation 3.82.

$$\pi(n,m) = G^{-1} \left(\frac{\upsilon}{\varphi} \right)^{n_1} \left(\frac{\lambda}{\varphi} \right)^{m_1} \binom{n_2+m_2}{n_2}$$

$$\times \left(\frac{\upsilon}{\varphi} \right)^{n_2} \left(\frac{\lambda}{\varphi} \right)^{m_2} \left(\frac{\upsilon}{\varphi} \right)^{n_3} \left(\frac{\lambda}{\varphi} \right)^{m_3} \tag{3.82}$$

Note the combinatorial term for the centre queue. The state reflects only the number of customers of each type at each queue and the combinatorial term accounts for all possible arrangements, which are all equally likely. (Equation 3.83.)

$$G^{-1} = \left(1 - \frac{\upsilon}{\varphi} \right)^2 \left(1 - \frac{\lambda}{\varphi} \right)^2 \left(1 - \frac{\upsilon}{\varphi} - \frac{\lambda}{\varphi} \right) \tag{3.83}$$

3.4.2 Fixed point models for closed queuing networks

In many communication applications, the distributions of system random variables may be known only rather imperfectly. Consider the distribution of sojourn (queuing plus transmission) time of a packet at a node within a communication network. This varies with the flow of packets through the node. It is possible to have a very good estimate of how the mean sojourn time depends on this quantity but not have more detailed information about the distribution than this.

In these circumstances detailed modelling of the sojourn time distribution appears inappropriate. As will now be shown it is possible to deduce a great deal about performance without having to make further assumptions which would be difficult to justify and which may also complicate analysis (Kelly, 1989). These models are capable of considerable generalisation including having priority queues although this extension will not be discussed here.

The nodes within the network are labelled 1, 2,...,J. Each customer class ,r, has N_r customers in it. For each such class there is a rule which determines how the customers in the class move around within the network. This rule is based on cycles with one being completed every time certain sequences of visits are executed.

A simple rule of this type is given if a route is determined by a list of nodes which have to be visited in order. A cycle is completed once all the nodes in the list have been visited. Note that repeat visits to nodes within the list are permitted.

A more general rule is given if it is supposed that routing in each class is determined by an irreducible homogeneous Markov chain. Let π_{jk} denote the probability that the customer visits node k immediately after departing node j. A cycle is completed when a given node is returned to.

As can be seen the routing rules include those mentioned in the previous section.

Given routing rules such as these, let the mean number of visits to each node per cycle be given by α_{jr}. Finally denote the mean rate at which class r complete cycles by θ_r and the flow of customers through node j by ρ_j. Conservation of flow gives ρ_j in terms of the θ_r's, as in Equation 3.84.

$$\rho_j = \sum_j \alpha_{jr} \theta_r \tag{3.84}$$

The model is determined once the mean sojourn time at each node is specified. In the simplest cases this will be a function of mean flow and service capacity only. (Equation 3.85.)

$$D_j = D_j(\rho_j ; \varphi_j) \tag{3.85}$$

This definition allows all the queuing models described in Sections 3.2.3 and 3.3.3 to 3.3.5.

The conservation of flow equation (Equation 3.85), together with Little's law applied to each customer class, gives Equation 3.86, which yield J +R equations in J+R unknowns.

$$N_r = \theta_r \sum_r \alpha_{jr} D_j(\rho_j ; \varphi_j) \tag{3.86}$$

If D_j is non-negative and an increasing function of ρ_j then the solution is unique. We now demonstrate this.

Define H as in Equation 3.87.

$$H = -\sum_j \int_0^{\rho_j} D_j \, d\rho_j' + \sum_r N_r \log \theta_r \tag{3.87}$$

However H is strictly concave because the D_j's are continuous and monotonic increasing. Furthermore any maximum of H must be unique since H is strictly concave. In addition the maximum must

be located at an interior point. This is therefore determined by the zeros of the derivative and must be satisfied at only that point.

H has a derivative as in Equation 3.88.

$$\frac{\partial H}{\partial \theta_r} = -\sum_j \alpha_{jr} D_j + \frac{N_r}{\theta_r} \tag{3.88}$$

It can now be seen that Equation 3.86 must have just one solution since the solution determines the unique maximum of H.

Repeated substitution is one of the most numerically efficient ways of solving the above sets of equations. One begins with an initial value of the ρ_j's, for example as in Equation 3.89. The θ_r's and ρ_j's may then be solved recursively as in Equations 3.90 and 3.91.

$$\rho_j^{(1)} = 0, \ j = 1, \ldots, J \tag{3.89}$$

$$\theta_r^{(n)} = \frac{N_r}{\sum_r \alpha_{jr} D_j(\rho_j^{(n)} ; \varphi_j)} \tag{3.90}$$

$$\rho_j^{(n+1)} = \sum_j \alpha_{jr} \theta_r^{(n)} \tag{3.91}$$

On many occasions the above recursion will not converge. However the use of damping gets over this problem. With damping factor γ, $0 < \gamma < 1$ Equation 3.90 can be written as in Equation 3.92.

$$\theta_r^{(n+1)} = \frac{\gamma N_r}{\sum_r \alpha_{jr} D_j(\rho_j^{(n)} ; \varphi_j)} + (1 - \gamma)\theta_r^{(n)} \tag{3.92}$$

On some occasions heavy damping may be needed i.e. values of γ close to 0.

As an example, consider again the model of a series of transmission links, access to which is regulated by window flow control, see Figure 3.10. Again there are N tokens which circulate at rate θ. From Figure 3.10 this is determined by the fixed point Equation 3.93.

$$N = \frac{\theta}{(\lambda - \theta)} + \frac{3\theta}{(\varphi - \theta)} \tag{3.93}$$

The rate of transmitting packets is θ of course and therefore the proportion of packets which are lost is given by expression 3.94.

$$1 - \frac{\theta}{\lambda} \tag{3.94}$$

3.5 Queuing models for multi-access channels

Queuing analysis has been successfully applied to determine the throughput of a wide range of access protocols used in radio communications and elsewhere. The following provide two examples illustrating a typical approach to the problem of determining the throughput. (See also Chapter 13.)

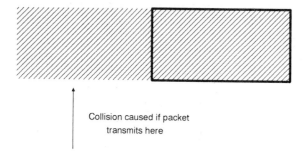

Collision caused if packet
transmits here

Figure 3.12   Vulnerable period for unslotted ALOHA

3.5.1   ALOHA models

Consider first asynchronous (unslotted) ALOHA, as shown in Figure 8.12. All packets are the same length and the transmission of a packet will be successful provided another packet does not transmit in it's vulnerable period. The probability of a successful transmission is therefore given by Equation 3.95, where γ is the total transmission attempt rate.

$$Pr\left\{\text{Successful transmission}\right\}$$
$$= Pr\left\{\text{No transmission in vulnerable period}\right\} = e^{-2\gamma} \quad (3.95)$$

The total throughput is the rate of making successful transmissions, as in Equation 3.96.

$$\text{Throughput} = \text{Transmission attempt rate}$$
$$\times \text{Probability of success}$$

$$= \gamma\, e^{-2\gamma} \quad (3.96)$$

This is maximum for $\gamma = \frac{1}{2}$ so that the throughput cannot exceed $\frac{1}{2}e$. Note that the total rate of transmissions and retransmissions is being modelled as a Poisson process of rate γ. Even if the process of fresh transmissions is Poisson, the assumption that the retransmissions are independent Poisson can only be justified if the retransmissions take place at random over long intervals following the collisions which give rise to them.

The throughput can be increased by adopting a slotted version of this protocol so that packets can only be transmitted at the beginning of each slot which was depicted in Figure 3.2. In this way if a collision takes place the two packets coincide completely, eliminating the possibility of packet loss by partly overlapping packets. The probability of success becomes $e^{-\gamma}$ and the throughput $\gamma\, e^{-\gamma}$. The maximum throughput becomes $\frac{1}{e}$ at $\gamma = 1$.

The above results must be treated with caution. The conclusions are correct but only if they are qualified. The reason for this is that the analysis does not take into account the nature of the underlying Markov chain which it purports to analyse. Indeed if an infinite station model is adopted the equilibrium can be shown not to exist (Kelly, 1985)! The slotted ALOHA channel will jam with probability 1.

Even in the case where the station population is finite the channel may perform inadequately. This is because the system may have bistable operation with one stable point at low traffic and most stations idle giving high throughput and a second one where most stations are busy and the throughput is low because of the large number of stations all attempting together. The system may remain in this second state for long periods.

The underlying difficulty is that the protocol does not adapt the number of transmission attempts according to the number of busy stations. The retransmission probability should be high if the number of busy stations is small but low when there are large numbers of busy stations. This problem is overcome by having the stations keep an estimate of the backlog which is updated following each slot according to whether it was idle contained a successful transmission or contained a collision (Gallager and Bertsekas, 1987).

3.5.2   Non-Persistent Carrier Sense Multiple Access

Under Carrier Sense Multiple Access (CSMA) mobiles in a communication network having packets to transmit do so if they "sense" the radio channel is not being used. We do not go into a description of how this is achieved but suppose that all mobiles become aware of a packet transmission within τ time units after it was begun. The period τ is called the vulnerable period.

The protocol has only two steps:

1. The channel is "sensed". If it is found to be idle the packet is transmitted immediately.
2. If the channel is "sensed" busy the packet transmission is rescheduled using the retransmission distribution. At the end of the delay period the protocol moves to step 1.

Figures 3.13(a) and 3.13(b) show successful and unsuccessful transmissions respectively. The analysis for non-persistent CSMA is as follows. During the start of a transmission there is a short period during which other transmissions may start before all other mobiles become aware that the transmission has started. This interval, in units of packet transmission time is τ as already mentioned. Making the usual assumption that transmission attempts are taking place at rate λ as a Poisson process, the probability that the packet is transmitted successfully is that there are no further transmission attempts during this vulnerable period, which is given by expression 3.97.

$$e^{-\tau\lambda} \quad (3.97)$$

Contending packets may arrive at any time during the initial vulnerable period and it is the last of these arrivals which determines when the contention period ends and the line goes idle. Let Z be a random variable defined as in Equation 3.98.

$$Z = \begin{cases} 0 \text{ No collisions} \\ \text{Time between first and last colliding packet} \end{cases} \quad (3.98)$$

Observe that Z must be less than τ. Given that there is at least one colliding packet the distribution of time between the last packet to arrive and the end of the vulnerable period is the same as the time until the first packet transmission. This observation shows that the distribution of Z is given by expression 3.99.

$$e^{-\lambda(\tau-z)} \quad (3.99)$$

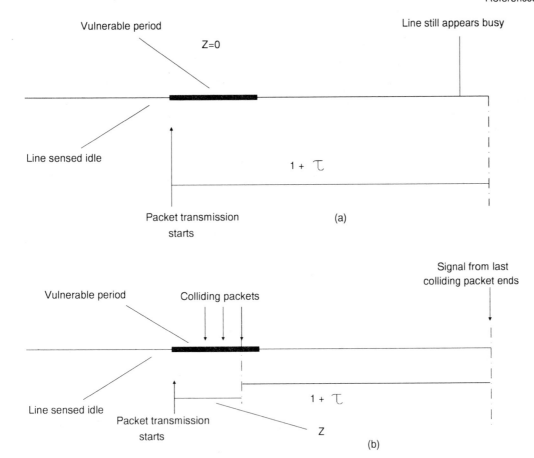

Figure 3.13 Transmission under the non-persistent CSMA protocol: (a) successful; (b) unsuccessful

From Equation 3.99 the mean value of Z is obtained, as in Equation 3.100.

$$E[Z] = \tau - \frac{1}{\lambda} + \frac{e^{-\lambda\tau}}{\lambda} \qquad (3.100)$$

Packet transmissions and contention go in cycles. There are only two kinds:

1. Successful transmission, equal to the idle period plus packet transmission time.
2. Unsuccessful period, equal to the idle period plus the contention period.

The mean duration of an idle period is $\frac{1}{\lambda}$.

The definition of Z takes into account both contention and a successful transmission. The mean for this second part of the cycle is given by expression 3.101.

$$1 + \tau + E[Z] \qquad (3.101)$$

The system throughput C is then determined as in Equation 3.102.

$$C = \frac{e^{-\tau\lambda}}{1 + \tau + E[Z] + \frac{1}{\lambda}} = \frac{\lambda e^{-\tau\lambda}}{\lambda + 2\lambda\tau + e^{-\tau\lambda}} \qquad (3.102)$$

The maximum possible throughput can now be found from examining C over all possible values of λ. Other forms of CSMA protocol are discussed in (Kleinrock, 1975b). Note, once again that these results must be treated cautiously too; stability questions arise with CSMA protocols as well.

3.6   References

Benes V.E. (1956) On Queues with Poisson Arrivals, *Annals of Mathematical Statistics*, **28**, pp. 670-677.

Feller W. (1958) *An Introduction to Probability Theory and Its Applications*, **1**, 3rd edn., Wiley.

Feller W. (1970) *An Introduction to Probability Theory and Its Applications*, **2**, Wiley.

Gallager R.G. (1977) A Minimum Delay Distributed Routing Algorithm, *I.E.E.E. Transactions on Communications*, **Com 23** (1) January, pp. 73-85.

Gallager R.G. and Bertsekas D.M. (1987) *Data Networks*, Prentice-Hall.

Kelly F.P. (1979) *Reversibility and Stochastic Networks*, Wiley.

Kelly F.P. (1985) Stochastic Models of Computer Communication Systems, *Journal Royal Statistical Society*, Series B, **47** (3), pp. 379-395.

Kelly F.P. (1989) On a Class of Queuing Approximations for Closed Queuing Networks, *Queuing Systems*, **4**, pp. 69-76.

Kleinrock L. (1975a) *Queuing Theory*, **1**, Wiley Interscience.

Kleinrock L. (1975b) *Queuing Theory*, **2**, Wiley Interscience.

Tackacs L. (1962) *An Introduction to the Theory of Queues*, Oxford University Press.

4　Information theory

William J Fitzgerald
University of Cambridge

Contents

4.1 Introduction

In this chapter, the ideas associated with information and entropy are considered and related to probability defined in terms of incomplete knowledge. Mutual and self information are introduced and these concepts are applied to various models for communications channels.

The concepts of Information and the related quantity Entropy, date back to the early days of thermodynamics. The concept of entropy arose in considerations connected with the theory of heat, and its relationship to information was not at first realised. However, in retrospect it is not surprising that the analytical treatment of information should have its origin in this area of physical science, for the subject of thermodynamics is primarily concerned with the determination of the laws that govern the conversion of mechanical and other forms of energy, into heat energy. Heat is characterised by its disorder, and ultimately by the irreversibility of certain processes which involve heat transfer. The degree of organisation of a system can also be interpreted as a measure of the quantity of information incorporated in it. This idea, was developed by Szilard in 1929, after which time the notion of entropy was another term for information, and that the physical measure of entropy was also a measure of the quantity of information or degree of organisation of the corresponding physical system. More precisely, the difference in the quantity of information between two states of a physical system is equal to the negative of the corresponding difference in entropy of the two states.

In nature it is found that self contained systems change from more highly organised structures to less organised ones, i.e. from states of higher information content to states of lower information content.

It is important to note that in the above context a physical system corresponds to many different thermodynamic systems, and entropy is not simply a property of the system, but of the experiments chosen to undertake on the system. For example, one normally controls a set of variables for the physical system, and one measures the entropy for that set. A solid with N atoms has approximately 6N degrees of freedom, of which only a few, e.g. pressure, temperature, magnetic field, are usually specified to obtain the entropy. By increasing this set, one obtains a sequence of entropy values, each corresponding to the chosen constraints.

According to Jaynes (1978), the entropy of a thermodynamic system is a measure of the degree of ignorance of a person whose sole knowledge about its microstate consists of the values of the macroscopic quantities, e.g. pressure and temperature, which define its thermodynamic state, and it is a completely objective quantity in the sense that it can be measured in the laboratory.

A very good source of reference concerning both the thermodynamic and the information processing approach to entropy and information can be found in the recent book edited by Leff and Rex (1990).

Before we concentrate on information theory proper, it will be worth laying a few foundations concerning the role of probability theory in information, and in trying to use probability theory in information theory, one immediately sees that there exist many different views as to what probability theory is, a sample of the various views being:

1. Kolmogorov; The theory of additive measures.
2. Jeffreys; The theory of rational belief.
3. Fisher; The theory of frequencies in random experiments.
4. de Morgan; The calculus of inductive reasoning.
5. Laplace; Common sense reduced to calculation.
6. Bernoulli; The art of conjecture.
7. von Mises; The exact science of mass phenomena and repetitive events.

For over one hundred years, controversy has raged between those holding these, and other views. However, these views just reflect the particular problems that were being addressed by the authors, and one should take the view that the above are valid and useful in different contexts, but that some views are more general than others, and it is this general approach that will now be discussed before we apply it to information theory.

According to the view put forward by Jeffreys, probability expresses a state of knowledge about any system under investigation, and as such applies to a very wide range of problems. This approach to probability theory incorporates many of the above mentioned interpretations.

It should not be considered wrong to adopt a narrow view of probabilities in terms of random experiments and frequencies of occurrence, but there is certainly nothing to be lost in adopting a broader view in terms of states of knowledge, and if the problem requires the concept of relative frequencies etc., this should emerge out of the broader formulation.

Consider propositions A and B. Using Boolean algebra, we may construct new propositions from A and B by conjunction, disjunction and negation, as in Equations 4.1 to 4.3.

$$A B = Both \ A \ and \ B \ are \ true \tag{4.1}$$

$$A + B = At \ least \ one \ of \ the \ propositions \ is \ true \tag{4.2}$$

$$\bar{A} = A \ is \ false \tag{4.3}$$

The conditional probability that A is true given that B is true, is a real number between 0 and 1, and is represented by the symbol $P(A|B)$. Therefore $p(A+B|CD)$ is the probability that at least one of the propositions (or hypotheses) A,B, is true, given that both C and D are true, etc.

In this formulation of probability as a state of knowledge, or a representation of incomplete knowledge, all probabilities are conditional on some information, and there does not exist an absolute probability.

The rules for conducting scientific inference follow from the simple laws of probability as in Equations 4.4 and 4.5.

$$P(AB|I) = p(A|I)p(B|AI) = p(B|I)p(A|BI) \tag{4.4}$$

$$p(A|B) + p(\bar{A}|B) = 1 \tag{4.5}$$

If $p(B|I) \neq 0$ then Bayes' theorem follows as in Equation 4.6, where I stands for any prior information.

$$p(A|BI) = \frac{(pA|I)p(B|AI)}{p(B|I)} \tag{4.6}$$

Using Bayes' theorem, it is possible to incorporate chains of evidence into one's reasoning, the posterior probability becoming the prior for the next iteration as new data become available. This method of inference goes back to Laplace in the 18th century, but the mathematics necessary to show that Bayesian inference is the only logical way to proceed was given in 1946 by R.T. Cox. However, the formalism does not show us how to assign the initial probabilities. There are several methods that may be used to assist in the initial assignment of probabilities, the first one to consider being symmetry. For example, if one considers coins or dice that are unbiased, it would seem reasonable to express this state of knowledge by assigning equal probabilities to the allowed states, and this allows us to make the best predictions we can from our state of incomplete knowledge. This is referred to as Laplace's law of insufficient reason.

Boltzmann in 1877 wished to determine how gas molecules distribute themselves in a conservative field such as gravity. He divided the 6-d 'phase space', 3 spatial dimensions and 3 momentum dimensions, into equal cells, with N_i molecules present in the *i*th cell.

The number of ways this distribution can be realised is as in Equation 4.7.

$$W = \frac{N!}{N_1! N_2! .... N_n!} \qquad (4.7)$$

The prior knowledge that Boltzmann was able to use was that the total energy and the total number of molecules in the gas was constant, as in Equations 4.8 and 4.9.

$$N = \sum_i N_i = constant \qquad (4.8)$$

$$E = \sum_i N_i E_i = constant \qquad (4.9)$$

Boltzmann considered that the most probable distribution for this case was the one that maximises W subject to the constraints given above.

If the total number of gas molecules is large, then Stirling's approximation gives Equation 4.10, which may be seen to be related to the Shannon entropy.

$$\frac{1}{N} \log W = - \sum_i \left(\frac{N_i}{N} \right) \log \left(\frac{N_i}{N} \right) \qquad (4.10)$$

Thus the most likely distribution is obtained by maximising entropy subject to the constraints of the problem. This methodology has, over the years, been applied to a vast range of problems, with remarkable success.

Information theory says that a random variable, X, which has an associated probability density function, p(x), has an entropy given by Equation 4.11 which means that H bits are sufficient to describe X on the average.

$$H = - \sum p(x) \log p(x) \qquad (4.11)$$

Kolmogorov similarly described algorithmic complexity, K(x), to be the shortest binary program that describes X. According to Kolmogorov, Information theory must precede probability theory, and should not be based on it, and his contribution to information theory followed by a direct development of his ideas in algorithmic complexity. In particular, he was interested in finding any determinism in random events, and his work on turbulence must be seen in this light as an attempt to find deterministic order in chaotic processes, and indeed turbulence was one of the key phenomena that motivated the resurgence of interest in non-linear dynamical systems, and the range of chaotic phenomena and strange attractors.

It is interesting that many of the ideas borrowed from information theory are used to classify many of the chaotic signals, such as heart beats, brain waves, chemical reactions, lasers, flames, etc., and Dimensions, Entropies and Lyapunov exponents are used routinely.

4.2 Information capacity of a store

Figure 4.1(a) shows a system with two possible states. If the position of the points is unknown, a priori, and we learn that the point is in the left hand box, say, we gain information amounting to 1 bit. If we obtain this information, we save one question in order to locate the point. Hence the maximum information content of a system with two states is one bit.

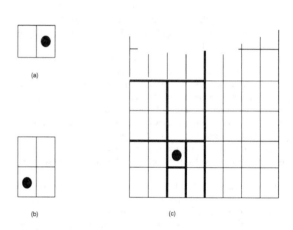

Figure 4.1 Information capacity of a store: (a) a box with two states; (b) it takes two questions and their answers to locate a point in a system with four states: right or left ? up or down ? (c) in order to locate a point on a board with 64 = 2^6 states, six questions are required

For a box with two states, one needs two questions in order to locate the point, (such as, is the point to the right or left and up or down?) and the maximum amount of information is two bits. This can, of course, be written as the logarithm to the base 2 of the number of allowable states. In general, the maximum information content associated with a system having N states, is given by Equation 4.12.

$$I = \log_2 N \qquad (4.12)$$

We can also consider the outcome of statistical events, and calculate the average gain of information associated with such events. As an example, consider coin tosses, such that the outcome, heads or tails, occurs with equal probability of 1/2.

The information gain acquired by learning that the outcome of an experiment is heads, say, is given by Equation 4.13.

$$I = - \left(\frac{1}{2} \log_2 \frac{1}{2} + \frac{1}{2} \log_2 \frac{1}{2} \right) = 1 \qquad (4.13)$$

In general, therefore, the information gain associated with many states having probabilities associated with each state, is given by Equation 4.14.

$$I = -\sum_i p_i \log_2 p_i \qquad (4.14)$$

4.3 Information and thermodynamics

Boltzmann realised that entropy was a measure of disorder of the configuration of the system being considered. This viewpoint was extended by Szilard in 1929, and he identified entropy with information, and the measure of information with the negative of the measure of entropy. This laid the foundations of information theory.

This viewpoint came about due to a paradox conceived of by Maxwell concerning two chambers separated by a common partition which could be removed to allow objects (gas molecules) to move freely between the two chambers. Normal experience tells us that if one of the chambers initially has gas present and the partition is withdrawn, then gas will rapidly diffuse to fill both chambers. The reverse never occurs.

Maxwell proposed his famous 'demon' whose purpose was to open a small frictionless door present in the partition, and when a particle, due to thermal motion heads towards the door, the demon opens the door to let the particle through the partition, in one direction only, and as time passes, one chamber gets filled up with particles at the expense of the other, thus seeming to violate the second law of thermodynamics. This paradox was explained by Szilard, who pointed out that in order for the demon to perform, it had to be very well informed about the position and velocity of the particle as it approached the door. Szilard's argument is very well given in the book by Leff and Rex, (1990), and led to the realisation of the connection between entropy and information.

4.3.1 Entropy of finite schemes

Consider a complete system of events, $A_1, A_2,...A_n$ such that one and only one event may happen at a given trial, e.g. tossing a coin, for which $n = 2$, and the events are mutually exclusive.

Every finite scheme describes a state of uncertainty, and we only know the probability of possible outcomes, i.e. a one in six chance of a particular face of a dice being uppermost (for a fair dice).

If for one scheme the particular probabilities are different, then there will be different degrees of uncertainty associated with states having different probabilities. It is therefore essential to derive a measure of uncertainty of a particular scheme, and the quantity given in Equation 4.15 is a very suitable measure.

$$H(p_1, p_2, ... p_n) = -\sum_{i=1}^{n} p_i \log p_i \qquad (4.15)$$

The logarithm is taken to be an arbitrary base, and $p_i \log p_i = 0$ if $p_i = 0$. The quantity H is called the entropy of the finite scheme.

Around the time when Szilard was considering Maxwell's demon and the connection between entropy and information, the whole of physics was undergoing vast changes due to the development of quantum theory. Of particular interest is the work of J. Von Neumann, who in 1932, showed that in the process of making measurements, the observer must be taken into account, and this gathered together ideas of entropy, information and irreversibility.

It was R.V. Hartley (1928), of the Bell Telephone laboratories who gave the logarithmic definition of information from a communications viewpoint, and it was C. Shannon who further refined the ideas in 1949.

Suppose that X is a random variable or random vector that can be described by its probability density function p (x), where x takes values in a certain alphabet, A_x. Shannon (1949), defined the entropy of X by Equation 4.16.

$$H = -\sum_{x \in A_x} p_x(x) \log p_x(x) \qquad (4.16)$$

Similarly, given two discrete random variables X and Y, one can define various entropies H(X,Y), H(X), H(Y) as well as the conditional entropy as in Equation 4.17 (see the next section).

$$H(X|Y) = H(X,Y) - H(Y) \qquad (4.17)$$

It should also be mentioned that the statistician R.A. Fisher in 1922 defined the information content of a statistical distribution, and this Fisher information still plays a fundamental role in statistical estimation and parameter estimation in general, and allows one to put bounds on the accuracy with which one can estimate parameters.

4.4 Mutual and self information

Let X and Y be two discrete variables with possible outcomes x_i, $i = 1,2,...,n$, and y_i, $i = 1,2,...,m$, respectively. If an outcome $Y = y_j$ is observed, and we wish to quantitatively determine the amount of information that this observation provides about the event $X = x_i$, $i = 1,2,...n$, then the appropriate measure of information has to be selected. If X and Y are statistically independent, then the occurrence of $Y = y_j$ provides no information about the occurrence of $X = x_i$. If, however, the random variables are fully dependent on one another, then the outcome of one determines the outcome of the other. An obvious measure that satisfies these 'boundary conditions' is that of the logarithm of the ratio of the conditional probability $P(x_i|y_i)$ divided by $P(x_i)$, and this defines the mutual information $I(x_i, y_j)$ between x_i and y_j as in Equation 4.18.

$$I(x_i, y_i) = \log \frac{P(x_i|y_j)}{P(x_i)} \qquad (4.18)$$

When the random variables are statistically independent, Equation 4.19 and therefore Equation 4.20 are obtained.

$$P(x_i|y_i) = P(x_i) \qquad (4.19)$$

$$I(x_i, y_j) = 0 \qquad (4.20)$$

However, when the occurrence of event $Y = y_i$ uniquely determines the occurrence of event $X = x_i$, the conditional probability above is unity, and therefore Equation 4.21 is obtained which is called the self information of the event $X = x_i$.

$$I(x_i, y_j) = \log \frac{1}{P(x_i)} = -\log P(x_i) \qquad (4.21)$$

It should be noted that an event that occurs with high probability conveys less information than a low probability event.

Consider the expression given above for the mutual information, and since we can write Equation 4.22 then the mutual information obeys the symmetry relation given in Equation 2.23 by virtue of Bayes' theorem.

$$\frac{P(x_i|y_j)}{P(x_i)} = \frac{P(x_i|y_j)P(y_j)}{P(x_i)P(y_j)}$$
$$= \frac{P(x_i,y_j)}{P(x_i)P(y_j)} = \frac{P(y_j|x_i)}{P(y_j)}$$
(4.22)

$$I(x_i,y_j) = I(y_j,x_i)$$
(4.23)

The average value of the mutual information defined above is given by Equation 4.24

$$I(X,Y) = \sum_{i=1}^{n}\sum_{j=1}^{m} P(x_i,y_j) I(x_i,y_j)$$
$$= \sum_{i=1}^{n}\sum_{j=1}^{m} P(x_i,y_j) \log\frac{P(x_i,y_j)}{P(x_i)P(y_j)}$$
(4.24)

Likewise, the average value of the self information, H(X) is defined by Equation 4.25.

$$H(X) = \sum_{i=1}^{n} P(x_i) I(x_i)$$
$$= -\sum_{i=1}^{n} P(x_i) \log P(x_i)$$
(4.25)

For any given communication source transmitting an 'alphabet' of symbols, the entropy of the source is a maximum when the output symbols are equally probable, as is clear since if the symbols are equally probable, Equations 4.26 and 4.27 and in general Equation 4.28 are obtained.

$$P(x_i) = \frac{1}{n} \quad \text{for } all \ i$$
(4.26)

$$H(X) = -\sum_{i=1}^{n} \frac{1}{n} \log\frac{1}{n} = \log n$$
(4.27)

$$H(X) \leq \log n$$
(4.28)

It is very straightforward to show that Equation 4.29 follows with equality if and only if X and Y are independent, and that Equation 4.30 is true where $H(X|Y)$ is a conditional uncertainty, etc.

$$H(X,Y) \leq H(X) + H(Y)$$
(4.29)

$$H(X,Y) = H(X) + H(Y|X)$$
$$= H(Y) + H(X|Y)$$
(4.30)

The above definitions of mutual information, self information and entropy for discrete random variables may be easily extended to the case of continuous random variables, and if the joint probability density functions and the marginal probability density function are p(x,y), p(x) and p(y) respectively, then the average mutual information between X and Y (or the cross entropy) is given by Equation 4.31 and the entropy of X in the continuous case by Equation 4.32 where m(x) is an appropriate measure function (Jaynes, 1989).

$$I(X,Y) = \int_{-\infty}^{\infty}\int_{-\infty}^{\infty} p(x)p(y|x)$$
$$\log\frac{p(y|x)P(x)}{p(x)p(y)} \ dx \ dy$$
(4.31)

$$H(X) = -\int_{-\infty}^{\infty} p(x)\log\frac{p(x)}{m(x)} \ dx$$
(4.32)

4.5 Discrete memoryless channels

The discrete memoryless channel serves as a statistical model with an input X and an output Y which is a noisy version of X, and both X and Y are random variables.

The channel is said to be 'discrete' when both the alphabets from which X and Y are selected have finite size, not necessarily the same size, and the channel is said to be 'memoryless' when the current output symbol depends only on the current input symbol and not on any previous ones (c.f. Markov models and ARMA processes etc.).

In terms of the elements of the input and output alphabets, one can define a set of transition probabilities for all j and k, as in Equation 4.33 and this is just the conditional probability that the channel output is $Y = y_k$ given that the channel input is $X = x_j$.

$$p(y_k|x_j) = P(Y = y_k|X = x_j)$$
(4.33)

Due to transmission errors, when k = j, the transition probability represents the conditional probability of correct reception, and when $k \neq j$ the conditional probability of error.

Just as for Markov processes, one can define a transition probability matrix as follows.

$$P = \begin{bmatrix} p(y_0|x_0) & p(y_1|x_0) & \cdots & p(y_{K-1}|x_0) \\ p(y_0|x_1) & p(y_1|x_1) & \cdots & p(y_{K-1}|x_1) \\ \cdot & \cdot & \cdots & \cdot \\ \cdot & \cdot & \cdots & \cdot \\ \cdot & \cdot & \cdots & \cdot \\ p(y_0|x_{J-1}) & p(y_1|x_{J-1}) & \cdots & p(y_{K-1}|x_{J-1}) \end{bmatrix}$$

This is a J by K matrix called the channel matrix. The sum of elements along any row is given by Equation 4.34 for all j.

$$\sum_{k=0}^{K-1} p(y_k|x_j) = 1$$
(4.34)

If the inputs to a discrete memoryless channel are selected according to the probability distribution p(x), j = 0,1,...,J-1, then the event $X = x_j$ occurs with probability given by Equation 4.35.

$$p(x_j) = P(X = x_j)$$
(4.35)

The joint probability distribution of the random variables X and Y is given by Equation 4.36 and the marginal distribution of the output variable Y is obtained by integrating out, or averaging out, the dependence on x_j for (j = 0,1,..., J-1), as in Equation 4.37 for k = 0,1,...,K-1.

$$p(x_j,y_k) = P(X = x_j, Y = y_k)$$

$$= P(Y = y_k | X + x_j) P(X = x_j)$$

$$= p(y_k | x_j) p(x_j) \tag{4.36}$$

$$p(y_k) = \sum_{j=0}^{J-1} p(y_k | x_j) p(x_j) \tag{4.37}$$

This is a very important equation, since if we are given the input a priori probabilities p(x_j) and the channel matrix, then we may obtain the probabilities of the various output symbols from the above equation.

4.5.1   Channel capacity

Regardless of whatever means, or channel, is used for transmission, there is a maximum rate of transmission, called the 'capacity' of the channel, which is determined by the intrinsic properties of the channel and is independent of the content of the transmitted information and the way it is encoded. This is measured in bits per second. As an example, in order to transmit a colour television picture, a channel with a capacity of about 200 million bits per second is required.

For a discrete memoryless channel with transition probabilities $p(y_k | x_j)$ as before, the average mutual information between the output and the input is given by Equation 4.38.

$$I(X,Y) = \sum_{j=0}^{J-1} \sum_{k=0}^{K-1} p(x_j, y_k) \log \frac{p(y_k | x_j)}{p(y_k)} \tag{4.38}$$

Also as before, Equations 4.39 and 4.40 may be obtained.

$$p(x_j, y_k) = p(y_k | x_j) p(x_j) \tag{4.39}$$

$$p(y_k) = \sum_{j=0}^{J-1} p(y_k | x_j) p(x_j) \tag{4.40}$$

From the expression for the average mutual information, it is seen therefore that the average mutual information depends both on the channel characteristics expressed in terms of the elements of the channel matrix, and also on the input probability distribution, which is clearly independent of the channel. Therefore, by changing the input probability distribution, the average mutual information will change, and we can define the 'channel capacity' in terms of the maximum average mutual information with respect to the input probability distribution.

We can therefore write the channel capacity as in Equation 4.41.

$$C = \max \; I(X, Y) \tag{4.41}$$

The calculation of C is a constrained optimisation, since the constraints of Equations 4.42 and 4.43 have to apply to p(x_j).

$$p(x_j) = 0 \tag{4.42}$$

$$\sum_{j=1}^{J-1} p(x_j) = 1 \tag{4.43}$$

This may be compared to the method employed for the maximum entropy analysis of images and inverse problems (Jaynes, 1989; Skilling, 1988).

The channel capacity is an extremely important quantity, since it is possible to transmit information through a channel at any rate less than the channel capacity with an arbitrary small probability of error; completely reliable transmission is not possible if the information processed is greater than the channel capacity. However, in general, the calculation of the channel capacity is a difficult problem.

Before calculating the channel capacity for some simple channel models, it is useful to introduce certain classes of channel, as follows:

1. A channel is lossless if $H(X|Y) = 0$ for all input distributions, which means that the input is determined by the output, and hence no transmission errors can occur.
2. A channel is deterministic if $p(y_j | x_i) = 1$ or 0 for all i, j, which means that Y is determined by X, and hence $H(Y|X) = 0$ for all input distributions.
3. A channel is noiseless if it is lossless and deterministic.
4. A channel is useless or zero capacity if $I(X|Y) = 0$ for all input distributions.
5. A channel is symmetric if each row of the transition matrix contains the same set of numbers, and if each column contains the same set of numbers (different in general for the row set).

It is a consequence of the definition of the symmetric channel that $H(Y|X)$ is independent of the input distribution p(x), and depends only on the channel probabilities $p(y_j | x_i)$.

The best known model for a symmetric channel is the binary symmetric channel shown in Figure 4.2. As an example of the calculation of the channel capacity, a closed form expression for a symmetric channel will be given.

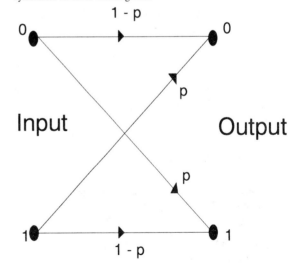

Figure 4.2   Binary symmetric channel

Let us consider a symmetric channel with input alphabet $x_1, ..., x_M$, and output alphabet $y_1, ..., y_L$, and a channel matrix with row probabilities $p_1', ..., p_L'$ and column probabilities $q_1', ..., q_M'$. Since $H(Y|X)$ does not depend on the input distribution, the problem of maximising the information reduces to the problem of maximising the output uncertainty H(Y) as in Equation 4.44.

$$I(X|Y) = H(Y) - H(Y|X) \quad (4.44)$$

It is known that Equation 4.45 holds with equality if and only if all values of Y are equally likely.

$$H(Y) \leq \log L \quad (4.45)$$

Therefore, if an input distribution can be found for which all values of Y have the same probability, then that input distribution would maximise $I(X|Y)$. The uniform distribution does this, since Equation 4.46 holds and for a uniform distribution Equation 4.47 holds.

$$p(y_j) = \sum_{i=1}^{M} p(x_i) p(y_j|x_i) = \frac{1}{M} \sum_{i=1}^{M} p(y_j|x_i) \quad (4.46)$$

$$p(x_i) = \frac{1}{M} \text{ for all } i \quad (4.47)$$

However, the term $\sum_{i=1}^{M} p(y_j|x_i)$ is the sum of the entries in the jth column of the channel matrix, and since the channel is symmetric, Equation 4.48 is obtained, which is independent of j, and hence $p(y_j)$ does not depend on j, or equivalently all values of Y have the same probability.

$$\sum_{i=1}^{M} p(y_j|x_i) = \sum_{k=1}^{M} q_k' \quad (4.48)$$

The maximum, given by Equation 4.49, is therefore attainable and the channel capacity can be written as in Equation 4.50 since Equation 4.51 is also true.

$$H(Y) = \log L \quad (4.49)$$

$$C_{sym} = \log L + \sum_{j=1}^{L} p_j' \log p_j' \quad (4.50)$$

$$H(Y|X) = -\sum_{j=1}^{L} p_j' \log p_j' \quad (4.51)$$

For the binary symmetric channel shown in Figure 4.2, the channel capacity can be written as in Equation 4.52 and the variation with β is shown in Figure 4.3.

$$C_{BSC} = \log 2 + \beta \log \beta + (1-\beta) \log(1-\beta)$$
$$= 1 - H(\beta, 1-\beta) \quad (4.52)$$

4.5.2 Source encoding

An important problem in communications is how to efficiently represent data generated by a discrete source. This is called source encoding. For a source encoder to be efficient, one needs knowledge of the statistics of the source. For example, if some source symbols

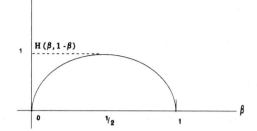

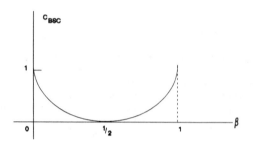

Figure 4.3 Capacity of a binary symmetric channel

are known to be more probable than others, then this feature may be exploited by assigning short code words to frequent source symbols and vice versa, e.g. the Morse code.

The average length of a code word, L can be written as in Equation 4.53.

$$L = \sum_{k=1}^{K} P_k l_k \quad (4.53)$$

This represents the average number of bits per source symbol used in the source encoding process. If L_{min} represents the minimum possible value of L, the coding efficiency of the source encoder is defined as in Equation 4.54 and the source encoder is said to be efficient when η approaches unity.

$$\eta = \frac{L_{min}}{L} \quad (4.54)$$

One question of importance is how to determine the minimum length code. The answer to this is given in Shannon's first theorem, also called the source coding theorem. This states that given a discrete memoryless source of entropy H(X), then the average code word length L for any source encoding is bounded as in Equation 4.55.

$$L \geq H(X) \quad (4.55)$$

Therefore, the entropy H(X) represents a fundamental limit on the average number of bits per source symbol necessary to represent a discrete memoryless source. Thus Equation 4.56 can be obtained and the efficiency of the source encoder may be written in terms of the entropy as in Equation 4.57.

$$L_{min} = H(X) \quad (4.56)$$

$$\eta = \frac{H(X)}{L} \qquad (4.57)$$

A theorem which is complementary to Shannon's first theorem and applies to a channel in which the noise is Gaussian is known as the Shannon-Hartley theorem, which states that the channel capacity of a white, bandlimited Gaussian channel is given by Equation 4.58, where B is the channel bandwidth, S the signal power, and N is the total noise within the channel bandwidth.

$$C = B \log_2\left(1 + \frac{S}{N}\right) \qquad bits/s \qquad (4.58)$$

This theorem, although restricted to Gaussian channels, is of fundamental importance, since many channels are approximately Gaussian, and the results obtained by assuming a Gaussian channel often provide a lower bound on the performance of a system operating over a non-Gaussian channel. The Shannon-Hartley theorem indicates that a noiseless Gaussian channel $\left(\frac{S}{N} = \infty\right)$ has an infinite capacity. However, when noise is present in the channel, the capacity does not approach infinity as the bandwidth is increased, since the noise power increases as the bandwidth increases, and the channel capacity reaches a finite upper limit with increasing bandwidth if the signal power remains constant. This limit is easily calculated using the fact that the total noise within the channel bandwidth is given by Equation 4.59 where $\frac{\eta}{2}$ is the two-sided power spectral density. The Shannon-Hartley theorem may now be written as in Equations 4.60 and 4.61.

$$N = \eta B \qquad (4.59)$$

$$\begin{aligned} C &= B \log_2\left(1 + \frac{S}{\eta B}\right) \\ &= \left(\frac{S}{\eta}\right)\left(\frac{\eta B}{S}\right)\log_2\left(1 + \frac{S}{\eta B}\right) \end{aligned} \qquad (4.60)$$

$$C = \frac{S}{\eta}\log_2\left(1 + \frac{S}{\eta B}\right)^{\eta B/S} \qquad (4.61)$$

Using Equation 4.62 gives Equation 4.63.

$$x = \frac{S}{\eta B} \qquad (4.62)$$

$$\lim_{B \to \infty} C = \frac{S}{\eta}\log_2 e = 1.44\frac{S}{\eta} \qquad (4.63)$$

The Shannon-Hartley theorem allows for a trade off between bandwidth and signal to noise ratio, in the following sense. If, for example, the signal to noise ratio S/N = 7, and B = 4kHz, we obtain C = 12x10³ bits/s. If the signal to noise ratio is increased to 15, and the bandwidth increased to 3kHz, the channel capacity remains the same.

We have seen that in the case of a noiseless channel, the capacity is infinite, and no matter how restricted the bandwidth, it is always possible to receive a signal without error, as predicted by the Shannon limit. The question of how in practice one achieves this performance is complex, one method being the use of orthogonal signals.

Let us now consider the problem of the reliable transmission of messages through a noisy communications channel. We therefore need the best decoding scheme to enable us to obtain the input sequence after seeing the received symbols. Assuming the input alphabet $x_1,...,x_M$, output alphabet $y_1,...,y_L$, and channel matrix $p(y_j|x_i)$ as before, and consider the special case where a sequence of symbols, chosen at random according to a known distribution, p(x), is transmitted through the channel. For this given distribution p(x), we wish to construct a decision scheme that minimises the overall probability of error. Such a scheme is called an ideal observer.

Consider a sequence $x = (\alpha_1, ..., \alpha_n)$ chosen in accordance with the distribution p(x). The probability that the output sequence $\beta_1, ..., \beta_n$ is produced is given by Equation 4.64, which may also be written as Equation 4.65.

$$\begin{aligned} p(\beta_1, ..., \beta_n &= \sum_{\alpha_1,...,\alpha_n} p(\alpha_1,...,\alpha_n) \\ &\times p(\beta_1,...,\beta_n | \alpha_1,...,\alpha_n \end{aligned} \qquad (4.64)$$

$$\begin{aligned} p(\beta_1,...,\beta_n) &= \sum_{\alpha_1,...,\beta_n} p(\alpha_1,...,\alpha_n) \\ &\times p(\beta_1|\alpha_1(p(\beta_2|\alpha_2)\cdots p(\beta_n|\alpha_n) \end{aligned} \qquad (4.65)$$

A decoder scheme may be defined as a function that assigns to each output sequence $(\beta_1,...,\beta_n)$ an input sequence $(\alpha_1,...,\alpha_n)$ and the ideal observer is the scheme which minimises the overall probability of error for the given input distribution, and this is found by maximising the conditional probability as given by Equation 4.66.

$$\begin{aligned} p(\alpha_1,...,&\alpha_n | \beta_1,...,\beta_n) \\ &= \frac{p(\alpha_1,...,\alpha_n)\,\Pi_{k=1}^n\,p(\beta_k|\alpha_k)}{p(\beta_1,...,\beta_n)} \end{aligned} \qquad (4.66)$$

When all the inputs are equally likely, then Equation 4.67 may be obtained and for a fixed y, maximising $p(x_i|y)$ is equivalent to maximising the inverse probability $p(y|x_i)$. This is referred to as the maximum likelihood decision scheme.

$$p(x_i|y) = \frac{p(x_i)p(y|x_i)}{p(y)} = \frac{1}{M\,p(y)}p(y|x_i) \qquad (4.67)$$

4.6   Discrete channels with memory

Previously we have described channels that have no memory, that is channels in which the occurrence of errors during a particular symbol interval does not influence the occurrence of errors during succeeding symbol intervals. However in many realistic channels, errors do not occur as independent random events, but tend to occur in bursts. These channels are said to have memory. Examples of channels with memory would be telephone channels that suffer from switching transients, and microwave radio links that suffer from fading, etc.

It is useful to give two simple models for discrete channels with memory, before going onto ideas associated with capacity and coding for these channels. The first model is due to Blackwell

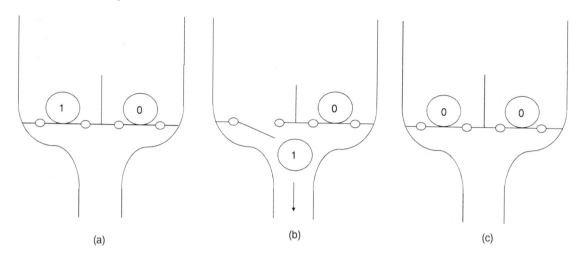

Figure 4.4 Trapdoor channel

(1961), and considers 'trapdoors' as shown in Figure 4.4. Initially a ball labelled with 0 or 1 is placed in each of the two slots. One of the trapdoors is then opened, with each door having the same probability of being opened. The ball then falls through the open door, and the door then closes behind it. The empty compartment then has another ball placed in it, and the whole process starts all over again. This model defines a channel whose inputs correspond to the balls placed in the empty compartment and whose outputs correspond to the balls which fall through the trapdoors. If the symbol b_i corresponds to the condition in which a ball labelled i remains in an occupied slot, and time is started after one of the doors is opened, four states s_{ij}, for i,j = 0 or 1 may be defined as follows. The channel is in state s_{ij} at time t = n, if the condition b_i holds at time t = n and condition b_j hold at time t = n-1. An input k therefore corresponds to the placing of a ball labelled k in the unoccupied slot, and the opening of the trapdoor then determines the corresponding output and the next state.

If at time t = n the channel is in state s_{10}, and an input 1 is applied, then one ball labelled 0 and one ball labelled 1 rest over the trapdoors. With a probability of 1/2 the ball 1 falls through, leaving the ball 0 in the occupied slot. The channel then moves to state s_{00} and emits an output of 1. With probability 1/2 the 0 ball falls through, sending the channel into the state s_{01}, and an output 0 is emitted. The behaviour of this channel may thus be described by two matrices, M_0 and M_1, called the channel matrices, and whose components are the state transition probabilities under the input 0 and 1 respectively, and a function that associates an output with each input-state pair, Figure 4.5.

Another model that is successful in characterising error bursts and impulsive noise in channels is the so called Gilbert model, where the channel is modelled as a discrete memoryless binary symmetric channel for which the probability of error is a time varying parameter. The changes in probability of error are modelled as a Markov process as shown in Figure 4.6. The error generating mechanism in the channel occupies one of the three states. When the channel is in state 2, the probability of error during a bit interval is 10^{-2} and the channel stays in this state during the succeeding bit interval with a probability of .998. The channel may make a transition to state 1, which has a bit error probability of 0.5, and since the

system stays in this state with probability .99, errors tend to occur in groups.

The models developed for the case of a discrete channel with memory are those for which the channel has a finite number of internal states, for which the present state of the channel represents a summary of its past history. The application of an input will result in a transition to another state, with the production of an output. The resulting source channel matrix then determines a finite Markov chain with states (a_i, s_k) where a_i are the states of the source and s_k are the states of the channel. If the chain associated with the source channel matrix has steady state probabilities, then given the pair (a_i, s_k) one can determine the corresponding input $f_1(a_i, s_k) = f(a_i)$ and output $g_1(a_i, s_k) = g(f(a_i), s_k)$. Thus the chain associated with the source channel matrix determines a stationary sequence of input-output pairs (X_n, Y_n), for n = 1,2,... An input, output and joint

$$
\text{input = 0} \quad
\begin{array}{c}
 \\
S_{00} \\
S_{10} \\
S_{01} \\
S_{11}
\end{array}
\begin{array}{cccc}
S_{00} & S_{10} & S_{01} & S_{11} \\
\left[\begin{array}{cccc}
1 & 0 & 0 & 0 \\
1 & 0 & 0 & 0 \\
0 & \frac{1}{2} & 0 & \frac{1}{2} \\
0 & \frac{1}{2} & 0 & \frac{1}{2}
\end{array}\right]
\end{array} = M_0
$$

$$
\text{input = 1} \quad
\begin{array}{c}
 \\
S_{00} \\
S_{10} \\
S_{01} \\
S_{11}
\end{array}
\begin{array}{cccc}
S_{00} & S_{10} & S_{01} & S_{11} \\
\left[\begin{array}{cccc}
\frac{1}{2} & 0 & \frac{1}{2} & 0 \\
\frac{1}{2} & 0 & \frac{1}{2} & 0 \\
0 & 0 & 0 & 1 \\
0 & 0 & 0 & 1
\end{array}\right]
\end{array} = M_1
$$

Figure 4.5 Channel matrices for the trapdoor channel

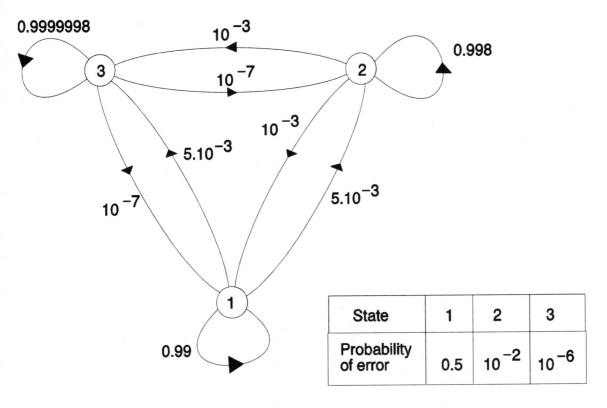

State	1	2	3
Probability of error	0.5	10^{-2}	10^{-6}

Figure 4.6 A three state Gilbert model

uncertainty may therefore be defined respectively as in Equations 4.68 to 4.70.

$$H(X) = \lim_{n \to \infty} H(X_n | X_1, \dots X_{n-1}) \qquad (4.68)$$

$$H(Y) = \lim_{n \to \infty} H(Y_n | Y_1, \dots Y_{n-1}) \qquad (4.69)$$

$$H(X,Y) = \lim_{n \to \infty} H[(X_n, Y_n)|(X_1, Y_1), \dots$$
$$\dots (X_{n-1}, Y_{n-1})] \qquad (4.70)$$

The information conveyed about the process X by the process Y is given by Equation 4.71.

$$I[X|Y] = H(X) + H(Y) - H(X,Y) = I[Y|X] \qquad (4.71)$$

The capacity of the given channel is defined as the least upper bound of $I[X|Y]$, taken over all regular Markov sources, and it can be proved that it is possible to transmit information at any rate less than the capacity with an arbitrarily small probability of error.

The above discussion says nothing about how one calculates the channel capacity of a given finite-state channel. This is an extremely complex task, and details may be found in Proakis (1987).

It is possible to model a channel such that the model combines features of the discrete memoryless channel with those of the discrete channel with memory, and this defines a compound channel.

4.7 Continuous channels

Communications channels may be continuous in two senses. In the first sense, we may allow the input and output alphabets to contain an infinite number of elements, but we require that the transmitted material be in the form of a discrete sequence of symbols. This type of channel is called a time-discrete, amplitude continuous channel.

For the second type of continuous channel, we allow the transmission of information to be continuous in time.

Consider an analog source that emits a message waveform x(t) which is a sample function of a stochastic process X(t). If X(t) is a stationary stochastic process with autocorrelation function $\Phi_{xx}(\tau)$ and power spectral density function $\Phi_{xx}(f)$, and if X(t) is a bandlimited process such that Equation 4.72 is satisfied, then X(t) has a representation given by the sampling theorem as in Equation 4.73.

$$\Phi_{xx}(f) = 0 \quad \text{for } |f| > W \qquad (4.72)$$

$$X(t) = \sum_{n=-\infty}^{\infty} X\left(\frac{n}{2W}\right) \frac{\sin 2\pi W\left(t - \dfrac{n}{2W}\right)}{2\pi W\left(t - \dfrac{n}{2W}\right)} \tag{4.73}$$

This means that the bandlimited signal can be represented by a sequence of samples as in Equation 4.74 sampled at the rate given by Equation 4.75 the so called Nyquist rate. These samples may then be encoded using various techniques giving a digital representation of the analog signal.

$$X_n = X\left(\frac{n}{2W}\right) \tag{4.74}$$

$$f_s = 2W \quad samples \ per \ second \tag{4.75}$$

One such technique is Pulse Code Modulation (PCM), the essential operations being sampling, quantising and encoding, usually performed in the same circuit, called an analog-to-digital converter (ADC). It should be noted that PCM is not modulation in the conventional sense of the word, since modulation usually refers to the variation of some characteristic of the carrier wave in accordance with an information bearing signal. The only part of PCM that is similar to this definition, is sampling. The subsequent use of quantisation, which is basic to PCM, introduces a signal distortion that has no counterpart in conventional modulation.

Let $x(t)$ denote a sample function emitted by a source, and let x_n represent the samples taken at a sampling rate greater than the Nyquist rate, 2W, where W is the highest frequency present in the signal. In PCM, each sample is quantised to one of 2^b amplitude levels, where b is the number of binary digits used to represent each sample. The rate from the source is therefore bf_s bits per second, where f_s is the sampling frequency.

The quantisation may be represented as in Equation 4.76, where $\tilde{x}_n$ represents the quantised value of x_n and q_n represents the quantisation error which is treated as additive noise.

$$\tilde{x}_n = x_n + q_n \tag{4.76}$$

If an uniform quantiser is used, the quantisation noise is well represented by an uniform probability density function, and the mean square value of the quantisation error can be shown to be as in Equation 4.77, where $\Delta = 2^{-b}$ is the step size of the quantiser.

$$E(q^2) = \frac{\Delta^2}{12} = \frac{2^{-2b}}{12} \tag{4.77}$$

Measured in decibels, the mean square value of the noise is as in Equation 4.78.

$$10 \log \frac{\Delta^2}{12} = -6b - 10.8 \ dB \tag{4.78}$$

For example, a 7-bit quantiser gives a quantisation noise power of -52.8 dB.

A uniform quantiser provides the same spacing between successive levels throughout the entire dynamic range of the signal. In practice this can cause problems since for many signals, speech for example, small signal amplitudes occur more frequently than large signal amplitudes, and a better approach would have more closely spaced levels at low signal amplitudes, and vice versa. The desired form of nonuniform quantisation can be achieved by using a compressor followed by a uniform quantiser. By cascading this combination with an expander complementary to the compressor, the original signal samples are restored to their correct values apart for quantisation errors. This combination of compressor and expander is called a compander.

There are basically two types of compander in current use, μ-law and A-law.

The transfer characteristic of the compressor is represented by a memoryless nonlinearity $c(x)$, where x is the sample value of a random variable X denoting the compressor input. In the μ-law compander, $c(x)$ is continuous, approximating a linear dependence on x for low input levels and a logarithmic one for high input levels, as in Equation 4.79 for $0 \leq \dfrac{|x|}{x_{max}} \leq 1$.

$$\frac{c(|x|)}{x_{max}} = \frac{\ln\left(1 + \dfrac{\mu |x|}{x_{max}}\right)}{\ln(1 + \mu)} \tag{4.79}$$

The special case of uniform quantisation corresponds to the case where $\mu = 0$. The μ-law is used for PCM telephone systems in the USA, Canada and Japan.

In A-law companding, the compressor characteristic is piecewise, made up of a linear segment for low-level inputs and a logarithmic segment for high-level inputs. This type of compander is used for the PCM telephone systems in Europe.

In PCM each sample of the waveform is encoded independently of all the other samples. However, most source signals sampled at or above the Nyquist rate exhibit significant correlation between successive samples, i.e. the average change in amplitude between successive samples is relatively small. An encoding scheme that exploits the redundancy in the samples will result in a lower bit rate for the source output, and one such system called Differential pulse code modulation (DPCM) does this by encoding the differences between successive samples rather than the samples themselves.

A sub-class of DPCM is delta modulation in which the code word is only one binary digit in length. Delta modulators have the advantage over more conventional PCM systems of having a particularly simple architecture, which forms the basis of 'single-chip' coder-decoder (CODEC) integrated circuits. Because delta modulation is a 1-digit code, sampling rate and output digit rate are the same. However, in order for delta modulation to achieve performance comparable to that of conventional n-digit PCM systems, the sampling rate must be increased substantially over that required for a PCM system.

Most real signal sources are nonstationary in nature, which means that the variance and the autocorrelation function of the source output vary with time. PCM and DPCM encoders are designed on the basis that the source output is stationary, and the performance of these encoders can be improved by using adaptive methods. One such method being the use of an adaptive quantiser.

PCM, DPCM and the adaptive counterparts are source encoding techniques that attempt to represent the output waveforms. Consequently these methods are known as waveform encoding techniques. In contrast to these methods, Linear Predictive Coding models the source as a linear system, which when excited by an appropriate input signal gives rise to an observed source output. Instead of transmitting the samples of the source waveform to the receiver, the model parameters of the linear system are transmitted together with the appropriate excitation signal.

4.8   References

Cox, R.T. (1946) *Am.J.Phys.* 17.1.1946.

Gull, S. (1988) Developments in Maximum Entropy data analysis. *In Maximum Entropy and Bayesian Methods* (ed. J. Skilling). Kluwer Academic Press.

Hartley, R.V.L. (1928) Transmission of Information. *Bell Systems Technical Journal*, July.

Jaynes, E.T. (1978) Where do we stand on Maximum Entropy. *In The Maximum Entropy Formulism* (ed. R.D. Levine and M. Tribus) M.I.T. Press.

Jaynes, E.T. (1989) *Papers on probability, statistics and statistical physics* (ed. R.D. Rosenkranz) Kluwer Academic Press, 1989.

Leff, H.S. and Rex, A.F. (1990) *Maxwell's Demon, Entropy, Information, Computing*. Adam Hilger Press.

Proakis, J. (1987) *Digital Communications*. McGraw-Hill.

Shannon, C. (1949) *The Mathematical Theory of Communication*, University of Illinois Press.

Skilling, J. (ed) (1988) *Maximum Entropy and Bayesian Methods*. Kluwer Academic Press.

5 Teletraffic theory

R J Gibbens
MA, Dip Math Stat, PhD
University of Cambridge

Contents

5.1 Introduction

The subject of Teletraffic Theory has a long history dating back to the work of the Danish mathematician, A.K. Erlang (Brockmeyer, 1948), first published in 1917. Today the subject has grown enormously and is still growing at a rapid pace with research into the performance modelling of areas as diverse as, for example, dynamic routeing strategies, cellular mobile radio systems and the application of fast packet switching techniques proposed for use in a broadband integrated services digital network. Hui (1990) is a good text for some of these more recent developments.

In Section 5.2 the basic model of a single link in a circuit switched telecommunication network is studied. This section also introduces the important control mechanism of trunk reservation.

Section 5.3 shows how the single link models studied in Section 5.2 can be incorporated into models of networks of links using the effective link independence approximation to construct the Erlang fixed point systems of equations. These equations allow the investigation of the rich behaviour of dynamic routeing strategies in the setting of symmetric fully connected networks. This section on network based results ends with two bounds on the overall best possible behaviour of dynamic routeing strategies.

Section 5.4 presents some of the dynamic routeing strategies that have been either implemented or proposed for real networks. This is an area which has received much attention over the last decade and is one in which teletraffic theory has provided the models and understanding leading to more efficient, flexible and reliable networks.

5.2 Single link models

5.2.1 Erlang's loss formula

The first model to be considered is the classical model for a single link in a circuit switched network. Suppose that the arrival process of calls offered to a link is a Poisson process of rate λ. Let the holding times of calls be exponentially distributed with a mean of 1 independently of the arrival process. Suppose that the link has a capacity of C circuits. See Figure 5.1 and Chapter 3 for an introduction to the theory of stochastic processes applied to queueing networks.

This system may be modelled by the stochastic process, n, the number of circuits occupied by the link with n taking values in the range 0 to C inclusive. It can be seen that n is a birth and death

process since n either increases by one when a new call is accepted on the link or decreases by one when an existing call clears down. The transition rates for the birth and death process are therefore given by Equations 5.1 and 5.2.

$$q(n, n+1) = \lambda \quad n = 0, 1, ..., C-1 \tag{5.1}$$

$$q(n, n-1) = n \quad n = 1, ..., C \tag{5.2}$$

A general result, (Kelly, 1979) on birth and death processes gives the equilibrium distribution in terms of the birth and death rates, as in Equation 5.3 where π_0 is determined from the normalisation condition of Equation 5.4.

$$\pi_n = \pi_0 \prod_{i=1}^{n} \frac{q(i-1, i)}{q(i, i-1)} \tag{5.3}$$

$$\sum_{n=0}^{C} \pi_n = 1 \tag{5.4}$$

Hence, from Equations 5.1 and 5.2 one can obtain Equations 5.5 and 5.6.

$$\pi_n = \pi_0 \prod_{i=1}^{n} \frac{\lambda}{i} = \pi_0 \frac{\lambda^n}{n!} \tag{5.5}$$

$$\pi_0 = \left[\sum_{n=0}^{C} \frac{\lambda^n}{n!} \right]^{-1} \tag{5.6}$$

In summary, the equilibrium distribution for the utilisation, n, of a single link is given by Equation 5.7.

$$\pi_n = \frac{\dfrac{\lambda^n}{n!}}{\displaystyle\sum_{i=0}^{C} \frac{\lambda^i}{i!}} \quad (n = 0, 1, ..., C) \tag{5.7}$$

In particular, the probability, L, that an arriving call finds the link full to capacity is π_C given by Equation 5.8.

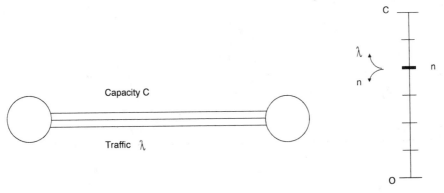

Figure 5.1 Single link model

$$L = \pi_C = \frac{\lambda^C}{C!} \left[\sum_{i=0}^{C} \frac{\lambda^i}{i!} \right]^{-1} \qquad (5.8)$$

Equation 5.8 is known as Erlang's loss formula and is undoubtedly the most widely used result in teletraffic theory. The standard notation $E(\lambda,C)$ for the quantity given in Equation 5.9 will be used.

$$E(\lambda,C) = \frac{\lambda^C}{C!} \left[\sum_{i=0}^{C} \frac{\lambda^i}{i!} \right]^{-1} \qquad (5.9)$$

Later the question of how best to compute $E(\lambda,C)$ in such a way as to reduce numerical inaccuracies caused by rounding errors will be considered. First, let us look at some of its properties.

In Figure 5.2 the loss probability $L = E(\lambda,C)$ is shown as a function of the traffic intensity $\rho = \lambda/C$ for C held fixed at the values C = 100, 250, 1000 and 10000. This figure demonstrates the important trunking efficiency effect where for a fixed level of the traffic intensity, ρ, the loss probability, L, decreases with increasing link capacity, C: larger links are more efficient at carrying calls. Also shown in the figure is the limiting case as C increases to infinity which is given by Equation 5.10.

$$L = \max \left(1 - \frac{1}{\rho}, 0 \right) \qquad (5.10)$$

5.2.1.1   Numerical considerations

Several methods are available for the efficient and accurate numerical evaluation of Erlang's loss formula. For small values of C, perhaps up to several hundreds of circuits, $E(\lambda,C)$ can be computed using the recursive formula of Equation 5.11 and $E(\lambda,0) = 1$.

$$E(\lambda,C) = \frac{\lambda E(\lambda,C-1)}{C + \lambda E(\lambda,C-1)} \qquad (5.11)$$

This result can be derived by substituting the expression for $E(\lambda,C)$ given in Equation 5.9 and simplifying the resulting expression.

For larger values of C, which make a recursive computation impractical, a second method is available which avoids the direct calculation of large factorials. After some re-arrangement Equation 5.12 may be obtained.

$$E(\lambda,C) = \left[1 + \frac{C}{\lambda} + \frac{C(C-1)}{\lambda^2} + \ldots + \frac{C!}{\lambda^C} \right]^{-1} \qquad (5.12)$$

Written in this form each successive term in the summation is a simple multiple of the previous one and so direct calculation of factorials may be avoided. The final sum is then inverted to give the loss probability.

5.2.2   Multiple priorities and trunk reservation

Consider again a single link with C circuits but now suppose that there are two independent Poisson arrival streams offered at rates λ_1 and λ_2. Suppose we wish to give priority to the calls at rate λ_1 over those at rate λ_2. A very simple mechanism has been devised to implement these priorities known as trunk reservation. In this mechanism, calls of the low priority stream are only accepted when there are at least r + 1 free circuits available. In contrast, the high priority calls are accepted so long as there is at least 1 free circuit available. The integer value, r, is known as the trunk reservation parameter. An equivalent notation which is sometimes more convenient is to let C^i be the capacity available to calls of priority i or lower so that $C^1 = C$ and $C^2 = C - r$.

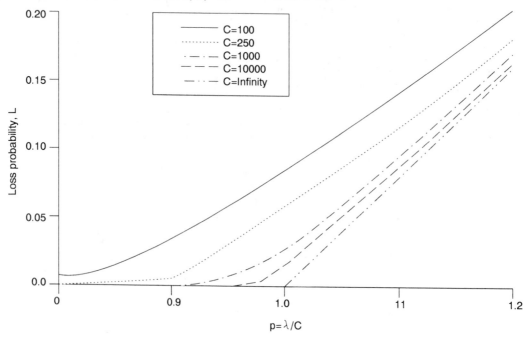

Figure 5.2   Erlang's blocking formula

Again, a birth and death process can be used to model the system. The transition rates are now given by Equations 5.13 and 5.14.

$$q(n, n+1) = \begin{cases} \lambda_1 + \lambda_2 & n = 0, ..., C-r-1 \\ \lambda_1 & n = C-r, ..., C \end{cases} \tag{5.13}$$

$$q(n, n-1) = n \quad n = 1, ..., C \tag{5.14}$$

The equilibrium distribution, using the general result in Equation 5.3 is given, after some re-arrangement, by Equation 5.15, where π_0 is determined by Equation 5.16.

$$\frac{\pi_n}{\pi_o} = \begin{cases} \dfrac{(C-r)!}{n!}(\lambda_1 + \lambda_2)^{n-(C-r)} & n = 0, ..., C-r \\ \dfrac{(C-r)!}{n!}\lambda_1^{n-(C-r)} & n = C-r+1, ..., C \end{cases} \tag{5.15}$$

$$\sum_{n=0}^{C} \pi_n = 1 \tag{5.16}$$

The above procedure to avoid computing large factorials in Erlang's loss formula can also be used here to calculate the distribution π_n.

Two criteria for selecting the trunk reservation parameter r will now be considered.

5.2.2.1 Optimality criterion for r

Consider the situation given by Equations 5.17 and 5.18.

$$B_1(r) = \pi_C \tag{5.17}$$

$$B_2(r) = \sum_{k=C-r}^{C} \pi_k \tag{5.18}$$

Then $B_1(r)$ and $B_2(r)$ are the blocking probabilities to the high and low priority streams respectively when the trunk reservation parameter level is set at the value r.

A criterion for choosing r, which is applicable in much of the work to follow on control in routeing strategies in fully connected networks, is to minimise with respect to r the expression of 5.19.

$$\lambda_1 B_1(r) + \frac{1}{2}\lambda_2 B_2(r) \tag{5.19}$$

This would correspond to a valuation by the link that the carrying of a low priority call is worth just half the carrying of a high priority call. Here we think of high priority calls as the directly routed calls and the low priority calls as the overflow calls using two links.

In Figure 5.3 the value of r minimising expression 5.19 is illustrated with λ_1 held fixed in such a way that $E(\lambda, C) = 1\%$ for two values of C.

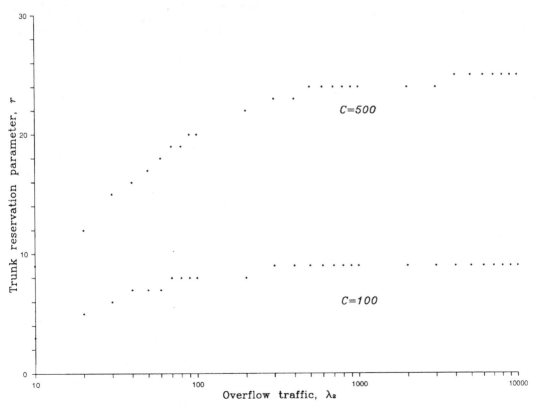

Figure 5.3 Optimality criterion

The value of expression (5.19) is relatively insensitive to r above a low threshold. Thus, while minimising the value of r can be quite sensitive to the precise values of C, λ_1, and λ_2 close to optimal performance over a wide range of values of C, λ_1 and λ_2 can be obtained by quite a crude choice of the parameter r.

5.2.2.2   *Secondary criterion for r*

A further criterion which may be applied to selecting the trunk reservation parameter r is as follows. The approach begins by first recognising that the offered traffics in a network are in practice very uncertain and large low priority overflow traffics may occur. Trunk reservation may then be used to guarantee performance in the worst case conditions of infinite overflow traffic, where the number of circuits in use on a link is forced to remain in the states {C − r, ..., C}, where r > 0 is the trunk reservation parameter. Then the transition rates for the birth and death process are simply as in Equations 5.20 and 5.21.

$$q(n, n+1) = \lambda \quad n = C - r, ..., C - 1 \tag{5.20}$$

$$q(n, n-1) = n \quad n = C - r + 1, ..., C \tag{5.21}$$

If B(λ,C,r) is the blocking probability for fresh traffic under these circumstances then Equation 5.22 may be obtained.

$$B(\lambda, C, r) = \left[\sum_{n=c-r}^{C} \frac{C(C-!) \dots (n+1)}{\lambda^{C-n}} \right]^{-1} \tag{5.22}$$

A rationale for choosing the trunk reservation parameter is then to relate λ and C by Equation 5.23, where B > 0 is a fixed constant, and to take the trunk reservation parameter, R(C), as in Equation 5.24 for some constant K with 1 < K < 1/B.

$$E(\lambda, C) = B \tag{5.23}$$

$$R(C) = \min\{r : B(\lambda, C, r) \le KB\} \tag{5.24}$$

Suppose that fresh traffic alone would suffer a blocking probability of B. Then the trunk reservation mechanism with parameter r = R(C) chosen in accordance with this criterion ensures that the blocking probability for fresh traffic under arbitrary conditions of overflow traffic is no worse than K times that without overflow traffic. Figure 5.4 gives some examples of R(C) with several values of the parameter K.

5.3   Network models

5.3.1   Erlang fixed point

In section 5.2 models of a single link was described. In this section the scope will be broadened to investigate models of networks of links. The simplest, and most commonly used, approach to creating a model of a network of links is to use an approximation that blockings on links within a route are statistically independent. In order to describe this approximation consider a simple situation of a network of nodes fully connected by links each of capacity C and with independent Poisson arrival streams of traffic offered between the pairs of nodes each of rate λ.

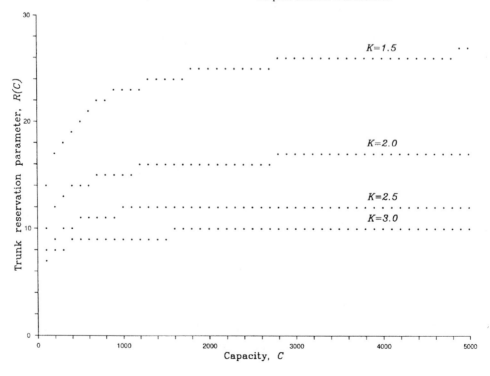

Figure 5.4   Secondary criterion

The fully connected network architecture has been the focus of much attention in recent years in relation to studies of dynamic routeing strategies for national trunk networks. Section 5.4 considers in some depth the various strategies that have so far been proposed. In this section a simple strategy for symmetric fully connected networks is considered, that will suffice to illustrate many of the modelling aspects. In practice, networks are not symmetric, and in particular traffics may not be well matched to capacity. Nevertheless, one can learn much about the behaviour of routeing schemes from a consideration of the symmetric case (see Gibbens 1990 for further discussion on dynamic routeing strategies).

This simple strategy is called random routeing and operates as follows: a call arriving at the network from the source destination pair (i, j) is routed along link (i, j) if there is at least one free circuit on this link; otherwise an intermediate node k(k ≠ i, j) (sometimes called a tandem node) is chosen at random and the call is routed along the two link path between nodes i and j via node k provided that there are at least r + 1 free circuits on each of the links (i, k) and

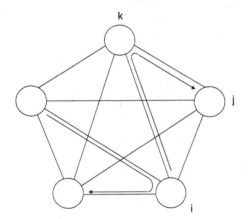

Figure 5.5 A fully connected network

(k, j); otherwise the call is lost. Notice that each link receives direct and overflow traffic. (See Figure 5.5.) Let B_1 and B_2 be the blocking probabilities of a link for direct and overflow traffic respectively. Observe that B_1 and B_2 will differ as a result of the use of the trunk reservation mechanism with parameter r.

Consider a single link in such a network and let, n, be the number of circuits in use. The process, n, can be modelled by a birth and death process with transition rates as in Equations 5.25 and 5.26, where σ is the rate of overflow traffic.

$$q(n, n+1) = \begin{cases} \lambda + \sigma & n = 0, ..., C - r - 1 \\ \lambda & n = C - r, ..., C - 1 \end{cases} \quad (5.25)$$

$$q(n, n-1) = n \quad n = 1, ..., C \quad (5.26)$$

The independent blocking approximation allows σ to be expressed in terms of B_1 and B_2 by Equation 5.27.

$$\sigma = 2\lambda B_1 (1 - B_2) \quad (5.27)$$

The interpretation of Equation 5.27 is that blocking conditions of different links are approximately independent, and that overflow traffic arriving at a link is approximately Poisson. A call blocked

with probability B_1 on its direct route will attempt an alternative route through two links, but may be blocked at either of these links. The transition rates correspond to the acceptance by a link of direct traffic and overflow traffic (at rates λ and σ respectively) in states {0, ..., C − r − 1} and of direct traffic only (at rate λ) in states {C − r, ..., C − 1}.

If L is the probability that a call offered to the network is lost then Equation 5.28 may be obtained.

$$1 - L = (1 - B_1) + B_1 (1 - B_2)^2 \quad (5.28)$$

Since calls are first offered to the direct links and are accepted with probability $(1 - B_1)$ and with probability B_1 they overflow to a randomly chosen two-link alternative path on each link of which they are independently accepted with probability $(1 - B_2)$.

The task is now to solve for B_1 and B_2. Let $\{\pi_n : n = 0, ..., C\}$ be the stationary distribution of the process, n, then Equations 5.29 and 5.30 are obtained.

$$B_1 = \pi_C \quad (5.29)$$

$$B_2 = \sum_{n = C - r}^{C} \pi_n \quad (5.30)$$

The distribution $\{\pi_n : n = 0, ..., C\}$ is itself a function of B_1 and B_2 and so Equations 5.25 to 5.30 define B_1 and B_2 implicitly as in Equations 5.31 and 5.32 for some functions φ_1 and φ_2.

$$B_1^{l+1} = \varphi_1 (B_1^l, B_2^l) \quad (5.31)$$

$$B_2^{l+1} = \varphi_2 (B_1^l, B_2^l) \quad (5.32)$$

Choosing initial starting values for B_{10} and B_{20} one can use repeated substitution in Equations 5.31 and 5.32 to readily obtain a solution. By the Brouwer fixed point theorem there exists a solution, and indeed as will be seen later there may be more than one solution.

Now, suppose that a call blocked on its direct route is allowed to attempt not just one but up to M two-link alternatives before it is lost. Again, use trunk reservation to insist that at least r + 1 circuits be free on a link before it accepts an alternatively routed call. Then the process, n, modelling the utilization of a link is again a birth and death process with rates as given by Equations 5.25 and 5.26 but now with the overflow rate (σ) given by Equation 5.33 and the loss probability (L) given by Equation 5.34.

$$\sigma = 2\lambda B_1 (1 - B_2)^{-1} \left\{ 1 - [1 - (1 - B_2)^2]^M \right\} \quad (5.33)$$

$$L = B_1 [1 - (1 - B_2)^2]^M \quad (5.34)$$

Note that these expressions reduce to those in Equations 5.27 and 5.28 with the choice M = 1. The repeated substitution method can again be used to determine a solution for B_1 and B_2 given some initial starting values.

Figure 5.6 shows solutions to these fixed point equations when r = 0 (i.e. no trunk reservation is applied) with M = 1,5 and a range of values of λ and C. Note that when r = 0 we have that $B_1 = B_2 = B$, say. Observe the possibility of multiple solutions for B for C large

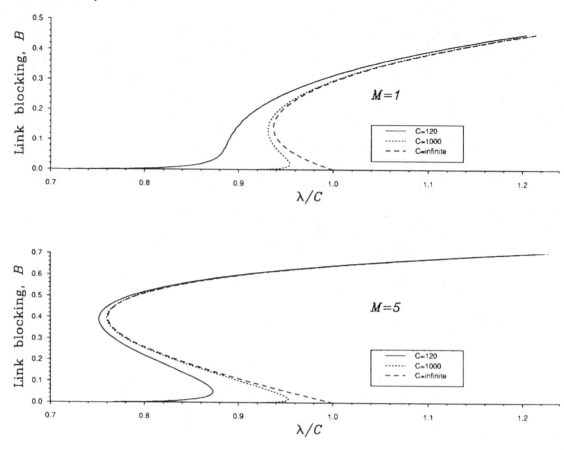

Figure 5.6 Blocking probability B with M = 1, 5

enough and for a narrow range of the ratio λ/C and that these effects are magnified in the case of larger M. The upper and lower solutions correspond to stable fixed point solutions while the middle solution corresponds to an unstable fixed point.

Simulations also exhibit this bistable behaviour where the network has two quasi-stable states. A high blocking state corresponding to many calls being carried on two-link routes and a low blocking state corresponding to only a few calls carried over two links with the majority carried on one-link routes.

Trunk reservation has been found to be an ideal way of preventing this bistable behaviour in the network performance and for providing more efficient use of network resources. In Figure 5.7 the loss probability, L, is shown as a function of r for values M = 1 and 5, λ = 110, and C = 120. Observe that a value of r in a broad range will give close to optimal performance.

Now consider the effect of increasing the number of retries M. Figure 5.8 shows the loss probability for varying λ and C = 120 and for various values of the retry parameter M. The curves are obtained by choosing the optimal choice of r for each traffic (as in Figure

5.7). The optimal choices of r are also shown in Figure 5.8 together with the limiting case where M tends to infinity.

5.3.2 Implied costs

Now examine the issue of implied costs (see Kelly, 1990) in the context of fixed routeing strategies. Suppose that the circuit switched network consists of links labelled k = 1,2,...,K with link k comprising C_k circuits. A subset $r \subset \{1, 2, ..., K\}$ identifies a route. Calls requesting route r arrive as independent Poisson processes of rate v_r. A call requesting route r is blocked and lost if on any link k $\in$ r there are no free circuits. Otherwise, the call is connected and simultaneously holds one circuit on each link k $\in$ r for the holding period of the call. The call holding period is independent of earlier arrival times and holding periods; holding periods of calls on route r are identically distributed with unit mean. Write R for the set of possible routes.

The Erlang fixed point equations for this set up are as in Equation 5.35 and the proportion of calls requesting route r that are lost is given by Equation 5.36.

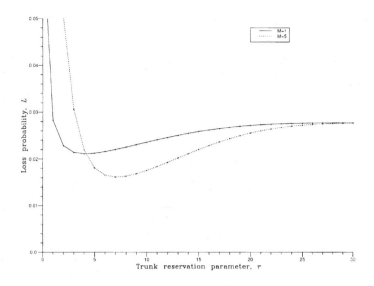

Figure 5.7 Optimal choice of r

$$B_k = E\left(\sum_{r:k \in r} \nu_r \prod_{j \in r - \{k\}} (1 - B_j), C_k \right) \qquad (5.35)$$

$$L_r = 1 - \prod_{k \in r} (1 - B_k) \qquad (5.36)$$

$$W(\nu;C) = \sum_{r \in R} \omega_r \lambda_r \qquad (5.37)$$

$$\lambda_r = \nu_r \prod_{k \in r} (1 - B_k) \qquad (5.38)$$

Suppose that a call accepted on route r generates an expected revenue ω_r. The rate of return from the network will be as in Equation 5.37 where λ_r is given by Equation 5.38.

Let $c = (c_1, c_2, ..., c_k)$ be the unique solution of the systems of equations given by Equation 5.39.

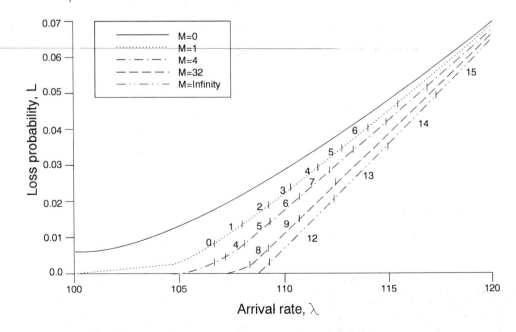

Figure 5.8 Loss probability with varying number of retries, M

$$c_k = \eta_k (1 - B_k)^{-1} \sum_{r:k \in r} \lambda_r \left(\omega_r - \sum_{j \in r - \{k\}} c_j \right) \quad (5.39)$$

The values of λ_k and ρ_k are given by Equations 5.40 and 5.41.

$$\eta_k = E(\rho_k, C_k - 1) - E(\rho_k, C_k) \quad (5.40)$$

$$\rho_k = \sum_{r:k \in r} \nu_r \prod_{j \in r - \{k\}} (1 - B_k) \quad (5.41)$$

Thus, ρ_k is simply the traffic offered to link k under the approximation procedure. It may be proved that Equations 5.42 and 5.43 hold.

$$\frac{d}{d\nu_r} W(\nu; C) = (1 - L_r) \left(\omega_r - \sum_{k \in r} c_k \right) \quad (5.42)$$

$$\frac{d}{dC_k} W(\nu; C) = c_k \quad (5.43)$$

The definition of Erlang's loss formula can be extended to non-integral values of capacity C by linear interpolation and at integer values of C_k define the derivative of $W(\nu; C)$ with respect to C_k to be the left derivative.

Equation 5.42 shows that the effect of increasing the offered traffic on route r can be assessed from the following rule of thumb: an additional call offered to route r will be accepted with probability $1 - L_r$; if accepted it will earn ω_r directly, but at a cost c_k for each link $k \in r$. The costs c measure the knock-on effects of accepting a call upon the other routes in the network. From Equation 5.43 it follows that the costs c also have an interpretation as shadow prices, with c_k measuring the sensitivity of the rate of return to the capacity C_k of link k. Note that Equation 5.39 can be rewritten in the form shown in Equation 5.44 where s_r is given by Equation 5.45.

$$c_k = \eta_k (1 - B_k)^{-1} \sum_{r:k \in r} \lambda_r (c_k + s_r) \quad (5.44)$$

$$s_r = \omega_r - \sum_{j \in r} c_j \quad (5.45)$$

Here s_r is the surplus value of a call on route r.

5.3.3 Applications of implied costs

5.3.3.1 *Network dimensioning*

The Equations 5.42 and 5.43 can be used directly as the basis for an efficient hill climbing algorithm to maximise the expression (5.37). Through analogies with deterministic network flow the shadow price interpretation of Equation 5.43 could be used in algorithms to aid capacity expansion decisions (see Key, 1988). The overall approach also has important economic implications for pricing policies and for the apportionment of revenue between different sections of the network operation.

5.3.3.2 *Decentralised adaptive routeing strategy*

Note that the implied cost, c_k, can be written in the form shown in Equation 5.46 (where s_r is given by Equation 5.47) in terms of observables such as the carried traffics on routes and links.

$$c_k = \rho_k \eta_k \sum_{r:k \in r} \frac{\text{carried traffic on route } r}{\text{carried traffic through link } k} (c_k + s_r) \quad (5.46)$$

$$s_r = \omega_r - \sum_{k \in r} c_k \quad (5.47)$$

Hence, we may construct over time estimates of the implied costs c_k and surplus values s_r. This might be achieved by using, for example, moving average estimators. Suppose that the loss probability, L_r, on route r has also been estimated by similar means. A call offered to route r will generate a net expected revenue of $(1 - L_r)s_r$. Should this quantity be negative for any route then that route should be avoided: more revenue will be lost elsewhere in the network than can be generated by accepting calls on this route. Otherwise, traffic should be shared out between possible routes so as to reflect the net expected revenues $(1 - L_r)s_r$. Routes with higher values of $(1 - L_r)s_r$ than others should receive an increased share of the traffic. Adjustments to routing patterns made on this basis will need to be gradual since the effect of increasing the traffic to a route will be to push up the loss probability of the route and the implied cost c_k along that route, and hence reduce the net expected revenue $(1 - L_r)s_r$.

5.3.4 Network bounds

In this section the aim is to obtain bounds on the performance of any dynamic routeing scheme under a fixed stationary pattern of offered traffic. Consider two approaches. The first makes minimal assumptions concerning the stochastic structure of the system, and within this rather weak framework the bounds are the best possible. The second approach considers various ways to improve these bounds when the offered traffic can be assumed Poisson.

5.3.4.1 *Max-flow bound*

For $(\lambda_{ij} : i < j)$, let $F(\lambda)$ be the maximum attained in the linear programme of Equation 5.48, subject to Equations 5.49 to 5.51.

$$\text{maximise } F(\lambda) = \sum_{i<j} \left(x_{ij} + \sum_{k \neq i,j} x_{ikj} \right) \quad (5.48)$$

$$x_{ij} + \sum_{k \neq i,j} x_{ikj} \leq \lambda_{ij} \quad \forall i < j \quad (5.49)$$

$$x_{ij} + \sum_{k \neq i,j} (x_{ijk} + x_{jik}) \leq C_{ij} \quad \forall i < j \quad (5.50)$$

$$x_{ij} \geq 0, \ x_{ijk} \geq 0, \ x_{ikj} = x_{jki} \quad \forall i, j, k \quad (5.51)$$

The interpretation of this problem is as follows. Regard x_{ij} as the direct flow between nodes i and j along the link (i, j), and x_{ikj} as the flow between nodes i and j through the tandem node k. Regard λ_{ij} as the offered traffic between nodes i and j. Then the linear programme has as its objective function the total flow through the network, and has as constraints the limits imposed by the levels of offered traffic and the capacities of the links.

It may be shown that the bound of expression 5.52 holds for the overall network loss probability, L, where Λ is given by Equation 5.53.

$$L \geq 1 - \frac{F(\lambda)}{\Lambda} \tag{5.52}$$

$$\Lambda = \sum_{i<j} \lambda_{ij} \tag{5.53}$$

In this equation Λ is just the total offered traffic to the network and $F(\lambda)$ is the maximum carried load obtained by solving the above linear programme.

Note also that if the arrival streams are in fact deterministic, then the bound can be attained by a dynamic routeing strategy which routes traffic according to a solution to the linear programme.

5.3.4.2   *Erlang bound*

Suppose now that calls arrive to be connected between nodes i and j (i, j = 1, 2,...,J) as a Poisson process with rates λ_{ij} and that as the pair $\{i, j\}$ varies it indexes independent Poisson streams. Suppose also that a connected call has a duration which is arbitrarily distributed with unit mean, is independent of earlier arrival times and call durations and of the node pair $\{i, j\}$, and is unknown to the dynamic routeing strategy at the time of the call arrival. Let L be the overall network loss probability. Then it may be shown that a lower bound on L is provided by l, the optimum attained in the linear programme of expression 5.54 subject to expressions 5.55 and 5.56.

$$minimise \ l = \sum_{i<j} \frac{\lambda_{ij} b_{ij}}{\sum_{i<j} \lambda_{ij}} \tag{5.54}$$

$$\sum_{i \in S, j \notin S} \lambda_{ij} b_{ij} \geq \left(\sum_{i \in S, j \notin S} \lambda_{ij} \right)$$

$$\times \ E \left(\sum_{i \in S, j \notin S} \lambda_{ij}, \sum_{i \in S, j \notin S} C_{ij} \right) \quad \forall S \subset \{1, 2, ... J\} \tag{5.55}$$

$$b_{ij} = b_{ji} \geq 0 \quad \forall i < j \tag{5.56}$$

5.4   Dynamic routeing strategies

Advances in the technology of modern telecommunication systems have led to considerable interest in schemes which can dynamically control the routeing of calls within a network. The purpose of such dynamic routeing schemes is to adjust routeing patterns within the network in accordance with varying and uncertain offered traffics, to make better use of spare capacity in the network resulting from dimensioning upgrades or forecasting errors, and to provide extra flexibility and robustness to respond to failures or overloads.

Two approaches in particular have received considerable attention. In the United States, AT&T (see Ash, 1981) implemented a scheme called Dynamic Non-Hierarchical Routeing (DNHR) which uses traffic forecasts for different times of day in a large scale

optimisation procedure to predetermine a routeing pattern. This pattern may be changed hourly, typically in relation to time zone differences.

In Canada, Bell Northern Research has proposed a scheme called Dynamically Controlled Routeing (DCR), based on a central controller which receives information on the current state of all links at regular intervals of about 5–10 seconds. This information is used by the controller to determine a routeing pattern which is then distributed back to the nodes.

More recently further dynamic routeing strategies have been proposed such as Dynamic Alternative Routeing (DAR) for the British Telecom national network (see Stacey, 1987). Key, 1990 gives a recent survey of distributed dynamic routeing strategies.

5.4.1   Dynamic Non-Hierarchical Routeing (DNHR)

The DNHR strategy has been in operation throughout the entire AT&T trunk network since 1987 following initial operation within a sub network since 1984. The strategy maintains fixed sequences of alternative routes for each source destination node pair but where the sequences are changed during the day to follow changes in the offered traffic patterns. It is designed to take advantage of traffic non coincidence whereby not all the nodes in the network reach their peak traffic at the same time of day. In international networks, and in trunk networks of geographically large countries, such hourly non coincidence is due to the presence of multiple time zones.

Figure 5.9 shows an example of how this might operate in practice. Traffic between Boston and Miami during the morning peak period may experience congestion on the direct route. A sequence of alternative routes for this time of day might be to attempt overflowing via Chicago, then to try via Phoenix and then finally San Francisco using links which are only lightly congested with direct traffic thanks to the time zone effect which makes the peak periods for traffic between San Francisco and Boston and between San Francisco and Miami, say, occur a few hours later in the day.

In DNHR these patterns are calculated in a network management centre at intervals of months with weekly updates using data on traffics and circuit capacities provided by the nodes. This procedure is integrated within a large scale optimisation procedure for updating the link capacities to cope with the growth in forecasted traffic demands. By taking advantage of idle capacity which can be found in the network due to traffic non coincidence overall network cost savings can be achieved. In a case study of a 24 node network model it was reported that with DNHR the trunk cost was reduced by about 15% compared with fixed routeing strategies. In international networks even greater savings of the order of 25% have been reported.

5.4.2   Learning automata

Learning automata schemes have been applied to telephone routeing problems (see Narenda, 1983). They continually offer calls across the available routes r = 1, 2,...,R, say, for calls between each source destination node pair according to a probability distribution $(p_r : r = 1, 2,...,R)$. This probability distribution is updated over time according to the acceptance or rejection of offered calls. A scheme can thereby reward a route on which a call is successful and punish a route on which a call fails.

For example, the learning automation scheme called $L_{R-\epsilon P}$ updates the route selection probabilities as follows. If route i is chosen at time step n and the call is successful then Equations 5.57 and 5.58 are used.

Figure 5.9 DNHR alternative routes

$$p_i(n+1) = p_i(n) + a[1 - p_i(n)] \qquad (5.57)$$

$$p_j(n+1) = (1-a)p_j(n) \qquad j \neq i \qquad (5.58)$$

However, if the call fails, then Equations 5.59 and 5.60 are used.

$$p_i(n+1) = (1 - \in)p_i(n) \qquad (5.59)$$

$$p_j(n+1) = (1 - \in)p_j(n) + \frac{\in p_i(n)}{R-1} \qquad j \neq i \qquad (5.60)$$

The learning parameter, a, and the penalty parameter, $\in$ are two parameters of the scheme such that $0 < \in < a < 1$ and $\in$ is small compared to a. The value a is typically small so that the updating step is gradual. If B_r is the probability that a call is blocked on route r then it can be shown that the $L_{R-\in P}$ scheme tends to approximately equalise blocking probabilities, B_r, while an L_{R-P} scheme (where $\in$ = a) equalises the blocking rates $B_r p_r$ over routes r = 1, 2, ...,R.

In practice, in a fully connected network it is preferable to first try the direct route between two nodes and then apply the automaton to the choice of two-link overflow routes, rather than to use the automaton to include the single link direct route.

5.4.3 Dynamic Alternative Routeing (DAR)

DAR is a simple, decentralised dynamic routeing strategy that was originally designed for the British Telecom trunk network consisting of between 50 and 60 main switches or nodes which are fully connected. The strategy operates as follows (see Gibbens, 1990). Calls arriving between a source destination node pair first attempt the direct route and are accepted so long as there is at least one free circuit available. If there are no free circuits on the direct route then the call attempts a currently nominated two-link alternative route

via a tandem node. The call is attempted on this route with trunk reservation applied against it on both links. If the call is successful then this tandem node remains the currently nominated tandem node for overflow calls. Otherwise, if the call is rejected by this two-link route the call is lost and the tandem node for future overflow calls is re-selected by choosing at random from amongst the set of feasible tandem nodes for that source destination node pair. Note that the tandem node is not re-selected if the call is successfully routed on either the direct route or the two-link alternative route. The term sticky random routeing has been coined to emphasise this property of the strategy.

The design of the DAR strategy attempts to construct a random search algorithm to find and then efficiently utilise spare capacity available within a network under varying conditions of traffic and capacity mismatches.

The simplicity of DAR permits us to extend the Erlang fixed point models of Section 5.3 to model DAR's long run average behaviour. Suppose that n_{ij} is the birth and death process for the utilization of the link (i, j). Then as in Equations 5.25 and 5.26, Equations 5.61 and 5.62 may be obtained where C_{ij} and r_{ij} are the (i, j) link capacities and trunk reservation parameters respectively.

$$q(n_{ij}, n_{ij} + 1) = \begin{cases} \lambda_{ij} + \sigma_{ij} & n_{ij} = 0,..., C_{ij} - r_{ij} - 1 \\ \lambda_{ij} & n_{ij} = C_{ij} - r_{ij},..., C_{ij} - 1 \end{cases} \qquad (5.61)$$

$$q(n_{ij}, n_{ij} - 1) = n_{ij} \qquad n_{ij} = 1,..., C_{ij} \qquad (5.62)$$

Now suppose that $p_k(i, j)$ (where $k \neq i, j$) is the long run proportion of (i, j) overflow traffic offered via node k. Then Equation 5.27 generalises to the asymmetric case of Equation 5.63 where $B_1(i, j)$ and $B_2(i, j)$ are the (i, j) link blocking probabilities for fresh and overflow calls respectively.

$$\sigma_{ij} = \sum_{k \neq i,j} \lambda_{ik} B_1 (i,k) p_j (i,k) [1 - B_2 (j,k)]$$

$$+ \sum_{k \neq i,j} \lambda_{ij} B_1 (j,k) p_i (j,k) [1 - B_2 (i,k)] \qquad (5.63)$$

Let $L_k(i, j)$ be the blocking on the two-link alternative route via tandem node k given by Equation 5.64.

$$1 - L_k (i,j) = [1 - B_2 (i,k)] [1 - B_2 (k,j)] \qquad (5.64)$$

In the case of DAR, it may be shown that the route blocking rates are approximately equalised. Hence expression 5.65, which does not depend on k. Therefore $p_k(i, j)$ may be determined by the relation of Equation 5.66 in terms of $L_k(i, j)$ and hence $B_2(i, j)$ by Equation 5.64.

$$p_k (i,j) L_k (i,j) \qquad (5.65)$$

$$\sum_{k \neq i,j} p_k (i,j) = 1 \qquad (5.66)$$

The proportions $p_k(i, j)$ may then be used to calculate new estimates for the offered traffics and hence for the link blockings $B_1(i, j)$ and $B_2(i, j)$. Using the method of direct repeated substitution has been found to lead to oscillatory behaviour in some cases. In practice, this may be readily overcome by damping the iteration in the sense that, if solving the fixed point Equation 5.67 for some function f, then one should update x by Equation 5.68 where a (0 < a ≤ 1) is the damping factor. A value around a = 0.8 has been found to be satisfactory in practice.

$$x = f(x) \qquad (5.67)$$

$$x_{n+1} = (1-a) x_n + a f(x_n) \qquad (5.68)$$

5.4.3.1   DAR applied to the BT network

Figure 5.10 shows a typical routeing problem similar to those that were faced in the British Telecom national trunk network. A call

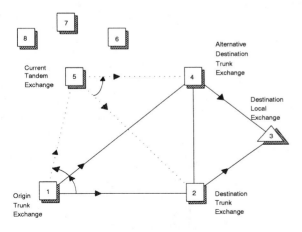

Figure 5.10   DAR in the BT network

requires a route from its trunk exchange (labelled as node 1) to its destination local exchange (node 3). There are two trunk exchanges that connect to node 3 — namely, nodes labelled 2 and 4. This situation, where a local exchange connects to two trunk exchanges, is often repeated throughout the network and is called 'dual-parenting'. First, the call attempts the route (1,2,3) and if a free circuit can not be found on each of these two links it overflows to the route (1,4,3) via the alternative destination trunk exchange (node 4). If this second route does not have a free circuit available on each link then the call is either lost or further, but necessarily longer, routes are attempted.

A situation where a network may implicitly judge it better to lose the call rather than accept it using routes containing many links is when it is subject to a general overload of traffic. Accepting calls over long routes in these circumstances just adds to the levels of congestion felt by all calls.

The 'sticky random' or Dynamic Alternative Routeing (DAR) strategy handles this situation by remembering a current tandem trunk exchange (labelled node 5) through which to send calls attempting to overflow to longer routes. First, it attempts the route (1,5,2,3) and then overflows to the alternative destination trunk exchange along route (1,5,4,3). For each of these two routes the trunk reservation is used to give priority to the more directly routed calls in preference to the indirect calls using longer routes. If none of these routes is prepared to accept the call then it is at this stage finally rejected from the network. The sticky random strategy then again comes into play to reset the current tandem trunk exchange by choosing at random from amongst a pre-defined set (nodes 5,6,7,8,...). In this way, the sticky random strategy is able to shift the patterns of offered traffic to match the presence of spare capacity that it finds to form these longer paths. It should be pointed out that this strategy applies in parallel, in a decentralised fashion, throughout the network. In an example such as the British Telecom national trunk network there could well be 60 trunk exchanges spread throughout the United Kingdom.

5.4.4   Least busy alternative (LBA)

The least busy alternative routeing strategy is an example of a state dependent routeing strategy defined for fully connected networks which operates as follows. A call is first attempted on the direct route and is accepted so long as at least one free circuit is available. Otherwise, the strategy looks at the occupancies of all the available two-link alternative routes and attempts to route the call along the least busy such route subject to trunk reservation. Specifically, if m_{ik} and m_{kj} give the number of circuits free on the links (i, k) and (k, j) then the alternative chosen is via tandem node k which maximises $\min\{m_{ik}, m_{kj}\}$ over all tandem nodes $k \neq i, j$. Then trunk reservation with parameter r will mean that the chosen alternative is only used if $\min\{m_{ik}, m_{kj}\} > r$.

It is possible to obtain an Erlang fixed point model for the LBA strategy (see Wong, 1990). We present the model in the simpler case of a symmetric network of N nodes with link capacities C and offered traffics at rate λ. Let n be the birth and death process representing the utilization of a link then the transition rates are as in Equations 5.69 and 5.70.

$$q(i, i+1) = \begin{cases} \lambda + \sigma_i & i = 0,..., C - r - 1 \\ \lambda & i = C - r,..., C \end{cases} \qquad (5.69)$$

$$q(i, i-1) = i \quad i = 1,..., C \qquad (5.70)$$

In this equation σ_i is a state dependent birth rate given in terms of the equilibrium distribution $\{\pi_i : i = 0,..., C\}$ for n as in Equation 5.71 where y_i is given by Equation 5.72 and φ_i by Equation 5.73.

$$\sigma_i = 2N \left[y_i \sum_{j=0}^{i} \pi_j + \sum_{j=i+1}^{C-1} y_j \pi_j \right] \tag{5.71}$$

$$y_i = \frac{\lambda \pi_C}{N} \sum_{j=0}^{N-1} (\Phi_i)^j (\Phi_{i+1})^{N-1-j} \tag{5.72}$$

$$\Phi_i = 1 - \left(\sum_{j=0}^{i-1} \pi_j \right)^2 \tag{5.73}$$

The loss probability, L is then as in Equation 5.74 where B_1 and B_2 are the link blocking probabilities for fresh and overflow traffics respectively and are given by Equations 5.75 and 5.76.

$$L = B_1 \left[1 - (1 - B_2)^2 \right]^N \tag{5.74}$$

$$B_1 = \pi_C \tag{5.75}$$

$$B_2 = \sum_{i=C-r}^{C} \pi_i \tag{5.76}$$

In the United States, AT&T has recently started implementing a closely related dynamic routeing strategy called Real Time Network Routeing (RTNR) (see Ash, 1991).

5.5 Bibliography

Ash, G.R., Cardwell, R.H. and Murray, R.P. (1981) Design and optimization of networks with dynamic routeing, *Bell Syst Tech J*, **60**, (8), pp. 1787–1820.

Ash, G.R., et al. (1991) Real time network routeing in a dynamic class of service network In *Proc. 13th International Teletraffic Congress*, Copenhagen, North Holland, Amsterdam.

Brockmeyer, E., Halstrom, H.L. and Jensen, A. (1948) *The life and works of A.K. Erlang*, Academy of Technical Sciences, Copenhagen.

Gibbens, R.J. and Kelly, F.P. (1990) Dynamic routeing in fully connected networks, *IMA J. Math Control Inform*, **7**, pp. 77–111.

Hui, Y.J. (1990) *Switching and traffic theory for integrated broadband networks*, Kluwer, Boston.

Kelly, F.P. (1979) *Reversibility and stochastic networks*, Wiley, Chichester.

Kelly, F.P. (1990), Routeing in circuit switched networks: optimization, shadow prices and decentralization, *Adv. in Appl. Probab.*, **20**, pp. 112–144.

Key, P.B. and Whitehead, M.J. (1988), Cost effective use of networks employing Dynamic Alternative Routing. In *Proc. 12th International Teletraffic Congress*, Turin, North-Holland, Amsterdam.

Key, P.B. and Cope, G.A. (1990) Distributed dynamic routeing schemes, *IEEE Communications Magazine, Advanced traffic control methods for circuit switched telecommunication networks*, **28**, (10), pp. 54–64.

Narenda, K.S. and Mars, P. (1983) The use of learning algorithms in telephone traffic routeing — A methodology, *Automatica*, **19** (5) pp. 495–502.

Stacey, R.R. and Songhurst, D.J., (1987) Dynamic alternative routeing in the British Telecom trunk network, *Int Switching Symposium*, Phoenix.

Wong, E.W.M. and Yum, T.S. (1990) Maximum free circuit routeing in circuit switched networks, *Proc. IEEE Infocom '90*, IEEE Computer Society Press, pp. 934–937.

6

Electromagnetic waves

J H Causebrook
BSc PhD CEng MIEE
Vodafone Ltd.

R V Goodman
CEng MIEE
Broadcasting and Telecommunications
Engineering Consultant

Contents

6.1 Principles

6.1.1 Fundamental laws of electromagnetism

Many engineering aspects of propagation do not need a knowledge of the historically derived principles, but these do provide a good background. The fundamental laws of electromagnetism are:

1. Gauss' electrostatic theorem: the normal component of electric displacement (flux) D, integrated over any closed surface equals the total charge ρ within the surface.
2. Gauss' magnetic theorem: the normal component of magnetic induction B, integrated over any closed surface is zero.
3. Faraday's law of electromagnetic induction: the parallel component of electric field E, integrated round a closed path is proportional to the rate of change of the flux of magnetic induction enclosed by the path (Lenz's law: the constant of proportionality is minus one).
4. Ampere's law for magnetomotive force: the parallel component of magnetic field H, integrated round any loop equals the total current J, flowing through the loop.

6.1.2 Maxwell's equations and wave equations

Maxwell combined these laws and added the concept of displacement current to give a set of equations. These are expressed below in differential form, using the rationalised M.K.S. units as in Equations 6.1 to 6.4.

$$\nabla D = \rho \tag{6.1}$$

$$\nabla B = 0 \tag{6.2}$$

$$\nabla \wedge E = -\frac{\partial B}{\partial t} \tag{6.3}$$

$$\nabla \wedge H = J + \frac{\partial D}{\partial t} \tag{6.4}$$

For an infinite homogeneous medium, with no free charges ρ and zero conductivity σ, these equations become as in Equations 6.5 to 6.8, where ε is the permittivity (dielectric constant) which equals $\varepsilon_r \varepsilon_o$, the relative permittivity multiplied by the permittivity of free space, and μ is the magnetic permeability which equals $\mu_r \mu_0$, the relative permeability multiplied by the permeability of free space.

$$\varepsilon \nabla E = 0 \tag{6.5}$$

$$\mu \nabla H = 0 \tag{6.6}$$

$$\nabla \wedge E = -\mu \frac{\partial H}{\partial t} \tag{6.7}$$

$$\nabla \wedge H = J + \varepsilon \frac{\partial E}{\partial t} \tag{6.8}$$

Elimination of H from this set of simultaneous equations produces a wave equation, as in Equation 6.9.

$$\nabla^2 E = \mu \varepsilon \frac{\partial^2 E}{\partial t^2} \tag{6.9}$$

Equally E could have been eliminated, to give Equation 6.10.

$$\nabla^2 H = \mu \varepsilon \frac{\partial^2 H}{\partial t^2} \tag{6.10}$$

If E or H is disturbed at a point within a homogeneous non-conductive medium, a 'wave' is produced which propagates away from the point with a velocity v metres/sec. When this disturbance is a sinusoidal oscillation of frequency f Hertz, the wave equations may be solved for a general wave front of any shape, by considering it to be composed of a set of plane waves. One of these plane waves can be expressed in a cartesian frame, such that it progresses along the Z axis with electric field along the Y axis. Then it has a solution, at time t, proportional to expression 6.11, where β is 2π divided by the wavelength in metres.

$$e^{-j(Z-vt)\beta} \tag{6.11}$$

Analysis shows that this plane wave has its magnetic component along the X axis i.e. the electric vector is at right angles to the magnetic vector, and both are perpendicular to the direction of propagation. The velocity is given by Equation 6.12.

$$v = \frac{1}{\sqrt{\mu \varepsilon}} \tag{6.12}$$

If the relative permittivity and permeability are both unity, v is the velocity of the wave in free space c, and λ is the free space wavelength λ_0. The value of μ_0 is defined as $(4\pi)10^{-7}$ Henry per metre, and measurements have set ε at $(8.8547)10^{-12}$ Farad per metre. This leads to a velocity of the wave in free space of $(2.998)10^8$ metre per second. This is the same as the velocity determined by direct measurement, at least within the limits of experimental error. For most practical purposes it is adequate to take this velocity to be equal to 3×10^8 metres per second.

The refractive index of a medium is defined by Equation 6.13.

$$n = \frac{c}{v} = \sqrt{\mu_r \varepsilon_r} \tag{6.13}$$

By analogy to Ohm's law, the impedance of the medium is given by Equation 6.14.

$$\eta = \frac{E}{H} = \left(\frac{\mu}{\varepsilon}\right)^{1/2} \tag{6.14}$$

For free space this impedance is equal to 377 ohms.

The energy which is carried by the wave is given by the Poynting vector as $E \wedge H$ Watts per square metre. Historical understanding of the fields from electric charges and magnets led to the prediction of the electromagnetic wave travelling through space. Two major categories of receiving antenna (rods and loops) extract from the wave, voltages related to the electric and magnetic fields. Furthermore many other features of the wave can be accurately formulated from the theory (some of which are given here, and others may be found in text books with mathematical derivation). Thus, there is a tendency to attach more significance to the theory than is justified. It does not prove that the wave is composed of distinct electric and magnetic vectors. It only shows that it is very convenient for us to make the distinction.

6.1.3 Boundary conditions

If there are discontinuities in the electrical properties of the medium, determination of the wave behaviour requires a knowledge of what are called 'the boundary conditions'. The most relevant of these is that components of both E and H tangential to a surface must be continuous. Thus, it is possible to determine how a wave behaves if it is incident on a plane surface where there is a change of impedance from η_1 to η_2 and of refractive index from n_1 to n_2. If the incident wave-normal makes an angle α_1 with the plane-normal, as shown in Figure 6.1, Snell's law gives the angle α_2 for the wave passing into medium 2.

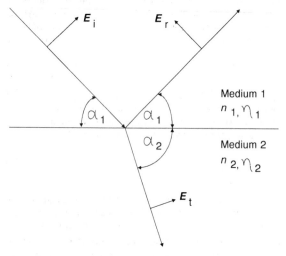

Figure 6.1 Reflection and refraction at a boundary with the electric vector in the plane of incidence

$$n_1 \cos \alpha_1 = n_2 \cos \alpha_2 \qquad (6.15)$$

To determine the reflection r and transmission t coefficients it is necessary to consider two cases, as follows.

6.1.3.1 Case 1

Electric vector in the plane of incidence (equivalent to a vertically polarised transmitter), as shown in Figure 6.1, gives Equations 6.16 and 6.17.

$$r_v = \frac{\eta_1 \sin \alpha_1 - \eta_2 \sin \alpha_2}{\eta_1 \sin \alpha_1 + \eta_2 \sin \alpha_2} \qquad (6.16)$$

$$t_v = \frac{2 \eta_2 \sin \alpha_2}{\eta_1 \sin \alpha_1 + \eta_2 \sin \alpha_2} \qquad (6.17)$$

At high frequencies this may be simplified because it is possible to neglect magnetic permeability, giving Equation 6.18.

$$r_v = \frac{\cot(\alpha_1 - \alpha_2)}{\cot(\alpha_1 - \alpha_2)} \qquad (6.18)$$

For $n_1 < n_2$ Snell's law gives $\alpha_1 < \alpha_2$ so for $(\alpha_1 + \alpha_2)$:

1. Greater than $\pi/2$: r_v is positive, i.e. no phase change.
2. Less than $\pi/2$: r_v is negative, i.e. a π phase change.
3. Equal $\pi/2$: r_v is zero and α_1 equals the Brewster angle.

6.1.3.2 Case 2

Electrical vector perpendicular to the plane of incidence (equivalent to a horizontally polarised transmitter), as shown in Figure 6.2, gives Equations 6.19 and 6.20.

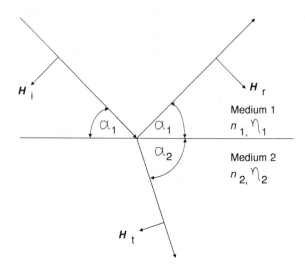

Figure 6.2 Reflection and refraction at a boundary with the magnetic vector in the plane of incidence

$$r_h = \frac{\eta_2 \sin \alpha_1 - \eta_1 \sin \alpha_2}{\eta_2 \sin \alpha_1 + \eta_1 \sin \alpha_2} \qquad (6.19)$$

$$t_h = \frac{2 \eta_2 \sin \alpha_1}{\eta_2 \sin \alpha_1 + \eta_1 \sin \alpha_2} \qquad (6.20)$$

These results allowed for a relative magnetic permeability of non-unity, but conductivity was zero. For propagation over the Earth's surface, it is more appropriate to approximate magnetic permeability to unity, but allow for the finite conductivity of the medium. It is also reasonable to assume unity for the refractive index of air, to obtain formulas for reflections off the Earth's surface. Then, for a wave of angular frequency ω Equation 6.21 may be obtained.

$$n = n_2 = \left(\varepsilon_r - j \frac{\sigma}{\omega \varepsilon_o} \right)^{1/2} \qquad (6.21)$$

Then the reflection coefficient modulus and phase are given by Equations 6.22 and 6.23.

$$r_v = \frac{n^2 \sin\alpha_1 - \left(n^2 - \cos^2\alpha_1\right)^{1/2}}{n^2 \sin\alpha_1 + \left(n^2 - \cos^2\alpha_1\right)^{1/2}}$$ (6.22)

$$r_h = \frac{\sin\alpha_1 - \left(n^2 - \cos^2\alpha_1\right)^{1/2}}{\sin\alpha_1 + \left(n^2 - \cos^2\alpha_1\right)^{1/2}}$$ (6.23)

Examples of the use of these formulas are given by Figures 6.3 and 6.4 for the land, and by Figures 6.5 and 6.6 for the sea.

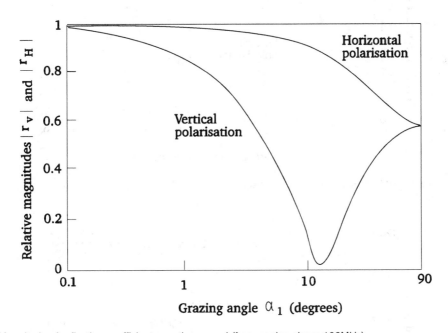

Figure 6.3　Magnitude of reflection coefficient over the ground (frequencies above 100MHz)

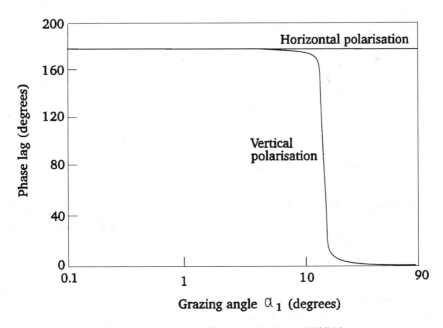

Figure 6.4　Phase of reflection coefficient over the ground (frequencies above 100MHz)

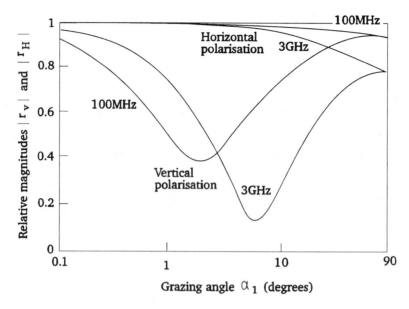

Figure 6.5 Magnitude of reflection coefficient over the sea

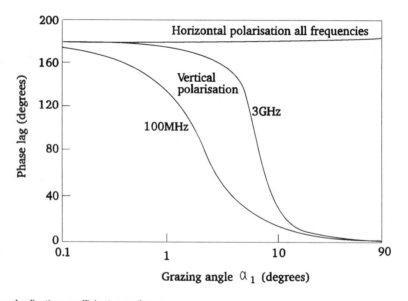

Figure 6.6 Phase of reflection coefficient over the sea

6.1.4   Huygen's principle and Fresnel diffraction

An earlier solution to propagation phenomena came via Huygen's principle, which states that every point on a wave front acts as a source of a secondary wavelet. This provides an explanation for some propagation phenomena. Most importantly, it helped to quantify diffraction.

Diffraction effects can be formulated via the wave equation and Kirchhoff's integral (Longhurst, 1967), but the original derivation by Fresnel was via the Huygen principle. A semi-infinite opaque screen is assumed to exist between transmitter and receiver, as shown in Figure 6.7. Then, Fresnel's integral states that the attenuation is related to free-space, in amplitude and phase, by the complex function F, given by Equation 6.24, where v is given by Equation 6.25.

$$F(v) = \frac{1+j}{2} \int_{v}^{\infty} e^{-j\frac{\pi}{2}(t^2+v^2)} \, dt \qquad (6.24)$$

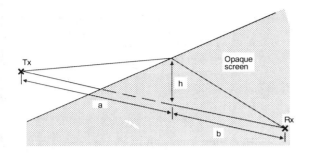

Figure 6.7 Fresnel diffraction parameters

$$v = h \left(\frac{2(a+b)}{\lambda\,a\,b} \right)^{1/2} \qquad\qquad (6.25)$$

6.1.5 Propagation mechanisms

The principles of propagation enable the communications engineer to produce convenient calculation techniques. This process is facilitated by recognising three major propagation mechanisms, which tend to dominate in different wave bands:

1. Space wave, below 10 metres i.e. frequencies above 30MHz.
2. Sky wave, 10 to 200 metres i.e. from 1.5 to 30MHz.
3. Surface wave, above 200 metres i.e. below 1.5MHz.

This division into three categories should not be regarded as rigidly defining the propagation mechanisms for the frequency ranges specified. Firstly, it should be appreciated that the stated ranges are only approximate. Secondly, there can be a considerable

overlap, where more than one mechanism is relevant. For example, m.f. broadcast stations normally provide coverage via the surface wave, but this coverage may be reduced, at night time, by sky wave interference.

6.2 Generation of the electromagnetic wave

Electromagnetic waves, as distinct from electrostatic fields or steady magnetic fields, involve a continuous net transfer of energy, or radiation, through a medium and are produced by current and charge distributions which vary with time.

The types of antenna employed to generate such waves are many, depending on the radio frequency to be transmitted, the radiation pattern required to fulfil the needs of the system and the environment in which the antenna is required to operate.

The following sections deal with several fundamental antenna elements from which the performance of many practical antennas may be derived.

6.2.1 Radiation from an infinitesimal linear element

The electromagnetic field equations for many complex antenna systems may be derived from a knowledge of the fields produced by an oscillating current in an infinitesimal linear element (Jordan and Balmain, 1968, pp. 317-321; Balanis, 1982, pp. 164-176). For such an element, the current may be assumed to be constant throughout its length.

Consider a current element of length δl carrying a current $I \cos \omega t$, located at the origin of a spherical co-ordinate system in a homogeneous, isotropic, non-conducting medium as shown in Figure 6.8. The formulation of the electric and magnetic field magnitudes generated by such a current element is made more succinct by

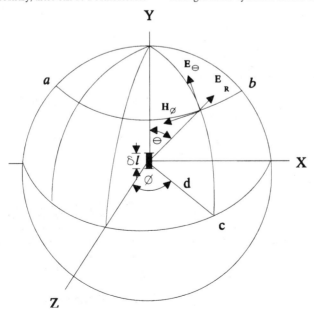

Figure 6.8 Radiation from an oscillating current in an infinitessimal linear element (δL) at the centre of a spherical co-ordinate system

the introduction of two variables, as in Equations 6.26 and 6.27, from which Equations 6.28 to 6.30 are obtained.

$$\Psi = \frac{I \delta l \beta \sin \theta}{4 \pi d} \qquad (6.26)$$

$$\alpha = \frac{j}{\beta d} \qquad (6.27)$$

$$H_{\varphi} = \Psi (1 - \alpha) \qquad (6.28)$$

$$E_{\theta} = \eta \Psi (1 - \alpha + \alpha^2) \qquad (6.29)$$

$$E_r = 2 \eta \Psi \alpha (1 - \alpha) \cot \theta \qquad (6.30)$$

Terms in α and α^2 are known as the induction and electrostatic fields respectively. They are also known as the near field terms, representing energy which ebbs and flows between the field and the current source. At $d = 16\lambda$, α is equal to 0.01 and can effectively be set to zero. This leaves us with the radiation field terms.

The total power radiated (P_{rad}) by the current element may be obtained by integration of the radial Poynting vector over a spherical surface with the element at the centre, to give Equation 6.31, where I is the peak current and I_o is the r.m.s. current.

$$P_{rad} = 10 (\beta I \delta l)^2 = [20 (\beta \delta l)^2] I_0^2 \qquad (6.31)$$

From Equation 6.31 it can be seen that the part in square brackets has the dimensions of resistance. This is known as the radiation resistance of the current element.

6.2.2 Radiation from an oscillating current in a small loop

The magnetic equivalent to the infinitesimal linear element is the small loop, of radius a. Consider such a current loop at the centre of a spherical co-ordinate system.

The electric and magnetic field components generated by such a loop may be derived, as for the infinitesimal linear current element, and are given by Equations 6.32 to 6.34, where χ is given by Equation 6.35.

$$E_{\varphi} = \eta \chi (1 - \alpha) \qquad (6.32)$$

$$H_{\theta} = \chi (1 - \alpha + \alpha^2) \qquad (6.33)$$

$$H_r = 2 \chi \cot \theta \alpha (1 - \alpha) \qquad (6.34)$$

$$\chi = \frac{\beta^2 a^2 I \sin \theta}{4 d} \qquad (6.35)$$

Integration of the Poynting vector over the surface of a surrounding sphere gives the total radiated power as in Equation 6.36.

$$P_{rad} = \eta \left(\frac{\pi}{12} \right) \left(\frac{c}{\lambda} \right)^4 I^2$$

$$= \left[20 \pi^2 \left(\frac{c}{\lambda} \right)^4 \right] I_o^2 \qquad (6.36)$$

Again the part in square brackets is the radiation resistance, which may be increased by constructing the loop from N turns, wound so that the magnetic field passes through all the turns. The radiation resistance is then given by Equation 6.37.

$$R_{rad} = 20 \pi^2 \left(\frac{c}{\lambda} \right)^4 N^2 \qquad (6.37)$$

6.2.3 Radiation from a short dipole

The derivation of the radiation characteristics of practical antennas, from the equations for the infinitesimal current element, requires a knowledge of the current distribution in the practical antenna.

In the case of the centre fed short dipole (Figure 6.9) the current distribution may be regarded as linearly tapering from a maximum value at the centre to zero at the tips, provided that the electrical length is small i.e. less than 0.1 wavelength. In this figure the current

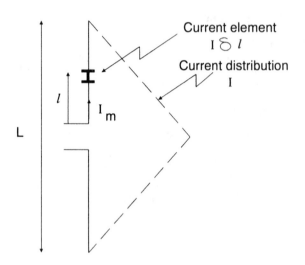

Figure 6.9 The short dipole

distribution is given by Equation 6.38.

$$Current\ distribution\ I = I_m \left(1 - \frac{2l}{L} \right) \qquad (6.38)$$

The mean value of the current along the dipole is half the current at the centre. Thus, the magnitudes of the far field terms are half what would be given by Equations 6.26 to 6.30 for a current element of the same length. Therefore, the total power radiated and the radiation resistance, expressed in terms of the r.m.s. current I_o at the centre of the dipole, are a quarter of that given by Equation 6.31.

6.2.4 Radiation from a half wavelength dipole

The radiation characteristics of the half wavelength dipole may be derived on the basis that, for a thin dipole, the current distribution along the antenna is approximately sinusoidal, as shown in Figure

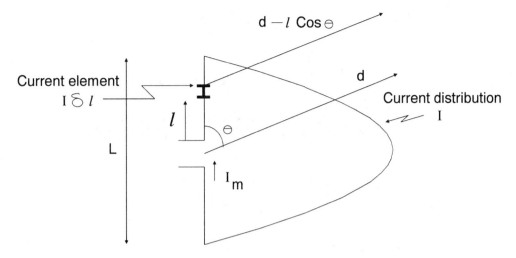

Figure 6.10 The half wavelength dipole

6.10. In this figure the value of the current distribution is given by Equation 6.39 and E_θ by Equation 6.40.

$$I = I_m \cos \beta \, l \qquad (6.39)$$

$$E_\theta = \frac{60 \, \pi \, I_m \sin \theta}{\lambda \, d} \, e^{-j \beta d} \int_{-\frac{L}{2}}^{\frac{L}{2}} \cos \beta \, l \, e^{j \beta \, l \cos \theta} \, d \, l \qquad (6.40)$$

Using the same system of spherical co-ordinates defined earlier, the far field radiation terms in free-space are given by Equations 6.41 and 6.42.

$$H_\varphi = \frac{I_m}{2 \, \pi \, d} \frac{\cos \left(\frac{\pi}{2} \cos \theta \right)}{\sin \theta} \qquad (6.41)$$

$$E_\theta = \eta \, H_\varphi \qquad (6.42)$$

The average power flux density through the surface of a surrounding sphere is given by the Poynting vector.

The total power P radiated by the dipole is equal to the total power radiated through the surface of the sphere and is given by Equation 6.43.

$$P = \frac{\eta \, I_m^2}{4 \, \pi} \int_0^\pi \frac{\cos^2 \left(\frac{\pi}{2} \cos \theta \right)}{\sin \theta} \, d \theta \qquad (6.43)$$

Evaluation of this integral is dealt with by Jordan and Balmain (1968, pp. 330-331) and (for I_o given by Equation 6.45) gives Equation 6.44.

$$P = 73.1 \, I_o^2 \quad watts \qquad (6.44)$$

$$I_o = \frac{I_m}{\sqrt{2}} \qquad (6.45)$$

The radiation resistance of the thin half wavelength dipole is given by the coefficient of I_o^2 in Equation 6.46 and is, therefore, equal to 73.1 Ohms.

It is now possible to determine the r.m.s. value of the electric field in the direction of maximum radiation by combining Equations 6.41, 6.42 and 6.44, with θ equal to zero, giving Equation 6.46 where E is in Volts per meter, with P in Watts and d in meters.

$$E \approx 7 \frac{\sqrt{P}}{d} \qquad (6.46)$$

6.2.5 Radiation from a short monopole

Figure 6.11 shows a vertical monopole on a perfectly conducting, infinite, flat ground plane. The current distribution (given by Equation 6.47), for a thin monopole is approximately sinusoidal and, as a result of the perfect image in the ground plane, the radiation pattern above the plane is identical to that of a dipole of length 2H.

$$Current \; distribution \; I = I_m \sin \left[\beta \left(H - l \right) \right] \qquad (6.47)$$

Thus, for a short monopole ($H < 0.1 \, \lambda$), the current may be assumed to taper linearly from a maximum at the base to zero at the top. The radiation pattern above the plane will be identical to that of the short dipole.

However, since power can only be radiated into the hemisphere above the reflecting plane, the total power radiated (for a given value of current at the base of the monopole) is half that for the short dipole of length $2H$ with the same current at its centre.

Thus, in free space, Equation 6.48 may be obtained.

$$P = \left[40 \, \pi^2 \frac{H^2}{\lambda^2} \right] I_o^2 \qquad (6.48)$$

Once again the radiation resistance is given by the term in square brackets.

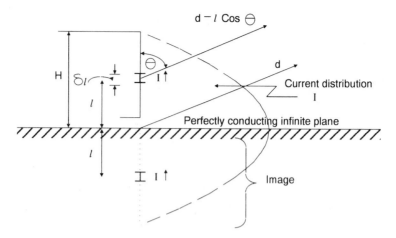

Figure 6.11 Vertical monopole over a ground plane

The maximum field strength at a given distance from the monopole, in the far field, occurs at the surface of the conducting plane and is $\sqrt{2}$ times that for a short dipole radiating the same total power, because all the energy is confined to a hemisphere. By choosing units of power in kilowatts, distance in kilometres and r.m.s. electric field in mV/m, the maximum electric field strength is given by Equation 6.49.

$$E = \frac{300\sqrt{P}}{D} \tag{6.49}$$

The quantity $300\sqrt{P}$ is called the Cymomotive Force (CMF).

6.2.6 Radiation from a quarter wavelength monopole

The quarter wavelength monopole above the conducting surface may be compared to the half wavelength dipole with the same base current: it has the same radiation pattern above the surface, half the total radiated power and the maximum field strength is given by Equation 6.50, where E is in mV/m, P in kW and D in km.

$$E = \frac{313\sqrt{P}}{D} \tag{6.50}$$

6.2.7 The isotropic radiator

The hypothetical isotropic radiator, which radiates power equally in all directions, is widely used as a reference with which to compare the performance of practical antennas.

Such a radiator located at the centre of a large sphere of radius, d metres, and radiating a total power, P Watts, produces a uniform power flux density $E \wedge H$ over the surface of the sphere, as in Equation 6.51.

$$E \wedge H = \frac{P}{4\pi d^2} = \frac{E^2}{\eta} \tag{6.51}$$

Therefore, in free space, the electric field strength in Volts/metre, for P in Watts and d in metres, is given by Equation 6.52.

$$E = \frac{\sqrt{30\,P}}{d} \tag{6.52}$$

6.2.8 Antenna gain and effective radiated power

The term antenna gain defines the degree to which an antenna concentrates radiated power in a given direction, or absorbs incident power from that direction, compared with a reference antenna. The logical reference antenna is the isotropic radiator, in view of its lack of directional properties, though the half-wavelength dipole is also often used. Antenna gain is most easily derived by considering all antennas as transmitting antennas.

If the r.m.s. field strength in free space produced at a distance d is given by E, the total power radiated by the antenna is given by the surface integral as in Equation 6.53.

$$P = \frac{d^2}{120\,\pi} \int_0^{2\pi} \int_0^{\pi} E^2 \sin\theta \, d\theta \, d\varphi \tag{6.53}$$

If the field strength in a particular direction is E_n the gain relative to an isotropic antenna is given by Equation 6.54.

$$G_i = \frac{4\pi E_n^2}{\int_0^{2\pi} \int_0^{\pi} E^2 \sin\theta \, d\theta \, d\varphi} \tag{6.54}$$

If a choice is made such that E_n is in the direction of maximum radiation, the maximum intrinsic gain of the antenna is obtained.

G_i is the gain solely attributable to the directional characteristics of the radiation pattern of the antenna and takes no account of dissipative losses in the antenna itself or in the transmission line between the antenna and the transmitter. These losses may be combined and expressed as a power ratio, K so that the antenna gain referred to the transmitter output becomes $K\,G_i$ for the gain in any direction. This gives the effective gain relative to an isotropic antenna. The product of transmitter power and effective antenna gain relative to an isotropic antenna is called the Effective Isotropically Radiated Power (EIRP).

When the half wavelength dipole is used as the reference antenna, instead of the isotropic antenna, the gain figures are reduced by the maximum intrinsic gain of the half wavelength dipole. The product of transmitter power and effective antenna gain relative to a half wavelength dipole is called the Effective Radiated Power (ERP). The numerical power gain of a half wave dipole relative to an isotropic source is 1.641 (2.15dB).

The computation of the intrinsic or directive gain of an antenna requires a complete knowledge of the three dimensional radiation pattern. Fortunately, for many practical cases, a sufficiently accurate approximation to the three dimensional pattern may be obtained from the radiation patterns measured in two mutually perpendicular planes. These patterns represent cross sections of the three dimensional pattern and are normally measured in the horizontal plane and the vertical plane. Under these conditions, the patterns are called the Horizontal Radiation Pattern (HRP) and the Vertical Radiation Pattern (VRP), respectively. They may also be referred to as the H-PLANE and E-PLANE radiation patterns, respectively, for a vertically polarised antenna and vice versa for a horizontally polarised antenna.

It is not uncommon for transmitting antennas to have the main lobe, or beam, of the VRP tilted down below the horizontal to reduce the power wasted in radiation above the horizon. In such cases, the HRP is measured for θ equal to the beam-tilt angle, not 90 degrees.

Figure 6.12 shows a vertical radiation pattern for a typical high-

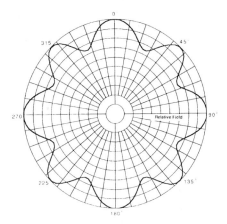

Figure 6.13 Horizontal radiation pattern of a typical u.h.f. broadcast antenna

The three dimensional radiation pattern may be more fully represented in two dimensions by a family of polar patterns, each contour line joining directions having equal ERP.

6.2.9 Polarisation

The polarisation of an electromagnetic wave defines the time varying behaviour of the electric field vector at a point.

6.2.9.1 Linear polarisation

When the electric vector lies wholly in a single plane, the wave is said to be linearly polarised. In terrestrial communications, when this plane is parallel to the surface of the Earth, the wave is defined as horizontally polarised and, when the plane is perpendicular to the surface of the Earth, the wave is defined as vertically polarised.

6.2.9.2 Circular polarisation

A wave is said to be circularly polarised where the electric field vector rotates in the plane normal to the direction of propagation such that the locus of the extremity of the vector describes a circle. The agreed convention for defining the sense of rotation of the electric vector is in terms of the direction of rotation for an observer looking in the direction of propagation i.e. towards the receiver.

Clockwise rotation is often called right-hand circular polarisation and counter clockwise, left-hand circular polarisation. The electric field vector rotates at the angular frequency ω of the wave and describes one revolution in the period $2\pi/\omega$.

6.2.9.3 Elliptical polarisation

A wave is defined as elliptically polarised where the electric field vector rotates in the plane normal to the direction of propagation whilst its amplitude varies such that the locus of the extremity of the vector describes an ellipse. The vector rotates by one revolution during the period of oscillation $2\pi/\omega$ of the source, though the angular velocity is not constant throughout the revolution, as it would be for circular polarisation.

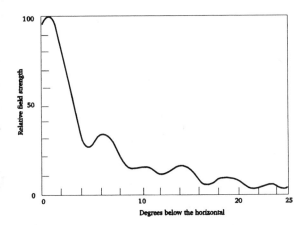

Figure 6.12 Vertical radiation pattern of a typical u.h.f. broadcast antenna

power UHF television broadcasting antenna and Figure 6.13 shows the associated HRP. The maximum intrinsic gain or directivity may be computed by performing an integration, provided the functional form of the radiation pattern is known. The maximum effective gain may then be derived by subtracting all the dissipative losses and the maximum effective radiated power then obtained for any particular value of transmitter power.

The ERP for any direction may be derived by measuring the relative field coefficients r and s from the radiation patterns and computing as in Equation 6.55, where P_m is the maximum ERP.

$$P = r^2 s^2 P_m \tag{6.55}$$

Elliptical polarisation should be regarded as the most general form of polarisation, circular and linear being special cases of elliptical polarisation with axial ratios of unity and zero, respectively. An elliptically polarised wave may be completely defined by three parameters, axial ratio, orientation angle and sense of rotation. These are defined as follows, using Figure 6.13 as a reference. In this figure γ is given by Equation 6.56.

$$\tan \gamma = \frac{Ey}{Ex} \tag{6.56}$$

1. Axial ratio: The axial ratio is defined as the ratio of the minor axis to the major axis. This ratio is often expressed in decibels.
2. Orientation angle: The orientation angle β is defined as the angle between the major axis and the reference axis. In terrestrial communications this reference axis is normally taken as parallel to the surface of the Earth.
3. Sense of rotation: The convention for defining the sense of rotation of the electric vector is the same as for circular polarisation and the commonly used terms are clockwise (or right hand) and counter clockwise (or left hand).
4. Ellipticity angle: This is an alternative way of defining the axial ratio and is equal to the angle α defined in Figure 6.14 for the circumscribing rectangle CDEF.

6.3 Reception of the electromagnetic wave

6.3.1 The simple rod antenna

It can be assumed that a receiving rod antenna consists of an infinite number of current generators of length dx driven by fields $E(x)$. Then, if the total impedance at the terminals is z and the current generators have a normalised value of $D(x)$ relative to the value at the terminals ($x = 0$), the elemental current generators will each contribute an amount $E(x)D(x)dx/z$ to the current I. The current distribution $D(x)$ on a rod antenna is assumed to be analogous to the sinusoidal standing wave pattern obtained on an open circuited transmission line of the same length as the antenna, along which a

wave is propagating with the speed of light. This statement lacks some rigour, but is accurate enough for most practical purposes and has stood the test of time.

The current distribution shown as a dotted line on Figure 6.15, is for a half wavelength dipole antenna. In this case, if the field is

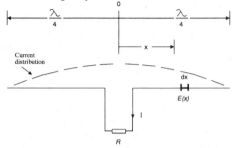

Figure 6.15 Current distribution on a half wavelength dipole

considered constant along the antenna, the current is given by Equation 6.57 where R is the load impedance and the intrinsic radiation resistance of the half wavelength dipole is 73 ohms.

$$I = \frac{E \displaystyle\int_{-\frac{\lambda}{4}}^{\frac{\lambda}{4}} \cos \beta x \, dx}{73 + R} = \frac{\lambda E}{\pi(73 + R)} \tag{6.57}$$

From Equation 6.57 it follows that the open circuited voltage e across the terminals is given by Equation 6.58.

$$e = \frac{\lambda E}{\pi} \quad volts \tag{6.58}$$

Figure 6.16 gives the simple equivalent circuit for a half wavelength dipole receiving antenna. For maximum power transfer R also equals 73 ohms, thus the power absorbed by the load is as in

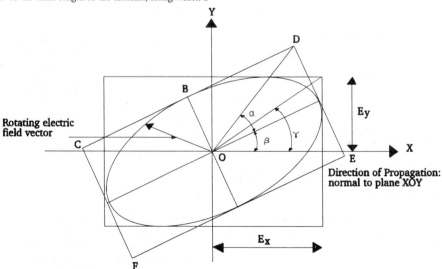

Figure 6.14 Polarisation ellipse and circumscribing rectangles

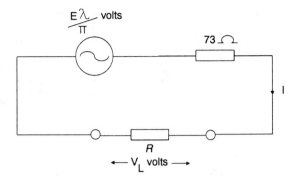

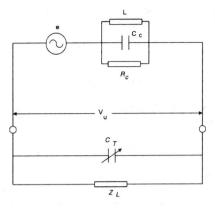

Figure 6.16 Simple equivalent circuit for a half wavelength dipole

Figure 6.17 Equivalent circuit of a loop antenna

Equation 6.59 and the voltage across the load is $\dfrac{E}{\beta}$, where β is given by Equation 6.60.

$$P = \frac{1}{73}\frac{E^2}{\beta^2} \tag{6.59}$$

$$\beta = \frac{2\pi}{\lambda} \tag{6.60}$$

The effective capture area, or aperture, S of an antenna is defined as the ratio of the received power to the incident power flux density. For the half wavelength dipole this is given by Equation 6.61.

$$S_d = \frac{5.15}{\beta^2} \tag{5.61}$$

6.3.2   The hypothetical isotropic antenna

The concept of an isotropic receiving antenna creates conceptual problems, since such an antenna has to be infinitesimally small. Nevertheless, an effective receiving aperture may be derived by taking that of a physically realisable antenna divided by its power gain relative to an isotropic antenna.

Equation 6.61 gives the effective aperture of a half wavelength dipole which has a maximum power gain of 1.64, relative to an isotropic antenna. The effective aperture of an isotropic antenna is, therefore, given by Equation 6.62.

$$S_i = \frac{\pi}{\beta^2} \tag{6.62}$$

6.3.3   The loop antenna

An application of Lenz's Law gives the open circuited voltage of a loop antenna as in Equation 6.63 where N is the number of turns in the loop and A is its area.

$$e = \omega\mu HNA \tag{6.63}$$

The equivalent circuit of the antenna is shown in Figure 6.17, with L being the self inductance, C_c the self capacitance, R_c the winding resistance, C_T a tuning capacitor, and Z_L the load impedance.

This circuit will have a 'Q' value, such that the unloaded output voltage (V_u) at resonance is given by Qe volts.

A sufficiently large voltage is only obtained from an air filled loop by making its area large. Large voltages are often achieved by winding the loops on ferrite rods. In this way m.f. receivers can have antennas with cross sectional areas some thousands of times smaller than would be necessary if they were air filled.

6.3.4   High gain rod antennas

Frequently a simple dipole is inadequate for practical reception purposes. More gain is required, together with the ability to reject unwanted signals coming from directions other than that of the wanted signal. This is often achieved with a yagi antenna consisting of a driven element with a passive reflector and directors (Yagi, 1928; Balanis, pp. 393-409). The reflector is more efficient if it consists of a mesh of rods effectively forming a back screen. Gain may also be achieved by having several dipoles spaced and combined to give directivity. It may also be a requirement that the antenna has a wide band response as well as gain relative to a dipole; this is neatly achieved with a log-periodic antenna (Balanis, 198, pp. 423-439).

The terminated voltage (V_μ) expressed in decibels relative to $1\mu V$, for a practical receiving system with antenna gain, GdB, relative to a half wave dipole and attenuation of the feeder system LdB, is given by Equation 6.64, assuming perfect impedance matching to the load resistance, R.

$$V_\mu = 20\log E - L + G - 120$$
$$- 20\log\beta + 10\log\frac{R}{73} \tag{6.64}$$

6.4   The space wave

6.4.1   Free space field strength

Earlier expressions were derived for field strength in free space. It is convenient to convert these to field strength expressed in decibels relative to $1\mu V/m$, as in Equation 6.65, where D is the distance in kilometres and P is the ERP in Watts.

$$E_{\mu} = 76.9 + 10\log_{10}P - 20\log_{10}D \qquad (6.65)$$

Some workers prefer to base an equation on the isotropic transmitting antenna. The difference is that $10\log_{10}P$ becomes 2.1dB greater, because EIRP is used, which is compensated by the constant 76.9 becoming 74.8.

6.4.2 Free space path loss

A transmission path may also be characterised by the free space path loss, which is defined as the ratio received power P_r to transmitted power P. Expressed in decibels, in a non-dissipative medium, this is given by Equation 6.66.

$$L = 17.7 + 20\log_{10}d$$
$$- 20\log_{10}\lambda - G_t + L_t - G_r + L_r \qquad (6.66)$$

G_t and G_r are the antenna gains relative to a half wavelength dipole and L_t and L_r are the antenna feeder losses; subscripts t and r being for transmitter and receiver.

Again some workers prefer to base an equation on the isotropic antenna. In which case the gains G_t and G_r are each increased by 2.1dB to be relative to isotropic antennas instead of half wavelength dipoles, which is compensated by the constant 17.7 becoming 21.9. There may also be a preference to convert d in metres to D in kilometres, and λ (metres) wavelength to frequency in Megahertz, which must be matched by an appropriate change of constant.

6.4.3 Variation from the free space values

Free space values rarely occur in practice because factors such as the Earth's surface, buildings, trees, and the atmosphere cause variations. It is, therefore, necessary to be able to predict an excess loss which is dependent on the particular propagation path under consideration. This loss prediction is complicated by the fact that the real world does not provide simple geometric shapes for the boundary conditions, and nearly all calculation systems have been based on such simple geometries. It is, therefore, convenient to stylise the real world into shapes which can be handled, and the following sections discuss these and the predictions based upon them.

6.4.4 Knife edge diffraction

Fresnel's diffraction formula is still one of the most useful tools for prediction of the loss over a hilly terrain. A rigorous analysis for a path obstructed by many edges involves a multiple integral but, as this is difficult to solve, attempts have been made to get acceptable results from a sum of single integrals. It is now well established that a method originally devised by Deygout (1966) gives the best results in most cases. It consists of taking each hill as if it alone existed on the path, to establish which one gives the largest predicted loss. This hill is then taken as a terminal to divide the path into two sub-paths, and the process repeated. Further subdivisions may then be made. The total diffraction loss is taken as the sum, in decibels, of the primary loss and the losses on each sub-path.

This process is illustrated by the profile drawn in Figure 6.18, which is stylised into the construction shown in Figure 6.19. From this, three Fresnel limit parameters may be derived, of the type introduced in Equation 6.24, as in Equations 6.67 to 6.69.

$$v_1 = h_1\left(\frac{2(a+b+c+e)}{\lambda(a+b)(c+e)}\right)^{1/2} \qquad (6.67)$$

$$v_2 = h_2\left(\frac{2(a+b+c+e)}{\lambda a(b+c+e)}\right)^{1/2} \qquad (6.68)$$

$$v_3 = h_3\left(\frac{2(a+b+c+e)}{\lambda(a+b+c)e}\right)^{1/2} \qquad (6.69)$$

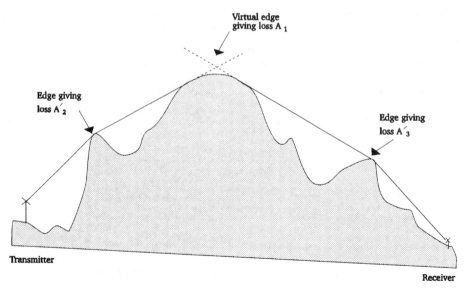

Figure 6.18 Example of a path profile with multiple obstructions

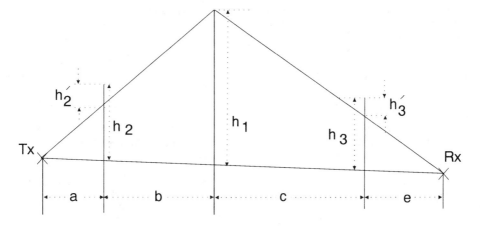

Figure 6.19 Construction for the Deygout method

Let us assume that v_1 is the largest of these so that we then get Equations 6.70 and 6.71.

$$v_2' = h_2' \left(\frac{2(a+b)}{\lambda\, a\, b} \right)^{1/2}$$ (6.70)

$$v_3' = h_3' \left(\frac{2(c+e)}{\lambda\, c\, e} \right)^{1/2}$$ (6.71)

To avoid the complication of evaluating the Fresnel integral, it is possible to go directly from the above parameters to the required losses in dB via a graph of the type shown in Figure 6.20.

The diffraction attenuation assumed for the path is as in Equation 6.72.

$$A_k = A_1 + A_2' + A_3'$$ (6.72)

As stated, this method is generally the most accurate of the approximations. However, it is liable to overestimate the loss by up to 6dB if either A_2 or A_3 is nearly equal to A_1

6.4.5 Surface diffraction

The rounded nature of hill tops, and reflections from elsewhere on the Earth's surface, is liable to make losses greater than that derived from the simple screens assumed for the Deygout approximations. To overcome this, the profile can be assumed to consist of geometric shapes, for which calculations are possible, such as a system of spheres, cylinders or wedges.

6.4.6 Rounded hill tops

One method of stylising the profile is to assume a rounded top on each of the obstructions, rather than assuming a knife edge. This technique has a problem in its application because it requires the radius of a hill top to be known and, with most maps in common use,

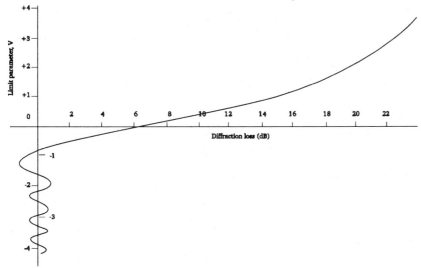

Figure 6.20 Fresnel diffraction loss chart

it is not possible to determine this radius with sufficient accuracy. However, a useful analysis of this method is given in an IEE paper by Hacking (1970), where extra terms are derived to add to the knife edge loss.

6.4.7 Diffraction over a sea path

If it is only sea which interrupts the line of sight path, a spherical diffraction calculation can be made from a method which has its origins in work by Van der Pol and Bremmer (1937, 1949). These methods have a complicated formulation and will not be detailed here. However, for many applications a simplification, based on a paper by Vogler (1964) is of value for frequencies above 400MHz.

6.4.8 Approximating a land path to a cylindrical surface

On a land path with many diffraction edges, a useful prediction is made with a cylindrical surface stylisation of 4 radii joining each other with common tangents, as shown in Figure 6.21. Point 'a' is the transmitter horizon, and 'b' is the receiver horizon. Arc ac just clears the terrain between point 'a' and the transmitter site, and has a tangent to the horizon line Ta at point 'a'. This condition defines the radius r_t. Radius r_r is defined similarly at the receiver end. The radii r_1 and r_2 are defined such that arcs ae and be form tangents with horizon lines Ta and Rb at points a and b, respectively, and have a common tangent at e. The curved surface attenuation can then be approximated by Equations 6.73 to 6.77.

$$A_c = G(Z_t + Z_r + Z_1 + Z_2)$$
$$- R(Z_t) - R(Z_r) - 20 \tag{6.73}$$

$$Z_i = 448 \lambda^{-1/3} r_i^{-2/3} d_i \tag{6.74}$$

$$G(Z) = 0.058 Z - 10 \log Z \tag{6.75}$$

$$Z \le 2000: \quad R(Z) = 0.058 Z - 33 \tag{6.76}$$

$$Z > 2000: \quad R(Z) = G(Z) \tag{6.77}$$

The calculation does not allow for the roughness of the terrain and, as a result, the loss of signal on the path is usually over estimated. A better result is obtained from an interpolation between this and the knife edge calculation. The form of interpolation can be determined by obtaining a best fit with a set of measured data. In the UK it was found that an averaging of losses, expressed in decibels, gave good results.

6.4.9 Approximating a single hill to a wedge shape

On a land path with one diffraction edge, a prediction can be made by assuming a wedge shaped profile. This wedge has its peak at the diffraction edge, and surfaces which clear the terrain on both sides of the profile, as shown in Figure 6.22, with an angle between the horizon lines of θ. The angles between the wedge surfaces and these horizon lines are φ and Ψ. The diffraction loss is given by Equation 6.78 to 6.83 where F is given in Equations 6.24.

$$A_D = -20 \log [F(v_1) + \rho_r F(v_2) $$
$$+ \rho_t F(v_3) + \rho_r \rho_t F(v_4)] \tag{6.78}$$

$$v_1 = \theta u \tag{6.79}$$

$$v_2 = (\theta + 2\varphi) u \tag{6.80}$$

$$v_3 = (\theta + 2\Psi) u \tag{6.81}$$

$$v_4 = (\theta + 2\varphi + 2\Psi) u \tag{6.82}$$

$$u = \left(\frac{2ab}{\lambda(a+b)} \right)^{1/2} \tag{6.83}$$

Simulated reflection coefficients ρ_r and ρ_t depend on how the actual profile deviates from the wedge surface and the values should

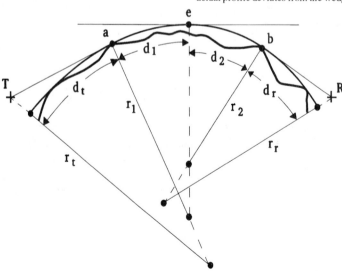

Figure 6.21 Geometry for curved surface diffraction calculation

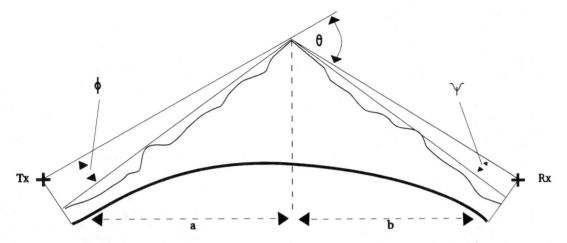

Figure 6.22 Geometry for wedge diffraction calculation

range from about –0.9 for a very smooth wedge like profile, to about –0.1 for a rough 'peaky' edge.

6.4.10 Attenuation by buildings and trees

Attenuation is also caused by buildings and trees. The effects are complicated in these conditions, but allowance can be made by specifying categories.

For reception at 10m above ground level, a clutter loss A_{CL} is given approximately by Table 6.1.

6.4.11 Ground reflections

If the path between transmitter and receiver is well clear of intervening terrain and obstacles, the Earth's surface is still liable to modify the received field due to reflections. It is often difficult to accurately predict the effect of such reflections because the resultant field strength is a vector addition between the direct and reflected waves, so that a small uncertainty about terrain can result in a significant uncertainty about relative phases, especially for the higher frequencies.

The strength and phase of the reflected wave depends upon:

1. The surface conductivity.
2. The surface dielectric constant.
3. The general shape of the ground profile, e.g. flat, convex, or concave.
4. The roughness of the ground.
5. The presence of buildings and trees.

If the surface of the ground is rough, the reflected energy is scattered. Smoothness may be judged by an application of the, so called, Rayleigh criterion: for small angles of Ψ radians between the reflected ray and the ground plane, this criterion states that the undulations shall not be greater than $\dfrac{\lambda}{16\,\Psi}$ for the surface to be treated as smooth.

Of course, the irregular shape of the terrain can result in many reflected waves arriving at a reception point.

Despite all these difficulties, it is instructive to consider the formulation for a simple case, with the reflected path longer than the

direct by δ and a reflection coefficient of magnitude ρ and phase change φ. From a summation of vectors (applying the cosine rule), the received field is reduced from the free space value by Equation 6.84.

$$A_r(dB) = -10\log\left[\,1+\rho^2-2\,\rho\cos(\beta\,\delta-\varphi+\pi)\,\right]\quad(6.84)$$

For horizontal polarisation and angles of incidence below 10 degrees at frequencies above 400MHz it is reasonable to assume $\rho = 1$ and $\varphi = \pi$.

6.4.12 Tropospheric refractive index effects

A further influence on the received field strength is the refractive index of the troposphere. Irregularities in this region bend, scatter and reflect the wave. This is the main cause of time variability, particularly on a long distance path.

The refractive index n of the atmosphere differs by only a small amount from unity and it is more convenient to use the, so called, N factor. This factor is dependent upon the pressure P (millibars), temperature T (K) and relative humidity W of the atmosphere, as given by Equation 6.85.

$$N = (n-1)\,10^6 = \frac{77.6}{T}\left(P+\frac{4810\,W}{T}\right)\quad(6.85)$$

Table 6.1 Clutter loss

	V.h.f. (dB)	U.h.f. (dB)
Urban	8	12
Suburban	6	8
Wooded	4	8
Rural	2	4
Rx foreground slope:	Change above by:	
Facing Tx	–2	–4
Away from Tx	2	4

In 'normal' conditions, the refractive index of the atmosphere decreases with height by an amount which slightly bends the wave back towards the earth. However, it is still more convenient to think of the wave travelling in straight lines, which can be done theoretically if the Earth's radius is suitably modified. Under normal atmospheric conditions this modification involves multiplying the true Earth radius by 4/3.

Changes of meteorological conditions can greatly alter the refractive index from the normal, and hence influence the mode of propagation of signals through the troposphere.

If the refractive index decreases from ground level at a sufficiently high rate to bend the wave with a curvature greater than that of the Earth, propagation of high field strengths to great distances can occur via the ground based ducts created by such meteorological conditions. Under these conditions the wave is refracted back to Earth, where it is reflected back towards the troposphere to be refracted back again towards the Earth and so on, to produce a wave guide type of propagation. Where such a rapid decrease in refractive index occurs at a higher level in the atmosphere, it can produce an elevated propagation duct, without involving reflection off the ground.

If the change of refractive index is very rapid over a small height interval, the wave may be effectively reflected from it and again off the ground, followed by reflection back from the layer, to produce high fields at large distances.

In addition, the refractive index changes may be patchy and 'blob' like, in which case energy is returned to earth in the form of scattered waves. In this case, the resultant received signal level changes rapidly with time as the tropospheric discontinuities move. A satisfactory parameter for the prediction of such scatter fields is the angle between the receiver and transmitter horizons, as shown in Figure 6.23. An empirical relationship can then be determined to relate the field strength to this angle.

The signals resulting from abnormal tropospheric conditions usually represent unwanted interference to services sharing the same frequencies at some considerable distance away. However, they are made use of for some purposes, such as over the horizon radar and communication systems.

6.4.13 Atmospheric absorption

Electromagnetic waves propagating in the non-ionised region of the atmosphere around the Earth are subject to attenuation due to absorption and scattering by hydrometeors (rain, snow, ice particles, fog and cloud) and absorption by atmospheric gases. Curves showing the variation of specific attenuation with frequency are published by the CCIR (1990f).

For most practical purposes, this source of attenuation may be ignored for frequencies below 1 GHz.

Waves passing through rain precipitation are subject to attenuation due to absorption and scattering, the attenuation being a function of frequency, polarisation, the microstructure of the precipitation and the distance the wave travels through the precipitation cell.

In practice, due to air resistance, falling raindrops, other than very small droplets, assume an approximately oblate spheroidal shape and this causes the specific attenuation coefficient to be higher for horizontal polarisation than for vertical polarisation. The calculation of the total rain attenuation along a radio path requires a knowledge of the rainfall rate distribution along the path and an allowance for inclined paths. The total attenuation is obtained by integrating the specific attenuation coefficient over the path length. In most practical cases, predictions are required for the attenuation

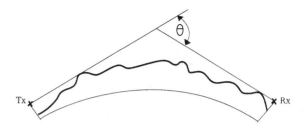

Figure 6.23 The angle of scatter calculations

likely to be exceeded for small percentages of time and this, therefore, requires a knowledge of the cumulative long term statistics for rainfall in the geographical area concerned. In the absence of such measured rainfall data for the area concerned, the rainfall data presented by the CCIR, for various geographical areas throughout the world, may be used.

The attenuation, in dB/km, due to a cloud of small droplets of diameter less than 0.1mm is given by the product of the specific attenuation factor, and the condensed water content of the cloud in g/m^3.

6.4.14 Effect of atmospheric absorption on sky noise temperature

The non-ionised atmosphere surrounding the Earth, in addition to causing attenuation of electromagnetic waves, acts as a source of radio noise. For many terrestrial communications systems, this is of little importance since the receiving antenna noise temperature is dominated by the noise temperature of the Earth. However, for satellite and space communications systems using low noise temperature antennas and receivers, the sky noise temperature plays an important role in determining the received carrier to noise power ratio.

If the temperature of the absorbing medium can be assigned a mean value, T_m (degrees Kelvin), and the total atmospheric absorption at a particular frequency for a given radio path is A (dB), the effective sky noise temperature T_S for the ground station receiving antenna is given by Equation 6.86 where T_E is the extraterrestrial noise temperature (usually taken as 2.7°K for the frequency range 2 to 50 GHz, unless the receiving antenna is pointing near the sun).

$$T_S = T_m (1 - 10^{-A/10}) + T_E 10^{-A/10} \qquad (6.86)$$

Figure 6.24 shows the variation of effective sky noise temperature for clear air with 7.5g/m^3 water vapour density for various elevation angles, for the frequency range 1 to 60GHz. Noise contribution due to absorption by rain or cloud may also be calculated from Equation 6.87, provided that the temperature and specific attenuation variations along the radio path are known. Figure 6.25 shows an example of the theoretical variation in sky noise temperature due to attenuation from clouds on a radio path.

6.4.15 Depolarisation due to hydrometeors

The use of orthogonal polarisation in communications systems is an important technique by which economy of frequency spectrum

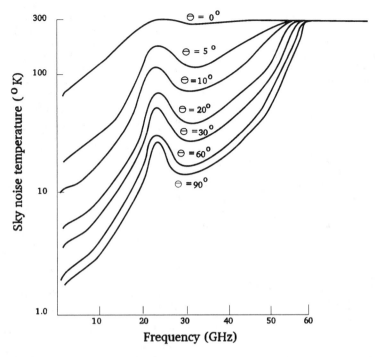

Figure 6.24 Sky noise for clear air and infinitessimal antenna beamwidth. (Water vapour concentration = 7.5g/m³; θ = path elevation angle; surface temperature = 15°C; surface pressure = 1023mb)

usage may be improved by reducing mutual interference between systems sharing the same, or adjacent, frequency channels. This technique relies on the cross polarisation discrimination (XPD) achieved by the careful design and alignment of the transmitting and receiving antennas involved.

A significant factor affecting the cross polarisation discrimination achieved in practice at SHF is the depolarisation caused by hydrometeors, in particular rain and ice crystals.

6.4.15.1   *Depolarisation due to rain*

For rain induced depolarisation, there is a strong statistical correlation between the degradation in XPD and the attenuation of the wanted polarisation, usually called the co-polarised path attenuation (CPA).

The relationship between XPD (XdB) and CPA (CdB) is, however, complex and depends on the frequency, polarisation, angle of

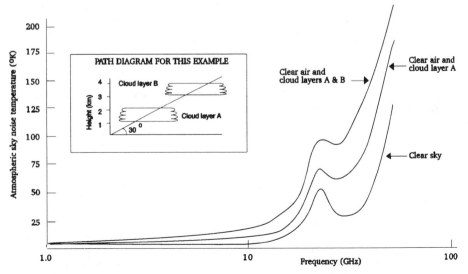

Figure 6.25 Example of the effect of cloud on sky noise temperature. (Clear air: water vapour 7.5g/m³ at surface. Cloud layer: 0.5g/m³ liquid water.)

inclination of the path and the raindrop size, shape and canting angle distributions along the path.

Data is continually being amassed from propagation experiments, in many cases using communications satellites, and semi-empirical relationships based on this data are in common use. One such semi-empirical relationship is given in CCIR (1990b) with further parameters in CCIR (1990c).

6.4.15.2 *Depolarisation due to ice crystals*

Depolarisation due to clouds of ice crystals can be considerable and can occur in the absence of significant attenuation and depolarisation due to rain. Since the major axes of the crystals are normally close to the horizontal, depolarisation tends to a minimum for horizontal or vertical polarisation. Abrupt changes in XPD have been observed to coincide with lightning strokes and this appears to be due to rapid changes in the orientation of the axes of the crystals as the electrostatic charge distribution changes.

The occurrence of depolarisation due to ice crystals and the magnitude of the effect on XPD vary with climate and geography; tending to be greatest in maritime climates. Further information on this subject may be obtained from CCIR (1990c) and Chu (1980).

6.5 The sky wave

6.5.1 The structure of the ionosphere

Ultraviolet and X-radiation from the sun and, to a lesser extent, particle radiation from sunspots and galactic cosmic rays, cause the gases of the upper atmosphere to become ionised. The degree of ionisation does not change uniformly with height, but there are relatively dense regions in layers above the Earth's surface. The properties of the four principal layers are:

D: About 50km – 90km in altitude. Greatly dependent on sun's intensity. Absorbs low frequency radio waves on passage through layer.

E: About 90km – 130km in altitude. Depends on sun's intensity – small residual level at night. Exhibits a 'sporadic' nature.

F1: About 130km – 210km in altitude – merges with F2 layer at sunset. Depends on sun's intensity

F2: About 210 – 400km in altitude – merges with F1 layer at sunset. Influenced by Earth's magnetic field. Depends on auroral zones, particularly in sunspot activity.

6.5.2 Reflection and refraction of waves in the ionosphere

Radio waves cause free electrons and ions to oscillate and re-radiate, increasing the phase velocity of the wave, but reducing the group velocity. Thus, the ionosphere behaves as a medium with a refractive index less than one. This value is formulated later when other influences have been discussed, but, for now, it is sufficient to know that the refractive index of the ionosphere deviates further from 1 for the lower frequencies, and for the higher electron densities.

The change of electron density with height results in a refractive index gradient, symbolised by dn/dh. This gradient will cause both reflection and refraction of the wave. Reflection dominates when the refractive index changes rapidly over a height range which is small compared with the wavelength. Thus, reflection is the main

mechanism for the low frequencies where the refractive index changes more rapidly with real height and, more specifically, height measured in wavelengths.

On the other hand, for the higher frequencies, refraction dominates over reflection, even though the amount of refraction decreases as the frequency increases. If the angle between the ionospheric layer and the direction of propagation is α, the wave will follow a path whose radius of curvature r is given by Equation 6.87.

$$\frac{1}{r} = -\frac{\cos \alpha}{n} \frac{dn}{dh} \tag{6.87}$$

This radius of curvature may be sufficient to return the wave to Earth, depending upon the angle α, frequency, intensity of ionisation, and other factors discussed later.

6.5.3 Ionospheric attenuation

Collisions occur between free electrons and gas molecules, which destroy the oscillatory energy acquired by the electron, converting it to random thermal energy. Thus, energy is taken from the wave which is consequently attenuated. At low heights, there are more gas molecules so more collisions i.e. more attenuation. The number of collisions also depends on the amplitude of the electron vibrations, which increases with increasing wave length and field strength.

In the l.f. and m.f. bands, i.e. 150kHz to 1.6MHz, the D layer almost totally attenuates the wave, so that ionospheric propagation is mainly restricted to night time, when the D layer is absent. Then, reflections take place off the lower edge of the E layer. This is rarely used as a means of communication, but is a source of interference to m.f. broadcast services.

At still lower frequencies, reflection off the lower edge of the ionosphere occurs before much attenuation takes place.

6.5.4 Gyrofrequency — the ordinary and extraordinary wave

In the absence of a magnetic field, electrons would oscillate in the direction of the electric vector of the wave. The presence of the Earth's magnetic field produces an additional force on the electron. The direction of this force is at right angles to the direction of motion of the electron, and to the magnetic field. In general a charged particle moves in a helix around the lines of magnetic field. The frequency of rotation only depends on the charge of the particle, its mass, and the strength of the magnetic field. Thus a resonance exists which is called the gyrofrequency.

If the wave frequency equals the gyrofrequency, the velocity of the electrons increases to large values, and the wave attenuation is increased. The frequency at which this occurs varies between 0.8MHz in equatorial regions to 1.6MHz near the magnetic poles. In the UK it is about 1.3MHz. The electrons, under these conditions, re-radiate with two polarisations, giving rise to the ordinary and extraordinary waves. The ordinary wave propagates as though the Earth's magnetic field were absent, but the electron motion of the extraordinary wave is in the plane perpendicular to the direction of the Earth's magnetic field.

6.5.5 Polarisation coupling loss

The energy in the extraordinary wave suffers more attenuation than the ordinary wave in its passage through the ionosphere, in fact it is largely lost. Also, the ordinary wave may suffer a polarisation change in its passage through the ionosphere and, where the receiving antenna is of the same polarisation as that transmitted, there is a further loss. These factors give rise to the, so called, polarisation coupling loss.

Polarisation coupling loss is small in temperate latitudes, because the Earth's magnetic field is nearer the vertical. Near the equator, the magnetic field is nearly horizontal. This means, that on North-South paths, there may be as much as 6dB coupling loss. The effect is at its greatest on East-West paths near the equator, where the polarisation coupling loss can be very large.

6.5.6 The refractive index of the ionosphere

The refractive index of an ionised medium without a magnetic field and negligible loss of energy is given by Equation 6.88 where N is the number of electrons per cubic centimetre, and f is the frequency in kilohertz.

$$n^2 = 1 - \frac{81 N}{f^2} \qquad (6.88)$$

If the Earth's magnetic field and electron collisions are included, the complex refractive index μ is given by the Appleton-Hartree formula, as in Equation 6.89 where Y is the gyrofrequency divided by wave frequency, θ is the angle between magnetic field and ray, and $2 \pi Z$ is the collision divided by wave frequencies.

$$\mu^2 = 1 - (1 - n^2) \left[1 - jZ - \frac{Y^2 \sin^2 \theta}{2(n^2 - jZ)} \right.$$
$$\left. \pm \left(\frac{Y^4 \sin^4 \theta}{4(n^2 - jZ)^2} + Y^2 \cos^2 \theta \right)^{1/2} \right]^{-1} \qquad (6.89)$$

The square root term takes the positive sign for the ordinary wave and the negative sign for the extraordinary wave.

6.5.7 The critical frequency

The maximum electron density of an ionospheric layer determines the critical frequency f_ckHz. This is the highest frequency for which a vertically incident ray can be returned to Earth. This corresponds to a refractive index of zero. The Earth's magnetic field and collisions can usually be neglected, resulting in Equation 6.90.

$$f_c = 9 \sqrt{N} \qquad (6.90)$$

6.5.8 Ionospheric cross modulation

The oscillatory energy given to an electron by a wave is normally small compared with the ambient thermal energy but, for a very strong wave, this may not be so. This increases the probability of electrons colliding with molecules, so that all other waves entering the ionosphere will have increased attenuation. If then, the strong wave is amplitude modulated, the ionospheric attenuation will vary with the instantaneous amplitude of this wave, and thus the modulation. All other waves are, therefore, modulated in amplitude by the strong wave. This is called ionospheric cross modulation.

6.5.9 Skip distance and maximum usable frequency

When a wave has a frequency greater than the critical frequency of the layer it can still be returned to earth if the angle of incidence α is such that inequality 6.91 is satisfied, where n_o is the refractive index associated with the maximum electron density.

$$\cos \alpha > n_o \qquad (6.91)$$

This results in no skywave energy being returned to Earth closer to the transmitter than a range referred to as the 'skip distance', as shown in Figure 6.26.

For any given distance, at a particular time, there is a maximum frequency that can be used, such that the signal will arrive at the receiver via the ionosphere. This frequency is called the 'maximum usable frequency' or MUF. This frequency is also liable to be the one giving the strongest sky wave signal. The MUF is an important parameter in the propagation of short waves i.e. frequencies from 1.6MHz to 30MHz. It is given by Equation 6.92.

$$MUF = f_c \, cosec \, \alpha \qquad (6.92)$$

The maximum skip distance is about 1700km for the E layer and 3300km for the F layer. Transmission can also take place by two or more hops, to be received at much greater distances.

6.5.10 Sporadic E propagation

Sometimes, waves are returned to Earth by the E layer at frequencies greater than the nominal MUF. This phenomenon is called sporadic E. It is assumed that this is caused by strongly ionised 'clouds' in the lower part of the E-region. By this means, it is possible for propagation to occur over long distances at frequencies as high as about 100MHz.

6.5.11 Sunspots

H.F. propagation is strongly influenced by sunspot activity. It can cause loss of communication or permit very extensive communication. The presence of sunspots is accompanied by a large increase in ultraviolet radiation.

Sunspots vary cyclically in number and size with a period of about 11 years. This activity is approximately quantified by the relative Zurich sunspot number, also called the Wolf number, derived from observations of the number and size of sunspots.

6.5.12 Prediction of field strengths, received via the ionosphere

So far, descriptions have been given of a variety of Ionospheric phenomena. This is helpful in qualitative terms, but most engineers require an ability to make quantitative predictions of the field strength likely to be received in given circumstances. Such calculations should allow for each of the ionospheric features, which means they are complicated and lengthy. It is, therefore, not practicable to give a comprehensive description of the calculations here, but references listed below may be used. It must also be realised that these predictions are largely empirically derived, it does not seem possible to be deterministic about such a problem.

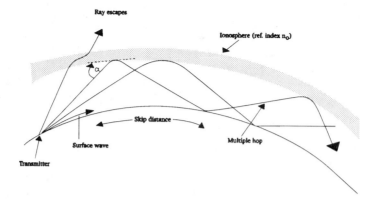

Figure 6.26 Sky wave and surface wave transmission showing skip distance

For h.f. predictions CCIR (1970) is recommended. This, in its turn, has a comprehensive set of references, and lists a lengthy computer program for completing the predictions, described in the text.

For m.f. and l.f. predictions CCIR (1982a) is recommended. Of course, a problem exists because of the large differences associated with different geographical locations. For this reason it is also recommended that CCIR (1982b) is consulted.

6.6 The surface wave

6.6.1 Ground wave and surface wave

The terminologies of ground wave and surface wave are often considered as synonymous, but it is useful to make a distinction. The influence of the ground in producing a reflected ray was discussed previously for elevated antennas and high frequencies. This ray or wave may usefully be described as the ground wave. With frequencies below about 1.5MHz, and with antennas at ground level, another mechanism of propagation tends to dominate. This is a wave which is guided along the boundary between the surface of the Earth and the air above it. The best term to be applied to this mechanism is the surface wave.

6.6.2 Reference field strength

Equation 6.49 gave the field strength for a short monopole on a perfectly conducting plane. In practice, allowance must be made for:

1. The power gain g of a particular antenna in a given direction, relative to the short monopole, assuming a perfect ground plane.
2. The imperfect conductivity of the ground plane, which causes a significant fraction of transmitter power to be lost as heat in the ground, and not radiated as electro-magnetic energy. This is taken into account by the transmitter antenna system efficiency τ.
3. The reduction in field strength for the real path relative to that for a perfectly conducting flat plane. This is taken into account by the path attenuation factor A.

The quantity P' given by Equation 6.93 is called the effective monopole radiated power in kilowatts (E.M.R.P.), which is analogous to the E.R.P. defined previously for the space wave.

$$P' = P_{kW}\, g\, \tau \qquad (6.93)$$

Thus an E.M.R.P. of 1kW gives a field strength of 0.3volts/metre at 1km on a perfectly conducting ground.

Monopole antennas that are longer than 0.1 wavelengths have gains given by the graph of Figure 6.27. A practical antenna may obtain additional gain, in a given direction, by many means. This may be allowed for, as with the space wave, by the use of a horizontal radiation pattern (H.R.P.).

The field strength for the practical case now becomes as in Equation 6.94.

$$E = \frac{300 \left(P_{kW}\, g\, \tau \right)^{1/2}}{d}\, A \quad volts/metre \qquad (6.94)$$

6.6.3 The Sommerfeld-Norton theory

The Sommerfeld-Norton theory (Jordan and Balmain, 1986, pp. 635-649; Terman, 1943) gives a method for prediction of attenuation over a homogeneous smooth earth. This method will not be fully described here but, for a vertical antenna, it is convenient to define this calculation via the surface impedance concept. Thus, for a ground conductivity σ, relative permittivity ε_r, and for a wave of length λ, the relative surface impedance at grazing incidence, may be given by Equation 6.95.

$$\eta = \frac{\left(\varepsilon_r - j\, 60\, \sigma\, \lambda - 1 \right)^{1/2}}{\varepsilon_r - j\, 60\, \sigma\, \lambda} \qquad (6.95)$$

For a given distance d a parameter w may be defined by Equation 6.96.

$$w = -j\, \pi\, \eta^2\, \frac{d}{\lambda} \qquad (6.96)$$

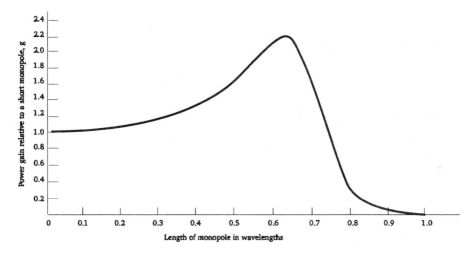

Figure 6.27 Relative power gain of a monopole antenna

From this, the complex surface wave attenuation factor A is given by Equation 6.97 where $erfc$ denotes the complimentary error function (Aboramowitz and Stegun, 1964).

$$A = 1 - j\sqrt{\pi w}\, e^{-w}\, erfc\,(j\sqrt{w})\qquad(6.97)$$

6.6.4 The realistic terrain – A solution via an integral equation

A realistic terrain is covered by clutter of man made and natural objects which significantly modify the surface impedance, in ways described in Causebrook (1978a). This modification can result in attenuation varying as shown in Figure 6.28 i.e. instead of a simple monotonic curve, there is an initial rise and a significant dip at $\frac{d}{\lambda}$ equal to about 100.

In practice, it is desirable to have a calculation system which allows for:

1. The curvature of the Earth.
2. A terrain which varies in height.
3. A surface impedance modified by clutter.

Hufford (1952) gives an integral equation which, at least in principle, provides a general solution for attenuation of radio waves. This can be written as in Equation 6.98.

$$A(R) = 1 - \int_0^R (\eta + \Psi)\, e^{-j\beta\xi}\, A(r) \left(\frac{jR}{\lambda r(R-r)} \right)^{1/2} dr \qquad(6.98)$$

In this equation R is the distance of path over which attenuation is required; Ψ is the angle in radians between the line from the receiver to the surface at range r and the tangent to the surface, at this point; ξ is the distance between terminals subtracted from the sum of distances from terminals to surface at r, see Figure 6.29; η is the relative surface impedance at r.

The integral contains quantities which do not have 'mathematically closed' forms, so an analytical solution is unobtainable. To overcome this it is, first, possible to divide the distance R into N quanta of length Δ to give Equation 6.99, where I_n is given by Equation 6.100.

$$A(r) = 1 - \sum_{n-1}^{N} Q_n I_n \qquad(6.99)$$

$$I_n = \int_{(n-1)\Delta}^{n\Delta} A(r) \left(\frac{jN\Delta}{\lambda r(N\Delta-r)} \right)^{1/2} dr \qquad(6.100)$$

Q_n is a part of the integrand which may be considered constant in the interval Δ to be given by Equation 6.101 with quantities defined by Figure 6.29.

$$Q_n = (\eta_n + \Psi_n)\, e^{-j\beta\xi_n} \qquad(6.101)$$

The next barrier to simple solution is that $A(r)$ is initially an unknown function. Up to a distance of 2Δ this presents little problem because terrain variations will not greatly modify the result. Thus the Sommerfeld-Norton function may be used to determine attenuations A_1 and A_2 at distances Δ and 2Δ, respectively, by Equation 6.102.

$$w = -j\pi \eta_1 \eta_2 \frac{n\Delta}{\lambda} \qquad(6.102)$$

Also, I_1 can be determined analytically by putting $A(r)$ equal to a power series expansion of the Sommerfeld-Norton formula.

Further values of I_n and A_n may be obtained by assuming that $A(r)$ varies linearly within an interval, as in Equation 6.103 where S_n and R_n can be derived from integrals which are amenable to analytic solution.

$$I_n = S_n A_{n-1} + R_n A_n \qquad(6.103)$$

Of course, A_n is unknown, initially, for n greater than two, but it is solvable from Equation 6.104.

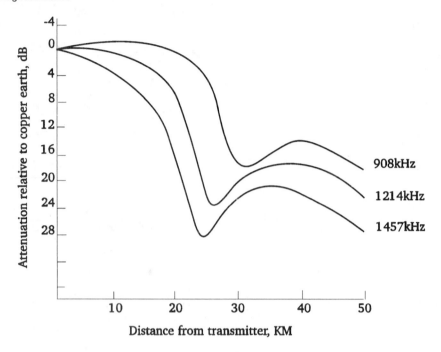

Figure 6.28 Attenuations of m.f. signals through a built up area

$$A_n = \frac{1 - \sum_{m=1}^{n-1} Q_m I_m - Q_n S_n A_{n-1}}{1 + Q_n R_n}$$

(6.104)

This equation must be applied repeatedly from n = 3 until n = N, at which point the required attenuation at distance R is obtained

6.6.5 Electric to magnetic field ratio in cluttered environments

The attenuation, calculated by the method of the previous section, is only rigorously applicable just above the top of the clutter (buildings, trees, etc.). However, most reception of m.f. and l.f. signals takes place on antennas well in the clutter.

For antennas like the ferrite rod, designed to respond to the magnetic field, the attenuation experienced should, on average, be close to the calculation. This is not true for the electric field, like that received by a rod antenna on a car, because this can suffer more attenuation in the clutter.

In the open environment, the electric field is related to the magnetic field by the free space impedance. However, in the cluttered environment this is not the case. In fact, the impedance is less than the free space value. Further details on this subject are available in Causebrook (1978b).

6.6.6 Curves for surface wave field strength prediction

For many practical purposes it may be considered that calculating the field strength with mathematical techniques is too difficult, cumbersome or time consuming. In this case a prediction may be obtained from a set of published curves. These curves usually show the variation in surface wave field strength with distance as a function of both frequency and ground conductivity (relative permittivity is a less relevant parameter). The trend is for attenuation

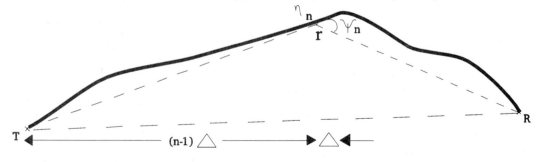

Figure 6.29 Profile data (quantised form)

with distance to be greater at higher frequencies and when ground conductivity is low. A comprehensive set of these curves is to be found in CCIR (1990d).

6.6.7 The ground conductivity

It is necessary to add a few words about the way a conductivity figure is ascribed to the Earth for the present purposes. In the case where the ground is uniform and composed of similar material at all depths, and composed of material having a conductivity which remains constant independent of frequency, the meaning of the term is fairly clear. However, the geological structure of the real Earth has considerable variations in the constituent materials near the surface. To determine the depths to which the characteristics of the Earth's surface are significant, the 'skin depth' of the current flow must be calculated. This skin depth varies between 70m for low frequencies and poor ground conductivity to 20m for high frequencies and more conductive ground. For the sea, with its greater conductivity, the skin depth at medium frequencies is less than 1m. The effective conductivity, for land, is best taken as a mean value averaged over the values obtainable down to the skin depth.

Electricity undertakings have measured conductivity, for 50Hz, to a depth of about 20m. This gives a good guide for values which can be used in the m.f. band. Various methods are quoted in published literature for the determination of ground conductivity (CCIR, 1990e). Also a method developed in Finland (Koskenniemi and Laiho, 1975) appears to be accurate, and can be measured quickly from an aircraft.

In the UK, ground conductivity can be as high as 20mS/m (milli-Siemens per metre) but is more likely to be 10mS/m in fertile regions, and about 1mS/m in the mountainous regions. If the ground conductivity changes by a small amount over the path in question, a mean value will normally produce a reasonable result but, for large variations, calculations must take account of the different characteristics in different segments of the path. A useful method for dealing with this problem was proposed by Millington (1953).

6.7 References

Aboramowitz, M. and Stegun, I.A. (1964) *Handbook of Mathematical Functions*, Dover, Chapter 7.

Balanis, C.A. (1982) *Antenna Theory Analysis and Design*, Harper and Row.

Bremmer, H. (1949) *Terrestrial radio waves; Theory of propagation*, Amsterdam, Elsevier.

Causebrook, J.H. (1978a) Medium-wave propagation in built-up areas, *Proc. IEE*, **125**, (9), pp. 804–808.

Causebrook, J.H. (1978b) 'Electric/Magnetic Field Ratios of Ground Waves in a Realistic Terrain', *IEE Electronic Letters*, **14**, (19)(614).

CCIR (1970) *CCIR interim method for estimating sky-wave field strength and transmission loss at frequencies between the approximate limits of 2 and 30MHz*, CCIR Report 252-2, New Delhi.

CCIR (1982a) *Prediction of sky-wave field strength between 150kHz and 1600kHz*, CCIR Recommendation 435-4, XVth Plenary Assembly, **VI**, Geneva.

CCIR (1982b) *Analysis of sky-wave propagation measurements for the frequency range 150 to 1600kHz*, CCIR Recommendation 431-3, XVth Plenary Assembly, **VI**, Geneva.

CCIR (1990a) *Radiometeorological Data*, CCIR Report 563, XVIIth Plenary Assembly, **V**, Dusseldorf.

CCIR (1990b) *Cross-Polarisation due to the atmosphere*, CCIR Report 722, XVIIth Plenary Assembly, **V**, Dusseldorf.

CCIR (1990c) *Propagation data required for space telecommunications systems*, CCIR Report 564, XVIIth Plenary Assembly, **V**, Dusseldorf.

CCIR (1990d) *Ground-wave Propagation Curves for Frequencies between 10kHz and 30MHz*, CCIR Recommendation 368, XVIIthe Plenary Assembly, **V**, Dusseldorf.

CCIR (1990e) *Electrical Characteristics of the Surface of the Earth*, CCIR Report 229, XVIIth Plenary Assembly, **V**, Dusseldorf.

CCIR (1990f) *Attenuation by Atmospheric Gases* CCIR Report 719, XVIIth Plenary Assembly, **V**, Dusseldorf.

Chu, T.S. (1980) Analysis and prediction of cross–polarisation on Earth-space links. In *Proc. URSI (Commission F), International Symposium on Effects of the lower atmosphere on radio propagation at frequencies above 1GHz*, Lennoxville, Canada.

Deygout, J. (1966) 'Multiple knife–edge diffraction of Microwaves', *IEEE Trans. Antennas and Prop.*, **AP-14**, (4) pp. 480–489.

Hacking, K. (1970) UHF Propagation Over Rounded Hills, *Proc. Inst. Elect. Engrs.*, **117**, (3), pp. 499–511.

Hufford, H.A. (1952) An integral equation approach to wave propagation over an irregular surface, *Q.J. Appl. Math.*, **9**, pp. 391–404.

Jasik, H. (1961) *Antenna Engineering Handbook* 1st Ed., McGraw Hill, Chapter 6, 'Loop Antennas' by Blass, Judd.

Jordan, E.C. and Balmain, K.G. (1968) *Electromagnetic Waves and Radiating Systems*, 2nd. Ed., Prentice Hall, pp. 317–321.

Koskenniemi, O. and Laiho, J. (October, 1975) Measurement of Effective Ground Conductivity at Low and Medium Frequencies in Finland *EBU Technical Review* **153**, pp. 237–240.

Laws, J.O. and Parsons, D.A. (1943) The relation of raindrop size to intensity *Transactions of American Geophysical Union*, **24**, pp. 452–460.

Longhurst, R.S. (1967) *Geometrical and Physical Optics*, 2nd. Ed., Longmans.

Millington, G. (1953) Surface Waves, *Proc. IEE*, **3**, (100).

Terman, F.E. (1943) *Radio Engineers' handbook*, McGraw–Hill, pp. 675–682.

Tsukiji, T. and Tou, S. (1980) On Polygonal Loop Antennas, *IEEE Trans. Antennas and Propagation*, **AP-28**, (4) pp. 571–575.

Van Der Pol, B. and Bremmer, H. (1937) The diffraction of electromagnetic waves from an electrical point source round a finitely conducting sphere, with applications to radiotelegraphy and the theory of the rainbow (2 parts). *Phil. Mag.*, **XXIV**, pp. 141–176, and pp. 825–863.

Vogler, L.E. (1964) Calculation of groundwave attenuation in the far diffraction region. *Radio Sci. J. Res. MBS.*, **68D**, (7) pp. 819–826.

Yagi, H. (1928) Beam Transmission of Ultra Short Waves, *Proc. IRE*, **26**, pp. 715–741.

7 Optics and vision

D R Heath
BSc PhD CPhys MInstP
British Aerospace

Contents

7.1 Basic concepts of optical radiation

In describing the measurement of light and its interaction with matter, three complementary properties of electromagnetic radiation need to be invoked: ray, wave and quantum. At microwave and longer wavelengths it is generally true that radiant energy exhibits primarily wave properties while at the shorter wavelengths, x-ray and shorter, radiant energy primarily exhibits ray and quantum properties. In the region of the optical spectrum ray, wave, and quantum properties will have their importance to varying degrees.

7.2 The optical spectrum

Light is electromagnetic radiant energy and makes up part of the electromagnetic spectrum. The term optical spectrum is used to describe the light portion of the electromagnetic spectrum and embraces not only the visible spectrum (that detectable by the eye) but also the important regions in optoelectronics of the ultraviolet and infrared.

The optical spectrum forms only a very narrow region of the complete electromagnetic spectrum. Figure 7.1 is an expanded diagram showing more detail of the ultraviolet, visible and infrared regions. By convention, optical radiation is generally specified according to its wavelength. The wavelength can be determined from a specific electromagnetic frequency from Equation 7.1, where λ is the wavelength (m), f is the frequency (Hz) and c is the speed of light in a vacuum (approximately $2.99 \times 10^8 \text{ms}^{-1}$).

$$\lambda = \frac{c}{f} \qquad (7.1)$$

The preferred unit of length for specifying a particular wavelength in the visible spectrum is the nanometre (nm). Other units are also in common use, namely the *angström* (A^o) and the micrometre or micron. The relation of these units is as follows:

1. 1 nanometre (nm) = 10^{-9} metre.
2. 1 *angström* $(A^o) = 10^{-10}$ metre.
3. 1 micron (μm) = 10^{-6} metre.

The micron tends to be used for describing wavelengths in the infrared region and the nanometre for the ultraviolet and visible regions.

The wavenumber (cm^{-1}) is the reciprocal of the wavelength measured in centimetres, i.e. $\frac{1}{\lambda}$ (cm) = wavenumber (cm^{-1})

The term monochromatic light is often encountered and refers to the situation where most of the electromagnetic energy is concentrated into a small range of wavelengths. If light from a discharge lamp such as sodium is examined by some sort of spectrum analyser it is possible to observe the various wavelengths of the components which it contains. Typically these would be a number of fairly narrow wavelength ranges which contain most of the energy and which are separated by much wider regions of darkness. Each narrow band of energy constitutes what is known as a spectral line which can be termed monochromatic. However it should be noted that the spectral lines are never infinitely sharp. They always consist of a small band of frequencies however narrow which make up what is called the linewidth. A laser line is monochromatic but again will have a finite linewidth.

7.3 Radiometry and photometry

Radiometry is the science and technology of the measurement of radiation from all wavelengths within the optical spectrum. The basic unit of power in radiometry is the watt (W).

Photometry is concerned only with the measurement of light detected by the eye, i.e. that radiation which falls between the wavelengths 380nm and 750nm. The basic unit of power in photometry is the lumen (lm).

In radiometric measurements the ideal detector is one which has a flat response with wavelength whereas in photometry the ideal detector has a spectral response which approximates to that of the average human eye. To obtain consistent measurement techniques the response of the average human eye was established by the Commission Internationale de l'Eclairage (CIE) in 1924. The response known as the photopic eye response is shown in Figure 7.2 and is observed to peak in the green/yellow part of the visible spectrum at 555nm. The curve indicates that it takes approximately ten times as many units of blue light as green light to produce the same visibility effect on the average human eye.

The broken curve in Figure 7.2 with a peak at 507nm is termed the scotopic eye response. The existence of the two responses arises out of the fact that the eye's spectral response shifts at very low light levels. (See Section 7.8.2.)

In normal circumstances photometric measurements are based on the CIE photopic response and all photometric instruments must have sensors which match this response. At the peak wavelength of 555nm of the photopic response one watt of radiant power is defined as the equivalent of 680 lumens of luminous power.

In order to convert a radiometric power measurement into photometric units both the spectral response of the eye and the spectral output of the light source must be taken into account. The conversion is then achieved by multiplying the energy radiated at each wavelength by the relative lumen/watt factor at that wavelength and summing the results. Note that in the ultraviolet and infrared portions of the optical spectrum although one may have high output in terms of watts the photometric value in lumens is zero due to lack of eye response in those ranges. However, it should be said that many observers can see the 900nm radiation from a GaAs laser or the 1.06μm radiation from a Nd:YAG laser since in this instance the intensity can be sufficiently high to elicit a visual response. Viewing of these sources in practice is not to be recommended for safety reasons and the moderately high energy densities at the eye which are involved.

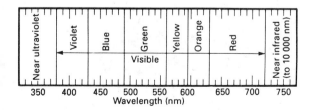

Figure 7.1 The visible spectrum

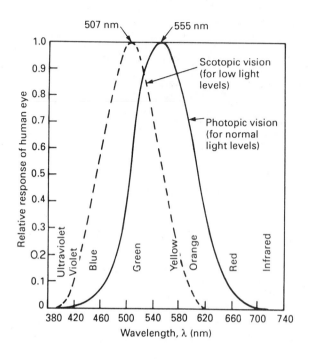

Figure 7.2   The photopic and scotopic eye responses

7.4   Units of measurement

There are many possible measurements for characterising the output of a light source. The principles employed in defining radiometric and photopic measurement terms are very similar. The terms employed have the adjective radiant for a radiometric measurement and luminous for photometric measurement. The subscript e is used to indicate a radiometric symbol and the subscript v for a photometric symbol. A physical visualisation of the terms to be defined is given in Figure 7.3. Figure 7.4 illustrates the concept of solid angle required in the visualisation of Figure 7.3.

7.4.1   Radiometric terms and units

These are as follows:

1. Radiant flux or radiant power, Φ_e. The time rate of flow of radiant energy emitted from a light source. Expressed in Js^{-1} or W.
2. Irradiance, E_e. The radiant flux density incident on a surface. Usually expressed in $W\,cm^{-2}$.
3. Radiant intensity, I_e. The radiant flux per unit solid angle travelling in a given direction. Expressed in $W\,sr^{-1}$.
4. Radiant excitance, M_e. The total radiant flux divided by the surface area of the source. Expressed in $W\,cm^{-2}$.

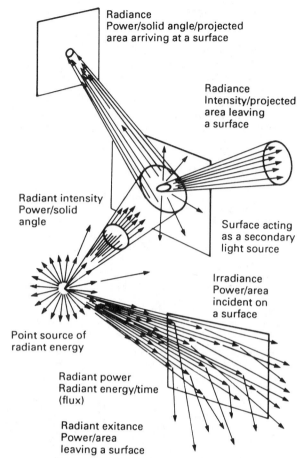

Figure 7.3   A visualisation of radiometric terms (from Zaha, 1972)

5. Radiance, L_e. The radiant intensity per unit area, leaving, passing through, or arriving at a surface in a given direction. The surface area is the projected area as seen from the specified direction. Expressed in $W\,cm^{-2}\,sr^{-1}$.

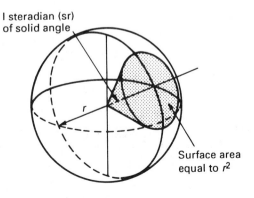

Figure 7.4   Diagram illustrating the steradian (from Zaha, 1972)

7.4.2 Photometric terms and units

The equivalent photometric terminologies to the radiometric ones defined above are as follows:

1. Luminous flux or power, Φ_v. The time rate of flow of luminous energy emitted from a light source. Expressed in 1m.
2. Illuminance or illumination, E_v. The density of luminous power incident on a surface. Expressed in lm cm^{-2}. Note the following: 1 lm cm^{-2} = 1 phot; 1 lm m^{-2} = 1 lux; 1 lm ft^{-2} = 1 footcandle.
3. Luminous intensity, I_v. The luminous flux per unit solid angle, travelling in a given direction. Expressed in 1m sr^{-1}. Note that 1 1m sr^{-1} = 1 cd.
4. Luminous exitance, M_v. The total luminous flux divided by the surface area of the source. Expressed in lm cm^{-2}.
5. Luminance, L_v. The luminous intensity per unit area, leaving, passing through or arriving at a surface in a given direction. The surface area is the projected area as seen from the specified direction. Expressed in im cm^{-2} sr^{-1} or cd cm^{-2}.

Mathematically if the area of an emitter has a diameter or diagonal dimension greater than 0.1 of the distance of the detector it can be considered as an area source. Luminance is also called the photometric brightness, and is a widely used quantity. In Figure 7.5 the projected area of the source, A_p varies directly as the cosine of θ i.e. is a maximum at 0° or normal to the surface and minimum at 90°. Thus Equation 7.2 may be obtained.

$$A_p = A_s \cos \theta \qquad (7.2)$$

Luminance is then the ratio of the luminous intensity (I_v) to the projected area of the source (A_p), as in Equation 7.3.

$$luminance = \frac{luminous\ intensity}{projected\ area} = \frac{I_v}{A_p}$$

$$= \frac{I_v}{A_s \cos \theta}\ lm\ sr^{-1}\quad per\ unit\ area \qquad (7.3)$$

Since one lm sr^{-1} = one cd, depending on the units used for the area we have:

1. 1 cd cm^{-2} = 1 stilb.

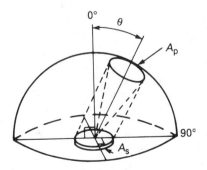

Figure 7.5 Diagram illustrating the projected area

2. $\frac{1}{\pi}$ cd cm^{-2} = 1 lambert.

3. $\frac{1}{\pi}$ cd ft^{-2} = 1 footlambert.

Table 7.1 provides a summary of the radiometric and photometric terms with their symbols and units. Some typical values of natural scene illumination expressed in units of lm/m^2 and footcandles are given in Table 7.2. Table 7.3 gives some approximate values of luminance for various sources.

Table 7.1 Radiometric and photometric terms

Quantity	Symbol	Unit(s)
Radiant flux	Φ_e	W
Luminous flux	Φ_v	lm
Irradiance	E_e	W cm^{-2}
Illuminance	E_v	lm cm^{-2}=phot
		lm m^{-2}=lux
		lm ft^{-2}=footcandle
Radiant intensity	I_e	W sr^{-1}
Luminous intensity	I_v	lm sr^{-1}=cd
Radiant exitance	M_e	W cm^{-2}
Luminous exitance	M_v	lm cm^{-2}
Radiance	L_e	W cm^{-2}sr^{-1}
Luminance	L_v	lm cm^{-2}sr^{-1}
(Photometric brightness)		cd cm^{-2}=stilb
		$1/\pi$ cd cm^{-2}=lambert
		$1/\pi$ cd ft^{-2}=footlambert

Most extended sources of radiation follow what is known as Lambert's Law, as in Equation 7.4, where I_v is the intensity of an incremental area in a direction at an angle from the normal to the surface and I_{vn} is the intensity of an incremental area in the direction of the normal.

Table 7.2 Approximate levels of natural scene illumination

	Footcandles	lm m^{-2}
Direct sunlight	1.0 - 1.3 x 10^4	1.0 - 1.3 x 10^5
Full daylight	1-2 x 10^3	1 - 2 x 10^4
Overcast day	10^2	10^3
Very dark day	10	10^2
Twilight	1	10
Deep twilight	10^{-1}	1
Full moon	10^{-2}	10^{-1}
Quarter moon	10^{-3}	10^{-2}
Starlight	10^{-4}	10^{-3}
Overcast starlight	10^{-5}	10^{-4}

Table 7.3 Approximate levels of luminance for various sources (Zaha, 1972)

	Footlamberts	cd m^{-2}
Atomic fission bomb (0.1ms after firing 90 ft diameter ball)	6x10^{11}	2x10^{12}
Lightning flash	2x10^{10}	6.8x10^{10}
Carbon arc (positive crater)	4.7x10^6	1.6x10^7
Tungsten filament lamp (gas filled 16 lm W^{-1})	2.6x10^5	8.9x10^5
Sun (as observed from the earth's surface at meridian)	4.7x 10^3	1.6x10^4
Clear blue sky	2300	7900
Fluorescent lamp (T-12 bulb cool white 430 mA medium loading)	2000	6850
Moon (as observed from earth's surface)	730	2500

$$I_v = I_{vn} \cos \theta \qquad (7.4)$$

Thus in direction θ, Equation 7.5 is obtained.

$$luminance = \frac{I_{vn} \cos \theta}{A_s \cos \theta} \qquad (7.5)$$

The luminance or brightness is therefore constant with respect to θ. The brightness of a diffuse source is the same, regardless of the angle from which it is viewed.

7.5 Instrumentation

A wide variety of commercial instruments is available for carrying out optical radiation measurements. The terminology used to describe them can be confusing although in many instances the basic component make up is in fact very similar.

7.5.1 Photometers

From the definition of photometric units and its relation to eye response, photometric measurements will be appropriate when evaluating a light source or lighting from the point of view of its effect on human vision. Typical measurements could be on room lighting, panel light indicators or warning light systems. For such measurements a photometer is used. The eye itself is a very limited photometer; the only photometric determination it can make is whether two adjacent white areas are or are not equally bright. In the past a number of photometers were developed which were based on visual measurements namely the matching of luminances. However, such systems are slow and tedious to use and many instruments have now been developed where a photocell replaces the eye as a detector.

In photometric measurement the luminance and illuminance of sources with any spectral content and spatial distribution are required. The spectral response of the photometer must be matched closely to that of the human eye. In addition, the geometrical response provided must accurately follow a cosine law in order to mimic the geometric response of the eye.

A typical photometer head for illuminance measurements employs a photoconductive or photovoltaic silicon photodiode contained in a light tight housing. In front of the detector is a filter specially designed such that the combination of detector and filter spectrally matches the response of the eye. In front of the filter is an opal glass disc which in combination with the geometry of the housing produces the required cosine response. The photometer head is connected to a calibrated readout unit.

In a telephotometer used for luminance measurements the measuring head incorporates a telescopic optical system focused onto the detector. A beam splitter enables the operator to look through the telescope and point the instrument at the surface whose luminance is required. In some instruments the dial of the readout meter appears in the eyepiece field so that the observer can read off the luminance of any part of the scene without removing the instrument from his eye.

7.5.2 Radiometers and spectral analysis

Radiometry is concerned with the emission and detection of radiant energy. The radiant energy is taken wavelength by wavelength through the entire radiation spectrum from the extreme ultraviolet to the extreme infra-red. To detect this radiation an instrument will normally employ a detector which is responsive to radiant power which is expressed in watts. A radiometer might employ a photodiode, photomultiplier or photoconductive cell as its detector. Here the sensitivity of each of these detectors varies with wavelength. It is therefore necessary to take account of this variation in sensitivity when calibrating the instrument in which the detector is used. Alternatively, a thermopile, bolometer or pyrometer might be used. Such detectors generate signals which can be related to the incident power as a result of a change in temperature which is caused by absorption of the radiant energy. These detectors have an advantage that their response as a function of wavelength is almost flat (constant with wavelength) but are limited to the measurement of relatively high intensity sources and normally at wavelengths greater than 1μm.

The choice of a radiometer is usually defined by its application. A spectral radiometer is an instrument which disperses optical radiation that is to say it employs an 'element' which is capable to some extent of separating the constituent wavelength components of a polychromatic light beam. The 'element' referred to will be a prism or diffraction grating. The instrument then analyses the radiation as a function of wavelength using one of the detector types described. A long list of names have been given to such instruments. Most commonly found are spectroradiometers, spectrophotometers, spectrometers, spectrum analysers, spectrocolorimeters.

In essence all of these instruments employ similar basic components. The methods of assembly, integration and output for these components can create significant variations in performance. Such instruments have a wide range of applications. They can be used to monitor and measure absolute spectral emission from sources and the transmission or reflectance of materials. In addition to this, recent advances in detector array technology has opened up the capabilities to the analysis of time dependent optical emissions where rapid acquisition of spectral data is required.

7.5.3 Spectroradiometers

Figure 7.6 (Ruff, 1991) illustrates the basic components of the traditional spectroradiometer. Here the dispersing element is a dif-

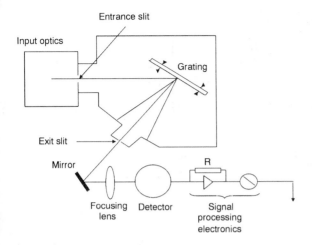

Figure 7.6 Tradional spectroradiometer. (Grating rotates to illuminate detector in discrete steps, wavelength by wavelength)

fraction grating which is rotated to illuminate the detector in discrete steps. The function of the instrument can be broken down into steps: Input-collection optics to assure proper collection geometry, the dispersing element to break the light flux into its spectral constituents, a detector to measure the amount of flux and a means of processing and displaying the output signal. Important specifications which will need to be assessed for a specific application will be the wavelength range of the instrument and the resolution (the smallest resolvable spectral element which the instrument can detect). These will be determined by the slit width and the specification of the grating in use, plus the type of detector employed in the output optics. Also, knowledge of the total beam angle or solid angle of emission of the source under investigation is important since this parameter could determine the necessary field of view for the measuring instrument. Scanning a spectrum with this type of instru-

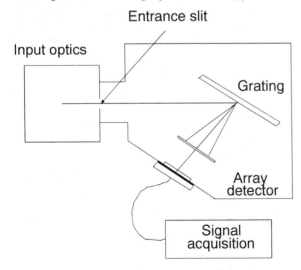

Figure 7.7 Array-detector based spectroradiometer receives all wavelengths at once

ment is relatively slow, usually of the order of several minutes. This is because of the need to rotate the grating in discrete increments, where the detector captures the output at each position.

An alternative configuration is shown in Figure 7.7 (Ruff, 1991) which uses a linear array detector. There are two advantages to this type of design. There are no moving parts and the elements of the array are exposed simultaneously to the entire spectrum. Signal acquisition from the spectrum in this case can be as short as 10-20 milliseconds.

In this type of instrument the type of detector which is available in array form may not be as sensitive as say a photomultiplier tube. However, with detector cooling, quite acceptable performance can be achieved for many applications. Many array based instruments use a 256 pixel array to cover a region from 400nm to 600nm in wavelengths. Such a configuration results in about a 2nm resolution. Arrays at 1024 elements are available which can achieve about a 0.6nm resolution.

7.5.4 Optical power meter

The term optical power meter is normally applied to an instrument without a dispersing element and with a broad band sensitivity. Typically such an instrument would be used to measure power or energy from a narrow band source such as a laser. Using a range of calibrated detector probes which would be typically pyroelectric silicon and thermopile it is possible to measure both energy and power from pulsed and CW lasers from the UV to the far infrared.

7.5.5 Interferometers

An interferometer is an instrument which can be constructed to measure changes in distance, refractive index or wavelength by comparing the relative phase differences between two or more beams through changes in an interference pattern. The coherence property of laser light leads to many interference related applications. Laser interferometry (usually with He-Ne lasers) is used for measuring the flatness, physical dimensions of objects and also distance between objects. The dispersive action of the diffraction grating used in the spectroradiometer is due to multiple beam interference. For resolving power larger than that provided by a grating instrument the Fabry Perot etalon can be used. This is a Fabry Perot Interferometer with a fixed separation between its plates, see for example Hecht and Zajac (1974). Such an instrument is frequently used to examine the detailed structure of spectral lines and laser emissions. Figure 7.8 shows a set up for what is called the central spot scanning technique. It is applicable when only a few wavelengths are present in a source so that preliminary separation can be accomplished with a filter or grating. Light is collimated by lens L_1 and after passage through the etalon is focused by lens L_2. In the focal plane of lens L_2 a circular fringe pattern is seen. A pin-hole is positioned in front of the detector in the centre of the pattern such that the flux density of the centre spot of the pattern is recorded. Purely monochromatic light generates a particular circular fringe system. However, if two such monochromatic components were present then two superimposed ring systems would result. The etalon is commonly scanned by varying the plate separation. The condition for an interference maximum is as in Equation 7.6, where m is an integer called the order of interference, λ is the wavelength, d is the plate separation and n is the refractive index of the gas between the plates.

$$m\lambda = 2nd \qquad (7.6)$$

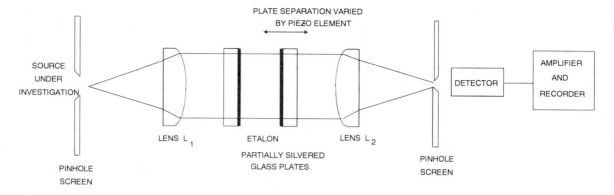

Figure 7.8 Fabry Perot etalon for central spot scanning

In the case of air, $m\lambda = 2d$. For the case of the two monochromatic lines above the intensity variation might have a form as shown in Figure 7.9. The fringe peaks are repeated as the order of interference increments by one, m, m+1, m+2, etc. and are equally spaced with respect to $\frac{1}{\lambda}$ or frequency. When d and λ are known the wavelength or frequency differences of component lines lying in what is called the 'free spectral range' can be evaluated, where the free spectral range is the separation between adjacent orders of interference. A study of the width and shape of individual spectrum lines can also be carried out. If the instrument has high resolving power the fringes will have a contour corresponding closely to the line itself. The etalon is particularly suited to the measurement of laser emission and the resonant modes of a laser cavity.

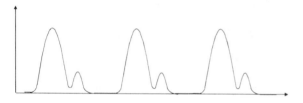

Figure 7.9 Recoder output from the set up of Figure 7.8

Fourier Transform Spectroscopy is another application of the interferometer and has emerged as a direct alternative to the dispersive prism or grating spectrometer previously discussed. Its main application is in the field of organic chemical analysis. The basic optical element in the Fourier Transform Spectrometer is normally a Michelson interferometer as shown in Figures 7.10 and 7.11. As the mirror in one of the arms of the interferometer is moved the detector records the interference pattern produced by the superposition of the two beams which are split and recombined by the beam splitter. The detector is fixed at the centre of the ring pattern of the interferometer. The recorded interference pattern is called the interferogram. The interferogram is digitised and sent to a computer. The computer reduces the interferogram to a spectrum by means of a Fourier Transform algorithm.

Although more sophisticated than the grating instrument the instrument has benefited greatly from advances in digital computing. It does have an energy throughput advantage over dispersion instru-

ments and a multiplexing advantage in that all spectral elements are observed throughout the recording of the interferogram. However, as we have seen the advent of detector arrays and their use in the grating instrument tends to cancel out the second advantage of the Fourier Transform Instrument. The built in computer of a rapid scan commercial instrument is mainly there to perform the Fourier transformation but it can also be used to store reference spectra and these can be used in a ratio to yield solely the spectrum of the desired component. This is equivalent to the double beam operation of a commercial conventional dispersive instrument where the incident beam is split into two beams one of which traverses the specimen and the other passes through a reference channel. Great care should be taken in selecting the instrument which is most suited to a particular application.

7.5.6 Accuracies

Blackbody sources and electrical substitution radiometers are used as primary standards for the calibration of radiometric instruments. Absolute calibrations are transferred from these primary standards to the broad variety of sources and power meters used in working laboratories with special incandescent lamps. Errors that can build up with transfer of calibrations result in field instruments with calibration accuracies which are typically around the 5 per cent

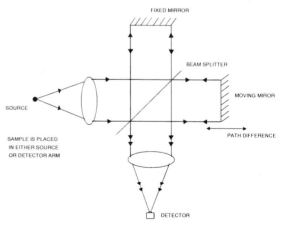

Figure 7.10 Michelson interferometer

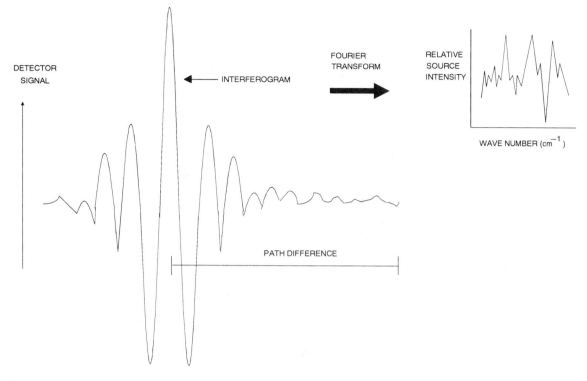

Figure 7.11 Interferogram from the interferometer of Figure 7.10

level. Advances are being made in the calibration field with the use of cryogenic electrical substitution radiometers and silicon photodiode light traps, (Hoyt and Zalewski, 1990). These are emerging technologies which will undoubtedly lead to a substantial improvement in the uncertainties of working standards and field instruments.

7.6 The human eye

As stated earlier, the science of photometry is concerned only with the measurement of light detected by the human eye. It was stated that the human eye is sensitive to radiant energy from 380nm to 750nm in wavelength. In fact, the limits of visibility for young eyes are about 313nm to 900nm but for practical purposes, the narrower range is representative for average eyes. The human eye is a positive lens system and casts a real image on a light sensitive surface which is curved to fit the curved field of the lens. In addition, the eye has the facility of automatic diaphragm and automatic focusing control.

7.7 Structure of the eye

Figure 7.12 illustrates the structure of the human eye. It is an almost spherical organ with the viscous mass inside held in place by a tough outer shell, the sclera. The sclera is a whitish colour and is opaque. However, it has a transparent front area which protrudes with a greater curvature. This is the cornea. The surface of the cornea provides the first and strongest element of the lens system of the eye. This is because the greatest change in refractive index occurs at this surface; the refractive index of air = 1.000 and the refractive index

of the cornea = 1.376. Light entering the eye through the cornea then passes through a chamber called the anterior chamber which is filled with a clear watery fluid called aqueous humour. The refractive index of the aqueous humour is 1.336.

Immersed in the aqueous humour is the iris. The iris is essentially a diaphragm with an opening in the centre, the pupil. The size of the pupil is controlled by means of the circular and radial muscle fibres in the iris. The iris can expand or contract the pupil over a range from 2mm in bright light to about 8mm in darkness. The variation in pupil diameter depending on the amount of light, is an involuntary property. When doing close work the iris also closes down the pupil in order to increase image sharpness. Immediately behind the iris is the lens which is a transparent elastic body with an outer capsule, a less dense cortex and a denser inside core. The lens is normally quite pliable with the refractive index varying from 1.406 in the inner core to about 1.386 at the cortex. The lens of the eye changes curvature in order to focus light onto the retina.

Both the lens and the iris are part of the ciliary body whose muscles control the lens curvature and the size of the pupil. The space at the back of the lens and the ciliary body is filled with vitreous humour of refractive index 1.337. Within the sclera is the choroid which contains an opaque pigment and which is well supplied with blood vessels. This is the absorber of stray light. The retina covers much of the surface of the choroid behind the ciliary body and contains the first co-ordinating nerve cells of the visual system. At the back of the retina is a thin layer of light sensitive photoreceptor cells known as rods and cones under a protective pigment. Millions of rod and cone cells are intermingled non-uniformly over the retina. The rods contain rhodopsin which is bleached by light. In turn the products formed by this bleaching stimulate nerve conduction. Rods are extremely sensitive and per-

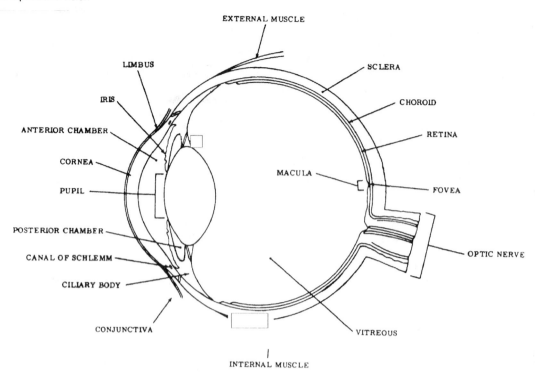

Figure 7.12 Horizontal section of right eye

form in light too dim for the cones to operate. This is the region of scotopic vision. As an ensemble they are unable to distinguish colour and the images relayed are not well defined.

There is a smaller population of cones than rods. The cones contain isodopsin and respond in bright light giving detailed coloured images. This is the region of photopic vision. The optic nerve is spread over the back of the area of the retina. Signals from the retina are then brought out via the optic nerve. The point of exit contains no receptors and is therefore insensitive to light. This is known as the blind spot.

Almost in the centre of the retina is a small depression known as the macula which is around 2.5mm to 3mm in diameter. In the centre of the macula there is an area of about 1.5mm in diameter called the fovea. In turn in the centre of the fovea there is a tiny area of about 0.5mm in diameter where there are no rods. In this region the cones are longer and thinner and more densely packed than cones elsewhere in the retina. In terms of sensitivity of the retina to light, this varies depending on the area stimulated.

The fovea is the most sensitive area and provides the finest detail and colour. To take advantage of this an image is constantly shifted across different receptor cells by continuous eyeball movement in order to keep the area of prime interest of an object on the fovea. The exact mechanism of vision is not fully known. The complexity may be conveyed by the fact that the cones of the fovea are connected individually on to a single nerve fibre and have direct path to the optic nerve. Outside the fovea the rods and some cones are multiply connected to nerve fibres which enables pattern vision.

The time varying signals from the millions of nerve fibres are continuously interpreted by the eye-brain combination in order to construct the perception of a scene. The brain of course, does not rely only on the information it receives from one eye but analyses the images formed simultaneously on the retina of two eyes. Since the two eyes are in different positions the image received by one is slightly different from the image received by the other. By this means the degree of parallax occurring between objects at different distances is measured by the brain. This enables it to conceive the objects in three dimensions and to estimate the distance of the objects.

7.8 The eye as an optical instrument

7.8.1 Resolving power

The rods and cones of the retina of the eye give it a mosaic structure which determines resolution. Minimum resolution depends on the retinal location of the image, the nature of the image and the resolution criteria used and adequate time for stimulation. Two small dark objects can be resolved as two when their images spread over two cones provided the diffraction patterns are sufficiently separated. This is the case for a 4mm diameter pupil eye where the angular limit of resolution is about 0.5 minute of arc due to the diffraction patterns.

The arc subtense of a cone is about 1 minute of arc so that the average eye is able to resolve details subtending 1 minute of arc at the eye. Even so, most people can only achieve this resolution under the most favourable conditions. It is important to distinguish between seeing and resolving. The eye can 'see' a star subtending an angle of less than an arc second but it cannot 'resolve' two stars separated by such a small angle.

7.8.2   Sensitivity

The photopic and scotopic spectral sensitivity of the eye is shown in Figure 7.2. The photopic response applies at higher levels when the eye is adapted to any light level from the brightest sunlit scene to that lit by early twilight. Here cone vision dominates. In much darker conditions, for instance at just before nightfall, the peak of the eyes sensitivity has shifted towards the blue end of the spectrum from 555nm to 507nm. When the eye is adapted to very dim light, rod vision is dominant.

The process of adaptation where the eye brain combination automatically adjusts the sensitivity of the system to light allows comfortable viewing of scenes differing in luminance by about a factor of 10^{11}. If one compares the minimum intensities which effectively switch on rod vision and cone vision then it is found that rod vision is 100 to 1000 times more sensitive than cone vision. This is illustrated in Figure 7.13 where the relative spectral sensitivity of rod and cone vision is shown.

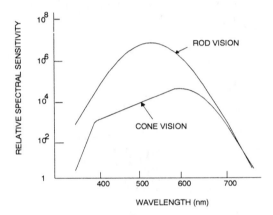

Figure 7.13   Relative spectral sensitivity of cone and rod vision

7.8.3   Persistence of vision

The process of adaptation is not instantaneous. Dark adaptation takes several minutes whilst light adaptation is much faster. If an observed illuminated image is switched on and off rapidly a sensation of flicker is produced. However if the flicker frequency is sufficiently high, the successive images merge into one another and all flicker vanishes. The maximum flicker frequency that the eye can detect increases as the amplitude of the flicker increases. For square wave flicker the maximum detectable frequency is about 50Hz at a level of luminance of 100 foot lamberts in the bright half of the cycle, (Kingslake, 1983).

7.9   Defects of vision

7.9.1   Accommodation

In a normal completely relaxed eye, the light from an object at infinity will be sharply focused on the retina and as the object moves closer to the eye the power of the lens increases automatically to maintain sharp focus. This process is called accommodation. It is enabled by the ciliary muscles bringing about a change in shape and power of the crystalline lens. With age the crystalline lens becomes stiffer and the available range of accommodation diminishes. The closest point on which the eye can focus, the near point, might be about 7 cm for a teenager, 25cm for an adult and around 100cm in older adult. The far point is the most distant object which can be brought into focus. In a normal or emmetropic eye this distance is infinity.

7.9.2   Short sightedness

Myopia is the condition of the eye where parallel rays are brought to focus in front of the retina. The eye lens is unable to relax sufficiently to focus parallel light. On the other hand when the ciliary muscles are tensed the eye can usually see objects much closer to the eye than normal. Hence the name of the defect short sightedness. For correction a concave spectacle lens enables the eye to see distant objects because it makes the light diverge as though from a less distant object.

7.9.3   Far sightedness

Hypermetropia is the condition where the eye lens is unable to focus on objects close at hand. The condition is called far sight in that distant objects are seen more clearly than closer ones. The ciliary muscles cannot contract sufficiently to bring the image of near objects on to the retina. For correction a convex spectacle lens converges light from a near object and makes it appear to come from a more distant position which the eye can cope with.

With advancing years, the range of accommodation reduces until myopia or hypermetropia or even both are present. This may necessitate two pairs of spectacles or a single pair of bifocal lenses.

7.9.4   Astigmatism

Many people suffer from some degree of astigmatism in the middle of their visual field, mainly due to pressure of the eyelid on the soft cornea. The result is that vertical and horizontal lines cannot be focused simultaneously. The cure for this refractive error is to use a lens which is itself asymmetric in its powers. A cylindrical lens can be used to correct simple astigmatism. Where it is combined with other defects the corrective lens has a more complex shape.

7.10   Interaction of light with matter

Light may interact with matter by being reflected, refracted, absorbed or transmitted. Two or more of these are usually involved.

7.10.1   Reflection

Some of the light impinging on any surface is reflected away from the surface. The reflectance varies according to the properties of the surface and the wavelength of the impinging radiation.

Regular or specular reflection is reflection in accordance with the laws of reflection with no diffusion (surface is smooth compared to the wavelength of the impinging radiation).

Diffuse reflection is diffusion by reflection in which on the microscopic scale there is no regular reflection (surface is rough when compared to the wavelength of the impinging radiation).

Reflectance (p) is the ratio of the reflected radiant or luminous flux to the incident flux.

Reflection (optical) density (D) is the logarithm to the base ten of the reciprocal of the reflectance, as in Equation 7.7, where $\rho(\lambda)$ is the spectral reflectance.

$$D(\lambda) = \log_{10}\left(\frac{1}{\rho(\lambda)}\right) \qquad (7.7)$$

7.10.2   Absorption

When a beam of light is propagated in a material medium its speed is less than its speed in a vacuum and its intensity gradually decreases as it progresses through the medium. The speed of light in a material medium varies with the wavelength and this variation is known as dispersion. When a beam traverses a medium, some of the light is scattered and some is absorbed. If the absorption is true absorption the light energy is converted into heat. All media show some absorption. Some absorb all wavelengths more or less equally, others show selective absorption in that they absorb some wavelengths very much more strongly than others. The phenomena of scattering, dispersion and absorption are intimately connected.

7.10.2.1   *Absorption coefficient*

Lambert's law of absorption states that equal parts in the same absorbing medium absorb equal fractions of the light that enters them. If in traversing a path of length dx the intensity is reduced from I to I – dI then Lambert's law states that dI/I is the same for all elementary paths of length dx. Thus Equation 7.8 may be obtained, where K is a constant known as the absorption coefficient.

$$\frac{dI}{I} = -K\,dx \qquad (7.8)$$

Therefore Equation 7.9 follows, where C is a constant.

$$Log\,I = -Kx + C \qquad (7.9)$$

If $I = I_o$ at x = 0 then Equations 7.10 and 7.11 follow.

$$C = \log I_o \qquad (7.10)$$

$$I = I_o\,e^{-Kx} \qquad (7.11)$$

Note that in considering a medium of thickness x, I_o is not the intensity of incident light due to there being some reflection at the first surface. Similarly I is not the emergent intensity owing to reflection at the second surface. By measuring the emergent intensity for two different thicknesses the losses due to reflection may be eliminated.

7.10.3   Polarisation

For an explanation of polarisation of light we need to invoke the wave concept and the fact that light waves are of a transverse nature possessing transverse vibrations which have both an electric and magnetic character. Figures 7.14 and 7.15 set out to illustrate the meaning of unpolarised and linearly polarised light.

In Figure 7.14 a wave is propagating in the x direction with vibrations in a single plane. Any light which by some cause pos-

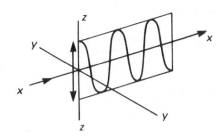

Figure 7.14   Linearly polarised light

sesses this property is said to be linearly polarised. Ordinary light, such as that received from the sun or incandescent lamps, is unpolarised and in this case the arrangement of vibrations is in all possible directions perpendicular to the direction of travel, as in Figure 7.15.

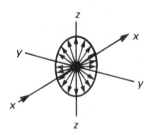

Figure 7.15   Unpolarised light

There are numerous methods for producing linearly polarised light, those most widely known being birefringence or double refraction, reflection, scattering and dichroism. Double reflection occurs in certain types of natural crystal such as calcite and quartz and will divide a beam of unpolarised light into two separate polarised beams of equal intensity. By eliminating one of the polarised beams a very efficient linear polariser can be made.

Dichroic polarisers make up the great majority of commercially produced synthetic polarisers. They exhibit dichroism, the property of absorbing light to different extents depending on the polarisation form of the incident beam.

The light emerging from a linear polariser can be given a 'twist' so that the vibrations are no longer confined to a single plane but instead form a helix. This is achieved by inserting a sheet of double-refracting material into the polarised beam which divides the beam into two beams of equal intensity but with slightly different speeds, one beam being slightly retarded. The light is said to be circularly polarised.

The application and uses of polarised light are considerable: liquid crystal displays, control of light intensity, blocking and prevention of specular glare light, measuring optical rotation, measuring propagation of stress and strain are some notable ones.

7.11 References

Bruening, R.J. (1987) Spectral irradiance scales based on filtered absolute silicon photodetectors, *Appl. Optics*, **26**, (6).

Clayton, R.K. (1971) *Light and Living Matter: The Biological Part*, McGraw-Hill, New York.

Grum, F. and Bechener, R.J. (1979) *Optical Radiation Measurements: Vol.1, Radiometry*, Academic Press, London.

Hecht, E. and Zajac, A. (1974) *Optics*, Addison Wesley pp. 309-311.

Hoyt, C. and Zalewski, E. (1990) Radiometry - Attaining absolute accuracy in the 1990's, *Photonics Spectra*, **24** (12) pp. 83-7.

Jenkins, F.A. and White, F.E. (1957) *Fundamentals of Optics*, 3rd edn, McGraw-Hill, New York.

Keys, R.J. (1980) *Optical and infrared detectors*, Springer Verlag.

Kingslake, R. (1983) *Optical system design*, Academic Press, p. 174.

Klein, M.V. and Furtak, T.E. (1986) *Optics* 2nd edn, J. Wiley and Sons.

Land, E.H. (1951) Some aspects on the development of sheet polarisers, *J. Opt. Soc. Am.* **41**, p. 957.

Lerman, S. (1980) *Radiant energy and the eye*, Macmillan.

Longhurst, R.S. (1957) *Geometrical and physical optics*, Longman, Green & Co., London.

McEwen, R.S. (1987) Liquid crystals, displays and devices for optical processing. *J. Phys. E. Sci. Instrum.*, **20**, p. 364.

Mayer-Arendt, J.R. (1972) *Introduction to classical and modern optics*, Prentice Hall, Englewood Cliffs, N.J.

RCA (1974) *Electro-optics handbook*, RCA Commercial Engineering, Harrison, NJ.

Ruff, R. (1991) Array detectors increase spectroradiometer flexibility, *Laser Focus World*. April issue pp. 155-158.

Smith, W.J. (1966) *Modern Optical Engineering*, McGraw-Hill, New York.

Taylor, J.H. (1987) Radiation exchange, *Appl. Optics*, **26** No.4, p. 619.

Walsh, J.W.T. (1965) *Photometry*, Dover, New York.

Zaha, M.A. (1972) Shedding some needed light on optical measurements, *Electronics*, 6 Nov. pp. 91-6.

8

Sound, speech and hearing

Michael Talbot-Smith
BSc CPhys MInstP
Independent Consultant

Contents

8.1 Sound waves

Sound consists of longitudinal waves in the air. The term is loosely used also for corresponding vibrations in other media. The term longitudinal means that the mode of transmission is by oscillatory movements of the air particles (in reality molecules of oxygen, nitrogen, etc.) the direction of oscillation being the same as the direction of the wave. Alternatively sound waves can be regarded as a succession of compressions followed by rarefactions. It is usual, however, to represent sound waves by graphs of convenient parameters. Particle displacement is an obvious one but the most useful is normally pressure, as shown in Figure 8.1.

Particle velocity is another useful parameter for graphical representation and this is also shown in Figure 8.1. Note that particle velocity and pressure are in phase since pressure arises from the impact of the moving particles, but pressure and particle displacement are 90° out of phase. In general we shall refer to pressure, this being the most important of the parameters as it is the sound wave pressure which causes movements of microphone diaphragms and the human ear drum.

Various units may be found to express r.m.s. (root mean square) sound pressures. The generally preferred one is the Pascal, (Pa), which is equivalent to 1 Newton/metre^2 (N/m^2). Older literature may be found which uses the dyne/cm^2.

The relationship between these is: $1Pa = 1N/m^2 = 10\ dyne/cm^2$.

Other units, used mostly for static pressures, as in meteorology for example, are the bar and torr. $1\ bar = 10^5 Pa$ and $1\ torr = 133.322 Pa$.

Pressure on its own is a very useful unit but it gives no indication of the available power or energy in a sound wave. For this the term intensity is used, the basic unit for which is the Watt/metre^2. How-

ever sound wave intensities are frequently so small that $\mu W/m^2$ is frequently more convenient. (Note that in everyday speech intensity is often equated with loudness. It is important to realise that the two things, although having some relationship, are in fact quite different.)

8.1.1 The Inverse Square Law

It is quite obvious that almost any form of wave energy diminishes in intensity as the distance from the source is increased. In practice this rate of diminution varies greatly with different conditions. An idealised relationship is given by the Inverse Square Law, as in Equation 8.1, which states that, for a point source of waves, capable of radiating omnidirectionally and with no obstructions in the vicinity (free field conditions) the intensity, I, decreases with the square of the distance, d, from the source.

$$I \propto \frac{1}{d^2} \tag{8.1}$$

In real situations sources of waves are never infinitely small and neither do they radiate omnidirectionally. Further there are almost always obstacles. Nevertheless the law can be an useful approximation in circumstances where, for example, the source is a small loudspeaker and obstacles and reflecting surfaces are relatively distant. The wavefronts then approximate to concentric spheres and are known as spherical waves. (Circumstances with spherical waves where reflecting surfaces and other obstacles are sufficiently far away for their effect to be negligible are often referred to as near field conditions.)

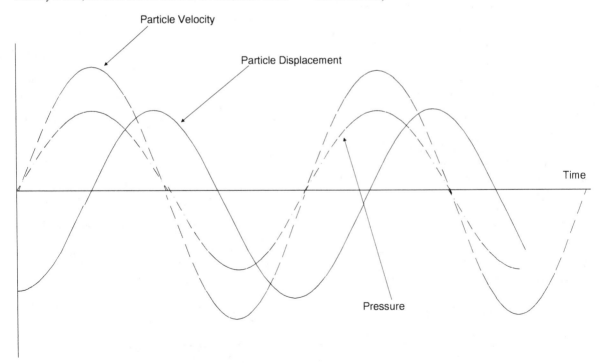

Figure 8.1 Sound wave parameters

It is important to note that intensity is proportional to (pressure)^2, so that, denoting pressure by P, Equation 8.1 may be rewritten as in Equation 8.2.

$$P \propto \frac{1}{d} \tag{8.2}$$

8.1.2   The velocity of sound

Sound velocity (c) depends upon the medium and also, in the case of gases, upon the temperature (but not, within normal limits, on pressure). Some typical values for c are given in Table 8.1. The large value of c for helium accounts for the raised pitch of speech when an oxygen/helium mixture is breathed.

Table 8.1   Examples of sound velocity

Substance	c m/s (approx.)
Water	1500
Concrete	3400
Steel	5000 - 6000
Wood	3000 - 4000
Helium gas	965 (at 0°C)
Air (dry)	331 (at 0°C)

A general expression for the velocity of sound in gases is given by Equation 8.3, where γ is the ratio of the specific heats of the gas (1.414 in the case of air), P is the pressure and ρ is the density of the gas.

$$c = \left(\frac{\gamma P}{\rho} \right)^{1/2} \tag{8.3}$$

It follows that, provided the gas obeys Boyle's Law, increasing the pressure will increase the density in the same proportion, so that under constant temperature conditions the velocity c is independent of pressure. Increase of temperature, however, causes expansion so that, under constant pressure conditions, an increase in temperature results in a decrease in density. To summarise, an expression showing how c (in m/s) varies with temperature, t (in °C), is given by Equation 8.4.

$$c = 331 + 0.6t \tag{8.4}$$

Therefore at −10°C the value of c is 325m/s; at 0°C it is 331m/s; at 10°C it is 337m/s; at 20°C it is 343m/s. A fair approximation at normal temperatures is 340m/s.

8.1.3   Frequency and wavelength

The frequency of any wave is defined as the number of complete waves emitted or received in one second. The unit is the Hertz. The wavelength is the distance between corresponding points on adjacent cycles.

Frequency f and wavelength λ are related by Equation 8.5.

$$c = f\lambda \tag{8.5}$$

For sound waves, the frequency range which can be detected by the normal human ear is approximately 16Hz to 16kHz, and Table 8.2 shows some values of wavelength in this frequency range.

Table 8.2   Examples of wavelength and frequency within range of the human ear

Frequency (Hz)	Wavelength (m)
16	21.25
20	17.0
50	6.8
100	3.4
500	0.68
1000	0.34
5000	.068
10000	.034
16000	.021

8.1.4   The Doppler effect

This is the apparent change of frequency of a received sound when there is relative movement between the source and the observer. (The Doppler Effect applies to all waves, but here we are concerned only with sound.)

For a source moving with velocity v_s towards the observer the apparent sound frequency is given by Equation 8.6.

$$f' = \frac{fc}{c - v_s} \tag{8.6}$$

Taking c as 340m/s and a source velocity of 10m/s, then a sound of true frequency 1kHz would be received as 1030.3Hz (from Equation 8.6)

For an observer moving with velocity v_o towards a stationary source, apparent sound frequency is given by Equation 8.7.

$$f' = \frac{f(c + v_o)}{c} \tag{8.7}$$

Again taking c as 340m/s and the observer's velocity as 10m/s, a sound of frequency 1kHz would be received as 1029.4Hz (from Equation 8.7).

Note that for the same relative velocities the apparent change in frequency depends on whether it is the source or the observer which is in motion. When the relative velocity approaches c the apparent frequency for a moving source approaches infinity, whereas for a moving observer the frequency approaches 2f.

8.2   Decibels

8.2.1   The fundamental decibel

The decibel (dB) is basically a unit of comparison of power using a logarithmic scale, so that the difference, n, in dBs between two powers is given by Equation 8.8 where P_1 and P_2 are the two powers (all logs are to base 10 unless stated).

$$n = 10log\left(\frac{P_1}{P_2}\right) \quad (8.8)$$

If P_1 is less than P_2 then n is negative. Powers in audio circuits are not easy to measure but voltages are. If V and R are voltage and resistance, then power is given by Equation 8.9, and from this Equation 8.10 may be obtained.

$$P = \frac{V^2}{R} \quad (8.9)$$

$$n = 20log\left(\frac{V_1^2/R_1}{V_2^2/R_2}\right) \quad (8.10)$$

If $R_1 = R_2$ Equation 8.11 follows.

$$n = 20log\left(\frac{V_1}{V_2}\right) \quad (8.11)$$

In many audio circuits a common impedance is 600 ohms and Equation 8.11 valid. However there are cases when the impedances at different points in the chain differ from each other and strictly Equation 8.11 should not be used. In fact, though, it is convenient to continue to use this equation and usually the context makes clear that the dBs are of voltage comparison rather than of power. (See Table 8.3.)

Table 8.3 Power and voltage ratios at different decibels

Decibels	Power ratio	Voltage ratio
0	1	1
1	1.26	1.12
2	1.58	1.26
3	2.0	1.41
4	2.51	1.58
5	3.16	1.78
6	3.98	2.0
7	5.01	2.24
8	6.31	2.51
9	7.94	2.81
10	10.0	3.16
20	100.0	10.0
30	1000.0	31.6
40	10^4	100.0
50	10^5	316.0

Although the decibel is a unit of comparison there are many cases where it is useful to have an agreed reference as a base, so that powers, voltages or, as we shall see, sound pressures may be compared with it. A particularly common instance in audio engineering is to refer powers to 1 milliwatt (1mW) and this is indicated by dBm.

Thus one may speak of a level of (say) +3dBm, which means that the signal in question is 3dB above 1mW, (=2mW).

8.2.2 Other versions of the decibel

These may be listed as:

1. dBmV; the reference is 1mV.
2. dBV; the reference is 1 volt.
3. dBu; this is less obvious and is based on the fact that if 1mW of power is dissipated in 600 ohms the voltage across the 600 ohms is 0.775V. Thus +6dBu is 6dB above 0.775V, (=1.55V).
4. dBA; a non-electrical unit which is intended to approximate to an unit of loudness.

Finally it should be mentioned that dBs are used without any further abbreviations when service areas of transmitters are shown with field strength contours. In such instances the reference level is 1μV/m, unless there are statements to the contrary.

An alternative to the decibel is the Neper, based on natural logarithms, as given by Equation 8.12.

$$Nepers = log_e(voltage\ ratio) \quad (8.12)$$

It follows that 1dB = 0.115 neper and 1 neper = 8.686dB.

8.3 Hearing

8.3.1 The Ear

Figure 8.2 shows a simplified section through the human ear. The visible part, the outer ear or pinna, is generally of little use although it may help in the location of high frequency sounds where the wavelengths are comparable with the dimensions of folds and ridges. The ear drum, or tympanum, is a delicate membrane which is caused to move by sound wave pressures and attached to it is a chain of bones called the ossicles. These serve as an impedance transforming set of levers to match the impedance of the air to the impedance of the fluid in the inner ear, thus ensuring that as much sound energy as possible is conveyed to the actual receptor system inside the cochlea.

The inner ear is represented in Figure 8.3 where the cochlea is shown straightened out.

The final bone in the ossicles operates a small membrane, the oval window or fenestre ovalis. The section through the cochlea shows the basilar membrane which runs the length of the cochlea. This membrane varies in width, being widest at the far end, near the helicotrema which is a small aperture allowing vibrations to pass into the lower section below the basilar membrane. The round window simply gives compliance to the system; without it very little wave energy would enter the cochlea because of the relative incompressibility of fluids.

Along the basilar membrane is a complex structure called Corti's Organ. When sound waves enter the ear, because of the shape and other physical characteristics of the cochlea, regions of maximum vibration occur depending on the sound frequency. The lowest frequencies reach a maximum near the helicotrema, the highest peaking near the oval window. Corti's organ is thus set into vibration at places corresponding to the frequency. Part of Corti's Organ consists of an array of haircells, small hairs which are attached to

Pinna
Middle ear
Inner ear
Ossicles
Meatus
To semicircular canals
Cochlea
Round window
Oval window
Tympanum
Eustachian tube

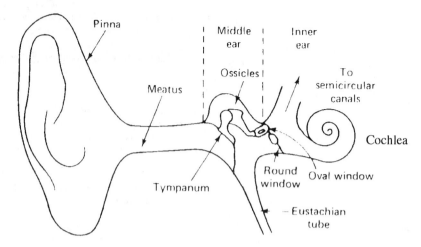

Figure 8.2 Section through the ear

nerve endings so that as the hairs are set into vibration the nerves are stimulated and signals are sent to the brain.

8.3.2 The response of the ear

A curiosity about the human ear is that not only does it not have a flat frequency response but that this response varies with sound level; in other words its sensitivity depends on both frequency and level. This is best illustrated by the curves in Figure 8.4, sometimes known as the Fletcher-Munsen curves because of the original work by these men in the 1930s, but also, and more correctly, referred to as the NPL curves, from work done at the National Physical Laboratory in the UK in the 1960s.

It will be seen from the curves in Figure 8.4 that:

1. The normal ear is most sensitive at frequencies in the region 2 to 5 kHz, when the intensity required to produce a just-detectable sensation is less than 10^{-12}W/m^2. (Taking the opening of the ear canal as being of the order of 1cm^2, or 10^{-4}m^2, the power needed to produce a sensation is roughly 10^{-16}W or 10^{-10}μW!)
2. At low frequencies, about 20Hz, the ear is relatively insensitive and requires a sound intensity of 10^{-5}W/m^2 to cause an audible sensation.
3. The sensitivity also decreases at high frequencies. This is in practice less obvious as the most important speech and music frequencies are below 5 to 6kHz.
4.

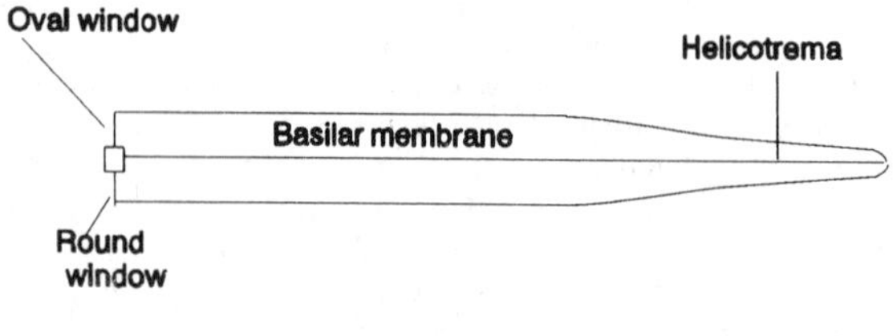

Oval window
Helicotrema
Basilar membrane
Round window

Figure 8.3 The cochlea (unwound)

The curvature of the lines becomes less pronounced at higher levels.

Although not shown explicitly in Figure 8.4 it can be stated that the average adult ear has a hearing range from about 16 to 16 000Hz. The lower figure is difficult to measure accurately and the upper figure varies very much with age and individual persons. Young people in their teens and early twenties may have an upper limit of over 20kHz, falling with age. There is, however a great deal of variation. 16kHz may be taken as a useful value for the upper limit of audibility of the average adult.

Figure 8.4 also shows a decibel scale. The reference (0dB) is standardised as a sound pressure level of 0.00002Pa. This is near to the pressure required to produce a sensation in the average ear at about 3kHz.

8.3.3 Loudness

An important point about the curves in Figure 8.4 is that they are equal loudness curves. The lowest of all is usually referred to as the Threshold of Hearing (or Threshold of Audibility).

The use of the decibel for comparison of sound pressures is fortunate in that the ear has a generally logarithmic response to sound pressure, and the decibel, being logarithmic by definition, thus has a roughly proportional relationship with loudness. For example it is found that, for most sounds, a 1dB change in level is just detectable with steady, pure tones; a 3dB change is just detectable with speech or music, while a change of 10dB is perceived as approximately a doubling (or halving) of loudness.

It will be noticed that the curves in Figure 8.4 are labelled Phons. The Phon is an unit of loudness, and it must be remembered that loudness is a subjective effect and cannot therefore be measured by external means, although there are, as we shall see, methods of making measurements which correlate sufficiently well with subjective assessments to be useful.

The Phon is defined in the following way: a sound is said to have a loudness of n phons if it has the same loudness as a pure tone at a level of n dB above 0.00002Pa at a frequency of 1kHz. It will be noted that, for example, the 60 phon curve passes through the 60dB line at 1kHz, and similarly for the other curves.

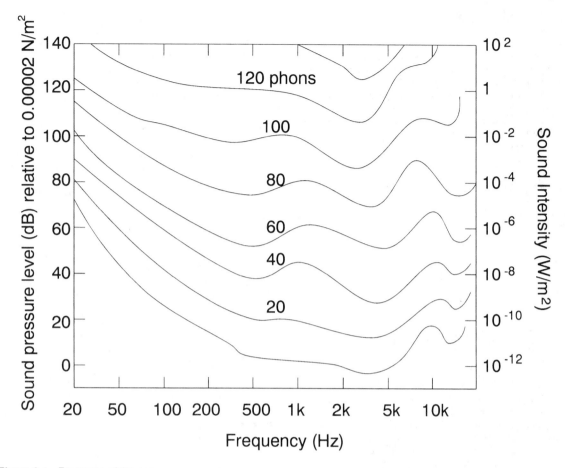

Figure 8.4 Response of the ear

A further unit of loudness is the Sone, although this seems to have found limited favour. It is intended to reflect the fact that a 10dB change in level produces in general an approximate doubling or halving of loudness, as mentioned above. For P phons the loudness in sones (S) is given by Equation 8.13.

$$S = 2^{(P - 40)/10} \qquad (8.13)$$

Thus a loudness of 40 phons corresponds to 1 sone, 50 phons to 2 sones, etc.

8.3.4 Loudness measurement

As has been stated above this is not strictly possible because loudness is a subjective phenomenon. Further, the use of a microphone, amplifier and suitably calibrated meter would give erroneous indications because such a system would make no allowance for the variation in the ear's response with frequency. However the use of appropriate weighting networks having frequency responses approximating to the response of the ear means that fairly good correlations exist between such observations and perceived loudness. The most commonly used frequency weighting network is known as the A network. This matches roughly the 40 phon curve and was originally intended to be used only with fairly quiet sounds, other networks (B and C) being designed to match higher sound

levels. However it has been found that, regardless of the sound level, the A network gives measurements which correlate reasonably well with subjective assessments of loudness. Measurements made in this way are given in dBA. This is sometimes written dB(A) but the former unit, dBA, is generally preferred. Table 8.4 lists some typical measurements.

Table 8.4 Typical dBA measurements

Sound	dBA
Jet aircraft at 150m	120
Chain saw at 1m	100
Loud motor horn at 5m	100
Busy street	90
Fairly busy road (at roadside)	80
Radio or TV set (set to loud) at 2m	70
Speech at 1m	60
Inside fairly quite car	60
Inside quite house	30 - 40

8.3.5 Hearing impairment

It is well known that exposure to excessively loud sounds can lead to hearing damage. The subject is a complicated one and can be the matter of considerable debate. The following is a summary of what is generally accepted in the UK and most of Europe. (In the UK the Health and Safety Executive (HSE) issue specific recommendations.) Below 90dBA there is probably little serious risk of hearing damage, although in industrial situations some type of ear defenders should be worn for levels above 85dBA. Above 90dBA permissible exposures depend on the sound level and the duration per day as given in Table 8.5.

Table 8.5 Permissible exposure times above 90dBA

dBA	Hours
90	8
93	4
96	2
99	1
102	0.5
105	0.25

Note that the exposure time halves for each 3dBA increase in level. There is a complication in that few noises are constant in level, or a worker in an industrial environment may not stay in the same noise conditions for very long, moving to other areas on the factory floor, for example. This has led to the concept of an equivalent noise, or personal noise dose. The terms L_{eq} for Equivalent noise Level, or $L_{ep,d}$ for Equivalent Personal Daily exposure have been adopted. The term L_{eq} is being generally discarded in favour of $l_{ep,d}$ at least in health and safety contexts. Briefly, an $L_{ep,d}$ of n dBA is the equivalent in noise dosage to a steady sound of n dBA, although the actual sound levels may have varied widely. It should be emphasised that $L_{ep,d}$ is not a simple average of individual noise levels. Computation from dBA readings and their durations is possible but suitable measuring instruments are usually to be preferred.

Other commonly encountered units are:

1. L_{90}; the noise level in dBA which is exceeded for 90% of the time.
2. L_{50}; the noise level which is exceeded for 50% of the time.
3. L_{10}; the noise level which is exceeded for 10% of the time.

8.4 Speech and music

8.4.1 Components of sounds

A sound is characterised, at least in the human ear/brain system, by various parameters. One, loudness, has been outlined above. Two others are pitch and timbre.

Pitch is generally described, rather unsatisfactorily, as the position of a note in the musical scale. It is, like loudness, a subjective phenomenon, but in technical terms it is permissible to regard pitch as being very similar to frequency. The difference arises because the pitch of a sound can vary with loudness. If a pure tone from an oscillator is fed into a loudspeaker and the level is abruptly changed by about 20dB, most listeners will experience a change in the pitch, upwards or downwards depending on the original frequency and also depending on the individual person. The higher the frequency of the sound the higher the pitch. A portion of a keyboard, as shown in Figure 8.5 can be used to aid explanation.

The letters given to different notes correspond, at least ideally, to the frequencies given in Table 8.6. The note A is adopted as a standard and is known as International A.

The subject of musical scales and pitch is beyond the scope of this book and it must be sufficient here to state that an octave, the eight white notes on a keyboard from say, c to C, contains in fact twelve equally spaced notes. The frequency ratio 2:1 is an octave, as for example a to A (220Hz to 440Hz). The frequencies of two adjacent notes, semitones in the table above, are in the ratio $2^{1/12}$ or 1.05946. It should be noted that to a trained musical ear the mathematical relationship stated here is not quite correct, so that, for instance, a semitone above F, written as F# is different from a semitone below G, written Gb.

Timbre (pronounced tarmbre) is the term used to describe the quality of a sound i.e. that which distinguishes the sound of, for instance, a trumpet from a clarinet. There are two principal factors which determine the timbre of a sound: the harmonic content and the starting transients.

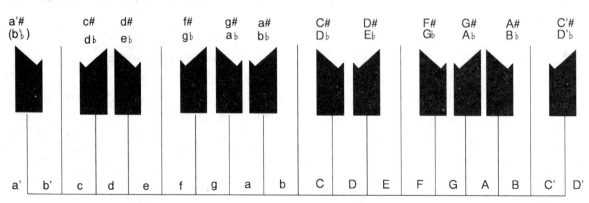

Figure 8.5 Portion of a keyboard

Table 8.6 Frequencies corresponding to musical notes

Note	Frequency (Hz)
a	220.00
a#	233.08
b	246.94
C	261.63
C#	277.18
D	293.66
E	311.13
E#	329.63
F	349.23
F#	369.99
G	392.00
G#	415.30
A	440.00
A#	466.16
B	493.88
C'	523.25

Harmonics are of course exact multiples of a fundamental frequency and the number and relative strengths of the various harmonics go some way towards giving a sound its individual quality. At least as important are the starting transients. These are additional frequencies, not in general related to the fundamental, which last for only a brief time at the start of a sound. It is probably true to say that their duration is typically no more than about ten cycles of the fundamental. Thus in a sound of basic frequency 400Hz (period 1/400=2.5mS) the starting transients would probably have died

away in about 25mS. The ear/brain attaches great importance to the starting transients and if they are missing or distorted accurate identification of the source, say a musical instrument, may be difficult or even impossible.

8.4.2 Frequency ranges of typical sounds

Figure 8.6 shows typical ranges. It should be noted that the fundamental frequencies of speech and music go only to about 4 kHz, but the harmonics may in some circumstances go well into the 10 to 20 kHz range, or maybe even higher.

It is of interest to take the example of a square wave (Figure 8.7). This consists of a fundamental together with, strictly, an infinite number of harmonics of diminishing amplitude, as in Equation 8.14.

$$x = A \sin (\omega t) + \frac{A}{3} \sin (3 \omega t) + \ldots\ldots$$
$$\ldots\ldots\ldots + \frac{A}{n} \sin (n \omega t) \tag{8.14}$$

In practice a good square wave is obtained with some thirty terms.

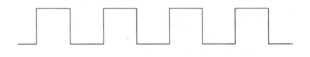

Figure 8.7 A square wave

Square wave signals, or waveforms approaching them, can be a serious source of interference because of the likely existence of high frequencies. For example a square wave of 1kHz fundamental will contain frequencies of 1kHz, 3kHz, 5kHz, etc. and the 21st harmonic will be 21kHz, albeit of low amplitude.

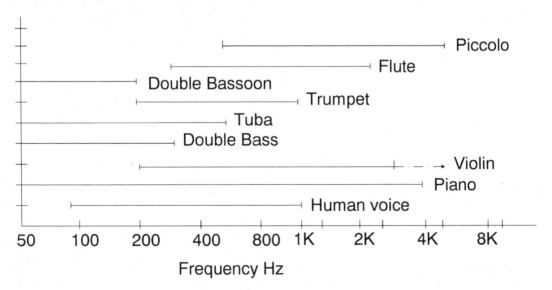

Figure 8.6 Typical frequency ranges

8.5 Acoustics

8.5.1 Reverberation time

In any room or enclosure a sound created within it will undergo repeated reflections at the various surfaces, wall, floor, ceiling, etc., losing energy at each reflection. Some energy will also be lost in travelling through the air but this is not usually significant below a frequency of about 4kHz and even then is often not important in small rooms. Such multiple-reflected sound energy is known as the reverberant sound.

Reverberation Time (T_{60}) is defined as the time taken for the reverberant sound in a room to decay through 60dB. In practice this can be regarded as being roughly the time taken for a fairly loud sound to decay to inaudibility. T_{60} can be calculated to a reasonable accuracy by a formula devised by WC Sabine, as in Equation 8.15, where V is the volume of the room and S is the total absorption in the room in Sabines.

$$T_{60} = \frac{0.16\ V}{S} \qquad (8.15)$$

The Sabine is an unit of sound absorption and is equivalent to $1m^2$ of 100% sound absorber. S is found from Equation 8.16, where S_n is the area of a material having an absorption coefficient a_n.

$$S = S_1 a_1 + S_2 a_2 + S_3 a_3 + \ldots\ldots \qquad (8.16)$$

Absorption coefficient is defined as the fraction (or percentage) of incident sound energy absorbed by the material. Some typical values of absorption coefficient are given in Table 8.7.

Table 8.7 Examples of absorption coefficient

Material	125Hz	500Hz	4000Hz
Brickwork	0.02	0.03	0.07
Rough concrete	0.01	0.04	0.10
Wood (typically)	0.06	0.009	0.12
Breeze blocks (unplastered)	0.25	0.60	0.45
Heavy curtains	0.1	0.4	0.5
Thick carpet	0.09	0.21	0.37
50mm mineral wool	0.11	0.96	0.82
75mm mineral wool	0.34	1.00	0.86

Proprietary materials, such as the mineral wool quoted above, may be retained behind perforated hardboard for protection and also to make them visually acceptable. There can be significant variations in the absorption characteristics depending upon the percentage of perforation.

Very effective absorbers can be made by using 25mm of mineral wool, faced with perforated hardboard, and with some 150 to 200mm of air space behind, the air space being divided with hardboard or even cardboard into nesting boxes 120 to 200mm square. Isolated troublesome resonances, particularly in the low frequencies, can sometimes be treated with some form of Helmholtz resonator, represented in Figure 8.8.

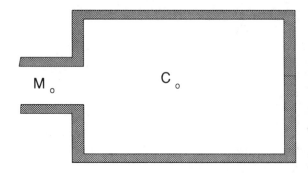

Figure 8.8 Helmholtz resonator

The action, briefly, is that the mass of air in the neck m_o, vibrates against the compliance, C_o, provided by the air in the main body of the device. The device may be compared with a weight oscillating vertically on the end of a coiled spring. The frequency of resonance is given approximately by Equation 8.17, where S the cross-sectional area of the neck, l is its length and V is the volume of the body.

$$f = \frac{c}{2\pi} \left(\frac{S}{l\,V} \right)^{\frac{1}{2}} \qquad (8.17)$$

It should be noted that a Helmholtz resonator absorbs or re-radiates sound depending on the amount of damping (i.e. acoustic friction) in the neck. Gauze across the opening has been found to be effective.

The Sabine formula given above is reasonably accurate provided that:

1. The absorptive material is fairly evenly dispersed.
2. The enclosure does not differ greatly in the ratio of its dimensions from the conventional (corridors are thus excluded).
3. The mean absorption coefficient does not approach unity.

Where there is very heavy absorption a more accurate result is given by a formula due to Eyring, as in Equation 8.18, where a' is the mean absorption coefficient.

$$T_{60} = \frac{0.16\ V}{-S \log_e (1 - a')} \qquad (8.18)$$

A further refinement is to make allowance for the absorption by the air which, as stated above, varies with frequency and also with relative humidity. Figure 8.9 gives the relationship between T_{60}, volume and absorption units (Sabines), based upon the Eyring formula.

Calculation of T_{60}, even with the aid of diagrams like Figure 8.9 is tedious and apt to be at best only approximate, if only because

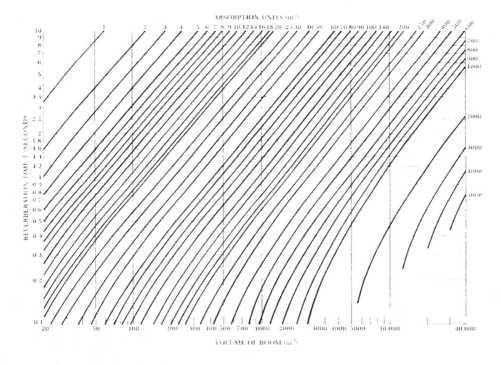

Figure 8.9 Determination of T₆₀ (Courtesy Klark-Teknik plc)

there can be considerable uncertainties about the actual absorption coefficients of materials present. Such uncertainties are likely to be made worse because diffraction effects can make the effective area of a material greater than its physical dimensions would indicate. Measurement of T_{60} with suitable apparatus is almost certainly going to give better results with much less tedious calculation or observation. A usual technique is to produce a warble tone from a loudspeaker, the warble being used to minimise excitation of particular acoustic resonances, and a microphone picks up the decaying sound when the warble tone is cut. A microprocessor device can be used to calculate T_{60}. Measurements are usually made at a number of points in the room, and at several centre frequencies of the warble.

T_{60} is at its most crucial in concert halls and recording and broadcasting studios. In other less critical circumstances it is still important as a major parameter in deciding intelligibility of speech. Typical values are given in Table 8.8.

8.5.2 Acoustic resonances

Resonances can occur between two parallel surfaces when their spacing is equal to an odd number of half-wavelengths. In these conditions there is a pressure antinode (maximum) at the surface with one or more nodes in the region between, as in Figure 8.10. Such maxima and minima are known as standing waves.

The frequencies of resonance are then given by Equation 8.19, where l is the spacing between the parallel surfaces, c is the velocity of sound and n =1, 2, 3 etc.

$$f = \frac{n\,c}{2\,l} \tag{8.19}$$

It will be quickly appreciated that with relatively small spacings (l of the order of 2 to 10m) the lowest resonance will occur well into the audible range. For example, taking l as 5m the resonant frequencies are 34, 68, 102 Hz etc., and this can result in a 'boominess' which may, in extreme cases, impair intelligibility.

With larger spacings, say l = 40m, the lowest frequencies of resonance are approximately 4.25, 8.5, 12.75, 17 Hz, etc. The lowest frequencies are below the audible range and the higher ones are sufficiently close together for their effect to be probably less objectionable.

A formula due to Lord Rayleigh (Equation 8.20) takes account of the fact that a room will normally have at least three pairs of parallel surfaces, so that not only are there potential resonances between each pair but there will also be diagonal resonances between opposite edges and between opposite corners, where p, q and r are integers and l, w and h are the room dimensions.

Table 8.8 Typical values of T₆₀

Location	Typical T_{60} (seconds)
Lecture rooms and similar auditoria	0.5 - 1.0
Theatres	1.0 (approx.)
Average domestic sitting room	0.5
Large cathedral (low frequencies)	10 - 15
Radio talks studio	0.4
Large television studio	1.1
Large concert hall	2.0

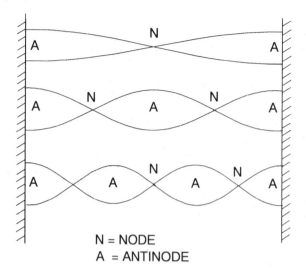

N = NODE
A = ANTINODE

Figure 8.10 Standing waves

$$f = \frac{c}{2}\left[\left(\frac{p}{l}\right)^2 + \left(\frac{q}{w}\right)^2 + \left(\frac{r}{h}\right)^2\right]^{1/2} \qquad 8.20$$

8.5.3 Background noise criteria

Table 8.9 lists typical acceptable background noise levels.

Table 8.9 Acceptable background noise levels

Location	dBA
Radio studio (drama)	20
TV studio	30
Hospital operating theatre	40
Hotel corridor	45
Open plan office	45
Public library	40
Lecture room	40

8.5.4 Sound isolation

In deciding how much noise needs to be reduced it is clearly necessary first to consider the permissible noise levels as outlined in the previous section. The present section will concentrate on reduced external noise.

Noise ingress to an enclosure may basically be by two means: structure-borne sound or airborne sound. Structure-borne sound is that which travels as vibration in the fabric of a building. Concrete, metal water pipes etc. are good conductors of sound and vibrations created in one part of a building can often be a nuisance throughout the whole structure. The problem is often compounded because of many parallel (flanking) paths. Figure 8.11 illustrates this.

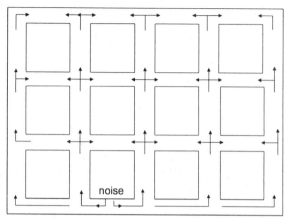

Figure 8.11 Transmission of vibrations in a building

Reduction of structure-borne sound is generally very difficult and/or expensive. The easiest solution is to reduce the noise at source, even by stopping the offending equipment if this is possible. Fitting flexible anti-vibration mounts between the machine and the ground may be very effective if properly done. Broadcast and recording studios, unless well away from any sources of vibration, are frequently isolated from the structure of the building by resilient supports below the studio floor, but to be effective this also means that the walls and ceiling must be similarly isolated from the main structure. Flexible tie-rods, for example, are needed in cavity walls.

Airborne sound is generally easier to control. In the case of walls the most effective treatment is mass; the heavier the partition the better the sound isolation. Figure 8.12 shows what is often called the 'Mass Law', relating (approximately) sound reduction with mass per unit area of partition. It will be noted that a single leaf brick wall will provide a sound reduction of about 45 dB, assuming that there are no flanking paths. It should also be noted that doubling the mass

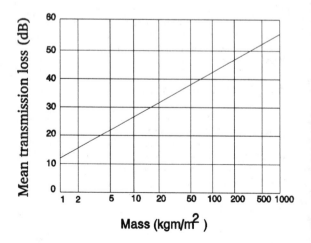

Figure 8.12 The 'Mass Law'

per unit area will in general increase the sound reduction by only about 5 dB.

Typical mass/unit area figures for a few well-known materials are given in Table 8.10.

Table 8.10 Typical mass per unit area

Material	Mass in kgm/m^2 surface area
6mm glass	15
100mm breeze block	150
12mm plasterboard with studs	60
115mm brickwork	160
150mm concrete	300

There are light-weight partitions which can be effective. Figure 8.13 illustrates in simplified form such a partition and Figure 8.14 shows the sound reduction against frequency graph for such a partition.

It is a common misconception that sound absorbing materials are also sound insulators. Polystyrene ceiling tiles seem often to have been used for this purpose and it may be useful to point out that such tiles, while effective for thermal insulation, are too light to have any value for sound isolation. Further, their sound absorption qualities are also negligible, so they are of almost no use in trying to reduce reverberation time.

Effective reduction of airborne noise involves the careful sealing of all crevices, however small. These can sometimes be difficult to locate. Typical sources of trouble are places where services such as water and electricity enter the area.

Windows can be major points of noise ingress and the best solution is to have double or even triple-glazing. It is important to realise here that the few millimetres which are appropriate for thermal insulation are very little use for acoustic purposes. A minimum of about 20mm is needed for any real effect, while for observation windows in broadcasting and recording studios the spacing of the sheets of glass should be not less than about 200mm. A further point is that such windows should have the two sheets of glass of different thickness, 6mm and 10mm for example. This is to prevent both sheets having the same acoustic resonant frequencies. Good sealing of gaps round doors is important. Some form of magnetic seal, somewhat after the fashion of the seals around refrigerator doors, is generally desirable.

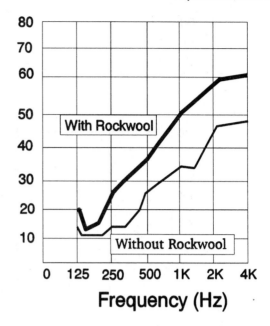

Figure 8.14 Sound reduction characteristic for the partition shown in Figure 8.13. (Courtesy Rockwool Ltd.)

8.6 Psychoacoustics

By this term we mean the somewhat obscure region between the physical characteristics of sound and the psychological interpretation of them by the brain. Only a few aspects will be outlined here.

8.6.1 Location of sounds

Several factors are involved in locating a sound, including visual clues. However the single most important one is the time of arrival difference (t) at the two ears, as illustrated in Figure 8.15.

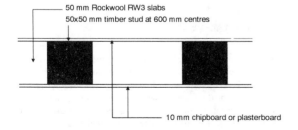

Figure 8.13 Typical lightweight partition. (Courtesy Rockwool Ltd.)

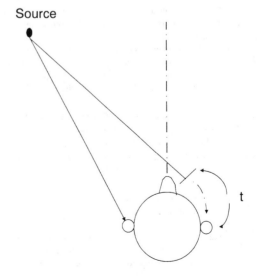

Figure 8.15 Time of arrival differences

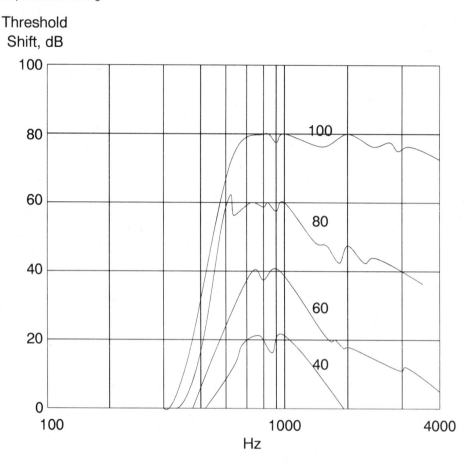

Figure 8.16 Noise masking

Clearly there is no time-of-arrival difference for sounds arriving from directly in front of the person. The maximum value of t, for sounds arriving from the extreme left or right, is of the order of a millisecond or less. Most people, in reasonable listening conditions, can detect aurally the shift of a sound source through about 1° from the centre line and t is then in the region of 10μs. The time-of-arrival difference effect is the major factor in sound location up to several hundred hertz, above which the head is big enough in relation to wavelength to begin to have an obstacle effect. Consequently there start to be amplitude differences at the ears and these can play a part in location.

It is a common observation that steady tones are difficult or even impossible to locate and there needs to be a relatively low frequency envelope for the location process to occur.

Sounds above or below the person, or in the arc behind the head, seem to be located by one or more of the following:

1. Successive head movements, often ending with the person looking at the apparent source.
2. Visual indications.
3. Common sense (bird song heard from inside a sitting room is unlikely to come from anywhere except a window!).
4. The effect of the folds and ridges in the outer ear, as mentioned previously.

8.6.2   The Cocktail Party Effect

This term is given to the ability of the brain to concentrate on sounds from a particular direction and largely ignore those from other directions. The effect is easily demonstrated by stopping up one ear. It is then found that one becomes aware of extraneous noises, room reverberation, etc. that one was largely unconscious of before. It is a well known fact that sound recordings made in a non-acoustically treated room often contain disturbing amounts of unwanted noises that were not apparent to the ears at the time of making the recording.

8.6.3   The Haas Effect

The ears tend to judge the location of a sound according to the direction of the first arrival, even though the later arrival is higher in level. The Haas Effect, as it is known, is significant in high quality sound reinforcement systems, where loudspeakers close to parts of an audience may be fed with a delayed signal so that the direct sound from the stage, platforms etc. arrives first at the listeners. The illusion is then that the sound originates only from the stage, whereas the received level from the loudspeakers may be as much as 10dB higher than the direct sound. Table 8.11 gives the approxi-

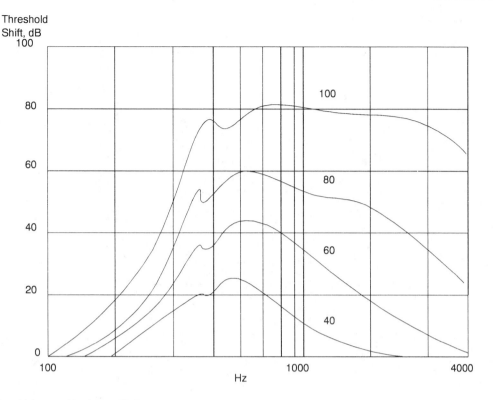

Figure 8.17   Noise masking by 400Hz tone

mate relationship between level differences in dBs and the time delay for the Haas Effect to occur.

8.6.4   Echo

Brief mention may be made of the subjective effect of repetition of a sound. Echo is defined as a repetition when there is a perceptible time interval between the first and second sound, it being assumed that the repeat has essentially the same characteristics as the first sound.

For the brain to recognise the existence of an echo there must be a time gap of more than 30 to 40mS between the first arrival and the echo. Time intervals less than this are not perceived as two distinct

Table 8.11 Time delay and level difference relationship for Haas effect

Time delay (ms)	Level difference (dB)
5	7
10	10
20	10
30	9
40	7
50	6

and separate sounds but an awareness of a time gap nevertheless can manifest itself in a different way: a mental assessment of the proximity of reflecting surfaces. Thus a person with normal hearing can generally judge the approximate size of a room, even without visual clues, simply by speaking in it. In such cases the nearest wall may be no more than two or three metres away so that the time intervals are of the order of 10 to 15mS or even less.

8.6.5   Masking

If a steady sound is detected and then another, at a different frequency, is started from a low level and increased, there may come a point where the first sound is no longer detected. It is said to be masked. In general a high frequency sound can be easily masked by a low frequency but low frequency masking by a high frequency is much more difficult. Figure 8.16 shows the effect of an 800Hz masking tone on other frequencies.

The numbers by each curve give the level of the 800Hz tone above the threshold of audibility while the vertical axis shows the threshold shift, the difference in level between the normal threshold of audibility and the level at which the otherwise masked tone becomes audible. It will be noticed that the effect on frequencies greater than, in this case 800Hz, is considerable but there is little or no effect on lower frequencies. In contrast Figures 8.17 and 8.18 show the effect of masking tones of frequencies 400Hz and 1200Hz respectively.

It is worth commenting that noise reduction techniques used in analogue audio recording, such as the Dolby[TM] system, make use of noise masking.

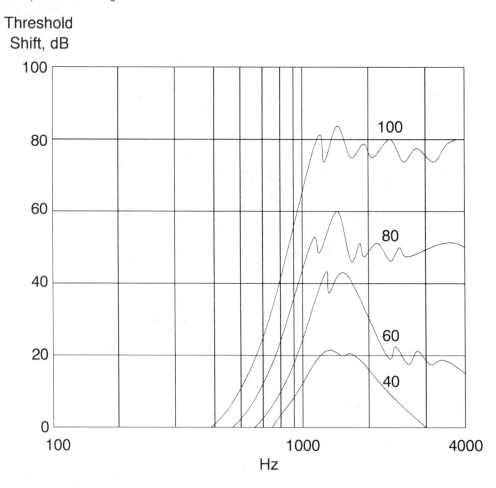

Figure 8.18 Noise masking by 1200Hz tone

8.7   References

Gilford (1972) Acoustics for Radio and Television Studios, *Peter Peregrinus*.

Richards (1973) *Telecommunication by Speech*, Butterworths, London.

Smith (1970) *Acoustics,* Longmans, London.

Taylor C.A. (1965) *The Physics of Musical Sounds*, English Universities Press.

9

The Ionosphere and the Troposphere

P A Bradley
BSc MSc CEng MIEE
Rutherford Appleton Laboratory
(Sections 9.1 - 9.6)

J A Lane
DSc CEng FIEE FInstP
Radio Communications Agency
(Sections 9.7 - 9.11)

Contents

9.1 The ionosphere

The ionosphere is an electrified region of the Earth's atmosphere situated at heights of from about fifty kilometres to several thousand kilometres. It consists of ions and free electrons produced by the ionising influences of solar radiation and of incident energetic solar and cosmic particles. The ionosphere is subject to marked geographic and temporal variations. It has a profound effect on the characteristics of radio waves propagated within or through it. By means of wave refraction, reflection or scattering it permits transmission over paths that would not otherwise be possible, but at the same time it screens some regions that could be illuminated in its absence (see Figure 9.1)

The ability of the ionosphere to refract, reflect or scatter rays depends on their frequency and elevation angle. Ionospheric refraction is reduced at the higher frequencies and for the higher elevation angles, so that provided the frequency is sufficiently great rays 1 in

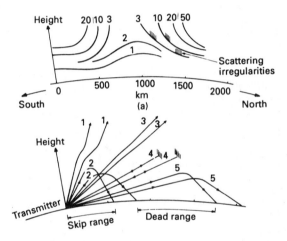

Figure 9.1 High frequency propagation paths via the ionosphere at high latitudes: (a) sample distribution of electron density (arbitrary units) in northern hemisphere high-latitude ionosphere (adapted from Buchau, 1972); (b) raypaths for signals of constant frequency launched with different elevation angles

Figure 9.1 escape whereas rays 2 are reflected back to ground. Rays 3 escape because they traverse the ionosphere at latitudes where the electron density is low (the plasmapause trough (Muldrew, 1965)). Irregularities in the F-region are responsible for the direct backscattering of rays 4. The low-elevation rays 5 are reflected to ground because of the increased ionisation at the higher latitudes. Note that for this ionosphere and frequency there are two ground zones which cannot be illuminated.

The ionosphere is of considerable importance in the engineering or radio communication systems because:

1. It provides the means of establishing various communication paths, calling for system-design criteria based on a knowledge of ionospheric morphology.

2. It requires specific engineering technologies to derive experimental probing facilities to assess its characteristics, both for communication-systems planning and management, and for scientific investigations.

3. It permits the remote monitoring by sophisticated techniques of certain distant natural and man-made phenomena occurring on the ground, in the air and in space.

9.2 Formation of the ionosphere and its morphology

There is widespread interest in the characteristics of the ionosphere by scientists all over the world. Several excellent general survey books have been published describing the principal known features (Davies, 1990; Ratcliffe, 1970) and other more specialised books concerned with aeronomy, and including the ionosphere and magnetosphere, are of great value to the research worker (Rishbeth and Garriott, 1969; Davies, 1969; Ratcliffe, 1972). Several journals in the English language are devoted entirely, or to a major extent, to papers describing investigations into the state of the ionosphere and of radio propagation in the ionosphere.

The formation of the ionosphere is a complicated process involving the ionising influences of solar radiation and solar and cosmic particles on an atmosphere of complex structure. The rates of ion and free-electron production depend on the flux density of the incident radiation or particles, as well as on the ionisation efficiency, which is a function of the ionising wavelength (or particle energies) and the chemical composition of the atmosphere. There are two heights where electron production by the ionisation of molecular nitrogen and atomic and molecular oxygen is a maximum. One occurs at about 100km and is due to incident X-rays with wavelengths less than about 10nm and to ultraviolet radiation with wavelengths near 100nm; the other is at about 170km and is produced by radiation of wavelengths 20- 80nm.

Countering this production, the free electrons tend to recombine with the positive ions and to attach themselves to neutral molecules to form negative ions. Electrons can also leave a given volume by diffusion or by drifting away under the influences of temperature and pressure gradients, gravitational forces or electric fields set up by the movement of other ionisation. The electron density at a given height is governed by the so-called Continuity equation in terms of the balance between the effects of production and loss.

Night-time electron densities are generally lower than in the daytime because the rates of production are reduced. Figure 9.2 gives examples of a night-time and a daytime height distribution of electron density. The ionisation is continuous over a wide height range, but there are certain height regions with particular characteristics, and these are known, following EV Appleton, by the letters D, E and F. The E-region is the most regular ionospheric region, exhibiting a systematic dependence of maximum electron density on solar-zenith angle, leading to predictable diurnal, seasonal and geographical variations. There is also a predictable dependence of its electron density on the changes in solar radiation which accompany the long-term fluctuations in the state of the sun. Maximum E-region electron density is approximately proportional to sunspot number, which varies over a cycle of roughly 11 years.

In the daytime the F-region splits into two, with the lower part known as the F1-region and the upper part as the F2-region. This splitting arises because the principal loss mechanism is an ion- atom interchange process followed by dissociative recombination, the former process controlling the loss rates in the F2-region and the latter in the F1-region. Although maximum production is in the

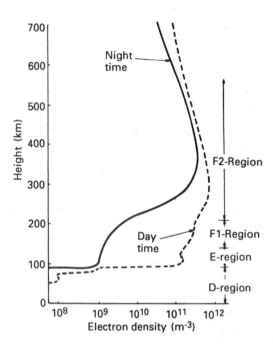

Figure 9.2 Sample night-time and daytime height distributions of electron density at mid-latitudes in summer

for its formation principally involve nitric oxide and other minor atmospheric constituents.

The D-region is mainly responsible for the absorption of radio waves because of the high electron-collision frequencies at such altitudes (see below). While the electron densities in the upper part of the D-region appear linked to those in the E-region, leading to systematic latitudinal, temporal and solar-cycle variations in absorption, there are also appreciable irregular day-to-day absorption changes. At middle latitudes anomalously high absorption is experienced on some days in the winter. This is related to warmings of the stratosphere and is probably associated with changes in D-region composition. In the lower D-region at heights below about 70km the ionisation is produced principally by energetic cosmic rays, uniformly incident at all times of day. Since the free electrons thereby generated tend to collide and become attached to molecules to form negative ions by night, but are detached by solar radiation in the daytime, the lower D-region ionisation, like that in the upper D-region, is much greater by day than night. In contrast, however, electron densities in the lower D-region, being related to the incidence of cosmic rays, are reduced with increase in the number of sunspots. Additional D-region ionisation is produced at high latitudes by incoming particles, directed along the lines of force of the Earth's magnetic field. Energetic electrons, probably originating from the Sun, produce characteristic auroral absorption events over a narrow band of latitudes about 10° wide, associated with the visual auroral regions (Hartz, 1968).

From time to time disturbances occur on the Sun known as solar flares. These are regions of intense light, accompanied by increases in the solar far ultraviolet and soft X-ray radiation. Solar flares are most common at times of high sunspot number. The excess radiation leads to sudden ionospheric disturbances (SIDs), which are rapid and large increases in ionospheric absorption occurring simultaneously over the whole sunlit hemisphere. These persist for from a few minutes to several hours giving the phenomena of short-wave fadeouts (SWFs), first explained by Dellinger. Accompanied by solar flares are eruptions from the Sun of energetic protons and electrons. These travel as a column of plasma, and depending on the position of the flare on the Sun's disc and on the trajectory of the Earth, they sometimes impinge on the ionosphere. Then, the protons, which are delayed in transit from fifteen minutes to several hours, produce a major enhancement of the D-region ionisation in polar regions that can persist for several days. This gives the phenomenon of polar cap absorption (PCA) with complete suppression of h.f. signals over the whole of both polar regions (Bailey, 1964). Slower particles, with transit times of 20-40 hours, produce ionospheric storms. These storms, which result principally from movements in ionisation, take the form of depressions in the maximum electron density of the F2-region (Matsushita, 1967). They can last for several days at a time with effects which are progressively different in detail at different latitudes. Since the sun rotates with a period of about 28 days, sweeping out a column of particles into space when it is disturbed, there is a tendency for ionospheric storms to recur after this time interval.

Additional ionisation is sometimes found in thin layers, 2km or less thick, embedded in the E-region at heights between 90 and 120km. This has an irregular and patchy structure, a maximum electron density which is much greater than that of the normal E-region, and is known as sporadic-E (or Es) ionisation because of its intermittent occurrence. It consists of patches up to 2000km in extent, composed of large numbers of individual irregularities each less than 1km in size. Sporadic-E tends to be opaque to the lower h.f. waves and partially reflecting at the higher frequencies. It results from a number of separate causes and may be classified into

F1-region, maximum electron density results in the F2- region, where the loss rates are lower. The maximum electron density of the F1-region closely follows that of the E-region, but there are significant and less predictable changes in its height. The maximum electron density and height of the F2-region are subject to large changes which have important consequences to radio wave propagation. Some of these changes are systematic but there are also major day-to-day variations. The F2-region is controlled mainly by ionisation transport to different heights along the lines of force of the Earth's magnetic field under the influence of thermospheric winds at high and middle latitudes (Rishbeth, 1972) and by electric fields at low latitudes (Duncan, 1960). These effects, taken in conjunction with the known variations in atmospheric composition, can largely explain characteristics of the F2-region which have in the past been regarded as anomalous by comparison with the E-region, namely, diurnal changes in the maximum of electron density in polar regions in the seasons of complete darkness, maximum electron densities at some middle-latitude locations at times displaced a few hours from local noon with greater electron density in the winter than the summer, and at low latitudes longitude variations linked more to the magnetic equator than to the geographic equator, with a minimum of electron density at the magnetic equator and maxima to the north and south where the magnetic dip is about 30°. At all latitudes electron densities in the F2- region, like those in the E- and F1-regions, increase with increase of sunspot number. The electron densities at heights above the maximum of the F2-region are controlled mainly by diffusion processes.

The D-region shows great variability and fine structure, and is the least well understood part of the ionosphere. The only ionising radiations that can penetrate the upper regions and contribute to its production are hard X-rays with wavelengths less than about 2nm and Lyman-α radiation at 121.6nm. Chemical reactions responsible

different types (Smith and Matsushita, 1962), each with characteristic occurrence and other statistics. In temperate latitudes sporadic-E arises principally from wind shear, close to the magnetic equator it is produced by plasma instabilities and at high latitudes it is mainly due to incident energetic particles. It is most common at low latitudes where it is essentially a daytime phenomenon.

Irregularities also develop in the D-region due to turbulence and wind shears and other irregularities are produced in the F-region. The F-region irregularities can exist simultaneously over a wide range of heights, either below or above the height of maximum electron density, and are referred to as spread-F irregularities. They are found at all latitudes but are particularly common at low latitudes in the evenings where their occurrence is related to rapid changes in the height of the F-region (Cohen and Bowles, 1961).

9.3 Ionospheric effects on radio signals

A radio wave is specified in terms of five parameters: its amplitude, phase, direction of propagation, polarisation and frequency. The principal effects of the ionosphere in modifying these parameters are considered as follows.

9.3.1 Refraction

The change in direction of propagation resulting from the traverse of a thin slab of constant ionisation is given approximately by Bouger's law in terms of the refractive index and the angle of incidence. A more exact specification including the effects of the Earth's magnetic field is given by the Haselgrove equation solution (Haselgrove, 1954). The refractive index is determined from the Appleton-Hartree equations of the magnetoionic theory (Ratcliffe, 1959; Budden, 1961), as a function of the electron density and electron-collision frequency, together with the strength and direction of the Earth's magnetic field, the wave direction and the wave frequency. The dependence on frequency leads to wave dispersion of modulated signals. Since the ionosphere is a doubly refracting medium it can transmit two waves with different polarisations (see below). The refractive indices appropriate to the two waves differ. Refraction is reduced at the greater wave frequencies, and at v.h.f. and higher frequencies it is given approximately as a function of the ratio of the wave and plasma frequencies, where the plasma frequency is defined in terms of an universal constant and the square root of the electron density (Ratcliffe, 1959). Table 9.1 lists the magnitude of the refraction and of other propagation parameters for signals at a frequency of 100MHz which traverse the whole ionosphere.

9.3.2 Change in phase-path length

The phase-path length is given approximately as the integral of the refractive index with respect to the ray-path length. Ignoring spatial gradients, the change in phase-path length introduced by passage through the ionosphere to the ground of signals at v.h.f. and higher frequencies from a spacecraft is proportional to the total electron content. This is the number of electrons in a vertical column of unit cross-section.

9.3.3 Group delay

The group and phase velocities of a wave differ because the ionosphere is a dispersive medium. The ionosphere reduces the group velocity and introduces a group delay which for transionospheric signals at v.h.f. and higher frequencies, like the phase-path change, is proportional to the total electron content.

Table 9.1 Effect of one way traverse of typical mid-latitude ionosphere at 100MHz on signals with elevation angle above 60 degrees (CCIR, 1990a)

Effect	Day	Night	Frequency dependence (f)
Total electron content	5×10^{13} per cm^2	5×10^{12} per cm^2,	
Faraday rotation	15 rotations	1.5 rotations	f^{-2}
Group delay	12.5µs	1.2µs	f^{-2}
Change in phase-path length	5.2km	0.5km	f^{-2}
Phase change	7500 radians	750 radians	f^{-2}
Phase stability (peak-to-peak)	±150 radians	±15 radians	f^{-1}
Frequency stability (r.m.s.)	±0.04Hz	±0.004Hz	f^{-1}
Absorption	0.1dB	0.01dB	f^{-2}
Refraction	≤1	Negligible	f^{-2}

9.3.4 Polarisation

Radio waves that propagate in the ionosphere are called characteristic waves. There are always two characteristic waves known as the ordinary wave and the extraordinary wave; under certain restricted conditions a third wave known as the Z-wave can also exist (Ratcliffe, 1959). In general the ordinary and extraordinary waves are elliptically polarised. The polarisation ellipses have the same axial ratio, orientations in space that are related such that under many conditions they are approximately orthogonal, and electric vectors which rotate in opposite directions (Ratcliffe, 1959). The polarisation ellipses are less elongated the greater the wave frequency. Any wave launched into the ionosphere is split into characteristic ordinary and extraordinary wave components of appropriate power. At m.f. and above these components may be regarded as travelling independently through the ionosphere with polarisations which remain related, but continuously change to match the changing propagation path and associated ionospheric conditions. The phase paths of the ordinary and extraordinary wave components differ, so that in the case of transionospheric signals when the components have comparable amplitudes, the plane of polarisation of their resultant slowly rotates. This effect is known as Faraday rotation.

9.3.5 Absorption

Absorption arises from inelastic collisions between the free electrons, oscillating under the influence of the incident radio wave, and the neutral and ionised constituents of the atmosphere. The absorption experienced in a thin slab of ionosphere is given by the Appleton-Hartree equations (Ratcliffe, 1959) and under many conditions is proportional to the product of electron density and collision frequency, inversely proportional to the refractive index and inversely proportional to the square of the wave frequency. The absorption is referred to as non-deviative or deviative depending on whether or not it occurs where the refractive index is close to unity. Normal absorption is principally a daytime phenomenon. At frequencies below 5MHz it is sometimes so great as to completely suppress effective propagation. The absorptions of the ordinary and extraordinary waves differ, and in the range 1.5-10MHz the extraordinary wave absorption is significantly greater.

9.3.6 Amplitude fading

If the ionosphere were unchanging the signal amplitude over a fixed path would be constant. In practice, however, fading arises as a consequence of variations in propagation path, brought about by movements or fluctuations in ionisation. The principal causes of fading are:

1. Variations in absorption.
2. Movements of irregularities producing focusing and defocusing.
3. Changes of path length among component signals propagated via multiple paths.
4. Changes of polarisation, such as for example due to Faraday rotation.

These various causes lead to different depths of fading and a range of fading rates. The slowest fades are usually those due to absorption changes which have a period of about 10 minutes. The deepest and most rapid fading occurs from the beating between two signal components of comparable amplitude propagated along different paths. A regularly reflected signal together with a signal scattered from spread-F irregularities can give rise to so-called flutter fading, with fading rates of about 10Hz. A good general survey of fading effects, including a discussion of fading statistics, has been produced (CCIR, 1990b). On operational communication circuits fading may be combated by space diversity or polarisation-diversity receiving systems and by the simultaneous use of multiple-frequency transmissions (frequency diversity).

9.3.7 Frequency deviations

Amplitude fading is accompanied by associated fluctuations in group path and phase path, giving rise to time and frequency-dispersed signals. When either the transmitter or receiver is moving, or there are systematic ionospheric movements, the received signal is also Doppler-frequency shifted. Signals propagated simultaneously via different ionospheric paths are usually received with differing frequency shifts. Frequency shifts for reflections from the regular layers are usually less than 1Hz, but shifts of up to 20-30Hz have been reported for scatter-mode signals at low latitudes (Nielson, 1968).

9.3.8 Reflection, scattering and ducting

The combined effect of refraction through a number of successive slabs of ionisation can lead to ray reflection. This may take place over a narrow height range as at l.f. or rays may be refracted over an appreciable distance in the ionosphere as at h.f. Weak incoherent scattering of energy occurs from random thermal fluctuations in electron density, and more efficient aspect-sensitive scattering from ionospheric irregularities gives rise to direct backscattered and forward-scatter signals. Ducting of signals to great distances can take place at heights of reduced ionisation between the E- and F-regions, leading in some cases to round-the-world echoes (Fenwick and Villard, 1963). Ducting can also occur within regions of field-aligned irregularities above the maximum of the F-region.

9.3.9 Scintillation

Ionospheric irregularities act as a phase-changing screen on transionospheric signals from sources such as Earth satellites or radiostars. This screen gives rise to diffraction effects with amplitude, phase and angle-of-arrival scintillations (Ratcliffe, 1956).

9.4 Communication and monitoring systems relying on ionospheric propagation

Ionospheric propagation is exploited for a wide range of purposes, the choice of system and the operating frequency being largely determined by the type and quantities of data to be transmitted, the path length and its geographical position.

9.4.1 Communication systems

Radio communication at very low frequencies (v.l.f.) is limited by the available bandwidth, but since ionospheric attenuation is very low, near world-wide coverage can be achieved. Unfortunately the radiation of energy is difficult at such frequencies and complex transmitting antenna systems, coupled with large transmitter powers, are needed to overcome the high received background noise from atmospherics, the electromagnetic radiation produced by lightning discharges. Despite the expanding introduction of alternate satellite links such as NAVSTAR and GPS, because of the stability of propagation, v.l.f. systems continue to be used for the transmission of standard time signals and for c.w. navigation systems which rely on direction-finding techniques, or on phase comparisons between spaced transmissions as in the Omega system (10-14kHz) (Pierce, 1965). At low frequencies (l.f.) increased propagation losses limit area coverage, but simpler antenna systems are adequate and lower transmitter powers can be employed because of the reduced atmospheric noise. Low frequency systems are used for communication by on-off keying and frequency-shift keying. Propagation conditions are more stable than at higher frequencies because the ionosphere is less deeply penetrated. Low frequency signals involving ionospheric propagation are also used for communication with submarines below the surface of the sea, with receivers below the ground and with space vehicles not within line-of-sight of the transmitter. Other l.f. systems (Stringer, 1969) relying principally on the ground wave, which are sometimes detrimentally influenced by the sky wave at night, include the Decca c.w. navigation system (70-130kHz), the Loran C pulse navigation system (100kHz) and long-wave broadcasting.

At medium frequencies (m.f.) daytime absorption is so high as to completely suppress the sky wave. Some use is made of the sky wave at night-time for broadcasting, but generally medium frequencies are employed for ground-wave services. Despite the advent of reliable multichannel satellite and cable systems, high frequencies continue to be used predominantly for broadcasting, fixed and mobile point-to-point communications, via the ionosphere; there are still tens of thousands of such circuits.

Very high frequency (v.h.f.) communication relying on ionospheric scatter propagation between ground-based terminals is possible. Two-way error-correcting systems with scattering from intermittent meteor trains can be used at frequencies of 30-40MHz over ranges of 500-1500km (Sugar, 1964). Bursts of high-speed data of about one second duration with duty cycles of the order of 5% can be achieved, using transmitter powers of about 1kW. Meteor-burst systems find favour in certain military applications because they are difficult to intercept, since the scattering is usually confined to 5-10 degrees from the great-circle path. Forward-scatter communication systems at frequencies of 30-60MHz, also operating over ranges of about 1000km, rely on coherent scattering from field-aligned irregularities in the D-region at a height of about 85km (Bailey et. al., 1955). They are used principally at low and high latitudes. Signal intensities are somewhat variable, depending on the incidence of irregularities. During magnetically disturbed conditions signals are enhanced at high latitudes, but are little affected at low latitudes. Directional transmitting and receiving antennas with intersecting beams are required. Particular attention has to be paid to avoiding interference from signal components scattered from sporadic-E ionisation or irregularities in the F-region. Special frequency-modulation techniques involving time division multiplex are used to combat Doppler effects. Systems with 16 channels, automatic error correction and operating at 100 words per minute, now exist.

9.4.2 Monitoring systems

High frequency (h.f.) signals propagated obliquely via the ionosphere and scattered at the ground back along the reverse path may be exploited to give information on the characteristics of the scattering region (Croft, 1972). Increased scatter results from mountains, from cities and from certain sea waves. Signals backscattered from the sea are enhanced when the signal wavelength is twice the component of the sea wavelength along the direction of incidence of the signal, since round-trip signals reflected from successive sea-wave crests then arrive in phase to give coherent addition. The Doppler shift of backscatter returns from sea waves due to the sea motion usually exceeds that imposed on the received signals by the ionosphere, so that Doppler filtering enables the land- and sea-scattered signals to be examined separately (Blair et. al., 1969). Doppler

filtering can also resolve signals reflected or scattered back along ionosphere paths from aircraft, rockets, rocket trails or ships. This technique is exploited in military over-the-horizon (OHD) radar systems which involve huge steered antenna arrays for fan-beam surveillance (Anderson, 1986; Headrick and Skolnik, 1974).

Studies of the Doppler shift of stable frequency, h.f., c.w. signals propagated via the ionosphere between ground-based terminals provide important information about infrasonic waves in the F-region originating from nuclear explosions (Baker and Davies, 1968), earthquakes (Davies and Baker, 1965), severe thunderstorms (Baker and Davies, 1969), and air currents in mountainous regions.

High-altitude nuclear explosions lead to other effects which may be detected by radio means (Pierce, 1965). An immediate wideband electromagnetic pulse is produced which can be monitored throughout the world at v.l.f. and h.f. Also, enhanced D-region ionisation, lasting for several days over a wide geographical area, produces an identifiable change in the received phase of long-distance v.l.f. ionospheric signals. Other more localised effects which can be detected include the generation of irregularities in the F-region.

Atmospherics may be monitored at v.l.f. out to distances of several thousand kilometres and by recording simultaneously the arrival azimuths at spaced receivers the locations of thunderstorms may be determined and their movements tracked as an aid to meteorological warning services.

9.5 Ionospheric probing techniques

There are a wide variety of methods of sounding the state of the ionosphere involving single- and multiple-station ground-based equipments, rocket-borne and satellite probes (see Table 9.2). A comprehensive survey of the different techniques has been produced by a Working Group of the International Union of Radio Science (URSI) (Smith, 1970). Some of the techniques involve complex analysis procedures and require elaborate and expensive equipment and antenna systems (Figure 9.3), others need only a single radio receiver.

Figure 9.3 The EISCAT radar antenna (Photograph courtesy of Rutherford Appleton Laboratory)

Table 9.2 Principal ionospheric probing techniques

Height range	Technique	Parameters monitored	Site
Above 100km	Vertical-incidence sounding	Up to height of maximum ionisation-electron density	Ground
	Topside sounding	From height of satellite to height of maximum ionisation-electron density; electron and ion temperatures; ionic composition	Satellite
	Incoherent scatter	Up to few thousand km - electron density; electron temperature; ion temperature; ionic composition; collision frequencies; drifts of ions and electrons	Ground
	Faraday rotation and differential Doppler	Total electron content	Satellite-ground
	In-situ probes	Wide range of parameters	Satellite
	C.W. oblique incidence	Solar flare effects; irregularities; travelling disturbances; radio aurorae	Ground
	Pulse oblique incidence	Oblique modes by ground backscatter and oblique sounding; meteors; radio aurorae; irregularities and their drifts	Ground
	Whistlers	Out to few Earth radii-electron density; ion temperature; ionic composition	Ground or satellite
Below 100km	Vertical-incidence sounding	Absorption	Ground
	Riometer	Absorption	Ground
	C.W. and pulse oblique incidence	Electron density and collision frequency	Ground
	Wave fields	Electron density and collision frequency	Rocket-ground
	In situ probes	Electron density and collision frequency; ion density; composition of neutral atmosphere	Rocket
	Cross-modulation	Electron density and collision frequency	Ground
	Partial reflection	Electron density and collision frequency	Ground
	Lidar	Neutral air density; atmospheric aerosols; minor constituents	Ground

The swept-frequency ground-based ionosonde consisting of a co-located transmitter and receiver was developed for the earliest of ionospheric measurements and is still the most widely used probing instrument. The transmitter and receiver frequencies are swept synchronously over the range from about 0.5-1MHz to perhaps 20MHz depending on ionospheric conditions, and short pulses typically of duration 100μs with a repetition rate of 50/s are transmitted. Calibrated film or computer digitised records of the received echoes give the group path and its frequency dependence.

In practice these records require expert interpretation because:

1. Multiple echoes occur, corresponding to more than one traverse between ionosphere and ground (so-called multiple-hop modes) or when partially reflecting sporadic-E or F-region irregularities are present.
2. The ordinary and extraordinary waves are sometimes reflected from appreciably different heights.
3. Oblique reflections occur when the ionosphere is tilted.

Internationally agreed procedures for scaling ionosonde records (ionograms) have been produced (Piggott and Rawer, 1972). Automatic scaling software has been developed for use with digital ionograms (Reinisch and Huang, 1983) and comparisons with manual scaling lead to periodic refinements.

Since reflection takes place from a height where the sounder frequency is equal to the ionospheric plasma frequency, and since the group path can be related to that height provided the electron densities at all lower heights are known, the data from a full frequency sweep can be used to give the true-height distribution of electron density in the E- and F-regions up to the height of maximum electron density of the F2-region. The conversion of group path to true height requires assumptions regarding missing data below the lowest height from which echoes are received and over regions where the electron density does not increase monotonically with height. The subject of true-height analysis is complex and has been considered by several research groups for many years (Beynon, 1967). An internationally agreed procedure is now available (Titheridge, 1985). Commercially manufactured pulse sounders use transmitter powers of about 1kW. Sounders with powers of around 100kW and a lower frequency limit of a few kHz have been operated successfully in areas free from m.f. broadcast interference, to study the night time E-region. This has a maximum plasma frequency of around 0.5MHz.

Pulse-compression systems (Coll and Storey, 1964) and c.w. chirp sounders (Fenwick and Barry, 1966) offer the possibility of improved signal/noise ratios and echo resolution. In the chirp sounder system, originally developed for use at oblique incidence, the transmitter and receiver frequencies are swept synchronously so that the finite echo transit time leads to a frequency modulation of the receiver i.f. signals. These signals are then spectrum-analysed to produce conventional ionograms. Receiver bandwidths of only a few tens of hertz are needed so that transmitter powers of a few watts are adequate. Other ionosondes have been produced and used operationally which record data digitally on magnetic tape (Piggott and Rawer, 1972). An ionosonde has been successfully flown in an aircraft to investigate geographical changes in electron density at high latitudes (Whalen, et. al., 1971). Over 100 ground-based ionosondes throughout the world make regular soundings each hour of each day; data are published at monthly intervals (Rutherford, 1991).

Over several years beginning in 1962 swept-frequency ionosondes have been operated in satellites orbiting the earth at altitudes of around 1000km. These are known as topside sounders and they give the distributions of electron density from the satellite height down to the peak of the F2-region. They also yield other plasma-resonance information, together with data on electron and ion temperatures and ionic composition. Fixed-frequency topside sounders have been used to study the spatial characteristics of spread-F irregularities and other features with fine structure.

Many different monitoring probes have been mounted in satellites orbiting the earth at altitudes above 100km, to give direct measurements of a range of ionospheric characteristics. These include r.f. impedance, capacitance and upper-hybrid resonance probes for local electron density, modified Langmuir probes for electron temperature, retarding potential analysers and sampling mass spectrometers for ion density, quadrupole and monopole mass spectrometers for ion and neutral-gas analysis and retarding potential analysers for ion temperature measurements.

Ground measurements of satellite beacon signals permit studies of total-electron content, either from the differential Doppler frequency between two harmonically related h.f./v.h.f. signals (Garriott and Nichol, 1965) or from the Faraday rotation of a single v.h.f. transmission (Ross, 1965). Beacons on geostationary satellites are valuable for investigations of temporal variations. The scintillation of satellite signals at v.h.f. and u.h.f. gives information on the incidence of ionospheric irregularities, their heights and sizes (Aarons, 1973).

A powerful tool for ionospheric investigations up to heights of several thousand kilometres is the vertical-incidence incoherent-scatter radar. The technique makes use of the very weak scattering from random thermal fluctuations in electron density which exist in a plasma in quasi-equilibrium. Several important parameters of the plasma affect the scattering such that each of these can be determined separately. The power, frequency spectrum and polarisation of the scattered signals are measured and used to give the height distributions of electron density, electron temperature, ionic composition, ion-neutral atmosphere and ion-ion collision frequencies, and the mean plasma-drift velocity. Tristatic receiving systems enable the vertical and horizontal components of the mean plasma drift to be determined. Radars operate at frequencies of 40-1300MHz using either pulse or c.w. transmissions. Transmitter peak powers of the order of 1MW, complex antenna arrays (Figure 9.3), and sophisticated data processing procedures are needed. Ground clutter limits the lowest heights that can be investigated to around 100km.

Electron densities, ion temperatures and ionic composition out to several Earth radii may be studied using naturally occurring whistlers originating in lightning discharges. These are dispersed audio-frequency trains of energy, ducted through the ionosphere and then propagated backwards and forwards along the Earth's magnetic-field lines to conjugate points in the opposite hemisphere. Whistler

dispersions may be observed either at the ground or in satellites (Helliwell, 1965).

Continuous wave and pulsed signals, transmitted and received at ground-based terminals, may be used in a variety of ways to study irregularities or fluctuations in ionisation. Cross-correlation analyses of the amplitudes on three spaced receivers, of pulsed signals of fixed frequency reflected from the ionosphere at near vertical incidence, give the direction and velocity of the horizontal component of drift (Mitra, 1949). The heights, patch sizes and incidence of F-region irregularities responsible for oblique-path forward-scatter propagation at frequencies around 50MHz may be investigated by means of highly-directional antennas and from signal transit times (Cohen and Bowles, 1961). Measurements of the Doppler frequency variations of signals from stable c.w. transmitters may be used to study:

1. Ionisation enhancements in the E- and F-regions associated with solar flares.

2. Travelling ionospheric disturbances (Munro, 1950).

3. The frequency-dispersion component of the ionospheric channel-scattering function (Bello, 1965).

Sporadic-E and F-region irregularities associated with visual aurorae may be examined by pulsed-radar techniques over a wide range of frequencies from about 6MHz to 3000MHz. They may also be investigated using c.w. bistatic systems in which the transmitter and receiver are separated by several hundred kilometres. Since the irregularities are known to be elongated and aligned along the direction of the Earth's magnetic field and since at the higher frequencies efficient scattering can also occur under restricted conditions, the scattering centres may readily be located. Using low-power v.h.f. beacon transmitters, this technique has proved very popular with radio amateurs. Pulsed meteor radars incorporating Doppler measurements indicate the properties and movements of meteor trains (Sugar, 1964).

Two other oblique-path techniques, giving information on the regular ionospheric regions, are high-frequency ground backscatter sounding and variable-frequency oblique sounding. The former uses a nearby transmitter and receiver, and record interpretation generally involves identifying the skip distance (see Figure 9.1) where the signal returns are enhanced because of ray convergence. It is important to use antennas with azimuthal beamwidths of only a few degrees to minimise the ground area illuminated. Long linear antenna arrays with beam slewing, and circularly-disposed banks of log-periodic antennas with monopulsing are used. Oblique-incidence sounders are adaptions of vertical-incidence ionosondes with the transmitter and receiver controlled from stable-synchronised sources. Atlases of characteristic records obtained from the two types of sounder under different ionospheric conditions have been produced. Mean models of the ionosphere over the sounding paths may be deduced by matching measured data with ray-tracing results (Croft, 1968).

Large upwards-pointing antenna arrays fed from very high power transmitters operating at v.l.f. through to u.h.f. are capable of leading to ionospheric modification at F-region heights with the excitation of plasma instabilities by non-linear wave-interaction processes. Measurements mainly at h.f. are the subject of ongoing research involving a variety of phenomena including the generation of plasma waves and artificial aurorae (CCIR, 1990c).

So far, no mention has been made of the height region below about 100km. As already noted, the D-region is characterised by a complex structure and high collision frequencies which lead to large daytime absorption of h.f. and m.f. waves. This absorption may be measured using fixed-frequency vertical-incidence pulses (Appleton and Piggott, 1954), or by monitoring c.w. transmissions at ranges of 200-500km, where there is no ground-wave component and the dominant signals are reflected from the E-region by day and the sporadic-E layer by night. There is then little change in the raypaths from day to night so that, assuming night absorption can be neglected, daytime reductions in amplitude are a measure of the prevailing absorption. Multifrequency absorption data give information on the height distributions of electron density (Beynon and Rangaswamy, 1969). Auroral absorption is often too great to be measured in such ways, but special instruments known as riometers can be used (Hargreaves, 1969). These operate at a frequency around 30MHz and record changes in the incident cosmic noise at the ground caused by ionospheric absorption.

D-region electron densities and collision frequencies may be inferred from oblique or vertical-path measurements of signal amplitude, phase, group-path delay and polarisation at frequencies of 10Hz to 100kHz, with atmospherics as the signal sources at the lower frequencies. Vertically radiated signals in the frequency range 1.5-6MHz suffer weak partial reflections from heights of 75-90km. Measurements of the reflection coefficients of both the ordinary and extraordinary waves, which can be of the order of 10^{-5}, enable electron density and collision-frequency data to be deduced (Belrose and Burke, 1964). Pulsed signals with high transmitter antenna systems and very sensitive receivers are needed. As well as in-situ probes in rockets, there are a wide range of other schemes for determining electron density and collision frequency, involving the study of wave-fields radiated between the ground and a rocket. These use combinations of frequencies in the v.l.f.-v.h.f. range and include the measurement of differential-Doppler frequency, absorption, differential phase, propagation time and Faraday rotation.

Theory shows that signals propagated via the ionosphere can become cross-modulated by high-power interfering signals which heat the plasma electrons through which the wanted signals pass. This heating causes the electron-collision frequency, and therefore the amplitude of the wanted signal to fluctuate at the modulation frequency of the interfering transmitter. Investigations of this phenomenon (known as the Luxembourg effect after the first identified interfering transmitter) usually employ vertically transmitted and received wanted pulses, modulated by a distant disturbing transmitter radiating synchronised pulses at half the repetition rate. Changes in signal amplitude and phase between successive pulses are measured, and by altering the relative phase of the two transmitters, the height at which the cross-modulation occurs can be varied. Such data enable the height distributions of electron density in the D-region to be determined (Fejer, 1955).

Using a laser radar (lidar), the intensity of the light back- scattered by the atmospheric constituents at heights above 50km gives the height distributions of neutral-air density and the temporal and spatial statistics of high-altitude atmospheric aerosols. Minor atmospheric constituents may be detected with tunable dye lasers from their atomic and molecular-resonance scattering.

9.6 Propagation prediction procedures

Long-term predictions based on monthly median ionospheric data are required for the circuit planning of v.l.f.-h.f. ground-based systems. Estimates of raypath launch and arrival angles are needed for antenna design, and of the relationship between transmitter power and received field strength at a range of frequencies, so that the necessary size of transmitter and its frequency coverage can be determined. Since there are appreciable day to day changes in the electron densities in the F2-region, in principle short-term predictions based on ionospheric probing measurements or on correlations with geophysical indices should be of great value for real-time frequency management. In practice, however, aside from the technical problems of devising schemes of adequate accuracy:

1. Not all systems are frequency agile (e.g. broadcasting).
2. Effective schemes may require two-way transmissions.
3. Only assigned frequencies may be used.

An alternative to short-term predictions is real-time channel sounding; certain procedures involve a combination of the two techniques.

9.6.1 Long-term predictions

The first requirement of any long-term prediction is a model of the ionosphere. At v.l.f. waves propagate between the Earth and the lower boundary of the ionosphere at heights of 70km by day and 90km by night as if in a two-surface waveguide. Very low frequency field-strength predictions are based on a full-wave theory that includes diffraction and surface-wave propagation. For paths beyond 1000km range only three or fewer waveguide modes need to be considered. A general equation gives field strength as a function of range, frequency, ground-electrical properties and the ionospheric reflection height and reflection coefficients (CCIR, 1990d). Unfortunately the reflection coefficients vary in a complex way with electron density and collision frequency, the direction and strength of the Earth's magnetic field, wave frequency and angle of incidence, so that in the absence of accurate D-region electron-density data, estimates are liable to appreciable error. At l.f. propagation is more conveniently described by wave-hop theory in terms of component waves with different numbers of hops. As at v.l.f. reflection occurs at the base of the ionosphere and the accuracy of the field-strength prediction is largely determined by uncertainties in ionospheric models and reflection coefficients. Medium-frequency signals penetrate the lower ionosphere and are usually reflected from heights of 85-100km, except over distances of less than 500km by night when reflection may be from the F-region. Large absorptions occur near the height of reflection and daytime signals are very weak. It is now realised that because of the uncertainties in ionospheric models, signal-strength predictions are best based on empirical equations fitted to measured signal-strength data for other oblique paths.

Prediction schemes for h.f. tend to be complicated because they must assess the active modes and elevation angles; these vary markedly with ionospheric conditions and transmitter frequency. Equations are available for the raypaths at oblique incidence through ionospheric models composed of separate segments of simple analytic form (Appleton and Beynon, 1947; Croft and Hoogasian, 1968). Combinations of parabolic, quasiparabolic, linear and quasilinear segments are typically employed (Bradley and Dudeney, 1973; Dyson and Bennett, 1988) with the segment parameters determined from numerical prediction maps of the vertical-incidence ionospheric characteristics, as given by data from the world network of ionosondes (CCIR, 1990e) (see Figure 9.4). Calculations over a fixed path for a range of frequencies indicate the largest frequency (the basic m.u.f. or maximum usable frequency) that propagates via a given mode. Assuming some statistical law for the day to day variability of the parameters of the model they also give the availability, which is the fraction of days that the mode can exist. Received signal strengths are then determined in terms of the transmitter power and a number of transmission loss and gain

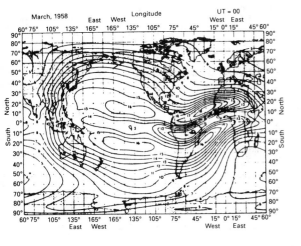

Figure 9.4 Predicted median, foF2, MHz for 00h, UT in March 1958 (Reproduced by permission of the Institute for Telecommunication Sciences, Boulder, USA)

factors. These include transmitting and receiving antenna gain, spatial attenuation, ray convergence gain, absorption, intermediate-path ground-reflection losses and polarisation-coupling losses. Predictions may be further extended by including estimates of the day to day variability in signal intensity. Calculations are prohibitively lengthy without computing aids and a number of computerised prediction schemes have been produced (CCIR, 1990f; Teters, et. al., 1983). Nowadays such procedures are available for microcomputer evaluation. By means of estimates of background noise intensity, and from the known required signal/noise ratio, the mode reliability may also be determined. This is the fraction of the days that the signals are received with adequate strength. For some systems involving fast data transmission, predictions of the probability of multipath, with two or more modes of specified comparable amplitude with propagation delays differing by less than some defined limit, are also useful and can be made.

9.6.2 Short-term predictions and real-time channel sounding

Some limited success has been achieved in the short-term prediction of the ionospheric characteristics used to give the parameters of the ionospheric models needed for h.f. performance assessment. Schemes are based either on spatial or temporal extrapolation of near real-time data or on correlations with magnetic activity indices. Regression statistics have been produced for the change in the maximum plasma frequency of the F2-region (foF2) with local magnetic activity index K, and other work is concerned with producing joint correlations with K and with solar flux.

In principle at h.f. the most reliable, although costly, way of ensuring satisfactory propagation over a given path and of optimising the choice of transmission frequency involves using an oblique-incidence sounder over the actual path; in practice, however, sounder systems are difficult to deploy operationally, require expert interpretation of their data, lead to appreciable spectrum pollution,

and give much redundant information. Some schemes involve low-power channel monitoring of the phase-path stability on each authorised frequency, to ensure that at all times the best available is used. Real-time sounding on one path can aid performance predictions for another. Examples include ray tracing through mean ionospheric models simulated from measured backscatter or oblique-incidence soundings. Many engineers operating established radio circuits prefer, for frequency management, to rely on past experience, rather than to use predictions. This is not so readily possible for mobile applications. Real-time sounding schemes involving ground transmissions on a range of frequencies to an aircraft, but only single-frequency transmission in the reverse direction, have proved successful (Stevens, 1968).

9.7 The troposphere

The influence of the lower atmosphere, or troposphere, on the propagation of radio waves is important, in several respects. At all frequencies above about 30MHz refraction and scattering caused by local changes in atmospheric structure become significant, especially in propagation beyond the normal horizon. In addition, at frequencies above about 5GHz, absorption in oxygen and water vapour in the atmosphere is important at certain frequencies corresponding to molecular absorption lines. An understanding of the basic characteristics of these effects is thus essential in the planning of very high frequency communication systems. The main features of tropospheric propagation are summarised from a practical point of view as follows. There are two general problems: firstly, the influence of the troposphere on the reliability of a communication link. Here attention is concentrated on the weak signals which can be received for a large percentage of the time, say 99.99%. Secondly, it is necessary to consider the problem of interference caused by abnormal propagation and unusually strong, unwanted signals of the same frequency as the wanted transmission.

In both these aspects of propagation, the radio refractive index of the troposphere plays a dominant role. This parameter depends on the pressure, temperature and humidity of the atmosphere. Its vertical gradient and local fluctuations about the mean value determine the mode of propagation in many important practical situations. Hence the interest in the subject of radio meteorology, which seeks to relate tropospheric structure and radio-wave propagation. In most ground-to-ground systems the height range 0-2km above the Earth's surface is the important region, but in some aspects of Earth-space transmission, the meteorological structure at greater heights is also significant.

9.7.1 Historical background

Although some experiments on ultra-short-wave techniques were carried out by Hertz and others more than 90 years ago, it was only after about 1930 that any systematic investigations of tropospheric propagation commenced. For a long time it was widely believed that at frequencies above about 30MHz transmission beyond the geometric horizon would be impossible. However, this view was disputed by Marconi as early as 1932. He demonstrated that, even with relatively low transmitter powers, reception over distances several times the optical range was possible. Nevertheless, theoreticians continued for several years to concentrate on studies of diffraction of ultra-short waves around the Earth's surface. However, their results were found to over-estimate the rate of attenuation beyond the horizon. To correct for this disparity, the effect of refraction was allowed for by assuming a process of diffraction around an Earth with an effective radius of 4/3 times the actual value. In addition, some experimental work began on the effect of irregular terrain and the diffraction caused by buildings and other obstacles.

However, it was only with the development of centimetric radar in the early years of World War II that the limitations of earlier concepts of tropospheric propagation were widely recognised. For several years attention was concentrated on the role of unusually strong refraction in the surface layers, especially over water, and the phenomenon of trapped propagation in a duct. It was shown experimentally and theoretically that in this mode the rate of attenuation beyond the horizon was relatively small. Furthermore, for a given height of duct or surface layer having a very large, negative, vertical gradient of refractive index, there was a critical wavelength above which trapping did not occur; a situation analogous to that in waveguide transmission.

Again however it became apparent that further work was required to explain experimental observations. The increasing use of v.h.f., and later u.h.f., for television and radio communication emphasised the need for a more comprehensive approach on beyond-the-horizon transmission. The importance of refractive-index variations at heights of the order of a kilometre began to be recognised and studies of the correlation between the height variation of refractive index and field strength began in several laboratories.

With the development of more powerful transmitters and antennae of very high gain it proved possible to establish communication well beyond the horizon even in a 'well-mixed' atmosphere with no surface ducts or large irregularities in the height variation of refractive index. To explain this result, the concept of tropospheric scatter was proposed. The trans-horizon field was assumed to be due to incoherent scattering from the random, irregular fluctuations in refractive index produced and maintained by turbulent motion. This procedure has dominated much of the experimental and theoretical work since 1950 and it certainly explains some characteristics of troposphere propagation. However, it is inadequate in several respects. It is now known that some degree of stratification in the troposphere is more frequent than was hitherto assumed. The possibility of reflection from a relatively small number of layers or sheets of large vertical gradient must be considered, especially at v.h.f. At u.h.f. and s.h.f. strong-scattering from a 'patchy' atmosphere, with local regions of large variance in refractive index filling only a fraction of the common volume of the antenna beams, is probably the mechanism which exists for much of the time.

The increasing emphasis on microwaves for terrestrial and space systems has recently focused attention on the effects of precipitation on tropospheric propagation. While absorption in atmospheric gases is not a serious practical problem below 40GHz, the attenuation in rain and wet snow can impair the performance of links at frequencies of about 10GHz and above. Moreover scattering from precipitation may prove to be a significant factor in causing interference between space and terrestrial systems sharing the same frequency. The importance of interference-free sites for Earth stations in satellite links has also stimulated work on the shielding effect of hills and mountains. In addition, the use of large antennae of high gain in space systems requires a knowledge of refraction effects (especially at low angles of elevation), phase variations over the wavefront, and the associated effects of scintillation fading and gain degradation. Particularly at higher microwave frequencies, thermal noise radiated by absorbing regions of the troposphere (rain, clouds, etc.) may be significant in space communication. Much of the current research is therefore being directed towards a better understanding of the spatial structure of precipitation.

In addition, there has been a recent revival of interest in the effects of terrain (hills, buildings, etc.) at v.h.f., u.h.f. and s.h.f., especially in relation to the increasing requirements of the mobile services.

9.8 Survey of propagation modes in the troposphere

Figure 9.5 illustrates qualitatively the variation of received power with distance in a homogeneous atmosphere at frequencies above about 30MHz. For antenna heights of a wavelength or more, the propagation mode on the free-space range is a space wave consisting of a direct and a ground-reflected ray. For small grazing angles the reflected wave has a phase change of nearly 180° at the Earth's surface, but imperfect reflection reduces the amplitude below that of the direct ray. As the path length increases, the signal strength exhibits successive maxima and minima. The most distant maximum will occur where the path difference is λ/2 where λ is the wavelength.

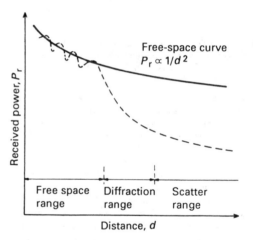

Figure 9.5 Tropospheric attenuation as a function of distance in a homogeneous atmosphere. Direct and ground reflected rays interfere in the free space range; obstacle diffraction effects perdominate in the diffraction range; and refractive-index variations are important in the scatter range

The range over which the space-wave mode is dominant can be determined geometrically allowing for refraction effects. For this purpose we can assume that the refractive index, n, decreases linearly by about 40 parts in 10^6 (i.e. 40 N units) in the first kilometre. This is the equivalent to increasing the actual radius of the Earth by a factor of 4/3 and drawing the ray paths as straight lines. The horizon distance d, from an antenna at height h above an Earth of effective radius a is given by Equation 9.1.

$$d = (2ah)^{1/2} \tag{9.1}$$

For two antennae 100m above ground the total range is about 82km, 15% above the geometric value.

Beyond the free-space range, diffraction around the Earth's surface and its major irregularities in terrain is the dominant mode, with field strengths decreasing with increasing frequency and being typically of the order of 40dB below the free space value at 100km at v.h.f. for practical antenna heights. As the distance increases, the effect of reflection or scattering from the troposphere increases and the rate of attenuation with distance decreases. In an actual inhomogeneous atmosphere the height-variation of n is the dominant factor in the scatter zone as illustrated in Figure 9.6. However, in practice the situation is rarely as simple as that indicated by these simple models.

At frequencies above about 40GHz, absorption in atmospheric

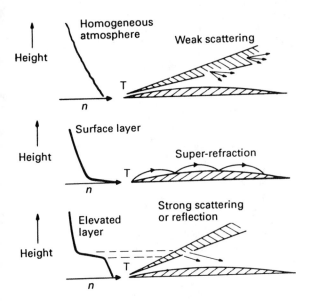

Figure 9.6 Tropospheric propagation modes and height-variation index, n

gases becomes increasingly important. This factor may determine system design and the extent to which co-channel sharing is possible; for example, between terrestrial and space communication services. There are strong absorption lines due to oxygen at 60 and 119GHz, with values of attenuation, at sea level, of the order of 15 and 2dB km^{-1} respectively. At 183GHz, a water vapour line has an attenuation of about 35dB km^{-1}. Between these lines there are 'windows' of relatively low attenuation; e.g. around 35, 90 and 140GHz. These are the preferred bands for future exploitation of the millimetric spectrum, such as short-range communication systems or radar. Further details are given in Report 719 of the CCIR.

9.8.1 Ground-wave terrestrial propagation

When the most distant maximum in Figure 9.5 occurs at a distance small compared with the optical range, it is often permissible to assume the Earth flat and perfectly reflecting, particularly at the low-frequency end of the v.h.f. range. The space-wave field E at a distance d is then given by Equation 9.2.

$$E = \frac{(90W^{1/2}h_t \, h_r)}{\lambda d^2} \tag{9.2}$$

W is the power radiated from a $\lambda/2$ dipole, and h_t and h_r are the heights of the transmitting and receiving antennae respectively.

The effects of irregular terrain are complex. There is some evidence that, for short, line-of-sight links, a small degree of surface roughness increases the field strength by reducing the destructive interference between the direct and ground-reflected rays. Increasing the terrain irregularity then reduces the field strength, particularly at the higher frequencies, as a result of shadowing, scattering and absorption by hills, buildings and trees. However, in the particular case of a single, obstructing ridge visible from both terminals it is sometimes possible to receive field strengths greater than those over level terrain at the same distance. This is the so-called obstacle gain.

In designing microwave radio-relay links for line-of-sight operation it is customary to so locate the terminals that, even with unfavourable conditions in the vertical gradient of refractive index (with sub-refraction effects decreasing the effective radius of the Earth), the direct ray is well clear of any obstacle. However in addition to multipath fading caused by a ground-reflected ray, it is possible for line-of-sight microwave links to suffer fading caused by multi-path propagation via strong scattering or abnormal refraction in an elevated layer in the lower troposphere. This situation may lead to a significant reduction in usable bandwidth and to distortion, but the use of spaced antennae (space diversity) or different frequencies (frequency diversity) can reduce these effects. Even in the absence of well defined layers, scintillation-type fading may occasionally occur at frequencies of the order of 30-40GHz on links more than say 10km long. The development of digital systems has further emphasised the importance of studies of the effect of refractive index variation on distortion, bandwidth and error rate.

As a guide to the order of magnitude of multipath fading, Report 338 of the CCIR gives the following values for a frequency of 4GHz, for the worst month of the year, for average rolling terrain in northwest Europe:

0.01% of time:	path length 20km; 11dB or more below free space
	path length 40km; 23dB or more below free space

Over very flat, moist ground the values will be greater and, for a given path length, will tend to increase with frequency. But at about 10GHz and above, the effect of precipitation will generally dominate system reliability.

The magnitude of attenuation in rain can be estimated theoretically and the reliability of microwave links can then be forecast from a knowledge of rainfall statistics. But the divergence between theory and experiment is often considerable. This is partly due to the variation which can occur in the drop-size distribution for a given rainfall rate. In addition, many difficulties remain in estimating the intensity and spatial characteristics of rainfall for a link. This is an important practical problem in relation to the possible use of route diversity to minimise the effects of absorption fading. Experimental results show that for very high reliability (i.e. for all rainfall rates less than say 50 100 mm/h in temperate climates) any terrestrial link operating at frequencies much above 30GHz must not exceed say 10km in length. It is possible, however, to design a system with an alternative route so that by switching between the two links the worst effects of localised, very heavy rain can be avoided. The magnitude of attenuation in rain is shown in Figure 9.7(a) and the principle of route diversity is illustrated in Figure 9.7(b). For temperate climates, the diversity gain (i.e. the difference between the attenuation, in dB, exceeded for a specified, small percentage of time on a single link and that exceeded simultaneously on two parallel links) varies as follows:

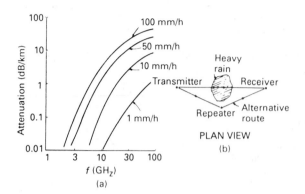

Figure 9.7 (a) Attenuation in rain; (b) the application of route diversity to minimise effects of fading

1. It tends to decrease as the path length increases from 12km, for a given percentage of time and for a given lateral path separation.
2. It is generally greater for a spacing of 8km than for 4km, though an increase to 12km does not provide further improvement.
3. It is not strongly dependent on frequency in the range 20-40GHz for a given geometry.

The main problem in the v.h.f. and u.h.f. broadcasting and mobile services (apart from prediction of interference) is to estimate the effect of irregularities in terrain and of varying antenna height on the received signal. The site location is of fundamental importance. Prediction of received signal strengths, on a statistical basis, has been made using a parameter Δh, which characterises terrain roughness (see CCIR Recommendation 370 and Reports 239 and 567). However, there is considerable path-to-path variability, even for similar Δh values. Especially in urban areas, screening and multipath propagation due to buildings are important. Moreover, in such conditions, and especially for low heights of receiving antenna, depolarisation effects can impair performance of orthogonally polarised systems sharing a common frequency. At the higher u.f.h. frequencies, attenuation due to vegetation (e.g. thick belts of trees) is beginning to be significant.

The problem of field-strength prediction becomes especially difficult at the frequencies specified for a range of future public and private mobile systems. For example, existing 'cellphone' services operating at about 950MHz will be supplemented by 'personal communication networks' (PCNs) at around 1.5 to 2.5GHz. At present, relevant data for such frequencies are very limited. Work is in progress to produce prediction models for various categories of path; e.g. over dense buildings, sparse buildings, woodland, bare ground, etc. Satellite imagery may assist in this, supplementing data on terrain height obtained from detailed maps. Preliminary results at 1.8GHz suggest that the path losses can be some 20dB or more greater than at 900MHz when trees and buildings are along the path.

9.8.2 Beyond-the-horizon propagation

Although propagation by surface or elevated layers (see Figure 9.6) cannot generally be utilised for practical communication circuits, these features remain important as factors in co-channel interference. Considerable theoretical work, using waveguide mode theory, has been carried out on duct propagation and the results are in qualitative agreement with experiment. Detailed comparisons are difficult because of the lack of knowledge of refractive index structure over the whole path, a factor common to all beyond-the-horizon experiments. Nevertheless, the theoretical predictions of the maximum wavelength trapped in a duct are in general agreement with practical experience. These values are as follows:

λ (max) in cm	Duct height in m
1	5
10	25
100	110

Normal surface ducts are such that complete trapping occurs only at centimetric wavelengths. Partial trapping may occur for the shorter metric wavelengths. Over land the effects of irregular terrain and of thermal convection (at least during the day) tend to inhibit duct formation. For a ray leaving the transmitter horizontally, the vertical gradient of refractive index must be steeper than 157 parts in 10^6 per kilometre.

Even when super-refractive conditions are absent, there remains considerable variability in the characteristics of the received signal usable in the 'scatter' mode of communication. This variability is conveniently expressed in terms of the transmission loss, which is defined as $10 \log (P_t/P_r)$, where P_t and $_r$ are the transmitted and received powers respectively. In scatter propagation, both slow and rapid variations of field strength are observed. Slow fading is the result of large-scale changes in refractive conditions in the atmosphere and the hourly median values below the long-term median are distributed approximately log-normally with a standard deviation which generally lies between 4 and 8 decibels, depending on the climate. The largest variations of transmission loss are often seen on paths for which the receiver is located just beyond the diffraction region, while at extreme ranges the variations are less. The slow fading is not strongly dependent on the radio frequency. The rapid fading has a frequency of a few fades per minute at lower frequencies and a few hertz at u.h.f. The superposition of a number of variable incoherent components would give a signal whose amplitude was Rayleigh-distributed. This is found to be the case when the distribution is analysed over periods of up to five minutes. If other types of signal form a significant part of that received, there is a modification of this distribution. Sudden, deep and rapid fading has been noted when a frontal disturbance passes over a link. In addition, reflections from aircraft can give pronounced rapid fading.

The long-term median transmission loss relative to the free-space value increases approximately as the first power of the frequency up to about 3GHz. Also, for most temperate climates, monthly median transmission losses tend to be higher in winter than in summer, but the difference diminishes as the distance increases. In equatorial climates, the annual and diurnal variations are generally smaller. The prediction of transmission loss, for various frequencies, path lengths, antenna heights, etc. is an important practical problem. An example of the kind of data required is given in Figure 9.8.

At frequencies above 10GHz, the heavy rain occurring for small percentages of the time causes an additional loss due to absorption, but the accompanying scatter from the rain may partly offset the effect of absorption.

Other problems related to fine structure are space and frequency diversity. On a v.h.f. scatter link with antennae spaced normal to the direction of propagation, the correlation coefficient may well fall to say 0.5 for spacings of 5-30λ in conditions giving fairly rapid fading. Again, however, varying meteorological factors play a dominant role. In frequency diversity, a separation of say 3 or 4MHz may ensure useful diversity operation in many cases, but occasionally much larger separations are required. The irregular structure of the troposphere is also a cause of gain degradation. This is the decrease in actual antenna gain below the ideal free-space value. Several aspects of the irregular refractive-index structure contribute to this effect and its magnitude depends somewhat on the time interval over which the gain measurement is made. Generally, the decrease is only significant for gains exceeding about 50dB.

9.9 Tropospheric effects in space communications

In space communication, with an Earth station as one terminal, several problems arise due to refraction, absorption and scattering effects, especially at microwave frequencies. For low angles of elevation of the Earth station beam, it is often necessary to evaluate the refraction produced by the troposphere, i.e. to determine the error in observed location of a satellite. The major part of the bending occurs in the first two kilometres above ground and some statistical correlation exists between the magnitude of the effect and the refractive index at the surface. For high-precision navigation systems and very narrow beams it is often necessary to evaluate the variability of refraction effects from measured values of the refractive index as a function of height. A related phenomenon important in tracking systems is the phase distortion in the wave-front due to refractive index fluctuations, a feature closely linked with gain degradation. This phase distortion also affects the stability of frequencies transmitted through the troposphere.

Absorption in clear air may affect the choice of frequencies, above about 40GHz, to minimise co-channel interference. Figure 9.9

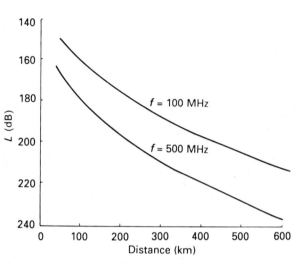

Figure 9.8 Median transmission loss, L, between isotropic antennas in a temperate climate and over an average rolling terrain. The height of the transmitting antenna is 40m, and the height of the receiving antenna is 10m

9.8.3 Physical basis of tropospheric scatter propagation

Much effort has been devoted to explaining the fluctuating trans-horizon field in terms of scattering theory based on statistical models of turbulent motion. The essential physical feature of this approach is an atmosphere consisting of irregular blobs in random motion which in, turn produce fluctuations of refractivity about a stationary mean value. Using this concept, some success has been achieved in explaining the approximate magnitude of the scattered field but several points of difficulty remain. There is now increasing evidence, from refractometer and radar probing of the troposphere, that some stratification of the troposphere is relatively frequent.

By postulating layers of varying thickness, horizontal area and surface roughness, and of varying lifetime it is possible in principle to interpret many of the features of tropospheric propagation. Indeed, some experimental results (e.g. the small distance-dependence of v.h.f. fields at times of anomalous propagation) can be explained by calculating the reflection coefficient of model layers of constant height and with an idealised height-variation of refractive index such as half-period sinusoidal, exponential, etc. The correlation between field strength and layer height has also been examined and some results can be explained qualitatively in terms of double-hop reflection from extended layers. Progress in ray-tracing techniques has also been made. Nevertheless, the problems, of calculating the field strength variations on particular links remain formidable, and for many practical purposes statistical and empirical techniques for predicting link performance remain the only solution (see CCIR Report 238).

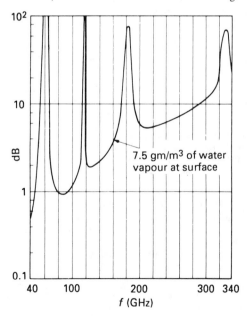

Figure 9.9 Zenith attenuation (dB) in clear air

shows the zenith attenuation from sea level for an average clear atmosphere as a function of frequency. It illustrates the 'window' regions mentioned in the survey of propagation modes. From an altitude of 4km, the values would be about one-third of those shown. This indicates the potential application of frequencies above 40GHz for communication on paths located above the lower layers of the troposphere.

Clouds produce an additional loss which depends on their liquid-water content. Layer-type cloud (stratocumulus) will not cause additional attenuation of more than about 2dB, even at 140GHz. On the other hand, cumulonimbus will generally add several decibels to the total attenuation, the exact value depending on frequency and cloud thickness.

Absorption in precipitation (see Figure 9.7(a) has already been mentioned in relation to terrestrial systems. Water drops attenuate microwaves both by scattering and by absorption. If the wavelength is appreciably greater than the drop-size then the attenuation is caused almost entirely by absorption. For rigorous calculations of absorption it is necessary to specify a drop-size distribution; but this, in practice, is highly variable and consequently an appreciable scatter about the theoretical value is found in experimental measurements. Moreover, statistical information on the vertical distribution of rain is very limited. This makes prediction of the reliability of space links difficult and emphasises the value of measured data. Some results obtained using the Sun as an extraterrestrial source are shown in Figure 9.10.

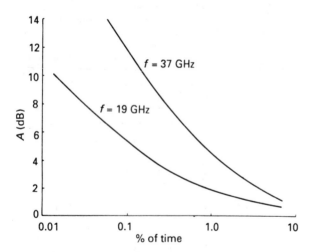

Figure 9.10 Measured probability distribution of attenuation A on earth-space path at 19GHz (southeast England: elevation angles 5° to 40°. Data from solar tracking radiometers)

Scatter from rain (and ice crystals at and above the freezing level in the atmosphere) can cause significant interference on co-channel terrestrial and space systems even when the beams from the two systems are not directed towards each other on a great-circle path; such scattering being, to a first approximation, isotropic. It may also be significant in the case of two Earth stations with beams elevated well above the horizon: for example, with one a feeder link transmitter to a broadcasting satellite and the other a receiver in the fixed-satellite service. This mode of interference may be dominant when hills or other obstacles provide some 'site-shielding' against signals arriving via a ducting mode.

Because precipitation (and to a smaller extent atmospheric gases) absorb microwaves, they also radiate thermal-type noise. It is often convenient to specify this in terms of an equivalent blackbody temperature or simply noise temperature for an antenna pointing in a given direction. With radiometers and low-noise receivers it is now possible to measure this tropospheric noise and asses its importance as a factor in limiting the performance of a microwave Earth space link. For a complete solution, it is necessary to consider not only direct radiation into the main beam but also ground-reflected radiation, and emission from the ground itself, arriving at the receiver via side and back lobes. From the meteorological point of view, radiometer soundings (from the ground, aircraft, balloons or satellites) can provide useful information on tropospheric and stratospheric structure. Absorption in precipitation becomes severe at frequencies above about 30GHz and scintillation effects also increase in importance in the millimetre range. However, for space links in or near the vertical direction the system reliability may be sufficient for practical application even at wavelengths as low as 3-4mm. Moreover, spaced receivers in a site-diversity system can be used to minimise the effects of heavy rain.

In recent years, extensive studies of propagation effects (attenuation, scintillation, etc.) have been carried out by direct measurements using satellite transmissions. Special emphasis has been given to frequencies between 10 and 30GHz, in view of the effect of precipitation on attenuation and system noise. Details are given in Report 564 of the CCIR. For typical elevation angles of 30° to 45°, the total attenuation exceeded for 0.01% of the time has values of the following order:

f=12GHz: 5dB in temperate climates
        (e.g. northwest Europe)
        20dB in tropical climates (e.g. Malaysia)
        10dB in East Coast USA (Maryland)
f=20GHz: 10dB (northwest Europe)

Site-diversity experiments using satellite transmissions show that site spacings of the order of 5-10km can give an useful improvement in reliability. However, the improvement may depend on the site geometry and on topographical effects. At frequencies above say 15GHz, the advantage of site diversity may be quite small if the sites are so chosen that heavy rain in, for example, frontal systems tends to affect both sites simultaneously.

Frequency re-use is envisaged, in space telecommunication systems, by means of orthogonal polarisation. But this technique is restricted by depolarisation due to rain and ice clouds and, to a lesser extent, by the system antennas. Experimental data on polarisation distortion, obtained in satellite experiments, are given in CCIR Report 564.

Further data are still needed, especially from satellite transmissions and at frequencies up to at least 40GHz. In this context, the availability of signals from the Olympus satellite at 12, 20 and 30GHz, from 1989 onwards, is important. Measurements at 20, 40 and 50GHz on the ITALSAT satellite are also planned. But an on-going need also still remains for improved predictions for reception in low-latitude (equatorial) regions. This has recently been the subject of study in a Working Party of the CCIR.

9.10 Propagation and co-channel interference

The increasing need for different microwave terrestrial systems, satellite communications and broadcast systems to share frequencies has produced a correspondingly greater likelihood of mutual interference. The development of interference prediction methods leading to the efficient co-ordination of communication systems sharing a frequency band requires modelling the transmission loss due to all possible propagation mechanisms as a function of frequency, distance and time percentage. Until recently, the primary concern had been for situations occurring less than 1% of time, for which the main clear-air mechanisms are ducting and layer reflection. However the small antenna systems used in new services have generated a need for time percentages up to 20%, for which diffraction and tropospheric scatter are important.

In addition, scattering from different types of hydrometers can be important at frequencies above about 10GHz. This propagation mechanism may couple energy into the receiving antennas of unrelated systems, despite precautions such as site-shielding. Up to now there have been only very limited data available to develop prediction models.

A third group of studies in response to this general area has reflected that an accurate estimation of diffraction effects due to buildings and terrain is essential in the planning of radio services in the microwave bands. Significant data exist from diffraction over large-scale features of terrain, e.g. hills and mountains, which are of major concern at VHF and UHF, but little data are available on the diffraction losses for microwaves that can be produced by buildings or trees which could be used to shield antennas from interference signals.

All these aspects have been studied in recent years in a collaborative European Project 'COST 210' (Influence of the Atmosphere on Interference Between Radiocommunication Systems at Frequencies Above 1GHz). The full report should be consulted for details of the procedures developed.

9.11 Techniques for studying tropospheric structures

The importance of a knowledge of the structure of the troposphere in studies of propagation is clearly evident in the above sections. The small-scale variations in refractive index and in the intensity of precipitation are two important examples. They form part of the general topic of tropospheric probing.

Much useful information on the height-variation of refractive index can be obtained from the radio-sondes carried on free balloons and used in world-wide studies of meteorological structure. However, for many radio applications these devices do not provide sufficient detail. To obtain this detail instruments called refractometers have been developed, mainly for use in aircraft, on captive balloons or on tall masts. They generally make use of a microwave cavity for measuring changes in a resonance frequency, which in turn is related to the refractive index of the enclosed air. Such refractometers are robust, rapid-response instruments which have been widely used as research tools, though they have yet to be developed in a form suitable for widespread, routine use.

High-power, centimetric radar is also a valuable technique. By its use it is possible to detect layers or other regions of strong scatter in the troposphere, and to study their location and structure. Joint radar-refractometer soundings have proved of special interest in confirming that the radar does indeed detect irregularities in clear-air structure. The application of radar in precipitation studies is, of course, a well-known and widely used technique in meteorology; although to obtain the detail and precision necessary for radio applications requires careful refinements in technique.

Optical radar (lidar) and acoustic radar have also been used to probe the troposphere, although the information they provide is only indirectly related to radio refractive index.

The millimetre and sub-millimetre spectrum, as yet not exploited to any significant degree for communications, is nevertheless a fruitful region for tropospheric probing. In particular, the presence of several absorption lines (in water vapour, oxygen and minor constituents such as ozone) makes it possible to study the concentration and spatial distribution of these media. Near the ground, direct transmission experiments are feasible; for example, to study the average water-vapour concentration along a particular path. In addition, it is possible to design radiometers for use on the ground, in an aircraft or in a satellite, which will provide data on the spatial distribution of absorbing atmospheric constituents by measurement of the emission noise they radiate. This topic of remote probing is one exciting considerable current interest in both radio and meteorology.

9.12 References

Aarons, J. (1973) *Total-electron content and scintillation studies of the ionosphere*, ed. AGARDograph 166, NATO, Neuilly- sur-Seine, France.

Anderson, S.J. (1986) Remote sensing with the JINDALEE sky-wave radar, *I.E.E.E. J. Ocean. Eng.*, OE-11(2), 158.

Appleton, E.V. and Beynon, W.J.G. (1940), (1947) The application of ionospheric data to radio communications, *Proc. Phys. Soc.* **52**. 518 and **59**. 58.

Appleton, E.V. and Piggott, W.R. (1954) Ionospheric absorption measurements during a sunspot cycle, *J. Atmosph. Terr. Phys.* **5**. 141.

Bailey, D.K. (1964) Polar cap absorption, *Planet. Space Sci.* **12**. 495.

Bailey, D.K., Bateman, R. and Kirby, R.C. (1955) Radio transmission at VHF by scattering and other processes in the lower ionosphere, *Proc. IRE*, **43**. 1181.

Baker, D.M. and Davies, K. (1968) Waves in the ionosphere produced by nuclear explosions, *J. Geophys. Res.* **73**. 448.

Baker, D.M. and Davies, K. (1969) F2-region acoustic waves from severe weather, *J. Atmosph. Terr. Phys.* **31**. 1345.

Bean, B.R. and Dutton, E.J. (1966) *Radio meteorology*, Monograph 92, US Government Printing Office, Washington.

Bello, P.A. (1965) Some techniques for instantaneous real-time measurements of multipath and Doppler spread. *IEEE Trans. Comm. Tech.* **13**. 285.

Belrose, J.S. and Burke, M.J. (1964) Study of the lower ionosphere using partial reflections, *J. Geophys, Res.* **69**. 2799.

Beynon, W.J.G. (1967) *Special issue on analysis of ionograms for electron density profiles*, ed. URSI Working Group, *Radio Science* **2**. 1119.

Beynon, W.J.G. and Rangaswamy, S. (1969) Model electron density profiles for the lower ionosphere, *J. Atmosph. Terr. Phys.* **31**. 891.

Blair, J.C., Melanson, L.L. and Tveten, L.H. (1969) HF ionospheric radar ground scatter map showing land-sea boundaries by a spectral separation technique, *Electronics Letters*, **5**. 75.

Bradley, P.A. and Dudeney, J.R. (1973) A simple model of the vertical distribution of electron concentration in the ionosphere, *J. Atmosph. Terr. Phys.* **35**. 2131.

Boithias, L. (1988) *Radio-wave propagation*, North Oxford Academic Publishers, London.

Buchau, J. (1972) *Instantaneous versus averaged ionosphere*. Air Force Surveys in Geophysics No. 241 (Air Force Systems Command, United States Air Force), 1.

Budden, K. (1961) *Radio waves in the ionosphere*, Cambridge University Press, Cambridge.

Castel, F. Du, (1966) *Tropospheric radiowave propagation beyond the horizon*, Pergamon Press, Oxford.

CCIR (1990a) REPORT 263-7. *Ionospheric effects upon Earth-space propagation*, Documents of XVIIth Plenary Assembly, Dusseldorf, ITU, Geneva.

CCIR (1990b) REPORT 266-7. *Ionospheric propagation and noise characteristics pertinent to terrestrial radiocommunication systems design and service planning (Fading)*, Documents of XVIIth Plenary Assembly, Dusseldorf, ITU, Geneva.

CCIR (1990c) REPORT 728-3. *Ionospheric modification, by ground-based, high-power radio transmissions*, Documents of XVIIth Plenary Assembly, Dusseldorf, ITU, Geneva.

CCIR (1990d) REPORT 265-7. *Sky-wave propagation and circuit performance at frequencies between about 30kHz and 500kHz*, Documents of XVIIth Plenary Assembly, Dusseldorf, ITU, Geneva.

CCIR (1990e) REPORT 340-6. *CCIR atlas of ionospheric characteristics*, Documents of XVIIth Plenary Assembly, Dusseldorf, ITU, Geneva.

CCIR (1990f) REPORT 894-2. *CCIR HF propagation prediction method (Third CCIR computer-based method for estimation of MUF, sky-wave field strength, signal-to-noise ratio, LUF and basic circuit reliability)*, Documents of XVIIth Plenary Assembly, Dusseldorf, ITU, Geneva.

Cohen, R. and Bowles, K.L. (1961) On the nature of equatorial spread-F. *J. Geophys. Res.* **66**. 1081.

Coll, D.C. and Storey, J.R. (1964) Ionospheric sounding using coded pulse signals, *Radio Science*. **68D**. 1155.

Croft, T.A. (1968) Special issue on ray tracing, *Radio Science*. **3**. 1.

Croft, T.A. (1972) Skywave backscatter: a means for observing our environment at great distances, *Rev. Geophys. and Space Physics*. **10**. 73.

Croft, T.A. and Hoogasian, H. (1968) Exact ray calculations in a quasi-parabolic ionosphere with no magnetic field, *Radio Science*. **3**. 69.

Davies, K. (1969) *Ionospheric radio waves*. Blaisdell, Waltham, Mass.

Davies, K. (1990) *Ionospheric radio*. Peter Peregrinus, London.

Davies, K. and Baker, D.M. (1965) Ionospheric effects observed around the time of the Alaskan earthquake of March 28 1964. *J. Geophys. Res.* **70**. 2251.

Duncan, R.A. (1960) The equatorial F-region of the ionosphere, *J. Atmosph. Terr. Phys.* **18**. 89.

Dyson, P.L. and Bennett, J.A. (1988) A model of the vertical distribution of the electron concentration in the ionosphere and its application to oblique propagation studies. *J. Atmosph. Terr. Phys.* **50**(3). 251.

EEC (1990) COST Project 210; *Influence of the atmosphere on interference between radio systems at frequencies above 1GHz*. (L- 2920, Luxembourg).

Fejer, J.A. (1955) The interaction of pulsed radio waves in the ionosphere, *J. Atmosph. Terr. Phys.* **7**. 322.

Fenwick, R.B. and Barry, G.H. (1966) Sweep frequency oblique ionospheric sounding at medium frequencies, *IEEE Trans. Broadcasting*, **12**. 25.

Fenwick, R.B. and Villard, O.G. (1963) A test of the importance of ionosphere reflections in long distance and around-the-world high frequency propagation, *J. Geophys. Res.* **68**. 5659.

Garriott, G.K. and Nichol, A.W. (1965) Ionospheric information deduced from the Doppler shifts of harmonic frequencies from earth satellites, *J. Atmosph. Terr. Phys.* **22**. 50.

Hall, M.P.M. (1979) *Effects of the troposphere on radio communication*, Peter Peregrinus (for IEE) London.

Hall, (1989) *Radiowave propagation*; edited by M.P.M. Hall and L.W. Barclay. IEE Electromagnetic Waves Series 30, London.

Hargreaves, J.K. (1969) Auroral absorption of H.F. radio waves in the ionosphere — a review of results from the first decade of riometry. *Proc. IEEE*, **57**. 1348.

Hartz, T.R. (1968) The general pattern of auroral particle precipitation and its implications for high latitude communication systems, in *Ionospheric Radio Communications*, ed. K. Folkestad, Plenum, New York, 9.

Haselgrove, J. (1954) Ray theory and a new method for ray tracing. In *Report on conference on physics of ionosphere*, Phys. Soc. London, 355.

Headrick, J.M. and Skolnik, M.I. (1974) Over-the-horizon radar in the HF band. *Proc. IEEE* **62**(6). 664.

Helliwell, R.A. (1965) *Whistlers and Related Ionospheric Phenomena*, Stanford University Press, Stanford, California.

Matsushita, S. (1967) Geomagnetic disturbances and storms, in *Physics of geomagnetic phenomena*, ed. Matsushita, S. and Campbell, W.H., Academic Press, London, 793.

Mitra, S.N. (1949) A radio method of measuring winds in the ionosphere, *Proc. IEE*, **46** Pt.III, 441.

Muldrew, D.B. (1965) F-layer ionisation troughs deduced from Alouette data. *J. Geophys. Res.* **70**.2635.

Munro, G.H. (1950) Travelling disturbances in the ionosphere, *Proc. Roy. Soc.* **202A**. 208.

Nielson, D.L. (1968) The importance of horizontal F-region drifts to transequatorial VHF propagation, *Scatter propagation of radio waves*, ed Thrane, E. *AGARD Conference Proceedings*, No.37, NATO, Neuilly-sur-Seine, France.

Pierce, E.T. (1965) Nuclear explosion phenomena and their bearing on radio detection of the explosions, *Proc. IEEE*, **53**. 1944.

Pierce, J.A. (1965) OMEGA, *IEEE Trans. Aer. and Elect. Syst.* 1. 206.

Piggott, W.R. and Rawer, K. (1972) *U.R.S.I. handbook of ionogram interpretation and reduction*, 2nd edn. Rep. UAG-23, Dept. of Commerce, Boulder, USA.

Ratcliffe, J.A. (1956) *Some aspects of diffraction theory and their application to the ionosphere*, Reports on Progress in Physics, Phys. Soc., London, **19**. 188.

Ratcliffe, J.A. (1959) *The magnetoionic theory*, Cambridge University Press.

Ratcliffe, J.A. (1970) *Sun, Earth and Radio — an introduction to the ionosphere and magnetosphere*, Weidenfeld and Nicolson, London.

Ratcliffe, J.A. (1972) *An introduction to the ionosphere and magnetosphere*, Cambridge University Press, Cambridge.

Reinisch, B.W. and Huang Xueqin (1983) Automatic Calculation of electron density profiles from digital ionograms, 3. Processing of bottomside ionograms. *Radio Science*, **18**(3). 477.

Rishbeth, H. (1972) Thermospheric winds and the F-region, a review, *J. Atmosph. Terr. Phys.* **34** 1.

Rishbeth, H and Garriott, O.K. (1969) *Introduction to ionospheric physics*, Academic Press, London.

Ross, W.J. (1965) Second-order effects in high frequency transionospheric propagation, *J. Geophys. Res.* **70**. 597.

Rutherford (1991) *Catalogue of ionospheric vertical sounding data*, World Data Centre C1 for Solar-Terrestrial Physics, Rutherford Appleton Laboratory, Chilton, England.

Saxton, J.A.(Ed) (1964) *Advances in radio research*, Academic Press, London.

Smith, E.K. (1970) *Electromagnetic probing of the upper atmosphere*, U.R.S.I. Working group, *J. Atmosph. Terr. Phys.* **32**. 457.

Smith, E.K. and Matsushita, S. (1962) *Ionospheric sporadic- E.* Macmillan, New York.

Stevens, E.E. (1968) *The CHEC sounding system, in Ionospheric radio communications*, ed. K. Kolkestad, Plenum, New York, 359.

Stringer, F.S. (1969) Hyperbolic radionavigation systems, *Wireless World* **75**. 353.

Sugar, G.R. (1964) Radio propagation by reflection from meteor trails, *Proc. IEEE* **52**. 116.

Teters, L.R., Lloyd, J.L., Haydon, G.W. and Lucas, D.L. (1983) *Estimating the performance of telecommunication systems using the ionospheric transmission channel — Ionospheric Communications Analysis and Prediction Program,* Report 83-127, National Telecommunications and Information Administration, Dept. of Commerce, Boulder, U.S.A.

Titheridge, J.E. (1985) *Ionogram analysis with the generalised program POLAN*, Rep. UAG-93, Dept. of Commerce, Boulder, U.S.A.

URSI Commission F. Colloquium Proceedings; La Baule, France (CNET, Paris, 1977). Also at Lennoxville, Canada (Proceedings edited by University of Bradford, England, 1980).

Whalen, J.A., Buchau, J. and Wagner, R.A. (1971) Airborne ionospheric and optical measurements of noontime aurora, *J. Atmosph. Terr. Phys.* **33**. 661.

10 Signals and noise

John Price
Northern Telecom Europe

Terry Goble
Northern Telecom Europe

Contents

10.1 Definition of a signal

The definition of a signal may take a variety of forms:

1. The conveying of information through a medium.
2. The physical embodiment of a message.
3. A media manifestation conveying information or direction from one end of a transmission medium to another

Two further definitions associated with a signal are :

1. Signal frequency, the frequency of the carrier wave upon which the signal information has been impressed.
2. Signalling, the use of a signal to convey coded direction or instructions to a person or piece of apparatus at a distance, such a signal normally being associated with the establishment, servicing or breaking of a connection.

Signals that follow the instantaneous variation of the original information energy are defined as analogue. A digital signal is in the form of a pre-determined code of pulses or variations, which represent symbols taken from a selected set of symbols.

A direct current signal is when the flow of current is only in one direction. However, the strength of the current may be varied. A direct current can be produced from an energy source such as a dry battery.

A steady direct current flowing in a circuit cannot convey information. The inclusion of a simple on-off switch enables the current to be regulated into a series of pulses. These pulses represent symbols which have an agreed meaning at the transmitting and receiving ends of the link. A series of the symbols can be concatenated to form a message.

If the connections to the direct current source are reversed, then the direction of the current is also reversed. The current direction can therefore be considered to be positive or negative according to the way it is flowing around the circuit, and this is known as the polarity of the circuit.

There are two principal methods for creating signals with direct current sources. Firstly the information may be carried by the alternate presence and absence of current or, secondly, by the switching of the direct current sources between two distinct values. The feature common to both of these methods is the variation in the amplitude of the current.

A typical use of direct current signal, using the alternate presence and absence of a pulse, is between a telephone and the local exchange. The state of the signal indicates on-hook, off-hook, dial pulses, or the status of the connection. On-hook is indicated by an open circuit and no current flow. Off-hook is indicated by a closed circuit and continuous current flow. Dial pulses consist of current flow interrupted at a specified rate.

There are various difficulties associated with direct current signalling :

1. Circuits that have long transmission lines are subject to attenuation and distortion, although these can be rectified using regeneration and amplification.
2. Connecting wires are needed for the whole of a telecommunications circuit.

A rotating alternator or an electronic oscillator causes the current to reverse direction at regular intervals to create a particular repeating pattern or waveform. This is known as an alternating current. The advantages of alternating current signals are :

1. The strength and amplitude can easily be altered allowing transmission over long lines.
2. Connecting wires are not necessary for the whole of a telecommunications circuit.

10.1.1 Bits and bauds

Bits are defined as the number of binary digits that are transmitted through a transmission medium per second. The baud is the unit of modulation rate. When a modulation method is used that has binary values then the line rate for the modulation directly corresponds with the transmission of bits, and the bit rate and baud rate are equal. When a multi-level modulation method is used each modulation can represent more than one bit. If one modulation equals two bits, each modulation represents a dibit. A tribit is when each modulation represents three bits. In the latter case the bit rate is three times the modulation rate.

An example of the dibit operation is found in CCITT V.22 recommendations which uses four phase changes for modulation, as in Table 10.1. The baud rate is 600 whilst the bit rate is 1200 per second.

Table 10.1 Example of a dibit operation

Dibits	Phase
00	+90
01	0
10	+180
11	+270

CCITT V.29 uses 4 bits per baud which are carried using 8 different phase changes, 45 degree apart, and two different amplitude changes.

10.2 Waveform and frequency

There are a wide variety of waveforms that are possible with alternating currents. One of the simplest to produce, a sinusoidal waveform, shown in Figure 10.1, is created by rotating a loop of wire in a uniform magnetic field.

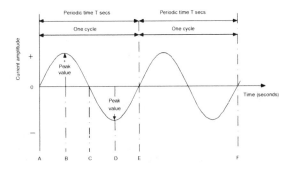

Figure 10.1 Sinusoidal alternating current waveform

In Figure 10.1 between points A and B the current increases from zero to a peak value in a positive direction. Between points B and C the current gradually reduces to zero. Then between points C and D the current moves to a peak value in the opposite or negative direction. Finally between points D and E the current gradually returns to zero again. The whole sequence from point A to point E represents one complete rotation of the wire loop in the magnetic field and is called one cycle of an alternating current waveform.

The periodic time, which is measured in seconds, is the time required for one complete cycle of the alternating current waveform to be produced.

The frequency of the waveform is the number of complete cycles that occur in one second and is therefore the reciprocal of the periodic time. Frequency is measured in Hertz (Hz).

The amplitude of the waveform represents the strength of the current at any instance, with the direction of the current, positive or negative, being referred to as the polarity.

The rotation of the wire loop within the magnetic field can be expressed in terms of rotation. The wire loop for each cycle will move through 360 degrees. Figure 10.2 shows the sinusoidal waveform plotted against angular rotation.

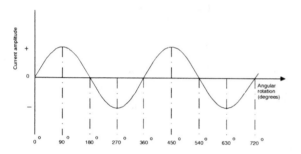

Figure 10.2   Angular rotation

At the same point in each cycle the amplitude of the waveform has the same value. The identification of a particular point in the cycle as the degree of rotation is called the phase of the alternating current waveform.

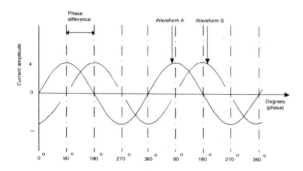

Figure 10.3   Phase difference

Phase difference describes two waveforms that are identical except for their phase. Figure 10.3 illustrates two sinusoidal waveforms that have a phase difference.

Amplitude, frequency and phase represent the characteristics of a waveform, that may by varied so that symbols may be transmitted along the media, thus allowing a complete message to be sent.

The energy of an alternating current waveform will travel along a transmission medium at a particular velocity, therefore a certain distance will be travelled in one cycle. The alternating current waveform repeats complete cycles over equal distances. The distance representing each cycle is called the wavelength and is conventionally measured in metres.

Equations 10.1 to 10.3 represent the relationships between velocity, wavelength, time and frequency.

$$Velocity = \frac{Wavelength}{Time} \tag{10.1}$$

$$Frequency = \frac{1}{Periodic \ time} \tag{10.2}$$

$$Velocity = Wavelength \ x \ Frequency \tag{10.3}$$

10.2.1   Waveshapes

All component waveforms are made of a sinusoidal waveform which has a certain frequency, called the fundamental frequency and a number of other sinusoidal waveforms having frequencies that are direct multiples of the fundamental frequency. These direct multiples are harmonics of the fundamental frequencies.

For a complex waveform having a fundamental frequency, f, the harmonics with multiple values of f (e.g. 2f, 3f, 4f, etc.) may also be present. The square waveform is made of a fundamental frequency and all the odd harmonics rising to infinity, i.e. 3f, 5f, 7f, 9f, and so on. Figure 10.4 shows the square waveform with the associated

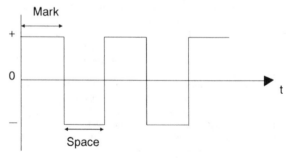

Figure 10.4   Square waveform

terminology of space and mark.

The amplitude of the various harmonics are added to give a resultant waveshape that approximates to a square wave. The addition of the fundamental with the 3rd and 5th harmonics is illustrated in Figure 10.5. A more exact square wave would be created by the addition of further odd harmonics.

A second common waveshape is the saw tooth waveform which contains a fundamental frequency and all the odd and even harmonics to infinity.

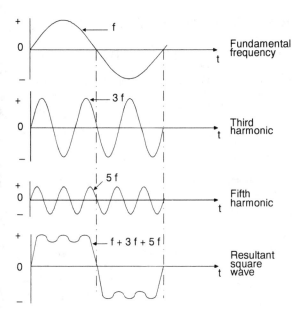

Figure 10.5 Amplitude addition

10.3 Digital signals

There are three ways in which a digital signal may be transmitted to a line :

1. A single (unipolar) current.
2. The presence or absence of a voltage.
3. Two voltages (bipolar) one positive and one negative with respect to earth.

The use of digital transmission instead of analogue gives the following advantages :

1. A better signal to noise ratio. Noise and interference are accumulative with distance on an analogue system, but not on a digital system.
2. Improved signalling capability.
3. Time division multiplexing, used with digital signals, is simpler than frequency division multiplexing, which is used with analogue signals.
4. Digital switching is more straightforward to implement.
5. In digital systems different kinds of signals, e.g. data, telegraph, telephone speech and television, have the same representation on the medium and therefore can be treated in a similar manner during transmission and switching.

10.4 Examples of signals

10.4.1 Voice and music

The sounds produced by a human voice are variations of air pressure above and below normal pressure. Such sounds are alternating in nature and have a complex waveform that is different for each voice. The voice contains fundamental frequencies and associated har-

monics. Therefore the sound waves produced by human voices contain a range of frequencies which is known as bandwidth.

Voice frequencies lie within the band 100Hz to 10000Hz. The pitch of the voice is determined by the fundamental frequency of the vocal chords and is between 200Hz and 1000Hz for women and between 100Hz and 500Hz for men. The tonal quality and the individuality are determined by the higher frequencies that are produced.

The power content of speech is small, an average being between 10 and 20 microwatts. The distribution of the power is not even, with most of it being contained in the region of 500Hz for men and 800Hz for women.

The notes produced by musical instruments occupy a much larger frequency band than occupied by speech. Some instruments, such as the drum, have a fundamental frequency of 50Hz or less, while others, such as the violin, can produce a note which has a harmonic content in excess of 15000Hz. An orchestra may generate a peak power in the region of 90 to 100 watts.

In practice not all frequencies produced are transmitted to the receiver. There are two principal reasons for this. Firstly, it is more economic to use devices in circuits that have a limited bandwidth and, secondly, on long distance routes a number of circuits are transmitted over a single telecommunications link and this provides a further limitation on bandwidth.

At the receiving end of the speech or music the sound waves impact on the ear and cause the ear drum to vibrate. The ear can only hear sounds that lie within certain limits. The minimum sound level that can be detected by the ear is known as the threshold or audibility, with the sound level that produces a feeling of discomfort being known as the threshold of feeling.

Figure 10.6 illustrates the threshold of feeling and audibility by plotting sound pressure against frequency. It can be seen that the most sensitive region is between 1000Hz and 2000Hz although response is capable with the 30Hz to 16500Hz range.

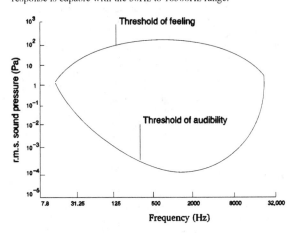

Figure 10.6 Audability

10.4.2 Telephone and telegraph

By international agreement the audio frequency for a commercial quality speech circuit routed over a multi-channel telephone system is restricted from 300Hz to 3400Hz. The suppression of all frequencies above 3400Hz reduces the quality of sound but does not affect the intelligibility.

A telegraphy system is one that passes messages by means of a pre-agreed signalling system. Typical codes that have frequently been used are Morse and Murray, the latter also being known as the International Alphabet 2 (IA2).

The characters in Morse code are represented by 'dot' and 'dash' signals. A dot is differentiated from a dash by differing time periods. Spacings between, signals, words and letters are distinguished by different time periods. Morse code is not adopted for use with automatic receiving equipment as the number of signals elements that comprise a symbol varies, as does the actual length of the signal element. The bandwidth required for Morse code lies in the range of 100Hz to 1000Hz.

The teleprinter system uses the Murray code which has signal elements that are of equal length, and all characters have exactly the same number of signal elements. Each character is represented by a negative potential and a space by a positive potential.

Teleprinters normally operate at a speed of 50 baud. The maximum periodic time for one cycle of an alternating waveform is 40ms, giving a fundamental frequency of 25Hz.

10.4.3   Radio and television

The bandwidth for speech on a circuit operated over a high frequency radio link is 25Hz to 3000Hz. Land line circuits that connect studio and transmission sites have a bandwidth of 30Hz to 10000Hz, which allows very high quality sound. Long and medium wave broadcasting cannot use such a wide bandwidth because the high demand from other broadcasting stations.

By international agreement medium waveband broadcasting stations in Europe are spaced at approximately 9000Hz apart. The receiver is therefore confined to about 4500Hz so as to avoid interference.

The bandwidth for a television picture signal depends on a number of factors such as: the number of lines that make up the picture; the number of fields transmitted per second: and the duration of the synchronising pulses. In general the normal bandwidth is 5.5MHz. The bandwidth of the audio signal is 20Hz. A colour television picture consists of a brightness (luminance) component which corresponds to the monochrome signal plus colour (chrominance) information which is transmitted as amplitude modulation side bands of two colour sub-carriers which are of the same frequency approximately 4.434MHz but 90 degrees apart. No extra bandwidth is needed to accommodate the colour information.

10.4.4   Radar

When a radio wave strikes an object some of the energy in the signal is reflected back to the transmitter so that the object may be detected. If the transmitted radio wave is in the form of pulses, then by measuring the item delay between the transmitted and the received pulse (the echo) the distance of the object can be calculated. Highly directional transmitting aerials also allow the bearing of the distant object relative to transmitter to be calculated.

Radar is different from other transmission methods discussed, since the transmission does not carry actual information. A typical transmitter produces pulses of radio waves in the frequency range of 150MHz and 30000MHz. The duration of the pulses will generally lie between 0.25µs and 50µs. The time interval between the pulses depends on the maximum distance at which the radar system is effective.

10.5   Classification of signals

10.5.1   Energy and power signals

A voltage or current represents a signal in an electrical system. In the time interval t_1 to t_2 the energy dissipated by a voltage in a resistance is given by Equation 10.4.

$$E = \int_{t_1}^{t_2} \frac{V^2(t)}{R} \, dt \tag{10.4}$$

The current would therefore be given by Equation 10.5.

$$E = \int_{t_1}^{t_2} R \, i^2(t) \, dt \tag{10.5}$$

A conventional way of referring to the energy is by considering the case of one-ohm resistance. Equations 10.1 and 10.2 then take the same form. A description may then be given of the energy associated with any signal x(t) in dimensionless form, as in Equation 10.6.

$$E = \int_{t_1}^{t_2} x^2(t) \, dt \tag{10.6}$$

An energy signal is one for which Equation 10.6 is finite. The condition that must be satisfied is given in expression 10.7.

$$\int_{-\infty}^{\infty} x^2(t) \, dt < \infty \tag{10.7}$$

There are many signals that do not satisfy expression 10.7. Periodic signals are the principal group although there are also some aperiodic signals that are included in this group. If this expression is not satisfied, then it is more appropriate to consider the average power of the signal. If a one-ohm basis is considered then the average power, from Equation 10.6, is given by Equation 10.8.

$$P = \frac{1}{t_2 - t_1} \int_{t_1}^{t_2} x^2(t) \, dt \tag{10.8}$$

A power signal satisfies the condition given in Equation 10.9.

$$\varphi < \lim_{T \to \infty} \frac{1}{2T} \int_{-T}^{T} x^2(t) \, dt \tag{10.9}$$

Therefore an energy signal has zero average power and a power signal has infinite energy. Thus this type of signal classification is mutually exclusive. However, there are some signals that fit into neither classification.

10.5.2   Periodic and aperiodic signals

A periodic signal is one that repeats the sequence of values exactly after a fixed length of time, known as the period. In mathematical terms a signal x(t) is periodic if there is a number T such that for all t Equation 10.10 holds.

$$x(t) = x(t + T) \tag{10.10}$$

The smallest positive number T that satisfies Equation 10.10 is the period and it defines the duration of one complete cycle. The fundamental frequency of a periodic signal is given by Equation 10.11.

$$f = \frac{1}{T} \tag{10.11}$$

It is important to distinguish between the real signal and the quantitative representation, which is necessarily an approximation. The amount of error in the approximation depends on the complexity of the signal, with simple waveforms, such as the sinusoid, having less error than complex waveforms.

A non-periodic or aperiodic signal is one for which no value of T satisfies Equation 10.11. In principle this includes all actual signals since they must start and stop at finite times. However, aperiodic signals can be presented quantitatively in terms of periodic signals.

Examples of periodic signals include the sinusoidal signals and periodically repeated non-sinusoidal signals, such as the rectangular pulse sequences used in radar.

Non-periodic signals include speech waveforms and random signals arising from unpredictable disturbances of all kinds. In some cases it is possible to write explicit mathematical expressions for non-periodic signals and in other cases it is not.

In addition to periodic and non-periodic signals are those signals that are the sum of two or more periodic signals having different periods. T will not be satisfied in Equation 10.10, but the signal does have many properties associated with periodic signals and cannot be represented by a finite number of periodic signals.

10.5.3 Random and deterministic signals

Signals may be classified as random or deterministic, the deciding criteria being the predictability of a signal before it is generated. Random or stochastic signals are those which have variations in magnitudes that occur in an unpredictable manner. Interference and noise constitute random features of signals. If the possible future values of a signal can be predicted from the study of previous signals then no suitable quantitative expression can be derived.

Under some circumstances, following the observation of signals, a mathematical expression can be constructed to describe a waveform form, but there are some factors associated with parameters such as phase that are unpredictable in the first instance.

A deterministic signal is one about which there is no uncertainty before it occurs and in almost all cases an explicit mathematical expression can be written for it.

10.6 Signal representation

10.6.1 Time and frequency domains

A signal x(t) may be represented in terms of sinusoids having frequencies that are multiple of the fundamental frequency $\frac{1}{T}$. Coefficients are added to give the magnitude and phase of the sinusoids and this combination represents the frequency domain description of the signal.

The explicit time function x(t) is the time domain description of the signal.

10.6.2 Complex representation

Signals may be represented mathematically in different ways. The basis for many waveforms is the sinusoidal form and thus sine and cosine representation is a convenient mathematical method of describing signals.

A second method, often preferred for mathematical convenience, is the representation of a pair of real value signals in complex mathematics. A complex signal consists of a real signal and an imaginary signal, which may be visualised as two voltages across two resistors. Complex valued signals are processed just as real valued signals, except the rules of complex arithmetic are used. Conventionally j is taken to represent the imaginary part.

The relationship between the sine and cosine representation and the complex representation is given in Equation 10.12, where ω_0 is given by Equation 10.13.

$$e^{\pm j n \omega_0 t} = \cos n \omega_0 t \pm j \sin n \omega_0 t \tag{10.12}$$

$$\omega_0 = \frac{2\pi}{T} \tag{10.13}$$

10.6.3 Fourier series representation

The use of real and complex sinusoids to represent signals are called Fourier methods, after the mathematician who first investigated these techniques. In the case of signals the Fourier representation has direct physical interpretation through measured quantities. Fourier analysis of signals also lends itself to automatic calculation on a computer based system.

Various waveforms have Fourier series expressions. The series for a general periodic wave that has an arbitrary period T is given in Equation 10.14, the coefficients being given by Equations 10.15 and 10.16.

$$\frac{a_0}{2} + \sum_{n=1}^{\infty} a_n \cos \frac{2\pi n t}{T} + b_n \sin \frac{2\pi n t}{T} \tag{10.14}$$

$$a_n = \frac{2}{T} \int_{t_1}^{t_1 + T} f(t) \cos \frac{2\pi n t}{T} \, dt \tag{10.15}$$

$$b_n = \frac{2}{T} \int_{t_1}^{t_1 + T} f(t) \sin \frac{2\pi n t}{T} \, dt \tag{10.16}$$

The waveform depicted in Figure 10.7 has the Fourier series given by expression 10.17 with the coefficient given in Equation 10.18.

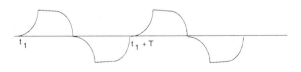

Figure 10.7 Waveform with the Fourier expression of 10.17

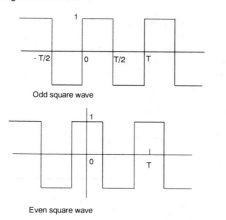

Odd square wave

Even square wave

Figure 10.8   Odd and even square waveforms

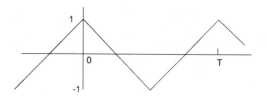

Figure 10.10   Triangular waveform with the Fourier expression given by Equation 10.22

The triangular waveform is illustrated in Figure 10.10 and the Fourier expression is given in 10.22.

$$\frac{8}{\pi^2} \sum_{n=1}^{\infty} \frac{1}{(2n-1)^2} \cos \frac{2\pi(2n-1)t}{T} \tag{10.22}$$

Figure 10.11 illustrates the sawtooth waveform and Equation 10.23 gives the expression corresponding to that figure.

$$\frac{2}{\pi} \sum_{n=1}^{\infty} \frac{(-1)^{n+1}}{n} \sin \frac{2\pi nt}{T} \tag{10.23}$$

$$\sum_{n=-\infty}^{\infty} a_n \varepsilon^{j(2\pi n/T)t} \tag{10.17}$$

$$a_n = \frac{1}{T} \int_{t_1}^{t_1+T} f(t)\varepsilon^{-j(2\pi n/T)t} \tag{10.18}$$

There are two varieties of square waveforms that can be described by Fourier series, one being odd and the other even. Figure 10.8 illustrates the two waveforms with expression 10.19 giving the Fourier representation of the odd square wave and expression 10.20 giving the representation for the even square wave.

$$\frac{4}{\pi} \sum_{n=1}^{\infty} \frac{1}{2n-1} \sin \frac{2\pi(2n-1)t}{T} \tag{10.19}$$

$$\frac{4}{\pi} \sum_{n=1}^{\infty} \frac{(-1)^{n+1}}{2n-1} \cos \frac{2\pi(2n-1)t}{T} \tag{10.20}$$

A regular pulse train, illustrated in Figure 10.9, has the Fourier expression given in 10.21.

$$\frac{2t_a}{T} = \frac{4t_a}{T} \sum_{n=1}^{\infty} \frac{\sin \dfrac{2\pi n t_a}{T}}{\dfrac{2\pi n t_a}{T}} \cos \frac{2\pi nt}{T} \tag{10.21}$$

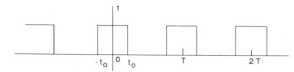

Figure 10.9   Rectangular pulse train with the Fourier expression given by Equation 10.21

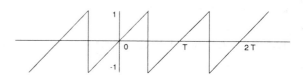

Figure 10.11   Sawtooth waveform with the Fourier expression given by Equation 10.21

10.7   Distortion of signals

10.7.1   Types of distortion

Distortion of a signal may be expressed in a variety of ways :

1.   Distortion has occurred if the output signal from a channel is not the exact replica of the input to that channel.
2.   Distortion is the difference in time between the output signal of a receiver and the input signal causing that output.
3.   Distortion occurs if there is a change in waveform between the input and output terminals.

In general distortion arises when the output waveform contains frequency components that are not present in the original signal, or where complex signals are involved when the phase relationships between the various components of the signal may be altered. The relative amplitudes of the harmonic components may also be altered.

The relationship between the input and output voltage is known as the transfer characteristic. The gain therefore varies with the instantaneous magnitude of the input signal and non-linear distortion occurs.

10.7.1.1 *Attenuation distortion*

If all frequencies involved in the transmission were subject to the same gain and the same loss then attenuation distortion would not occur. However, in all transmission media some frequencies are attenuated more than others, therefore attenuation distortion results from imperfect amplitude frequency response.

Attenuation distortion across the voice channel is measured against a CCITT reference frequency of 800Hz. In North America 1000Hz is commonly used as the reference frequency. If a signal at 10dBm is placed on the input of a channel, then assuming no gain or loss the output would be 10dBm at 800Hz, whereas the output at 2500Hz could be 11.9dBm and at 1100Hz it could be 9dBm. The attenuation distortion for a voice channel is illustrated in Figure 10.12.

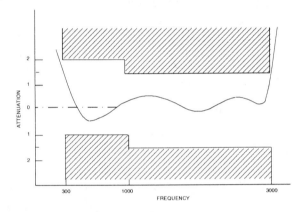

Figure 10.12 Attenuation distortion voice channel

10.7.1.2 *Delay distortion*

The velocity with which a signal travels through a medium is a function of the velocity of propagation, which varies between mediums. The velocity tends to vary with frequency, with an increase towards the band centre and a decrease towards band edge. The finite time the signal takes to pass through the voice channel of the

transmission link is called the delay. At a reference frequency the delay a signal experiences is referred to as the absolute delay.

10.7.1.3 *Phase distortion*

With the propagation time being different for different frequencies, the wave front of one frequency will arrive before the wave front of another frequency, thus the phase has been shifted or distorted. The result is that the relative phases of the harmonic components of a signal are not maintained.

10.7.1.4 *Harmonic distortion*

With non-linear distortion the application of a sinusoidal input voltage results in a periodic output waveform that is non-sinusoidal. Fourier analysis shows that spurious harmonics are present, the result being known as harmonic distortion. Total harmonic distortion is measured as the root of the sum of the squares of the r.m.s. voltages of the individual harmonics divided by the r.m.s. of the total output signal, V, where V_{H2}, V_{H3} are the r.m.s values of the harmonic components. Equation 10.24 gives the total harmonic distortion.

$$D = \frac{(V_{H2}^2 + V_{H3}^2 + V_{H4}^2 + ... + V_{Hn}^2)^{1/2}}{V} \ 100 \ \% \tag{10.24}$$

10.7.1.5 *Intermodulation distortion*

Intermodulation distortion is a form of non-linear distortion whereby the amplitude of a signal of one frequency is affected by the amplitude of a simultaneously applied signal of a lower frequency. Combination frequencies are produced which have values equal to the sum and difference of the two applied frequencies. The non-linear transfer characteristics reduce the amplitude of the higher frequency signals at times when the lower frequency signal is near to maximum and minimum voltages (Figure 10.13.)

10.7.2 Distortion of digital signals

10.7.2.1 *Attenuation distortion*

The attenuation of signals in the voice frequency range increases with an increase in frequency and so the various harmonics contained in a digital waveform will be attenuated to a greater extent than the fundamental frequency. The greater attenuation on the higher order harmonics means the rectangular waveshape will grad-

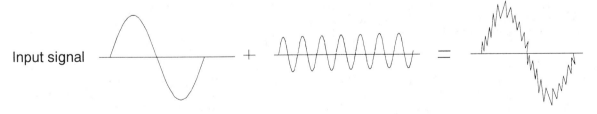

Input signal

Figure 10.13 Illustration of intermodulation distortion

ually be lost. The effect is accentuated by the length of the line and so pulses will be more rounded.

10.7.2.2 *Synchronisation distortion*

Synchronisation is the principal whereby the receiver will at all times sample the incoming bit at the correct instance in time. Distortion can occur if the sampling drifts from the correct sample period. The two methods of synchronisation, isochronous and aniochronous, the latter often being referred to as start-stop, can both suffer from distortion.

10.8   Types of noise

10.8.1   Thermal or Johnson noise

Thermal or Johnson noise, first documented by J.B. Johnson of Bell Laboratories in 1928, is often called white noise. It is of a gaussian nature which means it is completely random. Any circuit operating at a temperature above absolute zero ($-273°C$) will display thermal noise. This random noise is caused by the random motion of discrete electrons in the conductive path.

The work of Johnson states that the available power per unit bandwidth of thermal noise is given by Equation 10.25, where K is Boltzmann's constant (1.3805×10^{-23} joules/degree K), and T is the absolute temperature of the source in degrees K.

$$\text{Noise power } P_n = k\,T \quad \text{watts/Hz} \qquad (10.25)$$

Using measurements it has been shown that across the entire frequency range the available power P_a is directly proportional to the product of the system bandwidth B_w and the absolute temperature of the source T, as in Equation 10.26, which may be expressed in dBm at room temperature as in Equation 10.27.

$$P_a = k\,T\,B_w \quad watts \qquad (10.26)$$

$$P_a = -174 + 10\log B_w \quad dBm \qquad (10.27)$$

10.8.2   Noise voltage equivalence circuit

A resistor is a good example of a thermal noise source, and therefore a suitable equivalent circuit is an r.m.s. noise voltage generator connected in series with a hypothetically noiseless resistor having the same resistance. If these are connected in series with a load resistor, as shown in Figure 10.14, then the maximum noise power in the circuit may be calculated. The maximum power will be delivered with $R_1 = R$. Therefore the maximum power is given by Equations 10.28 and 10.29, leading to Equation 10.30.

$$P_a = \frac{(V_n)^2}{4R} \qquad (10.28)$$

$$P_a = k\,T\,B_w \qquad (10.29)$$

$$V_n = (4\,k\,T\,B_w\,R)^{1/2} \qquad (10.30)$$

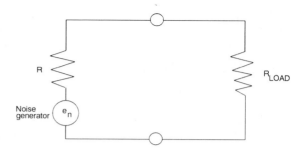

Figure 10.14   Equivalent circuit for resistor noise

Reactive elements do not contribute to thermal noise but they do affect its frequency shape.

10.8.3   Effective noise bandwidth

The effective noise bandwidth is defined as the width of a rectangular frequency response curve having a height equal to the the maximum height of the frequency response curve and corresponding to the same total noise power (see Figure 10.15). It is given by Equation 10.31.

$$B_w = \frac{1}{|H_0|^2} \int_0^\infty (H_f)^2\,df \quad Hz \qquad (10.31)$$

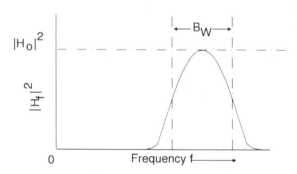

Figure 10.15   Effective noise bandwidth

10.8.4   Shot noise

Shot noise is the name given to noise generated in active devices such as valves, transistors and integrated circuits. It is caused by the random varying velocity of electron movement under the influence of externally applied potentials or voltages at the terminals or electrodes.

It is similar to thermal noise in that it has a gaussian distribution and a flat power spectrum. It differs, however in that it is not directly affected by temperature. Its magnitude is proportional to the square root of the direct current through the device and thus may be a function of signal amplitude.

The r.m.s. value of the shot noise current is given by Equation 10.32, where I_a is the average anode current; B_w is the effective bandwidth; and e is electronic charge.

$$I_s = (2\,e\,I_a\,B_w)^{1/2} \qquad\qquad (10.32)$$

10.8.5 Partition noise

Partition noise occurs in multi-electrode devices such as transistors and valves. It is due to the current through the device being divided between the various electrodes.

10.8.6 Intermodulation noise

Intermodulation noise is due to the presence of the products of intermodulation. If a number of signals are passed through a non-linear device the result will be intermodulation products that are spurious frequency components. These components may be inside or outside the frequency band of interest for the device.

The non-linearities cause each signal to combine with the other signals in the set, to produce a series of second order sum and difference products, third order products etc.

For most analogue systems with many multiplexed channels, the addition of the very large combination of signals results in an output noise spectrum which is approximately flat with a frequency across a narrow band of about 4kHz.

Intermodulation noise differs from thermal noise since it is a function of the signal power at the point of non-linearity.

10.8.7 Crosstalk

Crosstalk is the unwanted coupling between signal paths. There are essentially three causes of crosstalk:

1. Electrical coupling between transmission media such as between wire pairs on a VF cable system, or a capacitance imbalance between wire pairs in a cable.
2. Poor control of frequency response in an analogue multiplexer system caused by defective filters or poor filter design.
3. Non-linear performance in analogue multiplexer systems.

There are two types of crosstalk:

1. Intelligible crosstalk, where at least four words are intelligible to the listener from extraneous conversations in a seven second period.
2. Unintelligible crosstalk, which is crosstalk resulting from any other form of disturbing effects from one channel to another.

Intelligible crosstalk causes the greatest problem to the listener. This is caused by the fear of loss of privacy or the fact that the listener has great difficulty in differentiating between the party to which he is connected and the interfering circuits.

10.8.8 Impulse noise

Impulse noise consists of short spikes of power having an approximately flat frequency response over the spectrum range of interest.

It is considered to be a voltage increase of 12 dB or more above the r.m.s. noise for a period of 12 ms or less.

This type of noise may be caused by a number of sources such as the switching of relays in electro-mechanical telephone exchanges. Although these "clicks and pops" are annoying to the human ear, it is reasonably tolerant. However impulse noise may cause many serious error rate problems on data or digital circuits.

The effects of impulse noise can be alleviated by the use of a wide band clipping circuit followed by a band limiting filter. This procedure first reduces the amplitudes of the spectral components and then reduces the number of components.

10.8.9 Flicker noise

Flicker noise is sometimes known as low frequency (1/f) noise or excess noise. It is because of its unusual increase at very low frequencies that it is also called low frequency noise.

Its cause is associated with contact and surface irregularities in cathodes of valves and semiconductors and it appears to be caused by fluctuations in the conductivity of the medium. Because of the advances in cleaning and passivation techniques, which are employed during component manufacturing process, a good device will exhibit negligible flicker noise above 1kHz.

10.9 Noise units and measurements

10.9.1 Terms of measure

The measurement of noise is an effort to characterise a complex signal. The noise measurement in telephone channels is further complicated by the subjective nature of the annoyance caused to users, rather than the absolute magnitude of the noise power. A noise measuring set must therefore measure the subjective interference effect as a function of the frequency as well as magnitude and give the same readings for different types of noise which cause equal interference.

The value of 10^{-12} watts or -90dBm has been chosen arbitrarily as the noise reference value. The markings on a noise meter are in decibels and measurements are expressed in dB above reference noise dBrn. A 1000Hz tone having a magnitude of -90dBm will give a reading of 0dBrn regardless of weighting, but all other measurements must specify the type of weighting.

10.9.2 Equivalent noise resistance

In a circuit using valves or transistor devices shot noise is produced. For noise calculation purposes this shot noise can be thought of as the thermal noise produced by an 'equivalent resistor'.

For a triode the hypothetical resistor is inserted in series with the grid and its value is given by Equation 10.33, where g_m is the mutual conductance of the triode.

$$R_{eq} = \frac{2.5}{g\,m} \qquad\qquad (10.33)$$

10.9.3 Noise temperature

The thermal concept can be applied to other types of noise sources such as diodes and noise tubes. The noise temperature of such a device is the temperature of a thermal noise source which produces the same available noise power as the device under consideration regardless of the actual physical temperature of the device.

The concept of noise temperature is not confined to noise sources. For example the noise power measured at the output of an amplifier or antenna can be expressed in terms of the equivalent noise temperature. In the case of an antenna the noise is due to radiation from objects on earth as well as in outer space and the antenna noise temperature is used.

Another concept which is used is excess noise temperature T_x which is the difference between the noise temperature of the source T and the noise temperature T_o of a thermal noise source at room temperature (17^0 C or 290^0 K). (Equation 10.34.)

$$T_x = T - T_o \qquad (10.34)$$

Many commercially available noise sources with resistive terminations are calibrated in these terms. In use care must be taken to correct for actual temperature in such devices.

10.9.4 Effects of noise on speech telephony

Noise is a complex signal and the measurement of its effects in telephone channels carrying speech is made more difficult by the fact that, to the telephone user, it is the annoyance that is caused by noise that is important rather than the absolute magnitude of the noise power. The subjective interfering effect of noise is a function of frequency as well as magnitude and may be the combination of a number of dissimilar forms of noise.

The results of many experiments involving telephone users have shown that, within the normal telephone frequency range of 300Hz to 3400Hz, lower frequencies cause less annoyance than higher frequencies. It has also been shown that if simultaneous noises are present then the effect to the user is additive on a power basis, i.e. if tones of an equal interfering effect are used a meter indication would be 3dB higher.

A further effect to be noted is that it has been shown by experiment that the human ear does not fully respond to sounds shorter than 200ms and therefore does not fully appreciate the true power.

10.9.5 Line weighting for channel noise

In order to conduct measurements of channel noise it is necessary to recognise the effects of annoyance to the telephone user of frequency. The results of experiments have produced a number of line weighting curves with respect to frequency. This weighting must take account of the relative annoyance of tones, both in the presence of speech and in its absence, with respect to a tone of a specified frequency.

This weighting also must take account of the effects of attenuation caused by the telephone handset. Thus standard line weighting networks have been produced which take account of these factors and provide a frequency shaping effect which matches that of a telephone user and telephone handset.

10.9.6 Psophometric

Psophometric line weighting is the standard produced by the International Telegraph and Telephone Consultative Committee (CCITT). It is defined as the noise measured on a telephone line using a psophometer, which is an instrument for measuring channel noise and includes a weighting network. For most purposes it is sufficient to assume that the psophometric weighting of 3kHz white noise decreases the average power by about 2.5dB.

The reference frequency specified at the point of minimum attenuation in the voice channel is 800 Hz. The full specification is provided in the CCITT G series Recommendations.

It is common to refer to average noise power delivered to 600 ohms instead of r.m.s. noise voltage, this power is expressed in picowatts.

The noise units used are picowatts psophometric (pWp) or decibels psophometrically weighted (dBmp), as in Equations 10.35 and 10.36, for noise which is flat from 0kHz to 3kHz.

$$pWp = \frac{(psophometric \ mV) \times 10}{600} \quad pwatts \qquad 10.35)$$

$$dBmp = 10 \log (pWp) \qquad (10.36)$$

10.9.7 FIA C-message noise units

In North America there are two forms of line weighting that are encountered, FIA and C-message.

FIA line weighting is so called because it is based upon the FIA handset developed by Western Electric Company. It uses a reference frequency of 1000Hz and a reference power level of –85 dBm. The unit of noise measurement for FIA weighting is dBa (dB adjusted). FIA line weighting is being phased out.

The second line weighting, which is now the preferred standard in North America, is C-message line weighting which is based upon a more sensitive handset. It uses a reference frequency of 1000Hz and a reference power level of –90dBm. The unit of noise measurement used for C-message weighting is dBrnC (dB above reference noise C-message).

10.9.8 Noise measurement instruments

Instruments for measuring noise are usually built specially for the purpose because of the random nature and considerable fluctuations of the noise voltage.

10.9.8.1 *Voltmeters*

The use of an a.c. voltmeter to measure noise voltage is possible under limited conditions. However, a large amount of fluctuation would be seen due to the random nature of the noise voltage. If a rectifying a.c. voltmeter is used then form factor correction should be used for the measurements. This requires knowledge of the character of the noise to be measured.

A voltmeter will indicate the total r.m.s. voltage of the noise if the voltmeter has a frequency response greater than the bandwidth of the noise spectrum to be measured. If the voltmeter has a frequency response less than that of the bandwidth of the noise then the reading will be proportional to the noise within the bandwidth of the meter.

When the noise to be measured is in a narrow frequency band within a broadband spectrum, then a filter of the required bandwidth must be used between the voltmeter and the point to be measured. It is also common to use frequency shaping, in addition to band limiting, which is known as noise weighting.

10.9.8.2   Noise meter

The measurement of noise in a system or device is often performed using a noise meter. This is actually an a.c. voltmeter preceded by a filter which is tunable or switchable over a range of frequencies much greater than their noise bandwidths. In most cases these meters will have a fixed input impedance and are often calibrated in terms of power rather than voltage.

In the case of an average reading voltmeter form factor correction must be applied.

10.9.8.3   Impulse noise counter

Impulse noise is voltage spikes on the line which, although tolerable on voice circuits, will cause errors on circuits used for data transmission.

To measure these noise spikes requires a weighting network, a rectifier, a threshold detector and a counter to record the events above the threshold. A means of measuring time is also provided so that a count may be recorded for a fixed time interval.

A typical impulse counter for the voice frequency band has a threshold adjustable in 1dB steps from 40dBrn to 99 dBrn, with a choice of terminating (600 ohms) or bridging (high) input impedance. The timer can be set in 1 minute intervals up to 15 minutes, a 5 minute interval being standard for message circuits. On some instruments there are several counters in order to make counts at different threshold levels simultaneously, which allows the measurement of the distribution of impulse magnitudes.

10.10   Signal to noise ratio

10.10.1   Definitions

Signal to noise ratio is the ratio of the required signal power to the noise power, as in Equation 10.37

$$S/N = \frac{Required\ signal\ power}{Noise\ power}$$

$$= 10\log\frac{Required\ signal\ power}{Noise\ power}\quad dB \qquad (10.37)$$

In some systems it is useful to compare the input signal to noise ratio $\frac{S_i}{N_i}$ with the output signal to noise ratio $\frac{S_o}{N_o}$.

The performance of a system may be judged in terms of the signal to noise ratio, and for the best results it must be as large as possible.

The theoretical maximum data rate of a transmission medium is related to the signal to noise ratio and can be determined using a formula attributed to Shannon and Hartley. This formula, known as the Shannon-Hartley Law is given in Equation 10.38, where C is the data rate, B is bandwidth in Hz, and N is the random noise power in watts.

$$C = B\log_2(1 + \frac{S}{N})\quad bits\ per\ second \qquad (10.38)$$

10.10.2   Effect of amplification

The effect of amplification upon the signal to noise ratio is to degrade it at the output of the amplifier as compared to its input.

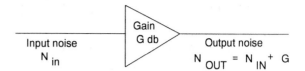

Figure 10.16   Output noise in terms of input noise

This is caused because the noise is amplified as well as the the signal and in addition the amplifier itself will introduce noise into the system, usually thermal noise and/or shot noise.

A term often used in connection with amplifiers is "equivalent noise input" which is defined as the amount of noise that would be required to be present at the input of a completely noiseless amplifier in order to produce the same noise level at the output as that of a practical amplifier.

From this definition it follows that the output noise of an amplifier is equal to the input noise plus the gain of the amplifier in decibels. (See Figure 10.16 and Equation 10.39.)

$$N_{out} = N_{in} + G\quad dB \qquad (10.39)$$

10.10.3   Effect of tandem connections

The doubling of noise power, by adding two identical amplifiers in tandem with equal input levels, increases the noise power by 3dB. If the input level remains the same and the noise power level is increased by 3dB, then the signal to noise ratio is reduced by 3dB.

Thus every doubling of the number of amplifiers will show a 3dB reduction in the signal to noise ratio. Figure 10.17 shows the effect of adding more amplifiers upon this ratio. However it should be noted that this will only hold true for amplifiers of identical noise figures. A similar graph may be produced for other combinations of amplifiers.

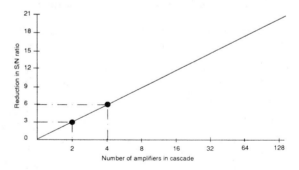

Figure 10.17   Effect on S/N of multiple amplifier connections

10.11   Noise factor

10.11.1   Definition of noise factor (noise figure)

The noise factor, usually of an amplifier, is defined as the ratio of the signal to noise ratio at the input to the signal to noise ratio at the output of the amplifier stage. It indicates the "noisiness" of the amplifier, as in Equation 10.40.

$$Noise\ factor\ =\ \frac{Signal\ to\ noise\ ratio\ at\ input}{Signal\ to\ noise\ ratio\ at\ output} \tag{10.40}$$

As the units on the top and bottom of this equation are the same then it will be seen that the noise factor is just a number.

It is convenient to work in decibels and to this end the term noise figure is used, which is the noise factor expressed in decibels, as in Equation 10.41.

$$Noise\ figure\ =\ 10\log(Signal\ noise\ ratio\ at\ input)$$
$$-\ 10\log(Signal\ noise\ ratio\ at\ output) \tag{10.41}$$

It may be seen from this equation that the noise figure is the number of decibels by which the signal to noise ratio is degraded by an amplifier.

10.11.2 Noise factor in terms of equivalent noise resistance

As has already been stated, for calculation purposes the shot noise produced by valves and transistor devices may be represented by the the thermal noise produced by an "equivalent resistor".

The relationship between the equivalent resistance and the noise factor is: the higher the equivalent resistance the higher the noise factor or noisiness of a device. For triode valve circuits the relationship is given by Equation 10.42, where F is the noise factor, R_{eq} is the equivalent resistance, and R_s is the resistance in series with the input supply.

$$F\ =\ 1+\frac{R_{eq}}{R_s} \tag{10.42}$$

10.11.3 Noise factor and noise temperature

These measures are used to indicate the amount of noise generated in a network. In both cases the higher the value the more noise is generated in the network.

The relationship between noise factor and noise temperature are given by Equations 10.43 and 10.44, where F is the noise factor and T is the noise temperature in degrees Kelvin.

$$T\ =\ (F-1)\,290 \tag{10.43}$$

$$F\ =\ \frac{T}{290}+1 \tag{10.44}$$

Note that for low noise systems, where F is small, then it is more convenient to use T for calculations which is larger in both range and magnitude.

10.11.4 Amplifier input noise in cascaded amplifiers

The concept of equivalent input noise of an amplifier may be used to calculate the noise level in cascaded amplifiers. It may be shown that the noise level at the input of the second amplifier is given by Equation 10.45.

$$N_{total}\ =\ N_{in}+10\log 2 \tag{10.45}$$

In a similar manner, for system with x amplifiers, the noise input at the xth amplifier (N_x) will be given by Equation 10.46.

$$N_x\ =\ N_{in}+10\log x \tag{10.46}$$

10.11.5 Noise factor measurement

The most convenient method of measurement of noise factor is using a noise diode, as in Figure 10.18, as this method does not require the bandwidth of the system to be known. The system bandwidth is very difficult to measure to any degree of accuracy.

A noise diode produces mainly shot noise, which may be adjusted by varying the input current to it. It produces a broad spectrum of frequencies up to at least 5MHz. The input resistance of the active network is R_g, the output power is P_o, and the noise factor is F. The

Figure 10.18 Method of measurement of noise factor

following method is used. First measure P_o when the diode current and the attenuation are zero. The diode current is then adjusted to give the same power reading with an attenuation of 3dB (a doubling of the output power). By using the same meter reading any discrepancies caused by the meter are avoided. Equation 10.47 can be obtained, and this reduces to Equation 10.49 if Equation 10.48 holds.

$$F\ =\ \frac{e\,I_a\,R_g}{2\,k\,T} \tag{10.47}$$

$$\frac{e}{2\,k\,T}\ \approx\ 20 \tag{10.48}$$

$$F\ =\ 20\,I_a\,R_g \tag{10.49}$$

10.12 Noise waveforms

10.12.1 Mathematical model

Thermal noise is a combination of a very large number of random events and satisfies the conditions of gaussian distribution, as in Figures 10.19 and 10.20, and Equation 10.50.

$$\rho(V)\ =\ \frac{1}{\sigma_n\sqrt{2\pi}}\ \exp\left(\frac{-V^2}{2\,\sigma_n^2}\right)$$
$$=\ \frac{1}{\sigma\sqrt{2\pi}}\int_{-\infty}^{V}\exp\left(\frac{1}{2}\frac{x^2}{\sigma_n^2}\right)dx \tag{10.50}$$

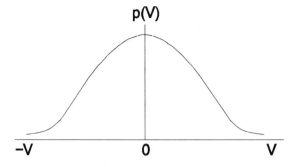

Figure 10.19 Gaussian density function

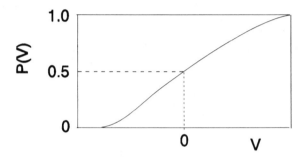

Figure 10.20   Gaussian distribution function

the midband frequency, modulated in amplitude by low frequency wave whose highest frequency is dependent on the bandwidth of the noise. (See Figures 10.21 and 10.22.)

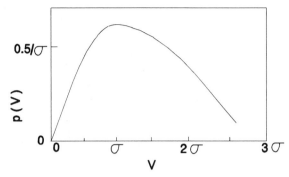

Figure 10.21   Rayleigh density function

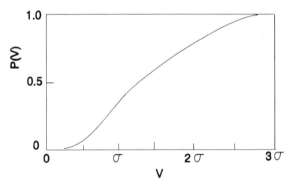

Figure 10.22   Rayleigh distribution function

10.12.2   Band limited white Gaussian noise

In most practical applications where white noise is produced it will be passed through a band limiting filter. Filtering uncorrelated white noise produces correlated band limited white noise or coloured noise. The autocorrelation function is given by Equation 10.51.

$$R_\tau = N_o B \, \frac{\sin (2 \pi B_\tau)}{2 \pi B_\tau} \qquad (10.51)$$

10.12.3   Narrowband Gaussian noise

Narrowband gaussian noise is called Rayleigh noise and it is defined as narrowband if the noise bandwidth is small compared to the midband frequency. It has the appearance of a sinusoidal carrier at

10.13   Bibliography

Bell (1979) *Transmission Systems for Communications*, Bell Telephone Laboratories.

Freeman, R.L. (1989) *Telecommunication System Engineering*, John Wiley.

Lee, E.A. et. al. (1990) *Digital Communications*, Kluwer Academic Publications.

Slater, J.N. (1988) *Cable Television Technology*, John Wiley.

11

The telecommunications industry

Fraidoon Mazda
MPhil DFH DMS MBIM CEng FIEE
Northern Telecom

Contents

11.1 Introduction

It has long been recognised that availability of information is crucial if a country is to be globally competitive. Telecommunications is the method for transmission of this information. In fact the word telematics is derived from a contraction of the French words for telecommunications and computing.

The requirements placed on a telecommunications system are:

1. A modern infrastructure to support the economic growth of the nation.
2. Availability of a range of services at prices which the user can afford.
3. Continual investment in the infrastructure, which often requires a suitable economic and regulatory environment (Geeslin, 1989).

This chapter provides an overview of the telecommunications field, some of the topics then being developed in greater detail in subsequent chapters in this book.

11.2 The telecommunications model

Telecommunications is a complex entity containing many interwoven factors. Figure 11.1 shows a simplified representation of a telecommunications model, which illustrates the 'chicken and egg' syndrome occurring in any high tech industry.

Services or customer demand is at one end of the model and enabling technology at the other. Which comes first? Which is the chicken and which is the egg? Do the services pull through the technology or is it that, once a technology is discovered, the corresponding services follow automatically? As in all such considerations there is no single answer which fits every occasion.

Telepoint (mobile public telephony) licences were granted to several operators in the UK in 1989, but the service failed to catch on immediately. The technology was available to provide the service but there was no customer demand for it. Similarly ISDN was developed as a technology long before its widespread acceptance by users, primarily because of lack of suitable services. However personal global communications, also known as 'any' communications (anyone, anytime, any place) was in demand as a supplement or even replacement for fixed networks, but the technology to deliver the service at an economic price (facilities for global roaming and compact handsets) were to come much later.

Technology is subject to frequent change or evolution (Gilhooly, 1990) which means that:

1. The telecommunications network must be designed to evolve with its technological base, leading to the concept of open network architecture. The network should be able to provide new services and respond in real time to changes in traffic flow, and to changes from switched to permanent or semi-permanent connections, and all this must be achieved under control of the service provider or the customer.
2. Investment decisions are based on short payback periods. There must be rapid growth in the revenues resulting from introduction of a service based on a new technology.

Many telecommunication technologies are being developed which will form the network of the future, such as SDH, broadband ISDN using ATM, and universal mobile communications. These developments in their turn are dependent on enabling component technologies such as in photonics (optical components and optical fibre), integrated circuits, software structures and languages and software development processes.

Telecommunications is creating an information oriented society, resulting in a change in business practices and in individual life styles. The customer is becoming increasingly sophisticated and is

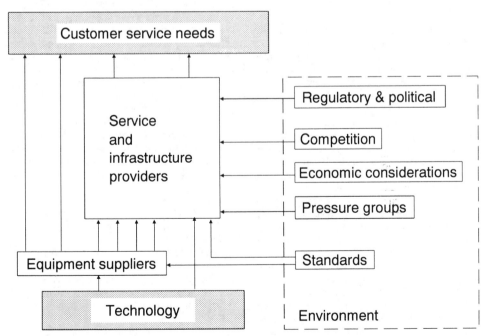

Figre 11.1 A simplified telecommunication model. Vertical arrows are enablers. Horizontal arrows are constraints.

demanding continually improving services, for use at the workplace and at home. However customers must obtain a significant benefit from a new service before they will use it. The fact that it is based on a new technology does not interest them. The service must meet actual needs at an economical price and be universally available. It is important that the services are integrated into the network so that multiple services are provided by a single network.

The growth of VCRs has been largely attributed to the fact that users can record a television programme and then view it in their own time. This is a different market from that at which the VCR was originally targeted. Users bought to meet their actual needs, not that which was assumed by the marketer. It is also assumed that once high definition television has been viewed users will be unwilling to return to conventional television, just as they moved from monochrome television to colour.

Remote banking and shopping, available around the clock, is a convenience which the user is likely to want, at the right price. Multimedia promises to be a service in widespread use at the workplace for communication between individuals. Autotranslation also has many applications, when it becomes available. The obvious application is the real-time translation between different languages, a must as the European Community develops. However another use is in the translation between sound and video, such as would be required if a blind person were communicating with a deaf one.

Developments in telecommunication and component technology have the greatest impact on the equipment suppliers. There are many of these competing and dependent on technology and efficient work practices to provide them with a competitive edge. The equipment suppliers sell to the service providers as well as direct to the customer, primarily such things as customer premise equipment.

The service providers are affected by many factors. Political considerations have resulted in the privatisation of most of the modern PTTs and deregulation has resulted in increasing competition. The prime aim of deregulation is to provide the user with greater choice, and reduce prices, so stimulating the economy of the country.

Apart from added value service providers, there now also exist other PTOs who own their own communications infrastructure. In order to ensure that these new PTOs thrive, governments have often placed restrictions on the established operators, such as price caps and limiting the services which they can offer. It is primarily new services which provide PTOs with their competitive edge, generating new traffic and increasing revenue.

Many countries have appointed telecommunications 'watchdogs' to regulate the operations of their PTOs, so separating out the regulatory and operational activities. They carry out many functions, such as licensing new operators and services, applying regulatory pressure on them to improve the grade of service, setting guidelines on prices, establishing rules on interconnection between the operators, and ensuring that uneconomic services continue to be provided where they are in the public interest, these sometimes being funded publicly. Some countries also use these same regulatory procedures to protect their internal markets from external competition.

Competition between equipment suppliers helps the service provider, whilst competition between service providers helps the equipment supplier. The establishment of standards also helps service providers since interoperability between equipment provides them with the option to source from many different suppliers. On the other hand the need to conform to standards is often a constraint on the equipment suppliers, sometimes increasing the cost of their equipment.

Economic considerations vary between countries, and is often a matter of perception in the importance of telecommunications. In the developed countries, for example, telephones serve between 50% and 80% of the population, whilst in many developing countries it is well below 10%. Part of the reason for this is the lower finance available in these countries, but they also spend a much smaller part of their GDP (below 1%) on telecommunications compared to developed countries (between 1.25% and 2.0%).

Investment by a service provider in telecommunications cannot usually be justified only on the cost savings it introduces, but future revenues generated must also be taken into account. Other considerations are the need to minimise the total network life cycle (initial cost plus ongoing maintenance), and the impact on any existing investment and when it should be phased out. Generally older technologies are phased out much faster in developed countries compared to developing countries. For example telegraphy and telex have been largely replaced by the telephone in the US, and is approaching that stage in Europe, whilst it is still an important means of communications in many developing countries (Andrews, 1989).

Also shown in Figure 11.1 are pressure groups. These may be user groups, or manufacturers' associations, of which there are many world wide. The service providers often join some of these associations, especially where they are working towards introducing a new technology or standard. Furthermore the operators often have their own groups, the best known being CEPT (and now ETNO) for European PTTs.

11.3 The key players

Because of the strategic importance of telecommunications on the economy of a country, governments have traditionally played a prominent role in this area. Usually the PTT has been a monopoly national operator, wholly owned by the government. However, one by one, governments have loosened the reins on these PTTs, the process used in most cases being illustrated in Figure 11.2.

The first step has usually been to liberalise the services market and open it to competition. The PTT has still been state owned and it provided the infrastructure to carry these services. Usually a regulatory body, part of the government, is set up to ensure that the new service providers get equable treatment from the monopolistic carrier, and that they operate in a responsible manner.

The next step usually involves the privatisation of the PTT, the government often maintaining some of the shares in the company. Coincidental with this move a second telephone operator is given a licence, in order to provide competition in the infrastructure area. The regulatory body is once again used to ensure that the new operator is given fair treatment by the established PTO, and that competition grows between the two.

New services and infrastructures, such as cellular or satellite communications, are often opened to competition at an early stage, frequently before the public PTT has been privatised. Sometimes the PTT is barred from entering these new markets in order to prevent them dominating it.

As illustrated in Figure 11.2 investment (usually foreign) frequently flows into the new competing services and infrastructure which are set up. There are several reasons for this:

1. PTOs are sometimes prohibited by legislation from carrying out certain activities in their own countries, and are eager to take the opportunity to expand overseas. This activity provides

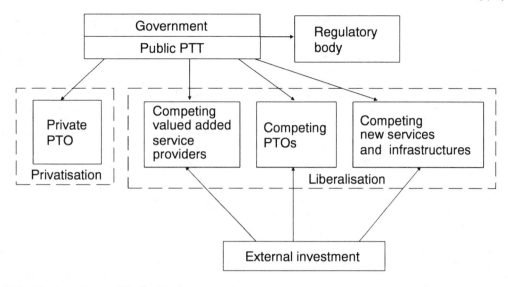

Figure 11.2 The key players within the telecommunications market

them with valuable experience, so that they can more readily enter their own markets when legislations have been relaxed.

2. PTOs, especially if they have a near monopoly in their own country, sometimes move overseas in order attack the dominant PTO of that country in their home territory, before the PTO concerned also moves overseas. A case of 'the best line of defence is attack!'

3. Local players are critically dependent on the local regulatory environment and the state of the local economy. Spreading their activities over several countries also helps to cushion them against adverse conditions in any local area. The motto is very clearly, 'think globally, act locally.'

4. Equipment suppliers sometimes also become service providers and vice versa (vertical integration). An equipment supplier will operate globally in order to increase the addressable market and so recoup the considerable investment which he has made in developing new technology, which often has a relatively short life. Equipment suppliers may also prefer to become service providers in countries where they are not the dominant equipment provider to the local PTO, so avoiding competition with their main customer.

The telecommunication operator who wishes to operate globally often faces a difficult decision. The temptation is to gain market share, usually at the expense of the local operator. Many of the large telecommunication users are also multinational organisations who prefer to obtain services from a single supplier, no matter in which country they operate. The PTOs therefore offer 'one-stop shopping', providing global services and single billing. However they also very often need to form alliances with the local country PTO, especially if the country has a near monopoly in its telecommunications system.

Alliances are also formed between a foreign and local PTO where a country is just starting to grant new operator licences. In these instances the foreign investor brings money and his experience to the table, whilst the local partner has knowledge of local conditions and is also likely to be looked on more favourably by the local government. Buying a local operator is another alternative to forming an alliance; a case of 'if you can't beat them, buy them.'

It is generally recognised that monopolies do not result in effective services, and that privatising an operator is not sufficient in itself. Economically there is no advantage to having a private monopoly compared to a public monopoly. Competition is usually introduced for three reasons:

1. To lower the price of a service. It is assumed that several suppliers would compete, causing the price to the end user to fall. The side effect of this is that suppliers are forced to become more efficient in order to maintain their margins.

2. To improve the quality of service, such as low disruptions and quick installations. Users make a choice between competing suppliers on the basis of price and quality.

3. To improve innovation and investment in services and infrastructure. Governments are not effective in making investment decisions, and there is little incentive for a supplier, who is in a monopolistic position, to make investments in improved infrastructure. Competition usually ensures infrastructure choices and the most efficient allocation when capital is scarce.

It has been argued that the telecommunication network is a natural monopoly, and that it is wasteful to duplicate access to subscribers, It is reasonable to have competition in services which run over this infrastructure, so long as legislation is introduced to ensure equal access to the service providers. Certainly it is very difficult for a newcomer to set up his own network, due to the large investment needed to compete with the established operator.

This situation is made worse by the conditions usually attached to the licence being granted, where the new entrant has to guarantee coverage of a high percentage of the country within a specified period in time, many of the locations covered having a low population density and therefore being uneconomical. Where the technology is new, for example radio based PCN services, all operators are on equal grounds in having to set up their networks.

Many of the new entrants to the telecommunications operators' sector are organisations with established telecommunication network, such as the utilities. They are niche players, their network being primarily used to carry their own traffic, and the excess capacity being sold. Examples of such operators are the electricity companies and the railway operators, who often have miles of optical fibre cable laid alongside the rail tracks.

Telecommunications provision may be considered to be at three levels: infrastructure, i.e. the physical network; transport services, i.e. that which provides the delivery mechanism (often switched); and higher level services, also called value added services, which process the information being transported. The lower the level, and the more established the technology, the less likelihood that competition will occur.

The prime role of regulation is to ensure effective competition. In a monopoly situation regulation is needed to protect the user (e.g. price cap), and to spur the supplier to improve efficiency. Cost plus pricing should never be used as it encourages 'gold plating'.

Competition may be said to benefit everyone. It stimulates the market so that it grows, ensuring revenue increase even though the percentage market share held by an individual supplier decreases. Furthermore the new service providers may take business from an established PTO, but they provide him with increased revenue by using his network to carry these new services (Aamoth and Smith, 1991). The problem the regulator faces is to determine the rate at which the market should be opened to competition. If, after a second supplier has been introduced, a third supplier is granted a licence, he is more likely to take business from the new entrant than from the established PTO.

The world population is about five billion, and it has a GDP of approximately nineteen trillion dollars. The world communications market is about five hundred billion dollars. The North American, European and Japanese markets account for about 15% of the world population but they represent over 60% of its GDP and over 90% of the telecommunications revenue.

11.3.1 USA

The USA telecommunications market is the most liberalised in the world, and the lessons learnt there are often studied by other countries starting down the privatisation and liberalisation path.

The regulatory framework of US telecommunications was set by the 1934 Communications act which also set up the Federal Communications Commission (FCC). The FCC has the responsibility to administer telecommunications on behalf of the US government.

Telecommunications competition can be considered to have started in 1959 when the FCC authorised the use of private micro-

wave systems. Amongst the FCC's duties are the regulation of prices, allocation of frequencies and granting of licences to new operators.

For some time AT&T owned the whole of the US telecommunications network, the Bell system. It also owned a manufacturing subsidiary (Western Electric) which produced equipment exclusively for the Bell system. AT&T was therefore a vast private, vertically integrated monopoly, the largest privately owned company in the world. Its activities were closely regulated by the FCC.

From this position the major steps in the deregulation of telecommunications within the US were as follows:

1968. The FCC ruled that equipment could be connected to the Bell system, even though it had not been produced by AT&T. This was known as the Carterfone decision.

1971. Licences were granted to specialised common carriers to provide switched telecommunications services connected to existing local networks. This was the specialised common carrier decision. In the same year the integrated office automation systems market was opened to competition (Computer Inquiry I). AT&T was allowed to supply these services through independent subsidiaries only.

1976. The market for terminals was opened further by simplifying the certification procedures. This was referred to as the equipment registration programme.

1980. Introduction of the concept of value added services, covering basic services and enhanced services. The terminals market was deregulated and AT&T was allowed to enter this through independent subsidiaries, only.

1982. Ruling by the District Court for the District of Columbia that the regional Bell system had to be split off from AT&T. The long distance services of the Bell system, as well of the Bell Laboratories and Western Electric were to be retained by AT&T. Competition was subsequently introduced in the long distance network, but the regional network remained a monopoly. (Modified Final Judgement or MFJ).

1984. On 1 January 1984 the MFJ ruling became effective, resulting in the AT&T divestiture.

Following divestiture the twenty-two local operating companies of the Bell system were formed into seven regional holding companies, often referred to as Regional Bell Operating Companies (RBOCs) or 'Baby Bells'. They are shown in Figure 11.3. They

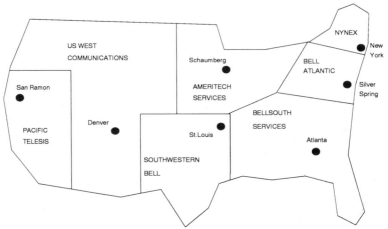

Figure 11.3　Regional Bell Operating Companies

provide the bulk of the local exchange infrastructure and are referred to as local exchange carriers (LEC). Under the terms of the MFJ the RBOCs had to provide equal access to all long distance carriers.

In addition there are several other local operators, referred to as bypass carriers. They generally provide a service to large businesses, linking them to one or two long distance companies at competitive rates and also ensuring security of supply.

AT&T continued to provide long distance or interexchange (IXC) services along with other competitive carriers, such as MCI Communications and Sprint International.

Access charges, i.e. the amount paid by long distance operators to local exchange carriers for interconnection, form a large part of the transmission costs, and bypass carriers often charge less for these services. Competition in long distance and local markets can therefore ensure equal access without the need to regulate it. In addition the Open Network Architecture (ONA) was introduced in 1987 to ensure that the dominant carriers provide fair access to value added service providers.

The Modification of Final Judgement (MFJ) which outlined the terms of the divestiture of AT&T, set three restrictions on the operations of the RBOCs:

1. They were to be infrastructure and service providers only, and were not allowed to manufacture equipment.
2. They were not allowed to offer information services, such as electronic yellow pages, audio text and video text.
3. They were not allowed to offer interexchange long distance services.

The RBOCs have been fighting to free themselves from these restrictions, and succeeded in having the restriction on provision of information services lifted in 1991. It is likely to be only a matter of time before all the restrictions have been removed. In the meantime the RBOCs have been very active in moving overseas in these areas, since the restrictions only apply to operations carried out in the USA.

11.3.2 Japan

The regulatory body for telecommunications within Japan is the Ministry of Posts and Telecommunications (MPT). Since the 1950s all domestic services in Japan was been provided by Nippon Telegraph and Telephone Corporation (NTT) and all international services by Kokusai Denshin Denwa Co. Ltd. (KDD). NTT is one of the largest telecommunications companies in the world.

Deregulation and liberalisation in telecommunications was started in 1985. Two laws were introduced, which became effective on 1 April 1985: the Telecommunications Business Law and the Nippon Denshin Denwa Kabushiki Kaish Law. These laws ended the domestic and international monopolies of NTT and KDD and restructured NTT as a private corporation.

There are two types of operators in Japan:

1. Type I carriers, who own and maintain their own telecommunications infrastructure. These include long distance and international carriers, satellite service providers and mobile services, including paging.
2. Type II carriers, who do not own their own infrastructure, but provide services. Anyone can become a Type II carrier simply by informing the MPT, and in the region of a thousand exist.

In order to increase competition and to ensure that the dominant carriers provide fair access to service providers, the Open Network Doctrine (OND) was introduced (Patel, 1982).

11.3.3 Europe

11.3.3.1 *The European Community*

The European Community can be considered to be made from three separate communities:

1. The European Coal and Steel Community (ECSC) which was formed by the Treaty of Paris, and signed by France, Germany, Italy, The Netherlands, Belgium, and Luxembourg. It came into effect on 25th August 1952 and aimed to create a common market for coal and steel.
2. The European Economic Community (EEC) which was formed by the Treaty of Rome on 25th March 1957. It has wide ranging aims, to result in an economic union within Europe.
3. The European Atomic Energy Community (Euratom), established by the Treaty of Rome to increase the energy availability within Member States, primarily by the adoption of nuclear power.

The European Economic Community (EEC) officially came into being on 31 December 1992, although this date is largely symbolic; changes began long before this time and continued after it. On this date all tariffs, custom regulations and other trade barriers between Member States were removed. The EEC is a single market made from twelve countries: Ireland, United Kingdom, Denmark, Germany, France, Spain, Portugal, Italy, Greece, The Netherlands, Belgium, and Luxembourg. Ten different languages are spoken and the population is well over 300 million (Frazer, 1991).

The key dates in the evolution of the European Economic Community are as follows:

1957. The Treaty of Rome was signed on 25 March 1957 by six countries (France, Germany, Italy, Belgium, The Netherlands and Luxembourg), which established the EEC (as well as the European Atomic Energy Community). Soon after that the European Free Trade Association (EFTA) was formed by Denmark, Norway, Austria, Portugal, Sweden, United Kingdom and Switzerland, and a treaty was signed between the EEC and EFTA. The EEC treaty came into effect on 1 January 1958 and the EFTA treaty on 3 May 1960.

1968. All custom duties between Member States was removed on 1 July 1968. (The Custom Union.)

1972. The Treaty of Accession was signed on 22 January 1972 by which the United Kingdom, Ireland and Denmark joined the EEC, bringing its membership up to nine. The treaty came into effect on 1 January 1973.

1974. The European Monetary System (EMS) was agreed, which went into effect on 9 March 1979. There were four elements to the agreement: a European Unit of Account (EAU); a mechanism for exchange and information; transfer arrangements; and credit arrangements.

1979. First direct elections to the European Parliament, by the citizens of the EEC. (Before this time its members had been appointed.)

1981. Greece joined the EEC, bringing its membership up to ten. The European Currency Unit (ECU) was also created and replaced the EAU.

1986. On 1 January 1986 Portugal and Spain joined the EEC, bringing the number of countries up to twelve.

1986. On 17 and 28 February 1986 the Single European Act was signed which amended the earlier treaties of Paris and Rome and defined the goal to be reached by the single European market by 31 December 1992.

The European Community works through five main bodies:

1. The Commission of the European Communities, which may be considered to be the civil service of the Community as well as its think-tank and its referee. It is charged with guarding the European treaties, and defending the Community's interests. It has seventeen members, appointed by Member States, and is divided into twenty-three Directorates General, each with specific responsibilities. Directorate General XIII (DG XIII) is responsible for Telecommunications, Information Industries and Innovation. Members of the Commission perform functions similar to those of ministers within their own countries, each being responsible for specific portfolios within the Community's activities. The Commission meets once a week in Brussels.

2. The Council of Ministers, consisting of ministers from the Member States. It meets to take decisions on specific topics. There are specific councils, such as the Agriculture Council in which Agricultural ministers sit. In addition the Council contains many small working groups of staff (mainly civil servants seconded from the Member States) who hammer out details of legislation. The Council of Ministers meets in Brussels, and twice a year the heads of states convene in what is known as the European Council.

3. The European Parliament (EP), consisting of five hundred and eighteen Members of the European Parliament (MEPs), which are directly elected by the citizens of the Member States, the number of representatives from each country varying according to its size. The MEPs belong to European political groupings and sit accordingly in the Parliament, which meets in Strasbourg. The Parliament has a consultative and advisory role, rather than a legislative one. It makes recommendations to the Council of Ministers.

4. The European Court of Justice (ECJ) consists of thirteen judges and sits in Luxembourg. It hears cases which are concerned with the implementation and interpretation of Community law. Rulings made by the ECJ are binding on members and take precedence over national courts.

5. The Economic and Social Committee (ESC), which is an advisory body of 156 members, consisting of representatives of employers, trade unions and consumers. It provides opinions on Commission proposals.

There are several legal instruments available under the Treaty of Rome, in order to enforce community regulations. These are as follows:

1. The direct application of Treaty rules, in which the Commission can obtain enforcement before the European Court of Justice. Persons within Member States also have rights which they can bring to the ECJ.

2. Directives. The aims of all directives are binding on Member States, but the method of attaining the aim is left to the legal system within individual Member States. Directives are usually issued by the Council, on proposals from the Commission, although the Commission can also issue directives.

3. Regulations. These are issued by the Council, or sometimes by the Commission. They are legally binding in their entirety to all Member States.

4. Decisions. These are issued by the Council and sometimes by the Commission. They are addressed to a Member State or a legal person and are binding in their entirety on those to whom they are addressed.

5. Recommendations. A recommendation has no legal power, being a recommendation for a course of action. It may be issued by the Commission or the Council.

11.3.3.2   *Telecommunications within the EC*

Telecommunications represents one of the biggest challenges to the united European Community. It is very visible, having a major impact on every business and individual. The technology used is advanced and it is one of the least integrated sections of the EC. By the turn of the century telecommunication services are expected to account for about seven percent of the gross output of the EC, making it one of the largest industrial sectors.

Historically telecommunications within the EC was in the hands of individual national operators, who were government owned, worked in isolation, set their own standards, acted as their own regulatory authorities, and procured equipment almost exclusively from national suppliers who designed to their local PTT's specifications.

The telecommunications market is not distributed evenly throughout the European Community. Although this market is approximately the same size as that of the USA, 70% of this is concentrated in the UK, France, Germany and Italy. The growth rate between countries is also uneven. For example, the Nordic countries have a very high concentration of telecommunication equipment and the market is therefore reaching saturation with a low growth rate.

Many of the current policies within the EC on telecommunications were outlined in the June 1987 Green Paper on 'The Development of the Common Market for Telecommunications Services and Equipment.' The principal aims of the EC's policies are (Cordaro, 1991):

1. Creation of a pan-European market for equipment by ensuring harmonised standards and approval procedures. This was further strengthened by the Terminals Equipment Directive of May 1988 which opened the terminal equipment market to competition, and included proposals for fair type approval. It required Member States to set up organisations, which were independent from their PTT, to specify and carry out type approval testing. The Directive also abolished the PTT's exclusive rights on the sale, maintenance and installation of terminal equipment.
   The June 1989 Type Approvals Directive followed, whose aim was to ensure mutual recognition of type approval testing. It required that terminals could be sold in all Member States following approval by a recognised testing house in any one Member State.

2. Liberalisation of the telecommunications services market. The EC aim is to provide open access to harmonised services across Europe, separating out services, products and regulation, previously all these being provided by monopolistic nationalised operators. In this context the EC Council Decision of February 1990 on Open Network Provision (ONP) is key (Sharma, 1991). ONP specifies the conditions for a network which is open to users and service providers. It has three components:

technical interfaces, usage and supply conditions and traffic principles. ONP covers a wide range of applications, such as leased lines, ISDN, voice telephony, packet switching, mobile services (including paging), telex, intelligent networks and broadband.

3. Opening up of public procurement in telecommunications. This was accomplished by the Council Directive of February 1990 which required fair procurement decisions to be taken by PTTs within Member States, based on commercial considerations only (Schwarz, 1991).

4. Development of an Europe-wide infrastructure in telecommunications.

The creation of Europe's single infrastructure is being achieved by several initiatives:

1. By common research programmes, the main one being RACE, as described in the next section.

2. By the establishment of a single standards making authority for Europe, which is ETSI, formed in March 1988.

3. By agreeing the joint introduction of new services. For example in June 1987 a Council Recommendation covered the co-ordinated introduction of a public pan-European cellular digital land mobile communication system, and in June 1989 another Recommendation covered the co-ordinated introduction of a land based public radio paging system (ERMES).

4. By investing in the peripheral regions of the Community, so as to improve their access to advanced telecommunications services. This aim was achieved primarily by the Special Telecommunications Action for Regional Development (STAR) programme, introduced in October 1986 and covering the period 1987 to 1991 (Martin, 1991). Close to one billion ECUs were provided by the European Regional Development Fund (ERDF), which covered part of the funding for this project, the rest being made up by public and private investors in the regions concerned.

11.3.3.3 *RACE*

The RACE (Research and development in Advanced Communication technologies in Europe) programme represents a major EC initiative for the 'introduction of Integrated Broadband Communications (IBC), taking into account the evolving ISDN and national introduction strategies, progressing to Community-wide services by 1995'. The aim is to ensure that the telecommunications network is truly integrated, by having one homogeneous network rather than a collection of national ones (Huber, 1991).

RACE I started in 1988 and ended in 1992. The initial funding from the EC was set at ECU 550 million. Further funding of ECU 489 million was added in 1992 to take the programme through to 1994, and this is known as RACE II. EFTA countries are also involved, supported by additional EFTA funding. Several hundred companies and organisations are taking part, and they are expected to match the EC contributions so the total funding is about ECU 2 billion.

There are three types of projects within RACE:

1. Part I projects. The aim of these projects is to establish the conceptual feasibility of IBC, working closely with international standards making bodies.

2. Part II projects. These projects establish the technical feasibility of IBC. They involve technology co-operation between participants, at the pre-competitive stage. The projects often lead to the development of prototypes, which run on test beds.

3. Part III projects. These establish the application feasibility of IBC and develop user applications. The aim is to produce real live applications, which are used in experiments and can be proved on test beds.

Work within RACE is being done in several areas:

1. IBC development projects, which are primarily focused on optical network, including optical components and optical switching. The projects are also studying ATM techniques and Fibre to The Home (FTH).

2. Intelligence in the network, which covers various aspects of communications management including the TMN (Telecommunications Management Network).

3. Mobile communications, which includes a wide range of areas such as mobile broadband systems; third generation mobile communications, including UMTS; and implications of mobiles in fixed networks.

4. Image communications, covering broadcasting and multimedia, coding/transcoding, digital recording, image synthesis, and HDTV transmission.

5. Service engineering, which is looking at providing architectures for flexible integration of telematic services.

6. Information security, covering security relating to communications management and service administration.

7. Advanced communications experiments. These develop applications for IBC and include various areas of business e.g. banking, publishing, distribution, manufacturing, etc.

8. Test infrastructure and interworking, which are concerned with looking at interworking between broadband systems and also with the testing of application projects.

Figure 11.4 shows the main stages in the RACE programme leading to the introduction of the first IBC commercial service from the end of 1995. The key target dates are:

1993. Completion of major standardisation activities and the early introduction of prototypes for commercial customers. Investment decisions for the pan-European IBC network and services firmed up.

1994. Optical link connecting capital cities of the EC are in place.

1995. Initial installation of IBC for major customers and continuation of field trials.

1996. Offering of first basic commercial IBC services, based on 155Mbit/s data rates.

11.3.3.4 *Supplier initiatives*

There have been several telecommunications initiatives within Europe, driven by suppliers, a few of these being as follows (Patel, 1992c):

1. The European Broadband Interconnect Trial (EBIT), which was started in 1989 with the aim of developing a switched broadband network across Europe to support the RACE programme. Several PTOs from CEPT countries were involved.

2. The International X.25 Infrastructure (IXI), which is provided by PTT Telecom of The Netherlands. It uses leased lines from

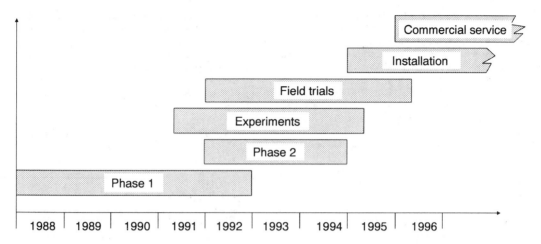

Figure 11.4   RACE programme leading to IBC commercial service

other PTOs in order to provide a high speed backbone interconnecting national research networks. Some funding for this came from the CEC's EUREKA COSINE programme.

3. ETSI is defining standards for the Connectionless Broadband Data Service (CBDS), which is a variation of Bellcore's SMDS, based on IEEE 802.6. The aim is to enable suppliers to speed up the introduction of MAN interconnections across Europe.

4. Managed European Transmission Network (METRAN), which is a CEPT initiative for the introduction of a high speed transmission backbone across Europe. It will be based on SDH and is targeted for introduction in 1995.

5. Global European Network (GEN), which is a joint venture between several major European PTOs for the early introduction of a high speed network based on leased lines. This would eventually be replaced by the METRAN development.

6. Hermes, which is a consortium of European railway companies, co-operating in providing a high speed network by using optical fibre laid along their railway rights of way. Several foreign partners, mainly USA based telecommunications operators, are involved. If successful this development could provide a strong challenge to the European PTO's own network infrastructure.

11.3.3.5   *UK*

The United Kingdom represents the most open market in Europe and one of the most open in the world. The market began to be deregulated well before those of others within the EC, and today there are two major suppliers (BT and Mercury) with many niche suppliers. Granting of licences to local telephone operators commenced in 1992, and involved several cable television operators and utilities, who already had extensive telecommunications networks for their own use (e.g. the Post Office, British Rail and the electricity supply authorities).

The early major steps in the development of the UK telecommunications market were as follows:

July 1991.   The British Telecommunication Act was passed, which separated the telecommunications arm from the Post Office and created British Telecom (which was subsequently renamed BT).

Feb. 1982.   Mercury Communications Ltd. was licensed to run a network in full competition with BT. The company began investing heavily in its infrastructure. Safeguards were introduced to ensure equitable access arrangements between Mercury and BT.

Oct. 1982.   General licence was granted for the provision of a range of value added network services over UK networks. In effect this opened up the services market to competition.

April 1984.   Telecommunications Act was passed, which established the regulatory framework within the UK, policed by Oftel (Office of Telecommunications).

Nov. 1984.   BT was privatised, the UK government selling 51% of its shares in a public flotation, which was heavily over-subscribed.

March 1986.   Two licences were awarded for provision of nationwide Private Mobile Radio (PMR).

Oct. 1988.   Six Specialised Satellite Service Operators (SSSOs) were licensed.

Jan. 1989.   Four telepoint licences were announced. The initial launch of telepoint within the UK was unsuccessful, primarily due to poor marketing and the threat from PCN.

Dec. 1989.   Three PCN licences were announced.

11.4   Economic considerations

Economic considerations play a major role within the telecommunications model of Figure 11.1, and are linked closely to other factor such as competition, technology, regulatory controls and political pressures. Figure 11.5 shows the price model in greater detail. In setting the price of a service the operator needs to consider the objectives of his business, the costs of providing the service, and the pressures on him, such as competitive and regulatory.

11.4.1   Pricing

The prices set need to cater for several factors, such as:

1. Entry strategy. When a new service is introduced there are usually very few competitors. The temptation is therefore to set a high price, especially since the relative low initial usage will result in high unit costs for providing the service. Unfortunately

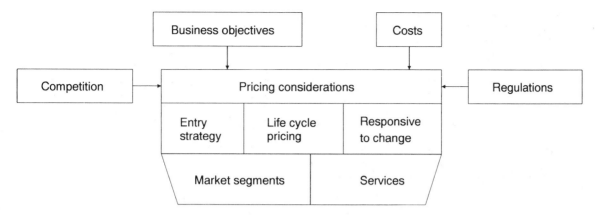

Figure 11.5 A price model

the higher the price the lower the take-up, so the price has to be determined based on the need to rapidly build up a large number of users and establish market share and economies of scale before the number of competitors grow.

2. Life cycle pricing. The price of a service will vary over its life cycle, typically as shown in Figure 11.6. At the post-competitive stage the number of new entrants grows rapidly, forcing down the price of the service, until it reaches an equilibrium, the margin obtained by each of the remaining suppliers being low enough not to encourage new entrants or further price cuts. Eventually the product or service will reach obsolescence, being replaced by a new service. The number of suppliers left will decline, and as this starts to happen the price of the service, to the few customers still requiring it, may actually increase for a short time before falling back, until eventually the service is totally discontinued.

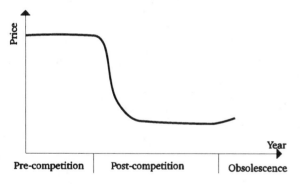

Figure 11.6 Typical price variation during a product's life cycle

3. Responsiveness to change. All pricing policies must be flexible so that they can be adjusted rapidly to changing environments, such as regulatory pressures, introduction of new technology, entry or exit of strong competitors.

4. Market segments and services. The price set will clearly depend on the service being provided, its costs and consumer demand, and the market segment into which the service is being supplied. It is common for the same service to be priced differently depending on the market segment, e.g. private and corporate users. Local calls are also usually priced at below costs,

whereas other calls are above costs, the PTO's profit increasing as the distance increases.

11.4.2 Costs

The general drive world-wide is towards pricing which is related to costs, and the ONP proposals specify that tariffs should be 'cost oriented.' The problem is that whereas it is relative easy to find the cost of a network it is not so easy to accurately determine the cost of providing a service over this network. This is primarily because the network is shared between several services, and there are problems associated with allocating overheads, such as administration and research costs, which can account for a third to half the total costs.

The most common method of cost allocation is to use fully absorbed accounting, where all the costs from the previous year are allocated to the different products or services, rather than trying to predict what the future costs are likely to be. Clearly this is not the best method since costs can vary considerably from one year to the next.

If the PTO treats its whole business as a profit centre then cross-subsidies will occur between services. However it is important that each service is treated as a profit centre so that the true costs for any service are known. It is then possible to determine how much profit is being made by that service, and to respond more effectively to price changes by competitors.

A large element of any cost is the interconnect charges (also called access charges) between suppliers, especially on international lines. Closely related to this is the accounting rate system, where international operators agree how the revenue from an international call is shared between them. This area is often linked to regulatory and political considerations.

11.4.3 Regulatory influences

In markets which have recently been liberalised, new entrants usually target the profitable areas first (Gandhi, 1992). Their main weapon for gaining market share is to cut prices, so forcing the existing supplier to also cut his price and to reduce his costs in order to stay competitive. Generally the existing supplier cannot cut operating costs quickly, since he has an established network to support and older work practices.

The existing supplier is also usually burdened by regulatory considerations which force him to continue to provide services, even though they may be uneconomical. This is the case of the social cross-subsidy, where the profitable areas of a business have to subsidise the non-profitable ones, a concept which is difficult to maintain in a fiercely competitive market.

It is worth noting that if a PTO has to agree its tariffs with another authority, such as a government agency, then it is less likely to base these tariffs on costs than if it is driven to do so by competition.

11.4.4 Developing countries

The greatest problem within developing countries, especially if they are a large agricultural country, is economic investment within their telecommunication infrastructure. The cost of introducing new telephone lines in rural areas is five times greater than in urban areas (ITU, 1986). Two thirds of the world do not have access to telephone services (ITU, 1988a) and 15% of the population own 85% of the telephone sets world-wide. Telephone densities in industrial countries exceeds 45 per thousand inhabitants, whilst in developing countries it is less than one per thousand inhabitants.

The problem is that in developing countries telecommunications is only a part of the country's overall infrastructure, competing for scarce funds with other essential services such as post, transport and power. The amount of investment possible is closely related to the GNP of the country and there is a good correlation between the telephone density in the country and its per capita GNP (ITU, 1988b; Varakin, 1989).

Figure 11.7 shows a typical curve for the usage of a technology during its life cycle, and it should be compared to the price curve of Figure 11.6. Following its introduction usage increases until it reaches saturation and then begins to decline as it is gradually replaced by a newer technology.

However the rate of technology usage varies, there being considerable variation between developed and developing countries. The telephone will be the most common form of communications well into the next century, especially in developing countries. New services, such as ISDN, need more expensive terminals and high user densities to justify their introduction, which is unlikely to occur in developing countries for some time. The usual route is for households to have telephones first and for these then to be upgraded to cater for more sophisticated services. Older technologies are often introduced into developing countries, usually just as they

are becoming obsolete in developed countries. The prime reasons for this are:

1. The lower capital costs involved; the initial investment in the product having being recouped and its price therefore being low as suppliers compete to gain marginal revenue.
2. Labour is generally cheap in developing countries, so the greater installation, maintenance and operational costs which are associated with older technologies is not a great disadvantage.
3. The greater simplicity and lack of advanced services in the older technologies does not present a disadvantage since the prime requirement is for basic services.

11.4.5 Competition

The powerful influence which competition has in determining the economic environment within telecommunications has already been covered in the previous sections. Competition can be beneficial in forcing suppliers to become more efficient, so reducing costs and prices. It can also be destructive when competitors concentrate on the most profitable areas of service provision, so ignoring the other markets, allowing the prices in these areas to rise.

In a non-competitive market there is very little price elasticity. Large users subsidise the smaller ones. However, the large users are the ones most sensitive to small price differentials, and they are also sophisticated enough to shop around for the best prices. Therefore, in a competitive environment, the telecommunication operators give them the best terms and now it is usually the smaller users who subsidise the larger ones. The small user funds the operator's telecommunications infrastructure, whilst the larger user provides the marginal revenue on this, so giving the carrier the flexibility needed to price for its preferential customers.

Competition can arise from many sources. The PTO's customers may themselves be competitors, for example reselling spare capacity to other users. The problem can get worst when international resale is concerned. This presents a dilemma to the primary supplier: if the prices are too low then it in effect invites resellers to take away its most lucrative business. If too high no one will use the service in the first place (Wood and Turton, 1992). The solution is clearly to sell services, not clear channels, if this is possible. One

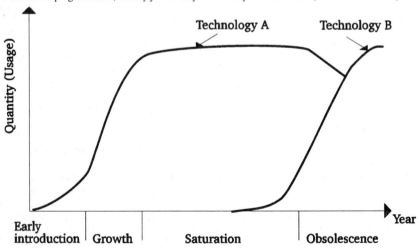

Figure 11.7 Technology usage curve

form is the use of virtual private circuits, the customer buying circuits on demand to match his current needs.

11.4.6 Customer perception

Price is the key to the adoption of a service by the mass market. Households spend a fixed proportion of their income on the media, but expect more for their money over time. Therefore prices need to fall in real terms to meet their expectations.

Telecommunications is unique in that, in the majority of cases, the invoice for the service comes much after consumption of the service has taken place (Weiss and Lewis, 1991). Consumers therefore do not have direct price feedback; they have to depend on their experience of previous usage of the service. To some extent this is no different to other services, such as gas and electricity, although household meters are more common here, which may be checked periodically.

Lack of direct price feedback means that customer perception of price differentials is not usually very high, and there is a lag in time before consumers take advantage of these differentials. If the consumer is an infrequent user then price comparisons may not be possible at all. For example a consumer on the move, using fixed and mobile telephones within various locations, such as hotels, would not be able to obtain an accurate price comparison of these services if they were supplied by competing service providers.

11.5 Services and technology

The two major elements of the telecommunications model of Figure 11.1, are the customer demand for services and the underling tech-nology which enables this service to be presented in an efficient and economic form. In some cases the technology and the service which it supports are clearly separable, whilst in others they are interde-pendent. For example in mobile communications the need for per-sonal communications is so closely related to the technology that provides it, that the same term is often used for both, PCN meaning the service and the network which delivers it.

11.5.1 Service and technology trends

Figure 11.8 shows the development of technology and services over the past century. This illustrates two important developments:

1. The exponential growth curve, with the introduction of many new technologies and services over the past two decades.
2. Like old soldiers, technologies do not die; they fade away, but that too takes a long time. Therefore telegraphy has been around for over a century and is still very much in use. The prime reason for this is that, as stated earlier, older technologies usually move from developed countries to the developing coun-tries, which suits their economies.

It is instructive to look at telegraphy, as a technology and as a service. Prior to its invention it took many weeks for messages to be taken over relatively short distances, usually on horseback and sail boat.

The first use of telegraphy was optical, and the word was coined by the French Chappe brothers who founded a 145 mile optical telegraph line between Paris and Lille in 1794. Towers with tele-scopes and mechanical semaphores were used, coded messages being passed from tower to tower with people doing the translation.

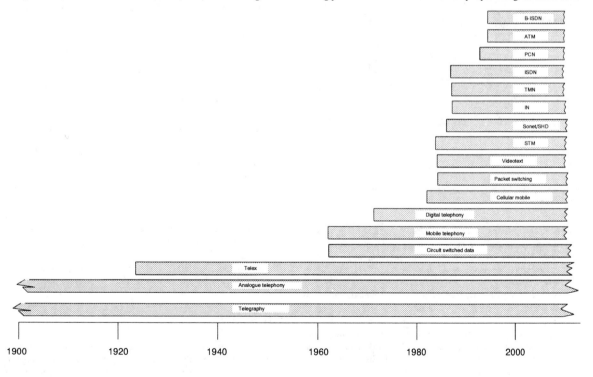

Figure 11.8 Service and technology introductions

The Moscow to Warsaw system opened in 1838 and had 220 stations with almost one and a half thousand operators and support staff (Andrews, 1989).

Electrical telegraphy was invented by Samuel Morse and Alfred Vail in 1838. The electrical current was carried through wire suspended between poles, a system which could only be used when crossing a relatively narrow expanse of water. Invention of a suitable cable insulation in 1847, by Werner Siemens, solved this problem; the English Channel was crossed in 1850 and the Atlantic in 1866.

Since then there has been rapid progress in international communications, driven first by a demand for the service and followed by the enabling technology. The first transatlantic telephone cable was laid in 1956 (TAT-1); the first transatlantic fibre optic cable, capable of carrying 40000 simultaneous telephone conversations, was laid in 1988 (TAT-8); and the first international communications satellite (Intelsat I, also called Early Bird) was launched in 1965, followed by many others world-wide.

11.5.2 Core and application technologies

Technologies may be considered to be of two types: core and application, a few of these being illustrated in Figure 11.9. Core technologies are primarily of four types:

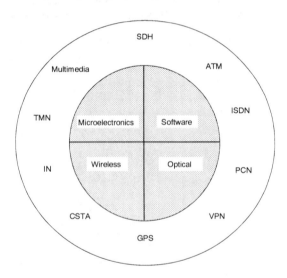

Figure 11.9 Core technologies and application technologies

1. Microelectronics, where the implementation of increasing functions on a silicon chip, having submicron channel structures, high speeds and low power consumption, has resulted in enhanced performance, reduced costs and smaller equipment sizes.
2. Software, where advances in technology and development standards have resulted in enhanced reliability and performance.
3. Optical, which includes optical fibres, with increasing capacities and the ability to transmit over longer distances without amplification; optoelectronic integrated circuits; optical amplifiers; and optical switches.
4. Wireless, which covers a wide range of technologies for the efficient transmission of radio signals, including by satellite.

There are many application technologies, a few of these being given in Figure 11.9. Most of these are relatively new, such as SDH and ATM, whilst others have been established for longer but are developing, such as ISDN into broadband ISDN and the telecommunications management networks (TMN). Wireless and optical applications have grown rapidly. Mobile communications, from personal communication networks (PCN) through to wireless PABX, cellular, telepoint and paging, are in increasing use. The trend is a change from accessing locations (e.g. a person's office desk) to accessing the person directly by a personal number. Satellite based telephony services have provided global coverage, and have introduced a new phase into the traveller's vocabulary: phoning and non-phoning airline seats!

11.5.2.1 The local loop

The local loop can act as a monopoly and a technology bottleneck. It is freely available to the user, although the user may not have a choice to which carrier he is connected. However the loop is restricted to service providers, and therefore acts as a barrier between them and their customers.

The original local loop was one wire, and used the earth for the return path. This was too noisy and so two copper wires were introduced, to allow speech circuits to flow around; hence the use of the term 'loop'. Copper is suitable for low transmission rates, such as voice or data using modems. However, for the broadband applications which are increasingly being used in businesses and homes, it is too slow.

Optical fibre is competing with traditional copper lines in the local loop (Fibre In The Loop, or FITL), although the cost of replacing copper to all homes is high. Many techniques are used, such as Fibre To The Home (FTTH) and Fibre To The Curb (FTTC), which use star, bus or rings with passive optical waveguide couplers and converters per group of subscribers.

Radio In The Loop (RITL) is also being used for ease and quickness of implementation.

11.5.2.2 Intelligent networks

Intelligent Networks (IN) are based on processing within the public network architecture. They enable PTTs and other service providers to give a service to their customers which would be difficult to provide on a private network. The key advantages of intelligent networks, in service provision, are:

1. The ability to offer new and advanced facilities.
2. All staff within an organisation can have access to equal services, irrespective of the branch in which they are located.
3. It enables operational services to be more easily sub-contracted.
4. It provides flexibility of services, and the ability to change quickly between the various services being subscribed to.

11.5.2.3 ISDN

ISDN has a very important roll to play in the local loop. Most of the network, apart from the subscriber loop to the local exchange, is now digital in the developed countries. ISDN provides the means for obtaining digital channels over these analogue lines. Basic access ISDN provides two digital channel (plus a signalling channel) whilst primary access ISDN provides 30 digital channels (23 in North America) plus signalling. Broadband ISDN gives much higher speeds. There are many applications for ISDN (Wood, 1991) such as:

1. The connection of a PABX to the public network.
2. The connection of small branches to the headquarters of an organisation.
3. As a back up to leased lines use within an organisation, either as an added security measure, or to carry overflow traffic.
4. To provide enhanced features, such as Calling Line Identification (CLI).

11.5.2.4 *Multimedia*

Figure 11.10 provides a simplified definition of multimedia services, as the convergence of voice or sound, text and image, usually on the same computer workstation (Francik et al., 1991; Weber, 1992). The components within a multimedia system are: the network; still image; video telecommunications; audio; motion video; graphics.

Television or a computer may be used as the delivery vehicle.

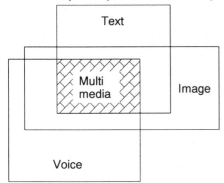

Figure 11.10 Simplified illustration of multimedia services

Television may have an optical disk associated with it for accessing games, training courses, etc.

Multimedia will play an increasing roll in telecommuting (Payne, 1991). It allows remote users to participate fully in joint work, including database access. However the bandwidth needed can be very high, requiring broadband to the home. This would arise, for example, if five users were conferencing and each had a workstation with sound and five images, along with the document being reviewed.

ISDN is key to the growth of multimedia applications, especially for the home market. Applications include videophony, videoconferencing, desktop conferencing, where files can be shared between participants and changed in real time, etc.

11.5.2.5 *Private and virtual private circuits*

Two factors are impacting the use of private circuits (Wright, 1992):

1. Users are demanding high bandwidth at random times due to increasing use of services such as teleconferencing and high speed inter-network traffic.

2. The PTOs want to move users away from leased private circuits, partly to avoid them reselling unused capacity to the PTO's other customers. The preference is to move customers onto the PSTN which is featured to meet their diverse needs.

The advantage of virtual private networks to the customer are:

1. They are cheaper to set up since no expensive transmission equipment is needed.
2. The services provided over a VPN can be rapidly changed to meet changing customer needs.
3. They are based on the PSTN, which is designed to high standards to meet public network needs.
4. Bandwidth can be provided on demand or on an agreed basis, e.g. at certain times of the day or night to cater for transmission of large data files.
5. The VPN in effect provides a managed service of the user's network, so they can get on with managing their core business.
6. There is greater reliability compared to a private circuit, since the PSTN can provide diversity of traffic routing, which is only possible in large private networks.

Small organisations, with few small remote sites, cannot justify having their own private network but can more readily justify the use of a virtual private network. Large organisations may wish to use private circuits, but would still use virtual private networks in order to:

1. Increase network resilience by providing a secondary routing for the main traffic, as illustrated in Figure 11.11.
2. Access the smaller locations of the company which are not linked by a private line, as also illustrated in Figure 11.11.

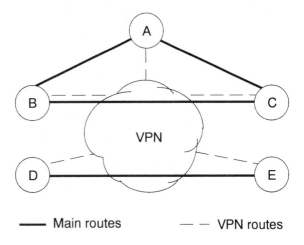

Main routes   **— —** **VPN routes**

Figure 11.11 A hybrid network of private and public (VPN) links

3. To extend the private network to other businesses with whom the company deals, or even to the home of key employees.
4. To provide an overflow to the private network in times of heavy use.

Security within virtual private networks is usually provided by use of encryption techniques.

Virtual private networks are often associated with the concept of outsourcing, although they are quite different. In outsourcing (Kirvan, 1992) a separate company provides an agreed level of service to the customers, relating to the operation of their communications network. This company may be the original supplier of the telecommunication facilities or it could be a third party. The company may also provide virtual private networks. Outsourcing may be considered to be the equivalent of Facilities Management (FM) as used in the IT industry.

There are several advantages to the customer in outsourcing:

1. The customers can concentrate on managing their core business and leave the management of their telecommunications network to the outsourcing company.
2. Often the capital cost of transmission equipment required for the private network can be rolled into the running costs of the network, so the customer does not need to meet a large up-front bill.
3. The outsourcing company usually has a large pool of skilled resources it can draw on in solving network problems, if they arise.

Figure 11.12 shows the relationship between private, outsourced and virtual private networks, and the most usual migration paths between them.

11.5.2.6 *CSTA*

In CSTA or Computer Supported Telephony Applications (Piggott, 1991; Walters, 1992) the computer is used to help in the telephony services. A popular example is illustrated in Figure 11.13. Client information is held on a computer database which can be accessed by the PABX. On an incoming call which is recognised by the PABX, the relevant data is sent to the operator's terminal (usually a VDU) at the same time that the call is put through to the operator. Therefore the operator can see details of the customer whilst speaking to him. Orders can be taken, or queries answered, and entered into the database in real time.

Outgoing calls can also be made by the PABX automatically, by dialling out to more customers than there are sales operators. This is done on the assumption that not all calls will be answered (predictive calling). When a client answers he is routed to a free sales operator. The system therefore avoids the sales operator having to wait for a successful connection, and is therefore more efficient.

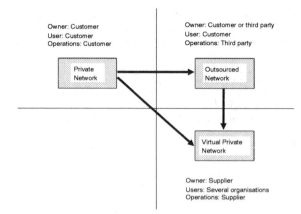

Figure 11.12 The relationship between a private network, an outsourced network and a VPN

Other examples of CSTA are the use of different numbers which provide various recorded messages to the callers; the use of interactive voice selection (yes/no answers to recorded questions); and the ability to pass records and customer calls between operators, in order to deal with specialised services or queries.

The advantages of CSTA are:

1. Saving in customer's and operator's time, due to the simultaneous transfer of the call and all relevant data.
2. Reduced telephone call time, which is important if the company is paying for the customer's call via a toll-free service.
3. Personal service provided to the customer, enhancing customer-vendor relationship.
4. Use of voice processing techniques to save on operator's time.
5. Apart from client details, the operating software can also be changed relatively quickly so as to provide different servics.

11.5.3 Service values

Changing consumer life styles are providing opportunities to the telecommunication service provider, who needs to support entertainment, leisure, learning, hobbies, home automation, etc.

Businesses are also operating globally, and demand global services. They usually prefer to deal with their local PTO, negotiating all their international services and charges. The requirement is also

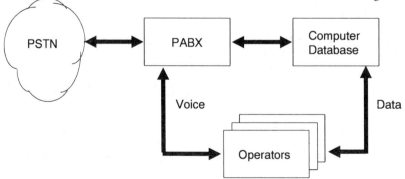

Figure 11.13 Example of a CSTA application

for a single bill, i.e. single-end ordering and single-end billing. This is the concept of One Stop Shopping or OSS (Gasbarrone, 1992) and One Stop Billing.

OSS clearly requires co-operation between PTOs in different countries for it to be successful on an international scale. OSS concepts were defined by CEPT's Commercial Action Committee (CAC) in 1986 and in September 1989 most of the CEPT countries signed a memorandum of understanding on the provision of OSS. International agreements are also required in order to provide International Private Virtual Circuit (IPVC) and International Closed User Group (ICUG) services.

Customer needs with regard to telecommunication services are: low cost; high quality; wide choice; services customised to meet their specific needs; intelligence in the network to allow them to manage the service functions.

Operator needs with regard to the same telecommunication service provisioning are: ability to provide a wide range of services from the same network; rapid deployment of new services to meet customer changing requirements; ease of upgrade to new technologies; low costs, especially whole life costs involved in providing the service; high reliability; world-wide networks.

Figure 11.14 shows the trend in the different types of services over the last decade. It shows that telephone based services will decrease as a percentage of the total, but they will dominate well into the next century. Similarly the telecommunication services in the developed countries will continue to dominate that of the rest of the world, as shown in Figure 11.15.

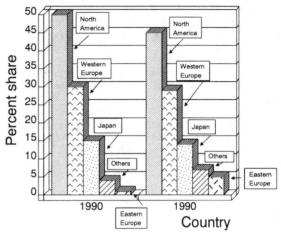

Figure 11.15 Service trends by region

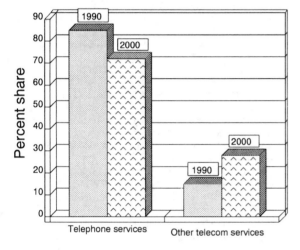

Figure 11.14 Service trends

11.5.4 Service classification

Services have been classified by the CCITT as in Figure 11.16 (CCITT, 1988; Wright and To, 1990). The two major groupings are interactive services, where transmission is in both direction, and distribution services, where transaction is in one direction only at any time.

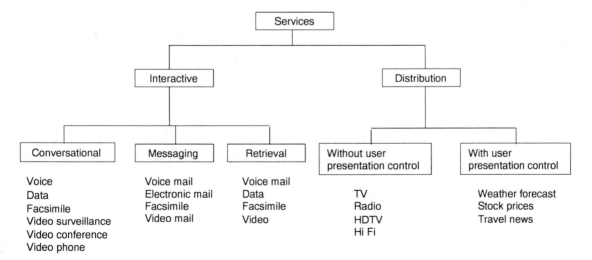

Figure 11.16 CCITT grouping of services

Interactive services can be further subdivided into conversational, messaging and retrieval. Conversational services usually apply to small user groups and require low end to end delays, and relatively high bandwidth. Since a human operator is involved accuracy (i.e. low loss) is usually less important since it can be compensated for. Examples of interactive conversational services are voice conversation and videoconferencing.

Interactive messaging services are similar to conversational services except that only the 'send' part of the action is carried out, the 'retrieval' being considered to be part of a separate service. Examples are logging of voice onto a voice mail system, sending electronic mail, and sending a facsimile message. In this service accuracy is important since a human operator is not available to compensate for loss. Delay is less important unless the system is waiting for an acknowledgement.

Interactive retrieval services are the other half of messaging services, and usually consists of retrieving information from a database.

Distribution services are subdivided into those with user control and those without user control. Examples of services without user control are broadcast television or radio. In distribution services with user control the user has presentation control, for example selecting the material for viewing from a broadcast. Examples are weather forecasts and stock price broadcasts.

11.6 References

Aamoth, R.J. and Smith, R. (1991) Competitive markets, *Communications International*, October.

Anerews, F.T. (1989) The Heritage of Telegraphy, *IEEE Commun. Magazine*, August.

CCITT (1.88) Part C of the Report of the Seoul Meeting (Jan. 25 – Feb. 5), *Study Group XVIII*, Report R55(c).

Cordaro, G. (1991) The Telecommunications Single Market, *Telecommunications*, January.

Francik, E. et al. (1991) Putting Innovation to Work: Adoption strategies for multimedia communication systems, *Communications of the ACM*, **34**, (12), December.

Frazer, J. (1991) The economic challenge of a united Europe, *EDN*, November 7.

Gasbarrone, G. (1992) One-Stop Shopping: A Global Approach, *Telecommunications*, February.

Geeslin, B.M. (1989) Funding the Future Telecommunications Infrastructure, *IEEE Commun. Magazine*, August.

Ghandhi, S. (1992) What price service?, *Communications Networks*, June.

Gilhooly, D. (1990) A look at the arbiters of change, *Commun. Week Internat.*, 12 November.

Huber, R. (1991) Europe's IBC Strategy, *Communications International*, October.

ITU (1986) Girmaw, I. and Morman, E.: *Investing in Telecommunications*, Geneva, October.

ITU (1988a) Centre for Telecommunications Development, December.

ITU (1988b) *Telecommunications and the national economy: A quantitative study using a macroeconomic cross-sectional analysis*, Geneva, May.

Kaplan, G. (1990) EC '92: status report, *IEEE Spectrum*, June.

Kirvan, P. (1992) The perks and pitfalls of opting to outsource, *Communications Networks*, May.

Martin, W.J. (1991) The European Community's STAR Programme, *European Business Review*, **91**, (2).

Patel, V. (1992a) Realising Broadband: The Regulatory Hurdles, *Telecommunications*, March.

Patel, V. (1992b) Speeding toward a single market, *Communications International*, January.

Patel, V. (1992c) Pan-European High-Speed Networks: Fact or Fiction?, *INTE NET*, April.

Payne, M. (1991) Telecommuting: the need for broadband, *Communications International*, October.

Piggott, J. (1991) THe status of CSTA, *Communications International*, December.

Schwarz, T. (1991) Public Procurement in Telecommunications, *Telecommunications*, 1 January.

Sharma, P. (1991) Opening the European Network for Services, *Telecommunications*, May.

Sweeney, D. (1992) The coming of satellite-based mobile phone service, *Cellular & Mobile International*, Winter.

Varakin, L.E. (1989) The macroeconomics of telecommunications, *Elektrosvyaz*, **2**, pp. 34–39.

Walters, R.E. (1992) The missing link: Computer-supported telephony, *IEE Review*, April.

Weber, S. (1992) The telephone's new frontier, *Electronics*, April.

Weiss, M.B.H. and Lewis, C.M. (1991) Telecommunications pricing and consumer expectations, *Telecommunications Policy*, December.

Wood, H. (1991) Strategy for users, *Communications International*, October.

Wood, H. and Turton, P. (1992) Telcos solve the high speed tariff dilemma, *Communications International*, April.

Wright, A. (1992) Virtually there! *Communications Networks*, July.

Wright, DJ and To, M. (1990) Telecommunication Applications of the 1990s and their Transport Requirements, *IEEE Network Magazine*, March.

12

Open systems interconnection reference model

Harold C Folts
BSEE MSSM
Omnicom Inc

Contents

12.1 Introduction

Effective and meaningful interchange of information is an essential element in the operation of enterprises and the conduct of business activities. The dramatic advances in computer/communications technology are now providing comprehensive capabilities for the establishment and evolution of distributed information systems fully interconnected and integrated to serve as the foundation of business around the world.

These distributed information systems have diverse operational requirements and will be supported by continually advancing technologies through a vast world-wide multivendor market-place of products. The question that immediately arises is: "How can compatibility among the variety of systems, designs, technologies, and manufactures be realised without constraining innovation, performance, and ongoing evolution?"

In 1978, the International Organization for Standardization (ISO) established a massive standards development programme called Open Systems Interconnection to establish an architecture and family of standards that will serve as the generic basis for compatibility among systems for information interchange. This chapter presents the perspective, concepts, and functions of the Reference Model for Open Systems Interconnection (OSI), defined in International Standard ISO 7498, and the structure of the comprehensive family of International Standards that have been established for distributed information systems.

12.2 OSI environment

The OSI architecture and family of standards, which specify the services and protocols for interchange of information between systems, have been defined to provide an operating environment for the implementation of distributed information systems from a multivendor market-place. Interchange of information is in digital form and can convey data, voice, and image communications. The interconnected telecommunication resources can be dedicated transmission paths or switched services on a demand basis. Switched paths interconnecting communicating users can be on a fully-reserved basis or on a demand basis using various switching technologies.

An illustrative distributed information system is shown in Figure 12.1. The many different types of systems shown contain Application Processes (APs) that may need to communicate. APs can be manual, computerised, or physical. For example:

1. A manual process could be a person operating a "point of sale" terminal entering data or receiving an output.
2. A computerised process could be an operational program in a "host" computer performing its task, such as an accounting program processing a payroll.
3. A physical process could be the operation of a "robot" in a manufacturing plant.

Communications are often required in order for APs to perform their designated tasks. The data that an AP requires may need to be retrieved from a remotely located data base. The operations that an AP requires may not be supported by its local processing resources, and therefore, it must share additional resources in a remotely located system to accomplish its task. Finally, upon completion of its operations, the AP may need to deliver the resulting data to a remotely-located data base for further processing or analysis.

The interconnecting network shown in Figure 12.1 provides the telecommunication paths for information interchange between the systems. The OSI architecture defines an orderly structure of functionality to facilitate successful communications between APs. There are two basic components to ensure successful communica-

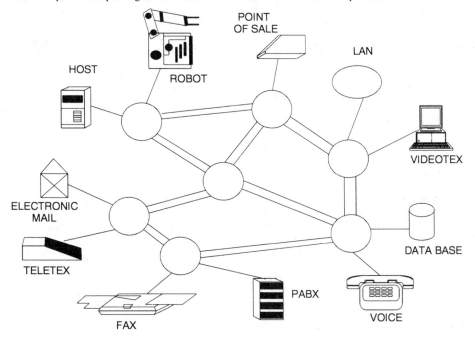

Figure 12.1 Distributed information systems

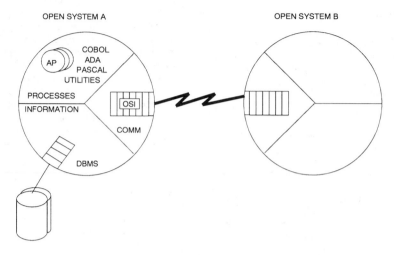

Figure 12.2 Functional components of a computer based system

tions. The first is the transparent movement of the data between systems. The second is ensuring that the data arriving for the destination AP is in a meaningful form that can be immediately recognised and processed.

OSI standards only define those functions that are necessary to facilitate communications between systems. They do not describe the specific implementation, design, or technology that is used. These are left to the innovation of the system developer.

The functional components of a computer based system are shown in Figure 12.2. The processing part, information and memory part, and internal communications (comm) part are not constrained by the standards. The OSI elements are additional functions in the communications part that are only invoked when communications with other systems are required. Systems that implement the OSI functions are therefore called Open Systems and can participate in information interchange using the OSI environment.

12.3 Layered architecture

12.3.1 Basic Principles

There are many ways to describe and characterise systems for information technology applications. Many arbitrary alternatives could be just as effective, but it is imperative to have as much inherent flexibility as possible in the structure and to have a solution that is globally agreeable. Only then can an architecture be established as a generic basis that will continue to evolve to accommodate advancing technology and expanding operational requirements.

The concept of layering has been widely accepted. Only a minimum number of layers has been defined, thereby keeping the structure basically simple, whilst no individual layer should be so functionally complex that it is unwieldly. The modular structure of layering provides a great deal of flexibility by enabling implementations to change over time with new technology, by allowing tailoring of the invoked functions to optimise a specific operating configuration, and by satisfying the broadest range of applications.

A layered architecture, as shown in Figure 12.3, can be referred to as an "onion skin structure" to describe a communications environment. The users on either side represent the corresponding APs that

are interchanging information. In the communication process, the functions of each of the layers (layer 7 through 1) are invoked in the originating system and conveyed to the destination system where they are executed from layer 1 through 7 in the destination system. Very simply, in a point-to-point configuration, each layer is traversed twice, firstly for initiation and secondly for execution of the appropriate functions to ensure a successful communication. As interconnecting configurations become more complex with diverse paths through switched telecommunication resources, some of the layers may be traversed multiple times in performing relaying functions to support the information flow between systems.

An overlay of the layered architecture to real systems is shown in Figure 12.4. Each open system has its local system environment (LSE), which includes the basic processing, information, and communication components shown earlier in Figure 12.2. Part of the OSI environment (OSIE) is also shown in each system. The AP

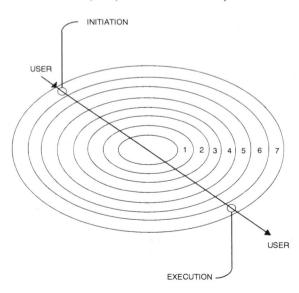

Figure 12.3 Onion skin structure

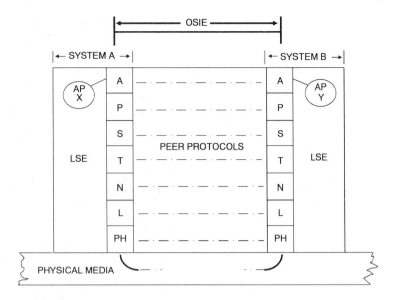

Figure 12.4 OSI environment

resides in the LSE of a system and binds to the OSIE for communicating with another AP in a remotely-located system. Each system has a component of each of the layers that are referred to as layer entities. An instance of a layer entity represents the set of functions of the specific layer that are active in a system to support the instance of communication. The functions are invoked in the layer entities in the originating system and executed by the respective layer entity in the destination system. Specifically, the functions invoked by the entity in layer 7 of system A are executed by the entity in layer 7 of system B. These functions are logically conveyed between systems using peer protocols, which are defined for each of the layers to perform particular tasks. Each of the descending layers in the originating system adds its functions to the layer above as the communication proceeds layer-by-layer. The physical media,

which are not part of the OSIE, provide the interconnecting transmission paths between the systems. At the destination system, each layer in turn executes its functions and passes the action to the next layer above, in ascending order.

12.3.2 Layer Concept

The concept of a layer is illustrated in Figure 12.5. OSI characterises an (N)-layer as a subdivision of the OSI architecture that interacts with elements in the next layer above, the (N+1)-layer, and the next layer below, the (N-1)-layer. The (N)-entity is an active element within the (N)-layer in a real system, and peer-entities are (N)-entities within the same layer, but in different systems.

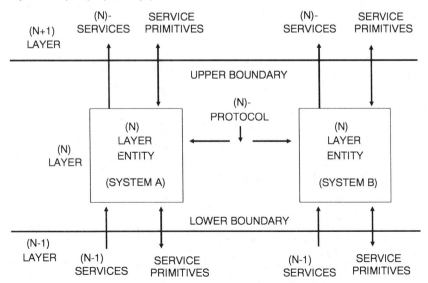

Figure 12.5 Concept of a layer

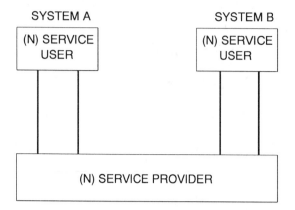

Figure 12.6 Layer service model

The (N)-service relates the collective capability of the (N)-layer and underlying layers provided to support the (N+1)-entity. Associated with each (N)-service are primitive interactions that pass various parameters. The primitives will be described later in this chapter. The semantics of the services and primitive interactions are defined in the family of OSI standards to facilitate an understanding of the dynamics of the OSIE but are not critical to OSI conformance and interoperability between systems.

Peer-entities communicate with each other using an (N)-protocol, which is a set of rules and procedures to facilitate an orderly communication in the performance of the associated functions. The peer protocols are the critical specifications of the OSI family of standards that facilitate interoperability between systems and are the basis for determining OSI conformance.

In the case of the uppermost layer, there is no (N+1)-layer, but this is the point at which the AP binds to the OSIE during an instance of a communication. There is also no (N-1)-layer associated with the lowest layer because that is the point of interface between the OSIE and interconnecting physical transmission media.

12.3.3 Layer services

Whilst each layer performs its functions independently of other layers, interaction between layers is essential to ensure full co-operation in support of the communication. The services are provided to the (N+1)-layer (see Figure 12.5), which is characterised as the (N)-service-user in each system by the companion technical report, ISO TR 8509. This concept is illustrated in Figure 12.6, which applies to any of the layer boundaries. The (N+1)-entity in each system is the service user of the functions of the (N)-layer and any lower layers, which are characterised collectively in Figure 12.6 as the (N)-service-provider. Therefore, each of the layer services can be defined from specific vantage points using this model.

Four interaction primitives are defined to further characterise the semantics of the dynamics of operation within a system as follows:

1. REQUEST is provided by the originating service user to activate a particular service by the service provider.
2. INDICATION is provided by the service provider to the destination service user to advise that a particular service is activated.
3. RESPONSE is provided by service user back to the service provider in response to an incoming indication primitive.

4. CONFIRM is returned by the service provider to the originating service user to acknowledge completion of a requested service.

The primitives carry important parameter information between the layers. The nature of the parameters may vary for different services, but they can include address information, data to be transferred, and invocation of service options. The specifics of the services and associated primitives for each layer are covered by the specific layer service definitions, which are part of the OSI family of standards.

12.3.4 Communication between peer entities

Two modes of communication are defined in the OSI Reference Model: connection-mode and connectionless-mode. Connection-mode operation was the original basis for OSI. Later, the connectionless-mode was defined in ISO 7498 AD1.

The connection-mode functions through three phases of operation in support of an instance of communication. These are establishment, data transfer, and release. The initial definition of the OSI Reference Model included only the connection-mode for all the layers.

An (N)-connection represents an association that has been established between (N+1)-entities and establishes the path for information flow that is maintained for the duration of the instance of communication, as shown in Figure 12.7. It is a result of the (N)-layer and the underlying layers collectively. Each layer operating in the connection-mode follows the procedure to establish the association, or connection, with its peer entity. Upon termination of the communication, the connection of each layer is released.

The establishment of a connection allows negotiation of parameter values and options between corresponding entities. It has a distinguishable lifetime that can support interchange of multiple data units over a period of time.

In contrast, the connectionless-mode does not establish and maintain a relationship between corresponding entities. Each transfer of data in the connectionless-mode is a separate independent action for that layer. It has often been called the "message mode" or "datagram mode" where each data unit is routed to the destination on an individual basis with no regard to data units transferred before or after it.

The connectionless-mode simplifies operations where the overhead of error control and recovery is not needed. It also eliminates the overhead of establishment and release of connections for a faster

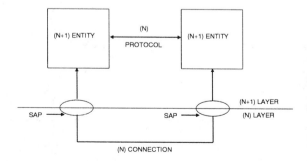

Figure 12.7 (N) connection

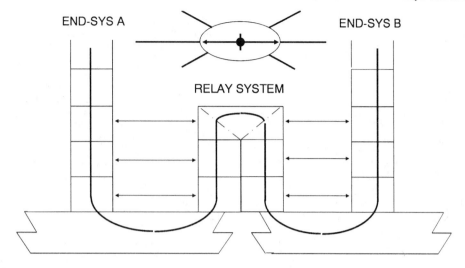

Figure 12.8 Relay function

reaction communication. Typically, the connectionless-mode has been applied to routing data to destination systems through telecommunication resources. In this case, some layers are operated in the connectionless-mode, whilst others are operated in the connection-mode. A discussion regarding the use at different layers is included later in this chapter.

In the future, the upper layers directly supporting applications may also use the connectionless-mode for certain operations, such as broadcast to multiple APs.

12.3.5 Relaying

A layer entity can also provide a relaying function to facilitate the routing of data along the path to the destination system. An (N)-relay-entity does not provide any service to an (N+1)-entity but only uses the services from a receiving (N-1)-entity. It processes the incoming data unit and forwards it to the (N-1)-entity associated with the next path for the data to flow through. This concept is illustrated in Figure 12.8. The relay system is identified between the two end systems, which are the source and destination systems for the instance of communication.

A relay system may have a number of possible paths to select from for routing data to the addressed destination, as illustrated by the lines radiating from the elipse in Figure 12.8. Relay systems apply to both packet and circuit switching and can function in either the connection-mode or connectionless-mode depending upon the specific operational configuration. The circles in Figure 12.1 along the paths interconnecting the end systems are examples of intermediate relay systems that participate in OSIE to support the communications.

12.3.6 Identifiers

The principles of naming and addressing have been included in the OSI structure to facilitate the mapping of the information flow through the layers within a system and to find the path between systems for transmission of the data to the destination system. The conceptual port between an (N)-layer and an (N+1)-layer is called a Service Access Point (SAP), which is shown in Figure 12.7. The location of the SAP is identified by an (N)-address, which may be globally unique or may only be specific to a particular instance of communication, depending on the layer involved.

A single SAP can support multiple instances of connections, which are identified by (N)-connection-endpoint-identifiers. A layer boundary may support more than one SAP between the same or different entities of the (N)-layer and (N+1)-layer.

The provision of (N)-titles is used to uniquely identify individual (N)-entities to facilitate the routing and relaying functions. An (N)-directory is the function that is used to translate a global title into an (N-1)-address to which the (N)-entity is attached. The complex and abstract subject of Naming and Addressing is dealt with in detail in Part 3 to ISO 7498, and the provisions for global Network SAP addressing is defined in the OSI Network Layer Service Definition ISO 8348 AD2. The addressing structure of the upper layers is defined in the Application Layer Structure of ISO 9545.

12.3.7 Data units

As discussed earlier in this chapter, a communication activity from an AP in a system progresses from layer to layer as the required functions are initiated to support the communication. In turn, at the destination system, the incoming communication ascends through the layers as the functions are executed to provide a successful communication to the destination AP.

This transfer of information between the systems involves the construction and forwarding of control information and data units that convey the actions and substance of the communication. Figure 12.9 presents the basic data unit structure that passes layer-by-layer within a system. A service data unit (SDU) is the data that is passed to the (N)-layer from the (N+1)-layer for forwarding to the peer (N+1)-entity in the destination system. Therefore, the (N)-layer is responsible for transferring the SDU transparently, so that it is delivered to the destination (N+1)-entity exactly as it was received by the (N)-entity in the source system.

The SDU is received by the (N)-entity as a parameter of a request primitive issued by the (N+1)-entity. The (N)-entity then produces the protocol control information (PCI), which initiates the required functions and provides the appropriate parameter information for execution by the peer (N)-entity in the destination system.

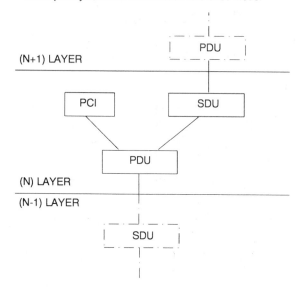

Figure 12.9 Data units

The combination of the SDU and PCI becomes the protocol data unit (PDU) for transfer to the peer (N)-entity via the (N-1)-connection or connectionless path, depending upon the mode of operation. the (N)-PDU becomes the (N-1)-SDU, which is them processed in a similar manner with the addition of a (N-1)-PCI to produce the (N-1)-PDU for the next layer below. Recursively, this process occurs in each descending layer until the data leaves the OSIE in transmission on the physical media.

At the destination system, the PDU enters a layer as a parameter of an indication primitive. The layer entity processes the PCI part, executes the functions, and discards the PCI, leaving the SDU to pass to the next ascending layer via an indication primitive. Again, each layer in turn recursively processes the data units until the final data is delivered to the destination AP in a form that is meaningful for processing in the local environment of the destination system.

The layer protocols in the family of OSI standards support the many functions in the different layers. The protocols define the peer entity interactions, along with the syntax and information content of the PCIs that convey the actions between communicating systems. These protocol standards are the specifications that provide the compatibility and interoperability between systems in the world-wide multivendor market-place of products for information technology applications.

12.4 Additional layer elements

The OSI Reference Model defines many additional layer elements that further characterise the OSIE. The various elements defined can apply at some or all layers, depending on the specific service requirements for the particular layer.

12.4.1 Multiplexing and splitting

The layer entities have been shown as mapping on a one-to-one basis from layer to layer. However, additional flexibility is provided through the mapping of multiple entities to provide for more effective use of resources as needed.

Multiplexing involves the mapping of multiple (N)- connections to a single (N-1)-connection. This configuration enables bandwidth sharing of the connection to support multiple communications. The demultiplexing is done in the respective peer entity in the destination system.

Splitting involves the mapping of a single (N)- connection to multiple (N-1)-connections. This configuration enables expansion of the bandwidth to support a communication that requires a higher throughput of data than can be supported by the bandwidth of a single (N-1)-connection. Splitting can also apply to high survivability situations where the loss of a sole (N-1)-connection would be seriously disruptive to an operation, whereas the loss of one of many connections in a split configuration would only reduce the bandwidth.

12.4.2 Data transfer

There are two basic types of data transfer: normal and expedited. The unit of transfer by a layer is its protocol data unit (PDU). Every layer has the function for transfer of data in support of the instance of communication.

12.4.2.1 *Connection-mode*

In the connection-mode, normal data transfer is accomplished by a layer through an (N-1)-connection that has been established with the destination (N)-entity. Some of the layers will also employ the following additional functions:

1. Flow control regulates the rate of data transfer, so that PDUs do not arrive at the destination (N)-entity faster than they can be processed. Peer-to-peer protocol flow control mechanisms are generally employed to co-ordinate the rate of transfer between the peer (N)-entities. Flow control may also be applied across the layer interface between an (N+1)-entity and an (N)-entity.
2. Segmenting enables a single (N)-SDU to be broken up into smaller units for processing into multiple (N)-PDUs. At the destination (N)-entity, the SDU segments are reassembled into a single (N)-SDU before passing to the (N+1)-layer. An (N)-protocol mechanism is employed to keep track of the segments during transfer so they can be recombined at the destination.
3. Blocking enables multiple (N)-SDUs to be mapped into a single (N)-PDU. Although this function is specified in the OSI Reference Model, it has not been employed in any of the OSI protocols or configurations.
4. Concatenation enables multiple (N)-PDUs to be mapped to a single (N)-SDU in the (N-1)-layer.
5. Sequencing returns data units to the same order at the destination (N)-entity that they were sent in from the originating (N)-entity. This situation could particularly occur in connectionless-mode data transfer where each data unit could take a different route to the destination system. The (N)-protocol PCI contains a sequence number that is used for the resequencing function.
6. Acknowledgement provides confirmation for delivery or receipt of PDUs by a destination (N)-entity. Generally, the (N)-protocol PCI provides the acknowledgement mechanism and sequence numbers to facilitate this function, which generally provides for recovery of lost data units.
7. Error detection and notification identifies corruption of data during the transfer process between (N)-entities. Recovery from such errors can be accomplished by the same mechanism

used for lost data units found by the acknowledgement function.

8. Reset provides for reinitialisation of an (N)-connection without the loss of associations and connections of the upper layers.

9. Routing provides for relaying PDUs across multiple (N)-entities for establishing a connection and transferring data, or for connectionless-mode data transfer.

The connection-mode data transfer also provides for expedited data, which is not intended to be used on a regular basis. Generally, expedited data is limited in amount of data transferred and its frequency of transfer. It is not subject to the same flow-control constraints, if any, as normal data transfer. The basic rule is that an expedited data unit should not arrive at the destination any later than a normal data unit sent after the expedited data unit. In other words, it should not be any slower than normal data but may be faster. Expedited data service is invoked as required by the upper layers. Expedited data may also be acknowledged by the destination (N)-entity.

12.4.2.2   *Connectionless-mode*

Data transfer in the connectionless-mode involves minimal functionality. Data units are sent, routed, and delivered with no knowledge being maintained by the (N)-layer of their status along the way. Some have referred to this mode as "send and pray" because there is no assurance that delivery has been successful. On the other hand, the shortcomings of this simple approach can be compensated for by use of appropriate functions at higher layers, which are operating in the connection-mode.

12.5   Specific OSI layers

As explained earlier in this chapter, the number and functional configuration of the specific layers for the OSIE is somewhat arbitrary. A number of arrangements to satisfy the requirements are possible. However, the agreement has been made internationally for the OSI configuration, which provides a solid generic basis to characterise distributed information systems whilst establishing a structure for accommodating advances in technology and expanding operational requirements through continuing evolution.

The required functions to support successful communications between APs are distributed among seven architectural layers. The layers, as shown in Figure 12.10, are defined below.

In summary, the upper three layers provide the functions for a meaningful communication so that information reaching the destination AP is processible and compatible with the local systems environment, The lower four layers provide the connectivity for interchange of data between systems and collectively represent the "bit pipe" for transparent data transfer.

12.5.1   Application layer

The structure of the application layer has changed from that defined in the OSI Reference Model of ISO 7498. The current concept defines the application layer entity as consisting of two types of service elements. The Association Control Service Element (ACSE) of ISO 8649 and ISO 8650 establishes the association between communicating APs and sets the context of the communication. The context refers to the other operational elements that are needed to support the specific nature of the communication. These are defined

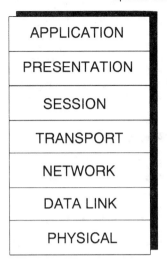

Figure 12.10   Layers of the OSI model

as the Application Service Elements (ASEs), which may be used individually or in multiples to satisfy specific operational contexts. Example ASEs include: File Transfer, Access, and Management (ISO 8571); Virtual Terminal (ISO 9040 and ISO 9041); Transaction Processing (ISO 10025); Commitment, Concurrency, and Recovery (ISO 9804 and ISO 9805); Remote Operations (ISO 9072); Reliable Transfer (ISO 9066); Remote Database Access (ISO 9579); and others. There is a richness of functionality to select from in the application layer.

12.5.2   Presentation layer

The application layer is defined in terms of its semantics and described in terms of an abstract syntax of the data types involved. The Abstract Syntax Notation No. 1 (ASN.1) of ISO 8824 has been widely accepted for use in OSI specifications. When data are transferred through the OSIE, an encoding agreed upon by the peer presentation entities is needed. The common presentation layer service and protocol of ISO 8822 and ISO 8823 are used to establish the transfer syntax that will be used to support the communication. The Basic Encoding Rules of ISO 8825 are now widely used in OSI applications, but other transfer syntaxes can also be selected.

12.5.3   Session layer

The session layer facilitates orderliness in a communication. A session connection is established, and the specific functions that are to be used are selected. Among the choices in typical use are: use of either two-way simultaneous or two-way alternate data transfer, expedited data transfer, synchronisation and recovery of data, activity management, and exception reporting. The session service and protocol are specified in ISO 8326 and ISO 8327, respectively. The connectionless-mode in the upper three layers is under development.

12.5.4   Transport Layer

The transport layer provides for the transparent transfer of data between peer session layer entities and ensures that the appropriate quality of service, which was requested by the originating session entity, is maintained. In this regard, the transport layer is required to select the network layer service that most closely matches the requested requirement. In addition, it may also have to invoke additional functionality to ensure the proper quality of service. Five classes of connection-mode protocol have been defined in ISO 8073 to accommodate the variety of operational conditions. The transport service is defined in ISO 8072. There is also a connectionless- mode transport protocol specified in ISO 8602.

12.5.5 Network layer

The network layer provides the functions for the telecommunication resources that provide the paths for transfer of data between systems. Real telecommunication services, such as may be provided by a public data network, are defined by OSI as subnetworks. Paths between systems may involve switched services and interconnection of multiple subnetworks en route. Both connection-mode and connectionless-mode operations have been widely applied in the network layer. The Network Service Definition is provided in ISO 8348 and a number of standards are available for the various protocols and configurations that can be employed.

12.5.6 Data link layer

The data link layer provides the means for synchronising the bit stream flowing to and from the physical layer and for detection of errors due to transmission problems. Typically, Local Area Networks (LANs) operate the data link in connectionless-mode, whilst wide area network applications operate in the connection-mode. In the connection-mode, the additional functions of flow control and error recovery are included. The Data Link Layer Service Definition is specified in ISO 8886.

12.5.7 Physical layer

The physical layer provides the functions for transparent transmission of the bit stream between data link entities. When the physical layer is active, the bits flow through to the transmission medium. The electrical characteristics and physical connector serve as the interface between the OSIE and the external transmission media. The Physical Layer Service Definition is specified in ISO 10022. A number of physical interfaces are available for a variety of transmission environments.

12.6 Additional provisions

Three additional parts of the OSI Reference Model have been published that cover some other very important aspects of distributed information systems. These are summarised as follows:

1. ISO 7498-2: Security Architecture provides the framework for development of various security provisions to protect system integrity and unauthorised access to user data.
2. ISO 7498-3: Naming and Addressing provides the concepts and principles for identifying objects through naming and location of objects through addressing mechanisms.
3. ISO 7498-4: Management Framework provides the concepts and principles for management of the resources of the OSIE to ensure continuing and effective operation.

12.7 Conclusions

The OSI architecture establishes a generic foundation for implementation and evolution of distributed information systems to support a diversity of operational requirements. Whilst the richness of functionality that is available can lead to significant complexity, not all the capabilities are needed for every application. It is important to select only those functions that are needed for particular operational configurations, and no more. Therefore, the complexity will vary as needed to fulfill specific requirements.

OSI is a living architecture that will facilitate evolution to new technologies and operational requirements, but the basic structure must be preserved to ensure an orderly transition on a common basis. New functions may be added to layers in the future, whilst some of the existing functions will become disused. Even some layers may be inactive in certain applications. Nevertheless, keeping the basic OSI structure intact will ensure a consistent evolution in the future.

12.8 Appendix 12.1

The following references used in this chapter are International Standards published by the International Organization for Standardization, 1 rue Varembe, Geneva, Switzerland. They are also available from national standards bodies such as the British Standards Institution in the UK.

For brevity, the following abbreviations have been used in the titles below:

IPS - Information Processing Systems
OSI - Open Systems Interconnection
IT - Information Technology
TC - Text Communication

ISO 7498, IPS - OSI - Basic Reference Model
ISO 7498 AD1, IPS - OSI - Basic Reference Model - Addendum 1: Connectionless-Mode Transmission
ISO 7498-2, IPS - OSI - Basic Reference Model - Part 2: Security Architecture
ISO 7498-4, IPS - OSI - Basic Reference Model - Part 4: Management Framework
ISO 7498-3, IPS - OSI - Basic Reference Model - Part 3: Naming and Addressing
ISO 8072, IPS - OSI - Transport Service Definition
ISO 8073, IPS - OSI - Connection Oriented Transport Protocol Specification
ISO 8326, IPS - OSI - Basic Connection Oriented Session Service Definition
ISO 8327, IPS - OSI - Basic Connection Oriented Session Protocol Specification
ISO 8348, IPS - DC - Network Service Definition
ISO 8348 AD2, IPS - DC - Network Service Definition, Addendum 2: Network Layer Addressing
ISO TR 8509, IPS - OSI - Service Conventions
ISO 8571, IPS - OSI - File Transfer, Access and Management - (5 parts)
ISO 8602, IPS - OSI - Protocol for Providing the Connectionless-Mode Transport Service
ISO 8649, IPS - OSI - Service Definition for the Association Control Service Element
ISO 8650, IPS - OSI - Protocol Specification for the Association Control Service Element

ISO 8822, IPS - OSI - Connection Oriented Presentation Service Definition

ISO 8823, IPS - OSI - Connection Oriented Presentation Protocol Specification

ISO 8824, IT - OSI - Specification of Abstract Syntax Notation One (ASN.1)

ISO 8825, IT - OSI - Specification of Basic Encoding Rules for Abstract Syntax Notation One (ASN.1)

ISO 8886, IPS - Data Communication - Data Link Service Definition for OSI

ISO 9040, IT - OSI - Virtual Terminal Basic Class Service

ISO 9041, IT - OSI - Virtual Terminal Basic Class Protocol - (2 parts)

ISO 9066, IPS - TC - Reliable Transfer - (2 parts)

ISO 9072, IPS - TC - Remote Operations - (2 parts)

ISO 9545, IT - OSI - Application Layer Structure

ISO 9579, IT - Database Languages - Remote Database Access - (2 parts)

ISO 9804, IT - OSI - Service Definition for the Commitment, Concurrency and Recovery Service Element

ISO 9805, IT - OSI - Protocol Specification for the Commitment, Concurrency and Recovery Service Element

ISO 10022, IT - OSI - Physical Service Definition   .

ISO 10026, IT - OSI - Distributed Transaction Processing - (5 parts)

13

Multiple access techniques

Fraidoon Mazda
MPhil DFH DMS MBIM CEng FIEE
Northern Telecom

Contents

13.1 Introduction

Communication bandwidth is a scarce commodity, whether it be carried on copper wire, fibre optic cable or by the air waves. The need to share this bandwidth fairly and efficiently between multiple users is therefore crucial. Many techniques have been developed to enable multi-users to share, and especially to access, the same communication channel, and these have all been employed in various applications. Each technique has advantages in certain environments, but often different techniques are used for the same or similar application. For example, in digital cordless telephone, CT2 uses FDMA whereas DECT and CT3 are based on the TDMA. Also, in the UK, personal communication networks (PCN) is based on TDMA multiple access techniques, whereas the system proposed by Nynex in the USA is to use CDMA.

This chapter describes and compares the various multiple access techniques and introduces a classification system for the many systems which exist. No reference will be made to any particular application, these being covered in other chapters. Differences between mobile and fixed systems are also narrowing and there are many ways in which mobile communications occur, for example wireless local and wide area networks, PMR, cellular, PCN and satellite.

Network topology sometimes plays a role in the selection of the multiple access technique. Figure 13.1 shows the most commonly used forms. The star network is usually seen in configurations such as lines terminating within a central controller or switch. It is well suited to carry out a polling mechanism from the central location to outlying nodes, for multiple access.

Ring topologies are often preferred since they are not dependent on a single control site, and can generate traffic in either direction around the ring, so providing alternate transmission paths and therefore survivability. The ring architecture is suited to multiple access methods such as token passing and slotted ring, as described later.

The bus structure provides simultaneous access to a central bus by several nodes, and this is the most commonly used structure within local area networks of office buildings, with CSMA/CD (Ethernet) the most popular multiple access mechanism. Tree topologies can be considered to be generalised forms of bus structures and have similar characteristics.

Another consideration in the choice of a multiple access technique is the geographical area covered by the network. Local Area Networks (LAN) spread over a few kilometres, usually an industrial site or university campus, and are owned by a single organisation. They can operate at high data rates.

Wide Area Networks (WAN) cover a much larger geographical area and are usually composed of LANs interconnected by other communication links hired from a PTT or common carrier. Their operating speed is usually restricted by these links.

Metropolitan Area Networks (MANs) fall in-between LANs and WANs in geographical area and characteristics.

Although multiple access techniques can be used irrespective of the transmission technology, their performance is often different. For example radio networks have a relatively low propagation time, of the order of a few milliseconds. They are largely omnidirectional and are usually sent as a broadcast to all receivers, although some may be out of reach or screened from the source. Satellite based radio systems broadcast their information, but can be made to have a relatively small footprint on the earth. They suffer from long delays, of the order of a quarter of a second (up-link and down-link), which would seriously hamper the performance of some multiple access techniques.

13.2 Queuing theory

Queuing theory is covered in Chapter 3 and in Kleinrock (1976). The basic parameters are introduced in this section.

Queuing analysis usually refers to queues by a notation such as A/B/m. This applies for an infinite population of users, which is usually the assumption made when analysing multiple access techniques.

In this notation A represents the interarrival time probability density, i.e. the time between consecutive arrivals into the queue. B is the service time probability density, i.e. the time required to serve an arrival. The letter m represents the number of servers which are present to accommodate the arrivals.

Values of A and B vary from M (representing Markov or exponential probability density); D (representing Deterministic i.e. all arrivals have the same value); and G (representing General or arbitrary probability density).

The most common is the M/M/1 queue, and this is used in the analysis in this chapter. The assumption is also made that no arrivals are lost, i.e. leave or are rejected from the queue because of long waiting times. Arrivals are also assumed to be served on a first come first served basis, unlike, for example, a hospital queue where the most urgent cases are served first.

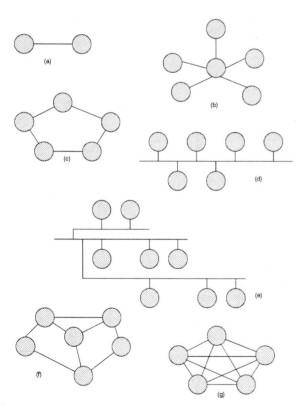

Figure 13.1 Popular network topologies:
(a) point-to-point; (b) star; (c) ring or loop; (d) bus; (e) tree;
(f) mesh; (g) fully interconnected

If λ is the arrival rate in number per unit interval of time and μ is the service rate in number per unit time, then the traffic intensity (ρ is given by Equation 13.1.

$$\rho = \frac{\lambda}{\mu} \tag{13.1}$$

The average number (N) in the queue is given by Equation 13.2.

$$N = \frac{\rho}{1 - \rho} \tag{13.2}$$

As the traffic intensity grows, i.e. the arrival rate approaches the service rate, the value of the traffic intensity factor ρ approaches unity, and the number in the queue rapidly increases towards infinity. The queue is now said to be unstable.

The total waiting time (T_w) in the queue for any arrival is equal to the time before service begins and the actual service time. It is equal to the time between an arrival into the end of the queue and its departure from the queue, with service having been completed. It is given by Equation 13.3 and, for a transmission channel capacity of C bits per unit time, it may be rewritten as in Equation 13.4.

$$T_w = \frac{N}{\lambda} = \frac{1}{\mu - \lambda} \tag{13.3}$$

$$T_w = \frac{1}{\mu C - \lambda} \tag{13.4}$$

13.3 Performance parameters

This section introduces some of the concepts which need to be considered when comparing the performance of different multiple access techniques. These will then be used in the following sections which describe the methods in more detail.

The key performance measures are:

1. The elapsed time between a packet of information being ready for transmission at a transmitting node and when it is successfully received at the receiving node. This is referred to as the delay and is usually denoted by D.
2. The total rate of information flow, the carried load, between the nodes on the network. This is referred to as the throughput, S. As will be seen later, throughput is also a measure of utilisation.
3. The fraction of the total capacity of the transmission medium which is used to carry information between nodes. This is referred to as the utilisation, U.

Several parameters need to be considered when defining the performance of a network. These are:

1. The number of nodes (N) on the network.
2. The average arrival rate (λ) at each node, assumed to have a Poisson distribution and to be the same for all nodes. This is also the rate of data generated by each node.
3. The capacity (C) of the transmission medium usually specified in bit/s, and also referred to as its bandwidth.
4. The velocity of propagation (v) within the medium. For example, for coaxial cable this is about 65% the velocity of light, or 2×10^8 m/s.
5. The average length (L) of the message frame in bits.

6. The offered traffic (G), i.e. the total rate of information presented to a network for transmission. Whereas the average arrival rate is a measure of the data traffic, the offered traffic includes items such as control data (e.g. acknowledgements), packets destroyed due to collision, retransmissions, etc.
7. The length (l) of the communication path.

Generally the throughput (S) and offered traffic (G) are normalised, i.e. expressed as a fraction of the capacity of the transmission medium. For example, if the successful transmission between nodes totals 10Mbit/s, and the capacity of the medium is 100Mbit/s, then the throughput S is stated to be 10/100 or 0.1. Therefore S is also a measure of the utilisation of the medium, as stated earlier. For stability the steady state arrival rate at a network must not exceed the rate at which this data can be transmitted over the network, otherwise the queue would grow without control.

Under ideal conditions the relationship between the throughput (S) and offered traffic (G) is as in Figure 13.2. The traffic throughput increases linearly, as more traffic is presented to the network, until it reaches the maximum capacity of the transmission medium, at which stage the throughput flattens out.

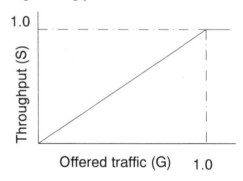

Figure 13.2 Idealised curve of S/G or medium utilisation

The length of the medium in bits is give by Equation 13.5 and it is a measure of the number of bits which are in transit between communicating nodes at any time.

$$l_{bit} = \frac{C \, l}{v} \tag{13.5}$$

A very important dimensionless parameter used in the definition of the performance of multiple access systems is denoted by α as in Equation 13.6.

$$\alpha = \frac{\textit{Length of medium between nodes (in bits)}}{\textit{Length of data frame (in bits)}} \tag{13.6}$$

Using Equation 13.5 gives the value of α as in Equation 13.7.

$$\alpha = \frac{\dfrac{C \, l}{v}}{L} = \dfrac{\dfrac{l}{v}}{\dfrac{L}{C}}$$

$$= \frac{\textit{Propagation time in the medium}}{\textit{Transmission time of the message}} \tag{13.7}$$

For satellite systems α is usually large, of the order of 10–100, due to the round trip delays, whilst for terrestrial systems it is normally relatively small, usually less than 1.

The utilisation factor (U) is therefore given by Equation 13.8, and the theoretical curve of Figure 13.2 can be modified to take factor α into account, as in Figure 13.3.

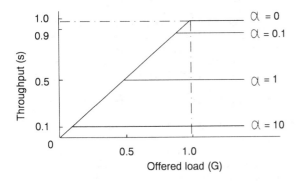

Figure 13.3   Effect of α on the idealised curve of Figure 13.2

$$U = \frac{\text{Total information flow or throughput } (S)}{\text{Total capacity of the medium } (C)}$$

$$= \frac{1}{1 + \alpha} \tag{13.8}$$

13.4   Classification of multiple access techniques

Figure 13.4 provides a classification for the many different multiple access techniques which have been developed and gives a few examples, described later in this chapter. In pure contention systems a source transmits its data independently of other users, i.e. does not take any action to avoid collision with data being transmitted by other users. If collisions occur these are sensed and the data is retransmitted.

In contention minimisation systems the source takes some action to minimise the occurrence of collisions but does not avoid these altogether, whilst in non-contention systems each source takes due regard of all other sources transmitting on the common line, so that data collisions are avoided. These three major classifications can be subdivided further, as described in the following sections.

13.5   Pure contention systems

The pure contention multiple access techniques are the simplest to implement since a source having data to transmit does so without regard for any other user of the common transmission medium. Very little sensing or synchronisation mechanism is required, the prime requirement is for an acknowledgement system which can detect when the data has not been correctly received, usually due to a collision with information transmitted by another source, so that it can be retransmitted.

In contention protocols any overhead involved in assigning channel access is independent of the number of users, but depends instead on the channel traffic. This system is most efficient when there are a large number of users, each sending small amounts of 'bursty' traffic.

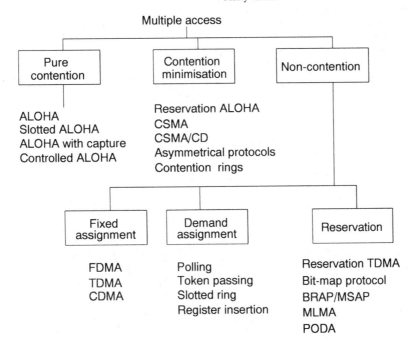

Figure 13.4   Classification of multiple access techniques

13.5.1 Pure ALOHA

The pure ALOHA multiple access system (usually referred to simply as ALOHA) was developed by the University of Hawaii for use with satellite based transmission systems. Its operation can be explained by the simplified flow diagram of Figure 13.5. Whenever

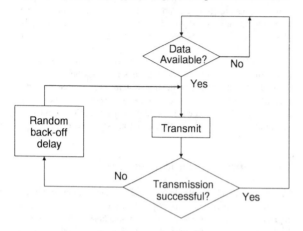

Figure 13.5 Flow diagram of a pure ALOHA access system

a data source has information to send, usually a packet of data, it does so without regard for any other data source which may also be using the transmission medium. It then waits the appropriate amount of time for an acknowledgement. If this is not obtained the source assumes that a collision has occurred. It then waits for a random amount of time before retransmitting the same information.

A random wait or back-off time is required to ensure that two sources, which have just collided, do not again collide when they retransmit their data. Many algorithms are in use for calculating this random time. Also the acknowledgement process varies depending on the transmission system being used. For broadcast systems, such as satellites, the sender listens for its message to be broadcast from the satellite, and if it does not occur within a given time (allowing

for up-link, down-link and processing delays) then it assumes a collision has occurred.

Figure 13.6 illustrates the process of packet collision within ALOHA. If any part of two packets overlap (e.g. the first bit of one and the last bit of another) then they are both destroyed. This means that there is a vulnerable period equal to the the sum of the two packet lengths (or twice a packet length, if all packets have the same length) when collision can occur.

In Figure 13.6 packets from users B and D are seen to overlap and collide. After this has occurred it is assumed that there is a finite time t which both senders take to detect that a collision has occurred. They then wait random periods of time (T_1 and T_2) before retransmitting their data, which in this case does not collide with any other data on the line.

The data which is transmitted from the source and eventually reaches its destination is the throughput S. The total traffic on the line, which includes all retransmissions, is the offered traffic G, both usually being normalised to the channel capacity, as stated earlier. Also, as seen from Figure 13.6, collisions and retransmissions add to the delay between the transmission of a packet and it being correctly received at the source.

The performance of an ALOHA system have been analysed by many researchers (e.g. Abramson, 1977; Binder et al., 1975a). It will be assumed that there are a very large number of users (infinite) each sending small amounts of data, in the form of packets, with a Poisson distribution and having a mean of S packets per unit time. For stability $0 < S < 1$. The offered load (G) is also assumed to have a Poisson distribution and $G \geq S$, with $G \rightarrow S$ when the load is low and there are few collisions. It is also assumed that all users are equal, i.e. they have equal probability of transmission.

The performance of an ALOHA channel is given by Equation 13.9 and is plotted in Figure 13.7.

$$S = G e^{-2G} \tag{13.9}$$

From this it is seen that the maximum throughput of an ALOHA channel occurs when $G = 0.5$ and is equal to 0.184, i.e. the channel utilisation is limited to 18.4%. This is the maximum possible utilisation since, as seen later, the delay in packet transmission reaches unacceptable values as this theoretical utilisation figure is approached.

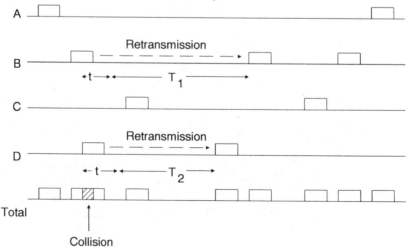

Figure 13.6 Illustration of packet collision and retransmission in ALOHA

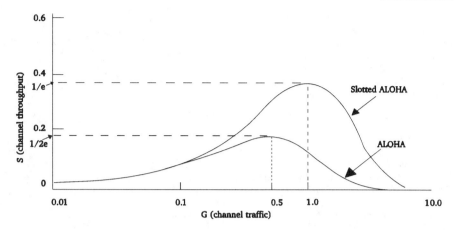

Figure 13.7 Throughput in pure ALOHA and slotted ALOHA channels

If the offered load exceeds 0.5 the number of collisions increases at a rapid rate, so that although the offered load is increasing this is made up of retransmitted traffic and the useful traffic, or throughput, actually decreases, until it eventually falls to zero.

Although ALOHA has low utilisation it is frequently used for systems which have many users who are transmitting low volume bursty traffic.

If the average length of a message is equal to T_m seconds, the average propagation delay in the medium is T_p seconds, and the average number of retransmissions required before a message is successfully transmitted is n_r, then these are given by Equations 13.10 to 13.12.

$$T_m = \frac{Message\ length\ in\ bits}{Channel\ capacity\ in\ bits\ per\ second} = \frac{L}{C} \quad (13.10)$$

$$T_p = \frac{Length\ of\ medium\ (m)}{Velocity\ in\ medium\ (m/s)} = \frac{l}{v} \quad (13.11)$$

$$n_r = \frac{G}{S} \quad (13.12)$$

The random back-off delay is usually an integral number of packets, if fixed length packets are being used. If this varies between 1 and x packets, then the average back-off delay (T_b) is given by Equation 13.13, and the overall delay or waiting time (T_w) in the communication channel is given by Equation 13.14.

$$T_b = \frac{1 + x}{2} \quad (13.13)$$

$$T_w = (T_m + T_p) + (T_m + T_p + T_b) n_r \quad (13.14)$$

In Equation 13.14 the first bracketed term is the delay experienced due to the initial transmission and would be the overall delay if no collisions were to occur. The second bracketed term accounts for the delays due to collisions. Delay is also often normalised to the packet length in seconds (which is also the message transmission time), and is denoted by D, as in Equation 13.15.

$$Delay\ D = \frac{T_w}{T_m} \quad (13.15)$$

Figure 13.8 shows the plot of delay for a systems operating over channels with significant and variable delay. This also indicates the very large delays which are experienced as the theoretical maximum throughput of the ALOHA channel is approached.

In order to increase throughput the retransmission should be randomised over longer intervals, to reduce the probability of collisions on retransmission. This means that the value of x, in Equation 13.13, should be large. However, as seen from Equations 13.14, this would also result in increased delay, so that design of multiple access system often require a trade off between throughput and delay.

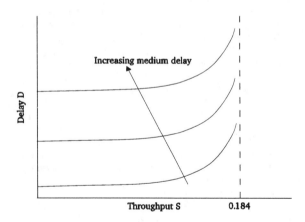

Figure 13.8 Delay-throughput characteristic of an ALOHA channel

13.5.2 Slotted ALOHA

In the pure ALOHA system collisions will occur whenever any part of one packet overlaps any part of another packet. The vulnerable period is therefore equal to the sum of their two packet lengths, or to two packet lengths if all packets are the same size. An alternative version of ALOHA was developed (Roberts, 1972; Kleinrock and Lam, 1973) which uses fixed length packets and synchronises all transmissions to the start time of the packet. The flow diagram for this system is as in Figure 13.5 except that transmissions can only occur at the start of a packet period.

The disadvantage of slotted ALOHA is the added complexity of requiring a method for synchronising all sources to the start of a packet frame, and the use of fixed length packets. The advantage is that the vulnerable period is now halved, i.e. is equal to the length of one packet. Assuming that all packets are full during transmission, then the throughput is given by Equation 13.16.

$$S = G e^{-G} \qquad (13.16)$$

Figure 13.7 shows the plot of the throughput curve for a slotted ALOHA channel. It has twice the theoretical maximum throughput (0.368) compared to the pure ALOHA channel and this occurs at a value of G equal to one. This however assumes that all the packets are full, since if they are only half full then the actual throughput is the same as for pure ALOHA.

So far the discussions have assumed an infinite number of users. If they are finite, and equal to N, then the throughput for the ith user (S_i) is given by Equation 13.17.

$$S_i = G_i \prod_{j \neq i} (1 - G_j) \qquad (13.17)$$

For N identical users, this reduces to Equation 13.18.

$$S = G \left(1 - \frac{G}{N} \right)^{N-1} \qquad (13.18)$$

As N tends towards a very large number, S approaches the value given in Equation 13.16.

In a slotted ALOHA channel each time a user has information to transmit it must wait for the start of a slot before doing so. This applies also to retransmitted data. There is therefore, on average, an extra half packet time delay compared to pure ALOHA. At the theoretical peak transmission point (G = 1 and S = 0.368) there are an average of 2.7 (= G/S) transmissions for every successful transmission, resulting in an extra delay t_d given by Equation 13.18.

$$t_d = 2.7 \times \frac{Packet\ length}{2} \qquad (13.18)$$

Figure 13.9 compares the delay curves between a typical pure ALOHA and slotted ALOHA system, where it is seen that for low throughput (few users and low traffic) pure ALOHA has a lower delay.

13.5.3 ALOHA with capture

ALOHA with capture is a modification to the basic slotted ALOHA system (Roberts, 1975) which works on the principle that if two signals have different strengths, then on collision the stronger one will be 'captured' by the receiver and will get through, so that only the weaker signal needs to be retransmitted. This, in effect, reduces the retransmissions by half, and gives almost a 50% increase in throughput over slotted ALOHA, as seen by Equation 13.19. It is assumed that if three stations collide none of them get through, i.e. no one station is strong enough to dominate any two others.

$$S = G e^{-G} \left(1 + \frac{G}{n} \right) \qquad (13.19)$$

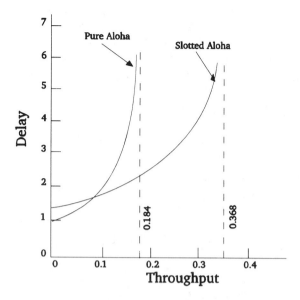

Figure 13.9 Delay-throughput characteristics for pure ALOHA and slotted ALOHA

In this equation n equals 2 if, for the colliding packets, one or the other gets through; n equals 3 if one gets through a third of the time, the other gets a third of the time, and neither gets through at the other times. For n equal to 2 the value of S is about 50% greater than that attained with a slotted ALOHA system, as stated earlier.

Figure 13.10 compares the performance of ALOHA with capture with pure ALOHA and slotted ALOHA.

Many techniques exist for allocating signal strength to users. For example this could depend on the priority of the user, or could be allocated on a random or pseudo-random basis.

13.5.4 Controlled ALOHA

An ALOHA channel can rapidly move into congestion if the traffic approaches the theoretical maximum, due to collisions and retransmissions. Several methods have been devised (Lam and Kleinrock, 1975) for controlling the traffic so as to reduce congestion. The prime methods are to reduce the probability of retransmission of collided packets in a time slot, so reducing G, and to deny certain users the right to transmit over a period of time, which in effect reduces the number of users.

13.6 Contention minimisation systems

In pure contention systems a user takes no account of other users, and therefore transmits when it has any data available. There are however several multiple access protocols which, although basically of the contention type, attempt to minimise the amount of contention between users. Some of these contention minimisation systems are described in this section.

13.6.1 Reservation ALOHA

This multiple access method is very similar to the ALOHA (pure and slotted) systems described in the previous section, but uses

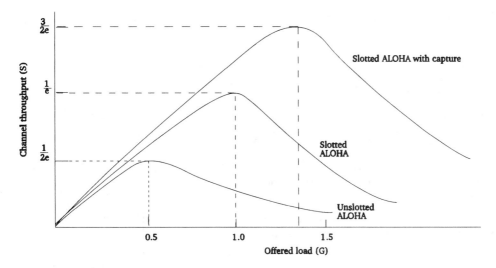

Figure 13.10 Comparison of throughput for pure ALOHA, slotted ALOHA, and ALOHA with capture

some form of reservation of capacity as a means of minimising contention. There are several variants of these as described below, and they can be grouped as those needing implicit reservations and those with explicit reservations.

13.6.1.1 *Implicit reservations*

In one such system (Binder, 1975b) the transmission slots are grouped into frames, the number of slots exceeding the number of users. Each user is nominated as being the owner of a slot position within the frame. (Frame 0 in Figure 13.11.)

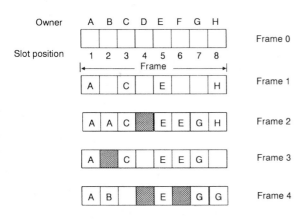

Figure 13.11 Illustration of an implicit reservation ALOHA system

Each user has priority for transmission on his slot. If there are more slots than users then all users contend for the spare slots, using ALOHA or slotted ALOHA. Whilst an owner is transmitting on his allocated slot no other user can interfere. However, if a slot falls idle for a frame, then in the next frame other users can contend for its use. Once a slot has been so seized only the owner is allowed to interfere with the new user. The owner gets his slot back by trans-

mitting on it. A contention occurs and in the next frame only the owner is allowed to transmit.

In Figure 13.11 in Frame 1 owners A, C, E and H transmit on their allocated slots, the other being free. In the following frame (Frame 2) user A and E successfully seize another slot each, whilst G commences transmission. In addition a collision occurs in slot 4, either due to the owner and another station or two other stations simultaneously transmitting.

In Frame 3 slot 4 is vacant, which means that the owner was not involved in the collision in Frame 2, so each station had to wait to make sure. Also a collision has occurred in slot 2, which is due to the owner wanting his slot back.

In Frame 4 the owner B commences transmission in his slot. The two users who collided in slot 4 during Frame 2 operate an appropriate back-off algorithm and will try again. In the meantime other users have decided to contend for slot 4 (one of these may be the owner of the slot) so again contention occurs. In addition the owner of slot 6 has forced a contention to regain his slot.

From this illustration it is seen that the reservation protocol gives high efficiency when users have stream type traffic, with owners transmitting on their slots. However, for bursty traffic, there will be many collisions, and since all users (apart from the owner) need to wait for a frame following a collision, slots can go empty (such as slot 4 in Figure 13.11).

Slots must also remain vacant for one frame following the end of transmission from its owner, although this can be overcome by having a header on each frame which announces that the owner of particular slots will cease transmission in the following frame, allowing contention for these frames.

Another disadvantage of this protocol is that the number of users must be known in advance to allow slots to be allocated to them.

An alternative implicit reservation system (Crowther et al., 1973) does not have permanent owners allocated to slots, and it may therefore be used even when the number of users is not known. Users seize slots using normal ALOHA contention, but once a slot is seized the user becomes its owner and can continue sending data so long as it has any left. (Rules to prevent a user 'hogging' a slot are often applied.) If the slot falls idle for a frame contention can start on it, all users again being treated as equals. Clearly this system can be used even when the number of slots is less than the total number of users.

13.6.1.2 Explicit reservations

In one such technique (Roberts, 1973) one or more slots within a frame is divided into smaller slots, called reservation slots. Users content for these slots, using a technique such as ALOHA, and if successful they place a reservation for a slot over a given number of frames. They can then transmit over these slots without risk of contention from other users. It is therefore required that each user keeps a record of the queue associated with each slot so that they know when to transmit their data. This mode of operation is called the reservation mode.

When there are no remaining reserved slots in the queue (i.e. no stations waiting to transmit data) the whole frame is divided into smaller reservation slots, and it is now in the ALOHA mode. Figure 13.12 illustrates the reservation and ALOHA modes.

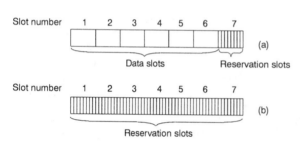

Figure 13.12 Illustration of an explicit reservation ALOHA system: (a) reservation mode; (b) ALOHA mode

13.6.1.3 Analysis of reservation ALOHA

The throughput (S_R) of a reservation ALOHA system is affected by whether an end of use flag is included or not in the header of the last packet sent. Such a flag allows users to contend for the slot at the next frame rather than having to wait a frame to discover whether it is empty. Equation 13.20 gives the throughput when no flag is included and 13.21 when it is included. Both equations compare the throughput of the reservation ALOHA with the throughput (S_S) of a slotted ALOHA system.

$$S_R = \frac{S_S}{\frac{1}{k} + S_S} \quad For\ no\ flag \tag{13.20}$$

$$S_R = \frac{S_S}{\frac{1}{k} + S_S - \frac{S_S}{k}} \quad For\ flag \tag{13.21}$$

In these equations k is the average number of packets transmitted before the user gives up his reserved slot. It varies between 1 and infinity.

The maximum throughput of a reservation ALOHA (S_{RM}) is given by Equations 13.22 and 13.23, where the value for slotted ALOHA is given by $\frac{1}{e}$.

$$\frac{1}{1 + e} \le S_{RM} \le 1 \quad For\ no\ flag \tag{13.22}$$

$$\frac{1}{e} \le S_{RM} \le 1 \quad For\ flag \tag{13.23}$$

13.6.2 Carrier Sense Multiple Access

The Carrier Sense Multiple Access (CSMA) technique relies on the sender sensing the state of the transmission channel and basing its actions on this. It can therefore only be effectively used in channels which have short propagation delays, since for channels with long delays (e.g. satellite) the sensed data is considerably out of date. This is usually specified as having a small α as given by Equation 13.7. In a perfect channel (zero transmission delay) the sender could listen to the state of the channel when it was ready to transmit and only send when the channel was free, so avoiding any collision.

Let t be the time from the start of a transmission from one user to when all users sense the presence of the signal on the line, i.e. the propagation delay on the network plus the sense time. The vulnerable period when collisions can occur is then 2t, i.e. t after the end of one transmission and t to complete a transmission. This is shown in Figure 13.13. If the channels are slotted into t second time slots,

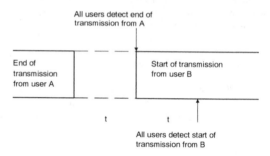

Figure 13.13 Vulnerable period in CSMA

then the vulnerable period is reduced to t since transmission must start at the start point of each slot. t is small for low propagation delays on the medium.

CSMA can operate in three modes, 1-persistent, non-persistent and p-persistent. In addition there is a variant called CSMA/CD, as described in the following sections.

13.6.2.1 1-persistent CSMA

In the 1-persistent CSMA all users listen to the line prior to transmitting. If they sense traffic they wait. When the line becomes free the users who have been waiting transmit immediately, i.e. transmit with probability one. Collisions will occur if two stations start transmission simultaneously, or if the delay in the transmission channel is such that after one channel has started transmission the second ready channel has not heard this and also starts transmission. After a collision the stations wait a random amount of time before listening to the channel again.

If all transmitted packets are assumed to be of constant length and the load (G) has a Poisson distribution, then the throughput is given by Equation 13.24. It is also assumed in this calculation that all users can sense the transmission of all other users.

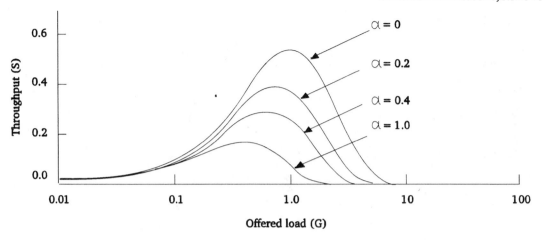

Figure 13.14 Effect of channel propagation delay on the channel throughput for 1-persistent CSMA

$$S = \frac{G e^{-G}(1 + G)}{G + e^{-G}}$$ (13.24)

This equation holds for slotted or unslotted channels, it being assumed that for slotted channels the slot time is much shorter than the packet time.

Figure 13.14 shows the variation of throughput with offered load for different channel delays, including zero delay.

13.6.2.2 *Non-persistent CSMA*

In a non-persistent CSMA a user who is ready to send data senses the line, and if it is free it commences transmission. Provided the delay in the transmission line is small (given as a low α) then there is good chance of success.

If the line is busy then the user does not continue sensing, but backs off for a random time before sensing it again, and so on. This method therefore gives a better utilisation of the line, but also results in larger delays than the 1-persistent CSMA.

13.6.2.3 *p-persistent CSMA*

This system is usually used with slotted channels. When a user has data to transmit it senses the channel and if it is free it transmits with probability p i.e. delays transmission to the next slot with probability 1-p.

If the next slot is idle then the user will again transmit with probability p, and so on. If the slot is not free at any time then the user waits a random amount of time and starts again. If initially the user had found that the slot was busy then it would have waited until the next slot and applied the algorithm.

The throughput of the system is given by Equation 13.25, where K is given by Equation 13.26.

$$S = \frac{G e^{-G}(1 + p G K)}{G + e^{-G}}$$ (13.25)

$$K = \sum_{k=0}^{\infty} \frac{(q G)^k}{(1 - q^{k+1}) k!}$$ (13.26)

Figure 13.15 shows the throughput for various CSMA systems and compares this with slotted ALOHA. The delay curves are given in Figure 13.16. Pure contention protocols are best at low loads and have high channel utilisation and low delay. Contention minimisation systems are best at high loads, when they have higher efficiency, but also higher delay at low loads.

13.6.2.4 *CSMA/CD*

In the previous CSMA systems once transmission commences it is completed even if a collision occurs on the first bit. This is clearly wasteful of bandwidth. In a modification, known as Carrier Sense Multiple Access with Collision Detection (CSMA/CD), a user monitors the line even when it commences transmission and stops once a collision is detected (Metcalfe and Boggs, 1976). After that the user waits a random time before sensing the line again. This multiple access method has been standardised by the IEEE as 802.3 (IEEE, 1985).

It is also not always possible for a sender to effectively sense the line during its transmission since the strength of the transmitted signal may be so strong as to swamp any signal returned back. Often CSMA/CD algorithms require that each user which detects a collision transmit a short jamming signal to immediately inform all other users that a collision has occurred on the line.

13.6.3 Asymmetrical protocols

We have so far been considering the case where all users have an equal probability (p) for transmission. This is know as a symmetrical protocol. If somehow it were possible to divide the users into a smaller number of groups, even if this meant splitting the overall channel capacity, then it can be shown that there is a greater overall chance of users being able to transmit without contention, resulting in enhanced throughput.

The ideal system would divide all users in such a way that in any one group there is only one active user, so that the chance of a successful transmission is assured. The trick is in determining a

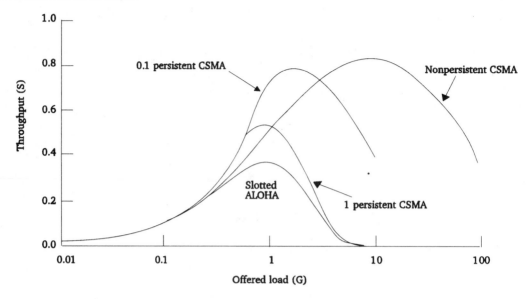

Figure 13.15 Comparison of channel throughput for ALOHA and CSMA, with channel delay factor α = 0.01.

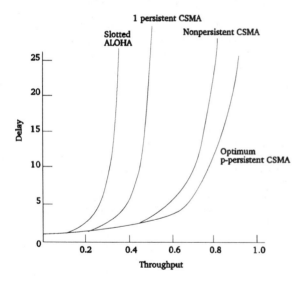

Figure 13.16 Delay-throughput curves for CSMA and ALOHA

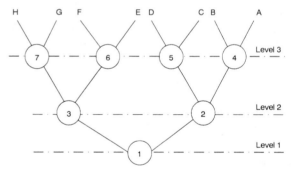

Figure 13.17 Operation of an adaptive tree walk protocol

method for allocating users to the available slots within a transmission system. Dynamic allocation is usually used, where the number of users per slot decreases as the load increases.

A dynamic allocation method which has been described (Capetanakis, 1979a and 1979b) is known as the adaptive tree walk protocol, and is illustrated in Figure 13.17 for eight users A to H.

Initially all users who wish to transmit data contend for a slot, and the protocol is at Level 1 and node 1. If a collision occurs then the protocol moves up the tree to Level 2 and node 2. Now only the users below this node (A to D) are permitted to contend for the slot. If a transmission is successful then the slot in the next packet is reserved for users under node 3. If, however, there was contention

at node 2 then the protocol moves further up the tree to Level 3 and node 4, limiting the users to A and B.

By moving up the tree each time a collision occurs, the protocol eventually finds users who have information to transmit, and limits their number so that transmission is successful. To ensure fairness users on either side of the tree are searched in turn following a successful transmission or if there is no data available for transmission on one side.

If the loading on the channel is heavy, i.e. many users waiting to transmit, then clearly it is more efficient and quicker to start searching at an intermediate level rather than at Level 1. It can be shown that this optimum level is related to the number of users 'n' who have data to transmit and is given by Equation 13.27.

$$Optimum\ search\ level\ =\ \log_e n \tag{13.27}$$

Other asymmetrical protocols have been developed, but are not considered here. For example Kleinrock and Yemini (1978) describe the urn protocol. All these have the same aim, to limit the number of users per slot so that the probability of transmission increases, ideally reaching one, with one ready user per slot.

13.6.4 Contention rings

Ring architectures are very powerful and often used in networks. The property of a ring is that the communication line passes through the nodes, and these are not just interfacing to it. The information passing through a node is stored a bit at a time and then forwarded. There is therefore a one bit delay, which can become significant if there are many users on the ring.

Contention rings use a token, similar to the token passing method described later. A token is a unique combination of bits which gives a user authorisation to transmit its data. There is only one token on the line at any time and the only user who can transmit data is the one holding the token, so contention is avoided.

Unlike the token passing method, a contention ring does not have a continuously circulating token, so when none of the users has data to transmit the ring is empty. If a user wishes to transmit it checks to see if a bit is passing though it. If not it commences transmission and at the end of this it puts a token onto the ring. When the token again comes round to the originator he removes it from the ring.

If there is traffic on the ring when a user wishes to commences transmission it waits until the token passes through it. This is then converted to a 'connector', usually by changing the polarity of the last bit, and then it commences transmission. Since there is now no token on the line no other station can transmit.

If two stations start transmission simultaneously, because they both checked the line and did not find a bit passing them, then they will read each other's data as it goes around the ring and will know that a contention has occurred. Both then back off for a random time and start again.

When the ring is full, i.e. many users have data to transmit, the system operates basically as a token passing ring, each user transmitting in turn. On light loads it operates as a contention ring, with low delay since a ready station does not need to wait for a token to arrive before it can begin its transmission.

13.7 Non-contention systems

The previous two sections have examined systems in which pure contention is used in order to access a communication channel and where contention is used but steps are taken to minimise it wherever possible. The present section will look at the large class of systems which avoid contention altogether.

These systems are subdivided into fixed assignment systems, where the channel capacity is divided out amongst users and is fixed; demand assignment systems, where the capacity is divided into segments, but is allocated to users according to their needs at any time; and reservation systems, where the capacity is not rigidly divided and can by reserved in advance by potential users.

13.7.1 Fixed assignment systems.

Three techniques are covered under fixed assignment systems: frequency division multiple access (FDMA) which uses the same principles as frequency division multiplexing described in Chapter 20; time division multiple access (TDMA) which again is based on the time division multiplexing principles of Chapter 21; and code division multiple access (CDMA) also sometimes referred to as spread spectrum multiple access (SSMA).

13.7.1.1 *Frequency division multiple access*

FDMA works on the principle of dividing the total bandwidth of the communication channel into a number of discrete segments, and allocating each segment exclusively to a user. This is shown pictorially in Figure 13.18. Guard bands are used between each segment of the frequency band to prevent interference between users.

The advantage of the FDMA system is its simplicity, since once the channel capacity is divided amongst users each can operate

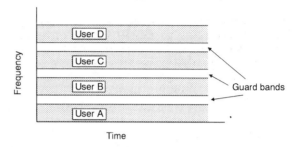

Figure 13.18   User assignment within FDMA

independently of each other. Since each user has exclusive use of its allocated bandwidth there is no contention and therefore no wastage of bandwidth or delays caused by collisions and retransmissions. Because of this the throughput (S) of non-contention systems equals the offered load (G) if retransmissions due to secondary causes, such as line errors, are ignored. The idealised curve is therefore as in Figure 13.3.

The disadvantage of FDMA systems is that there is wastage of bandwidth, firstly caused by the guard bands and secondly due to the fact that users can only use their own allocated frequency bands. Therefore if a user does not have any information to transmit its allocated band lies idle, even though other users may have a considerable amount of information to send and are experiencing delays on their channel. FDMA is therefore best for use in systems where all users have a stream of data to send, and it is unsuitable for users with 'bursty' traffic, where contention systems, such as ALOHA, perform better.

One of the results of dividing the overall channel capacity amongst multiple users is increased delay (Rubin, 1979). For example, if there are N users sharing a total channel capacity of C and the total traffic they generate is λ with a mean packet length of $1/\mu$, then the delay is given by Equation 13.28.

$$Delay\, D_1 = \frac{1}{\mu C - \lambda} \tag{13.28}$$

If the channel is now divided equally amongst the N users, each having exclusive use of its capacity (C/N) only, and the total traffic each user generates is λ/N, then the delay is given by Equation 13.29, which shows the increased delay over the case where the total channel resource is shared amongst all users, using some form of contention system.

$$Delay\, D_2 = \frac{N}{\mu C - \lambda} = N D_1 \tag{13.29}$$

Another disadvantage of fixed assignment systems, such as FDMA, is that the number of users cannot easily be changed. This would require the overall channel frequency band to be redivided amongst the new users.

FDMA is also not suitable for use in systems which require broadcast of data to many users. Since each user is allocated a single frequency band, it sends on this band and the receiver also monitors this band.

13.7.1.2 *Time division multiple access*

TDMA works on the principle that the complete bandwidth of the channel is allocated to all users, but these users have use of this for a limited time period only (Lam, 1976; Lam, 1977; Hayes, 1984; Stevens, 1990). This is shown pictorially in Figure 13.19.

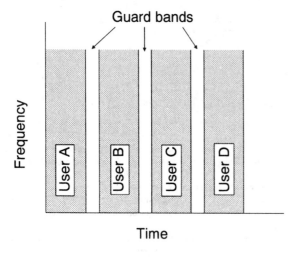

Figure 13.19 User assignment within TDMA

The user time slots are combined into frames, as in Figure 13.20, which shows a six user system (users A to F). The frames repeat after a frame period of T_F. This is the most usual assignment method where each user has equal allocation of the channel. Alternatively some users can have a greater share, and this is accommodated by grouping the frames and varying the user repetition period. This is illustrated in Figure 13.21 where users A and B are allocated increase capacity (with frame repetition period T_F) over users C to F (with frame repetition period T_G).

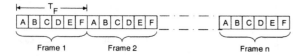

Figure 13.20 The frame structure within TDMA

Because the users always occupy the same position within a frame the receiver knows where to look to collect its data. It is essential to ensure, however, that some form of synchronisation system is used

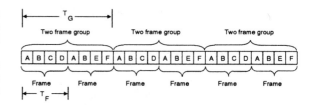

Figure 13.21 Unequal slot assignment within TDMA

so that user data is correctly timed with the start of their allocated time slots.

As illustrated in Figure 13.19 guard bands (time periods) must be used to prevent interference between users, caused by variations in the synchronisation times. This is shown in Figure 13.22. User A is allocated the first slot and transmit data which is correctly timed but which only occupies a part of its allocated slot. (This again illustrated the inefficiency of fixed assignment systems with fixed packet lengths, when a user does not have data ready to transmit during his allocated time, or only has data which partially fills his allocated time slot.)

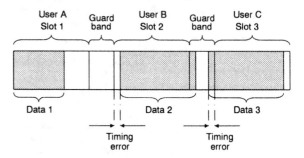

Figure 13.22 Effect of timing variations in TDMA (hypothetical case)

Users B and C have data which completely fill their time slots but, due to timing variations, they do not start at the correct times. The guard band period now absorbs this timing variation and prevents interference between adjacent transmissions.

The advantages and disadvantages of TDMA are similar to those for FDMA. It is most suited to systems where the number of users is fixed and each user has a continuous stream of traffic to send. However, since all users are continuously listening to the channel, but only accepting data during their allocated time slots, this method can cope with broadcast systems. Generally TDMA is more efficient than FDMA for the same conditions of operation.

Since there are no collisions and retransmissions within TDMA (as for FDMA) the offered load equals the throughput, if the retransmissions due to transmission errors are ignored. Also, once the time slots have been allocated to users, the performance of any user is unaffected by the loading of other users. Each user experiences a delay determined by the frame period (T_F), the propagation delay within the medium, the transmission time of an average message, and any queueing delays it may have. Assuming that the channel capacity C is equally divided between N users (i.e. each user has full use of the channel for 1/N of the time or has an average capacity of C/N), the normalised transfer delay is given by Equation 13.30.

$$Delay\ D\ =\ 1\ +\ \frac{N}{2}\ +\ \frac{N\,S}{2\,(1\ -\ S)} \qquad (13.30)$$

Figure 13.23 shows typical average delay curves for TDMA. As expected the delay increases as the throughput increases, due to queuing for access to the user's time slots, and also increases as the number of users is increased, since this results in further division of the communication channel and an increase in the frame repetition period, T_F.

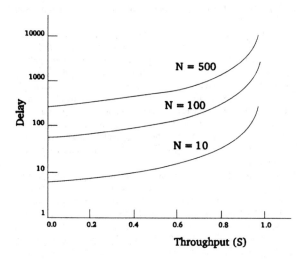

Figure 13.23 Averaged normalised delay within TDMA

The dependency of delay on number of user is shown more generally in Figure 13.24, so that this is an important parameter in the choice of TDMA systems. These perform best when there is a relatively small number of users, each sending a large amount of traffic. Figure 13.25 shows the reduction of average delay as the average traffic per user is increased.

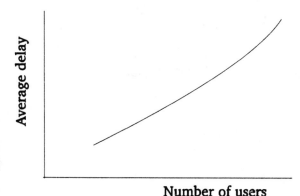

Figure 13.24 Effect of number of users on average delay within a fixed assignment multiple access system

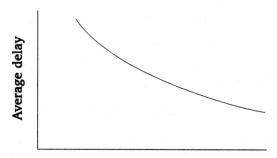

Figure 13.25 Effect of average traffic per user on average delay within a fixed assignment multiple access system

13.7.1.3   *Code division multiple access*

The most common application of CDMA is spread spectrum multiple access (SSMA) and the two terms are often used synonymously (Schilling, 1990; Schilling, 1991).

CDMA allows the transmission from various users to overlap in frequency and time (unlike FDMA and TDMA, where one of these parameters are used for separation) but segregation between users is obtained by using different codes which are matched between corresponding senders and receivers. (This coding clearly occupies bandwidth.)

SSMA is the most common form of CDMA. Two techniques are used, frequency hopping and phase coding. In phase coded SSMA the phase modulation of the carrier is changed in a coded pattern, whilst in frequency hopping the transmission frequency is varied according to the coded pattern. Figure 13.26 shows a simplified

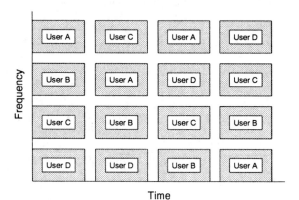

Figure 13.26 Simplified view of user assignment within CDMA (frequency hopping)

representation of CDMA using frequency hopping. The transmissions are shown synchronised to each other, although in practice no such synchronisation is needed between users. As seen from Figure 13.26 each user 'hops' around between frequency bands, these varying from one time slot to another.

CDMA has several advantages. It has high security against jamming, since no one frequency is used, and for this reason it is used in military systems. In addition it can co-exist with other systems since separation is via coding, and it is resilient to fading. If fading occurs in a given frequency band then for FDMA all users within this band are affected, but since CDMA only uses a frequency band for a certain portion of time, which varies between uses, the effect of fading is spread over many users.

13.7.2 Demand assignment systems

The demand assignment systems are part of non-contention systems in which the communication channel is allocated to a user as demanded, rather on a fixed basis, as in the previous section.

Four types of demand assignment multiple access techniques are described here: polling, token passing, slotted ring and register insertion.

13.7.2.1 Polling

Polling techniques are ideally suited to star, bus or tree structures although, in practice, any of the systems of Figure 13.1 may be used. The principles of polling have been described and analysed in several texts, such as Betsekas and Gallager (1987), Hammond and O'Reilly (1986), Hayes (1984), Schwartz (1987) and Chou (1983).

In polling each user in turn is interrogated to see if they have any data to transmit. If they have data then they will commence transmission and stop when their buffers are empty. At the end of this they send a 'complete' message and the next user in turn is polled. If a user does not have any data to send he simply returns the 'complete' message. This is therefore a demand assignment system since the more data a user has the longer he is able to transmit. (There may be some rules to prevent a station from hogging all the transmission time.)

Since only one station is polled at any time and is therefore able to transmit, there is no collision. It is also possible to introduce a priority system in which some users are polled more often than others in any period.

The time taken to go around and poll all the users in a system is referred to as its poll cycle. The portion of this period used for overheads (e.g. channel propagation delays, transmission time for the poll messages, synchronisation times when stations receive the poll request) is referred to as the walk time. It is in effect the time needed to transfer permission to transmit from one station to the next, and to complete the messages. Walk time represents the minimum delay time irrespective of whether any data is transmitted.

Three types of polling are considered here: roll call polling, hub polling and probing.

Figure 13.27 illustrates the principle of roll call polling. A central station, which may be a specified user who has taken on this task, polls each of the other users in turn. When a user receives a poll he puts his messages on the common line and the addressed user retrieves it. When all messages have been completed the user sends a 'complete' message to the central station, which then polls the next user in its planned sequence. The central station can be programmed to poll some users more often than others, giving them priority, or it can be made to poll users who consistently transmitting large volumes of data more often, so that it acts as a demand assignment system.

In hub polling the central station commences the poll cycle by sending a poll to the first user. If this user has any data to transmit it puts this onto the common line for the addressed user to retrieve. When all data has been completed (of if there was no data in the first place) a 'complete' signal is sent to the next user in line (which need not be the next adjacent user). The 'complete' signal is treated as a poll by the recipient, and so on, as shown in Figure 13.28. Finally the last user in the chain returns the 'complete' signal to the central station, so ending the poll cycle.

Hub polling can result in reduced walk time between users, since control is not passed back and forth to a central site, although it is more difficult to implement since each user needs greater intelligence.

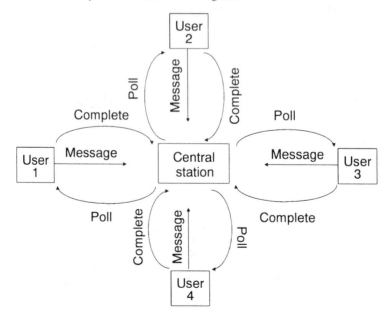

Figure 13.27   Illustration of roll call polling

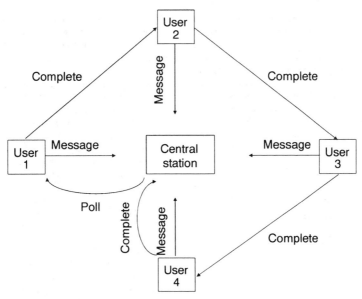

Figure 13.28 Illustration of hub polling

Assume that there are N identical users, and that all data is held at these user stations in buffers, the buffers being emptied at each poll. The average cycle time (t_c) is related to the average walk time (t_w) by Equation 13.31, where the traffic intensity (ρ) is as in Equation 13.1. Figure 13.29 shows the delay curves.

$$t_c = \frac{N t_w}{1 - N\rho} \qquad (13.31)$$

The cycle time will therefore be large, leading to poor performance, if the walk time is large, for example as experienced with satellite channels, or if there are a large number of users. This results in large delay.

Polling all users in turn can be a slow process if there are a large number of users and only a few of these have data to send at any time. In these circumstances a technique called probing is used to reduce the number of polls required and so reduce the overall delay in the system.

Probing is a technique in which groups of users are polled at a time, to find the users who are ready for transmission. It is similar to the tree walk protocol illustrated in Figure 13.17. The N users are divided into groups and these are probed simultaneously. The users who have data ready for transmission reply to this probe. For example in Figure 13.17 suppose user F is the only ready user and that node 1 is probed and it provides a ready response. Node 2 is then probed and, as there is no response, the probe is moved to node 3. A response is now received so node 7 is probed (no response) followed by node 6 (response). Finally user E is polled followed by a poll of user F. Therefore, in the worst case, the process of locating and polling the ready user took 5 probes and two polls.

Probing is a good technique to use if the overall loading of the system is light (i.e. few users ready to transmit). If there are 2^n users on the system and only one of them is ready to transmit, then the number of probes (including polls) needed to locate it are given by Equation 13.32.

$$Number\ of\ probes = 2n + 1 \qquad (13.32)$$

If, however, all the users are ready to transmit then the number of probes (and polls) needed is given by Equation 13.33, which is clearly larger than a simple sequential poll method. It is therefore important, during probing, to choose the initial group size so as to minimise the number of probes.

$$Number\ of\ probes = 2^{n+1} - 1 \qquad (13.33)$$

13.7.2.2 Token passing

Token passing is described and analysed in several papers, such as Bux (1989), Black (1989) and Farber and Larson (1972). It is commonly used in a ring topology and is then referred to as a token

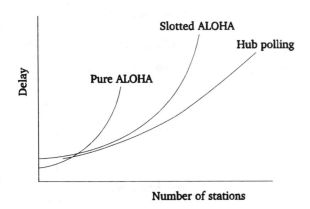

Figure 13.29 Variation of delay in hub polling compared to ALOHA

ring. It uses active termination points between the users and the network, unlike a polling system which users passive terminators.

In token passing a special bit pattern, called a token (for example eight logical ones, 11111111) circulates amongst users. This special pattern is prevented from being generated by a user, as part of its normal data, by bit stuffing techniques. Users operate in one of two mode, listen and transmit, as in Figure 13.30. During the listen mode all the bits are read off the line and then regenerated, one bit at a time. If the data is for the user, as indicated by the address, then it is read, otherwise it is just passed on. The user knows a token is present by the special sequence of bits.

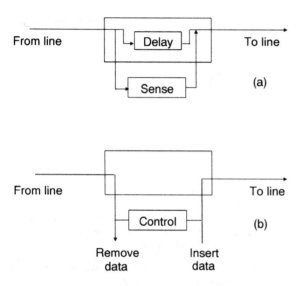

(a)

(b)

Figure 13.30 Interface to a token passing network: (a) listen mode; (b) transmit mode

Because of the requirement to read and regenerate each bit, there is a bit delay at each user node, which can become quite significant if many users are connected to the line. In addition the delay in the overall line must be high enough to permit a whole token to circulate at any time.

If the user wishes to transmit data then it waits for a token to appear. It knows this by the unique bit pattern, and as soon as the token passes through the user's node it is marked as busy. This can be done, for example, by reversing the polarity of the last bit (i.e. 11111110). The user is now in the transmit mode. All the data input from the line is absorbed (since it is not relevant, no user being permitted to transmit without the token) and the data from the user's buffer is emptied out onto the line, immediately after the busy token.

After all the data has been transmitted the user regenerates the token which can now be seized by the next ready user in the chain. When the traffic is light the token circulates from user to user around the ring. When the traffic is heavy the token is seized and marked as busy by each user in turn. As only one token circulates at any time there is no contention.

Token passing is similar to hub polling where no central station is used to commence the poll. Also hub polling is usually applied to bus structures whereas token passing is more often used in ring structures. The scan time in a token passing system is the time it takes for the token to be passed around all users, whilst the walk time is the time taken for a bit to go around the ring (i.e. one bit delay

within a user node plus propagation delay in the ring). The performance equations are the same as those derived for hub polling.

In token passing three strategies may be used for the transmitting user regenerating the token. These are:

1. Multiple token operation, where the token is sent straight after the user has completed his data transmission. This allows the next user to 'piggy-back' his data onto it, and is a useful technique to use if the ring is long and has appreciable delays.
2. Single token operation, where the user who has sent data (after having sent the busy token) waits to receive the busy token and his original transmission back again and following the last bit of his data he regenerates the token. This is the system used in the IEEE 802. standards.
3. Single packet operation, where the token is regenerated after the last bit of the busy token is received back (the user not waiting for his original transmission to be received).

The time for which a token is held by a user can be limited to prevent 'hogging'. If this is long the user will be able to empty his buffers and this is known as exhaustive transmission. If it is very short he will only be able to send a packet every time he receives the token. A master clock is required in all instances to synchronise all users. This clock can be maintained by one of the users (who is referred to as a monitor station). This station also carries out other functions, such as checking for loss of token.

Priority operation is achieved by having a priority slot in the token and assigning each user a priority level. When a user wishes to transmit it waits for a token to pass and, if it is busy, it puts its priority number into the priority slot, if its priority is higher than any which may already be in this slot. The token is then allowed to circulate round the ring. When the original user receives this busy token back it generates a free token and marks it with the priority level which it received. Now stations with this priority level, or above, are only allowed to seize the token.

Figure 13.31 shows typical throughput curves for token passing, comparing this with a contention system such as CSMA/CD. Although the throughput is relatively constant as the number of users increases, above a certain minimum, the delay also increases, as for polling.

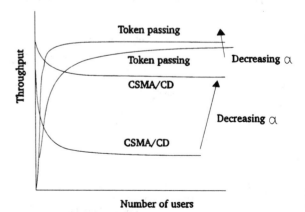

Figure 13.31 Variation of throughput with number of users for token passing and CSMA/CD

IEEE 802.5 describes the token ring protocols, and IEEE 802.4 the token bus. The bus structure can be considered to be a logical ring, as in Figure 13.32, the token moving between users as shown by the dotted line.

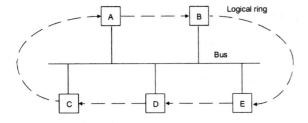

Figure 13.32 Illustration of a logical ring

13.7.2.3 *Slotted ring*

In the slotted ring (Pierce, 1972) the ring is divided into a number of slots. These slots can hold packets of data, and contain an indication bit which shows whether the slot is empty or full. The ring needs to have a considerable amount of delay, often introduced artificially, in order to hold a reasonable number of circulating slots.

When a user wants to transmit data it waits for an empty slot to arrive. This is then marked as busy and the data in placed in it. The receiver retrieve the data from the slot and once again marks it as free. Clearly the data needs to be the same size as the slot, so this system uses fixed slot sizes.

13.7.2.4 *Register insertion ring*

Operation of this method (Liu, 1978) is best explained by the simplified representation of the interface of a node to the ring, as in Figure 13.33. Data from the line feeds into a shift register and its

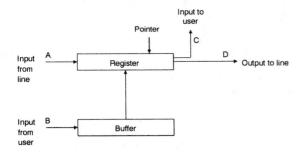

Figure 13.33 A simplified representation of the interface to a register insertion network

position is located by a pointer. As the register fills up the pointer moves to the left. Initially the pointer is at the extreme right, indicating that the register is empty. Data is clocked into the register one bit at a time and clocked out again. If the line is very busy the register will be full, but if it is lightly loaded then empty periods will build up and there will be spare room in the register.

When the user wishes to transmit data this is moved into the buffer. It then checks to see there is sufficient room in the register,

and if that is the case the data is loaded from the buffer into the register and clocked out onto the line.

If the loading is light the user can continue to send data, but if it is heavy it must wait between transmissions for gaps in the line, and for these to build up in the register. This method therefore automatically prevents users from 'hogging' the line. It also permits variable length packets (as in token passing) and several frames to be on the ring at any time (as in slotted ring).

13.7.3 **Reservation systems**

There are a large number of different multiple access techniques which are based on some form of reservation. One such system has already been described, that of Reservation ALOHA. This was introduced under contention systems, since some form of contention is used to access the reservation slots, although once this has been done the use of the data slots is contention free.

Reservations can be made using any of the techniques described earlier, pure contention, contention minimisation, or non-contention (fixed assignment or demand assignment). Furthermore, the control mechanism for allocation of slots can be centralised or distributed. In distributed systems each user needs to maintain knowledge of the queue length and its position in the queue. Often all users transmit information of the queue status within their packet headers, so that new users who join the queue can acquire its history. For centrally controlled systems this function would be performed by the master station.

In distributed control it is also required that data and reservation requests from each user is broadcast, so that it is received by all other users, and they know the state of the queue. In a centrally controlled system it is only necessary for the central controller to know about the reservations being made, and for it to be able to instruct the other users.

The efficiency of a reservation system is closely related to the overhead which is used to make reservations. If, for example, the fraction γ of the bandwidth is used for making reservations, as given by Equation 13.34, then the maximum throughput of a reservation channel is given by Equation 13.35.

$$\gamma = \frac{Bandwidth\ occupied\ by\ reservation\ slots}{Total\ channel\ bandwidth} \qquad (13.34)$$

$$Maximum\ throughput = 1 - \gamma \quad where\ \gamma < 1 \qquad (13.35)$$

Figure 13.34 compares the delay-throughput characteristics of slotted ALOHA and a general reservation systems. Slotted ALOHA reaches a maximum throughput of 1/e (0.368), as in Equation 13.16, whilst typical values of γ for reservation systems is 0.1 to 0.3, giving maximum throughputs from 0.7 to 0.9. However the delay within the reservation systems is higher than in ALOHA, especially when there are a relatively small number of users, and the data is 'bursty'.

13.7.3.1 *Reservation TDMA*

Reservation TDMA (Weissler et al., 1978) is similar to the reservation ALOHA system except that TDMA is used to access the reservation slots.

The channel is divided into N reservation slots and kN data slots per frame, as in Figure 13.35, where N is the number of users. Each user is allocated one data slot within each of the k subgroups, for his use, and one reservation slot. Reservations are made in the reserva-

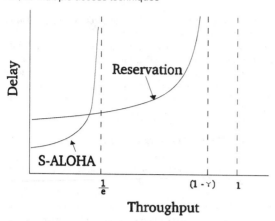

Figure 13.34 Delay-throughput characteristic for slotted ALOHA and reservation systems

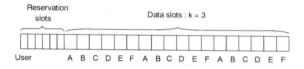

Figure 13.35 Frame structure for R-TDMA

tion slot and now there is no contention since no other user can transmit in it.

If the owner of a data slot does not wish to use it then it is assigned to other ready users. This is usually done in a round robin fashion.

13.7.3.2 *Bit-map protocol*

This uses a structure similar to R-ALOHA, with explicit reservations, except that no contention is used to access the reservation slots. Figure 13.36 illustrates its operation for six users, A to F.

If there are N users, then initially there will be N reservation slots with each user allocated exclusive use of one of these reservation slots. If a user wishes to transmit it puts a '1' into its allocated slot, and if it does not wish to transmit then it leaves this slot empty. After all the reservation slots have been so accessed, all stations know which users wish to transmit.

Priority is now given to low valued users. The first station who puts a '1' in its slot transmits in the first data slot following the end of the reservation slots. In Figure 13.36 this is user A. The next slot is allocated to the next user in sequence who marked its reservation slot, i.e. user D.

When all the users who reserved slots have transmitted, the reservation slots begin again. If the load is low then reservation slots will repeat continuously until a user is ready to transmit and makes a reservation.

If a user is ready to transmit data after its reservation slot has passed it must wait until the next cycle for it to reappear before it can make a reservation and transmit. The worst case delay occurs for a user located towards the end (user F in Figure 13.36). On average it must wait N/2 reservation slots before it has access to its reservation slot and then, if all users have made reservations, it must wait a further (N-1) data slots before it can begin transmission. To this must be added the transmission propagation time and access times, to obtain the total delay. Users who are allocated reservation slots at the beginning of the reservation cycle (user A in Figure 13.36) only have an average delay of N/2 plus propagation and access delays.

13.7.3.3 *The BRAP and MSAP*

The Broadcast Recognition with Alternating Priorities (Chlamtac, 1976) and the Mini Slotted Alternating Priorities (Scholl, 1976) protocols are very similar in operation, and overcome the two major limitations of the bit-map protocol. These are:

1. The delay under light load, caused by ready users who have made a reservation but have to wait until the end of the reservation cycle before they can transmit.
2. The asymmetry in the protocol, where some users get preferential treatment over others, depending on their position within the reservation frame.

Figure 13.37 illustrates the operation of the MSAP and BRAP protocols. As for the bit-map protocol reservation slots are allocated for exclusive use of a user. However as soon as a user makes a reservation it completes its transmission in a data slot. Also the reservation slot sequence now does not start from the beginning but from the last user who transmitted. These therefore overcome the two limitations of the bit-map protocol given earlier. However every user still has to wait for a reservation slot, and has an average delay of N/2 reservation slots.

In a variant of the MSAP a user who has just transmitted is given the option to transmit immediately in another data slot, and only if it does not do this does control pass to the next user. The system therefore gives improved performance under conditions of 'stream'

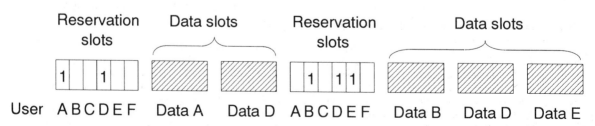

Figure 13.36 Illustration of the bit-map protocol

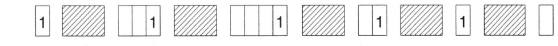

Figure 13.37 Principle of the MSAP/BRAP protocols

traffic, although it does result in an idle slot under conditions of light traffic, if the user does not take up the invitation to transmit again.

MASP and BRAP may be considered to be similar in operation to roll call polling, but they have a shorter walk time. Generally they have better performance than polling (Kleinrock and Scholl, 1977) but are more complex since users need to be intelligent to make and recognise reservations, and be synchronised to the reservation slots.

13.7.3.4   *MLMA*

The Multi-level Multi-Access protocol (Rothauser and Wild, 1977) overcomes the problem of high delay on light loads, experienced by MSAP/BRAP when there are many users. For example for a 1000 user system the worst case delay could be 1000 reservation time slots with a mean of 500 slots.

In MLMA a user broadcasts its reservation in a given format, for example radix 10, as illustrated in Figure 13.38 for 100 users. Suppose that users numbered 45, 49, 66 and 61 wish to transmit data. They will first broadcast their most significant station number in Frame A. The system now knows that any number of twenty users in the 40s and 60s group wish to transmit.

In Frame C the 40s users are invited to place their reservations, indicating their second digit. Stations 45 and 49 do so and are therefore positively identified. Similarly in frame D users 61 and 66 identify themselves by their second digit. Therefore in this example 30 reservation time slots are used as opposed to 100 which would be needed in MSAP/BRAP. As before each user keeps track of how many reservations have been made and the queue length.

13.7.3.5   *PODA*

The Priority-Oriented Demand Assignment protocol (Jacobs and Lee, 1977; Jacobs, Binder and Hoverstein, 1978; Hsu and Lee, 1978; Jacobs et al., 1979) is a demand assignment system. Like R-ALOHA the channel is divided into frames and each frame has data and reservation slots. Sophisticated scheduling and control algorithms are used, which makes this protocol unique.

Users make reservations for a number of slots and are allocated a priority for transmission on data slots. (There can be two types of data slots, one reserved for particular users and one shared.) A central station then allocates the data slots to users according to their priority and demand. There are usually three classes of traffic, priority, normal and bulk, and these are served in that order.

Fixed assignment can be used to access the reservation slots, when the protocol is called Fixed assignment PODA (FPODA). Alternatively, when there are a large number of users, with light traffic, contention can be used for access to the reservation slots, the system being called Contention PODA (CPODA). However a central station still manages the allocations based on reservations.

13.8   References

Abramson, N. (1977) The Throughput of Packet Broadcasting Channels, *IEEE Trans. Commun.*, **COM-25**, January.

Betsekas, D. and Gallager, R. (1987) *Data Networks*, Prentice-Hall.

Binder, R. et al. (1975a) ALOHA Packet Broadcasting — A Retrospect, *Proc. NCC*.

Binder (1975b) A Dynamic Packet Switching System for Satellite Broadcast Channels, *Proc. ICC*, pp. 41-1 to 41-5a.

Black, U. (1989) *Data Networks: Concepts, Theory and Practice*, Prentice-Hall.

Bux, W. (1989) Token Ring Local-Area Networks and Their Performance, *Proceedings of the IEEE 77*, (2), February.

Capetanakis, J.I. (1979a) Generalised TDMA: The Multi-Accessing Tree Protocol, *IEEE Trans. Commun.*, **COM- 27**, pp. 1476–1484, October.

Capetanakis, J.I. (1979b) Tree Algorithms for Packet Broadcast Channels, *IEEE Trans. Inf. Theory*, **IT-25**, pp. 505–515, September.

Chen, M.S. et al. (1990) A Multi-Access Protocol for Packet-Switched Wavelength Division Multiaccess Metropolitan Area Networks, *IEEE J. Selected Areas in Commun.*, **8**, (6), August.

Chlamtac, I. (1976) *Radio Packet Broadcasted Computer Network — The Broadcast Recognition Access Method*, MS thesis, Tel Aviv University.

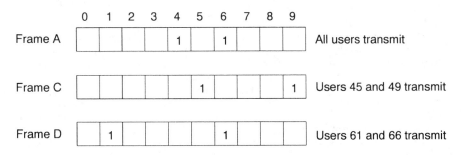

Figure 13.38 Illustration of MLMA

Chou, W. (ed.) (1983) *Computer Communications*, Prentice-Hall.

Clare, L.P. et al. (1990) A performance comparison of control policies for slotted ALOHA frequency-hopped multiple access systems. In *Proceedings of the new era IEEE military communications conference, MILCOM 90, (2), September.*

Clark, D.D., Pogran, K.T. and Reed, D.P. (1978) An Introduction to Local Area Networks, *Proc. IEEE*, **66**, pp. 1497–1517, November.

Crowther, W. et al. (1973) A System for Broadcast Communication: Reservation ALOHA, *Proc. 6th Hawaii Int. Conf. Syst. Sci.*, pp. 371–374.

Dono, N.R. (1990) A Wavelength Division Multiple Access Network for Computer Communication, *IEEE J. on Selected Areas in Commun.*, **8**, (6), August.

Farber, D.J. and Larson, K.C. (1972) The System Architecture of the Distributed Computer System — the Communications System, *Symp. on Comput. Networks*, Polytechnic Institute of Brooklyn, April.

Gerla, M. and Kleinrock, L. (1977) Closed Loop Stability Controls for S-ALOHA Satellite Communications, *Proc. 5th Data Commun. Symp.*, pp. 2-10 to 2-19.

Hammond, J.L. and O'Reilly, P.J.P. (1986) *Performance Analysis of Local Computer Networks*, Addison-Wesley.

Hayes, J.F. (1978) An Adaptive Technique for Local Distribution, *IEEE Trans. Commun.*, **COM-26**, August.

Hayes, J.F. (1984) *Modelling and Analysis of Computer Communication Networks*, Plenum Press.

HSU, N. and Lee, N. (1978) Channel Scheduling Synchronisation for the PODA protocol, *Proc. Internat. Conf. on Commun.*, Toronto, June.

Hwa, H.R. (1975) A framed ALOHA system, *Proc. PACNET Symposium*, Sendai, Japan, August.

IEEE (1977) Special Issue on Spread Spectrum Communications, *IEEE Trans. Commun.*, **COM-25**, August.

IEEE (1985) *IEEE 802.3: IEEE Standards for Local Area Networks — Carrier Sense Multiple Access with Collision Detection (CSMA/CD) Access Method and Physical Layer Specifications*, New York, IEEE.

Jacobs, I.M. and Lee, L.N. (1977) A Priority-Oriented Demand Assignment (PODA) protocol and an Error Recovery Algorithm for Distributively Controlled Packet Satellite Communication Network, *EASCON '77 Convention Record*, pp. 14-1A to 14-1F.

Jacobs, I.M., Binder, R. and Hoversten, E.V. (1978) General Purpose Packet Satellite Networks, *Proc. IEEE*, **66**, (11), November.

Jacobs, I.M. et al. (1979) Packet Satellite Network Design Issues, *Proc. National Telecom. Conf.*, November, pp. 45.2.1–45.2.12.

Khansefid, F. et al. (1990) Performance analysis of code division multiple access techniques in fibre optics with on- off and PPM pulsed signalling. In *Proceedings of the new era IEEE military communications conference, MILCOM 90, (3) September.*

Kleinrock, L. and Lam, S. (1973) Packet switching in a slotted satellite channel, *Nat. Computer Conf., AFIPS Conf. Proc.*, **42**, AFIPS Press, pp. 703–710.

Kleinrock, L. and Tobagi, F. (1975) Random Access Techniques for Data Transmission over Packet-Switched Radio Channels, *Proc. NCC*, pp. 187–201.

Kleinrock, L. (1976) *Queueing Systems*, John Wiley.

Kleinrock, L. and Scholl, M. (1977) Packet Switching in Radio Channels: New Conflict-Free Multiple Access Schemes for a Small Number of Data Users, *Conf. Rec. Int. Conf. Commun.*, Chicago, June.

Kleinrock, L. and Yemini, Y. (1978) An Optimal Adaptive Scheme for Multiple Access Broadcast Communications, *Proc. ICC*, pp. 7.2.1 to 7.2.5.

Ko, C.C., Lye, K.M. nad Wong, W.C. (1990) Simple priority scheme for multichannel CSMA/CD local area networks, *IEE Proc.*, **137**, (6), December.

Lam, S.S. and Kleinrock, L. (1975) Packet Switching in Multiaccess Broadcast Channels: Dynamic Control Procedures, *IEEE Trans. Commun.*, **COM-23**, pp. 891–904, September.

Lam, S.S. (1976) Delay Analysis of a Packet-switched TDMA System, *Proceedings of the National Telecommunications Conference*, December.

Lam, S.S. (1977) Delay Analysis of a Time Division Multiple Access (TDMA) Channel, *IEEE Transactions on Communications*, **COM-25**, (12), December.

Liu, M.T. (1978) Distributed Loop Computer Networks. In *Advances in Computers*, M.C. Yovits (ed.), Academic Press.

Mark, J.W. (1978) Global Scheduling Approach to Conflict-Free Multiaccess via a Data Bus, *IEEE Trans. Commun.*, September.

Metcalfe, R.M. and Boggs, D.R. (1976) Ethernet: Distributed Packet Switching for Local Computer Networks, *Commun. ACM*, **19**, pp. 395–404, July.

Morris, M.J. and Le-Ngoc, T. (1991) Rural telecommunications and ISDN using point-to-multipoint TDMA radio systems, *Telecom. J.*, **58**.

Pierce, J. (1972) How Far Can Data Loops Go? *IEEE Trans. Commun.*, **COM-20**, pp. 527–530, June.

Roberts, L. (1972) Extensions of Packet Communications Technology to a Hand Held Personal Terminal, *Proc. SJCC*, pp. 295–298.

Roberts, L. (1973) Dynamic Allocation of Satellite Capacity through Packet Reservation, *Proc. NCC*, pp. 711–716.

Roberts, L. (1975) ALOHA packet system with and without slots and capture, *Comput. Commun. Rev.*, **5**, pp. 28–42, April.

Rodrigues, M.A. (1990) Evaluating Performance of High Speed Multiaccess Networks, *IEEE Network Magazine*, May.

Rothauser, E.H. and Wild, D. (1977) MLMA — A Collision-Free Multi-Access Method, *Proc. IFIP Congr. 77*, pp. 431–436.

Rubin, I. (1979) Message delays in FDMA and TDMA communication channels, *IEEE Trans. Commun.*, **COM-27**, May.

Schilling, D.L. et al. (1990) CDMA for personal communications networks. In *Proceedings of the new era IEEE military communications conference, MILCOM 90, (2), September.*

Schilling, D.L. et al. (1991) Spread Spectrum for Commercial Communications, *IEEE Commun. Magazine*, April.

Scholl, M. (1976) *Multiplexing Techniques for Data Transmission over Packet Switched Radio Systems*, PhD thesis, UCLA.

Schwartz, M. (1987) *Telecommunication Networks: Protocools, Modelling and Analysis*, Addison-Wesley.

Stallings, W. (1988) *Data and Computer Communications*, Macmillan.

Stevens, D.S. et al. (1990) Evaluation of slot allocation strategies for TDMA protocols in packet radio networks. In *Proceedings of the new era IEEE military communications conference, MILCOM 90, (2), September.*

Strole, N.C. (1987) The IBM Token-Ring Network — A Functional Overview, *IEEE Network*, (1), January.

Tsiligirides, T. and Smith, D.G. (1991) Analysis of a p-persistent CSMA packetized cellular network with capture phenomena, *Computer Communications*, **14**, (2), March.

Weissler, R.R. et al. (1978) Synchronisation and Multiple Access Protocols in the Initial Satellite IMP, *Fall COMPCON*, September.

14

Coding

Dr M D Macleod
MA PhD MIEEE
University of Cambridge

Contents

14.1 The need for error control coding

In a digital (discrete) communication system, information is sent as a sequence of digits, which are first converted to an analogue (continuous) form by modulation at the transmitter, and then converted back into digits by de-modulation at the receiver. An ideal communication channel would transmit information without any form of corruption or distortion. Any real channel introduces noise and distortion, however, and these cause the corruption or loss of some digits at the receiver. The system designer can try to reduce the probability of digit errors by appropriate design of the analogue parts of the communication system, but it may be either impossible or too costly to achieve a sufficiently small probability of error in this way. A better solution will often be to use error control coding (ECC).

14.2 Principles of ECC

Error control coding is the controlled addition of redundancy to the transmitted digit stream in such a way that errors introduced in the channel can be detected, and in certain circumstances corrected, in the receiver. It is therefore a form of channel coding, so called because it compensates for imperfections in the channel; the other form of channel coding is transmission (or line coding), which has different objectives such as spectrum shaping of the transmitted signal. ECC is used to lower the probability of error from the input to the output of the communication system. The added redundancy means, however, that extra digits have to be transmitted over the channel, so that either the channel transmission rate must be increased, or the rate of transmission of digits from input to output must be reduced.

The controlled addition of redundancy in ECC contrasts with source coding (data compression) in which redundancy is removed from the source signal. For a signal (such as speech) with a high degree of intrinsic redundancy it would in principle be possible to perform some error detection and correction at the receiver without adding further redundancy. However this is generally too complex and too dependent on the uncontrolled redundancy of the source signal to be attractive. The functions of error control coding and source coding are therefore usually separated.

The functional blocks used for error control coding are a coder preceding the modulator in the transmitter, and a decoder following the demodulator in the receiver. The decoder may be designed to detect digit errors, or it may be designed to correct them. These functions are known as error detection and error correction respectively.

14.2.1 Types of ECC

There are two main types of ECC: block coding and convolutional coding. In block coding, the input is divided into blocks of k digits. The coder then produces a block of n digits for transmission, and the code is described as 'an (n,k) code'. Each block is coded and decoded entirely separately from all other blocks. In convolutional coding, the coder input and output are continuous streams of digits. The coder outputs n output digits for every k digits input, and the code is described as 'a rate k/n code'.

If the input digits are included unmodified in the coder output the code is described as systematic. The additional digits introduced by the coder are then known as parity or check digits. As well as the conceptual attractiveness of systematic codes, they have the advantage that a range of decoder complexities is made possible. The simplest decoder can simply extract the unmodified input digits from the coded digit stream, ignoring the parity digits. A more sophisticated decoder may use the parity digits for error detection, and a full decoder for error correction. Unsystematic codes also exist, but are less commonly used.

14.2.2 Feedforward and feedback error correction

In feedforward error correction (FEC) the decoder applies error correction to the received codeword, and it may also detect some uncorrectable errors. However, no return path from the receiver to the sender is assumed. Either block or convolutional codes may be used for feedforward error correction.

In feedback error correction, for which only block codes can be used, the receiver only attempts to detect errors, and sends return messages to the sender which cause repeat transmission if any errors are detected in a received block. In the OSI model for packet data networks, this function is carried out within the data link layer, by the return of a positive or negative acknowledgement (ACK or NAK) to the sender on receipt of a data block, a system known as stop-and-wait ARQ. In go-back-N ARQ, receipt of a NAK by the transmitter makes it retransmit the erroneous codeword and the N−1 following ones, where N is chosen so that the time taken to send N codewords is less than the round trip delay from transmitter to receiver and back again. This obviates the need for a buffer at the receiver. In selective repeat ARQ, only the codewords for which NAKs have been returned are re-transmitted. Performance analysis (Lin, 1983) shows that this is the most efficient system, although it requires an adequate buffer in the receiver.

14.2.3 Arithmetic for ECC

In a digital communication system, each transmitted digit is selected from a finite set of M values and is described as an M-ary digit. For example, binary digits (bits) have one of two values, which may be represented as 0 and 1. (The actual values of the physical signal used to transmit the digits, for example +12V and −12V, are irrelevant here). We shall assume that the input message digits use the same value of M as the transmitted digits; if not, the message digits can simply be converted to M-ary before coding.

The analytical design of coders and decoders for M-ary digits requires the use of Galois field arithmetic, denoted GF(M). If M is a prime number (including the important case of binary digits, where M = 2), Galois field arithmetic is equivalent to arithmetic modulo-M. GF(M) arithmetic also exists when M is equal to a power of a prime, so coders using the principles described below can be designed for quaternary (4-valued) and octal (8-valued) digit systems, for example, but in these cases GF(M) arithmetic is not equivalent to modulo-M arithmetic.

In the case of binary systems (M = 2), the addition and multiplication operations in GF(2) (i.e. modulo-2) arithmetic are as follows:

$$(0 + 0) = (1 + 1) = 0$$
$$(0 + 1) = (1 + 0) = 1$$
$$(0 \times 0) = (0 \times 1) = (1 \times 0) = 0$$
$$(1 \times 1) = 1.$$

Clearly, addition in this system is equivalent to the logical exclusive OR (XOR) function, and multiplication is equivalent to the logical AND function. For non-binary systems, multiplication and addition operations can be implemented using either dedicated logic or lookup tables.

Note that in modulo-2 arithmetic, addition and subtraction are equivalent. Some textbooks only discuss binary coders, and therefore treat all subtractions as additions. However for values of M other than 2 addition and subtraction are not equivalent, and it is essential to implement subtractions correctly.

14.2.4 Types of error

If the physical cause of digit errors is such that any digit is as likely to be affected as any other, the errors are described as random. A typical cause of random errors is thermal noise in the received signal. Other types of interference, however, may make it likely that when an error occurs, several symbols in succession will be corrupted; this is known as a burst error. A typical cause of burst errors is interference. Although the true behaviour of the channel may be more complex than either of these simple models, the random error and burst error models are simple, effective, and universally used for describing channel characteristics and error control code performance.

A channel used for transmitting binary digits is known as a binary channel, and if the probability of error is the same for 0s and 1s, the channel is called a Binary Symmetric Channel. The probability of error in binary digits is known as the bit error rate (BER).

14.2.5 Coding gain

Coding gain is a parameter commonly used for evaluating the effectiveness of an error correcting code, and hence for comparing codes. It is defined as the saving in energy per source bit of information for the coded system, relative to an uncoded system delivering the same BER. The effects of both error correction and the increase in transmission rate by a factor of n/k must be included when calculating the coding gain.

14.2.6 Criteria for choosing a code

The primary objective of error control coding will be to achieve a desired end-to-end probability of either uncorrected or undetected digit errors. The choice of code will depend on the error characteristics of the channel (particularly the random and burst error probabilities). The other important factors are likely to be the value of n/k (the increase in transmission rate over the channel), and the implementation complexity and cost of the coder and decoder.

14.3 Block coding

14.3.1 Single parity checks

The simplest block coder appends a single parity digit to each block of k message digits. This produces a systematic $(k + 1, k)$ code known as a single parity code. For binary digits, the parity bit may be either the modulo-2 sum of the message bits or 1 minus that sum. The former case is known as even parity, because the sum of the $k + 1$ bits of the codeword (including the parity bit) is 0, and the latter is known as odd parity.

The decoder forms the sum of the bits of the received codeword. For even parity a sum of 1 means that there has been an error, and a sum of 0 is assumed to mean that the received codeword is correct. (For odd parity 0 indicates an error, and the correct sum is 1). Note that when an error is detected there is no way to deduce which bit(s) are in error; also, if more than one error occurs, and the number of

errors is even, the single parity code will fail to detect them. This code is therefore a single error detecting (SED) code.

14.3.2 Linear block codes

The even parity code is the simplest example of a powerful class of codes called linear block codes. For such codes, the block of k message digits is represented as the k-element row vector d and the n digit codeword produced by the coder is represented by the n-element vector c. The function of the linear block coder is described by the Equation 14.1 where G is the (k x n) generator matrix.

$$c = d\,G \tag{14.1}$$

The multiplications and additions in this equation are carried out in GF(M) arithmetic (i.e. modulo-2 for binary digits). The codewords generated by the equation are called valid codewords. Since there are 2^k possible datawords, only 2^k of the 2^n possible n-digit words are valid codewords.

Systematic linear block codes are produced by a generator matrix of the form shown in Equation 14.2, where I_k is the (k x k) unit matrix.

$$G = [\,I_k\,|\,P\,] \tag{14.2}$$

When G has this form, the codeword c has the form of Equation 14.3, in other words the first k digits of the codeword equal the dataword, and the last $n - k$ digits are parity digits.

$$c = [\,d\,|\,d\,P\,] \tag{14.3}$$

Let r be the received codeword; in the absence of errors $r = c$. The decoder performs the operation of Equation 14.4, where H is the $((n - k)$ x n) parity check matrix, to produce the $(n - k)$ element syndrome s.

$$s = r\,H^T \tag{14.4}$$

H is chosen so that all valid codewords produce a zero syndrome; the syndrome then plays a crucial role in error correction. For the systematic code given above, the optimum form of parity check matrix is simply as in Equation 14.5.

$$H = [\,P^T\,|\,I_{n-k}\,] \tag{14.5}$$

For unsystematic codes, construction of the parity check matrix is more difficult.

14.3.3 Distance and code performance

The Hamming distance between two codewords is simply the number of bit positions in which they differ. If the Hamming distance between two codewords c_1 and c_2 is d, and c_1 is transmitted, then d errors would have to occur for codeword c_2 to be received. More generally, if the minimum Hamming distance between codeword c_1 and any other valid codeword is d_M and c_1 is transmitted, then the received codeword will not be a valid codeword if between 1 and $d_M - 1$ errors occur. The decoder could therefore detect up to $d_M - 1$ errors.

Assume that an invalid codeword is received. The distance (number of discrepancies) between it and all the valid codewords can be calculated at the decoder; let the distance between the received codeword and valid codeword c_i be d_i. If it is found that one of these distances d_i is less than all the others, then assuming random errors it is more likely that the transmitted codeword was c_j than any other. (This is because for realistic bit error rates the probability that the number of errors will be between 1 and d diminishes rapidly as d increases). The decoder could therefore be made to output the 'most probably correct' codeword c_j; this is known as Maximum Likelihood or Minimum Distance error correction. Such error correction is only possible if the number of errors is less than d/2, because otherwise the distance to two codewords could be equal, or the distance to a wrong codeword could be less than the distance to the correct one.

In general it is possible to trade off error detection and correction ability; a code which is required to allow correction of n_C errors and detection of a further n_D errors must have a minimum distance given by Equation 14.6.

$$d_M = 2 n_C + n_D + 1 \tag{14.6}$$

Determining the minimum distance of a code by comparing every pair of codewords would be time consuming for large codeword lengths. The following useful theorem means that only the 2^k valid codewords themselves need to be checked:

'The minimum Hamming distance of a linear block code is equal to the minimum Hamming weight among its non-zero codewords'. (The Hamming weight of a codeword is simply the number of ones in it).

14.3.4 Hard and soft decision decoding

There are two types of decoding: hard decision and soft decision decoding. In hard decision decoding the demodulated input signal is sliced to produce a digit stream; in the case of binary transmission, slicing is a simple thresholding operation. The decoder performs error detection and correction using this (possibly corrupted) received digit stream. In soft decision decoding the input to the decoder is the unsliced (analogue) sample stream; since the decoder implementation is usually digital, the sample stream is digitised to an adequate precision before input to the decoder. It has been found that in practice very low resolution digitisation (for example to only 8 or 16 levels) is often adequate. Soft decision decoding is computationally more demanding than hard decision decoding, but is used, particularly with convolutional codes (Section 14.5), to give an extra coding gain, typically of about 2dB. Soft decision decoding of this kind is hardly ever used with powerful block codes such as cyclic codes (Section 14.5) because of its large processing penalty. However, some codes such as Reed-Solomon codes (Section 14.4.4) can handle erasures (i.e. digits that are known to be in error) as well as erroneous digits, and this can be viewed as a form of soft decision decoding.

14.3.5 Hard decision decoding of linear block codes

The detection and correction of errors is based on analysis of the syndrome. For linear block codes, the syndrome of all valid codewords is zero as in Equation 14.7.

$$s = c H^T = 0 \tag{14.7}$$

If the syndrome of the received codeword is zero, the decoder assumes that it is correct, and the output dataword can be extracted directly from it (very easily, for a systematic code).

A non-zero syndrome is a certain indication of errors. If the transmitted codeword c is corrupted by the (modulo-2) addition of the n-bit error pattern e, the syndrome becomes as in Equation 14.8, which is a function only of the error pattern.

$$s = (c + e) H^T = e H^T \tag{14.8}$$

Hence the syndrome can be used to deduce, and remove, the errors. There are only $2^{(n-k)} - 1$ different non-zero syndromes, but there are $2^n - 1$ different error patterns, so every syndrome (including zero) may be generated by many different error patterns. However, as mentioned above, error patterns with small numbers of errors are more likely than those with large numbers of errors, so the most likely cause of a given non-zero syndrome is the corresponding error pattern with the fewest 1s. (This is why the decoder assumes no errors if the syndrome is zero).

One way to implement the decoder is to store in a look-table (called the Standard Array) the chosen error pattern for each syndrome. The decoder then calculates the syndrome, reads the corresponding error pattern from the table, and subtracts it (using bit-by-bit XOR) from the received codeword. Finally, the output dataword is extracted from the corrected codeword.

14.3.6 Hamming codes

Hamming codes are distance-3 linear block codes, so they can be used for single error correction (SEC) or dual error detection (DED). For binary Hamming codes, the codeword length is given by Equation 14.9, the number of parity bits is r, and the number of message bits is therefore given by Equation 14.10.

$$n = 2^r - 1 \tag{14.9}$$

$$k = n - r \tag{14.10}$$

The first four Hamming codes, for example, are (3,1), (7,4), (15,11), and (31,26) codes.

In Hamming codes, the submatrix P in Equations 14.2 and 14.5 is chosen so that its k rows are different from each other, and none of them is all-zero. It is then easy to show that each of the n possible single bit errors generates a different non-zero syndrome, so that any single bit error may be corrected.

14.3.7 2-D parity codes

The single parity code described in Section 14.3.1 is a distance 1, single error detecting (SED) code. A more powerful parity code can be created by arranging the message bits on a rectangular array, and calculating parity bits for each row and each column. Changing any one message bit changes one row parity and one column parity as well, so this is a distance 3-code, which can be used for single error correction or dual error detection.

The SEC decoder works as follows: the sums are formed of each row including its parity bit, and each column including its parity bit. If all the sums are zero, the codeword is assumed to be correct. If only a row sum or only a column sum is 1, the error is assumed to be in the corresponding parity bit. If one row sum and one column sum are 1, the error is assumed to be in the databit in that row and column, which is therefore corrected. If 2 or more row sums, or 2 or more column sums, are 1, a larger number of errors has occurred, which cannot be corrected.

14.3.8   Other codes

The most important linear block codes are the cyclic codes, which are considered in Section 14.4. In addition, many other linear and non-linear block codes have been developed. These include:

1. Hadamard codes. The code words are the rows of a Hadamard matrix, which is a binary n x n matrix (n even), in which each row differs from any other row in exactly n/2 positions; if the matrix elements are denoted +1 and −1, the rows are also orthogonal. Using this matrix and its complement (i.e. the matrix formed by exchanging the +1 and −1 elements), a blocklength n, distance n/2 code, with 2n code words can be formed.
2. Golay code. The Golay code is a (23,12) triple error correcting (TEC) code.
3. Constant ratio codes. Also known as m-out-of-n codes, have blocklength n, and each codeword has m bits set. These are non-linear codes of primarily historical interest.

14.3.9   Shortened codes

If no convenient code exists with exactly the required value of the dataword length k, a code having a larger value of k, say k' can be shortened. The number of check (parity) bits is unaltered by shortening, but the dataword and codeword lengths are both reduced by the same amount, so the (n', k') code becomes $(n' + k - k', k)$. An example would be the use of a (15,11) Hamming code, shortened to (12,8), for the byte-by-byte transmission of data. Shortening may or may not increase the minimum distance, and hence the error control ability, of the code.

At its simplest, shortening the code consists simply of encoding k' databits, of which k are the required data and $k' - k$ are zero. The main advantage arises when a systematic code is used, because then the first $k' - k$ bits in the codeword can be set to zero and need not be transmitted. In principle, the received codeword can then be lengthened to n' bits again by the reinsertion of $k' - k$ zeros prior to decoding with the (n', k') decoder.

In practice, however, the decoder should be modified, because errors in untransmitted bits are impossible. Consider the example of a shortened Hamming code. The Hamming code can normally correct any single error. However, if on receiving a shortened codeword the decoder calculates a syndrome which would normally imply an error in one of the untransmitted bits, that cannot be the true cause. The next most likely cause is a double error pattern in the transmitted bits. If there were only one double bit error pattern which could produce that syndrome, then the decoder could apply the corresponding double bit correction. If, however, more than one double bit error pattern could have given rise to that syndrome, the decoder cannot guarantee to correct the error. If this is the case, the minimum distance of the shortened code is no greater than that of the unshortened code.

In decoders for shortened cyclic codes, further modifications are desirable to reduce decode time. These are discussed in Section 14.4.6.

14.3.10   Extended codes

An odd-distance code may be extended by adding an overall (even) parity bit; for binary codes this is just the modulo-2 sum of the codebits. This increases the code distance by 1. If the original distance is 2t + 1, the code is t-error correcting; the extended code can correct up to t errors and detect the case when there are t+1 errors, which is often useful. An example of an extended code is the (24,12) extension of the Golay (23,12) code, which has a convenient rate k/n of exactly 0.5.

14.4   Interleaved and concatenated codes

Interleaving (also known as interlacing) is a technique used to combat burst errors, such as those which occur in fading radio channels. As an illustration, consider ten 15-bit codewords produced by a Hamming (15,11) coder. Assume that these are stored as the 10 rows of a 10 x 15 bit array, and that the array is then transmitted column by column. This means that the 10 first bits of the 15 codewords will be transmitted, then the 10 second bits, and so on. The receiver re-groups the received bits into the original pattern of ten 15-bit codewords before decoding.

In this example, if there is a burst error of up to 10 bits duration, no more than one bit in each codeword will be affected. Because the code is single-error-correcting, the receiver can clearly correct these errors, so the use of 10-way interleaving allows correction of 10-bit burst errors. The extension of this technique to more powerful codes is straightforward, and permits correction of combinations of random and burst errors.

Concatenated coding means the application of one error correcting code to the input data, followed by the application of another code to codewords output by the first coder, and so on. Concatenated coding is valuable when the different codes can combat different types of error (e.g. burst vs. random errors). It is used when the overall efficiency (k/n) of the concatenated code is higher than that of any single code with the same error correcting ability.

14.5   Cyclic codes

Cyclic codes are a very important class of linear block codes, for two reasons: firstly, cyclic codes are available for a wide range of error detecting and correcting requirements, including burst error correction; and secondly, the encoders and decoders can be implemented efficiently using feedback shift registers.

14.5.1   The mathematics of cyclic codes

In the theory of cyclic codes, polynomial notation is used rather than the vector notation used earlier. In this notation the k digits of the input data word are treated as the coefficients of a polynomial d(x). For example the 4-binary digit data word (1011) is represented by the polynomial of Equation 14.11. Similarly, the n digit codeword is represented by polynomial c(x).

$$d(x) = 1.x^3 + 0.x^2 + 1.x^1 + 1.x^0 \qquad (14.11)$$

The mathematical basis of cyclic codes is the 'algebra of polynomials over GF(M)'; this means that when adding, subtracting, multiplying or dividing polynomials, the arithmetic which has to be carried out on the coefficients is done in GF(M). Binary cyclic codes use polynomials over GF(2) so the coefficient arithmetic is modulo-2. In this case, for example, the product of the polynomials given by equations 14.12 and 14.13 is as in expression 14.14.

$$g(x) = 1.x^1 + 1.x^0 \qquad (14.12)$$

$$p(x) = 1.x^2 + 1.x^1 + 1.x^0 \qquad (14.13)$$

$$1.x^3 + (1+1).x^2 + (1+1).x^1 + 1.x^0 \qquad (14.14)$$

But Equation 14.15 holds, resulting in Equation 14.16.

$$GF(2)(1+1) = 0 \qquad (14.15)$$

$$g(x)p(x) = 1.x^3 + 0.x^2 + 0.x^1 + 1.x^0 \qquad (14.16)$$

The variable x never needs to be evaluated; it serves only a 'place keeping' role.

An (n,k) cyclic code for M-ary digits is completely defined by a generator polynomial. This generator polynomial must be a factor of x^n-1 and it must be of degree r given by Equation 14.17. In other words it is of the form given by expression 14.18.

$$r = (n - k) \qquad (14.17)$$

$$1.x^r + g_{r-1}x^{r-1} + \ldots + g_o x^o \qquad (14.18)$$

It therefore has r + 1 coefficients, the most significant of which is always 1. There is a very large number of known binary cyclic codes, and published tables are available which give for each code the values of n and k, the coefficients of g(x), and the distance of the code and hence its error detection and correction ability. In such tables it is common practice to represent the binary coefficients of the generator polynomial in actual notation. For example, if the generator of a (7,3) cyclic code (which therefore has 7–3+1=5 coefficients) is written '35' in octal, the binary coefficients are (11101), and the generator polynomial is given by Equation 14.19.

$$g(x) = 1.x^4 + 1.x^3 + 1.x^2 + 0.x^1 + 1.x^0 \qquad (14.19)$$

Unsystematic codewords c(x) can be generated from input data words d(x) by calculating Equation 14.20.

$$c(x) = g(x)d(x) \qquad (14.20)$$

Of much more interest are systematic cyclic codes, in which the first k bits of the codeword are equal to the data word and the last r bits are parity bits. In polynomial notation Equation 14.21 is obtained, where the parity check polynomial, p(x) is set equal to the remainder after dividing $x^r d(x)$ by g(x).

$$c(x) = x^r d(x) + p(x) \qquad (14.21)$$

This remainder operation can be conveniently calculated by feedback shift register circuits described in the next section.

If the received, possibly corrupted, codeword is r(x), the decoder calculates a syndrome polynomial, s(x), which is used for error detection and correction. s(x) is defined in one of two ways: as the remainder after dividing either r(x) or $x^r r(x)$ by g(x); the second of these two options allows maximum commonality between the coder and decoder, as explained below. In either case a valid codeword produces a zero syndrome.

14.5.2 Implementation of cyclic coders and decoders

Cyclic coders and decoders are implemented using Linear Feedback Shift Registers (LFSR). The general form of a systematic cyclic coder is shown in Figure 14.1, for the code with generator g(x) given by Equation 14.22.

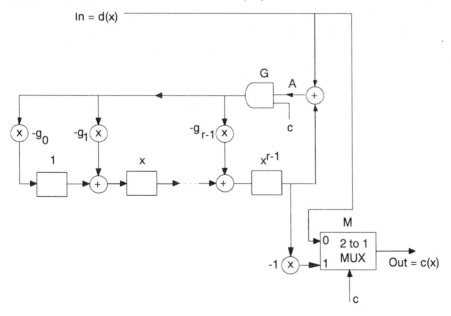

Figure 14.1 General form of a systematic cyclic coder

$$g(x) = 1.x^r + g_{r-1}x^{r-1} + \dots + g_0 x^0 \qquad (14.22)$$

All multiplications and additions are in GF(M), for example in modulo-2 for binary digits. The rectangular boxes are latches which store the results from multipliers or adders, as appropriate; there are r multipliers and latches (where $r = n - k$ as before). The latches are initially cleared. During the first k cycles of operation control line c is ON and the k digits of the data word are fed through the 2-to-1 multiplexer M to the output; also AND gate G is open, so the adder output A is fed back to the coefficient multipliers. These multiply A by the values $-g_0$ to $-g_{r-1}$. For the last r cycles of operation, control line c is OFF, so gate G is closed and the multiplier inputs and outputs are all zero. The r values stored in the shift register are therefore sequentially output through the 2-to-1 multiplexer.

The function of this circuit is equivalent to the polynomial division $x^r d(x)/g(x)$; the digits produced at A are the quotient of the division, and the contents of the shift register after the kth cycle are the remainder (x^0 term at the left, x^{r-1} term at the right).

For binary coders, all the coefficients are 0 or 1; multiplication by 0 is equivalent to removal of the corresponding path and adder, and multiplication by -1 is equivalent to multiplication by 1 (in modulo-2 arithmetic), which in turn is equivalent to a direct connection to the adder input. Each adder is a modulo-2 adder, or XOR gate. Hence the systematic binary coder for the (7,4) code with generator polynomial given by Equation 14.23 (which would be represented in tables as 1011 in binary, or 13 in octal) is as shown in Figure 14.2.

$$g(x) = x^3 + x + 1 \qquad (14.23)$$

The decoder calculates the syndrome of the received (possibly corrupt) codeword. This is done using a linear feedback shift register circuit exactly as in the coder. If the received codeword is represented as r(x), the circuit performs the polynomial division $x^r r(x)/g(x)$, and the contents of the shift register after the nth cycle are the remainder of this calculation, in other words the required syndrome. As mentioned above, other syndromes are sometimes used; in particular it is possible to produce a circuit to perform the division r(x)/g(x). This is achieved by removing the input from the right-hand end of the LFSR circuit and instead placing an adder at the left-hand end, one of whose inputs is the input data word, and the other the output of the $-g_0$ multiplier. Although this produces a

different syndrome, the basis of decoder operation is the same in either case.

In a decoder which is only designed to detect errors, the syndrome is tested using an r-input OR gate, whose output is 1 (indicating an error) if the syndrome is non-zero. In an error correcting decoder, further processing is required to correct the error. The general form of a cyclic error correcting decoder of the Meggitt or error trapping variety is shown in Figure 14.3. During the first n cycles control line

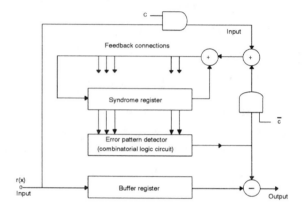

Figure 14.3 General form of a Meggitt or error trapping cyclic error correcting decoder

c is ON and the syndrome is calculated as already described; while this is happening the received codeword is stored in a buffer register. During the second n cycles, c is OFF and the received codeword is output from the buffer register. The error pattern detector circuit outputs a 1 (in the binary case) whenever the corresponding bit of the received codeword has been deduced to be in error. This inverts, and hence corrects, the output codeword. Since the code is systematic, its first k digits are the required data word. It can be seen from Figure 14.3 that the signal from the error pattern detector circuit is also fed back to the linear feedback shift register input. This produces an 'updated' syndrome; after the whole codeword has been

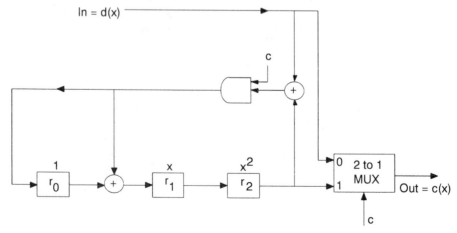

Figure 14.2 A systematic binary cyclic coder

corrected the remaining syndrome in the shift register should be zero. If it is not, it indicates that more errors have occurred than can be corrected by the code. Depending on the system requirements, this condition can be detected and flagged.

The internal details of the error pattern detector are simple for single error correcting codes. In this case, the syndrome corresponding to an error in the first (most significant) bit of the codeword is calculated. The error pattern detector is then simply a combinational logic circuit which outputs a 1 when it detects this pattern in the shift register. For multiple error correcting decoders, as discussed in the following section, the design of the error pattern detector is more complex.

14.5.3   BCH codes

BCH codes are the most extensive and powerful family of error-correcting cyclic codes, and because of their mathematical structure allow decoders to be implemented reasonably easily, even for multiple error correction. Both binary and non-binary BCH codes exist; there are two classes of binary BCH codes: primitive BCH codes, which have a block length $n = 2^m - 1$, and non-primitive BCH codes, where n is a factor of $2^m - 1$. For any positive integers m and $t(t < 2^{m-1})$ there exists a primitive BCH code with the parameters n and r given by Equations 14.24 and 14.25 and minimum distance by Equation 14.26.

$$n = 2^m - 1 \tag{14.24}$$

$$r = n - k \leq m t \tag{14.25}$$

$$d_M \geq 2 t + 1 \tag{14.26}$$

Such a code can therefore be used as a t-error-correcting code.

Detailed discussion of both the algebraic basis of BCH codes and the decoder algorithms is described in many textbooks. Primitive BCH codes include cyclic forms of the Hamming SEC codes, and non-primitive BCH codes include a cyclic form of the (23, 12) Golay TEC code.

The two main procedures used in decoding are:

1. Peterson's direct solution, suitable for up to about 6-error-correction.
2. The Berlekamp/Massey algorithm, an iterative algorithm applicable to any BCH code.

Some decoder algorithms have also been developed for specific BCH codes, for example, the Kasami algorithm for the (23, 12) TEC code.

14.5.4   Reed-Solomon codes

Reed-Solomon (RS) codes are an important subclass of non-binary BCH codes. RS codes have a true minimum distance which is the maximum possible for a linear (n, k) code, as in Equation 14.27. They are therefore examples of maximum-distance-separable codes.

$$d = n - k + 1 \tag{14.27}$$

For decoding RS codes, both Peterson's method and the Berlekamp/Massey algorithm can be used. The latter is also known as the FSR synthesis algorithm, because it is equivalent to the generation

of the coefficients of a certain LFSR. A further technique for decoding RS codes is called transform decoding, which uses a finite field analogue of the Fourier transform.

A particularly important ability of RS codes (and non-binary BCH codes in general) is their ability to perform errors and erasures decoding. This is of value if the receiver can under some circumstances signal the loss of a received digit. If such a code has distance d, it can correct combinations of l errors and s erasures provided that $2l + s < d$.

While RS codes are naturally suited to non-binary digits they can sometimes be used very effectively for binary channels by treating groups of m bits as 2^m-ary digits. It has been shown that such codes outperform binary codes with the same rate and block length at low output error rates. Also, when used in this way RS codes have a natural burst-error correcting ability, because, for example, a burst of up to m bit errors will affect at most 2 'digits'.

14.5.5   Other cyclic codes

14.5.5.1   *Majority logic decodable codes*

These codes are slightly inferior to BCH codes in terms of error correction, but have simple decoder implementations in which the error pattern detector circuit is a combination of XOR and majority logic gates.

14.5.5.2   *Burst error correcting codes*

Fire codes are a widely used class of algebraically constructed burst error correcting cyclic codes, which require a minimum of 3b − 1 parity bits to correct bursts of up to b bits in length. Other, more efficient, burst error correcting cyclic codes, found by computer search, are also available.

14.5.6   Shortening cyclic codes

Cyclic codes may be shortened; the design of a systematic cyclic coder is unaffected by this, except that only k bits are clocked in rather than k' before the control line is switched to output the parity check bits. In the decoder, the same approach of simply reducing the number of clocks can be used for syndrome polynomial calculation; however, if error correction is to be carried out the error pattern detector must be modified to deal with the missing leading bits, and the fact that there cannot be errors in those missing bits.

14.6   Convolutional codes

A convolutional coder operates on the source data stream using a 'sliding window' and produces a continuous stream of encoded symbols. Many of the concepts related to block codes also apply to convolutional codes; they can for example be systematic or unsystematic, and can be used for error detection or correction. However, there are many good block codes which can be used for error detection with simple encoding and decoding, so when only error detection is required, block codes are almost always used.

By contrast with the analysis and design of block codes, much less mathematical analysis is needed for convolutional codes, and some of the best codes are found by computer search. A rigorous mathematical treatment is however available in Forney (1970). Tables of good convolutional codes for various values of k, n, and L are

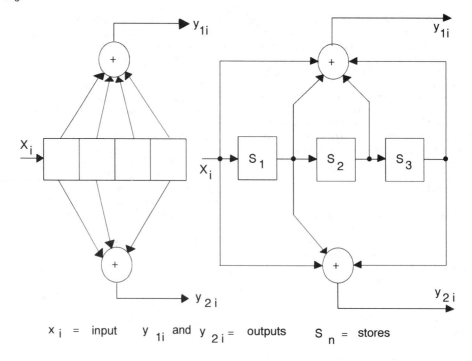

x_i = input y_{1i} and y_{2i} = outputs S_n = stores

Figure 14.4   Two commonly used representations for convolutional coders, for the example of a binary rate 1/2 constraint length 4 code

available in reference books, together with measures of their performance, such as their coding gain at different output BERs.

14.6.1   Convolutional coding

A convolutional coder takes M-ary input digits in groups of k at each time-step and produces groups of n output digits. Since the input and output data rates are k and n digits per time-step, the code is known as a rate k/n code. The coder contains k parallel shift registers of maximum length L − 1, where L is known as the constraint length of the code. Two common pictorial representations of such a coder (with k = 1, n = 2 and L = 4) are shown in Figure 14.4.

The output digits are formed as weighted sums of the input digit(s) and the digits in the shift register(s), with arithmetic in GF(M) as for block codes. In binary, the only possible weights are 0 and 1, so the output bits are formed by selected modulo-2 sums of the input bit(s) and register contents. After the output digits have been formed, the input digit(s) are shifted into the shift register(s).

An alternative representation of a convolutional coder is as a single shift register of length ≤ (L − 1)k digits. In each time-step the n output digits are calculated and then the k input digits are loaded sequentially into this register. Sometimes Lk is called the constraint length (a conflicting definition with the one above).

The digits in the shift register(s) (s_1 to s_3 in Figure 14.4) define the state of the coder at each time-step; there are therefore $M^{(L-1)k}$ possible coder states. The possible transitions from a given coder state at one time-step to another state at the next time step are determined by the shift register arrangement. The actual output code digit stream is determined by both the shift register arrangement and the particular summations chosen to form the output digits.

There are M^k patterns of k input digits, so from each state there are M^k possible next states. The behaviour of the coder can therefore

be described using a trellis diagram, as shown in Figure 14.5. In this, the possible states of the coder are represented as $M^{(L-1)k}$ nodes in a vertical column, and the state-to-state transitions at each time-step are represented by a rightwards step of one column. From each node at time-step i there are M^k branches to successor states at time-step i + 1. In a worthwhile code no two different patterns of input digits give the same transitions.

14.6.2   Viterbi decoding

The error correcting power of a convolutional code arises from the fact that only some of the possible sequences of digits are valid outputs from the coder; these sequences correspond to possible paths through the trellis. The job of the decoder is to find which valid digit sequence is closest to the received digit sequence. This is analogous to the job of a block decoder, but because the input digit sequence is continuous the coder must operate continuously, and must have an acceptably small delay between the arrival of particular input digits and output of the corresponding decoded digits.

The optimum (in the sense of Maximum Likelihood) decoding of convolutionally coded sequences can be carried out using the Viterbi algorithm, which can be applied to both hard-decision and soft-decision decoding. Calculating the most likely digit sequence output by the coder is equivalent to calculating the most likely path followed by the coder through the trellis. In a hard-decision decoder (and assuming a binary symmetric channel for simplicity) the most likely coder path is the one which has the smallest number of disagreements with the received bit stream. In a soft-decision decoder the most likely path is the one with the smallest squared difference from the received signal. These measures of discrepancy between the received signal and possible transmitted signals are referred to as path metrics.

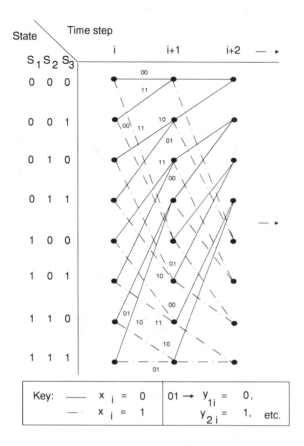

State | Time step

Key:
  —— $x_i = 0$ $01 \rightarrow y_{1i} = 0,$
  — — $x_i = 1$ $y_{2i} = 1,$ etc.

Figure 14.5 The trellis diagram for the coder of Figure 14.4

It appears at first sight that the number of candidate paths grows exponentially with each time-step. However, at time step i the decoder only needs to keep track of the single best path so far to each node; any worse path to that node cannot be part of the overall best path through the node. The number of paths to be remembered therefore remains constant and equal to the number of nodes. For each node the decoder must store the best path to that node and the total metric corresponding to that path. By comparing the actual n received digits at time-step i + 1 with those corresponding to each possible path on the trellis from step i to step i + 1, the decoder calculates the additional metric for each path. From these, it selects the best path to each node at time step i + 1, and updates the stored records of the paths and metrics.

In theory the decoder has to wait until the hypothetical end of transmission before it can decide the overall maximum likelihood path from start to finish. Fortunately it can be shown that a fixed finite delay between input and output is all that is necessary to give nearly optimum performance. In particular, it can be shown that if all the reasonably likely paths at time-step i are traced backwards in time, they will converge to the same path within about 5L time-steps. The decoder therefore operates with a fixed delay of δ steps, where δ ≥ 5L; at time i it selects one of the reasonably likely paths and the bit from that path at time i − δ is output as the decoded

output. The path stores within the decoder can therefore be implemented as δ bit shift registers.

14.6.3 Code performance

A decoding error occurs when the path through the trellis selected by the decoder is not the correct path. The result will almost always be a burst error; it is even possible, for some codes, for the worst error to be infinite in extent. Such codes are clearly unusable. Analysis of the exact statistics of the error bursts (their probability as a function of their duration) is very complex; approximations can however be derived using the minimum free distance of the code. This is obtained by considering all possible error paths, that is, incorrect paths which depart from the correct path at one symbol time and rejoin it later. The minimum free distance is the minimum number of symbol differences between any of these error paths and the correct path. Note, however, that calculation of the true error rates involves analysis of many other interacting effects.

In practice, the user of a convolutional code will normally use the published graphs of output BER as a function of SNR (E_b/n_o). The coding gain is also often quoted, but it is important to remember that this varies with SNR.

14.7 Encryption

14.7.1 Applications of encryption

It is sometimes the case that a sender wishes to send a recipient a message which he wants to keep secret from an eavesdropper. This message, which in its usable form is called plaintext, must be transmitted over a channel to which the eavesdropper is presumed to have access. The process by which the sender and recipient can achieve secrecy is called encryption or encipherment.

In encryption, the plaintext is transformed into a message called the ciphertext in such a way that the recipient can recover the plaintext from the ciphertext, while the eavesdropper cannot. The transformation of plaintext to ciphertext and back is controlled by one or more strings of symbols or digits called keys.

A further use of encryption is for authentication, when it is necessary to check that you are communicating with the correct person and not an impostor.

14.7.2 Principles of encryption

Encryption algorithms have two possible components: substitution, in which plaintext symbols are mapped to different symbols, and transposition, in which the locations of symbols in the ciphertext are altered from the locations of the corresponding symbols in the plaintext. The need for substitution is obvious; many symbols have sufficient significance that an eavesdropper could deduce information from them wherever they were, and perhaps alter them. Transposition is desirable to prevent the eavesdropper deducing information by comparing messages, or corrupting known parts of a message, even if he does not know what they have been altered to.

The most completely secure system is known as the one-time pad. This is a symbol-by-symbol substitution system in which the key is as long as the message; hence no deductions about one part of the ciphertext help the eavesdropper to decipher the rest. The problem is in distribution of the key itself (key management), which is now as big a problem as the original problem of sending the message securely.

Practical encryption systems must have manageable keys, and are based on algorithms for which it is too difficult, rather than theoretically impossible, to decrypt the ciphertext. Various (worst case) assumptions are made in designing and analysing the security of the system; it is normally assumed that the eavesdropper knows the encryption and decryption algorithms, but not the key. When a very high degree of security is required, it is also assumed that the eavesdropper has obtained (by other means) the plaintext corresponding to some of the intercepted ciphertext.

In conventional or symmetric cryptosystems, it is easy to deduce the deciphering key from the enciphering key (they may even be the same), so both must be kept secret. In public key cryptosystems, however, the enciphering key can be made public by the recipient; despite this, it is believed to be computationally infeasible for an eavesdropper to work out the decipherment key. A further technique, public key-distribution (Diffie, 1976) applies the same principles to the secure distribution of keys for conventional cryptosystems.

In stream ciphers, a stream of plaintext symbols is enciphered symbol by symbol. Instead of a true one time pad, the stream of enciphering symbols is generated by a symbol generator under the control of the control of the enciphering key. A simple example for binary data is the use of a pseudo random binary sequence (PRBS) generator, initialised by the chosen key. This produces a stream of 0s and 1s, which are XORed with the databit stream. Clearly, recovery of the original bit stream requires exactly the same operation, so the decipherment key is the same as the encipherment key. Such systems are widely used in communications; their advantages include ease of encryption and decryption, and the fact that single bit errors in the channel cause only single bit errors in the decrypted plaintext. Disadvantages include the effort of initial synchronisation and resynchronisation if synchronisation is lost, and the fact that there is no transposition element in this system.

In block ciphers, the message is divided into n-bit blocks and the blocks are input sequentially to the algorithm. At each stage the key (which is usually constant for the whole message) is also entered, and the encryptor typically uses both substitution and transposition to produce consecutive blocks of ciphertext. In such systems an error in transmission usually results in corruption of the whole received block.

In all these systems, it is essential that the key is changed frequently; the security of an otherwise satisfactory cryptosystem may be compromised if the key is reused.

14.7.3 Specific cryptosystems

Many cryptosystems have been developed, both by government establishments and commercial organisations. The first public standard system is the American National Bureau of Standards Data Encryption Standard (DES), which is a block cipher with a 64-bit blocklength involving both substitution and transposition under the control of a 56-bit key (NBS, 1977), the original proposal was for a 64-bit key and there is debate about whether the 56-bit key is secure enough. Many hardware and software implementations of this standard exist.

The RSA algorithm (Rivest, 1978) is a public-key encryption algorithm in which the recipient publishes an encipherment key N, consisting of the product of two primes, each of order 10^{100}, together with another number E. The sender breaks the plaintext into blocks which can be represented by numbers less than N, then encrypts the blocks using a simple modulo-N arithmetic operation involving E. The recipient recovers the plaintext using further simple modulo-N operations which rely on knowledge of the factors

of N. The difficulty of factoring numbers of order 10^{200} means that the eavesdropper cannot work out the two factors of N and cannot decrypt the message.

14.8 Spread spectrum systems

14.8.1 Applications

Spread spectrum systems (Proakis, 1989; Dixon, 1976) are used in digital communications for:

1. Combating interference arising from jamming other users, or self-interference due to multipath effects.
2. Making it difficult to detect the signal, to achieve covert operation.
3. Making it difficult to demodulate the signal, to achieve privacy.

Signals in which spread spectrum techniques are used to make detection difficult are referred to as Low Probability of Intercept (LPI) signals. The use of spread spectrum techniques to allow several users to share a common channel is known as code division multiple access (CDMA) or spread spectrum multiple access (SSMA). In conventional approaches to multiple access (such as FDMA) the channel transfer function may be very poor at some frequencies and good at others. The advantage of using spread spectrum signals for CDMA and for combating multipath is that by using a much wider channel bandwidth, all users get a uniformly acceptable service, rather than a good service for some, and bad for others. For this reason there is currently interest in spread spectrum systems for wireless LANs within buildings.

14.8.2 Direct sequence spread spectrum

In direct sequence spread spectrum (DSSS), the transmitter and receiver contain identical psuedo-random sequence generators producing a pseudo-noise (PN) signal. In the transmitter, the input data stream is XORed with the PN signal before transmission. In the receiver the received signal is XORed with the PN stream to recover the original data stream; this is equivalent to correlation with the known PN sequence. There is an obvious analogy between this process and stream ciphering (Section 14.8) but with the crucial difference that in DSSS the PN sequence is at a much greater clock frequency than the data stream. Each bit of the PN sequence is called a chip, and the clock rate of the PN generator is called the chip rate. In practical systems the chip rate is a large integer multiple L of the databit rate. The bandwidth of the transmitted signal is therefore L times greater than that of the data stream.

The DSSS signal gives LPI (a low probability of intercept) because the total signal power is spread over a wide bandwidth and the signal is noise-like, making it hard to detect. In anti-jamming (AJ) applications, the transmitter introduces an unpredictable element into the modulation of the signal, known also to the receiver but kept secret from opponents, as in stream ciphering. This, together with the wide bandwidth of the transmitted signal, makes jamming more difficult than for conventional signals. In CDMA applications, the various transmitters which are sharing the channel use different fixed PN sequences which are chosen so that their cross-correlation is low. After a receiver has correlated the received signal with its particular PN pattern, the interference from the other PN sequences is therefore low. The chosen sequences must also have noise-like autocorrelation functions, to help the receiver to synchronise correctly to the partially unknown timing of the transmitter. Some often-used sequences with these properties are called Gold and Kasami sequences (Proakis, 1989).

Direct sequence spread spectrum requires the overall channel (including, where relevant, equalisation in the receiver) to have approximately unity gain, pure delay characteristics over the whole signal bandwidth. This is achievable for local radio systems and transmission lines, but can be much harder to achieve over a wide bandwidth in long distance radio links.

14.8.3 Frequency hopping spread spectrum

In Frequency Hopping Spread Spectrum (FHSS), the available channel bandwidth LW is divided into L slots of bandwidth W. In any signalling interval the signal occupies only one slot or a few ($\ll$ L) slots. The spreading of the spectrum arises because the active slot frequency 'hops' around pseudo-randomly. Because of the difficulty of maintaining phase references as the frequency hops, FSK modulation and non-coherent demodulation are normally used in FHSS, rather than PSK and coherent demodulation.

In block hopping FHSS, the input signal is first modulated using a conventional binary or M-ary FSK modulator, whose output is one of M frequencies within a bandwidth W. This block of frequencies is then shifted to somewhere in the full bandwidth LW by mixing it with a local oscillator signal derived from a frequency synthesiser controlled by a PN generator. The receiver has a matching PN generator, frequency synthesiser and mixer, which shift the frequency block down to baseband again, where it is demodulated by a conventional FSK demodulator. An alternative approach, which has better resistance to some kinds of jamming, but requires a more complex demodulator, is called independent tone hopping. In this, each digit value is combined with the output of the PN generator, to control the frequency synthesiser directly. The resulting frequency separation of the tones corresponding to different digit values at any particular time can be up to the full channel bandwidth.

The frequency hopping rate is usually chosen to be equal to or faster than the symbol rate. If they are equal, it is referred to as slow-hopping, and if the hop rate is faster it is referred to as fast hopping. Fast hopping is used to combat a follower jammer, which attempts to detect the tone(s) and immediately broadcasts other tones with adjacent frequencies. However, when fast hopping is used, the fact that phase coherence cannot be maintained across hops means that the energy from the successive hops in one symbol must be combined incoherently; this causes a non-coherent combining loss.

FHSS signals are primarily used in AJ and CDMA systems. Usually, FHSS is preferred over DSSS because it has less severe timing requirements and is less sensitive to channel gain and phase fluctuations.

14.9 References

Diffie, W. and Hellman, M.E. (1976) New direction in cryptography, *IEEE Trans. Inform. Theory*, pp. 644-654.

Dixon, R.C. (1976) *Spread Spectrum Systems*, Wiley, New York.

Forney, G.D. (1970) Convolutional codes 1: Algebraic structure, *IEEE Trans. Info. Theory*, (IT-16) pp. 720-738.

Lin, S. and Costello, D.J. (1983) *Error control coding: fundamentals and applications*, Prentice-Hall, Englewood Cliffs, NJ.

Michelson, A.M. and Levesque, A.H. (1985) *Error-control techniques for digital communication*, Wiley-Interscience, New York.

NBS (1977) National Bureau of Standards. *Data encryption standard*, Federal Information Processing Standard (FIPS) Publication No. 46.

Peterson, W.W. and Weldon, E.J. (1972) *Error-correcting codes*, 2nd ed., MIT Press, Cambridge, MA.

Proakis, J.G. (1989) *Digital communications*, 2nd ed., McGraw-Hill, New York.

Rivest, R.L., Shamir, A. and Adelman, L. (1978) A method for obtaining signatures and public-key cryptosystems, *Commun. ACM*, pp. 120-126.

15 Telecommunication cables

P J Howard
Telecommunication Consultant

Contents

15.1 Introduction

Cables provide the transmission medium for the majority of tele-communication systems. The installed cost of cables is a significant proportion of total investment in any network. A fascinating aspect of telecommunication transmission history has been the achievement of progressive upgrades in traffic capacity over existing cable links. For example, the application of 30 channel systems to de-loaded audio pairs, the operation of coaxial cables initially with 300 channel (1.3MHz) systems and many years later with either 2700 channel (12MHz) systems or 1920 (140Mbit/s) digital systems.

Today, virtually all new cables except for the local area, are of optical fibre and of single mode design. Not only does single mode provide economic solutions to today's requirements, it also holds the greatest promise for exploitation as the bearer for high capacity systems yet to be designed.

This section gives a description of the various cables used in telecommunication networks and their impairments on signal trans-mission. Copper pairs, coaxial cables and various optical fibres are included.

15.2 Symmetric pair cables

Symmetric pair or balanced pair cables provide the most economic solution for the direct provision of audio circuits over short dis-tances, for example from local exchange to street cabinets and distribution pillars. Notwithstanding new techniques in mobile radio and optical fibre, conventional copper pair cables for new communities, and for the enhancement and replacement of very old cables in established areas, continue to be in substantial demand.

A typical local area cable is of unit twin construction. The conduc-tors are insulated with cellular polyethylene of various colours which provides for pair identification within the cable. Two insu-lated conductors are twisted together to form a pair, the twist length and that of the other pairs, being specially chosen to minimise crosstalk. The pairs are then assembled into basic units of either twenty-five, fifty or one hundred pair units. Each unit is identified by a lapping of coloured tape.

To prevent the cables filling with water in the event of damage to the cable sheath, or due to a faulty joint sheath closure, the cable can be fully filled with petroleum jelly during manufacture. The cable sheath is of polyethylene with an internal Glover barrier. This vapour barrier comprises an aluminium polyethylene laminate tape which is applied longitudinally with a small overlap, and with the polyethylene surface facing outwards. As the polyethylene sheath is extruded around the finished cable it bonds to the laminate. This

APL sheath provides an effective moisture barrier and electrostatic screen.

Cables of this design can be supplied with conductor diameters ranging from 0.32mm to 0.9mm, and in sizes ranging from 100 pairs to 3200 pairs or more. The maximum average resistance and mutual capacitance is shown in Table 15.1. Overall cable diameters are in the range 17mm to 70mm, depending on conductor gauge and number of pairs. The capacitive unbalance at voice frequency is generally less than 275pF in a 500m length.

For longer circuits, cables with a lower mutual capacitance and less capacitance unbalance are required. These requirements are met with a star quad construction i.e. diagonally opposite conduc-tors form a pair. A typical cable is formed from 0.63mm or 0.9mm cellular polyethylene insulated conductors, four being twisted into a star quad formation. The quads are then stranded into a concentric layered cable, the direction of standing alternating in successive layers. The complete cable of between 14 and 520 quads is then sheathed as described for the unit twin design. The resultant cable has a smaller diameter then the equivalent unit twin design and a more tightly toleranced characteristic as shown in Table 15.2. The capacitance unbalance at voice frequency in a 500m length is generally less than 40pF between pairs in the same quad, less than 25pF between pairs in adjacent quads and less than 150pF to earth.

Table 15.2 Typical characteristics of star quad cable

Wire diameter (mm)	Average mutual capacitance (nF/km)			Nominal resistance (ohm/km @ 10^{0}C)
	Nominal	Minimum	Maximum	
0.63	45	38	49	53.2
0.9	41	39	44	26.0

15.2.1 Analysis of balanced pair cables

The characteristics of a cable can be defined in terms of its primary coefficients, where the distributed characteristics are represented by circuit elements lumped at unit lengths apart.

The primary coefficients of a uniform transmission line are:

R = Resistance in Ohms per unit length
G = Leakance in Siemens per unit length
L = Inductance in Henries per unit length
C = Capacitance in Farads per unit length

The secondary coefficients are the propagation coefficient P and the characteristic impedance Z_O given by Equations 15.1 and 15.2.

$$P = [(R + j\omega L)(G + j\omega C)]^{1/2} \qquad (15.1)$$

$$Z_O = \left[\frac{(R + j\omega L)}{(G + j\omega C)} \right]^{1/2} \qquad (15.2)$$

The propagation coefficient P is complex, as in Equation 15.3.

$$P = \alpha + j\beta \qquad (15.3)$$

Table 15.1 Typical characteristics of unit twin cable

Conductor diameter (mm)	Maximum average resistance (ohms/km @ 20^{0}C)	Maximum average mutual capacitance (nF/km)
0.32	223	56
0.40	143	56
0.50	91	56
0.63	58	56
0.90	28	56

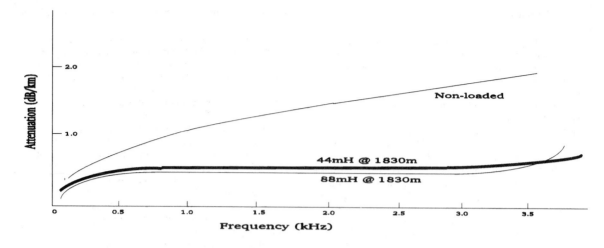

Figure 15.1 Effect of loading. 0.63mm conductors of mutual capacitance 45nF/km

The real part α of the propagation coefficient thus gives the attenuation of the line (in nepers per unit length) and is the attenuation coefficient. The imaginary part β is called the phase coefficient.

The relationship between the attenuation and phase coefficients and the primary coefficients is given by Equation 15.4.

$$\tanh(\alpha + j\beta) = [(R + j\omega L)(G + j\omega C)]^{1/2} \qquad (15.4)$$

By expanding real and imaginary parts, Equations 15.5 and 15.6 can be obtained.

$$\alpha = [\tfrac{1}{2}((R^2 + \omega^2 L^2)(G^2 + \omega^2 C^2))^{1/2} \\ + \tfrac{1}{2}(RG - \omega^2 LC)]^{1/2} \qquad (15.5)$$

$$\beta = [\tfrac{1}{2}((R^2 + \omega^2 L^2)(G^2 + \omega^2 C^2))^{1/2} \\ - \tfrac{1}{2}(RG - \omega^2 LC)]^{1/2} \qquad (15.6)$$

At low frequencies, $\omega L \ll R$ and $\omega C \ll G$ giving Equation 15.7.

$$\alpha = (RG)^{1/2} \qquad (15.7)$$

At audio frequencies $\omega L \ll R$ but $\omega C \gg G$ giving Equation 15.8.

$$\alpha = (\tfrac{1}{2}\omega CR)^{1/2} \qquad (15.8)$$

At very high frequencies $\omega L \gg R$ and $\omega C \gg G$ giving Equation 15.9.

$$\alpha = \tfrac{1}{2}\left(\frac{R}{Z_O} + GZ_O\right) \qquad (15.9)$$

The value of Z_O is given by Equation 15.10.

$$Z_O = \left(\frac{L}{C}\right)^{1/2} \qquad (15.10)$$

But, at high frequencies skin effect causes R to increase in proportion to the square root of the frequency, and so at high frequencies the line attenuation increases as the square root of the frequency.

15.2.2 Loaded lines

A special case arises if LG = RC. Substituting this condition in Equation 15.5, then the attenuation coefficient $\alpha = (RG)^{1/2}$ which at voice frequencies is independent of frequency. In a real cable, RC will be larger than LG and increasing G would increase the attenuation. However, L can be increased by inserting lumped inductance in each leg of a pair. Loading a line in this way was an important technique for providing long distance audio circuits. However, the lumped inductance forms a low pass filter with cable capacity which limits the line bandwidth as illustrated in Figure 15.1.

In order to apply PCM systems to such cables the loading coils have to be removed. Hence the term 'deloaded audio'.

15.2.3 Performance of balanced pair cables

Table 15.3 gives typical performance characteristics of 0.9mm star quad cable at audio frequencies. In this table 44mH/1800m indicates 44mH loading coils placed at 1800m. The line would only be operated at about 75% of the cut-off frequency. It will be seen that loading can reduce attenuation to one third of the unloaded value, but at the expense of restricted bandwidth.

Table 15.4 gives typical data for unit twin cable and shows how conductor size influences attenuation and impedance.

Table 15.3 Performance of 0.9mm star quad cable

Parameter	Non-loaded	44mH/1800m	88mH/1800m
Impedance @ 1kH	470Ω	820Ω	1130Ω
Attenuation @ 1kH	0.66dB/km	0.31dB/km	0.22dB/km
Cut-off frequency	-	5.7kHz	4kHz

Table 15.4 Performance of unloaded unit twin cable

Parameter	Conductor size			
	0.4mm	*0.5mm*	*0.63mm*	*0.9mm*
Impedance @ 1kHz (Ω)	910	725	567	400
Attenuation @ 1kHz (dB/km)	1.8	1.4	1.1	0.76

15.2.4 Pair cables for HF carrier systems

High frequency symmetric pair cables have been developed for analogue carrier telephone systems providing 12, 24, 36, 48, 60 and 120 channels on each pair, necessitating operation at up to 550kHz. These cables have polyethylene insulated pairs in star quad formation, and conductor sizes from 0.9mm to 1.3mm. A typical cable is described in CCITT Rec. G.611 (CCITT, 1989) from which Table 15.5 is an extract.

Table 15.5 Pair cables for analogue transmission (From CCITT G.611)

Parameter	Value
Conductor diameter	1.2mm
Mutual capacity	26nF/km
Characteristic impedance @ 60kHz	178Ω
Characteristic impedance @ 120kHz	174Ω
Characteristic impedance @ 240kHz	172Ω
Attenuation @ 10°C, 120kHz	2.0dB/km
Attenuation @ 10°C, 240kHz	2.9dB/km
Attenuation @ 10°C, 552kHz	4.8dB/km

Far end crosstalk between pairs operating in the same direction has to be of the order of 70dB and this is achieved with the use of capacitive crosstalk balancing frames during cable installation.

15.2.5 Pair cables for digital transmission

As previously indicated, many 1.5Mbit/s and 2Mbit/s pcm systems have been provided over deloaded audio cables with regenerative repeaters equipped at the old loading coil sites. For this application the cable loss at 1MHz must not exceed about 30dB. However, the limiting factor on cable fill (the percentage of pairs in a given cable which can be equipped with pcm) is crosstalk within the cable, and within the cable terminations to the repeaters. One solution is to recode the standard format with a reduced high frequency content so that crosstalk effects are mitigated. This has served to significantly raise the pcm occupancy on existing cables of unit twin design.

For new digital installations, the cable pairs are split into 'go' and 'return' directions by means of an aluminium screen, i.e. a D screen or Z screen cable.

Typical characteristics of a new pair cable for 2Mbit/s systems are given in CCITT Rec. G.613, from which Table 15.6 is extracted. FEXT (far end crosstalk) is measured with the detector at the end of

Table 15.6 Pair cables for digital transmission. (From CCITT G.613.)

Parameter	Value
Operational bit rate	2048 kbit/s
Construction	Unit twin
Conductor diameter	0.6mm
Nominal impedance	130Ω
Attenuation @ 20° C, 1MHz (f_o)	15.5dB/km
Attenuation @ f MHz	$15.5\left(\dfrac{f}{f_o}\right)^{1/2}$
Attenuation @ t$^{\circ}$	$\alpha_{20^{\circ}C}\,(1 + 0.002\,(t^{\circ} - 20))$
Sinusoidal NEXT	78 dB (nominal)
Sinusoidal FEXT	64 dB
Direct current resistance @ 20°C	63Ω/km
Nominal mutual capacitance	44nF/km

the cable remote from the disturbing source. NEXT (near end crosstalk) is measured at the same end of the cable as the disturbing source. Higher rate digital systems, 6Mbit/s and 34Mbit/s, have been used over the symmetric pair cables designed for HF carrier systems discussed in Section 15.2.4.

15.2.6 Balanced pair cables for information systems

New office blocks and industrial complexes involve the use and interconnection of many data terminal equipment and other IT products. The contending transmission technologies have been reviewed by (Flatman, 1988, 1989). His main points relating to pair cable are as follows.

Unscreened twisted pair (UTC) as used for telephone cabling, has been evaluated by a number of independent bodies. 10Mbit/s transmission is technically feasible over distances of up to 100m within the general office environment. Screened twisted pair (STP) can be operated at data rates of tens of Mbit/s over hundreds of metres. The advantage of twisted pair for this application is that it is sufficiently low cost, low weight and small size to plan for 'saturation' cabling at the outset and so avoid expensive upheavals as demand changes.

15.3 Coaxial pair cables

The limitations of balanced pair cables for telecommunication use at higher frequencies are the crosstalk between pairs, and the lack of predictability in transmission performance. These problems are overcome in a coaxial cable. (Schelkunoff).

Considering the operation of a coaxial cable, at high frequencies skin effect causes the currents to be concentrated on the outer layer of the inner conductor and inner layer of the outer conductor. The field is then contained between the two conductors of a pair and mutual interference between cables is greatly reduced.

The effective depth of penetration of an electric current flowing over a plane surface is given by Equation 15.11.

$$\delta = \left(\frac{\rho}{\pi \mu f} \right)^{1/2} \tag{15.11}$$

δ is the depth at which the current at the surface I_o has reduced to I_o/e. (At a penetration of 4δ the current will only be $0.02I_o$)
ρ is the electrical resistivity in ohm cm.
μ is the magnetic permeability in Henry cm.
f is the frequency in Hz.

From this equation it will be seen that δ increases with resistivity and decreases with frequency. Table 15.7 gives the value of δ for copper.

The greater depth of penetration in a higher resistivity material, tends to offset the effect of its greater resistivity, as in Equation 15.12

$$H.F. \ resistance \ R_f = (\pi \rho \mu f)^{1/2} \tag{15.12}$$

Thus, although the relative d.c. resistance of aluminium to copper is 1.64, the relative HF resistivity is 1.28. Thus skin effect is the most important factor determining the functioning of a coaxial cable because it controls the resistance losses and screening efficiency at high frequencies.

15.3.1 Design for minimum loss

The primary coefficients of a coaxial cable are related to the secondary coefficients in the same way as in the balanced pair case discussed in Section 15.2.1.

$$Z_O = \left(\frac{(R + j\omega L)}{(G + j\omega C)} \right)^{1/2} \tag{15.13}$$

$$\rho = \alpha + j\beta = [(R + j\omega L)(G + j\omega C)]^{1/2} \tag{15.14}$$

At high frequencies ω is large, giving Equations 15.15 to 15.19

$$Z_O = \left(\frac{L}{C} \right)^{1/2} \tag{15.15}$$

$$\alpha = \frac{1}{2} \left(\frac{R}{Z_O} + GZ_O \right) \tag{15.16}$$

$$\beta = \omega(LC)^{1/2} \tag{15.17}$$

$$Z_O = \frac{13\delta}{\sqrt{\varepsilon}} \log \frac{D}{d} \quad ohm \tag{15.18}$$

$$\alpha = \frac{7.83 \ x \ 10^{-2} (\rho \varepsilon f)^{1/2}}{\log_{10} \dfrac{D}{d}} \left(\frac{1}{d} + \frac{1}{D} \right)$$
$$+ 9.08 \ x \ 10^{-5} f (\varepsilon \tan \delta)^{1/2} \tag{15.19}$$

Table 15.7 Effect of frequency on δ in copper

Frequency (MHz)	δ (mm) approximately
10	0.03
100	0.009
1000	0.003

Where ρ conductor resistivity ohm.cm
ε is the dielectric constant (= 1 in air)
D is the inside diameter of outer conductor
d is the diameter of the inner conductor
f is the frequency
tan δ is the power factor of the dielectric

It will be seen that only the first term of the expression for attenuation is dependent on the ratio of conductor diameters as in Equation 15.20.

$$\alpha_c = \frac{7.83 \ x \ 10^{-2} (\rho \varepsilon f)^{1/2}}{\log_{10} q} \left(\frac{1}{d} + \frac{1}{D} \right) \tag{15.20}$$

where $q = \dfrac{D}{d}$

Then for a given attenuation α_c Equation 15.21 can be obtained.

$$D = \frac{7.83 \ x \ 10^{-2} (\rho \varepsilon f)^{1/2}}{\alpha_c} \frac{(q + 1)}{\log_{10} q} \tag{15.21}$$

By partial differentiation, D will be a minimum when Equation 15.22 holds.

$$q (\log_e q - 1) = 1 \tag{15.22}$$

or q = 3.59.

Thus for a given diameter of coaxial cable, the attenuation is a minimum when the ratio of conductor diameters is 3.59. The characteristic impedance is given by Equation 15.23, which equals 76.7ohm for a dielectric constant of 1(air) and 50.6ohm for a dielectric constant 2.3(polyethylene).

$$Z_O + \frac{13\delta}{\sqrt{\varepsilon}} \log_{10} \frac{D}{d} \tag{15.23}$$

Most air spaced cables are 75ohm impedance and flexible polyethylene insulated cables of 50ohm impedance. Cables can, of course, be proportioned for different optimisations and complexities of materials (Dummer, 1961).

15.3.2 Coaxial cable construction

For general telecommunication use, coaxial cables are manufactured with a nominal impedance of 75ohms. By using a minimum amount of dielectric material, e.g. widely spaced polyethylene discs, they are effectively air spaced. The inner conductor is a solid copper wire and the outer usually formed from a folded copper tape with a longitudinal seam.

One commonly used manufacturing process, developed and licensed world-wide by STC plc, incorporates the following features. The insulation between the centre and the outer conductors consists of an air filled moulding made from high density polyethylene copolymer which is continuously applied to the centre conductor of 1.2mm diameter. The insulation is formed by an on line moulding process in which two half mouldings are consolidated together around the centre conductor as shown in Figure 15.2. The effective dielectric constant of this composite insulator is 1.15. The outer conductor is formed from 0.180mm copper tape into a tube closely fitting around the centre moulding. The tape edges are corrugated in order to prevent overlap at the tube seam. The stages

Coaxial pairs, or tubes of the type described are laid up into cables of 4, 6, 8, 12, 18 and even 40 coaxial pairs. Balanced pairs are sometimes provided in the interstitial spaces between the coaxials for the control and supervision of the main transmission equipment.

Some operating companies combine the coaxial pairs with complete layers of balanced pairs to be used for local circuits. However, the initial saving has to be balanced against the extra complication of installation, and maintenance operations on the layer pairs. The complete cable is sheathed in polyethylene preceded by a Glover barrier of 0.2mm aluminium foil. Steel tape or wire armouring can be added if the cable is to be directly buried.

15.3.3 Coaxial cable parameters

15.3.3.1 *Impedance*

In a transmission system the source, cable and load impedances are all matched. An impedance mismatch causes a reflected backward travelling wave which serves to reduce the power of the forward travelling wave, causing an apparent increase in transmission loss. Manufactured cable lengths can be selected to be of the nominal impedance at repeater points, and of matching impedances at other joints. However, this practice is not viable on cables carrying a large number of pairs, and is not necessary if the impedance is controlled in manufacture to within 1ohm at 1MHz. The biggest source of reflections arise at the cable/repeater interface and these accumulate along a repeatered line to steep attenuation frequency rolls which are difficult to equalise. To limit these effects the CCITT recommend that the cable and repeater impedances satisfy Equation 15.24. (G332.5).

$$N = 2A + 20\log_{10}\left[\frac{Z_E + Z_L}{Z_E - Z_L}\right] + 20\log_{10}\left[\frac{Z_L + Z_R}{Z_L - Z_R}\right] \quad (15.24)$$

where N = 55dB minimum for a 12MHz line system and 65dB minimum for a 60MHz line system

A = section loss at frequency f
Z_E = repeater output impedance at frequency f
Z_L = cable impedance at frequency f
Z_R = repeater input impedance at frequency f

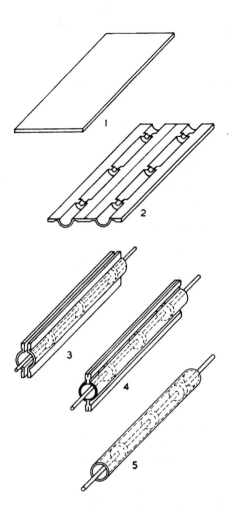

Figure 15.2 Stages in the construction of the STC moulded shell insulation

in the construction of the STC moulded shell insulation are as follows:

Stage 1. Continuously extruded strip of high density polyethylene copolymer.

Stage 2. Two half-insulations moulded into strip by embossed rollers.

Stage 3. Moulded strip divided and centre conductor introduced.

Stage 4. Two halves heat-consolidated together around centre conductor, forming single tube with integral spacing discs and two longitudinal fins.

Stage 5. Fins removed to give insulated conductors.

Two soft steel tapes of thickness 0.1mm are lapped around the outer copper, in opposite directions in such a manner as to cross each other at right angles. The inner tape has a nominal 5% gap between turns, and the outer which is wider but applied at the same lay length has a nominal 15% overlap. Two thickness of insulating tape, with colour coding are then applied. The novel method of steel tape application ensures high crosstalk immunity between coaxial pairs at low frequencies and the whole manufacturing process can be controlled to ensure a consistent product.

15.3.3.2 *Impedance irregularities*

Impedance irregularities within a manufactured length of cable can arise, for example, from variations in the concentricity of the inner conductor, imperfect circularity of the inner and outer, and variation in the dielectric support. Further disturbances can arise during factory operations prior to and during the laying up of a multipair cable, for example, roughness on an intermediate process drum.

The resultant reflections can be assessed by pulse echo testing and swept frequency reflectometer testing as a routine factory test and the product quality controlled to system requirements.

15.3.3.3 *Attenuation*

The attenuation coefficient is specified at 1MHz in dB/km. To a close approximation the loss at other frequencies is inversely proportional to the square root of the frequency. For example, the loss at 9MHz is three times the loss at 1MHz. More exact formulae are provided for a 1.2/4.4mm and 2.6/9.5mm Coaxial Pair, in Section

15.3.4, which include a constant and an f term. Alternatively the consistency of product is such that manufacturers can provide measured data on which the equalisation of analogue systems can be based.

The attenuation variation with temperature is also important. In a buried cable, the temperature change will not exceed an annual variation of $\pm 10^o$ C, and the prevailing annual mean temperature will lie typically between $+5^o$ C and $+15^o$ C. The temperature coefficient is taken as $2x10^{-3}$ per degree centigrade at frequencies of 500kHz or more, increasing at lower frequencies to $2.8x10^{-3}$ per degree centigrade at 60kHz.

15.3.3.4 *Crosstalk*

As previously discussed, the structure of coaxial pairs is such that high values of crosstalk suppression are obtained between pairs. Poor crosstalk on an installed cable is evidence of a fault condition, such as a broken outer conductor.

The most demanding systems crosstalk requirement arises from consideration of sound programme transmission in the same carrier frequency band on adjacent coaxial pairs. In practice the limiting factor tends to be crosstalk within the carrier and repeater equipment and not within the coaxial cable system.

15.3.3.5 *Group delay*

The phase delay/frequency characteristic of a coaxial cable is very smooth and consequently the group delay distortion is low across a telephony or wideband data channel. However, both baseband and carrier TV transmission will require group delay equalisation, but the dominant contributions arise from band limiting components of the system and not from the cable.

15.3.4 Standard coaxial pair cables

Three sizes of coaxial pair have been standardised by the CCITT for telecommunication use. These are designated by the diameter of the inner conductor and inside diameter of the outer conductor. The largest 2.6mm/9.4mm, is the oldest design and is in extensive use in many parts of the world. Initially installed for low capacity analogue systems (600/960 channel) it has been successfully exploited for high capacity analogue systems (up to 60MHz for 10,800 channel systems) and for 560Mbit/s digital systems. The 1.2mm/4.4mm design has been particularly successful as a bearer for short and medium haul routes operating at up to 18MHz (3600 channel analogue) and 140Mbit/s digital. The smallest and newest cable, 0.7mm/2.9mm, has had limited application as a 34Mbit/s digital system bearer.

The performance of these cables is summarised in Appendix 15.1 to 15.3. In each case the CCITT recommendations make some practical distinctions between the performance demanded on a factory length and the results obtainable on a complete and installed repeater section. For the complete recommendations and explanatory notes the reader is referred to the CCITT publication.

15.3.5 Coaxial cables for data networks

Coaxial cable offers better noise immunity and crosstalk than pair cable for cabling within a building. It can also be operated at higher bit rates and has less loss per kilometre.

A commonly used technique is to multiplex many information channels into a broadband spectrum extending up to 450MHz on a single coaxial tube. Similar transmission equipment to that used on multichannel cable TV systems can then be employed. However, system costs are high compared with alternative technologies (Flatman, 1989).

15.3.6 Coaxial cable for submarine telecommunications

The special requirements of submarine telecommunication systems, which provide many international telephone links across oceans and shallower seas, result in a coaxial cable design rather different from the land-line product. Both cable and submerged repeater equipment have to be designed and manufactured to rigorous standards of performance and consistency coupled with high reliability and long life expectancy.

The preferred system configuration uses a single coaxial cable with the two directions of transmission transmitted in different frequency bands separated by directional filters at each repeater (Worthington, 1986).

15.3.6.1 *Deep-sea cable*

This cable is used where there is no risk of damage from fishing activity or ships' anchors. It needs no mechanical protection but must have tensile strength and be able to withstand deep water pressure. The design used by STC comprises a central strength member of high tensile steel wires which can tolerate the loads of 10 tons or more arising when a repeatered cable is recovered in a rough sea. This is covered in a copper tape welded longitudinally forming the inner conductor. The dielectric is solid polyethylene which, as well as having excellent electrical properties, is virtually incompressible. The outer conductor is a single metal tape closed in a longitudinal overlap.

This can be of copper, but aluminium is often used. The attenuation is then increased by 6%, as is the number of repeaters, but the overall system costs will be lower. Finally, an overall polythene sheath is extruded to apply compression to the outer conductor and provide some abrasion resistance. The dimensions of such a cable are considerably greater than standard land-line cable. Thus the inner conductor has an outside diameter of approximately 9.3mm, the dielectric a diameter of 37.3mm, the outer tape a thickness of 0.46mm and the overall diameter over the sheath is 44.5mm.

15.3.6.2 *Shallow-water cable*

In shallower seas, i.e. less than about 1000m, the risk of damage from ships' anchors and fishing activity, particularly trawling, can be high. The solution is to add one or two layers of mild steel armouring wires to the lightweight deep-sea cable, packed in a polypropylene bedding.

Sometimes in vulnerable situations a trench is ploughed on the sea floor as the cable is laid and the cable buried for extra protection.

15.3.6.3 *Cable performance*

This cable design conforms with the outer to inner conductor diameter ratio of 3.6 to 1 for minimum loss as derived in Section 15.3.1 above. As the dielectric is solid polythene, the characteristic

Table 15.8 Loss of 37.3mm submarine coaxial cable at 10°C

Parameter	Value			
Frequency	1	5	15	45
Loss (dB/nm)	1.69	3.84	6.84	12.54
Loss (dB/km)	0.91	2.07	3.69	6.76

impedance of the cable is 50ohm. The pressure coefficient of the cable is remarkably low at about 0.5% per 2km of sea depth.

This cable has been used for 1840 circuit systems operating up to 13.7MHz and for 5520 circuit systems operating up to 44.3MHz. The cable loss is given in Table 15.8. (The standard unit of length in submarine system work is the nautical mile (n.m.) of 6087 feet (1.855km).) Laboratory studies demonstrated that systems of much higher frequencies were feasible, but this work has been dropped in favour of the development of optical fibre systems.

Many thousands of nautical miles of STC's submarine coaxial cable systems give reliable service throughout the world.

15.4   Line plant for copper cables

Cables can be installed underground or overhead. For overhead installation the cable can be lashed tightly against a previously installed messenger wire. Alternatively, the messenger wire, or catenary, can be built into the cable sheath to give a figure-of-eight section and clamped to each supporting pole. Cable joint housings are usually mounted part way down the pole. Two techniques are used for underground installation, by duct and by direct burial. Ducts have the advantage that additional cables can be added and obsolete cables removed relatively easily. Ducts are the normal solution in urban areas and are preferred by some operating companies (e.g. British Telecom) for virtually all applications. For many years lead was the preferred cable sheath as it is totally impervious and waterproof joints can be made. Plastic, particularly polyethylene offers lower cost, greater toughness and lighter weight, but its widescale adoption had to wait until sheath jointing by either welding or epoxy adhesives were developed. The polyethylene sheath is applied over and bonded to an aluminium/polyethylene laminate moisture barrier. This aluminium foil also provides the equivalent electrical screen to a lead sheath.

For direct burial the cable is armoured with layers of steel wire or tape appropriate to the installation conditions. In open country cable ploughs are employed which open the trench, lay the cable and backfill in one operation.

Two techniques are used to resist water penetration through a damaged sheath. The cable core can be saturated with petroleum jelly or a similar compound. The disadvantage is the difficulty of cleaning all the cable elements when joining and it is not appropriate to air cored coaxial cables. The second technique is by air pressure, either continuous flow or static. Static pressure systems rely on total air integrity of the cable. Regularly spaced pressure sensitive switches e.g. at each joint, close across a monitor control pair when pressure drops. Resistance measurements from the terminal stations identify the location. Continuous flow systems tolerate some leakage from the cable and damage is sensed by an increase in flow rate. Cables to be used with either of these systems must have a sufficiently low pneumatic resistance.

A repeatered cable line includes accommodation for equipment e.g. PCM regenerators at 1.8km on pair cable; coaxial line repeaters spaced in the range 1.5km to 9km on large core cable and 2.0 to 4.0km on small core cable. These are robust steel or cast iron housings with a removable lid which when sealed will withstand several metres of water pressure. Several housings may be used to support one large cable which is separated out into individual pairs at a segregating joint.

The individual tail cables have to be air tight and to retain the electrical characteristics of the main cable. For convenience of equipment installation and maintenance, the housings are best mounted to one side of the main cable in a dedicated shallow manhole or footway box. Water tightness of the repeater housings is assured by air pressurisation which may be integrated into the main cable system.

15.5   Optical fibres

Telecommunication transmission systems operating over light guiding optical fibre waveguides were first proposed in 1966 by Hockham and Kao working at the STC Technology Ltd. laboratories in Harlow, Essex. One of the earliest and most ambitious field trials of an optical fibre system was the 140Mbit/s system designed, manufactured and installed by STC plc between Hitchin and Stevenage in 1977. Since then the technology has progressed to the extent that optical fibres have virtually ousted metallic cables for new telecommunication work except for the local area network and short distance applications.

Optical fibres, or light guides, operate by total internal reflection at a core cladding boundary where the refractive index of the cladding is less than that in the core. A multimode fibre supports many hundreds of modes which can be conceptually considered as light rays. Each ray is totally reflected at the core/cladding boundary and progresses along the fibre by multiple reflections back into the core. Axially injected rays experience fewer reflections than rays injected at an angle to the axis.

Before considering the properties of optical fibres, it is useful to have some appreciation of how fibres are made.

Fibre manufacture requires a high purity glass which is generally achieved by fabrication from compounds in a gaseous form. A typical process is by chemical vapour deposition (CVD) the principles of which are as follows: silicon tetrachloride, oxygen and germanium chloride gases are fed into a silica tube which is rotating in a lathe. A hot burner traverses along the tube causing a chemical reaction at that point and glass to be deposited on the inside wall of the tube. At each traverse of the burner the percentage of germanium dopant can be modified and the refractive index of the glass changed. Other dopants are phosphorous and fluorine. A hundred or more passes are typically involved and the whole process is computer controlled. Finally the burner temperature is raised and the support tube collapses into a solid rod or preform.

It will be apparent that an advantage of this technique is that as well as pure starting materials, the complicated deposition and collapse process take place in a closed environment, minimising the problems of contamination by handling or from the atmosphere.

In the next operation, the preform is fitted in a pulling tower and its end heated to a temperature at which a fibre filament can be drawn off, at about 2200°C. At the bottom of the tower is the take up drum the speed of which is controlled by a diameter monitor just below the drawing furnace. Following the diameter monitor, the fibre is drawn through a primary coating vessel, coating curing oven, and then finally the fibre is wound on the take up drum. It will

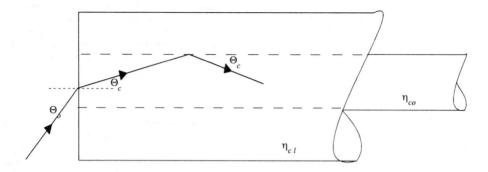

Figure 15.3 Illustration of numerical aperture

be noted that the primary protective coating is applied virtually as the fibre is drawn.

15.5.1 Features of multimode fibres

Standard multimode fibre for telecommunication application has a core diameter of 50μm and a cladding surface diameter of 125μm.

The numerical aperture (N.A.) of a fibre is a measure of the angle of acceptance of the light rays presented to it as shown in Figure 15.3 which illustrates numerical aperture. Rays at too steep an angle will not be totally reflected and not be guided.

If θ_c is the critical angle for total reflection, and θ_a is the maximum incident angle, then the numeric aperture is given by Equation 15.25.

$$N.A. = Sin\,\theta_a = (\,n_{co}^{\,2} - n_{ce}^{\,2}\,)^{1\!/2} \qquad (15.26)$$

Where n_{co} is the maximum refractive index of the core and n_{ce} is the minimum refractive index at the cladding boundary. The larger the NA, the more modes the fibre will support but the baseband response may be limited. Fibres for telecommunication purposes have an NA of typically 0.2.

The simplest form of multimode fibre is a step-index design in which there is a well defined step in the refractive index between the core glass and the cladding. In such a fibre the light rays (highest order modes) experiencing most reflections travel a longer path down the fibre than rays experiencing fewer reflections (lower order modes). Consequently the arrival time of the higher order modes at the end of the fibre is later. A transmitted pulse at the output end of a fibre will be longer than that inputted. To an analogue signal this effect shows as a bandwidth limitation.

The most commonly encountered form of multimode fibre is the graded index type in which the refractive index decreases with offset from the centre to an approximately parabolic law. The difference between the refractive index at the axis and the boundary of the core is about 1%. This has two effects. Firstly, the fibre becomes self focusing and secondly, transit speed in the outer, lower refractive index regions of the fibre is faster than in the higher refractive index region at the core. That is, there is an equalising effect on the transit times of the higher order modes and the pulse spreading effect is reduced by a factor of 100.

For many fibres the pulse spreading which results from these multipath differential propagation times is of a Gaussian shape.

Then, 1ns of pulse distortion measured at half amplitude, corresponds to a drop of 6dB measured in the amplitude/frequency response at 440MHz.

In an installed cable of jointed fibre lengths, mode mixing takes place at the joints and at small irregularities within the fibre lengths and this has the effect of reducing the effects of modal dispersion. The summation of modal dispersion in a real route is given by dL^c where d is the dispersion per kilometre, L is the length in kilometres and c is the concatenation index. The concatenation index for most fibres lies between 0.5 and 1.0 and is usually taken as 0.7.

Commercially the modal dispersion of multimode fibres is usually expressed in terms of bandwidth per kilometre. A typical grading would be from 400MHz to 1600MHz in 400MHz steps.

The refractive index of glass is a function of the light wavelength. As the propagation rate is a function of the refractive index it follows that different wave lengths have different propagation speeds in the fibre.

Thus pulse dispersion arises from variation of the refractive index across the band of wavelengths emitted by the light sources used in the equipment, i.e. lasers and LEDs.

A typical value for graded index fibres is 120ps/km per nm at a centre wavelength of 850nm, that is a pulse emitted from a 10nm width source would be subjected to 1.2ns widening in a 10km length. With increasing wavelength, material dispersion in silica fibres falls and becomes negative above about 1270nm. As attenuation also falls with wavelength, 1300nm is an attractive operating window. The value of material dispersion at 1300nm is usually taken as 6ps/km nm.

Material dispersion in the next transmission window of 1550nm where attenuation is still lower, is around 17ps/km nm. By increasing doping concentrations, the material dispersion zero can be shifted to 1550nm, but at the expense of some slight increase in attenuation at 1550nm (See paragraph 15.4.2. on single mode fibres).

In systems planning calculations, the effects of both material and modal dispersion can be considered to be of Gaussian shapes and added by taking the square root of the sum of the squares.

Low attenuation coupled with wide bandwidth, is probably the most remarkable property of optical fibres and accounts for their outstanding success. Values of around 0.5dB/km at 1300nm are commonly achieved on cables for general telecommunication applications, and even lower values at 1550nm for submarine telecommunication systems.

There are two basic loss mechanisms in optical fibres. These are absorption and scattering:

1. Absorption loss. Pure silica is transparent in the wavelength range from approximately 200nm to 10000nm, with a maximum transparency at a wavelength of 1550nm. Small traces of metallic impurities in the silica can increase the loss of the fibre considerably and metallic ion (fe, Cu, Ni etc.) concentrations must be limited to less than 0.01ppm. A common impurity is water in the form of hydroxyl ions (OH) which can produce rather wide absorption bands of overtones of the 2800nm fundamental which can typically be seen around 1400nm, 1250nm, 970nm and 750nm. In modern fibres the water content can be reduced to less than 1 part in 10^8.
2. Scattering loss. Rayleigh scattering of the light occurs within the molecules of glass material itself. This loss is independent of the light intensity but varies inversely with the fourth power of wavelength. Hence the advantage of operating at longer wavelengths. These loss mechanisms result in three operating transmission windows in the loss spectrum of silica optical fibre in the region of 800nm, 1300nm and 1500nm. Historically 850nm was the first to be commercially exploited and 1550nm is the most recent. However, interest continues in the use of the 850nm window for short distance applications because the electro-optic devices are considerably cheaper. Most commercial activity is directed at 1300nm with 1550nm limited to applications where very long spans are warranted, such as submerged cable systems.

15.5.2 Single mode fibre

The bandwidth limitations of multimode fibres arise from the variation in multipath propagation times. The best graded index fibre offers a bandwidth of about 1.5GHz/km and is expensive and difficult to produce. (On a 30km route this would reduce to something like 140MHz which is inadequate for high bit rate systems.)

This major limitation is overcome in single mode fibre designs. The number of modes propagated by a fibre is given approximately by Equation 15.26.

$$N = \frac{2\pi^2 a^2}{\lambda^2} \left(\eta_{co}^2 - \eta_{cl}^2 \right) \tag{15.26}$$

where a is the core radius

λ is the wavelength

η_{cl} is the refractive index of cladding

η_{co} is the refractive index of the core.

As the fibre diameter is reduced, the number of modes which can be propagated falls, and in the extreme only a single mode is transmitted. In order to obtain a usable core size the core cladding index difference is also reduced from the order of 1% to 0.1%.

In a single mode fibre the core size is about one tenth of that of a graded index fibre (5 micron) and obviously the practical problems of injecting light into the fibre, jointing fibres and connector design are more difficult. However, solutions are now well established and single mode fibres have become the standard for virtually all new telecommunication work.

In a single mode fibre, part of the power is carried in the fibre cladding, and is still guided. The concept of mode field diameter is therefore more useful than core diameter and can be defined as the width between the points across the fibre where the optical field amplitude measured is $\frac{1}{e}$ of the maximum value.

The overall diameter over the cladding of the fibre as drawn is 120 micron, the same as for standard multimode fibre. The cladding is thus very much larger than the core and is of optically low loss. One consequence of this is that care has to be taken to exclude cladding light when making measurements, for example by taking the fibre through a bath of liquid of higher refractive index than the cladding. Some fibre protective coatings are also designed to act as cladding mode strippers.

A single mode guide will only be single mode above a certain wavelength and below this value second order modes will also be propagated. The cut-off wavelength is usually in the range 1100-1280nm.

Reference has already been made to dispersion shifted fibres in the earlier section on material dispersion. This involves increasing the dopant concentrations to shift the naturally occurring zero value at 1270nm in silica fibre to the lower loss window of 1550nm. However, this also serves to increase the loss at 1550nm. The effect can be mitigated by changing the refractive index profile of the fibre from a rectangular to a triangular shape.

Single mode fibre provides a low loss and high bandwidth transmission bearer which is economic over a wide range of digital bit rates using either laser or LED sources, and thus provides an operating administration with a "future-proof" investment.

The low values of pulse dispersion make system planning a relatively straightforward task up to about 600Mbit/s. At higher bit rates additional allowances may have to be made for very short term laser wavelength changes during the 'on' period which are converted by the small but finite dispersion of the fibre to an additional noise source.

15.6 Optical fibre cables

There are two primary considerations determining the design of an optical fibre cable:

1. To minimise optical attenuation increments associated with the manufacture and use of the cable.
2. To maintain the physical integrity of the fibre during the cabling process and its subsequent installation and service environment.

Macrobending loss arises due to a partial loss of guidance in the fibre when it is bent into a curve having a radius less than a few tens of millimetres. When the fibre is so bent, the evanescent wave in the cladding needs to travel above the velocity of light in the medium, which it cannot do, and so guiding is lost and energy is radiated. At wavelengths approaching the mode cut-off wavelength, more energy is carried in the evanescent field in the cladding and bending loses more easily occur. In multimode fibres, there are always some modes close to cut-off and less tightly bound than the lower order modes. Minor perturbations in the fibre geometry causes coupling between modes and hence replacement of those vulnerable to loss.

Microbending loss occurs when a fibre is in contact with a rough surface that imposes many very small bends on the fibre. Bending loss can be reduced by designing the fibre to have a small mode field diameter, but this conflicts with the need for a large spot size to reduce splicing and connector difficulties.

Standard fibre has a mode field diameter between nine and ten micrometres.

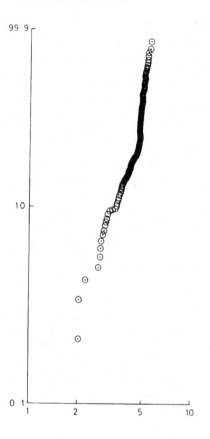

Figure 15.4 Weibull plot of strain at fibre break (147 sambles; 10m gauge length tests). Reproduced with permission of STC Technology Ltd.)

Glass fibre, unlike steel or copper wire, does not have a well defined or controllable breaking strain because failure is initiated in flaws that are usually at the surface, but may also be within the fibre. These flaws cause local intensification of any applied stress.

For a typical telecommunication fibre, a flaw only one micrometre deep will cause failure at about 1% strain. Flaws arise from a number of sources during fabrication, for instance: imperfections in the substrate tube, scratches introduced by handling, discontinuities during deposition, stresses introduced during collapse or pulling, impurities implanted from the furnace during pulling and foreign matter trapped during coating.

Tests on a number of fibre lengths will give a range of breaking strains depending on the largest flaw in each length tested, and the longer the sample lengths, the greater probability of finding larger flaws and hence lower strengths would be recorded. Results must be treated statistically, for example as the cumulative failure probabilities a function of strain (Figure 15.4).

Below the critical strain at which a flaw will cause immediate fracture, the flaw will increase in size until fracture occurs. It can be shown (Allard, 1990) that the time to failure is inversely proportional to the nth power of the applied stress or strain, where n lies in the range of 14 to 25, the higher value being in dry conditions and the lower value at 100% humidity.

Fibres with the largest flaws can be eliminated by applying a proof test, typically of 0.6% strain, as an online manufacturing process, and ensuring by cable design that the stress on the fibre at all stages in its life remains low.

A fibre buffer or primary coating serves the dual purpose of protecting the fibre from rough surfaces which would introduce microbending losses, and, of preserving the pristine strength of the fibre. Hence, the coating is applied on the pulling tower within a second or two of the fibre being drawn in such a way that the fibre is not scratched or marked.

Thermally cured polydimethyl silicone (e.g. Sylgard) provides a marked increase in a usable fibre strength and very small temperature dependence. More recently acrylate resin coatings have been widely adopted as these offer advantages in fibre drawing speeds and in more versatile buffering techniques. A typical system employs a low modulus inner coating with a high modulus outer coating, giving a package which provides a tough smooth exterior capable of withstanding subsequent handling and abrasion, while the soft inner protects against microbending losses.

The coated fibre requires further protection before it can be incorporated into a cable. A common solution is to extrude a loose tube over the fibre, and if the fibre is made to lie in a long helix within the tube by overfeeding, strain relief of 0.2 to 0.4% can

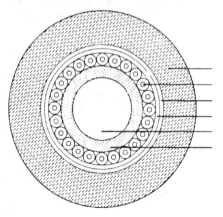

Polyethylene sheath
Optical fibres
Aluminium polyethylene laminate
Paper tape
Central strength member
Polyethylene bedding layer

Figure 15.5 Tightly buffered optical fibre trunk cable

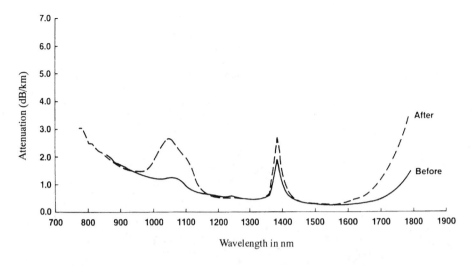

Figure 15.6   Single mode fibre before and after cabling

readily be obtained. However, there is clearly some uncertainty on the positional stability of the fibre, and contacts between the fibre and inside wall of the tube (which is relatively rough) can give rise to microbending loss.

Long term movement and water blocking problems can be overcome by introducing a gel into the tube. Thixotropic gel compounds have been especially developed for optical fibre cables (Bury, 1985) with a wide temperature range and a fine granular structure. The gel is normally highly viscous and supportive of the fibre, but changes to low viscosity under stress and allows rapid movement of the fibre during cable elongation of compression. With this arrangement good protection of a fibre with a single hard acrylic coating is obtained.

A common alternative to loose tube encapsulation is tight buffering. In this the coated fibre has extruded an additional jacket of polymer such as nylon 12 to an overall diameter of between 0.5 and 1.0mm. This can be applied in such a manner to apply a longitudinal compression to the fibre and obtain a strain relief of 0.2% or more.

Multifibre encapsulation in a gel filled loose tube for high fibre count cables is also attractive e.g. up to 12 fibres can be inserted in a tube of 2mm inside diameter and gel filled.

15.7   Cable design

With the essential building block of well buffered and encapsulated fibres, optical cables can be manufactured in a similar way to conventional cables.

A design for installation in long underground ducts is shown in Figure 15.5. Tight jacketed buffered fibres are laid helically around

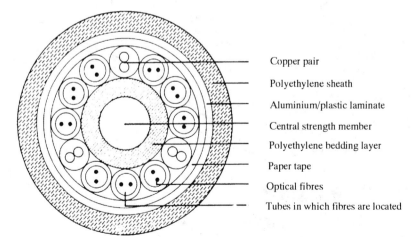

Copper pair

Polyethylene sheath

Aluminium/plastic laminate

Central strength member

Polyethylene bedding layer

Paper tape

Optical fibres

Tubes in which fibres are located

Figure 15.7   Optical fibre loose tube cable

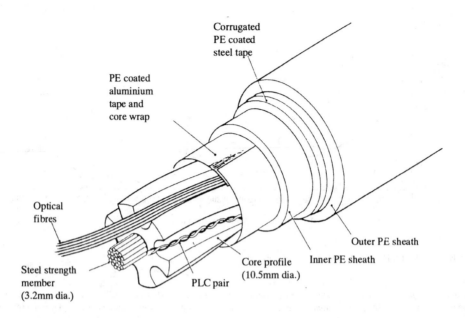

Figure 15.8   Slotted core cable with rodent protection

a strength member of stranded steel wires. The cable is pulled through the duct via a mechanical fuse which ruptures if the intended stress is exceeded, which is well before stress on the fibres exceeds 0.2% to 0.3%. Attenuation increments during the cabling process are very low as shown in Figure 15.6. The same general design is also used with fibres encapsulated in loose tubes and in gel-filled loose tubes (Figure 15.7). For applications where non-metallic cables are required - alongside electrified railways or in regions of high lightning activity, the aluminium plastic laminate is omitted and dielectric strength members (e.g. Kevlar) replace the steel core.

The slotted core construction (Figure 15.8) is effective for high fibre count cables. Figure 15.9 shows a more recent design with several fibre bundles laid in a large protective soft gel-filled tube. This cable is for direct burial and is shown completed with outer sheath's lightning and rodent protection.

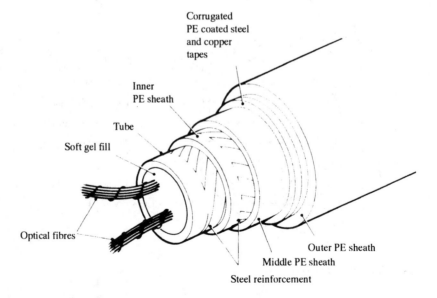

Figure 15.9   Alternative cable design with rodent protection

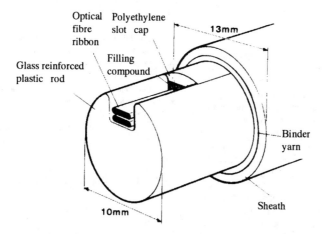

Figure 15.10 Self-supporting optical fibre cable

15.7.1 Self supporting cable

The advantages of interference free operation have encouraged the installation of optical fibres on high voltage power lines. Although the communication needs of an electricity authority are relatively modest, the high voltage power transmission and distribution network potentially provides an alternative communication route for use by common carriers. In an earlier development, optical fibres have been incorporated into overhead line conductors, but application is limited to new or reconstructed routes.

The cable shown in Figure 15.10 (Rowland, 1987) has been developed by STC Telecommunications for economic retrospective installation on live power transmission lines operating at voltages up to 150kV.

The strength member is a pultruded glass reinforced plastic (grp) rod at the top of which is a small rectangular slot. Within this gel filled slot are two twelve-fibre ribbons covered with a cap. The cable is sheathed in a track-resistant material to an overall diameter of only 13mm. In temperate climates, subject to simultaneous ice and wind loading the maximum span between towers is 550m and 720m over river crossings. Without ice loading, spans can be significantly larger.

The optical loss of the fibres is designed to remain within 0.5dB/km at 1300nm during all conditions of service. This includes temperature excursions from -40°C to +70°C and a 25 year service life. The cable is supplied in 4km lengths and supported on the bottom crossarms. The installation fittings and procedures are compatible with safe working practices on live routes.

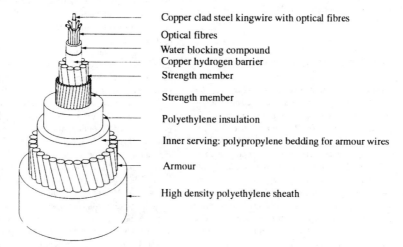

Figure 15.11 Submarine optical fibre cable

Ongoing research is expected to extend the area of application of this self supporting all dielectric communication cable to include 400kV power lines.

15.7.2 Submarine optical cables

A second example of an optical fibre cable for special application is one for submarine system use. These are now in service in both shallow waters and in trans-oceanic links. Consideration has to be given to the high strains during installation and in any recovery and repair operations. In shallow waters additional protection must be provided against damage by anchors and trawling operations.

An example of cable manufactured by STC is shown in Figure 15.11 and the optical characteristics are given in Appendix 15.4 (Mazda, 1989). An interesting feature of this cable is the copper tube around the fibres which is the system power feeding conductor and also a hydrogen barrier.

Hydrogen causes adverse changes to the attenuation of optical fibre (Barnes, 1985). This is of no consequence on land line cable, but of much greater significance in a deep sea cable because of the high pressure. Loss mechanisms arise from interstitially dissolved hydrogen, hydroxyl formation, and the formation of defect centres. The hydrogen can arise by galvanic corrosion, metallic outgassing, polymer degradation, magnetic hydrodynamic effects and other causes. By careful choice of fibre and cable materials, and by appropriate design the hydrogen effect can be limited to a tolerable level (Worthington, 1986).

15.7.3 Optical cable for information systems

Much attention has been devoted to using optical fibre technology in a 10Mbit/s ethernet. Another current project is FDDI-II (fibre distributed data interface) which is a 100Mbit/s dual optical fibre ring (Flatman, 1989).

Clearly the wideband transmission characteristics of optical fibre, and its immunity to interference make it an ideal medium for this work. The inhibiting factors are the relatively high cost of optical devices and connectorisation in the context of short distance, high density links. An elegant solution to this problem has been reported by workers at STC Technology Limited (Cannell, 1988). Access to a single mode fibre is accomplished via a non-intrusive tap and a 10Mbit/s ring with a capacity of 100 nodes is described.

15.8 Line plant for optical cables

Generally it has proved feasible to adapt conventional cable hardware to the requirements of optical fibre. The preferred fibre jointing technique is by fusion of the two fibre ends, either in a gas flame or more commonly by an electric arc. Proprietary machines are available in which the fibre coatings are stripped, the fibre ends cleaved, and fusion applied. Surface tension forces centre the mating fibres with respect to the cladding surface diameters. Finally, the surface coatings are reinstated and the splice given mechanical support. Machines with various levels of automation are available and some provide light injection and detection (LID) so that splice loss can be minimised during the operation. It is common practice to check splice losses by OTDR (optical time domain reflectometer) progressively as work proceeds along a route.

The completed splice, with its reinforcement splint, must be carefully stowed within a splice housing and organiser. It is normal to allow surplus fibre for a splice remake and this too must be stowed within the constraints of the minimum bending radius specified. The complete splice housing is finally rendered integral with the cables by polyethylene injection welding or heat shrink techniques.

Intermediate repeaters on long optical cable routes can readily be accommodated in the same design of underground housings used for metallic cable systems. It is only necessary to design an appropriate pressure tight cable termination and tail cable which is spliced to the main cable. With repeater spans up to 30km it is feasible to power feed these repeaters over 0.9mm copper conductors in the cable. Although still practical at longer spacings, the voltage drop in the cable becomes increasingly significant and local power sources, such as solar power can be considered as an alternative.

15.9 CCITT standardised optical fibre

Probably the most important contribution of the CCITT to the rapid development of fibre optic technology has been the achievement of internationally accepted definitions and reference test methods (RTM).

The recommended fibre characteristics in G.651 and G.652 are generally sufficient to ensure compatibility between conforming cables and manufacturers' optical repeater equipment. Key parameters from these recommendations are given in Appendix 15.5 and 15.6.

15.10 Future developments

The current standard single mode telecommunication fibre provides remarkably low attenuations of 0.5dB/km in the 1300nm window and, optionally, 0.2dB/km at 1500nm. These values, in conjunction with a variety of transmitters and receivers of different powers, sensitivities and costs, enable system designers to produce economic and technically attractive solutions to most telecommunication needs. This fibre is the culmination of many years development in laboratories throughout the world, and it is unlikely that it will be superseded as a general transmission bearer for some years. Optical device development will certainly continue and new system designs offering advantages in transmission bit rates and costs will continue to emerge. Cable designs incorporating standard fibre will also continue to evolve in response to new opportunities and special needs.

There are however two, perhaps three, market sectors of special interest where a new fibre design might be justified. The first is in submarine cable systems where the benefit of lower loss means fewer underwater repeaters and potentially higher reliability. Some research into new glass compounds offering very low losses at long wavelengths (10 μm) has been reported. The second market sector is the proposal for optical links into telephone subscribers premises. This application would probably benefit from larger core fibres facilitating the design of the necessarily low cost optical devices and connectors. A third possible area is application in local area networks which is in some respects similar to the problem of subscriber connection. However, current sentiment seems to be in favour of standard fibre for this application.

It is evident that any alternative fibre design in terms of operating wavelength or core size, must be supported by a corresponding range of transmitters, receivers, connectors and test equipment - and that the resulting system has to be cost competitive with standard alternatives. Technological prediction is a dangerous game, but it would seem that today's standard fibre has an assured future by virtue of its outstanding performance and the massive investment already committed by operators in their cable networks.

15.11 References

Allard, R.C. (1990) *Fiber Optics Handbook for Scientists & Engineers.* McGraw-Hill, Section 2.1.1.

Barnes, S.R. et. al. (1985) The Effect of Hydrogen on Submarine Optical Cables. *Electrical Communication* **59** (4).

Bury, J.R. and Joiner, D.A. (1985) Versatile High Performance Filling Compounds for Telecoms Cable Applications. *In Proceedings of the International Wire and Cable Symposium.*

Cannell G.J. et. al. (1988) Access Methods for Non-Intrusive Optical Fibre Networks. *In Proceedings of the International Wire and Cable Symposium.*

CCITT (1989) *Blue Book.* Vol 111, ITU Geneva.

Dummer, G.W.A. and Blackband, W.T. (1961) *Wires and R.F. Cables.* Pitman.

Flatman, A.V. (1988) Universal Communications Cabling - A Building Utility. *ICL Technical Journal* pp. 117-136.

Flatman, A.V. (1989) Open Systems Cabling as a Building Utility. *Electronics and Communication Engineering Journal (IEE)* **1** pp. 152- 158.

Mazda, F.F. (1981) *Electronics Engineers Reference Book 5th Edition,* Butterworth Scientific, Section 56.18.

Mazda, F.F. (1989) *Electronics Engineers Reference Book 6th Edition,* Butterworth Scientific, Section 55.18.

Rowland, S. et. al. (1987) The Development of a Metal-Free Self-Supporting Optical Cable for Use on Long Span, High Voltage Overhead Power Lines. *In Proceedings of the International Wire and Cable Symposium.*

Schelkunoff, S.A. The Electromagnetic Theory of Coaxial Transmission Lines and Cylindrical Shields. *Bell Syst. Tech. J.* **13**.

Worthington, P. et. al. (1986) The Design and Manufacture of Submarine Optical Cables in the U.K. *In Proceedings of the Sub-Optic Conference, Paris.*

15.12 Acknowledgements

The writer wishes to thank Mr. M.M. Ramsay and Dr. John Lees of BNR Europe (formerly STC Technology) for their generous assistance, and the directors of NT Europe (formerly STC) for permission to publish this paper.

15.13 Appendix 15.1

2.6/9.5mm coaxial pair (CCITT G.623) characteristics

(a) Factory Length

Impedance
Characteristic impedance is given by Equation A15.1.

$$Z = 74.4 \left[1 + \frac{0.0123}{\sqrt{f}} \ (1-j) \right] \quad ohm \tag{A15.1}$$

Table A15.1 Far end cross talk ratios for 2.6/9.5mm coaxial pair.

Section length	Frequency band	FEXT ratio
9km	0.06 to 4.3MHz	85dB
4.5km	0.3 to 12.5MHz	94dB
1.5km	4 to 62MHz	130dB

Where f is the frequency in MHz, and the tolerance on impedance is ±1ohm.

Attenuation
The nominal attenuation is 18.00 ±0.3dB/km at 60MHz at 10°C.
Nominal at 1MHz is 2.32dB/km.
Above 1MHz it is $0.01 + 2.3\sqrt{f} + 0.00 ff$ dB/km.

Construction
Inner diameter is 2.6mm solid wire.
Outer conductor is 0.25mm copper tape.
Internal diameter is 9.5mm over insulation.

Impedance regularity
A cable suitable for 60MHz analogue or 560Mbit/s digital systems must exhibit reflections of at least 54dB down on the inputted signal, measured with a 2ns pulse.

(b) Installed cable

Crosstalk
The far-end crosstalk ratio between two coaxial pairs shall not be less than the values given in Table A15.1.

Dielectric Strength
The pair shall measure not less than 5000Mohm-km at 500V dc, after electrification for one minute at 2000V dc. (Transmission systems frequently incorporate high voltage power feeding of dependent repeaters).

15.14 Appendix 15.2

1.2/4.4mm coaxial pair (CCITT G.622) characteristics

(a) Factory Length

Impedance
The characteristics Impedance is 75ohm ±1ohm at 1MHz.

Table A15.2 Far end cross talk ratios for 1.2/4.4mm coaxial pair

Section lenght	Frequency band	FEXT RATIO
8km	0.06 to 1.3MHz	87dB
4km	0.06 to 4.5MHz	93dB
2km	0.3 to 12.5MHz	99dB

Typically, then Z at 60kHz is 79.8ohm; at 500kHz it is 75.8ohm; at 4.5MHz it is 74 ohm; at 18MHz it is 73.5 ohm.

Attenuation

Nominal attenuation at 1MHz is 5.3dB/km ±0.2dB/km.
Attenuation above 2MHz is $0.07 + 5.15\sqrt{f} + 0.005f$.
The lay up factor causes the attenuation of multipair cables to be about 0.5% greater per sheath km.

Construction

Inner conductor is 1.2mm diameter copper wire.
Outer conductor is 0.15mm or 0.18 copper tape.
Internal diameter is 4.4mm over insulation.

Impedance Regularity

The most demanding requirement is for 140Mbit/s digital operation. Reflections from a 10ns pulse shall be at least 49dB down.

(b) Installed Cable

The far-end crosstalk ratio between any two coaxial pairs shall not be less than that given in Table A15.2.

Dielectric Strength

The pair shall measure not less than 5000Mohm-km at 500V d.c. after electrification for one minute at 1000V d.c. If in normal use the outers are not earthed, outers to sheath shall withstand 2000V d.c. (Isolated outers are one technique for reducing induced currents from railway traction and lightning strokes).

15.15 Appendix 15.3

0.7/2.9mm coaxial pair (G.621) characteristics

(a) Factory Length

Impedance

The characteristics impedance at 1MHz is 75 ±2.5 ohm.
Typically, then Z at 0.2MHz is 77.7ohm; Z at 5MHz it is 73.4 ohm; Z at 20MHz it is 72.8 ohm.

Attenuation

Nominal attenuation at 1MHz is 8.9dB/km at 10°C.
Typical attenuation at 0.2MHz is 4.5dB/km; at 0.5MHz it is 6.5dB/km; at 5MHz it is 19.8dB/km; at 20MHz it is 39.6dB/km.

Mechanical Construction

Inner is solid copper wire 0.7mm diameter.
Outer is 0.1mm thick copper tape, laid lengthwise.
Screen is 0.1mm thick steel tape, laid lengthwise.
Insulation has an external diameter of 2.9mm.

Impedance Regularity

The reflection from a 100ns pulse shall be at least 39dB down.

(b) Installed Cable

Crosstalk

The near-end crosstalk attenuation between coaxial pairs, measured in the frequency band 0.5 to 20MHz on 2km or 4km sections, should be greater than 130dB.

Dielectric

The pair shall measure not less than 5000Mohm-km at 500C, after electrification for one minute at 1000V d.c. Outer to screen shall withstand 2000V d.c. for 1 minute.

15.16 Appendix 15.4

Submarine optical fibre characteristics

Core diameter = 8.4μm (germanium doped).
Refractive index difference = 0.004
Fibre diameter = 125μm
Cut-off wavelength = 1.15 - 1.28μm
Wavelength of zero dispersion = 1.315μm
Attenuation at 1.310μm = 0.34dB/km
Attenuation at 1.55μm = 0.19dB/km
Dispersion at 1.55μm = 17ps(km.nm)
Mode field diameter = 9.8μm

Alternative Dispersion Shifted Fibre

Core diameter = 6.9μm (at base of triangular profile)
Refractive index difference = 0.011
Cut-off wavelength = 0.84μm
Wavelength of zero dispersion = 1.53μm
Attenuation at 1.55μm slightly greater than 0.19dB/km

15.17 Appendix 15.5

Multimode graded index optical fibres (CCITT G.651) key parameters

Core diameter = 50μm, deviation less than ±6%
Cladding surface diameter = 125μm, deviation less than ±2.4%
Concentricity error less than 6%
Core non circularity less than 6%
Cladding non circularity less than 2%
Attenuation at 850nm generally less than 4dB/km
Attenuation at 1300nm generally less than 2dB/km
Modal bandwidth 850nm generally greater than 200MHz.km
Modal bandwidth 1300nm generally greater than 1000 MHz.km
Chromatic dispersion 850nm generally less than 120ps/km.nm
Chromatic dispersion 1300nm generally less than 6ps/km.nm

NOTE

1. The optical performance quoted is for guidance only. Fibres offering 2 to 2.5dB/km at 850nm and 0.5 to 0.8dB/km are available. Similarly, bandwidths of greater than 1000MHz.km at 850nm and 2000MHz.km at 1300nm have been achieved.
2. The CCITT recommend specific dimensional tolerance to ensure that fibres can be interconnected with an acceptably low loss. Provisional results indicate that acceptable splice loss and adequate strength can be achieved when splicing different high-silica fibres.

15.18   Appendix 15.6

Singlemode optical fibre cable (CCITT G.652) key parameters

Cladding diameter = 125μm, deviation less than ±2.4%

Mode field diameter = In range 9mm to 10mm at 1300nm

Mode field concentricity error less than 1.0μm (up to 3.0μm may be appropriate for some jointing techniques and joint loss requirements).

Cladding non-circularity, less than 2%

Cut off wavelength (fibre) in range 1100 - 1280nm

Cut off wavelength (cable) less than 1270nm

Loss at 1300nm less than 1dB/km (typical)

Dispersion (1270 - 1340nm) 6ps/km.nm max

Dispersion (1550nm) 20ps/km.nm max

Bend loss at 1550nm. The loss at 1550nm shall not increase by more than 1dB when measured on 100 turns of fibre loose wound on a 75mm diameter mandrel.

16

Network management

Fraidoon Mazda
MPhil DFH DMS MBIM CEng FIEE
Northern Telecom

Contents

16.1   The need for network management

Network management has traditionally been the last item to be planned when designing a new network, whilst it should always be the first. A system which can provide interconnectivity and data interchange may be thought of as having met its objectives, but if it cannot be managed then it will soon prove to be worthless.

The function of a network is to satisfy the needs of the business that it serves, and it is only through effective network management that one can ensure that these aims are being met.

Figure 16.1 shows the wide variety of network combinations within which network management has to operate. Networks can be privately owned, either leased from a public operator or be fully private, such as the vast optical infrastructure of the utility companies. The transmission media can be copper, optical or radio based, for example PMR or satellite. The network can be analogue or digital and it can carry a mix of services.

Within this range of networks there exists an equally wide spread of equipment needing management. Modern devices often conform to some standardised interface, and have on-board intelligence which allows sophisticated management functions. Older equipment have interfaces which do not conform to any standards, and are therefore very difficult to manage as part of an integrated network. Furthermore, with liberalisation growing throughout the world, users are free to shop around for the most economical equipment to meet their needs. The networks will therefore contain a mix from many suppliers, and all of these need to be managed as one unit.

16.2   Network management structure

The elements within a network manager can be conveniently considered to be structured into four sections or layers, as in Figure 16.2. At the lowest level is the platform on which the manager runs.

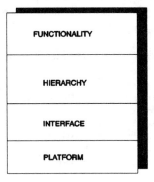

Figure 16.2   Simplified representation of the elements of network management

This not only consists of the hardware, such as a workstation or mainframe computer, but also any associated platform related software, such as the operating system and commercially obtained database.

Above this platform sits the interfaces to the elements outside the manager. This may consist of the elements being managed, such as

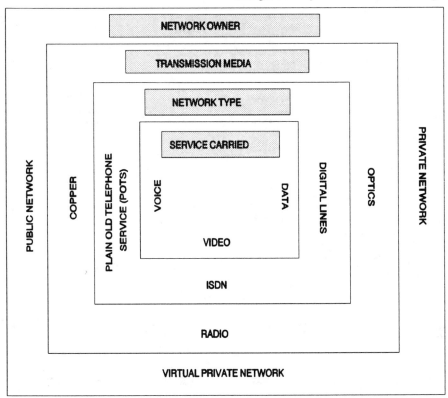

Figure 16.1   The hierarchical structure of a network

a modem, multiplexer, or cross connect, or it may be another manager within a management hierarchy, as described in the next section. These interfaces have traditionally been proprietary to the vendors who supplied the equipment, but more and more they are conforming to standards, such as OSI or SNMP, as described in the following sections. Above the hierarchy is the final 'layer', the functions which the management system needs to perform.

16.3 Network management hierarchy

A convenient hierarchical structuring of network management has been to consider the geographical location and span of control. For example the managers can be split into local, metropolitan, national and international. At the local level, which is usually intrafacility, speed of response and quality of service tend to be the most important considerations. Equipment being managed are limited in scope, such as local area networks and modems. The greater the distances, the greater the likelihood that the service will be interfacility, and now low cost and the importance of an uninterrupted flow of information, become important. There is also a much greater variety of equipment involved, spanning the range from circuits, switches and services.

Figure 16.3 shows alternative hierarchical structuring of network management. In the centralised management structure of Figure 16.3(a) all management functions are carried out at one central location, usually by a large mainframe computer. Although suitable for small networks, spread over a limited geographical area, this solution becomes difficult to operate where information has to be transported over long distances. Wide area bandwidth is expensive and the management information carried over the links competes for this bandwidth with the normal data traffic. If, therefore, all management instructions and operations have to be carried over these channels, the system can become quickly overloaded when a problem arises.

The tree structure of Figure 16.3(b) provides a distributed management hierarchy which overcomes this limitation. The element level (or plant level) manager carries out all the local servicing of alarms and disaster recovery, feeding back only major alerts to the next higher level of manager. Data processing has been moved closer to the network element that generates the data. This enables faster response to faults and also avoids the problem of a single failure of the central manager bringing down the whole network. A distributed management structure, in which set functions are carried out on separate machines, also makes it easier to design controllers operating on the principles of knowledge based systems, which can perform certain routine actions autonomously.

The peer-to-peer structure shown in Figure 16.3(c) divides the network into segments, which can then be controlled by separate but interlinking managers. This structure is often used when resilience is important. In these circumstances each manager has total jurisdiction over its own segment of the network, but maintains a monitoring brief over other segments. If one of the managers were to fail

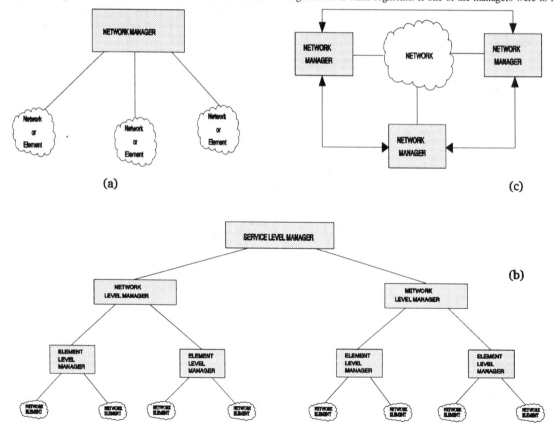

Figure 16.3 Network manager hierarchical structures: (a) centralised; (b) tree; (c) peer-to-peer

then its neighbour steps in and assumes temporary responsibility over this additional part of the network.

16.4 Network management functions

The prime function of a network manager is to ensure that the network meets the aims of the organisation which it serves. This implies that the network will consist of a set of objectives against which its performance can be measured and controlled. Unfortunately these parameters are often not easy to define or to measure. The usual indicators are as follows:

1. Grade of service, which is a subjective measure of the satisfaction expressed by the users of the service.
2. Call completion rate, which is easier to measure, but which is dependent on factors such as the rapidity with which retries occur, and the frequency of customer generated errors.
3. Network utilisation, both in terms of under utilisation, which implies wasted investment, and over utilisation, which can result in congestion and delays. Network utilisation requires careful planning and control to enable overloads to be handled satisfactorily.
4. Return on investment, which is a prime measure. However, although investment can be easily determined, return is much more complicated, since one needs to put monetary values on user frustration and time lost in getting through a congested network, and lost revenue due to customers taking their business elsewhere.

The functions required from a network management system have been conveniently classified by ISO into five groups: fault management; configuration management; performance management; security management; and accounting management. These can be considered to occur at all the three hierarchical levels, illustrated in Figure 16.3(b), giving an overall functional structure of network management, as in Figure 16.4.

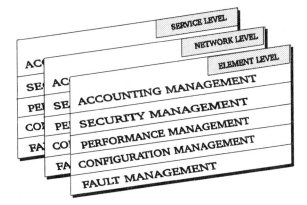

Figure 16.4 Network management functional structure

Fault management involves the detection, diagnosis and correction of network faults. These faults may be transient or persistent. The network management system should be able to zoom into the network so as to highlight the area where the fault has occurred, the node containing the fault, the card within that node and the circuit on the card. Remote diagnostics is important so that the service engineer is well prepared, often with spares, before he visits the site to fix the fault. The system should be able to issue work tickets, monitor the work being done on site, and keep track of all items returned for repair.

Fault management involves much more than reacting to problems after they have occurred. The helpdesk should be in a position to inform users of faults or potential faults, before they are affected by the fault and the complaints start to jam the helpdesk's telephones.

Configuration management provides a mechanism for managing the network elements, often called managed objects, which are under the control of the management system. The system should have the facility for changing the configuration, initialising managed objects, shutting them down and removing them from service, collecting state information on a regular and on an on-demand basis, and provisioning services and resources to meet demand. Examples of such activities are: connecting end-to-end service; setting up alternative routing options under fault conditions; configuring gains on cards; providing alternative configurations depending on time of day; and downline loading of information.

An important aspect of configuration management is name management. This allows the user to symbolically name and refer to resources on the network. Several techniques exist for this, the most popular, and the ones for which ISO is developing standards, are called the 'white pages' and 'yellow pages' protocols. In the white pages system the user looks up the values associated with any name, in much the same way that the telephone numbers are associated with people's names on the white pages of a telephone directory. In yellow pages the name of an object can be found by reference to certain attributes associated with that name, again in analogy with the yellow pages of telephone directories. Distributed facilities are often used for name management in which each area is responsible for managing the names within its territory. This prevents the delays involved in searching through vast lists and enables faster retrieval by use of an hierarchical naming structure.

The aim of performance management is to monitor and improve on the performance of the network. It gathers statistical information to enable both long term planning and prediction of short term trends. A large network would require many monitor points for collection of information and some method of local analysis and filtering to prevent the network and the user from being swamped with data. Performance monitoring requires the maintenance of logs of objects and states, so as to show trends, and the adjustment of network resources in response to trends.

Security management includes the authentication and authorisation of access to the network by users. Although shown as a separate function, security management cuts across several other functional areas, for example the need to limit access to users for certain configuration management functions. Security management therefore determines who may do what in controlling a network. It is usual to provide security access in a layered structure, the upper layers being able to perform all the functions available to the lower layers.

Accounting management aids in the preparation of bills for network users and for tracking their payment. It also helps in the sale of network resources. It is the set of facilities which enables charges to be determined for the use of the network resources and for costs to be identified and allocated to each resource. This management function depends on statistics provided by the objects on the network. Once again there is interaction between the various functions, for example accounting management and configuration management. The lowest cost is often determined by the cheapest route or the cheapest time zone, both of which are controlled by configuration management.

Accounting management is frequently considered to include inventory management. This is the function which keeps track of the individual elements being managed on the network, their characteristics, asset values and ownership and contractual information.

Although, in Figure 16.4, the five functions of fault, configuration, performance, security and accounting management are shown spread across the three levels of element management, network management and service management, they tend to be more relevant at certain levels compared to others. The element level is primarily concerned with day-to-day management of the network. It deals with faults as they occur and makes planned changes to the configuration, for example loading a predetermined configuration down to the elements depending on the time of day. This level helps in maintaining an inventory of the network resources and for updating the trouble tickets database, which contains information on the date and time of a fault, what action was taken to correct it and who took the action. This database is used by the next level manager, at the network level.

The prime function of the network level manger is to maintain a network level view of the system being managed and to carry out network wide tasks, such as setting up a service path between two elements on the network. Whereas the element level manager deals with problems associated with faulty equipment, the network level manager is concerned with items such as traffic congestion and throughput on the network.

The service level manager manages the services which are carried over the network, for example an X.25 service, and it deals with faults which result in end customer complaints. A fourth level of management is also sometimes included, the business level manager. It is here that the plans for the overall network are formulated, bearing in mind the present and predicted aims of the organisation. It takes a longer term view in considering items such as capacity and growth, and costs in terms of inventory, operations and damage to the company and its reputation caused by downtime or congestion.

Questions like the level of network resilience also need to be answered. This functional level is more concerned with long term trends than with short term variations. For example Figure 16.5

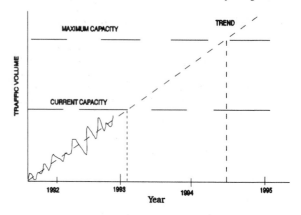

Figure 16.5   Traffic volume trends on a network

shows a trend curve of traffic demand, from which the operator would deduce that capacity will need to be expanded after 1993 and that a major re-design would be required by 1995, assuming that occasional overloads before then are acceptable.

16.5   Trends in network management

Figure 16.6 illustrates some of the trends in network management systems. The network management process, which currently has to be known and closely controlled by the user, will in future be transparent, so that the overall job is greatly simplified. The re-

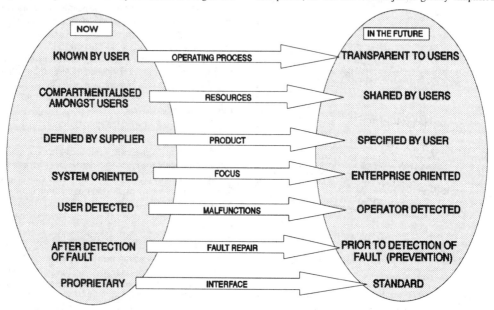

Figure 16.6   Trends in network management

sources on the network are also currently available to relatively small groups of users, but in the future they will be shared by much wider groups, and will often be a mix of privately owned and publicly owned resources. Currently it is the supplier who determines what the product will do, a case of having a car of any colour provided that it is black. In the future it will be the sophisticated user who will determine which product, out of the many standards based systems available, meets his requirement.

At the present time the focus of network management is on system management, whereas this will gradually change to be more clearly focused on managing the overall enterprise. The management systems will also be much more intelligent, being able to detect faults before the user has found them, and often monitoring trends and taking actions autonomously, so that breakdowns are prevented.

The key evolution, however, will be the change from proprietary based management systems to those which incorporate standard interfaces. This will be driven by many of the factors described above. The change from proprietary to standard based systems will be evolutionary rather than revolutionary. Currently two networks supplied by different vendors can only be controlled by their own proprietary managers. The two systems cannot communicate and the nearest one can get to in integration terms is to run them on one workstation using different windows. This eliminates the need for the operator to stare at a multitude of screens, but he still needs to be familiar with the syntax and command formats of the two systems, and human intervention is needed to pass any information between the different systems.

Figure 16.7 shows an evolution from this where the network elements still maintain proprietary interfaces but the two managers are able to converse using a common, standards based, protocol. Once again the two systems can be located on the same hardware, but now there is interchange of information between networks A and B via their managers.

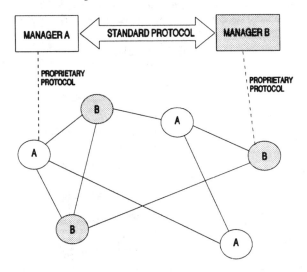

Figure 16.7 Interaction between two proprietary networks at the manager level

Summarising, currently management systems are used primarily to control mono-services, such as a telephone network, a packet switch network, telex, etc. These are usually dedicated to homogeneous groups of users. In the future multi-services will be the norm, using a mix of carrier networks, some privately owned and

some owned by public operators, so that it will be important to be able to share tasks. Currently the management of a network is treated as separate from the management of services carried on the network (intelligent networks), but in the future the two will be managed as one entity.

16.6 The OSI model

In the area of network management the standards activity with the greatest long term impact is that based on the ISO Seven Layer, Open System Interconnect, Basic Reference Model, often called the OSI model. The International Standards Organisation (ISO) started work on the OSI model in 1977. The aim was to allow computers from different manufacturers to talk to each other. OSI ideas have been accepted by many organisations, including the CCITT, and a considerable amount of work is being done to extend and develop the model.

OSI principles are now being incorporated into many types of equipment, which need to communicate with each other. Figure 16.8 illustrates that as more of these network elements begin to conform to standards so too will their managers. Eventually a large

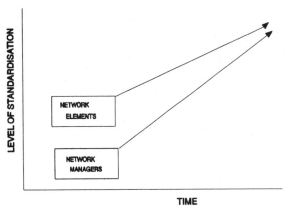

Figure 16.8 Convergence of the amount of standardisation on network elements and network

proportion of systems will be based on OSI standards, resulting in the original aim of ISO of global interworking. Further development of the OSI model is now being done by a joint technical committee (JTC1) set up by ISO and the IEC, which works very closely with CCITT study groups. The OSI architecture is covered in ISO standards ISO 7498, which has been accepted by CCITT as Recommendation X.200.

It is important to remember that OSI deals with communications between systems and not processing within these end systems. It gives an abstract structure for the subdivision of communication functions and so forms a framework for co-ordination of current and future standards, rather than defining the standards themselves. In a related area JTC1 is working on a second reference model, the Reference Model of Open Distributed Processing (ODP) which will define the standards to enable distributed processing, i.e. the ability to run systems on equipment supplied by several different manufacturers.

Base OSI standards provide several options, so that the same set of standards can be applied to many different applications, and also because, to be useful, standards operate in combinations within the seven layer stack.

Functional standards or profiles specify a subset of these base standards for particular applications, often adding details which are missing from the base standards, and it is these profiles which largely enable interworking between systems. Several different groups are involved in defining profiles, for example the Manufacturing Automation Protocol (MAP), and the Technical and Office Protocol (TOP). For network management the key activities are those within CCITT Study Group IV on the Telecommunications Management Network (TMN); within CCITT Study Group XV on the management of the synchronous digital hierarchy (SHD); and within CCITT Study Groups XI and XVII on ISDN management. ANSI subcommittees T1M1 and T1X1 are also developing standards for management in fibre optic based systems (Sonet).

Other special interest groups (see Chapter 22) are the OSI Implementors Workshop (OIW), mainly with participants from North America, the European Workshop for OSI Standardisation (EWOS) and the Asia and Oceania Workshop for OSI Standardisation (AOWS). Many of these profiles, and others developed by various OSI Workshops, are submitted to JTC1 in order to have them incorporated as International Standardised Profiles (ISPs).

Another area, as important as the standards, is that of conformance testing. Items which pass these tests can then be certified, so that the user knows that two such items within his network will interwork with each other. Conformance test specifications have been developed by various interest groups, such as the OSI Network Management Forum, and independent conformance testing is carried out by other bodies, such as the Corporation for Open Systems (COS) in North America, the Standards Promotion and Application Group (SPAG) in Europe, and the Promoting Conference for OSI (POSI) in Japan. ISO has published the OSI Conformance Testing Methodology and Framework (ISO 9646) which provides a general framework for conformance testing. It outlines principles which should be applied in developing conformance tests for specific OSI standards.

16.6.1 The seven layers

Figure 16.9 shows the traditional OSI seven layer model in which communications is taking place between two end systems, using an intermediate or relay system. The operation of this model is covered in more detail in Chapter 12 and is briefly reviewed here.

The OSI concept assumes that exchanges of data between systems involve at least four components:

1. The communications path between the systems.
2. The systematic delivery of the data along this path, which requires a structured exchange of information.
3. A common language (the syntax) which is understood by all parties involved in the data interchange.
4. The same conceptual interpretation of the data on all sides, i.e. the semantics.

OSI has divided these requirements into a hierarchical structure within its reference model. The basic concept is that the functions involved in any communications can be divided into seven separate and well defined layers. Communications between layers within different systems is defined by service primitives. OSI standards define the services each layer provides, and service definitions are then the basis for the protocol defining how layers in one system communicate with layers at the same level within another system. This means that, in theory if not in practice, protocols in one layer can be replaced without affecting other layers.

Figure 16.10 illustrates this concept of service provision within a layer. Layers provide services to its own users and to the layers above, using their own functions or those contained within services provided by the layer below. There are four basic types of service primitives, request, indication, response and confirm. Primitive full names consist of a letter, indicating the layer (e.g. S for the Session layer) a verb indicating the operation, and the basic type of service primitive, for example 'S- DISCONNECT confirm.' In an actual

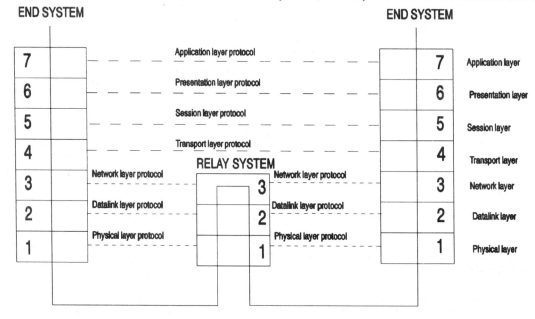

Figure 16.9 The OSI model showing communications between two end systems using an intermediate relay system

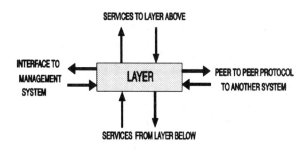

Figure 16.10 Communications using services within the seven layer OSI model

system data from the originator has headers (and sometimes a trailer) added to it as it moves down the stack. At the receiving end these are stripped off as the message moves up the stack, and this information is used by those layers, until eventually the end user receives the raw data from the sender.

The Application Layer includes both the Application Entities (AEs), which provide the semantics (the communications between the end user applications) as well as the Application Service Elements (ASEs) such as CMISE, ACSE and ROSE, which provide the communication services according to a defined protocol.

The Presentation Layer transforms the local syntax used in the Application Layer, which may be unique, into a transfer syntax, which is common between communicating applications. The local syntax for a given system is derivable from a machine independent abstract syntax, such as Abstract Syntax Notation one (ASN.1). The transfer syntax is operated at the Presentation Layer according to standardised encoding rules, such as Basic Encoding Rules (BER).

The Session Layer controls the exchange of information between the Presentation Layers within the different systems, by establishing connection, synchronisation, disconnection, flow control to prevent flooding, etc. The Session Layer (and the Transport Layer) has only one standard specified within it, but they have different classes or subsets which provide options to enable the lower layers to be matched to the needs of the upper layers, depending on the application.

The Transport Layer ensures the correct quality of service, requested by the applications, and informs the Session Layer if it cannot maintain this service quality. There are five classes of service, characterised by parameters such as transmission delay, throughput, residual error rate, and connection set-up delay. Class 0 is used when the bearer is of good quality and Class 4 when it is not as good.

The Network Layer's prime aim is to provide a transparent path for the transmission of data between the Transport Layers within the communicating systems. It handles addressing and routing of circuits. The Data Link Layer provides the error free circuit between the Network Layers, and it has facilities for detecting and correcting errors, and for retransmissions. The Physical Layer interfaces to the physical transmission media and converts the data into signals which are compatible with it, e.g. optical, electrical and radio. The services in these last three layers is what is normally provided by the public X.25 network.

As stated earlier the OSI reference model describes a general structure only, whilst other standards define the services and protocols which need to be provided at the various layers. Some of these

are shown in Figure 16.11. This illustrates the choice which exists when communicating up and down the OSI stack. The standards are of two types: those used in different applications and those which are specific to one type of application.

16.6.1.1 *Common Application Layer standards within OSI*

Association Control Service Element (ACSE)

This Application Service Element has functions to enable the identification and approval of communicating end users; negotiation of the protocol functional units which will be used by the applications concerned; the establishment and release of application associations between processes. ACSE can be used directly by an application, or it may be used by other Layer 7 Application Service Elements.

Remote Operation Service Element (ROSE)

This Application Service Element has functions for supporting remote operations in a distributed open system environment. It has the ability to request that a remote operation be performed on another open system, a response or an error being returned.

Commitment, Concurrency and Recovery (CCR)

This provides a facility for ensuring the correct performance of a multi-step operation, where a step is dependent on the previous one being successfully implemented. It is used when there is need to guarantee distributed data consistency amongst two or more interworking open systems.

Reliable Transfer Service Element (RTSE)

These elements ensure reliable communications, protecting against failures and informing the sender when errors occur.

16.6.1.2 *Specific Application Layer standards within OSI*

File Transfer, Access and Management (FTAM)

This Application Service Element provides functions for accessing and modifying files on another open system and for transferring them between open systems.

Message Handling System (MHS)

This comprises a set of standards for use in electronic mail, where the message may consist of data, speech, text or graphics. MHS is a CCITT standard, the ISO equivalent being Message Oriented Text Interchange System (MOTIS).

Directory services

These are a set of standards for the electronic supply and update of information covering, for example, applications or people. It can consist of application addresses, telephone numbers, telex numbers, etc. The directory may be located on distributed databases, in which case the standard also specifies the interconnection between these and the user.

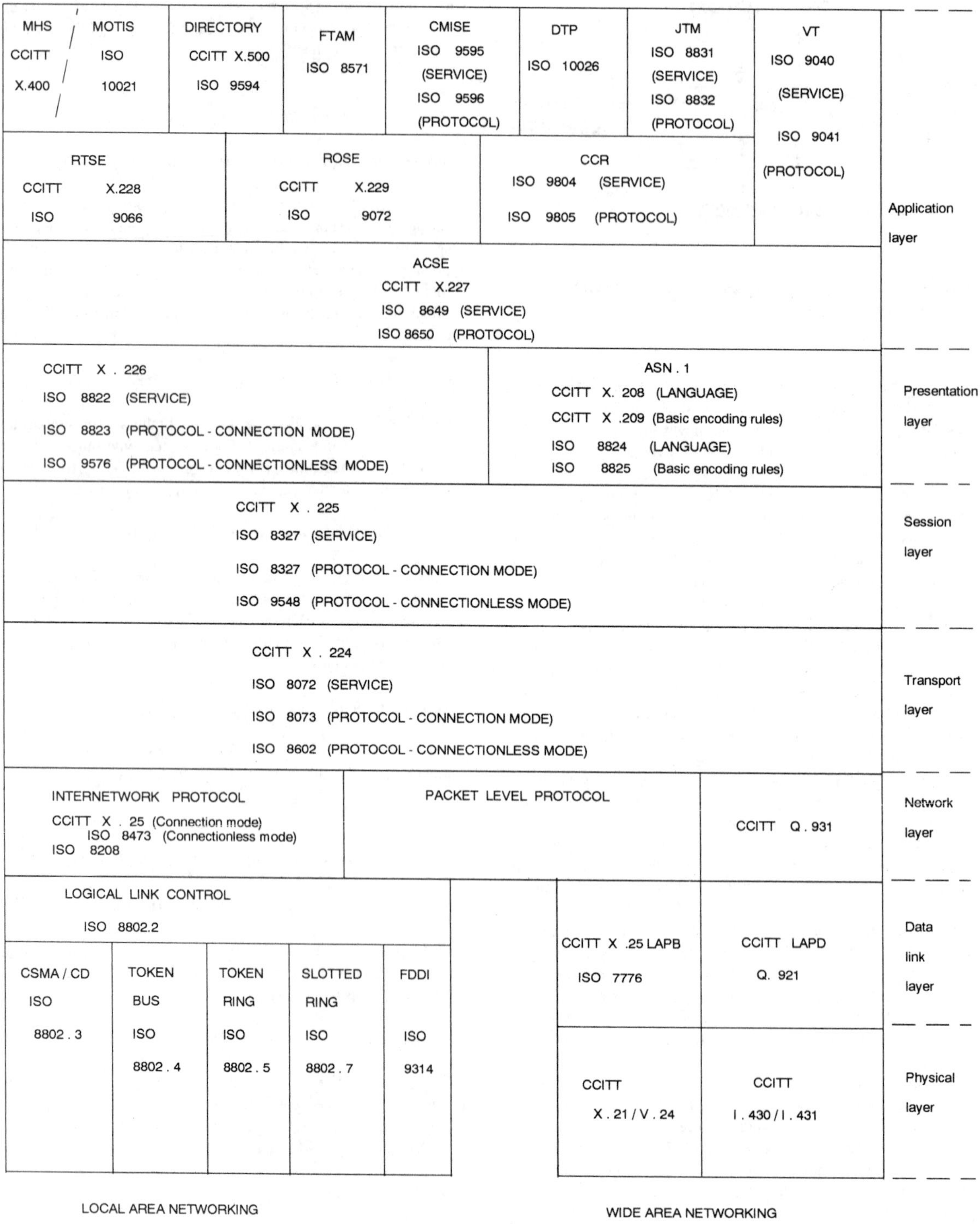

MHS / MOTIS CCITT / ISO X.400 / 10021		DIRECTORY CCITT X.500 ISO 9594	FTAM ISO 8571	CMISE ISO 9595 (SERVICE) ISO 9596 (PROTOCOL)	DTP ISO 10026	JTM ISO 8831 (SERVICE) ISO 8832 (PROTOCOL)	VT ISO 9040 (SERVICE) ISO 9041 (PROTOCOL)

Application layer

RTSE CCITT X.228 ISO 9066	ROSE CCITT X.229 ISO 9072	CCR ISO 9804 (SERVICE) ISO 9805 (PROTOCOL)

ACSE
CCITT X.227
ISO 8649 (SERVICE)
ISO 8650 (PROTOCOL)

Presentation layer

CCITT X . 226 ISO 8822 (SERVICE) ISO 8823 (PROTOCOL - CONNECTION MODE) ISO 9576 (PROTOCOL - CONNECTIONLESS MODE)	ASN . 1 CCITT X. 208 (LANGUAGE) CCITT X .209 (Basic encoding rules) ISO 8824 (LANGUAGE) ISO 8825 (Basic encoding rules)

Session layer

CCITT X . 225
ISO 8327 (SERVICE)
ISO 8327 (PROTOCOL - CONNECTION MODE)
ISO 9548 (PROTOCOL - CONNECTIONLESS MODE)

Transport layer

CCITT X . 224
ISO 8072 (SERVICE)
ISO 8073 (PROTOCOL - CONNECTION MODE)
ISO 8602 (PROTOCOL - CONNECTIONLESS MODE)

Network layer

INTERNETWORK PROTOCOL CCITT X . 25 (Connection mode) ISO 8473 (Connectionless mode) ISO 8208	PACKET LEVEL PROTOCOL	CCITT Q . 931

Data link layer

LOGICAL LINK CONTROL ISO 8802.2						

CSMA / CD ISO 8802 . 3	TOKEN BUS ISO 8802 . 4	TOKEN RING ISO 8802 . 5	SLOTTED RING ISO 8802 . 7	FDDI ISO 9314	CCITT X .25 LAPB ISO 7776	CCITT LAPD Q. 921

Physical layer

CCITT X . 21 / V . 24	CCITT I . 430 / I . 431

LOCAL AREA NETWORKING   WIDE AREA NETWORKING

Figure 16.11 Some of the standards contained within the OSI seven layers

Virtual Terminal (VT)

This provides functions for remote terminal access between open systems.

Distributed Transaction Processing (DTP)

This provides functions which enable distributed transaction-oriented processing between open systems. It uses CCR as an underlying service provider.

Job Transfer and Manipulation (JTM)

This provides functions to control processes in a remote computer. It enables work to be submitted to one open system and to be run on another system.

Common Management Information Service Element (CMISE)

This Application Service Element provides functions for transmitting management information between open systems and is therefore of prime importance in network management. It is a transaction oriented standard which uses services of common standards, such as ACSE and ROSE. Contained within CMISE are CMIS (Common Management Information Service), which provides the service necessary to support CMISE capabilities, and CMIP (Common Management Information Protocol) which is the protocol used to carry CMIS.

16.7 OSI network management concepts

There are several management concepts defined within OSI, as described in the following sections.

16.7.1 Managed objects

OSI management standards are dependent on the principles of object modelling. The managed object forms an abstract representation of a resource looked at from the perspective of management. It may, for example, be a physical item, such as a multiplexer, or it may be logical, such as a connection. Managed objects contain attributes, each attribute having a value. Objects and their attributes are stored within what is known as a Management Information Base (MIB).

The collection, or set, of managed objects which share identical properties is referred to as a managed object class. Every occurrence of a managed object, which conforms to the same class, is called a managed object instance. Managed object classes are important since, if a management system knows the class of a managed object, then it knows unambiguously the management services which it can expect to be provided by the object.

In OSI the Structure of Management Information (SMI) defines the modelling principle to be used for designing managed objects, along with the description associated with them. It provides sets of templates to describe the managed objects. Abstract Syntax Notation One (ASN.1) is used for these, so that they are independent of the architecture of the machine on which they run. An ASN.1 compiler would then take these ASN.1 object definitions and provide the data structures and the source code routines needed to encode and decode management information relating to the managed objects.

16.7.2 Managers and Agents

Two illustrations are usually used to demonstrate the concept of a manager process and an agent process, as in Figure 16.12 and Figure 16.13. The concept is that since a manager cannot effectively control a large number of objects directly, it employs agents (also known as agent managers or agent processes) who control subsets. Manager and agent applications in the same or different open system exchange management information using CMIS/CMIP. The agent performs the following functions on behalf of the manager:

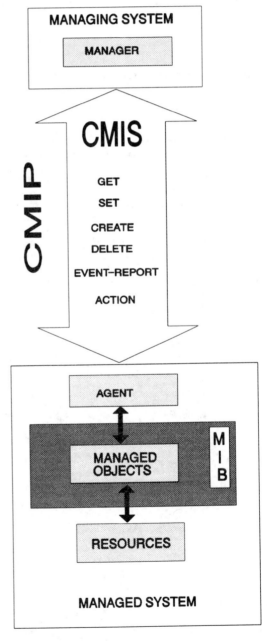

Figure 16.12 Illustration of Manager and Agent process

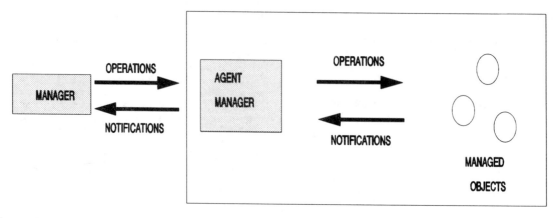

Figure 16.13   Alternative representation of a Manager and Agent process

1. Handles the representation of the resources being controlled in the form of managed objects.
2. Gives the manager a management view of the objects being managed.
3. Handles management requests from the manager to the managed objects and responses from the objects to the manager. These may be categorised as operations and notifications. The agent therefore performs an amplifying and filtering role.

As stated earlier, the manager interacts with the remote agent using the Common Management Information Service (CMIS) which is transmitted by the Common Management Information Protocol (CMIP). The manager can request management information from the agent manager (solicited responses), for example by the use of the following services provided by CMIS:

GET, which fetches the attribute values, from the MIB.
SET, which replaces the attribute values specified by the new values contained within the SET command.
CREATE, which adds a new instance of a managed object, and can be used, for example, to create a new 'connection' in a telecommunication network.
DELETE, which deletes the instance of a managed object.
ACTION, which provides a general facility for requesting actions, against existing managed objects, for example carrying out a test to determine the cause of an alarm. The service therefore contains a specific action identifier.

Each of the above single requests (except for CREATE) in CMIS can themselves trigger off a large number of subsidiary actions, by the agent, on managed objects selected by scoping and filtering.

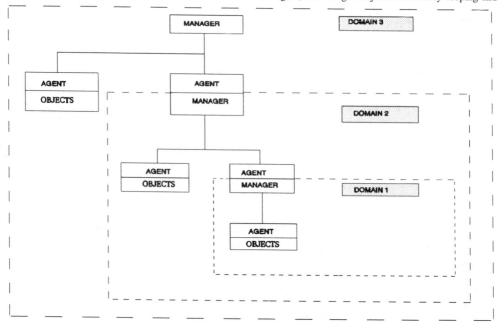

Figure 16.14   Manager and Agent within management domains

Operations requests may refer to more than one managed object. The agent performs the necessary scoping and filtering as specified by the manager to select target objects, applies the operation to each object, thus resulting in a (linked) response from each to the manager. Facilities also exist to request the agent to either:

1. Only do all operations if they can be successfully completed, otherwise to do none of them ('atomic' action).
2. Do as many operations as it can complete ('best effort' action).

In addition to the above solicited requests, unsolicited reports may be received by the manager from the managed object. This is achieved by means of the CMIS **EVENT-REPORT** service, which allows the agent to send events and alarms.

A complex system would have several managers and several agents. A manager can be a managing process for its own agents and an agent for another managing process. Managers and agents can therefore form a hierarchy of management domains, as shown in Figure 16.14, each domain defining the scope of its manager.

16.7.3 The Management Information Base

The set of managed objects, made visible by the agent to the manager, is called the Management Information Base (MIB), as illustrated in Figure 16.12. For example the managed resources may be the seven layers of the OSI stack. This gives an abstract image of the managed objects within the network, such as the routing table objects which form the layer 3 functions used by the nodes. Because the data relating to managed resources is often stored in a physical database, this database is often spoken of as the MIB.

The MIB provides a method for relating managed objects to each other. It is by manipulation of the virtual object held within the MIB that the real database held within the node can be examined or changed.

The Management Information Base (MIB) contains a virtual image of how a network is behaving at any time. It should not be confused with the configuration databases, which are located at management centres and which keep information on how the node should be behaving. The MIB must span all seven layers, as shown in Figure 16.15(a), since it must be able to access and change the management information in all layers of the stack. A problem can arise when controlling devices which do not have a full seven layer implementation, such as modems, bridges and routers. Two solutions are possible in these instances: use of a thin stack, or of a proxy node (translator node).

Figure 16.15(b) shows a device which uses a thin stack. In this arrangement the device which does not have the full seven layers only performs the minimum functionality needed to support network management. The use of a proxy node is illustrated in Figure

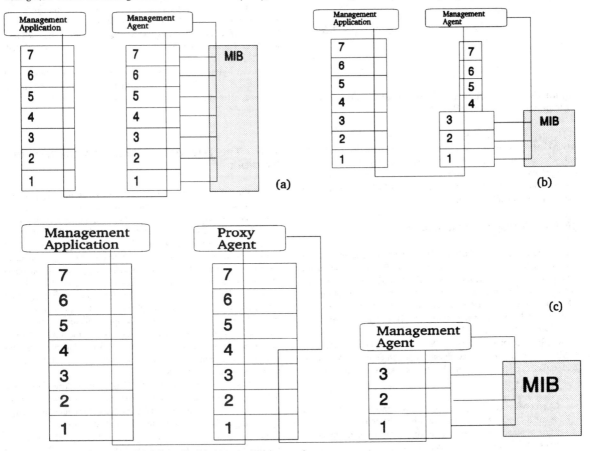

Figure 16.15 MIB options: (a) full stack; (b) thin stack; (c) use of a proxy agent

15(c). These devices use the lower layer protocols for communications; in the example shown this is layer 3. A proxy node has exclusive control over the node to which it is attached. Translator nodes are similar to proxy nodes but in this case they consist of a group of nodes which share control over a common device.

Within the MIB the managed objects are organised in a containment hierarchy or tree structure, as in Figure 16.16, where the subordinate nodes on the tree are contained within superior objects. This tree is called a Management Information Tree (MIT). Operations on managed objects within the MIB needs a knowledge of this containment hierarchy. Each managed object has a name and this name is formed by concatenating the names of all its superior objects within the MIT. The object at the head of the tree is the ROOT and an object's name relative to the root is called its distinguishing name (DN). The name of an object relative to any other superior object below the root is called its relative distinguishing name (RDN). For example, in Figure 16.16, object D has an RDN

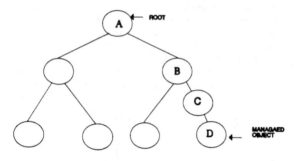

Figure 16.16 Containment relationship of objects within a Management Information Base (MIB)

of D, relative to C and an RDN of CD relative to B. It has a DN of ABCD. All DNs are unique within an entire system, but RDNs are only unique within a limited confine, such as a network, a switch or a geographical area. Names are important since they are used to select managed objects, in the exchanges which occur between managers and agent managers.

16.7.4 Management functions

Layer 7 within the OSI model has the Systems Management Application Entity (SMAE), which contains the System Management Application Service Element (SMASE). An SMASE is associated with each manager and its agent, and for communication the SMASE uses the services of CMIS which are carried to the remote system via CMIP. This manipulates the MIB using low level operations such as SET and GET.

SMASE encompasses a set of System Management Functions (SMF) which define the mechanism by which certain tasks can be undertaken on the managed objects. Examples of these are as follows:

1. Object Management, covering the mechanism used to create, delete and manage the attributes within the objects.
2. State Management, covering the object states, and the mechanisms which may be used to change them.
3. Relationship management, covering the principles of containment, that is the mechanism used for establishing the relationships between the managed objects.

4. Alarm Management Reporting, covering the syntax and the semantics of the alarms originated by the managed objects.
5. Security Alarm Reporting, covering the syntax and the semantics for alarms which are used to report security events on a system.
6. Event Management Reporting, covering the reporting and control of events.
7. Log Control, covering the mechanism for setting up and maintaining a log of events.
8. Confidence and Diagnostic Testing, covering the methods to be used for carrying out and controlling diagnostic tests performed on a system.
9. Accounting and Metering, covering the procedure for logging and reporting the amount of network resources used, so that effective accounting and billing can be carried out.
10. Workload Monitoring, covering the method to be used for monitoring the use of network resources in order to evaluate its performance.
11. Measurement Summary, covering the method for statistical analysis of the performance of elements connected to the network.

The various SMFs, which may be used by network management applications, are grouped by ISO into five System Management Functional Areas (SMFA): accounting management, security management, performance management, configuration management, and fault management. These were described earlier with reference to Figure 16.4. The SMFA define which SMFs are to be used and which OSI applications are to be involved, for example CMIP, FTAM, etc.

Table 16.1 gives a list of OSI network management standards and their availability. In this the suffix IS implies a full international standard, DIS indicates a draft international standard and CD a committee draft.

16.8 The Telecommunication Management Network

As mentioned earlier, several groups have taken the OSI network management model and developed it further for specific applications. The best known of these is the Telecommunications Management Network (TMN). Work started on TMN in 1985 and it has since been developed by ANSI, CCITT and ETSI. ANSI approached this on a bottom up basis, first determining what management data, and in what format, the network elements can provide to the operator, before specifying management requirements. CCITT and ETSI, on the other hand, started by first defining the network management functions which would be needed to control a telecommunications network, and then working downwards to define the data and format needed to implement these functions. All three groups are co-ordinating their activities closely. The principles for a Telecommunications Management Network are described in CCITT Recommendation M.30.

The basic concept behind a TMN is to provide an organised network structure, to achieve the interconnection between various types of Operations Systems (OS) and telecommunications equipment using an agreed architecture and with standardised interfaces. Figure 16.17 shows the relationship between the TMN and a telecommunications network. The telecommunications network can consist of both digital and analogue telecommunications equipment. As in the case of the OSI model, the telecommunications network is considered to consist of managed objects (network

Table 16.1 OSI management standards and availability

Standard number	Standard description	Expected date for full IS
Architecture		
IS 7498-4	Reference model of open systems communication - Part 4 Management framework	Dec. 1989
Structure of Management Information		
IS 10165-1	Structure of Management information - Part 1 Management information model	July 1991
IS 10165-2	Structure of Management information - Part 2 Definition of management information	July 1991
IS 10165-4	Structure of Management information - Part 4 Guidelines for the definition of managed objects	July 1991
Management Information Services and Protocols		
IS 9595	Common management information service plus: Addendum 1 Cancel Get. Addendum 2. Add/Remove	Jan. 1991
IS 9596	Common management information protocol plus: Addendum 1 Cancel Get. Addendum 2. Add/Remove	Jan. 1991
Systems Management Functions		
IS 10164-1	Object management function	July 1991
IS 10164-2	State management function	July 1991
IS 10164-3	Relationship management function	July 1991
IS 10164-4	Alarm reporting function	July 1991
IS 10164-5	Event report management function	July 1991
IS 10164-6	Log control function	July 1991
IS 10164-7	Security alarm reporting function	July 1991
DIS 10164-8	Security audit trail function	April 1992
CD 10164-9	Objects and attributes for access control	April 1992
CD 10164-10	Accounting meter function	April 1992
CD 10164-11	Workload monitoring function	April 1992
CD 10164-12	Test management function	April 1992
CD 10164-13	Measurement summarisation function	August 1992
Managed Object Definitions		
DIS 10589	IS-IS routing exchange protocol	July 1992
CD 10733	Elements of management information related to OSI network layer standards	July 1992
CD 10737	Elements of management information related to OSI transport layer standards	July 1992

elements). These may be physical elements, such as exchanges, transmission equipment, cable, cross-connects, or it may consist of abstract elements, such as maintenance entities and support entities.

The interchange of information within the TMN uses the OSI seven layer model and the services within these layers. For example Figure 16.18 illustrates the flow of information when an alarm is raised by a network element and sent to its Operations System. The alarm is sensed by the relevant TMN application. This sends a request (A) to CMISE to set up a connection to the Operations System. The CMISE primitive used is 'M-INITIALISE request. CMISE forwards this request to ACSE using 'A-ASSOCIATE request' as at (B). ACSE passes this request on and it goes down the OSI stack, is transmitted to the Operations System, and up its stack until it reaches the application layer at (D) with the primitive 'M-INITIALISE request.' The Operations System acknowledges this request via (E) until it arrives at the originating network element at

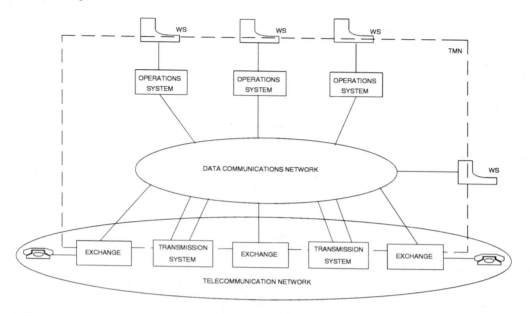

Figure 16.17 Relationship between the TMN and a telecommunication network

(F) as 'M-INITIALISE confirm'. Alarm information is now sent by the network element as 'M-EVENT REPORT request' at (G) to CMISE, which calls ROSE at (H) with 'RO-INVOKE request'. Eventually the alarm message reaches the Operations System as 'M- EVENT-REPORT indication' at (I).

16.8.1 The TMN architecture

The TMN architecture consists of three elements: functional architecture; information architecture; and physical architecture.

The functional architecture may be considered to be the building blocks which allow complex systems to be built.

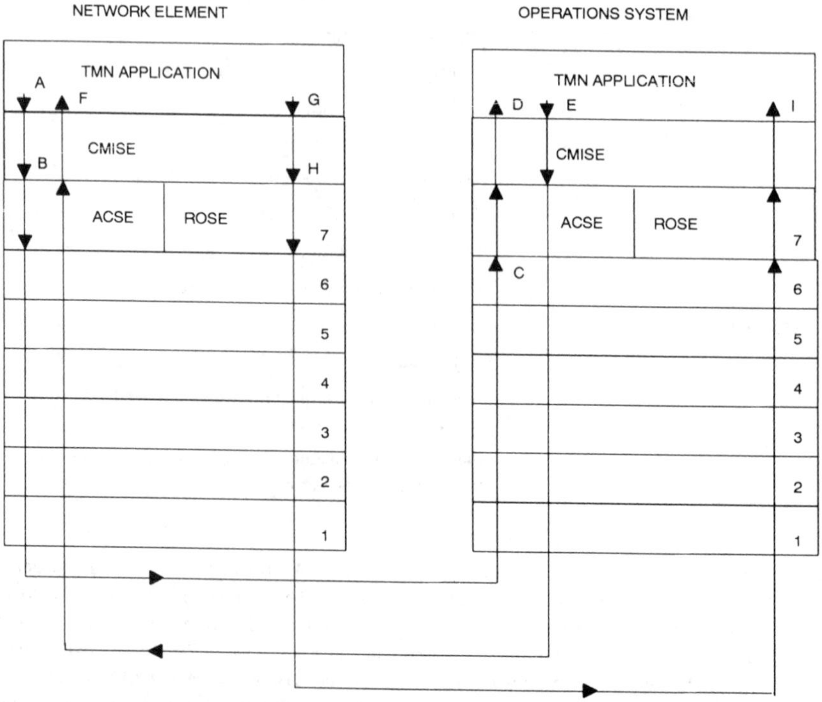

Figure 16.18 Interchange of information between a Network Element and Operations System within a TMN

The information architecture describes the nature of information which needs to be exchanged between the functional building blocks.

The physical architecture of TMN describes the interfaces which have to be implemented, along with examples of physical components which make up the TMN.

16.8.1.1   The TMN functional architecture

The TMN functional architecture is based on a number of functional building blocks which enable a TMN to perform its application functions. They consist of principle blocks, such as the Operations Systems Function (OSF) and the Work Station Function (WSF), and complementary blocks, such as the Data Communication Function (DCF), the Mediation Function (MF) and the Q Adaptor Function (QAF). Some of these blocks are only partly within TMN, as explained later and illustrated in Figure 16.19.

The Operations Systems Functions (OSF) processes information to support and control the realisation of various telecommunication management functions. Many types of OSFs are realisable, depending on the TMN, and can range from business, customer, service, network and basic levels of abstraction. Business OSFs are concerned with the management and co-ordination of the total business or enterprise. Service OSFs usually provide the interface to customers, and are primarily involved in service aspects of the network. The network OSFs cover the realisation of the network, based on TMN application functions, by communicating with the basic OSFs. In small networks these basic OSFs may not be present and then the network OSFs need to communicate with the Network Element Functions or directly with the Mediation Functions.

The Mediation Function (MF) is responsible for adapting, filtering and condensing information which passes from the NEFs, and sometimes from the QAFs, to suit the requirements of the OSFs.

The Network Element Function (NEF) communicates with the TMN in order that it may be monitored and controlled. It includes

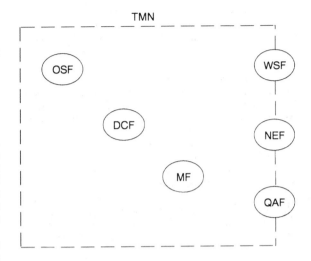

Figure 16.19   The TMN function block

some telecommunication functions which do not form part of TMN, but which are represented to it by the NEF for purposes of management. Hence this function is shown partly outside the TMN in Figure 16.19.

The Work Station Function (WF) is responsible for providing the user with the means to interpret the information coming from the TMN. It also includes support for the interfaces to the user, these aspects being considered to be outside the TMN. The WSF contains the Presentation Function (PF) which provides the user with human readable displays and with a method of data entry, such as a terminal.

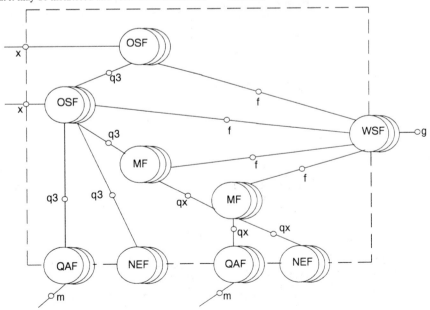

Figure 16.20   Example of the TMN functional reference model and classes of reference points

The Q Adaptor Function (QAF) provides the translation between a TMN interface and a proprietary or non-TMN interface, this latter part being outside the TMN in Figure 16.19. The QAF is therefore used to connect those network elements which do not support TMN interfaces to a TMN.

Within the TMN the concept of reference points is introduced, these being used to define the boundaries between the management function blocks, as in Figure 16.20. Reference points describe the service interface between two management function blocks and identify the information which passes between them. There are three classes of TMN reference points (q, f and x) and two classes of non-TMN reference points (g and m).

The q reference points are located between OSF, QAF, MF and NEF. There are qx reference points between two MFs, or between an MF and a QAF or NEF. There are q3 reference points between OSFs, or between an OSF and a NEF or QAF or MF. q3 interfaces are very communicative. Less intelligent functions need to use one or more mediation functions, via qx interfaces, to allow them to be controlled using a q3 interface.

The f reference points are those located between the WSF and OSF or between the WSF and the MF, via the Data Communications Function (DCF).

The x reference point provides the interface between OSF functional blocks within different TMNs, or the equivalent functions in a non-TMN system.

The g reference point provides the interface between the workstation and the human user. It conveys TMN information but is considered to be outside the TMN. Similarly an m reference point is considered to be located outside the TMN. It is situated between the QAF and a managed entity which does not conform to TMN.

16.8.1.2 *TMN information architecture*

The information architecture for TMN is based very closely on that of OSI, these principles being developed further by TMN within Recommendation M.30.

An object oriented approach is used throughout. M.30 also defines the principles of managed objects and their relationship to real resources. The concepts of attributes and the concept of manager and agent manager are also described, as in Figure 16.13.

16.8.1.3 *TMN physical architecture*

Figure 16.21 illustrates a simplified example of the physical architecture for a TMN. The Operations System (OS) is a stand alone system which performs the Operations System Functions. The Mediation Device (MD) performs the Mediation Functions. MDs can be implemented as a hierarchy of cascaded devices, as in Figure 16.20. The Q Interface Adapter (QA) is the device which network

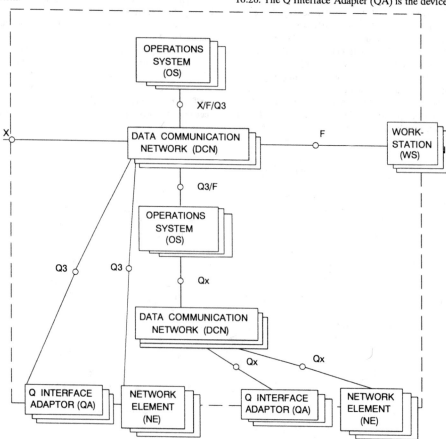

Figure 16.21 Simplified example of the physical architecture for a TMN

elements (NEs) without a TMN interface connect to, using the m interface point. QAs may incorporate mediation functions, therefore the interface they present to the TMN may be Q3 or Qx.

The Data Communication Network (DCN) is the communication network within a TMN which supports the Data Communication Function (DCF). It consists of the dedicated communications paths, such as X.25 and voice channels.

The network element (NE) is made up of the telecommunication equipment, groups of equipment or parts of equipment. It supports any item which performs NEFs and has one or more standard Q-type interfaces. Equipment which does not have this standard interface needs to connect to the TMN via a Q Interface Adapter, as above, which converts between the non-standard and standard management interfaces.

The Work Station (WS) is the system which performs the WSFs, these latter translating the information from the f reference point to a suitable format for the user at the g reference point and vice-versa.

The relationship between the TMN building block names and the TMN functional blocks is shown in Table 16.2.

Table 16.2 Relationship of the TMN building block names to the TMN functional blocks

	NEF	MF	QAF	OSF	WSF
NE	M	O	O	O	O
MD		M	O	O	O
QA			M		
OS				M	
WS					M

Note: M=Mandatory   O=Optional

Standard interfaces are also defined in the TMN physical architecture, corresponding to the reference points of Figure 16.20. The Q interface is applied at the q reference points, and for flexibility there are sub-classes for the Q interfaces. Qx connects MDs to MDs, NEs to MDs, QAs to MDs, and NEs to NEs when one or both NE includes a mediation device.

Table 16.3 Relationship of TMN to the TMN building blocks

	Qx	Q3	X	F
NE	O	O	O	O
MD	M	O	O	O
QA	O	O		
WS				M
OS		O	O	O

Notes: (1)An MD must always have a Qx interface to be part of the TMN.
(2) At least one of the interfaces inside the boxes must be present.

The Q3 interface is intended to connect MDs, QAs, NEs (containing MF) and OSs to OSs via a DCN.

The F interface is applied at f reference points. When a F interface connects workstations remotely to the OSF or MF through a data communication network it is included within TMN, whilst direct connections of WSF to OSF or NEF is not included within TMN.

The X interface is applied to the x reference point. The purpose of the X interface is to interconnect two management systems or TMNs. These TMNs may belong to separate administrations or to an administration and a private service provider.

Table 16.3 shows the possible interfaces which each TMN building block can support. It is based on Table 16.2, i.e. the functional blocks associated with each building block.

16.9   The Simple Network Management Protocol

The Simple Network Management Protocol (SNMP) is widely used to manage networks which employ the Transport Control Protocol and Internet Protocol (TCP/IP) as the transport mechanism. These protocols are reviewed in this section and compared with those based on OSI.

16.9.1   The TCP/IP

The Transport Control Protocol and the Internet Protocol have their origins in the USA, and unfortunately they are therefore considered to be protocols which are primarily intended for use there, whilst Europe and the rest of the world uses OSI protocols. This is not strictly true since TCP/IP is widely supported world-wide, for use within local and wide area networks.

TCP/IP was devised by the US Defence Advanced Research Projects Agency (DARPA), in the late 1970s, as the transport mechanism for use in the Arpanet research network.

The Arpanet network developed into the Internet programme, which is the largest collection of heterogeneous networks in the world, consisting of over five thousand interconnected networks with several million potential users. It is administered by the Internet Activities Board (IAB) and is primarily associated with the

National Science Foundation and the US Department of Defence (known as Internet). It has a mix of local area networks (LAN) and wide area networks (WAN) all operating as a single network using TCP/IP.

Internet Protocol is equivalent to layer three, the network layer, of the OSI model, and TCP is equivalent to layer 4, the transport layer. Alongside TCP exists an alternative level 4 protocol, the User Datagram Protocol (UDP).

Above level 4 there are several higher level protocols, associated with various services, some being illustrated in Figure 16.22. SMTP is used for mail transfer, FTP for file management and transfer, and TELNET for terminal sessions.

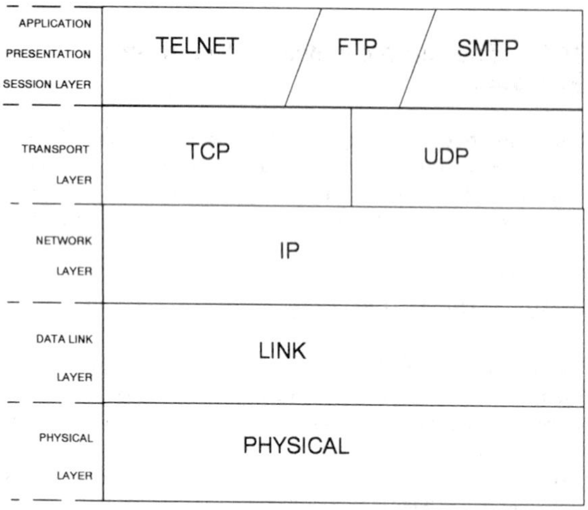

Figure 16.22   A TCP/IP protocol stack

Below level 3 of the TCP/IP stack the protocols can be chosen to match the application. Examples are HDLC for point-to-point networks, Ethernet for local area networks and X.25 for wide area networks.

Comparing with the OSI system of Figure 16.11 it is evident that the TCP/IP stack is relatively simple. OSI has a width of standards, with a choice of connectionless or connection oriented operation. It also covers a wider range of network technologies. Items can therefore be chosen at the various levels, in order to obtain optimum communication efficiency for any application.

16.9.2   Management of TCP/IP networks

Work on managing the large base of TCP/IP networks started in 1987, the emphasis at that time being on developing a manager for the routers (gateways) used to interconnect the widely spaced networks. The first demonstration of such a system, called the Simple Gateway Monitoring Protocol (SGMP), was conducted in August 1987.

In March 1988 SGMP was developed by the IAB into the Simple Network Management Protocol (SNMP), the intention being that the protocol would be used as an interim, until full OSI based protocols became available. A system was envisaged which would be able to carry OSI messages over TCP/IP and this was called

CMOT, the Common Management Information Protocol over TCP/IP.

The IAB published three RFCs (Request for Comment) in August 1988 to define SNMP. These were RFC 1065, Structure of Management Information; RFC 1066, Management Information Base; and RFC 1067, Simple Network Management Protocol. In June 1989 an ad hoc meeting of the IAB was called to discuss the present and future direction for the management of Internet. RFC 1109 was published as a result of this, which confirmed that SNMP had long term relevance for network management, which seemed to negate the original aim of moving to OSI.

A measure of SNMP's success and ease of implementation, can be gauged by the fact that at the 1990 Interop, only two years after publication of the RFCs, almost fifty individual companies took part in the SNMP solutions showcase, demonstrating an interconnected and managed network.

16.9.3   The SNMP structure

SNMP has three main elements, and these are defined in the RFCs issued by the IAB.

The Structure of Management Information (SMI) is specified in RFC 1065, upgraded to RFC 1155. It provides the administrative and organisational policies for defining managed objects. For each managed object SMI provides a low level syntax, based on ASN.1, status information on the object, access rights to that object, and guidelines for naming objects. This ensures that a manager can use a common format when controlling equipment from several vendors, provide they support SNMP variables on their product.

The second element is the Management Information Base for Network (MIB), published as RFC 1066, upgraded to RFC 1156. This provides a list of the network objects that can be interrogated on any agent, and also defines the information which can be retrieved.

MIB variables can have a status of mandatory or optional. Mandatory items need to be supported by everyone, but optional items are usually vendor specific.

The MIB document defines a series of objects as given in Table 16.4. A total of about 120 objects can be held in MIB I, which has been updated to MIB II (RFC 1158) with a capacity of about 200 objects. This will mean that more vendor specific data can be accommodated, increasing the ability of the system to control a mix of networks. Vendor specific objects are referred to as extended variables. They are put in the public domain so that anyone can design a manager to control them.

The SMI defines a registration sub-tree structure for the MIB, as shown in Figure 16.23. Three branches come from the root, branch 1 administered by ISO, branch 2 by CCITT and branch 3 jointly by ISO and CCITT. Under the ISO branch are other sub-branches, number 3 being assigned by ISO to 'other standards organisations' (org). The US Department of Defence has been assigned sub-branch 6 (dod) under org. The DOD then assigned its first sub-branch (1) to Internet.

Under Internet there are four sub-branches. Management (mgmt) holds all the standard MIBs and the private sub-branch holds vendor specific MIBs. The experimental sub-branch holds MIBs which will eventually become standard but are awaiting test. Under mgmt there is presently one standard mib, referred to as the Internet MIB. This is MIB I which has MIB II as a superset.

Each node on the tree has a superset and a symbolic name. Either numeric or object description forms may to used for representing an MIB object. For example the ifPhysAddress variable is stored as an

Table 16.4 MIB Object Groups and functions within SNMP. The first five Object Groups are mandatory. The last Object Group is from MIB II

Group name	Description
system	System wide information about the managed node itself
interfaces	Information about parts and interfaces on the node
at	The (address translation) table which gives translation from network address to IP address
ip	Information covering all the IP counters and tables having routing and addressing data
icmp	Information covering all the Internet Control Message Protocol Counters
tcp	Information covering all the Transmission Control protocol counters and TCP connections to the SNMP agent
udp	Information covering all the User Datagram Protocol Counters
egp	This is the exterior gateway protocol and is used for Internet core gateways
snmp	Statistical information on SNMP traffic

object string, described by iso org dod internet mgmt mib interfaces ifTable ifEntry ifPhysAddress or by 1.3.6.1.2.1.2.2.1.6.

Individual object entries can be grouped into tables, SNMP defining five kinds of tables, as shown in Table 16.5.

Table 16.5 MIB tables within SNMP

Table type	Type of values stored
IF Table	Status of the interfaces on the agent
AT Table	Address translation values
IP Address Table	IP address of all interfaces on the agent
IP Routing Table	IP destination addresses
TCP Con Table	Status of TCP connections

The third main element of SNMP is provided in RFC 1067, upgraded to RFC 1157, which covers SNMP itself. Whereas the SMI and MIB documents define the set of managed objects, the SNMP document defines the means for getting information between management stations and managed objects. SNMP usually uses the User Datagram Protocol (UDP/IP) instead of TCP/IP.

TCP checks for error, whilst UDP assumes a reliable transmission path and does not carry out checks. SNMP messages have the potential to be carried over any transport mechanism that supports bi-directional flow and addressability. Figure 16.24 shows a communication architecture within SNMP. The messages, described in the next section, are packaged using ASN.1 and sent over the UDP/IP services.

SNMP uses a simple polling access process and no sessions are maintained between the manager and its managed objects. The rate of polling can be varied, which provides a means for trading off between the response time and the amount of bandwidth used. A single packet is employed for polling, and a relatively small number of packets would be expected in reply.

Figure 16.25 shows the way in which a SNMP message is contained in a typical frame structure. The packet lengths vary, depending on the transport mechanism being used. If this mechanism allows a very small data size, such as 128 bytes for X.25, then the datagrams are broken into smaller sections by the sender and reassembled by the receiver.

SNMP is basically a request-response protocol having five message types.

> **GET-REQUEST** is used by the manager to ask for one or more network management variables from an agent MIB.
> **GET-NEXT-REQUEST** has a similar function to GET-REQUEST, but it enables portions of the MIB to be stepped through, and the next variable to be asked for. The command is therefore used for traversing tables, so avoiding the overhead of a separate state synchronisation mechanism.
> **GET-RESPONSE** is used by the agent to provide the information requested by the manager.
> **SET-REQUEST** is used by the manager to change the value of an MIB object or variable, including booting and re-booting devices.
> **TRAP** is slightly different from the above four messages, since it originates from the managed element and allows them to send events to the manager. It is an unsolicited, asynchronous message sent from the managed agent to the manager, usually to

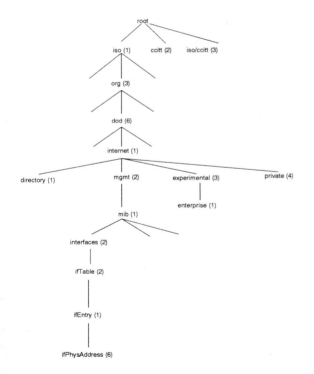

Figure 16.23 Registration sub-tree for MIB definitions used in SNMP

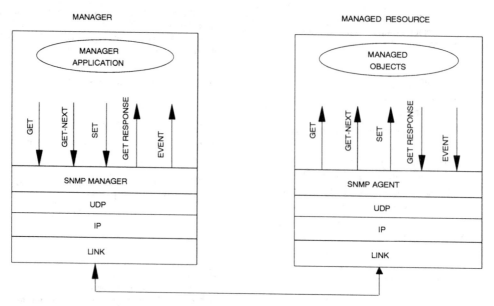

Figure 16.24 Communications using SNMP

indicate that threshold condition has been exceeded. Table 16.6 shows the traps used within SNMP. Vendors can add their proprietary traps for indicating alarms raised by their equipment.

The agent will return any protocol errors which occur, following any of the above requests (except for TRAP) by a manager, as shown in Table 16.7

As an example, suppose the manager wants to know the length of time the agent has been running. The variable which determines this is called sysUpTime and is represented by 1.3.6.1.2.1.1.3. The manager sends the following message to the agent:

GET-REQUEST <sysUpTime>

The agent replies with:

GET-RESPONSE <sysUpTime:TimeTicks 211930>

This indicates to the manager that the variable is of type Time-Ticks, having a value of 211930 or about three quarters of an hour.

16.9.4   SNMP, CMOT and CMIP

SNMP was designed initially to be an interim standard, until full OSI based network management standards (CMIP) were available. However the popularity of SNMP, with several hundred vendors supporting it, means that it is likely to be in the network for many years to come. Transition to OSI could therefore be delayed and many vendors have even spoken confidently of SNMP displacing OSI.

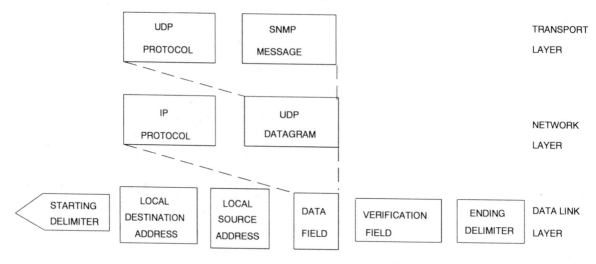

Figure 16.25   Structure of an SNMP protocol

Table 16.6 Traps used in SNMP

Trap sent	Description
coldStart	Agent is initialising and this may give a changed configuration
warmStart	Agent is re-initialising and the configuration will not change
linkDown	One of the agent's links has failed
linkUp	One of the agent's links has (re) started
authenticationFailure	A message has been received by the agent which fails SNMP authentication procedure
egpNeighbourLoss	A neighbour has gone down resulting in the loss of EGP peer-peer mapping

Table 16.7 Protocol errors returned by an SNMP agent following a management request

Error	Meaning
noError	Standard response
tooBig	Response too big
noSuch	Unknown variable
badValue	Wrong value type
readOnly	Variable of read-only type
genError	Generic error

In order to bridge the gap between SNMP and OSI a working group, called the OSI Internet Management (OIM) working group was set up to develop a protocol for transition from SNMP to OSI. This protocol has been called CMOT, the transport of CMIP over TCP/IP, as illustrated graphically in Figure 16.26. SNMP protocol runs over TCP/IP transport mechanism and CMIP over OSI based

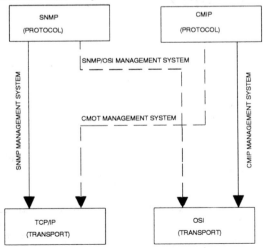

Figure 16.26 Alternatives for mixed SNMP/CMIP systems

transport. CMOT uses CMIP protocols but over TCP/IP transport. Similarly one could have SNMP transported over OSI (SNOO?), but the advantages of this are not evident. The aim of CMOT was to allow designs to carry out CMIP prototyping before OSI transport became available, and for deploying CMIP over the large existing base of the TCP/IP environments.

Figure 16.27 shows the structure of CMOT. The application layer is OSI, the transport layer is TCP/UDP and the network layer is IP. The presentation layer consists of a Lightweight Presentation Protocol (LLP), defined in RFC 1085, which provides a means for carrying OSI applications over the TCP/IP environment.

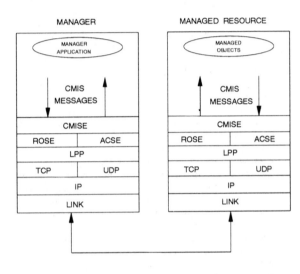

Figure 16.27 Communications within CMOT

Although SNMP is widely supported, CMOT has very few implementors, and this may mean that it will not become a popular migration path from SNMP to CMIP. In the meantime expect many more acronyms! For example iBM and 3Com Corp proposed CMOL, the transport of CMIP over Logical Link Control, the idea being to save memory by transporting OSI based messages over a shortened protocol stack.

SNMP has many similarities with CMIP and also many differences. The similarities are as follows.

1. At level 3, the IP layer used by SNMP is connectionless and it cannot be operated in a connection oriented mode. The Connection-Less Interworking Protocol (CLIP) of OSI is very close to IP, both acting as routers to send datagrams up and down the stack.
2. At level 4 the TCP service and protocol are similar to Class 4 of the OSI layer. Both use positive acknowledgement schemes with timer driven retries; both can reorder data if it is out of sequence on arrival; and both can use check-sums to protect against data corruption.
3. At layer 7 the TCP/IP applications look like subsets of the OSI applications. Therefore, for example, FTP performs services similar to that obtained from FTAM.
4. Both SNMP and CMIP use the concept of protocol data units (PDUs) which are messages exchanged between systems at the same layer. They also both use ASN.1 to specify the PDUs and the managed objects. However, SNMP uses a subset of ASN.1,

and although this reduces the amount of code, and memory, it does restrict the encoding of complex items, such as lists.

5. The structure of the MIB used in SNMP is similar to that within OSI.

6. Both SNMP and CMIP offer a method for managing devices which do not have SNMP or CMIP capability, via the use of proxy agents.

The differences between SNMP and CMIP are primarily related to their design aims, i.e. one providing a simple protocol and the other a powerful, extendible protocol. These differences are as follows.

1. SNMP uses a polling based management system, i.e. the managed devices are polled for information. CMIP (and CMOT) use an event based management system, the managed devices asynchronously sending predefined information (not only alarms) of interest to the manager. This allows CMIP to be much more efficient than SNMP when controlling large networks, since polling would result in the generation of volumes of SNMP messages, and give problems with detection and response times.

2. SNMP over UDP has poor security capability. This means that it is relatively easy for anyone with a LAN analyser to monitor and change settings on the network. Because of this many vendors have not implemented the SET command, so that under these circumstances SNMP is reduced mainly to being a network monitoring tool. CMIP, together with ACSE, provides powerful security capabilities.

3. CMIP can specify multiple operations within a single request, and CMIP operations can be specified to be on a best effort basis or on an atonomic basis, i.e. if all the operations cannot be carried out then none are done and an error is returned. SNMP can only work on one object at a time, so that the concept of best effort does not arise.

4. CMIP allows a single request to retrieve large amounts of data from managed objects, by having information sent back from the objects in multiple linked replies. SNMP does not allow linked replies, so it is limited in the volume of information which can be obtained from a single request. It is therefore inefficient when a large amount of information is to be retrieved. SNMP cannot, for example, retrieve or alter a table of N rows in less than N request/response pairs.

5. CMIP allows for powerful conditional commands, via scoping and filtering. SNMP, on the other hand, needs the name of the actual object instance being managed, except in the case of the GET-NEXT command which enables the application to retrieve the next MIB object, relative to its current position.

6. SNMP and CMIP both have three primitive operations, GET, SET and EVENT (or TRAP). CMIP has three further primitives, CREATE, DELETE and ACTION, which provide it with a powerful capability.

7. CMIP makes a clear distinction between objects and their attributes, an attribute being a condition or state of the device. SNMP does not differentiate between an object and its attribute, and not being able to do so means that re-use of attributes, or definitions, to represent generic information is not possible. Therefore the management of novel objects is difficult with SNMP. In CMIP very different objects can have common attributes, so that it is not necessary to assign a unique description to each object or operational state, as in SNMP. This means that CMIP is much more extendible (future proof) since the boundary between the agent and an object can be designed such that new objects can be added without affecting the agent's code.

8. CMIP uses the concept of inheritance whilst SNMP does not. Therefore in CMIP it is possible to define an object and then to use the same definition, with other added attributes, for another similar object, greatly simplifying the management task.

9. CMIP events may be confirmed or unconfirmed, whereas in SNMP all events (TRAP) are unconfirmed. One can therefore never be certain if the message reached its destination unless supplementary systems, such as handshaking, are introduced.

10. SMFs are being defined in OSI, but no such functions are available in SNMP. Some of the SMFs allow manager to manager communications, this facility being poorly implemented within SNMP.

11. CMIP has a naming hierarchy which is based on a flexible containment philosophy. Multiple CMIP object instances can be remotely created and deleted, and applications can manage objects via names which are not tied to network addressing systems. In SNMP managed devices are named directly, via IP addresses, and objects within these devices are named in a predefined tree, so it is much more restrictive. SNMP naming also does not cover proxy agents, which is required for the management of large networks, for example to enable manager X to manage Z through Y.

Summarising, the greatest advantage of SNMP compared to CMIP is its simplicity. The standard was developed relatively quickly, and it is easy and quick to implement. This accounts for its wide popularity. However, as the complexity of networks and devices grow, the protocol is called upon to perform a management function which it was not originally designed to do, and its limitations are becoming evident.

CMIP, on the other hand, is a powerful and complex protocol, which has been developed with future expandability very much in mind; it has been a long time in defining within the various standards bodies. Because of its complexity it needs more memory and more processing power than SNMP and is more complex to design to and to test against, for conformance.

16.10 Bibliography

Adiarous, S.E., Proudfood, D.A. and Dam, X.N. (1990) Service management in Intelligent Networks, *IEEE Network Magazine*, January.

Ben-Artizi, A., Chandna, A. and Warrier, U. (1990) Network management of TCP/IP networks: present and future, *IEEE Network Magazine*, July.

Bush, Nick (1991) The importance of open standards for network management, *Telecommunications*, May.

Caruso, R.E. (1990), Network management: a tutorial overview, *IEEE Communications Magazine*, March.

Cassel, L.N., Partridge, C. and Westcott, J. (1989) Network management architectures and protocols: problems and approaches, *IEEE Journal on Selected Areas in Communications*, September.

Corsi, N. and Iorio, N. (1990) OSI structures for network management, *CSELT Technical Reports*, August.

Embry, J., Manson, P. and Milhan, D. (1990) An open network management architecture: OSI/NM Forum architecture and concepts, *IEEE Network Magazine*, July.

Fleming, S. and Jakubson, J.E. (1989) Managing the multilevel network, *Telephony*, May 1.

Holter, R. (1990) Standards, standardizing, standardization, *TE&M*, May 1.

Joseph, C.A. and Muralidhar, K.H. (1990) Integrated Network Management in an enterprise environment, *IEEE Network Magazine*, July.

Klerer, S.M. (1988) The OSI management architecture: an overview, *IEEE Network Magazine*, March.

Mazda, F.F. (1991) Convergence or collision: SNMP and CMIP, *Telecommunications*, Part 1: September; Part 2, November.

Mazda, F.F. (1991) Structured network management, *Communications International*, December.

Sahin, V., Omidyar, C.G. and Bauman, T.M. (1988) Telecommunications Management Network (TMN) architecture and interworking designs, *IEEE Journal on Selected Areas in Communications*, May.

Trew, D. (1991), Network management: coming of age? *Telecommunications*, February.

Warrier, U.S. and Sunshine, C.A. (1990) A platform for heterogeneous interconnection network management, *IEEE Journal on Selected Areas in Communications*, January.

Yoshida, M., Kobayashi, M. and Yamaguchi, H. (1990) Customer control of network management from the service provider's perspective, *IEEE Communications Magazine*, March.

17

Antennas

Professor A D Olver
BSc PhD CEng FIEE FIEEE
Queen Mary and Westfield College

Contents

17.1 Types of antennas

Antennas form the link between the guided parts and the free-space parts of a communication system. The purpose of a transmitting antenna is to efficiently transform the currents in a circuit or waveguide into radiated radio or microwave energy. The purpose of a receiving antenna is to efficiently accept the received radiated energy and convert it to guided form for detection and processing by a receiver. The design and construction of an antenna usually involves compromises between the desired electromagnetic performance and the mechanical size, mass and environmental characteristics.

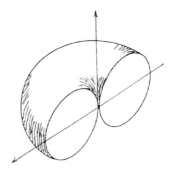

Figure 17.2 Toroidal radiation pattern

Figure 17.1 Pencil beam radiation pattern

Antennas for communication systems fall into two broad categories depending on the degree to which the radiation is confined. Microwave radio relay and satellite communications use pencil beam antennas, where the radiation is confined to one narrow beam of energy, Figure 17.1. Mobile communications are more likely to require antennas with omni-directional patterns in the horizontal plane and toroidal patterns in the vertical plane, Figure 17.2.

Pencil beam antennas usually consist of one or more large to medium reflectors which collimate the signals from a feed horn at the focus of the reflector. Both reflector and feed horn fall within the generic class of aperture antennas because they consist of an aperture which radiates into space. The design problem is to first determine the aperture fields which will yield the specified radiation

characteristics and secondly to design the reflectors and horns to produce the aperture fields. Aperture antennas can be designed to meet very stringent specifications. Omni-directional antennas consist of elements which are small in wavelengths, such as dipoles and monopoles. The radiation characteristics are influenced by the presence of surrounding objects. Non-electromagnetic factors such as the size are often as important in the design as the radiation performance. For this reason the design of omni-directional antennas is partly an empirical process in which expertise and previous experience play an equal part with theoretical knowledge.

In between the large aperture antennas and the small element antennas lies array antennas which consist of two or more elements. The radiation from an array antenna is determined principally by the physical spacing and electrical signals driving the elements rather than the radiation characteristics of the elements themselves.

The detailed theory of antennas can be found in Stutzman (1981); Elliot (1981); Balanis (1982); Silver (1984); Colin (1969). Design information and descriptions of particular types can be found in a

Table 17.1 Antennas used in communication systems

Use	Specific type	Generic type
Microwave line ofsight radio	Prime focus reflector with small feed	Apertures
Earth Stations (Large)	Dual reflector with corrugated horn feed	Apertures
Earth Stations (Medium)	Offset reflector with corrugated or dual mode horn feed	Apertures
Direct Broadcast Satellite Receiving Antennas	Prime focus symmetric or offset reflector	Apertures
	Flat plate antennas	Arrays
Satellite Antennas (Spot beams)	Offset reflector with single feed	Apertures
Satellite Antennas (Multiple beams)	Offset reflector with array feed	Aperture and Arrays
Satellite Antennas (Shaped beams)	Shaped reflectors	Apertures
	Offset reflector with array feed	Apertures and Arrays
VHF/UHF Communications	Yagis Dipole arrays Slots	Elements and Arrays
Mobile Communications (Base stations)	Dipole arrays	Elements and Arrays
Mobile Communications (Mobile)	Monopoles Microstrip	Elements
HF Communications	Dipoles Monopoles	Elements

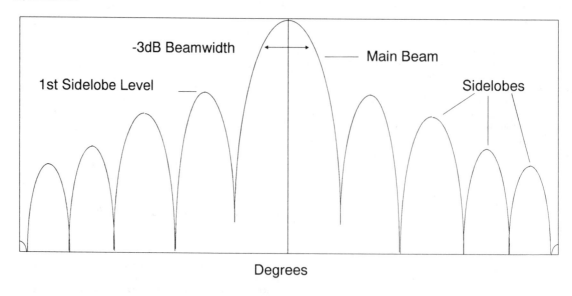

Figure 17.3 Typical rectangular radiation plot

number of handbooks, such as, Rudge (1986); Johnson (1984); Lo (1988); Milligan (1985).

17.1.1 Antennas used in communications

Table 17.1 lists the principal types of antennas which are used in communications. Under each category of communication system, the specific type of antenna which is usually used is given. The last column gives the generic type of either an aperture antenna, an array antenna or a small element antenna. The generic type describes the general radiation characteristics which can be obtained from the antenna and is useful because it makes the explanation of the performance easier.

The following sections describe first the generic antenna characteristics, then the specific antenna types and then brief discussion of the practical implementation of antennas in communication systems.

17.2 Basic properties

The principle of reciprocity is one of the most important properties of an antenna. It means that the properties of an antenna when acting as a transmitter are identical to the properties of the same antenna when acting as a receiver. For this to apply, the medium in between the two antennas must be linear, passive and isotropic, which is always the case for communication systems.

The directional selectivity of an antenna is represented by the radiation pattern. It is a plot of the relative strength of the radiated field as a function of the angle. A pattern taken along the principal direction of the electric field is called an E- plane cut, the orthogonal plane is called an H-plane cut. The most common plot is the rectangular decibel plot, Figure 17.3 which can have scales of relative power and angle chosen to suit the antenna being characterised. Other types of plots such as polar plots (used for small antennas and two dimensional), contour plots (or three dimensional), and isometric plots are also used. A radiation pattern is characterised by the main beam and sidelobes. The quality is speci-

fied by the beamwidth between the −3dB points on the main beam and the sidelobe level.

Communication antennas radiate in either linear polarisation or circular polarisation. In modern communications cross- polarisation is important. This is the difference between the two principal plane patterns and is specified relative to a reference polarisation, called the co-polar pattern. There are three definitions of the cross-polarisation. The one in normal use with reflector antennas and feed systems is Ludwig's third definition (Ludwig, 1973) which assumes that the reference polarisation is that due to a Huygens source. It most closely corresponds to what is measured with a conventional antenna test range.

The power gain in a specified direction is defined by the ratio of the power radiated per unit solid angle in direction θ,φ to the total power accepted from the source, as in Equation 17.1.

$$G(\theta,\varphi) =$$

$$4\pi\frac{\textit{Power radiated per solid angle in direction }\theta,\varphi}{\textit{Total power accepted source}} \quad (17.1)$$

This is an inherent property of an antenna and includes dissipative losses in the antenna. The dissipative losses cannot easily be predicted so a related parameter, the directivity, is used in calculations. The definition of the directivity is similar to that of the gain except that the denominator is replaced by the total power radiated. The terms gain and directivity are often used interchangeably in the literature. Normally only the peak gain along the boresight direction is specified. If the direction of the gain is not specified, the peak value is assumed. The value is normally quoted in dB's. The definitions given above are in effect specifying the gain relative to a loss-less isotropic source. This is sometimes stated explicitly by using the symbol dBi.

The efficiency of an aperture antenna is given by the ratio of the effective area of an aperture divided by the physical area. Normal aperture antennas have efficiencies in the range 50-80%.

As far as circuit designers are concerned the antenna is an impedance. Maximum power transfer will occur when the antenna is matched to the transmission line. The impedance consists of the self impedance and the mutual impedance. The mutual impedance accounts for the influence of nearby objects and of mutual coupling to other antennas. The self impedance consists of the radiation resistance, the loss resistance and the self reactance. Loss resistance is the ohmic losses in the antenna structure. Radiation resistance measures the power absorbed by the antenna from the incoming plane waves. It is one of the most significant parameters for small antennas where the problem is often to match very dissimilar impedances.

A receiving antenna is both a spatially selective filter (measured by the radiation pattern) and a frequency selective filter. The bandwidth measures the frequency range over which the antenna operates. The upper and lower frequencies can be specified in terms of a number of possible parameters: gain, polarisation, beamwidth and impedance.

A communication link consists of a transmitting antenna and a receiving antenna. If the transmitter radiates P_t watts, then the received power, P_r at a distance r is given by Equation 17.2 where G_t and G_r are the transmitter and receiver antenna gains respectively.

$$P_r = P_t \frac{G_t G_r \lambda^2}{(4\pi r)^2} \tag{17.2}$$

This formula is known as the Friis transmission equation. It assumes that the antennas are impedance and polarisation matched. If this is not the case then extra factors must be multiplied to the equation to account for the mismatches.

17.3 Generic antenna types

17.3.1 Radiation from apertures

The radiation from apertures illustrates most of the significant properties of pencil beam antennas. The radiation characteristics can be determined by simple mathematical relationships. If the electric fields across an aperture, Figure 17.4, is $E_a(x,y)$ then the radiated fields $E_p(\theta,\varphi)$ is given by Equation 17.3, where $f(\theta,\varphi)$ is given by Equation 17.4. (Oliver, 1986; Milligan, 1985).

$$E_p(\theta,\varphi) = \cos^2\frac{\theta}{2}\left(1 - \tan^2\frac{\theta}{2}\cos 2\varphi\right) f(\theta,\varphi) \tag{17.3}$$

$$f(\theta,\varphi) = \int_{-\infty}^{\infty}\int_{-\infty}^{\infty} E_a(x,y)\, e^{jk(x\sin\theta\cos\varphi + y\sin\theta\sin\varphi)}\, dx\, dy \tag{17.4}$$

For high or medium gain antennas the pencil beam radiation is largely focused to a small range of angles around $\theta = 0$. In this case it can be seen from Equation 17.3 that the distant radiated fields, and the aperture fields are the Fourier transformation of each other. Fourier transforms have been widely studied and their properties can be used to understand the radiation characteristics of aperture antennas. Simple aperture distributions have analytic Fourier transforms, whilst more complex distributions can be solved numerically on a computer.

The simplest aperture is a one dimensional line source distribution of length $\pm\frac{a}{2}$. This serves to illustrate many of the features of

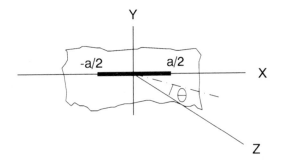

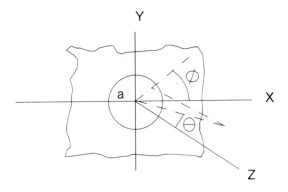

Figure 17.4 Radiation aperture in a ground plane

aperture antennas. If the field in the aperture is constant, the radiated field is given from Equation 17.3 as in Equations 17.5 and 17.6.

$$E_p = \frac{\sin(\pi u)}{\pi u} \tag{17.5}$$

$$u = \frac{a}{\lambda}\sin\theta \tag{17.6}$$

This distribution occurs widely in antenna theory. It is plotted in Figure 17.5. The beamwidth is inversely proportional to the aperture width and is $\frac{0.88\lambda}{a}$. The first sidelobe level is at −13.2dB which is a disadvantage of a uniform aperture distribution. The level can be reduced considerably by a tapered aperture distribution where the field is greatest at the centre of the aperture and tapers to a lower level at the edge of the aperture. For example if Equation 17.7 holds, then the first sidelobe level is at −23dB.

$$E_a(x) = \cos\left(\frac{\pi x}{2a}\right) \tag{17.7}$$

The energy which was in the sidelobes moves to the main beam with the result that the beamwidth broadens to $\frac{1.2\lambda}{a}$. In practice almost all antennas have natural tapers across the aperture which result from boundary conditions and waveguide modes. Rectangular apertures are formed from two line source distributions in orthogonal planes.

Circular apertures form the largest single class of aperture antennas. The parabolic reflector is widely used in communications

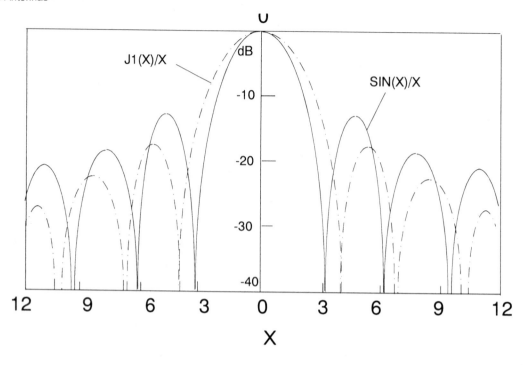

Figure 17.5 Dipole and radiation pattern

and is often fed by a conical horn. Both the reflector and the horn are circular apertures. For an aperture distribution which is independent of azimuthal angle the simplest case is uniform illumination which gives a radiated field as in Equation 17.8, where $J_1(x)$ is a Bessel function of zero order.

$$E_p = \frac{2 J_1 (\pi u)}{\pi u} \tag{17.8}$$

This can be compared to $\frac{\sin (x)}{x}$ and is also plotted in Figure 17.5. The first sidelobe level is at −17.6dB. Table 17.2 lists a number of circular aperture distributions and corresponding radiation pattern properties. The pedestal distribution is representative of many reflector antennas which have an edge tapers of about −10dB corresponding to $E_a(a) = 0.316$. The Gaussian distribution is also important because high performance feed horns ideally have Gaussian aperture distributions. The Fourier transform of a Gaussian taper which decreases to zero at the edge of the aperture gives a Gaussian radiation pattern which has no sidelobes.

17.3.2 Radiation from small antennas

Small antennas are needed for mobile communications operating at frequencies from HF to the low microwave region. Most of these are derivatives of the simple dipole, Figure 17.6, which is an electric current element which radiates from the currents flowing along a small metal rod. The radiation pattern is always very broad with energy radiating in all directions. An important design parameter is the impedance of the dipole which can vary considerably depending on the exact size and shape of the rod. This means that the imped-

ance matching between the antenna and the transmitting or receiving circuit becomes a major design constraint.

Table 17.2 Radiation characteristics of circular apertures

Electric field aperture distribution	3dB beamwidth	Level of first sidelobe
Uniform	$1.02 \frac{\lambda}{D}$	−17.6dB
Taper to zero at edge $$1 - \left(\frac{2r}{D} \right)^2$$	$1.27 \frac{\lambda}{D}$	−24.6dB
Taper on a pedestal $$0.5 + \left[1 - \left(2\frac{r}{D} \right)^2 \right]^2$$	$1.16 \frac{\lambda}{D}$	−26.5dB
Gaussian $$\exp\left[-p\left(\frac{2r}{D} \right)^2 \right]$$	$1.33 \frac{\lambda}{D}$	−40dB (p=3)

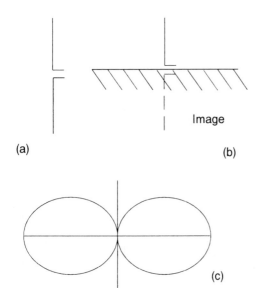

Figure 17.6 Dipole and radiation pattern: (a) dipole; (b) monopole; (c) polar pattern of dipole

The radiation fields from a dipole are obtained by integrating the radiation from an infinitesimally small current element over the length of the dipole. This depends on knowing the current distribution which is a function not only of the length but also of the shape and thickness of the rod. Many studies have been addressed towards obtaining accurate results (King, 1956; King, 1968). For most cases this has to be done by numerical integration. A simple case is a short dipole with a length $a << \dfrac{1}{10\lambda}$ when the current distribution may be assumed to be triangular. This results in radiated fields of the form given in Equation 17.9.

$$E = j\,30\,\pi\,I\,\frac{a}{\lambda}\,\sin\theta\,\frac{e^{-jkr}}{r} \tag{17.9}$$

The electric field is plotted in polar form in Figure 17.6. The radiation resistance is calculated by evaluating the radiated power and using $P = I^2 R$ to give Equation 17.10.

$$R = 20\pi^2\left(\frac{a}{\lambda}\right)^2 \tag{17.10}$$

A dipole of length $a = \dfrac{\lambda}{10}$ has a radiation resistance of 2.0ohms. This is low by comparison with standard transmission lines and indicates the problem of matching to the transmission line.

The half wave dipole is widely used. Assuming a sinusoidal current distribution the far fields are given by Equation 17.11.

$$E = j\,60\,I\,\frac{\cos\left[\,\pi/2\cos\theta\,\right]}{\sin\theta}\,\frac{e^{-jkr}}{r} \tag{17.11}$$

This gives a slightly narrower pattern than that of the short dipole and has a half beamwidth of 78 degrees. The radiation resistance must be evaluated numerically. For an infinitely thin dipole it has a value of 73 + j 42.5 ohms. For finite thickness the imaginary part

can become zero in which case the dipole is easily matched to a coaxial cable of impedance 75ohms. The half wave dipole has a gain of 2.15dB.

A monopole is a dipole divided in half at its centre feed point and fed against a ground plane, Figure 17.6. The ground plane acts as a mirror and consequently the image of the monopole appears below the ground. Since the fields extend over a hemisphere the power radiated and the radiation resistance is half that of the equivalent dipole with the same current. The gain of a monopole is twice that of a dipole. The radiation pattern above the ground plane is the same as that of the dipole.

17.3.3 Radiation from arrays

Array antennas consist of a number of discrete elements which are usually small in size. Typical elements are horns, dipoles, and microstrip patches. The discrete sources radiate individually but the pattern of the array is largely determined by the relative amplitude and phase of the excitation currents on each element and the geometric spacing apart of the elements. The total radiation pattern is the multiplication of the pattern of an individual element and the pattern of the array assuming point sources, called the array factor. Array theory is largely concerned with synthesising an array factor to form a specified pattern. In communications most arrays are planar arrays with the elements being spaced over a plane, but the principles can be understood by considering an array of two elements with equal amplitudes, Figure 17.7(a). This has an array factor given by Equation 17.12, where Ψ is given by Equation 17.13.

$$E = E_1 + E_2\,e^{j\Psi} \tag{17.12}$$

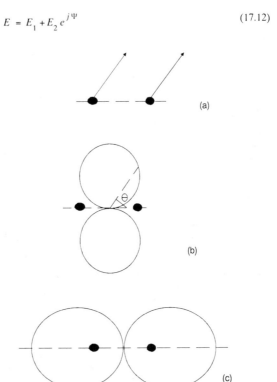

Figure 17.7 Two element array and radiation pattern: (a) two elements with equal amplitudes; (b) half wavelength spacing; (c) 180° phase difference

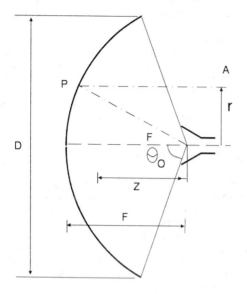

Figure 17.8 Geometry of reflector antenna

$$\Psi = \delta + k\,d\cos\theta \tag{17.13}$$

The pattern for small spacings will be almost omnidirectional and as the spacing is increased the pattern develops a maxima perpendicular to the axis of the array. At a spacing of half a wavelength, a null appears along the array axis, Figure 17.7(b). This is called a broadside array. If a phase difference of 180 degrees exists between the two elements then the pattern shown in Figure 17.7(c) results. Now the main beam is along the direction of the array and the array is called the end-fire array. This illustrates one of the prime advantages of the array, namely by changing the electrical phase it is possible to make the peak beam direction occur in any angular direction. Increasing the spacing above half a wavelength results in the appearance of additional radiation lobes which are generally undesirable. Consequently the ideal arrays spacing is half wavelength, though if waveguides or horns are used this is not usually possible because the basic element is greater than half a wavelength in size. Changing the relative amplitudes, phases and spacings can produce a wide variety of patterns so that it is possible to synthesise almost any specified radiation pattern. The array factor for an N element linear array of equal amplitude is given by Equation 17.14.

$$E = N\,\frac{\sin\,(\,N\,\Psi\,/\,2\,)}{\sin\,(\,\Psi\,/\,2\,)} \tag{17.14}$$

This is similar to the pattern of a line source aperture, Equation 17.5, and it is possible to synthesise an aperture with a planar array. There is a significant benefit to this approach. The aperture fields are determined by the waveguide horn fields which are constrained by boundary conditions and are usually monotonic functions. This constraint does not exist with the array so that a much larger range of radiation patterns can be produced. Optimum patterns with most

of the energy radiated into the main beam and very low sidelobes can be designed.

17.4 Specific antenna types

17.4.1 Prime focus symmetric reflector antennas

17.4.1.1 *Parabolic reflectors*

The axi-symmetric parabolic reflector with a feed at the focus of the paraboloid is the simplest type of reflector antenna. The geometry is shown in Figure 17.8. The paraboloid has the property that energy from the feed at F goes to the point P on the surface where it is reflected parallel to the axis to arrive at a point A on the imaginary aperture plane. The equation describing the surface is given by Equation 17.15, where F is the focal length.

$$r^2 = 4F(F-z) \tag{17.15}$$

At the edge of the reflector, of diameter D, Equation 17.16 applies.

$$\frac{F}{D} = \frac{1}{4}\cot\left(\frac{\theta_0}{2}\right) \tag{17.16}$$

The depth of the paraboloid is usually specified by its F/D ratio. Common sizes are between F/D = 0.25 (θ_0 = 90 degrees) to F/D = 0.4.

17.4.1.2 *Aperture fields and radiation patterns*

Ray optics indicates that the path length from F to P to A is equal to twice the focal length. Hence the phase across the aperture is constant. The amplitude across the aperture plane will peak at the centre and taper towards the edge for two reasons. Firstly because the feed will have a tapered radiation pattern and secondly because the action of a parabola in transforming a spherical wave from the feed into a plane wave across the aperture introduces a path loss which is a function of angle θ. The aperture electric field is then given by Equation 17.17, where $F(\theta,\varphi)$ is the pattern of the feed.

$$E_a(\theta,\varphi) = F(\theta,\varphi)\cos^2\left(\frac{\theta}{2}\right) \tag{17.17}$$

Feeds suitable for reflector antennas are discussed in a later section, but it is often convenient in initial design to take the feed pattern as being given by Equation 17.18.

$$F(\theta,\varphi) = \cos^q(\theta) \tag{17.18}$$

Experience has shown that good quality feeds approximate well to this function.

The radiation patterns can be predicted from the aperture fields by using the Fourier transform relations described in Section 17.3.1. This works well for large reflectors but for detailed design of small to medium reflectors it is necessary to take account of the precise form of the currents on the reflector surface and the diffraction that occurs at the edges of the reflector surface. The former can be accomplished with Physical Optics theory (Rusch, 1970; Rusch, 1986) and is good for predicting the main beam and near-in sidelobes. The diffracted fields influence the far-out sidelobes and can be predicted using the Geometrical Theory of Diffraction (GTD) (James, 1986).

17.4.1.3   Gain of reflector antennas

The gain of a reflector antenna can be calculated from Equation 17.19, where η is the efficiency of the reflector.

$$G = \eta \left(\frac{\pi D}{\lambda} \right)^2 \tag{17.19}$$

The total efficiency is the product of six factors:

1. The illumination efficiency is the gain loss due to the non-uniform aperture illumination.
2. The spillover efficiency is the gain loss caused by energy from the feed which radiates outside the solid angle subtended by θ_0 called the spillover. It is the fraction of the power which is intercepted by the reflector. As the aperture edge taper increases, the spillover decreases and the spillover efficiency increases, whilst the illumination efficiency decreases. There is an optimum combination which corresponds to an edge illumination of about −10dB.
3. The phase error efficiency is a measure of the deviation of the feed face front away from spherical and is usually nearly 100%.
4. The crosspolarisation efficiency is a measure of the loss of energy in the orthogonal component of the polarisation vector. For a symmetric reflector no crosspolarisation is introduced by the reflector so the efficiency is determined by the feed characteristics. For good feeds this factor is also nearly 100%.
5. The blockage efficiency is a measure of the portion of the aperture which is blocked by the feed and the feed supports. The fields blocked by the feed do not contribute to the radiation so it is desirable to keep the proportion of the area blocked to less than 10% of the total area of the aperture because otherwise the sidelobe structure becomes distorted. The feed support blocking is more complicated because it depends on the shape and orientation of the supports (Lamb, 1986). It is electrically desirable to keep the cross-section of the supports small which means that a compromise with the mechanical constraints is needed.
6. The surface error efficiency is a measure of the deviations of the aperture wavefront from a plane wave due to surface distortions on the parabolic surface. Assuming that the errors are small and randomly distributed with a root mean square (r.m.s.) surface error, the efficiency is given by Equation 17.20. This is a function of frequency and falls-off rapidly above a certain value which means that the upper frequency for which a reflector can be used is always given by the surface errors. The effect on the radiation pattern of random surface errors is to fill in the nulls and to scatter energy in all directions so that the far out sidelobes are uniformly raised.

$$\eta_S = \exp\left[-\left(\frac{4\pi\varepsilon}{\lambda} \right)^2 \right] \tag{17.20}$$

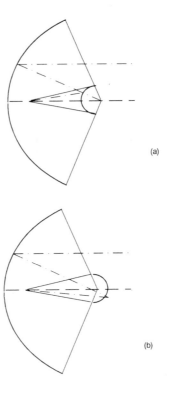

Figure 17.9 Dual reflector antennas: (a) Cassegrian; (b) Gregorian

17.4.2   Dual symmetric reflector antennas

The performance of a large reflector antenna can be improved and the design made more flexible by inserting a sub-reflector into the system, Figure 17.9. There are two versions, the Cassegrain, where the subreflector is a convex hyperboloid of revolution placed on the inside of the parabola focus, and a Gregorian where a concave elliptical subreflector is placed on the outside of the parabola focus. In symmetric reflectors the Cassegrain is more common because it is more compact, but the electrical performance is similar for both systems.

The advantages of the dual reflectors are:

1. The feed is in a more convenient location.
2. Higher performance feeds can be used because the subtended angle is such that wide aperture diameter feeds are needed.
3. Spillover past the subreflector is directed at the sky which reduces the noise temperature.
4. The depth of focus and field of view are larger.

The study of the radiation characteristics and the efficiency of dual reflectors is similar to that for the prime focus reflector. Analysis of the radiation patterns depends partly on the size of the subreflector. If it is small then physical optics or GTD must be used on the subreflector. The main reflector is usually large so geometric optics is adequate.

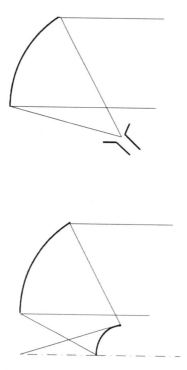

Figure 17.10 Offset reflector antennas

The limiting factor to obtaining high efficiency in a standard parabola is the amplitude taper across the aperture due to the feed pattern and the space loss in the parabola (i.e. the illumination efficiency). By shaping the surfaces of a dual reflector antenna it is possible to increase the efficiency and produce a more uniform illumination across the aperture. A well known method to produce a high efficiency Cassegrain symmetric reflector antenna is due to Galindo and Williams (Galindo, 1964; Williams, 1965). It is a geometric optics technique in which the shape of the subreflector is altered to redistribute the energy more uniformly over the aperture. Then the shape of the main reflector is modified to refocus the energy and create a uniform phase across the aperture. After this process the reflector surfaces are no longer parabolic and hyperbolic. The method works well for large reflectors. For small or medium size reflectors geometric optics is not adequate and physical optics including diffraction must be used at least on the subreflector.

17.4.3 Offset reflectors

In recent years the growth in communication systems has led to a tightening in the radiation pattern specifications and the consequent need to produce reflectors with low far-out sidelobes. Symmetric reflectors cannot be made to have low sidelobes because of the inherent limitations caused by scattering from the feed and feed supports. This blockage loss can be entirely eliminated with the offset reflector, Figure 17.10, which consists of a portion of a parabola chosen so that the feed is outside the area subtended by the aperture of the reflector. The projected aperture is circular, though the edge of the reflector will be elliptical. The removal of the blockage loss also means that smaller reflector antennas can be

made efficient which has led to their widespread use as DBS receiving antennas.

In addition to the unblocked aperture, the offset reflector has other advantages, (Rudge, 1986, Page 185; Rahmat-Samii, 1986). The reaction of the reflector upon the primary feed can be reduced to a very low order so that the feed VSWR is essentially independent of the reflector. Compared to a symmetric paraboloid, the offset configuration makes a larger F/D ratio possible which in turn enables a higher performance feed to be used. The removal of the feed from the aperture gives greater flexibility to use an array of feeds to produce multiple beams or shaped beams.

The offset reflector antenna also has some disadvantages. It is much more difficult to analyse and design due to the offset geometry and it is only with the advent of powerful computers that this has become feasible. The lack of symmetry in the reflector means that when a linearly polarised feed is used, a cross-polarised component is generated by the reflector surface. When circular polarisation is used, a cross-polarised component does not occur but the offset surface causes the beam to be 'squinted' from the electrical boresight. Lastly the construction of the offset reflector is more difficult. However if the reflectors are made by fibreglass moulding this is not really significant. Also the structural shape can be put to good use because it is convenient for deployable configurations on satellites or transportable earth stations.

17.4.4 Horn feeds for reflector antennas

A reflector antenna consists of the reflector plus the horn feed at the geometric focus of the reflector. Thus the correct choice and design of the feed is an important part of the design of the total

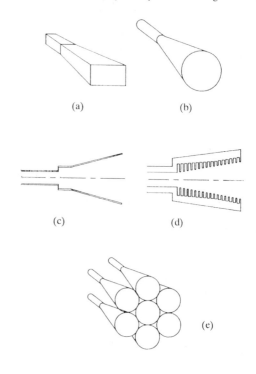

Figure 17.11 Types of feed horns for reflector antennas: (a) rectangular or square; (b) small conical; (c) small conical with chokes; (d) conical corrugated; (e) array feed

reflector antenna. High performance feeds are necessary to achieve high performance antennas. The diameter of the feed in wavelengths will be determined by the angle subtended by the reflector at the feed. A prime focus reflector with an F/D between 0.25 and 0.5 will have a subtended half angle of between 90 degrees and 53 degrees. Application of the general rule that beamwidth is approximately equal to the inverse of the normalised aperture diameter shows that this means a feed with an aperture diameter of between about one and three wavelengths. Dual reflectors (Cassegrain or Gregorian) and offset reflectors have subtended angles between 30 degrees and 7 degrees, leading to feed diameters of between three and ten wavelengths.

Of particular interest in horn feed design is the polarisation performance and the quality of a feed is usually expressed by the level of the peak cross-polarisation. The radiation characteristics of horns are predicted by a two part process. Firstly the fields in the aperture are computed from a knowledge of the guided wave behaviour inside the horn. Secondly the aperture fields are used to compute the radiated fields. The Fourier transform method has been found to work very well for the case of horns. The main types will now be briefly described. For more details see (Love, 1976; Love, 1986).

17.4.4.1 *Rectangular or square horns*

These are the simplest type of horn, Figure 17.11(a) but they are rarely used as feeds for reflectors because they have very high cross-polarisation unless the aperture size is large.

17.4.4.2 *Small conical horns*

These can have reasonably good cross polarisation performance, Figure 17.11(b). They are widely used as prime focus feeds in small symmetric and offset reflectors. The basic design will have an aperture diameter of about one wavelength and is essentially an open-ended circular waveguide propagating a TE_{11} mode. The radiation pattern can be improved by adding one or more rings or chokes around the aperture, Figure 17.11(c). These have the effect of changing the distribution of current on the flange and creating a more symmetric radiation pattern. The theoretical design of the open-ended waveguide is straightforward, but the analysis of the choked version is much more complicated. As a consequence most small feeds are designed empirically with measured data.

17.4.4.3 *Multi-mode conical horns*

These improve the performance of conical horns by generating a second mode inside the horn in such a manner that the aperture fields are linearised. The second, TM_{11} mode, is generated by a step change in the conical horn diameter and the length of the horn is determined by the need to have the modes in the correct phase relationship at the aperture. The dual mode horn gives low crosspolarisation over a narrow band of frequencies. Although narrow band it is simple to make and of low weight.

The concept of adding higher order modes in a horn can be extended for other purposes. In tracking feeds a higher order mode is used to provide tracking information. The inherent crosspolarisation which occurs in offset reflectors can be cancelled by the appropriate addition of higher order modes (Love, 1986). Finally the main beam can be shaped to provide higher efficiency in prime focus reflectors although only over a narrow frequency band.

17.4.4.4 *Conical corrugated horns*

These are the leading choice for a feed for dual reflector and medium size offset reflectors, Figure 17.11(b). They have excellent radiation pattern symmetry and radiate very low crosspolarisation over a broad range of frequencies.

A corrugated horn propagates a mixture of TE_{11} and TM_{11} modes called a hybrid HE_{11} mode. The corrugations are approximately quarter of a wavelength deep so that the electric short circuit at the base of the slot is transformed to a magnetic short circuit at the top of the slot. The result is that the azimuthal magnetic field is forced to zero at the corrugations and the azimuthal electric field is zero due to the ridges. Consequently the boundary conditions of the TE and TM modes are identical and the mutual propagating modes are linear combinations of the two parts. The design procedure for corrugated horns is well understood (Clarricoats, 1984a) and it is possible to accurately predict the radiation characteristics.

17.4.4.5 *Array feeds*

They are used to form multiple beam and shaped beam reflector antennas used on satellites, Figure 17.11(e). The individual elements of the array can be any type of horn, although for compactness small diameter open ended waveguides are preferred. The

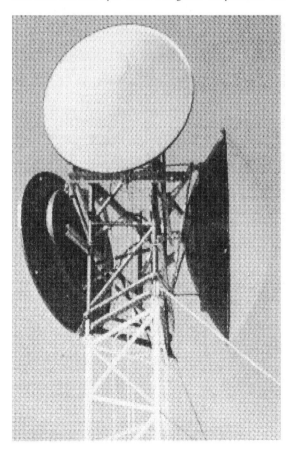

Figure 17.12 Microwave line of sight reflector antenna

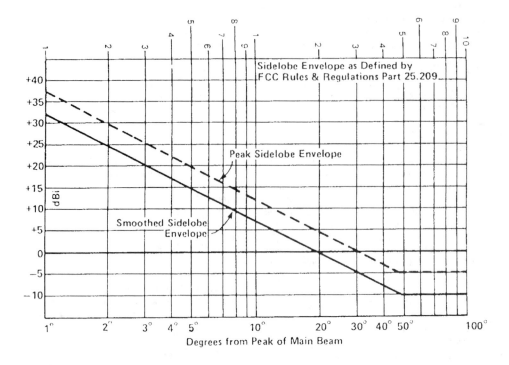

Figure 17.13 FCC earth station antenna pattern specification

radiation patterns of the array are mainly determined by the element spacing and the amplitudes and phases of the signals sent to the individual elements. In addition to being able to form a wide range of multiple or shaped beams, the array has the advantage that the cross-polarisation of the total array is lower than that of an individual element. However the closeness of the array elements gives rise to mutual coupling between the aperture fields which can distort the radiation patterns (Clarricoats, 1984b; Clarricoats, 1984c). A significant disadvantage of an array is that a beam forming network of waveguide components must be used behind the array elements to produce the correct amplitudes and phases to the array. For large arrays this can be heavy, expensive and a significant part of the design of the complete antenna system.

17.5 Antennas used in communication systems

17.5.1 Microwave line of sight radio

A typical microwave radio relay system consists of two axi-symmetric parabolic reflector antennas on towers, Figure 17.12, with a spacing of the order of 50km apart in a line of sight path. The relationship between the transmitted and received powers and the antenna and path parameters is given by the Friis transmission formulae, Equation 17.2. The typical antenna gain is about 43dBi which means a diameter of about 3 metres at 6GHz.

In addition to the pattern envelope specifications (which must be low because two or more antennas are normally mounted next to each other on a tower), there are a number of other important criteria

for microwave radio antennas. The front-to-back ratio must be high, and the cross-polar discrimination needs to be high for dual polarisation operation, typically better than −25dB within the main beam region over a bandwidth of up to 500MHz. The VSWR needs to be low (typically 1.06 maximum) in a microwave radio relay system in order to reduce the magnitude of the round trip echo. The supporting structure must be stable to ensure that the reflector does not move significantly in high winds. The reflectors must operate under all weather conditions, which means that a radome is often required. This poses extra design problems because inevitably it degrades the electrical performance. A long waveguide or coaxial cable feeder must be provided from the transmitter to the antennas. Not only must this be low loss but it must also be well made so that there is no possibility of loose joins introducing non-linear effects. Finally the cost must be relatively low because a large number of reflectors are required in a microwave communication system.

The majority of antennas in use are prime focus symmetric reflectors often with shields and radomes. The design of the prime focus reflectors follows the procedure discussed in earlier sections. The need to have a high front-to-back ratio means that either a low edge illumination must be used or baffles and shields must be used. The latter methods are preferable, but increase the weight and cost. The most common feed is a modified TE_{11} circular waveguide, which is designed to have a low VSWR and good pattern symmetry. Sometimes operation in two frequency bands is needed in which case the feed must combine two waveguides and operate at the two frequencies. The VSWR can be reduced by replacing the centre portion of the paraboloid with a flat plate, called a vertex plate. This minimises the VSWR contribution from the dish although it also degrades the near-in sidelobes and reduces the gain.

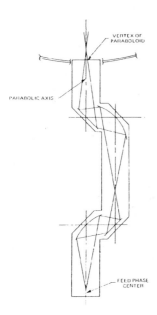

Figure 17.14 Beam waveguide feed system for large earth stations

17.5.2 Earth station antennas

Earth station antennas are at the earth end of satellite links. High gain is needed to receive the weak signals from the satellite, or to transmit strong signals to the satellite. The antennas can be divided into three types:

1. Large antennas required for transmit and receive on the INTEL-SAT type global networks with gains of 60 to 65dBi (15 to 30 metres diameter).
2. Medium sized antennas for cable head (TVRO) or data receive only terminals (3-7 metres diameter)
3. Small antennas for direct broadcast reception (0.5-2 metres diameter).

Types 1 and 2 have to satisfy stringent specifications imposed by regulatory bodies. When the recommended spacing of satellites in the geostationary arc was 3 degrees, the pattern envelope was specified by $32 - 35 \log\theta$. This could be met with a symmetric reflector antenna. With the new spacing of 2 degrees, the pattern spec has been improved to $29 - 25 \log\theta$, Figure 17.13. This can best be met with low sidelobe, offset reflector designs.

The minimum receivable signal level is set by inherent noise in the system. Earth stations are required to detect small signals so the control of the noise parameters is important. The noise appearing at the output terminals of an earth station used as a receiver has three components; the noise received by the main beam of the reflector; the spillover noise due to the spillover from the feed; the receiver noise. The first component may be due to natural sources or to man made interference. The natural noise emitters are the earth and sea absorption, galactic noise, isotropic background radiation, quantum noise and absorption due to the oxygen and water vapour in the

Earth's atmosphere. A minimum isotropic background radiation of about 3K is always seen by any antenna. The value of the other factors depends on frequency. The spillover noise is the only component under the control of the antenna designer. Its value can be reduced by designing an antenna with very low sidelobes. The receiver noise is normally the dominant noise factor. It depends on the method of amplification and detection. Early earth stations all used cooled receivers which have low noise temperatures. Modern earth stations use uncooled receivers which are dependent on the noise performance of the front-end transistor. This was improved dramatically in recent years, especially for small DBS terminals where the economies of scale have supported considerable research to reduce the noise temperature.

The ratio of the gain to noise temperature, the G/T ratio, is a useful measure of the influence of the noise components. Typical values are 40.7dBK^{-1} for an INTELSAT A, 30 metre diameter antenna operating at 4/6GHz (Pratt, 1986)

Large earth station antennas are expensive to construct and to maintain so that there is a premium in obtaining the maximum efficiency from the system. The axi-symmetric Cassegrain antenna (see Section 17.4.2.) is the favourite choice for a number of reasons:

1. The gain can be increased over the standard parabola- hyperbola combination by shaping the reflectors. Up to an extra 1dB is possible.
2. Low antenna noise temperatures can be achieved by controlling spillover using a high performance corrugated horn and by using a beam waveguide feed system.
3. Beam waveguide feed systems place the low noise receivers and high power transmitters in a convenient, stationary, location on the ground.

The beam waveguide feed system (Rudge, 1986), Figure 17.14, consists of at least four reflectors, whose shape and orientation is chosen so that the transmitter and receiver can be stationary whilst the antenna is free to move in two planes. The free-space beam suffers very little loss. The dual polarised transmit and receive signals need to be separated by a beam-forming network placed behind the main feed horn. For 4/6GHz operation, this will also incorporate circular polarisers.

The narrow beam from the large antenna necessitates the incorporation of some form of tracking into the antenna because even a geostationary satellite drifts periodically. There are a number of schemes available, including monopulse, conical scan and hill climbing. The favourite is a monopulse scheme using additional modes in the feed horn to electromagnetically abstract the tracking data.

The first generation of medium earth station antennas were axi-symmetric Cassegrain reflector antennas, sometimes shaped. However the advent of tighter pattern specifications has led to the widespread use of single or dual offset reflector antennas (see Section 17.4.3). These can meet the low sidelobe specifications by removing blockage effects from the aperture. Very high efficiency designs have been produced by shaping the reflectors to optimise the use of the aperture (Bergman, 1988; Cha, 1983; Bjontagaard, 1983). For these high efficiency designs, the r.m.s. surface error on the main reflector needs to be less than 0.5mm for operation in the 11GHz to 14GHz band. The feed is a high performance corrugated horn. The offset reflector configuration lends itself to deployment and portable designs have been produced where the offset reflector folds for transportation.

Cost is the main driver for small earth station antennas for mass market applications. Receive only terminals in the 4/6GHz band for

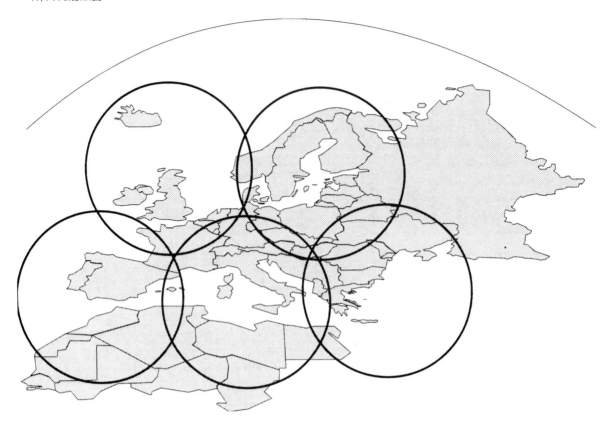

Figure 17.15 Multiple spot beams generated by an array feed on a space craft

data or TV reception are usually symmetric prime focus paraboloid which are made by spinning an aluminium sheet. In the 11GHz communication band or the 12GHz DBS band, prime focus offset reflectors made from fibreglass moulds are popular. A simple open-ended waveguide type feed is incorporated on a sturdy feed support with the first stage low noise converter incorporated directly into the feed. There is considerable interest in making flat-plate array antennas which can be mounted flush against buildings and incorporate electronic scanning to look onto the satellite signals. The technology for electronic scanning is available from military radars but not so far at a price which is acceptable to the domestic market.

17.5.3 Satellite antennas

17.5.3.1 *Telemetry, tracking and command (TT&C)*

The ideal TT&C antenna would give omnidirectional coverage so that the orientation of the satellite would be irrelevant. Wire antennas are used for VHF and UHF coverage but the spacecraft is a few wavelengths across at these frequencies and therefore considerable interaction between the antenna and the satellite distorts the radiation pattern. An alternative approach is to use a low gain horn antenna to provide full earth coverage. This is particularly useful for spin stabilised spacecraft. The earth subtends 17 degrees from a geostationary satellite which can be met with a small conical horn.

17.5.3.2 *Spot beams*

Spot beam antennas are required to produce a beam covering a small region of the earth's surface. The angular width of the beam is inversely proportional to the diameter of the antenna. Size considerations virtually dictate that some form of deployable mechanism is needed on the satellite and this leads to the use of offset reflectors with a dual-mode or corrugated feed horn. The constraints of the launcher mean that the maximum size for a solid reflector is about 3.5 metres. Larger reflectors can only be launched by using some form of unfurlable mesh or panel reflector. The trend towards smaller footprints on the earth can be met either by using a larger reflector or by using a higher frequency, both of which involve higher costs. To date most spot beam communication satellite have used two prime focus offset reflectors, one for transmit and one for receive, producing footprints on the earth's surface which are elliptical because of the curvature of the earth.

17.5.3.3 *Multiple beams*

It was early recognised that by using a single reflector and an array of feeds it was possible to produce multiple beams on the earth, Figure 17.15. This has the advantage that most of the antenna sub-system is re-used with the penalty of having to design and make the array of feed horns and the beam forming network behind the array. The array feed elements must be compact so that they occupy

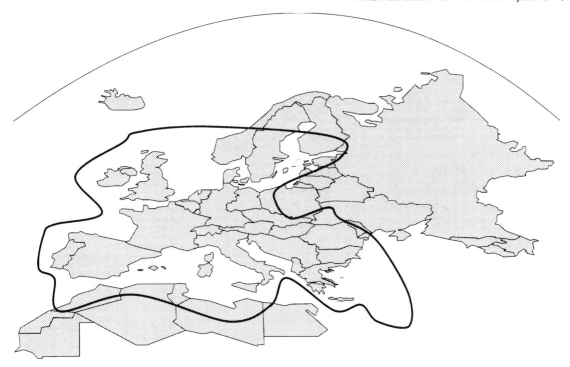

Figure 17.16 European contoured beam

the minimum space in the focal plane of the offset reflector. At the same time the crosspolarisation must be low. This tends to mean that corrugated horns cannot be used and small diameter dual-mode rectangular or circular horns are preferred. The maximum number of beams depends on the tolerable aberrations since array elements which are off-axis will have degraded performance.

17.5.3.4 *Shaped beams*

It is desirable to optimise the shape of the satellite beam on the earth's surface so as to conserve power and not waste energy by illuminating portions of the oceans. An example is shown in Figure 17.16. Shaped beams can be produced in two ways. Multiple, overlapping beams produced by an offset parabolic reflector and an array of feeds can be used. This approach is an extension of the multiple beams and has the advantage that it is possible to design for reconfiguration by incorporating switching systems into the beam forming network. The alternative approach is to use a single, high performance feed and to physically shape the surface of the reflector so that power is distributed uniformly over a shaped beam region. Both approaches have received considerable attention in recent years.

The multiple beam approach is well illustrated by the INTELSAT VI communication satellite, Figure 17.17, which produces multiple shaped beams to cover the main population regions of the earth. (Figure 17.18.) In order to be able to use the same satellites over the Atlantic, Indian or Pacific Oceans, the array feed consists of 146 elements which can be switched to produce the appropriate shaped beams (Bennett, 1984).

The shaped reflector approach has the advantage of mechanical simplicity and lower weight at the penalty of fixed beams. The theoretical design process is quite extensive and involves a synthesis process with the input of the required beam shape and the output of the contours of the reflector surface. A single offset reflector constrains the possible shapes because it is not possible to

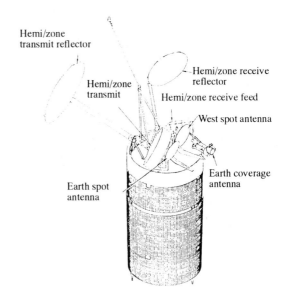

Figure 17.17 INTELSAT IV antenna system

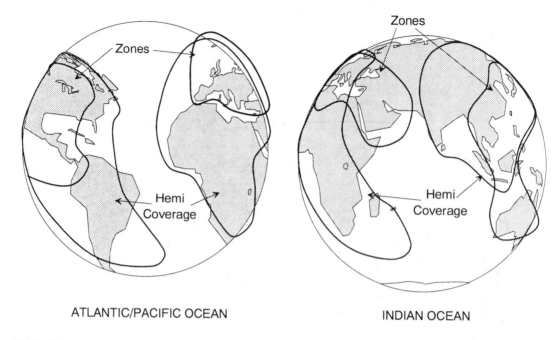

ATLANTIC/PACIFIC OCEAN   INDIAN OCEAN

Figure 17.18 Shaped beam generated by INTELSAT VI antenna

arbitrarily specify the amplitude and the phase of the synthesised pattern. This constraint is removed with a dual reflector design.

17.5.4 VHF and UHF communications

Antennas for VHF and UHF communication systems take on a wide variety of specific forms, but the vast majority are derivatives of the generic dipole type antenna. The physical, mechanical and environmental aspects are generally more significant than for microwave antennas because the smaller size of the antenna means that the radiation and impedance characteristics are partly determined by these aspects.

A comprehensive survey of VHF and UHF antennas can be found in (Rudge, 1986; Johnson, 1984). Antennas that give near uniform coverage in one plane can be obtained from half wave dipoles or monopoles. Complementary antennas such as loops and slots will work equally well and the actual shape will be determined more by the application than by the basic electromagnetic performance. The bandwidth of these simple elements is limited by the impedance

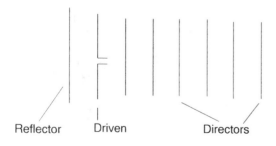

Reflector   Driven   Directors

Figure 17.19 A Yagi-Uda array

characteristics, although most communication applications only require relatively narrow bandwidths. With small elements, some form of impedance matching network is required. One problem with balanced dipole type antennas is that they are required to be fed by an unbalanced coaxial cable. A balun is needed to match the balanced to unbalanced system and this is inevitably frequency sensitive.

Antennas for point-to-point links need to be directional and have as high a gain as possible. This is achieved with Yagi-Uda array, Figure 17.19, which consists of one driven elements, one reflector element and a number of director elements. Only the driven element is connected to the feed line; the other elements are passive and currents are induced in them by mutual coupling, the spacing ensuring that this is in the correct amplitude and phase to give a directional radiation pattern. Gains of up to about 17 dBi are possible from one Yagi-Uda array. Higher gains can be obtained by multiple arrays. The Yagi-Uda array is inherently linearly polarised. Circular polarised arrays can be made either from crossed dipoles or from helixes.

Antennas for mobile communications can be divided into those for base stations and those for the mobiles. Base station antennas are mounted on towers and usually require to have nearly uniform patterns in the horizontal plane with shaping in the vertical plane to conserve power. This can be achieved with a vertical array of vertical dipoles or other panelled dipoles. The influence of the tower on the antenna must be taken into account in the design.

Mobile antennas on vehicles, ships, aircraft or near humans present challenging problems to the antenna designer. In most cases the physical, mechanical and environmental aspects take precedence over the electromagnetic design. In consequence the ingenuity of the antenna designer is required to produce an antenna which works well in adverse conditions. For instance antennas on aircraft must not disturb the aerodynamic profile so cannot protrude from the body of the aircraft. The effects of corrosion, temperature, pressure, vibration and weather are other factors to be taken into account. Antennas for personal radios are constrained by the role of the operator and by the need for very compact designs commensurate with satisfying radiation safety levels. The human body acts partly as a director and partly as a reflector depending on the frequency of use and the relative position of the antenna to the body. The portable radio equipment has to be considered a part of the antenna system including the radio circuits, batteries and case. In general, improved performance will result when the antenna is held as far from the body as possible and as high as possible.

17.5.5   HF communications

HF antennas are used in the range of frequencies from 2 to 30MHz for mobile communications and some fixed communications. Space precludes more than a brief mention of the types of HF antennas. Surveys can be found in (Rudge, 1986; Johnson, 1984). HF antenna design is constrained by the ionospheric propagation characteristics which change both daily, seasonally and with the sun-spot cycle. Antennas can receive either the sky wave reflected from the ionosphere or the ground wave if transmitter and receiver are close together. The wavelength in the HF band is such that antennas are usually only a fraction of a wavelength in size and this in turn means that the local environment around the antenna will have a major impact upon the performance. This is particularly true for antennas mounted on vehicles, ships and aircraft. The analysis of the antenna must take account of the environment by techniques such as wire grid modelling (Mittra, 1975). This is computer intensive and inevitably approximate which means that much HF antenna design is empirical.

Most HF antennas are based on dipoles, monopoles or wire antennas. Complementary elements such as loops or slot antennas are also used. Directionality or gain is achieved by arrays of elements. A prime requirement of most HF antennas is that they are broadband in order that the optimum propagation frequency can be used. The radiation patterns of the basic elements are wide band but the input impedance or VSWR is narrow band. To overcome this limitation a tuning unit has to be incorporated into the system. The wide band operation is achieved with automatic tuning units.

17.6   References

Balanis, C.A. (1982) *Antenna Theory: Analysis and Design* Harper & Row, New York.

Bennett, S.B. and Braverman, D.J. (1984) INTELSAT VI - A Continuing Evolution *Proc. IEEE* , **72**, 1457.

Bergman, J., Brown, R.C., Clarricoats, P.J.B. and Zhou, H. (1988) Sythesis of Shaped Beam Reflector Antenna Patterns, *Proc. IEE*, **135 (H)**, (1) 48.

Bjontagaard, G. and Pettersen, T. (1983) An Offset Dual Reflector Antenna Shaped from Near-Field Measurements of the Feed Horn; Theoretical Calculations and Measurements, *IEEE Trans.*, **AP-31**, 973.

Cha, A.G. (1983) An Offset Dual Shaped Reflector with 84.5 Percent Efficiency, *IEEE Trans.*, **AP-31**, 896.

Clarricoats, P.J.B. and Olver, A.D. (1984a) *Corrugated Horns for Microwave Antennas*, Peter Peregrinus (IEE), London.

Clarricoats, P.J.B., Tun, S.M. and Parini, C.G. (1984b) Effects of Mutual Coupling in Conical Horn Arrays, *Proc. IEE*, **131 (H)**, (1), 165.

Clarricoats, P.J.B., Tun, S.M. and Brown, R.C. (1984c) Performance of Offset Reflector Antennas with Array Feeds, *Proc IEE*, **131 (H)**, (1) 172.

Collin, R.E. and Zucher F.J. (1969) *Antenna Theory (Pts 1 & 11)*, McGraw Hill, New York.

Elliot, R.S. (1981) *Antenna Theory and Design*, Prentice Hall, Englewood Cliffs, N.J.

Galindo, V. (1964) Design of Dual Reflector Antennas with Arbitrary Phase and Amplitude Distribution, *IEEE Trans.*, **AP- 12**, 403.

James, G.L. (1986) *Geometrical Theory of Diffraction for Electromagnetic Waves*, Peter Peregrinus (IEE), London.

Johnson, R.C. and Jasik, H. (Eds) (1984) *Antenna Engineering Handbook*, McGraw-Hill, New York.

King, R.W.P. (1956) *The Theory of Linear Antennas* , Havard Univ. Press. Cambridge, Mass.

King, R.W.P., Mack, R.B. and Sandler, S.S. (1968) *Arrays of Cylindrical Dipoles*, Cambridge Univ. Press, New York.

Lamb, J.W. and Olver, A.D. (1986) Blockage Due to Subreflector Supports in Large Radiotelescope Antennas, *Proc. IEE*, **133(H)** 43 (1).

Lo, Y.T. and Lee, S.W. (1988) *Antenna Handbook*, Van Nostrand, New York.

Love, A.W. (1976) *Electromagnetic Horn Antennas*, Selected Reprint Series, IEEE Press, New York.

Love, A.W., Rudge, A.W. and Olver, A.D. (1986) Primary Feed Antennas. *In The Handbook of Antenna Design, (eds. A.W. Rudge et al)*, Peter Peregrinus (IEE), London.

Ludwig, A.G. (1973) The Definition of Cross- Polarisation, *IEEE Trans.*, **AP-211** (1), 116.

Milligan, T. (1985) *Modern Antenna Design*, McGraw-Hill, New York.

Mittra, R. (1975) *Numerical and Asymptotic Methods in Electromagnetics*, Springer Verlag, Berlin.

Olver, A.D. (1986) Basic Properties of Antennas. *In The Handbook of Antenna Design (eds. A.W. Rudge, et al)* Peter Peregrinus (IEE), Chapter 1.

Pratt, T. and Bostian, C.W. (1986) *Satellite Communications*, Wiley, New York.

Rahmat-Samii, Y. (1986) Reflector Antennas. *In Antenna Handbook (eds. Y.T. Lo and S.W. Lee)* Van Nostrand, New York. Chapter 15.

Rudge, A.W., Milne, K. Olver, A.D. and Knight, P. (Eds.) (1986) *The Handbook of Antenna Design*, Peter Peregrinus (IEE), London.

Rusch, W.V.T. and Potter, P.D. (1970) *Analysis of Reflector Antennas*, Academic Press, New York.

Rusch, W.V.T., Ludwig, A.C. and Wong, W.G. (1986) Analytical Techniques for Quasi-Optical Antennas. *In The Handbook of Antenna Design (eds. A.W. Rudge, et al)* Peter Peregrinus (IEE). Chapter 2.

Silver, S. (Ed.) (1984) *Microwave Antenna Theory and Design*, Peter Peregrinus (IEE), London.

Stutzman, W.L. and Thiele, G.A. (1981) *Antenna Theory and Design*, Wiley, New York.

Williams, W.F. (1965) High Efficiency Antenna Reflector, *Microwave J.*, **8**. 79.

18

Analogue modulation

Professor J E Flood
OBE DSc FInstP CEng FIEE
Aston University

Contents

18.1   Introduction

The processing of a signal to make it suitable for sending over a transmission medium is called modulation. Reasons for using modulation are:

1. Frequency translating (e.g. when an audio frequency baseband signal modulates a radio frequency carrier).
2. Improving signal/noise ratio by increasing the bandwidth (e.g. using frequency modulation).
3. Multiplexing i.e. enabling many baseband channels to share the same wideband transmission path.

Modulation is performed by causing the baseband modulating signal to vary a parameter of a carrier wave. A sinusoidal carrier, as given by Equation 18.1, is defined by three parameters: amplitude A, frequency $\omega / 2\pi$ and phase φ. Thus there are three basic modulation methods: amplitude modulation (AM), frequency modulation (FM) and phase modulation (PM).

$$v_c = A \cos(\omega t + \varphi)$$ (18.1)

When modulation is employed, a modulator is needed at the sending end of a channel and a demodulator at the receiving end recovers the baseband signal from the modulated carrier. The combination of modulator and demodulator at a terminal is often referred to as a modem.

18.2   Amplitude modulation

18.2.1   Simple amplitude modulation

The simplest form of modulation is amplitude modulation. The modulator causes the envelope of the carrier wave to follow the waveform of the modulating signal and the demodulator recovers it from this envelope.

If a carrier, given by Equation 18.2, is modulated to a depth m by a sinusoidal modulating signal given by Equation 18.3, the resulting AM signal is as in Equation 18.4.

$$v_c = V_c \cos \omega_c t$$ (18.2)

$$v_m = V_m \cos \omega_m t$$ (18.3)

$$\begin{aligned} v &= (1 + m \cos \omega_m t) V_c \cos \omega_c t \\ &= V_c [\cos \omega_c t + \frac{1}{2} m \cos(\omega_c + \omega_m) t \\ &\quad + \frac{1}{2} m \cos(\omega_c - \omega_m) t] \end{aligned}$$ (18.4)

If the modulating signal contains several components, f_1, f_2, ..., etc., then the modulated signal contains $f_c - f_1$, $f_c - f_2$, ..., etc., and $f_c + f_1$, $f_c + f_2$, ..., etc. in addition to f_c. If the modulating signal consists of a band of frequencies, as shown in Figure 18.1(a), the modulated

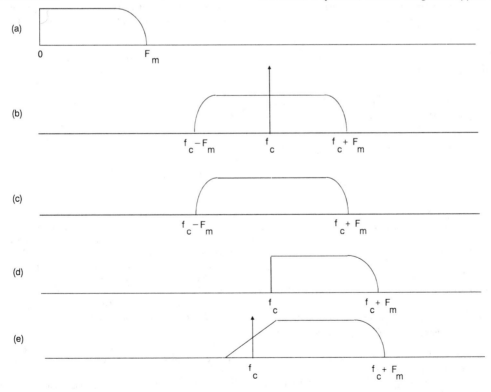

Figure 18.1   Frequency spectra for amplitude modulation: (a) baseband signal; (b) simple amplitude modulation (AM); (c) double sideband suppressed carrier (DSBSC) modulation; (d) Single sideband suppressed carrier (SSBSC) modulation; (e) vestigial sideband (VSB) modulation

signal consists of two sidebands, each occupying the same bandwidth as the baseband signal, as shown in Figure 18.1(b). In the upper sideband, the highest frequency corresponds to the highest frequency in the baseband; this is therefore known as an erect sideband. In the lower sideband, the highest frequency corresponds to the lowest frequency in the baseband; this is known as an inverted sideband.

Simple amplitude modulation makes inefficient use of the transmitted power, as information is transmitted only in the sidebands but the majority of the power is contained in the carrier. If a carrier as in Equation 18.2 is modulated to a depth m by the sinusoidal baseband signal of Equation 18.3, the output power is given by Equation 18.5.

$$\overline{v^2} = V_c^2 \left(\frac{1}{2} + \frac{1}{8} m^2 + \frac{1}{8} m^2 \right)$$

$$= \frac{1}{2} V_c^2 \left(1 + \frac{1}{2} m^2 \right) \tag{18.5}$$

The maximum sideband power is obtained with 100% depth of modulation. The power in the sidebands is then a third of the total transmitted power. For smaller modulation depths, it is even less.

One method of producing AM is to add the baseband signal to the carrier and apply them to a non-linear amplifier, as shown in Figure 18.2. If the input/output characteristic of the non-linear circuit is

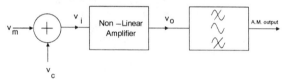

Figure 18.2 Low level amplitude modulator

given by Equation 18.6 and its input voltage by Equation 18.7, then the output voltage is as in Equation 18.8.

$$v_o = a_o + a_1 v_i + a_2 v_i^2 + \ldots\ldots \tag{18.6}$$

$$v_i = v_m \cos \omega_m t + V_c \cos \omega_c t \tag{18.7}$$

$$
\begin{aligned}
v_o = &\ a_o + a_2 (V_m^2 + V_c^2) \\
&+ a_1 (V_m \cos \omega_m t + V_c \cos \omega_c t) \\
&+ a_2 (\frac{1}{2} V_m^2 \cos 2\omega_m t + \frac{1}{2} V_c^2 \cos 2\omega_c t \\
&+ V_c V_m [\cos (\omega_c - \omega_m) t \\
&+ \cos (\omega_c + \omega_m) t]) + \ldots\ldots \tag{18.8}
\end{aligned}
$$

The bandpass filter is required to remove all components except those which comprise the AM wave. These are shown in bold in the above equation.

Another form of modulator is shown in Figure 18.3. This uses a gain controlled amplifier whose input signal is the carrier and whose control voltage is the modulating signal. For example, the carrier may be applied to the base of a transistor and the modulating signal superimposed on the collector supply voltage.

If the gain of the amplifier is given by Equation 18.9 and the carrier and modulating waveforms by Equations 18.2 and 18.3 then

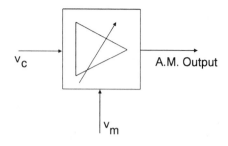

Figure 18.3 High level amplitude modulator

the output voltage is given by Equation 18.10, which is the required AM wave.

$$A = A_o (1 + k v_m) \tag{18.9}$$

$$
\begin{aligned}
v_o = &\ A_o V_c \cos \omega_c t + k A_o V_m V_c \cos \omega_m t \cos \omega_c t \\
= &\ A_o V_c (\cos \omega_c t + \frac{1}{2} k V_m [\cos (\omega_o - \omega_m) t \\
&+ \cos (\omega_c + \omega_m) t]) \tag{18.10}
\end{aligned}
$$

The first method is used for low level modulators before the power amplifier of a transmitter. The second method is used for high level modulators in the final stage of amplification.

An AM wave can be demodulated by the simple diode circuit shown in Figure 18.4. The rectified output voltage across the load resistor follows the envelope of the modulated input signal as in

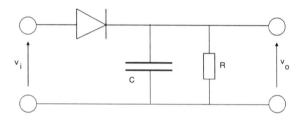

Figure 18.4 Envelope demodulator circuit

Figure 18.5. The time constant CR must be large compared with the period of the carrier to prevent the output voltage decaying substantially between the peaks of the carrier. However, time constant CR in Figure 18.4 must be sufficiently small for the output voltage to decay as rapidly as the envelope changes when the baseband signal has its maximum frequency, F_m. If $f_c > > F_m$, this is easily arranged.

Other demodulators, which give a better performance at poor input signal/noise ratios, are the coherent demodulator (described later) and the phase locked loop AM demodulator (Gardner, 1979; Gosling, 1986).

18.2.2   Suppressed carrier modulation

It is possible, by using a balanced modulator (Tucker, 1953) to eliminate the carrier and generate only the sidebands, as shown in Figure 18.1(c). This is known as double sideband suppressed carrier modulation (DSBSC). The modulator acts as a switch, which multiplies the baseband signal by a quasi square wave carrier. Its output

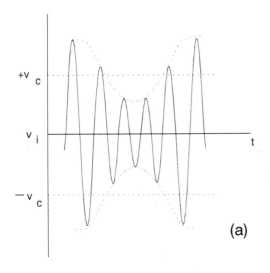

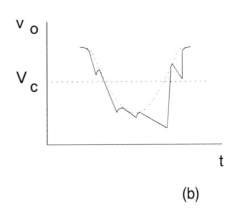

Figure 18.5 Envelope demodulator waveforms: (a) input; (b) output

thus contains upper and lower sidebands about the fundamental and harmonics of the carrier frequency. As shown in Figure 18.6(a), a bandpass filter is used to remove all components except the wanted sidebands. Thus, for a sinusoidal baseband input signal, the output signal is given by Equation 18.11.

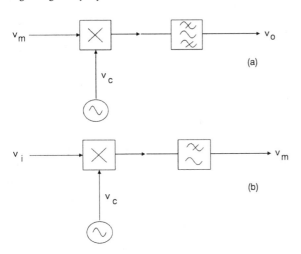

Figure 18.6 Applications of balanced modulator: (a) product modulator; (b) coherent demodulator

$$v_o = V_m \cos \omega_m t \cos \omega_c t$$

$$= \frac{1}{2} V_m \left(\cos (\omega_c - \omega_m) t + \cos (\omega_c + \omega_m) t \right) \quad (18.11)$$

A balanced modulator used in this way is often called a product modulator.

To demodulate a DSBSC signal, it is necessary to use a coherent demodulator, consisting of a balanced modulator supplied with a locally generated carrier as shown in Figure 18.6(b) instead of the

envelope demodulator used with simple AM. If the incoming DSBSC signal is given by Equation 18.12 and the coherent demodulator multiplies this with a local carrier given by Equation 18.13, its output voltage is as in Equation 18.14.

$$v_i = \frac{1}{2} m V_c \left(\cos (\omega_c + \omega_m) t + \cos (\omega_c - \omega_m) t \right) \quad (18.12)$$

$$v_c = \cos (\omega_c t + \theta) \quad (18.13)$$

$$v = \frac{1}{4} m V_c (\cos [(2 \omega_c + \omega_m) t + \theta]$$
$$+ \cos [(2 \omega_c - \omega_m) t + \theta]$$
$$+ \cos (\theta + \omega_m t) + \cos (\theta - \omega_m t)) \quad (18.14)$$

The components at frequencies $(2\omega_c \pm \omega_m)$ are removed by a low pass filter and the baseband output signal is given by Equation 18.15.

$$v_o = \frac{1}{4} m V_c \left(\cos (\theta + \omega_m t) + \cos (\theta - \omega_m t) \right)$$

$$= \frac{1}{2} m V_c \cos \theta \cos \omega_m t \quad (18.15)$$

Thus v_o represents the original baseband signal, provided that the phase θ of the local carrier is stable.

A further economy in power, and a halving in bandwidth, can be obtained by producing a single sideband suppressed carrier (SSBSC) signal, as shown in Figure 18.1(d). If the upper sideband is used, the effect of the modulator is simply to produce a frequency translation of the baseband signal to a position in the frequency spectrum determined by the carrier frequency. If the lower sideband is used, the band is inverted as well as translated.

The SSBSC signal requires the minimum possible bandwidth for transmission. Consequently, the method is used whenever its complexity is justified by the saving in bandwidth (Pappenfus, 1964). An important example is the use of SSBSC for multichannel carrier telephone systems (Kingdom, 1991). An error in the frequency of the local carrier of the demodulator results in a corresponding shift in the frequencies of the components in the baseband output signal. For speech transmission, frequency shifts of the order of ±10Hz are not noticeable, but the errors that can be tolerated for telegraph and data transmission are less. The CCITT specifies that the frequency shift should be less than ±2Hz.

A SSBSC signal can be generated by using a balanced modulator and a bandpass filter, as for DSBSC. However, the filter in Figure 18.6(a) is designed to pass only one of the sidebands, instead of both.

An alternative method of generating a SSBSC signal is the quadrature method shown in Figure 18.7. This uses two product modulators. The baseband signal, v_m, and the carrier, v_c, are applied to

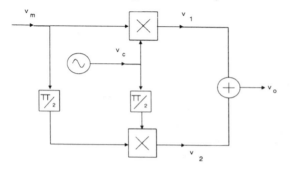

Figure 18.7   Quadrature method of SSBSC generation

one directly, and to the other after a phase shift of 90°. If the carrier and modulating signals are as in Equations 18.2 and 18.3, the outputs of the two modulators are given by Equations 18.16 and 18.17 and v_o by Equation 18.18.

$$v_1 = V_m \sin \omega_m t \sin \omega_c t \qquad (18.16)$$

$$v_2 = V_m \cos \omega_m t \cos \omega_c t \qquad (18.17)$$

$$v_o = v_1 + v_2 = V_m \cos (\omega_c - \omega_m) t \qquad (18.18)$$

Alternatively, subtracting v_1 from v_2 gives Equation 18.19.

$$v_o = V_m \cos (\omega_c + \omega_m) t \qquad (18.19)$$

It is straightforward to provide a 90° phase shift at the single carrier frequency, but not over the band of frequencies of a modulating signal. Instead, the baseband signal is applied to the modulators through a pair of networks whose phase shifts differ by approximately 90° over the required band (Coates, 1975). The quadrature method is not widely used, since small phase errors result in unwanted frequency components in the output signal.

A coherent demodulator is required for demodulating a SSBSC signal. Since only one sideband is present, the demodulated output signal, from Equation 18.15, is as in Equation 18.20.

$$v_o = \frac{1}{4} m V_c \cos (\omega_m t \pm \theta) \qquad (18.20)$$

If a SSBSC signal is corrupted by noise, the coherent demodulator acts on each component of the noise spectrum in the same way as it

does on each component of the signal. Consequently, the signal to noise ratio at the output of the demodulator is the same as the input signal to noise ratio.

For a DSBSC signal, the output of the demodulator produced by a signal component at $f_c + f_m$ is in phase with that produced by the component at $f_c - f_m$. Thus, the output signal voltage is twice the input signal voltage (c.f. Equation 18.15 with $\theta = 0$) and the output signal power is four times that for SSBSC. For noise, the outputs produced by components at $f_c - f_m$ and $f_c + f_m$ have a random phase difference. Thus, the output noise power is twice the input noise power. Consequently, the output signal to noise ratio is twice the input signal to noise ratio, an apparent improvement of 3dB over SSBSC. However, the bandwidth required for DSBSC transmission is twice that for SSBSC. This doubles the received noise power, so no overall improvement is obtained.

For simple AM, a coherent demodulator acts in the same way as for DSBSC. So does the envelope demodulator of Figure 18.4 at good signal to noise ratios. The diode acts as a switch operated by the incoming carrier and this multiplies the input signal by $\cos \omega_c t$, as does a coherent demodulator.

At poor input signal to noise ratios, this is no longer true. The diode is switched by peaks of the noise voltage and the output signal to noise ratio is worse than for a coherent demodulator (Brown and Glazier, 1974; Coates, 1975). The signal to noise ratio performance of simple AM is, of course, worse than that of DSBSC because the input power includes that of the carrier as well as the sidebands. For 100% depth of modulation, the sideband power is only a third of the total power. Thus, for equal transmitter powers and receiver noise power densities, simple AM gives an output signal to noise ratio 4.8dB worse than for DSBSC or SSBSC transmission.

By using SSBSC, it is possible to transmit two channels through the bandwidth needed by simple AM for a single channel; one uses the upper sideband of the carrier and the other uses the lower sideband. This is known as independent sideband modulation and is used in h.f. radio communication (Hills, 1973). However, it is also possible to do this using DSBSC. The transmitter uses two modulators whose carriers are in quadrature. The receiver uses two coherent demodulators whose local carriers are in quadrature. Equation 18.15 shows that each demodulator produces a full output from the signal whose carrier is in phase (since cos 0=1) and zero output from the signal whose carrier is in quadrature (since cos π/2=0). This is called quadrature amplitude modulation (QAM). In practice, the method is not used for analogue baseband signals since small errors in the phases of the local carriers cause a fraction of the signal of each channel to appear as crosstalk in the output from the other. However, the method is used for transmitting digital signals.

18.2.3   Vestigial sideband modulation

If the sideband signal extends down to very low frequencies, as in television, it is almost impossible to suppress the whole of the unwanted sideband without affecting low frequency components in the wanted sideband. Use is then made of vestigial sideband (VSB) transmission instead of SSBSC. A conventional AM signal (as shown in Figure 18.1(b)) is first generated and this is then applied to a filter having a transition between its pass and stop band that is skew symmetric about the carrier frequency. This results in an output signal having the spectrum shown in Figure 18.1(e).

If a coherent demodulator is used, the original baseband signal can be recovered without distortion. It is also possible to use a simple envelope demodulator for VSB, but some non linear distortion then results (Black, 1953). VSB transmission does, of course, require a greater channel bandwidth than SSB. However, for a wideband signal such as television, the bandwidth saving compared with DSB is considerable.

18.3   Frequency and phase modulation

18.3.1   General

The instantaneous angular frequency of an alternating voltage is given by Equation 18.21. This relationship between frequency and phase means that frequency modulation (FM) and phase modulation (PM) are both forms of angle modulation.

$$\omega = \frac{d\varphi}{dt} \quad radians/s \tag{18.21}$$

A sinusoidal carrier modulated by a sinusoidal baseband signal may be represented by Equation 18.22 where β is the modulation index.

$$v = V_c \cos\left(\omega_c t + \beta \sin \omega_m t\right) \tag{18.22}$$

The maximum phase deviation is given by Equation 18.23 and, since Equation 18.24 holds, the maximum frequency deviation is given by Equation 18.25.

$$\Delta\varphi = \pm\beta \tag{18.23}$$

$$\frac{d\varphi}{dt} = \omega_m \beta \cos \omega_m t \tag{18.24}$$

$$\Delta F = \pm\beta f_m \tag{18.25}$$

In PM the phase deviation is proportional to the modulating voltage; therefore β is independent of its frequency and the frequency deviation is proportional to it. In FM, the frequency deviation is proportional to the modulating voltage; therefore the deviation frequency is independent of its frequency and β is inversely proportional to it. Thus, for FM, the modulation index may be defined as in Equation 18.26.

$$\beta = \frac{maximum\ frequency\ deviation\ of\ carrier}{maximum\ baseband\ frequency}$$
$$= \frac{\Delta F}{F_m} \tag{18.26}$$

In angle modulation, the information is conveyed by the instantaneous phase of the signal. Consequently, phase distortion in the transmission path causes attenuation distortion of the received signal. The differential delay of the transmission path must therefore be closely controlled over the bandwidth required to transmit the signal. However, since the information is not conveyed by the amplitude of the signal, the receiver can contain a limiter to maintain a constant signal amplitude. Consequently, non linear distortion in the transmission path does not cause distortion of the demodulated output signal; nor does attenuation/frequency distortion.

Use of a limiter in the receiver also removes amplitude variations due to noise and so enables angle modulation to give a better output signal to noise ratio than AM. Moreover, since the amplitude of an angle modulated wave is constant, the transmitter can deliver its full rated power all the time, whereas for AM this only occurs for peak amplitudes of the baseband signal. This contributes a further improvement in signal to noise ratio.

In PM, the frequency deviation (βf_m) is proportional to the frequency of the modulating signal as well as to its amplitude. Consequently, for signals (such as speech) that have the major proportion of their energy at the lower end of the baseband, PM makes inefficient use of the transmission path bandwidth compared with FM. Moreover, to demodulate a PM signal, the receiver must compare the phase of the incoming carrier with that of a locally generated carrier which must be very stable. FM is therefore preferred to PM for the transmission of analogue signals. It is used whenever sufficient bandwidth can be provided. However, PM is widely used for the transmission of digital signals as described in Chapter 19.

18.3.2   Modulators and demodulators

To generate FM, a voltage controlled oscillator is needed to enable the instantaneous frequency of the carrier to be varied by the baseband signal. This usually employs a varactor diode or a transistor reactance circuit to provide a voltage controlled capacitance (Coates, 1975).

The frequency of the oscillator is given by Equation 18.27. Thus, if C is given by Equation 18.28 then Equation 18.29 may be obtained.

$$f = \frac{1}{2\pi\sqrt{LC}} \tag{18.27}$$

$$C = C_o(1 + kv_m) \tag{18.28}$$

$$f = \frac{1}{2\pi\sqrt{LC_o}}\left(1 - \frac{1}{2}kv_m + \frac{3}{8}k^2 v_m^2 + ...\right) \tag{18.29}$$

To achieve linearity, it is therefore necessary for the frequency deviation to be kept to a small fraction of the centre frequency. Since the frequency depends on device parameters, which may change, a frequency stabilisation loop is usually added to control the centre frequency from a crystal oscillator.

Phase modulation can be generated by Armstrong's method shown in Figure 18.8. A product modulator produces a DSBSC

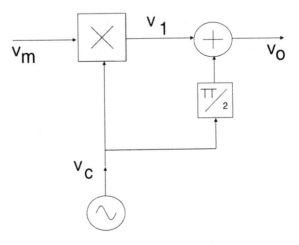

Figure 18.8   Phase modulation by Armstrong's method

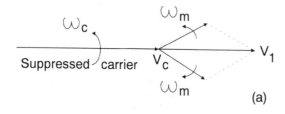

(a)

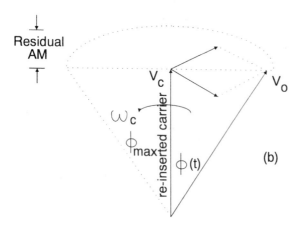

(b)

Figure 18.9 Phasor diagrams for Armstrong's phase modulator of Figure 18.8: (a) product modulator output (V_1); output from circuit (V_o)

wave, as shown in Figure 18.9(a), and the carrier is added to this after shifting its phase by 90°. This produces a phase deviation of the resultant signal, V_o, as shown in Figure 18.9(b). This method is only suitable for small values of modulation index. It produces an output containing only two side frequencies, whereas it is shown in the next section that significant additional side frequencies are present with high index modulation. These higher order side frequencies serve to keep the amplitude of the signal constant, whereas the circuit of Figure 18.8 produces some residual amplitude modulation. The locus of the end of phasor V_o is a straight line, whereas it would be a circle for perfect phase modulation.

Frequency modulation may be produced by using a phase modulator whose modulating signal is the integral of the baseband signal, as shown in Figure 18.10. Therefore Equations 18.30 and 18.31 may be obtained and this corresponds to FM.

$$v_o = V_c \cos\left(\omega_c t + k \int_0^t v_m \, dt \right)$$

$$= V_c \cos\left(\omega_c t + \varphi(t) \right) \tag{18.30}$$

$$\omega = \omega_c + \frac{d\varphi}{dt}$$

$$= \omega_c + k v_m \tag{18.31}$$

The Armstrong modulator of Figure 18.8 can therefore be used to generate FM. Similarly, phase modulation may be generated with a frequency modulator by differentiating the baseband signal, as shown in Figure 18.10(b). The Armstrong circuit only produces low index modulation. The frequency deviation can be increased by

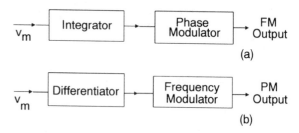

Figure 18.10 Alternative methods of generating angle modulation: (a) use of phase modulator to generate FM; (b) use of frequency modulator to generate PM

applying its output to a non-linear circuit to generate harmonics, one of which is selected by a bandpass filter. If the nth harmonic is selected, the frequency deviation is increased by a factor n.

A phase modulated wave can be demodulated by using a coherent demodulator whose local carrier is in quadrature with the incoming carrier when unmodulated. When the incoming carrier is modulated, the output voltage is given by Equation 18.32.

$$v = V_c \cos\left(\omega_c t + \varphi(t) \right) \sin \omega_c t$$

$$= \frac{1}{2} V_c \cos\left(2\omega_c t + \varphi(t) \right) + \frac{1}{2} V_c \sin \varphi(t) \tag{18.32}$$

The component at frequency $2\pi\omega_c$ is removed by the low pass filter and the output signal is as in Equation 18.33.

$$v_o = \frac{1}{2} V_c \sin \varphi(t)$$

$$\approx \frac{1}{2} V_c \varphi(t) = k v_m \tag{18.33}$$

One method of demodulating FM is to use the incoming carrier to generate a train of pulses and to count the number of these per unit of time (Gosling, 1986). However, more widely used circuits operate indirectly by converting frequency variations of the incoming signal to variations of amplitude or phase and demodulating these. Such circuits are called discriminators.

A simple discriminator can use a parallel tuned circuit whose resonant frequency is offset from the centre frequency of the incoming FM signal. As shown in Figure 18.11(a), a deviation of the input frequency varies the output voltage and this is rectified by an envelope demodulator to give a baseband output voltage. Improved forms of discriminator use a pair of tuned circuits, one resonant on each side of the centre frequency, to obtain linearity of conversion over a greater range of frequency deviation (Langford-Smith, 1960; Sturley, 1965). Since the output voltage of a discriminator is proportional to the amplitude of the input signal as well as its frequency, the discriminator must be preceded by a limiter to ensure that its input is of constant amplitude.

A tuned circuit can also produce a phase shift depending on the frequency deviation, as shown in Figure 18.11(b). The baseband signal can therefore be recovered by a coherent demodulator. The incoming FM carrier is fed directly to the coherent demodulator, but it is shifted 90° (by a small series capacitance) before being applied to the discriminator. The circuit is therefore known as a quadrature FM demodulator (Gosling, 1986).

A form of demodulator which is increasingly used for FM is the phase locked loop circuit shown in Figure 18.12. When the voltage

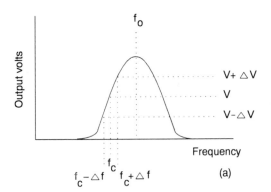

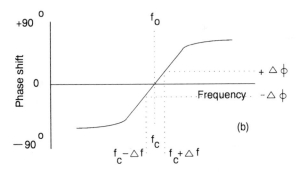

Figure 18.11 Principles of tuned circuit discriminators: (a) frequency to amplitude conversion; (b) frequency to phase conversion

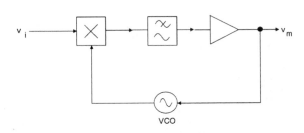

Figure 18.12 Phase locked loop circuit for demodulating FM

controlled oscillator (VCO) has zero control voltage, its output frequency is that of the unmodulated carrier. When the frequency of the input signal begins to change, the resulting phase difference between it and the output of the VCO causes the coherent demodulator to produce an output voltage. This is fed back to the VCO to change its frequency and so reduce the phase error. In this way, the frequency of the VCO tracks the varying frequency of the incoming carrier. If the characteristic of the VCO is linear, its control voltage is thus proportional to the incoming carrier frequency and provides a demodulated baseband output signal. The low pass filter eliminates noise and interference at frequencies above the baseband.

The phase locked loop demodulator is less complicated than a discriminator because it has no tuned circuits to align. It also has a better output signal to noise performance at low values of input

signal to noise ratio (Pappenfus et al., 1964; Viterbi, 1966; Roberts, 1977).

18.3.3 Frequency spectra

From Equation 18.22, a sinusoidal carrier modulated by a sinusoidal baseband signal may be represented by Equation 18.34.

$$v = R V_c e^{j \omega_c t} e^{j \beta \sin \omega_m t} \tag{18.34}$$

However Equation 18.35 holds, where $J_n(\beta)$ is the Bessel function of the first kind of order n, resulting in Equation 18.36.

$$e^{j \beta \sin \theta} = \sum_{n = -\infty}^{\infty} J_n(\beta) e^{j n \theta} \tag{18.35}$$

$$v = R V_c e^{j \omega_c t} \sum_{n = -\infty}^{\infty} J_n(\beta) e^{j n \omega_m t} \tag{18.36}$$

$$= V_c \sum_{n = -\infty}^{\infty} J_n(\beta) \cos(\omega_c + n \omega_m) t$$

Thus, the spectrum of the angle modulated wave has an upper and a lower sideband, each containing frequencies separated from the carrier by all the harmonics of the baseband signal.

Equation 18.36 shows that angle modulation is non linear. If the baseband signal contains two frequencies, f_1 and f_2, the sidebands contain many components at frequencies $f_c \pm qf_1 \pm rf_2$ (where q = 1,2,3,..., r = 1,2,3,...) in addition to $f_c \pm nf_1$ and $f_c \pm nf_2$. If the spectrum of the baseband signal contains many components, the spectrum of each sideband is extremely complicated (Black, 1953). It can be represented by a band of Gaussian noise (Roberts, 1977).

Tables of $J_n(x)$ have been published (Jahnke and Emde, 1945). Some values of $J_n(\beta)$ are given in Table 18.1 and some typical voltage spectra of angle modulated signals are shown in Figure 18.13. It will be seen that for low index modulation ($\beta < 1$) only the components at $f_c \pm f_m$ are significant. Thus, the bandwidth required for transmission is no greater than for AM. However, for high index modulation, the bandwidth is much greater than for AM.

In general, the magnitudes of $J_n(\beta)$ are small for $n > \beta + 1$. As a result, the bandwidth W required is approximately given by Equation 18.37 (Carson's rule).

$$W = 2 F_m (1 + \beta) \tag{18.37}$$

Thus, for FM, Equation 18.38 may be obtained where ΔF is the maximum frequency deviation.

$$W = 2 (F_m + \Delta F) \tag{18.38}$$

18.3.4 Interference and noise

In FM, the amplitude of the signal conveys no information. The receiver contains a limiter, so amplitude variations due to interference and noise (unless very severe) have no effect. However, interference and noise also perturb the phase of the signal and thus its instantaneous frequency.

Table 18.1 Bessel functions of the first kind

β	$J_0(\beta)$	$J_1(\beta)$	$J_2(\beta)$	$J_3(\beta)$	$J_4(\beta)$	$J_5(\beta)$	$J_6(\beta)$	$J_7(\beta)$	$J_8(\beta)$	$J_9(\beta)$	$J_{10}(\beta)$
0	1.000										
0.2	0.990	0.099	0.005								
0.4	0.960	0.196	0.019	0.001							
0.6	0.912	0.286	0.043	0.004							
0.8	0.846	0.368	0.075	0.010	0.001						
1.0	0.765	0.440	0.114	0.019	0.002						
2.0	0.223	0.576	0.352	0.128	0.034	0.007	0.001				
3.0	−0.260	0.339	0.486	0.309	0.132	0.043	0.011	0.002			
4.0	−0.397	−0.066	0.364	0.430	0.281	0.132	0.049	0.015	0.004		
5.0	−0.177	−0.327	0.046	0.364	0.391	0.261	0.131	0.053	0.018	0.005	0.001
6.0	0.150	−0.276	−0.242	0.114	0.357	0.362	0.245	0.129	0.056	0.021	0.006
7.0	0.300	−0.004	−0.301	−0.167	0.157	0.347	0.339	0.233	0.128	0.058	0.023
8.0	0.171	0.234	−0.113	−0.291	−0.105	0.185	0.337	0.320	0.223	0.126	0.060
9.0	−0.090	0.245	0.144	−0.180	−0.265	−0.055	0.204	0.327	0.305	0.214	0.124
10.0	−0.245	0.045	0.254	0.058	−0.219	−0.234	−0.014	0.216	0.317	0.291	0.207

The phasor diagram in Figure 18.14(a) represents an unmodulated carrier with a small interfering signal separated from it by a frequency difference f_i. If the interfering voltage $V_x \cos(\omega_c + \omega_i)t$ is added to the carrier $V_c \cos \omega_c t$, the resultant is as in Equation 18.39.

$$v = V_c \cos \omega_c t + V_x \cos(\omega_c + \omega_i)t$$

$$= (V_c + V_x \cos \omega_i t) \cos \omega_c t - V_x \sin \omega_c t \sin \omega_i t \quad (18.39)$$

The first term represents amplitude modulation of the carrier and the second term represents a phase displacement, $\varphi_i(t)$, given by Equation 18.40.

$$\varphi_i(t) = \tan^{-1}\left(\frac{V_x \sin \omega_i t}{V_c + V_x \cos \omega_i t} \right) \quad (18.40)$$

But $V_x \ll V_c$, so Equation 18.41 may be obtained.

$$\varphi_i(t) \approx \frac{V_x}{V_c} \sin \omega_i t \quad (18.41)$$

For FM, the demodulated output voltage is proportional to $d\varphi/dt$. Thus, the output voltage due to the interference is as in Equation 18.42, for values of f_i within the pass band of the receiver's output low pass filter, which corresponds to the baseband (F_m) to be handled. If $f_i > F_m$, no interference reaches the output.

$$v_{ox} = k\frac{d\varphi}{dt} = \frac{k\omega_i V_x}{V_c} \cos \omega_i t \quad (18.42)$$

If the carrier is frequency modulated, the signal output voltage is given by Equation 18.43, where $\Delta\Omega$ is the maximum deviation of angular frequency.

$$v_{os} = k\Delta\Omega \cos \omega_m t = V_{os} \cos \omega_m t \quad (18.43)$$

Thus, the ratio between the output interference and signal voltages is as in Equation 18.44.

$$\frac{V_{ox}}{V_{os}} = \frac{\omega_i V_i}{\Delta\Omega V_c} \quad \text{for } \omega_i < \Omega_m$$

$$= 0 \quad \text{for } \omega_i > \Omega_m \quad (18.44)$$

For a large modulation index, $\Delta\Omega > \omega_m$. Thus, as shown in Figure 18.14(b), the output signal to interference ratio is much greater than V_c/V_x. It is therefore much better than that obtained with AM, the improvement being proportional to the modulation index $\Delta\Omega/\omega_m$.

If the interference is at the same frequency as the carrier (which is the worst situation for AM), Equation 18.44 shows that there is zero interference present at the receiver output. Thus, when two transmissions at the same frequency are received, the output corresponds to the stronger. This is known as the capture effect.

Gaussian noise can be considered as consisting of an infinite number of interference components, $V_x(q)$ (where $q = 0, \pm1, \pm2,...$), spaced at infinitesimal intervals $\delta\omega$. Since $V_{ox} \propto \omega_i$, the noise spectrum at the output of the receiver is parabolic, i.e. the noise power density increases with the square of the frequency.

The power of each component, $v_x(q)$, is equal to the noise power in its frequency band, giving Equation 18.45 where n is the input noise power density.

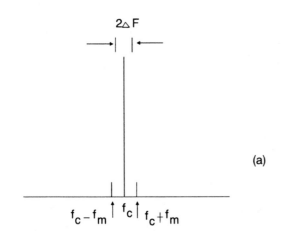

(a)

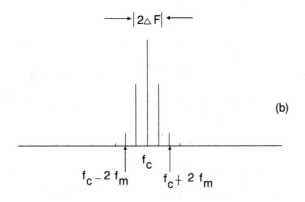

(b)

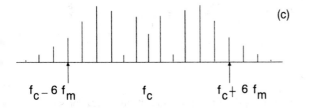

(c)

Figure 18.13 Amplitude/frequency spectra of angle modulated waves: (a) $\beta = 0.2$; (b) $\beta = 1.0$; (c) $\beta = 5.0$

$$\frac{1}{2} V_x^2(q) = \overline{v_x^2(q)} = n\delta\omega \tag{18.45}$$

The total output noise power, from Equation 18.42, is given by Equation 18.46.

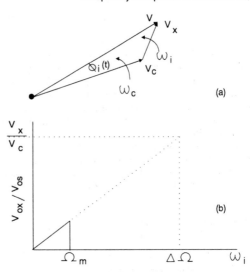

Figure 18.14 Effect of interfering signal on FM receiver: (a) phasor diagram of input signal; (b) output signal due to interference

$$N_o = \sum_{q=-\infty}^{\infty} k^2 \left(\frac{V_i(q)}{V_c} \right)^2 \omega_i^2(q)$$

$$= \frac{k^2 n}{V_c^2} \int_{-\Omega_M}^{\Omega_M} \omega^2 d\omega = \frac{2 k^2}{3 V_c^2} n \Omega_M^3 \tag{18.46}$$

The output signal power, from Equation 18.43 is as in Equation 18.47.

$$S_o = \frac{1}{2} V_{os}^2 = \frac{1}{2} (k \Delta\Omega)^2 \tag{18.47}$$

Thus, the output signal to noise ratio is given by Equation 18.48.

$$\frac{S_o}{N_o} = \frac{3 V_c^2 (\Delta\Omega)^2}{4 n \Omega_M^3} = \frac{3}{4} \frac{\beta^2 V_c^2}{n \Omega_m} \tag{18.48}$$

The input signal power is as in Equation 18.49.

$$S_i = \frac{1}{2} V_c^2 \tag{18.49}$$

If wideband (high index) FM is used, the bandwidth is approximately $2\Delta\Omega$, so the input noise power is given by Equation 18.50 and the input signal to noise ratio by Equation 18.51.

$$N_i = 2 n \Delta\Omega \tag{18.50}$$

$$\frac{S_i}{N_i} = \frac{V_c^2}{4 n \Delta\Omega} \tag{18.51}$$

Therefore Equation 18.52 may be obtained.

$$\frac{S_o/N_o}{S_i/N_i} = 3\,\beta^3 \tag{18.52}$$

Although the improvement in signal to noise ratio is proportional to β^3 (i.e. to ΔF^3), the input noise power is proportional to the bandwidth ($2\Delta F$). Thus, the output signal to noise ratio is proportional to the square of the bandwidth used. An octave increase in the frequency deviation and bandwidth increases the output signal to noise ratio by 6dB.

The bandwidth required is β times that for AM, so for equal noise power densities, the noise power at the input to the receiver is β times that for AM. Consequently, for fully modulated AM and the same carrier power, the improvement is given by Equation 18.53.

$$\frac{\text{Output signal noise ratio for FM}}{\text{Output signal noise ratio for AM}} = 3\,\beta^2 \tag{18.53}$$

For example, FM broadcasting typically has a baseband of 15kHz and a maximum frequency deviation of 75kHz, i.e. $\beta = 5$. The improvement in signal to noise ratio compared with AM with 100% modulation is $3 \times 25 = 75$, i.e. 19dB.

It has been shown above that the output noise spectrum for FM is parabolic. The output signal to noise ratio can therefore be improved further by making the signal power also increase with frequency. It is common practice to insert in front of the modulator at the transmitter a pre-emphasis network which has a rising gain-frequency characteristic across the baseband. The receiver contains a de-emphasis network with the inverse gain-frequency characteristic, to obtain a channel having a flat overall gain-frequency characteristic and a uniform noise spectrum. For single channel telephony or broadcasting this provides a better output signal to noise ratio. When FM is used to transmit a wideband signal consisting of a block of telephone channels assembled by frequency division multiplexing, the use of pre-emphasis is essential. Otherwise, there would be a large difference between the signal to noise ratios of channels at the top and the bottom of the band.

It has been assumed above that amplitude variations due to noise have no effect on the output signal of a FM receiver. For this assumption to be valid, the input signal to noise ratio must exceed a threshold of approximately 12dB (Brown and Glazier, 1974). When the input signal to noise ratio decreases below this, peaks of noise begin to obliterate the carrier and the output signal to noise ratio deteriorates rapidly, as shown in Figure 18.15. Radio links used for commercial telecommunications must therefore have signal to noise ratios well above the threshold.

18.4 Pulse modulation

18.4.1 General

In the preceding sections, it has been assumed that the carrier wave is sinusoidal. However, it is also possible to modulate carriers having other waveforms. For example, it is possible to modulate trains of pulses to produce pulse amplitude modulation (PAM), pulse frequency modulation (PFM) or pulse phase modulation (PPM), which is sometimes called pulse position modulation. It is also possible to produce pulse length modulation, which is sometimes called pulse duration modulation (PDM) or pulse width modulation (PWM).

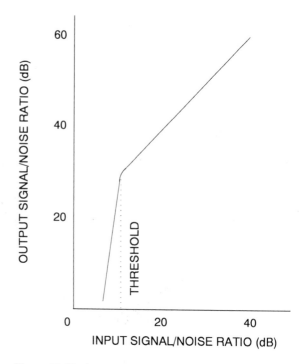

Figure 18.15   Improvement in signal to noise ratio given by frequency modulation ($\beta = 5.0$)

18.4.2 Pulse amplitude modulation

A basic PAM system is shown in Figure 18.16. If a train of pulses as shown in Figure 18.17(b) is amplitude modulated by the baseband signal shown in Figure 18.17(a) the resulting PAM signal is shown in Figure 18.17(c). The baseband signal is represented by a sequence of samples of it, so the process is also called sampling.

A train of pulses having a pulse repetition frequency (PRF) f_r may be represented by a Fourier series, as in Equation 18.54.

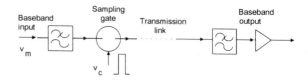

Figure 18.16   Basic pulse amplitude modulation system with one direction of transmission only

$$v_c = \frac{1}{2}a_o + \sum_{n=1}^{\infty} a_n \cos n\,\omega_r t \tag{18.54}$$

Its spectrum thus contains a d.c. component, the PRF and its harmonics, as shown in Figure 18.17(d). If the pulses are of short duration, the amplitudes a_n of the harmonics are approximately equal up to large values of n.

If the pulse train is amplitude modulated by a sinusoidal baseband signal, the resulting PAM signal is given by Equation 18.55.

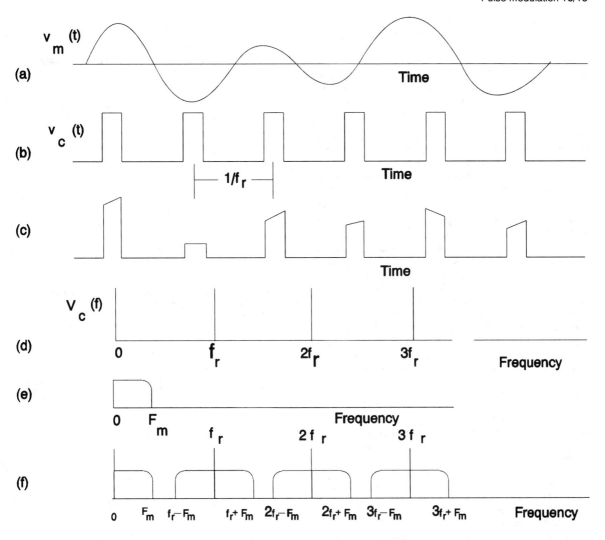

Figure 18.17 Pulse amplitude modulation waveforms: (a) baseband signal; (b) unmodulated pulse train; (c) modulated pulse train; (d) spectrum of unmodulated pulse train; (e) spectrum of baseband signal; (f) spectrum of modulated pulse train

$$v = (1 + m \cos \omega_m t) v_c$$

$$= \frac{1}{2} a_o + \frac{1}{2} a_o m \cos \omega_m t + \sum_{n=1}^{\infty} a_n \cos n \omega_r t$$

$$= \frac{1}{2} m \sum_{n=1}^{\infty} a_n [(\cos (n \omega_r + \omega_r) t$$

$$+ \cos (n (\omega_r - \omega_m) t)] \tag{18.55}$$

Thus, the spectrum of the PAM signal contains all the components of the original pulse train, together with the baseband frequency f_m and upper and lower side frequencies $(nf_r \pm f_m)$ about the PRF and its harmonics. If the modulating signal consists of a band of frequencies, as shown in Figure 18.17(e), the spectrum of the PAM signal contains the original baseband, together with upper and lower sidebands about the PRF and its harmonics, as shown in Figure 18.17(f).

The PAM signal can be demodulated by means of a low pass filter which passes the baseband and stops the lower sideband of the PRF

and all higher frequencies. For this to be possible, Equation 18.56 must hold, where F_m is the maximum frequency of the baseband signal and f_o is the cut off frequency of the filter. Thus Equation 18.57 must hold.

$$F_m \le f_o \le f_r - F_m \tag{18.56}$$

$$f_r \ge 2 F_m \tag{18.57}$$

Equation 18.57 is a statement of the sampling theorem. This may be expressed as follows: if a signal is to be sampled and the original signal is to be recovered from the samples without error, the sampling frequency must be at least twice the highest frequency in the original signal. The sampling theorem is due to Nyquist and the lowest possible rate at which a signal may be sampled, $2F_m$, is often known as the Nyquist rate. If the sampling frequency is less than the Nyquist rate, the lower sideband of the PRF overlaps the baseband

and it is impossible to separate them. The output from the low pass filter then contains unwanted frequency components; this situation is known as aliasing.

To prevent aliasing, it is essential to limit the bandwidth of the signal before sampling. Thus, practical systems pass the input signal through an anti-aliasing low pass filter of bandwidth $\frac{1}{2}f_r$ before sampling as shown in Figure 18.16. Practical filters are non-ideal; it is therefore necessary to have $f_r > 2F_m$ in order that the anti-aliasing filter and demodulating filter can have both very low attenuation at frequencies up to F_m and very high attenuation at frequencies down to $f_r - F_m$. For telephony, a baseband from 300Hz to 3.4kHz is provided and a sampling frequency of 8kHz is used. Thus $f_r - F_m$ = 4.6kHz and there is a guardband of 1.2kHz to accommodate the transition of the filters between their pass band and their stop band.

18.4.3 Pulse time modulation

Pulse frequency modulation, pulse phase modulation and pulse length modulation all vary the times of occurrence of the individual pulses of a pulse train. They can therefore be collectively called pulse time modulation. Since the modulating signal is not carried by the amplitude of the pulses, pulse time modulation can be almost immune to amplitude variations caused by interference and noise and so give a better output signal to noise ratio than PAM.

When pulse time modulation is used, the sidebands about the PRF and its harmonics contain sideband components at frequencies $nf_r \pm qf_m$ (where $q = 1,2,3,...$), just as do the sidebands of a sinusoidal carrier when angle modulation is used (Fitch, 1947; Moss, 1948; Black, 1953). It is therefore necessary to use a sampling frequency greater than $2F_m$ to minimise aliasing.

The voltage of the d.c. component in the spectrum of an unmodulated train of rectangular pulses is equal to the pulse height multiplied by the duty ratio of the pulse train (i.e. the ratio of pulse duration to pulse repetition period). If modulation causes changes in either pulse height or duty ratio, there is a corresponding modulation of the d.c. component. Equation 18.55 shows that the spectrum of a PAM wave contains a voltage at the modulating frequency (f_m) whose ratio to the d.c. component ($\frac{1}{2}a_0$) is equal to the depth of modulation (m) of the pulse height. For PLM, the duty ratio varies with pulse duration, so the baseband frequency component is proportional to the depth of modulation of the pulse duration. In PFM, the duty ratio increases if more pulses are generated in a given period and decreases if fewer are generated. Consequently, a low pass filter can be used for demodulating PLM and PFM, just as for PAM.

In PPM, there is no change in pulse height or pulse duration and the mean number of pulses per unit of time is constant. Consequently, the spectrum has only a small component at the modulating frequency. PPM is therefore demodulated by converting it to PLM before low pass filtering.

In pulse time modulation, the pulse amplitude conveys no information. It is therefore possible to use a 'slicer' at the receiver, as shown in Figure 18.18, to produce pulses from which amplitude variations due to interference or noise have been removed. If the input pulses could have zero rise and fall times, no interference or noise would reach the output of the slicer. In practice, however, pulses have finite rise and fall times. As shown in Figure 18.19 interference or noise produces a displacement of the time at which the input pulse crosses the slicing level and thus of the time at which the output pulse appears from the slicer. This results in noise or interference in the demodulated output signal. This time displacement is given by Equations 18.58 and 18.59.

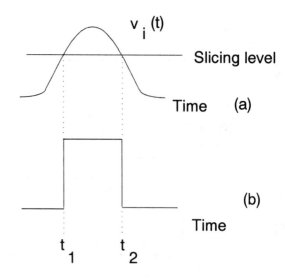

Figure 18.18 Use of slicer in pulse time modulation: (a) input pulse; (b) output pulse

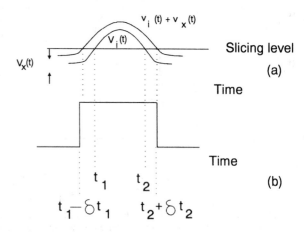

Figure 18.19 Operation of a slicer in the presence of interfering voltage (v_x): (a) input pulse; (b) output pulse

$$\delta t_1 = \left(\frac{dt}{dv_i} \right)_{t_1} v_x(t_1) \qquad (18.58)$$

$$\delta t_2 = -\left(\frac{dt}{dv_i} \right)_{t_2} v_x(t_2) \qquad (18.59)$$

These equations show that the demodulated output voltage varies inversely with the slope (dv_i / dt) of the input pulse. This slope is proportional to the bandwidth of the transmission path. Thus, the improvement in output signal to noise power ratio is proportional to the square of the bandwidth (Jelonek, 1947; Kretzmer, 1950; Black, 1953). It is assumed above that the noise voltage itself does not cross

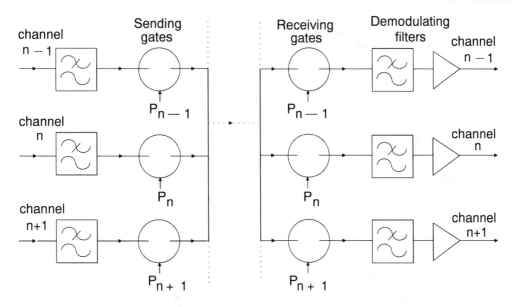

Figure 18.20 Elementary TDM system with one direction of transmission only

the slicing level; if it does, misoperation of the slicing circuit occurs and there is a severe deterioration of the output signal to noise ratio. Thus, there is a threshold phenomenon similar to that shown in Figure 18.15.

18.4.4 Time division multiplexing

Pulse modulation is used for time division multiplexing (TDM). It enables channels to share a wideband transmission path by using it at different times. The principle is shown in Figure 18.20. At the sending terminal, a baseband channel is connected to the common transmission path by means of a sampling gate which is opened for short intervals by means of a train of pulses. In this way, samples of the baseband signal are sent at regular intervals by means of amplitude modulated pulses.

Pulses with the same repetition frequency f_r but staggered in time, as shown in Figure 18.21 are applied to the sending gates of the

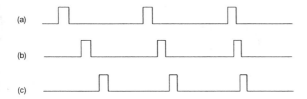

Figure 18.21 Channel pulse trains for the TDM system of Figure 18.20: (a) (n-1)th channel; (b) nth channel; (c) (n+1)th channel

other channels. Thus the common transmission path receives interleaved trains of pulses, modulated by the signals of different channels. At the receiving terminal, gates are opened by pulses coincident with those received from the transmission path so that the demodulator of each channel is connected to the transmission

path for its allotted interval and disconnected throughout the remainder of the pulse repetition period. The combination of a multiplexer and a demultiplexer at a TDM terminal is sometimes referred to as a muldex.

The pulse generator at the receiving terminal must be synchronised with that at the sending terminal to ensure that each incoming pulse train is gated to the correct outgoing baseband channel. A distinctive synchronising pulse signal is therefore transmitted in every repetition period in addition to the channel pulses. The complete waveform transmitted during each repetition period contains a number of time slots: one is allocated to the synchronising signal and the others to the channel samples. The complete waveform is called a frame, by analogy with a television signal waveform, and the synchronising signal is called the frame alignment signal.

The elementary TDM system shown in Figure 18.20 uses PAM. Pulse length modulation and pulse position modulation can also be used. Pulse frequency modulation is unsuitable. If the PRF of one channel changes, its pulse will leave its allotted time slot and drift across the time slots of the other channels.

Attenuation and delay distortion of a transmission path cause pulse dispersion. The pulse of each channel spreads into the time slots of adjacent channels, as shown in Figure 18.22. This causes inter-channel crosstalk (Flood and Tillman, 1951; Flood, 1952). Consequently, analogue pulse modulation is now mainly used as an

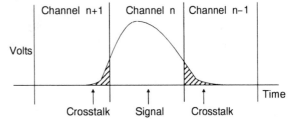

Figure 18.22 Inter-channel crosstalk in TDM systems

intermediate stage towards pulse code modulation (PCM), in order to obtain immunity to crosstalk by using digital transmission. Digital modulation methods are discussed in the next chapter.

18.5 Acknowledgement

This chapter contains material reproduced by permission of the Institution of Electrical Engineers from Flood, J.E. and Cochrane, P. (1991) *Transmission Systems*, Peter Peregrinus.

18.6 References

Black, H.S. (1953) *Modulation Theory*, Van Nostrand.

Brown, J. and Glazier, E.V.D. (1974) *Telecommunications* (2nd edition), Chapman and Hall.

Coates, R.F.W. (1975) *Modern Communication Systems*, Macmillan.

Fitch, E. (1947) *The Spectrum of Modulated Pulses*, J. Inst. Elect. Engrs. **94**, Pt. 111A, p. 556.

Flood, J.E. (1952), *Crosstalk to Time Division Multiplex Communication Systems Using Pulse Position and Pulse Length Modulation*, Proc. Inst. Elec. Engrs., **99**, Pt. IV, p. 64.

Flood, J.E. and Tillman, J.R. (1951) *Crosstalk in Amplitude Modulated Time Division Multiplex Systems*, Proc. Inst. Elec. Engrs., **98** Pt. III, p. 279.

Gardner, F.M. (1979) *Phaselock Techniques*, EUP.

Gosling, W. (1986) *Radio Receivers*, Peter Peregrinus.

Hills, M.T. and Evans, B.G. (1973) *Transmission Systems*, Allen & Unwin.

Jahnke, E. and Emde, F. (1945) *Tables of Functions with Formulas and Curves*, Dover.

Jelonek, Z. (1947) *Noise Problems in Pulse Communication*, J. Inst. Elec. Engrs. **94**, Pt. IIIA, p. 533.

Kingdom, D.J. (1991) *Frequency Division Multiplexing*, Chap.5 in Flood, J.E. and Cochrane, P. (Eds) *Transmission Systems*, Peter Peregrinus.

Kretzmer, E.R. (1950) *Interference Characteristics of Pulse Time Modulation*, Proc. Inst. Radio Engineers, **38**, p. 252.

Langford-Smith, F. (1960) *Radio Designer's Handbook*, (4th edition), Iliffe.

Moss, S.H. (1948) *Frequency Analysis of Modulated Pulses*, Phil, Mag., **39**, p. 663.

Pappenfus, E.W., Bruene, W.B. and Schoenike, E.O. (1964) *Single Sideband Principles and Circuits*, McGraw-Hill.

Roberts, J.H. (1977) *Angle Modulation*, Peter Peregrinus.

Sturley, K.R. (1965) *Radio Receiver Design*, (3rd edition), Chapman & Hall.

Tucker, D.G. (1953) *Modulators and Frequency Changes for Amplitude Modulated Line and Radio Systems*, Macdonald.

Viterbi, A.J. (1966) *Principles of Coherent Communication*, McGraw-Hill.

19

Digital modulation

Professor J E Flood
OBE DSc FInstP CEng FIEE
Aston University

Contents

19.1 Introduction

The term digital modulation is used in two senses, both of which are discussed in this chapter:

1. Modulation of an analogue carrier by a digital baseband signal.
2. Modulation of a digital carrier by an analogue baseband signal.

A digital signal may modulate an analogue carrier by using amplitude modulation, frequency modulation or phase modulation, as discussed in Chapter 18. Examples are wireless telegraphy and the use of modems for transmitting data over analogue telephone circuits.

An important example of the use of a digital carrier for transmitting an analogue baseband signal is the use of pulse code modulation (PCM) for sending voice signals over digital circuits. This enables telephony to obtain the advantages of digital transmission, namely effective immunity to distortion, interference, crosstalk and noise and a constant transmission performance regardless of the length of a telephone connection and its routeing.

19.2 Digital transmission

In a digital transmission system, a modulator lies between the baseband input channel and the transmission path and a demodulator lies between that and the baseband output channel. The baseband input signal and the modulator determine the form of the transmitted signal and the demodulator is required to reconstruct the baseband signal with adequate fidelity. The overall channel between the modulator input and demodulator output must have the required properties and these will now be considered.

19.2.1 Bandwidth requirements

The minimum bandwidth needed to transmit a digital signal at B bauds has been shown by Nyquist (1928) to be $W_{min} = \frac{1}{2}B$ Hertz. This can be demonstrated as follows. Consider a binary signal consisting of alternate '0's and '1's. This produces a square wave of frequency $\frac{1}{2}B$. Let this be applied to an ideal low pass filter. If the cut off frequency of the filter is as in Equation 19.1 where ε is small, the output is a sine wave of frequency $\frac{1}{2}B$ and the original square wave can be recovered by sampling it at its positive and negative peaks.

$$Filter\ cut\ off\ frequency\ =\ \frac{1}{2}B\ +\ \varepsilon \tag{19.1}$$

If the cut off frequency is reduced to the value given in Equation 19.2, the output consists only of the d.c. component and the signal is lost.

$$Cut\ off\ frequency\ =\ \frac{1}{2}B\ -\ \varepsilon \tag{19.2}$$

Consequently, the minimum bandwidth required is given by Equation 19.3.

$$\frac{1}{2}B\ -\ \varepsilon\ <\ W_{min}\ <\ \frac{1}{2}B\ +\ \varepsilon \tag{19.3}$$

In the limit when ε tends to zero, Equation 19.4 is obtained.

$$W_{min}\ =\ \frac{1}{2}B \tag{19.4}$$

This result can also be demonstrated for the case when the transmitted symbols are very short pulses (which approximate to impulses), instead of the full width pulses considered above. The impulse response, h(t), of the ideal low pass filter of bandwidth W is given by Equation 19.5.

$$h(t)\ =\ \frac{\sin 2\pi Wt}{2\pi Wt} \tag{19.5}$$

This response has its maximum at t = 0 (where h(0) = 1) and is zero for t given by Equation 19.6 where T is as in Equation 19.7.

$$t\ =\ \pm nT \tag{19.6}$$

$$T\ =\ \frac{1}{2}W \tag{19.7}$$

If pulses are transmitted at rate B = 2W and each is detected by sampling at the time when it has its maximum output voltage, the outputs due to all preceding and following pulses are zero at that time, i.e. there is no intersymbol interference (ISI). Thus, it is possible to transmit pulses at rate B bauds through a channel of bandwidth W = $\frac{1}{2}$B without any ISI.

In practice, it is not possible to obtain a channel with an ideal low pass characteristic. (Equation 19.5 shows that, if it were possible, an output voltage would appear before the input pulse is applied!) However, Nyquist showed that zero ISI can also be obtained if the gain of the channel changes from unity to zero over a band of frequencies with a gain frequency response that is skew symmetrical about f = $\frac{1}{2}$B. It is also impossible to generate a perfect impulse (since it has zero duration and infinite amplitude). The transfer characteristic of the channel should therefore be equalised so that the output signal has the required spectrum. A commonly used signal is that having the raised-cosine spectrum given by Equation 19.8 to 19.10.

$$F(f)\ =\ 1\quad for\ 0\le f\le \frac{(1-\alpha)}{2T} \tag{19.8}$$

$$F(f)\ =\ \frac{1}{2}\left(1+\sin\frac{\pi}{2\alpha}(1-2fT)\right)$$
$$for\ \frac{1-\alpha}{2T}\le f\le \frac{1+\alpha}{2T} \tag{19.9}$$

$$F(f)\ =\ 0\quad for\ f\ge \frac{1+a}{2T} \tag{19.10}$$

This gain/frequency response rolls off sinusoidally from unity to zero in the frequency band from $\frac{(1-\alpha)}{2T}$ to $\frac{(1+\alpha)}{2T}$. Thus, for 100% roll off (i.e. $\alpha = 1$), the spectrum occupies a bandwidth of 1/T, which is twice the theoretical minimum requirement. Bandwidth is used most efficiently by using as small a roll off α as possible, but problems of timing and equalisation increase as α is reduced.

19.2.1.1 Equalisation

Digital transmission systems can use gain and phase equalisation to obtain an output signal spectrum corresponding to a pulse waveform

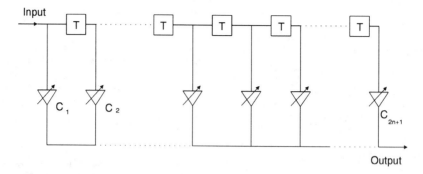

Figure 19.1 Block diagram of a transversal equailiser

with negligible intersymbol interference, e.g. the raised cosine spectrum described above. However, time domain equalisers are often employed.

A common form of time domain equaliser is the transversal equaliser (TVE) shown in Figure 19.1. This consists of a delay line tapped at intervals equal to the intersymbol interval T. Each tap is connected to an amplifier (which may be an inverter to obtain negative gain). The output of the equaliser is the sum of the outputs of these amplifiers. It is possible to adjust the gains of the amplifiers (in magnitude and sign) to cancel ISI by adding appropriately weighted versions of preceding and following pulses at the time of each symbol, and thus cancel interference between them.

A TVE can be adjusted manually. However, if the characteristics of the transmission path change with time, it is preferable for the equaliser to be adjusted automatically. A TVE which does this for itself during normal operation is called an adaptive equaliser (Lucky et al., 1968; Clark, 1985). Adaptive equalisers are used in data modems which may be used on a variety of different connections in a switched telecommunication network. They are also used for digital radio links, which must cater for varying propagation conditions (de Belin, 1991).

So far, it has been assumed that the objective of equalisation is to eliminate intersymbol interference. An alternative is to have a large but well defined ISI. This is known as partial response equalisation (Lender, 1963; Kretmer, 1966). It effectively turns a binary signal into a 3-level signal and enables a smaller bandwidth to be used.

This can also be done digitally by combining adjacent pulses at the sending end of the transmission link. This form of partial response operation is called duobinary coding (Lucky et al., 1968; Taub and Schilling, 1986; Dorward, 1991).

19.2.2 Effects of noise

The principal advantage of PCM and other forms of digital transmission is that it is possible to obtain satisfactory transmission in the presence of very severe crosstalk and noise. In the case of binary transmission, it is only necessary to detect the presence or absence of each pulse. Provided that the interference level is not so high as to cause frequent errors in making this decision, the output signal will be almost noise free.

Consider an idealised train of unipolar binary pulses, as shown in Figure 19.2(a). If the symbols '0' and '1' are equiprobable, i.e. as in Equation 19.11 the mean signal power corresponds to Equation 19.12. Thus, the signal to noise ratio is given by Equation 19.13, where σ is the r.m.s. noise voltage.

$$P(0) = P(1) = \frac{1}{2} \tag{19.11}$$

$$S = \frac{1}{2} V^2 \tag{19.12}$$

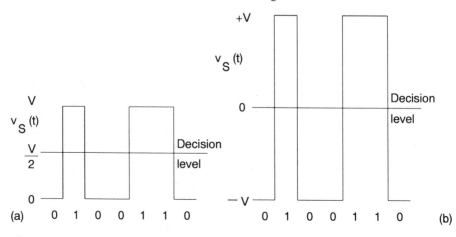

Figure 19.2 Detection of digital signals: (a) unipolar binary signal; (b) bipolar binary signal

$$\frac{S}{N} = \frac{V^2}{2\sigma^2} \tag{19.13}$$

The receiver compares the signal voltage v_s with a threshold voltage of $\frac{1}{2}V$, giving an output '0' when $v < 1/2V$ and '1' when $v > \frac{1}{2}V$. If a noise voltage v_n is added, an error occurs if $v_n < -\frac{1}{2}V$ when $v_s = +V$, or if $v_n > +\frac{1}{2}V$ when $v_s = 0$. Thus, the probability of error, P_e, is given by Equation 19.14.

$$P_e = P(0)P(v_n > +\frac{1}{2}V) + P(1)P(v_n < -\frac{1}{2}V) \tag{9.14}$$

But Equation 19.15 holds and, for white noise, Equation 19.16 is obtained. Therefore Equation 19.17 is also obtained.

$$P(0) + P(1) = 1 \tag{19.15}$$

$$P(v_n < -\frac{1}{2}V) = P(v_n > +\frac{1}{2}V) \tag{19.16}$$

$$P_e = P(v_n > \frac{1}{2}V) \tag{19.17}$$

White noise has a normal or Gaussian probability density distribution, given by Equation 19.18 where σ is the standard deviation of v_n and is thus the r.m.s. noise voltage. Therefore Equation 19.19 is obtained.

$$p(v_n) = \frac{1}{\sigma\sqrt{2\pi}} \exp\left(\frac{-v_n^2}{2\sigma^2}\right) \tag{19.18}$$

$$P(v_n > \frac{1}{2}V) = \int_{+\frac{V}{2}}^{\infty} p(v_n)\,dv_n = \frac{1}{2} - \int_0^{+\frac{V}{2}} p(v_n)\,dv_n$$

$$= \frac{1}{2} - \frac{1}{\sigma\sqrt{2\pi}} \int_0^{\frac{V}{2}} \exp\left(\frac{-v_n^2}{2\sigma^2}\right) dv_n \tag{19.19}$$

Now the probability integral is defined as in Equation 19.20 and the complementary function is as in Equation 19.21. Therefore Equation 19.22 is obtained. Substituting from Equation 19.13 gives Equation 19.23.

$$Erf\,x = \frac{1}{\sigma\sqrt{2\pi}} \int_0^x \exp\left(\frac{-z^2}{2}\right) dz \tag{19.20}$$

$$Erfc\,x = \frac{1}{2} - Erf\,x \tag{19.21}$$

$$P_e = P(v_n > \frac{V}{2}) = Erfc\,\frac{V}{2\sigma} \tag{19.22}$$

$$P_e = Erfc\left(\frac{1}{2}\frac{S}{N}\right)^{\frac{1}{2}} \tag{19.23}$$

Many authors use the form of error function defined as in Equation 19.24 and 19.25. Consequently Equations 19.26 and 19.27 are obtained.

$$erf\,x = \frac{2}{\sqrt{\pi}} \int_0^x \exp\left(-z^2\right) dz \tag{19.24}$$

$$erfc\,x = 1 - erf\,x \tag{19.25}$$

$$Erf\,x = \frac{1}{2}erf\left(\frac{x}{\sqrt{2}}\right) \tag{19.26}$$

$$P_e = \frac{1}{2}erfc\left(\frac{1}{2}\sqrt{\frac{S}{N}}\right) \tag{19.27}$$

Tables of $erf\,x$ have been published (e.g. Jahnke and Emde, 1960; Betts, 1970). However, for $x > 3$, $erf\,x$ is so close to unity that it is usually not tabulated. In these cases, the asymptotic expression for the error function (Beckmann, 1967) should be used as in Equation 19.28.

$$erf\,x \approx 1 - \frac{\exp(-x^2)}{x\sqrt{\pi}} \tag{19.28}$$

This expression enables calculations to be made of the very low error probabilities obtained with good signal to noise ratios. The variation of error probability over a range of signal to noise ratios is shown in Figure 19.3.

If the signal to noise ratio is calculated for the peak power (v^2/σ^2) instead of the mean power ($v^2/2\sigma^2$), then Equation 19.29 is obtained.

$$P_e = Erfc\left(\frac{1}{2}\sqrt{\frac{S}{N}}\right) = \frac{1}{2}erfc\left(\frac{1}{2}\sqrt{\frac{1}{2}\frac{S}{N}}\right) \tag{19.29}$$

If a bipolar binary signal is used, as shown in Figure 19.2(b), the mean signal power is given by Equation 19.30 and the signal noise ratio by Equation 19.31.

$$S = V^2 \tag{19.30}$$

$$\frac{S}{N} = \frac{V^2}{\sigma^2} \tag{19.31}$$

The receiver gives an output '0' when $v < 0$ and '1' when $v > 0$. An error will occur if $v_n < -V$ when $v_s = +V$, or if $v_n > +V$ when $v_s = -V$. Thus, the probability of error is given by Equation 19.32.

$$P_e = P(0)P(v_n > +V) + P(1)P(v_n < -V)$$

$$= P(v_n > +V)$$

$$= \int_V^{\infty} p(v_n)\,dv_n = \frac{1}{\sigma\sqrt{2\pi}} \int_V^{\infty} \exp\left(-\frac{v_n^2}{2\sigma^2}\right) dv_n$$

$$= Erfc\,\frac{V}{\sigma} = Erfc\,\sqrt{\frac{S}{N}} = \frac{1}{2}erfc\,\sqrt{\frac{1}{2}\frac{S}{N}} \tag{19.32}$$

Consequently, the same error rate is obtained with a 3dB lower signal to noise ratio. Alternatively, a much lower error rate can be obtained for the same signal to noise ratio.

The above analysis can be extended to multilevel digital signals, by replacing the pulse amplitude with the spacing between adjacent signal levels. If the number of levels is large, the error rate is nearly doubled. This is because all the intermediate levels can be misinter-preted in either direction, owing to noise voltages of either polarity.

For the case of a unipolar binary signal disturbed by white noise, the bit error rate, calculated from Equation 19.23, varies with the signal to noise ratio as shown in Figure 19.3. For example, if the signal noise ratio is 20dB, less than one digit per million is received in error. For telephone transmission, an error rate of 1 in 10^3 is intolerable, but an error rate of 1 in 10^5 is acceptable. Lower error rates are required for data transmission; if the error rate of the transmission link is inadequate, it is necessary to use an error detecting or error correcting code for the data (Lucky et al, 1968; Taub and Schilling, 1986).

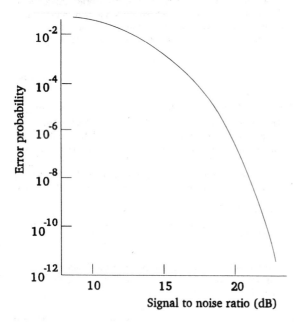

Figure 19.3 Error rate for transmission of unipolar binary signal disturbed by white noise

On a long transmission link, it is possible to use regenerative repeaters instead of analogue amplifiers. A regenerative repeater (Dorward, 1991) samples the received waveform at intervals corresponding to the digit rate. If the received voltage at the sampling instant exceeds a threshold voltage, this triggers a pulse generator which transmits a pulse to the next section of the link. If the received voltage is below the threshold, no pulse is generated. If both positive and negative pulses are transmitted, the regenerator is required to determine whether the received voltage is positive or negative and to retransmit pulses of either polarity.

19.2.3 Optimal detection

In a digital transmission system, the receiver attempts, at the required instants of time, to determine whether a pulse is present that represents valid information or just noise. Optimum strategies for doing this have been developed.

If a digital signal uses symbols $s_1(t), s_2(t),...., s_r(t),...., s_n(t)$, each of duration T, these should ideally be orthogonal; i.e. there should be no correlation between them. This can be expressed mathematically as in Equation 19.33, where φ_{qr} is a cross correlation function and φ_{rr} is an autocorrelation function.

$$\varphi_{qr} = \int_0^T s_q(t) s_r(t)\,dt = 0 \quad \text{for } q \neq r$$
$$\neq 0 \quad \text{for } q = r \qquad (19.33)$$

This suggests that an ideal receiver for the signal would be a bank of correlators, as shown in Figure 19.4. Each consists of a multiplier followed by an integrator. The signal is applied to one input of each multiplier and the waveform corresponding to one of the symbols is applied to the other. In the absence of noise, only one correlator will produce an output. If noise is present, other correlators will also produce some output. However, that corresponding to the symbol actually received should produce the largest output and this is selected as being the one most likely to be present. This maximum likelihood strategy has been shown to be the optimum for additive Gaussian noise when the symbols are equally probable (Harman, 1963).

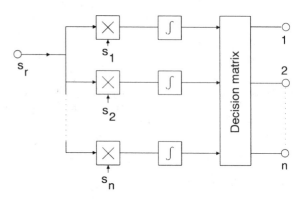

Figure 19.4 Correlation receiver

Since an integrator is a low pass filter, each of the correlators in Figure 19.4 is equivalent to a coherent demodulator. Thus, a coherent demodulator with the appropriate waveform applied as its local carrier acts as a correlation detector.

It may be noted that the incoming pulses to a correlation receiver do not need to be a baseband signal. They can be pulses of a modulated carrier.

Another approach is to postulate that there can be a filter which enhances the signal and reduces the noise voltage as much as possible. Such a filter is called a matched filter, because its transfer function is tailored to the particular input signal to be detected.

It has been shown (Betts, 1970; Brown and Glazier, 1974; Schwartz, 1970; Taub and Schilling, 1986) that the impulse response of the required filter is given by Equation 19.34, where T is the duration of the signal.

$$h(t) = s_r(T - t) \qquad (19.34)$$

The impulse response of the matched filter is thus the signal waveform with time reversed. It must be zero for t > T, at which time a decision is made as to whether $s_r(t)$ was present.

The output voltage, $v_o(t)$, due to the signal $s_r(t)$ is given by its convolution with h(t) as in Equation 19.35.

$$v_o(t) = \int_0^t s_r(\tau) s_r(t - T - \tau)\,d\tau \qquad (19.35)$$

Since this integral is zero outside the interval for which $s_r(t)$ and $s_r(t - T - \tau)$ exist, Equation 19.35 corresponds to the autocorrelation function φ_{rr} of $s_r(t)$. Consequently, the matched filter is equivalent to a correlation detector.

Since the impulse response of the matched filter is the time inverse of the input signal, if the latter is symmetrical in time, both are of the same shape. For example, if the signal is a pulse of $(\sin x)/x$ shape, so is the impulse response of the filter. The $(\sin x)/x$ pulse has a uniform spectrum up to frequency W, so the matched filter is an ideal low pass filter with cut off frequency W. This is hardly surprising, since it passes all the energy of the pulse and stops all noise outside the band of the signal. In the case of a sinusoidal carrier which is amplitude modulated by a $(\sin x)/x$ pulse, the matched filter will be an ideal band pass filter of bandwidth 2W, centred on the carrier frequency.

In a digital communication system, the input to the receiver should be band limited by a well designed filter. Consequently, the improvement obtained by using a matched filter or correlation detector is likely to be only about 1dB (Brown and Glazier, 1974).

19.3 Digital modulation of a carrier

19.3.1 Amplitude shift keying

If a binary signal is used to modulate the amplitude of a carrier to the greatest possible depth, the carrier is switched on and off. This is known as amplitude shift keying (ASK) or on off keying (OOK). The method is widely used in wireless telegraphy. Another important example is its use in optical communication systems. At the sending end, a binary electrical signal switches on and off a laser or light emitting diode. At the receiving end, a photodiode is switched on and off to reproduce the binary electrical signal.

In ASK, the spectrum of the transmitted signal consists of a component at the carrier frequency, together with an upper sideband which is a translated version of the baseband spectrum and a lower sideband which is an inverted version. It was shown earlier that the minimum bandwidth required to transmit the baseband signal is W $= \frac{1}{2}B$ (where B is the digit rate in bauds). It therefore follows that the minimum bandwidth required to transmit the ASK signal is 2W $= B$. If the baseband signal has a raised cosine spectrum with 100% roll off, the bandwidth of the ASK signal is increased to 2B.

If the carrier amplitude is V_c, the power when it is switched on corresponds to $\frac{1}{2}V_c^2$. If the on and off states are equiprobable, the mean power is equal to half this value. The transmitted signal is a fully modulated carrier of amplitude $\frac{1}{2}V_c^2$, so that the power at the carrier frequency, fc, corresponds to $\frac{1}{8}V_c^2$. Therefore, half of the total transmitted power is in the carrier and half is in the sidebands.

ASK can be demodulated by an envelope demodulator, as shown in Figure 18.5 (Chapter 18). However, at poor input signal/noise ratios, a coherent demodulator gives a better output signal/noise ratio and so a smaller bit error rate. Comparing Figures 18.6(b) (Chapter 18) and Figure 19.4 shows that the coherent demodulator is an optimum detector for the signal $s(t) = V_c \cos \omega_c t$.

For binary coded data, a coherent demodulator gives an output of +V for '1' and zero for '0'. The error rate thus corresponds to that of a unipolar baseband system and is given by Equation 19.27, where the signal/noise ratio is that at the output of the demodulator. It is shown in Chapter 18 that the output signal/noise ratio, S_o/N_o, of the coherent demodulator is twice the input signal/noise ratio, S_i/N_i, when the latter is calculated from the sideband power alone. However, in this case, the sideband power is only half the total

transmitted power. Therefore, $S_o/N_o = S_i/N_i$ and the error probability is given by Equation 19.27, where S/N is the input signal/noise ratio of the coherent demodulator.

The output voltage from a coherent demodulator is proportional to $\cos \theta$, where θ is the phase angle between the incoming carrier and the local carrier. Thus, ideal demodulation depends on keeping the local carrier in phase with the incoming carrier at all times. This is not obtained when the carrier at the transmitter is switched on at arbitrary instants. Consequently, the carrier must be synchronised with the baseband signal and be an exact multiple of its digit rate.

If this is not possible, an envelope demodulator should be used to remove the effect of carrier phase variation. Use of a matched filter only improves the signal/noise ratio by about 1dB, so the difference between the input signal/noise ratios required for coherent and non-coherent ASK is only about 1dB (Bylanski and Ingram, 1980). It can be shown (Peebles, 1976) that the bit error probability for a binary non-coherent ASK system is approximately given by Equation 19.36.

$$P_e = \frac{1}{2}\left(1 + \frac{1}{\sqrt{\pi(S/N)}}\right)\exp\left(-\frac{1}{4}\frac{S}{N}\right) \qquad (19.36)$$

Single sideband suppressed carrier (SSBSC) transmission is unsuitable for digital data, because the baseband signal has a substantial low frequency content. Vestigial sideband (VSB) transmission (see Chapter 18) can be used. It enables a significant bandwidth saving to be obtained at high data rates (Bennett and Davey, 1965). For example, 9600 baud transmission can be obtained over telephone circuits with 8-level ASK using VSB transmission.

19.3.2 Frequency shift keying

If a digital signal is used to modulate a carrier in frequency, this is known as frequency shift keying (FSK). It is used in voice frequency telegraph systems (Chittleburgh et al., 1957) and for wireless telegraphy in the h.f. band (Hills and Evans, 1973). It is also widely used for data transmission over telephone connections in public switched telecommunication networks (Bennett and Davey, 1965; Lucky et al., 1968). A typical data modem for use on telephone circuits uses frequencies of 1.3kHz and 1.7kHz to transmit at 600 bauds or 1.3kHz and 2.1kHz to transmit at 1200 bauds (CCITT Recommendation V.23).

As shown in Figure 19.5, binary FSK is equivalent to applying ASK to two carriers of frequencies f_1 and f_2, one being switched on when the baseband signal is '0' and the other when it is '1'. In fact, some systems use two separate oscillators, instead of one whose frequency is shifted. However, this is not true frequency modulation, since there is no continuity of phase at the instants of frequency transition. It may be termed non-coherent FSK.

For each of the constituent ASK signals in Figures 19.5(c) and 19.5(d), half of the power lies in the sidebands and half in the carrier. Therefore the complete FSK signal has half of its power in sidebands and one quarter at f_1 and at f_2.

If the frequency deviation is large compared with the digit rate (high index f.m.), the resulting spectrum is that corresponding to amplitude shift keying of f_1 and f_2, with the energy concentrated about these two frequencies as shown in Figure 19.6(a). If the frequency deviation is reduced to become comparable to the digit rate (low index f.m.), the sidebands about f_1 and f_2 merge, as shown in Figure 19.6(b). Consequently, little more bandwidth is required than for ASK.

A high value of modulation index gives an improvement in signal to noise ratio, as in analogue systems. However, this may be un-

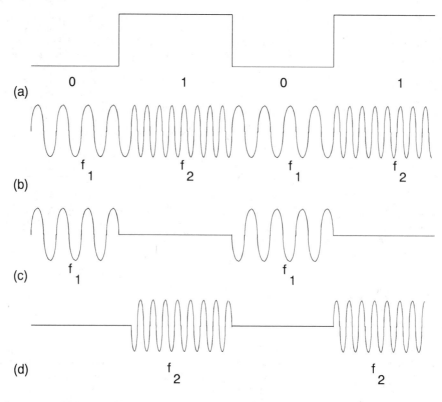

Figure 19.5   Frequency shift keying: (a) baseband signal; (b) FSK signal; (c) & (d) constituent ASK signals

necessary for a digital signal. Moreover, it would reduce the data throughput obtainable in a given bandwidth. Sunde (1954) obtained a solution to satisfying Nyquist's minimum bandwidth condition for the case of FSK. He showed that, with certain assumptions, the minimum bandwidth is obtained when the frequency shift $(f_2 - f_1)$ is equal to the data rate in bauds. It is therefore common practice to use a frequency shift equal to the digit rate.

If the bandwidth occupied by the sidebands about f_1 and f_2 is approximately B and $f_2 - f_1 = B$, then the spectrum in Figure 19.6(b)

occupies a bandwidth of approximately 2B. This is twice that needed for ASK. However, if coherent demodulation is used, it is possible to use a frequency shift of only 0.7B (Clark, 1983). In a multi-level FSK system, a similar separation is needed between the frequencies representing each of the levels. Thus, for a given symbol rate, the bandwidth increases with the number of levels.

An FSK signal can be demodulated by a frequency discriminator, as described in Chapter 18. Alternatively, a pair of filters tuned to f_1 and f_2 may be used with a pair of envelope demodulators. This is

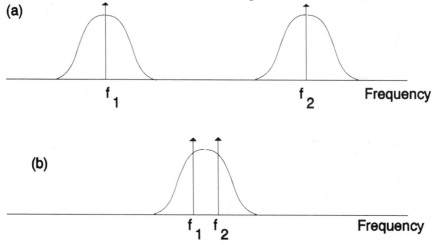

Figure 19.6   Spectra for frequency shift keying: (a) large frequency deviation; (b) small frequency deviation

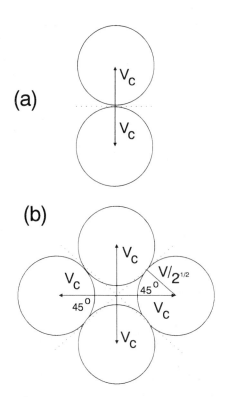

Figure 19.7 Signal-space diagrams for pulse phase modulation: (a) binary PSK; (b) 4-phase PSK

equivalent to two non-coherent ASK systems, so a similar error rate performance may be expected. It has been shown (Schwartz et al., 1966) that the error probability is approximately given by Equation 19.37.

$$P_e = \frac{1}{2} \exp\left(-\frac{1}{4} \frac{S}{N} \right) \qquad (19.37)$$

If the phase of the FSK signal is coherent, a lower error rate can be obtained at low input signal/noise ratios by using two coherent demodulators, with local carriers f_1 and f_2 respectively. Since this is equivalent to a pair of coherent ASK systems, the error probability is the same and is given by Equations 19.23 and 19.27.

19.3.3   Phase shift keying

If phase modulation is used to transmit a digital signal, this is known as phase shift keying (PSK). If the signal is binary, the phase of the carrier is shifted between two positions which are $180°$ apart. This is sometimes known as phase reversal keying (PRK).

If a binary baseband signal, v_m, with values of -1 and $+1$ is applied to a product modulator to produce double sideband suppressed carrier (DSBSC) modulation of a carrier v_c given by Equation 19.38, the output voltage is given by Equation 19.39.

$$v_c = V_C \cos \omega_c t \qquad (19.38)$$

$$v_o = V_c \cos \omega_c t \quad \text{for } v_m = +1$$
$$= -V_c \cos \omega_c t = V_c \cos(\omega_c t + \pi) \quad \text{for } v_m = -1 \qquad (19.39)$$

Thus, binary PSK with a phase shift of $180°$ is identical with binary DSBSC transmission. At the receiver, a coherent demodulator with a local carrier $\cos \omega_c t$ will produce an output signal of $+1$ and -1.

Since PSK uses DSBSC amplitude modulation, it requires the same bandwidth as ASK and this is less than that needed for FSK. Moreover, since PSK is a suppressed carrier system, all the transmitted power is in the sidebands which convey the information. Compared with FSK and ASK which have only half of their power in the sidebands, this gives a 3dB advantage. Hence, the bit error probability is given by Equation 19.32. Consequently, for the same transmitted power, PSK gives a much lower error rate than FSK or ASK.

PSK signals may have more than two levels. For example, a 4-level PSK signal uses four carrier phases, separated by $90°$. It is therefore sometimes known as quadrature phase shift keying (QPSK). In order to transmit a binary baseband signal, a pair of binary digits is combined to form a 4-level signal (00, 01, 10, 11) corresponding to the four phases transmitted. At the receiver, each of the four output values is used to generate two consecutive binary output digits. By this means, the digit rate on the transmission path and the required bandwidth are halved.

Alternatively, a higher digit rate can be achieved with a given bandwidth. Multiphase PSK is therefore used in digital radio systems for terrestrial links (de Bellin, 1991) and for satellite communication systems (Evans, 1987; Nouri, 1991).

The penalty for the increased data rate obtained with multiphase PSK is a lower immunity to noise. Figure 19.7(a) shows that, for two phase PSK, an interfering voltage must exceed V_c before an error can occur by detecting a '1' as '0' or vice versa. Figure 19.7(b) shows that, in four phase PSK, the tolerable interfering voltage is reduced by a factor of $1/\sqrt{2}$, i.e. 3dB. This is a disadvantage in the case of impulsive noise, such as that encountered on some switched telephone connections (Alexander et al., 1960; Williams, 1966). However, the bandwidth required for four phase PSK is only half that for two phase PSK. Consequently, in the case of white noise, the noise power is reduced by 3dB and the error rates are the same.

PSK requires a synchronous demodulator and synchronism is often difficult to maintain, particularly at high carrier frequencies. It is especially difficult to maintain if the transmission takes place through a fading medium or if either the transmitter or receiver is in a vehicle whose movement causes a Doppler shift of frequency. The difficulty can be overcome by transmitting a pilot carrier or by using a phase locked loop to control generation of the local carrier at the receiver (Viterbi, 1966).

The signal output voltage from a coherent demodulator is proportional to $\cos \theta$, where θ is the angle between the incoming and local carriers (see Chapter 18). Any departure from $\theta = 0$ reduces the amplitude of the output signal from the demodulator. However, there is no reduction in the noise output, so there is an increase in the error rate. Even if phase synchronism is correctly established initially, it may occasionally be lost. There can be a shift of $180°$ and this results in a sign inversion of all the output data.

The need for accurate carrier recovery can be avoided by using differential phase shift keying (DPSK). This does not require the generation of a local carrier at the demodulator. In DPSK, the information is conveyed by changes in phase between digits, instead of by the phase deviation of each from a reference carrier.

The principle of differential encoding is shown in Figure 19.8. The coder is fed with a sequence of binary symbols $s_1(1), s_1(2), ..., s_1(n)$, ..., where $s_1(n) = \pm 1$. Its output signal, $s_2(n)$, is obtained by multiplying $s_1(n)$ by the previous output from the coder, i.e. $s_2(n - 1)$, resulting in Equation 19.40.

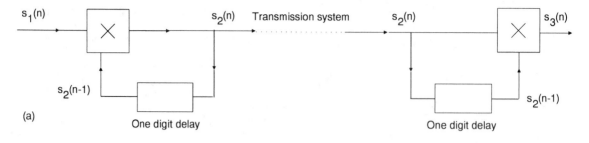

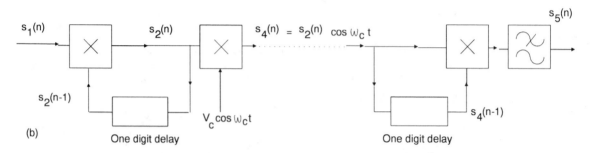

Figure 19.8 Principle of differential phase shift keying (DPSK): (a) differential coding and decoding; (b) DPSK system

$$s_2(n) = s_1(n)s_2(n-1) \tag{19.40}$$

Thus, s_2 only changes sign if $s_1(n) = -1$.

Since $s_1(n)$ and $s_2(n-1)$ are single digit binary numbers, their multiplication can be carried out simply by means of an exclusive-OR logic gate.

Assuming error free transmission, the output signal from the decoder is given by Equation 19.41, regardless of whether $s_2(n-1)$ is +1 or −1 and whether the initial condition of s_2 was $s_2(0) = +1$ or $s_2(0) = -1$.

$$s_3(n) = s_2(n)s_2(n-1)$$

$$= s_1(n)s_2(n-1)s_2(n-1) = s_1(n) \tag{19.41}$$

In differentially encoded pulse phase modulation (DEPSK), the coder shown in Figure 19.8(a) is followed by a PSK modulator and the demodulator is followed by the decoder. However, the decoder can be incorporated in the coherent demodulator of the receiver, as shown in Figure 19.8(b). This is known as differential phase shift keying (DPSK). Then, the output signal of the demodulator is $s_5(n)$ = +1 if $s_4(n)$ and $s_4(n-1)$ are represented by carriers of the same phase and $s_5(n) = -1$ if the phase has shifted by $180°$ between $s_4(n-1)$ and $s_4(n)$. However, the phase of s_4 will only have shifted if s_2 has changed in polarity as a result of $s_1(n) = -1$. Therefore Equation 19.42 is obtained.

$$s_5(n) = -1 \quad \text{when} \quad s_1(n) = -1$$

$$s_5(n) = +1 \quad \text{when} \quad s_1(n) = +1 \tag{19.42}$$

Although DPSK has the advantage of no errors due to loss of synchronism, the probability of error due to noise is greater than for PSK. Each input digit to the demodulator contributes to determining the values of two output digits. Consequently, a noise peak that would produce a single error with PSK can produce two errors with DPSK.

Calculation of the bit error probability for DPSK is complicated. It has been shown (Schwartz et al., 1966) that the error probability is given by Equation 19.43.

$$P_e = \frac{1}{2} \exp\left(-\frac{1}{2}\frac{S}{N}\right) \tag{19.43}$$

19.3.4 Comparative performance of ASK, FSK and PSK

Figure 19.9 shows, for signals perturbed by added Gaussian noise, how the bit error probability varies with the signal to noise ratio for binary systems using coherent and non-coherent ASK, coherent and non coherent FSK, PSK and DPSK. These curves were obtained from Equations 19.27, 19.32, 19.36, 19.37 and 19.43. For comparison, the error probabilities for unipolar and bipolar baseband transmission (from Equations 19.27 and 19.32) are also shown.

None of the modulation schemes, except PSK, gives as good an error performance as bipolar baseband transmission. Coherent ASK and FSK both achieve as good a performance as unipolar baseband transmission. Non coherent ASK and FSK are about 1 dB worse than the corresponding coherent systems. DPSK is about 1 dB worse than PSK.

Determination of the error probabilities for multilevel systems is more complex and will not be considered here. The reader is referred to Arthurs and Dym (1962), Bylanski and Ingram (1980) and Taub and Schilling (1986). For 4-level systems, it is found that coherent FSK nearly equals the performance of PSK and ASK gives the worst performance (Bylanski and Ingram, 1980). For more than four levels, a better performance is obtained by using the hybrid modulation schemes described in the next section.

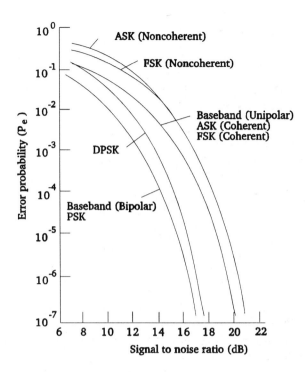

Figure 19.9 Bit error probability for various digital sytems

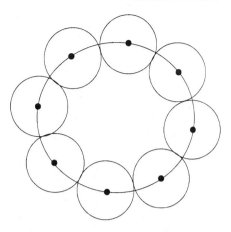

Figure 19.11 Signal-space diagram for eight state phase modulation

19.3.5 Quadrature amplitude modulation

If a carrier is modulated by a digital signal, its amplitude and phase can only have a finite number of values. These can be represented in a signal space diagram, as shown in Figures 19.10 and 19.11. These show an 8-level ASK signal and an 8-level PSK signal. The circles show the maximum permissible perturbation from the ideal signal before an error may occur in the transmission. It is obvious that, in this respect, PSK is superior to ASK.

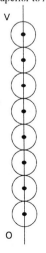

Figure 19.10 Signal-space diagram for eight state amplituded modulation

It is possible to combine ASK and PSK to obtain hybrid modulation, as shown in Figure 19.12. The 8-level scheme shown in Figure 19.12(b) has a similar error threshold voltage to the PSK scheme of Figure 19.11. However, it has a lower mean transmitted power, because four of the eight states have a smaller carrier amplitude than those in Figure 19.11.

These hybrid modulation schemes can be implemented using quadrature amplitude modulation (QAM), i.e. modulation of two carriers in quadrature as shown in Figure 19.13. If a 2-level signal is applied to each modulator, the output has a constant amplitude, as shown in Figure 19.12(a). It therefore produces quadrature phase shift keying (QPSK).

If a 3-level signal ($s_1 = -1$, $s_2 = 0$, $s_3 = +1$) is applied to each of the two modulators, the sum of their outputs has three values of its in phase component and three values of its quadrature component. This permits duobinary partial response coding and the system is known as a quadrature partial response (QPRS) system (Taub and Schilling, 1986).

If a 4-level signal is applied to each of the two modulators, the sum of their outputs has four values of its in phase component and four values of its quadrature component. This produces the sixteen state signal constellation shown in Figure 19.12(c). The demodulators reproduce the two 4-level signals at their outputs.

Four state QAM is used to produce QPSK to transmit data at 2400bit/s over switched telephone circuits with a signalling rate of only 1200 bauds (CCITT Recommendations V.26 and V.27). Sixteen state QAM is used to provide 2400bit/s data transmission over switched telephone circuits with a signalling rate of only 600 bauds (CCITT Recommendation V.22 bis) and 9.6kbit/s over private circuits with a signalling rate of only 2400 bauds (CCITT Recommendation V.32).

19.4 Pulse code modulation

Pulse code modulation (PCM) can be produced by applying a train of amplitude modulated pulses to an analogue to digital (A/D) converter, as shown in Figure 19.14. Each analogue sample is thus converted to a group of on/off pulses which represents its voltage in a binary code. At the receiving terminal, a digital to analogue (D/A) converter performs the decoding process. The combination of a coder and decoder at a PCM terminal is often referred to as a codec. The group of bits (i.e. binary pulses) representing one sample is

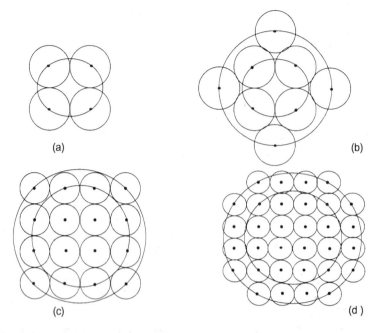

Figure 19.12 Signal-space diagrams for m-state quadrature amplitude modulation: (a) four state; (b) eight state ; (c) sixteen state; (d) thirty-two state

called a word or a byte. An 8-bit byte is sometimes called an octet. In a time division multiplex (TDM) system, the coder and decoder are required to perform their operations within the time slot of one channel. They can therefore be common to all the channels of a TDM system, as shown in Figure 19.14.

For telephony, speech samples are usually encoded in an 8-bit code. Since sampling is at 8kHz, a telephone channel requires binary digits to be sent at the rate of 8 x 8 = 64kbit/s. It was shown earlier that the minimum bandwidth required to transmit pulses is half the pulse rate. Thus, a bandwidth of at least 32kHz is required to transmit a single telephone channel. The advantages of digital transmission are won at the expense of a much greater bandwidth requirement.

19.4.1 Sampling

In order to produce a digital signal, an analogue signal must first be sampled by a periodic pulse train to convert it from continuous to discrete time. If a continuous signal has a bandwidth W, then the minimum sampling frequency, f_s, that can be used is $f_s = 2W$. This is called the Nyquist rate. Subsequent removal of all frequency components except the original baseband by a low pass filter at the receiver recovers the original signal.

If the sampling rate is less than 2W, the lower sideband about f_s overlaps the baseband and it is impossible to separate them. This is called aliasing. It can be avoided by passing the input signal through a low pass filter before sampling it. It is essential to include such an anti-aliasing filter at the input of a sampling system. Since the nominal band of telephone signals is from 300Hz to 3.4kHz and the internationally agreed sampling frequency is 8kHz, there is a guard band of 1.2kHz between the top of the baseband and the bottom of the lower sideband of the sampling frequency. This must accommodate the transition between the pass band and the stop band of the anti-aliasing filter at the sending end and of the demodulating filter at the receive end.

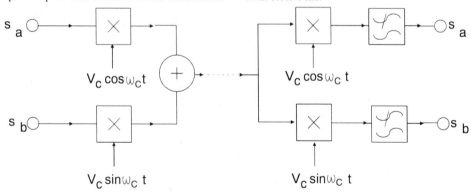

Figure 19.13 Quadrature amplitude modulation (QAM) system

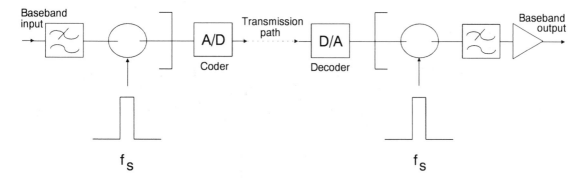

Figure 19.14 Block diagram of a PCM system (one direction of transmission only)

Anti-aliasing filters can be implemented in many ways. High order passive LC filters have often been used, offering low distortion and low noise, but with the physical drawbacks of large size and weight, and inevitable insertion loss. A more up to date approach might be the use of a Sallen-and-Key active filter (1955), which is smaller, lighter and loss free, but adds more noise, and can be more difficult to trim than the corresponding LC filter. Switched capacitor filters (Sedra and Smith, 1982) can be highly integrated, requiring only off chip capacitors, and hence lead to a cheap package which does not require large amounts of PCB area. They do, however, add considerably more noise than the passive and active filters.

The analogue sampler, commonly known as the 'sample-and-hold', performs the task of sampling the input analogue voltage and maintaining that voltage until the next sampling instant. A simple sample-and-hold is illustrated in Figure 19.15. When the Sample command is given, the buffer is connected via the FET switch to the storage capacitor, the voltage on which tracks the input voltage thereafter. The capacitor is at all times buffered by a voltage follower. When the Sample command is removed, the capacitor is isolated from the input buffer. The voltage across the capacitor, and hence the voltage follower, will then remain steady until the next Sample command.

Such a simple design is marred by a number of adverse properties, so more complex designs are sometimes used (Wallace et al., 1991).

19.4.2 The coder

The analogue sampler performs the transformation from continuous time to discrete time representation. The coder or analogue to digital converter (ADC) performs the complementary operation of transformation from continuous amplitude to discrete amplitude. There are a variety of techniques which may be used in an ADC, such as

dual slope conversion, successive approximation and flash conversion (Wallace et al., 1991).

The successive approximation ADC is built from a digital to analogue converter, a comparator, a storage register and controlling logic, as shown in Figure 19.16. This type of converter essentially operates by performing a binary search through the ADC dynamic range to find the input voltage.

Upon receiving the Convert command, the storage register is cleared. The output from the storage register is passed to the digital to analogue converter (DAC), but with the most significant bit set. This causes the DAC to output its half range voltage. This voltage is then compared with the input sample by the comparator. The comparator output is then stored in the most significant bit (MSB) of the storage register. The converter has thus decided whether the input voltage is in the lower or upper half of the ADC's dynamic range.

On the next clock cycle, the storage register output is passed to the DAC with its 2nd most significant bit set. The comparator output then indicates whether the input signal lies in the upper or lower half of that portion of the dynamic range selected in the previous decision. The comparator output is stored in the 2nd most significant bit of the register.

This process continues, passing through as many cycles as there are bits in the storage register, with each pass determining whether the input voltage lies in the upper or lower half of the range selected in the previous cycle. The storage register then contains the ADC conversion value.

The successive approximation ADC must perform several operations in sequence to encode each sample. For high sampling rates (e.g. above 1MHz), in order to reduce the conversion time, it is necessary to use a circuit which requires fewer operations to be performed.

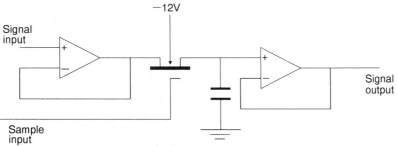

Figure 19.15 Simple sample-and-hold circuit

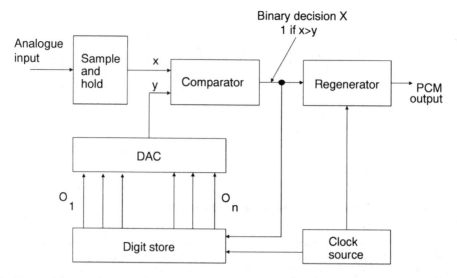

Figure 19.16 Successive approximation ADC

The flash converter, shown in Figure 19.17, consists of a chain of fast comparators, with one input of each comparator driven by the voltage to be converted. The other input of each successive comparator is connected to the corresponding point of a resistor chain, containing as many resistors of equal value, as there are comparators. The number of comparators, and hence resistors, in the divider chain, is equal to the number of levels which must be coded. For example, for the case of a 4-bit flash converter, capable of coding voltages in the range 0 to 1 V, 16 comparators are needed, connected to a resistor chain containing 16 equal resistors, connected across a

1 V reference. The comparators thus compare the input voltage with $\frac{1}{16}$V, $\frac{1}{8}$V, $\frac{3}{16}$V, and so on.

The comparator outputs are then passed to a priority encoder, which determines the position of the last comparator in the chain to indicate that its reference voltage is lower than the flash encoder input voltage. This indicates directly which segment of the converter's dynamic range contains the input signal and gives the corresponding binary code output.

The main feature of the flash converter is its extremely rapid conversion time. They are often used for video ADC's. or any other application which requires a sample rate in excess of 1MHz. The penalty for the speed is the rapid increase in complexity, and therefore power consumption and cost, as the desired number of bits increases. Indeed, it is rare to find a flash converter operating to more than 8-bit accuracy because of the cost of an array of more than 256 comparators. Variation of input offset voltage between adjacent comparators can set a further limit to ultimate resolution. However, analogue and digital pipelining can be combined to implement two stage flash conversion, giving accuracy up to twice the number of bits with the same sample rate, and only twice the conversion time.

The above converters encode voltages between ground and some upper limit. It is more usual to want to convert voltages of both polarities. This can be achieved either by

1. The addition of a voltage equal to half the upper limit, with two's complement coding of the signal then easily achieved by inversion of the resulting MSB.
2. The use of a precision full wave detector, which results in an output signal of fixed polarity, together with information about whether the signal is positive or negative.

The latter scheme results naturally in the production of a 'sign-plus-magnitude' code.

19.4.3 The decoder

After the digitally encoded signal has been transmitted, it is often necessary to reconstruct an analogue signal at the receiver. Conver-

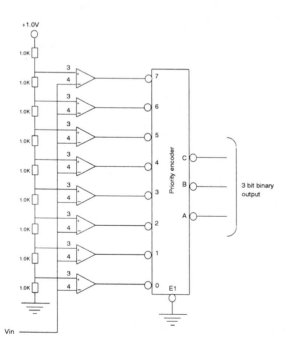

Figure 19.17 A 3 bit flash converter

sion from digital to analogue is generally easier to achieve than conversion from analogue to digital. There are again many techniques which may be used for this conversion, each possessing its own blend of merits and demerits.

The simplest form of DAC is shown in Figure 19.18. It consists of an array of resistors connected via an analogue switch either to a reference voltage, if the corresponding bit in the digital word is 'one', or to ground otherwise. The resistors are all connected to the virtual earth input of a current summing amplifier, and their values are chosen such that the currents flowing through the resistors when the corresponding bits are 'one' are binary weighted.

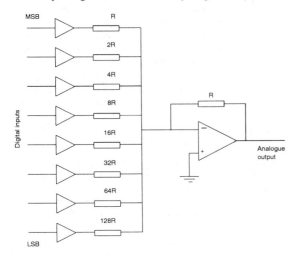

Figure 19.18 Simple digital to analogue converter

The output voltage of the summing amplifier is proportional to the sum of the input currents, and hence to the numerical value of the digital codeword.

The circuit illustrated in Figure 19.18 is simple, but it suffers some drawbacks. The linearity and monotonicity are both critically dependent on the precision of the resistors used. Any errors in resistor value will show particularly around the transition between the lower and upper halves of the converter's dynamic range. The resistor values will also almost certainly drift slowly with time and temperature. More elaborate designs based on the resistor ladder network overcome this drawback (Wallace et al., 1991).

19.4.4 Quantisation distortion

The digital signal can only represent a finite number of input signal voltages. For example, a binary code of k digits can only represent 2^k different input voltages. When the signal is reconstructed at the receiver, it is an approximation to the original signal, since it can only change in discrete voltage steps. This signal is said to be quantised, and a form of non-linear distortion, known as quantisation distortion, has been introduced.

The difference between the original signal and the reconstructed signal is the error voltage. Because the error voltage varies randomly with time, it is often referred to colloquially as 'quantisation noise'. Indeed, in PCM telephony, it sounds just like noise. If the acceptable r.m.s. noise voltage in an analogue signal is σ, then a discrete representation with a voltage level spacing of the order of σ will be adequate to represent the analogue signal.

Obviously, the closer the spacing of the discrete levels, the smaller will be the quantisation distortion. However, the smaller the spacing, the greater is the number of levels. This increases the number of digits in the code words representing the levels (e.g. doubling the number of levels increases the length of a binary code word by one bit). An increase in the number of digits representing every sample increases the bandwidth required to transmit them.

Consider a quantiser where the ith interval is centred around Q_i and possesses width Δ_i. Any input signal x in the range given by Equation 19.44, will be represented by the quantised amplitude Q_i.

$$Q_i - \frac{1}{2}\Delta_i \leq x < Q_i + \frac{1}{2}\Delta_i \tag{19.44}$$

The squared quantisation error will clearly be $(x - Q_i)^2$. Let us also assume that the probability density of the input signal is p(x). Therefore, to obtain the mean square error over the ith range, the squared error value must be averaged over all possible values of the input signal for that quantisation interval, as in Equation 19.45.

$$E_i^2 = \int_{Q_i - \frac{1}{2}\Delta_i}^{Q_i + \frac{1}{2}\Delta_i} p(x)(x - Q_i)^2 \, dx \tag{19.45}$$

If the signal varies widely in comparison to the size of a single quantisation interval, it can be assumed that p(x) is constant across that quantisation interval, having value $\frac{1}{\Delta_i}$. Therefore Equation 19.46 is obtained.

$$E_i^2 = \frac{1}{\Delta_i}\int_{Q_i - \frac{1}{2}\Delta_i}^{Q_i + \frac{1}{2}\Delta_i} (x - Q_i)^2 \, dx = \frac{1}{\Delta_i}\frac{\Delta_i^3}{12} = \frac{\Delta_i^2}{12} \tag{19.46}$$

We may now calculate the mean square noise over the entire quantiser dynamic range by averaging E_i over all values of i as in Equation 19.47, where P_i is probability of the signal voltage being in the ith interval and N is total number of quantisation intervals in the entire converter dynamic range.

$$E^2 = \frac{\sum_{i=1}^{N} P_i E_i^2}{\sum_{i=1}^{N} P_i} = \frac{1}{12}\sum_{i=1}^{N} P_i \Delta_i^2 \tag{19.47}$$

For the important case of a uniform quantiser, where all intervals have the same width (Δ) Equation 19.48 is obtained.

$$E^2 = \frac{\Delta^2}{12}\sum_{i=1}^{N} P_i = \frac{1}{12}\Delta^2 \tag{19.48}$$

For a sinsuoidal input signal, the maximum amplitude which can be handled is given by Equation 19.49, so the signal power is given by Equation 19.50.

$$V_m = \frac{1}{2}N\Delta \tag{19.49}$$

$$S = \frac{1}{2} V_m^2 = \frac{1}{8} N^2 \Delta^2 \quad volts \qquad (19.50)$$

Therefore, the signal/quantisation noise ratio (SQNR) is as in Equation 19.51.

$$SQNR = \frac{S}{E^2} = \frac{3}{2} N^2 \qquad (19.51)$$

Expressing this in decibels gives Equation 19.52.

$$SQNR = 1.8 + 20 \log_{10} N \quad dB \qquad (19.52)$$

Now, for binary encoded PCM, $N = 2^k$ where k is the number of bits in the codeword. Substituting in Equation 19.51 gives Equation 19.53.

$$SQNR = 1.8 + 20 k \log_{10} 2 \quad dB$$
$$= 1.8 + 6 k \quad dB \qquad (19.53)$$

Equation 19.53 shows that adding one digit to the code improves the SQNR by 6dB. Since the quantisation noise level is independent of signal level, a signal whose level is xdB lower than the maximum will have a SQNR which is xdB worse than that given by Equations 19.52 and 19.53.

19.4.5 Companding

In typical telephone speech, the probability distribution of signal amplitudes has a maximum at zero amplitude and becomes progressively smaller for high amplitudes, having a near Gaussian distribution. In addition, substantial level variations exist between one conversation and another, depending on such factors as the line length between the subscriber and the exchange, the sensitivity of the subscriber's handset and the loudness of the talker. These factors

can lead to a variation of up to 30dB between one speaker and another (Purton, 1962). There is, therefore, a requirement for a wide dynamic range to be coded by the ADC for a speech signal.

A uniform quantiser has a constant noise power, independent of the signal level. Equation 19.53 shows that to code a signal with a dynamic range of 50dB, maintaining a signal to noise ratio of at least 30dB over that dynamic range, would require a 13-bit uniform quantiser. The ear, however, is a very non-linear sensor and, in the presence of a speech signal, any broadband noise which is 30dB quieter than the signal is masked by that speech. So, why use a uniform quantiser with its fixed noise power, unaffected by speech level? What is really needed is a quantiser which has a constant signal to noise ratio of 30dB over a 50dB dynamic range.

The signal/quantising noise ratio for small signals could be improved by compressing the level range before coding and using expansion after decoding at the receiver (i.e. companding).

It is not necessary to use a 'syllabic' compander, because the process can be performed independently on each speech sample. Such an 'instantaneous' compressor could be implemented by a non-linear characteristic for which constant increments (δ_y) in output voltage correspond to input voltage increments (δ_x) which are proportional to the input voltage x, as shown in Figure 19.19(b). Thus Equations 19.54 and 19.55 are obtained. However, log 0 = $-\infty$ and a practical ADC must give zero output for zero input. A compression law is therefore needed which is logarithmic for large values of x but corresponds to a straight line through the origin for small values of x, as shown in Figures 19.19(c) and (d).

$$dy = \left(\frac{b}{x} \right) dx \qquad (19.54)$$

$$y = b \log cx \qquad (19.55)$$

One compression law that is used is the A-law shown in Figure 19.19(c). This is given by Equation 19.56.

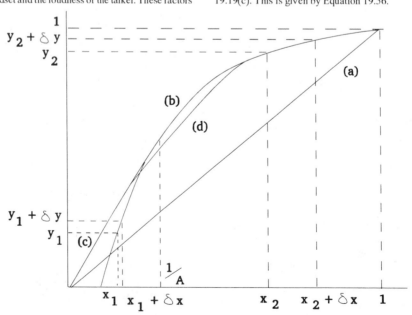

Figure 19.19 Compression characteristics: (a) linear law; (b) logarithmic law; (c) A-law; (d) μ-law

$$y = \frac{1 + \log_e A\, x}{1 + \log_e A} \quad \text{for } \frac{1}{A} \le x \le 1$$

$$= \frac{A\, x}{1 + \log_e A} \quad \text{for } 0 \le x \le \frac{1}{A} \tag{19.56}$$

The section below $x = 1/A$ is linear. The section between $1/A$ and 1 is logarithmic and, for $A = 87.6$, this gives constant SQNR over a range of $20 \log_{10} 87.6 = 38\text{dB}$. For small signals, the A-law gives Equation 19.57.

$$\frac{dy}{dx} = \frac{A}{1 + \log_e A} \tag{19.57}$$

However, for uniform quantisation, $dy/dx = 1$. Thus, if the A-law companding advantage is defined as the improvement in SQNR compared with uniform quantisation, it is as in expression 19.58. For $A = 87.6$, this is 24dB.

$$20 \log_{10}\left(\frac{dy}{dx}\right) \tag{19.58}$$

Another compression law that is used is the μ-law shown in Figure 19.19(d). This is given by Equation 19.59.

$$y = \frac{\log_e(1 + \mu x)}{\log_e(1 + \mu)} \quad \text{for } 0 \le x \le 1 \tag{19.59}$$

This approximates to the logarithmic law for $x \ge \frac{1}{\mu}$ and to a linear law for $x \ll \frac{1}{\mu}$ since Equation 19.60 holds.

$$\log_e(1 + \mu x) = x - \frac{\mu^2 x^2}{2} + \frac{\mu^3 x^3}{3} - \dots \tag{19.60}$$

From Equation 19.59, the slope of the characteristic is as in Equation 19.61.

$$\frac{dy}{dx} = \frac{1}{\log(1 + \mu)} \frac{\mu}{1 + \mu x} \tag{19.61}$$

Equation 19.61 shows that, when $\mu = 255$, the SQNR changes by less than 3dB over an input level change of 40dB. For small signals Equation 19.62 is obtained.

$$\frac{dy}{dx} = \frac{\mu}{\log_e(1 + \mu)} \tag{19.62}$$

This corresponds to the companding advantage; thus, for $\mu = 255$, this is 33dB.

Early PCM systems use non-linear networks in conjunction with uniform encoding. Later systems used piecewise linear approximations to the compression law, since these are easy to implement digitally. Two such logarithmic quantising schemes for 8-bit encoding have been defined by CCITT Recommendation G.711. They correspond respectively, to the A-law with $A = 86.7$ and the μ-law with $\mu = 255$. The A-law is used across Europe, and the μ-law is used across America and Japan. Both schemes use codewords which bear a remarkable similarity to 8-bit binary floating point numbers. One bit is reserved for the sign, three bits for the exponent, and four

bits for the mantissa, with the leading bit (which is always one) removed. The A-law characteristic is shown in Figure 19.20.

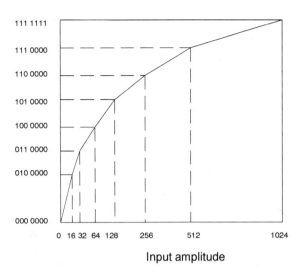

Figure 19.20 CCITT A-law characteristic

19.5 Differential pulse code modulation

19.5.1 Basic differential PCM

Conventional PCM permits any sample to have any value. The system can therefore cope with adjacent samples having values at the extreme opposite ends of the range. For example, it can transmit a signal of maximum amplitude at the maximum baseband frequency. Such rapidly changing signals rarely occur, so it should be possible to convey the baseband signal with adequate fidelity by transmitting fewer bits per second than is needed by conventional PCM. Differential pulse code modulation (DPCM) does this by encoding the difference between each sample and the previous one, instead of encoding the actual value of each sample (Peebles, 1976; Taub and Schilling, 1986).

The block diagram of a basic DPCM system is shown in Figure 19.21. Each sample presented to the coder is the difference between the present value of the baseband input voltage and the integrated value of previous transmitted samples. At the receiver, the output of the decoder is fed to the baseband output channel via a similar integrator. Thus, the coder at the sending end is constantly updating the output of the receiver's integrator by comparing the output of its own integrator with the voltage received from the baseband input channel and transmitting the difference. Usually, the difference will be much smaller than the full amplitude of the input signal, so it can be encoded with fewer digits. Typically, 4-digit coding can be used instead of 8-digit coding, thereby halving the transmitted digit rate and the bandwidth required.

Occasionally, the input signal may change so rapidly that the difference between it and the integrator output exceeds the maximum voltage that can be encoded. This is known as slope overload. There is then an error in the output voltage from the receiver. However, this rapid rate of change is unlikely to persist, so the receiver output will be corrected over the next few samples.

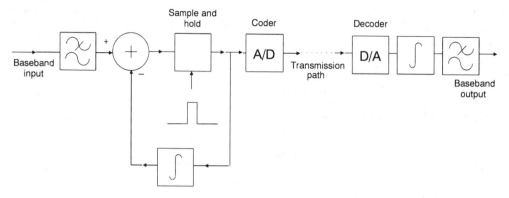

Figure 19.21   Block diagram of a differential PCM system

19.5.2   Adaptive differential PCM

The basic DPCM system of Figure 19.21 may be thought of as predicting that each sample will not change from the previous one and transmitting the difference between each sample and this predicted value. Thus, the integrators at the sending and receiving ends are a simple form of predictor. The performance of the system can be improved, or the digit rate reduced, by using a more sophisticated form of predictor based on the a priori knowledge that the baseband signal to be encoded is a speech signal.

The predictor can be a self adaptive filter based on a model of the vocal tract (Wallace et al., 1991). This removes a large amount of the redundancy contained in voiced sounds, thereby reducing the magnitude of the difference signal to be encoded. This scheme is known as adaptive differential pulse code modulation (ADPCM). It enables a SQNR of about 40dB to be obtained with 4-bit encoding. Telephone transmission can therefore use only 32kbit/s instead of 64kbit/s.

The CCITT has specified an algorithm for 32kbit/s ADPCM (Recommendation G.721). This is embodied in a transcoder, whose input is a normal 64kbit/s PCM signal (with A-law or μ-law companding) and whose output is 32kbit/s ADPCM. Block diagrams of this encoder and the corresponding decoder are shown in Figures 19.22 and 19.23.

Alternatively, ADPCM can be used to enable a 64kbit/s digital channel to transmit speech having a bandwidth of 7kHz instead of only 3.4kHz (CCITT Recommendation G.722).

19.5.3   Linear predictive coding

Linear predictive coding (LPC) takes the idea of using a model of the vocal tract one stage further (Atal and Schroeder, 1970). A short block of speech, typically 20ms in duration, is processed to extract pitch period and formant information, which describe respectively the activity of the vocal chords and the resonances of the vocal tract. Then, rather than transmitting speech samples, the LPC coder sends the pitch period and formant model coefficients for the block of speech. The decoder uses this information to reconstruct the speech block from the model.

Because of the small amount of information transmitted, LPC coders can use digit rates as low as 4.8kbit/s, although error protection of the code is essential. However, LPC coders have the severe disadvantage of introducing a coding delay of two or three times the length of the speech block. Consequently, echo suppressors or echo cancellers must be used with LPC.

The Group Speciale Mobile (GSM), which was formed by the European PTTs, had the task of specifying the speech encoding algorithm for a pan European digital cellular radio system. It has chosen a variant of LPC, known as regular pulse excitation long term prediction (RPE-LTP) (ETSI, 1989). This will use a speech block of 20ms and will operate at 13kbit/s, with an additional 3kbit/s for error protection.

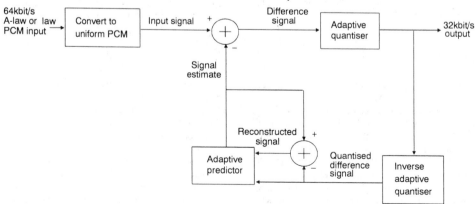

Figure 19.22   ADPCM encoder

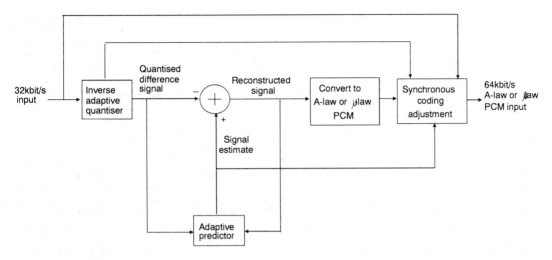

Figure 19.23 ADPCM decoder

19.6 Delta modulation

19.6.1 Basic delta modulation

The limiting case of DPCM is when the number of bits in the code is reduced to only one. This is possible if over sampling is used, i.e. the sampling frequency is made much greater than the Nyquist rate. The difference that can occur between adjacent samples is then reduced, so that it rarely exceeds one quantum step. The method is called delta modulation (DM) (Steele, 1975).

A basic DM system is shown in Figure 19.24. At the sending end, the comparator causes the pulse generator to transmit +V when the input voltage exceeds the output voltage from the integrator and −V when it is less. As well as being transmitted, each of these pulses causes the output voltage from the integrator to rise or fall by one quantum step, so that it closely tracks the input voltage. At the receiving end, each incoming positive or negative pulse causes the output voltage from a similar integrator to rise and fall by one quantum step, thereby reproducing the input signal of the sending end.

Alternatively, instead of transmitting a bipolar pulse train, a unipolar pulse train can be used (i.e. '1' = +V and '0' = zero volts). The integrators are then discharged at a constant rate, so that their output voltages decrease by one quantum step during a sample period not containing '1'.

As shown in Figure 19.24, a delta modulator is very simple and therefore cheap. It also has the useful property that all transmitted digits have equal weight, corresponding to one quantum step. Thus, a one bit error in transmission only causes an error of one quantum in the output signal. In PCM, an error in the most significant digit causes an error of half the maximum signal amplitude, with disastrous results if this occurs frequently. Thus, DM is very robust in the presence of frequent transmission errors. It has therefore been used in military systems.

In theory, there is no limit to the amplitude of baseband signal which the system can transmit. It can handle a signal of any amplitude, providing that it is not changing so rapidly that it causes slope overload. To avoid slope overload, the input signal, v_m, must not change by more than one quantum step (Δ) in the sampling interval, $1/f_s$, i.e. as in Equation 19.63. If v_m is given by Equation 19.64 then Equation 19.65 is obtained, its maximum value being given by Equation 19.66 so that V_m must satisfy Equation 19.67.

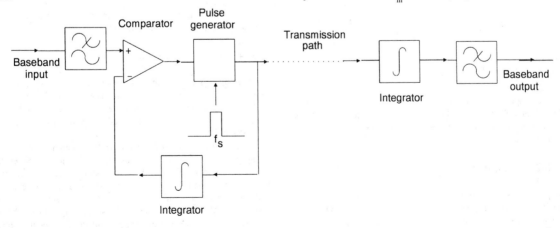

Figure 19.24 Basic delta modulation system

$$\frac{d v_m}{d t} \frac{1}{f_s} \leq \Delta \qquad (19.63)$$

$$v_m = V_m \cos \omega_m t \qquad (19.64)$$

$$\frac{d v_m}{d t} = - \omega_m V_m \sin \omega_m t \qquad (19.65)$$

$$\omega_m V_m = 2 \pi f_m V_m \qquad (19.66)$$

$$V_m \leq \frac{\Delta}{2 \pi} \frac{f_s}{f_m} \qquad (19.67)$$

Thus, DM has a dynamic range which is large at low frequencies, but which decreases with frequency. This is satisfactory for speech, since speech signals contain little energy at high frequencies.

In DM, the output voltage increases and decreases in increments of one quantum step; it cannot remain stationary. The maximum quantising error is thus $\pm \Delta$ whereas in PCM it is $\pm \frac{1}{2} \Delta$. Consequently, the quantisation noise power is four times that given by Equation 19.48 i.e. as in Equation 19.68.

$$E^2 = \frac{1}{3} \Delta^2 \qquad (19.68)$$

However, the quantisation noise power spreads over a wider frequency band than for PCM, because of the higher sampling frequency (Wallace et al., 1991). If it is assumed that the noise power is uniformly distributed up to frequency f_s, then the fraction of the noise power reaching the output is F_m/f_s, where F_m is the cut off frequency of the baseband output channel, resulting in Equation 19.69.

$$N_o = \frac{\Delta^2}{3} \frac{F_m}{f_s} \qquad (19.69)$$

For a sinusoidal signal which just avoids slope overload, V_m is given by Equation 19.67 and the output signal power is given by Equation 19.70 and the SQNR by Equation 19.71.

$$S_o = \frac{1}{2} \left(\frac{\Delta}{2 \pi} \frac{f_s}{f_m} \right)^2 \qquad (19.70)$$

$$SQNR = \frac{3}{8 \pi^2} \frac{f_s^3}{f_m^2 F_m} \qquad (19.71)$$

For example, if f_s = 64kHz, F_m = 3.4kHz and f_m = 800Hz, the SQNR is 36.6dB. This is similar to that obtained with 64kbit/s PCM, but there is no companding to maintain the SQNR at lower signal levels.

19.6.2 Adaptive delta modulation

Simple DM is susceptible to slope overload. Moreover, since it provides uniform quantisation, the SQNR decreases when the level of the input signal is reduced. Several schemes of adaptive delta modulation (ADM) have been introduced to minimise these disad-

vantages by adapting the step size under changing signal conditions (Steele, 1975; Peebles, 1976; Taub and Schilling, 1986).

In a basic DM system, a rapidly changing input signal results in a long sequence of 1's or 0's being transmitted. In continuously variable slope delta modulation (CVSDM), the rate of change of the integrator output is increased if there is a sequence of several 1's or 0's. Thus, the CVSDM coder can follow a rapidly changing signal more accurately (Taub and Schilling, 1976).

19.6.3 Delta sigma modulation

Because slope overload causes the dynamic range to decrease with frequency, simple DM is unsuitable for baseband signals having a flat frequency spectrum. This disadvantage can be overcome by preceding the delta modulator by an integrator to reduce the high frequency energy of its input signal, as shown in Figure 19.25(a). This is known as delta sigma modulation (DSM), (Steele, 1975; Peebles, 1976). In order to obtain a flat overall gain/frequency response, a corresponding differentiator can be added at the output of the demodulator, as shown in Figure 19.25(a). However, the DM demodulator consists of an integrator, so differentiation of the output can be obtained by simply omitting it. The demodulator then consists only of a low pass filter, as shown in Figure 19.25(b).

Slope overload of the delta modulator within the delta sigma modulator occurs when dv_i/dt is too large. However v_i is given by Equation 19.72, resulting in Equation 19.73, and slope overload of this delta modulator corresponds to amplitude limiting of the input signal to the delta sigma modulator. Consequently, the signal amplitude that can be handled and the SQNR are both independent of frequency.

$$v_i = k \int_0^t v_m \, d t \qquad (19.72)$$

$$\frac{d v_i}{d t} = k v_m \qquad (19.73)$$

For a sinusoidal baseband signal of maximum amplitude, it can be shown (Johnson, 1968) that, SQNR is given by Equation 19.74.

$$SQNR = \frac{9}{8 \pi^2} \left(\frac{f_s}{F_m} \right)^3 \qquad (19.74)$$

Thus, as with simple DM, the quantisation noise power decreases with the cube of the sampling frequency.

19.6.4 Conversion filters

The various digital modulation schemes can be represented by a general theoretical model (Flood and Hawksford, 1971), which applies time and amplitude quantising to an analogue modulated signal. For PCM, the analogue modulation is AM; for DM, it is PM; for DSM, it is FM.

It follows that one type of digital modulation can be converted to another. If DM is generated with a sampling frequency n times the Nyquist rate and the output of the delta modulator feeds an up-down binary counter, then output readings from the counter at intervals of n digits give PCM code words at the Nyquist rate. (Goodman, 1969). If DSM is used, the number of 1's in the digit stream should be counted over a period of n digits and the counter then reset (Wallace et al., 1991).

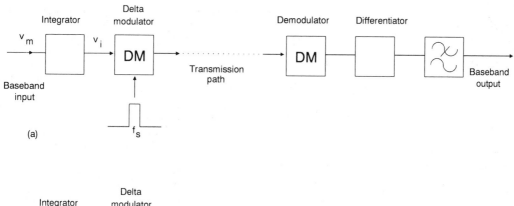

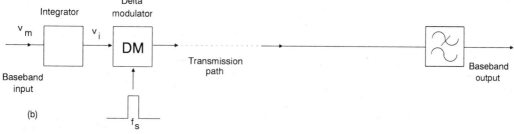

Figure 19.25 Delta sigma modulation: (a) derivation of delta sigma modulation; (b) delta sigma modulation system

Counters used in this way are called conversion filters. Use of a delta modulator or a delta sigma modulator, together with a conversion filter, provides an alternative to A/D converters.

19.7 Coding programme quality sound

For broadcast programmes, the bandwidth and dynamic range required are greater than those needed for telephony and the permissible degradation is much smaller. The CCIR has set a standard of 32 kHz sampling and 14-bit coding for sound channels of 14 kHz bandwidth.

The CCITT has recommended two alternative companding schemes: an 11-bit A-law, giving a reduction from 14 bits to 11 bits per sample, and a five range 'near instantaneous' companding scheme (NIC), giving a reduction from 14 bits to 10 bits per sample (Wallace et al., 1991).

19.8 Coding video signals

Composite video signals for colour television contain a luminance signal, together with colour components modulated onto quadrature sub carriers at 4.43 MHz. Since the total bandwidth exceeds 5 MHz, it might appear that the sampling frequency must exceed 10 MHz. However, the spectrum about the colour sub carrier frequency is concentrated in lines at intervals equal to half the line repetition frequency. This enabled a lower sampling rate, f_s, to be chosen, such that the aliases from those lines above $f_s/2$ fall into gaps in the spectrum below $f_s/2$ and can be removed by comb filtering.

A sampling frequency of 8.86 MHz and 8-bit encoding gives a digit rate of about 70 Mbit/s. In practice, 68 Mbit/s is used, but addition of error protection increases the digit rate further. The CCIR has recommended that 140 Mbit/s transmission be used in order to provide a higher quality than that provided by analogue transmission (CCIR Report 962).

A number of techniques have been developed to reduce the bandwidth required for a 70 Mbit/s video signal. Differential PCM can be used instead of conventional PCM. With non uniform quantisation, 4 to 6 bits are sufficient for the luminance signal and 2 to 4 bits for the colour information. This enables 34 Mbit/s to be used for programme quality signals or 8 Mbit/s for video telephony (CCIR Report 629-2).

More complex coding techniques have been developed to achieve further bandwidth reductions. (Jain, 1981). For example, the application of conditional replenishment and motion prediction enables the digit rate to be reduced to about 384 kbit/s (Wallace et al., 1991). The performance obtained is adequate for colour video conferencing applications (CCITT Recommendation H.261).

19.9 Acknowledgements

This chapter contains material reproduced by permission of Messrs. L.D. Humphrey, M.J. Sexton and A.D. Wallace and the Institution of Electrical Engineers from Chapter 6 of Flood, J.E. and Cochrane, P. (1991) Transmission Systems, Peter Peregrinus.

19.10 References

Alexander, A.A., Gryb, R.M. and Nast, D.W. (1960) Capabilities of the telephone network for data transmission, *Bell Syst. Tech. Jour.*, **39**, p.431.

Arthurs, E. and Dym, H. (1962) On the optimum detection of digital signals in the presence of white Gaussian noise, *IRE Trans.*, **CS-10**, pp. 336–373.

Atal, B.S. and Schroeder, M.R. (1970) Adaptive predictive encoding of speech signals, *Bell Syst. Tech. Jour.*, **49**, pp. 1973–1986.

Beckmann, P. (1967) *Probability in Communication Engineering,* Harcourt, Brace and World.

Bennett, W.R. and Davey, J.R. (1965) *Data transmission,* McGraw-Hill.

Betts, J.A. (1970) *Signal processing, modulation and noise,* English Universities Press.

Brewster, R.L. (Ed) (1986) *Data communication and networks,* Peter Peregrinus.

Brown, J. and Glazier, E.V.D. (1974) *Telecommunications* (2nd ed.), Chapman and Hall.

Bylanski, P. and Ingram, D.G.W. (1987) *Digital transmission systems* (3rd edn.), Peter Peregrinus.

Cattermole, K.W. (1969) *Principles of pulse code modulation,* Iliffe.

Chittleburgh, W.F.S., Green, D. and Heywood, A.W.A. (1957) A frequency-modulated voice-frequency telegraph system, *Post Off. Electr. Engrs. Jour.*, **50**, p. 69.

Clark, A.P. (1983) *Principles of digital data transmission* (2nd edn.), Pentech Press.

Clark, A.P. (1985) *Equalisers for digital modems,* Pentech Press.

de Belin, M. (1991) Microwave radio links, Chapter 12 in Flood, J.E. and Cochrane, P. (eds.) *Transmission Systems,* Peter Peregrinus.

Dorward, R.M. (1991) Digital transmission principles, Chapter 7 in *Transmission Systems,* Peter Peregrinus.

ETSI (1989) European Telecommunications Standards Institute *GSM full-rate speech transcoding,* GSM 06.10, version 3.01.02, April.

Evans, B.G. (Ed.) (1991) *Satellite communication systems* (2nd edn.), Peter Peregrinus.

Flood J.E. and Hawksford, M.J. (1971) An exact model for delta-modulation processes, *Proc. IEE*, **118**, pp. 1155–1161.

Goodman, D.J. (1969) The application of delta modulation to analogue-to-PCM encoding, *Bell Syst. Tech. Jour.*, **48**, pp. 321–343.

Harman, W.W. (1963) *Principles of the statistical theory of communication,* McGraw-Hill.

Hills, M.T. and Evans, B.G. (1973) *Transmission systems,* Allen and Unwin.

Jahnke, E. and Emde, F. (1960) *Tables of higher functions,* McGraw-Hill.

Jain, A.K. (1981) Image data compression: a review, *Proc. IEEE*, **69**, pp. 349–389.

Johnson, F.B. (1968) Calculating delta modulator performance, *IEEE Trans.*, **AU-16**, pp. 121–129.

Kretzmer, E.R. (1966) Generalisation of a technique for binary data transmission, *IEEE Trans.*, **COM-14**, pp. 67–68.

Lender, A. (1963) The duobinary technique for high speed data transmission, *AIEE Com. and Electron.*, **82**, pp. 214–218.

Lucky, R.W. and Hancock, J.C. (1962) On the optimum performance of N-ary systems having two degrees of freedom, *IRE Trans.*, **CS-10**, pp. 185–193.

Lucky, R.W., Salz, J. and Weldon, E.J. (1968) *Principles of data communication,* McGraw-Hill.

Nouri, A.M. (1991) *Satellite Communication,* Chapt. 13 in Flood, J.E. and Cochrane, P. (eds.) *Transmission Systems,* Peter Peregrinus.

Nyquist, H. (1928) Certain topics in telegraph transmission theory, *Trans. AIEE*, **47**, pp. 617–644.

Peebles, P.Z. (1976) *Communication system principles,* Addison-Wesley.

Purton, R.F. (1962) Survey of telephone speech-signal statistics and their significance in the choice of a PCM companding law, *Proc. IEE*, **109B**, pp. 60–66.

Ralphs, J.D. (1985) *Principles and practice of multi-frequency telegraphy,* Peter Peregrinus.

Sallen, R.P. and Key, E.L. (1955) A practical method of designing RC active filters, *IRE Trans.*, **CT-2**, pp. 74–85.

Saltz, J., Sheehan, J.R. and Paris, D.J. (1971) Data transmission by combined a.m. and p.m., *Bell Syst. Tech. Jour.*, **50**, pp. 2399–2419.

Schwartz, M. (1970) *Information transmission, modulation and noise,* McGraw-Hill.

Schwartz, M., Bennett, W.R. and Stein, S. (1966) *Communication systems and techniques,* McGraw-Hill.

Sedra, A.S. and Smith, K.C. (1982) *Microelectronic circuits,* Holt, Rinehart and Winston.

Steele, R. (1975) *Delta modulation systems,* Pentech Press.

Sunde, E.D. (1959) Theoretical fundamentals of pulse transmission, *Bell Syst. Tech. Jour.*, **33**, pp. 721–788 and 987–1010.

Taub, H. and Schilling, D.L. (1986) *Principles of communication systems,* (2nd edn.), McGraw-Hill.

Viterbi, A.J. (1966) *Principles of coherent communication,* McGraw-Hill.

Wallace, A.D., Humphrey, L.D. and Sexton, M.J. (1991) Analogue/digital conversion, Chapt.6 in Flood, J.E. and Cochrane, P. (eds.) *Transmission systems,* Peter Peregrinus.

Williams, M.B. The characteristics of telephone circuits in relation to data transmission, *Post Off. Electr. Engrs. Jour.* **59**, p.151.

20

Frequency division multiplexing

David Lockstone
Bell Northern Research

Contents

20.1 FDM principles

Frequency Division Multiplex (FDM) is the frequency translation of a number of individual standard telephony channels so that they can be stacked side by side and form a single wide band signal. This principle is illustrated in Figure 20.1.

Two identical telephony channels C_1 and C_2 (0.3 to 3.4kHz) are each mixed with a carrier frequency and combined. Only the lower sideband is selected from the mixing process and thus the channel frequencies are inverted on the combined signal. The spacing of the carrier dictates the spacing between the combined channels and is normally 4kHz i.e. $f_2 - f_1 = 4$kHz. The received path at B undergoes the opposite process.

As the carrier is not transmitted with the signal then f_1' and f_2' are separately generated at B. Any frequency difference between the carriers at A or B will impose a frequency shift on the recovered channel of $f_n - f_n'$.

The function of filters Fa1 and Fa2 is to select the wanted lower sideband and suppress the unwanted carrier signal, upper sideband etc. Fb1 and Fb2 filters select the required set of frequencies from the broadband line frequency spectrum for demodulation.

In the higher orders of translation it is not normally economic to design Fb filters with sufficient selectivity, such that only the required band of frequencies are selected. The signal presented to the demodulator in this case can contain some information from the adjacent channels. These unwanted signals are removed by the greater selectivity of the lower order demodulating equipments.

An additional requirement for Fb filters is to limit the total band of frequencies applied to the demodulator and thus keep the inter-modulation noise generated to a minimum. Fa and Fb filters are normally the same design.

The filters Fc1 and Fc2 remove the unwanted products from the demodulation process before presentation to the user or to the next lower order of translation.

The FDM system represents the most efficient use of bandwidth. With only the lower sideband of the modulation products transmitted the system limitations of bandwidth and overload are maximised.

20.2 History

The first UK FDM cable systems started service with a 12 channel system between Bristol and Plymouth in 1936. (Young, 1983)

Previously all telephony transmission was at audio frequency and the move to FDM was inspired for economic reasons and the pressure on cable utilisation. From then onwards the drive was for lower loss and higher bandwidth cables to support ever higher bandwidth systems.

The period during the 1960's to the mid 1970's saw the peak of FDM systems in service and the development of transistorised systems to 60MHz. However during this period developments of digital systems started to fully occupy the R&D budgets and penetration of digital into the trunk transmission network rapidly overtook the FDM analogue network.

20.3 FDM hierarchy

20.3.1 General considerations

A number of different transmission media are available, such as open wire cable, coaxial cable, radio or satellite systems, all with different bandwidth capability. The multiplexing schemes use a hierarchy of building blocks to construct systems to the required bandwidth. Many stages of translation may be required with the final stages of modulation only being specific to the particular transmission medium.

The building blocks are optimised for cable transmission. The dimensions of the various blocks are largely historic and based on the economics of filter design.

20.3.2 Channel bandwidth

Channel spacing is standardised on 4kHz. This provides enough space between the voice frequencies (0.3 to 3.4kHz) to economically filter the carrier, pilots, outband signalling tones, etc. that are positioned in the gaps between the speech signals.

Where transmission bandwidth is at a premium then the channel spacing may alternatively be based on 3kHz (voice bandwidth 0.2 to 3.050kHz). This provides a 4/3 increase in channel capacity but is only achieved with increased cost of the channel translation stage.

20.3.3 Group and supergroup

With reference to Figure 20.2 the channel translating section converts 12 voice frequency channels (or 16 if 3kHz channelling) and assembles them into a basic 'group' in the range 60 to 108kHz.

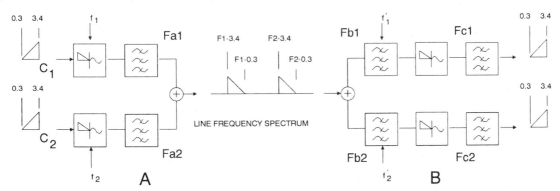

Figure 20.1 Frequency division multiplexing

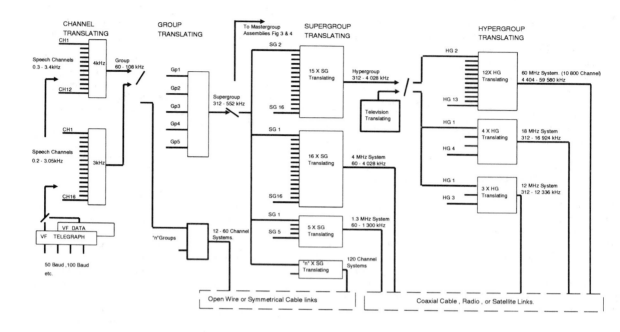

Figure 20.2 FDM hierarchy (U.K.)

Five groups are translated using carriers spaced 48kHz apart to form a 'supergroup' in the range 312kHz to 552kHz. A supergroup contains 60 channels.

Where a suffix has been added i.e. group 5 or supergroup 12, the suffix refers to the carrier that will be used to translate that particular set of channels and identifies it in the higher order band of frequencies.

Groups and supergroups are used to construct systems on open wire and symmetrical cable. The line frequency spectrum of the typical systems are shown in Figure 20.3.

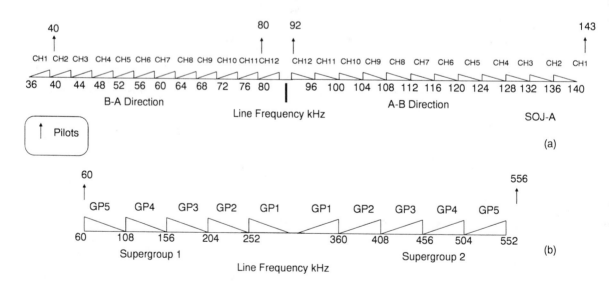

Figure 20.3 Typical open wire and symmetrical pair systems: (a) open wire, 12 channel; (b) symmetric pair, 120 channel

20.3.4   Higher order translation

Above supergroup level different administrations have adopted different hierarchies to build large systems. Three schemes have been identified and are described below:

1. The 15 supergroup assemblies (UK).
2. The mastergroup and supermastergroup assemblies (Europe).
3. The Bell mastergroup plan (USA).

20.3.4.1   *15 supergroup assemblies*

Supergroups 2 to 16 (Figure 20.2) are translated to the band 312 to 4028kHz and form the 15 supergroup assembly or 'hypergroup'. Note that supergroup 2 is not translated and passed forward directly to sit in the higher order spectrum at 312 to 552kHz.

Hypergroups (900 channels) are used as building blocks to assemble large groupings up to 60MHz, the most important is the 12MHz 2700 channel system. The carrier frequency chart up to 12MHz is shown in Figure 20.4.

20.3.4.2   *Mastergroup*

The mastergroup (Figure 20.5) is a 5 supergroup assembly using supergroups 4 to 8 and spans 812kHz to 2044kHz. This is an alternative scheme for building large systems, which avoids the large 15 supergroup blocks but introduces more stage of translation.

Three mastergroups, mastergroup 7, 8 and 9, are translated to a supermastergroup 8516kHz to 12338kHz and supermastergroups are used in further translations stages for 12MHz, 18MHz, and 60MHz systems.

20.3.4.3   *Bell system*

The Bell system (Figure 20.6) has adopted a different mastergroup arrangement in that 10 supergroups are required to form a mastergroup. The supergroup carrier frequencies vary according to the system usage resulting in different mastergroup frequency allocations. The U600 mastergroup is used as a building block for further translations whereas the L600 mastergroup is used directly for transmission as a 600 channel system. Six mastergroups form a supermastergroup of 3600 channels.

20.4   Frequency translation

The ring bridge modulator/demodulator typically provides the general features for frequency translation. With reference to Figure 20.7, a sinusoid carrier is supplied at a high level (+10dBm to +13

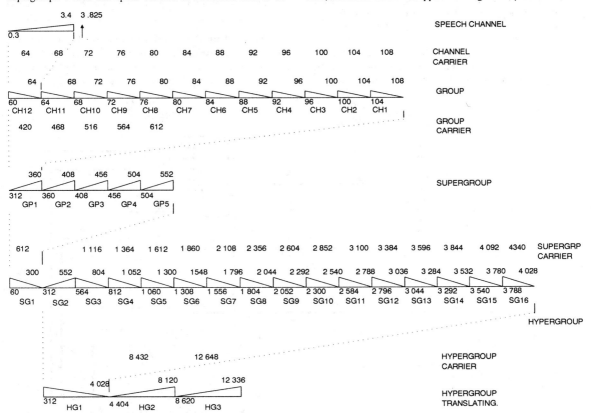

Figure 20.4   Translation frequencies and carriers (UK hierarchy)

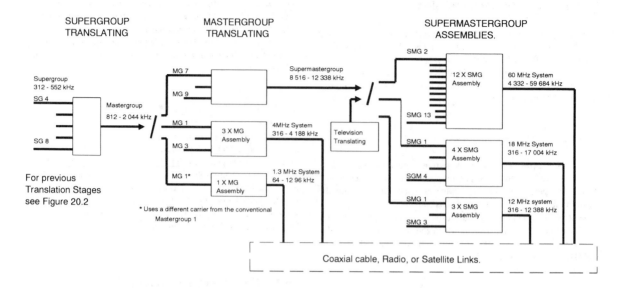

Figure 20.5   Mastergroup hierarchy

dBm) sufficient to forward bias the diodes D_1 and D_2 or D_3 and D_4 depending on the polarity of the carrier. The signal path, also through the diodes, is thus inverted on alternate half cycles of the carrier.

The current flowing, $i_c(t)$, due to the carrier signal is close to a square wave due to the clipping action of the diodes and by Fourier analysis is given by Equation 20.1, where k_1, k_3, k_5 etc. are circuit constants.

$$i_c(t) = k_1 \sin \omega_c t + k_3 \sin 3\omega_c t + k_5 \sin 5\omega_c t + \dots \quad (20.1)$$

If the input signal is represented by $i_{sig}(t)$ then the resulting modulated waveform at the output is given by Equation 20.2. i.e. the output frequency spectra is formed by the upper and lower sidebands about the carrier frequency and odd harmonics of the carrier frequency.

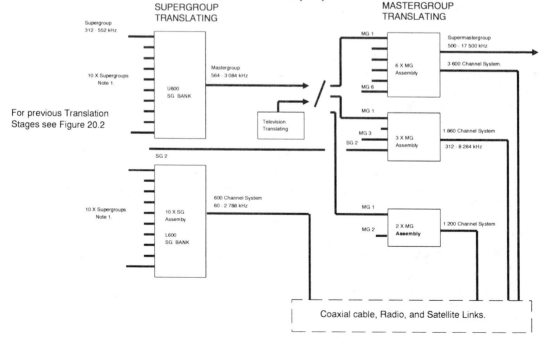

Figure 20.6   Bell FDM 'long haul' hierarchy. The Bell System Supergroup carrier frequencies do not always correspond to the CCITT supergroup carrier frequencies

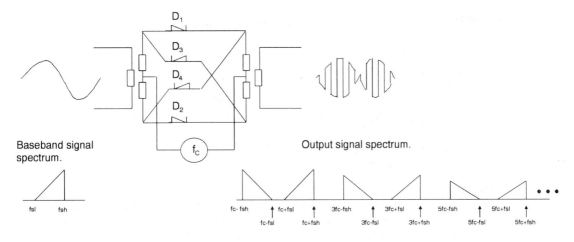

Figure 20.7 Ring bridge modulation

$$i_{out}(t) = i_c(t) i_{sig}(t)$$

$$= k_1 i_{sig}(t) \sin \omega_c t$$

$$+ k_3 i_{sig}(t) \sin 3\omega_c t + k_5 i_{sig}(t) \sin 5\omega_c t + ... \quad (20.2)$$

Note that neither the carrier frequency, carrier frequency harmonics, nor the original baseband signal is present at the output. i.e. the modulator is 'balanced'.

20.4.1 Ring bridge modulator/demodulator design considerations

20.4.1.1 *Carrier compression.*

With this type of modulator the ratio of the change in carrier power to the change in signal loss of the modulator, known as 'carrier compression', is approximately 10:1 so that accurate level stability of the carrier is not required.

20.4.1.2 *Carrier and signal suppression*

This is also known as carrier 'leak' and signal 'leak'. Perfect balance of modulator referred to above is not possible in practice. The best balance that can be achieved in a manufacturing environment is in the order of 30dB.

There will therefore be some unwanted products at the output of the modulator that will have to be removed by filtering before presentation to the combined path. Filter Fa (see Figure 20.1) requirements are shown in Table 20.1. The requirement is higher for the signal leak and the upper sideband as these products will give rise to crosstalk.

20.5 Carriers

20.5.1 Carrier frequency accuracy

For some services, particularly data circuits, it is desirable that the 'virtual' carrier difference over a network is maintained to within

Table 20.1 Filter Fa requirements

Product	Level at modulator output	Requirement	Filter suppression
Carrier leak	+20dBmO	−50dBmo	70dB
Signal leak	−30dBmO	−80dBmO	50dB
Upper sideband	−30dBmO	−80dBmO	50dB

2Hz. (CCITT, 1985.) To achieve this the carrier generation master oscillators receive regular maintenance adjustment using a reference frequency comparison pilot (see Section 20.6.2.2) or in later developed systems are phased locked to the frequency comparison pilot.

The recommended stability of the carrier frequencies are given in Table 20.2. With this carrier accuracy the end to end difference in virtual carriers will exceed 3Hz for 1% of the time and 4Hz for 0.1% of the time over a hypothetical international link of 2500km.

Table 20.2 Recommended stability of carrier frequencies

Carrier	Stability
Channel carriers	$\pm 1 \times 10^{-6}$
Group and supergroup	$\pm 1 \times 10^{-7}$
Hypergroup mastergroup and supermastergroup associated with 12MHz systems	$\pm 5 \times 10^{-8}$

20.5.2 Carrier purity

This is as follows:

1. Harmonics less than −20dBmO.
2. Purity against other carriers and side products related to 4kHz less than −80dBmO.

Spurious sidebands are produced by the carrier impurities during the modulation process and these create both intelligible and unintelligible crosstalk. The level of the 'ghost' sidebands is related to the level of the impurity of the carrier. (Tucker, 1948.)

20.5.3 Carrier level

Carriers are generated at a high level (+25dBm) for distribution to the translating equipment. Each equipment normally requires two supplies at a power level of approximately +10 to +13dBm in order to drive the modulator and demodulator.

20.6 Pilots

20.6.1 Translation equipment pilots

Reference pilots are discrete frequencies added to each translated band of traffic channels for monitoring and automatic gain control regulation at the far end of the transmission path. Some of the more common reference pilots are given in Table 20.3.

Additional pilots can be added for measurement or monitoring of wide band systems and are usually positioned in the gaps between supergroups. These are called intersupergroup pilots.

20.6.1.1   *Use of reference pilots for automatic gain control*

The normal practice is to provide gain or loss correction to the traffic path at the received end of transmission using the pilot to control the correction. (See Figure 20.8). This correction is applied most commonly at group and supergroup level.

Table 20.3   Some common reference pilots

Pilot	Frequency
Group reference pilot	84.080kHz
Supergroup reference pilot	411.920kHz
Hypergroup or mastergroup reference pilot	1552kHz
Supermastergroup reference pilot	11096kHz

Correction is applied to maintain the design traffic level across the circuit link which may contain many stages of translation and several tandem connected line systems. Seasonal temperature changes to the cable link is foremost in the contributing factors. The correction is applied equally across the frequency band and with an Automatic Gain Control ratio of approximately 10:1.

Thermistors are normally used as gain control elements to avoid any unlinearity distortion to the traffic path. In addition the slow thermal time constant is suited to the slow diurnal gain change of the cable system and the envelope gain of the AGC relatively easy to control. ± 4dB regulation range is normally required from AGC equipments.

20.6.2   Line equipment pilots

Specific pilots are combined with the traffic path for transmission over copper line systems.

20.6.2.1   *Regulation pilots*

Regulating pilots are placed at the high end of cable frequency spectrum close to the top traffic frequency where the cable loss is greatest and the pilot most sensitive to any loss changes. The gain of the line repeater is modified to keep the pilot level constant throughout the seasonal changes of cable loss and thus the traffic power level at the repeater output can be maintained close to the

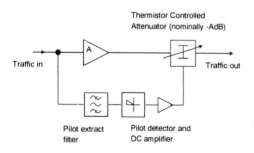

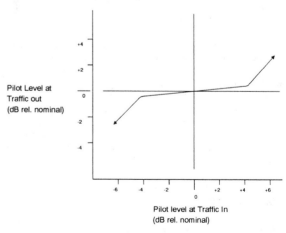

Figure 20.8   Automatic gain control (AGC)

thermal and intermodulation noise design optimum. The regulating pilot is transmitted at −10dBmO. (See also Section 20.14.3.)

Commonly used regulating pilot frequencies are given in Table 20.4.

Table 20.4 Commonly used regulating pilot frequencies

Coaxial system	Pilot frequency
1.3MHz, 300 channel	1364kHz
4MHz, 960 channel	4092kHz
4MHz, 900 channel	4287kHz
12MHz, 2700 channel	12435kHz
18MHz, 3600 channel	18480kHz
60MHz, 10800 channel	61160kHz

20.6.2.2 *Frequency comparison pilots*

The frequency comparison pilot is used at each translation point to maintain the carrier generation master oscillators to a high degree of frequency stability. The pilots are placed at the low end of the cable frequency spectrum for minimum phase error shifts. These phase shifts occur from the cable and equalisers. Some commonly used frequency comparison pilots are given in Table 20.5.

Table 20.5 Commonly used frequency comparison pilots

Coaxial system	Pilot frequency
1.3MHz, 300 channel	60kHz
4MHz, 960 channel	60kHz
4MHz, 900 channel	300kHz
12MHz, 2700 channel	308kHz
18MHz, 3600 channel	564kHz
60MHz, 10800 channel	564kHz

20.7 Noise contributions

Noise is the largest source of degradation to analogue systems.

Two contributions have to be considered, thermal and unlinearity noise. To evaluate the noise performance of an equipment both noise source contributions are calculated in pWOp and summated.

20.7.1 Definitions

There are three power levels in common use, dBr, dBm and dBmO.

20.7.1.1 *dBr*

The 0dBr point is the level at a reference point within the system that all the transmission levels refer. This used to be the 2 wire audio point or the 2 wire point of origin, as it was sometimes called.

This physical entity within a network has all but disappeared and a point of reference is now normally taken as the virtual outgoing switch point and is set at −4dBr. From the transmissions point of view the audio output from the channel translating equipment is adjusted to suit the required stated dBr level at that point and this becomes the level to which all the transmission levels within the system refer. Transmission levels are referred to in dBr.

20.7.1.2 *dBm*

The power at a various points in the transmission are referred to in dBm. If a test signal is injected into a 0dBr point at 0dBm then the test signal level throughout the transmission can be referred to in dBm.

It is sometimes the case that for noise calculations where the transmission level is required in dBm rather than dBr it is assumed that the power at the 0dBr point is 0dBm.

20.7.1.3 *dBmO*

This is the power of a signal in dBm referred to a point where the transmission level is 0dBm.

For instance if a signal power is −80dBm at a −30dBm transmission level point, then the signal is defined as −50dBmO.

20.7.2 Psophometric weighting

When noise, either thermal or unlinear noise, is added to a telephone conversation, the degree of annoyance or the effect on the intelligibility of the conversation is not the same for all frequencies of added noise.

A weighting curve has been constructed to characterise this effect. Various curves exist (CCITT , Bell System C message etc.) all giving weighting factors of 2 to 2.5dB. The UK adopt the CCITT curve in Figure 20.9 providing a weighting factor of 2.5dB. This

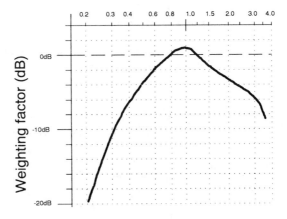

Figure 20.9 Psophometric weighting curve (CCITT)

factor allows that for a 4kHz channel, considered over the speech bandwidth of 3.1kHz, 2.5dB more Gaussian type noise can be tolerated from the system when weighting is applied.

When this correction is applied the suffix 'p' is added to the noise power figure (i.e. dBmOp). An additional weighting factor is included when the full channel width of 4kHz is considered.

The weighting factor for a 4kHz channel considered over the full 4kHz is 2.5 + 10log(4/3.1) or 3.6dB.

20.7.3 Thermal noise

This is sometimes called Browian or Gaussian noise and is noise that is associated with the random movement of electrons at temperatures above absolute zero.

For the FDM range of frequencies the noise power that is generated is given by Equation 20.3, where P is noise power in watts, k is Boltzmann's constant, T is the absolute temperature in degrees Kelvin, and B is bandwidth in Hz.

$$P = k\,T\,B \quad watts \tag{20.3}$$

If T = 310°K and B = 4000Hz then the available noise power is −137.5dBm.

The absolute thermal noise power at the output of a circuit element of gain GdB and noise figure FdB within a 4kHz channel is given by Equation 20.4.

$$- 137.5 + G + F \quad dBm \tag{20.4}$$

If the absolute power at the transmission level point T_L is known (TL in dBm) then the thermal noise contribution to the noise power in a 4kHz channel can be calculated in dBmOp (or pWattOp) as in expressions 20.5 and 20.6, where 3.6dB is the weighting factor for a 4kHz bandwidth. Definitions of the noise factor F are found in Connor, 1973.

$$- 137.5 + G + F - T_L - 3.6 \quad dBmOp \tag{20.5}$$

$$\frac{1}{1000} Antilog \left(\frac{- 137.5 + G + F - T_L - 3.6}{10} \right) \quad pWOp \tag{20.6}$$

20.7.4 Noise due to unlinearity

When carrying a traffic channel load the unlinear transfer characteristic of the active devices in the system generate harmonics and more complex intermodulation products that very quickly take on the characteristics of gaussian noise.

This noise source is referred to as intermodulation or cross modulation noise.

The initial problem is to define the power presented to the system by speech traffic.

20.7.4.1 *Single channel load*

The average power in each channel of a transmission band carrying normal 'busy hour' speech traffic referred to a 0dBr point of measurement is L_0 (dBmO) as in Equation 20.7 (Bell, 1971), where P_{vo} is the long term average power in a single talker dBm0, g is the standard deviation of the distribution of talker volumes and t is the traffic activity factor.

$$L_o = P_{vo} + 0.115\, g^2 + 10 \log t \quad dBmO \tag{20.7}$$

Single talker volume (P_{vo})

This is the power in dBmO of a continuous individual talker measured using a long term averaging meter (10 seconds) at a 0dBr point. This includes power due to signalling frequencies.

The precise value for P_{vo} has been the subject of much measurement and study over the years. The UK figure used for trunk networks is −12.9dBmO. In the Bell System a figure of −13.9dBmO has been adopted for International use. (Most of the figures have been derived from Holbrook and Dixon, 1939.)

Loud and soft talker factor ($0.115g_2$)

P_{vo} is the average power in an individual talker. However, analysing a large number of talkers will show that they all have different volumes compared to the standard talker i.e. there are loud and soft talkers.

The distribution of the talker volumes (in dB) has been found to be Normal, with a standard deviation of g. (Figure 20.10(a).)

In order to find the average power per talker from a distribution of talker volumes the average or expected value is derived from the log normal distribution (see Figure 20.10(b)). This derives that the average power per talker over a large number of talkers is $0.115g^2$ greater than the average power of a single talker. (Bennett, 1940)

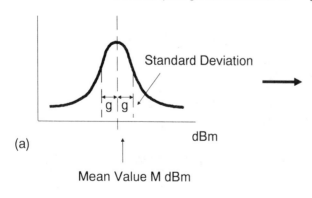

(a)

Standard Deviation

g g

dBm

Mean Value M dBm

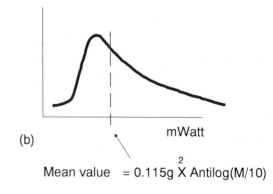

(b)

mWatt

Mean value $= 0.115g^2$ X Antilog(M/10)

Figure 20.10 Log normal distribution

Activity factor (10log t)

Not all the channels are fully occupied with continuous talkers. This gives rise to an activity factor t.

Conversation between two parties consist of 50% listening and 50% talking. The activity in any one direction is therefore 0.5.

In addition not all of the channels are in use. Even in the peak period only 70% of the circuits are occupied at any one time. The activity factor t is therefore reduced to 0.35. The figure normally used for t is 0.25.

Values for L_o, P_{vo}, g and t are given in Table 20.6. (CCITT, 1985; Bell, 1971.)

Table 20.6 Values for L_o P_{vo} g and t

	L_0 (dBmO)	P_{vo}(dBmO)	g	t
CCITT	−15.0	−12.9	5.8	0.25
Bell International	−14.5	−13.9	5.0	0.45

20.7.4.2   Multichannel load

The average traffic power P_n in a multichannel load of N channels is given by Equation 20.8, where $N \geq 240$, assuming that a single channel load figure is given by the −15dBmO value in Table 20.6.

$$P_n = -15 + 10 \log N \quad dBmO \tag{20.8}$$

For N < 240 the statistics of the activity factor dictate that a slightly higher value for the average load should be used. A best fit curve is given by Equation 20.9 (CCITT, 1985).

$$P_n = -1 + 4 \log N \quad dBmO \tag{20.9}$$

20.7.4.3   Unlinearity characterisation

For a sinusoid fundamental signal at the output of a typical amplifier, the output power of the second and third harmonics would appear as in Figure 20.11. In order to calculate the effect of the unlinearity on the transmission it is necessary to be able to quantify the harmonics and associated intermodulation products.

At the overload point, or clipping region, the harmonics increase very rapidly with increasing fundamental level and the characterisation of harmonic performance of the amplifier in this region is not practical.

As the output level is reduced and moves out of the overload region, the shape of the harmonic curve passes the knee and enters a linear portion of the graph where the second harmonic level reduces by 2dB and the third harmonic by 3db for every 1dB drop in fundamental signal. The harmonic performance is characterised in this region.

If the amplifier transfer characteristics in the 'linear' region are assumed to be a square law, Equation 20.10 is obtained, where v_i is the input voltage, given by Equation 20.11, v_o is the output voltage, and a_1, a_2, a_3 are constants of the amplifier.

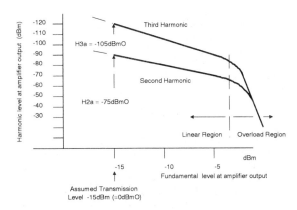

Figure 20.11 Amplifer characteristics

$$v_0 = a_i v_i + a_2 v_i^2 + a_3 v_i^3 + \dots \tag{20.10}$$

$$V_i = V \cos \omega t \tag{20.11}$$

From this transfer characteristic Equations 20.12 and 20.13 may be obtained.

$$v_0 = a_1 V \cos \omega t \tag{20.12}$$

$$\begin{aligned} v_o = \frac{1}{2} a_2 V^2 + \left(a_1 V + \frac{3}{4} a_3 V^3 \right) \cos \omega t \\ + \frac{1}{2} a_2 V^2 \cos 2 \omega t + \frac{1}{4} a_3 V^3 \cos 3 \omega t + \dots \end{aligned} \tag{20.13}$$

Thus the second harmonic (cos 2 ω t) is proportional to the square of input signal amplitude V. Likewise the third harmonic (cos 3 ω t) is proportional to the cube of the input signal amplitude.

In dB terms it can be shown (Bell, 1971) that at a transmission level of 0dBmO the power in a sinusoidal harmonic or intermodulation tone, $P_m(x)$ in dBmO, at the amplifier output is related to the output level of the fundamental tones A and B by Equations 20.14 to 20.18, where $P_m(x)$ is the harmonic or intermodulation power in dBmO, P(x) is the fundamental power in dBmO, H_{2a} and H_{3a} are the second and third harmonic powers in dBmO, characterised for the amplifier with fundamentals at 0dBmO. (Figure 20.11.)

$$P_m(2A) = H_{2a} + 2P(A) \tag{20.14}$$

$$P_m(A \pm B) = H_{2a} + 6 + P(A) + P(B) \tag{20.15}$$

$$P_m(3A) = H_{3a} + 3P(A) \tag{20.16}$$

$$P_m(2A \pm B) = H_{3a} + 9.6 + 2P(A) + P(B) \tag{20.17}$$

$$\begin{aligned} P_m(A \pm B \pm C) = H_{3a} + 15.6 \\ + P(A) + P(B) + P(C) \end{aligned} \tag{20.18}$$

Thus, once H_{2a} and H_{3a} have been determined by measurement, all the second and third order intermodulation products can be deduced for a specific transmission level.

20.7.4.4 Determination of unlinearity noise from a multi-channel load

The technique used (Bennett, 1940) is to show that, for the purpose of calculating unlinearity or intermodulation noise, a channel loaded with a single sinusoid can be considered equivalent to a channel loaded with gaussian (or speech) noise by the application of a suitable factor k(x) to the noise contribution . A band of n speech channels thus becomes a band of n sinusoids and the problem is reduced to one of counting intermodulation products falling into the channel of interest for each product (A + B, 2A– B, etc.).

The total intermodulation noise in any particular channel is the summated power contribution from each of these products.

Bennett's formula, rearranged to give the weighted noise contribution W(x) within a specified channel is as in Equation 20.19.

$$W(x) = P_m(x) - k(x) + P_{vo} e(x) + 0.115 g^2 d(x)$$
$$+ 10 \log(U(x) t^{u(x)}) - C \quad dBmOp \quad (20.19)$$

The suffix (x) refers to the type of intermodulation under consideration i.e. H(A + B) etc. (Table 20.7) In Equation 20.9 $P_m(x)$ is

Table 20.7 Types of intermodulation

Type(X)	k(x)	e(x)	d(x)	u(x)	C
A+B	0	2	2	2	3.6
A–B	0	2	2	2	3.6
A–2B	1.5	3	5	2	3.6
2A–B	1.5	3	5	2	3.6
2A+B	1.5	3	5	2	3.6
A+B+C	0	3	3	3	3.6
A+B–C	0	3	3	3	3.6
A–B–C	0	3	3	3	3.6

the power of the intermodulation product (x) in dBmO at the output of the system for 0dBmO fundamentals; k(x) is the speech tone modulation factor (a factor in dB to convert the sinusoid $P_m(x)$ to the equivalent intermodulation product power for bands of 4kHz gaussian noise); P_{vo} is the power in a single average talker in dBmO (see Table 20.6); g is the standard deviation of the distribution of all talkers from loud to soft (see Table 20.6); e(x) and d(x) are factors to account for the relationship between the power in the talker (the fundamental signal) and the resulting intermodulation product (e(x) is a factor to modify the talker volume P_{vo} and d(x) to modify the standard deviation of talker volumes g); t is the transmission activity factor or the probability that a particular channel is active (see Table 20.6); u(x) is the number of channels involved in forming the particular intermodulation product and therefore $t^{u(x)}$ is the probability that the particular intermodulation product from a particular set of channels is present; C is the psophometric weighting correction factor for 4kHz and is 3.6dB. U(x) is the number of intermodu-

lation products for a particular type (i.e. A + B, A + B, etc.) falling in a particular channel of interest.

The factor U(x) is derived from Bennett's formulae but for simplicity are usually shown in graphical form as in Figure 20.12.

These graphs are valid for systems of greater than 500 channels (Bell, 1971).

20.7.4.5 Approximate value for the weighted intermodulation noise contribution

For wide band systems there are three major intermodulation contributors A + B, A – B and A + B – C. Assuming the CCITT accepted values for channel loading (see Table 20.6) a rule of thumb calculation can be made for unlinearity contributions using Equations 20.20 to 20.22, where $W^*(x)$ is the approximate noise power in a selected channel, $P_m(x)$ is the power of the (x) product in dBmO for 0dBmO fundamentals, $U^*(x)$ is the factor obtained from Figure 20.13 for a channel at frequency f.

$$W^*(A + B) = P_m(A + B)$$
$$+ U^*(A + B) - 33.5 \quad dBmOp \quad (20.20)$$

$$W^*(A - B) = P_m(A - B)$$
$$+ U^*(A - B) - 33.5 \quad dBMOp \quad (20.21)$$

$$W^*(A + B - C) = P_m(A + B - C)$$
$$+ U^*(A + B - C) - 47 \quad dBmOp \quad (20.22)$$

20.7.4.6 Weighted noise power in pWOp

The total weighted intermodulation noise power can be determined from Equation 20.23, where x = all products, (A+B), (A-B), etc.

$$\sum \frac{1}{1000} Antilog\left(\frac{W(x)}{10}\right) \quad pWOp \quad (20.23)$$

20.7.4.7 Determination of unlinearity noise using spectral densities

The problem with Bennett's method is the difficulty of dealing with shaped frequency spectra (pre-emphasis at the output of Line repeaters for instance.)

A method using spectral densities (Bell, 1971) overcomes this difficulty and can be extended to include the shape of the H_{2a} and H_{3a} across the band.

From Equation 20.10 the ratio of the total second order distortion voltage to the fundamental signal at the output of the amplifier or system is given by Equation 20.24, where v_i is the system input signal (assumed Gaussian).

$$\frac{a_2 v_i^2}{a_1 v_i} \quad (20.24)$$

The terms in Equation 20.24 can be expressed as a power in volts squared where $S_1(f)$ and $S_2(f)$ are the power spectral densities in volts squared per Hertz. $S_1(f)$ is the figure for the multichannel input

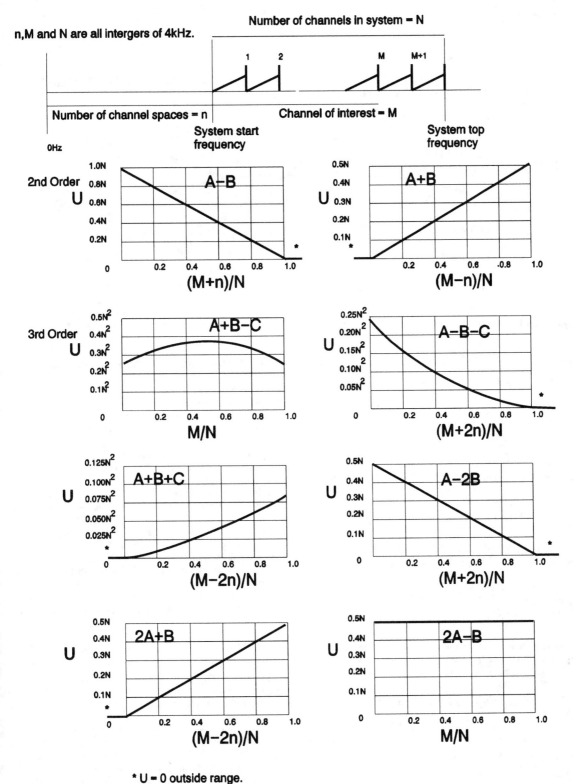

Figure 20.12 U(x) values for large sysems

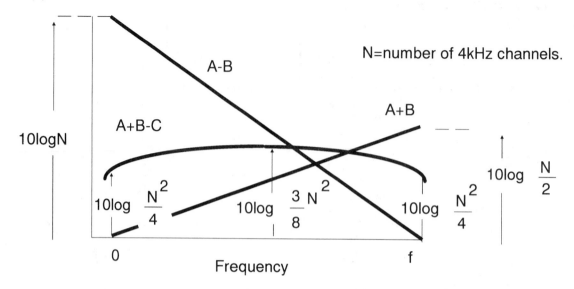

Figure 20.13 Approximate intermodulation factors $U^*(x)$

signal voltage, v_i, and $S_2(f)$ for the input signal voltage squared, v_i^2. This is shown in Equation 20.25.

$$\frac{a_2^2 S_2(f)}{a_1^2 S_1(f)} \tag{20.25}$$

If v_i is assumed Gaussian then Equation 20.26 may be obtained, ignoring d.c. terms and where * represents the convolution integral.

$$S_2(f) = 2[S_1(f) * S_1(f)] \tag{20.26}$$

The second order noise power NP_2 in watts is therefore given by Equation 20.27, where Pch is the traffic load per channel in watts.

$$NP2 = Pch \frac{a_2^2 2[S_1(f) * S_1(f)]}{a_1^2 S_1(f)} \tag{20.27}$$

Likewise the third order noise power NP_3 in watts is given by Equation 20.28, where the mean square voltage is given by Equation 20.29 and Pch is the traffic load per channel in watts.

$$NP_3 = Psch \frac{a_3^2 [9 V_{rms}^4 S_1(f) + 6(S_1(f) * S_1(f) * S_1(f))]}{a_1^2 S_1(f)}$$

$$\tag{20.28}$$

$$V_{rms}^2 = \int_{-\infty}^{+\infty} S_1(f) \, df \tag{20.29}$$

The convolution is best performed numerically on a per system basis.

20.8 Measurement of noise contributions

This is also referred to as white noise measurement. Both the thermal noise contributions and the intermodulation noise contributions can be measured directly with one test. This allows rapid field evaluation of installed systems and bench evaluation of individual circuits.

In Figure 20.14 the system is loaded with Gaussian noise from a generating source that has a flat frequency spectrum of noise, bandwidth limited by the filter F_{lim}.

A single defined channel at frequency f(c) is removed from the spectrum of noise by a filter F_{sc} before the noise band is transmitted into the system.

A measurement on the same channel at frequency f(c) selected by filter F_{pc} at the receiver will therefore measure noise that has been generated only within the system itself.

The system is loaded with noise power P_s that represents the expected multichannel load, as in Equation 20.30, where P_s The total power of the signal applied to the system, P_n is the multichannel load for N channels, and T_L is the transmission level point in dBm.

$$P_s = P_n + T_L \tag{20.30}$$

For instance, the figures for a 4MHz system at a −30dBm transmission level point will be P_n = +14.8dBmO (assuming the normal channel loading of −15dBmO). P_s will evaluate to −15.2dBm at T_L = −30dBm.

Two measurements are taken. The first is with the channel stop filter at the transmitter by-passed with the switch S in the closed position. This gives the power due to simulated traffic in a single channel referred to the meter calibration. Measured figure = N_s.

The second measurement is with the channel stop filter at the transmitter in circuit with the switch S open. This gives the noise power generated from the system referred to the same meter calibration. Measured figure = N_n.

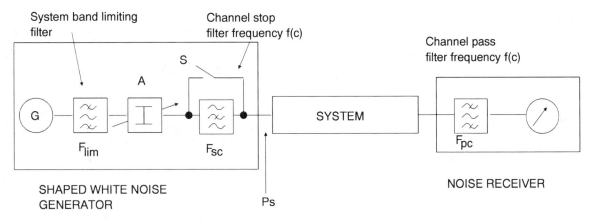

Figure 20.14 System loaded noise test

The Noise Power Ratio (NPR) is given by 10log(Ns/Nn) dB.

The total noise power falling into the channel can be determined from Equation 20.31, where N_c is the total weighted noise contribution over 4kHz in the specified channel in dBmOp, k = B/4N where B is the bandwidth of the system bandwidth limiting filter in kHz, and N is the number of channels.

$$N_c = -NPR - 18.6 - 10 \log k \quad dBmOp \quad (20.31)$$

The term 10log k is to correct for the fact that the actual traffic load has gaps between the channels and is not continuous.

The total noise power is also given in pWOp by Equation 20.32.

$$\frac{1}{1000} Antilog \left(\frac{N_c}{10} \right) \quad pWOp \quad (20.32)$$

Several channels are selected for measurement over the band by varying the frequency f(c) of both the channel stop filter in the transmitter and the channel pass filter in the receiver.

Also of interest is to vary the channel loading factor L_o (nominally −15dBmO) and determine the NPR for various conditions of traffic load. This is a measure of the system's robustness to peak loads and transmission level changes outside the normal design guides. The normal expected NPR curve is shown in Figure 20.15.

As the transmission load is lowered then the basic or Gaussian noise predominates. The NPR increases linearly with decreasing traffic power. As the transmission load is increased then intermodulation noise predominates and the NPR rapidly rises as more higher order intermodulation products contribute.

The optimum working point of the system is easily determined from Figure 20.15

20.9   Overload

Elements of the network have to be able to transmit the peak signal of the multichannel system load.

The system overload requirements are dimensioned such that the probability of the peak busy hour transmission signal exceeding the peak value of a sinusoid signal of power P_{eq} is 0.01.

P_{eq} in dBmO is given by Equation 20.33 (CCITT, 1985, Supplement 22) where t is the activity factor (see Table 20.6); L_o is the

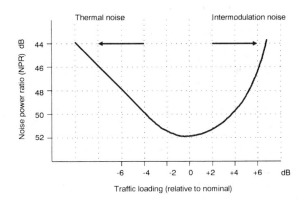

Figure 20.15 Noise power ratio variation for change in transmission loading

channel loading factor (see Table 20.6); and n is the number of active channels.

$$P_{eq} = L_o - 10 \log t$$
$$+ 10 \log \left[n + 2.33 \left(n \left(2 e^{0.23 g - 1} \right) \right)^{1/2} \right]$$
$$+ 9.9 + \frac{6}{1 + 0.07 n} \quad dBmO \quad (20.33)$$

The value of n is derived from assuming that the probability n channels are active in an N channel system is given by a binomial distribution and that n is only exceeded with a probability of 1% (i.e. the value of n is not exceeded 99% of the time) as in Equation 20.34. g is the standard deviation of loud/soft talkers (see Table 20.6) and N the system channel capacity.

$$n = N t + 2.33 \left(N t (1 - t) \right)^{1/2} \quad (20.34)$$

P_{eq} has been calculated for some of the more important systems, as in Table 20.8.

Table 20.8 Examples of P$_{eq}$

Number of channels	12	120	960	2700
Peq (dBmO)	19	21.2	27	30.5

20.9.1 Overload measurement.

The overload point is precisely defined according to one of two definitions, using harmonic/intermodulation products or using gain change.

20.9.1.1 *Harmonic/intermodulation products*

CCITT (1985) Recommendation G223, defines the overload as:

'The overload point or overload level of an amplifier is at that value of absolute power at the output at which the absolute power level of the third harmonic increases by 20dB when the input signal to the amplifier is increased by 1dB.'

If the 3rd harmonic is outside the frequency band of interest then the 2A–B intermodulation product may be used instead of the 3rd harmonic by the definition:

'The overload point or overload level of an amplifier is 6dB higher than the absolute power level in dBm, at the output of the amplifier, of each of two sinusoid signals of equal amplitude and of frequency A and B respectively, when these absolute power levels are so adjusted that an increase in 1dB of both of their separate levels at the input of the amplifier cause an increase, at the output of the amplifier, of 20dB in the intermodulation product of 2A–B.'

20.9.1.2 *Gain change*

From Equation 20.13 it can be seen the gain to the fundamental signal decreases by a factor given by expression 20.35 due to the non-linear characteristic.

$$20 \log \left(1 + \frac{3}{4} \frac{a_3}{a_1} v^2 \right) \qquad (20.35)$$

This effect can be used to give a definition of overload such that:

'The overload is the output power in dBm of a signal such that a further increase in 1dB of a fundamental sinusoid signal power at the input of the amplifier will give an increase in power at the output of the amplifier of the fundamental signal of 0.9dB.'

The advantage of this last method is that it is easy to perform and can be measured at any frequency in the band of interest.

20.10 Hypothetical reference system

Hypothetical reference systems (CCITT, 1985, G.212 — G.222 & G.229) have been constructed to define network building and how the various degradation factors are apportioned and planned. The longest proposed international link is 25000km (CCITT,1985, G.103) and is constructed of a number of sub hypothetical links of typically 2500km.

20.10.1 Noise contributions

Noise contributions are defined on a per channel basis in pWOp.

Table 20.9 Design targets for noise contributions from open wire systems with 2500km circuit length

Equipment	Number of equipments	Total noise allocation
Channel translation	3	2500pWOp
Line (group) frequency translation	6	2500pWOp
Line equipment noise		17500pWOp

Table 20.10 Design targets for noise contributions from metric pair cable systems, coaxial cable and radio systems with 2500 km circuit length

Equipment	Number of equipments	Total noise allocation
Channel translation 200pWOp	1	200pWOp
Group translation 80pWOp	3	240pWOp
Supergroup translation 60pWOp	6	360pWOp
Higher order translations 120pWOp	12	1440pWOp
Through connections etc.		260pWOp
Line equipment noise		7500pWOp

Recommended design targets are included in Tables 20.9 and 20.10. The line equipment noise figure in Table 20.10 corresponds to 3pWOp per km. For wideband services, such as TV transmission, the equivalent requirement is more onerous at 1.5pWOp mean noise contribution per km.

20.10.2 Line sections

The following applies:

1. The coaxial cable hypothetical systems are constructed from homogeneous line sections of 280km.
2. The change of gain of a regulated 280km homogeneous line section due to seasonal changes in the cable loss, time etc. will not be greater than 1dB.
3. Unwanted modulation products from low frequencies (50Hz etc.) will not be greater than 48dBmO for a 280km homogeneous line section. A similar requirement is placed on the multiplex equipment.

20.11 Companding

Companding (compression/expansion) enables a noise advantage by compressing the dynamic range of the transmitted voice channel and performing the opposite expansion of the signal at the receiving end. Companders are used on long circuits where the noise additions have rendered the circuits unacceptable, or where a noisy transmission medium can be made viable.

20.11.1 Compander characteristics

The Compander parameters (Bell, 1971) are Compression Ratio and Unaffected Level, where compressor and expandor power output are given by Equations 20.36 and 20.37.

$$\text{Compressor output } (dBm)$$
$$= \frac{\text{Compressor power input } (dBmO)}{K} + A \qquad (20.36)$$

$$\text{Expandor power output } (dBmO)$$
$$= K\left(\text{Expandor power input } (dBmO)\right) - KA \qquad (20.37)$$

K is normally 2 (the Compression Ratio) and KA equal 5 (the Unaffected Level). Compander characteristics are as in Figure 20.16.

The values for K and KA are limited by practical considerations. Increasing these values will improve the noise reduction but at the expense of other transmission properties. For instance increasing the compression ratio has the disadvantage of expanding any gain change or level error within the transmission.

20.11.2 Multichannel load increase

Companding gives an increase in the peak multichannel load. The increase is mainly determined by the compression ratio, but the unaffected level and both the attack and decay times all impact on the overall loading.

Considering the main contribution from the compression ratio, the power in an single average talker is given in Table 20.6 where $P_{vo} = -12.9dBmO$, $g = 5.8$ and $t = 0.25$ to derive $L_o = -15dBmO$. When compression is applied to the signal then the parameters above are modified by the compression ratio to give $P_{vo} = -12.9/2dBmO$, $g = 5.8/2$ and $t = 0.25$ to derive $L_o = -11.48dBmO$.

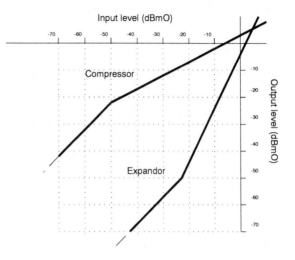

Figure 20.16 Idealised compressor and expandor characteristics

Using the new value for L_o (compressed) of $-11.48dBmO$ new values for P_{eq} (compressed) can be calculated from Equation 30.24. For example a 4MHz 960 channel system has an overload requirement of $+26.62dBmO$ with normal $-15dBmO$ single channel loading. With compression the overload requirement is $+29.73dBmO$ or 3.2dB higher.

It will therefore normally be necessary to drop the transmission level by 3.2dB (WdB) and to raise it again before expansion to avoid overloading the system (see Figure 20.17).

This adjustment to the transmission level will reduce some of the companding advantage by increasing the thermal noise contribution at the output of the expandor where the extra WdB gain is applied.

20.11.3 Compandor noise advantage

From Figure 20.16 it can be seen that while no speech is transmitted the noise power will be subject to an attenuation of 25dB at the expandor output.

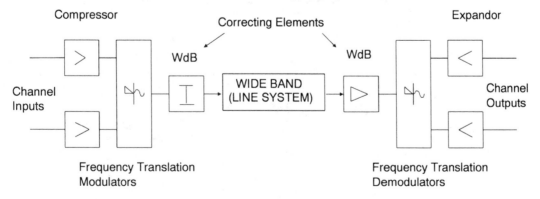

Figure 20.17 Transmission level correction for companding load increase

The theoretical noise advantage will therefore be given by Equation 20.38.

$$Noise\ advantage\ =\ 25 - W\ \ dB \qquad (20.38)$$

However, the circuit noise while speech power is transmitted is virtually unaffected by the compression/expansion process and there is no advantage. During talking, therefore, the conversation is subject to the full effect of the system noise. The effect of this noise produces an impairment to speech intelligibility that detracts from the companding advantage by an estimated 5dB.

Overall advantage is therefore given by Equation 20.39.

$$Noise\ advantage\ =\ 25 - W - 5\ \ dB \qquad (20.39)$$

20.11.4   Attack and decay time

The compression and expansion process is speech power activated and it therefore takes time to recognise the increase (attack time) or decrease (recovery time) in speech power. Attack time is normally set at 5ms and recovery time 22.3ms. (CCITT, 1985, Recommendation G.162.)

20.11.5   Usage of companders

Companders are recommended for use with speech transmission if the mean noise power of a circuit in any hour is greater than 40000pWOp (–44dBmOp). (CCITT, 1985, Recommendation G.143.) The comparable limit for telegraphy is 80000pWOp (–41dBmOp). (CCITT, 1985, Recommendation H.21.)

20.12   Through connections

Within the network it may be required that a band of channels (typically group or supergroup) are allocated as a through connection path without translation to voice band. This could be at a drop and insert point for instance as shown in Figure 20.18.

20.12.1   Through connection filter

In this situation the band of interest has to be cleaned before passed back into the modulation process. From Figure 20.1 and Figure 20.19 a typical demodulator filter F_b selects the required band of frequencies (band N) from the high order broadband of channels. Because of the selectivity of the filter F_b, the selected band of frequencies contain some of the adjacent channels from N+1 and N–1.

Normally these are removed by subsequent filtering and demodulation to voice level. If presented for re-translation however the adjacent channels must be removed to prevent crosstalk. Suppression of all such possible crosstalk paths is less than 80dBmO.

Such filters are large and complex and are usually separate equipments.

20.13   Transmultiplexers

A transmultiplexer provides a link between FDM and TDM hierarchies without having to translate to baseband voice frequencies.

The drive for transmultiplexer development came from analogue network operators updating to digital switches. With a digital switch the interface to the trunk network is at a 2.048kbit/s CEPT defined digital bit stream (or 1.554Mbit/s T1 for the USA digital hierarchy) i.e. there is no point that is suitable for direct connection into an FDM hierarchy without the cost and attendant distortions of translation to speech band.

As a prime function therefore transmultiplexers interface to 2048kbit/s 30 channel (1544kbit/s 24 channel).

An economic fit of this digital interface is normally achieved by taking 2 X 2048kbit/s 30 channel bit streams with a total of 60 channels and transmultiplexing to a single FDM supergroup. The alternatively fit for a T1 1544kbit/s 24 channel bit stream is transmultiplexed into 2 X FDM groups each carrying 12 channels. A block diagram of a typical 60 channel Transmultiplexer is shown in Figure 20.20 (Rossiter et. al.,1982).

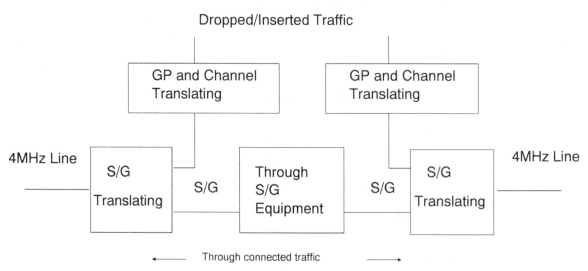

Figure 20.18   Drop and insertion of traffic

CONVENTIONAL DEMODULATION

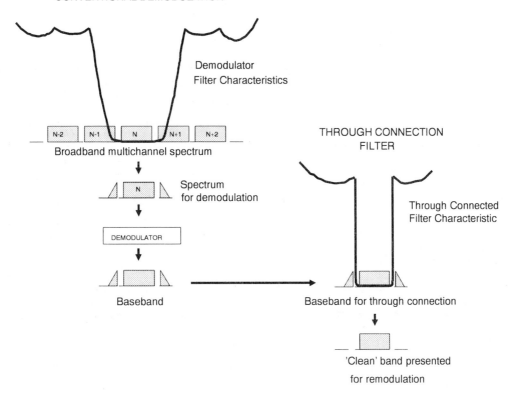

Figure 20.19 Through connection filters

The incoming supergroup is filtered to remove the adjacent side-bands. The gain is adjusted using an AGC from the supergroup pilot extracted within the Discrete Fourier Transform (DFT) and the complete band digitised through an analogue to digital converter. Using Digital Signal Processing (DSP) techniques the digitised band is split and then transformed into a TDM representation.

At this point the coefficients representing the pilots and signalling are extracted. The signalling is processed separately and the process algorithms depend on the type of signalling adopted (i.e. CCITT R1 or R2, E&M scheme etc.). The TDM band is then formatted for

A-law companding, PCM coding and time processed for the 2048kbit/s CEPT structure.

The opposite procedure is adopted for the PCM to FDM conversion.

20.13.1 Synchronisation

The frequency accuracy requirement of an FDM supergroup is better than 1 part in 10^7 whereas the TDM stream is 50 part in 10^6 (Ribeyre et. al., 1982). To achieve the FDM accuracy the transmulti-

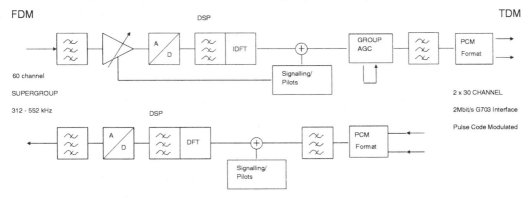

Figure 20.20 Supergroup transmultiplexer

plexer may have to be locked to an accurate reference and allowance made to frame slip the TDM data.

20.13.2 PCM alarms

Data and alarms carried on TS0 of the PCM frame, data services carried on either the TDM or FDM signals and common channel signalling schemes have to be terminated at the transmultiplexer and treated separately.

20.14 Repeatered cable line equipment

The main function of the line terminal equipment is to service the cable transmission equipment. A supervisory overlay system is usually provided whereby a faulty repeater can be located from the terminal end. A constant current d.c. supply is established on the copper transmission wires for supplying power to the dependent repeaters (usually 50 or 110 mA).

Dependent repeaters are installed at regular intervals along the cable, the recommended spacing is as in Table 20.11. Repeaters are normally housed in pressurised boxes, either pole mounted or buried depending on the siting of the cable.

A coaxial line is required to meet an average noise contribution per circuit of better then 1.5pWOp per km. In order to achieve this with a limited DC power budget optimal designs have to be used.

Table 20.11   Repeatered cable spans

System	Cable	Repeatered span
1.3MHz (300 channels)	1.2/2.4mm	8km
4MHz (960 channels)	1.2/2.4mm	4km
12MHz (2700 channels)	1.2/2.4mm	2km
18MHz (3600 channels)	2.6/9.5mm	4km
60MHz (10800 channels)	2.6/9.5mm	1.5km

20.14.1 Pre-Emphasis

The noise contributions from a single repeater are shown in Figure 20.21(a). The greatest contribution is thermal noise at high frequencies as the highest gain is required at this end to overcome to cable loss.

By applying deliberate shaping to the transmission path at the transmitting terminal end (pre-emphasis) and an opposite characteristic at the receiving terminal end (de-emphasis) the noise contributions can be flattened so that all the channels have a similar contribution and the worst channels are 3 to 4dB improved.

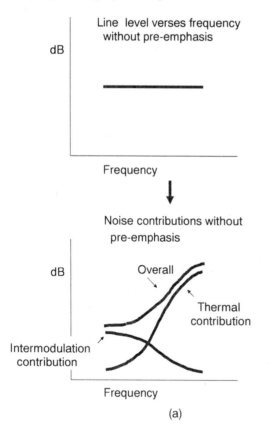

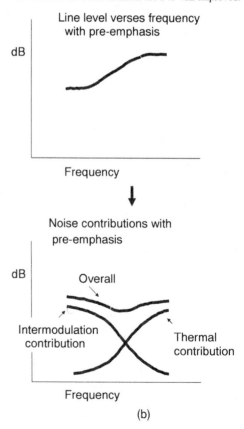

(a)   (b)

Figure 20.21 Principles of pre-emphasis

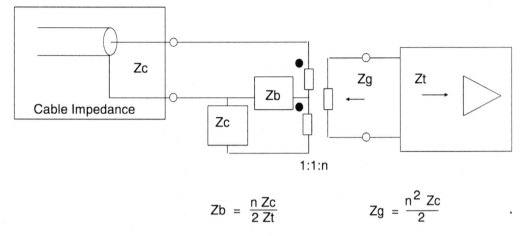

Figure 20.22 Hybrid input circuit

In other words, the shape of the pre-emphasis balances the multi-channel load and thermal noise contributions so that these are equally distributed over the line spectrum and all channels have ideally the same performance as Figure 20.21(b).

20.14.2 Thermal noise

To optimise the noise figure of the repeater and also to provide a good input impedance matching to the line produces conflicting requirements at the amplifier input. A good input impedance match to the cable is required with reflection losses normally kept to below 55dB and at the same time effective noise impedance matching is essential to give a low noise figure F.

Use of a Hybrid circuit at the input as shown in Figure 20.22 (Bell, 1971) provides a method of achieving both these requirements. The noise matching is improved by about 3dB compared to a conventional amplifier.

This technique can be extended further by including a hybrid transformer at the output and bridging the feedback between the input and output hybrid transformers.

20.14.3 Regulation

The gain shaping of a repeater is designed to match the loss characteristics of the cable. This is characterised by Equation 20.40, the loss being in dB.

$$Loss\ at\ frequency\ f\ =\ Loss\ at\ frequency\ f_r \left(\frac{f}{f_r} \right)^{1/2} \qquad (20.40)$$

Thus if the loss of the cable is known at one frequency f_r (normally the regulating pilot frequency) the loss at other frequencies can be deduced.

The change of the cable loss with temperature obeys the same law and thus correction for temperature is applied with a root f shape across the line frequency spectrum with the greatest correction at the highest frequency.

This equalisation which is controlled by the regulating pilot is not exact and small errors accumulate in the gain frequency response at each repeater equalisation point. The error systematically adds along the repeatered cable and to avoid excessive systematic error

build up, a requirement to maintain the error to within 1dB at any frequency over a 280km system is necessary.

20.14.3.1 *Regulation range*

The change in loss of typical coaxial cable is approximately 0.004% per °C. The change in buried cable temperature in the UK is ±10°C.

Thus for a typical cable section loss of 40dB at the regulating pilot frequency the maximum diurnal change is approximately ±1.6dB. Over two such sections the loss change would be 3.2dB and with reference to Figure 20.15 it can be seen that a change in transmission load of 3.2dB produces only a small increase in NPR.

Thus regulation points in the UK are established every two repeatered sections as in Figure 23(a) and allow for a loss change of ±4dB. A higher temperature shift would require regulation at every repeatered point with the greater cost and power feeding requirements this would entail.

An alternative method of regulation, applying pre-regulation to halve the diurnal changes in repeater levels, is shown in Figure 20.23(b).

20.14.4 Power feeding

A constant current is normally used to serially feed the repeatered cable. A constant current ensures a consistent power delivered to each repeater even though the cable resistance is continuously shifting with the cable temperature.

The power is normally fed from both ends of the section with a turn round break in the centre. This break is important as the induction of unwanted currents from services (rail traction, grid systems etc.) that may run parallel with the transmission is proportional to the square of the effective coupled path (CCITT, 1985, K17).

Under traction or grid faults where very large currents may flow for a short period in the service cable, excessive voltages may be coupled into the transmission cable and can damage the repeaters and cause an insulation breakdown within the cable.

Even under normal conditions a long coupled path with a.c. traction or similar installations can cause the transmission power feed current to be modulated with the traction frequency, or its

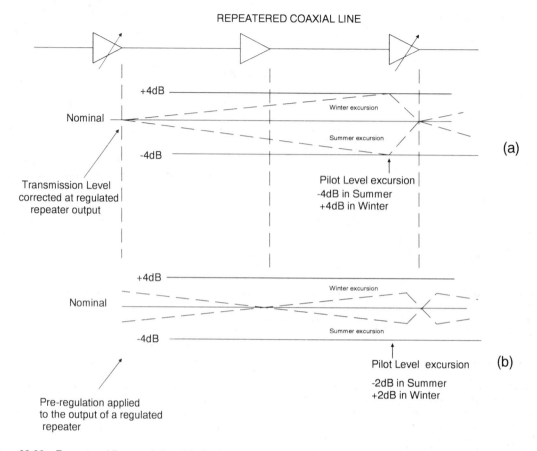

Figure 20.23   Repeatered line regulation: (a) pilot levels using conventional regulation; (b) pilot levels using pre-regulation

harmonics. This will create unwanted modulation products within the required multichannel traffic load.

20.15   References

Bell (1971) *Transmission systems for communications*, Bell Telephone Laboratories.

Bennett, W.R. (1940) Cross modulation requirements on multichannel amplifiers below overload, *Bell Systems Technical Journal*, (19) October.

CCITT (1985) Volume III, CCITT, Geneva.

Connor, F.R. (1973) *Introductory topics in electronics and telecommunications — Noise*, Edward Arnold, London.

Holbrook, B.D. and Dixon, J.T. (1939) Load rating theory for multichannel amplifiers, *Bell Systems Technical Journal*, (18), October.

Ribeyre, M. et. al. (1982) Exploration of transmultiplexers in telecommunication networks, *IEEE Trans. on Commun., COM-30*, July, pp. 1493-1497.

Rossiter, T.J.M. et. al. (1982) A modular transmultiplexer system using custom LSI devices, *IEEE Trans. on Commun., COM-30*, (7), July.

Tucker, D.C. (1948) *Journal Inst. Electrical Engineers*, Part III, May.

Young, P. (1983) *The power of speech*, George Allen, London.

21

Time division multiplexing

Michael J Simmonds
Telindus Ltd

Luc Ceuppens
Ind Ing
Telindus Ltd

Contents

21.1 General definition

In telephone systems a time division multiplexer, better known as a TDM, is generally defined as a device that distributes a number of channels periodically in time through the intermediary of pulse modulation. Each pulse corresponds to a channel and is interleaved between those of other channels. Hence, a time division multiplexed signal is always composed by means of synchronous sampling of the channels, with pulses shifted with respect to each other. This is illustrated in Figure 21.1. The interleaved channels form one frame of a duration corresponding to the sampling period T_s. The pulse modulation used can be analog (e.g. PAM, PPM) or digital (PCM).

With time division multiplexing time is a relative value, i.e. TDM requires a reference point in the frame cycle to which the receiver must be synchronised in order to correctly demultiplex the stream of pulses it receives and extract the signals concerning each channel individually. Since the receiver must be continuously synchronised in both frequency and phase this reference point is repeated periodically. The easiest way to understand this is to cyclically represent the time division multiplexing process as illustrated in Figure 21.2.

Figure 21.2 depicts a rotating switch S scanning a number of channels connected to its inputs. The channels are scanned one by one in the order they are encountered by the switch: channel 1 is sampled at time t_1, channel 2 at time t_2, and finally channel n at time t_n, after which the process is repeated. The resulting output signal is composed of the samples of the different channels, shifted over a time period given by Equation 21.1.

$$\Delta t = t_n - t_{n-1} \tag{21.1}$$

If the channels presented at the input are pulse amplitude modulated signals, we obtain a signal as depicted in Figure 21.1. At the other side of the connection we find an identical switch executing the opposite operation, i.e. scanning the composite input signal at

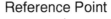
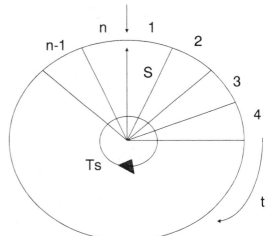

Figure 21.2 Cyclical representation of time division multiplexing

exactly the same frequency and phase, it demultiplexes the input signal and distributes the extracted signals over the respective channels. Both systems synchronise each time they pass the reference point.

Time division multiplexing has become very important, not only in transmission but also in switching, particularly in connection to the digital systems.

In the early days of electrical communications a medium such as copper wire carried a single information channel. For economic reasons, in terms of both cost and equipment, it was necessary to

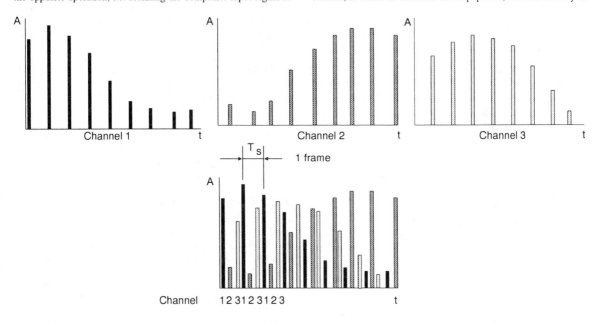

Figure 21.1 Time division multiplexing

find ways of packing multiple channels onto one physical link. The resulting system is referred to as a carrier. Digital signals are now transmitted from one location to another by transmission facilities or systems using a multitude of media (paired cable, coaxial cable, analog or digital radio systems, optical fibres, satellite communication).

The synchronous time division multiplexers typically are used as termination equipment of such carrier systems. These multiplexers are better known as T1 or E1 multiplexers, depending on the multiplexing scheme they use. T1 is generally used in America and is based on the PCM system that was originally designed by AT&T. The name T1 was derived from the identification number of the committee set up by the American National Standards Institute (ANSI). Europe, on the other hand, uses the E1 system, which is based on CEPT (Conference of Post and Telecommunications) recommendations. The delay with which CEPT has undertaken the definition of a primary digital PCM system has allowed it to profit from the experience of the American systems.

On the international level, the two types of system coexist although they are incompatible, and are a subject of two recommendations of the CCITT. Although both systems will be discussed later in this chapter, Table 21.1 compares their main characteristics. The

Table 21.1 Primary European and American systems

	E1 (European System) CCITT Recommendation G.732	T1 (American System) CCITT Recommendation G.733
Sampling Frequency	f_s = 8kHz	f_s = 8kHz
Bit rate per channel	D_i = 64kbit/s	D_i = 64kbit/s
Number of time slots	32	24
Number of channels	30	24
Number of bits/frame	32 x 8 = 256	24 x 8 + 1 = 193
Total bit rate	256 x 8kHz = 2.048kbit/s grouped word of 7 bits in the 0 channel of odd frames	193 x 8kHz = 1.544kbit/s distributed sequence 101010... consisting of the 193rd bit of odd frames
Signalling	Out-of-octet, grouped in channel 16, consisting of 4 bits per channel, distributed over 16 frames (=1 multiframe),	

meaning of the different items will become clear throughout the rest of this chapter.

Before discussing the T1 and E1 technologies in detail, consider first the general structure of a digital time division multiplex.

21.2 Digital time division multiplex structure

21.2.1 Frame organisation

For each digital channel there is assigned a group of b bits, called a word which corresponds to a digital message element (data). The groups belonging to the same channel are transmitted at a frequency f_s, equal to the sampling frequency. Thus, the bit rate of channel i can be calculated as in Equation 21.2.

$$D_i = f_s b \qquad (21.2)$$

In the case of digital PCM telephony, these words are composed of 8 bits and called octets. Hence the bit rate of each channel equals 64000bit/s.

When n digital channels are assembled into a time division multiplex, the collection of the n words of b bits (and eventually auxiliary bits which are added to them), within a period given by Equation 21.3, constitutes a frame.

$$T_s = \frac{1}{f_s} \qquad (21.3)$$

Although the structure of the frame is strictly repetitive, their content obviously is not because the channels contain variable digital information.

Two types of frame organisation can be considered, as shown in Figure 21.3:

1. Word interleaved, where the interleaving is performed on a character by character basis, i.e. a character from each data source is accumulated and combined as a word or frame for transmission. To do so, the frame is subdivided into y ≥ z time slots each containing b grouped bits corresponding to the same digital channel or auxiliary bits.
2. Bit interleaved, where the interleaving is performed on a bit by bit basis, i.e. one bit from each data source is accumulated and combined as a word or frame for transmission. To do so, the frame is subdivided into b groups each containing z bits of the same order belonging to each of the channels.

The word interleaved structure corresponds well to the mode of functioning of a PCM modulator, while the bit interleaved structure has advantages for time division digital switching because it suffers less throughput delay.

21.2.2 Frame alignment

The frame alignment or framing is typical of time division multiplexing. It consists of synchronising the receiving equipment both in frequency and in phase to the stream of symbols it receives. This operation is obviously necessary each time the receiver is switched on, but also during normal operation. Indeed, once aligned, the receiver needs a periodic time reference in order to check its isochronism and detects eventual shifts.

This necessary time reference consists of a particular pattern of several bits, called the framing pattern. When the receiver has lost frame alignment, it searches for this pattern in order to realign itself with as short a delay as possible. The framing pattern is periodically

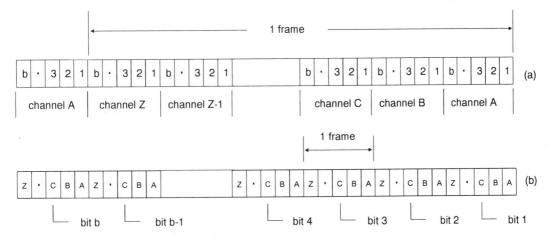

Figure 21.3 Digital TDM frame structures

carried by the frame according to one of the following organisations:

1. Grouped framing pattern, which consists of a number of consecutive bits at the beginning of a frame.
2. Distributed framing pattern which, as the name suggests, is spread over the frame on a bit by bit basis, or over several frames at one bit per frame.

There is of course a danger of simulating the framing pattern by chance combination of other information carrying bits. There are different ways to protect the system from this, such as:

1. One can choose a framing pattern with low autocorrelation, so that it is impossible to imitate by shifting and infringement on random neighbouring bits. Examples are the patterns 110 or 1110010 for for 3-bits or 7-bits grouped framing patterns respectively.
2. One can block all the channels of the frame when the framing is lost at reception. The frame would be replaced by the transmission of a resynchronisation signal. This necessitates an announcement warning in the opposite direction, which is assumed to be correctly aligned.
3. One could confirm correct framing by a criterion other than the presence of the framing pattern, e.g. absence of the pattern in one frame out of two.

In order to avoid reacting to each transmission error, the reaction to an incorrect reception of the framing pattern in an aligned situation, i.e. during normal data transfer, must be delayed. The solution to the framing problems of both T1 and E1 are given in the respective sections later.

21.2.3 Signalling

The transmission of multiple telephone calls is not the only requirement for a T1 or E1 network. The network also has to transfer signalling information. Signalling information is auxiliary information (digits, commands, acknowledgement signals, etc.) sent from exchange to exchange to control switching and management operation of the network.

Aside from analog signalling by sinusoidal carriers (in-band or out-band) used in analog systems and translatable by PCM modulation, digital systems lend themselves by nature much better to direct digital transmission of signalling information. Several solutions can be considered:

1. In-octet signalling, which is also called bit robbing. In this the least significant bit (LSB) among the 8 bits that represent a coded sample of speech is periodically (typically every six frames) assigned to signalling. This results in an imperceptible degradation of the telephone transmission. However, when data are transferred over the same network, the impact of losing the LSB every sixth byte is not acceptable.
2. Out-of-octet signalling, also referred to as channel by channel signalling. In this system each digital channel arranges, besides its octet, one or several signalling bits. These signalling bits of the n channels of the frame can be distributed, i.e. juxtaposed at each octet as a supplementary bit per time slot (possible signalling rate being 8kbit/s per channel), or grouped in a time slot reserved for this purpose and of which the bits are assigned in turn, cyclically, to the n channels of the frame (possible signalling rate being 64/n kbit/s per channel)
3. Common signalling, where one time slot per frame is reserved for signalling and assigned according to need to one channel, then to another. Signalling is done using labelled messages, of which the label indicates which channel the message belongs to. This technique allows an instantaneous signalling rate of 64kbit/s for one channel at a time.

21.3 The digital hierarchy levels

A range of digital systems with increasing capacity has been defined, the systems of each order being composed of four systems of the immediately lower order. In America the traditional TDM hierarchy is described as DS levels 0 through 4. Europe simply uses digits to indicate the digital order. These digital streams, produced by multiplexing equipment, are by design independent of the target transmission medium. In fact, in an end to end circuit, many different types of media may be encountered.

The 0kHz to 4kHz nominal voice band channels are first converted to digital information by PCM techniques and then stacked (multiplexed) onto higher bit streams. Each of the individual digitised 64kbit/s channels is referred to as DS0 levels (USA) or 0 order systems (Europe). Table 21.2 summarises the American and European digital hierarchies. In the USA 24 voice band analog channels are combined or multiplexed to form a DS1 signal (1.544Mbit/s), also called a digroup (for digital group). The rest of the digital hierarchy uses 3.152Mbit/s for 48 channels (DS1-C), 6.312Mbit/s for 96 channels (DS2), 44.736Mbit/s for 672 channels (DS3), and 274.176Mbit/s for 4032 channels (DS4).

Table 21.2 American and European digital hierarchy

Order		Number of telephone channels at 64kbit/s		Total bit rate (Mbit/s)	
Europe	USA	Europe	USA	Europe	USA
0	DS0	1	1	0.064	0.064
1	DS1	30	24	2.048	1.544
2	DS1-C	120	48	8.448	3.152
3	DS2	480	96	34.368	6.312
4	DS3	1920	672	139.264	44.736
5	DS4	7680	4032	565.148	274.176

The European telephone system is based on 30-channel blocks and uses transmission rates of 2.048Mbit/s to carry 30 channels (1st order), 8.448Mbit/s to carry 120 channels (2nd order), 34.368Mbit/s for 480 channels (3rd order), 139.264Mbit/s for 1920 channels (4th order), and 565.148Mbit/s for 7680 channels (5th order).

Figure 21.4 illustrates the coupling of the hierarchical systems. The high order services are structured around a point to point plesiochronous sectioned concept. This concept has a layered approach in which the 2Mbit data stream is supported by a 8Mbit server network. In turn this is supported by a 34Mbit server network which is itself supported by a 140Mbit server network. Starting from the second order, the equipment no longer contains an analog to digital converter and only deals with digital frames. The equipment essentially consists of multiplexers, combining into new frames the frames of four systems of the preceding order, called tributaries.

During the construction of an nth order multiplexer starting from frames with order n-1, we are confronted with the problem of anisochronism of the tributaries. In effect, the frames to be grouped come from different equipments which are geographically distinct and often far away, and whose clocks have neighbouring frequencies (plesiochronous tributaries) or, in the best case, equal (synchronous tributaries), but whose relative phases can certainly be anything and even vary, because the lines have different propagation delays which further depend on temperature.

The multiplexing of the four tributaries requires perfect isochronism between the bits. It is therefore necessary to bring them all to exactly the same rate. This is generally done with the aid of retime buffers, capable of storing an entire frame. The tributary writes the frame in the buffer at its own data rate, while the higher order multiplexer empties the buffer at the new internal rate.

21.4   The T carrier framing and coding formats

21.4.1   The superframe format

The T carrier was designed to carry 24 independent digitised voice channels, with each channel encoded as a 64kbit/s data stream. One of the earliest framing formats was the D4 framing pattern. This T1 frame format evolved principally to carry voice streams, and data to be transmitted over a T carrier system must conform to this format. The frame consists of 193 bits, with the last bit always being a framing bit. The first 192 bits correspond to 24 conversations, or channels, sampled with PCM type methods and generating 8-bit words. The combined signal is word interleaved, providing one frame.

A superframe (CCITT calls it a multiframe) is a repeating sequence of 12 such frames and thus contains 12 framing/signalling bits. In order to keep track of the frame structure, at least 1 bit in 15 bits of the combined stream (information plus signalling) must be a 1, and at least 3 bits in 24 bits of the stream must be 1s. The bandwidth used on voice frequency (VF) signalling is minimised by putting signalling information only in the LSB in the sixth and twelfth frames.

As illustrated in Figure 21.5, each superframe consists of 12 repeating frames. One frame corresponds to 125 microseconds; one superframe is thus 1.5 milliseconds in duration. Each frame contains one synchronisation bit to allow the receiving equipment to decode, demultiplex, and allocate the incoming bits to the appropriate channels.

From the above follows that each superframe contains a 12-bit word, composed of individual bits coming from each of the 12 frames. The framing bits are called BFf, and the signalling bits BFs. BFfs are the odd numbered framing bits, whilst BFss are the even

64kbit/s

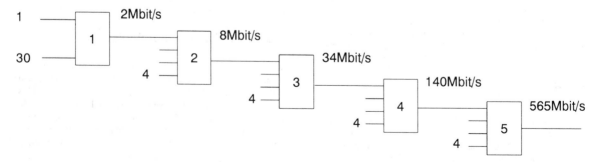

Figure 21.4   Hierarchy of digital systems

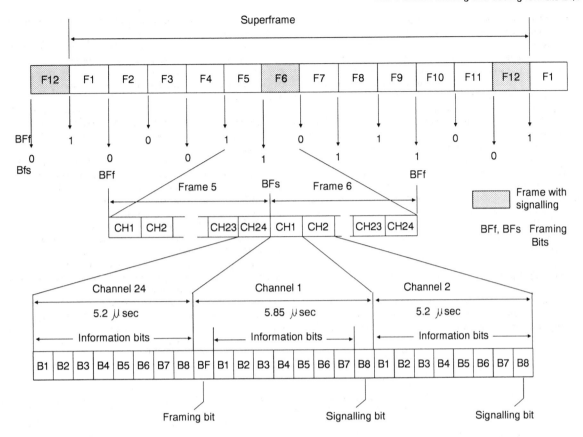

Figure 21.5 D4 framing patterns

numbered bits. The 12-bit word is used for synchronisation and for identifying frames number 6 and 12, which contain channel signalling bits. Each frame thus contains a BFf or BFs framing/signalling bit on the 193rd position. The resulting pattern of the 12-bit word is 100011011100. This entire process repeats every 1.5 milliseconds.

The BFf bit alternates (1, 0, 1, 0, 1, 0, ...) every other frame. The receiving multiplexer can identify this unique sequence in the incoming digital data stream to maintain or re-establish frame boundaries. Frame 6 is identified by the fact that it occurs when the BFs is a 1 preceded by three BFs which were 0s. Frame 12 is identified by the fact that it occurs when the BFs is 0, preceded by three BFs which were 1s. The receiver can easily identify this sequence, in the absence of severe line errors or impairments, and thus identify the desired frames which contain signalling information.

The 193rd bit signalling described above involves the management of the DS1 facility itself. As indicated in Section 21.3.2, each individual voice channel requires its own signalling information (call set-up, call completion, etc.). The signalling information must be transmitted along with the PCM samples. To achieve this the multiplexer will rob, or share the least significant bit, i.e. bit 8 from the user data stream. Consequently, this bit alternatively carries information or signalling data.

For five consecutive frames bit 8 will contain voice bits, and on the sixth, it will contain a signalling bit. This should not be confused with the mechanism described above for the superframe and the 193rd bit, though both mechanism and principle are similar. This bit robbing occurs totally within one voice sample, namely within one octet of bits. The sixth bit is also referred to as the A bit, while the twelfth bit is also called the B bit. These combinations of bits allow the end-user station equipment to carry out its signalling protocol, which involves indicating such states as idle, busy, ringing, no ringing, loop open, etc.

For data applications the A/B signalling has no relevance. However, when transferring data, the impact of losing the LSB every six frames is not acceptable. There are two ways to get around this inherent difficulty. Instead of transmitting data in 8-bit quantities, they are transferred in 7-bit quantities. Therefore, the fact that the LSB is robbed does not affect the overall performance because it is not used. To achieve this, data must be transmitted 7 bits at a time every 125 μsec. In practical terms this involves either using a device that is capable of outputting at 7-bit increments or providing a special timing pulse to enable the data output.

Many communications controller devices can be operated in the latter mode but only a few in the former. As only 7 bits are transmitted every 125 μsec, the data rate is reduced from the 64kbit/s available to 56kbit/s. With this method, 12% of the potential bandwidth is lost (see also Section 21.4.3).

21.4.2 The extended superframe format

The DS1 format described above was developed in the 1960s and is based on technology then available. The basic challenge of DS1 transmission is that of preserving bit and word synchronism. To do so, 24 eight-bit words (corresponding to samples for 24 telephone conversations) are followed by one bit (the 193rd bit) for frame tracking and management. There are 8000 repetitions of this pattern in one second, which results in an additional 8kbit/s bandwidth loss.

The extended superframe format, denoted as ESF, was announced in 1981 and adds two enhancements. First, the number of frames in a superframe is increased to 24, rather than 12. This provides extra signalling bits for telephone signalling, a C bit and a D bit. A 24 frame pattern makes an additional bandwidth available on the framing bit. This is used to send maintenance data between T1 interfaces.

The ESF has 24 frames in its definition of a superframe, but only six bits in its framing pattern. Rather than resynchronising every 1.5 milliseconds as in the regular format, the ESF only needs to resynchronise every 3.0 milliseconds. The 193rd bits are now being looked at as part of one 24-bit word. Substantial progress in VLSI technology has enabled the equipment to keep timing more accurately. This implies that fewer bits are required for this housekeeping function. The result is that 4000bit/s of channel are freed without losing any functionality or any additional bits. This bandwidth can be used for direct communication between intelligent network monitoring devices and centralised network monitoring computers.

Figure 21.6 depicts the ESF format. The successive 193rd bits are shown explicitly. There are 6 bits in the frame synchronisation word, rather than 12. The D bit represents link level data, while the C bit handles error checking and monitoring functions. With the extended superframe format all previous functionality, including

the VF signalling rule, remain available. No new bits from the 1.544Mbit/s are taken away from the user.

Since twenty four frames have now to be examined by the equipment to establish synchronisation and extract other channel information, it takes longer to regain lost synchronisation. However, with the newer sophisticated clocking mechanism this should only happen very rarely.

A 4000bit/s data link, also referred to as the Embedded Operations Channel (EOC) or Facilities Data Link (FDL), used for maintenance information, supervisory control, and other (future) needs, becomes available.

The ESF format also provides in a 6-bit Cyclic Redundancy Check (CRC). The check character is used for monitoring the transmission quality and overall performance of the DS1 facility. The CRC-6 is generated from the bits of the preceding frame. For the calculation, the framing bits of that frame are considered to equal 1. Since the CRC-6 allows detection of apparent degradation in transmission quality, problems may be fixed before a total failure occurs. The CRC-6 detects about 98.4% of single bit or multiple bit errors. The CRC 6 also provides false frame protection. This follows from the fact that if the wrong synchronisation boundary is selected, the CRC will not calculate correctly.

Under ESF new VF signalling capabilities become available by providing two additional robbed signalling bits, allowing representation of up to 16 states. These bits are known as C and D, which

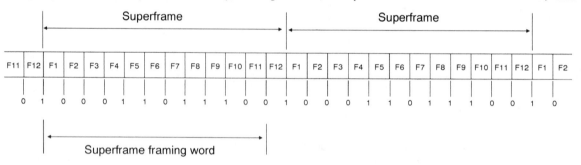

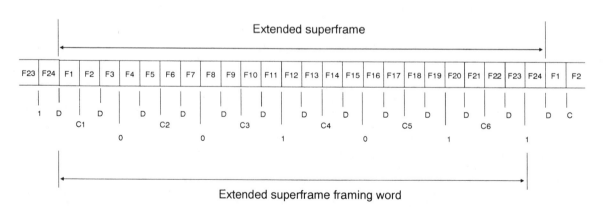

C bits = CRC-6 bits
D bits = Data link bits (maintenance)
001011 = 6 bit framing pattern

Figure 21.6 Extended superframe format

complement the A and B bits of the regular superframe format. Out of these, 16 codes options are available for transparency (no robbed signalling bits), two state signalling (A bit only), four state signalling (A and B bits), or sixteen state signalling (A, B, C, and D bits). In the transparent signalling option, all eight bits within a frame within the extended superframe are given to the user for data. When the A signalling mode is employed, the LSB of every sixth signalling frame is robbed to show the desired bit. When A/B signalling is used, the first and third signalling frames are robbed to carry the A bits, while the second and fourth signalling frames will carry the B bits. If the A/B/C/D signalling is employed, the desired bits are gained by robbing the first, second, third, and fourth frames, respectively.

From the above we can conclude that ESF has economically reallocated the 8kbit/s that have long been used to manage the DS1 facilities. 2000 bits are used for framing (6 bits distributed over 24 framing bits and there are 333 such 24-bit words per second). 2000 bits are used for error detection and performance determination (6 bits distributed over 24 framing bits). Finally, 4000 bits are used for telemetry and facility management and/or reconfiguration (12 bits distributed over 24 framing bits).

21.4.3 Clear channels for data applications

As already mentioned, users of T1 facilities are restricted from accessing the full 64kbit/s bandwidth of the PCM channel on any one circuit of the DS1, whether for voice or data applications, because the eighth bit of each word is unavailable. In voice transmission, the eighth bit has been used for in-band signalling (remember that only the sixth and twelfth frames are really affected). In speech, this generally does not cause any problem, but the same condition cannot be guaranteed for data. The implication has been the deployment of 56kbit/s facilities and a loss of 8kbit/s of usable bandwidth. The maximum data rate in a DDS channel (Bell's Dataphone Digital Service, see Section 21.8) is thus 57kbit/s, with 7 bits per frame used for customer data and the eighth bit reserved for network control. This causes complications, particularly for users interfacing with an international facility, e.g. a 64kbit/s satellite channel.

In many early repeaters that were installed along the transmission cables linking the T1 devices, the synchronisation circuitry was very simple. An oscillator was run at a frequency close to the line pulse stream. The pulses were then used to pull the oscillator on frequency. This method relied upon the availability of pulses in the data stream. Because there could be many repeaters over a T1 span, the cumulative effect of a drift in frequency could cause an unacceptable amount of error in the transmission. Therefore the number of pulses, or the ones density, on the line is important. For voice transmission this is not a problem. However, for data it is a different story. To be able to maintain the ones density, zero code suppression schemes are used. These schemes consist of replacing long sequences of zeros by a special pattern (for details on zero code suppression schemes, refer to Section 21.7).

The assumption on the DS1 stream was that at least one eighth, i.e. 12.5%, of the incoming bits were 1s. If that ratio was not maintained, synchronisation would be lost and an error would result. When the DS1 contains voice channels, work around techniques like changing the eight 0 to a 1 do not create major problems, since the distortion in the voice message is minimal and the human ear would not notice it. In contrast, changing a customer data bit is not acceptable, as that may imply a substantial difference in the received data (e.g. 0001 and 1001 are quite different numbers). Therefore, one bit out of eight in the customer channel is reserved

in each frame to inject a 1. This bit is called the network control bit and is not made available to the user. While this resolves the ones density problem, it imposes the speed restriction alluded to above.

The approach embodied in the current generation of equipment, of substituting a 1 in the LSB position of an all zeros word, may be acceptable for voice, because the difference between a 00000000 coded sample and a 00000001 coded sample is imperceptible to the ear. When the bits of a DS1 channel represent directly input digital data, such as DDS or ISDN, however, one is not at freedom to alter the data, and a technical solution must be achieved.

A possible solution has already been introduced. This concept, also referred to as the primary rate interface or PRI, is one of the central physical components of ISDN. Its implementation involves taking all of the signalling information of the individual 23 T1 channels and combining it into a 24th channel. Often referred to as the "23B + D" format, this framing and signalling scheme allows 23 T1 channels to carry up to 64kbit/s of voice, data, video, or other information, while the D channel transmits all of the control data, including sophisticated signalling techniques described in CCITT Recommendation I.431/Z.921/Q.931. (The "B" in this designation stands for bearer; the "D" stands for delta, i.e. the channel that transmits change information).

21.5 The CEPT PCM-30 framing format

The CEPT PCM-30 is a PCM format used for time division multiplexing of 30 voice or data circuits onto a single twisted pair cable using digital repeaters. As already mentioned, the delay with which CEPT has undertaken the definition of a primary digital PCM system has allowed it to profit from the experience of the American systems.

The basic characteristics of this primary PCM multiplex equipment are described in CCITT Recommendation G.732. Each voice circuit is sampled at 8 kHz using an 8-bit A-law companding analog to digital converter as specified in CCITT Recommendation G.711, and multiplexed with 29 other sampled channels plus one alignment and one signalling channel, resulting in 32 multiplexed channels.

The standard CEPT frame contains 32 channels of 8 bits each, or 256 bits. With 8000 samples per seconds, the CEPT data rate becomes 8000 x 256, or 2.048Mbit/s.

21.5.1 Frame composition

As with the DS1 D4 framing format, the CEPT PCM-30 frame structure is subject of CCITT Recommendation G.704. Each CEPT PCM-30 frame consists of 32 time slots to include 30 voice channels, one alignment signal and one signalling channel. Time slots 1 to 15 and 17 to 31 are assigned to the 30 voice or data channels. This frame composition is depicted in Figure 21.7.

The frame alignment signal FAS (0011011) is transmitted in bit positions 2 to 8 of time slot 0 of every other frame. Bit position 1 carries the International bit, while frames not containing the frame alignment signal, i.e. the odd frames, are used to carry National and International signalling bits and alarm indication for loss of frame alignment. The loss of frame alignment alarm is announced by alarm bit A, which is the third bit of the odd. To avoid imitation of the frame alignment signal, bit 2 of the odd frames are set to 1.

Time slot 16 in each CEPT 30 frame is used to transmit such signalling data as on-hook and off-hook conditions, dialling digits and call progress. Since a common channel is dedicated for the signalling data of all voice circuits, this method of signalling is referred to as common channel signalling. The signalling consists

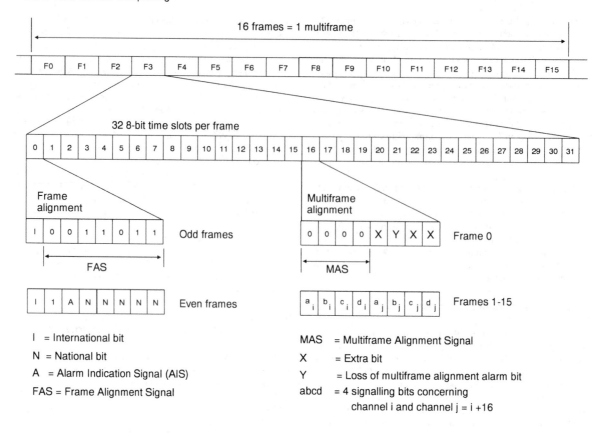

Figure 21.7 CEPT PCM-30 frame and multiframe composition

of four bits per channel, grouped in the two halves of time slot 16. It therefore requires 15 frames to carry the information of the 30 channels. Completed by a 16th frame (frame 0) they constitute a multiframe. Time slot 16 of this 16th frame contains a multiframe alignment pattern MAS which allows unambiguous numbering of the frames within the multiframe. Each channel thus arranges the signalling of 4 bits every 16 frames, i.e. every 2 milliseconds.

21.5.2   CRC-4 cyclic redundancy check

Where there is a need to provide additional protection against simulation of the frame alignment signal, and/or where there is a need for an enhanced error monitoring capability, then bit 1 of the frame, i.e. the International bit, is used for the 4-bit cyclic redundancy check described below.

Each CRC-4 multiframe, which is composed of 16 frames numbered from 0 to 15, is divided into two 8 frame sub-multiframes or SMF, designated SMF I and SMF II which indicates their respective order of occurrence within the CRC-4 multiframe structure. The SMF is the Cyclic Redundancy Check-4 block size, i.e. 2048 bits.

In the frames containing the frame alignment signal, bit 1 is used to transmit the CRC-4 bits. There are four CRC-4 bits, referred to as C1, C2, C3, and C4 in each SMF. In the frames not containing the frame alignment signal, bit 1 is used to to transmit the CRC-4 multiframe alignment signal and two CRC-4 error indication bits (E). The CRC-4 multiframe alignment signal is a 7-bit sequence having the form 0011011. The E-bits are used to indicate received

errored sub-multiframes by changing the binary state of one E-bit from 1 to 0 for each errored sub-multiframe. Recommendation G.704 requires the delay between the detection of an errored sub-multiframe, and the setting of the E-bit that indicates the error state, to be less than 1 second. Table 21.3 shows the allocation of bits 1 to 8 of the frames for a complete CRC-4 multiframe.

21.6   T1 and PCM-30 alarms and error conditions

21.6.1   Principal alarms

The principal alarms defined by both T1 and PCM-30 are the red alarm, generated by the receiving equipment to indicate that it has lost frame alignment, and the yellow alarm, which is returned to the transmitting terminal to indicate that the receiving terminal has lost frame alignment. Normally, the terminal will use the receiver's red alarm to request that a yellow alarm be transmitted. The name of these alarms simply comes from the colour of the lights on the original equipment.

Loss of frame alignment is detected simply by monitoring the frame alignment signal. PCM-30 differentiates between loss of frame alignment, being a failure to synchronise on the frame alignment signal FAS (0011011), and loss of multiframe alignment, which is caused by a failure to synchronise on the multiframe alignment signal (0000) contained in bits 1 to 4 of time slot 16 of

Table 21.3 CRC-4 multiframe structure.
E= CRC-4 error indication bits; S4 to S8 = Spare bits; C1 to C4 = CRC-4 bits; A = Alarm indication signal (AIS)

	Sub-multiframe (SMF)	Frame number	Bits							
			1	2	3	4	5	6	7	8
M		0	C_1	0	0	1	1	0	1	1
U		1	0	1	A	S_4	S_5	S_6	S_7	S_8
L		2	C_2	0	0	1	1	0	1	1
T		3	0	1	A	S_4	S_5	S_6	S_7	S_8
I	SMF I	4	C_3	0	0	1	1	0	1	1
		5	1	1	A	S_4	S_5	S_6	S_7	S_8
		6	C_4	0	0	1	1	0	1	1
		7	0	1	A	S_4	S_5	S_6	S_7	S_8
F		8	C_1	0	0	1	1	0	1	1
		9	1	1	A	S_4	S_5	S_6	S_7	S_8
A		10	C_2	0	0	1	1	0	1	1
M	SMF II	11	1	1	A	S_4	S_5	S_6	S_7	S_8
E		12	C_3	0	0	1	1	0	1	1
		13	E	1	A	S_4	S_5	S_6	S_7	S_8
		14	C_4	0	0	1	1	0	1	1
		15	E	1	A	S_4	S_5	S_6	S_7	S_8

frame 0. The former is the red alarm, the latter is the multiframe red alarm. Table 21.4 illustrates how these alarm conditions are transmitted. T1 multiplexers can also signal a blue alarm. This is a continuous ones pattern across all 24 channels (the F-bits, however, remain unchanged) to indicate an upstream failure.

21.6.2 Error conditions

The most basic impairment that T1 or E1 equipment can suffer from are bipolar violations (BPVs). A bipolar violation is a violation of bipolar coding in which two pulses occur consecutively with the same polarity. As will be discussed later in this chapter, T1 and E1 signals are encoded with a system that inverts the polarity of alternate one bits so that two pulses of the same polarity will not occur in a row. On metallic circuits, a bipolar violation will occur if a zero is changed to a one, or if a one is changed to a zero. Since bipolar violations occur one for one with bit errors, the BPV rate (the ratio of BPVs to correct bits) corresponds to the bit error rate.

CRC errors are a second possible T1/E1 error condition. The cyclic redundancy check error measurement is an alternative to frame error measurement, and is available to T1 circuits that employ the Extended Superframe (ESF) format and to E1 circuits that employ the CRC-4 multiframing.

CRC-n (n = 4 with PCM-30, n = 6 with T1 ESF) is an error checking method that uses an n-bit code to represent an entire multiframe of data bits. The n-bit code is arrived at by applying a complex mathematical function to each group of 24 (ESF) or 8 (PCM-30) frames of data. The result of this calculation, the n-bit code, is then transmitted in the CRC framing bit positions of the following frame.

At the other end of the circuit, the same mathematical function is performed on the same first group of frames. This newly calculated

n-bit code is compared with the code that was calculated by the transmitting equipment. Any discrepancies between the two codes are counted as CRC errors. CRC errors are by far the best in service performance measurements because the CRC scheme allows detection of errors on all of the data bits within each group of frames, with an accuracy of about 98 percent.

Slips are yet another impairment. Slips are the most common impairments caused by frequency deviations and timing problems. A slip is the insertion or deletion of data bits into or from the data stream. It is the direct result of equipment buffer overflow or underflow, resulting from improperly timed network equipment. Digital equipment uses input buffers of finite length to accommodate the momentary frequency fluctuations that can occur between the receiver and transmitter of a digital network node. These frequency differences become persistent when connecting to (or selecting) the wrong clocking source, causing buffers to overflow or underflow and then reset themselves. It is the buffer resetting that results in the addition or deletion of data bits from the bit stream.

Based on the source of the slips and their effects on the network, all slips can be placed in one of two categories, controlled slips or uncontrolled slips. Controlled slips are bit additions or deletions that do not disrupt frame synchronisation. Uncontrolled slips are bit additions or deletions that cause both framing and data to be displaced. This framing and data displacement results in a loss of frame synchronisation, effectively taking the circuit down momentarily.

Jitter, the cyclic offset of bits from their expected positions in time, is one of the most ominous of all T1/E1 impairments. Jitter can be intermittent and data dependent, which makes it difficult to isolate. Jitter occurs little by little, cumulatively over many bits, and can ultimately cause the missampling of the pulses resulting in bipolar violations and bit error conditions.

The most common cause of jitter is the network equipment itself. Jitter is inherent to the clock recovery timing used in transmission, and is typically added to the pulses at every regeneration point within the network. As long as each network component adds only a very small amount of jitter, the circuit will be unaffected. Problems arise when a failed or failing network component adds significant amounts of jitter. Less typically, jitter can come from crosstalk, electrical noise, and other types of interference.

Wander is an impairment very similar to jitter, and is defined as jitter occurring at a frequency of less than 10Hz. Wander, like jitter, is a back and forth (cyclic) displacement of bits from their expected positions. But, because wander occurs at such low frequencies, its cause within the network and effects on the network are very different from those of jitter. Wander is most often caused by instabilities in a master timing source, or by nocturnal cooling (cooling as the sun goes down). The end result is usually slips.

21.7 Coding schemes

Another aspect of digital transmission systems is the algorithm used for data transmission on the line. There are various ways in which the data can be represented as signals on the line. One of the important factors of a transmission system is the number of discrete levels a signal can have. For example, TTL has two levels to encode the binary data. One voltage level indicates a logic 1, and the other voltage level a logic 0. A single switching point, or decision level, is used to set the threshold. By comparing the coded signal to the threshold level, the binary information can be decoded. If the signal level is above the threshold, then a logic 1 is detected; conversely, if it is lower, a logic 0 is detected. Because the signal has two levels, it is known as a unipolar code. Unipolar coding is a very good system for TTL systems but is not suitable for transmission systems using copper cables over long distances.

The reason why lies in the construction and characteristics of such cables. A transmission cable is made of a group of wires, having two electrical properties. One is the d.c. resistance and the second is the self inductance value of the wire. When a group of wires is placed in a casing to form the cable, a third electrical property, capacitance between the wires, is brought to bear. The transmission cable now behaves like a low pass filter.

If a unipolar code is transmitted down the line, each high level signal will inject energy into the capacitor/inductor of the cable. Conversely, a low level signal will discharge the line. If the number of highs and lows is matched, then the net energy level on the line will be zero. But if the number is not matched (which is normally the case), the transmission line will have periods during which energy is stored. This stored energy will result in a d.c. offset being superimposed on the transmitted signal. The d.c. offset will interfere with the decoding of the received pulse by reducing the difference between the high and low signal levels and the threshold level. For instance, if the threshold level is 1.3V and a low level signal is 0.8V, then a DC offset of greater than 0.5V will stop the decoding of a low level signal and affect the overall performance of the transmission system.

To overcome this, transmission codes with three levels, positive high, zero, and negative low, have been developed. The highs and lows are used to represent the same logic level. The main difference between this system and the unipolar system is that the highs and lows are alternated for the same logic level. For example, in the system of coding known as alternate mark inversion (AMI), a high or a low level represents the logic level 1. A zero level represents the logic level 0. To transmit the sequence 10101 the following pattern would be output: high/zero/low/zero/high. This type of coding is known as pseudoternary coding. It is called "pseudo" because the zero voltage level is not really classified as a discrete level. The receiver needs two decision levels to decode the incoming data and also has to keep track of the level of the last logic 1 transmitted so that the correct level of the next logic 1 is sent as the

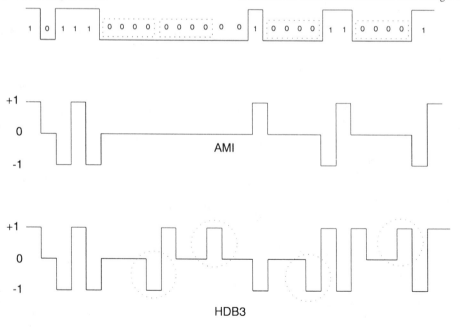

Figure 21.8   AMI and HDB3 pseudo-ternary codes

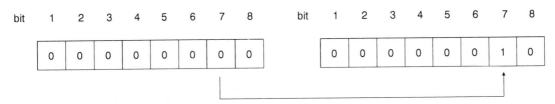

Figure 21.9 Typical B7 zero code suppression example

code alternates. In the case in which the wrong level is detected, i.e. a high followed by a high, a code violation is recorded. The advantage of this type of coding is that the d.c. level, or balance, is maintained by the transmission of alternate high and low pulses. The disadvantage is the extra circuitry required.

Many receivers extract clocking information from incoming data by detecting the occurrences of the incoming signal data crossing a decision threshold. Each time the signal crosses this point, a PLL can lock its output to it. To perform this task effectively there have to be sufficient crossings over a period of time. If the number of crossings is reduced, the PLL can drift from the frequency of the incoming signal. This will cause the incoming signal to be sampled incorrectly and result in data errors. With a ternary code, the logic levels encoded into alternate high and low output signals provide the clocking information. For example, in AMI coding, each time a logic 1 is transmitted the receiver can lock the PLL onto the incoming signal. Unfortunately, long series of zeros, which are impossible to prevent, may deprive the PLL of all synchronisation information. To avoid this, a group of several consecutive zeros is replaced by a group containing a factitious 1, signalled as such to the receiver by a polarity in violation of the law of alternation of the AMI mode. This principle is systematically applied to all primary and second order digital transmission systems.

The European digital system makes use of a pseudo-ternary mode called a high density bipolar 3-zero maximum code HDB3, which avoids the appearance of more than three consecutive zero symbols, as illustrated in Figure 21.8. It consists of replacing groups of four binary zeros by groups of four ternary symbols of which the the last is non-zero and transmitted with the same polarity as the last non-zero symbol, i.e. in violation of the alternation law of the AMI code. This allows the easy identification of such group at reception and its interpretation as four binary zeros. Furthermore, the first of the four ternary symbols is chosen to be positive, zero, or negative

in such way as to maintain or reset the d.c component to a zero value.

The American T1 system generally uses a technique called B7 zero code suppression (B7ZS). To keep telephone company T1 line repeaters and channel service units (CSU) in synchronisation, the digital bit stream permits a maximum of 15 consecutive zeros. As already mentioned, this is known as the Telco's ones density requirement (also refer to Section 21.4.3). To obtain compliance with the ones density requirement, communications carriers use the B7ZS technique.

As an example of B7 zero code suppression, consider the DS0 time slot illustrated in Figure 21.9. If all 8 bits are zeros, B7 zero code suppression will substitute a 1-bit in position 7. The adapted time slot is also depicted in Figure 3.9.

Figure 3.10 shows the worst case scenario, where channel 24 is followed by a 0 frame bit, and all bits in channel 1 are zeros, resulting in a total of 16 consecutive zeros. The illustration shows that in this case B7 zero code suppression reduces the number of consecutive zeros to 14.

As already mentioned in Section 21.4.3, this coding technique followed from the assumption that, in order to guarantee synchronisation, at least one eighth, i.e. 12.5%, of the incoming bits were 1s. However, if a data channel contains all 0s, the data will be corrupted due to B7 zero code suppression. As a result, a data channel is normally restricted to seven usable bits, with one bit set to a 1. This prevents the user data from being corrupted but limits the actual bandwidth to only 56kbit/s. When one bit is set to a 1 on a DS0 channel, the channel is said to be a non-clear channel. The 56 kbit/s on a non-clear channel is also known as a DS-A channel.

Clear channel capability can be obtained by using bipolar transmission with bipolar 8 zero substitution (B8ZS) in the T1 bit stream (Figure 21.11). With B8ZS no more than eight logic 0s can be transmitted sequentially. Therefore, the data stream to be transmitted is examined to determine if a long sequence of logic 0s is

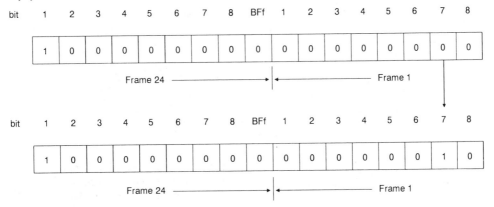

Figure 21.10 B&ZS worst case scenario

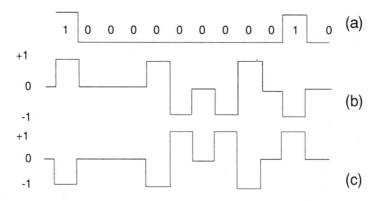

Figure 21.11 Bipolar 8 zero substitution coding

about to be transmitted. If such a sequence is detected, each eight consecutive 0s in a byte are replaced by a special pattern. If the pulse preceding the all zero byte is positive, the inserted B8ZS code is 000 +– 0 –+. If the pulse preceding the all zero byte is negative, the inserted B8ZS code is 000 –+ 0 +–. Both examples result in bipolar violations occurring in the fourth and seventh bit positions. This special pattern is unique because of the embedded code violations. When detected at the receive side it is removed and not seen as a code violation.

If a string of nine logic 0s were to be transmitted, then the first eight logic 0s would be replaced by the special pattern while the ninth 0 would be transmitted normally. At the receive end, the special pattern, which is expected by the receiver, is decoded back to the eight zeros removed. The data output by the receiver is still the nine logic 0s that were to be transferred. Two things can be seen from the example. The addition of the extra, special pattern gave the receiver the clocking data it required to allow the PLL to maintain synchronisation. Secondly, to transmit the sequence of nine binary digits still requires only eight pulses on the line. Although the receiver will be less likely to lose synchronisation, more complicated transmitters and receivers have to be used.

21.8 Examples of digital network services

This section provides a brief description of three digital network facilities that are based on T1 and PCM-30 time division Multi-plexers. Bell's Dataphone Digital Service (DDS) and AT&T's Accunet T1.5 are typical examples of T carrier multiplexer networks, while BT's KiloStream and MegaStream networks are based on the European standards.

21.8.1 Bell's DDS subrate facility

Bell's Dataphone Digital Service (DDS) was approved by the U.S. Federal Communications Commission in December 1974. Currently, there are over 100 cities connected to the DDS network in the United States as well as international connections to other digital networks.

DDS is an all synchronous facility. Currently supported transmission rates and services include 2400, 4800, 9600 and 56000bit/s leased circuits. Recently a 56kbit/s switched service has been added. For transmission at different data rates, specialised equipment to include multiplexers and/or converters must be employed.

The carrier structure of the DDS network is illustrated in Figure 21.12. DDS facilities are routed from a subscriber's location to an Office Channel Unit (OCU) located in the carrier's serving central office.

The signalling structure used on DDS facilities is a modified bipolar signalling code. The modification to bipolar return to zero signalling results in the insertion of zero suppression codes to maintain synchronisation whenever a string of six or more consecutive zeros is encountered.

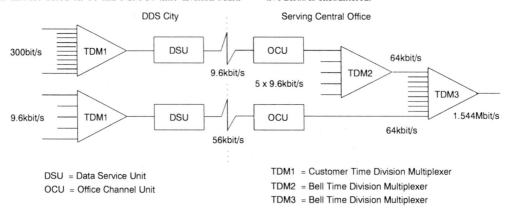

Figure 21.12 DDS carrier structure and multiplexing arrangement

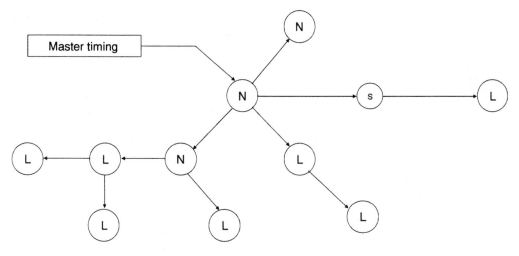

N = Nodal Timing Supply
L = Local Timing Supply
s = Secondary Timing Supply

Figure 21.13 DDS network timing

It should be clear by now that precise synchronisation is the key to the success of an all digital network. Timing ensures that data bits are generated at precise intervals, interleaved in time and read out at the receiving end at the same interval to prevent the loss or garbling of data. To accomplish the necessary clock synchronisation on the AT&T digital network, a master clock is used to supply a hierarchy of timing in the network. Should a link to the master clock fail, the nodal timing supplies can operate independently for up to 2 weeks without excessive slippage during outages. In Figure 21.13 the hierarchy of timing supplies as linked to AT&T's master reference clock is illustrated. As shown, the subsystem is a tree-like network containing no closed loops.

Within a DDS office, a composite timing signal is distributed over balanced pairs to each bay of equipment. This timing signal is a bipolar 64 kHz waveform having a 5/8 duty cycle. Each eighth pulse violates the bipolar rule. Hence, the basic waveform provides the bit clock information while the bipolar violation provides the byte clock information.

Connection to the DDS service originally required a channel service unit (CSU) and a data service unit (DSU) to terminate a DDS line. The DSU converts the signal from the terminal equipment into the bipolar format used with DDS and T1 facilities. The CSU performs line conditioning functions to include equalisation and signal reshaping as well as line loopback testing. Prior to deregulation, the CSU was provided by the communications carrier, while the DSU could be obtained from third party sources. After deregulation, several third party vendors started manufacturing devices that combined the functions of the DSU and the CSU.

21.8.2 BT's KiloStream

KiloStream is a point to point leased line digital service that was first offered commercially in January 1983. Like DDS, KiloStream is an all synchronous facility. BT provides a Network Terminating Unit (NTU) which is similar to a DSU/CSU to terminate the subscriber's line. The NTU encodes customer data for transmission via

a digital local line to the local exchange where it is fed into a CEPT 2.048 Mbit/s multiplexer, as illustrated in Figure 21.14.

The customer data rate can be 2400, 4800, 9600, 48000 or 64000bit/s. The DTE/NTU interface depends on the data rate. Speeds of 2400, 4800, and 9600bit/s can be serviced through a CCITT X.21 or CCITT X.21 bis/V.24 interface. 48kbit/s can be provided with a CCITT X.21 or CCITT X.21 bis/V.35 interface. A 64kbit/s channel is only available with an X.21 interface. At all data rates, except at 64kbit/s, the NTU encodes the user data into a 6+2 envelope structure as described in CCITT Recommendation X.50. Hence, the line data rate is higher than the customer data rate. For DTE data rates of 2400, 4800, and 9600bit/s the line data rate equals 12.8kbit/s, while a 48kbit/s user channel is transported at a 64kbit/s line rate.

Customer data is framed into a 6+2 format to provide the signalling and control information required by the network for maintenance assistance. This is known as envelope encoding and is illustrated in Figure 21.15. The rate of 8000 octets/s, imposed by the 8kHz sampling frequency of PCM systems, allows a total net rate of 48kbit/s per digital channel. One such channel could, for example, transport 5 sub-channels at 9600 bit/s, 10 sub-channels at 4800bit/s, or 20 sub-channels at 2400bit/s. CCITT Recommendation X.58 optimises this structure by minimising the signalling overhead and is able to transport up to 6 sub-channels at 9600bit/s.

The NTU provides a CCITT interface for customer data at 2.4, 4.8, 9.6 or 48kbit/s to include performing data control and supervision, which is known as structured data. At 64kbit/s, the NTU provides a CCITT interface for customer data without performing data control and supervision, which is known as unstructured data.

The NTU controls the interface via CCITT Recommendation X.21, which is the standard interface for synchronous operation on public data networks. An optional V.24 interface is available at 2400, 4800 and 9600bit/s, while an optional CCITT V.35 interface can be obtained at 48kbit/s. With the X.21 interface, the control circuit (C) indicates the status of the transmitted information, data or signalling, while the indication circuit (I) signals the status of information received from the line. The control and indication

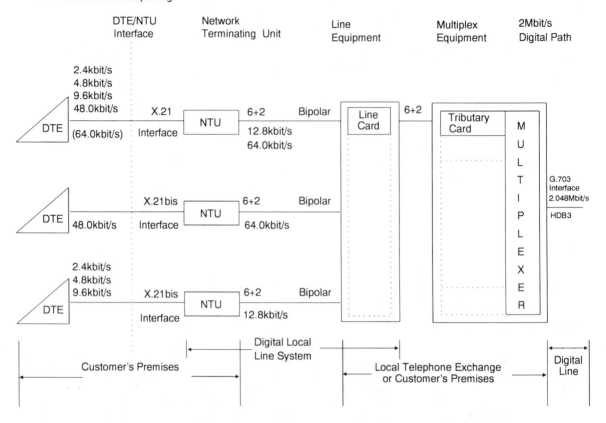

Figure 21.14 Basic KiloStream structure

circuits control or check the status bit of the 8-bit envelope used to frame six information bits.

21.8.3 AT&T's Accunet and BT's MegaStream

Both Accunet T 1.5 and MegaStream are carrier transmission facilities for high speed data and high volume speech communications. The Accunet T1.5 facility operates at 1.544Mbit/s. The MegaStream facility operates at 2.048Mbit/s. Both facilities offer full or fractional T1/E1.

Data sources that can be effectively serviced by these transmission facilities include digital PABXs, analog PABXs with voice digitisers, clustered terminals via multiplexer input, analog terminations, and video applications.

21.9 References

Bell (1982). *Bell System Technical Reference*, PUB 43801, November.

Bocker, P. (1988) *The Integrated Services Network*, Springer Verlag (West Germany).

Bylanski, P. and Ingram, D.G.W. (1976) *Digital Transmission Systems*, Peter Peregrinus, Stevenage.

CCITT (1989) *Blue Books, Volume III – Fascicle III.4, General Aspects of Digital Transmission Systems – Terminal Equipments, Recommendations G.700 – G.795*, CCITT, Geneva.

Lucky, R.W., Salz, J., Weldon Jr, E.J. (1968) *Principles of Data Communication*, McGraw-Hill, New York.

Matick, R.E. (1969) *Transmission Lines for Digital and Communication Networks*, McGraw-Hill, New York.

A = Alignment bit which alternates between 1 and 0 in successive envelopes to indicate the start and stop of each 8-bit envelope

S = Status bit which is set or reset by the control circuit and checked by the indicator circuit

I = Information bits

Figure 21.15 KiloStream 8-bit envelope encoding

22 Telecommunication standards

Fraidoon Mazda
MPhil DFH DMS MBIM CEng FIEE
Northern Telecom

Contents

22.1 The growth of telecommunication standards

Telecommunications is a major industrial sector for two reasons. Firstly it is vast in terms of revenue generated per annum, and secondly it impacts on all aspects of commercial and domestic life. Standardisation within telecommunications is intended to perform three basic functions:

1. Facilitate interconnection between different users. After all communications cannot be said to occur unless the parties involved can understand each other.
2. Facilitate the portability of equipment within different applications and regions, such that the market size is increased, resulting in reduced cost due to economies of scale. This benefits the supplier.
3. Ensure that equipment bought from one vendor can interface to that from another. This benefits the user in enabling competitive procurement.

Telecommunications standards were spurred by the growth in technology. The invention of the electric telegraph, and its use in civil and military applications, resulted in the first known treaty regulating telecommunications across national frontiers. On 3 October 1849 Prussia and Austria signed a treaty establishing the priority of telegraph traffic across their frontiers. The system was simple but effective; on odd dates Prussian traffic was given priority and on even dates the priority was assigned to Austria.

Other European treaties followed until, in 1865, the French Government invited major countries of the industrial world to a conference in Paris. This marked the birth of the International Telecommunication Union (ITU) and the signing of the first International Telegraph Convention on 17 May 1865 by 20 countries.

The United Kingdom could not join since, unlike the rest of Europe, its telegraph service was not under control of the state. It was not until 1871 that the service was nationalised and the UK joined the ITU. Key dates in the formation of the major international standards bodies are as follows:

1865 The ITU was established by 20 European states meeting in Paris.
1923 The CCIF was established in Paris, for the study of long distance telephony.
1925 The CCITT was established for the technical study of problems into telephony, and both it and the CCIF became part of the ITU.
1927 The CCIR was formed in Washington, with the mandate to concentrate on technical issues concerned with radio communications.
1947 In Atlantic City, USA, the ITU was recognised as an agency of the United Nations, specialising in telecommunication matters.
1959 The CCIF and the CCITT were combined, in Geneva, to form the CCITT, which continued to be part of the ITU.

22.2 The standards making process

The path towards global standards has been a difficult one. Historically each country had its own Post, Telephone and Telegraph (PTT) authority. They set standards and had the monopoly on local manufacture. There was little interest in standardisation and even when standard bodies were set up they produced standards which were recommendations (and therefore not enforceable), containing many country specific exceptions.

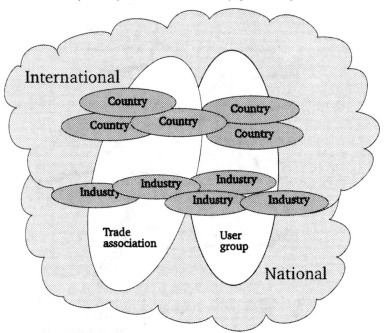

Figure 22.1 Groupings in the standards making process

Producing standards is not easy. It is important that standards formation does not hold back technology progress. At the same time once a technology becomes established, and companies have invested in rival systems, each player is eager to promote its method as the international standard. Furthermore the leaders in any field are reluctant to slow down, to agree standards which will eventually help their rivals.

Producing standards is an expensive business. It is estimated that several hundreds of millions of dollars a year are being spent on world-wide telecommunication standards activities.

The standards making process is one of co-operation at many levels, both nationally and internationally. This includes co-operation between industrial concerns within a country, between these concerns and their national governments and between nationals at the international level. User groups and trade organisations usually also have members from several countries. This interaction is shown in Figure 22.1, remembering that many industrial companies are multinational in operation and have turnovers which exceed the Gross National Product of some countries.

Co-operation is important to obtain agreement on standards, but there is a danger that the many separate groupings and interests can often result in different standards being prepared for the same item. Historically this has resulted in the world being divided into two transmission standards, 2.048 Mbit/s (and A-law codec) in Europe and 1.544 Mbit/s (and μ-law codec) in the USA and Japan. Even recently the CCITT has had to adopt two standards for ISDN rate adaption, V.110 promoted by ECMA and V.120 promoted by T1 and ANSI.

In order to accommodate the many conflicting interests, the international standards making organisations often concentrate on producing what are known as base standards. These contain permissible variants or alternative methods, which are implementor defined facilities. Adopting any of these variants would mean that the implementor was compliant with the standard, but there would be no guarantee that equipment based on separate variants would be able to interwork.

The problem of interworking is being tackled by regional and national standards bodies, often consisting of trade organisations and user groups, with well defined requirements. These groups may be manufacturers or users. They adapt international base standards as functional standards or profiles, which contain only a limited subset of the permissible variants. Agreed test specifications and methods are also developed, to ensure that equipment designed to the different variants, permitted within the functional standards, will be able to interwork. Independent test houses then carry out conformance tests against the selected profiles and certify products which meet this requirement. Figure 22.2 shows this three stage standards making process.

Three key problems are seen in standards formulation:

1. Standards take too long, primarily due to the need for obtaining consensus between rival fractions. This usually means that de facto standards, based on proprietary solutions, are available ahead of an international standard. The standard making bodies then have the problem of either accepting the de facto standard and abandoning their own, or of accepting the existence of two standards. If standards are developed too early then the danger is that technology will change and make the standard obsolete.
2. Standards often need to be developed to cover every aspect of the intended application. This would probably result in an overlap in standards, with duplication. The alternative is to avoid duplication, but allow de facto standards in areas which have not been covered.
3. It is difficult, when developing a new standard, to know when an intellectual property right (IPR) is being infringed. This is often due to the time lag between the filing of a patent and the

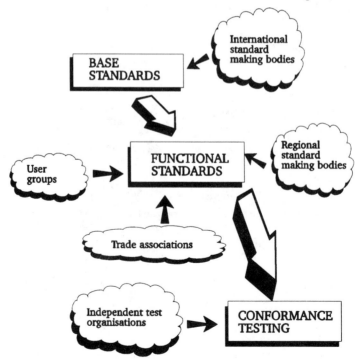

Figure 22.2 Base standards, functional standards and conformance testing

information being revealed by a search. This means that a standard may contain elements of an IPR. The problem is then of how it should be licensed to other users. Should the IPR holder be expected to license it to anyone who requests it, including his competitors? Furthermore, how should the licence be priced, especially if the standard is made mandatory?

22.3 International standards organisations

The structure of standard making bodies and the relationship between the international, regional and national bodies is shown in Figure 22.3. Trade associations and user groups can operate internationally, by geographical region, or nationally. The foremost international standard making body for telecommunications is the International Telecommunication Union (ITU) and for information technology standards it is the International Standards Organisation (ISO), although with the blurring of lines between telecommunications and information technology their activities often overlap.

22.3.1 The International Telecommunications Union

The ITU was founded in 1865 as the Union Telegraphique, with the prime aim of developing standards in telecommunications. In 1947 it became an specialised agency for telecommunications, of the United Nations, under the UN Charter Articles 57 to 63, when it was also renamed the International Telecommunications Union.

In its early years the ITU carried out its task of standard making very effectively, since the pace of technology was more leisurely than it is today. Telegraphy was invented in 1837, telephony in 1876, automatic switching in 1889 and telex in 1917. In fact up to 1960 the rate of change in telecommunications was manageable.

The discovery of the integrated circuit and its penetration into telecommunications changed that. The ITU found it difficult to keep up with the standards making requirements placed on it. Standards

took a long time to produce and the final output was often open to interpretation. It was at that stage that the principal responsibility for standards was delegated to other organisations such as CEPT, CCITT and CCIR.

22.3.1.1 *ITU aims*

Today the ITU has three major functions:

1. To encourage the interconnectivity of telecommunication equipment and services by promoting and establishing technical standards in these areas.
2. To promote the best use of scarce telecommunication resources, by the implementation of international regulations. This is especially important in the use of the radio frequency spectrum, which the ITU controls via the CCITT, CCIR and the International Frequency Registration Board (IFRB).
3. To encourage the growth of telecommunications in less developed countries. This is done via the Technical Co-operation Department (TCD) and the Telecommunications Development Bureau (TDB).

In addition the ITU carries out other ancillary tasks for its members, such as organising telecommunication exhibitions to keep members informed of the latest advances in telecommunication techniques. The best known is the Telecom exhibitions which are held every four years, Telecom 91 having been held in October 1991 in Geneva.

22.3.1.2 *ITU membership*

At the end of 1991 the ITU had 165 countries as its members, who had equal voting rights. Lithuania was the last to join and the first of the Baltic States to do so. Only Administrations, i.e. government departments concerned with telecommunications, can be ITU mem-

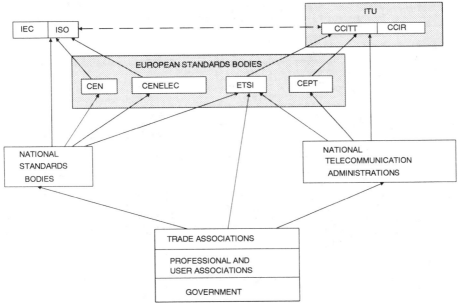

Figure 22.3 Organisations involved in the standards making process

bers. Therefore the UK is represented by the Department of Trade and Industry. Most other countries are represented by their Postal, Telegraph and Telephony (PTT) Administrations, which are State owned. For the USA the representation is by a complex mix of government, agencies and suppliers.

In addition other organisation groupings are recognised, who can attend meetings of the ITU and its other organisations but cannot generally vote. These organisations are:

1. Recognised Private Operating Agencies (RPOA). Over eighty of these have been recognised by the ITU and consist of telecommunication operators. Examples of these are BT and Mercury in the UK and Nippon Telephone and Telegraph Corporation (NTT) in Japan.
2. Scientific and Industrial Organisations (SIO). There are over one hundred and fifty of these and examples are IBM, Northern Telecom and Siemens.
3. International Organisations (IO), of which there are over fifty recognised. These are mainly trade organisations and user groups, such as the International Telecommunications User Group (INTUG).

RPOAs can be members of CCITT and CCIR and have voting rights, although SIOs and IOs can only be advisory members of these bodies.

22.3.1.3   *ITU structure*

The ITU is funded by voluntary contributions from member countries. (The 1990 budget for the ITU's operations was set at the 1989 Plenipotentiary at $77M.) The biggest contributors, providing over 40% of the funds, are USA, USSR, UK, France, Germany and Japan.

The structure of the ITU is illustrated in Figure 22.4. It may be considered to be made up of two parts:

1. A permanent organisation based in Geneva and consisting of a General Secretariat; the Administrative Council; the CCITT and the CCIR; the IFRB; and the TCD and BDT.
2. A series of conferences, which are held at various intervals. These are the Plenipotentiary; the WARC; the WATTC; the World and Regional Development Conferences; and the Plenary Assembly meetings of the CCITT and the CCIR.

Each ITU organ has its own elected head and there is not necessarily any co-ordination between them. The Secretary General has no direct jurisdiction over them either.

22.3.1.4   *The ITU General Secretariat*

The Secretary General, who is elected at the ITU Plenipotentiary conference, heads the General Secretariat. At the 1989 Plenipotentiary, held between 23 May 1989 and 30 June 1989, Mr. Pekka Tarjanne, Director General of the Finnish PTT, was elected to be Secretary General of the ITU for a six year term.

The General Secretariat is responsible for carrying out the directions of the Plenipotentiary Conference, for managing the finances of the ITU and for other administrative matters such as the organisation of meetings and conferences. It is also responsible for co-ordinating the work of the Union with other international organisations, and for all press contacts.

The Secretary General is assisted by a co-ordination committee, which he chairs, comprising of the directors of the CCIs and the BDT, and the chairman of the IFRB.

22.3.1.5   *The ITU Administrative Council*

The Administrative Council acts on behalf of the Plenipotentiary Conference and forms the governing body of the Union. The Coun-

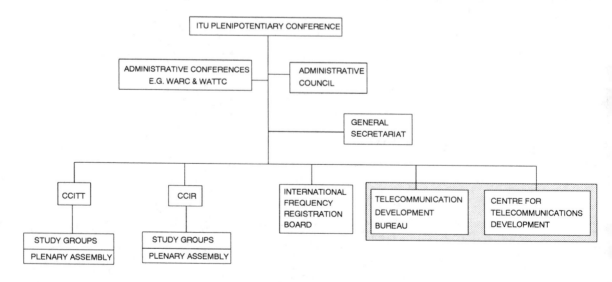

Figure 22.4   Structure of the ITU

cil meets annually and is responsible for setting budgets and for determining the agenda for conferences.

The Administrative Council monitors the work of the ITU between Plenipotentiaries, ensures the implementation of the Plenipotentiary convention and regulations, and carries out the decisions of the conferences. Its members are elected so as to represent all regions on an equitable basis.

22.3.1.6   *The CCITT*

The Comite Consultatif Internationale Telephonique et Telegraphic (CCITT) is the prime vehicle for developing technical standards in the telecommunications field.

In the 1989 Plenipotentiary the CCITT (and CCIR) were directed to conduct their activities with due consideration for the work of national and regional standardisation bodies, keeping in mind the need for the ITU to maintain its pre-eminent position in the field of world-wide standardisation for telecommunications. The two CCIs were therefore given a mandate for global standards.

22.3.1.7   *The CCIR*

The CCIR, develops standards in the radio field. Its activities mirror those of the CCITT in this area.

22.3.1.8   *The IFRB*

The International Frequency Registration Board (IFRB) is made up of five specialists elected by Plenipotentiary Conference. The IFRB acts as the custodian of an international public trust, it main duty being to decide whether new frequencies assigned to radio users are in line with the convention and the Radio Regulations. It also provides advice on improving the utilisation of the radio spectrum and in the preparation and organisation of the Administrative Radio Conferences.

The IFRB has its own secretariat of about 100. The technical secretariat of the IFRB has three departments: terrestrial services; space services; and informatic systems.

For frequency allocation purposes the world is divided into three regions. Region 1 covers Europe, Middle East, Africa and the USSR. Region 2 covers the Americas, Canada and Greenland. Region 3 covers the Far East, Australia and New Zealand.

The IFRB records the frequency assignments of all radio services and the associated orbital positions for space stations used throughout the world, after regulatory and technical examination, according to the provisions of the Radio Regulations and International treaty adapted by the members of the ITU. These records are kept in the Master Frequency Register, which gives it formal international recognition and protection. This register contains well over a million entries.

Central to Radio Regulations is the International Table of Frequency Allocations. This allocates all the frequency bands between 9kHz and 275GHz. In each region a band may be allocated exclusively to a service or shared between services. When shared the status of each can be defined as either a primary service, a permitted service or a secondary service. Secondary services have the lowest priority. They must not cause harmful interference with primary or permitted services, and they cannot claim protection from interference from these services. Primary and permitted services have

equal priority, except that when preparing new frequency plans primary services will have prior choice of frequencies.

22.3.1.9   *The TCD and the BDT*

The Technical Co-operation Department (TCD) has the task of co-ordinating the ITU's assistance to developing countries. It provides telecommunications training and technical assistance, and carries out studies on economic, financial or regulatory policy to help developing countries. This has been a contentious topic, with these countries continually complaining that not enough is being done in this area.

Support for developing countries was an issue during the 1986 Plenipotentiary and following this the Centre for Telecommunication Development was set up in 1986 in Geneva, to encourage the growth of telecommunications in developing countries. The topic was again raised at the 1989 Plenipotentiary and a new Telecommunications Development Bureau (BDT) was formed. The BDT now works in conjunction with the TCD in assisting the growth of telecommunication networks, particularly in developing countries; in encouraging investment by industry in these areas; and in organising world and regional development conferences.

22.3.1.10   *The Plenipotentiary*

The Plenipotentiary is held approximately every seven years. One was held in Nairobi in 1982, then in Nice in 1989 and the next is planned for Japan in 1994. One thousand delegates from 143 nations attended the 1989 Plenipotentiary over the period 23 May to 30 June. The Plenipotentiary Conference is the highest authority of the Union, responsible for setting its policies and for revisions to its constitution.

22.3.1.11   *The WARC, the WATTC and the RARC*

The World Administrative Radio Conference (WARC), the World Administrative Telephone and Telegraph Conference (WATTC), and the Regional Administrative Radio Conference (RARC) are held at irregular intervals, as required. These approve changes to the regulations in their respective fields, drawing up the ITU's binding regulations.

The WATTC establishes principles relating to the operation of international telecommunication public services. It sets rules applicable to administrations and RPOA.

The WATTC meetings started in 1850, the last one, WATTC 88 being held in Melbourne, Australia over 28 November to 9 December 1988. This was the 25th general telecommunication conference to be held. Over 500 representatives from governments and telecommunication organisations attended and over 1000 proposals for the new treaty were considered. The final acts were signed by 112 countries on 9 December.

The WARC revises regulations governing use of radio frequency spectrum and the geostationary satellite orbit. The RARC deals with specific radio communication questions of a regional nature.

The last WARC was held in Spain starting on 3 February 1992, the previous one being held in 1979. These meetings last about four weeks and consider revisions to Radio Regulations, which are a set of two large volumes published by the ITU. CCIR puts forward proposals for consideration at these conferences. Delegates from all ITU signatories attend the meetings.

22.3.1.12   *World and Regional Development Conferences*

The aims of these conferences are to promote international co-operation; assist development of telecommunication facilities and services, especially in developing countries; and establish targets for telecommunication development, both regionally and world wide.

22.3.1.13   *Plenary Assemblies*

The Plenary Assembly meetings of the CCITT and CCIR, are held every four years. They approve the new standards prepared by the working groups within these organisations and set the work for the next four years.

22.3.1.14   *ITU changes*

A high level committee, set up to review the ITU's structure, has recommended that the ITU is organised into three working directorates:

1. Standards, covering the CCITT and the network radio standards of the CCIR.
2. Radio communications, covering most of the other work currently carried out by the CCIR, and all the work of the IFRB.
3. Development, combining the TCD and TDB.

It also recommended that the ITU attract finance from industry for its work. The main proposals will need to be voted on at the 1994 ITU Plenipotentiary Conference, to be held in Kyoto, Japan, and will be considered at an ad hoc meeting called for in Geneva in December 1992. The committee also recognised that the ITU's standards work must fit with that of Europe's ETSI, USA's T1 committee, and Japan's TTC.

22.3.2   The CCITT

The Comite Consultatif Internationale Telephonique et Telegraphique was set up in 1925 as an agent of the ITU in order to carry out studies into the technical problems of telephony. Article 13 in the constitution of the ITU defines the role of the CCITT as being to study technical, operating and tariff questions and to issue recommendations on these with a view to standardising telecommunications on a world-wide basis. Radiocommunications are excluded as these come within the responsibility of the CCIR.

22.3.2.1   *CCITT organisation*

Members of the CCITT consist of:

1. Telecommunication administrations of all members of the ITU. BT, Mercury and the DTI represent the UK.
2. Any RPOA or SIO who wishes to participate in the work of the CCITT and is approved by its members to do so.

Membership fees to the ITU cover those of the CCITT, but RPOAs and SIOs are charged individually.

The technical work of the CCITT is undertaken by Study Groups (SGs). There are fifteen Study Groups, differentiated by Roman letters, those for the study period 1988 – 1992, being shown in Table 22.1. There are also three special groups, as shown in Table 22.2.

Table 22.1   CCITT Study Groups

Study Group	Activity
I	Services
II	Network operation
III	Tariff and accounting principles
Regional Tariff Groups of Study Group III	
GR TAF	Tariffs (Africa)
GR TAL	Tariffs (Latin America)
GR TAS	Tariffs (Asia and Oceania)
GR TEUREM	Tariffs (Europe and the Mediterranean Basin)
IV	Maintenance
V	Protection against electromagnetic effects
VI	Outside plant
VII	Data communications networks
VIII	Terminals for telematics services
IX	Telegraph networks and telegraph terminal equipment
X	Languages for telecommunications applications
XI	Switching and signalling
XII	Transmission performance of telephone networks and terminals
XV	Transmission systems and equipment
XVII	Data transmission over the telephone network
XVIII	ISDN

Table 22.2   CCITT Special Autonomous Groups

Group	Activity
GAS 7	Rural telecommunications
GAS 9	Economic and technical aspects of transition from an analogue to a digital network
GAS 12	Strategy for the introduction of new non-voice telecommunication services in developing countries

The Study Groups usually conduct their business by correspondence, meeting relatively infrequently, to produce draft standards for ratification by the Plenary assembly.

The director of the CCITT is assisted by a specialised secretariat, made up of four departments. Department A plans the committees and undertakes general affairs. Department B deals with the telecommunication network and network components (Study Groups IV, X, XI, XII, XV, XVIII, GAS 7, GAS 9). Department C deals with telecommunication services and tariffs (Study Groups I, II, III, V, VI, VII, VIII, IX, XVII, GAS12). It is also responsible for liaison with ISO. Department D is responsible for technical editing, for terminology and for the production of CCITT publications.

The CCITT works on a series of Plenary assemblies which meet every four years. Traditionally a Plenary meeting sets the study groups of the CCITT a series of 'questions' which are worked on over the four year period. The outcome of this work are 'Recommendations' which are approved by the next Plenary and published in volumes.

The tasks of the Plenary Assembly are to:

1. Approve the work programme for the Study Groups, based on new and existing questions.
2. Approve reports from Study Groups.
3. Decide on the Study Groups needed and allocate questions between them.
4. Approve, for submission to the Administrative Council, the budget of the CCITT covering the period to the next Plenary Assembly.

22.3.2.2   CCITT Recommendations

Every issue of the CCITT Recommendations has a different colour. Therefore the 1980 Recommendations were published as yellow coloured books, called Yellow Books, the 1984 issue was red, and were called the Red Books, whilst the 1988 issue was blue, called the Blue Books. Publication of a new set of Recommendations does not automatically make the preceding set of books obsolete. Most equipment would have been approved to the older set of standards and it is only user pressure which determines how soon the newer standards are adopted.

Apart from the Plenary Assembly, questions to the CCITT may also be referred by the Plenipotentiary or Administration Conference; the CCIR or IFRB; or at least 20 members of the ITU, in between Plenary Assemblies.

The task of the CCITT is vast and almost doubles with every Plenary. The 1980 issue of the recommendations occupied 6000 pages; the 1984 issue was in 11000 pages; whilst the 1988 issue runs to almost 20000 pages.

Because of the problems of producing standards in a timely fashion the CCITT, at its 1988 IXth Plenary held in Melbourne, Australia, agreed an accelerated procedure for the issue of standards. Recommendations are now adopted as soon as they have stabilised, rather than needing full ratification by the Plenary Assembly. This means that standards could be ready within one year of starting work.

The CCITT has also adopted more of a co-ordination role between the various national and regional standard making authorities. Key amongst these are the USA T1 committees, the Japanese TTC and the European ETSI. The ideas and work from these organisations, along with that from R&D organisations, manufacturers, users and service providers, flows into and back out of the CCITT until they are stable and accepted as standards.

Table 22.3 provides an overview of the content of the Blue Books covering CCITT Recommendations. These Recommendations are designated by a letter which signifies which Study Group was responsible for the recommendation and also its category. For example Study Group XVIII answers the questions relating to digital networks and ISDN and produces the I-Series Recommendations.

An area of contention of CCITT standard making activities is the work carried out by Study Group III which produces Recommendations covering pricing and supply conditions, especially for international leased circuits. The European Commission has stated in a Green Paper that this work conflicts with the Communities' competitive laws.

22.3.3   The CCIR

22.3.3.1   CCIR responsibilities

The CCIR was set up in 1927. It is an agent of the ITU, like the CCITT, but it concentrates on radio communications matters. Article 11 in the constitution of the ITU states the duties of the CCIR to be to study technical and operating questions relating specifically to radiocommunications without a limit of frequency range, and to issue recommendations on them, with a view to standardising telecommunications on a world-wide basis.

In carrying out these studies the CCIR is generally required to avoid addressing economic questions, except where technical options are being compared. To some extent this emphasis on technical rather than commercial considerations has resulted in the CCIR being more academic in its approach than its sister organisation, the CCITT.

CCIR's main responsibility are:

1. The development of technical bases for the international sharing and management of the frequency spectrum and geostationary satellite orbit resources.

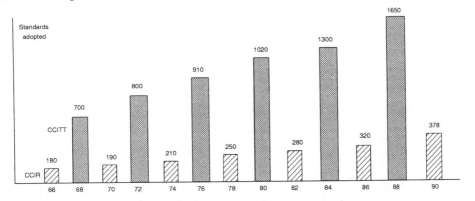

Figure 22.5   Comparison of standards produced by the CCITT and the CCIR

Table 22.3 CCITT Blue Books. (Continued on next page.)

Fascicle	Recommendations	Study group	Title
I.1			Minutes and reports of the Plenary Assembly. Opinions and resolutions.
I.2	C and A		Recommendations on the organisation and working procedures of the CCITT and general telecommunication statistics. List of study groups and questions under study.
I.3			Terms and definitions. Abbreviations and acronyms.
I.4			Index of the Blue Book.
II.1			General tariff principles — charging and accounting in international services.
II.2	E.100—E333	II	Telephone network and ISDN — operation numbering routing and mobile service.
II.3	E.401—E.880	II	Telephone network and ISDN — quality of service network management and traffic engineering.
II.4	F.1—F.140	I	Telegraph and mobile services — operations and quality of service.
II.5	F.160—F.353; F.600; F.601; F.710—F.730	I	Telematic data transmission and teleconference services — operations and quality of service.
II.6	F.400—F.422; F.500	I	Message handling and directory services — operations and definition of service.
III.1	G.101—G.181	XILXV	General characteristics of international telephone connections and circuits.
III.2	G.211—G.544	XV	International analogue carrier systems.
III.3	G.601—G.654		Transmission media — characteristics.
III.4	G.700—G.772	XV; XVIII	General aspects of digital transmission systems; terminal equipments.
III.5	G.801—G.956	XV; XVIII	Digital networks; digital sections and sigital line systems.
III.6	H and J	XV	Line transmission of non—telephone signals. Transmission of sound—programme and television signals.
III.7	1.110—1.257	XVIII	Integrated Services Digital Network (ISDN) — general structure and service capabilities.
III.8	1.310—1.470	XVIII	Integrated Services Digital Network (ISDN) — overall network aspects and functions; ISDN user—network interfaces.
III.9	1.500—1.600	XVIII	Integrated Services Digital Network (ISDN) — internetwork interfaces and maintenance principles.
IV.1	M.10—M.782	IV	General maintenance principles: maintenance of international transmission systems and telephone circuits.
IV.2	M.800—M.1375	IV	Maintenance of international telegraph; phototelegraph and leased circuits. Maintenance of the international public telephone network. Maintenance of maritime satellite and data transmission systems.
IV.3	N	IV	Maintenance of international sound—programme and television transmission circuits.
IV.4	O	IV	Specifications for measuring equipment.
V	P	XII	Telephone transmission quality. Series P Recommendations.
VI.1	Q.1—Q.118bis	XI	General Recommendations on telephone switching and signalling. Functions and information flows in the ISDN. Supplements.
VI.2	Q1.20—Q.180	XI	Specifications of Signalling Systems Nos. 4 and 5.
VI.3	Q.251—Q.300	XI	Specifications of Signalling System No. 6.
VI.4	Q.310—Q.490	XI	Specifications of Signalling Systems R1 and R2 (Study XI).
VI.5	Q.500—Q.554	XI	Digital local transit combined and international exchanges in integrated digital networks and mixed analogue—digital networks. Supplements

Table 22.3   (Continued from previous page.)

VI.6	Q.601—Q.699	XI	Interworking of signalling systems
VI.7	Q.700—Q.716	XI	Specifications of signalling system No.7
VI.8	Q.721—A.766	XI	Specifications of signalling system No.7
VI.9	Q.771—Q.795	XI	Specifications of signalling system No.7
VI.10	Q.920—Q.921	XI	Digital access signalling system; data link layer
VI.11	Q.930—Q.940	XI	Digital access signalling system; network layer; user—network management
VI.12	Q.1000—Q.1032	XI	Public land mobile network. Interworking with ISDN and PSTN
VI.13	Q.1051—Q.1063	XI	Public land mobile network. Mobile application part and interfaces
VI.14	Q.1100—Q.1152	XI	Interworking with satellite mobile systems
VII.1	S	IX	Telegraph transmission. Series R Recommendations. Telegraph Services terminal equipment
VII.2	U	IX	Telegraph switching
VII.3	T.o—T.63	VIII	Terminal equipment and protocols for telematic services
VII.4	T.64	VIII	Conformance testing procedures for the Teletex Recommendations
VII.5	T.65—T.101 T.150—T.390	VIII	Terminal equipment and protocols for telematic services
VII.6	T.400—T.418	VIII	Terminal equipment and protocols for telematic services
VII.7	T.431—T.564	VIII	Terminal equipment and protocols for telematic services
VIII.1	V	XVII	Data communication over the telephone network
VIII.2	X.1—X.32	VII	Data communication networks: services and facilities interfaces
VIII.3	X.40—X.181	VII	Data communication networks: transmission signalling and switching network aspects maintenance and administrative arrangements
VIII.4	X.200—X.219	VII	Data communication networks. Open Systems Interconnection (OSI — model and notation service definition
VIII.5	X.220—X.290	VII	Data communication networks: Open Systems Interconnection (OSI) — protocol specifications conformance testing
VIII.6	X.300—X.370	VII	Data communication networks: interworking between networks mobile data transmission systems
VIII.7	X.400—X.420	VII	Data communication networks: message handling systems
VIII.8	X.500—X.521	VII	Data communication networks: directory
IX	K L	V VI	Protection against interference Construction installation and protection of cable and other elements of outside plant
X.1	Z.100 and Annexes A;B;C;E Z.110	X	Functional Specification and Description Language (SDL) Criteria for using Formal Description Techniques (FDTs)
X.2	Z.100, Annex D	X	SDL user guidelines
X.3	Z.100, Annex F.1	X	SDL formal definition Introduction
X.4	Z.100, Annex F.2	X	SDL formal definition. Static semantics
X.5	Z.100, Annex F.3	X	SDL formal definition. Dynamic semantics
X.6	Z.200	XI	CCITT High Level Language (CHILL)
X.7	Z.301—Z.341	X	Man—machine Language (MML)
XI.1			Terms, definitions, abbreviations, acronyms, series and recommendations
XI.2			Index of Blue Book

2. For standards of radio systems world-wide, relating to compatible performance and interconnectivity.
3. For the production of information used for the development, planning and operation of radio systems, with special emphasis on the needs of developing countries.

22.3.3.2 *CCIR organisation and output*

The CCIR membership is similar to that of the CCITT and it operates on similar principles. CCIR Recommendations are published by Plenary Assemblies which meet every four years. The CCIR is not as active as its sister organisation, the CCITT, as can be seen from Figure 22.5 which compares their standards output over a twenty year period. This is partly due to the fact that whereas the CCITT devotes about 90% of its time to standards preparation, the CCIR devotes about 40% of its time to this, the rest being used on other studies, such as on spectrum utilisation.

The CCIR works through a series of Study Groups, similar to those of the CCITT. Study Groups are nominated at Plenary meetings and the scope of their responsibility defined. They set up Working Parties to prepare draft Recommendations for consideration by the Study Groups. For urgent topics smaller Task Groups may be assigned the work, the Groups being disbanded when this has been completed. Study Groups have the authority to adopt draft Recommendations between Plenary Assemblies.

Table 22.4 shows the Study Groups over the period 1990 – 1994, and Table 22.5 shows the CCIR/CCITT Joint Study Groups. These were set up at the XVIIth CCIR Plenary Assembly in Dusseldorf in 1990. The next Plenary is to be held in 1994. Table 22.6 gives the content of the CCIR 1990 Recommendations.

The XVIIth Plenary Assembly examined results of work by the Study Groups since the previous Plenary Assembly. Sixty new Recommendations were approved and 126 revised. This brought the total in force up to 378. Major areas considered were: high definition television, where five new Recommendations were adopted, and mobile systems, where eight new Recommendations were adopted and twelve revised. Many of the mobile Recommendations deal with frequency sharing and interference issues.

Table 22.4 CCIR Study Groups

Study Group	Activity
1	Spectrum engineering
2	Space research and radioastronomy
3	Fixed service at frequencies below about 30MHz
4	Fixed satellite service
5	Radio wave propagation in non-ionised media
6	Radio wave propagation in ionised media
7	Science services
8	Mobile
9	Fixed service
10	Broadcasting service (sound)
11	Broadcasting service (television)
12	Inter-service sharing and compatibility

Table 22.5 CCIR/CCITT Joint Study Groups

Study Group	Activity
CMTT	Television and sound transmission
CCV	Co-ordination committee for vocabulary

Table 22.6 CCIR 1990 Recommendations

Volume	Description
I	Spectrum utilisation and monitoring
II	Space research and radio astronomy service
III	Fixed service at frequencies below about 30MHz
IV—1	Fixed satellite service
IV/IX —2	Frequency sharing and coordination between systems in the fixed—satellite service and radio relay systems
V	Propagation in non-ionized media
VI	Propagation in ionized media
VII	Standard frequency and time signals
VIII	Mobile radiodetermination and amateur services including the associated satellite services
IX — 1	Fixed service using radio relay systems
X — 1	Broadcasting service (sound)
X/XI — 2	Broadcasting satellite service (sound and television)
X/XI — 3	Sound and television recording
XI — 1	Broadcasting service (television)
XII	Television and sound transmission (CMITT)
XIII	Vocabulary (CCV)
XIV	Administrative texts of the CCIR
XV — 1	Questions concerning Study Groups 1, 5, 6, 7 and 12
XV — 2	Questions concerning Study Group 8
XV — 3	Questions concerning Study Groups 10, 11 and CMTT
XV — 4	Questions concerning Study Groups 4 and 9

Following the 1990 Plenary Assembly a Working Party was set up to examine the structure of the Study Groups and to recommend changes to the next Plenary Assembly, in order to improve the efficiency and effectiveness of CCIR work.

The Director of the CCIR is assisted by a specialised Secretariat with four departments. Department A deals with broadcasting media (sound, television, satellite), broadcast programme transmission, and computer applications. It is responsible for Study Groups 10, 11, CMMT and liaison with the IEC. Department B is responsible for spectrum utilisation and monitoring, space research and radio astronomy, radiowave propagation, Study Groups 1, 2, 5, 6, and liaison with CISPR and URSI.

Department C is responsible for fixed satellite service; fixed service at h.f.; radio relay mobile service; standard time frequency; Study Groups 3, 4, 7, 8, 9 and liaison with IMO, ICAO. Department D is responsible for technical editing; production of CCIR publications; and for vocabulary (Study Group CMV).

In mobile radio and broadcasting the CCITT is becoming increasingly predominant as these services are integrated into the public network, so that the work of the CCITT and CCIR becomes difficult to separate. There are six CCITT study groups involved in mobile radio matters. The ITU has recognised this position by nominating CCITT Study Group XVIII as the prime focus for activities relating to mobile radio communications.

There is currently much debate about the benefits of integrating the CCITT and the CCIR. The ITU is likely to favour this move since it is becoming increasing difficult to fund these two organisations. In spite of its lower volume of output in standards, the CCIR requires almost as much funds as the CCITT in order to function effectively.

22.3.4 The ISO

22.3.4.1 *ISO aims*

The International Standards Organisation was founded in February 1947 following agreement between standards organisations from 25 nations meeting in London in October 1946. It has now grown to standards bodies from close to 100 countries.

ISO is a non-treaty organisation, based in Geneva, and a body of the United Nations. Its technical work is done by about 3000 technical bodies and 2000 working groups. It has published over 10000 international standards and drafts.

The prime aim of the ISO is to promote the development of international standardisation in order to facilitate international trade in goods and services. It also aims to develop world-wide co-operation in scientific, technological and economic matters. The ISO mainly works in the Information Technology area whilst its sister organisation, the International Electrotechnical Commission (IEC) is involved in standards for Electrical and Electronic engineering.

22.3.4.2 *ISO structure*

Membership of the ISO is primarily made up of national standards making bodies, such as ANSI (USA), BSI (UK) and DIN (Germany). Members can be active or participating, designated as 'P' members, or they can be corresponding members or observers, designated as 'O' members. 'P' members take the lead on technical committees or subcommittees.

All standards developed by ISO are published as International Standards. It is the responsibility of the individual national standards organisations to promote and distribute these standards within their own countries.

The organisation of ISO consists of:

1. A General Assembly, which meets once every three years and consists of delegates nominated from its member countries. Standards are approved by a vote in this Assembly or by mail ballot. All decisions are recommendations and not mandatory.
2. The Council, which consists of a President, Vice President, treasurer and representatives elected from member bodies. The

Council administers the ISO between General Assemblies, meeting once a year to receive reports from the various committees set up to do studies in designated areas. The Council is also responsible for preparing and managing the budget of the ISO, which is funded by members' fees and by sale of publications.

3. An Executive Board, which consists of the Vice President and nine other persons appointed by the Council. The Council delegates the duties of this Board.
4. The Technical Board, consisting of a Chairman and nine members appointed by the Council. The Technical Board appoints technical committees and monitors their work. It is also responsible for all external technical contacts with other standards making bodies such as IEC, and for joint activities with them.
5. Technical Advisory Groups (TAGs) which are established by the Technical Board to advise it in specific areas. These are shown in Table 22.7.

Table 22.7   ISO Technical Advisory Groups

TAG 1	Chemical and physico-chemical test methods and methods of analysis
TAG 2	Metals
TAG 4	Metrology
TAG 5	Fire tests
TAG 6	Medical equipment (joint TAG with IEC)
TAG 7	Information technology applications
TAG 8	Building
TAG 9	Distribution of goods
TAG 10	Image technology
TAG 11	Safety

6. Technical Committees (TCs), which are established by the Council. Every ISO member who is interested in its field of work can take part in its activities. The Technical Committees set up Sub Committees (SCs) and Working Groups (WGs). Technical Committees are allocated a number to differentiate them, starting with the number 1 in 1947. When a committee completes its work and is dissolved its number is not re-used. About 200 committees have been established so far.
7. A Central Secretariat, consisting of a Secretary General and staff, who are based in the same location as ISO, in Geneva, Switzerland.

The telecommunications equivalent of the ISO is the CCITT. These two organisations work closely together in areas of common interest. For example all ISDN activities within ISO are carried out in Technical Committee TC97, which is responsible for information processing systems. This committee has two subcommittees:

1. SC6 which is involved in telecommunications and information exchange between systems. This subcommittee is working with the CCITT on common channel signalling (CCS) and the relationship of ISDN to the Open System Interconnect (OSI) model.
2. SC21, which is responsible for developing the seven layer OSI model on which the CCITT has modelled ISDN.

22.3.4.3 *Joint ISO/IEC committee*

The ISO and the IEC work together in many areas through their Joint Technical Programming Committee (JTPC). This committee has the task of ensuring that overlap of work between the two bodies is avoided. The ISO and the IEC have also set up a Joint Technical Committee on Information Technology, called JTC1, to develop generic Information Technology standards. This Committee incorporates the ISO TC97 and the IEC TC83.

JTC1 is responsible for producing International Standards Profiles (ISPs). These profiles can also be proposed by bodies outside of JTC1, such as the regional workshops on OSI, and are then ratified and published by the JTC1. Regional workshops include the NIST OSI Implementors Workshop (OIW) in the USA, the European Workshop for Open Systems (EWOS) in Europe, and the Asia and Oceania Workshop for OSI Standardisation (AOWS) in Asia and Oceania. These workshops are backed by user organisations, vendors, etc.

Other organisations carry out conformance testing to the profiles, and prominent amongst these are the Standards Promotion and Application Group (SPAG) in Europe and the Corporation for Open Systems (COS) in the USA. All these organisations co-operate in the Feeders Forum, set up in 1987, which unifies their technical work and provides a forum for liaison with ISO and IEC.

22.3.5 The IEC

22.3.5.1 *IEC aims*

The International Electrotechnical Commission was founded in 1904 in Saint Louis, Missouri, USA, with the prime aim of carrying out standardisation work for domestic and commercial electrical and electronic equipment. It has over 40 member nations, each country being represented by a committee which is expected to reflect the views of that country's government establishments, manufacturers, users and educational bodies.

Draft standards are produced from over 80 technical centres and their related subcommittees.

22.3.5.2 *IEC output and organisation*

IEC standards are of two types:

1. Standards covering engineering design aspects, such as the definition of electrical units; the standardisation of symbols used in circuit diagrams; and the nomenclature used.
2. Standards for electrical equipment covering all aspects, such as material used, methods of test, safety, etc.

The IEC has a Council which administers it. It appoints a Committee of Action, consisting of the President of the IEC and twelve members nominated by the national committees, who regulate all the technical work of the IEC.

The IEC develops standards through Technical Committees, Subcommittees and Working Groups. The council meets annually to ratify standards produced by these Committees and Groups, which are then adopted by the member countries. In the USA the NIST has the responsibility for adopting these standards, and this is done in the UK by the British Standards Institute (BSI).

As the demarcation between the various areas of technology becomes blurred, it is increasingly important for the various standards making bodies to work together. To meet this aim the IEC has

a subcommittee, the IEC Information Technology Co-ordinating Group, whose prime responsibility is to ensure that the IEC's activities are co-ordinated with that of other standards making bodies, in particular with the CCITT, CCIR and ISO.

22.3.6 International trade and user groups

22.3.6.1 *The OSI/Network Management Forum*

The OSI/Network Management Forum is an international organisation, primarily interested in standards for network management. It was formed in June 1988 by Andahl Corporation, British Telecom, Northern Telecom, STC plc, AT&T, Hewlett-Packard Co., Telecom Canada and Unisys Networks. It currently has about one hundred members from seventeen countries, including the USA, Europe, and Japan, primarily representing the telecommunication and computing industries.

The aim of the OSI/NM Forum is to accelerate the implementation of OSI management standards and to demonstrate their use. However, the Forum accepts that the route to OSI may sometimes require the initial use of some other standards, including proprietary and de facto.

The policy of the Forum is to adopt international standards, where they exist, and to draw up its own functional standards (profiles) in other cases, replacing them with the international standards when they have become available.

In June 1990 the Forum published its Release 1 specifications, which has subsequently been updated. It lays the groundwork for multivendor network management by defining a common approach, or architecture, and common data communication protocols. It also includes application messages to support event and configuration management, plus the definitions of a first critical set of managed objects. In fact the nine documents which make up Release 1 contain everything a developer needs to build the Forum interface, and states requirements which must be met by a system in order to be considered conformant.

The OSI/NM Forum has also published technical reports (TRs), which are guidelines on Forum strategies and activities. Examples are: TR100 – Forum Testing Strategy, which explains the importance of conformance testing; TR101 – Conformance Testing Report Proforma, which explains how to document results of conformance tests and submit these to the Forum to claim conformance; TR102 – Modelling Principles for Managed Objects, which provides a set of principles to aid in the design of object classes.

The Forum operates a Showcase programme, which are usually shows within International trade exhibitions, where members can demonstrate products and interoperability. The Forum's user programmes also include the President's Roundtable, which are working sessions where users are informed about the progress made by the Forum and can provide feedback.

In June 1989 the OSI/NM Forum formed an alliance with SPAG and COS to set up an Executive Council, which reviews the work of each organisation, establishing joint policies regarding network management. The alliance has produced test tools for conformance testing.

22.3.6.2 *The International Telecommunications User Group*

The International Telecommunications User Group (INTUG) was formed in 1974 to represent the telecommunication user organisations from several countries, including the USA, UK, Australia and Japan. It is active in promoting the interests of its members, and lobbying associations such as the ITU, CEPT, PTTs, and CCITT. Any person or group can join except PTTs and manufacturers, who need to be represented as individual members.

22.4 European standards

22.4.1 The European Community

Table 22.8 shows a commonly used grouping for the countries in Europe, the European Community being the largest and with the greatest integration. There are four principal institutions within the EC:

Table 22.8 European country groupings

European Community (Population: 340 million)	Eastern Europe (Population: 120 million)	European Free Trade Association (Population: 40 million)
France	Czechoslovakia	Norway
Germany	Bulgaria	Finland
Italy	Albania	Sweden
Spain	Hungary	Switzerland
Greece	Poland	Iceland
Belgium	Romania	Austria
Denmark	Yugoslavia	Liechtenstein
Portugal		
Iceland		
The Netherlands		
Luxemburg		
United Kingdom		

1. The Council of Ministers, which is responsible for forming decisive views regarding policy and legislation. All the twelve members of the community are represented, different ministers from these countries attending, depending on the topic under consideration. Presidency of the Council rotates on a six monthly basis, between the twelve member countries.
2. The European Commission, which forms the executive arm (or civil service) of the Community. It has seventeen commissioners drawn from the member states, and is led by a president, who is also one of the commissioners. Larger countries, such as the UK, supply two representatives whilst smaller ones provide one. The European Commission meets once a week in Brussels. Members of the Commission perform functions similar to those of ministers within its individual countries, each being responsible for one or more portfolios within the Community's activities.
3. The European Parliament, which has five hundred and eighteen members. It is not empowered to make laws, but it does provide comments and views which are then referred to the Council of Ministers for action.
4. The European Court of Justice, which carries out judicial supervision of the community treaties and legislation, and was set up under the Treaty of Rome.

European Council meetings are held twice a year. These form summit meetings at which the heads of government from the EC member countries attend, accompanied by their foreign affairs ministers.

22.4.1.1 *DG XIII*

Directorate General XIII (DG XIII) is responsible for Telecommunications, Information Industry and Innovation. Its aims are to:

1. Assist in the development of the general European economy by building a sound telecommunications infrastructure throughout Europe.
2. To grow the telecommunications service sector so that it is effective and economically viable.
3. To develop the telecommunications industry within Europe so that it can compete effectively on the world stage.

DG XIII has six Directorates, as given in Table 22.9. It has contacts with the Senior Officials Group on Telecommunications (SOGT), which is composed of Ministers of Telecommunications and of Industry. They meet every six weeks under the chairmanship of the Director General. A subcommittee of SOGT is the Analysis and Forecasting Group (GAP) which studies industrial develop-

Table 22.9 Directorates within DG XIII

Directorate	Responsibility
A	Information Technology
B	Information
C	Exploitation of Research and Technology Development
D	Telecommunications
E	Support for Sector Activities
F	Policy

ments in selected areas, such as ISDN, broadband, cellular, etc. GAP organises meetings at which member states attend and provide opinions. The output are Recommendations which may be made mandatory within the Community.

One of the major aims of the single European market is to ensure the free movement of goods and services. This requires the co-ordination of standards activities, and a Green Paper in 1990 proposed the setting up of the European Standardisation Organisation (ESO) to oversee the activities of the European standards making bodies, CEN, CENELEC and ETSI.

22.4.2 CEPT

22.4.2.1 *CEPT aims*

The Conference European des Administrations des Postes et des Telecommunications (Conference of European Posts and Telecommunications) was formed in 1958 by the PTTs with the aim of harmonising standards. It presently consists of 31 members, covering all the countries of the European Community and the European Free Trade Association, plus PTTs from other European countries.

CEPT is a sister organisation to CEN/CENELEC and participates in many of its work programmes. The organisation is administered by one of the member nations for two years and meetings of the Plenary body are held every two years. Presidency of CEPT moved to Greece, from the UK, in October 1990.

Historically CEPT has been noted for its restrictive bureaucratic policies rather than its commercial outlook, an image which it is anxious to change. In the past most of the PTTs only paid lip service to standardisation, and since the output from CEPT were recommendations, which were not enforceable and contained many country specific exceptions, the standardisation effort was largely ineffectual. To some extent CEPT was an exclusive club in which non-telecommunication administrations and users were excluded and not even consulted.

A European Commission Green Paper in 1987, on competition in Europe within telecommunication markets, clearly defined the PTTs as commercial undertakings, rather than monopolistic telecommunication administrations, who were subject to competition, and with a separation of their regulatory and operational activities. This resulted in CEPT setting up an independent body, in January 1988, called the European Telecommunications Standard Institute (ETSI) to carry out all the standards activities on its behalf. CEPT still maintained the Technical Recommendations Application Committee (TRAC), formed in 1986, to approve standards for connection of equipment to public networks.

22.4.2.2   *CEPT organisation*

CEPT was set up when the PTTs and other public network operators worked in a monopolistic environment. This is rapidly changing, with the introduction of service providers in many areas, such as electronic mail and satellite based services. In a bid to improve its standing CEPT reorganised, in February 1990, to form several new groups. These are:

1. The European Telecommunications Network Operators group (ETNO). The prime aim of this group is to obtain the most favourable commercial, regulatory and technical terms for its members. The Commercial Action Committee (CAC) within CEPT has the responsibility for making the organisation more open in its outlook, and in April 1990 it organised its first meeting in which user groups and user associations were invited and consulted on various topics, such as electronic data interchange, international packet switching, videotext, and ISDN. The aim is that eventually CEPT could become an open forum for users, manufacturers, regulators and even competing service providers.
2. The European Committee for Telecommunications Regulatory Affairs (ECTRA), which represents the telecommunication regulatory authorities from CEPT's member countries. It sets policies, for example on licensing procedures for private value added service providers, to ensure commonalty across Europe; on international accounting principles and whether changes should be proposed to any CCITT recommendations; on the role of regulators within the European equipment testing and certification field; on the harmonisation of regulatory policy on mobile communications, across Europe; and on the collaboration on proposals for satellite communications.
3. The European Radio Committee (ERC), which has a permanent group of experts, to carry out studies and propose strategies for

the management of radio frequencies. It ensures that it confers with all interested parties in this field.
4. The European Telecommunications Information Services foundation (ETIS) which has as its members the information systems managers from the public telecommunication companies. Its aim is to allow CEPT members to share some of the development costs which they need to spend on software, required for carrying out their internal network administration.
5. The European Institute for Research and Strategic Studies in Communications (EURESCOM) which consists of research laboratories, based in Heidelberg, Germany, with the aim of carrying out R&D on behalf of CEPT members. It therefore has a function very similar to that of Bell Communications Research Inc. which does research for the US regional Bell companies.

22.4.3   ETSI

22.4.3.1   *The formation of ETSI*

The Commission of the European Communities (CEC) in its Green Paper 'The Development of the Common Market for Telecommunications Services and Equipment,' on 30 June 1987 stated that, for a community-wide open competitive terminal equipment and services market, 'a substantial reinforcement of resources applied to standardisation is a necessary requirement.'

The Green Paper went on to indicate the importance of forming a European Telecommunications Standards Institute, which was jointly financed and which, 'based on a small core team of permanent staff and independently managed according to best business practice, should draw flexibly on experts from both the Telecommunications Administrations and industry, in order substantially to accelerate the elaboration of standards and technical specifications.'

At the meeting of CEPT Director Generals, held in London between 14 – 15 January 1988, the proposals of the Green Paper were accepted, and the meeting decided to set up the European Telecommunications Standards Institute (ETSI). The starting date for ETSI was set at 31 March 1988, which was subsequently met. The first meeting of the Technical Assembly was held in June 1988.

22.4.3.2   *ETSI aims*

ETSI is a completely independent organisation. It is funded by its members, who decide on its programme of work. However, the EC and EFTA may fund ETSI to produce specific standards of interest to the Community.

The main interest of ETSI is in telecommunications, although it also has interests in information technology, for which it co-operates with CEN/CENELEC, and in broadcasting, where it works with the European Broadcasting Union (EBU). ETSI's main aims are:

1. To complete world-wide standards, in line with Europe's needs, and to choose a single option where many are allowed in international standards.
2. To anticipate the world-wide standards scene, by adopting European standards, and proposing these to international standards making bodies.
3. To prepare a common European position for input to world-wide standards bodies, e.g. CCITT, CCIR, IEC and ISO, and to support these bodies in their work.

22.4.3.3   *ETSI membership*

Membership of ETSI is open to a wide spectrum of organisations, unlike CEPT which was limited to PTTs. Members are from countries falling within the geographical area of the CEPT. There are six types or members:

1. Administrations, who are part of the public administration of a country. This can also cover groups of national bodies who seek to be represented via a standardisation organisation, this organisation carrying the national vote.
2. Public network operators, who are a recognised operator of a public telecommunications network or part of a network.
3. Manufacturer, who can be a national organisation or a European organisation, making or developing equipment for use in a public telecommunications network.
4. User, who could be any person, company or organisation (national or European) making use of a public telecommunications network.
5. Private service provider, defined as an organisation who uses a public telecommunications network in order to provide services to third parties.
6. Research organisations, who can be anybody doing research into telecommunications areas.

Members can participate individually, for example companies, or grouped together, such as in trade associations. Manufacturers can participate as parent companies, subsidiaries or both.

In addition ETSI has observers, who are European organisations entitled to become full members, but who do not wish to do so. These observers can speak but not vote in General Assemblies or Technical Assemblies. With the agreement of the Technical Assembly they may also take part in Technical Committees. Non European organisations concerned with telecommunications may also be invited to participate as observers, and this is usually done where reciprocal arrangements exist within their countries. Observers from Australia, New Zealand, Canada and the USA have taken part.

It is this diverse range of membership which is the prime strength of ETSI, since it ensures a healthy interchange of views.

In April 1991 there were 269 members of ETSI, of which manufacturers accounted for 63%, public network operators 14%, national administrations 10% and users/service providers 13%. Twenty three countries were represented, from the EC and EFTA, Turkey, Malta, Cyprus, Czechoslovakia and Poland. The largest number of members were from the UK (71), France (45) and Germany (36). There were 400 draft standards in preparation by the twelve technical committees and 110 standards had been sent for public enquiry. The target at that time was sixty days for producing a standard.

22.4.3.4   *ETSI's structure*

ETSI's structure is shown in Figure 22.6. The General Assembly is composed of representatives of members of the Institute, which may be grouped into national delegations. Representatives from the EEC and EFTA have a special status as counsellors. The General Assembly is the governing body of the Institute, determining its policy, appointing the Director and Deputy Director, and approving budgets and accounts.

The Technical Assembly consists of members of the Institute, and is the highest authority within the Institute for the production and approval of technical standards. It gives guidance to the Director on

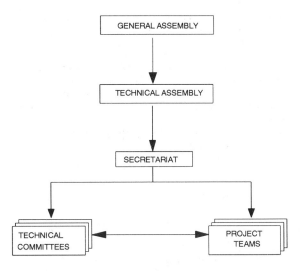

Figure 22.6   ETSI structure

the work to be undertaken and provides views on proposals from other sources, such as EEC, CEPT, EFTA. The Technical Assembly approves the costed annual work programme, and decides on the creation and cessation of Technical Committees and Project Teams, approving their terms of reference. The Technical Assembly adopts draft standards and ensures that public enquiry has been carried out on them. There are currently twelve Technical Committees, as follows:

> **RES**, Radio Equipment and Systems, which looks into basic standards for radio equipment, mobile systems, land, maritime and public aeronautical, and the harmonisation of measurement standards for mobile radio. It is responsible for developing standards for digital cordless telephony (DECT).
>
> **GSM**, Special Mobile Group, which has responsibility for developing technical standards for the pan-European digital cellular system in the 900MHz band, and for standards on type approval and security aspects.
>
> **PS**, Paging Systems, which is responsible for the technical aspects of new paging systems, such as the European system ERMES.
>
> **SES**, Satellite Earth Stations, covering applications and services, including mobile, for earth station equipment and for protocols involved in the interchange of information with satellites.
>
> **NA**, Network Aspects, covering network architecture, user interface service and charging, numbering and addressing, audio-visual services, broadband and intelligent networks.
>
> **BT**, Business Telecommunications, responsible for private network signalling, subscriber installations and ISPBX interconnection.
>
> **SPS**, Signalling Protocols and Switching, which covers all aspects of public digital switching and signalling, customer access to ISDN, and test methods.
>
> **TM**, Transmission and Multiplexing, which includes standards for cables and lines, multiplex and digital transmission and digital radio relay.
>
> **TE**, Terminal Equipment, covering all forms of equipment and access, such as videotext, text, voice, message handling service, ISDN terminal adaptors, and facsimile.

EE, Equipment Engineering, covering equipment practice.
ATM, Advanced Testing Methods.
HF, Human Factors.

The permanent Secretariat is based in Sophia, Antipolis, France, which is the headquarters of ETSI and houses most of its project teams. It is headed by the Director, who is responsible for the organisation of meetings, co-ordination of activities of the Technical Committees and Project Teams, for the administration of public enquiry on draft standards, and for maintaining records and finances. The Director is the legal representative of the Institute, and holds the authority of the Chief Executive.

22.4.3.5   *ETSI standards*

Technical Committees provide a forum for consensus building amongst European technical experts in developing new standards. They are also the focus for developing a harmonised European view on international standards, and consist of members of the Institute meeting on an ad hoc basis, as required. The Technical Committees pass standards, prepared by Project Teams, to the Technical Assembly for approval. Project Teams are created by the Technical Assembly for a defined task and limited time period. They consist of a small number of experts in the field under study.

Figure 22.7 shows the process for producing a standard. The draft standard, prepared by a project team, is debated, it being the respon-

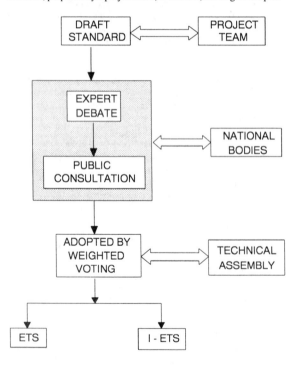

Figure 22.7 ETSI standards making process

sibility of the representative national bodies to ensure that this occurs within their countries. The modified standard is then adopted by the Technical Assembly, using a system of weighted voting, as described below, if required.

Standards are usually issued as European Telecommunication Standards (ETS). These are similar to the European Standard (EN) issued by CEN/CENLEC. An ETS is a voluntary standard, unless it is adopted as a NET, as described in the next section. In addition ETSI issues Interim European Telecommunication Standards (I-ETS). These are adopted when a standard is a provisional solution and a more advanced standard is to be prepared, or a standard is immature and needs a trial period.

From the date the Technical Assembly decides that ETSI should produce a standard on a specific matter, and for the duration, not exceeding fifteen months, the Technical Assembly sets down as being required to prepare and adopt that standard, no ETSI member is allowed to publish a new or revised national standard which is not completely in line with an ETS or EN in existence or in preparation on the specific matter in question, or take any other action which could prejudice the harmonisation intended. This is termed the 'standstill' agreement. In addition, when ETSI has approved an ETS on a specific topic then, on an agreed date set by the Technical Assembly, all ETSI members have to ensure that all conflicting national standards on that specific matter are withdrawn.

In order to develop standards rapidly, sometimes when the technology has not been completely developed, ETSI often adopts a 'working assumption' process. In this the Technical Committee, at the start of the development, draws up a proposal based on the best estimate of the technology. Following this anyone can suggest a change, but it is up to the proposer to show that the change would offer a significant improvement, technical or economical, over the existing proposal. In this way concepts can be put together quickly and adjusted to take account of changes, whilst still providing a measure of stability, which is so important for implementors.

Although members of ETSI try to get consensus, one of the reason why the Institute has been successful in passing standards quickly is that it can do so on the basis of national weighted voting. This applies in the General Assembly and the Technical Assembly, except that in the General Assembly individual voting is needed to approve the annual budget, and in the Technical Assembly the costed work programme requires a unanimous vote. The national weighted vote system allocates weights to nations, according to their contribution, and a 71% vote is needed to approve a proposal.

22.4.3.6   *ETSI's budget*

The budget for ETSI is voted annually by the General Assembly. It consists of two principal parts:

1. An amount to cover operating costs of the Secretariat, such as salaries, premises, etc. This is paid for by the major Administrations, in the form of national contributions. These contributions are based on a CEPT scale, and vary according to the size of the Administration.
2. The costed work programme, which covers all the costs of Project Teams whose work is included in the agreed programme for the year. In addition a contingency is kept for urgent work which arises in-between General Assembly meetings.

The costed work programme needs to be agreed unanimously by the Technical Assembly. It is financed by an annual fee paid by every member. This fee is made up of a number of units of contribution, the number of units relating to the turnover of the organisation or, in the case of Administrations, to the Gross Domestic Product of the country. The value of a single unit is set every year based on the estimated costs for the coming year.

In addition voluntary contributions are obtained for a voluntary account, to cover costs of any special work undertaken with the Technical Assembly's agreement, but which is not funded by the above. This includes translation costs, the official languages of the Institute being English, French and German. The Institute obtains revenues from sale of publications, and from fees charged to observers.

22.4.4 NETs

As stated earlier, an ETSI standard (ETS) is voluntary until it is converted into a NET (Norme Europeene de Telecommunication). This was originally done by weighted voting in TRAC, an organisation within CEPT. The membership of TRAC is limited to those European countries who have signed an MoU to give legal force to a NET as a technical requirement within their country. It includes all EC member countries, and applies to all telecommunication Administrations, to licensed public network carriers, and to equipment suppliers who want to attach equipment to any public network within these countries. In addition Administrations and network operators must use the relevant NET specification when procuring terminal equipment, unless it is a direct replacement for an earlier equipment.

NETs are basically of two types: access NETs, which specify access to the network but do not define any end-to-end compatibility; and terminal NETs, which ensure network-wide compatibility of a specific public service. The purpose of the NETs is to:

1. Ensure the safety of the user and of employees of public telecommunication network operators.
2. Protect the public telecommunication network from harm.
3. Ensure the interworking of terminal equipment, where this is justified.
4. Provide an uniform conformity testing programme, so that equipment approved in one member country can be used in another.

Table 22.10 lists early NETs. Some of these NETs are very comprehensive, running into a thousand pages in length.

22.4.4.1 *CTRs*

At the end of 1991 the procedure for the development of NETs was revised. Some of the NETs were now know as Common Technical Regulations (CTRs) and a new body was set up to be responsible for approvals, called the Approvals Committee for Terminal Equipment (ACTE). The ACTE represents the interests of all parties: operators, manufacturers and users. It is advised by TRAC. CRTs consist of subsets of ETSs, and the choice of which parts of ETSs are made mandatory is done by ACTE.

The process for development of a CTR is shown in Figure 22.8. The European Commission initiates the proposal for a new CTR and this is directed to ETSI by the Senior Officials Group on Telecommunications (SOGT). The process within ETSI is as in Figure 22.7, the ETS finally going to ACTE for approval and conversion to a CTR, and then to SOGT for enforcement.

A NET or CTR contains precise technical information, identifying clearly any national differences, caused by historic network differences. In addition it contains conformity test methods for all requirements.

Table 22.10 Some early NETs

NET	Description
1	X.21 Access
2	X.25 Access
3	ISDN Basic Access
4	PSTN Basic Access
5	Digital Telephony
6	X.32 Access
7	ISDN Terminal Adapter
10	Digital Cellular Radio Mobile Access
11	Mobile Terminal
20	Modem Category 1
21	Modem V.21
22	Modem V.22
23	Modem V. 22bis
24	Modem V.23
25	Modem V.32
30	Group 3 FAX
31	Group 4 FAX
32	Teletex
33	ISDN Terminal

22.4.4.2 *The CTS programme*

The European Commission has also been active in supporting test tool development through projects connected with conformance testing, called Conformance Test Services (CTS). This programme is concerned with setting up test services throughout Europe so that a vendor need only test his equipment once and receive approval for sale throughout the EC. This is covered by Memorandum M-IT-03 which allows countries within EC and EFTA to mutually recognise each other's test reports and certificates. Test laboratories are accredited at two levels: third party laboratories and operators of test procedures, to ensure equivalence of test results. In the UK the British Approvals Board for Telecommunications (BABT) is the responsible authority on testing and approvals.

Figure 22.9 illustrates the CTS process. The rules are formulated by the European Committee for IT Certification (ECITC), whose members consists of national representatives plus CEN, CENLEC and CEPT. For any specified area a Technical Support Service (TSS) is set up which provides advice to the ECITC and national members, and is responsible for definition and support of the test methods, and for co-operating with other standard bodies in this area.

The national certification co-ordinating member organises certification at the national level and confirms the certificates issued by other participating countries. It also accredits the test laboratories and the certifying bodies in its country, and this is supervised by ACTE. It is usually a government or a recognised agency which represents the government on ECITC. The Test laboratory performs

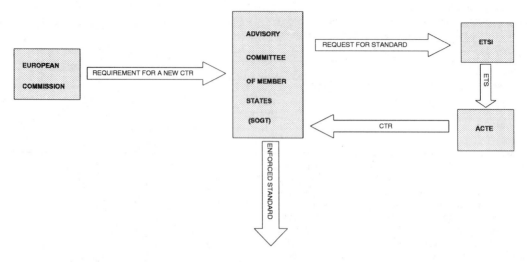

Figure 22.8 Process for development of a CTR

tests and issues harmonised test reports. These reports are then passed by the equipment manufacturer to the certifying body, who issues harmonised European certificates for the IT or telecommunication product. Conforming products are able to carry the CE mark.

22.4.5 CEN and CENELEC

Like ETSI both CEN and CENELEC are standards writing bodies rather than certifying authorities. CENELEC is primarily responsible for electro-technical matters and CEN for other areas. In this respect CENELEC is the European subset of IEC and CEN of ISO.

CEN and CENELEC function separately, except in the area of information technology where they combine as the Joint European Standards Institute (JESI). The secretariat for CEN/CENELEC is in Brussels and their membership is drawn from the European national standards organisations.

The information technology work programme is administered by an Information Technology Steering Committee (ITSTC) on which CEPT is also represented. This uses Expert Groups, formed as required, to develop standards. Included are ITAEGS for standards, ITAECM for manufacturing, ITAEGT for telecommunications, and ITAEGC for certification.

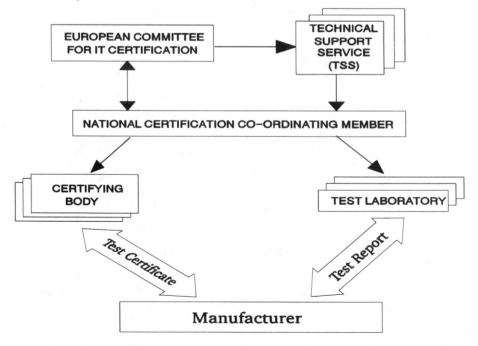

Figure 22.9 The CTS process

The output from CEN/CENELEC are European standards referred to as ENs (Europaische Norm) or European Standard. When in draft form they are called European pre-Standards, or ENVs. There is usually a two year conversion period from an ENV to an EN, to give users time to adopt them. Wherever possible these standards are based on international standards, such as from CCITT and ISO.

22.4.6 European national standards bodies

22.4.6.1 *France*

The standardisation authority in France is the Association Francaise de Normalisation (AFNOR). It was founded in 1926 and was made responsible for standardisation in France by the decree of 1984. It is responsible for preparing standards, and has its own permanent staff plus a large number who are sponsored by other organisations.

22.4.6.2 *Germany*

The Germany authority for standards making is the Deutsche Institut fur Normung (DIN). It is a private non-profit making association, which was founded in 1917. DIN standards are voluntary but they are accepted by industry and government, and are usually made the requirement for purchase agreements. All interested parties can participate in formulating DIN standards.

22.4.6.3 *UK*

In the UK the Telecommunications and Posts Division of the Government's Department of Trade and Industry (DTI) is involved in many aspects of standards formulation and enforcement, at the national and the international levels. It has three prime roles:

1. To act as the UK Administration for Post and Telecommunication matters, following the privatisation of its public operator (BT). Therefore the DTI represents the UK in CEPT.
2. To act as the Government department responsible for all UK legislation on telecommunication matters.

3. To champion the UK's interest overseas within the telecommunications arena, especially on standards related issues within the standards bodies.

The DTI represents the UK within CCITT, especially at Plenary Assemblies where it casts the UK vote approving its Recommendations. Figure 22.10 shows how it is organised to ensure that the UK view is effectively obtained and represented. For each CCITT Study Group the DTI organises a co-ordinating committee, which develops a common UK view. Individual members attending these Study Groups then support the UK view, and at the Plenary the DTI casts its vote.

A similar procedure is adopted for ETSI, except that individual members are more fully represented in ETSI committees. However the DTI uses co-ordinating committees, especially those set up through the British Standards Institute (BSI), to develop and sound out the UK view, and then casts its national vote accordingly in the ETSI Technical and General Assemblies.

As shown in Figure 22.11, the DTI takes advice from a policy committee (TAPC) on which a wide range of UK trade and user associations, network operators, and agencies such as BSI and OFTEL are represented. This committee is able to influence the DTI's view to the CEPT, especially in its vote within TRAC on the approval of NETs, and to the European Commission and its influential SOGT.

The British Standards Institute is the official standards body within the UK. It was formed in 1901 as the Engineering Standards Committee. It was granted a royal charter in 1929 for the co-ordination and preparation of standards and for marking and registering goods which complied with these standards. It took its present name in 1931.

Its activities cover a wide area such as building material, domestic electrical goods, and telecommunications. Its telecommunication standards responsibilities date back to the British Telecommunications Act 1981 (subsequently superseded by the Telecommunications Act 1984), when the BSI agreed to assist the DTI in the liberalisation process within telecommunications, by producing British Standards.

The Telecommunications Standards Policy Committee (TCT/-) first met in March 1981. Several committees have since been set up to look at various aspects of standardisation, for example Electrical Safety (TCT/1), Public Switched Telephone Network (TCT/2),

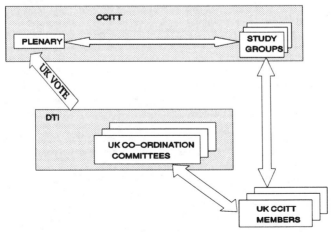

Figure 22.10 DTI's co-ordination role for CCITT representation

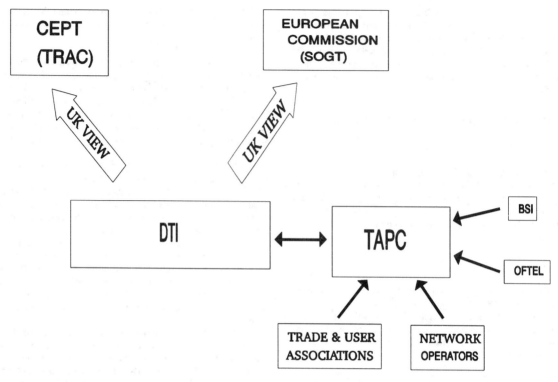

Figure 22.11 DTI's co-ordination role for CEPT and the EC

Telephone Instruments (TCT/2/1), Telex Network (TCT/3), Packet Switching Service (TCT/4), Private Circuits (TCT/5), Digital Networks (TCT/6), Installation Requirements (TCT/7) and Private Branch Exchanges (TCT/8). Its technical committees consist of individuals nominated by various organisations, such as manufacturers and user groups. It is financed by subscriptions and by a grant from the DTI.

The BSI represents the UK in the IEC, ISO and CEN/CENLEC, which have national standards bodies at meetings. It operates a series of technical committees which obtain the views of BSI members for presentation to these bodies. The BSI also has a Technical Committee (TCT/101) whose purpose is to co-ordinate the views of UK members to ETSI, and in this it works closely with the DTI.

22.4.7 European trade and user organisations

22.4.7.1 *The European Computer Manufacturers Association*

The European Computer Manufacturers Association was established in 1961 by European computer manufacturers to produce standards and interim guides for its members.

It has its Secretariat in Geneva, and now includes several North American companies as well. There are two classes of members, Ordinary Members, who are European companies making and marketing data processing equipment, and Associated Members, who have an interest and experience in the European area, or other areas of interest to the Technical Committees.

The organisation operates along ISO lines, with Technical Committees and Task Groups. It is dedicated to the production of data processing standards, which are not covered by other standards

making bodies, and technical reports for its members. These standards are voluntary and are submitted to the standards bodies as technical contributions or to propose new work. Several ECMA standards have been endorsed by ISO/IEC and by CENELEC and published by them as international or European standards. ECMA is a liaison member of the JTC1 set up by ISO/IEC.

22.4.7.2 *SPAG*

The Standards Promotion and Application Group (SPAG) was established in 1983, by twelve European IT companies, to promote OSI and to develop test services for OSI protocols. It is supported by the CEC. The group was incorporated in Brussels in October 1986 as SPAG SA, and SPAG Services was set up to provide a conformance and inter-operability testing service.

SPAG plays an active role on functional standards within the European Workshop on Open Systems (EWOS) and in the ISO work on ISPs. It has developed the European certification structure for OSI products, and is involved in the CEC programme for Conformance Testing Services (CTS). The group has close working ties with the Japanese Promoting conference for OSI (POSI) and the US Corporation for Open Systems (COS). It develops and markets conformance test tools and also carries out interoperability testing.

22.4.7.3 *The EWOS*

The European Workshop on Open Systems (EWOS) was formed in December 1987, by several suppliers and users, as the European forum for the development and promotion of OSI functional standards. It has a Secretariat in Brussels, under the auspices of

CEN/CENLEC. The Commission of European Communities supports it and DG IX is a member of the steering committee.

Membership of EWOS is primarily from the SPAG, European MAP and TOP User Groups, CEN/CENLEC national bodies, and ECMA.

The EWOS is similar in structure to the US National Institute for Standards and Technology (NIST). Its Steering Committee is drawn from constituent organisations and the CEC.

The EWOS technical programme is managed by a Technical Assembly, its standards work being done by Expert Groups. Their outputs are primarily technical guides and functional standards, which are submitted to CEN/CENLEC for adoption as ENVs and to ISO for adoption as International Standard Profiles (ISPs).

The EWOS works closely with ETSI, NIST – OIW and the Asia Oceania OSI Workshop, which is based in Japan, the three Workshops having set up a Regional Workshop Co-ordinating Committee (RWS-CC) to ensure that the profiles submitted to ISO are harmonised.

22.4.7.4 *The EUCATEL and ECTUA*

The European Conference of Associations of Telecommunication Industries (EUCATEL) is an organisation of European national trade associations of telecommunication equipment manufacturers. Its prime aim is to provide a forum for members to co-ordinate their views on standards being developed by other standards making bodies. It does not produce standards of its own.

The European Council of Telecommunication Users Association (ECTUA) was set up in 1986 with a similar purpose to that of the EUCATEL, but to represent users' views on standards. Its members are primarily national telecommunication user groups, but individual companies operating within Europe, who are telecommunication users, can also join as associated members.

ECTUA organises round table meetings of experts, at which all members can participate. This formulates the view of the organisation, which is then put to standards bodies and to governments.

22.4.7.5 *The TMA*

The Telecommunications Managers Association (TMA) is a UK company limited by guarantee and is a registered charity. Its activities are managed by an elected Executive Committee, which in turn elects a Chairman.

Membership of the TMA is on an individual basis, primarily by those responsible for planning, management or operations of telecommunication systems, and to consultants and project managers with special interest in telecommunications. Although this is essentially a user group, many of its members are from supplier organisations.

TMA activities are of three types:

1. Education and information exchange, where it organises conferences, exhibitions, and courses.
2. Liaison with government and other official bodies, such as the DTI and the Office of Telecommunications (OFTEL), and with ETSI and the European Community Telecommunications Users Association (ECTUA). The TMA is also a founding member of the International Telecommunications Users Group (INTUG) through which it promotes its members' interests at an International level.

3. Dialogue with suppliers, where TMA maintains a series of channels through which its members and principal suppliers, such as BT and Mercury, can interact. The prime aim is to encourage the development of a range of telecommunication services of sufficient quality and tariffed to address customer needs.

22.4.7.6 *The TUA*

The Telecommunications Users Association (TUA) was created in 1980 by a group of independent UK companies to represent their interests. It later merged with the Telephone Users Association, which was founded in 1965. It is a limited company, owned and funded entirely by its members, who elect a Board of non-executive Directors from its membership. It has about a thousand members, all being companies, such as banks, publishers, accountants, pharmaceutical companies and professional practices, although there is a special category of membership for domestic subscribers.

Some the TUA's objectives are the following:

1. To ensure that the UK telecommunications network matches the best of that available overseas.
2. To ensure that the telecommunication operators, the Office of Telecommunications (OFTEL) and suppliers become more responsive to user needs, particularly in the areas of pricing, installation, maintenance and attachment policy.
3. To provide expert advice to members and ensure that they are represented on all key strategy and regulatory committees.
4. To encourage competition in the supply of telecommunications services, nationally and overseas.

22.5 USA standards organisations

There are about six hundred organisations in the USA who are engaged in standardisation activities. Although this has resulted in some 90000 standards which are currently in use in the USA, only a handful have been adopted from international standards. This is changing rapidly, as many USA based manufacturers strive to enter the European market and find the need to adhere to International standards.

The reason for this is largely historical. After the break up of the USA's Bell telephone system, Bellcore was founded, in 1985, to carry out all the development work, including standardisation, needed to ensure interoperability. These have been used by the US telephone operators to buy against. Bellcore also determines and manages the North American numbering plan, trains personnel and provides consultancy services.

22.5.1 US Department of State

The US Department of State is the government agency primarily responsible for representing the USA in the ITU, as shown in Figure 22.12. It has discharged this responsibility to two public advisory committees, the United States Organisation for the International Telegraph and Telephone Consultative Committee (US CCITT) and the United States Organisation for the International Radio Consultative Committee (US CCIR). These bodies receive the input from ANSI accredited groups for consideration, before approving them and passing them onto CCITT and CCIR.

The US CCIs are headed by a director from the Bureau of International Communications and Information Policy, from the US

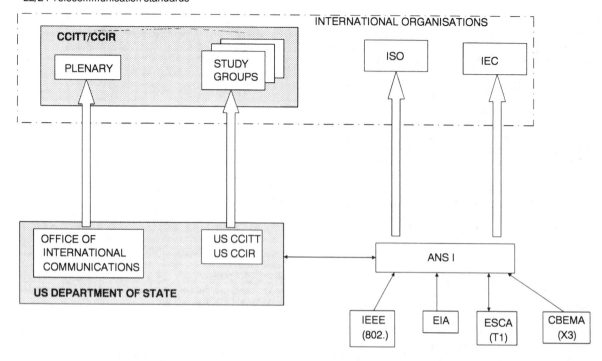

Figure 22.12 Primary USA telecommunication standards making bodies

Department of State. They represents US interests in the international CCI activities and advise the Department of State on policy matters, to prepare it for the plenary assembly meetings. They have national committees which administer them, and a series of study groups. The US CCITT has four study groups:

1. Study Group A: Telecommunications Services and Policy.
2. Study Group B: Switching, Signalling and ISDN.
3. Study Group C: Telephone Network Operations.
4. Study Group D: Data Networks and Telematic Terminal.

The US CCITT Study Groups divide the activities of the seventeen International CCITT Study Groups between them so as to be able to track their activities and to respond effectively to them. Members of the US CCITT Study Groups are drawn from individuals and organisations so as to obtain a broad view.

The State Department has also assigned to certain private sector telecommunication equipment and service suppliers the status of RPOA and SIO so that they can represent the USA in CCITT and CCIR.

22.5.2   ANSI

The American National Standards Institute (ANSI) is the principal standards forming body in the USA. It is a non-profit making non-government organisation, formed in 1918, and represents the USA in ISO and IEC.

ANSI does not directly develop standards, but it accredits other groups to do so, taking their outputs, approving it, and assigning numbers to them before publication. These standards, like those from CCITT and CCIR, are voluntary, although they are often used for equipment procurement. About ten thousand ANSI approved standards have been designated as American National Standards.

ANSI has accredited four groups as Accredited Standards Committees (ACS): IEEE; EIA; the T1 committee of the Exchange Carriers Standards Association (ECSA); and the X3 committee of the Computer Business Equipment Manufacturers Association (CBEMA).

22.5.3   NIST

The National Institute of Standards and Technology (NIST) was formerly known as the National Bureau of Standards (NBS). In 1968 it was given the responsibility for helping the US Federal Government make effective use of its vast base of computer and information technology equipment, and for developing Federal Information Processing Standards (FIPS).

Many FIPS's have been developed and published. The best known example is that on data encryption (FIPS 46), which has been adopted by ANSI as X3.92 and is being developed further by international standardisation bodies.

22.5.4   FCC

The Federal Communications Commission (FCC) was set up by the Communications Act of 1934 with the prime responsibility for regulating traffic carried by wire or radio, both between US states and internationally to and from the US. The FCC is administered by five Commissioners appointed by the President and approved by the Senate.

The FCC is involved in a wide range of telecommunication standardisation and regulatory issues, although it does not produce standards of its own. It issues radio licences within the US to those complying with its rules, and also takes part in organisations involved in making telecommunication standards in the US, such as ANSI, IEEE and EIA.

The main Bureau within FCC are:

1. The Mass Media Bureau, which regulates and issues licences for broadcast and cable television, direct broadcast satellites, and microwave radio.
2. The Common Carrier Bureau, which regulates and issues licences for communications via wire, radio or satellite, for interstate or international common carriers.
3. The Private Radio Bureau, which regulates and issues licences for use of radio spectrum by private users, covering land vehicles, ships and aircraft. Some three million licences have been granted to local and state governments, businesses, and individuals within the US.

22.5.5 North American trade, user and professional organisations

22.5.5.1 ECSA

The Exchange Carriers Standards Association is a trade association of wireline exchange carriers in the US and was formed to provide a central public forum for the US telecommunications industry. Its Standards Advisory Committee (SAC) is responsible to ANSI for the T1 Committee.

Following the recommendation from ECSA for a public standards committee which used ANSI procedures and which provided a public forum in telecommunications standards, ANSI set up the T1 Committee in 1983. The committee received its name from ANSI: T denoting Telecommunications and 1 for the first such committee.

T1 has four interest categories:

1. Exchange carriers.
2. Inter exchange carriers and resellers.
3. Manufacturers and vendors.
4. Government agencies, consultants and other users and general interest groups.

The T1 is composed of specialised technical subcommittees. Its output goes into ANSI for review as an American National Standard, and it also provides and input to the US CCITT where T1 formulates the US industry view on CCITT standards. T1 also produces reports for industry.

The T1 has six technical committees, each with working groups which are set up as needed. It also has an advisory group (T1AG) which manages its day to day activities, between T1 General Meetings. The main T1 committees are:

T1E1, which is responsible for standards relating to interfaces for user access to telecommunication networks. It concentrates on the physical layer and covers, for example, ISDN physical layer standards.
T1M1, which is responsible for standards on internetwork aspects of operations, administration, maintenance and provisioning of telecommunication networks. This covers network management aspects.
T1Q1, which is responsible for standards connected with performance parameters and service levels within the telecommunications network.
T1S1, which is responsible for standards dealing with architecture, signalling, and services, within the telecommunications network. It is, for example, responsible for ISDN services, architecture and signalling, and for common channel signalling.

T1X1, which is responsible for standards on the future digital hierarchical structures, and other related aspects, for example work on Sonet standards.
T1Y1, which is responsible for standards which are not covered by the other subcommittees, above.

22.5.5.2 EIA

The Electronic Industries Association is a trade organisation representing a large number of US electronic manufacturers, varying in size from small component suppliers to multinational organisations serving the defence industry. It was founded in 1924 as the Radio Manufacturers Association. Over four thousand government and industrial representatives participate in its two hundred or so committees.

The EIA is primarily involved in producing hardware oriented data communication standards. It has produced over six hundred standards, its best known being RS-232-C, now renamed EIA 232-C, which is used world-wide for computer interfaces.

In 1988 the telecommunications sector of the EIA merged with the US Telecommunications Suppliers Association (USTSA) to form the Telecommunications Industry Association (TIA).

22.5.5.3 CBEMA

The Computer and Business Equipment Manufacturers' Association (CBEMA) is a trade association of manufacturers and suppliers of hardware, software and services, to the computer, business and telecommunication industries. Within standards its activities are aimed at ensuring consensus amongst its members on the long term direction of the industry.

The standards activities within CBEMA are administered by its Standards Programme Management Committee (SPMC). The Committee does not make its own standards, but instead participates in other groups developing standards.

In 1960 ANSI accredited the X3 Committee (Information Processing Systems) to develop American National Standards in the area of media, languages, documentation and communications relating to computing devices and systems. Ever since it was formed CBEMA served as the secretariat to X3.

In addition to its sponsorship of X3, CBEMA has also been appointed by ANSI to be the technical administrator of the US Technical Advisory Group (TAG), which is responsible for developing the US contribution on information technology standards to ISO and IEC.

22.5.5.4 IEEE

The IEEE is a USA based professional organisation. It was formed in 1963 by a merger of the American Institute of Electrical Engineers (formed in 1884) and the Institute of Radio Engineers.

The IEEE is an international organisation with over a third of a million members in about a hundred and fifty countries. It has its headquarters in New York and is administered by a governing body of 32 volunteers, elected by its voting members.

The aim of the IEEE is to advance the theory and practice of engineering within the electronic and electrical disciplines, which includes information technology and telecommunications. It is structured into specialised divisions: Circuits and Devices; Industrial Applications; Communications Technology; Electromagnetic and Radiation; Computer; Engineering and Human Environment; Power Engineering; Signals and Applications; Systems and Control.

The IEEE is active in standards making, with about 700 standards published. Anyone with the right qualifications can join and take part in the IEEE's standards activities, and well over a hundred companies and universities are actively involved in its work. It is best known for its 802 committee, which defines standards for data communications, primarily in local area networks.

22.5.5.5 ICA

The International Communications Association (ICA) was formed in 1948 and is a member of the INTUG. It is the largest telecommunications users' group in the USA, representing government, industry and educational establishments.

The ICA sets standards, holds exhibitions and seminars for its members, and provides them with other relevant information.

22.5.5.6 COS

The Corporation for Open Systems (COS) was formed in North America in 1985 primarily due to an initiative from the Computer and Communications Industry Association (CCIA). About forty major US corporations took part in establishing COS.

COS aims to speed up the penetration of OSI by working closely with other standards making bodies. It is actively involved in standards setting and in conformance testing. It has members on many US technical committees, such as X3, T1, IEEE and EIA, and provides an input to CCITT Study Groups and to ISO on OSI standards.

22.6 Canadian standards organisations

Canada has several standards making organisations, under the control of a central statutory corporation, the Standards Council of Canada (SCC).

The SCC is a government body, founded in 1970. Its main aim is to approve standards, produced by other organisations, into a National Standards System. It encourages voluntary standardisation in areas not covered by law, e.g. health and safety.

22.7 Japanese standards organisations

22.7.1 The TTC

The Japanese Ministry of Posts and Telecommunications (MPT) is the body responsible for the country's postal, telecommunications and broadcasting services. In 1982 it set up the Telecommunications Technology Council to advise the Ministry on preparing contributions to international standards. Two years later, in 1985, the Telecommunications Technology Committee (TTC), which is a different organisation to the Council, was set up to prepare standards for telecommunications, in anticipation of deregulation in Japan.

Members of the TTC are Type I Telecommunication Carriers (i.e. those who own their own infrastructure), Type II Telecommunication Carriers (i.e. those who lease their infrastructure from other

carriers and resell), manufacturers, and users. Foreign bodies can also be members.

The TTC acts as a focus for receipt of standards and for comments on international standards. It maintains links with international standard organisations and sets technical requirements for broadcasting and telecommunications. It is run by an advisory committee of appointees by the MPT, drawn from academic institutions and industry.

The TTC also has expert sub-committees, drawn from a wide spectrum of public and private organisations, which study specific areas. Its four sub-committees are: network-to-network interfaces; network-to-terminal interfaces; special subjects; and higher layers and telematics. A system of weighted voting is used to adopt standards within TTC. The members are placed into groups, each with a fixed number of voting points, two thirds of all points voting being needed to adopt a TTC standard. The main standards work done by the TTC are the selection of profiles for use in Japan, based on international standards.

22.7.2 JISC

The Japanese Industrial Standards Committee (JISC) was formed in 1949 to advise the government on Japanese industrial standards. It contains over 1000 Technical Committees, drawn from a wide range of Japanese academic and industrial organisations, and from government and users, and its standards cover all aspects of industrial products, from building materials to electrical goods. It is responsible for marking goods which conform to its standards with a JIS (Japanese Industrial Standard) mark.

22.7.3 OSI standards

Two bodies are active in promoting OSI standards within Japan: the Promoting conference for OSI (POSI) and the Asia and Oceanic Workshop for OSI Standardisation (AOWS).

The POSI was formed in 1985. The founder members were Oki Electric Industry, Toshiba, Nippon Telegraph and Telephone (NTT), Mitsubishi Electric, Hitachi, NEC, and Fujitsu. Its prime aim is to further the use of OSI by international co-operation, and it is active on the Feeder's Forum and in AOWS.

The AOWS was formed in 1988 and includes OSI experts from Asia and Oceania. It contains a council, plenary meeting and special interest groups. Its members included organisations interested in OSI, such as researchers, standardisation organisations, manufacturers of OSI based equipment, and users of IT equipment.

22.8 Australian standards organisations

Australia is a member of the ITU where it is represented by its Department of Transport and Communications (DOTAC). It delegates co-ordination with CCITT to the Australian CCITT Committee (ACC).

22.8.1 The ACC

The Australian CCITT Committee administers Australia's CCITT activities and was formed as part of Australia's membership of the ITU. It co-ordinates all the technical activities and monitors the work done by other standards bodies in the region.

The ACC has representatives from Australian Electronics Industry Association (AEIA), Australian carriers, the Australian Telecommunications Authority (AUSTEL), DOTAC, Standards Australia and the Australian Information Industry Association (AIIA). Associated members are also included from other Australian organisations or from abroad.

The ACC sets up national Study Groups for each international CCITT Study Group. Any interested party can take part in this work. The ACC is chaired by AUSTEL.

22.8.2   The AUSTEL

The Australian Telecommunications Authority was formed to take over the country's standards activities from Telecom Australia, as required by the Telecommunications Act of 1989. It has a Standards Advisory Committee (SAC), which administers its standards work, and a series of Working Groups to whom standards are referred by the SAC. The AUSTEL is empowered by law to set mandatory Australian national standards relating to customer premises equipment and cabling.

22.8.3   Standards Australia

Standards Australia was formed in 1922 as the Standards Association of Australia. It received the Royal Charter in 1950 and in 1988 it was nominated as the leading standards setting body in Australia, when it was renamed Standards Australia.

Standards Australia is a member of international standards bodies, such as ISO and IEC, and has about 2000 Technical Committees which cover a wide range of industrial and domestic standards.

22.8.4   The ATUG

The Australian Telecommunications Users Group (ATUG) is a non-profit making user group. It aims to improve the services available to its members, including the range of services and its quality, and is involved in pricing issues.

The ATUG has its executive based in Sydney and members include individuals, organisations and government departments. It carries out political lobbying on behalf of its members and seeks to influence those organisations who are responsible for setting telecommunication regulations or legislation. Its executive or task force prepares papers on selected topics, which are submitted to relevant bodies, in order to influence them.

22.8.5   The AIIA

The Australian Information Industry Association (AIIA) is a manufacturers' association whose members include all major companies active within IT in Australia. This covers manufacturers and suppliers providing IT hardware and software.

22.9   New Zealand standards organisations

The Standards Association of New Zealand (SANZ) was set up in 1965 to develop standards for use within New Zealand. It is an organisation which is independent of the government. The role of SANZ was strengthened in the Standards Act of 1988.

SANZ standard committees cover a wide range of industrial and domestic goods and services. It prepares standards, is responsible for testing to these standards, and for marking goods which conform to the standards.

The Information Technology Association of New Zealand (ITANZ) represents manufacturers and suppliers of IT equipment and services. It seeks to influence the decision makers, such as government and PTT, on behalf of its members. To this aim it sets up task forces to deal with particular issues.

22.10   Bibliography

Barry, D. (1989) European standards gather pace, *Telecommunications*, January.

Bennett, B. and Darling, P. (1990) The importance of telecommunication standards, *Telecommunications Journal of Australia*, **40**, (3).

Bensen, S.M. and Farrell, J. (1991) The role of the ITU in standardisation, *Telecommunications Policy*, August.

Codding, G.A. and Gallegos, D. (1991a) The ITU's 'federal' structure, *Telecommunications Policy*, August.

Codding, G.A. (1991b) Evolution of the ITU, *Telecommunications Policy*, August.

Connor, S. (1990) The International Telecommunications Union — What it does and why we need it, *Telecommunication Journal of Australia*, **40**, (3).

Corsi, N. (1991) Developing testing and certification standards in Europe, *CSELT Technical Reports*, **XIX**, (3), June.

Fay, W.J. (1988) A European perspective on conformance testing and certification, *Telecommunications*, August.

Gibbons, R. (1989) Surveying Europe's standardisation scene, *Communications International*, Part 1, November; Part 2, December.

Pipe, G.R. (1989) The ITU Plenipotentiary: reconciling conflicting agendas, *Telecommunications*, August.

Rosenbock, K.H. (1991) ETSI — a central role for Europe, *Mobile Europe*, September.

Vinci, E. and Telkamper, W. (1991) European standardisation and the Green Paper, *TRR*, **5**, (4), August.

Williamson, J. (1991) Raising the European standard, *Telephony*, June 3.

Young, K. (1991) Meeting NETs needs, *Communications Networks*, November.

23 Safety and EMC

Robert S Ferguson
BSc (Eng)
Independent Consultant
(Sections 23.1–23.8)

Tim Williams
BSc CEng MIEE
ELMAC Services
(Sections 23.9–23.16)

Contents

23.1 Introduction

This chapter covers two topics which are of paramount importance in the consideration of any system, telecommunications or otherwise.

These topics are Safety and Electromagnetic Compatibility (EMC), also often known as Radio Frequency Interference (RFI), and they relate to personal and network safety, and as such they are controlled by government regulations.

In its least harmful form RFI is a nuisance, but in others it can lead to dangerous situations, for example when it causes interference in systems such as aircraft navigation and life support systems within hospitals.

23.2 Safety

This section deals with the design of safe telecom equipment, in particular in compliance with the available standards for safety. Which standards are to be used will probably be in the product specification and adherence to every aspect is necessary. The following guidance gives the background and principles to facilitate understanding these complex documents, and deciding what to do when the standards do not fit the case.

Emphasis is on the technical content of the standards, rather than the means of demonstrating compliance with them, or the legal framework in which they are enforced in some countries. Standards in Europe are the main consideration, because the situation (in 1992) is moving towards an unprecedented harmonized enforcement regime to facilitate movement of goods throughout the region. The situation is, however, far from stable and it can be foreseen that there will be some changes in technical requirements in the next few years.

The word 'safety' is used in the meaning of the avoidance of injury to persons, either those using the equipment or (in telecommunications applications) those working on the line or at the other end of it. Protection, meaning the avoidance of damage to equipment hardware, is not covered, although many design features for safety purposes will provide some protection.

Extensive reference is made to EN 41003, this being the only standard dealing only with telecom safety as currently conceived. The reader is advised to obtain copies of EN 41003 and of IEC 950, second edition, and to study the Principles of Safety in the latter.

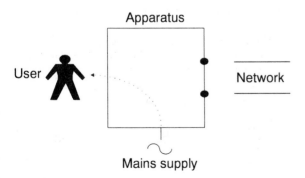

Figure 23.1 Safety of the user from electrical hazards in the equipment

Global consultation with test houses and approved authorities is recommended, especially in cases of doubt or ambiguity.

23.3 Basic elements of telecom safety

Some years ago IEC produced IEC Guide 105. This distinguishes between three objectives:

1. Safety of the user from electrical hazards in equipment (see Figure 23.1);
2. Safety of network service personnel, and other network users, from hazards in the equipment (see Figure 23.2);

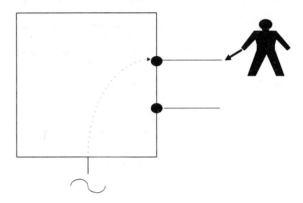

Figure 23.2 Safety of network personnel and other users

3. Safety of the equipment user from voltages on a network (see Figure 23.3).

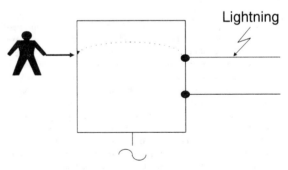

Figure 23.3 Safety of the user from network voltages

The 'network' in mind when this Guide was written (1984-1985) was the PSTN, Public Switched Telephone Network.

The first of these objectives has nothing to do with the telecom network and is the subject of the classical safety standards which exist for most electrical products. Figure 23.4 shows some of the international (IEC) standards for such products. Similar or identical national standards exist in many countries including Australia, Canada and USA.

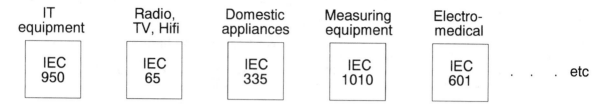

Figure 23.4 Classical product safety standards

In Europe there is a European version of each one (a European Norme, EN, or Harmonization Document, HD) which is substantially identical to the corresponding IEC standard and which in the case of an EN has to be adopted as the national standard by all member countries of CENELEC. Each EN or HD lists its deviations

Table 23.1 IEC standard and its EN equivalent

IEC standard	EN equivalent
IEC 950	EN 60950
IEC 65	HD 195 56
IEC 335	EN 60335
IEC 1010	HD 401 S1
IEC 601-1	EN 60601-1

from the IEC version. The corresponding standards are given in Table 23.1. In a few CENELEC countries some additional requirements are illegally imposed and CENELEC is endeavouring to enforce its rules to prevent this.

Any of the equipment mentioned in Figure 23.4 may be connected to a telecommunication network but IT (Information Technology) equipment is the commonest. With one exception, none of these IEC or CENELEC standards contains requirements to meet objectives (2) and (3), which only concern equipment connected to a network. Guide 105 shows in general terms how any IEC standard can be enhanced to cover (2) and (3) but being only a Guide is not precise enough for design or testing purposes. To provide a complementary but more precise European document, CENELEC produced EN 41003 which can be applied in conjunction with a classical safety standard so as to cover all the safety requirements for a product that is to be connected to a network, as shown in Figure 23.5. The

classical standard may be the IEC standard as shown, or the national or European version of it.

In one case, the telecom requirements have been included in the classical standard, namely in the 1991 second edition of IEC 950 (see Figure 23.6). However, the telecom requirements in IEC 950 are not precisely the same as those in EN 41003, although they are very similar. A document showing a side by side comparison is available, and this is being used by the authors of both standards to eliminate unnecessary differences. The main differences are:

1. EN 41003 covers line-powered equipment. IEC 950 at present does not, although a proposal has been made to amend it so that it would.
2. The rules in EN 41003 for the maximum levels of ringing signals are based on IEC 479 and they match European telecom practice. IEC 950 permits an alternative set of rules based on north American practice. Most analogue telephone equipment, it is believed, will satisfy both sets of rules.
3. The upper limit for the voltage of a telegraph signal is much higher in IEC 950 than in EN 41003 (135V peak vs. 96V peak) to cover existing practice in geographically large countries. However the high levels permitted in both standards are considered to be just as hazardous as mains voltage and must not be accessible to the user.

Later in this chapter the requirements and tests in EN 41003 will be considered in more detail.

23.4 Classical safety standards

23.4.1 Single fault principle

Most product safety standards are based on the principle of providing two levels of protection: the equipment must remain safe even in the presence of a single fault. The design must also make sure that

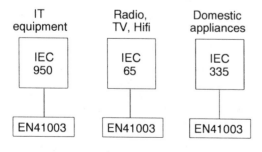
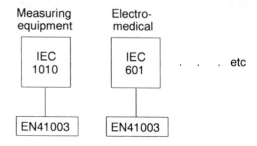

Figure 23.5 Addition of telecom safety section

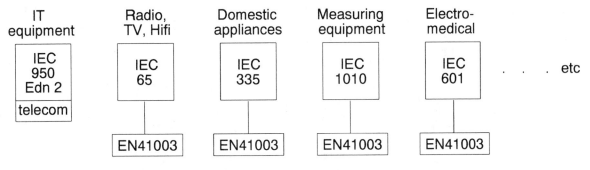

Figure 23.6 Telecom safety in IEC 950

a fault is unlikely, so that the possibility of two faults occurring simultaneously can be ignored. For example, basic insulation has to be designed to certain minimum dimensions and to withstand a voltage test, so that breakdown is very unlikely. However, if that were to break down, there must be another level of protection still in place. This second level may, for example, be added to basic insulation by earthing an accessible metal enclosure, such as a coffee pot, in conjunction with a fused supply; if either the basic insulation breaks down or the earth connection fails the equipment is still safe. This is class I protection (see Figure 23.7). Class II protection uses double or reinforced insulation (Figure 23.8), in

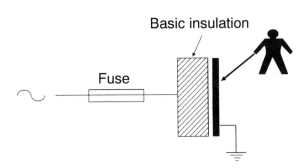

Figure 23.7 Class I protection

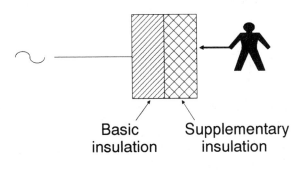

Figure 23.8 Class II protection

which supplementary insulation guards the basic. A plastic coffee pot is class II equipment.

23.4.2 Electric shock

Safety is concerned, among other things, with fire, mechanical and heat hazards but mainly with electric shock, and the telecom safety requirements are concerned only with electric shock.

The criterion for what is an unacceptable shock is the voltage on parts that are accessible to touch, or the current that can be drawn from accessible parts through a resistance representing the human body. These values are based on knowledge of the effect of current on the human body and will ensure that even if the condition is noticeable, it will be safe for the great majority of situations and people. IEC 479 gives the basis of these values.

So as to be unambiguous, the standard must also be clear about what is considered to be accessible. This is done by the use of a

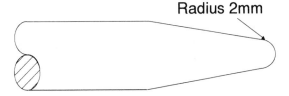

Figure 23.9 Tip of a standard test finger

standard metal test finger, which is like a human finger but smaller so as to give a margin of safety. Its main diameter is 12mm but the tip is 2mm radius (see Figure 23.9). The same test fingure is used in much the same way in all the classical safety standards. It will be noted that the criteria are binary (and therefore somewhat artificial, in the interests of unambiguous and repeatable testing): either the test finger can touch a part or it cannot; either the touch voltage is below a certain limit and safe, or it is considered to be hazardous and fails.

23.5 Telecom safety considerations

23.5.1 TNV circuits

Signals on telecom circuits, and ringing signals in particular, do not fit into this tidy scenario. They often have a higher voltage than is accepted in the classical standards as being safe to touch, yet in telephone practice, which has a good safety record, they have not traditionally been made as difficult to touch as, for example, mains circuits. There are several reasons for this apparent difference in philosophy, of which the most important are that a ringing signal is

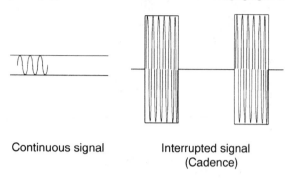

Continuous signal   **Interrupted signal
(Cadence)**

Figure 23.10   Cadenced ringing singal

cadenced (off part of the time, see Figure 23.10), and that a telephone circuit is not generally accessible to a large area of contact such as a whole hand, but only to a finger-tip.

To legitimise such designs in the framework of the classical standards, an intermediate level was invented, called a TNV circuit (telecommunication network voltage circuit), which is allowed to have a higher voltage but less accessibility. The maximum voltage for a ringing signal takes its cadence into account. A TNV circuit is allowed to be accessible to the standard test finger but only on the contacts of a connector (such as a telephone jack) and only then provided that it cannot be touched by a blunt version of the test

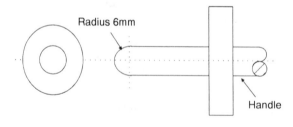

Figure 23.11   Blunt probe

finger. This blunt probe (see Figure 23.11) has a tip radius of 6mm. Its use ensures that a deliberate effort (such as poking a finger into a telephone jack) is needed to touch a TNV circuit; the very limited area of contact that is possible produces a higher body impedance and therefore a lower current through the body.

23.5.2   Indirect attachments

Before looking at detailed requirements and tests, it is worth considering what has been a difficult matter in the development of the telecom safety standards. A single box (for example a mains operated feature phone) can be designed with confidence to satisfy the safety requirements, in particular to present no safety hazard to the network. Electrical barriers are used to isolate the network from the mains and from any other hazardous voltages (see Figure 23.12).

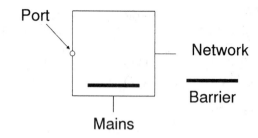

Figure 23.12   Directly connected equipment

However, most attachments, other than simple (or clever) telephones, have ports for other boxes to be connected. An example of this is a modem with a port for a PC, as in Figure 23.13.

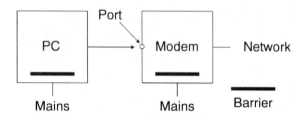

Figure 23.13   PC and modem connected to a network

In the present open market environment for telecom attachments, a user must be able to buy a modem and a PC separately and connect them together and to the network, without having to get specific approval for that particular pair of products. But can the direct attachment (the modem) be approved as being safe without examining the PC to be sure that it would not harm the network indirectly, even if it had a fault in it? BS 6301 (the British Standard that has the same intent as EN 41003) requires that the port in the modem must have an electrical barrier behind it (see Figure 23.14) to protect the

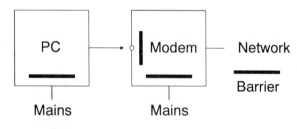

Figure 23.14   Barriered port

network; alternatively the user must make sure that the PC itself complies with BS 6301 and therefore that the circuit between the two boxes would never attain a hazardous voltage even in the presence of a single fault in the PC (an SELV circuit in IEC 950 terminology).

However, a PC is often not just one box but several, and it would not be practicable to test every PC add-on, including some not yet designed, when approving the modem. So BS 6301 is content with a warning label about what should be connected to a port, unless the port is barriered. Either way adds significantly to the cost of the equipment.

In EN 41003, however, there is no such requirement. The view was taken that if the PC and the modem are designed to co-operate with one another, they must use the same operational interface specification (RS 232 or V.24) and it is reasonable to assume that both boxes will be designed according to the appropriate safety specification at this interface. In the example of a modem and a PC, the appropriate safety specification on the interface between them is that of an SELV circuit, as defined in IEC 950. (If two boxes were not designed to co-operate with each other, the user is not likely to connect them together, or not for very long, because they will not work). So EN 41003 has no requirement for barriered ports or labelled ports; it is assumed that any other boxes connected to a port will have (in this example) SELV circuits, which are safe to touch directly and cannot indirectly impact the touch safety of the network.

In a different example, such as a PBX, the appropriate safety specification at the interface might be a TNV circuit. The principle is that the connection should be like to like: SELV to SELV or TNV to TNV.

23.6   EN 41003

This section considers some of the main requirements of EN 41003, using the clause numbers of the 1990/1991 first edition. The requirements of IEC 950 second edition are very similar but with different clause numbers.

23.6.1   Insulation

Much of EN 41003 is about TNV circuits and their insulation from other circuits, so it needs to specify certain types of insulation and minimum spacings. However EN 41003 does not contain detailed specifications for these; it refers to the specifications of SELV circuits and insulation that are given very fully in IEC 950 (and EN 60950).

23.6.2   Definitions

EN 41003 uses the definitions in EN 60950 plus some new ones. Clause 3 of EN 41003 contains a new definition for 'telecommunication network', a term which is quite difficult to define. This definition, unfortunately, can be read in different ways. However, for the current uses of the standard, which is invoked for permission to connect equipment to a PTT network, this lack of precision does not matter. The exclusions in this definition do not mean that there is no standard for mains signalling, TV distribution systems etc.; it means that they were not considered when EN 41003 was written. IEC 950, second edition, can be used as it stands for all the excluded systems.

The other definitions arise from the use of the concept of a TNV circuit. The term 'excessive voltage' is no different from 'hazardous voltage' in IEC 950, except that it allows a TNV circuit to be considered non-hazardous. Until the second edition of IEC 950, the definition of hazardous voltage conflicted with TNV circuit.

23.6.3   TNV circuit design

The maximum voltages on a TNV circuit must comply with one of three possibilities: steady state, a ringing signal or a telegraph signal. The formulae for ringing signals seem complex and daunting but are not difficult to use. This, and the telegraph signal, are those of existing technology where the operating voltage is some tens of volts; modern digital circuits in ISDN, and SCVF telegraphy, are SELV circuits operating at a few volts.

In the classical safety standards, where there are only two kinds of circuit, those that are safe to touch and those that are not, the rules for keeping these apart are fairly simple. With the addition of TNV circuits, which are somewhere in between, the separation and accessibility requirements are more complex. It is recognised that the rules in EN 41003 may not cover all future applications. In subclauses 4.1 and 4.2.2(c) (and in IEC 950) it is permitted to connect disparate circuits under some conditions, provided that the limit values are not violated. The principle of remaining safe in the presence of a single fault, mentioned above, governs these rules, and this principle should be applied when the standard does not seem to cover the situation.

TNV circuits that operate above SELV limits are permitted to be accessible only according to subclause 4.3 (see also Figure 23.11) and must be separated from accessible parts according to 4.2.1 or 4.2.2, depending on whether the accessible part is earthed or not. TNV circuits must also be separated from excessive voltages by two levels of protection, like SELV circuits, except that only two separation arrangements are permitted. These are double or reinforced insulation, and basic insulation plus an earthed screen. These restrictions reflect the long standing unwillingness of PTTs to rely on earth for the safety of their personnel.

23.6.4   Earthing

PTT concerns about earthing have led to a number of restrictions in addition to not relying on it, as noted above. At the subscriber's end, line wires and functional earth connections must be separated from earth, because they are generally earthed at the exchange end. Earthing at both ends could lead to electrical noise, malfunction, over heating and even hazardous touch voltages due to earth potential differences. Also, the green and yellow wire (protective conductor) can too often become disconnected or even acquire a hazardous voltage.

It can easily be seen from Figure 23.15 how a disconnected earth

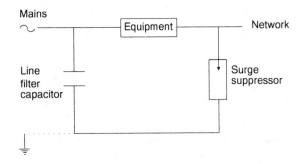

Figure 23.15   Hazard caused by disconnected earth

can allow a through connection between mains and network via an a.c. line filter and surge suppressors connected to line. Subclause 4.4.2 has a test for this particular circumstance: if this configuration of components cannot be avoided, 4.4.2 ensures that the mains current getting out to line will not exceed a safe value. In practice, to pass this test, the surge suppressors would preferably be of a type that did not conduct at all at 250V a.c. Even without this circuit configuration, the green and yellow wire has been known to be connected to the mains pin by inexpert users when re-wiring a plug. Equipment that will be installed by experts (including equipment with a hard wired or heavy duty pluggable mains connection) does not have this requirement. Equipment is also exempt if it needs an earth connection to enable it to function, provided that it is market to say so. However it is not clear in the standard if the earth connection of an interference filter is there 'to enable it to function'. (The corresponding phrase in IEC 950 'for functional reasons' leaves the same uncertainty). Filtering techniques not involving an earth connection are to be preferred. If a telecom 'functional earth' is needed, for earth signalling for example, this should preferably be a permanent and reliable connection, even though other ways are allowed by the standard. The simpler, the better, especially when offering the equipment for third party testing and approval. Finally, even if it is known that the line wires are earthed somewhere, they must not be used to obtain an earth connection for anything at the subscriber's end.

23.6.5   TNV superseding classical safety

Subclause 4.3.1 clearly states how EN 41003 is complementary to, and separate from, the classical safety standards, as shown in Figure 23.5. However, many of those standards contain rules which would preclude the use of TNV circuits as permitted in EN 41003, which is why 4.3.2 is stated to apply 'in place of any more restrictive requirement in the relevant standard'.

23.6.6   Voltages from the network

Unwanted voltages may arrive from the network due to lightning strikes, cross contact between overhead power and telephone lines, and other interference. While there are very few cases of injury to telephone users from such causes, 4.5 of the standard does require separation of the line terminals from various parts of the equipment. As well as avoiding discomfort and possible injury to the user, such separation is probably desirable for protection of any electronic circuits in the equipment. The separation is tested either with 10 impulses or with a steady state voltage for 60 seconds. The manufacturer has the choice. It is not forbidden to have surge suppressors connected to line (as in Figure 23.15 of this chapter) but special test conditions apply if this is done. IEC 950 is not quite the same regarding these test conditions.

The use of impulse testing is to be preferred when surge suppressors are used; the 60 seconds test may destroy them. It is also best to leave them in place during impulse testing, otherwise the parts they are there to protect may be damaged. However, it can be difficult to know whether or not such an arrangement passes the test, the criterion being breakdown of insulation. A technique is described in an annex for observing the characteristic waveforms across insulation (with or without a surge suppressor in parallel), to distinguish between proper operation of a suppressor and breakdown of insulation.

Annex F of EN 41003 contains out of date guidance on insulation spacings for 4.5 and should be ignored. It is not required to provide any particular spacings, only to withstand the voltage tests.

It will be noted that separation between the line and other parts may have to meet more than one requirement of the standard for different purposes, applying to the same physical piece of insulation. Of these, the requirements of 4.5 are probably least onerous and the most onerous must prevail; this should not be regarded as a contradiction within the standard.

23.6.7   Restricted access area

Inventing the TNV circuit was an attempt to include in classical IEC terms equipment that had traditionally been designed to different principles by the telecom industry. This convergence is seen as increasingly necessary, because a box of hardware used for data processing could equally well be used for switching telecom messages. Such a box should not have to conform with different safety standards depending on its application. The concept of a Restricted Access Area is a similar attempt, reflecting the telecom practice of locating hardware in a special room and locking the door, opening it again only to people who know what an electrical hazard looks like. In such a room, some of the accessibility requirements are relaxed, and for the purpose of containing a fire that might start in the equipment, the room may be regarded as the fire enclosure instead of the box itself. At the date of publication this concept lacks both maturity and the support of some experts. In particular the meaning of 'where access is controlled' is not precise. Until the subject becomes more stable, designers should if possible avoid using the relaxations proposed for equipment in a restricted access area.

23.6.8   Overlap of two ENs

EN 41003 and the telecom parts of IEC 950 are similar and may eventually be identical, so that two ENs, EN 41003 and EN 60950 will eventually have these similar or identical requirements. However, there will be a continuing need to keep EN 41003 in existence. For one reason, other standards are beginning to refer to it, and a standard that is referred to by another standard cannot be withdrawn. Secondly, as explained earlier, EN 41003 can be used with equipment designed to another of the classical safety standards.

23.7   Choice of relevant safety requirements

All of EN 41003 applies where the equipment has an interface to the PSTN, because it was written around that system. However, not all of it applies to every piece of telecom equipment. Subclause 4.4.2 and 4.5 may not apply; in some cases none of it applies. It is not always obvious to a hardware designer which parts do apply to the box he is designing. The problem does not arise with traditional IT equipment: if a circuit needs to be accessible it needs to be an SELV circuit or a limited current circuit, as specified in IEC 950; if a box contains no cathode ray tube, the section on cathode ray tubes clearly does not apply. But whether an interface should be an SELV circuit or a TNV circuit, to match its neighbouring box, may not be clear. For EN 41003, this information is given by ETSI (European Telecommunications Standards Institute) because EN 41003 was written for certain ETSI publications (those that become NETs or CTRs) that have mandatory effect.

ETSI is in the course of publishing a technical report, ETR 12, which summarises this information for a large number of possible interfaces on subscribers' terminal equipment. It also states, for each interface, whether or not 4.4.2 and 4.5 apply and whether or not SELV circuits as specified in 2.3.6 of IEC 950 can be used. (Designers of any kind of equipment would be well advised never to use 2.3.6 or 2.3.7, and not even 2.3.5 if it can be avoided). Additionally, ETSI has identified a possible safety hazard that arises on the ISDN 'passive bus' and has written tests and requirements that do not yet appear in EN 41003 (see ETSI ETS 300 046 and ETS 300 047). This hazard is the possibility of too much 'touch current' flowing through a person who touches the passive bus, due to the fact that the bus is floating with respect to earth. ETR 12 will also list protection requirements for each interface but this area needs further study.

Clearly, unspecified compliance with EN 41003 should never be claimed or demanded.

With IEC 950, the situation is less simple because designers and specifiers often claim or specify total compliance with the standard. There is no superior standard defining which bits of IEC 950 do apply. ETSI ETR 12 offers this information but it is a regional (European) document. IEC 950 itself tries to help by stating that an interface connected to a Telecommunication Network must be a TNV circuit, but the definition of Telecommunication Network is very imprecise. Is a Local Area Network, or the ISDN passive bus, or a long analogue telephone cable entirely on a subscriber's premises a telecommunication network?

There being no clear solution to this problem at present, there is a need for flexibility, common sense and mutual understanding between manufacturers, test houses and approval authorities. This is especially so where conformance with a standard is mandatory, and where non-compliance can mean that permission to connect the box to a network cannot be obtained.

Another area where rules need to be written and applied with practical understanding is that of the constant evolution of the standards, and in particular the adoption of successive modifications of IEC 950 into EN 60950 by CENELEC. This adoption process is currently nearly two years behind, but the mandatory requirements in Europe refer to EN60950, which may be faulty and out of date compared with IEC 950. Designs of hardware cannot change overnight and there must be room to accommodate these timing problems so that they do not cause unnecessary denial of 'permission to connect' and delays in the market-place.

Periods of overlap must be allowed between the old and new versions of a standard, during which either version can be used. There must also be room for 'grandfathered' equipment that has already been accepted under an earlier regime and is still being sold. Where problems of this kind arise, designers should consult with their approval authority to see what can be accepted, and perhaps persuade them to modify their rules to meet practical needs. The objectives of compliance with a safety standard should be safety, not the tidy adherence to bureaucratic rules and dates which may not have been fully thought out. Designers may also find that some test houses and approval authorities are more flexible than others, and they should act accordingly.

For new designs, designers are advised to use EN 41003 or IEC 950, second edition, including (or allowing for) amendments or proposed amendments to those standards for as far ahead as there is visibility. Visibility can be improved by designers becoming involved in the standards writing process through national standards institutes or trade associations. These organisations can quite likely benefit from such injections of practical experience.

23.8 Documentation

IEC Publications and corresponding European publications are given in Table 23.2. When the IEC Publication has been modified by CENELEC common modifications, indicated by (mod), the relevant EN/HD applies.

International (and national) standards can be obtained from national standards organisations or direct from IEC, 3 Rue de Varembe, 1211 Geneva 20, Switzerland.

ENs, ETRs, ETSs and NETs should be available from national standards organisations, especially in Europe. The English versions can be obtained from BSI, Linford Wood, Milton Keynes, MK14 6LE, UK.

Table 23.2 IEC, ETSI and CENELEC publications

IEC/ ETSI Publication	Date	Title	EN/HD	Date
		Particular electrical safety requirements for equipment to be connected to telecommunications networks	EN 41003	1991
IEC 65 (mod)	1965	Safety requirement for mains operated electronic and related apparatus for household and similar use	HD 195 S1	1989
IEC 335 (mod)		Safety of household and similar electrical appliances	EN 60335	
IEC 348	1978	Safety of electronic measuring apparatus	HD 401 S1	1980
IEC 479		The effects of current passing through the human body		
IEC 601-1	1988	Medical electrical equipment	EN 60601-1	1990
IEC 950 (mod)	1986	Safety of information technology equipment including electrically operated business machines	EN 60950	1988
IEC Guide 105	1985	Principles concerning the safety of equipment electrically connected to a telecommunications network		
ETS 300 046	1991/2	ISDN Primary Rate Access Safety and Protection,		
ETS 300 047	1991/2	ISDN Basic Access Safety and Protection		
ETR 12	1991/2	Safety categories and protection levels at various interfaces for telecommunications equipments in customer premises		

23.9 Electromagnetic compatibility

All electrical and electronic devices generate electromagnetic interference, and are susceptible to it. With the increasing penetration of solid state electronics into all areas of activity, acceptable levels of interference have become progressively tighter as physical separation between devices has reduced and reliance on their operation has increased. Solid state, particularly integrated circuit technology, is more susceptible than the vacuum tube devices of years ago, and the popularity of plastic cases with their lack of screening is a further factor. The ability of a device to operate within the limits of interference immunity and suppression is known as electromagnetic compatibility (EMC).

In some areas of electronics EMC has been a product requirement for a long time. Military electronics has severe limitations imposed on it, often because of the proximity of high power pulse equipment (radars) to sensitive signal processing equipment in the same aircraft, ship or vehicle, and military EMC standards first appeared in the 1960s. The increasing use of walkie-talkies on process plant and elsewhere has prompted users of safety critical instrumentation to specify a minimum immunity from r.f. interference. Measuring and weighing equipment must be prevented from giving incorrect readings in the presence of interference, and domestic broadcast receivers should be able to work alongside home computers.

Radio frequencies are not the only source of interference. Transients can be generated by power switching circuits, lightning, electric motors, spark ignition devices or electrostatic discharge. Microprocessor circuits are particularly susceptible to impulse interference and must be protected accordingly.

23.9.1 The importance of EMC

Poor EMC performance of a product can be extremely costly, both in terms of damaged reputation and in the measures needed to improve performance once a fault has been found. For this reason, many firms will test their products for EMC before releasing them even though there may be no applicable standard for that class of equipment. Others, whose markets may be less demanding or whose products are not used in a crowded electromagnetic environment, have not until recently considered it necessary to specify EMC performance.

This situation is now changing, both because of electromagnetic pollution which is bringing to light more cases of poor EMC, and because new legislation will compel manufacturers to consider their products' EMC. The technical constraints on equipment EMC are that the equipment should continue to function reliably in a hostile electromagnetic environment, and that it should not itself degrade that environment to the extent of causing unreliable operation in other equipment. EMC therefore splits neatly into two areas, labelled 'immunity' and 'emissions', and a list of some of the interference types and coupling methods is shown in Table 23.3.

23.9.2 Immunity

The electromagnetic environment within which equipment will operate and which will determine its required immunity can vary widely, as can the permissible definition of reliable operation. For instance, the magnitude of radiated fields encountered depends critically on the distance from the source. Strong r.f. fields occur in the vicinity of radars, broadcast transmitters and r.f. heating equipment (including microwave ovens at 2.45GHz). The free space electric field strength falls off linearly with distance from the trans-

Table 23.3 Electromagnetic compatibility phenomena

Immunity	Emissions
Mains voltage drop-outs, dips, surges and distortion	Mains distortion, transients or RFI generated within the equipment and conducted out via the mains supply
Transients and radio frequency interference (RFI) conducted into the equipment via the mains supply	Transient or RFI, generated within the equipment and conducted out via signal leads
Radiated transient or RFI picked up and conducted into the equipment via signal leads	RFI radiated directly from the equipment circuitry, enclosure and cables
RFI picked up directly by the equipment circuitry	
Electrostatic discharge	

mitting antenna in the far field, defined as greater than $\dfrac{\lambda}{2\,\pi}$ where λ is the wavelength. The value of the field strength in volts per metre can be calculated from Equation 23.1, where P is the radiated power in watts and d is the distance from the antenna in metres.

$$E = \frac{(30\,P)^{1/2}}{d} \tag{23.1}$$

In the near field closer than $\dfrac{\lambda}{2\,\pi}$ the field strength can be much greater depending on the type of antenna and how it is driven.

23.9.2.1 Radio transmitters

AM broadcast band transmitter power levels tend to be around 100kW to 500kW, but the transmitters are usually located away from centres of population. Field strength levels in the 1V/m to 10V/m range may be experienced occasionally, but at medium frequencies coupling to circuit components is inefficient, so these transmitters do not pose a great problem except when coupled via long cables. TV and FM band transmitters are more often found close to office or industrial environments and the greatest threat is to equipment on the upper floors of tall buildings, which may be in line of sight to a nearby transmitter of typically 10kW. Field strengths greater than 10V/m are possible, and although the building structure may give attenuation between 0 and 20dB, achieving immunity from even a 1V/m field is not trivial at these frequencies, where cable and track lengths approach resonance and coupling is correspondingly more efficient.

Portable transmitters (walkie-talkies, cellphones) do not have a high radiated power but they can be brought extremely close to susceptible equipment. Typical field strengths from a 1W u.h.f. hand held transmitter are 5V/m to 7V/m at half a metre distance.

23.9.2.2 Radars

Another serious threat is from radars in the 1GHz to 10GHz range, particularly around airports. Pulsed 50V/m field strengths can be found up to 3km from these radars. Again, building attenuation may give some relief, but set against this is the problem that pulsed RFI is particularly upsetting to microprocessor circuits.

From these considerations a minimum of 3V/m from, say, 10MHz to 1GHz represents a reasonable design criterion for RFI immunity, with 10V/m being preferred. Immunity from pulsed interference above 1GHz is extremely hard to quantify.

23.9.2.3 *Transients*

Conducted transient immunity is becoming relatively more important, because microprocessor based circuits are much more susceptible to transients than are analogue circuits. Mains transients, from many sources, are far more common than is generally realised. A study by the German ZVEI (Goedbloed, 1987) made a statistical survey of 28000 live to earth transients exceeding 100V, at 40 locations over a total measuring time of about 3400 hours. Their results were analysed for peak amplitude, rate of rise and energy content. Table 23.4 gives the average rate of occurrence of transients for four classes of location, and Figure 23.16 shows the relative

Table 23.4 Average rate of occurrence of transients

Area class	Average rate of occurrence (transients/hour)
Industrial	17.5
Business	2.8
Domestic	0.6
Laboratory	2.3

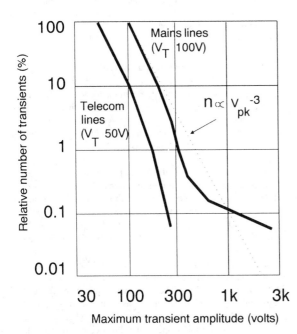

Figure 23.16 Relative number of transients (percent) vs. maximum transient amplitude (volts)

number of transients as a function of maximum transient amplitude. This shows that the number of transients varies roughly in inverse proportion to the cube of peak voltage.

Rate of rise was found to increase in proportion to the square root of peak voltage, being typically 3V/ns for 200V pulses and 10V/ns for 2kV pulses. Other field experience has shown that mechanical switching usually produces multiple transients (bursts) with rise times as short as a few nanoseconds and peak amplitudes of several hundred volts.

As a general guide, microprocessor equipment should be tested to withstand pulses at least up to 2kV peak amplitude. Thresholds below 1kV will give unacceptably frequent corruptions in nearly all environments, while between 1kV to 2kV occasional corruption will occur. For a belt and braces approach for high reliability equipment, a 4kV to 6kV threshold is not too much.

Work on common mode transients on telephone subscriber lines (Goedbloed and Pasmooij, 1990) has shown that the amplitude versus rate of occurrence distribution also follows a roughly inverse cubic law. Actual amplitudes were lower than those on the mains. A transient ringing frequency of 1MHz and rise times of 10ns to 20ns were found to be typical.

23.9.2.4 *ESD*

Electrostatic discharge is a further source of transient upset which most often occurs when a person who has been charged to a high potential by movement across an insulating surface then touches an earthed piece of equipment, thereby discharging themselves through the equipment. The achievable potential depends on relative humidity and the presence of synthetic materials (Figure 23.17), and the average human body equivalent circuit can be

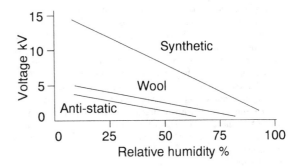

Figure 23.17 Maximum electrostatic charging voltages (Source: IEC 801 Part 2)

represented by a 150pF capacitance in series with 330Ω resistance, so that currents of tens of amps can flow for a short period with a very fast (sub-nanosecond) rise time. Even though it may have low energy and be conducted to ground through the equipment case, such a current pulse couples very easily into the internal circuitry.

23.9.2.5 *Effects of interference*

Required reliability of operation depends very much on the application. Entertainment devices and gadgets come fairly close to the bottom of the scale, whereas computers and instrumentation for control of critical systems such as fly by wire aircraft and nuclear power systems come near the top. The purchasers and authorities responsible for such systems have recognised this for some years and there is a well established raft of EMC requirements for them, but in less critical sectors this is not the case and EMC performance is mainly determined by market factors.

Actually determining whether a piece of equipment has been affected by interference is not always easy. Interference may cause a degradation in accuracy of measuring equipment, it may cause noticeable deterioration in audio quality or it may corrupt a microprocessor program. If the processor circuit has a program recovery mechanism this may correct the corruption before it is apparent, or the effects of the interference may be confused with a software glitch. Determining cause and effect in the operating environment is particularly difficult when the interference is transient or occasional in nature. When contemplating immunity testing, it is essential to be sure what will constitute acceptable performance and what is a test failure.

23.9.3 Emissions

By comparison with immunity requirements, equipment emissions are relatively easy to characterise. The majority of emissions from electronic equipment are due to either switching or other electro-mechanical operations, or digital clock and data lines. The former can be pulses at mains frequency, such as from thyristor phase controllers, motor commutator noise, individual switching 'clicks' or switch mode power supply harmonics, and they are generally conducted out of the equipment via the mains lead.

These emissions have been regulated for many years in order to minimise interference to AM broadcast and communications services.

Digital equipment with high frequency square wave clocks generates noise into the hundreds of MHz. The system clocks and their harmonics are the principal source because their energy is concentrated into a narrow band, but wideband noise from the data and address lines is also present. The noise amplitude and spectral distribution may vary depending on the operating mode of the circuit or its resident software.

Emissions from some classes of digital equipment, such as personal computers, have been regulated by some countries, again to control interference to broadcast and communication services.

Equipment emissions can be either conducted or radiated. Commercial emission standards differentiate between the two on the basis of frequency; the breakpoint is universally accepted to be 30MHz since it has in fact been found empirically that the coupling mechanisms are predominantly by conduction below 30MHz, and by radiation above it.

The regulation of emissions is intended only to reduce the threat to innocent 'victim' receivers. Some reasonable separation of the offending emitter and the victim is assumed. If a personal computer is placed right next to a domestic radio set one can still expect there to be interference. Regulations have nothing to say on the subject of intra-system interference, so that it is quite possible for two computer systems, both of which meet the appropriate standard, to be incompatible when they are placed together in the same rack or cabinet.

23.10 EMC legislation and standards

Up until the formulation of the European Community EMC Directive, the only countries to incorporate major product electromagnetic emission legislation (except for household products, fluorescent lights and vehicle ignition, which have been regulated

by specific Directives) have been Germany and the United States. In the US, emissions from digital devices are governed by FCC (Federal Communications Commission) Rules part 15. A 'digital device' is any electronic device that generates or uses timing signals or pulses exceeding 9kHz and uses digital techniques. There are some quite broad exemptions from the rules depending on application. Two classes are defined, depending on the intended market: class A for business, commercial or industrial use, and class B for residential use. These classes are subject to different limits, class B being the stricter. Before being able to market his equipment in the US, a manufacturer must either obtain certification approval from the FCC if it is a personal computer, or must verify that the device complies with the applicable limits.

23.10.1 The EMC directive

The relaxed EMC regime that had hitherto existed throughout Europe, with the exception of Germany, has now changed dramatically. In accord with the general objective of the single European market, the European Commission has put forward an EMC directive (89/336/EEC) (EEC, 1989) whose purpose is to remove any barriers to trade on technical grounds relating to EMC. Thus, EC member states may not impede, for reasons relating to EMC, the free circulation on their territory of apparatus which satisfies the directive's requirements.

23.10.1.1   *Scope and coverage*

The directive applies to all electrical and electronic equipment placed on the market or taken into service, so that it includes systems as well as individual products. It operates as follows: it sets out the essential requirements; it requires a statement to the effect that the equipment complies with these requirements; and it provides alternative means of determining whether the essential requirements have been satisfied.

The essential requirements are that:

'The apparatus shall be so constructed that:

(a) Equipment shall not generate electromagnetic disturbances exceeding a level allowing radio and telecommunications equipment and other apparatus to operate as intended.
(b) Equipment shall have an adequate level of intrinsic immunity from electromagnetic disturbances.'

Thus protection is extended not only to radio and telecomms but also to other equipment such as information technology and medical equipment, in fact any equipment which is susceptible to electromagnetic (EM) disturbances.

The second requirement states that the equipment should not malfunction in whatever hostile EM environment it may reasonably be expected to operate.

The range of EMC phenomena covered by the directive includes radiated emissions as well as those conducted along mains, signal, control or other cabling. The immunity requirement covers EM fields, spikes, dips, outages, distortions on the mains supply, electrostatic discharges, and lightning surges.

Equipment within the scope of the directive can be considered under the following generic classifications: industrial, scientific and medical; electricity supply and distribution; traction; lamps and luminaires; household appliances; building services; motor vehicles; broadcast; entertainment; ITE and telecomms; maritime; and aeronautical.

23.10.1.2   *Routes to compliance*

Without guidance, many manufacturers will not be able to assess whether their equipment is able to satisfy the two essential requirements, so the directive looks towards the development of harmonised European standards on EMC. Any equipment which complies with the relevant standards can be self certified as complying with the essential requirements. However, a manufacturer may choose to undertake his own technical assessment, indeed may have to if there is no relevant EMC standard in existence. In this case, he is required to keep a technical file containing details of the test method used, the test results and a supporting statement by an independent competent body. This file must be at the disposal of the national administration.

A further procedure for demonstrating compliance is transitional and will apply for four years after the Directive came into force on 1st January 1992. It allows apparatus to continue to be governed by the national arrangements in force in each member state, in the absence of European or approved national standards. Telecommunications Terminal Equipment (TTE) is subject to a separate Directive (91/263/EEC), but this does not prevent it also having to comply with the EMC Directive, except that EMC requirements 'specific to TTE' must be tested and certified as part of the TTE type approval process. The EMC aspects of radio transmitters are subject to type approval as part of the EMC Directive.

23.10.2   Standards

The European electrotechnical standards body is CENELEC (the European Organisation for Electrotechnical Standardisation) which has UK representation from the BSI (the British Standards Institution). The telecommunications standards body is ETSI (the European Telecommunications Standards Institute). Once CENELEC or ETSI have produced and agreed a European EMC standard all the CENELEC countries have to implement identical national standards, which will then be deemed to be 'relevant standards' for the purpose of demonstrating compliance with the Directive. The self certification route is the preferred method of demonstrating compliance with the Directive, and this depends on the availability of harmonized standards.

23.10.2.1   *Emission standards*

A number of product oriented standards already exist and can be applied to products where this is possible and reasonable. Since emission standards have evolved over a number of years there is a good deal of agreement not only in methods of measurement but also in the limits themselves. The principal standards are summarized in Tables 23.5 and 23.6, and a comparison of the emission limits is shown in Figure 23.18 for conducted and Figure 23.19 for radiated emission. Measuring equipment is defined in CISPR publication 16, which is aligned with BS727.

Note that there are detailed differences in the methods of measurement allowed between the various emission standards. Measurements on conducted emissions below 30MHz are made on the mains terminals and use an artificial mains network, or Line Impedance Stabilising Network (LISN), to define the impedance of the mains supply. Radiated measurements above 30MHz require the use of an

Table 23.5   Emission standards (– indicates that these standards are aligned)

Product sector	British		EN (CISPR)	FCC (US)	VDE (Germany)
Industrial scientific & medical	(BS4809)		EN55011 (11)	Part 18	0871
Radio & TV	BS905-1	—	EN55013 (13)		0872
Household appliances	BS800	—	EN55014 (14)		0875
Fluorescent lighting	BS5394	—	EN55015 (15)		0875
Information technology equipment	BS6527	—	EN55022 (22)	Part 15	0878
Generic emissions			EN50081		
Mains disturbances	BS5406	—	EN60555 (IEC555)		

Table 23.6   Immunity standards (– indicates that these standards are aligned)

Product sector	British	IEC/CISPR	EN	Notes
Industrial process measurement & control	BS6667	— IEC 801		RFI, ESD & transient susceptibility
Radio & TV receivers	BS905-2	— CISPR 20	EN55020	RFI only
Information technology equipment			EN55101	RFI, ESD etc.
Generic immunity			EN50082	

Open Area Test Site (OATS) to minimise reflections, with a calibrated attenuation characteristic. The limit levels shown in Figure 23.19 have been normalised to a measurement distance of 10m for ease of comparison; different standards call up distances of 3m, 10m or 30m. A direct translation of the levels (according to 1/d) from 10m to 3m is not strictly accurate because of the influence of near field effects.

23.10.2.2   *Immunity standards*

Since immunity standards are of more recent development they have not been adopted in the same way as emission standards. IEC

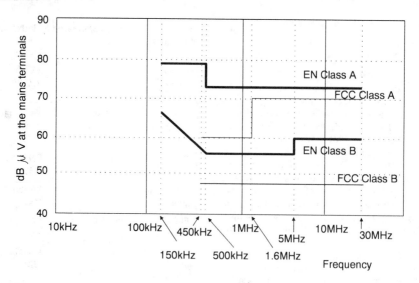

Figure 23.18 Conducted emission limits (CISPR16 quasi-peak detector, 50Ω/50μH LISN)

Publication 801, aligned with BS6667, was published initially in 1984 and refers specifically to requirements for industrial process control instrumentation, but it includes methods of assessment which can be applied to a much wider range of products and forms the basis for the CENELEC generic immunity standard. At the time of writing it covers electrostatic discharge, radiated RFI and fast transients, with draft parts in circulation covering switching and lightning surges and conducted RFI. Also, EN55020 lays down requirements for the immunity of radio and TV receivers to RFI. A further standard (EN55101, to be renumbered EN55024) is in preparation to cover the immunity of information technology equipment.

23.10.2.3 The generic standards

There are many industry sectors for which no product-specific standards have been developed. This is especially so for immunity.

In order to fill this gap, CENELEC have given a high priority to developing the Generic Standards. These are standards with a wide application, not related to any particular product or product family, and are intended to represent the essential requirements of the Directive. They are divided into standards for immunity (EN50082) and emissions (EN50081), each of which has separate parts for different environment classes.

Where a relevant product specific standard exists, this takes precedence over the generic standard. The tests defined in the generic standards are based only on internationally approved, already existing standards. For each electromagnetic phenomenon a test procedure given by such a standard is referenced, and a single test level or limit is laid down. Since the referenced standards are undergoing revision to incorporate new tests, these are noted in an 'informative annex' in each generic standard.

A particular problem with immunity is that the equipment under test may exhibit a wide variety of responses to the test stimulus. To account for this variety, the generic immunity standard includes

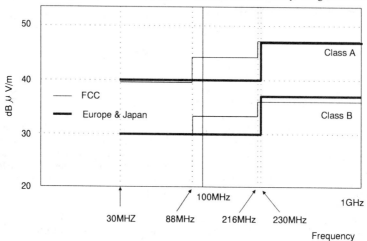

Figure 23.19 Radiated emission limits (CISPR16 quasi-peak detector, normalised (1/d) to a measuring distance of 10m)

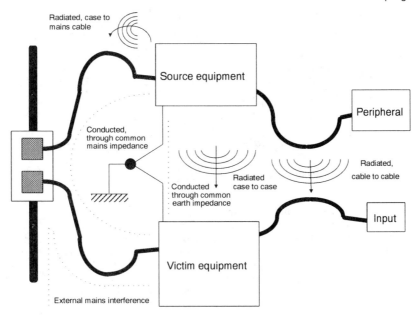

Figure 23.20 Coupling mechanisms

three generalised performance criteria for the purpose of evaluating test results. These are:

1. The apparatus continues to operate as intended with no degradation below a performance level specified by the manufacturer.
2. The apparatus continues to operate as intended after the test, but during the test some degradation of performance is allowed.
3. Temporary loss of function is allowed, provided that it is self recoverable or operator recoverable.

23.11 Interference coupling mechanisms

Interference can be coupled into or out of equipment over a number of routes (Figure 23.20). At low frequencies the predominant modes of coupling are directly along the circuit wires or by induction, but at high frequencies each conductor, including the equipment housing if it is metallic, acts as an aerial in its own right and will contribute to coupling.

23.11.1 Conducted

A very frequent cause of conducted interference coupling is the existence of a common impedance path between the interfering and victim circuits. This path is usually though not invariably in the ground return. A typical case of common impedance coupling might involve impulsive interference from a motor or switching circuit being fed into the 0V rail of a microprocessor circuit because they share the same earth return. Note that because of resonances, the impedance of earthing and bonding conductors is high at frequencies for which their length is an odd multiple of quarter wavelengths.

Another coupling route is through the equipment power supply to or from the mains. The power supply forms the interface between the mains and the internal operation of the equipment, and all emissions standards regulate the amount of interference that can be fed onto the mains via the power input leads. A great deal of work has been done to characterise the impedance of the mains supply, and perhaps surprisingly measurements in quite different environments show close agreement. This has allowed the development of the CISPR16 artificial mains network (LISN) referred to in the last section. The impedance can be simulated by 50Ω in parallel with $50\mu H$ with respect to earth (Figure 23.21) and Figure 23.22 shows its impedance-frequency plot. Power cables tend to act as low loss transmission lines up to 10MHz so that interference can propagate quite readily around the power distribution network, mainly attenuated by the random connection of other loads rather than by the cable itself.

23.11.2 Radiated

When source and victim are near one another (in the 'near field', d being given by inequality 23.2), radiated coupling is predominantly due either to magnetic or electric induction.

$$d < \frac{\lambda}{2\pi} \tag{23.2}$$

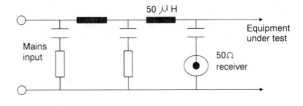

Figure 23.21 Equivalent circuit of an LISN

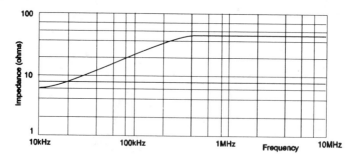

Figure 23.22 Impedance-frequency plot of the artificial mains network of Figure 23.21

Magnetic induction occurs when the magnetic flux produced by a changing current in the source circuit links with the victim circuit. The voltage induced in the victim circuit by a sinusoidal current I_s at frequency f due to a mutual inductance M henries is given by Equation 23.3.

$$V = 2\pi f I_s M \quad volts \tag{23.3}$$

M is proportional to the areas of the source and victim circuit loops, the distance between them, their relative orientation and the presence of any magnetic screening. It is normally hard to characterise accurately. For example, short lengths of cable within the same wiring loom have mutual inductances in the range of $0.1\mu H$ to $3\mu H$.

Magnetic induction is a current (low impedance) phenomenon, and it increases with increasing current in the source circuit. Electric induction, or capacitive coupling, is a voltage phenomenon and occurs when changing electric fields from the source interact with the victim circuit. The induced voltage due to a sinusoidal voltage V_s of frequency f on the source conductor coupled through a mutual capacitance C farads is given by Equation 23.4 where Z is the impedance to ground of the victim circuit.

$$V = 2\pi f V_s C Z \quad volts \tag{23.4}$$

Mutual capacitance between conductors depends on their distance apart, respective areas, and any dielectric material or electric screening between them. In some cases, component or cable manufacturers provide figures for mutual capacitance. It is generally in the range 1pF to 100pF for typical circuit configurations.

23.11.2.1 Electromagnetic induction

When the source and victim are further apart then both electric and magnetic fields are involved in the coupling, and the conductors must be considered as antennas. For conductors whose dimensions are much smaller than the wavelength then the maximum electric field component in the far field at a distance d metres due to a current I at frequency f flowing in the conductor is (Ott, 1985) given by Equation 23.5 for a loop and 23.6 for a monopole against a ground plane, where A is the area of the loop, and L is the length of the conductor.

$$E = 131.6 \times 10^{-16} \frac{(f^2 A I)}{d} \quad volts \, per \, metre \tag{23.5}$$

$$E = 4\pi \, 10^{-7} \frac{(f L I)}{d} \quad volts \, per \, metre \tag{23.6}$$

In the far field the field strength falls off linearly with distance. The electric and magnetic field strengths are related by the impedance of free space, $E/H = 377\Omega$. In the near field, a loop radiator will give a higher H (magnetic) field and this will fall off proportionally to $1/d^3$ while the E field falls off as $1/d^2$. Conversely, a short rod will give a high E field, which will fall off as $1/d^3$ while the H field falls off as $1/d^2$.

Once conductor lengths approach a quarter wavelength (one metre at 75MHz) then they cannot be treated as 'electrically small' and they couple much more efficiently with ambient fields.

23.12 Circuit design and layout

The most fundamental point to consider in designing for EMC is the circuit's grounding regime: the majority of post design interference problems can be traced to poor grounding. Printed circuit layout also has a significant impact. The common underlying problem is that all conductors have a finite impedance which is predominantly inductive above a few kHz, and so increases with frequency. Since EMC phenomena are critical at higher frequencies, two physically separate ground points cannot be regarded as being at the same potential unless no current flows between them. Ground tracks must be treated as low impedance routes by which return current is encouraged to flow (Ott, 1979), rather than as equipotential circuit reference points. The principles to follow in this regard are to:

1. Identify the circuits of high di/dt (for emissions) e.g. clocks, bus buffers and drivers, high-power oscillators.
2. Identify sensitive circuits (for susceptibility) e.g. low level analogue and fast digital data circuits.
3. Minimize their ground inductance by minimizing the length and enclosed area of their circuit traces or wires, and/or using a ground plane construction.
4. Partition sensitive and noisy circuits so as to be able to control the interfaces between them and to the external environment.
5. Ensure that internal and external ground noise cannot couple out of or into the system, by careful design of the cable ground connections.

23.12.1 Choice of logic

A careful choice of logic family will help to reduce high frequency emissions from digital equipment and may also improve r.f. and transient immunity. The harmonic spectrum of a trapezoidal wave, which approximates to a digital clock waveform, shows a roll off of amplitude with frequency which depends on the risetime (Figure 23.23). Using the slowest risetime compatible with reliable operation of the circuit will minimise the amplitude of the higher order harmonics where radiation is more efficient.

Therefore, the slowest logic family that will do the job should always be used. Where parts of the circuit must operate at high speed, fast logic should only be used for those parts and the clocks kept local.

23.12.1.1   *Noise margin and clock frequency*

Spurious signals coupled into a logic signal circuit will have no effect until they reach the logic threshold. At the same time, the amplitude of signals coupled into the circuit from a given field will depend on the impedance of the circuit, which is defined by the driver output impedance. 4000B series CMOS has around 10 times higher output impedance than LSTTL, depending on supply voltage, so although it has a higher input noise margin it is more susceptible to capacitively coupled interference. 74HC series has a roughly equivalent output impedance and a higher input noise margin, so it is to be preferred over ordinary 74LS series TTL.

The lowest possible clock frequency will minimize the amplitudes of the higher harmonics, and allow the smallest 'window' for disruptive transients in synchronous circuits. It may be possible to use low frequency multi-phase clocks rather than a single high frequency one. In some circumstances changing the spot frequency of the clock slightly may move its harmonics sufficiently far away from a particularly susceptible frequency, though this is more a case of EMC within a system than of meeting emission regulations.

23.12.2   Analogue circuits

Analogue circuits are also capable of unexpected oscillation at radio frequencies. Gain stages should be properly decoupled, loaded and

laid out to avoid this. Check them at the prototype stage with a high frequency oscilloscope or spectrum analyser, even if nothing appears to be wrong with the circuit function. Ringing on pulses transmitted along un-terminated transmission lines will generate frequencies which are related only to the length of the lines with perhaps sufficient amplitude to be troublesome. All long lines should be terminated, particularly if they end at a CMOS input, which provides no inherent termination.

Good r.f. and transient immunity at interfaces calls for a consideration of signal bandwidth, balance and level. Any cable connecting to a piece of equipment will conduct interference straight into the circuit and it is at the interface that protection is needed. This is achieved at the circuit design level by a number of possible strategies:

1. Minimising the signal bandwidth, so that interfering signals outside the wanted frequency range are rejected.
2. Operating the interface at the highest possible power or voltage level consistent with other requirements, such as dynamic range, so that relatively more interference power is required to upset it.
3. Operating the interface where possible with the signal balanced, so that interference is injected in common mode and is therefore attenuated by the common mode rejection of the input circuit.
4. In severe cases, galvanically isolating the input with an opto isolator or transformer coupling, so that the only route for the interference is via the stray coupling capacitance of the isolation components.

Not so obvious is the overload performance of the circuit. If the interference drives the circuit into non-linearity then it will distort the wanted signal, but if the circuit remains linear in the presence of interference then it may be filtered out in a later stage without ill effect. Thus, any circuit which has a good dynamic range and a high overload margin will also be relatively immune to interference.

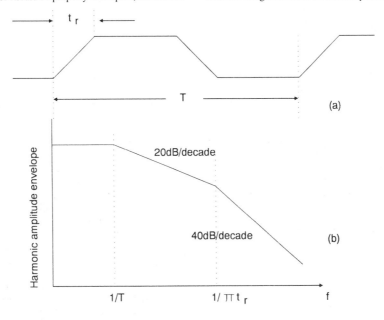

Figure 23.23   Harmonic spectrum of a trapezoidal waveform: (a) waveform; (b) harmonic spectrum envelope

23.12.3 Software

Microprocessor circuits with resident embedded software should use all the available software techniques to overcome likely data corruption. This will be due primarily to transients, but also to RFI. These are:

1. Incorporation of a watchdog timer. Any microprocessor without some form of watchdog is inviting disaster when it is exposed to disruptive transients.
2. Type checking and range checking all input data to determine its reliability. If it is outside range, it should be rejected.
3. Sampling the input data several times and either averaging it, for analogue data, or acting only on two or three successive identical logic states, for digital data, which is similar to digital switch de-bouncing.
4. Incorporating parity checking and data checksums in all data transmission.
5. Protecting data blocks in volatile memory with error detecting and correcting codes. How extensively this protection is used depends on allowable time and memory overheads.
6. Wherever possible relying on level triggered rather than edge triggered interrupts.
7. Not assuming that programmable interface chips (PIAs, ACIAs, etc) will maintain their initialized set up state indefinitely. They need to be re-initialised periodically.

23.13 Shielding

If despite the best circuit design practices, a circuit still radiates unacceptable amounts of noise or is susceptible to incoming radiated interference, the next step is to shield it. This involves placing a conductive surface around the critical parts of the circuit so that the electromagnetic field which couples to it is attenuated by a combination of reflection and absorption. The shield can be an all metal enclosure if protection down to low frequencies is needed, but if only high frequency (>30MHz) shielding is needed then a thin conductive coating deposited on plastic is adequate.

23.13.1 Shielding effectiveness

How well a shield attenuates an incident field is determined by its shielding effectiveness, which is the ratio of the field at a given point before and after the shield is in place. Shielding effectiveness of typical materials differs depending on whether the electric or magnetic component of the field is considered. Shielding effectiveness below 20dB is considered minimal, between 20dB and 80dB is average, and 80dB to 120dB is above average. Above 120dB is unachievable by cost effective measures. The perfect electric shield consists of a seamless box with no apertures made from a zero resistance material. This is known as a Faraday cage and does not exist. Any practical shield will depart from the ideal of infinite attenuation because of two factors:

1. It is not made of perfectly conducting material.
2. It includes apertures and discontinuities.

Shielding effectiveness of a solid conductive barrier can be expressed as the sum of reflection, absorption, and re-reflection losses (Figure 23.24) as in Equation 23.7.

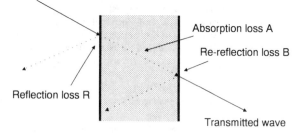

Figure 23.24 Losses due to a solid conducting barrier

$$SE_{(dB)} = R_{(dB)} + A_{(dB)} + B_{(dB)} \qquad (23.7)$$

The reflection loss depends on the ratio of wave impedance to barrier impedance, the barrier impedance being a function of its conductivity and permeability, and of frequency. Reflection losses decrease with increasing frequency for the E-field (electric) and increase for the H-field (magnetic). In the near field, closer than $\frac{\lambda}{2\pi}$, the distance between source and barrier also affects the reflection loss.

The re-reflection loss B is insignificant in most cases where A is greater than 10dB. A itself depends on the barrier thickness and its absorption coefficient. The inverse of the absorption coefficient is called the 'skin depth' (δ). Skin depth is the measure of a magnetic phenomenon that tends to confine ac current to the surface of a conductor. The skin depth reduces as frequency, permeability and conductivity increase, and fields are attenuated by 8.7dB (1/e) for every skin depth of penetration, as in Equation 23.8 where μ_r is relative permeability (1 for air and copper), and σ_r is relative conductivity (1 for copper).

$$\delta = 6.61 \, (\mu_r \, \sigma_r \, f)^{-\frac{1}{2}} \quad centimetres \qquad (23.8)$$

Thus at high frequencies, absorption loss becomes the dominant term. Figure 23.25 shows the combined reflection and absorption losses for copper and iron versus frequency.

23.13.2 Apertures

The curves in Figure 23.25 suggest that upwards of 200dB attenuation is easily achievable using reasonable thicknesses of common materials. In fact, the practical shielding effectiveness is limited by necessary apertures and discontinuities in the shielding.

Apertures are needed for ventilation, for control access, and for viewing indicators. Electromagnetic leakage through an aperture in a thin barrier depends on its longest dimension (d) and the minimum wavelength (λ) of the frequency band to be shielded against, and to a lesser extent on its width (h). For wavelengths less than or equal to twice the longest aperture dimension there is effectively no shielding. The frequency at which this occurs is the 'cut off frequency' of the aperture. For lower frequencies ($\lambda > 2d$) the shielding effectiveness increases linearly at a rate of 20dB per decade (Figure

23.26) up to the maximum possible for the barrier material, given by Equation 23.9 for $d \leq \frac{\lambda}{2}$ >> thickness.

$$SE(db) = 100 - 20 \log (d_{(mm)} F_{(MHz)})$$
$$+ 20 \log \left(1 + \ln \frac{d}{h} \right) \quad (23.9)$$

Comparing Figure 23.25 and Figure 23.26 shows that for all practical purposes shielding effectiveness is determined by the apertures. For frequencies up to 1GHz (the present upper limit for radiated emissions standards) and a minimum shielding of 20dB the maximum hole size you can allow is 1.6cm. If individual perforations are spaced closed together (hole spacing $< \frac{\lambda}{2}$) then the reduction in shielding over a single hole is approximately propor-

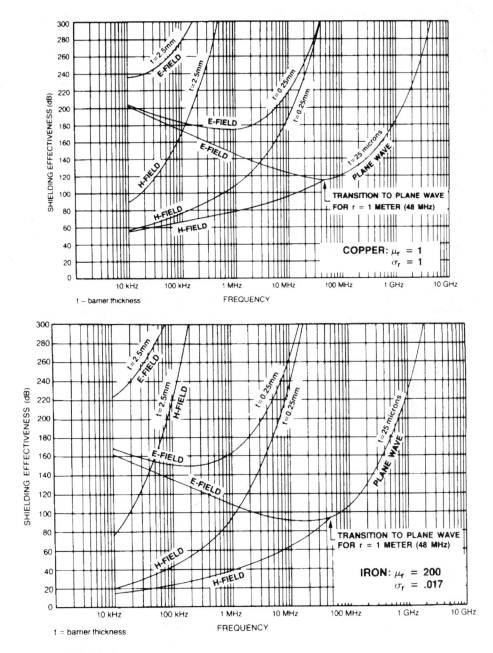

Figure 23.25 Composite reflection and absorption losses for copper and iron (Source: Tecknit)

tional to the square root of the number of holes. Thus a mesh of 100 4mm holes would have a shielding effectiveness 20dB worse than a single 4mm hole. Two similar apertures spaced greater than a half wavelength apart do not suffer any significant extra shielding reduction.

23.13.3 Seams

An electromagnetic shield is normally made from several panels joined together at seams. Unfortunately, when two sheets are joined the electrical conductivity across the joint is imperfect. This may be because of distortion, so that surfaces do not mate perfectly, or because of painting, anodising or corrosion, so that an insulating layer is present on one or both metal surfaces. Consequently, the shielding effectiveness is reduced by seams just as much as it is by apertures. The reduction of shielding effectiveness depends on the longest dimension of an aperture applies equally to a non-conductive length of seam.

The problem is especially serious for hinged front panels, doors and removable hatches that form part of a screened enclosure. The penalty of poor contact is mitigated to some extent if the conductive sheets overlap, since this forms a capacitor which provides a partial current path at high frequencies. An enclosure made of several ill fitting painted panels with large holes and few fastenings will give little or no shielding at typical frequencies.

There are a number of design options which will improve the shielding effectiveness at the seams:

1. Ensuring that supposedly conductive surfaces remain conductive. They must not be painted or anodised; alochrome is a suitable conductive finish for aluminium.
2. The area of overlap of two joined sheets is maximised. This can be done by lapped or flanged joints.

3. Where screwed or riveted fastenings are used they are spaced as closely as possible. A good rule is no farther apart than $\lambda/20$, where λ is the wavelength at the highest frequency of interest.
4. Keeping machining tolerances as tight as possible within cost constraints. Where this still does not give a flat enough mating surface (which is likely to be most cases) or an environmental seal is needed, or where good seam conductivity without fasteners is required, such as at a hinged panel, conductive gaskets may be used. These are available either as a wire mesh or spiral over rubber, or as an elastomer loaded with a conductive material such as silver flakes. Selection of the right gasket depends on environmental factors and the required conductivity.
5. Another way of improving shielding contact between two surfaces that frequently mate and un-mate is to use beryllium copper 'finger' stock either as a continuous strip or spaced at intervals subject to the limitations on spacing given above for fasteners.

23.14 Filtering

The purpose of filtering for EMC is almost invariably to attenuate high frequency components while passing low frequency ones. It is also, almost invariably, to block interfering signals which are coupled onto cables which enter or leave the equipment enclosure. There is little point in applying good shielding and circuit design practice to guard against radiated coupling if interference is then allowed to be coupled in or out via the external connections.

Interference can be induced directly onto the cable or can be coupled through the external connection, and a proper filter can guard against either or both of these, but some knowledge is re-

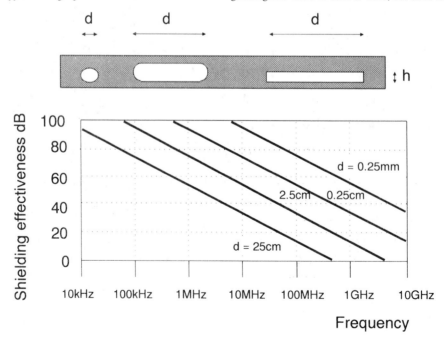

Figure 23.26 Attenuation through an aperture

quired of the characteristics of the circuit in which the filter will be embedded to design or select the best filtering device.

Filters fall broadly into three categories: those intended for mains terminals, for input/output connections and for individual power or signal wires. The basic principle is the same for all of these.

23.14.1 The low pass filter

The simpler circuit arrangements which offer a low pass response are shown in Figure 23.27. The attenuation of any given filter is conventionally quoted in terms of its insertion loss, that is the difference between the voltage across the load with the filter in and out of circuit. The insertion loss depends not only on the filter components but also on the source and load impedances. The simple inductor circuit, in which the inductor may be nothing more than a ferrite bead will give good results, better than 40dB attenuation, in a low impedance circuit but will be quite useless at high impedances. Conversely, the simple capacitor will give good results at high impedances but will be useless at low ones. The multi-component filters will give better results provided that they are configured correctly; the capacitor should face a high impedance and the inductor a low one.

Frequently, Z_S and Z_L are complex and perhaps unknown at the frequencies of interest for suppression. The mains supply impedance is fairly predictable and can be quite easily modelled. H.F. impedances for most signal circuits can be derived, but it is not so easy for power supply inputs, as power components such as transformers, diodes and reservoir capacitors are not characterised at h.f., and the impedances will either have to be measured or guessed.

When the source is taken to be a cable acting as an antenna any analytical method for deriving its impedance will be irrelevant when applied to the real situation, in which cable orientation and positioning is uncontrolled, and a nominal value has to be assumed, typically 150Ω. 50Ω is usually specified as the test impedance for filter units, but it should be remembered that published insertion loss figures in a 50Ω system are not likely to be obtained in the real application. This does not necessarily matter, provided the filter and circuit combination is carefully characterised and tested as a whole.

23.14.1.1   *Components and layout*

Filter components, like all others, are imperfect. Inductors have self capacitance, capacitors have self inductance. This complicates the equivalent circuit at high frequencies and means that a typical filter using discrete components will start to lose its performance above about 10MHz. The larger the components are physically, the lower will be the break frequency. As the frequency increases beyond capacitor or inductor self resonance the impedance of the capacitors in the circuit actually rises, or that of the inductors drops, so that the insertion loss begins to fall. This can be countered by using special construction for the capacitors.

The components are not the only cause of poor h.f. performance. Layout is another factor; lead inductance and stray capacitance can contribute as much degradation as component parasitics. Two common faults in filter applications are not to provide an adequate low inductance ground connection, and to wire the input and output leads in the same loom or at least close to each other, as in Figure 23.28.

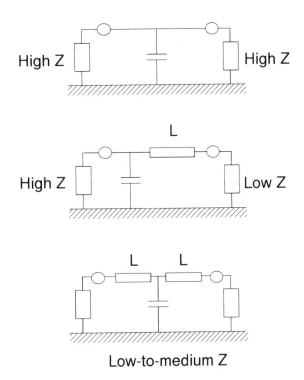

High-to-medium Z   Low-to-medium Z

Figure 23.27   Low pass filter

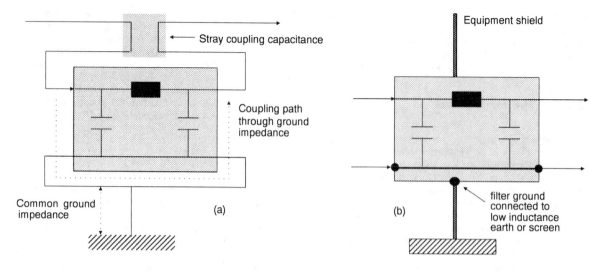

Figure 23.28 Filter wiring and layout: (a) bad; (b) good

A poor ground offers a common impedance which rises with frequency and couples h.f. interference straight through from one side to the other via the filter's local ground path. Common input-output wiring does the same thing through stray capacitance. The cures are obvious: always mounting the filter so that its ground node is directly coupled to the lowest inductance ground of the equipment, preferably the chassis, and keeping the input and output leads separate, preferably screened from each other. The best solution is to position the filter so that it straddles the equipment shielding.

23.14.2 Mains filters

RFI filters for mains supply inputs have developed as a separate species and are available in many physical and electrical forms from several specialist manufacturers. A typical 'block' filter for European mains supplies with average insertion loss might cost below £5. The reasons for this separate development are:

1. Mandatory RFI emission standards have concentrated on interference conducted out of equipment via the mains, and consequently the market for filters to block this interference is large and well established, with predictable performance needs.
2. There is an unfortunate tendency to add filtering as an afterthought, when it is discovered that equipment does not meet the regulations: add on block mains filters are well matched to this 'design' requirement.
3. Any components on the mains wiring side of equipment are exposed to an extra layer of safety regulatory requirements. Filter manufacturers are able to amortise the cost of designing and certifying their products to the plethora of national standards over a large number of units, thus relieving the equipment manufacturer to some extent of this particular burden.
4. Locating a filter directly at the mains inlet lends itself well to the provision of the whole input circuitry — connector, filter, fuse, on/off switch — as one block which the manufacturer can 'fit and forget'.
5. Many equipment designers are at a loss when it comes to r.f. filter design, and prefer a bought in solution.

On the other hand, mains filters can be designed in with the rest of the circuit, and this becomes a cost effective approach for high volume products and is almost always necessary if the optimum filter performance is essential. A typical mains filter circuit (Figure 23.29) includes components to block both common mode and differential mode interference currents.

The common mode choke L consists of two identical windings on a single high permeability, usually toroidal, core, configured in the circuit so that differential (line to neutral) currents cancel each other.

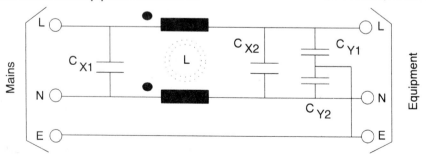

Figure 23.29 Typical mains filter circuit

This allows high inductance values, typically 1mH to 10mH, in a small volume without fear of choke saturation caused by the mains frequency supply current. The full inductance of each winding is available to attenuate common mode currents with respect to earth, but only the leakage inductance, which depends critically on the choke construction, will offer attenuation to differential mode interference.

Capacitors C_{X1} and C_{X2} attenuate differential mode only but can have fairly high values, $0.1\mu F$ to $0.47\mu F$ being typical. Either may be omitted depending on the detailed performance required, remembering that the source and load impedances may be too low for the capacitor to be useful. Capacitors C_{Y1} and C_{Y2} attenuate common mode interference and if C_{X2} is large, have no significant effect on differential mode.

Figure 23.30 gives the equivalent circuits for differential mode and common mode filtering.

23.14.2.1 *Safety requirements*

The values of $C_{Y1,2}$ are nearly always limited by the allowable earth return current, which is set by safety considerations. This current is due to the operating voltage at mains frequency developed across the capacitors. Several national safety authorities define maximum earth current levels and these depend on the safety class of the equipment and on the actual application. Values range from 0.25mA to 5mA.

BS613, which specifies requirements for mains RFI filters in the UK, gives the maximum value for Y-configured capacitors for class 1 appliances connected by a plug and socket as $0.005\mu F$, and this value is frequently found in general purpose filters. The quality of the components is also critical, since they are continuously exposed to mains voltage; failure of either C_X or C_Y could result in a fire hazard, and failure of C_Y could also result in an electric shock hazard. Therefore only components which are rated for mains use in these positions should be used.

23.14.3 Input/output filters

In contrast to the mains filter, a filter on an I/O line has to be more closely tailored to individual applications, and consequently ready made filters are not normally available. A major variable is the signal bandwidth of the I/O line. If the signal bandwidth extends into the r.f. range, as for example 10Mbit/s digital interfaces or video lines, then a simple low pass filter cannot be used except for u.h.f. and above. Conversely, a slow signal such as from a transducer or switch can easily be filtered with a simple capacitor.

A low pass filter may affect the signal waveshape even if its cut off frequency is higher than the signal bandwidth. More complex filter components with very steep cut off characteristics are becoming available to address this problem.

I/O filters may also be required to clamp transients to a safe level, determined by the over voltage capability of the circuitry inboard of

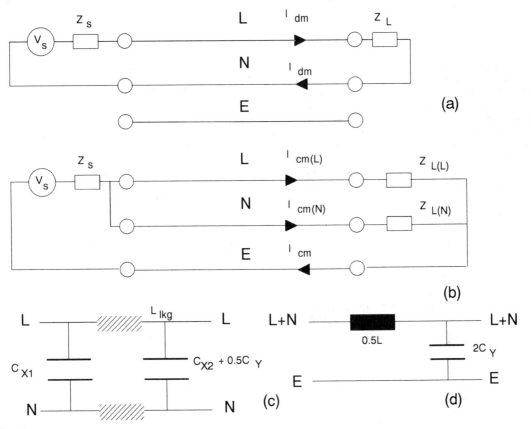

Figure 23.30 Filtering the mains port: (a) differential mode currents; (b) common mode currents; (c) equivalent circuit for differential mode; (d) equivalent circuit for common mode

the filter. This is invariably achieved by a combination of low pass filtering and transient suppression components, such as zener diodes or varistors. A discrete component approach may suffice for many applications, but where fast rising transients are expected the lead and wiring inductance has a significant effect on the circuit's ability to clamp the edge of the pulse. In these cases a combined capacitor/varistor component, in which the ceramic dielectric is treated to give it a predictable low voltage breakdown characteristic, can offer a solution.

23.14.4 Feedthrough and 3-terminal capacitors

Any low pass filter configuration, except for the simple inductor, uses a capacitor in parallel with the signal path. A perfect capacitor would give an attenuation increasing at a constant 20dB per decade as the frequency increased, but a practical wire ended capacitor has some inherent lead inductance which in the conventional configuration puts a limit to its high frequency performance as a filter. This lead inductance can be put to some use if the capacitor is given a three terminal construction (Figure 23.31).

The lead inductance now forms a T-filter with the capacitor, greatly improving its high frequency performance. Lead inductance can be enhanced by incorporating a ferrite bead on each of the upper leads. The 3-terminal configuration can extend the effectiveness of a small ceramic capacitor from below 50MHz to upwards of 200MHz, which is particularly useful for interference in the v.h.f. band.

23.14.4.1   *Feedthroughs*

Any leaded capacitor is still limited in effectiveness by the inductance of the connection to the ground point. For the ultimate performance, and especially where penetration of a screened enclosure must be protected at u.h.f. and above (this is more often the case for military equipment) then a feedthrough construction is essential.

Here, the ground connection is made by the outer body of the capacitor being screwed or soldered directly to the metal screening or bulkhead (Figure 23.32). There is effectively no inductance associated with this terminal and the capacitor performance is maintained well into the GHz region. The inductance of the through

lead can be increased, thereby creating a π-section filter, by separating the ceramic metallization into two parts and incorporating a ferrite bead within the construction.

Feedthrough capacitors are available in a wide range of voltage and capacitance ratings but their cost increases with size. Cheap solder-in types between 100pF and 1000pF may be had for a few tens of pence, but larger screw mounting components will cost £1–£2. If good performance is required down to the low-MHz region then the filters will be more expensive. A cheaper solution is to parallel a small feedthrough component with a larger, cheaper conventional unit which suppresses the lower frequencies at which physical construction is less critical.

23.14.4.2   *Circuit considerations*

When using any form of capacitive filtering, one has to be sure that the circuit can handle the extra capacitance to ground. This factor can be particularly troublesome when one needs to filter an isolated circuit at radio frequencies. The r.f. filter capacitance provides a ready made a.c. path to ground for the signal circuit and will seriously degrade the a.c. isolation, to such an extent that an r.f. filter may actually increase susceptibility to lower frequency common mode interference. This is a function of the capacitance imbalance between the isolated signal and return lines (Figure 23.33), and it may restrict the allowable r.f. filter capacitance to a few tens of pF.

Another problem may arise if several signal lines are being filtered together and a common earth point is being used, as is the case for example with the filtered-D range of connectors. Provided that the earth connection is low impedance there is no problem, but any series impedance in the earth path not only degrades the filtering but will also couple signals from one line into another (Figure 23.34), leading to designed in crosstalk. For this reason filtered connectors should be used with care, and they must always be well grounded to the case, as long as the case is the signal ground.

23.15   Cables and connectors

The EMC of any given product is always affected by the configuration of the cables that are connected to it.

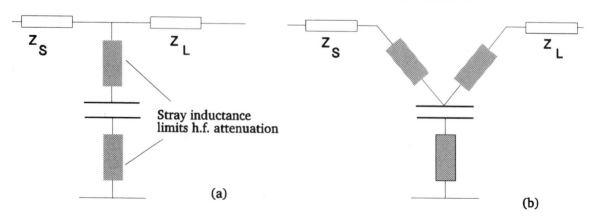

Figure 23.31   Two and three terminal capacitors: (a) two terminal; (b) three terminal

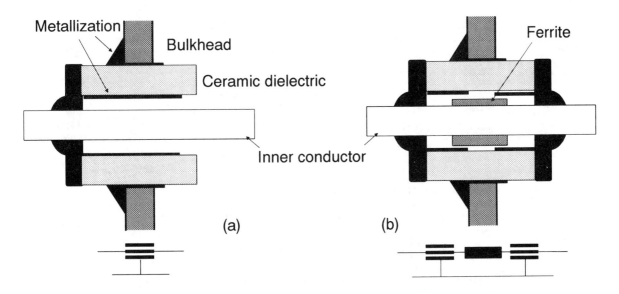

Figure 23.32   The feedthrough capacitor: (a) simple capacitor; (b) π-section filter

In the presence of an electromagnetic field any cable acts as an antenna and energy from the field is coupled onto it. The current induced on the cable depends on its physical orientation with respect to the field and any nearby conductive objects, and on its length. In a reciprocal manner, the field radiated by a cable carrying an r.f. current also depends on these parameters. Cable length is sometimes under the designer's control, but orientation is not, except occasionally in system design. Therefore, one needs to take steps to prevent interfering cable currents from affecting circuit operation, or to prevent circuit operation from generating interfering cable currents.

23.15.1   Cable shield termination

One approach is to filter the signal lines at the point at which they enter or leave the cable. Where this is inadequate or impossible, the other approach is to surround the signal conductors with a conductive shield which is grounded to the equipment screen. The function of this shield is to provide a return path for induced currents which does not couple onto the signal conductors, or conversely to confine radiating currents that are present on the signal conductors and prevent them from coupling with external fields.

Figure 23.35 shows the ideal connection of a shield to screen in which there is no discontinuity between the two. This can be most nearly achieved when the cable is fixed to the equipment and led through a conductive gland so that the cable screen makes contact all the way round its circumference, through 360°. As soon as a connector is used, some compromise has to be made.

Military style connectors are designed as above so that the cable screen makes 360° contact, but they attract military style prices and assembly costs. R.F. coaxial connectors, such as the common BNC type, also make 360° contact, but they carry only one signal line at a time. Many multi-way connectors do not have proper provision for terminating the shield, and this is where performance is degraded. Only too often, the shield is brought down to a 'pig tail' or drain wire and terminated to one of the connector pins (the EIA/RS-

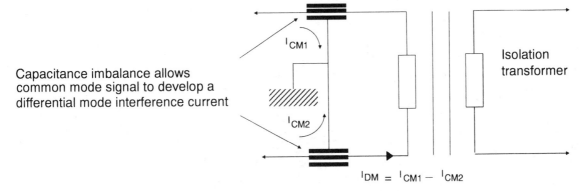

Figure 23.33   Unbalance between feedthrough capacitors

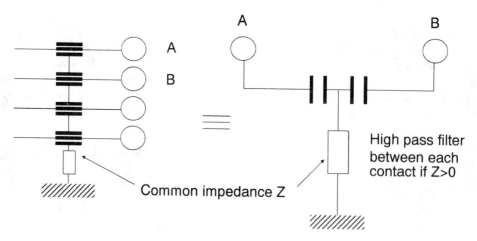

Figure 23.34 Common impedance coupling through filter capacitors

232D interface standard even has a pin allocated to this function, pin 1) or, worse still, it is not terminated at all (Figure 23.36).

The effect of no shield connection at all is to nullify the shielding effectiveness at high frequency. This is perhaps to be expected, but what is less intuitively obvious is that the pigtail connection is almost as bad (Paul, 1980). The difference in effectiveness between a pigtail connection and a full 360° connection is small below 3MHz, but can approach 40dB at higher frequencies. It is caused by the pigtail inductance appearing in series with the screen, and can show variations greater than 20dB over small changes in frequency.

23.15.2 Screened backshells

The best termination for a multi-way connector is to use a screened conductive backshell for the connector and to clamp the cable shield firmly to it. The backshell must make contact directly with the conductive shell of the connector itself, and this in turn must make good 360° contact with the shell on its mating connector, which must be bolted firmly and conductively to the equipment case. Any departure from this practice, in terms of not bolting directly to the case, not having mating conductive shells on the connectors, and not using a screened backshell, will compromise the high frequency shielding of the system.

Inexpensive subminiature D-type multi-way connectors are now available whose construction adheres to these principles, and if they are used correctly they can give good screening. It is quite possible to misuse them either in design or assembly and throw away all their advantages. Most other types of multi-way connector, in particular the popular insulation displacement two part units, have no potential for making shielded connections and should only be used for inter-board connections inside screened equipment, although certain manufacturers are now offering a type of screened backshell for shielded ribbon cable.

23.16 References

EEC (1989) Council Directive of 3rd May 1989 on the approximation of the laws of the Member States relating to Electromagnetic Compatibility (89/336/EEC), *Official Journal of the European Communities*, No L 139, 23rd May.

Goedbloed, J.J. (1987) Transients in Low-Voltage Supply Networks, *IEEE Transactions on Electromagnetic Compatibility*, **EMC-29**, (2), May, pp. 104-115.

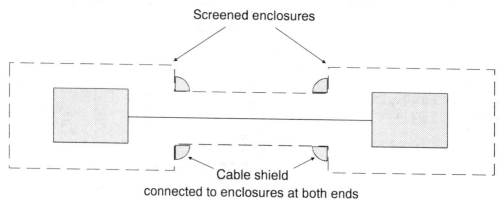

Screened enclosures

Cable shield
connected to enclosures at both ends

Figure 23.35 R.F. cable shield connections

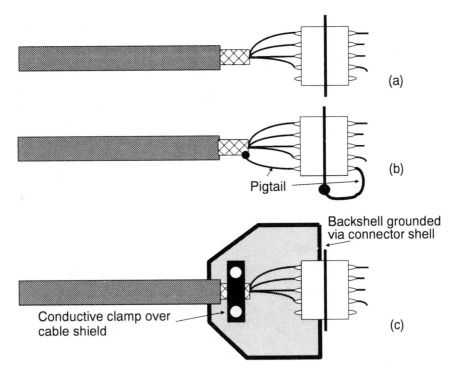

Figure 23.36 Cable screen terminations: (a) no connection (bad); (b) pigtail connection (poor); (c) screened backshell (good)

Goedbloed, J.J. and Pasmooij, W.A. (1990) Characterization of Transient and CW Disturbances induced in Telephone Subscriber Lines *IEE 7th International Conference on EMC*, York 28- 31st Aug, pp. 211-218.

Ott, H.W. (1979) Ground — A Path for Current Flow, *International Symposium on EMC*, IEEE, San Diego, October 9-11.

Ott, H.W. (1985) Controlling EMI by Proper Printed Wiring Board Layout *6th Symposium on EMC, Zurich, March 5-7.*

Paul, C.R. (1980) Effect of Pigtails on Crosstalk to Braided-Shield Cables, *IEEE Transactions on Electromagnetic Compatibility*, **EMC- 22**, (3), August.

24 Telecommunication power systems

Clive R Nightingale
Dip.EE CEng FIEE
Formerly Chief Power and
Building Services Engineer (BT)

Contents

24.1 Introduction

Power systems are a crucial element of any communications network, be the latter large or small, and they are one of the few elements capable of causing a total failure or malfunction of even the most sophisticated network. Hence the definition of the supplies, and their required level of reliability, has to be decided at an early stage of design. Neglect of this seemingly self evident fact, all too often results in a poor standard of service of the switching equipment etc., which will be difficult if not impossible to retrospectively put right in a cost effective manner.

In general there are no wholly defined international standards for complete power systems for any given communications service. These tend to be set by individual companies, or national administrations, although they inevitably follow a trend. This section therefore, sets out the principles of those most commonly employed in major networks, and not the least, those which have been, and are, so successfully employed in major organisations such as BT in the U.K.

24.2 A.C. systems

24.2.1 Public mains supplies

Where a public a.c. mains supply exists, it is normal to use this as the primary source of energy for a communications system, although rarely in an unmodified form. Indeed, the vast majority of energy consumed by equipment is d.c. and largely at low voltages.

For big centres with large power demands of the order of hundreds of kilowatts, electricity supply authorities often prefer to use high-voltage feeders. In the U.K. such supplies are commonly 11,000 volts, three phase, 50Hz, three wire. Such supplies would normally be transformed to a nominal voltage of 415 volts at a sub-station, which may be co-sited with the communications building, and be owned either by the supply authority, or the customer. Dependent on capacity these may be of a dry winding Class C air-cooled type for units of say 600kVA, or oil-cooled versions for capacities in the megawatt range. Because of safety considerations, such plant has to be installed in purpose built accommodation. In the case of oil filled plant, be they transformers or protective circuit breakers, oil catch-pits and comprehensive carbon dioxide automatic fire extinguishing systems have to be provided. Additionally, rigorous safety precautions and defined permit to work practices are essential operational prerequisites.

Medium voltage systems at 415 volts, 3-phase, 4-wire, 50Hz, or in the case of very small installations, 240 volts single phase, are widely employed for more modest sizes of communications unit. The incoming supply, with its metering and protective gear, (usually HRC fuses), may well be installed in a designated power room, which could also contain other power plant such as a standby engine generator system. The tolerance of the supply authority system to harmonics generated by customers' apparatus in the U.K. is becoming more stringent, and Recommendation G5/3 of the Electricity Council requires the total harmonic distortion to be limited to 5%, and individual harmonics limited dependent on the type of plant and its size. This means that in particular, larger thyristor controlled rectifiers must be carefully designed to take due account of any constraints imposed by particular supply authorities.

Where equipment is connected to such a supply without intervening power conversion plant, it is possible that electro-mechanical or electronic voltage regulators may be required if voltage variations are unacceptable. Typically, in the U.K., plant would have to be able to cope with voltage supply limits of +6% to –6%, and, of course, transients of short duration.

24.2.2 Local power supplies

In some locations site generation may be appropriate, based either on economic considerations, or in the case of remote installations, out of sheer necessity.

24.2.2.1 Site generation

In the U.K., a major telephone exchange at Cardiff was designed to work on a total energy scheme, using natural gas or diesel dual fuel prime mover engines driving medium voltage generators. This plant was conceived on the basis of a readily available, cheap, fuel source: natural gas, and a high electrical base load. The latter gave opportunities for the utilisation of waste heat from the engines to power absorption chiller plant used for air conditioning systems, and provide hot water for the space heating radiators in office accommodation. To give some idea of the scale of such an installation it comprised five 1300kW engine-generators, and associated gear. The plant has been highly successful, giving an acceptable level of reliability. However, the prime factors effecting such an installation; those of a higher initial capital cost; the need for a dedicated and highly skilled maintenance team; the necessity for an accurate forecast of load build up; and of key importance, the need of stable fuel costs, and their guaranteed availability; all need to be carefully evaluated (White, 1979; Johnson, 1980; Nightingale, 1983).

There is also the case of a BT installation at Goonhilly Downs. The installed engine-generator plant there has been operated on a site generation basis for long periods to overcome incoming a.c. supply instability and transients, arising from lightning ionisation and switching conditions on long and exposed overhead power lines (Nightingale, 1986; Woolley, 1986; Archer, 1979; Kageyama, 1982).

Whilst the foregoing cases quoted are elaborate examples, simpler multiple engine generator plant of just a few kilowatts are entirely feasible, and available. However, there are a limited number of examples in service in the U.K. because such excellent standards of power supply reliability, and availability, are at present generally available.

24.2.2.2 Wind, thermal, solar

Whilst not generally in service in much of Europe, or other densely populated parts of the developed world, the potential of plant such as wind and thermal generators, and solar cell plant, has received a lot of attention. Many examples are now in use in countries with the need to power remotely located communications buildings and equipment, or where extreme climatic conditions cause problems in securing the supply of energy (Lee, 1986). Such installations tend to be intermediate repeater stations in chains of land-line or radio links, and almost by definition, they are in environments of near desert (Lee, 1986), subject to ice and snow (Gahrn, 1987; Kolousek, 1986), in mountainous terrain, or subject to tropical and damp (high humidity) conditions (Olden, 1983) and have power demands of just a few kilowatts, or even watts.

Diesel-generator sets still have a part to play, either as the prime power source, or in combination with other systems, for example, a wind generator (Grant, 1983; Akerlund, 1983). But clearly, if access is a major problem, the difficulties of getting fuel (diesel oil or some form of bottled gas) to site, are significant. There are, therefore, advantages in the employment of wind and solar energy, but such systems have the disadvantage of being weather and time dependent. Hence they must always be associated with another power source to bridge the gap arising from windless or sunless conditions, a battery of secondary cells for instance. For situations where the energy demand is very small, tens to a few hundred watts, the thermoelectric generator (Grant, 1986) or Closed Cycle Vapour Generators (CCVT) (Gropper, 1985) may be considered, but gas or liquid fuels are, of course, still necessary.

24.2.3 Standby supplies

The level of standby plant provision is obviously related to the probability and duration of mains failures, but any studies inevitably give results which are very subjective, and like any generalisation cannot be specifically applied to any given location or point in time. Nevertheless, such assessments do give a yard stick to assess the type and nature of AC Standby plant necessary to meet given Mean Time Between Failure (MTBF) targets. If an assumption is made that the majority of a given communications system equipment is backed up by, say, a one hour battery, and the supply MTBF is of those orders shown in Table 24.1, then a.c. system MTBF rates of at least 75 years can be achieved, even in the worst case considered (Nightingale, 1985).

Since it is inevitable that failures of the supply authority a.c. mains supply will occur from time to time, and since long term standby using batteries would be prohibitively expensive in terms of capital cost and utilisation of accommodation, some form of prime mover standby generating plant provision becomes prudent in all but the smallest installations (Nightingale, 1971).

24.2.4 Prime movers

24.2.4.1 *Diesel engines*

Diesel engine driven generators (alternators) are the normal source of standby a.c. power (Jones, 1989). They tend to be used because they are capable of being made such that they are reliable in starting and operation, capable of being started automatically; they use readily available fuel which presents few problems in storage and handling; and there are a wide range of types and ratings available world-wide. Set speeds tend to be kept down to a maximum of 1500 revolutions per minute (rev/min); with larger sets operating at 1000 or even 750 rev/min. Such speeds, of course, give a synchronous alternator output at 50Hz. At these speeds the sets can be kept reliably in operation for long periods, weeks on end, and acoustic noise breakout, (which can be a major environmental nuisance to neighbours), can be contained within reasonable bounds at tolerable cost.

24.2.4.2 *Gas turbines*

Gas turbines are occasionally used, and offer substantial advantages over a diesel engine of comparable horse power in terms of both physical size and weight. However, the limited availability of suitable units in an appropriate range of outputs has rather limited their use hitherto, and in any event they tend to burn far more fuel than the diesel, perhaps as much as double the consumption of the latter. These factors then, rather restrict their use to special applications such as mobile plant.

24.2.4.3 *Petrol engines*

Petrol engines are not normally used for fixed installations because of their limitations in the automatic starting mode. They are of relatively low ratings not readily adapted to fixed industrial applications, and the fuel itself presents significant hazards in handling and large scale storage. However the very small sets are sometimes used where a manually transportable unit is needed.

To ensure the ability of any engine to operate over long periods of time, it is necessary to ensure that adequate fuel supplies are maintained. The usual arrangement is for a 'day' service tank to be located fairly close to the engine set; this being automatically replenished by pumping from bulk storage tanks, which can be buried or surface mounted outside the main building (Nightingale, 1986).

24.2.5 Alternators

Alternators used to supply communications equipment loads tend to be specified as having a good quality on-load wave form; a maximum total harmonic distortion of 5% is not unusual. Associated regulators capable of maintaining close limits of voltage, and control to within plus or minus 1% or 1½% of the nominal voltage are readily obtainable under steady state load conditions. Built in overload protection and discrimination can be obtained, and to limit transient output variations, and maintain the best possible compatibility with the normal mains supply, low impedance machines are desirable.

24.2.6 Control systems

Control systems (Mealing, 1984) for modern installations can give standby engine generator plant which is fully automatic in operation. Built in monitors are typically set to detect that the mains has fallen below say 10%, (or gone above 6%), and signal the engine plant to start. Once the plant has reached stable and optimum operating conditions, the load would be switched to the generator output. The integrity of the plant's fuel, lubricating oil, water and air cooling circuits would be continuously monitored, and pre-set alarms given in the event of any malfunctions. Plant can be automatically restored to the normal quiescent condition once the mains have returned to within acceptable limits for a predetermined time, or of course, the system can be restored manually as determined by the operator. Suitable hand operated by-pass switch-gear should be provided to allow the plant to be totally isolated for maintenance purposes, (without putting a break in the supply), or to allow by-passing under emergency conditions. A typical basic circuit configuration is shown in Figure 24.1.

24.2.7 Standby engine generator plant

The fundamental features of a typical plant comprise the main engine generator set, which more often than not in modern installations, (up to say 200kW), will be in the form of an unit package (Henderson, 1988). This set can be mounted on a rigid steel base frame which can be secured direct to the power room floor. In turn, this main frame can support a unit construction engine generator, fitted direct with anti-vibration mountings which prevent the transmission of vibration to the building structure. Alternatively, the set can be mounted on a sub-frame which supports the individual electrically started engine and generator, both the latter being interconnected by a flexible coupling. Vibration isolation is then

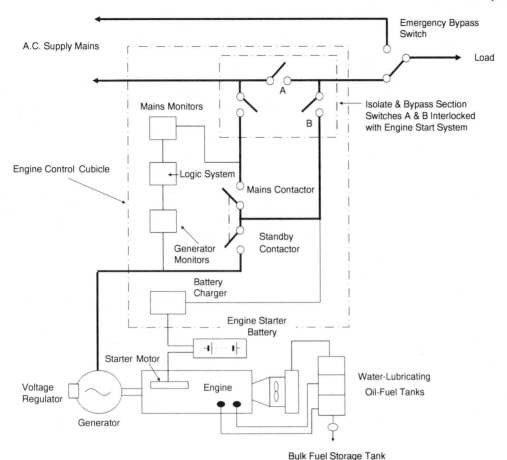

Figure 24.1 Basic engine-generator standby plant

achieved by the insertion of the mountings between the main and sub-frames.

The main set auxiliaries, day fuel service tank, fuel transfer pump, lubricating oil and water make-up tanks, (if required to achieve extended unattended engine running), together with, perhaps, an exhaust silencer, can then be mounted on the main frame work.

Associated with the set will be the control system, normally cubiclised, which can contain the control logic and monitors, supervisory lamp displays, and the isolating and emergency by-pass switch-gear. Additionally, the main power switching circuits and interlocked mains and standby supply contractors may be housed in the same cubicle, as can be the starter battery charging system.

To ensure adequate cooling air is available, automatically operated louvres are often fitted in wall openings to allow fresh air to be inducted to the engine room.

Similar principles apply to installations only requiring a few kilowatts of power, but whilst water cooled engines tend to predominate for most standby sets, air cooled machines are available, particularly in the lower horse power ratings. The latter find a ready application for small installations, such as rural exchanges, with loads up to about 10kVA (Nightingale, 1983; Mealing, 1982).

At the other end of the scale, come the very large centres, often housing multiple switching systems. These centres command significant attention to the provision of a.c. power plant, with loads often broken down into discrete blocks such that any single failure will

not lead to the complete isolation of the communications complex (Nightingale, 1971).

Figure 24.2 shows in schematic form a typical a.c. plant installation. With loads in the megawatt range, high voltage supplies have been assumed, and the essential loads have been divided into two modules, each fed by a discrete transformer. Each essential load is backed up by an engine-generator at the medium voltage stage. A separate transformer has been used to feed non-essential services. It will be noted that a spare transformer has been provided capable of backing up either the essential or non-essential, loads in the event of a failure; or when a working unit is withdrawn from service for maintenance purposes. Switching and isolating facilities are provided to ensure the safety of personnel and plant during maintenance operations. Additionally, a switching facility is shown allowing the ready interconnection of a mobile plant if, and when, required.

24.2.8 Short break systems

Sometimes it is possible to arrange with a supply authority for the provision of duplicate power feeders into a building, either at HV or MV, and to use them on a main and standby basis. Providing such supplies come from separate sub-stations, this will generally give an enhanced degree of power system security, but inevitably at some additional cost. It is possible to provide automatic switch-gear

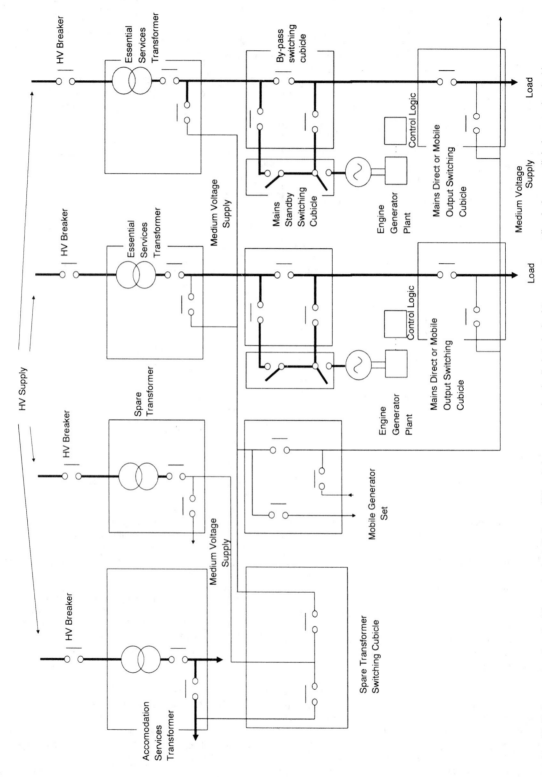

Figure 24.2 Multiple a.c. standby plant for major installations. (All switches are mechanically interlocked to prevent supplies being paralleled or overloaded.)

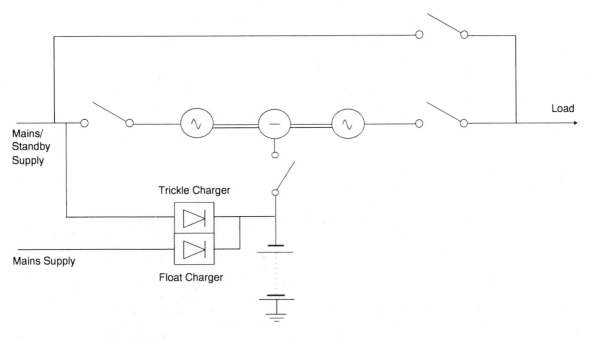

Figure 24.3 Three machine continuity set

between these supplies, (normally at MV), and even with interlocked electro-mechanical contactors, automatic change-over times
of the order of 250 milli-seconds can be achieved.

24.2.9 Interconnected a.c. systems

The reliability merits of feeding discrete load blocks from multiple
supply distribution sections, via appropriate engine generator plant,
is irrefutable, but in practical terms this is often very difficult to
achieve at acceptable cost. Also such systems can be relatively
inflexible once designed, and more difficult to adapt to changing
switching equipment designs. This is even more evident when the
introduction of new equipment technology is particularly volatile.
In these circumstances there are attractions to providing multiple
standby plant which is capable of being operated in parallel, the
second and subsequent plants being brought into service on demand
(Nightingale, 1985). This of course makes additional demands on
the provision of sophisticated monitoring and synchronising equipment, but state of art technology is making such plant design more
economic and reliable.

The increased use of directly operated a.c. powered switching or
computer equipment has created a situation in which even the on
load testing of standby plant, (which introduces change-over breaks
of just a few milli-seconds in switching from the mains to the engine
generator supply, and vice versa), is operationally unacceptable. In
these circumstances the ability to synchronise and work in parallel
with the mains without causing a transient disturbance is attractive.
However, it must be borne in mind that this form of operation, even
for short periods, is often unacceptable to some supply authorities
whose concurrence to such operations is essential, especially at MV.
Even in the case of HV generators, the ability to operate in parallel
with the supply feeder has to be conducted with plant which is fully
equipped with agreed synchronisation and protection devices.
Nevertheless, such systems can, in appropriate cases, be viable
(Nightingale, 1986).

24.2.10 No-break or uninterruptible power supplies

Where equipment design is such that any interruption of the power
supply, however short, causes malfunctions in the switching or
computer system, (and increasingly it is becoming difficult to differentiate between such systems), then additional power plant has
to be provided to guard against these breaks. Such plant is by
definition called a 'no break' power system, although popular jargon
is that of 'uninterruptible power systems', or more shortly UPS's.

24.2.10.1 Three machine continuity set

The three machine continuity set principle (Spurgin, 1970) consists
of an induction motor operating from the mains a.c. supply, driving
a d.c. motor, (which is in effect idling and acting to all intents and
purposes as a flywheel), coupled in turn to an alternator whose
output supplies the equipment load. On mains failure the d.c. machine is fully energised from a motor battery, and maintains the
drive to the set. The problems with this arrangement are that is an
economical induction motor is used as the primary drive, the slip
factor means that it runs a little below synchronous speed, and hence
the alternator output frequency is correspondingly lower than the
nominal value. Figure 24.3 shows the basic principles of the system.

24.2.10.2 Two machine continuity set

A two machine set (Spurgin, 1970) comprising a d.c. motor-alterna-
tor set gets away from the sub-synchronous speed feature, drawing
its energy from a rectifier floating an appropriate secondary battery.
The basic plant configuration is shown in Figure 24.4. There are
many versions of this type of plant, including some which have been
completely 'cubiclised' to enable factory assembled 'packages' to

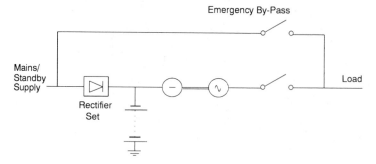

Figure 24.4   Two machine continuity set

be produced, with the resulting reduced on site installation time, as well as reducing acoustic noise and adding to their aesthetic appearance in equipment rooms (Woolley, 1986).

24.2.10.3   *Static inverters*

Static inverters (Henderson, 1986) are very prominent in installations requiring no-break power supplies, and vary in rating from a few VA to hundreds of kilowatts. The basic plant schematic is relatively straightforward, and is shown in Figure 24.5.

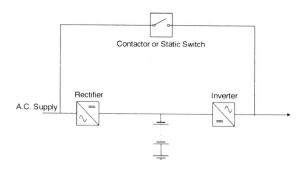

Figure 24.5   On line inverter system

For telecommunications purposes, no-break power loads tend to be in the kilowatts range, and in general terms there is little to choose between the two technologies of static and rotating plant, although there is inevitably much debate between the competing manufacturers. However, the transient response of the former may well have the edge. To counter balance this however, the rotary systems seem to have a rather better ability to cope with overload, as well as giving complete electrical separation stemming from the mechanical coupling of a motor generator set. It has also been argued that the static plant is more complex in its technology and hence is not so readily maintainable, but this is an issue rather conditioned by the viewpoint of the user, and the ready availability of suitably trained staff and spares.

There is an increasing use of switched mode power supplies for a.c./d.c. conversion, and this gives rise to the drawing of current from the a.c. supply for short periods of time, centred about the peak of the voltage waveform. The peak may be of the order of three to five times the r.m.s. current and can present problems where the equipment is fed from a UPS, (or indeed a standby generator set),

as such plant must have a limit in the current they can supply. Hence in specifying design criteria for a UPS it is essential that non-linear loads are defined as being present, and that the ability of a UPS is therefore designed to cope with such a load.

Some inverter UPS systems are not designed to work on load in the normal mode of operation. Such systems are sometimes termed as being on 'hot' standby, and are usually found in lower power ratings of plant. This arrangement, shown in Figure 24.6, means that the load is normally fed from, say, the mains, via a load conditioner such as a CVT. The inverter is only brought into service if a mains failure is detected. Such a system is usually cheaper in terms of capital cost, and can have a higher operating efficiency. However the load in these conditions does not necessarily have the advantage of any form of voltage and frequency control, and requires the off load inverter to suddenly switch from no to full load on mains failure. Also, there is the possibility of a short break as the inverter is switched into use.

Some plant designs also use various combinations of rotating

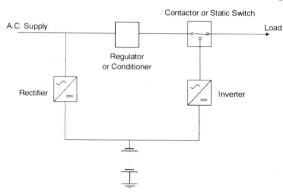

Figure 24.6   Standby or 'hot' standby inverter system

machines on a single shaft, plus a flywheel to provide carry over energy. A diesel engine is provided as part of the set and this is brought into operation on mains failure via forms of magnetic clutch (Dolezal, 1987) or induction coupling (Beems, 1981) to continue the drive to the generators.

24.3   D.C. systems

In the final analysis most communications equipment use d.c. power at a multiplicity of voltages, the value being dependent on the type of component. In the past (Pine, 1971) this has resulted in all manner of different power plants supplying loads, typical of which were a nominal -28 volts for transmission equipment, or ±80 volts for telegraphs. However, exchange switching equipment has traditionally been operated from a nominal -50 volts, and this continues to be the case world-wide.

For main network or private business systems, the source of back-up reserve has almost invariably been the ubiquitous lead acid secondary battery. Until comparatively recently, most users relied on a central battery type of plant to supply the equipment load, and for the most part modern systems derived the charging power from various configurations of rectifier (Wolpert, 1987) although the very earliest designs did, of course, use motor generator charging plant.

Electro-mechanical switching systems such as the Strowger, and the later Cross-bar systems, have power load patterns which to a greater or lesser extent, are traffic dependent. Electronic equipment however, tends to have a high level of standing load, and place different demands on power plant.

24.3.1 Single reserve systems

In simple terms such a plant comprises a rectifier to convert a.c. mains to low voltage d.c., and a battery which gives a reserve of energy, and the period of reserve and the power loading determine the capacity of the battery needed. Figure 24.7 shows the elemental circuit. Such a system is normally only viable for loads which are very light, such as tiny rural units, unless very large batteries capable of giving say 24 hours reserve can be accommodated, and the relatively high costs are acceptable.

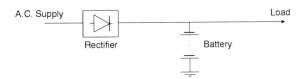

Figure 24.7 Single reserve system

24.3.2 Dual reserve systems

This basic system, Figure 24.8, consists of a similar plant to that of the single reserve, but to which has been added an engine generating set which acts as the long term source of reserve. This means that the d.c. plant battery can have a fairly short reserve capacity to bridge the gap between the incidence of a mains failure and the engine being started. Typically in the BT practice this reserve period is one hour, but the value chosen is of course a matter for an operator to choose dependent on the economics of the particular case.

24.3.3 D.C. power plant design

The variations in plant design are legion, but the fundamentals of some of the more common designs may be outlined.

24.3.3.1 *Transmission equipment plant*

Where the equipment can accept a fairly wide spread of voltages, it is possible to use the basic circuit set out in Figure 24.9. A typical plant used in association with transmission equipment at a nominal

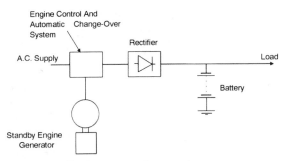

Figure 24.8 Dual reserve system

28 volts can comprise one or more rectifiers floating a single battery (Spurgin, 1970). Such a plant will typically float twelve lead acid Plante' type secondary cells at a constant potential of just under 2.3 volts per cell. Regulation of plus or minus 2% is common.

Such a plant will give a voltage variation of 28.2 volts under float conditions, down to 22.8 volts when the battery is discharged. At the normal float voltage of just under 2.3 volts per cell, gassing of the battery is limited, whilst maintaining the battery in a healthy charged condition. To give a high degree of plant security and hence reliability, it is usual to have two rectifiers capable of coping with the full load condition. A third rectifier is provided, which is connected to the mains supply only to reduce load to the standby engine set, and acts as a reserve should one of the other rectifiers fail, or be out of service for maintenance purposes. In the full availability situation this rectifier gives an enhanced recharge capability if the battery has been discharged. Most rectifiers of this type achieve regulation by static control methods comprising thyristors or transductors as the main elements. Such plant can be used to supply loads from a few amperes to hundreds of amperes, and achieve a very high level of service reliability.

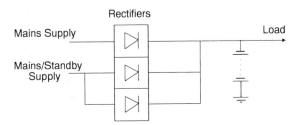

Figure 24.9 Basic d.c. plant

24.3.3.2 *Small exchange plant*

A typical example of an 'end cell switched' plant can be used to illustrate a method of switching in cells to maintain supplies to equipment within defined limits (Spurgin, 1970). The arrangement is shown in Figure 24.10. By floating the 22 cells at the optimum level of 2.27 volts per cell, the exchange load is supplied at a nominal −50.6 volts. The two 'end cells' (which are not connected to the load in the normal operating condition) are floated by a separate rectifier to give a voltage of −4.6 volts. The rectifiers are rated to cope with the full load of the exchange equipment, and recharge the battery as necessary.

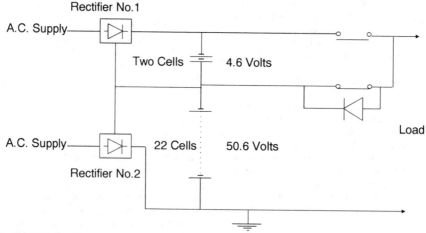

Figure 24.10 Small exchange plant

If the plant voltage should fall for any reason, for instance the a.c. mains fails, then at about –46.5 volts the full 24 cell battery is switched across the exchange load by the contactors. The plant voltage is therefore boosted to –48 volts. It should be noted that the contactors are interlocked to prevent their simultaneous operation which would short circuit the end cells. When the mains restores, the 24 cell battery recharges to –52 volts, and the contactor sequence is then reversed, and the two sections of cells continue to recharge to their full capacity, with the load again being fed at –50.6 volts. This sort of plant has a limited rating, about 100 amperes maximum.

More modern installations may well employ systems which do not need end cell switching techniques, and which instead use a single battery and a voltage regulator device (Pine, 1979).

For the future, the use of switched mode power systems in association with sealed lead acid cell batteries are likely to be used for the small exchange, with a small engine-generator set provided for long term standby power.

Where a reserve of more than a few hours is required for small exchanges, and it is provided by a standby engine generating plant, the accommodation needed, and the environmental problems due to noise for instance, tend to become substantial. This problem is becoming ever more prevalent as electronic equipment decreases in

volume per unit of switching capacity, leaving a disproportionately large power plant (O'Connor, 1990). The solution being developed for the future, is for the application of an a.c. to d.c. converter using switched mode techniques as later described in Section 24.3.3.6, and an associated operational battery. Instead of an engine-generator back up for any long duration a.c. supply failures however, an innovative design of fuel cell is proposed. With this system, if the associated battery approaches its designed point of discharge, a mechanically rechargeable aluminium-air fuel cell battery (O'Callaghan, 1989) is brought into use, and via suitable d.c. to d.c. converters, provides the primary source of energy.

24.3.3.3 Main exchange plant

For larger exchanges a double battery float system (Spurgin, 1970; Pine, 1971) can be used comprising two battery strings of 25 cells. The arrangement is shown in Figure 24.11. With this system, the battery is maintained at –51.5 volts, thus floating each cell at 2.06 volts per cell. The designed end of discharged voltage is 1.83 volts per cell, that is –46 volts across the exchange load. Cells floated at this voltage will lose of the order of 1% of their capacity each day,

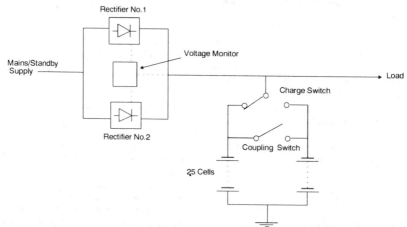

Figure 24.11 Main exchange plant. (Batteries are normally coupled. They are uncoupled during charging, one supplying the load whilst the other is being charged.)

and hence it is usual to uncouple and recharge each string of cells in turn every couple of weeks. This is done under manual control, and booster rectifier capacity has to be provided for the recharging process.

This basic form of design can be used to produce plants of many thousands of amperes capacity, by the simple expedient of adding additional rectifier units, but it suffers from the disadvantage of having a common control and distribution system. The latter factor can be a major problem because in practical terms it has to be determined at the outset of any particular plant installation, and accurate long term forecasting is notoriously difficult.

24.3.3.4   Booster converter plant

A Booster converter system (Wolpert, 1978) may be employed as an alternative to the arrangement previously described, and has significant advantages. This system may use a fixed number of cells, say 23, to achieve the nominal −50 volt system. See Figure 24.12. If, in periods of a.c. power failure, the battery discharges to an unacceptable value, then an a.c. to d.c. converter connected to the battery boosts the voltage output, and hence keeps the distribution voltage constant. The battery can also be automatically recharged.

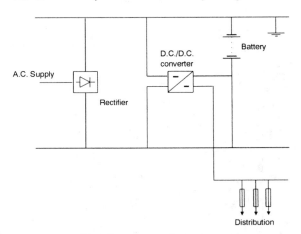

Figure 24.12   Booster converter plant

24.3.3.5   Modular plant

The diversity and complexity of larger communications systems, which require various voltages to power them, is such that the concept of centralised power plant with a tree and branch busbar distribution scheme rapidly becomes unwieldy electrically, and excessively difficult to safely extend without recourse to removing the plant, and the equipment it supplies, from service. Additionally the demands on accommodation to house the plant, and associated maintenance costs become onerous. As a result, in the U.K. during the 1970s (Pine, 1971; Nightingale, 1971) plant and switching equipment design philosophies evolved to cope with these problems. Firstly there was a design definition that to the maximum possible extent, all connected equipment should be capable of operating from a nominal −50 volt d.c. supply.

The actual power plant design was modular in approach and it is still widely used (Henderson, 1979). In essence the design brief requires power plant to be capable of safe extension so that it can

grow as the provision of the communications equipment load grows. Further, this sort of system does not require the use of common control systems, the failure of which could inhibit the safe functioning of the whole plant. The basic arrangement is set out in Figure 24.13. Once again a form of end cell switching is employed for the d.c. plant (Humphreys, 1971) with associated enclosed lead acid Plante' cells being maintained at their optimum constant potential float voltage of 2.27 volts.

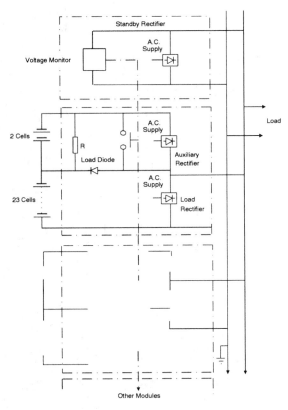

Figure 24.13   Modular plant

This fundamental plant arrangement has the merit of being relatively straightforward, and can be arranged to cater for virtually any configuration of communications equipment design. The system can be adapted to cater for all but the smallest installations, and single or multiple engine standby plant can be associated dependent on the overall degree of system reliability being sought.

24.3.3.6   Distributed plant

During the 1980s the development of new electronic switching equipment and related computer based systems, and the rapidly emerging additional services associated with communications systems, coupled with the development of a new generation of power switching devices and sealed secondary battery systems, has led to a totally new approach to d.c. power equipment (New, 1982; Wittey, 1983; Owen, 1985; Jacobs, 1984). In a nutshell, power plant has been modularised and miniaturised to the extent that both the power converter (Spooner, 1986) and its associated batteries can be closely

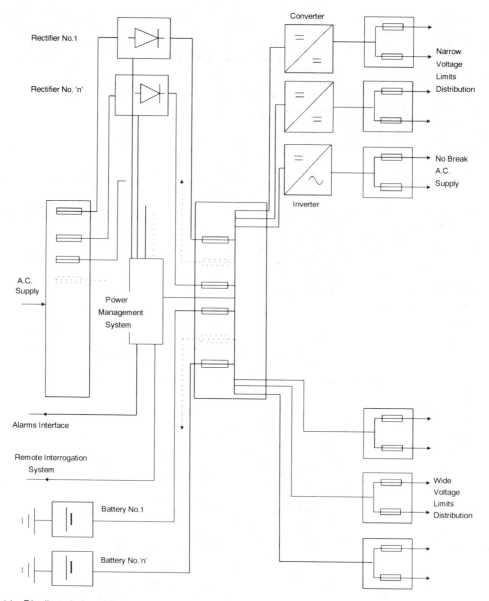

Figure 24.14 Distributed plant. All of this plant can be mounted on a power rack mounted en-suite with the equipment rack

associated with the equipment it serves. It has become rack mounted, purpose built accommodation is no longer needed; and this design arrangement reduces to a minimum the need for distribution cables or busbars.

This concept carries with it the merits of flexibility in the way that it is associated with the equipment it serves. Demands on purpose built accommodation are reduced, and there is an enhanced opportunity for factory assembly and testing of the power unit with the switching equipment concerned, together with reduced on site installation time (Yotsumoto, 1988; Luigi, 1989). Figure 24.14 shows the basic configuration of the power system, which has at its heart the switched mode power unit (Fry, 1982) and the valve regulated gas recombination design of secondary cell (Harrison, 1982) which is fully sealed under normal operational conditions.

24.4 Battery systems

Most communications d.c. power systems rely heavily on the lead acid secondary cell (Feder, 1987; Halliwell, 1979).

A high proportion use cells of the Plante' form of construction. Such cells have negative plates which have open grids which support a paste of active materials, and positive plates which are pure lead and have a ribbed form of construction to give a large surface area. A 'forming' procedure, which is achieved by the passage of a carefully controlled current in a special forming process results in the active material of the negative plate becoming pure lead, whilst the positive plates are converted to lead peroxide, and which has a characteristic brownish colour.

Early power plant tended to use various forms of automatic charge discharge systems, but these have largely disappeared in favour of the so called float trickle charge methods using the rectifier plant previously described. Given that batteries of this type are charged at about 2.27 volts per cell within the limits of plus or minus one percent, they will be maintained in a healthy condition with little need for boost or refresher charges. Maintenance tends to be at a minimum, and a life of 10 to 20 years is achievable. In the majority of capacities in regular use, the Plante' cells tend to be contained in glass boxes, which give the not inconsiderable advantage of allowing the condition of the cell plates to be inspected.

There are also pasted positive plate traction cells, and the tubular element or gauntlet cells. These have the merit of being rather smaller in overall size compared with the equivalent Plante', and are often of a more rugged construction, which in some cases can have considerable merit when used say for mobile units. However, they have some limitations which can give rise to a somewhat lower degree of reliability, or shorter life, in the applications previously described; and certainly organisations such as BT have used the Plante' cell as standard because they can be kept in good condition when maintained by the float trickle charge method, they have a long service life, and their condition can be determined by straightforward visual inspection.

Nickel-cadmium cells are also used, particularly where high capacities are not required, in applications such as for UPSs, or engine starting (Feder, 1987).

The more recent development of the valve regulated sealed lead acid battery (Harrison, 1986; Wittey, 1985) whilst not at present able to give the same high levels of capacity of the lead acid cells described earlier, now give the opportunity for the integration of the cells into the equipment racks. They also have the significant advantage of not requiring the use of purpose built accommodation, and for future U.K. telecommunications systems they are likely to become the dominant type of battery in service.

For some applications in the future, there is a prospect of a lithium polymer type of battery becoming available. It has been argued that this design may be regarded as the next logical step ahead from the so called valve sealed recombination lead acid battery. It shows promise of being far lighter and smaller than present cells, albeit that much development work will need to be carried out for it to meet its considerable potential.

Work generally in competing cells is a process of continuing development, and progress with the production of international standards is receiving increasing attention. Such standards will have the obvious advantages of uniformity of electrical performance and physical compatibility where they are adopted. IEC International Committee TC21, WG3, is for instance responsible for the international standards of lead acid batteries (Harrison, 1985).

24.5 Power supply distribution

The d.c. system distribution is not simply a function of providing conductors adequate to handle the current involved. For the most part the voltages involved are about 50 volts or less, and clearly the distance between the plant and its battery are significant in terms of the voltage drop, and the possibility of picking up spurious voltages as a result of induced or radiated interference.

The large centralised plants with ratings of hundreds or even thousands of amperes, are often interconnected with their associated batteries, and the load centres, by copper or aluminium busbar. Because of the lower conductivity of the latter material, a cost analysis to trade off the resulting increased physical size is desir-

able, and from a commissioning point of view, there is a need to take greater care with interbar joints.

As an alternative to busbar, hybrid arrangements using a combination of bar and cable distribution are feasible, or even all cable systems. This is especially the case with the more modern installations where power plant proper is distributed around a building, and hence the current values to be carried are well within the capability of cable conductors. The latter arrangements have, of course, the added merit of being generally simpler to install, and have a greater degree of flexibility in terms of extending existing plant and equipment schemes. Additionally, insulated cable conductors are in many ways inherently simpler to protect from accidental contact, and hence have a lower fault liability.

Electrical protection of the distribution systems chosen may be by means of fuses, or for very large systems, breakers; although interestingly it has been found by experience that fuses or circuit breakers of about 500 amperes do not often operate, even under severe fault conditions, the faults sometimes burning clear before the protective devices have time to operate (Wilson, 1979).

Power supply disturbances are of a more profound significance with modern electronic equipment than the old electro-mechanical systems. Faults impinging on the distribution, and clearing via the protective devices, (or 'burning off'), will cause voltage disturbances. Transients or 'spikes' so generated, whilst of very short duration, will often reach two or three times the nominal distribution voltage value, and are capable of causing actual damage or at the very least the malfunction of connected equipment. Hence it is of crucial importance that distribution schemes, and the selection of protective devices, are carefully considered in their basic design, e.g. anti-surge fuses are used where appropriate.

As an alternative to tree and branch types of distribution modern equipment schemes may use a radial-cable arrangement, with a single earthing system (Wilson, 1980). In such a system problems from contacts between different earthed elements tend not to arise because all parts of a given nominal earthed system are bonded together, (the mains earthing conductors excepted), into a single large system. By design these systems can enable the largest fault current to be drawn without an unacceptably high voltage disturbance. Fault currents can of course be limited by the use of fast acting fuses and the smallest practical conductor sizes.

The maximum noise on telecommunications power supplies used to be simply specified as 2mV weighted to 800Hz when related to a psophometric curve as defined by the CCITT 1960 (New Delhi) Standard (Howard, 1979). The weighting factors are set out in CCITT Recommendation P53. The more recent recommendations for 48 and 60 volts d.c. supplies for instance, are far more precisely defined to take account of narrow and wide band noise. These recommendations also cover electromagnetic radiations emitted into the immediate surroundings. Electromagnetic compatibility is a factor which must be taken into account in all equipment and distribution design, and IEC International Special Committee on Radio Interference (CISPR), and the Conference of European Posts and Telecommunications, (CEPT), as well as CCITT, are involved in the promulgation of recommendations concerning this topic (Wilson, 1984; Wilson, 1985; Scuka, 1987).

The requirements for Telecom's Centre Power Supply Interfaces have been set out in a CEPT Document T/TR02-02 which has as its objective the use of the same secondary supplies for all telecommunications equipment, the harmonisation of the latter, together with the power supply interfaces, maintenance, installation, safety and operation standards. There are also follow-up proposals by the European Telecommunications Standards Institute ETSI/TC (89) which are currently being considered.

24.6   Power for computer systems

Modern communications networks almost inevitably have associated computer systems which are likely to work both on and off line (Howard, 1990). All too often they are designed to be operated from a.c. supplies, sometimes even connected to raw supply authority mains. In consequence, such systems become vulnerable to transient interference due to disturbances incoming from the supply network, and of course, mains breaks both short and long term. For the most part, the interruptions created by such occurrences are so disruptive to operational work, that most operators may well find it prudent to provide a standby engine generator back-up to cater for breaks of more than a few minutes, (see Section 24.2.3), and probably a no-break power plant or UPS to cater for incoming transient interference and breaks (Nightingale, 1985; Henderson, 1986).

24.7   Customer systems

Business users will often have their own communications facility ranging from a few lines to quite major switching systems, sometimes in association with their own computer equipment. Such systems will merit the same consideration for reserve power plant as the main network providers, and the power plants available can be based on the same design criteria as previously outlined. In the case of modern systems of modest capacity it will be found that the power plant will be based on similar ideas to those for main exchange distributed power plant — see Section 24.3.3.6. However, the plant may also be made 'office compatible' by being mounted in line with the switching equipment in what at first sight appears to be a cupboard or filing cabinet (Banfield, 1984).

24.8   Power management systems

Power systems, comprising several plants in a single building, which may well be unattended for significant periods ranging from hours to weeks, or even months, require suitable alarm and surveillance systems to indicate to maintenance staff the status and availability of the individual plants or the collective systems. Limited information may be conveyed by audible or visual signals, and these can be physically extended as necessary, and in many cases this may be judged as being perfectly adequate.

However, the availability of the ubiquitous microprocessor now provides a capability for an operator, either locally or in a remote centre to obtain detailed information not only on current status, but plant history (Coppinger, 1984). Such systems can also be interactive, allowing a plants' status to be changed by remote commands (Nightingale, 1985; Mealing, 1984; Wittey, 1986). Additionally such systems can be linked with energy (say heating) and environmental (air conditioning perhaps) control systems, to give an overall picture of a given centres power and building services plant condition and performance (Allen, 1986). It is suggested that for the future these facilities will become an inherent feature of any system to ensure the most efficient use of technical and financial resources.

24.9   Maintenance and costs

Increasingly, prudent asset management will include data extracted from plant performance records which can be used to enhance financial management information covering the whole life costs of a given installation (Stephenson, 1985). For a large system, the annual cost of energy in all its forms may well amount to half the total expenditure for telecommunications and building services, whilst labour may account for a further 25% of the expenditure. To this will have to be added provision for factors such as plant replacement, perhaps some 10% to 15%, the price of training, stores and transport etc. making up the remainder.

Hence, key features of the selection of a particular plant design should include an evaluation of its quality, efficiency, and need for maintenance, besides aspects such as ease and speed of installation and commissioning, and the cost of the building structure in which it is to be housed.

The use of maintenance records to evaluate long term performance can make a significant contribution to the availability of management information, and the use of computerised records to produce appropriate data has much to commend it in achieving optimum operating efficiency. One such analysis of telecommunications power plant for instance, showed that major features of design which need to be considered are that common control features should be avoided, there is a paramount need to maintain high standards of electrical shrouding and insulation, plant alarm systems must fail safe, power distribution schemes must be capable of being safely extended, and that battery interconnections to its associated plant must be designed with the utmost care (Coppinger, 1987).

24.10   Mobile power plant

In some instances of difficult turn-round of plant replacement, or the catastrophic failure of an existing one, (especially in the case of A.C. engine-generating plant), mobile plant is of great value. Such plant (Nightingale, 1983) will desirably have similar performance and facilities to that of the permanently installed one, except of course that it has to be capable of withstanding the forces of transportation, and be suitably silenced to satisfy the constraints imposed by achieving acceptable environmental standards. Plant ratings from just a few watts to many kilowatts can be designed, and for the very largest, perhaps as much 0.5MW to 1MW, the valuable feature of the high power to weight ratio of the gas-turbine driven generator tends to come into its own.

24.11   Power plant accommodation

The accommodation used for power plant will often require features specific to the plant in question. It needs to be carefully considered in its own right, and not as is all to often the case, as an afterthought. Traditionally, and in many respects from a practical and economic point of view, major items of power plant tend to be located on the ground floor, or where available, the basement of a building.

In very large buildings, with a high power demand the supply authority mains intake may well be at high voltage, typically 11000 volts 50Hz in the U.K., and in many cases the sub-station for the transformer and its associated switchgear will be located on the premises in purpose built accommodation. Such accommodation must comply with the stringent regulations for such equipment set down by the supply and planning authorities, and will incorporate appropriate automatically operated fire extinguishing plant such as CO_2 systems. These systems will be subject to specific permit to work maintenance arrangements and regulations, conducted by properly trained and authorised engineering personnel (Carter,

1979). The regulations for high voltage systems used in buildings housing communications plant are not specific to them but are covered by the details set down, in the U.K. at least, by legislation embedded in the Electricity Factories Acts and Electricity Supply Regulations (IEE), together with the Health and Safety at Work Act.

The engine-generating plant will also generally be found in the basement or at ground floor level, where solid foundations to take the relatively high level of floor loading are likely to be found. Additionally, factors to be taken into account will include those of vibration insulation, prevention of noise breakout, clean air induction and cooling facilities, and the silencing and routing to high level of the exhaust system. Any associated fuel storage systems will have to be accommodated either internally or externally to the building, and appropriate fire and anti-pollution measures, and precautions to prevent the fuel freezing, are necessary (Nightingale, 1986).

Where very heavy centralised plant rectifiers and batteries are provided, adequate floor strength will clearly be needed, but with the increasing use of distributed or integrated d.c. power plant, the necessity for purpose built accommodation is markedly reduced or eliminated.

Batteries, other than those integrated into purpose built equipment racks, may well need specifically designed accommodation, especially where acid leakage, or fumes from battery charging are likely to occur.

24.12   Building engineering services

Building engineering services ar essential for the operational efficiency of any modern communications system. Prudent design will ensure that appropriate emergency lighting is included as part of the standby system load capability, and increasingly equipment and other operational accommodation will need to be cooled if plant life and performance is not to be degraded (Howell, 1989). Hence these loads will also need to be connected to the standby system as necessary. Matching modular plant designs to provide equipment cooling are increasingly seen as efficient and cost effective systems, and can be integrated into the main power system design to ensure overall high reliability targets can be achieved (Allen, 1990).

24.13   Reliability and cost

Terms such as reliability, failure, defect, mean- time to repair and so on and so forth, need adequate definition to have real meaning in a given situation. Failure may be defined as a complete loss of the mains supply, or it may be defined as the system voltage reducing to a level whereby equipment malfunctions start to occur, perhaps when the voltage becomes some 90% of the nominal value. This sort of analysis may then be continued for all aspects of a total communications scheme, of which power and cooling etc., form part. An operator must therefore define the acceptable limits or parameters of a given system for any meaningful consideration of reliability standards to be produced, and hence allow performance targets to be set. Table 24.1 gives a typical example of assumptions and definitions which can be used to assess the mean time between failure of an a.c. supply when an engine generating plant is available with a given failure to start rate. Other analysis can be repeated for all aspects of any system (Banfield, 1982; Banfield, 1984).

Cost is not an aspect against which a simple formula can be ascribed. First capital cost is not the sole arbiter; rather the whole life cost for a complete scheme must be considered. This can then be set against the cost of failure within the costing period, not the

Table 24.1   A.C. power plant reliability

Type of supply and location of centre	MTBF of mains supply exceeding one hour (years)	Engine failure to start rate	A.C. system MTBF of more than one hour (years)
City			
EHV underground	12	1 in 200	2400
HV underground	12	1 in 100	1200
0.3 to 5MVA	12	1 in 50	600
Large town			
EHV 70% underground	10	1 in 200	2000
HV underground	10	1 in 100	1000
0.3 to 5MV	10	1 in 50	500
Small town			
EHV 30% underground	1.5	1 in 200	300
HV 20% underground	1.5	1 in 100	150
0.3 to 5MVA	1.5	1 in 50	75

least being issues of the near imponderables of loss of reputation and opportunity.

24.14   Future developments

In broad terms, power systems may be divided into the two basic groups of a.c. and d.c. plant, and this format is like to continue for the future.

The trend for a.c. plant is likely to be for the mains equipment such as transformers, switchgear, cabling etc., to retain its robust construction. Similarly, the standby engine-generating plant, whilst achieving modest increases in efficiency and reduced fuel consumption, will continue to be the most cost effective solution to providing longer term reserve a.c. power supplies. What will change, and dramatically in some cases, will be the increasing use of electronics and the microprocessor to monitor and control the supplies; remotely if required, bringing in its train the more efficient utilisation of the facilities both operationally, and in maintenance terms.

The changes in d.c. plant have already been reflected in Section 24.3.3.6 which dealt with distributed power supplies. Increasingly, power conversion units will be capable of being embedded in the equipment it immediately serves, together with its reserve battery. New cell couples will undoubtedly be fully developed and produced, the lithium polymer type for instance, and perhaps, after so many false dawns, the fuel cell will come into its own.

The capability to build in the d.c. power conversion system will, therefore, greatly enhance an operator's ability to introduce new communications systems as required, without limitations arising from the use of centralised, or quasi centralised, power plant.

There are, nevertheless, dangers arising from this fragmented approach to overall power system design, that is the homogeneous nature of a.c. and d.c. systems, particularly the loss of the co-ordinated consideration of other services such as cooling; which are essential to the operational capability of a communications system. Lack of foresight in the co-ordination of all the power and building service systems, based on the outmoded concept of their being out of sight, out of mind services (tended by latter day troglodytes) can negate the whole integrity of high technology communications networks. The lessons of the infamous widespread losses of power supplies; in the north-eastern United States, including New York, in late 1965; the British power workers' strike in 1971; or the coal miners' strike of 1973 in the U.K.; all represent examples of major events which in the absence of adequate standby power supplies caused major disruptions to entire communities or even nations. And how much worse would the situation be today, where every other service comes to a halt when the mains supply fails or even has a transient blip. It has been eloquently summed up that such events 'can disrupt whole societies, very much like a collective loss of breath' (Roberts, 1989). It is appropriate therefore, to finish on the same note as at the beginning of this Section. Power is the lifeblood of any communications system, large or small, and is one of the few elements capable of causing a total failure or malfunction of even the most sophisticated network. It is neglected at one's peril.

24.15 References

The International Telecommunications Energy Conferences (IN-TELEC) were conceived to fill a significant need for a forum dealing exclusively with telecommunications power and building services developments and techniques. The first such conference was held in 1978 and has been held at about yearly intervals ever since.

Akerlund, J. (1983) Hybrid power systems for remote sites — solar, wind and mini diesel. *In Proceedings of INTELEC*, Tokyo.

Allen, P.A. (1986) An integrated power and building services management system. *In Proceedings of INTELEC*, Toronto.

Allen, P.A. (1990) The development of high reliability modular cooling systems in British Telecom, *Supplement to British Telecommun. Eng.*, **8**, Part 4, January.

Archer, C. (1979) Goonhilly satellite earth station — power plant, *British Post Office Elect. Eng. J.* **72**, October.

Banfield, K.E. (1982) Telecommunications power system reliability in the U.K. *In Proceedings of INTELEC*, Washington.

Banfield, K.E. (1984a) A new family of universal customer power units. *In Proceedings of INTELEC*, New Orleans.

Banfield, K.E. (1984b) Power systems and reliability, *British Telecommun. Engr. Journal*, **3**, April.

Barnett, P. (1987) Changing trends in the design of nninterruptible power supplies, *IEE Electronics and Power*, July.

Beems, P.L.M. (1981) The Heemaf dynamic diesel UPS system. *In Proceedings of INTELEC*, London.

CCITT (1985) *Primary sources of energy for the power supply of remote telecommunications systems.* International Telegraph and Telephones Consultative committee (CCITT) Gas IV ITU Geneva.

Carter, M.J. (1979) High voltage power systems for telecommunication plant: A safety aspect, *British Post Office Elect. Engrs. Journal* 72, July.

Coppinger, J.M., Hutchings, M.L., Cohen, A.L. (1984) Integrated power management scheme for telecommunications systems. *In Proceedings of INTELEC*, New Orleans.

Coppinger, J.M. (1987) Telecommunications power systems — the operations and maintenance perspective. *In Proceedings of INTELEC*, Stockholm.

Dolezal, H. (1987) UPS: Dynamic-Rotary systems with flywheel and diesel engine. *In Proceedings of INTELEC*, Stockholm.

Eoolley, J. (1986) A.C. power systems — operational experience at satellite earth stations. *In Proceedings of INTELEC,* Toronto.

Feder, D.O. and Kiehne, H.E. (1987). Changes and progress in battery technologies during the last decade. *In Proceedings of INTELEC*, Stockholm.

Fry, M.G.J. (1982) A switched mode power supply. *In Proceedings of INTELEC*, Washington.

Gahrn, V., Mueller, M.P., and Schlosser, H.G. (1987) Power supply systems for remote, unmanned microwave repeater stations in Greenland. *In Proceedings of INTELEC*, Stockholm.

Grant, W.T., Attwood, R. (1983) Autonomous multi-source power systems for telecommunications. *In Proceedings of INTELEC*, Tokyo.

Gropper, J. and Christopher, N. (1985) Experience with hybrid power systems using closed cycle vapour turbogenerators (CCVT's). *In Proceedings of INTELEC*, Munich.

Gumhalter, H. (1983) *Power supply systems in communications engineering*, Wiley and Sons.

Habock, A. and Schmalzl, F. (1979) Power supplies for telecommunications in remote areas. *In Proceedings of INTELEC*, Washington.

Higginbottom, J.C. and Lea, H.H. (1988) EMC considerations for telecommunications switching centres. *In Proceedings of INTELEC*, San Diego, U.S.A.

Halliwell, B. (1979) Battery options for standby power. *In Proceedings of INTELEC*, Washington.

Harrison, A.I., Bagshaw, N.E., and Thompson, E. (1982) Rack mounted power for modern telecommunications systems — a sealed for life lead acid battery. *In Proceedings of INTELEC*, Washington.

Harrison, A.I. (1986) Rack mounted battery power for modern telecommunication system — four years down the track. *In Proceedings of INTELEC*, Toronto.

Harrison, A.I. and Niklas, H. (1985) International standards for stationary lead acid batteries. *In Proceedings of INTELEC*, Munich.

Harris, W.P. (1987) UPS systems — static or rotary? *IEE, Electronics and Power*, July.

Henderson, P. (1979) A standard control system for thyristor rectifiers, *British Post Office Elect. Engr. Journal*, **72**, April.

Henderson, J.P. (1986) Uninterruptible power supplies for telecommunications. *In Proceedings of INTELEC*, Toronto.

Henderson, J.P. (1988) A.C. power systems in British Telecom for the 1990s. *In Proceedings of INTELEC*, San Diego, U.S.A.

Higginbottom, J.C. and Lea, H.H. (1988) EMC Considerations for Telecommunications Switching Centres. *In Proceedings of IN-TELEC*, San Diego, U.S.A.

Howard, R.H. (1979) Quality of the d.c. power supply for modern telecommunications systems. *In Proceedings of INTELEC*, London.

Howard, R.H. (1990) Secure power supplies for British Telecom's major computer centres, *Supplement to British Telecommun. Eng. Journal*, **8**, January.

Howell, P. (1989) Cooling requirements for small telephone exchanges. *In Proceedings of INTELEC*, Munich.

Humphreys, S.F. (1971) D.C. modular power plant, *British Post Office Elect. Eng. J.* **64** October.

IEE (1977) Reliability of power supply systems. *In Institution of Electrical Engineers International Conference. Pub. No.148*, February.

IEE (1985) *Colloquium on practical experiences with photovoltaic and wind power*. IEE Professional Group S1, April.

Jacobs, M.E., and Kunzinger, F.F. (1984) Distributed power architecture concepts. *In Proceedings of INTELEC*, New Orleans.

Johnson, N.G. (1980) The total energy installation at the Cardiff telephone exchange, *British Post Office Elect. Eng. J.* **73**, July.

Jones, D.L. and Bacon, D.M. (1989) Stand-by generators for telecommunications. *In Proceedings of INTELEC*, Florence.

Kageyama, T. (1982) Lightning protection of power equipment for telecommunications. *In Proceedings of INTELEC*, Washington.

Kolousek, M. (1986) Small energy systems for telecommunications equipment in cold climate remote areas. *In Proceedings of INTELEC*, Toronto.

Lee, G. and Thuan, N.K. (1986) Powering the Australian optical fibre trunk network. *In Proceedings of INTELEC*, Toronto.

Luigi, P. and Mario, B. (1989) Telecommunications power systems: one large power plant or many small ones? *In Proceedings of INTELEC*, Florence.

Mealing, A.W. (1982) Power supplies for small telecommunications centres, *British Post Office Elect. Eng. J.* **74** January.

Mealing, A.W., and Jones, W.R. (1984) SEMAC: A microprocessor system for remote monitoring and control engine generators. *In Proceedings of INTELEC*, New Orleans.

New, R. and Wittey, B.A. (1982) A rack mounted complete D.C. power system. *In Proceedings of INTELEC*, Washington.

Nightingale, C.R. (1971a) A.C. standby plant, *British Post Office Elect. Eng. J.* **64** July.

Nightingale, C.R. and Pine, R. (1971b) Power in the seventies, *British Post Office Telecom. Journal*, Summer.

Nightingale, C.R. (1983a) The design of mobile engine driven generating sets and their role in the British telecommunications network. *In Proceedings of INTELEC*, Tokyo.

Nightingale, C.R. and Mealing, A.W. (1983b) A new 3kVA standby diesel generating set for use in small remote telephone exchanges. *In Proceedings of INTELEC*, Tokyo.

Nightingale, C.R. and White, I.G. (1983c) Review of Cardiff telephone exchange total energy system after three years operation. *In Proceedings of INTELEC*, Tokyo.

Nightingale, C.R. (1985) A.C. power plant modernisation. *In Proceedings of INTELEC*, Munich.

Nightingale, C.R. (1986) A.C. standby power systems for satellite communications earth stations. *In Proceedings of INTELEC*, Toronto.

O'Callaghan, W.B., Fitzpatrick, N.P., and Peters, K. (1989) The aluminium-air reserve battery — a power supply for prolonged emergencies. *In Proceedings of INTELEC*, Florence.

O'Connor, J.A. (1990) A new dual reserve power system for small telephone exchanges, *Supplement to British Telecommun. Eng.* **8**, January.

Olden, A.H. (1983) Photovoltaic and other remote-site power generation systems for the Papua New Guinea telecommunications network. *In Proceedings of INTELEC*, Tokyo.

Owen, W.P. (1985) Power for system X, *British Telecommun. Engr. Journal*, **3**, January.

Pine, R. (1971) Telecommunications power supplies — the next decade, *British Post Office Elect. Eng. J.* **64**. April.

Pine, R., Krimholtz, R., and Crawley, A. (1979) A new British Post Office standard power plant. *In Proceedings of INTELEC*, Washington.

Roberts, G.K. (1989) *Electrification, from science, technology, and everyday life. 1870 — 1950* (Ed. C. Chant) Routledge and Open University 1989.

Scuka, V. et. al. (1987) Consequences of EMC. Requirements on the low voltage power distribution networks and installations. *In Proceedings of INTELEC*, Stockholm.

Spooner, F.E. (1986) Switched mode power supplies with idealised performance. *In Proceedings of INTELEC*, Toronto.

Spurgin, D.A. (1970) Power supplies for telecommunication services, *British Institution of Post Office Electrical Engineers*, Printed Paper No.230.

Stephenson, A.H. (1985) Asset management of power and building services plant in British Telecom. *In Proceedings of INTELEC*, Munich.

Taylor, M. (1987) Choosing the right UPS, *IEE, Electronics and Power*, July.

White, I.G. (1979) Cardiff telephone exchange — total energy project. *In Proceedings of INTELEC*, Washington.

Wilson, P.C. (1979) D.C. power supplies to telecommunications equipment: distribution, earthing and protection against induced transient voltages — Part 1, *British Post Office Elect. Engrs. Journal* **72**. October.

Wilson, P.C. (1980) D.C. power supplies to telecommunications equipment: distribution, earthing and protection against induced transient voltages — Part 2, *British Post Office Elect. Engrs. Journal*. **72**. January.

Wilson, P.C. and Coppinger, J.M. (1984) Electromagnetic compatibility in the telecommunication situation. *In Proceedings of INTELEC*, New Orleans.

Wilson, P.C. (1985) Electromagnetic compatibility; sources and levels of disturbances in the telecommunications environment. *In Proceedings of INTELEC*, Munich.

Wittey, B.A. and Henderson, J.P. (1983) Modern D.C. power systems: The power equipment rack, *British Telecom Engineering* **2** October.

Wittey, B.A. (1985) Sealed lead acid batteries — operational experience in a telecommunications application. *In Proceedings of INTELEC*, Munich.

Wittey, B.A. (1986) The introduction and operation of distributed D.C. power systems into the British Telecom switched network. *In Proceedings of INTELEC*, Toronto.

Woolley, J. (1986) A.C. Power Systems — Operational Experience at Satellite Earth Stations. *In Proceedings of INTELEC*, Toronto.

Wolpert, T. (1978) Some current trends in the design of D.C. power plants. *In Proceedings of INTELEC*, Washington.

Wolpert, T. (1987) Rectifier development during the last thirty years. *In Proceedings of INTELEC*, Stockholm.

Yotsumoto, K., et.al. (1988) Design for a highly efficient distributed power supply system based on reliability analysis. *In Proceedings of INTELEC*, San Diego, U.S.A.

24.16 Acknowledgement

Thanks are expressed the Directors, Network, BT U.K., for permission to use the information concerning its power systems. Also, acknowledgement is made of the work of those BT colleagues, past and present, and fellow engineers within the industry, who have contributed to the high standing of the British telecommunication power systems design.

25

Software systems in telecommunications

R S Hurst
BSc CEng
Bell Northern Research

Carolyn Story
BSc (Hons)
Bell Northern Research

Contents

25.1 Overview

Frequently more than half of the design cost of a telecommunications system lies in its software. This chapter offers an introduction to some of the software engineering techniques and technologies which are applied.

The technologies used are determined by the nature of the product and the telecommunications systems are diverse:

1. They can be large. Some public switching software can demand of the order of 20 million lines of code. This puts it in the class of major computer operating systems.
2. They can be real time. Much telecommunications software is embedded, and required to operate under severe timing constraints.
3. They can be flexible. Dynamic reconfigurability is a common requirement. The ability to interwork across vendor boundaries is becoming so.
4. They can be distributed. Sometimes the only way to provide the required service with the required performance is to exploit the most advanced distribution platforms.
5. They can involve very large volumes of data. Some of the directory assistance systems call for leading edge relational data base technology.
6. They demand intelligence. Knowledge based systems are applied in alarm analysis and in configuration.
7. They must be resilient, reliable, maintainable and usable, by all classes of people.

What all of this means is that there are few software and software engineering technologies which do not apply to the telecommunications world.

25.2 Stages in the software lifecycle

There are a number of generally recognised stages in software developments, known as the software lifecycle, as follows:

1. Requirements capture and analysis.
2. Specification.
3. Design.
4. Code and unit test.
5. Integration.
6. System testing.
7. Delivery and installation.
8. Acceptance testing.
9. Maintenance and enhancements

The name of the stage and its importance will vary according to the methods and techniques used to develop the software, as explained later.

25.2.1 Requirements capture and analysis

This stage identifies the requirements for the final software in terms of the user's needs. It answers the question "what does the user really want?" It may take the form of a user writing a document which is then analysed and clarified by the software team, or a set of recorded interviews, or a special team consisting of a customer representative and a software expert may generate the list of re-

quirements jointly. There are also a small number of methods, for example CORE which aim to address the problem of requirements capture and analysis more rigorously. Tools such as Lotos enable the user to capture protocol definition.

Often, during this stage, it is advisable to build a small model or prototype of certain aspects of the system (for example the screens which the user will use). If the system includes hardware (for example a telephone handset), producing a computer model of the hardware may help the user to understand his own needs more clearly.

It is frequently necessary to demonstrate compliance to a set of requirements. This is done by labelling each requirement and referencing back to the requirement during the analysis and design stages. This is called Requirements Traceability. Note that the requirements generated by the use may well be ambiguous and conflicting. In situations where requirements specification document is sufficiently large to hamper detection of anomalies, there are software tools to allow the user to pick out key words, phrases and concepts and to organise the data in such a way that these anomalies may be recognised. Hypertext technology is applicable here. (Pankaj, 1990.)

It is very important that any requirements documents or prototypes generated by the software team are validated and signed off by the users, as they can then form the basic definition for the main development.

25.2.2 Specification

This stage answers the question "What must the system do in order to satisfy the users' real needs?", and is normally carried out by a relatively small number of people in close consultation with the requirements specifiers.

In general, implementation considerations are ignored unless they are part of the user's requirements (for example, the user may insist that the software must run on a particular chip).

The main aims of this stage are to provide a modular, clear, correct, complete, and usually implementation free, definition of what the software must do. This then forms the basis for subsequent design and implementation by the complete software team, many of whom will not have (or need) a full understanding of all of the users' system requirements.

To ensure conformance to the user's requirements there should be frequent discussions, walk throughs and reviews with the user. Where appropriate, prototyping, modelling and simulation techniques should be used to ensure that the resultant software provides appropriate and effective facilities for the end user. It is also important that requirements traceability is provided via cross referencing back to labelled requirements wherever possible.

25.2.3 Design

This stage answers the question "How will the system be implemented?"

This is normally the stage when the team grows and individual groups are assigned subsystems to complete without necessarily having a complete knowledge of the systems as a whole.

Depending on the design method adopted, this stage may be split into two:

1. High Level Design which specifies the architecture of the system in terms of which facilities are in hardware and which -are in software; what software programs will be provided and

the interfaces between them; which programs will run on which processor; and so on.

2. Detailed Design which provides the detailed architecture of each program in terms of the functions how and when they are called, the implementation data model, and the detailed behaviour of the system.

Depending on the quality of the work in this phase, the resulting system will be resilient to change with many reusable components. If this stage is not completed properly the resultant software will tend to contain a large number of bugs often arising from unnecessary cross dependencies in the software; in this case the cost of maintenance will be high and the software will degrade rapidly, quickly needing replacement.

25.2.4   Code and unit test

Although tools are appearing on the market which will allow limited code generation from design specifications, currently coding and testing is still a relatively major part of a software lifecycle. The aim of the code and unit test phase is to provide clean, modular, correct pieces of code, with a complete set of associated tests. The code pieces will then be assembled as necessary to provide the functionality required of the complete system. The following are some general guidelines which should be observed during this phase:

1. Ensure that a detailed design is available; many potential bugs will have been corrected, and hence the coding and testing time will be reduced.
2. Ensure that coding conventions are available; any code produced may have a lifetime of several years, and therefore must be maintainable.
3. Ensure that code is simple, easy to read, well commented, and does not use clever tricks (e.g. self modifications) as this will enhance the resilience of the code to change.
4. Do not rely on special idiosyncrasies of a particular compiler. Compilers change as does the host hardware; high quality code will port easily to a different environment.
5. Testing should be carried out in a controlled, repeatable fashion. Test harnesses should be used whenever possible to exercise small , well defined parts of the code. All tests should be set up to be repeated as necessary as they will form an important part of the maintenance environments.

25.2.5   Integration

When the individual code sections are completed, then the complete system must be built and tested. This is the point at which the use of a good version control system (and preferably full configuration management) is essential. Builds should be automated as much as possible, and one person must be given the responsibility of ensuring the system built contains the correct software at all times.

Integration testing should concentrate on exercising the interfaces between individual pieces of code (as the internal functionality of the code elements should have been fully exercised during unit testing). This level of testing is against the specification produced . Sets of repeatable tests should be defined, built and run; all errors should be logged and at intervals a new build should be provided and the tests which identified bugs in the previous version should be rerun.

25.2.6   System testing

This is the final set of tests on the complete system to be run by the software team. The tests should be set up to be repeatable, and as automated as possible. The tests defined should be against the initial requirements specification and should aim to show that all requirements have been satisfied. If the user has provided acceptance tests then these should be run during this stage as part of system testing to ensure that:

1. There are no remaining misunderstandings between the user and the customer.
2. As an additional set of tests to exercise the complete system from the viewpoint of the customer.

25.2.7   Delivery and installation

The system will be reviewed and signed off by the software team before delivery. At this stage, the system must be baselined to ensure that:

1. All specification and design documentation is up to date.
2. The software and hardware comprising the delivered system is documented, and that version of the system may be rebuilt if necessary.
3. All user documentation is up to date.

A release of a system typically will consist of:

1. A delivery schedule.
2. The hardware component, if applicable.
3. A set of tapes containing the software.
4. Installation instructions, which will include the version number for any external hardware of software required.
5. Installation test and verification procedures, if applicable.
6. A definition of fault report and change request procedures together with the appropriate forms.
7. User documentation. For more complex systems, this may be split into a number of manuals, e.g. System Administration Guide, User Guide and Overviews, User Reference Manual.
8. A list of Fault Reports fixed.
9. A list of Change Requests and work arounds.

Normally releases are given numbers of the form a.b where a is the major version number and is only changed when a new release contains significant enhancements, and b is the minor version number which is increased for every release.

25.2.8   Acceptance testing

The user or customer, where feasible, should be encouraged to provide a set of tests which he will run in order to accept, and sign off, the software produced. These test will perform three functions:

1. They will ensure that there are no remaining misunderstandings between the customer and the software team.
2. They provide an invaluable insight into the user's view of how the system should be used.
3. They provide a mechanism for agreement that the software is to specification and correct.

The tests are usually performed after the software has been installed, although the system test team may also run them during system tests.

25.2.9 Maintenance and enhancements

These phases are often ignored, but in many ways may be deemed the most important as without them the software will have limited use and an even more limited lifetime.

25.2.9.1 *Maintenance*

All systems are prone to faults and however much testing has been performed during development, it is extremely difficult, and often not cost effective, to continue testing until one is virtually certain that all faults are removed. Equally, hardware can, and will, fail requiring some level of intervention. There are techniques available to assist with the provision of highly resilient systems (as described later), however in general some level of maintenance will be required.

Maintenance activities will usually start when a fault is reported via a Fault Report form; the maintenance team will, in general, not consist of the staff in the development team and therefore they will be heavily dependent on good documentation in the form of specification and design documents, comments within the code, and clear, comprehensive, well documented test definitions.

Equally, it is very important for the maintenance team to ensure that all documentation is kept up to date.

Normally, a group of bug fixes will form a maintenance release. However if the bug is sufficiently serious then a special release may be made for that bug fix; this is generally undesirable as before any release the integration testing system testing and release procedures must be performed, which can require significant effort.

To aid subsequent fault findings, the code corresponding to a fault report fix should be labelled as being part of that fault report fix. The description of the next release should include the list of faults fixed.

25.2.9.2 *Enhancements*

These will be triggered either by a set of approved Change Requests, or by the internal development plans for the system.

The lifecycle for the enhancements will be largely the same as for the main development. Care must be taken to ensure that all documentation (requirements, specifications, design, comments in the code, test specifications, user manuals) is kept fully up to date.

25.3 Software design techniques

There are many different software development techniques available; each addresses a particular section of the overall lifecycle and is applicable to a specific range of software applications. This section provides an overview of the main techniques used in the development of software in the telecommunication industry.

The main methodologies may be grouped under the following headings:

1. Formal methods.
2. Structured methods.
3. Object Oriented methods.
4. Knowledge Based Systems.

In general they provide a way of applying a set of techniques as well as the technique itself: they are explained further below.

In addition, there are specific techniques which may be used in conjunction with any software methodology; the main ones are modelling, simulation and prototyping, and are explained in Section 25.5.

25.3.1 Formal methods

This is a set of methods based on the mathematical definition of the problem and solution. The main Formal Methods are VDM and Z, with HOL being favoured for protocol specification work. For VDM and Z there are limited tools available to support the creation of the specification and some syntax checking. For a few languages (for example B), some advances are being made in the provision of proof related tools to allow formal verification of each subsequent stage of the design, proving correctness and completeness of each stage with respect to the previous stage. See also (Wing, 1990).

In 1990 an Esprit project called RAISE (Rigorous Approach to Industrial Software Engineering) was completed, providing an extremely rich formal language called RSL (RAISE Specification language) together with a method for using RSL to complete an initial specification, refine it and eventually produce code. RAISE is currently undergoing user trials and is beginning to gain usage within the industry. There is a comprehensive set of tools provided as part of RAISE, including editors, simplifiers and proof related tools. The graphics front end and built in library facilities for RSL modules provides the user with a high level of support during development.

Formal methods are particularly applicable for highly resilient safety critical software. They are not always the natural choice for other software domains as the development team must have a mathematics background, and the learning time can be high.

25.3.2 Structured methods

There are a range of methods using graphics based techniques which may be grouped together under this heading. The most commonly known ones in the telecommunications industry are JSD, SDL, SADT, Yourdon and the Yourdon based RT-SASD.

In general they address the portion of the lifecycle from the start of the Specification stage through to the end of the detailed design stage. (JSD addresses design stage only). Supporting tools often provide facilities for Requirements Capture, limited automatic code generation and occasionally some automatic generation of tests.

These methods provide support for describing data (in abstract and implementation terms) via Entity Relationship Diagrams and Entity life histories, data transformations (via Data Flow Diagrams) and behaviour (via State Transition Diagrams and event lists). Control is shown via Control Flow Diagrams, and the structure of the software is shown in a variety of ways (for example structure charts).

The method itself defines how to utilise these techniques to provide a complete specification, and then to derive the architectural and detailed designs in a way to produce a modular system with minimal interdependencies in the code. The resulting software tends to be more robust, maintainable and extendable.

Emphasis is placed on the fact that no unnecessary implementation constraints are imposed during design to allow a near perfect specification to be produced first. This is a powerful technique which ensures that artificial constraints due to, for example, current hardware limitations are not allowed to influence the specification, and therefore will be removed when a redesign is done for a new hardware platform.

These techniques also provide a mechanism for communication both with the software development teams, and with the user and/or customer, as no prior training is required to understand the diagrams.

The diagram elements have annotations which allow a more rigorous definition of the diagram element to be captured. Using this it is possible to combine the use of formal and structured methods to provide both an easy communication mechanism, and a formalised definition of the software components.

Structured methods are of most use where a system has one or more of the following characteristics:

1. The system is large and requires splitting into subsystems with clearly defined functionality before proceeding.
2. The software team has not got a strong mathematical background.

3. Resilience and safety critical issues are not paramount.

It is likely that, as object oriented methods develop and tools are available to fully support them, then structured methods may well be superseded by object oriented methods.

25.3.2.1 *SDL*

SDL (Specification and Description Language) is a notation recommended by the CCITT for the 'unambiguous specification and description of the behaviour of telecommunications systems'. It is to be used to describe both the required and the actual behaviour of telecommunications systems.

SDL has two different notations, a graphic representation (SD:/GR) and a textual phrase representation (SD:/PR). These are equivalent in that they share a common semantics. Figure 25.1 illustrates some of the elementary symbols.

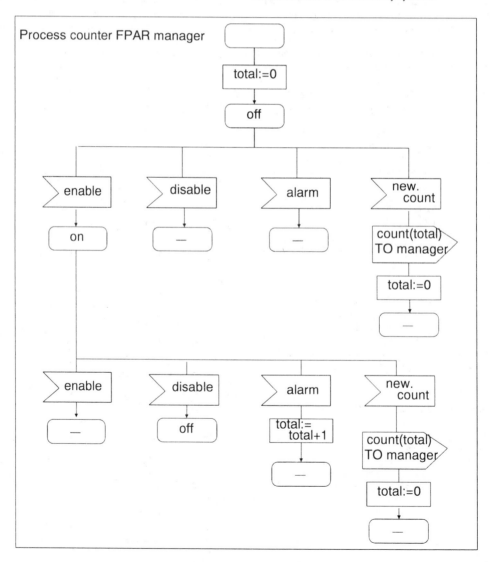

Figure 25.1   Some of the symbols used within SDL

25.3.3 Object oriented methods

Relatively recently it has been discovered that defining real world objects, and converting them into a software representation can provide a way of producing reusable software components which are very much tailored to the problem domain. A software "object" is a set of data together with its access and transformation code or "Methods". A user of an object merely needs to know how to invoke the appropriate method; all object internals, for example data details, are hidden.

In many areas the productivity gains through using object oriented languages have been significant. Object oriented methods to support this approach are being developed, and a number of notations exist. The main method supporting Object Oriented Design (OOD) is HOOD, for which a number of tools are available. However, the methods to support the full analysis and design phases are still being developed. The most commonly known analysis and design method emerging is Schlaer-Mellor's OOA/OOSD which is an extension of the 1989 OOD from Schlaer-Mellor, with others being produced.

Object oriented methods are particularly applicable for projects involving a large amount of data definition and manipulation although their general applicability and usage is growing.

These methods are graphically based, relying on annotations to provide a more rigorous definition of the data or the software (method) associated with each object. Thus it is possible to combine the use of a formal language with object oriented methods; the diagrammatic object oriented technique providing an accessible front end to the underlying formalisms which need be understood only by the designer of the object.

One of the major advantages of an object oriented approach, apart from the fact that the objects are easily traceable back to real world objects and events, is that it encourages the system designers to partition concepts with minimal interdependencies and maximum reuse. This approach enables large teams to work effectively together and as libraries of reusable software components are built up it should reduce development time significantly.

25.3.4 Knowledge based system techniques

There is a group of techniques concerned with logic programming and reasoning via rules and constraints. In the limit the techniques aim to produce software to simulate human reasoning i.e. artificial intelligence. The techniques most commonly used within the Telecommunications industry are Knowledge Based Systems (KBS) and provide the user with a means of solving problems using rule and constraint based data. Often the user can modify the rules, allowing the reasoning to be altered without any reprogramming.

Some of the domains in which KBS techniques are most applicable are:

1. Automated equipment configuration.
2. Diagnostic software.
3. Network management, in particular identification of faults from a set of symptoms and dynamic reconfiguration.
4. Simulating network behaviour.
5. Controlling and monitoring manufacturing processes.

KBS has, in the past, been seen as having limited applicability and there are few methods and supporting tools available. However, one such method which is being used within the industry is KADS (KBS Analysis and Design Support). This is a methodology which takes the user through the initial knowledge acquisition stages,

through analysis and design, and provides a basis from which to begin coding.

25.3.4.1 KADS

The following is reproduced from Hayball (1992) by kind permission of the authors:

The term 'knowledge-based system' (and related terms such as 'expert system', as well as the broader area of 'artificial intelligence') has been surrounded by unnecessary confusion and ambiguity. One reason for this is that the subject is an evolving and complex area. The complexity primarily derives from the definition of 'knowledge', but also from the breadth of coverage of such systems. Thus pragmatically, we define:

1. *A KBS is any computer system or subsystem which processes 'knowledge'.*
2. *Knowledge is a rich form of information, often stored by humans as expertise in some restricted domain, e.g. problem solving skills such as medical diagnosis or resource scheduling. It is often represented as facts, rules, concepts, assumptions, etc.*

Within this broad scope, it is possible to distinguish different types of KBS according to different criteria. For example, one may choose to distinguish systems according to the 'problem solving' task they perform or support; or one may wish to differentiate systems according to the 'role' that they play in relation to other systems or people in a co-operative working environment. Another simple way is used below. Five types of KBS have been found to be appropriate for development using the KADS methods using the following classification:

1. Generic Systems. Systems which are designed to be tailorable to a specific client's requirements, both in terms of the problem solving functionality and the clients' domain.
2. General Purpose Systems. Systems that operate in a domain common to many potential customers' requirements.
3. Bespoke Systems. Systems for specific users that are developed for specific clients requiring specific problem solving in specific domains.
4. Embedded Systems. The KADS methods can be combined with other software development methodologies to produce 'embedded' systems, i.e. those in which an expert problem solving component is nested within a larger application.
5. Adaptable Systems. The KADS methods provide an analysis and design framework that allows a high degree of adaptability to be built into a KBS so that the same system can be used by different people for different purposes.

25.4 Lifecycle for each software design technique

25.4.1 Formal methods lifecycle

The stages in the formal methods lifecycle are the same as those in the "standard" lifecycle. To a large extent, the same deliverables are produced, albeit in a slightly different format.

The key deliverables in a formal methods development are the initial specification of the system, the final design of the system and

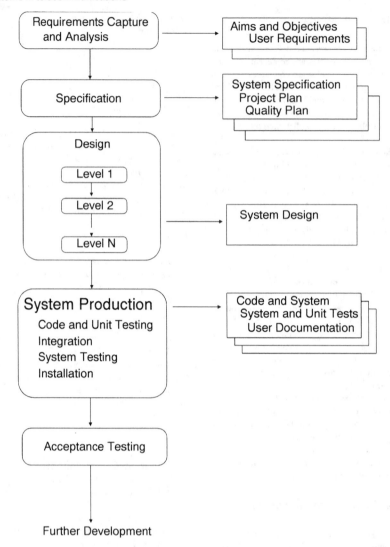

Figure 25.2 Main stages in the software lifecycle, with deliverables

the system itself. The initial specification is very important because this forms the basis for the whole development.

This initial specification is developed using an "invent and verify" paradigm. The specification is enriched (more details about the system is added) and refined (more details about how the system is to be implemented) to produce another description of the system. This new description is then checked or verified against the initial specification to ensure that this description is a "proper" development of the initial specification.

There may be several intermediate descriptions of the system before the final design is produced. The number of descriptions will depend on the size and complexity of the system, and should be defined at the start of the design stage. This allows the design stage to be broken up into several sub-stages, each sub-stage producing to new description of the system.

Modelling, simulation and rapid prototyping can all be used with formal methods, and will be based on the mathematical descriptions of the system. These descriptions will also form the basis for testing the system, as they define what the system is meant to do.

Considerable effort is required to produce and verify these intermediate descriptions. However, experience from other projects shows that a corresponding amount of effort is saved in the coding and testing stages of the lifecycle.

Figure 25.2 shows the main stages in the lifecycles together with the main deliverables from each stage. More detailed information may be found in Hughes (1992).

25.4.2 Structured methods lifecycle

The structured methods most widely used in the telecommunications industry are SSADM and Yourdon based techniques. In each case the lifecycle is essentially the same, although the terminology will differ. Figure 25.3 shows the stages used in RT-SASD (Real Time Structured Analysis Structured Design) a Yourdon extended

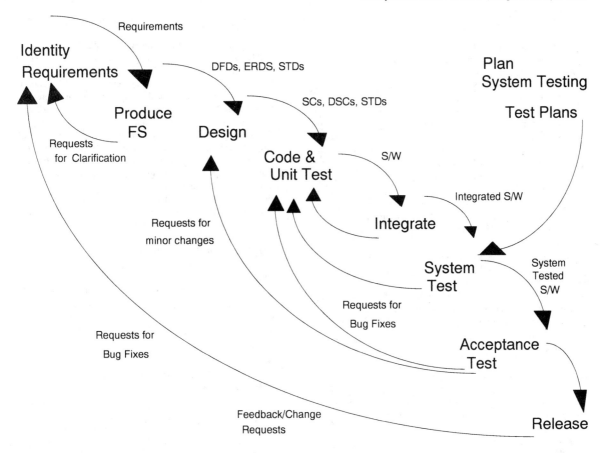

Figure 25.3 Real Time Structured Analysis Structured Design (RT - SASD)

method providing a stronger support for the user than classic Yourdon.

Modelling, simulation and rapid prototyping may all be used in conjunction with the main method. The stages where they are best utilised depends on the nature of the software being developed and should be decided at project initiation.

25.4.3 Object oriented methods lifecycle

As object oriented methods are relatively new, the lifecycle for these methods does not differ from the "standard lifecycle" significantly.

There are two noticeable changes to the activities carried out in the lifecycle however. These relate to the reuse of components and to the use of inheritance.

In order to take advantage of the reuse supported by object orientated methods, a library of standard components must be constructed. These standard components can then be used not only in the current development, but also, potentially, in future developments.

The effort required to create and catalogue these standard components can be considerable, with the attendant problems that savings may only be recouped in future developments. Nevertheless, the reuse of standard components is important to the use of object orientated methods, and this investment should be made.

The second change to the activities in the lifecycle involves the use of inheritance. Once the objects in the system have been ident-

ified, they need to be classified, so that commonality amongst objects is separated out. For example, if two objects in the system are cars and trucks, it may be possible to separate out properties common to both which relate to a vehicle. Cars and trucks are then simply special types of vehicles, inheriting the properties of a vehicle, but with some additional properties. This classification is not simple, and can require considerable effort with much rework.

In both cases, the overall stages of the lifecycle are not affected; what is affected is the amount of effort required in each stage.

25.4.4 Knowledge based systems lifecycle

The lifecycle described below is for KADS as this is the best known emerging method supporting KBS developments. The remaining text in this section has been reproduced from Hayball with kind permission from the author.

KADS (i.e. 'the KADS method') is a set of activities, and definitions of their results, for supporting the Analysis and Design stages of KBS development. KADS covers the following areas:

1. Structured activities for Analysis (Product Definition) & Design (High Level Design).
2. Framework definitions for the results produced by activities.
3. Tools and techniques for activities in KBS development.
4. Techniques and check lists for quality assessment and control (QAC).

5. Identified prototyping opportunities.

KADS is founded on modelling. Models in KADS are structured descriptions of observed or required behaviour. For example, human expert problem solving behaviour is represented in KADS as a four layer model of expertise. At each level qualitatively distinct aspects of the behaviour are addressed. Around this core idea a series of structural frameworks for representing a KBS at various points in development have been introduced. KBS development is thus viewed as consisting of a series of modelling tasks Q where the ultimate output of the development is an operational model, i.e. an implemented system.

Additionally, KADS supports the modelling of user/system interaction based on an analysis of the tasks to be performed using the system. It also provides a document framework for recording more general requirements and constraints. This ensures that any non KBS specific areas which still impact on the development are covered.

KADS is primarily concerned with the the Analysis (Product Definition) and Design (High Level Design) phases of the system development lifecycle. (See Figure 25.4). Accepting this, KADS covers the development activities required to build seven key models over these phases. The KADS modelling process involves translating the real world problem into an abstract form and mapping the abstraction onto a system design. The seven models produced are:

1. Process Model. An abstract representation of the overall organisational process that the system will be involved in. It describes the tasks to be performed within that process, down to the level where it can be decided whether they will be performed by the system or not.
2. Co-operation Model. An abstract representation of the way the future system will interact with its environment. In particular,

it records in a structured manner the requirements for user/system interaction.
3. Expertise Model. An abstract representation of the real world problem solving processes. It records in a structured manner the expert problem solving requirements of the system.
4. Global System Architecture. At the same level of abstraction as the Process Model, the Global System Architecture represents the structure and scope of the proposed system in terms of a set of subsystem and interface definitions.
5. Functional Design Model. This represents the structure and scope of the proposed system's problem solving component(s). It is a high level functional specification for the KBS. It is reached by a process of transforming the analysis models into a set of functional elements.
6. Behavioural Design Model. A representation of the design techniques (KBS or otherwise), algorithms and data structures which have been chosen to realise the elements of the Functional Design Model.
7. Physical Design Model. This represents the physical architecture of the target KBS in terms of a set of module definitions and module interfaces.

1 to 3 = Analysis – Specifying what the system will do.

4 = System Design – Specifying the overall system architecture.

5 to 7 = KBS Design – Specifying how the KBS subsystem is to work.

25.4.5 A Lifecycle based on Rapid Prototyping Techniques

The lifecycle given in Figure 25.5 has been shown to provide a powerful way of understanding and documenting the real needs of the user by building a prototype which is then subject to extensive user evaluation; successive iterations ensure that the final version

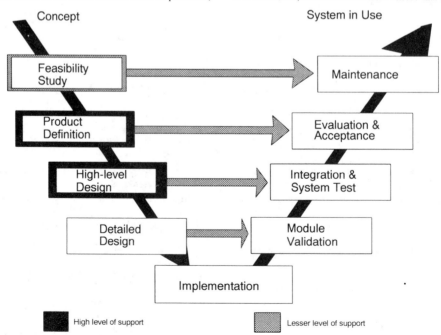

Figure 25.4 KADS in the product development lifecycle

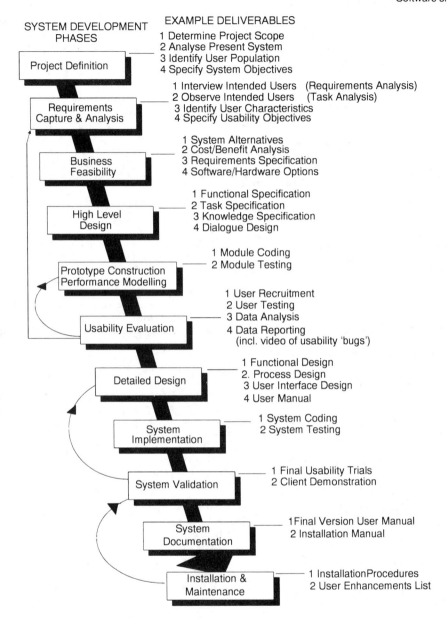

SYSTEM DEVELOPMENT PHASES

EXAMPLE DELIVERABLES

Project Definition
1 Determine Project Scope
2 Analyse Present System
3 Identify User Population
4 Specify System Objectives

Requirements Capture & Analysis
1 Interview Intended Users   (Requirements Analysis)
2 Observe Intended Users   (Task Analysis)
3 Identify User Characteristics
4 Specify Usability Objectives

Business Feasibility
1 System Alternatives
2 Cost/Benefit Analysis
3 Requirements Specification
4 Software/Hardware Options

High Level Design
1 Functional Specification
2 Task Specification
3 Knowledge Specification
4 Dialogue Design

Prototype Construction Performance Modelling
1 Module Coding
2 Module Testing

Usability Evaluation
1 User Recruitment
2 User Testing
3 Data Analysis
4 Data Reporting
   (incl. video of usability 'bugs')

Detailed Design
1 Functional Design
2. Process Design
3 User Interface Design
4 User Manual

System Implementation
1 System Coding
2 System Testing

System Validation
1 Final Usability Trials
2 Client Demonstration

System Documentation
1 Final Version User Manual
2 Installation Manual

Installation & Maintenance
1 Installation Procedures
2 User Enhancements List

Figure 25.5   Lifecycle based on rapid prototyping techniques

encapsulates not only the users' stated requirements, but also the additional facilities which would normally only become apparent once a real system is available.

25.5   Software simulation

In all branches of engineering it is common to make models, to obtain an impression of the nature of the end product before it is built. Software can be modelled.

It is sometimes worthwhile to model the behaviour of a proposed software system. Languages such as Prolog lend themselves to such work, and there are object oriented modelling tools. This approach,

however, is more usually applied to the software modelling of hardware.

Rather than its functional behaviour, the modelling of a software system focuses on its look and feel, performance or reliability.

25.5.1 · Look and Feel

There is a wide range of rapid prototyping tools (some mentioned above) for the simulation of user interfaces. Screen layouts, use of colour and grey scale, menu control and buttons can all be represented quickly, and it is possible to walk through the user processes and to adjust the user interface to best fit the way the user needs to work.

25.5.2 Performance

Discrete event modelling (Birtwistle, 1985) can be used to model the performance of hardware and software systems, identify bottle-necks, and to predict behaviour under various running conditions.

Tools exploiting queuing theory also exist.

25.5.3 Reliability

In hardware reliability models it is assumed that components will fail, but that they are replaced and can eventually fail again. In software reliability modelling, however, it is assumed that once a failure occurs its source can be located and the fault removed permanently.

Two leading models are the Jelinski-Moranda (Jelinski, 1972) and the Littlewood-Verrall (Littlewood, 1973). The former is based on the assumption that the failure rate of the software is proportional to the number of faults not yet corrected; the latter assumes that time between failures follows an experimental distribution.

These and others are discussed in Goel (1985) and Shanthikumar (1983).

25.6 Programming languages

25.6.1 Five generations

Programming languages are conventionally divided into five gener-ations:

25.6.1.1 *First generation*

Early computers were programmed by directly entering the machine code. The program was written as a sequence of bits, perhaps expressed in octal (base 8) or hexadecimal (base 16) notation. Code in such a notation would now be applied only as a patch (the software equivalent of cuts and straps, with all the same dangers and more) and even then rarely.

25.6.1.2 *Second generation*

The second generation allowed for a symbolic representation of the machine code. So, for example, the machine code to load a value from some memory location into a register might consist of:

1. 8 bits representing the code for the load instruction.
2. 4 bits giving the number (0 to 15) of the register to be loaded.
3. 4 bits giving the number (0 to 15) of an index register which addresses the area of memory in which the value resides.
4. 16 bits giving the displacement from the location addressed by the index register of the memory location in which the value required is to be found.

An assembly language might represent such a machine instruction by the notation L REG, VALUE, where 'REG' is the symbolic name of the register to be loaded and 'VALUE' represents the location, given by an appropriate index and displacement, of the required value.

The assembly language notation provides recognisable instruction mnemonics and allows meaningful variable names to be chosen. It

also provides for easier change of the program, since the symbolic name of a variable need not change when the variable is reassigned to a different memory location as a result of the change. The tool, as assembler, which translates the assembly language into machine code, can resolve the symbolic references.

25.6.1.3 *Third generation*

Most of the common programming languages, such as Fortran, Pascal, C and Ada belong to the third generation. Communications systems software is predominately written in languages of this generation, and some of their characteristics are described below.

25.6.1.4 *Fourth generation*

The fourth generation consists of problem oriented languages. Their main area of use is in commercial data processing for tasks such as report generation and data analysis. Statistical analysis packages generally provide fourth generation languages.

The spread of problem oriented languages into domains other than commercial data processing is slow but continuing. Some of the notations associated with text processing and font editing, for example, may be considered to belong to this generation.

25.6.1.5 *Fifth generation*

The fifth generation includes languages which are declarative rather than imperative; they specify the nature of the required solutions rather than the instructions which have to be followed to reach that solution.

The best known language in this class is Prolog (Colmerauer, 1983). A Prolog program consists of a series of logical assertions.

25.6.2 High level languages

The term 'high level language' is still often used to refer to lan-guages of the third generation. Some of the more widely used of these are the following.

25.6.2.1 *Pascal*

Pascal was designed by Wirth in 1968 as a tool to support the teaching of programming, and for a time it remained as no more than an educational aid. Eventually commercial compilers began to be introduced first for micro computers and then for larger machines. An ISO standard version of Pascal became available in 1982.

Pascal has been very influential. Among its features, which also appear in its descendants, are:

Type definition

In Pascal every variable must be declared to be of a chosen type, which determines what values may be associated with the variable and what operations may be performed upon it. The type may be one of the predefined types, 'real', 'integer','boolean' and 'char', or it may be a type defined by the programmer. The following are examples of user defined types:

```
type colour = (red,blue,green,yellow);
type digit = 0..9;
```

Addition is defined on type integer, but would not be defined on type colour. It would not be valid to assign a value of type boolean to a variable of type digit.

The use of types restricts the things a programmer can do, but the main area of restriction is in the errors that he can make. The chance of accidental misuse of data is reduced.

Conditional and loop statements

Pascal provides the if statement, which has an optional else part, and the case statement.

```
if test
  then begin
    hue := green;
    counter := counter + 1
  end
  else hue := red;

case selector [i] of
  'red' : status := stop;
  'amber': status:= stop;
  'green': status:= go
end;
```

There are three loop constructs: **for, while** and **repeat .. until.** Illustrating the first of these:

```
for m:= jan to dec do no.days[m]:=31;
```

These statements encourage the programmer to write clear well structured code. The encouragement can, of course, be ignored.

As a language for teaching Pascal has served admirably, and it has been used in a wide range of real applications. However, for some purposes it has deficiencies such as the coding of real-time systems demanding concurrent processing, and to cope with issues such as these more complex languages have been defined. Two such are Ada and CHILL.

25.6.2.2   *Ada*

Ada (Pyle, 1981) arose from an initiative by the United States Department of Defence to address the rapidly increasing cost of software by reducing the number of programming languages in use at the time. It was decided that none of those available was adequate to serve for all tasks and so a competition was set in place to find a new one. Ada was the result. (Ada is a trademark of the US Department of Defence, Ada Joint Program Office.)

Ada incorporates almost all the features of Pascal, and much more besides:

Information hiding

Ada introduced the notion of a package which was similar to that of the module in the language Modula, an earlier descendant of Pascal. The package has two parts, its definition and its body. Only those entities defined in the definition part of the package can be made available for use in other packages. Those defined in the package body are local. This means that it is possible through the package definition to provide details on how to use the package without disclosing the implementation details. Information is hidden except where it is explicitly made available.

Communication between tasks

A task is a piece of the Ada program which may be executed concurrently with other tasks. Again it divides into its specification part and the task body. The tasks may run on the same processor interleaved or on different processors.

Ada has a synchronous message passing mechanism known as a rendezvous, and associated with this are two statements, ACCEPT and SELECT.

The ACCEPT statement in a task defines a rendezvous in that task:

```
ACCEPT name (arguments) DO... END name;
```

This named rendezvous can be called by another task;

```
name (arguments);
```

This is an entry call.

Now, if a task A reaches an entry call x before an ACCEPT statement with the entry name x and another process has been reached then A is halted. Similarly, if a task B reaches an ACCEPT statement with entry name x before another task has reached a call to that entry then x is suspended. When the matched entry call and ACCEPT statement have both been reached, the rendezvous can take place.

If no other task is ready to call x in B then task B must wait. The SELECT statement allows conditions, known as guards, to be set on ACCEPT statements.

When the task reaches the SELECT statement:

1. All the guards are calculated.
2. One of those ACCEPTS for which the guard is true and for which entry calls are pending is chosen at random, and the rendezvous occurs.
3. If no rendezvous is possible the task is suspended until one of the open entry calls is made.

A comprehensive discussion of ways of expressing parallelism in programming languages is given in Bal (1989).

25.6.2.3   *CHILL*

CHILL (CCITT, 1980) was developed at the request of the CCITT. It is also descended from Pascal and has some features in common with Ada and some that are different.

CHILL has three mechanisms for communicating between processes:

1. Regions, which allow mutually exclusive access to information.
2. Buffers, in which information can be left by one process and retrieved by another.
3. Signals, which can be directly transmitted from one process to another without buffers.

Although CHILL is fairly well used in telecommunications, the total user population is not enough to attract tool makers from companies not in the communications business. The tool support therefore tends to be proprietary, and often limited. Other, more widely supported, languages are beginning to be used.

25.6.2.4 *C++*

The language C was originally developed as the systems programming language for the Unix operating system (Ritchie, 1978) but has been adopted widely as a programming language for software running not only on Unix but also on other operating systems. In the same way that new languages sprang from the Pascal route, C has its descendants, and of these the most important is C++ (Stroustrup, 1986) which adds object oriented programming constructs.

25.7 Testing procedures

Testing is a process used to give confidence that a system's behaviour or its attributes are acceptable. Tests do not prove that a system is free from faults; tests may find faults but cannot show absence of faults.

The main stages of testing, as described above, are unit testing, integration and system testing and acceptance testing. However, all outputs of each stage of the development process can be tested.

25.7.1 Testing by analysis

25.7.1.1 *Inspections and walk throughs*

Inspections (Fagan, 1976) and walk throughs are similar techniques. In each case the item to be examined, such as the specification of a system or the listing of a module of code, is made available a small number of days in advance of the inspection or walk through to its reviewers. They, and there is often just one reviewer, and usually no more than three, familiarise themselves with the item. At the review the author of the item talks through the item step by step, exploring what is happening and answering questions posed by the reviewers. The reviewers usually have check lists to remind them of the issues which need to be considered. The author is given at the end of the review a list of faults found.

The main difference between inspections and walk throughs lies in the route taken through the item by the reviewers. In an inspection, the item is considered line by line sequentially, beginning at the first line. In a walk through the reviewers may begin with test data, following the logic of the item as dictated by the way in which the test data would be processed.

A peer review is a special case of an inspection, in which the reviewers are drawn from the author's project team.

A simpler form of inspection is desk checking. Here just one person normally carries out the review and the review is informal. With desk checking the author is not called upon to explain his work, there is no real interaction or discussion, and there is no independent moderator. The process can be an economical way to find faults, but it tends to be less thorough than the more formal approaches.

25.7.1.2 *Code auditing*

There are tools which can automate some of the tasks which would be carried out by reviewers inspections and walk throughs. They are usually applied to program code, and look for violations of standards or of good practice. An example is the Unix tool 'lint' for analysis of code in the programming language C.

Little support exists for the auditing of specifications, designs and other textual outputs of the system development process. Usually all that can be applied is a spelling checker. As the representation of

specifications or designs becomes more formal, it will be possible to generate more formal tools.

25.7.1.3 *Static analysis*

Static analysers carry out a more detailed automated examination of the structure of a program, without executing it.

Complexity analysis

A complexity analyser will provide an estimate of the complexity of a module of code based on its structure. The estimate will be derived from features such as :

1. The number and the intricacy of the interfaces to the code.
2. The number and the linking of decision points within the code.
3. The nature of the data structures used.

Perhaps the best known complexity measure is McCabe's cyclomatic number (McCabe, 1976), which is the number of linearly independent control paths in the program.

Data flow analysis

Data flow analysers examine paths through the module of code, looking at the way data is defined and used. They report potential errors in cases, for example, where data variables are:

1. Defined and then redefined without being used.
2. Used without being defined.

Some special purpose data flow analysers exist (Korel, 1985).

More often this kind of check is provided as an extra service of a compiler.

25.7.2 Unit testing by execution

In conventional unit testing the code module is compiled, loaded in to the computer and set to run. Input data is supplied and the observed behaviour of the software is compared with the expected behaviour.

25.7.2.1 *'Top-down' and 'Bottom-up' testing*

A software unit is a component of the system. It is generally not a self contained program and cannot be run alone. It may rely on other components of the system. This means that the order of testing is important. If the unit to be tested depends on others, then it is convenient if those units on which it depends have already been tested.

Some systems are defined as a hierarchy of units, with a single top level module representing the complete program and calling on subordinate modules to carry out the main tasks. These in turn can call on their own subordinates.

With this architecture a 'top-down' approach can be used. Testing begins with the top level module, supported not by its subordinate units but by dummy modules known as 'stubs'. The stubs simply provide to the module under test the data it requires. The converse, 'bottom-up' approach starts with the lowest level modules. The tester either provides simple 'drivers' to control the unit under test, or employs a tool harness, which is a general purpose test aid able to feed data into the unit end to collect results. More comprehensive harnesses may also be able to compare the results with the expected outcome of the test automatically.

Usually unit testing proceeds with a harness in combination with stubs and drivers.

Software systems need not have this strict hierarchy. Telecommunications systems frequently make use of co-operating processes and of object oriented design, and here units need not be subordinate to each other in a strict sense. However, testing can still be carried out using harnesses, together with stubs and drivers as required.

25.7.2.2   *Test case generation*

For only the very simplest of pieces of software is it realistic to attempt to observe the behaviour in all possible circumstances.

The people who construct software and the systems on which it depends can make mistakes. We can call these errors. Human error may result (it need not) in one or several defects in the software that has been built. These can be called bugs or faults. Depending on the way in which the software is used, the presence of faults may cause it to misbehave. This will be a failure. So human error may lead to software fault, which may result in failure. The goal of testing is to reach an appropriately high level of confidence that any errors which have been made, and any faults which may therefore be present, will not result in system failure. To this end, a number of techniques for test case generation and a number of measures of the thoroughness of testing are sometimes used.

Black-box testing

Black-box testing is testing of software chosen without knowledge of the way in which the software is constructed. The tests are based on the requirements and specification, not on the internal design.

1. Equivalence classes. An equivalence class is a set of possible values for a particular input condition which might reasonably be expected to be treated in the same way by the software. Testing one value from the set can be assumed to serve for testing any other value in the set. For any input condition there would be expected to be at least two equivalence classes: the set of valid inputs and the set of invalid inputs. More usually there would be several and perhaps many equivalence classes. Having identified the classes a set of tests is designed which attempts to use at least one member of each class within the smallest convenient number of tests. Such a set of tests gives comprehensive coverage (though not exhaustive coverage; see below) without being unnecessarily wasteful.
2. Boundary testing. This technique concentrates on using test values which are near, at and just outside the extremes of equivalence classes, on the assumption that errors are more likely to be made at these limits. The designer or programmer may, for example, use 'less than' when comparing two values in cases where the correct relationship may have been 'less than or equal to'. By also making use of test values just outside the acceptable ranges, the tester can look for failure to detect invalid inputs. Boundary testing also considers equivalence classes of outputs. The tester attempts to create tests cases which deliver results just inside, at, and just outside the limits of expected output ranges.
3. Function testing. The common way of producing a test set for black-box testing is to examine the specification for the unit under test and to construct tests to match each of the functions which it is meant to provide. For each item in the specification it should be possible to show one or more tests which examine that item. Testing approaches using equivalence classes and boundary values mentioned above are forms of function testing.
4. Volume testing and stress testing. Individual unit tests tend to be small. However, some faults relate to an inability to handle large volumes of data; queues, buffers or work files may overflow. Volume testing is simply subjecting the unit to large quantities of data. Stress testing adds timing considerations to volume testing. Where the behaviour of the unit under test may vary within time, stress testing subjects the unit to large quantities of data in comparatively short periods of time.

White-box testing

White-box testing makes use of the way the unit under test has been constructed.

1. Structural testing. Here test cases are chosen so that together they satisfy some measure of coverage of the code. The simplest, and weakest, measure is the count of executable statements. A set of tests which together execute all the statements in the code will, except for the simplest logic, have tested only a small proportion of the possible paths through the code. Even so, it is often difficult or impossible to find test cases which meet this criterion; code to handle certain exceptions or error conditions may be inaccessible in normal operation and where there is parallel processing with indeterminacy, common in telecommunications systems, the test set may not force all possibilities.

    A stronger measure is branch coverage, in which the set of tests cases is chosen so that both 'true' and 'false' results are obtained at each decision point in the code.

    Stronger still is condition coverage. Here, where the decision point may depend on a compound condition, each condition in the decision is required to take all possible results at least once. So, for example, given the decision point: ' do x if A and B' the test cases must show instances of A 'true' and A 'false' and also B 'true' and B 'false'. [Note that this does not demand all possible combinations of conditions. In this example two tests might suffice: one providing both A and B 'true' and the other providing both A and B 'false'; the case A 'true; and B 'false' need not be examined yet the coverage criteria is met.]

    Even stronger measures may be based on the coverage of certain kinds of sub-paths through the code. One such example is the set of 'linear code sequence and jump' paths (LCSAJ) (Woodward, 1980) which considers combinations of decision points.
2. Mutation testing. In mutation testing faults are inserted systematically into the program, each fault generated being included into its own copy of the code. This version of the code with its inserted fault is known as a mutant. A set of test cases is run against each of the mutants which has been generated. If the test cases are sufficient to discover each of the mutants then there is confidence that they are enough to discover all faults of the class for which the mutants have been formed. If some mutants are not discovered then either the mutant code is equivalent to the assigned code, or the set of test cases needs to be improved. The technique is used to test the tests more than to test the unit under test.
3. Symbolic execution. This is a technique (King, 1976) in which program execution is simulated using symbols for input data, rather than actual values. The paths in the program are executed

algebraically, with branches chosen by some arbitrary criteria. When an end point is reached the user backs up to a previous decision point and selects a different subpath. Eventually the outputs from the symbolic execution are compared with the corresponding part of the specification. Symbolic execution is not widely used in practice, though there are some tools to support symbolic execution in languages such as Fortran and Lisp.

4. Proof. It is slowly becoming possible to specify software mathematically, and one of the anticipated benefits of this is that it then becomes possible to use mathematical proof methods to obtain confidence in the program. Proof tools now exist and it is practical, though still difficult, to produce proofs of small systems. The application of this technique is today in the verification of key components of a system, where the need for correctness is high enough to warrant the investment in the proof. Standards emerging for safety critical software are already beginning to demand the use of formal verification and proof (Ould, 1991). The ability to prove correctness does not take away the need for testing. The proof usually must assume some form of correctness of the environment in which the unit being proved is to exist, and some of the non functional attributes, such as usability, of the unit may not be susceptible to proof (Lindsay, 1988).

25.7.3 Testing systems

The approaches to testing summarised above tend to apply to components of a system. However, a system at one level is often a component of a system at a higher level, and so the division between system and component is to a degree arbitrary. Nevertheless, there are some issues in testing which relate to the testing of systems as aggregations of components, rather than to the components themselves.

25.7.3.1 *Integration testing*

Integration testing looks to see that the (partial) system built from a collection of components behaves as expected. This testing will include functional testing of the integrated system, but it focuses on the interfaces between components.

At this stage more importance tends to be given to be non-functional attributes of the system, such as performance and usability. At earlier stages of development these attributes may need to be examined by modelling (q.v.).

25.7.3.2 *System testing*

The system test of the completed, integrated system is the supplier's final check that the system meets its requirements. Here particularly it is important that the testing is carried out by a group other than that responsible for the development.

The system test team create test sets based on the understanding of the customer's or end user's requirements, which often are not and cannot be stated precisely, and on the user documentation provided by the developers. The tests exercise each required facility and examine attributes such as performance, reliability, installability and safety. Myers (1979) lists 15 categories of system test cases.

25.7.3.3 *Acceptance testing*

The acceptance test is the customer's check that the system meets its requirements. The tests will probably cover the same ground as the system test, though usually not so comprehensively.

25.7.3.4 *Regression testing*

Regression testing applies to an enhanced system or component, and is a check to see that modifications have not caused unintended effects and that the system or component still meets its requirements. The regression test usually consist of a battery of tests constructed during earlier development and enhancement of the system, often extracted from a test library and run automatically.

25.7.4 Debugging

Tests may discover faults in a system; debugging is the activity of isolating and correcting them.

25.7.4.1 *Dumps and traces*

The basic approaches to debugging involve the collection and presentation of information about the behaviour of a system as it moves towards the point of failure, assuming that the failure is repeatable. The values of variables may be displayed at selected points in the execution, and the path taken through the code may be traced.

25.7.4.2 *A process for debugging*

The usual steps taken are first to check that the failure can be reproduced and then to find the most simple case available which exhibits the failure. Then an attempt is made to localise the fault, focusing attention on some subset of the system. During this simplification and localisation a number of hypotheses will be developed, and some rejected. The likely hypotheses, if there are any, then need to be checked against all the symptoms of the failure. If a hypothesis checks out, a correction may be devised, installed and retested (Araki, 1991).

An isolated fault may represent a class of faults which exist elsewhere in the system, so having corrected the first instance of the problem consideration should be given to the possible presence of similar faults elsewhere.

25.7.4.3 *Stability*

Software evolves and decays (Lehman, 1980). As a software system is maintained the number of failures reported should tend to decline, but eventually there is decay and a point is reached at which the removal of a fault is likely to result in the introduction of at least one new fault.

25.8 Software development environments

Classically, a software development environment has been restricted to tools supporting the creation of code, compiling, linking and debugging. With the advent of methods and techniques addressing the earlier stages of the software lifecycle, and the recognition that time spent at the specification and design stages is more cost effective than putting all of the effort into the back end of the process then a typical software development environment is now expected to contain tools which support the method and all tasks associated with software development; in particular:

1. Analysis, and requirements traceability.
2. Design.
3. Automated code and data base generation wherever possible.
4. Automated extraction of design material, and inclusion into documentation.
5. Automated production of test cases.
6. Access to editors, compilers, debuggers.
7. Configuration management of all objects from design elements through to data structure definitions.
8. Reverse engineering.

In addition, it is expected that such environments are tailorable to match the project needs in a number of ways, for example:

1. Automatic production of function headers obeying project standards.
2. User definable annotation types to allow automatic extraction and inclusion of the text in documents.
3. Addition of menu options which when selected invoke a user program to perform a project specific task.

Each project requires a different level of tailoring which may be either trivial e.g. specifying a different function header layout, to substantial e.g. redefining or adding graphical symbols; or defining a change to the underlying method process supported by the environment.

These requirements have led to a number of environments being produced; in general they are in three categories:

1. Fixed environments supporting a given set of methods which are not easily changeable.
2. Environments which support a given set of methods but which are written in an open and modifiable way. They are characterised by the fact that all interfaces (for example to the underlying data repository) are clearly documented and available for use by non-experts, and that all menu options, formats for function headers etc. are in files which the user may modify according to the project needs.
3. Meta-environments which provide the facilities to create a software development environment which matches the user's needs exactly.

Category (1) is most suited to projects where the users wish to be guided by the environment and it is not desirable for any changes to the method to be made.

Category (2) is for users who wish to use a particular method, but are prepared to spend sometime (possibly weeks or months) customising the method and the items which are automatically generated.

Category (3) is for users who have developed their own method (possibly combining hardware and software development techniques) and wish to generate an environment containing tools to support the method. The input to a meta-environment is a set of notations, syntax and rules defining the semantics. Typically it will take several months to define such a method and use a meta-environment to create the necessary support environment, and care must be taken to ensure that the underlying method and techniques are complete, consistent and appropriate to the problem domain.

25.9 Software configuration management

Though no single lifecycle model necessarily fits all software developments, a common feature of the application of the models is that development is an ordered sequence of operations, where each operation has a tangible output acting as an input to its successor. This means that a software product can exist in a number of representations at the same time. There may be a specification, a design text, source code for the program and loadable code, each defining the final product. It is a function of configuration management to ensure that each representation is consistent with all of the others.

Software products tend not to be stable; faults are corrected and enhancements are made. Configuration management makes it possible to record the status of any representation of a software item, to be able to say which changes have been applied to it and which have not (Bersoff, 1979).

25.9.1 Baselines

A baseline is a fixed reference point in the software development. It is a good point from which change can be measured.

If the project management is applying a lifecycle model to the development then the work will move through a series of phases, from one phase of the lifecycle to the next. It is conventional to draw a baseline at the end of each of the phases. The end of the phase will be marked by a completion of appropriate documentation or computer files. This tangible output becomes the base line for the phase.

With most lifecycle models it becomes necessary to re-enter an earlier development phase. (A system design error may be discovered during the detailed design, for example, and so the system design has to be reworked). If a phase is re-entered then the rework of that phase will generate a change to its baseline. A configuration management system will record established baselines and all changes to those baselines.

There is a difference between work done to establish a baseline and rework done in the same phase of the lifecycle after the baseline is established. The path taken to reach the baseline need not be recorded but each step thereafter is.

25.9.2 Configuration identification

Configuration identification establishes the composition of the software item (what other items it is made from) and the documents and files which define it.

25.9.2.1 *Configuration items*

For all but the most simple software products, the product design activity will include breaking the product down into simpler components. As part of configuration management it has to be decided which components are to be given distinct formal identities and which are not. Those with formal identities are configuration items and are visible to the configuration management system.

25.9.2.2 *Documentation plans*

Each project should operate a documentation plan identifying all configuration items created or used by the project, and for each configuration item identifying the documents and files which comprise the item. Documentation plans are usually simple and generic.

25.9.2.3 *Parts list and 'where-used' lists*

For each configuration item constructed from other configuration items a parts list has to be maintained. This identifies the constituents of the item and also the other items needed for its construction (such as the tools used to build it).

The approximate inverse of the parts list is the 'where-used' list, allowing the consequences of changes to an item to be assessed.

Both parts lists and 'where-used' lists are nominally maintained automatically be configuration management tools.

25.9.3 Configuration control

Change control is the administrative mechanism for requesting, preparing, evaluating and authorising change proposals.

Change control applied both to delivered products and to products under development. Once a baseline has been drawn for a configuration item then all changes to that baseline should be controlled.

The terms used in change control are not consistent across usage, but the following are representative:

1. Change request. A request identified the effect required to be achieved by a change, the advantages of the change and the urgency of the change as seen by the initiator of the request.
2. Change Proposal. Proposals are responses to change requests, describing the way in which the change can be implemented and estimating its cost and ramifications.
3. Change control board. This is the formal or information decision making body which determines whether and then a change will be made.
4. Change note. The note authorises the change, describes it, and says what other configuration items are affected by it.

25.9.4 Status accounting

There is usually a delay between the approval of a change proposal and the completion of the change. A status accounting mechanism maintains a record of how the product has evolved and how it relates, at any time, to the issued baseline documentation and the set of authorised changes. Status accounting keeps track of changes, recording which parts of the changes have been implemented.

The kinds of data which may be kept include:

1. The formal name of each configuration item.
2. The baseline existing for each item.
3. The dates at which baselines were set.
4. Who is responsible for the item.
5. What change proposals affect each item.
6. The status of each proposed change.
7. The version number of each item.

In addition, copies of all change requests, proposals and notes are held.

25.9.5 Configuration auditing

The purpose of auditing in configuration management is to ensure that change to one representation of the product (such as the loadable code) is matched by equivalent change to another (such as the design documentation), and in particular that the change is consistent with customer requirements.

In the later stages of software development several baselines may have been drawn; specifications, design descriptions, code and test packages may all exist. When a change is made it may affect several of the baselines. The auditing function checks that the baselines are in step and that compatible documentation exists.

25.10 Software cost estimating

A number of approaches have been taken to software cost estimating, some fairly simple (Reifer, 1980) and some less so. The most common are COCOMO (Boehm, 1981), SLIM (Putnam, 1979) and Function Point Analysis (Albrecht, 1983).

25.10.1 COCOMO

COCOMO stands for Constructive Cost Model, and comes in three flavours, basic, intermediate and detailed.

Basic COCOMO first requires the project to be classed as one of 'organic', 'semidetached', or 'embedded'.

1. Organic projects tend to have small experienced teams producing a small product, using a stable environment.
2. Semidetached projects have a mix of experience in their teams, and may be producing a larger sized product.
3. Embedded projects work under tight constraints and require innovative solutions.

The effort required and the time to complete are then estimated in terms of the probable size of the product e.g. MM (man months), KDSI (thousands of delivered source instructions), TDEV (development time), as in Equations 25.1 to 25.3, for organic, semi-organic and embedded projects, respectively.

$$MM = 2.4\,KDSI^{1.05} \quad TDEV = 2.5\,MM^{0.38} \tag{25.1}$$

$$MM = 3.0\,KDSI^{1.12} \quad TDEV = 2.5\,MM^{0.35} \tag{25.2}$$

$$MM = 3.6\,KDSI^{1.20} \quad TDEV = 2.5\,MM^{0.32} \tag{25.3}$$

Intermediate COCOMO improves on these crude estimates by applying multipliers based on:

1. Product attributes, such as the required reliability.
2. Computer attributes, such as the performance constraints.
3. Personnel attributes, such as programmer or designer capability.
4. Project attributes, such as the degree of use of modern development practices.

Each attribute is scored and a corresponding multiplier is then applied to adjust the basic COCOMO estimates.

Detailed COCOMO provides the further refinement that the multipliers are sensitive to life cycle phases.

In each case, it is necessary for COCOMO to be calibrated to fit the organisation whose projects are being modelled, for no single attribute can be expected to have the same impact in two distinct organisations.

25.10.2 SLIM

The Putnam model applies the Rayleigh curve to the manpower profile as in Equation 25.4 and illustrated in Figure 25.6, where y(t) is the manpower at time t, K is the total life cycle effort, is the development time.

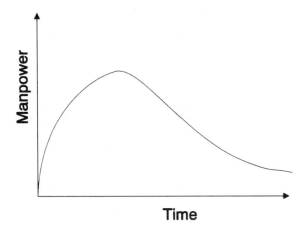

Figure 25.6 Manpower profile by the Rayleigh curve

$$y(t) = K \frac{t}{t_d^2} \exp\left(-\frac{t^2}{2\,t_d^2} \right)$$
(25.4)

25.10.3 Function point analysis

Albrecht's metric of function points (Albrecht, 1983) allocates scores to known sources of complexity, such as inputs and outputs. This offers a measure of size from which cost estimates can be inferred. The size metric corresponds rather more to the scale of the problem rather than the way it is programmed.

25.11 Software quality and reliability

25.11.1 Measuring quality

One of the difficulties in trying to achieve quality in a product is that of knowing what constitutes quality. To see whether quality is sufficient, and to check that there is a trend of improving quality, there need to be measures. However, quality is not single valued; there have to be a number of quality factors, which may be interdependent but which are distinct.

The following set of quality factors is due to McCall, Richards and Walters (McCall): correctness, reliability, efficiency, integrity, usability, maintainability, testability, flexibility, portability, reusability, interoperability.

However, these still do not lend themselves to easy measurement. One proposal for obtaining measurements is to represent each factor as a set of one or more criteria, and then to propose measures of the criteria. The measures which are available will not always correlate with the criteria, and therefore they will not always correlate with

the factors. A means of weighting the measures is therefore required. One proposal (Boehm, 1978) is to value in the range 1 to 4 each of:

1. The strength of the relationship between the metric and its quality factor.
2. The importance as an indication of final quality.
3. The degree to which measurement can be automated.

High scores in some or all of these lead to a high weighting. Multi-valued measures have been proposed for each of the factors listed above.

25.11.2 Specifying and predicting quality

Having the ability to measure quality leads to the ability to specify it. However, there is no common agreement on the metrics which relate to many of the quality factors.

The factors are not independent. Achieving efficient code might mitigate against, for example, achieving maintainable code. There are now prototype tools which assist in the breakdown of quality factors for the benefit of the person making the specification, and advise whether proposed values are inconsistent.

Similarly, there is at least one prototype constructive quality model which helps the user to predict quality levels based on the nature of the system to be built and of the techniques to be applied. Reliability is a special case and reliability modelling is summarised elsewhere.

25.11.3 Achieving quality

There are no tools or processes guaranteed to obtain software quality. Some help, and the early paragraphs of this chapter suggest elementary rules of software development.

Gilb offers three key approaches (Gilb, 1986) to achieving quality under deadline pressure:

1. Evolutionary delivery, not attempting to provide everything asked for at once.
2. Inspection, especially of the early specification and design outputs (Fagan, 1976).
3. Setting measurable quality objectives.

25.12 References

Albrecht, A.J. and Gaffney, J.E. (1983) Software function, source lines of code and development effort prediction: a software science validation, *IEEE Transactions on Software Engineering*, **SE-9**, (6), November.

Araki, A., Furnjawa, Z. and Cheng, J. (1991) A general framework for debugging, *IEEE Software*, **8**, (3), May.

Bal, H.E., Steiner, J.G. and Tanenbaum, A.S. (1989) Programming languages for distributed computing systems, *ACM Computing Surveys*, **21**, (3), September.

Bersoff, E.H., Henderson, U.D. and Siegel, S.G., (1979) Software configuration management: a tutorial, *Computer*, January.

Birtwistle, E.M. (1985) *Discrete event modelling on Simula*, Macmillan.

Boehm, B.W. et al. (1978) *Characteristics of Software Quality*, North Holland.

Boehm, B. (1981) *Software Engineering Economics*, Prentice Hall.

Burrell and Ouls, *A practical handbook for software development*, Cambridge University Press.

CCITT (1980) *Introduction to CHILL*.

CCITT (1989) *Functional specification and description language*. Recommendation Z100, CCITT Blue Book, Volume X Fascile X.1.

Colmerauer, A., Kanoui, H. and van Caneghem, M. (1983) Prolog, theoretical principles and current trends, *Technology and Science of Informatics*, **2** (4).

Fagan, M.E. (1976) Design and code inspections to reduce errors in program development, *IBM System Journal*, **3**.

Gilb, T. (1986) Deadline pressure: how to cope with short deadlines, low budgets and insufficient staffing levels, *Procs. of Information Processing 86*. (ed) H.J. Kugler, Elsevier Science Publishers B.V.

Glass, R.L. (1980) Real-time, the "lost world" of software debugging and testing, *Communications of the ACM*, **23**, (5).

Goel, A.L. (1985) Software reliability models: Assumptions, limitations and applicability, *IEEE Trans. on Software Engineering*, .**SE-11**, (12).

Hayball, C.C. and Tansley, D.S.W. (1992) *KADS methodology handbook*.

Hughes, S.W. (1992) *The RAISE development method*, Published by BNR Europe Ltd., London Road, Harlow, Essex.

Jelinski, Z. and Moranda, P.B. (1972) Software reliability research, *In Statistical Computer Performance Evaluation*, (ed. W. Freiberger), Academic Press.

King, J.C. (1976) Symbolic execution and program testing, *Communications of the ACM*, **19**, (7).

Korel, B. and Laski, J. (1985) A tool for data flow oriented program testing, *Proceedings of SoftFair 11*, San Francisco, IEEE.

Lehman, M.M.(1980) On understanding laws, evolution and conservation in the large-program life cycle, *J. of Systems and Software* **1**, (3).

Lindsay, P. (1988) A survey of mechanical support for formal reasoning, *Software Engineering Journal*, **3**, (1).

Littlewood, B. and Verrall, J. (1973) A Bayesian reliability growth model for computer software, *J. of the Royal Statistical Society, Series C*. **22**, (3)

McCabe, T.J. (1976) A complexity measure, *IEEE Transactions on Software Engineering*, **SE-2**, (4).

McCall, J.A., Richards, P.K. and Walters, G.E. (1980) Factors in software quality, *RADC Reports: NTIS AD/A 079 014, NTIS AD/A 049 015, NTIS AD/A 049 055*.

Myers, G.J. (1979) *The art of software testing*, John Wiley and Sons.

Ould, M.A. (1991) Testing – a challenge to method and tool developers, *Software Engineering Journal*, March.

Page-Jones, M. (1980) *The practical guide to structured systems design*, Yourdon.

Pankaj, K.G. and Scacchi, W. (1990) *A Hypertext system to manage software life-cycle documents*, IEEE Software, **7**, (3).

Putnam, L. and Fitzsimmons, A. (1979) Estimating Software Costs, *Datamation*, September to November.

Pyle, I.C. (1981) *The Ada programming language*, Prentice Hall.

Reifer, D.J. (1980) *A Poor Man's Guide to Estimating Software Costs*, Texas Instruments Inc. Technical Report RCI-TR-012.

Ritchie, D.M. et. al. (1978) The C programming language, *Bell System Technical Journal*, **57**, (6), July–August.

Scott, B.J. (1990) *User centre systems group*, BNR Europe Ltd., London Road, Harlow, Essex.

Shanthikumar, J.G. (1983) Software reliability models: a review. *Microelectronics and Reliability*, **23** (5).

Spurr and Layzell (eds) (1990) *CASE on Trial*.

Stroustrup, B. (1986) *The C++ reference manual*, Addison Wesley.

Turski and Maibaum. (1987) *The specification of computer programs*, Addison Wesley.

Wing, J.M. (1990) A specifier's introduction to formal methods, *Computer*, **23**, (9), September.

Woodward, M.R., Hedley, D. and Hennell, M.A. (1980) Experience with path analysis and testing programs, *IEEE Transactions on Software Engineering*. **SE-6**, (3).

26

Radio spectrum management

David J Withers
CEng FIEE
Telecommunications Consultant

Contents

26.1 Introduction

Governments manage the use of the radio spectrum to prevent the degradation by interference of a valuable resource, to ensure that radio systems use spectrum economically, leaving room for new users and new uses, and to provide for the orderly use of frequencies where this is necessary for practical reasons.

To ensure that these objectives can be attained, governments insist that there should be no transmission of radio signals without permission, signified by a licence. Licences are also required for many receiving stations. Exceptionally, a general authorisation may be given for specified frequency bands to be used for specific kinds of very low power device without formality, it being assumed that the possibility of interference can be disregarded in such cases.

Most licences specify the carrier frequency which has been assigned for use at a named station, together with other technical parameters of the emission (such as the transmitter power, the bandwidth that may be occupied and key antenna characteristics) and the purpose for which the system may be used. The assignment of a frequency usually implies an assurance that unacceptable interference is not likely to occur and that action will be taken by the licensing authority to eliminate such interference if it should occur. Typically a fee is charged for the licence, to cover the administrative costs of issuing it and a share of the cost of national spectrum management.

In pursuit of their policy towards industry, governments also regulate telecommunication systems and in particular, the operation of commercial systems set up to provide facilities for sale to other parties. Where the telecommunication systems use radio, the regulatory process may be implemented through the issuing, or withholding, of licences to operate radio stations. However, regulation of this kind is not discussed here.

If frequencies were assigned to stations at random from any technically suitable part of the spectrum, radio system development would be chaotic and the spectrum would be used inefficiently. The necessary degree of order is obtained by categorising radio systems into services and allocating specific frequency bands for each service. More detailed provisions are made for regulating the use made of assignments in some bands. The services and the allocations are outlined in Section 26.4 below.

Each government is sovereign in spectrum management within its country's frontiers. However, frontiers are no barrier to interference. Furthermore, operational radio equipment crosses frontiers on ships, on aircraft and by land and should desirably be usable wherever it goes. Governments collaborate where necessary in the management process to limit cross-frontier interference and to facilitate the operation of mobile radio stations. Much of this collaboration is done informally and bi-laterally or multi-laterally between the governments of neighbouring countries. Some specific management functions are co-ordinated through recognised international organisations with specialised responsibilities; for example, national use of some frequency bands allocated for civil aviation purposes is co-ordinated through the International Civil Aviation Organisation (ICAO). However, the International Telecommunication Union (ITU) is the primary world forum for radio spectrum management.

Governments set up bureaux to manage the spectrum. Usually such a bureau is part of a government department but some functions may be devolved to a body responsible to, but outside, government. The national authority, however it is constituted, is known as the administration.

26.2 Frequency assignment

26.2.1 National frequency assignment

Each administration maintains a register of the frequency assignments that it has made, recording where each assigned frequency is transmitted and received and the more important parameters of emissions. The use that is made of the spectrum is monitored, to ensure that unauthorised transmitting is stopped and that transmitting licences that are not put to use are withdrawn.

When a new assignment is to be made and the emission parameters required for satisfactory operation, such as the transmitter power and the bandwidth to be occupied, have been determined, a search can be made through the register to identify frequencies in appropriately allocated bands that may be suitable for assignment. The information in the register and predictions of propagation conditions are used to estimate whether any of these frequencies could be used for the new emission without causing unacceptable interference to other systems within the national jurisdiction. Similarly estimates are made of the interference that a new receiving station would suffer from established transmitting stations within the national jurisdiction if its receiver were tuned to a proposed new frequency. When an apparently interference free frequency has been found in this way, by inspection, it may be assigned for the new use, details being entered in the national register to prevent further assignments being made that would cause or suffer interference in the future.

Software is available for applying computer methods to the identification of interference free frequencies that could be used for new systems without causing interference to existing, registered, assignments. Spectrum efficient use of such techniques, however, requires the information in the register to be available in database form, together with adequate topographical and radio propagation information.

For some kinds of radio station, some administrations devolve the task of selecting frequencies for assignment to the owners of the stations. The relevant parts of the national register of frequency assignments and all proposals for new assignments are published and existing assignees, would-be assignees and the expert agents of both are free to argue before the administration whether a proposed new assignment should be made.

This description of the process of choosing frequencies for assignment by inspection is idealised, no mention being made of major practical problems. The most important of these problems is the international dimension, considered in Section 26.2.3. Other difficulties may arise within national frontiers. For example, the topographical and radio propagation data which are available may not be accurate enough to permit the wanted signal level and the interference levels to be determined with sufficient confidence, by calculation, to ensure that spectrum is used efficiently. The national register of frequency assignments may be inaccurate, leading to sub-optimal new assignments or interference when new assignments are taken into operation. Or there may not be a suitable frequency available in a heavily loaded frequency band without the re-arrangement of frequencies already assigned to other stations. Even without such complications, it is a labour intensive process demanding a lot of expertise. Furthermore, being a random process, it may not provide optimum use of the spectrum.

There are various ways of making this process more systematic, easier to apply and, in favourable circumstances, more efficient in using spectrum. Thus:

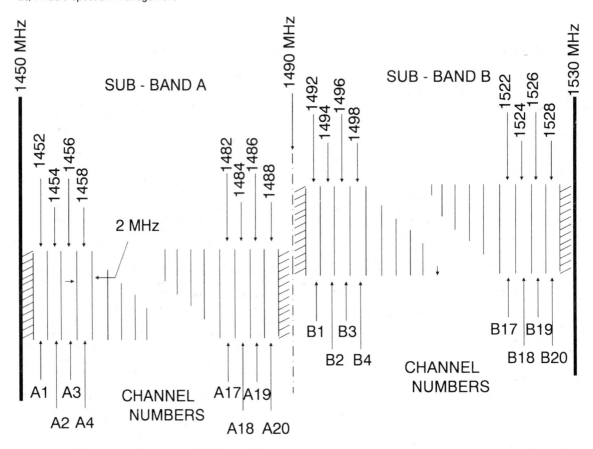

Figure 26.1 Radio channelling plan, providing channels 2MHz wide

1. A national radio channelling plan is sometimes drawn up. For example, when planning for bi-directional links, a frequency band would be split into two equal sub-bands, A and B, and each sub-band would be sub-divided into channels, each wide enough for a single uni-directional link. See for example Figure 26.1. One channel from each sub-band would be assigned to each bi-directional link, as in Figure 26.2. The plan shown in Figure 26.1 is suitable, for example, for multiplexed telephony links carrying 24 channel FDM with FM or 30 channel PCM with 4 phase PSK. Such a plan can facilitate the selection of frequencies for assignment. Where the planned frequency band is to be used for a large number of stations with similar characteristics, a regular radio channelling plan may give other advantages also; for example, the use of frequency synthesisers to determine the operating frequencies of transmitters and receivers may be facilitated and efficient spectrum utilisation may be more readily achieved through the imposition of strict type approval specifications for transmitters and receivers.

2. The radio channelling plan concept might be extended to become a national frequency allotment plan. A wide geographical area, perhaps nation-wide in extent, would be divided into cells, and a list of channels would be allotted for assignment within each cell. The same channel would be allotted for assignment in other cells, with enough geographical separation to make the probable level of interference acceptably low. The plan might, in the simplest case, consist of a regular tessellation of hexagonal cells, each allotted an equal number of channels. Alternatively, an irregular plan based, for example, on administrative areas and channel allotments proportionate to the local level of demand, might be more convenient to manage and would not necessarily be less efficient in spectrum use.

3. There will be circumstances in which the locations of stations that will need assignments in a frequency band in the future are known in advance. In such cases a frequency assignment plan, optimising the geographical dimension of spectrum utilisation, might be prepared at the outset, assignments being made in accordance with the plan as each station starts operating.

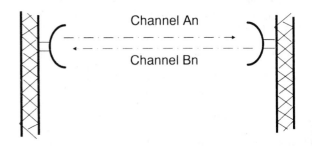

Figure 26.2 Channels An and Bn from the plan in Figure 26.1 are assigned to a bi-directional link

Other measures may also be implemented to reduce the burden of spectrum management that would otherwise fall on administrations. For example, where a single radio user has need of a great deal of spectrum, that user might be allotted a complete frequency band on condition that it is used efficiently. Administrations may also license stations or operators without undertaking to control interference. For example, the radio amateurs' societies are expected to discipline the use of bands allocated to radio amateurs.

There are alternatives to this method and some of them are described in Sections 26.4 and 26.6. However, despite the difficulties that are involved, the basic process of assigning for a new requirement a frequency that has been found to be suitable by inspection of the national register of frequency assignments, aided where feasible by national spectrum planning as indicated above, is in very general use.

26.2.2 International registration of assignments

Many transmitting stations in small countries and most stations in large countries do not radiate enough power to interfere with receiving stations abroad, particularly in the higher frequency ranges. Many receiving stations are likewise unlikely to suffer interference from abroad. The national frequency assignment management arrangements described in Section 26.2.1 are adequate for these stations. However, interference can cross frontiers; some radio links are international and some radio equipment moves from country to country and is used wherever it goes. The international aspects of frequency assignment management fall into three parts; the international machinery for registering frequency assignments is reviewed in this section, the management of spectrum in an international context follows in Section 26.2.3 and the elimination of interference if it should occur is considered in Section 26.2.4.

Before an administration makes a frequency assignment, it should ascertain whether the activation of the proposed new assignment will involve interference with already established foreign assignments. This often involves consultation with other administrations. In some circumstances, and in particular where it may be difficult to identify the foreign administrations that should be consulted, there are agreed mandatory procedures governing the consultation process (see Section 26.2.3.). However, informal contacts are used if consultation between the administration of adjacent countries is likely to be sufficient. Then:

1. If an assignment, when activated, may be capable of causing interference abroad or if it is to be used for an international link, details of the assignment must be notified to the International Frequency Registration Board (IFRB), one of the organs of the ITU.
2. The IFRB examines each notice to verify that the assignment is in accord with international agreements, and that any mandatory steps have been taken to ensure that interference will not occur to recognised foreign assignments. In some frequency bands below 28MHz, in which it is particularly difficult to assess whether interference is likely to occur, the IFRB itself makes a technical examination of the interference prospects. If the newly-notified assignment survives these examinations, it is registered in the Master International Frequency Register (MIFR) and dated. The essence of the MIFR is published twice a year in microfiche by the ITU, as the International Frequency List (IFL). A list of newly notified national assignments, together with an up-dating of the IFL, is circulated weekly to administrations by the IFRB.

Priority of registration in the MIFR helps to establish international recognition of the right of a station to operate on the frequency nationally assigned to it; see Section 26.2.4.

26.2.3 Limitation of cross-frontier interference

The use of the inspection method for identifying frequencies for assignment, laborious when interference from abroad can be disregarded, becomes even more difficult when cross frontier interference must be considered. There are indeed circumstances when effective international consultation on frequency assignments is virtually impossible, because the parties with whom consultation might be necessary cannot be identified with certainty or are too numerous. Such problems are made even more complex in many frequency bands by the practice of allocating spectrum, not to one service, but to several; this is called frequency allocation sharing.

Furthermore, many administrations reject the principle whereby the right to use a frequency may be based solely on priority of international registration of a national assignment. They consider that this benefits developed countries with long established radio systems, to the disadvantage of developing countries which are in the process of setting up their infrastructure. The impact of the "first come, first served" concept may be particularly serious where interference can arise at great distances, typically in the HF frequency range, 3 to 30MHz, and also where satellite systems are involved.

Various special measures have been adopted in particular frequency bands to deal with these problems and objections. The most important of these measures are as follows:

1. International radio channelling plans have been adopted in a number of frequency bands. These plans specify the carrier frequencies that should be used and the kinds of traffic that they should be used for. In some cases they specify also various parameters of the emissions that may be employed.
2. International frequency allotment plans have been formally agreed for some frequency bands. These plans extend the principle of radio channelling plans, typically by allotting channels to administrations for assignment to stations within their jurisdiction. See also Section 26.6.2.
3. International frequency assignment plans have been formally agreed for certain other frequency bands. These plans specify virtually all of the details of the foreseen assignments in a frequency band, including the location of stations, as well as many of the technical parameters of the foreseen emissions. See also Section 26.6.2.
4. In situations where it is difficult to identify all of the administrations that might be affected by a new frequency assignment, informal liaison between administrations would not be satisfactory. Detailed mandatory international frequency co-ordination procedures have been agreed in such cases.
5. Sharing constraints, such as constraints on transmitted power, are imposed on stations to limit the interference that other stations will suffer to an acceptably low level, in cases where frequency co-ordination would be impracticable.

Applications of these various specific measures are reviewed in Section 26.4.

26.2.4 Elimination of interference

If all the necessary preliminary checks and consultations have been carried out effectively before a new assignment is brought into operation, interference should not arise. However, radio propagation predictions are imperfect, the use that will be made of frequency assignments is not always clearly foreseen at the outset and the need grows every year to squeeze more and more systems into the most desirable frequency bands. Interference does arise.

If the station suffering interference provides what is called a safety service, typically a communication or radio navigation system upon which the safety of human life may depend, the interfering station stops using the assignment immediately.

If the assignment suffering interference and the assignment causing interference have both been made by the same administration, then that administration resolves the problem, typically by assigning another frequency to one of the links.

If the frequency assignments causing and suffering interference fall within the scope of an internationally agreed frequency allotment or frequency assignment plan, the interference may have arisen because system parameters assumed in planning have not been implemented; if so, the remedy is to bring the systems into line with the plan. Otherwise, it may be necessary to revise the plan to eliminate the interference. However, if the assignment suffering interference is operating in accordance with a plan and the interfering assignment, having been made by another administration which has ratified the plan, had not been planned, then the interfering assignment will be withdrawn.

Few frequency bands are allocated internationally for only one service; most bands are shared by at least two services, and some by several; see Section 26.3.1. The services sharing a band may have equal allocation status, but in other bands some allocations have primary status, and others have secondary status. Thus, station "S", of a service having secondary allocation status must stop using an assignment that causes harmful interference to station "P", belonging to a service with primary status, regardless of the dates of registration of the assignments, and station S has no remedy if station P interferes with its signals.

If safety considerations do not arise, if there is no internationally agreed plan, and if the radio services to which the stations involved belong are the same, or have equal allocation status in the frequency band, the operating organisations involved, assisted if necessary by their administrations, determine together what could be done to eliminate the interference. This may involve modifying one or other of the stations or modifying the emissions. As a last resort, it is customary for the opportunity to use the frequency without interference to be conceded to the station with the earlier date of registration in the MIFR but administrations are not committed to doing this.

26.3 International frequency allocation

26.3.1 Allocations for radio systems

In the early years of radio, only the lowest few megahertz of the radio spectrum were in use and they were used for point-to-point communication between fixed stations, communication with and between mobile stations, mainly ships, and broadcasting. These applications were called the fixed service, the mobile service and the broadcasting service respectively. By international agreement the spectrum then in use was divided into several frequency bands, different bands being allocated for each service.

This concept of dividing the spectrum between the different kinds of radio service is still found to be wise and its application has been extended and elaborated to serve modern requirements. The international table of frequency allocations (ITU, 1990, Article 8) now

covers the frequency range 9kHz to 275GHz, divided into hundreds of frequency bands, allocated for 33 different services.

Different countries need the various kinds of radio facilities in different proportions. Consequently, a rigid and uniform global pattern of frequency allocation would not be acceptable. The need for flexibility has been met in three ways:

1. Many frequency bands have been allocated, not for one but for several services; these bands are said to be shared. Usually all services sharing a band have equal rights of access to it, but there are bands in which one service is given primary status and another has an inferior, secondary status. As mentioned in section 26.2.4, the status of the allocation for a service affects the treatment that a station of that service receives if interference should arise.

2. The international frequency allocations are not uniform worldwide. Three geographical regions have been defined (ITU, 1990, para 392-399) and in some frequency bands there are different allocations in the different regions. The regions are approximately as follows:

   Region 1: Europe, Africa, USSR in Asia, Mongolia and Asian countries to the West of the Persian Gulf.

   Region 2: North and South America.

   Region 3: The parts of Asia not in Region 1, plus Australasia.

3. Footnotes to the international table of frequency allocations provide for departures from the world wide or regional allocations in various specified countries. See Section 26.5 below.

The frequency bands allocated to the various radio services and the methods which are applied internationally by regulation to manage the assignment of spectrum in the various bands are reviewed in Section 26.4 below.

Amendments to the international table of frequency allocations and the Radio Regulations are discussed and agreed at World Administrative Radio Conferences of the ITU.

26.3.2 Allocations for industrial, scientific and mqedical applications.

Not all generators of radio frequency energy are radio systems. Some industries use high frequency power, for example, for the heat treatment of metals and for drying and welding non-metallic materials. Some scientific machines, most notably sub-atomic particle accelerators, use radio frequency energy on a massive scale. Some apparatus used in medical diagnosis and treatment also uses radio frequency energy. Domestic and commercial microwave ovens are everywhere. All of these devices radiate some energy inadvertently. Similarly there is substantial radio frequency radiation from electrical power transmission plant, electrical traction systems and above all from petrol driven motor vehicles.

Often the radiation from such equipment is wide band and noise like but there may be a dominant spectral component. The designers and users of such equipment are urged to minimise both kinds of radiation. In addition, however, a dozen frequency bands spanning the spectrum from 6MHz to 250GHz have been identified by the ITU in collaboration with the International Electrotechnical Commission (IEC), to be used for Industrial, Scientific and Medical (ISM) equipment which has a narrow band radiation characteristic. These bands are also allocated for radio use, most commonly the fixed or the radiolocation services, it being understood that interference from ISM equipment must be tolerated in these bands.

26.4 International spectrum management

26.4.1 Overview

Almost all radio systems which provide telecommunications facilities fall into two broad categories, namely systems that link fixed stations and those providing links to, and between, mobile stations. These two categories, including the satellite systems for each, comprise the fixed services and the mobile services. Extensive frequency bands have been allocated for them, and many are shared between them. However, there are major differences in the regulatory methods used in the international management of frequency assignments to fixed and mobile stations and spectrum management for the two groups is considered separately in Sections 26.4.2 and 26.4.3. The amateur services follow in Section 26.4.4. The inter satellite service, providing spectrum for inter satellite links for systems of any radio service, is reviewed in Section 26.4.5.

However, there are other kinds of radio system. About one half of the spectrum below 1GHz is allocated for broadcasting. About one third of the spectrum between 1GHz and 20GHz is allocated for radars and similar position determination systems. There are lesser allocations for other specialised applications for radio. Some of this spectrum is shared with radio systems used for telecommunications and the conditions arising from sharing have significant impacts on the telecommunications services. There are brief accounts of these allocations for non-telecommunications radio services, as they affect telecommunications systems, in Sections 26.4.6 to 26.4.8.

26.4.2 Fixed station links

26.4.2.1 Terrestrial links

There are extensive allocations for the fixed service, comprising point to point and point to multipoint radio links, in most parts of the radio spectrum.

The fixed service allocations below 150kHz, at one time very important, are now little used. Those bands are occupied nowadays mainly by radionavigation systems.

About 55% of the bandwidth of the HF spectrum, in about 40 narrow bands between 4MHz and 28MHz, is allocated exclusively for the fixed service and is in substantial use, mainly for long distance ionospherically propagated links.

Substantial bandwidth is allocated for the fixed service between 28MHz and 1GHz. However, these bands are shared with broadcasting and the mobile services. The fixed service has little opportunity to use these bands in areas, like Europe, where there is heavy demand for these other services.

Very wide bands are allocated for the fixed service above 1GHz, much of this bandwidth being shared with the mobile service, the fixed satellite service or others. The means that have been adopted to deal with inter-service interference arising from this sharing pattern are considered in Sections 26.4.2.3 to 26.4.2.5. These allocations are heavily used, mostly for radio relay systems.

There are non mandatory CCIR radio channelling plans and similar national plans for microwave systems but in most other respects frequencies are chosen for assignment in the fixed service by inspection, with informal consultation between the administrations of neighbouring countries where necessary to ensure that interference is not likely to occur. After consultation, the responsible authority notifies the assignment to the IFRB, and the Board registers the assignment in the MIFR, provided that the assignments are in accordance with international agreements and subject below

28MHz to a technical examination to confirm that interference is unlikely to arise. However, if the station lies within the co-ordination area of an earth station operating in the same frequency band, the IFRB will not register a new assignment until its use has been co-ordinated with the earth station. Similar limitations apply in frequency bands around 12GHz that have been planned for the broadcasting satellite service and the associated feeder links around 14.6GHz and 17.7GHz (see Section 26.4.6).

26.4.2.2 Links via satellites

Wide microwave and millimetre wave frequency bands are allocated for the fixed satellite service. These allocations are used for links between fixed earth stations via satellites.

Feeder links may also be assigned frequencies in these bands. A feeder link connects an earth station at a given location with a satellite which is not of the fixed satellite service. The term covers, for example, links between coast earth stations and satellites serving ships, links feeding programme material to broadcasting satellites and links used for down loading data from a data collection satellite.

Some fixed satellite bands are allocated for transmission in the Earth to space direction (up links). The others are for the space to Earth direction (down links). The important up link allocations are around 6, 7, 8, 13, 14 and 30GHz. The corresponding down link allocations are around 4, 5, 7.5, 11, 12 and 20GHz. Three further up link bands, around 11GHz (Region 1 only), 14.6GHz and 17.7GHz, have been allocated for the fixed satellite service but reserved for feeder links to broadcasting satellites. Almost all of these allocations are shared with the fixed service and the mobile service. Some allocations are also shared with other satellite services, the directions of transmission being opposite to those of the fixed satellite service in some cases. With few exceptions, these allocations have primary status.

The modes of interference arising between fixed satellite stations and terrestrial stations are illustrated in Figure 26.3. The corresponding interference modes from one satellite network to another are illustrated in Figures 26.4 to 26.6. Special methods have to be used to prevent such interference, because it can occur over great distances and very large numbers of terrestrial stations operating in the same frequency band may be in the field of view of a satellite.

26.4.2.3 Constraints on satellite transmitters

Interference from satellite transmitters may enter fixed service receivers; this is interference mode 3 in Figure 26.3. It would not be feasible to control the level of this interference by negotiation, because of the very large numbers of stations that may be involved.

Most terrestrial stations are particularly sensitive to interference from satellites which are close to the horizon, that is, from energy which the satellite radiates towards the edge of the Earth's disc. See Figure 26.7. More powerful signals can be tolerated from sources higher in the sky. It has been estimated that interference would not exceed tolerable limits for terrestrial stations operating at 4GHz if the spectral power flux density from any one satellite, reaching the Earth's surface at an angle of elevation below 5°, does not exceed minus 152dB relative to 1 watt/m^2 in a sampling bandwidth of 4kHz. At angles of elevation greater than 25°, a flux density 10dB higher would be acceptable, with a linear dB transition between 5° and 25°.

Accordingly, these values have been adopted as a mandatory sharing constraint upon the fixed satellite service at 4GHz wherever

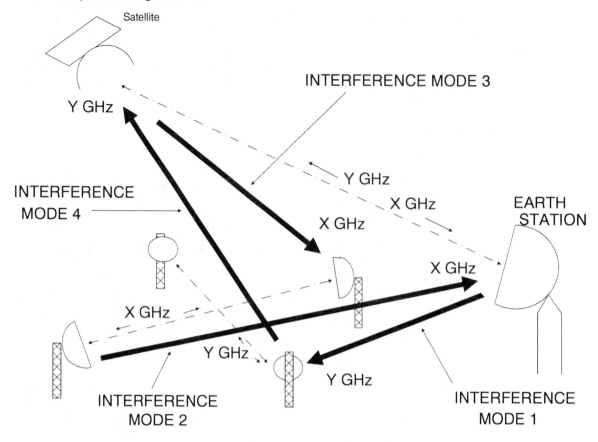

Figure 26.3 Interference modes between a fixed-satellite network and terrestrial links (Wanted signal paths are shown in broken line)

the frequency band is allocated internationally, with primary status, for the fixed service; see Figure 26.8. Slightly less stringent constraints have been agreed for down link bands at higher frequencies.

26.4.2.4 Constraints on terrestrial transmitters

Constraints on the power of fixed service transmitters operating in bands below 30GHz allocated for fixed satellite service up links (interference mode 4 in Figure 26.3) have been adopted to limit interference to satellite receivers for the same reasons as led to power flux density limits for satellite down links. The constraints are as follows:

1. The power input to the transmitting antenna shall not exceed +13dBW below 10GHz nor +10dBW above 10GHz.
2. The maximum equivalent isotropically radiated power (e.i.r.p.) shall not exceed 55dBW.

Below 10GHz the constraint is made more stringent in the direction of the geostationary satellite orbit. Thus, if the beam of a fixed service transmitter is directed within 0.5° of the orbit, usually because it is pointed towards one of the two azimuths at which the line of the orbit cuts the local horizon, the maximum e.i.r.p. is 47dBW, rising in a dB linear mode to 55dBW in directions 1.5° away from the orbit.

26.4.2.5 Frequency co-ordination around earth stations

There are agreed limits on the power radiated from earth stations at low angles of elevation in frequency bands shared with the fixed service. These limits are a sharing constraint, designed to keep within reasonable bounds the distances at which interference to terrestrial stations can occur. However, the limits are high, and they are unlikely to have much impact on the design of modern satellite networks.

The methods used in managing microwave spectrum for the fixed service assume that the incidence of interference will be relatively predictable and interference distances will be relatively short. Thus, administrations discuss proposed new assignments with their immediate neighbours, if it is thought necessary, before notifying the assignments to the IFRB for international registration, but this action is informal and non mandatory and international registration is not always sought if interference to or from future foreign terrestrial stations is thought to be unlikely.

However, earth stations have more powerful emissions than typical terrestrial stations and more sensitive receivers; interference may arise at great distances and such interference may be sporadic, depending, for example, on tropospheric duct propagation. A thorough and mandatory procedure is used to identify and eliminate potential cross frontier interference problems when an earth station is first set up. This procedure, once carried out, also provides a basis

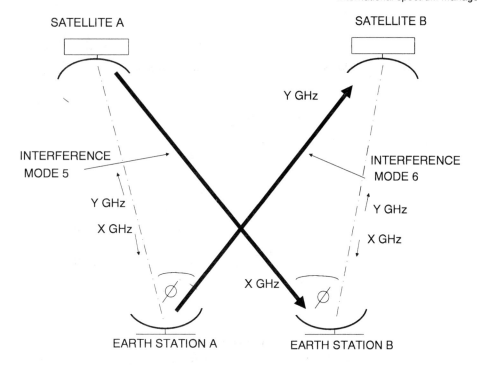

Figure 26.4   Interference modes from satellite network A to satellite network B, both using frequency band X for down-links and band Y for up-links. Interference from network B will enter network A by similar modes (Wanted signal paths are shown in boken line)

for co-ordination of subsequent significant changes of frequency assignments to both services in the vicinity of this earth station.

The procedure (ITU, 1990, Articles 11-13) is simple in principle, although somewhat complex in practice. The administration responsible for a proposed new earth station prepares a map, using agreed standardised parameters and techniques, showing the area around the proposed site within which, under worst case conditions, the earth station transmitter might cause significant interference to a receiver of the fixed service operating in the up link frequency band. A second map is drawn, showing the area within which, under worst case conditions, a transmitter of the fixed service operating in the down link frequency band might cause significant interference to the earth station receiver. These are interference modes 1 and 2 respectively in Figure 26.3.

If the co-ordination areas shown by these maps include any foreign territory where there is an agreed allocation of the same frequency bands for the fixed service, the two administrations exchange information on all relevant earth station and terrestrial station frequency assignments and co-operate to determine whether interference will exceed internationally agreed threshold levels. If interference problems are foreseen, acceptable solutions must be found before assignments are notified for international registration.

26.4.2.6   *Frequency co-ordination between satellite neworks*

A mandatory procedure is used to bring together for consultation the various administrations responsible for satellite systems that might interfere with one another. These consultations are often technically complex, since there are likely to be two bi-lateral interference

modes (modes 5 and 6 in Figure 26.4) between any pair of satellite networks. There may be three other bi-lateral interference modes (modes 7 and 8 in Figures 26.5 and 26.6, including the "quasi antipodal" form of mode 8) in the circumstances, so far relatively rare, in which a band used for up links in one network is used for down links in the other, and vice versa.

An administration responsible for a proposed new satellite network publishes the essential technical details up to six years before the launch. This is called "advance publication". It draws the attention of other administrations, responsible for existing satellite networks, to possible future inter network interference problems, enabling discussions to be held to seek ways of reducing prospective interference before the design and manufacture of the new satellite has progressed too far for changes to be made.

For a satellite that is not to be geostationary, the frequency assignments for the receivers and transmitters on board the satellite can be notified to the IFRB for registration in the MIFR when these discussions have been completed, without further formality. In operation, the transmitters on a non-geostationary satellite and at the associated earth stations must be switched off whenever this is necessary to avoid causing interference to a geostationary satellite network.

However, for a geostationary satellite network, formal procedures are used to ensure that interference to or from other geostationary satellite networks will not exceed agreed acceptable limits. These procedures must be completed, to the satisfaction of the IFRB, before the satellite frequency assignments can be registered in the MIFR. Two different kinds of procedure are used for this purpose, according to the frequency bands in which the new satellite is to operate.

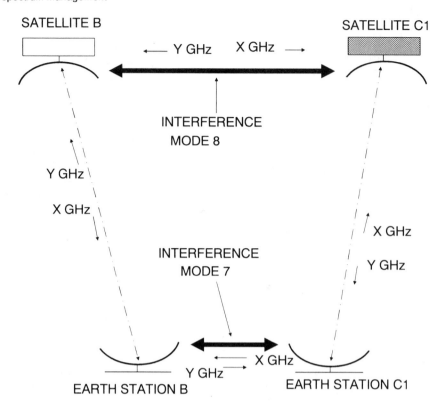

Figure 26.5 Interference modes between fixed-satellite networks having neighbouring satellites, both networks using frequency bands X and Y but in opposite directions of transmission (Wanted signal paths are shown in broken line)

A frequency and orbit allotment plan (ITU, 1990, Appendix 30B) has been drawn up for geostationary satellite networks of the fixed satellite service operating in the following frequency bands:

1. Up links at 6.725 to 7.025GHz and/or 12.75 to 13.25GHz.
2. Down links at 4.5 to 4.8, 10.7 to 10.95GHz and/or 11.2 to 11.45GHz.

This plan provides for each country to set up one satellite network covering its own territory, subject to broad limits on the parameters of the equipment and the emissions that are used, whenever it is ready to do so, without risk that networks set up by other countries will have pre-empted its option.

In all other frequency bands there is a detailed procedure of frequency co-ordination, designed to give every administration with a reasonable concern about interference the right to discuss prospective interference levels with the administration proposing to set up the new network. The chief parameters that are open to negotiation when excessive interference is foreseen are the orbital locations of the satellites, frequency assignments and earth station antenna characteristics.

As will be seen from Section 26.4.6. frequency assignment plans have been agreed for satellite broadcasting and the associated feeder links in several frequency bands between 11.7GHz and 18.3GHz, some of which are shared with the fixed satellite service. Special frequency co-ordination processes (ITU, 1990, Appendices 30 and 30A) additional to those outlined above, are used to ensure that

broadcasting suffers no significant interference from the fixed satellite service.

26.4.3 Links for mobile stations

26.4.3.1 *Terrestrial links*

Frequency bands are allocated for the mobile service, to be used for links with, or between, any kind of mobile station, but other allocations are made specifically for the aeronautical mobile, maritime mobile and land mobile services respectively. There is a further sub division of allocations for aeronautical use as between "Route" bands reserved for air traffic control purposes on civil air routes, and "Off route" bands, used for other aeronautical purposes. Narrow bands at various frequencies have been identified for use in distress and other emergencies; special measures are taken to prevent interference arising in these bands.

There are maritime mobile allocations below 160kHz but their use is declining. The maritime band around 500kHz, limited to radio-telegraphy, is in heavy use. Maritime and aeronautical allocations around 2MHz and 3MHz are also in substantial use, although the mobile services must share these bands with other services.

Over fifty narrow bands, mostly unshared, spread between 4MHz and 28MHz, have been allocated for the maritime service or the aeronautical service (Route or Off route) and a few bands have been allocated in this part of the spectrum for the land mobile service. These bands are used mainly for long distance, ionospherically propagated links. Most of the maritime bands have been sub divided

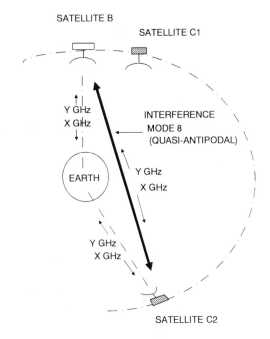

Figure 26.6 With frequency usage as in Figure 26.5, interference may also arise when the satellites are very wide apart in orbit, the quasi-antipodal case, as shown here

between radiotelephony and radiotelegraphy, elaborate radio channelling plans have been agreed for the radiotelegraph sub bands and there is a frequency allotment plan for the radiotelephone sub bands. Most of the aeronautical bands have been incorporated into frequency allotment plans (ITU, 1967; ITU, 1983), suitable for radiotelephony but available for other kinds of signal also.

There are important aeronautical mobile (Route) and maritime allocations around 125MHz and 160MHz respectively. There is a radio channelling plan for the aeronautical mobile band and the use of these channels is managed mainly by the national civil aviation authorities under the aegis of ICAO. There is also a radio channelling plan for the maritime band.

Wide bands between 28MHz and 470MHz and around 900MHz are allocated for the mobile services in general, shared mostly with broadcasting. These bands are used considerably for land mobile and aeronautical (Off route) systems but broadcasting is the major use.

Large amounts of spectrum are also allocated for mobile services above 1GHz, sharing with the fixed service (and in many cases the fixed satellite service). For technical reasons these allocations become less suitable for communication with moving vehicles as the frequency rises but considerable use is made of them for transportable equipment, often used for television outside broadcasting links. Where these bands are shared with up links of the fixed satellite service there are power constraints on mobile service transmitters similar to those which govern the fixed service sharing the same bands.

26.4.3.2 *Links via satellite*

As with the (terrestrial) mobile services, frequency bands are allocated for the mobile satellite service, usable for facilities for any kind of mobile station, but other allocations have been made speci-

fically for the aeronautical, maritime and land mobile satellite services. Some aeronautical mobile satellite allocations are specifically reserved for "Route" purposes.

The most important of the mobile satellite allocations are between 1530MHz and 1660MHz; sub bands in this part of the spectrum have been allocated for maritime, aeronautical (Route) and land mobile purposes. There is little sharing with other services. These bands are used entirely for links between satellites and mobile earth stations, any associated feeder links between satellites and earth stations at permanent locations on the ground being assigned frequencies in bands allocated to the fixed satellite service; see Section 26.4.2. There are also frequency allocations to the mobile satellite service in many other parts of the spectrum, many of them shared with the fixed satellite service.

26.4.3.3 *Spectrum management*

Very simple procedures are used for international registration when frequencies are assigned to stations at fixed locations (typically coast stations and aeronautical stations) in accordance with a frequency assignment or frequency allotment plan. In other bands, frequencies are chosen by inspection or from radio channelling plans, national or international, for assignment to coast stations, aeronautical stations, the base stations that communicate with land vehicles and the corresponding earth stations, typically after consultation with the administrations of neighbouring countries. These assignments are notified to the IFRB for registration after any necessary frequency co-ordination, as with the fixed and fixed-satellite services in corresponding ranges of frequency. The frequency co-ordination process for frequencies assigned to the satellites of mobile satellite systems is as described for the fixed satellite service in Section 26.4.2.

Many kinds of mobile station are authorised to use, not one frequency, but any of many frequencies, the assignment used on any occasion depending on the circumstances. Assignments to mobile stations for terrestrial mobile services are not notified to the IFRB. Assignments to mobile earth stations, on ships, aircraft and land vehicles, are not notified individually for registration, but a collective notification is made by the responsible administration, indicating the area in which the mobile earth stations operate.

In choosing frequencies for assignment to mobile stations, an administration must often take care to exclude from the vicinity of, for example, a radio astronomy observatory, the use of a frequency at which the observatory operates.

26.4.4 The amateur services

There are allocations for the amateur service in every part of the radio spectrum in use today. Many of these bands are allocated for the amateur satellite service also. However, many of these allocations are also shared with other services, typically the radiolocation service, and in some bands the amateur services have secondary status.

There are various internationally agreed technical constraints and operational constraints on amateur stations in the various bands. These constraints typically limit the power and bandwidth of emissions. Administrations authorising the launch of an amateur satellite operating in bands shared with other services undertake to ensure that the ground telecommand facilities will be good enough to keep interference from the satellite under control.

The regulation of the amateur services differs from that of other services in that the licence is awarded, not to the station, but to the

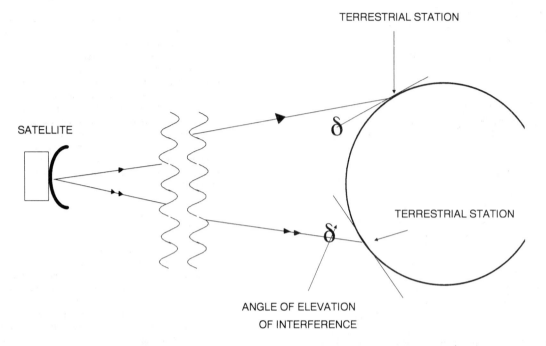

Figure 26.7 Geometry of interference from satellite transmitter to terrestrial service receiving station, showing angle of elevation δ of interference on arrival

operator, subject to proof of competence to operate a station. Formal assignments are made to amateur satellites and notified to the IFRB. Specific frequency assignments are not made to other amateur stations.

26.4.5 The inter-satellite service

Some research services have frequency allocations for satellite to satellite links but the other satellite using services, which may find need for inter satellite links in the future, have no suitable spectrum allocated for them. Instead, frequency bands have been allocated for the inter satellite service and frequencies in these bands may be assigned for any inter satellite links, regardless of the service to which the satellites belong.

The inter satellite service allocations are all above 20GHz and most of them are in parts of the millimetre wave frequency range where absorption is high, due to molecular resonances in the atmospheric gases. All the bands are shared with other services but the inverse distance squared attenuation on potential interference paths, augmented by atmospheric absorption where it arises, makes troublesome interference to or from stations of other services improbable.

A frequency co-ordination process, based on the one referred to in Section 26.4.2.6 above, is used to limit interference between inter satellite links.

26.4.6 The broadcasting services

26.4.6.1 *Terrestrial broadcasting*

In Region 1 there is a broadcasting allocation around 200kHz. World wide there is another allocation within the approximate limits of 530kHz and 1700kHz. Several relatively narrow bands between 2MHz and 5MHz are allocated for broadcasting, mainly in tropical areas. There are extensive broadcasting allocations world wide between 4MHz and 26MHz. Almost all of these allocations are exclusive to broadcasting and there are internationally agreed frequency assignment plans for the bands below 1700kHz.

There are broadcasting allocations around 60, 100, 200 and 500 to 900MHz, used for television and FM sound radio. The broadcasting service has primary status throughout but there is extensive sharing with the fixed and the mobile services. However, access to spectrum for these sharing services differs considerably from place to place. In Region 1 international frequency assignment plans have been agreed for broadcasting in all these bands and broadcasting use is intensive; substantial use is made of the mobile service allocations for land mobile systems, but only where this has been harmonised with the superior claim of the planned broadcasting assignments in nearby foreign countries. There are, however, no frequency assignment plans in Regions 2 and 3. In Region 2 the broadcasting service is protected from interference from the fixed and mobile services mostly by the secondary allocation status which the latter services have. In Region 3 all of these services have primary status and the partition of the bands between these various services is largely at the discretion of each administration, in consultation where necessary with neighbouring administrations.

Finally there are little used broadcasting allocations at 12, 42 and 85GHz. These bands are mostly shared with the fixed, mobile and broadcasting satellite services. It is likely that the availability of these bands for the telecommunication services will be determined mainly by broadcasting satellite developments.

26.4.6.2 *Satellite broadcasting*

World wide frequency assignment plans have been agreed for the broadcasting satellite service (ITU, 1990, Appendices 30 and 30A)

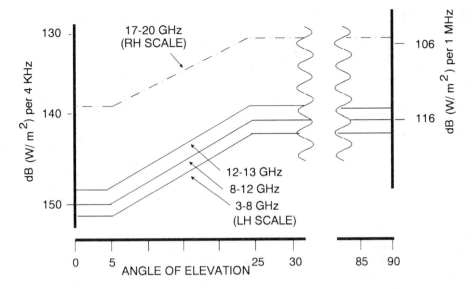

Figure 26.8 Constraints on the spectral power flux density at the Earth's surface from satellite transmitters operating in frequency bands shared with terrestrial services, as a function of δ and the frequency band

and for feeder links carrying programme material up to the satellites in the frequency bands given in Table 26.1.

In the down link bands, which are shared with primary allocations for the fixed service and terrestrial broadcasting and primary allocations (secondary in Region 1) for mobile services, these sharing allocations may be used only in ways that cause no significant interference to satellite broadcasting which is in accordance with the plans, regardless of the date when satellite broadcasting starts. Similar protection of the planned feeder link assignments is also provided by the terms of the plans.

26.4.7 Location by radio

The radiodetermination and radiodetermination satellite services include all systems which use radio to determine position, velocity or similar information, using terrestrial and satellite techniques respectively. Additional services have been defined to enable radionavigation systems, which provide safety services to be distinguished from radiolocation systems, which do not provide safety services, and to enable bands reserved for maritime systems to be distinguished from bands reserved for aeronautical systems.

With few exceptions the radionavigation service allocations are not shared with allocations to telecommunications services. Where such sharing does arise, radionavigation service assignments have advantages over those of the telecommunications services, if there should be interference, because the former always have primary allocation status, there are frequency assignment plans for it in some bands and additional protection arises from the "safety service" status of the radionavigation service. Radiolocation service allocations are sometimes shared with allocations for telecommunications services.

26.4.8 Exploration and research using radio

The last group of services consists of the space research, earth exploration satellite, meteorological satellite, radio astronomy, space operation, meteorological aids, standard frequency and time signal and standard frequency and time signal satellite services.

Several of these services need frequency bands suitably located in the spectrum, free from man made signals, in which radio frequency energy radiated naturally from the earth, from the atmosphere or from matter in space can be measured. Several need suitably located frequency bands in which the earth, including its atmosphere, can be probed for information from satellites, as by radar, using "active sensors". And most of them need frequency bands for the transmission of acquired data and for satellite management.

For passive observations there are a few allocations below 50MHz, and about 50 other allocations, wide or narrow, mostly above 1GHz. Some of these allocations are exclusive to the passive services but others are shared with telecommunications services; administrations do what they can, through their frequency assignment practices, to protect the exploration and research services from interference. For active sensors there are 11 allocations between 1GHz and 80GHz, all shared with terrestrial radar. For data links the earth exploration satellite and meteorological satellite services each have one or two allocations between 1GHz and 20GHz, wideband and shared on equal terms with telecommunications services. The other services have in aggregate a substantial number of allocations in many parts of the spectrum for communication, but most are narrow, many have secondary status and all are shared with telecommunications services.

Table 26.1 Frequency assignment plans for broadcasting satellite service

	Region 1	*Region 2*	*Region 3*
Broadcasting down-link bands (GHz)	11.7 — 12.5	12.2 — 12.7	11.7 — 12.2
Feeder up-link bands (GHz)	14.5 — 14.8 and 17.3 — 18.1	17.3 — 17.8	14.5 — 14.8 and 17.3 — 18.1

26.5 National frequency management

Governments, as members of the ITU, do not bind themselves to implement in all respects the worldwide or Region-wide provisions of the international table of frequency allocations. For example, many countries, claiming special needs, have obtained international agreement to the implementation of non-standard allocations within their territory; these agreements are recorded as footnotes to the international table. An administration is free to refrain from implementing within its jurisdiction any internationally agreed allocation. Also, an administration may assign frequencies for transmission in almost any frequency band to any kind of station, provided that the emission is not capable of causing interference abroad. Finally the Constitution of the ITU allows governments complete freedom of action with regard to military radio installations.

However, if use of an assignment contrary to the international table does cause harmful interference at a foreign receiving station which is operating in accordance with the table, then the interfering transmission must be stopped immediately.

Put briefly, governments do not bind themselves to implement the table, but they undertake to respect the right of other governments to do so.

Where a band is allocated internationally for several sharing services, it will often be desirable for an administration to limit the use of the band, or part of it, within its jurisdiction to some or only one of those services. For example, much of the spectrum between 47MHz and 960MHz is allocated internationally to both the broadcasting and the mobile services; in practice, within a given wide area, a given block of spectrum can be used for only one of these services. Likewise it is unsatisfactory for the same radio channel to be used by both aircraft and surface vehicles. Each country must decide for itself how to divide these bands between the various potential users, although these national decisions will often be harmonised with those of neighbouring countries.

An administration constructs a national frequency allocation table, based on options offered by the international table. Many frequency bands will be allocated nationally in the same terms as are found in the international table; this will often be true, for example, of the bands used for ships and aircraft. In recent years European countries have aimed to standardise the bands used for land mobile radiotelephones. Elsewhere in the spectrum, however, the national table will take into account the specific national requirements.

To allocate frequency bands to services as the ITU defines them is only the beginning of the process of planning how the spectrum is to be used within the jurisdiction of an administration. Thus:

1. Bands allocated internationally for the mobile service may be allocated for national purposes specifically for the maritime, the aeronautical or the land mobile service.
2. It will probably be desirable to designate solely for military use some of the bands allocated to the fixed, mobile, and radio-determination services and the corresponding satellite services.
3. It may be found expedient to allot whole bands, or sub-bands, to major civil users of radio. Thus the recognised providers of public telecommunications services may be authorised to use, and required to use efficiently, specified bands allocated to the fixed service. Other fixed service bands would be managed by the administration to provide frequency assignments for private fixed links.
4. Some bands allocated nationally for the land mobile service may be designated for private mobile radio systems; others would be designated for radio telephones giving access to the public telephone network, for communication with police and emergency service vehicles, for use by major public utilities, for cordless telephones, for wide area pagers, for citizens' band and so on.

Thus, the national frequency allocation table becomes an important and complex national planning document.

The uses of radio change with time, often because desirable new facilities have become technically and economically feasible and other, long established facilities have been superseded. It may be possible to provide for growth by assigning frequencies from frequency bands which are already in use, although it may first be necessary to re-organise the existing use so as to increase spectrum utilisation efficiency. Failing this, the usual alternative is to develop the use of vacant frequency bands, already appropriately allocated, high in the currently used spectrum.

However, in some countries most bands below 20GHz are already filling up and much higher bands are coming into use. Millimetre wave assignments are quite suitable for some kinds of radio system, such as short distance wide band fixed links, and they are acceptable for many other purposes, but they are unsuitable for, for example, most land mobile applications.

The emergence, in the 1980s, of technical means for providing convenient mobile radiotelephone facilities, car borne and hand portable, at an acceptable price has led to a massive demand for land mobile systems, cellular and trunked, and consequent pressure for spectrum below 1GHz. To clear spectrum for these mobile systems, it has been necessary to replace many assignments for fixed links below 1GHz by new assignments at higher frequencies and a critical examination has been made of the need for some of the VHF and UHF allocations for broadcasting. The next major stage in the expansion of mobile radio is involving the use of frequencies around 2GHz.

If provision cannot be made for a new allocation in a national table from amongst the options provided already by the international table, it will be desirable to get the international table amended at a competent world administrative radio conference (WARC). If there is general agreement that the addition of the new allocation to the international table is desirable, that allocation may be written into the international table of frequency allocations with worldwide, or perhaps Region-wide, applicability and with primary status. Often the already existing allocation will be retained for existing systems, creating a new sharing situation or extending one that was already in existence.

However, the need for changes of the international allocations may not be widely perceived and there may not be agreement as to what change should be made amongst the nations that do perceive the need. Failing agreement to a worldwide or regional primary allocation, international recognition of an allocation with sufficient status may be obtained by means of a secondary allocation, or a geographically limited footnote to the international table or by some combination of these measures by which the rights of existing stations of other services are protected.

26.6 Efficient spectrum utilisation

26.6.1 General measures

There are wise general principles of spectrum management, built into the ITU Radio Regulations, supported by the recommendations and reports of the International Radio Consultative Committee (CCIR) and applied by administrations everywhere. These principles enhance the value of radio as a communications medium, increasing the information transmission capacity of the spectrum as a whole and minimising link degradations due to interference.

Attention is given to certain broad technical principles of spectrum conserving system engineering. There are international standards for the suppression of spurious emissions (ITU, 1990, Appendix 8). The bandwidth occupied by emissions is required to be limited to what is necessary. Frequency tolerances are applied to radio carriers. Users of radio are discouraged from transmitting unnecessarily high power. Encouragement is given to the use of well designed receivers and antennas, capable of making the best of a medium which is interference limited in some frequency bands and some locations. These general requirements are undemanding, but more stringent measures are applied in particular situations and specific frequency bands where the need is evident; some of these latter cases are mentioned in Sections 26.6.2 to 26.6.4.

Above all, there is close collaboration between administrations at two main levels. In the absence of overriding political inhibitions, they co-operate to ensure that their frequency assignments do not cause or suffer interference. And they share expertise, in the technology of telecommunications and also in developing a precise statistical basis for predicting radio propagation conditions for wanted and interfering signals.

26.6.2   International frequency band planning

There are various forms of plan, drawn up internationally, for the arrangement of emissions within specific frequency bands. Typically, such plans cover frequency bands where radio propagation conditions lead to long interference distances and where system parameters are uniform and change only slowly. The other common application is for mobile systems, where the value of planning is mainly operational. The three basic forms of plan, namely radio channelling, frequency allotment and frequency assignment plans, are described briefly in Section 26.2.3.

Planning of this kind can make an important contribution to efficient spectrum utilisation. It provides a means of requiring radio users to implement a set of stringent spectrally efficient operational practices and technical standards in a specified frequency band if they are demonstrably necessary to enable that band to carry the traffic load which is required of it. Also frequency allotment and frequency assignment plans provide what may be an efficient method for optimising the geographical pattern of use of the channels in a frequency band. Plans also offer a basis for firm, mutual inter governmental undertakings to respect the rights of foreign stations to use specified frequency assignments.

A frequency assignment planning conference may also be a helpful forum at which an administration with an immediate requirement for a new assignment in a crowded frequency band can negotiate adjustments to established assignments which will make way for the new station.

Frequency assignment or frequency allotment planning may also be used to reserve a share of a frequency band, associated in the case of satellite services with an arc of the geostationary satellite orbit, for the exclusive use of specified, and typically every, country. Such a plan is sometimes drawn up for a frequency band which is not yet in general use, in case a country, at some time in the future, should find it impossible to get access to the band for a new system, because the whole band has by that time become filled by the systems of other countries. Recent examples of such planning are the frequency assignment plans for satellite broadcasting that were agreed in 1977 and 1983 (see Section 26.4.6.2) and the spectrum/orbit allotment

plan agreed in 1988 for the fixed satellite service (see Section 26.4.2.6).

However, no rational and acceptable basis has ever been devised for sharing out a band between the nations. The actual requirements for which these reserved parcels of spectrum might ultimately be assigned are not known at the time of planning and many may never arise. And the systems, possibly few, that are established within the terms of such plans may be made more costly by the high standards of equipment performance which are demanded in order to provide for the possibility of access by a much larger number of systems, many of which are never implemented. Planning for this purpose meets a need that many administrations feel acutely, but it does nothing for economy in system costs or spectrum use for the planned service, and it may significantly impede the use of the same band for sharing services.

26.6.3   International regulations and recommendations

In certain radio services and in specified frequency bands, as indicated in Section 26.6.2, sets of spectrum efficient operational practices and technical standards have been adopted as part of a plan. Exceptionally, in the fixed satellite service using geostationary satellites, which is ill suited in precise planning, a similar though less comprehensive set of international practices and standards is being adopted in all bands as they come into full use, to raise the efficiency with which this service uses its transmission medium.

There are regulations requiring frequency co-ordination between geostationary satellite networks, to ensure that the orbital separation between satellites can be minimised. The level of interference which is to be permitted, has been the basis of co-ordination, has been raised over the years, allowing the angular separation between satellites to be further reduced (CCIR, 1990, Recommendations 466, 483, 523) so that more satellites can operate satisfactorily. There are regulations setting tolerances on satellite East West station keeping (ITU, 1990), typically at $0.1°$. The accuracy of satellite antenna beam pointing is to be maintained within 10% of the half power beamwidth or $0.3°$, whichever is the greater.

However, as is apparent from Figures 26.4 to 26.6, interference between satellite networks arises largely from unwanted radiation of energy from antennas in the transmit mode (mainly satellite antenna radiation to locations outside the service area and earth station antenna radiation towards arcs of the geostationary satellite orbit away from where the wanted satellite is) and corresponding sensitivities to interference. In frequency co-ordination it may be possible to reduce such interference to an acceptable level by increasing the orbital separation between the satellites, but this option is of declining value as the number of satellites in use increases. In order to ensure that full use can be made of the medium, these entries of interference must be reduced by using earth station and satellite antennas with low sidelobe gain and by designing satellite networks to minimise the spectral power density of sidelobe radiation.

The CCIR recommends limits on the spectral power density radiated off beam by transmitting earth stations. For example, at 6GHz the e.i.r.p. due to a wide band emission radiated at φ degrees off axis should not exceed $(35 - 25 \log \varphi)$ dBW in any sampling bandwidth of 4kHz when φ lies between $2.5°$ and $48°$. The corresponding limit for off axis angles greater than $48°$ is minus 7dBW per 4kHz. More stringent limits apply to antennas installed since 1988.

Also, design objectives have been set for earth station antenna sidelobe gain levels (CCIR, 1990; Recommendation 580). For example, the CCIR recommends for a new antenna, 5 metres in diameter, operating at 14GHz, that the maximum gain of at least 90% of the sidelobes in the directions of greatest concern should not exceed the values indicated in Figure 26.9 within the solid angle indicated in Figure 26.10. It is likely that corresponding targets will be set soon for satellite antenna beam overspill suppression.

26.6.4 National spectrum optimisation

Two kinds of radio facility, which are needed nowadays in great quantity in some countries, are private fixed microwave links and vehicle borne radiotelephone systems of the land mobile service. Indeed, ensuring that such systems use spectrum efficiently, so that the demand for frequency assignments can be met from finite bandwidth resources in parts of the spectrum where the radio propagation characteristics are suitable, may be the most difficult task that administrations face. However, cross frontier interference is not a major problem for these systems and it has not been considered appropriate for the ITU to draw up international regulations or guidelines for the management of the spectrum that they use. Each administration, or group of administrations with a common policy in mobile radio, must find its own solutions.

A third major area of work for administrations is co-ordinating the frequencies assigned to earth stations (typically of the fixed satellite service) and terrestrial stations (typically of the fixed service) in shared frequency bands.

These three problem areas are touched on earlier but they are considered in rather more detail below.

26.6.4.1   *Fixed microwave links*

The main elements of efficient planning for private fixed links are:

1. Definition of radio channelling plans (such as, for example, Figure 26.1) for the available frequency band.
2. Publication of technical specifications for type approval of transmitting and receiving equipment, compatible with the radio channel plans. The specification would set standards of such factors as antenna sidelobe response, antenna polarisation performance and rejection of adjacent channel interference. These standards would be stringent if circumstances made high efficiency of spectrum utilisation necessary.
3. Determination of circuit noise and interference objectives. The target level for noise plus interference in channels should not be made unnecessarily good, and the ratio of interference to noise might favour the former if efficient spectrum utilisation was important.
4. Channels would then be assigned to links as the need arises, the transmitter power being determined in each case to ensure that the noise plus interference performance realised did not too greatly exceed the objective.

The key operation in this procedure is the assigning of channels to links. When a substantial number of assignments has been made, each frequency may be re-used several or many times over, with geographical separation. The separation may be quite small if good use can be made of the directional properties of the antennas. Computer software which is available does this task well, but digital maps giving very precise topographical data are necessary if the highest efficiency in the use of spectrum is to be attained.

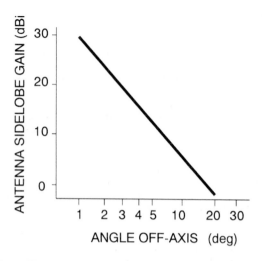

Figure 26.9   Recommended design objectives for the sidelobe gain of large earth station antennas installed after 1988.The maximum gain of 90% of the sidelobes within the solid angle shown in Figure 26.10 should not exceed (29 – 25 log φ) dBi where φ is the off-axis angle in degrees

26.6.4.2   *Mobile radiotelephones*

For land mobile radiotelephone facilities, different problems arise in managing spectrum. Here again a radio channelling plan is required. Channel frequencies will be re-used with geographical separation between service areas. The basic equipment type approval specification will emphasise:

1. Excellent suppression of spurious emissions from mobile transmitters and receivers.
2. Low adjacent channel emission in transmitters and low adjacent channel response in receivers.
3. Optimised channel bandwidth requirement, typically at present in the range 10kHz to 25kHz, and corresponding carrier frequency stability.
4. Freedom from receiver blocking by powerful signals off the tuning point.

However, traffic in the land mobile service typically consists of brief conversations between pairs of users, interrupted by periods of silence that may be long. The key to efficient spectrum utilisation lies in ensuring that a channel is not idle during the periods of silence. The nature of the user's business will determine what system architecture will provide efficient spectrum loading at acceptable cost.

A busy vehicle fleet operator, passing perhaps hundreds of short messages per hour to taxicabs, police cars etc. operating within an area some tens of kilometres in radius, may well make efficient use of spectrum as the sole assignee of a channel, using a simple transmitter receiver network.

An operator serving a small fleet of vehicles could seldom justify the exclusive use of a channel and a private user needing access from one vehicle would never do so. The level of use of the channel would usually be raised by assigning the same channel in the same area to several users. Simple control systems are available to stop one assignee from starting to transmit at a time when another assignee is using the channel. This provides a low cost system,

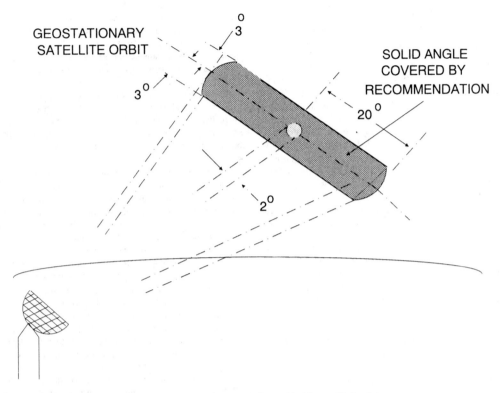

Figure 26.10   The solid angle to which the design objective indicated in Figure 26.9 relates

acceptable in spectrum utilisation efficiency in locations where the demand for spectrum is not high, although users find shared channels irksome.

In locations where demand is high, systems which offer access for each user to whichever of many channels is free at the moment when a call is to start can combine convenience to the user with very efficient spectrum utilisation. Multi channel trunked systems might be suitable if the vehicles remain for most of the time within range of a single base station. Cellular systems are necessary if the mobile station roams widely and are preferable where access to the public telephone network is required.

Given sufficient need for efficient spectrum utilisation, the spectrum manager must direct the users' choice of system towards appropriate system architecture.

26.6.4.3   *Frequency co-ordination around earth stations*

In shared frequency bands allocated to both the fixed and fixed satellite services, a frequency co-ordination procedure is used to limit interference between earth stations and nearby terrestrial stations. The procedure is outlined in Section 26.4.2.5. above. It is labour intensive but its application is quite feasible given the assumptions for which it was developed, namely that there are relatively few earth stations. However substantial numbers of new earth stations are now being installed, mostly Very Small Aperture Terminals (VSATs). The use of frequency co-ordination to manage spectrum in bands shared by large numbers of stations of both space and terrestrial services is likely to lead to inefficient use of spectrum for one or both services and spectrum management costs may become

disproportionate to the value of the telecommunication facilities made available.

Differences in the configuration of microwave terrestrial and satellite networks are a key factor here. If spectrum that is shared between these two services is to be used efficiently by both, the receivers of one service must be protected from the transmitters of the other by geographical separation or by obstacles in the direct propagation path between them. Now it is necessary for the antennas of most terrestrial stations to be mounted high on the skyline, on towers, the roofs of high buildings and hill tops; only in this way can line of sight propagation for terrestrial links of substantial length be obtained. Also, many terrestrial stations are located in city centres. There is no corresponding need for earth station antennas to be mounted high, and interference is reduced and co-ordination simplified if they are low. In considering how this basic factor affects practical spectrum management, three typical situations can be identified.

The first situation arises where the earth stations are used to provide high capacity network links, typically for international or trunk telecommunication connections or for television programme feeds, upwards to broadcasting satellites or downwards to terrestrial broadcasting transmitters or cabled networks. Such earth stations can be sited with due care, in locations which are remote from terrestrial stations or screened from terrestrial station antennas, typically by hills or massive buildings. Conventional frequency co-ordination is appropriate in such a situation and is in general use.

The second situation has evolved from the use of satellites operating in frequency bands allocated to the fixed satellite service for distributing television programmes to terrestrial broadcasting stations and cabled networks. Large numbers of small receiving antennas are now being used domestically in some countries to intercept these signals for home entertainment. In many residential localities interference from terrestrial transmitters may not be unacceptably high, but where interference is strong, there is no practical way in which frequency co-ordination can be used to reduce it.

The third situation concerns VSATs. Some of these earth stations are installed at remote locations, where interference to or from terrestrial stations may not be serious and conventional frequency co-ordination may be quite feasible, although the cost may be disproportionately high, relative to the value of the facilities provided by the VSAT station. However, installation of VSATs at city centre locations is more usual and rooftop antenna mounting would often be preferred. Spectrally efficient frequency co-ordination between these city centre VSATs and terrestrial systems operating from city centre towers is often not feasible.

The current indications are that the total bandwidth that VSAT networks will occupy in the foreseeable future may not be very great; a few hundreds of Megahertz may well be ample. If so, the best arrangement would be for VSAT networks to be assigned frequencies in fixed satellite allocations which are not shared in the earth station locality with terrestrial services. There are few unshared frequency allocations for the fixed satellite service in the international table of frequency allocations. The best prospects are as follows:

1. Up links; 14.0 to 14.5GHz (Region 2); 14.0 to 14.25GHz (Regions 1 and 3); 29.5 to 30.0GHz (all Regions).
2. Down links: 12.1 to 12.2GHz (Region 2); 12.5 to 12.75GHz (Region 1); 19.7 to 20.2GHz (all Regions).

Even these narrow bands are allocated to terrestrial services in very large numbers of countries by footnotes to the international table. However, one highly significant footnote (ITU, 1990, para 837) to the table reduces the terrestrial allocations in the band 11.7GHz to 12.1GHz to secondary status in Canada, Mexico and the U.S.A., effectively extending to 11.7GHz to 12.2GHz in those countries the band where earth station assignments do not have to be co-ordinated. Other countries, where footnotes to the international table provide a terrestrial allocation in the bands listed above, may decide not to activate those allocations nationally if substantial use of VSAT networks is foreseen.

26.6.5 Market forces in spectrum management

So far it has been assumed that the criterion for effectiveness in spectrum utilisation is enabling the largest quantity of radio services of all useful kinds to operate effectively in a large but not limitless spectrum. The means that are used for achieving this objective have been regulatory and technical. However, it has been argued that other objectives are to be preferred.

Economists point out that radio spectrum is exceptional among factors of substantial economic importance in that it is available at virtually no cost. Levin (1971), for example, argues that in consequence there is no satisfactory mechanism for ensuring that spectrum is distributed between users in an economically optimum way. The application of market forces should lead to spectrum being used, not necessarily to provide the greatest quantity of radio services, but for radio services of the greatest aggregate market value. He recognises that the establishment of a completely free market in spectrum presents special problems and is probably impracticable but he concludes that some substantial application of market forces would be beneficial.

The use of market forces in this way seems indeed to present major problems. Any system which takes authority over radio systems which can cause international interference out of the hands of governments raises problems, solutions to which are not evident. Also, loss of the benefits of internationally standardised frequency allocation in such areas as mobile communication and radionavigation would cause widespread difficulties and dangers. Furthermore, it is not obvious that facilities that only radio can provide can properly be denied to society because their market value is small.

However, there are situations where economic pressures of some kind would seem to be justifiable. In particular, the decision to use a microwave link between fixed points, instead of a cable connection, will often be influenced by the fact that cabling may be costly. If there is plenty of spectrum, the use of radio is a welcome benefit to the user. Where spectrum is in great demand, however, a case could be made for adding a leasing charge to the licence fee to encourage frugal use of bandwidth and to ensure that cables are used where economically feasible, leaving radio for the user for whom cable is a particularly costly option.

26.7 References

CCIR, (1990) *The Recommendations and Reports of the CCIR*, ITU, Geneva.

HMSO, (1985) *United Kingdom Table of Radio Frequency Allocations*.

ITU, (1967) *Appendix 26, Radio Regulations*. The International Telecommunications Union, Geneva.

ITU, (1983) *Appendix 27, Radio Regulations*. The International Telecommunications Union, Geneva.

ITU (1990) *Radio Regulations*, The International Telecommunication Union, Geneva.

Levin, H.J. (1971) *The invisible resource, use and regulation of the radio spectrum*. The Johns Hopkins Press.

Withers, D.J. (1991) *Radio spectrum management*, Peter Peregrinus Ltd. London.

27

Radiowave propagation

Mark Holker
CEng FIEE MBIM
Hiltek Ltd.

Contents

27.1 Introduction

Electromagnetic energy radiates outwards from the source, usually an antenna, at approximately the speed of light and it is attenuated and influenced by the medium through which it travels. Radio communications necessitates launching r.f. energy into the propagation medium, detecting its presence at some remote point and recovering the information contained within it, whilst eliminating noise and other adverse factors introduced over the transmission path. An understanding of radio wave propagation is therefore essential in the planning and operation of radio communications systems, to ensure that communications can be established and that there is an optimum solution between costs (capital and running costs) and link availability.

This chapter examines radio wave propagation in the frequency bands from v.l.f. (10kHz) to the millimetric band (100GHz), and the influence of the earth, the atmosphere and the ionosphere on such transmissions. It is assumed that propagation is in the far field i.e. several wavelengths from the antenna, where the electric and magnetic components of the wavefront are at right angles and normal to the direction of propagation. The process by which energy is launched into the propagation medium in the near field is described in Chapter 17, on antennas.

Radio waves may be propagated in one or more of five modes, depending upon the medium into which they are launched and through which they pass. These modes are:

1. Free space propagation, where radio waves are not influenced by the earth or its atmosphere.

2. Ground wave propagation, where radio waves follow the surface of the earth.
3. Ionospheric propagation, where radio waves are refracted by ionised layers in the atmosphere.
4. Tropospheric propagation, where transmission is "line of sight" with some atmospheric refraction occurring.
5. Scatter propagation, where natural phenomena such as tropospheric turbulence or ionised meteor trails are used to scatter radio waves.

27.2 The radio frequency spectrum

The radio frequency spectrum is divided into a number of bands which have been given designations such as l.f., m.f., h.f. etc. for ease of reference. These are shown in Figure 27.1 and are presented on a logarithmic scale. The microwave band, usually taken to be from 1GHz to 30GHz has been subdivided into a number of sub-bands which have been given letter designations such as X band (8GHz to 12GHz), but differing definitions are used and can cause confusion. 30GHz to 100GHz is commonly referred to as the millimetric band. Allocations have been made up to 275GHz by the ITU, but there is little activity other than experimental work above 100GHz.

Frequency and wavelength are shown in Figure 27.1. As radiowaves propagate at 3×10^{8} metres per second in free space, frequency and wavelength are related by Equation 27.1, where λ is wavelength in metres, and f is frequency in cycles per second.

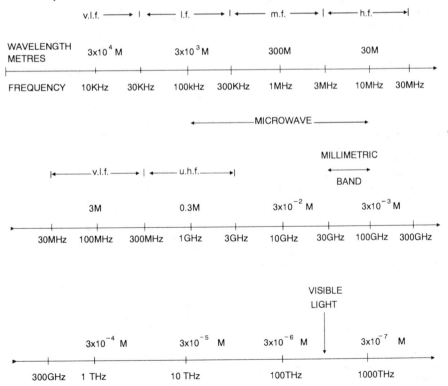

Figure 27.1 Radio frequency bands and designations

$$\lambda \times f = 3 \times 10^8 \qquad (27.1)$$

27.3 Free space propagation

This is seldom a practical situation, but it occurs when both transmitting and receiving antennas are situated away from the influence of the earth's surface or other reflecting and absorbing objects, including the transmitter and receiver themselves. If power is fed to an isotropic antenna, i.e. an antenna that radiates equally in all directions in azimuth and elevation, the wave front will radiate outwards from the antenna in an ever expanding sphere at 3×10^8 metres per second (186,282 miles per second). The strength of the signal obviously decreased with distance as a given amount of power is spread over a greater area, and the incident power density at a remote point can be calculated as in Equation 27.2 (CCIR, 1978), where P_r is received power density in watts per meter^2, P_t is transmitted power in watts and r is distance in metres.

$$P_r = \frac{P_t}{4 \pi r^2} \qquad (27.2)$$

Because of the very large differences in power density over long propagation paths, particularly in the microwave bands, it is usual to measure power density in decibels (dB) relative to 1 watt i.e. dBW, or 1 milliwatt i.e. dBm.

At frequencies below the microwave range, field strength in volts per metre is a more usual measurement than power density, partly because volts per metre has historically been used for the measurement of signal strength and partly because the thermal heating effect of power absorption is easier to use for microwave measurements. The conversion can be made for power density to field strength using the simple derivation of Ohm's law (Braun, 1986) as in Equation 27.3, where V is voltage, R is resistance in ohms and P is power in watts.

$$V^2 = R P \qquad (27.3)$$

In this case, R is substituted for Z_o, the characteristic impedance of free space, which is a constant of 377 ohms. Field strength can therefore be converted to power density by (Maslin, 1987) Equation 27.4, where E is field strength in volts per metre, Z_o is the impedance of free space (377 ohms), P_d is power density in watts per metre, and P_d is power density in watts per metre^2.

$$E^2 = Z_o P_d \qquad (27.4)$$

Equation 27.5 can be used to convert directly from dBW to dBμV, where E is in dB.

$$E = P_d \ dB \ (1W/m^2) + 145.6 \qquad (27.5)$$

On the left hand side of this equation, the dB represents a voltage and not a power ratio.

The voltage at the centre of an un-terminated half wave dipole in the path of a radiowave and aligned along the axis of the electric vector (i.e. no polarisation loss) is given by Equation 27.6, where V is the voltage at the centre of the dipole, E is the field strength in volts per metre, and λ is the wavelength in metres.

$$V = \frac{E \lambda}{\pi} \qquad (27.6)$$

If the dipole is connected to a feeder of matching impedance, E is halved. If polarisation and feeder losses are taken into account, the input to a receiver can be calculated.

A useful formula for calculating free space attenuation, derived from the power density Equation 27.1 and from 27.6, and published in CCIR Report 252-2 is given by Equation 27.7, where L_{fr} is the free space loss in decibels, f is the frequency in megahertz and d is distance in kilometres.

$$L_{fr} = 32.44 + 20 \log f + 20 \log d \qquad (27.7)$$

It will be noted that Equation 27.7 introduces a frequency component into the calculation.

As an example, the power density from a 500 watt transmitter working into a lossless isotropic antenna at a distance of 1 kilometre is $0.039W^{-3}/m^2$, and at 16 kilometres is $0.155W^{-6}/m^2$. This is a power ratio of 24dB, which is to be expected as there is a 6dB power loss every time the distance is doubled. The CCIR formula (Equation 27.7) gives a free space loss of 72.4dB at 1km and 96.5dB at 16km, again a difference of 24dB. Figure 27.2 shows the free space loss for frequency and distance based on this formula.

27.4 The propagation medium

Almost all propagation involves transmission through some of the earth's atmosphere, and the structure of the atmosphere and features within are shown in Figure 27.3. Most meteorological activity and cloud formation occur in the first 10km, and jet aircraft cruise at between 10km and 15km. Air pressure falls with height and at 30km, radiation from the sun is sufficient to generate some free electrons, but the first distinct ionised layer, the D layer occurs at 70km. Above the D layer, temperature and incident radiation increase and the E, F_1 and F_2 layers are formed between 120km and 450km. The ionosphere, which is the region in which the ionised layers are formed, spans the region from 50km to 600km. Ionised trails from meteors occur at around 100km and the lowest satellite orbit is at about 150km.

The primary influence on the atmosphere is radiation from the sun, which causes the ionised layers to form and creates global climatic and regional weather patterns. Solar radiation follows an 11 year sun spot cycle, which has a direct correlation with ionisation and is recorded on a scale from 0 to about 200. This is a smoothed average of the number of sunspots, which are observed disturbances on the sun's surface. A sunspot number is issued by the Sunspot Data Centre in Brussels and also the Telecommunications Services Centre in Boulder, Colorado, U.S.A. and is a smoothed 12 month average of solar activity indicating the degree of ionisation that can be expected. High sunspot numbers are an indication of better conditions for long range h.f. communication and this may also lead to unwanted long distance propagation in the v.h.f. bands creating interference in mobile communications and FM and TV broadcasting services.

The sunspot number being a running average may not be an accurate indication of daily or hourly conditions. The solar flux is a measure of solar activity taken at 2.8GHz and is a better indication of real time ionospheric conditions. It is measured continuously and quoted on a scale usually in the range from 60 to 260. The US

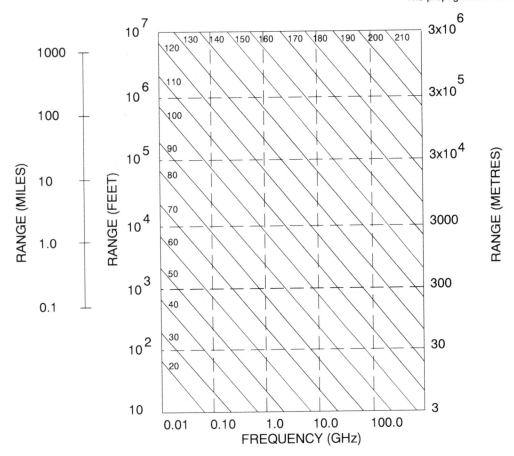

Figure 27.2 Free space loss versus distance for frequencies from 1 MHz to 100 GHz. (The units on the diagonal lines are in dB)

National Bureau of Standards radio station WWV transmits ionospheric data information hourly.

The signal to noise ratio (S/N) is often the determining factor in establishing communications, and it depends upon the absolute level of signal, the external noise in the propagation medium and the internal noise in the transmitting and receiving equipment. At h.f., communications are normally externally noise limited so that it is the noise in the propagation medium which predominates, whilst at v.h.f. and above the noise generated within the first stages of the receiver is usually the determining factor. Therefore there may be no benefit in trying to increase the received strength of h.f. signals by using larger and higher gain antennas as noise may increase proportionally with no improvement in signal to noise ratio.

External noise is from three sources; galactic noise, atmospheric noise and man made noise. Noise power in a communication link is given by Equation 27.8, where N is the noise power in watts, T is the temperature in degrees absolute, often taken as 290^0 as this corresponds to the normal room temperature of 17^0C and B is Boltzmanns constant (1.38×10^{-23}).

$$N = kTB \qquad (27.8)$$

In communications links, noise is measured in terms of the noise power available from a lossless antenna and may be expressed as in Equation 27.9, where P_n is the total power in dBW, F_a is the antenna noise figure in dB, $B = 10\log$ bandwidth (in hertz), and 204 is $10\log kT^o$, assuming $T^o = 290K$.

$$P_n = F_a + B - 204 \qquad (27.9)$$

Atmospheric and man made noise information is given in CCIR publications and typical values are shown in Figure 27.4. Galactic noise originates from sources outside the Earth's atmosphere, such as the sun and the stars, and extends from about 15 MHz to 100 MHz. It is limited by ionospheric absorption below this frequency range and atmospheric absorption above it. Atmospheric noise is the major source of noise in the m.f. and h.f. bands and is primarily due to lightning discharges so it is particularly severe in the rainy season in tropical regions such as equatorial Africa, and at its lowest value in high latitudes at night. It is transmitted over long distances by skywave paths. Man made noise may be similarly transmitted and emanates from power lines, industrial machinery and fluorescent tubes. Four standard levels for business, residential, rural and quite rural sites are defined in the CCIR report (CCIR, 1978).

Analysis of a propagation path usually requires a calculation of distance from transmitter to receiver and it is useful to know the great circle bearing. This information can be calculated from Equations 27.10 and 27.11 for two points A and B on the surface of the

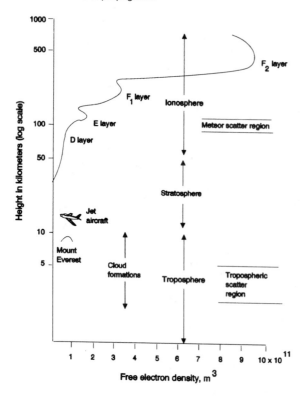

Figure 27.3 The Earth's atmosphere; major features and ionisation

Earth, where A is point A latitude in degrees; B is point B latitude in degrees; L is the difference in longitude between A and B; C is the true bearing of the receiver from the transmitter, which may be 360° - C if a negative value is calculated; D is the distance along the path in degrees of arc, which may be converted to kilometres by multiplying by 111.111 (i.e. 1 degree of arc = 111.111 kilometres).

$$\cos D = \sin A \sin B + \cos A \cos B \cos L \qquad (27.10)$$

$$\cos C = \frac{\sin B - \sin A \cos D}{\cos A \sin D} \qquad (27.11)$$

27.5 Low and medium frequency ground waves

In the low and medium frequency bands up to 3MHz, ground wave (rather than sky wave) propagation is used, because sky wave is heavily absorbed in daytime by the D layer. L.F. and m.f. antennas are generally short in terms of wavelength so vertical mast radiators are used. These have the advantages of maximum radiation at low angles to the horizon and also radiating vertically polarised transmissions.

The attenuation of vertically polarised ground wave transmissions is very much less than for horizontal polarisation, for example the ground wave attenuation of a 2MHz vertically polarised transmission over medium soil is 45dB at 30km whereas a horizontally polarised signal would be attenuated by nearly 95dB. Vertical polarisation is therefore almost always employed.

Because currents are induced in the ground by vertically polarised ground wave transmissions, attenuation is also dependent on ground conductivity and dielectric constant. Salt water offers low attenuation whereas desert sand or polar ice offer high attenuation, and consequent reduced communications coverage. Terrain irregularities such as hills and mountains, and also rough (as compared with calm) seas also reduce coverage.

Received field strength at any distance can be calculated theoretically (Braun, 1986; Maslin, 1987), however CCIR publish a series of graphs showing received field strength in microvolts per metre and in dBs relative to 1 microvolt, for distances up to 1000km. Frequencies from 500khz to 10MHz, and homogeneous surface conditions from sea water to dry soil are shown. Some of the curves are shown in Figure 27.5 and are calculated on the basis of a 1kW transmitter working into a short omni-directional monopole antenna. The field strength values are proportional to the square root of the power and will have to be adjusted accordingly for different powers or for higher gain or directional antennas.

The CCIR curves shown in Figure 27.5 assume propagation over homogeneous terrain, but discontinuities occur in paths over land and sea or over different types of soil, and the field strength over such a path can be calculated by a method developed by Millington, 1949. An example of the field strength over a land and sea path is shown in Figure 27.6 and it is interesting to note that the field strength rises after the wave front passes from land to sea.

M.F. groundwave propagation offers the advantage of predictable but limited communications coverage, which is largely independent of ionospheric conditions and diurnal or seasonal variations. Distances of up to 1000km are achievable over sea water, but in desert conditions this may be limited to tens of kilometres unless very high powers and directional antennas are used. A limitation that often occurs in medium frequency broadcasting is interference between groundwave and skywave from the same transmitter during darkness due to the absence of the absorbing D layer causing deep and rapid fading in received signals. The only practical solution is limiting power radiated at night when the D layer is no longer present, and designing the antenna to minimise high angle radiation. At l.f. and v.l.f., very long distance and global communications can be achieved, but this necessitates the use of high transmitter powers and very large antenna systems.

27.6 High frequency skywave propagation

Propagation in the h.f. band from 3MHZ to 30MHz is probably the most variable and least predictable of all transmission modes, as it depends upon the height and intensity of the ionised layers in the ionosphere. A wealth of data has been collected and incorporated in comprehensive computer programmes to enable predictions to be made with a reasonable degree of statistical accuracy, and modern ionospheric sounders can evaluate conditions on a real time basis. Unpredictable events such as solar flares do however mean that h.f. propagation always contains some degree of uncertainty (as does most radio wave propagation), and predictions can only be made on a statistical probability basis.

The ionosphere which is the primary influence on h.f. propagation extends from approximately 80km to 300km above the Earth's surface, and divides into a number of distinct ionised layers. Variations in the height and intensity of the layers occurs on a diurnal and seasonal basis due to the rotation and position of the earth in relation to the sun, and also on the longer term 11 year sunspot cycle. The diurnal variation is shown in Figure 27.7, and it will be seen that at night time when incident radiation is at a minimum as the

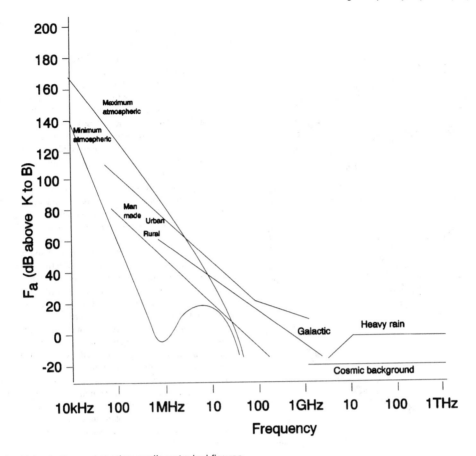

Figure 27.4 Noise in the propagation medium; typical figures

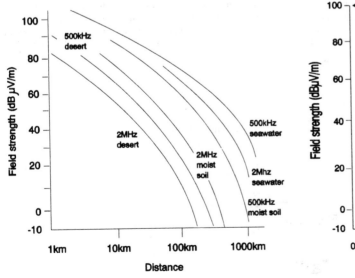

Figure 27.5 Ground wave propagation; field strength for different frequencies and surface conditions

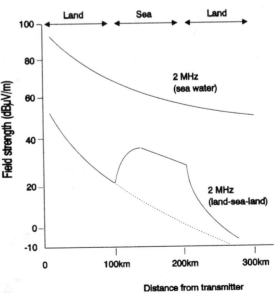

Figure 27.6 Ground wave field strength curve for a hypothetical non-homogeneous path

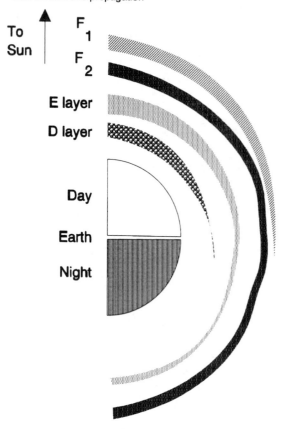

Figure 27.7 The diurnal variation in the Earth's ionised layers

occur with the seasons so there is greater level of ionisation in northern latitudes during July (summer) than in January (winter), but the reverse applies in the southern hemisphere.

The D layer actually spans an altitude from 50km to 90km and absorbs frequencies in the m.f. and lower h.f. bands. Higher frequencies will pass through the D layer suffering some attenuation and may be reflected back to earth by the E layer at distances up to 2000km. Still higher frequencies within the h.f. band will pass through the E layer and may be reflected by one of the F layers, providing very long distance communications. Frequencies in the v.h.f. bands and above (i.e. above 30MHz) will generally pass through all the layers and into space, except in unusual conditions of strong ionospheric activity.

Although a radio wave can be visualised as being reflected by the ionosphere, the process is in fact one of refraction, and the angle of refraction is proportional to both the angle of incidence and the frequency. When the wave front enters an ionised layer, it excites free electrons into oscillation which re-radiate electromagnetic energy, and this re-radiation modifies the direction of the wavefront, tending to bend it back to earth. For a given frequency, this tendency increases as the angle of incidence is reduced, so at the critical angle, the wave will be refracted back to earth, but at greater angles (i.e. nearer the vertical) only partial or no refraction will occur. This is illustrated in Figure 27.8. Similarly, for a given angle of incidence, refraction will decrease with increase in frequency, so at a critical frequency the wavefront will pass through the layer. As the wavefront passes through an ionised layer, it imparts energy to the electrons and a small amount of this energy is lost as heat. In the D layer, this transfer of energy is sufficient to completely absorb medium frequencies during daylight but at higher frequencies it causes some attenuation in the refraction process. Refracted waves also undergo a change of polarisation due to the complex movement of the free electrons, and this phenomenon is called Faraday rotation.

In planning an h.f. skywave link, it will be necessary to know the distance between the transmitter and receiver, or the area to be covered, and this can be calculated by Equations 27.10 and 27.11. It is desirable to minimise the number of 'hops' i.e. refractions from the ionosphere and reflections from the earth's surface, to minimise path attenuation and the inherent variability associated with ionospheric refraction. Maximum radiation from the antenna should therefore be at an angle (the take off angle) that results in refraction

ionosphere is in the earths shadow, the ionosphere comprises two comparatively thin layers at 110km and 210km, called the E and F layer respectively. During daylight, these two layers increase in thickness and intensity, and the F layer divides into the two separate F_1 and F_2 layers at 210km and 300km. In addition, the D layer forms at 80km during daylight but disappears at night. Similar variations

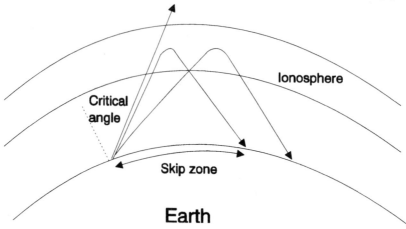

Figure 27.8 The critical angle of ionospheric refraction

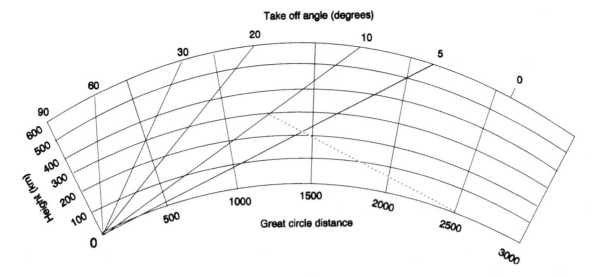

Figure 27.9 Take off angle for single hop sky wave paths

from the ionosphere onto the target area. Figure 27.9 is a diagrammatical representation of the surface of the earth from which the optimum take off angle of radiation from the antenna can be derived if the distance and refracting layer height are known. A lower take off angle is required for longer distances and for distance of greater than 2000km, two or more hops will normally be required.

In practice, a number of different propagation modes may be established on multi-hop links, which makes field strength predictions for the receive site difficult and uncertain. Three possible modes are shown in Figure 27.10. A first approximation can be

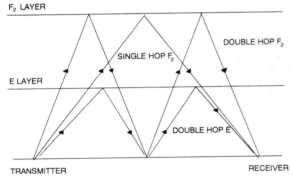

Figure 27.10 Possible multi-hop sky wave paths

obtained by calculating the free space loss using Equation 27.7, taking into account increased distance due to ionospheric refraction and applying this to the field strength at the transmitter site. Additional losses of up to 20dB will result from ionospheric and ground reflections, but these are very approximate values.

Actual sky wave refraction losses can be calculated (Braun, 1986), as can received field strength (Damboldt, 1975). Computer propagation prediction programmes are now generally employed for analysing h.f. paths and predicting received signal strength because of the large number of cancellations required, rather than

their inherent complexity. Such programmes run on desktop PC computers (Hitney, 1990) although many research establishments have larger and more sophisticated programmers (Dick, 1990).

Figure 27.11 shows a typical printout of a link from London to

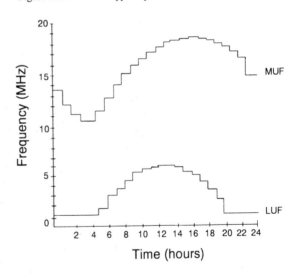

Figure 27.11 Frequencies for an h.f. link from London to Lisbon

Lisbon, a great circle distance of 1656 kilometres and a single hop F2 distance of 1757 kilometres. The programme shows the maximum usable frequency (MUF) and the lowest usable frequency (LUF), and at times when the LUF exceeds the MUF, h.f. skywave communication is not possible. The MUF is determined by the degree of layer ionisation whilst the LUF is generally determined by the multi-hop path attenuation and the noise level at the receive site. The frequency of optimum transmission (FOT) is the frequency with maximum availability and minimum path loss, and is generally taken as 90% of the MUF.

H.F. groundwave and skywave communications are still widely used for long distance low capacity services such as aeronautical ground to air transmissions, despite the increasing availability of satellite services. Defence forces are a major user, but the effects of the electromagnetic pulse (EMP) released by a nuclear explosion on the ionosphere and on equipment require special consideration in military systems. Much of the information on this topic is classified, but some papers are available.

27.7 Terrestrial line of site propagation

In the v.h.f., u.h.f. and microwave bands, the ionosphere has a minimal effect on propagation although anomalous conditions such as sporadic E propagation do affect the lower frequencies in this range. The frequencies are generally well above the critical frequency so that transmissions pass through the ionised layers and out into space. This offers the considerable benefit that the same frequencies can be used and re-used many times without causing mutual interference, provided sensible frequency planning is carried out and adequate physical separation is provided.

Communications link calculations can be carried out using the Friis power transmission formula as in Equation 27.12, where P_r is received power in watts, P_t is transmitted power in watts, G_t is the gain of the transmitting antenna in the direction of the receiving antenna, G_r is the gain of the receiving antenna in the direction of

the transmitting antenna, and r is the distance in metres between antennas.

$$P_r = \frac{P_t G_t G_r \lambda}{(4 \pi r)^2} \tag{27.12}$$

For systems calculations, the formula can be expanded to include transmit and receive antenna VSWR and polarisation mismatch as in Equation 27.13, where ρ_r is the magnitude of the voltage reflection coefficient at the receive antenna, ρ_t is the magnitude of the voltage reflection coefficient at the transmit antenna, and p is the polarisation mismatch.

$$\rho_r = \frac{P_t G_t G_r \lambda^2 (1 - \rho_r^2)(1 - \rho_t^2) p}{(4 \pi r)^2} \tag{27.13}$$

Voltage reflection coefficient can be calculated from the VSWR as in Equation 27.14.

$$p = VSWR - \frac{1}{VSWR} + 1 \tag{27.14}$$

The mismatch between two elliptically polarised waves is given by Equation 27.15, where R_t is given by Equation 27.16 and R_r by Equation 27.17. R_t is the transmit antenna axial ratio, and R_r is the receive antenna axial ratio.

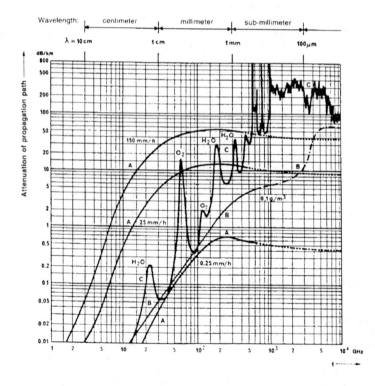

Figure 27.12 Atmospheric and rainfall attenuation versus frequency. (A: rainfall at 0.25, 25 and 150mm per hour; B: fog at 0.1 gram per m^3; C: molecular absorption by water vapour and air)

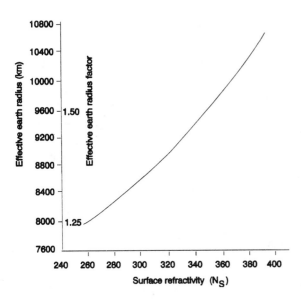

Figure 27.13 Atmospheric surface refractive index versus effective earth radius

$$p = \frac{1 + R_t{}^2 R_r{}^2 + R_t R_r \cos 2\theta}{(1 + R_t{}^2)(1 + R_r{}^2)} \qquad (27.15)$$

$$R_t = r_t + \frac{1}{r_t} - 1 \qquad (27.16)$$

$$R_r = r_r + \frac{1}{r_r} - 1 \qquad (27.17)$$

Equation 27.13 assumes free space conditions, however absorption occurs due to rain and fog and also water vapour and oxygen in the air, as shown in Figure 27.12. It will be noted that the first water absorption band occurs at 2.45GHz, a phenomenon that is put to good use in microwave ovens. The attenuation figure taken from this graph must be added to the figure calculated from the Friis formula.

Although v.h.f., u.h.f. and microwave point to point communications is frequently referred to as 'line of sight', the change in the refractive index of the atmosphere with height does in fact cause radio waves to be bent in the same direction as the earth's curvature. This in effect extends line of sight, and the relationship between the surface refractivity and the effective earth's radius is shown on Figure 27.13. The refractive index of air does in fact depend on atmospheric pressure, water vapour pressure and temperature and all these factors vary. An average effective earth radius factor of 1.33 or 'four thirds earth' is therefore assumed for most link assessments and this is shown diagrammatically in Figure 27.14 for a

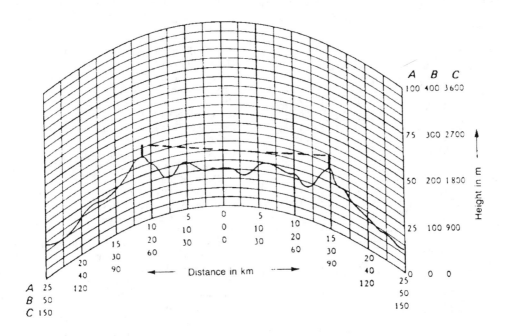

Figure 27.14 'Four thirds earth' line of sight link diagram

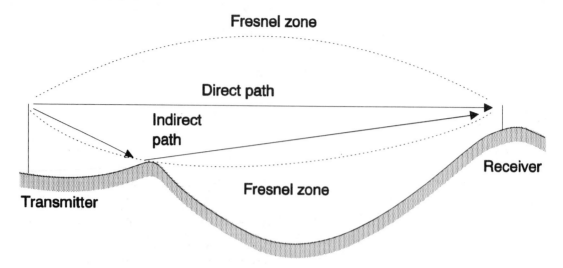

Figure 27.15 The Fresnel zone

hypothetical link. This presentation has the advantage that transmission paths can be plotted as straight lines.

The profile of the topology between transmitting and receiving antenna can also be plotted. It is desirable to avoid any obstructions within the first Fresnel zone which is defined as the surface of an ellipsoid of revolution with the transmitting and receiving antennas at the focal points in which the reflected wave has an indirect path half a wavelength longer than the direct paths. Figure 27.15 illustrates this and the radius of the first Fresnel zone at any point (P) is given by Equation 27.18, where R is the radius, and d_1 and d_2 are the distances from point P to the ends of the path.

$$R^2 = \frac{\lambda \, d_1 \, d_2}{d_1} + d_2 \tag{27.18}$$

The height of the transmitting and receiving antennas above the intervening terrain and the roughness of the terrain has a marked effect on path attenuation and received field strength in the v.h.f. and u.h.f. bands. The Friis formula will generally yield results that are too optimistic i.e. attenuation is too low and field strength is too high. CCIR Recommendation 370 (CCIR, 1982) reproduced in Figure 27.16 shows received field strength values at 10 metres above ground level for a radiated power of 1kW for different transmit antenna heights. The field strengths are modified by correction factors for the terrain irregularity between transmit and receive antennas which can increase attenuation by up to 18dB or reduce it by 7dB depending upon the topology. Average terrain irregularity is defined as differences in height above and below 50 metres in only 10% of the path length. Figure 27.17 (CCIR, 1982) gives attenuation correction factors for field strength for various terrain height differences.

Frequencies at 900MHz and 1800MHz are used for comparatively short distance "cellular" services, and communications will often be limited by multi-path interference cause by single or multiple reflections, particularly in urban environments. The only practical solution is to try different positions for the transmit antenna to minimise this problem. Multi-path interference can also be a problem on microwave links for TV outside broadcasts where transmissions may be from moving vehicles or aircraft. This can be minimised by using circular polarisation, as the reflected signals will undergo a polarisation reversal which will enable the receive antenna discriminate against them.

As the propagation medium is continuously changing, the figures derived from CCIR curves are based on statistical probabilities, generally 50% signal levels for 50% of the time, and therefore diversity transmission and a larger link margin may be required to increase channel availability.

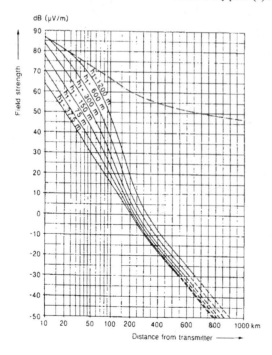

Figure 27.16 Received field strengths for different transmit antenna heights, v.h.f. and u.h.f. bands

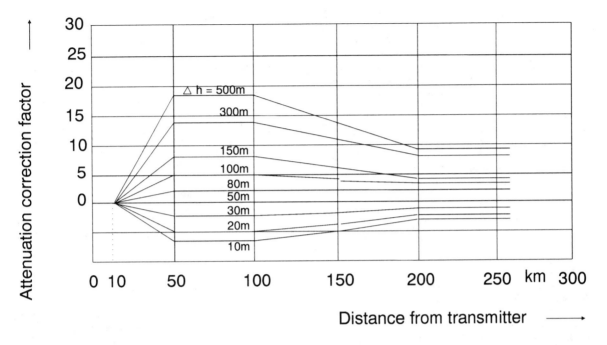

Figure 27.17 Attenuation correction factors for different terrain roughness

27.8 Over the horizon transmissions

The four thirds earth radius does extend transmission beyond the horizon in normal conditions, but a natural phenomenon known as ducting can extend this considerably. Ducting happens in stable weather systems when large changes in refractive index with height occur and causes propagation with very low attenuation over hundreds of kilometres. The propagation mode is similar to that in a waveguide. Ducting is not a very predictable form of propagation and therefore cannot be used commercially, but information is available in CCIR Report 718 (CCIR, 1982)

Tropospheric scatter and meteor scatter communications both provide over the horizon communications on a regular and predictable basis. Tropospheric scatter relies on small cells of turbulence in the troposphere between 2km and 5km above the Earth surface which scatter incident radiation, as illustrated in Figure 27.18. Frequencies in the lower part of the microwave range from 1.0GHz to 5.0GHz are generally used as this gives the maximum amount of forward scatter, nevertheless the amount of energy that is scattered forward is extremely small and the losses in the scatter volume are in the order of 50dB to 70dB in addition to the free space loss. Large short term variations following the Rayleigh law also occur and therefore quadruple or multiple diversity is almost always used.

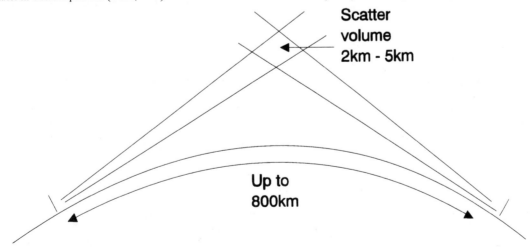

Figure 27.18 A tropospheric scatter communications link

This is achieved by employing two antennas, horizontal and vertical polarisation, different scatter volumes (angle diversity) and different frequencies. Space and polarisation diversity generally yield the best results. Tropospheric scatter can provide communications up to 500km, but paths as long as 800 kilometres have been operated.

Meteor scatter communications makes use of ionised trails of meteors burning up on entering the earth's atmosphere. This is not such a rare event as might be thought, and there is a steady shower of material entering the earth's atmosphere although there are random and predictable variations. Meteors that leave usable trails have diameters between 0.2mm and 2mm, and the trails which last for around half a second to several seconds occur at a height of about 120km. They may extend up to 50km although 15km is a typical value. The number of particles entering the earth's atmosphere is inversely proportion to size, so larger meteors occur too infrequently to be of use whilst the numerous very small particles do not generate sufficient ionisation. The variation in the number of usable ionised trails occurs on a daily basis with more occurring during daylight as the earth's rotations tends to sweep up more meteors than at night. There are also predictable showers occurring throughout the year.

Meteor scatter communications can be established for paths from 200km to 2000km, but information has to be transmitted in bursts when a link is established so the medium cannot be used for services such as speech. Radio waves are reflected from the trails by different mechanisms depending upon the density of ionisation; however frequencies in the 30MHz to 100MHz range are most effective with 50MHz being the optimum frequency. Horizontal polarisation is generally preferred. When a link is established, path attenuation is high due to the scattering process, and is typically 175dB for a 40MHz, 1000km path (Cannon, 1987). This is approximately 50dB greater than the free space attenuation of the same distance.

27.9 Propagation for satellite communications

Most communications satellites are placed in geo-stationary orbits 36000km above the equator, therefore transmitting and receiving earth stations can fix their antenna positions with only minor adjustments being required for small shifts in satellite position or changes in atmospheric propagation conditions. Such orbits also have the advantage of providing potential coverage of almost one third of the earth's surface, but the disadvantage of high free space loss compared with lower non stationary orbits. The systems planner will need to calculate the link budget taking into account such factors as the satellite EIRP (equivalent isotropically radiated power) and receiver noise performance. The free space loss can be calculated using Equation 27.7 and distance will have to take into account both the difference in latitude and longitude of the position of the satellite on the earth's surface to that of the transmitting or receiving station. If the distance and great circle bearing is calculated using Equations 27.10 and 27.11, the elevation and distance of the satellite can also be calculated. In addition to the free space loss, the loss due to atmospheric attenuation must be taken into account, and this will depend upon precipitation conditions in the earth station area. Typical values at 11GHz would be 1.0dB for an "average year" increasing to about 1.5dB for the worst month. The actual figures to be used should be calculated from local meteorological data and the attenuation curves given in Figure 27.12.

Calculation of satellite paths is not often required as operators usually publish "footprint" maps showing the received power con-

tours in dBW, taking into account the path loss and the radiation pattern of the satellite transmitting antenna.

27.10 Summary of radio wave propagation

27.10.1 V.l.f. and l.f.: 10kHz to 300Khz

Long distance (greater than 1000km) ground wave transmission for communications and radio navigation. Propagation unaffected by ionospheric conditions. High power and large antennas required. Very limited spectrum availability.

27.10.2 M.f.: 300kHz to 3MHz

Medium to short distance (up to 1000km) ground wave transmission for sound broadcasting and mobile communications. Propagation little affected by ionospheric conditions, but night time interference can be a problem.

27.10.3 H.f.: 3MHz to 30MHz

World wide communications using comparatively low power (1kw), but heavily dependent on ionospheric conditions. Limited channel availability. Used for sound broadcasting, point to point and mobile maritime and aeronautical communications.

27.10.4 V.h.f. and u.h.f.: 30MHz to 1GHz

Officially, u.h.f. extends to 3GHz. Lower frequencies are affected by anomalous propagation conditions. Line of sight communications, typically 80km (meteor scatter on 50MHz can provide services up to 2000km). Used for multi-channel point to point communications, FM sound and TV broadcasting and mobile communications.

27.10.5 Microwave: 1GHz to 30GHz

Unaffected by ionospheric conditions, but some attenuation at higher frequencies due to rain. Line of sight communications, typically 50km (tropospheric scatter can provide services up to 500km). Satellite services provide world wide coverage. Wide band multi-channel communication available. Extensively used for terrestrial point to point and satellite communications, also radar.

27.10.6 Millimetric: 30GHz to 100GHz

Unaffected by ionospheric conditions but moderate to severe attenuation due to atmospheric conditions. Limited line of sight communications, typically 10km. Limited usage, mainly short distance speech and data links but increasing usage is likely.

27.11 References

Boithias, Lucien (1987) *Radio wave propagation*, North Oxford Academic Publishers.

Braun, G. (1986) *Planning and engineering of short-wave links*, 2nd Ed. John Wiley & Sons, Chichester.

Budden, K.G. (1985) *The propagation of radio waves*, Cambridge University Press.

Cannon, P.S. (1987) The evolution of meteor burst communications systems. *J. IERE*. **57** (3) (May/June).

CCIR (1978) *Man-made radio noise*, Report 258- 3, ITU, Geneva.

CCIR (1982) *Volume V, Propagation in non-ionised media*, Geneva.

CCIR (1984) *World distribution and characteristics of radio noise*, Report 233-1, ITU Geneva.

Damboldt, T. (1975) A comparison between Deutsche Bundespost ionospheric h.f. propagation predictions and measured field strengths, *NATO AGARD, Radio systems and the ionosphere, Conf. Proc. 173*, Athens, (May).

Dick, M.I. (1990) *Propagation model of CCIR report 894,* Rutherford Appleton Laboratories, (May).

Friis, H.T. (1946) A note on a simple transmission formula, *IRE Proc.* (May), pp. 254-256.

Hitney, H.V. (1990) *IONOPROP, ionospheric propagation assessment software and documentation*, Artech House, London.

Johnson & Jasick (1984) *Antenna Engineering Handbook*, McGraw Hill.

Longmire, C.L. (1978) The electromagnetic pulse produced by nuclear explosions, *IEEE Transactions on Electromagnetic Compatibility*, **EMC-20** (1) (February).

Maslin, N.M. (1987) *H.F. Communications, A systems approach*, Pitman, London.

Millington, G. (1949) Ground wave propagation over inhomogeneous smooth earth, *J. Inst. Electr. Eng. Part 3*.

Picquenard, Arme (1984) *Radio wave propagation*, Philips Technical Library, McMillan Technical Press.

Radio Society of Great Britain, *Radio Communication Handbook*.

Stanniforth, J.A. (1972) *Microwave Transmission*, English University Press.

Stark, Axel (1986) *Propagation of Electromagnetic Waves*, Rohde & Schwarz.

28 Digital transmission

Edwin V Jones
BSc MSc PhD CEng MIEE
University of Essex

Contents

28.1 Design principles

28.1.1 System requirements

A simplified block diagram of a digital communication system is shown in Figure 28.1. Information from a data source is processed so that it can be reliably transmitted via a communication channel to a distant data terminal. The user will measure reliability in terms of the difference between the transmitted data and the received data. The system designer's task is to ensure that this difference is always acceptably low.

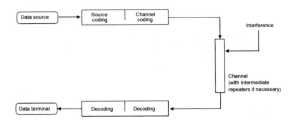

Figure 28.1 A digital communication system

The processing tasks in the transmitting terminal fall into two categories:

1. Source coding is concerned with the structure and statistics of the data source. It will involve the conversion of the data into a more suitable form for subsequent processing. Word alignment and frame alignment (when multiplexing several data sources together) can also be regarded as part of the source coder's task.
2. Channel coding is concerned with the characteristics of the transmission channel, it must ensure that the processed data is compatible with the requirements of the channel. For example, it may be necessary to add redundancy to the transmitted data symbols to combat the effects of transmission errors by providing some error detection and/or correction capability. Symbol timing information may also need to be added. In addition, coding must ensure that the frequency spectrum of the processed data is compatible with that of the channel, thus line coding for low-pass channels and modulation (carrier keying) for band-pass channels, are also tasks for the channel coder.

In practice it is not always possible to make a clear distinction between source and channel coding functions. Indeed, improved efficiency can sometimes be obtained by combining some tasks (Hamming, 1980).

We now concentrate on the fundamental aspects of digital transmission with emphasis on transmission over low-pass channels. These same principles apply to band-pass channels which are treated elsewhere.

28.1.2 The baseband waveform

Figure 28.2(a) shows a binary data signal, assumed to be in a suitable form for transmission over a low-pass channel, this is often referred to as the baseband waveform. After transmission over the restricted bandwidth of a channel (and if necessary, some equalisa-

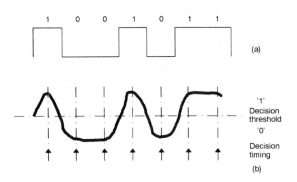

Figure 28.2 Baseband waveforms: (a) transmitted signal; (b) bandlimited received signal

tion to partially compensate for the characteristics of the channel) the signal may look like Figure 28.2(b).

The task of the receiver is to establish the transmitted sequence. For a binary sequence, a single decision threshold is required. Each amplitude decision will have to be made in the presence of any distortion and interference superimposed upon the data sequence during transmission. The decision making process will be more reliable if it is timed by a clock which distinguishes when each received symbol has reached an optimum value. The accuracy with which the decision threshold and sample times must be placed will depend upon the severity of distortion suffered during transmission. Wideband channels lead to less critical amplitude and time placement requirements, but they may admit more noise into the receiver. A compromise must therefore be struck.

The tasks of equalisation, clock extraction and decision making are shown in Figure 28.3. Also shown is the output stage which, under the control of the extracted clock, produces a retimed baseband waveform. Most digital transmission systems use such a self-timed fully regenerative arrangement at the distant terminal. A similar configuration is common at intermediate repeaters (if used), although untimed amplifiers are being considered for some optical systems.

28.1.3 Noise and the decision process

The effect of noise on the decision process is treated in many textbooks (Carlson, 1986; Sklar, 1988; Lee, 1988). For zero-mean Gaussian noise, the probability of making an erroneous decision is given by Equation 28.1, where a is the voltage difference between the received signal and its associated decision threshold at the decision time and σ is the r.m.s. noise voltage.

$$P_e = \frac{1}{\sigma\sqrt{2\pi}} \int_a^\infty e^{-x^2/2\sigma^2} \, dx \qquad (28.1)$$

This is known as the Gaussian tail area formula and is often shortened to Equation 28.2.

$$P_e = T\left(\frac{a}{\sigma}\right) \qquad (28.2)$$

Unfortunately, there is no analytic solution to this equation and so tables (Carlson, 1986; Sklar, 1988), bounds or approximation for-

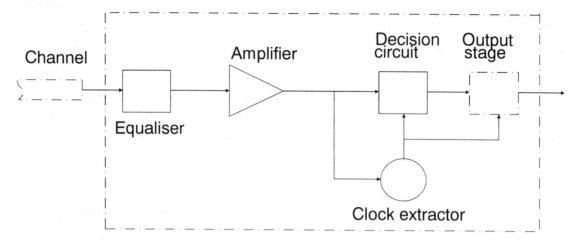

Figure 28.3 A baseband regenerator

mulae (Beaulieu, 1989) have to be used. The solid line of Figure 28.4 shows the error probability (P_e) plotted as a function of the signal-to-noise ratio $20 \log_{10} \frac{a}{\sigma}$ at the input to the decision circuit. This line is equivalent to the case of binary transmission. For an m-level transmitted signal (requiring m − 1 decision thresholds at the receiver), it can be shown (Bennett and Davey, 1965) that for a given symbol error probability an improvement in signal-to-noise ratio of approximately $(m^2 - 1)/3$ is required relative to the binary case. This analysis assumes a constant mean signal power and that all transmit levels are equiprobable.

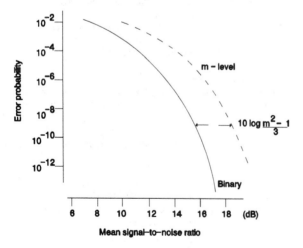

Figure 28.4 Error probability due to Gaussian noise

The steepness of the curve in Figure 28.4 means that small changes in signal-to-noise ratio have a significant effect on error probability. Thus digital systems need an adequate design margin to ensure both short and long term reliability. We also see that multi-level systems require much better signal-to-noise ratios. This may be partially compensated by the narrower bandwidth requirements made possible by a trade-off between the number of transmit levels and the symbol rate. However for baseband transmission the bal-ance is usually in favour of binary or 3-level transmission at the most.

28.1.4 Waveform shaping and bandwidth requirements

In order to use the transmission medium efficiently and to reduce received noise, the channel bandwidth should be minimised. However, this conflicts with the requirement to restrict the spreading of the pulse waveform at the receiver. For reliable decision making, a transmitted symbol must be shaped by the channel and its associated equaliser so that it does not interfere with other received symbols. Figure 28.5 shows a common pulse shaping objective. Symbols are transmitted with time spacing T and shaped before presentation to the decision circuit to yield a peak (at the time a decision is made) with zero amplitude at all other decision times. Such a signal is said to exhibit zero intersymbol interference (i.s.i.) with respect to neighbouring received signals.

Nyquist (Nyquist, 1928) showed that the minimum transmission bandwidth (channel plus equaliser) which meets this condition is one which passes all frequencies up to 1/2T and stops all others, as illustrated by the dashed lines of the frequency and time domain pair of Figure 28.6. This result is only of theoretical interest because a transmission characteristic with an infinitely sharp cut-off cannot be realised in practice. Furthermore, small errors in decision timing can lead to large amounts of i.s.i. Both problems can be overcome, but only at the expense of extra bandwidth. A popular solution, which preserves the zero crossing points, is to provide an equaliser such that the overall transmission characteristic has a raised cosine shape in the frequency domain. A full (100%) raised cosine is shown as the solid lines on Figure 28.6. This is seen to have a compact time response in that it always remains within the magnitude of the Nyquist pulse envelope. Thus, at the cost of more bandwidth, tolerance to (small) timing errors is good. The full raised cosine has the added feature that the waveform at time T/2 is half the peak amplitude. This leads to good eye shape (see next section), and also has application to some partial response systems (Bennett and Davey, 1965). Other pulse shaping strategies which aim to give good timing tolerance are to be found in (Franks, 1968).

It should be noted that the characteristics of Figure 28.6 imply linear phase properties. Deviations from this condition can lead to severe waveform distortion (Sunde, 1961). Equalisers must there-

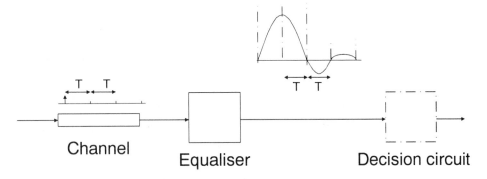

Figure 28.5 Waveform shaping for zero intersymbol interference (basic requirement)

fore take account of both phase and amplitude. Practical solutions, which can only approximate to the theoretical requirements, aim to give acceptably low (but usually not zero) i.s.i.

28.1.5 The eye diagram

Degradations in digital systems fall into two categories:

1. Deterministic degradations such as errors in equalising, offsets in decision timing, gain errors and possibly transmission echoes.
2. Stochastic degradations such as noise, interference, crosstalk and timing jitter.

Some degradations, it could be argued, should appear in both categories.

The deterministic degradations are conveniently assessed by means of an eye diagram. This is obtained, on an oscilloscope for example, by writing all possible received sequences on top of each other whilst triggering the oscilloscope timebase from the data clock as illustrated in Figure 28.7(a) and (b).

The eye diagram provides a great deal of information about the performance of a digital system. In the absence of noise, the width of the eye opening gives the time interval over which the received signal can be sampled without error from i.s.i. The sensitivity of the

system to decision timing errors is determined by the rate of closure of the eye as the sampling time is varied. The height of the eye, at a specified decision time, determines the margin over noise.

Given distribution probabilities for the noise and timing jitter, it is then possible to determine the optimum sample time and decision threshold voltage. Figure 28.7(c) gives a diagrammatic view of these points. The diagram serves to illustrate how the worst case signal margin can be very much less than the ideal design value. Noting the steepness of the error probability curve (Figure 28.4), it can be seen how worst case conditions can dominate performance. It follows that reliable estimates for the worst case signal margin are crucial if the performance of a system is to be predicted accurately.

28.2 Transmission error performance

28.2.1 The need for performance measures

Transmission errors are usually the most significant impairment to be found in a digital communication system. They are also difficult to predict and therefore difficult to quantify. Consequently, the study of their occurrence and the means of specifying their characteristics has been and continues to be the subject of considerable

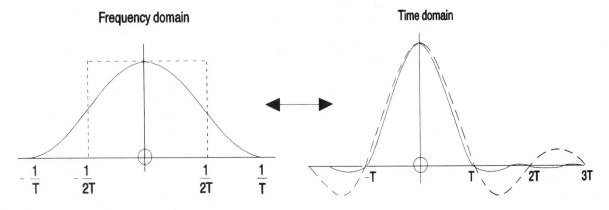

Figure 28.6 Waveform shaping for zero intersymbol interference (Nyquist shown in dashed line and full raised cosine in solid line)

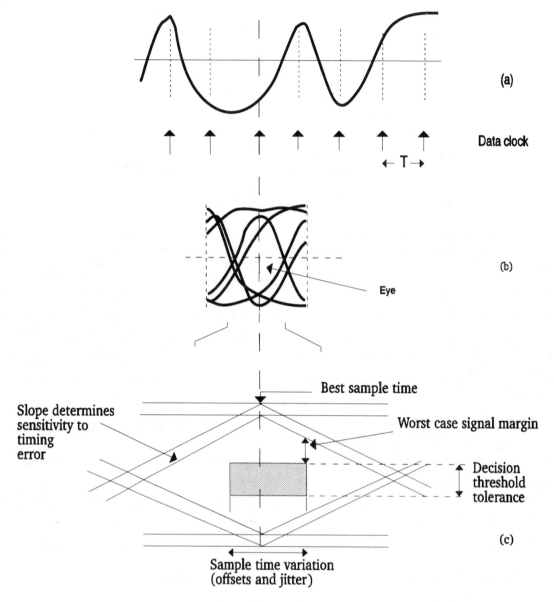

Figure 28.7 Construction of a binary eye: (a) equalised binary signal; (b) eye diagram; (c) interpretation of the eye diagram

activity; see for example (Yamamoto and Wright, 1989) and references therein.

The principal causes of transmission errors in a communication system are:

1. Noise, in particular thermal noise for metallic cable and radio systems, and quantum noise for optical systems.
2. Impulsive interference, often from nearby electro-mechanical equipment.
3. Cross-talk and intermodulation, from other interfering transmission systems.
4. Echoes and signal fading, arising from mismatches in transmission channels and from multi-path effects in radio systems.
5. Terminal equipment limitations and misettings, such as errors in equalisation and decision timing.
6. Network problems, including frame synchronisation errors and lost bits.

Various methods have been used to model these causes of degradation and interference (Kanal and Sastry, 1978; Knowles and Drukarev, 1988). Suffice it to note here that at the receiving terminal or regenerator in a digital link, the probability of making an erroneous decision (the error probability) is critically dependent upon the received signal-to-interference ratio. A small change in this ratio will result in a large change in error probability. It is thus vital to establish error performance measures so that both users and transmission system providers can anticipate an end-to-end performance which is compatible with the requirements of the digital information to be carried. Such performance standards are now emerging, from the CCITT for example. Recommendations for error performance are often based on three performance measures, bit-error ratio, available time and error-free seconds, as described in the following sections.

28.2.2 Bit-Error Ratio (BER)

The bit-error ratio (CCITT, 1988a) sometimes referred to as the bit-error rate, is defined as the number of bits received in error divided by the total number of bits transmitted in a specified time interval. Within the specified interval, it is numerically equal to the bit-error probability.

Studies have been conducted to quantify the BER requirements for various digital services (Yamamoto and Wright, 1989). Some typical objectives, expressed in terms of a long term mean BER, are given in Table 28.1.

However, the long term mean BER will usually be an insufficient performance measure by itself. For many digital services the degree of burstiness of the errors, that is their distribution, will also be important. Figure 28.8 shows a typical result where, for a given long term mean BER, the BER over shorter measurement intervals is seen to exhibit considerable variation with time. During some measurement intervals no errors are recorded whilst at the other extreme bursts of interference can cause bursts of errors and thus a high short term BER.

Within the illustrative limits quoted in Table 28.1 speech, video and data services will have quite different long and short term BER requirements. For speech, a listener will usually be tolerant to the low level of background noise caused by randomly distributed errors (Takahashi, 1988). Burst errors usually cause more objection-

Table 28.1 Some typical BER objectives

Digital service	Transmission rates (approx.)	Long term mean BER
Voice: Log-law PCM	64kbits/s	2×10^{-5}
Voice: ADPCM	32kbits/s	10^{-4}
Video: Linear PCM	60Mbits/s	2×10^{-7}
Video: Inter-frame coding	2Mbits/s	10^{-10} (approx.)
Data	16kbits/s to 600Mbits/s	10^{-7} (approx.)

able audible clicks but are still tolerable if they do not occur too often. Errors in a digital video signal will impair quality (CCIR, 1986), and again a viewer will usually be happier with the effects of random rather than burst errors. With video however, additional care is needed as excessive bursts of errors can result in a sudden and catastrophic loss of picture synchronisation. A similar sharp bound on acceptability may also occur with data if error control coding is used to protect the data from transmission errors. Occasional errors in an encoded block or even bursts of limited duration may be acceptable (in a retransmission scheme for example). However, a point will come when the error control coding system can no longer cope and then significant numbers of decoded data blocks may contain errors, now the proportion of error free blocks becomes a useful measure of performance.

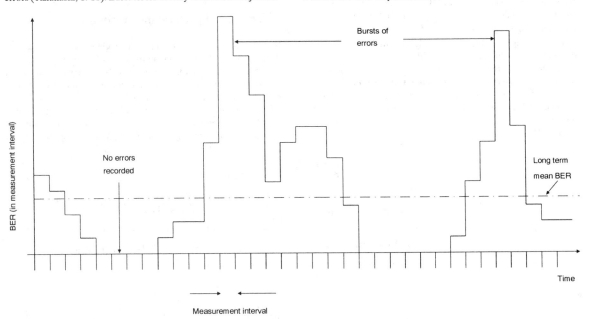

Figure 28.8 Variation of BER with time in a burst error environment

Thus, in order to quantify the error distribution characteristics, the BER measure must be refined by the addition of other measures.

28.2.3 Available time

This is the percentage of time, in a specified time interval, in which the BER is less than a specified threshold.

This measure is especially useful when blocks of data are protected by an error control coding scheme. The coding algorithm will usually be able to handle a given number of errors in a block.

Blocks with more errors will be decoded erroneously. If the BER measurement interval corresponds to the error control block length then, with the appropriate BER threshold, the available time will correspond to the percentage of error free blocks after decoding the received data.

28.2.4 Error-Free Seconds (EFS)

This is the proportion of one-second intervals, in a specified time interval, in which the transmitted data is delivered error free. Again it is usually expressed as a percentage.

For modern high bit rate transmission systems a second may be too long (it will contain many bits) and so an error-free millisecond, and error-free microsecond or more specifically, an error free data block (as mentioned above) may become more appropriate measures.

28.2.5 Performance standards — an example

The parameters BER, available time and EFS and adaptations of them are used in the emerging error performance standards for digital links (McLintock and Kearsey, 1984). The important CCITT Recommendation G.821 (CCITT, 1988a) serves as an example. It specifies error performance objectives for long distance 64kbit/s data connections (Table 28.2).

These are long term objectives, usually measured over many days, and apply only to the available time. When the error performance is consistently bad (a BER worse than 10^{-3} in ten consecutive one-second intervals is specified) the connection is deemed to be unavailable for information transmission. Figure 28.9 illustrates the relationship between the various performance parameters. Some subtleties of the terminology are to be found in the full specification (CCITT, 1988a).

Table 28.2 Error performance objectives; an example (CCITT, 1988a)

Performance parameter	Objective
Degraded minutes	Fewer than 10% of one-minute intervals to have a BER worse than 10^{-6}
Severely errored seconds	Fewer than 0.2% of one-second intervals to have a BER worse than 10^{-3}
Errored seconds	Fewer than 8% of one-second intervals to have any errors (i.e. EFS > 92%)

From the network operators point of view, this specification is somewhat incomplete. With the increasing deployment of digital networks a connection will often comprise a number of links perhaps of very different type. The network operator needs to consider the effects of these individual links on the overall G.821 objectives which the customer expects. Outline Recommendation M.550 (CCITT, 1988b) attempts to address these matters by defining performance objectives for:

1. The long-term (several days); for bringing a digital link into service.
2. The short-term (several minutes/hours); for removing an unsatisfactory link for maintenance.

However, this is a complex and challenging topic which remains the subject of continuing study, such as (Yamamoto and Wright, 1989; Kubat and Bollen, 1989).

28.2.6 Error performance monitoring

For many applications it is considered highly desirable to monitor the occurrence of transmission errors while a system is in service. This enables problems to be seen quickly and appropriate action taken such as reducing the transmission rate to ensure better performance or switching to an alternative link.

Errors are monitored by adding redundancy to the information signal. This added redundancy may also be used for other purposes (such as with line coding and frame alignment) or specifically for

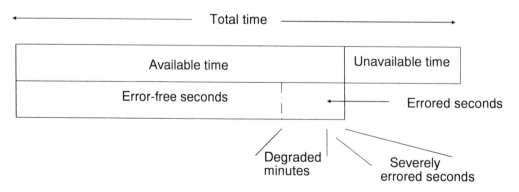

Figure 28.9 Relationship between error performance parameters

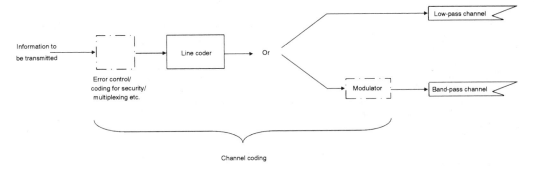

Figure 28.10 Relationship between line coding and other channel coding functions

error detection (as with error control coding). These topics are dealt with in more detail in following sections, and are briefly introduced below.

28.2.6.1 *Line coding*

Codes such as HDB3, 7B8B and the Manchester code can provide a monitoring capability on a per link basis. These codes have well defined coding rules which can be verified at a regenerator or subsequent link terminating point. Once any requisite code word synchronism has been obtained, any violations of the coding rules can be attributed to transmission errors and so the error performance of the link can be estimated.

28.2.6.2 *Frame alignment*

Here redundancy is added for synchronisation purposes. Once correct alignment is assured, any variation from the known frame alignment word can again be attributed to transmission errors. As with line codes, care has to be taken to distinguish between word misalignment conditions and transmission errors. The decision algorithms are often quite complicated but nevertheless can give a reasonable estimate of transmission error performance. Frame alignment words usually remain associated with the transmitted information over more than a single link and so can offer the opportunity for error monitoring over a greater portion of a connection.

28.2.6.3 *Error control coding*

It may not always be viable to provide an end-to-end level of error performance which is compatible with the most demanding digital service likely to be supported. In such circumstances error control coding (detection and then correction) over certain problem links or end-to-end over the whole connection may be used. This is the most direct method of error performance monitoring as the redundancy will usually have been specifically added, and so optimised, for the detection of errors. Of course certain error combinations may go undetected or only partially detected and this can lead to erroneous action in a subsequent error corrector. However, this problem can usually be reduced to an acceptable level by using coding which is appropriate to the error characteristics of the particular transmission link. It then becomes possible to ensure that transmission errors in

blocks of data for example, are monitored to a high degree of confidence.

28.3 Line codes

28.3.1 Definition

A line code defines the equivalence between sets of digits generated in a terminal and the corresponding sequence of symbol elements transmitted over a channel. It must be chosen to suit the characteristics of the particular channel (Cattermole, 1983; Waters, 1983).

For metallic cables which have an essentially low-pass frequency characteristic it will usually be the last coding function performed before transmission. For band-pass channels such as optical fibres, radio and the analogue telephone network, where modulation is required before transmission, the line coding function will either immediately precede the modulator or be incorporated within the modulation process. The relationship between line coding and other channel coding functions is shown in Figure 28.10. From this we see that the line coder may have to operate at the transmitted symbol rate, in which case a reasonably simple design will usually be essential, especially for high speed systems.

28.3.2 Purpose of a line code

A line code provides the transmitted symbol sequence with the necessary properties to ensure reliable transmission and subsequent detection at the receiving terminal. In order to achieve this the following have to be considered:

1. Spectrum at low frequency. Most transmission systems are easier to design if a.c. coupling is used between stages. This means that decoding must not rely on receiving a d.c. component. Furthermore, the coupling components (capacitors or transformers) will introduce a low frequency cut-off and this will put a limit on the permissible low frequency content of the line code if long term intersymbol interference is to be avoided (Cattermole, 1983).
2. Transmission bandwidth required. If transmission bandwidth is at a premium, a multi-level line code, in which each transmitted symbol represents more than one bit of information, will enable the transmitted symbol rate to be reduced. However, for a given bit error ratio, a multi-level line code will require a better signal-to-noise ratio than a corresponding binary code.
3. Timing content. There must always be sufficient embedded timing information in the transmitted symbol sequence so that

the distant receiver (and intermediate repeaters if used) can extract a reliable clock to time their decision making processes. This usually means ensuring that the line code provides an adequate density of transitions in the transmitted sequence.

4. Error monitoring. By adding redundancy into the information stream a line code can provide a means of in-service monitoring of the error rate of a transmission link. For example, a line coder can be constrained so that it never produces certain symbol sequences. Thus, the occurrence of these sequences at the receiver provides a means of estimating the link error performance.

5. Efficiency. In order to provide the above features it will usually be necessary to add extra information (redundancy as far as the data is concerned) into the digit stream. This will lower the efficiency of the line code which can be defined as the ratio of the average information carried per transmitted symbol to the maximum possible information per symbol (when assuming no added redundancy), expressed as a percentage.

28.3.3 Classification of line codes

Line codes can be classified in a variety of ways, one method is to identify the following categories:

1. Bit-by-bit codes.
2. Block codes: bit insertion and block substitution.
3. Partial response codes.

Some codes will fall into more than one of these classes. The following are representative examples from each category.

28.3.3.1 Manchester code

This is also called diphase or WAL1 code and is a simple example of a bit-by-bit code. Each information bit is coded into a two-bit symbol for transmission, as shown in Figure 28.11(a). No d.c. component is generated because the polarity and amplitude of the first half of each transmitted symbol is complemented by the second half. Also, the resulting signal transition in the centre of each symbol ensures an adequate clock content. The absence of such a transition indicates a transmission error and so error monitoring is also possible. However, only one bit of information is carried for every two bits transmitted and so the efficiency is only 50%. In this case, this results in a channel bandwidth requirement of twice the uncoded bandwidth. However, its simplicity makes it attractive for applications where transmission bandwidth considerations are less crucial; it is used in the magnetic recording of digital signals and in the Ethernet local area network system (ANSI/IEEE 802-3)

28.3.3.2 Code mark inversion (CMI)

It is shown in Figure 28.11(b) and is similar to the Manchester code except that it achieves a polarity balance over a longer term by alternating between a positive symbol and a negative symbol when a binary one (mark) is to be transmitted. It is specified by CCITT (CCITT, 1988c) as an interface code for short distance connections between certain types of transmission equipments.

28.3.3.3 Alternate Mark Inversion (AMI).

This differs from the above line codes in that the transmitted symbol rate is the same as the binary information rate. It provides the desired features by using a redundant signal set with three possible amplitude levels as shown in Figure 28.11(c). The zero d.c. property is achieved by sending marks as a positive or negative symbol alternately. An estimate of the link error performance is obtained by counting violations of this alternating mark inversion rule. We note that AMI has a potential weakness; if many successive zero-level symbols are transmitted, then the clock will fail. Thus, either the number of successive zeros has to be restricted, which is undesirable

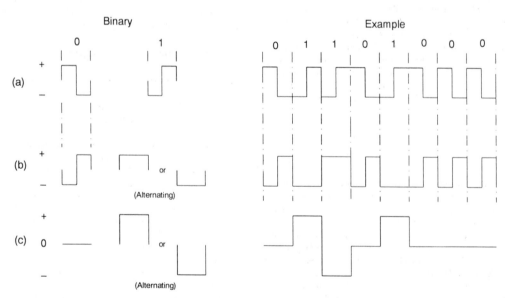

Figure 28.11 Some bit-by-bit line codes: (a) Manchester code; (b) code mark inversion (CMI); (c) alternate mark inversion (AMI)

for a transparent data link, or a code substitution has to be made to prevent this potential hazard. Such AMI based substitution codes are used in 24 and 30 channel PCM telephone systems, where they are known as B6ZS and HDB3 respectively (Waters, 1983).

28.3.3.4   *mB1C*

This (Yoshikai et al., 1984) is an example of a block code of the bit insertion type. A block of m information bits has added to it a single extra bit which is selected in an attempt to provide a long term polarity balance and so no d.c. component. For this to work reliably, the source data may need to be scrambled first to ensure that it is adequately randomised. The added bit also ensures a minimum clock content and some redundancy to permit transmission error monitoring. Binary codes of this type feature high efficiency (m has ranged in practice from 7 to at least 23) and simple hardware, and they are thus attractive for high speed applications such as in optical fibre systems. Codes such as mB1P (Dawson and Kitchen, 1986) and DmB1M (Kawanishi et. al., 1988) are similar in concept but offer slightly different features.

28.3.3.5   *mBnB*

These (Brooks and Jessop, 1983) are block codes where m binary source bits are mapped into n binary bits for transmission. Redundancy is built into the code to provide the desired transmission features by making n > m. Several such codes have been proposed (and used), in particular where n = m + 1. They differ from the previous category in that the m-bit transmitted block may bear little similarity to its input source block. This gives greater flexibility for providing the desired line code features for a given level code efficiency, but is achieved at the expense of increased encoder and decoder circuit complexity.

By way of example, part of the translation table for the balanced polarity 7B8B code (Sharland and Stevenson, 1983) is illustrated in Table 28.3. Each 7-bit input source word is mapped into one or two possible 8-bit output words depending on the polarity balance, or

Table 28.3   Part of the translation table for 7B8B

Input (7 bits)	Output as transmitted (8 bits)		
	Word disparity		
	Negative	*Zero*	*Positive*
1111111		− + − + − + − +	
1010001	+ − − − + − − +	or	− + + + − + + −
0101001	− + − − − + − −	or	+ − + + + − + +
0000000		+ + + − + − − −	

disparity, of the transmitted words. Output words which are balanced in themselves (that is, have zero disparity) are to be preferred in that a single input-to-output mapping is sufficient. However, there will only be a limited number of these and so the table has to be completed by using non-zero disparity pairs where members of each pair have a disparity of opposite sign. The selection of output words is then made on the basis of minimising the cumulative disparity. It follows that some possible output words will not be

needed, this redundancy provides the necessary design flexibility. The selection of words and their mappings from input-to-output is made on the basis of ensuring: good timing content, error monitoring, word alignment and of minimising the opportunity for transmission error multiplication in the decoding process. A computer search may be used to optimise this mapping.

Many such binary-to-binary balanced codes have been designed. A similar design philosophy can also be used for bandwidth efficient multi-level codes, of which 4B3T (4 binary bits converted to 3 ternary symbols) (Catchpole, 1975) and subsequent variations on it are perhaps the best known.

28.3.3.6   *Partial response*

These codes (Lender, 1981), known also as correlative or multiple response codes, deliberately introduce a controlled amount of inter-symbol interference into the received signal. This known amount of correlated interference produces a multi-level received signal which, with suitable pre-transmit coding, can be designed to provide the requisite line code features.

A simple example of the class is duobinary (Lender, 1966) in which a binary signal is transmitted at twice the rate required to give zero intersymbol interference. With suitable coding and equalisation the resulting intersymbol interference can be arranged to give a 3-level received signal. Figure 28.12 gives waveforms for this code. Figure 28.12(a) shows an input step applied to a transmission channel which, after appropriate equalisation, produces the requisite output at the receiver after time T (ignoring channel delay) Figure 28.12(b). Now, if signals are launched into the channel with a time spacing of less than T, the output will have time to only partially respond to the input stimuli. Figure 28.12(c) shows such an input where the symbol period is only T/2, that is, signalling is at twice the conventional rate. With duobinary, some pre-transmit coding is used as detailed in Figure 28.12(d), the waveform being shown in Figure 28.12(e). This signal is launched into the channel and its associated equaliser, the result is shown in Figure 28.12(f). This received signal can then be applied to a 3 level digital decision circuit and decoded in accordance with the rules given in Figure 28.12(g) to yield an output which is the same as the original binary input. Thus, a binary data signal has been transmitted at twice the conventional rate, the price paid being a 3-level signal at the receiver. The code features adequate transitions for clock extraction and also some redundancy suitable for transmission error monitoring, by noting that the output cannot change between the two outer levels in adjacent decision times.

For well behaved channels (where intersymbol interference can be accurately controlled), partial response codes can provide a bandwidth efficient transmission technique. They have been used in radio systems and also to convert existing 24-channel PCM systems into 48-channel systems with a minimum of equipment change.

28.3.3.7   *Other line codes*

Many line codes, designed to meet the requirements of a variety of transmission systems are known. Useful surveys, together with references to further details, are to be found in for example (Duc and Smith, 1977; International J. of Electronics, 1988; Bylanski and Ingram, 1987). A rather different approach suitable for high bit rate systems which currently require simple encoding and decoding procedures is to be found in (Fair et. al., 1991).

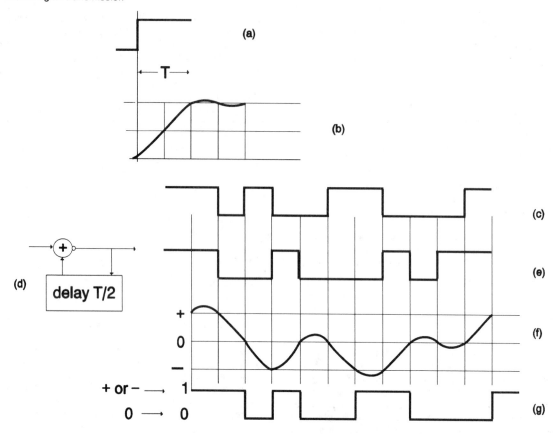

Figure 28.12 Duobinary, a partial response code: (a) step input to channel; (b) channel equaliser response; (c) binary input; (d) pre-transmit coding; (e) waveform for pre-transmit coding; (f) received signal; (g) decoded output

28.4 Clock extraction

28.4.1 Self-timed systems

Clock extraction, (known also as timing recovery or bit synchronisation), is the process by which a digital regenerator obtains a synchronising signal which enables it to optimise the timing of its decision making process. (Decision making and its relationship to the eye of the received signal has been discussed elsewhere.)

Most digital transmission systems are self-timed in that they extract the clock from the incoming data stream. This avoids the need for a separate timing channel, as used in most computers for example, and makes it easier over the longer transmission distances involved, to maintain the crucial phase relationship between the data and the clock at the point of decision making.

Self-timing requires that the data signal is coded to ensure that there is either a clock component present in the transmitted signal or that such a component can be reliably extracted after processing at the receiver. The words reliably extracted imply that a satisfactory clock can be recovered which has a frequency, phase and amplitude which is adequately immune from transmission distortions and interference, and from the effects of different data sequences. The latter requirement is found to be especially important in transmission systems containing a number of regenerative repeaters in tandem. Each repeater will experience some pattern dependent variation or jitter on the phase of its extracted clock and this will be passed on via the regenerated data stream to the next repeater. Thus the locally generated phase jitter will combine with the incoming signal jitter, a situation which will lead to a progressive build-up of jitter at subsequent regenerators. Careful design is required to ensure that this potential timing problem remains within acceptable bounds.

28.4.2 Timing content of a digital signal

All pulse sequences have symmetries in the amplitude and phase of their spectral structure. Even if the received signal lacks a component at the clock frequency, its spectral symmetry, which is independent of sequence statistics can, after further processing, be used to provide a clock for retiming purposes.

Analysis (O'Reilly, 1984) reveals that any repetitive impulse sequence, including the important case where the sequence length tends to infinity, will possess a frequency spectrum with even amplitude symmetry and odd phase symmetry (that is, Hermitian symmetry) about half the clock frequency. These symmetry conditions, which are independent of sequence statistics, arise from the periodic structure associated with the signal clock.

Now, if a received sequence has little or no d.c. component, it follows directly from the above symmetry property that it will also have little or no f_c component. Most transmission codes, which deliberately aim to suppress any d.c. content in a data sequence will fall into this category. For such sequences further processing is

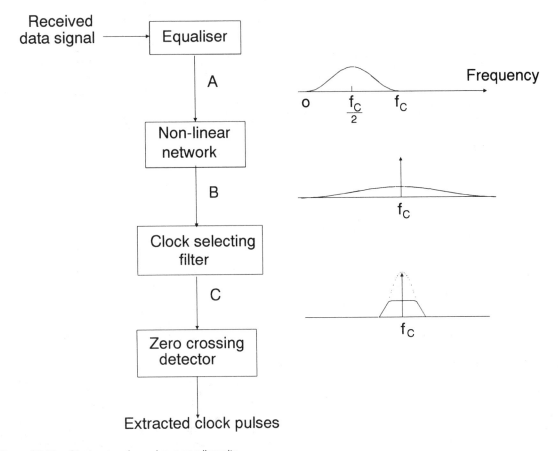

Figure 28.13 Clock extraction using a non-linearity

required before a clock component can be extracted. This can be achieved by subjecting the received signal to a non-linearity such as rectification, clipping or squaring or, often in practice, a combination of these. The Hermitian symmetry within the received signal, when subjected to the non-linearity results in pairs of spectral components, at frequency f_c, with equal amplitude and complementary phase. These components combine in a constructive manner to produce a non-zero spectral line at frequency f_c (Blackman and Mousavinezhad, 1990).

28.4.3 Clock extraction circuits

A commonly used method of clock extraction for data signals which have little or no spectral energy at the clock frequency is shown in Figure 28.13. The previous section has discussed how a signal spectrum with Hermitian symmetry about $f_c/2$ will, after non-linear processing, produce a spectral component at the clock frequency. Ideally, to ensure this symmetry property, it is necessary to have a separate equaliser for the timing path. In practice, the equaliser of Figure 28.13 will often be optimised for the decision path and provide little more than noise bandlimiting for the timing path. Nevertheless, a Hermitian symmetry component will be present at point A even if it is diluted by the characteristics of the transmitter and channel.

The non-linear network then produces, at point B, a discrete spectral line at the clock frequency f_c together with a continuous spectrum arising from the random data pattern. The purpose of the clock selecting filter is to select the wanted clock whilst rejecting as much as possible of the pattern related spectrum together with any associated noise. The selection filter may be a narrow bandpass filter or a phase locked loop with effective Q factors ranging in practice from about 80 to in excess of 200. The choice of Q will depend critically upon the stability of the incoming data rate and the tuning accuracy of the filter. A high Q will minimise the unwanted spectral components but will give rise to large phase shifts in the extracted clock if the tuned frequency deviates from the incoming clock frequency f_c.

Finally, the signal at point C is applied to a zero crossing detector or hard limiter which removes the amplitude variations and give clock pulses for use in the decision making and regenerating circuits.

28.4.4 Jitter

Short term variations from the optimum timing of a digital decision making process are known as jitter. It can be regarded as a phase modulation of the extracted clock relative to the original system clock and as such is sometimes referred to as phase jitter. The effect of jitter on the decision making process within a regenerator is illustrated in Figure 28.14(a), where it can be seen that clock edge jitter can cause decisions to be made at sub-optimum times, thereby

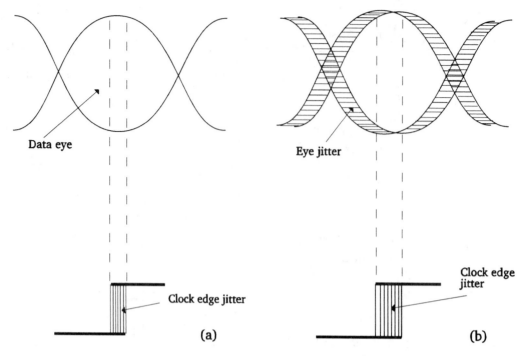

Figure 28.14 Timing jitter and the data eye: (a) clock edge jitter; (b) effect of jitter accumulation

increasing the probability of error. This jitter is caused by a combination of:

1. Incoming noise affecting the extraction process.
2. Data dependent timing effects arising from imperfections and limitations in the clock extraction process.

Both of these effects arise from the unwanted continuous spectral components getting through the clock selecting filter to point C in Figure 28.13. They combine with the spectral component of the wanted incoming clock to produce a resultant output clock which exhibits both amplitude and phase modulation. The mechanism for

a single interfering component is shown by way of example in Figure 28.15. Figure 28.15(a) shows the wanted and unwanted spectral components as they might appear at the output of a clock selecting filter. The equivalent phasor representation is given in Figure 28.15(b) where it is seen that the resultant has both amplitude and phase modulation. This is again apparent in the corresponding waveform of Figure 28.15(c). The amplitude variations can be effectively removed by a zero-crossing detector provided that the clock component is always adequately large. However, the phase modulation will remain giving rise to timing jitter.

In practice appropriate noise bandlimiting at the regenerator input means that the contribution to jitter from the noise is usually small,

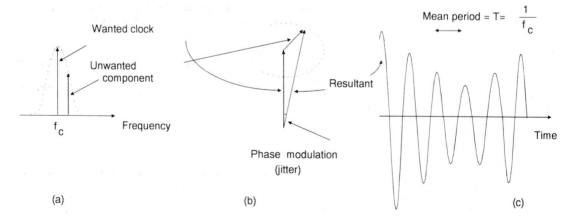

Figure 28.15 Jitter arising from an interfering spectral component: (a) spectrum from clock selecting filter (Figure 26.13 point C); (b) phasor representation of (a); (c) resulting waveform with amplitude and phase modulation

that is, the data dependent timing effects tend to dominate. These effects can be removed if the output spectrum of the clock selecting filter also has Hermitian symmetry, but which is now centred on f_c (Franks and Bubrowski, 1974). This can be explained by considering the phasor diagram of Figure 28.15(b). If the unwanted components always had Hermitian symmetry centred on f_c each pair would produce a vector of equal amplitude but opposite phase with respect to the unwanted clock. These would rotate about the f_c vector in opposite directions and so would produce a resultant which had amplitude modulation but no phase modulation, that is, no jitter.

It has already been noted that any data sequence (in impulse form) will have Hermitian symmetry properties which, after squaring, will produce the requisite Hermitian symmetry about f_c. It thus remains to provide equalisation to compensate for finite width and channel characteristics to ensure that the spectral symmetry condition is preserved at the output of the clock selecting filter. Unfortunately this requirement is not consistent with the skew symmetry spectral requirements for a good received eye and so must be provided by separate spectral shaping within the clock path. Although this demonstrates a theoretical requirement, in practice separate clock path equalisation is not always found to be necessary. Acceptably low jitter performance can often be obtained by a judicious combination of: careful transmission coding, to ensure an adequate clock component relative to the continuous spectrum after non-linear processing (Jones and Zhu, 1987), received noise limiting, and an appropriate choice of Q for the clock selecting filter.

28.4.5 Jitter accumulation

Jitter arising from the clock extraction and retiming process in a regenerator will be transmitted to subsequent regenerators where it may combine with any locally generated timing variations to cause an overall accumulation of jitter. When assessing the effect of this jitter accumulation in a self-timed system, two inter-related factors have to be taken into account. These are eye jitter and clock edge jitter and are depicted in Figure 28.14(b). Eye jitter is a direct consequence of any timing variations already present on the incoming data signal. Clock edge jitter arises as described in the previous section (which refers to Figure 28.14(a)) except that now a contribution will also be made to it by the incoming data signal.

The decision making process at the regenerator may not be as difficult as implied by Figure 28.14(b). The extracted clock will tend to follow any phase variations in the incoming data. What matters as far as the instantaneous signal-to-noise ratio and so decision error probability is concerned, is the relative timing of a particular decision instant. That is, the difference between the time position at the clock edge with respect to the optimum decision time for the particular incoming data symbol. Although this jitter tracking may help the decision making process at a particular regenerator, jitter will still accumulate from one regenerator to another. Problems can arise at the end of a link where the data signal may have to relate to a more rigid network clock. At this point, the incoming data signal may contain timing jitter which amounts to several clock periods. If data slips (loss or gain of bits) are to be avoided quite large data buffers may be required. The way in which jitter builds up has been extensively studied in the literature (Byrne et al., 1963). Suffice it to say here that it is the data pattern dependent effects which cause most trouble as they tend to reinforce each other at subsequent repeaters. In long chains of regenerators it is usually preferable to prevent the build up of excessive jitter in the first place by using carefully designed phase locked loops rather than band-pass filters in the clock selection circuits. Alternatively, data scramblers may be installed at intervals to break up the data patterns and

so control the main contributor to the problem, namely, the build-up of data dependent jitter.

The amount of jitter passed through a regenerator will depend upon the detail of the clock extraction process and in particular on the parameters of the clock selecting filter. For a simple tuned circuit the jitter power transfer characteristic (Byrne et al., 1963) will depend upon the Q of the filter as shown in Figure 28.16. Thus, low

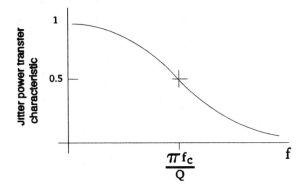

Figure 28.16 Jitter transfer characteristic for a tuned circuit

frequency jitter will be transferred through a regenerator with very little attenuation whilst higher frequency jitter will be reduced. It follows that any jitter suppressors or data buffers will need to be designed to deal especially with low frequency jitter, thus they may need to store large numbers of consecutive data bits so that slow timing variations can be smoothed out.

28.4.6 Jitter specifications

Specifications for jitter accumulation in digital systems have to take account of the low frequency build-up implied in Figure 28.16. A typical specification for jitter limits for a digital transmission system comprising many regenerators is given in Figure 28.17 where peak-to-peak jitter, expressed in clock periods, is plotted against jitter frequency. (It should be noted that r.m.s. values will be typically a factor of ten less than these figures.) This representative example is loosely based on figures given in CCITT Recommendations G823

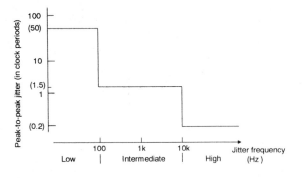

Figure 28.17 Typical jitter limits for a digital transmission system

and G824, although reference to these will show that the higher multiplex levels in the transmission hierarchy attract somewhat tighter specifications. The figure serves to highlight the low frequency timing jitter (or wander) which can amount to many clock intervals.

28.4.7 Further reading

Apart from the references given in the text, useful chapters on clock extraction are to be found in (Bylanski and Ingram, 1986) and also in (Lee and Messerschmitt, 1988), the latter includes details of waveform sampling methods which are applicable to fully digital realisations. For detailed analytical treatment the early work on timing and jitter published in the Bell System Technical Journal should be consulted (in particular the papers by Bennett and the one by Rowe, all in Vol 37, 1958 and also the paper by Manley in Vol 48, 1969). On jitter in digital networks, (Kearsey and McLintock, 1984) is a helpful paper which relates closely to the CCITT recommendations.

28.5 Frame alignment

28.5.1 The task

In addition to clock extraction, most signal formats used for digital transmission will entail some further structure which must be reliably extracted at the receiving terminal. In particular, when several information streams are combined before transmission using time division multiplexing, a frame structure will be involved. The boundaries between frames are usually marked by inserting a carefully selected frame alignment word (also called a marker, flag or frame sync pattern) which the receiver has to locate before demultiplexing can be performed (Figure 28.18).

The reliable frame alignment of such multiplexed signals is essential for the proper functioning of many digital communication systems. A loss of alignment will result in the failure to correctly identify the received bits and so will cause the disorientation of the demultiplexing process. This leads to a catastrophic loss of both message and control information. Thus the choice of frame alignment word (FAW) and the design of reliable alignment detection, misalignment detection and searching algorithms is crucial. Figure

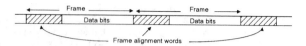

Figure 28.18 Frame structure

28.19 shows the principal tasks which have to be performed, with the desirable state shown shaded.

In practice, the aligner's task is made yet more challenging when one notes that:

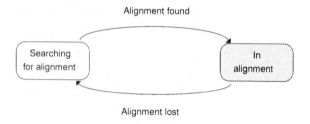

Figure 28.19 The alignment task

1. The frame alignment word may, in most systems, be temporarily imitated in random positions within the data region.
2. The frame alignment word may be mutilated by transmission errors.
3. In some systems bit slips can occur, that is, frames may temporarily lose or acquire erroneous bits.

To deal with these problems the 2-state model of Figure 28.19 has to be extended to at least the 3-state model of Figure 28.20. This model distinguishes between two locked (not searching) states; the desirable in alignment and locked state and the highly undesirable out of alignment but locked state. In this latter state a misalignment condition has occurred but the system has not yet detected it. The causes for transition from one state to another are given in the diagram and it can be seen that they relate directly to the conditions (1) to (3) listed above.

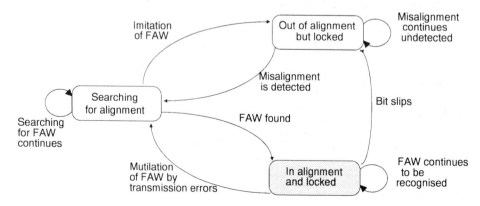

Figure 28.20 A state transition diagram for frame alignment

Before considering the mechanisms involved in such an alignment process there are two variations to the above which can be found in practice. The FAW may not be transmitted in the bunched format shown in Figure 28.18. If a system is known to be prone to short bursts of transmission errors, some protection against them may be afforded by distributing the FAW in known positions throughout the frame. Whichever method is adopted, the alignment principles are similar. Secondly, some systems use a unique FAW, that is, the data bits are encoded so that in the absence of transmission errors the FAW can never be imitated (e.g. the frame marker flag 01111110 in CCITT Recommendation X.25). For a given level of confidence in the alignment process, this will simplify the requisite algorithms but at the expense of some redundancy in coding the data bits.

28.5.2 The alignment process

When a system is operating correctly the aligner should reside in the in alignment and locked state of Figure 28.20, with the equipment verifying that the FAW occurs in the predicted position in each frame. If a misalignment condition is then detected, the mechanism must transfer to the searching state and begin an inspection of all possible FAW positions. When the correct position has been found the search can be abandoned and the equipment allowed to revert to the locked condition.

In practice the alignment mechanism needs to be yet more complicated than that shown in Figure 28.20. This is because it is desirable to try and verify that the current state really is incorrect before transferring to another state. For example, when the equipment is in alignment and locked, transmission errors may occasionally mutilate the FAW in a given frame; it may be sensible to wait and check the next frame (or the next few frames) to minimise the probability of setting off on an unnecessary search. Similarly, when in the searching state, a match to the FAW may be found which in fact is an imitation caused by the data bits. This condition is unlikely to be duplicated in the same position in successive frames (unless the FAW chosen is a bad one!) and so again, a check on subsequent frames may be sensible before reverting to the locked condition. Thus in practice, a series of check states are inserted between the locked and searching states of Figure 28.20 to reduce the probability of erroneous transitions between states. Of course a compromise is necessary, if a genuine transition to another state is required, it is equally undesirable to waste time making unnecessary checks. Unfortunately the equipment cannot instantaneously distinguish between necessary and erroneous transitions. Table 28.4 gives some examples of practical frame alignment arrangements, the last two columns detail the number of frame checks recommended before changing state.

To summarise, when in alignment, a good frame alignment process should exhibit a low probability of losing alignment and, when, out of alignment, a high probability of fast recovery to the aligned condition. To achieve these objectives the following features are required:

1. Reliable verification of the in alignment condition.
2. An efficient search procedure which ensures rapid location and verification of the position of the FAW.
3. Rapid detection of a genuine out of alignment condition caused by bit slips.
4. Robust performance in the presence of FAW imitations and transmission errors.

Table 28.4 CCITT Recommendations for frame alignment, for the 30 channel multiplexer hierarchy

Multiplexer level	CCITT Rec.	Frame length (bits)	Frame alignment word	Number of frame checks before changing state	
				Lock-to-search	Search-to-lock
Primary (approx. 2Mbits/s)	G732	512	0011011 (7 bits)	3 or 4	3
Second (approx. 8Mbits/s)	G745	1056	11100110 (8 bits)	5	2
Third (approx. 34Mbits/s)	G751	1536	1111010000 (10 bits)	4	3
Fourth (approx. 140Mbits/s)	G751	2928	111110100000 (12 bits)	4	3

Ideally these features should be obtained with a minimum of added redundancy in the data stream (in the form of an FAW) and with reasonably simple alignment equipment.

28.5.3 Searching techniques

A simple bit-by-bit aligner is outlined in Figure 28.21. A test window, of length equal to the FAW, is shown to be correctly aligned with the incoming signal. That is, a comparator (or pattern matcher) indicates that there is agreement between the received FAW and a locally stored version. This causes a bit counter to count through the known frame length and so locate and verify the position of the next FAW, and so on. If an FAW is not found in the expected position the control circuit will initiate a bit-by-bit search through the frame until a new alignment position is found.

As discussed in the previous section, it will usually also be necessary to guard against erroneous action being taken when an FAW is mutilated by transmission errors or when an imitation of an FAW occurs within the data region. We have seen that this can be done by checking an appropriate number of frames before entering or leaving the search state. A further sophistication is that of off-line searching in which extra equipment commences a search as soon as a misalignment condition is suspected. This takes place in parallel with the normal receiver processing and offers the considerable advantage that if the search proves to have been unnecessary no damage will have been done. It also benefits the true out of alignment condition in that an early start will have been made on the searching process.

The bit-by-bit searching technique can be relatively slow in establishing the aligned condition when there are random FAW imitations within the data region. This arises because each time an imitation is found the search will stop and a check made for an FAW one frame later. On failing to find the requisite pattern, the search will resume. This temporary halt in the searching process will occur

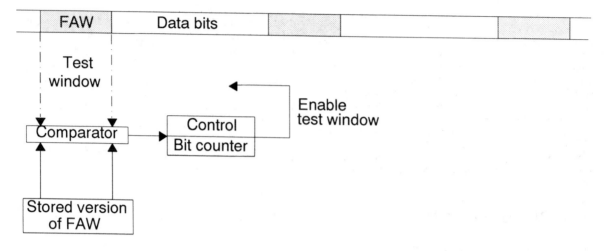

Figure 28.21 Basic configuration for a frame aligner

every time an FAW imitation is found. A faster search can be achieved by using more memory. For example, the location of sequences which match the FAW can be simply recorded and the search allowed to continue. Those which do not repeat at one-frame intervals are ignored. This process continues until the location of the true FAW becomes apparent. The aligner can then be made to jump directly to this new position. Thus, there is a trade-off; faster searches are possible but at the expense of equipment complexity.

28.5.4 Choice of frame alignment word

Some recommended patterns have been given in Table 28.4. By way of example, Figure 28.22 takes the first pattern in the Table (for 30-channel pcm) and plots the mean number of bit matches from the alignment comparator for different window positions. When the test window is in the correct position (and there are no transmission errors) the comparator will register seven agreements. If the posi-

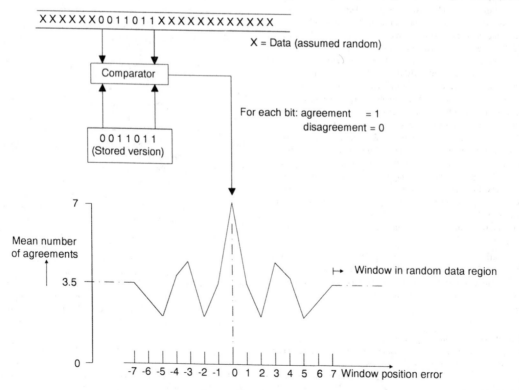

Figure 28.22 Mean number of bit agreements for different window positions

tion of the window is in error by 1 bit (in either direction), then it can be seen that three agreements and three disagreements will be registered, with the seventh bit overlapping into the data region. For random data this last bit will register an agreement or disagreement with equal probability, thus overall, the mean number of agreements for a window position error of 1-bit will be 3.5. Repeating this calculation for other window positions generates the plot of Figure 28.22. This confirms that the sequence 0011011 is a good FAW in that it produces a strong correlation spike when in alignment with relatively low sidelobes associated with the out of alignment window positions. In this respect we note that the correlation values for alignment errors of 1 or 2 bits are especially low, that is, it is a good word to use for well behaved systems which rarely experience more than 1 or 2 bit slips. Under such circumstances the pattern is thus seen to be reasonably immune to unfavourable data bit combinations and/or isolated transmission errors, both of which could increase the apparent number of agreements but are unlikely to achieve the in alignment peak value.

The choice of FAW for a particular system will depend upon many factors. For example, in contrast to the above well behaved application, systems which have to acquire alignment frequently, particularly if from a random starting position, will usually require longer FAWs. On the other hand, long FAWs are more liable to experience transmission errors. Thus, the word choice and the alignment strategy are closely linked. For example, in the presence of transmission errors it may be worthwhile to accept window positions that demonstrate a close but not necessarily exact match to the expected FAW. The implications of this and other variations on the basic alignment approach described above are to be found in the literature.

28.5.5 Further reading

A good introduction to frame alignment is to be found in (Bylanski and Ingram, 1986) and in several more recent books which refer to them and adopt a similar approach. Some of the subtleties of the alignment process with examples based on CCITT specifications are discussed in (Jones and Zhu, 1985), a similar method of analysis (using probability generating functions) is adopted in a tutorial article (Choi, 1990). Barker (Barker, 1953) was first to study the selection of good frame alignment words, since then many variations have been investigated to provide for optimum performance under a variety of system conditions, a recent study with references to earlier work is to be found in (Al-Subbagh and Jones, 1988).

28.6   References

Al-Subbagh, M.N. and Jones, E.V. (1988) Optimum Patterns for Frame Alignment, *Proceedings IEE (Part F)*, **135**, pp. 594-603.

Barker, R.H. (1953) Group Synchronising of Binary Digital Systems. In *Communication Theory, (ed. W. Jackson)*, Academic Press, pp. 273-287.

Beaulieu, N.C. (1989) A Simple Series for Personal Computer Computation of the Error Function, *IEEE Transactions on Communications*, **3**, pp. 989-991, (September).

Bennett, W.R. and Davey, J.R. (1965) *Data Transmission*, McGraw-Hill.

Blackman, N.M. and Mousavinezhad, S.H. (1990) The Spectrum of the Square of a Synchronous Random Pulse Train, *IEEE Transactions on Communications*, **38**, pp. 13-17.

Brooks R.M. and Jessop, A. (1983) Line Coding for Optical Fibre Systems, *International Journal of Electronics*, **55**, pp. 81-120.

Bylanski, P. and Ingram, D.G.W. (1987) *Digital Transmission Systems*, 2nd edn. Peter Peregrinus.

Byrne, C.J., Karafin, B.J. and Robinson, D.R. (1963) Systematic Jitter in a Chain of Digital Regenerators, *Bell System Technical Journal*, **42**, pp. 2679-2714.

Carlson, A.B. (1986) *Communication Systems*, McGraw-Hill, 3rd edn.

Catchpole, R.J. (1975) Efficient Ternary Transmission Codes, *Electronic Letters*, **11**, pp. 482-484, (October)

Cattermole, K.W. (1983) Principles of Digital Line Coding, *International Journal of Electronics*, **55**, pp. 3-33.

CCIR (1986) Report 967-1, *Digital Television: Transmission Impairments and Methods of Protection*.

CCITT (1988a) Recommendation G.821, *Error Performance of an International Digital Connection Forming Part of an Integrated Services Digital Network*, Blue Books, Geneva.

CCITT (1988b) Recommendation M.550. *Performance Limits for Bringing into Service and Maintenance of Digital Paths, Sections and Line Sections*, Blue Books, Geneva.

CCITT (1988c) Recommendation G.703, *General Aspects of Interfaces*, Blue Books, Geneva.

Choi, D.W. (1990) Frame Alignment in a Digital Carrier System — a Tutorial, *IEEE Communications Magazine*, pp. 47-54 (February).

Dawson, P.A. and Kitchen J.A. (1986) TAT-8 Supervisory System, *British Telecom Engineering Journal*, **5**, (July).

Duc, N.Q. and Smith B.M. (1977) Line Coding for Digital Data Transmission, *Australia Telecommunications Research Journal*, **11**, pp. 14-27.

Fair, I.J., Grover, W.D., Krzymien, W.A. and MacDonald, R.I. (1991) Guided Scrambling: A New Line Coding Technique for High Bit Rate Fibre Optic Transmission Systems, *IEEE Transactions on Communications*, **39**, pp. 289-297 (February).

Franks, L.E. (1968) Further Results on Nyquist's Problem in Pulse Transmission, *IEEE Transactions on Communications*, **16**, pp. 337-340.

Franks, L.E. and Bubrowski J.P. (1974) Statistical Properties of Timing Jitter in a PAM Timing Recovery System, *IEEE Transactions on Communications*, **22**, pp. 913-920.

Hamming, R.W. (1980) *Coding and Information Theory*, Prentice-Hall.

International Journal of Electronics (1983) **55**, Special Issue on Line Codes.

Jones, E.V. and Al-Subbagh, M.N. (1985) Algorithms for Frame Alignment — Some Comparisons, *Proceedings IEE (Part F)*, **132**, pp. 529-536.

Jones, E.V. and Zhu, S. (1987) Data Sequence Coding for Low Jitter Timing Recovery, *Electronics Letters*, **23**, pp. 337-338.

Kanal, L.N. and Sastry, A.R.K. (1978) Models for Channels with Memory and their Applications to Error Control, *Proceedings IEEE*, **66**, pp. 724-744.

Kawanishi, S. et al. (1988) DmB1M code and its Performance in a Very High Speed Optical Transmission System, *IEEE Transactions on Communications*, **36**, pp. 951-956, (August).

Kearsey, B.N. and McLintock, R.W. (1984) Jitter in Digital Telecommunication Networks, *British Telecommunications Engineering*, **3**, pp. 108-116 (July).

Knowles, M.D. and Drukarev, A.L. (1988) Bit Error Rate Estimation for Channels with Memory, *IEEE Transactions on Communications*, **36**, pp. 767-769.

Kubat, P. and Bollen, R.E. (1989) A Digital Circuit Performance Analysis for Tandem Burst-Error Links in an ISDN Environment, *IEEE Transactions on Communications*, **37**, pp. 1071-1076.

Lee, E.A. and Messerschmitt, D.G. (1988) Digital Communication, Kluwer Academic.

Lender, A. (1966) Correlative Level Coding for Binary-Data Transmission, *IEEE Spectrum*, pp. 104-115 (February).

Lender, A. (1981) Correlative (Partial Response) Techniques. In *Digital Communications: Microwave Applications (ed. K. Feher)*, Prentice Hall, Chapter 7.

McLintock, R.W. and Kearsey, B.N. (1984) Error Performance Objectives for Digital Networks, *The Radio and Electronic Engineer*, **54**, pp. 79-85, (February). (A later version which includes changes in CCITT Recommendations is to be found in: *British Telecommunications Engineering*, **3**, pp 92-98, July 1984.)

Nyquist, H. (1928) Certain Topics in Telegraph Transmission Theory, *Transactions AIEE*, **47** pp. 617-644.

O'Reilly, J.J. (1984) Timing Extraction for Baseband Digital Transmission. In *Problems of Randomness in Communication Engineering (ed. Cattermole and O'Reilly)* Pentech Press, 1984.

Sharland, A.J. and Stevenson, A. (1983) A Simple In-Service Error Detection Scheme Based on the Statistical Properties of Line Codes for Optical Fibre Systems, *International Journal of Electronics*, **55**, pp. 141-158.

Sklar, B. (1988) *Digital Communications*, Prentice-Hall.

Sunde, E.D. (1961) Pulse Transmission by AM, FM, and PM in the Presence of Phase Distortion, *Bell System Technical Journal*, **40**, pp. 353-422.

Takahashi, K. (1988) Transmission Quality of Evolving Telephone Services, *IEEE Communications Magazine*, pp. 24-35, (October).

Waters, D.B. (1983) Line Codes for Metallic Cable Systems. *International Journal of Electronics*, **55**, pp. 159-169.

Yamamoto, Y. and Wright, T. (1989) Error Performance in Evolving Digital Networks Including ISDNs, *IEEE Communications Magazine*, pp. 12-18 (April).

Yoshikai N.; Katagiri, K. and Ito, T. (1984) mB1C Code and its Performance in an Optical Communication System, *IEEE Transactions on Communications*, **32**, pp. 163-169.

29

Telephone networks

J E Flood
OBE DSc FInstP CEng FIEE
Aston University

Contents

29.1 Introduction

A public switched telecommunication network (PSTN) contains transmission links between different locations known as nodes (Flood, 1975). A node may be either a subscriber's station, which originates and terminates calls, or a switching centre (i.e. an exchange). Thus, any two subscribers may communicate by means of the appropriate combination of transmission links connected together at switching nodes for the duration of their call.

Although other services are growing rapidly, telephony is still the predominant service provided by public telecommunication operators (PTOs). Thus, most of the traffic carried on their networks is voice traffic. It is uneconomic to provide entirely separate networks for other services, so these make use of transmission links in the telephone network as bearers for their traffic. For example, a single telephone channel can convey 24 multiplexed telegraph channels, or a variety of data channels operating at different digit rates. Conversely, the bandwidth which could accommodate over a thousand telephone channels can, instead, be allocated to a single television channel. Consequently, the design of telecommunication networks is mainly dictated by the needs of telephony, as discussed in this chapter.

The transmission links in a national network act as common bearers for a variety of different services, as shown in Figure 29.1. A subscriber has access to these services over his local-line loop to the local exchange. For switched services, such as those provided for telephony, telex and packet switching of data, the transmission links provide circuits which are temporarily connected together as required by switching equipment at the nodes. Private circuits leased from the PTO, either analogue or digital, are provided by circuits in the same transmission bearer network. However, these circuits are connected together in a semi-permanent fashion at the nodes in order to provide fixed routings.

In a PSTN, in order to route the call to the required address, the calling subscriber must signal to the exchange that a call is required and then send it to a signal indicating the number of the called subscriber. At the end of the call, the subscriber sends a 'clear' signal causing the switches to release the circuits used in the connection. In the case of the simplest telephone call, the call and clear signals are respectively a loop and a disconnection of the subscriber's line, produced by the 'off hook' and 'on hook' states of the telephone handset. The called number is sent by a succession of disconnections produced by the telephone dial. A more complex call may be routed through several nodes. It is then necessary for this signalling

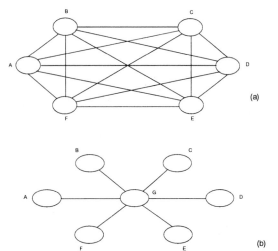

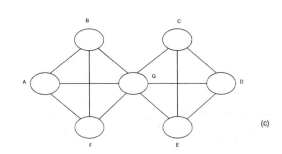

Figure 29.2 Simple network configuration: (a) fully interconnected network; (b) star network; (c) partially interconnected network

information to be transmitted between the exchanges at all these nodes (Welch, 1981).

It can therefore be seen that a telecommunication network may be considered to consist of the following interacting sub-systems:

1. Transmission systems.
2. Switching systems.

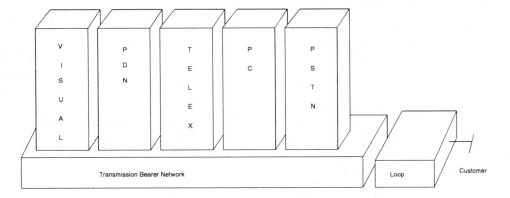

Figure 29.1 Provision of different services over common transmission bearer networks

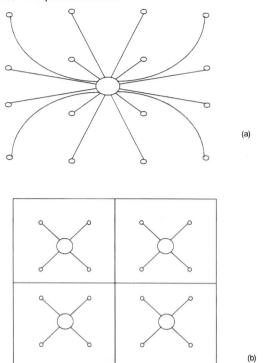

(a)

(b)

Figure 29.3 Effect of number of exchanges on length of subscribers' lines: (a) single-exchange area (b) multi-exchange area

3. Signalling systems.

These systems are discussed in more detail in Chapters 30, 31 and 43, respectively.

29.2 Network architecture

If each subscriber's station in a telecommunication system must be able to communicate with every other station, one possibility would be to provide a circuit between each pair of stations, as shown in Figure 29.2(a). If there are n stations, the number of circuits required is $\frac{1}{2}n(n-1)$. Thus, the cost is approximately proportional to n^2. If n is large, such a fully-interconnected mesh network would obviously be enormously expensive. Instead, each station is provided with a circuit to a central switching system, or exchange, as shown in Figure 29.2(b). The number of circuits required is then only n. Clearly, the star network of Figure 29.2(b) is much cheaper than the mesh network of Figure 29.2(a), unless n is very small.

If an exchange area is large and contains a large number of stations, many of the subscribers' circuits will be long and therefore expensive, as shown in Figure 29.3(a). If the area is divided into several separate areas, each with its own exchange, as shown in Figure 29.3(b), subscribers' circuits are shorter and their total cost is less. However, the costs of switching equipment and its accommodation increase with the number of exchanges. Thus, as shown in Figure 29.4, there is an optimum number of exchanges for which the total cost of the network is a minimum.

In a multi-exchange area, subscribers connected to each exchange will wish to communicate with subscribers connected to other exchanges. Thus, there is a need for circuits between the exchanges. These circuits are called junctions. The number of junctions required on each route between a pair of exchanges depends on the traffic between them. If a direct junction route is provided between every pair of exchanges, these routes form a fully interconnected mesh network, as shown in Figure 29.2(a). An alternative is to provide a junction route from each exchange to a central switching centre, to form a star network as shown in Figure 29.2(b). The exchanges to which subscribers' circuits are connected are called local exchanges and the central switching centre is called a tandem exchange.

In a star junction network with a tandem exchange there are fewer junction routes than in a fully-interconnected mesh. However, each route incurs the additional cost of its associated switching equipment in the tandem exchange. Consequently, if there is sufficient traffic between a pair of local exchanges to ensure that direct junctions are heavily loaded and they are cheap because the distance is short, it is more economical to provide direct junctions between these exchanges than to route the traffic indirectly through a tandem exchange. Consequently, a multi-exchange area will often contain direct junction routes between nearby local exchanges which have a high community of interest, and traffic between the other exchanges will be routed indirectly via a tandem exchange. The network thus consists of a mixture of a star and meshes, as shown in Figure 29.2(c).

In a multi-exchange area, only a minority of calls generated at a local exchange will be to other subscribers served by that exchange. Most traffic will be to or from other exchanges, either in the same area or outside it. Thus, the principal function of a local exchange is not to carry traffic between its own subscribers, but to provide an interface between these subscribers and the rest of the network.

A national telecommunication network links many towns and cities; it thus contains many of these multi-exchange areas. There is thus a need for a network of long-distance routes between them; this constitutes the trunk network. It is obviously uneconomic for the trunk network to interconnect all the local exchanges. However,

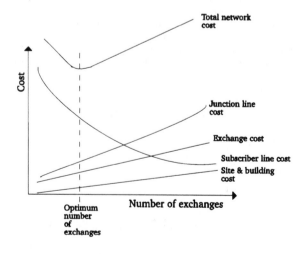

Figure 29.4 Variation of network cost with number of exchanges

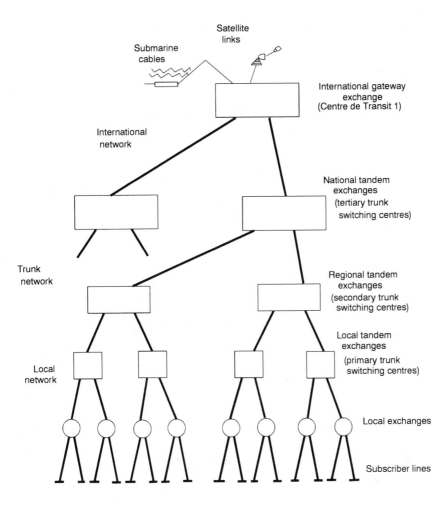

Figure 29.5   National telecommunication network

each local exchange has junctions to a tandem exchange, so this provides a convenient interface with the trunk network. In CCITT terminology, it is called the primary trunk switching centre. In the UK it was called a group switching centre (GSC) and in North America a class 4 office. A GSC in the UK usually acted as a trunk exchange, as a tandem exchange and as a local exchange serving nearby subscribers. However, in a large city, these functions may be performed by separate exchanges.

Just as it is usually uneconomic for all local exchanges to be directly interconnected in a multi-exchange area, it may be uneconomic for all primary trunk switching centres to be directly interconnected. Thus, a primary centre may have direct trunk routes to those nearest to it, but traffic to other primary centres is routed via tandem switching centres, known as secondary trunk centres, each serving a region of the country. Again, these may not be fully interconnected and traffic between secondary centres is routed via tertiary centres.

It can be seen that a complete national network contains a hierarchy of exchanges, as shown in Figure 29.5. At the apex of the hierarchy there will be one or more international gateway exchanges, which provide the interface between the national network and the rest of the world. In CCITT terminology, these are called CT3 exchanges (centres du transits).

A national network can be seen to consist of a hierarchy of interconnected networks, as follows:

1. A subscriber's private network. For example, this may consist of extension lines connected to a private automatic branch exchange (PABX) for telephony or a local-area network (LAN) for data.
2. The subscribers' distribution network, which is sometimes called the access network or local-loop plant. This connects subscribers' telephones or PABXs to a local exchange.
3. The junction network, which interconnects a group of local exchanges and connects them to the primary trunk centre.
4. The trunk network, which interconnects primary centres throughout the country.

There are variations in practice and in terminology throughout the world. In North America, junctions are called trunks and trunk circuits are called toll circuits. In CCITT terminology, networks (2)

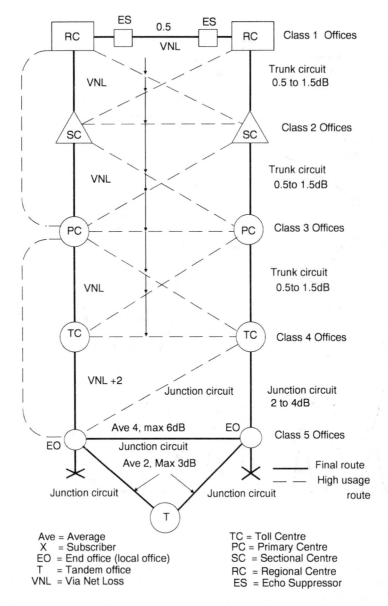

Figure 29.6 North American analogue network

and (3) together are called the local network; however, in the UK this term is usually reserved for (2) alone.

In some countries, where subscribers' distribution areas are large, it is economic to locate the switching equipment directly associated with a group of subscribers at a location close to the subscribers but remote from the exchange. This equipment is called a remote concentrator (Flood, 1975). It concentrates traffic from a number of subscribers' circuits onto a smaller number of circuits leading to the exchange. A concentrator may also be used as a temporary expedient when unexpected development in one part of an exchange area uses up all the cable pairs leading to it. In this way, service can be provided to new subscribers before an additional cable can be laid. If remote concentrators are used, an additional level of switching is introduced into level (2) of the hierarchy.

A subscribers' private network may use a private automatic exchange (PAX) which, unlike a PABX, does not connect its lines to the PSTN. On the other hand, a private network may extend over many different locations using circuits in networks (2), (3) and (4) rented from the PTO. Multinational companies may have private circuits extending through the international network to link their offices in different countries.

In a national network, as shown in Figure 29.5, the minimum configuration of star-connected exchanges is usually augmented by direct routes interconnecting exchanges where a high community of interest generates sufficient traffic. There is thus a backbone route joining each switching centre at the lowest level to the highest-level centre via intermediate centres, together with transverse branches between centres at the same level. There may also be some direct routes between centres at different levels, which violate this pattern, if there is sufficient traffic to justify them.

The number of levels in the hierarchy of a national network depends on the relative costs of transmission and switching. A country which is small and densely populated will have relatively short distances between its primary centres and large amounts of traffic between them. A country which is large and sparsely populated will have longer distances and less traffic between its primary centres. Consequently, the cost per circuit of providing direct routes between primary centres is much less in the former case than the latter. As a result, a small densely-populated country will have more of its primary centres directly connected and fewer levels in its hierarchy than a country which is large and sparsely populated.

These differences are illustrated in Figures 29.6 and 29.7 which show, respectively, the analogue networks of North America (Clarke, 1952) and of BT (British Telecom) (Barron, 1959). The former has four levels of trunk exchanges (toll offices classes 1 to 4), whereas the latter had only three. These were called group switching centres (GSCs), district switching centres (DSCs) and main switching centres (MSCs). The DSCs and MSCs were collectively called trunk transit exchanges and the network interconnecting them was the trunk transit network. The large number of direct circuits between GSCs handled most of the trunk traffic. Only a small proportion of trunk traffic reached the transit network. How-

ever, the transit network was necessary because of the very large number of different possible connections which could not be made over direct circuits between GSCs, although each of these generated relatively little traffic.

The introduction of digital switching and transmission has had a profound effect on the economics of network provision. As a result, the architectures of integrated digital networks (IDNs) now being developed differ greatly from the analogue networks described above. The changes are considered in section 29.5.

29.2.1 The International network

The introduction of international subscriber dialling (ISD) necessitated the introduction of a world-wide automatic-switching network. In 1964 the CCITT recommended a plan for a hierarchy of automatic international exchanges. This plan is shown in Figure 29.8.

The international network has three levels of switching centre (centre du transit) designated CT1 to CT3. The international gateway exchanges in each country, which connect national to international circuits, are centres CT3, whereas centres CT1 and CT2 interconnect only international circuits. A complete international connection consists of three parts:

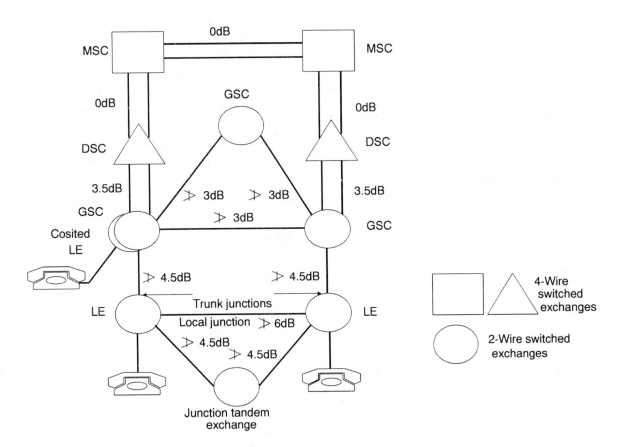

Figure 29.7 BT (British Telecom) former analogue network

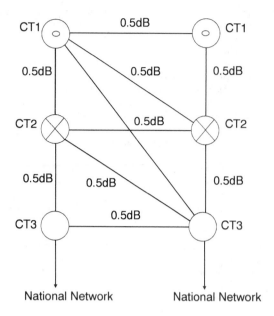

Figure 29.8 International network

1. From the calling subscriber through the national network of the country to a gateway exchange (CT3).

2. An international chain, which may consist of up to five international circuits (or exceptionally six). These are interconnected on a 4-wire basis via international transit centres (CT1 and CT2) between the gateways (CT3) of the two countries.

3. The national network of the country of the called subscriber.

29.3 Network standards

In designing a public switched telecommunication network (PSTN), consideration must be given to the following factors:

1. The transmission plan.
2. The numbering plan.
3. The charging plan.
4. The routing plan.
5. The signalling plan.
6. The grade of service required (end to end).
7. The capabilities of switching systems.
8. The economics of direct and indirect routing.

These considerations are inter-related. For example, charging, routing and numbering are closely related. Both the route for a call and its charging rate are determined by the directory number of the called station. The flexibility with which these can be handled is governed by the capabilities of the switching equipment employed. Either transmission or signalling standards may limit the size of a local-exchange area, or the number of links that may be used in tandem for a trunk connection. These place restrictions on the routings that may be employed.

The national plans for numbering, charging, transmission and signalling thus form a set of standards that govern planning both for

a national network and its constituent local networks. The specified grade of service determines the number of circuits required on each route within it, i.e. the dimensioning of the network.

29.4 Transmission

29.4.1 General

The overall (i.e. mouth to ear) performance of a telephone connection is described by its loudness rating or reference equivalent. This is determined by the performances of the two telephones (which partly depend on the DC feeding currents they receive from their local exchanges) and on the losses (attenuations) of all intervening circuits in the connection through the PSTN (Richards, 1973). These circuits comprise the subscribers' lines to their local exchanges, together with any junctions and trunk circuits used in the connection.

A national transmission plan should allocate the permissible overall attenuation so as to obtain the most economical design. Subscribers' exchange lines are most numerous and contribute very significantly to the total cost of a network. In order to minimise this cost, subscribers' lines use the minimum size of cable conductors. Consequently, the transmission plan should allocate as much loss as possible to the subscribers' lines at the two ends of a connection. Junction circuits between local exchanges and between them and primary trunk switching centres are much less numerous. It is thus economic to use cables with larger conductors which have lower losses. Trunk circuits can justify still higher cost, so they contain amplifiers and have very small losses.

In an analogue PSTN, the economic necessity of allocating a large limiting attenuation to subscribers' lines, together with the loss variations of other circuits, results in some connections which are unsatisfactory. If present limiting standards were consistently encountered, the performance obtained on complex trunk calls would be totally unacceptable. Fortunately, most calls do not follow the most adverse routing permitted by the transmission plan. By means of statistical studies of routings and of the various transmission impairments, it is possible to design a network which is economic and yet provides an acceptably small proportion of unsatisfactory connections.

29.4.2 Four-wire circuits

Long-distance circuits use amplifiers to overcome their high attenuation. Amplifiers are usually unilateral devices. An amplified circuit therefore has a separate channel for transmission in each direction, as shown in Figure 29.9. Such a circuit is called a four-wire circuit, although the channels may be provided in high-capacity multiplex systems over optical fibres or microwave radio instead of wires. A connection made up of such circuits will be joined at each end to two-wire circuits leading to the subscribers' stations. A four-wire circuit is connected to its two-wire terminations by means of a four-wire to two-wire terminating set containing a hybrid transformer and a line-balance impedance.

If the four-wire circuit were to be directly connected to the two-wire circuit at each end, this would complete a loop round the channels in the two directions which could oscillate or 'sing'. The terminating set prevents this. If the balance impedance exactly matches the impedance of the two-wire line, the hybrid transformer provides transmission between the two-wire lines and the four-wire circuit (with 3dB loss), but there is infinite loss across it between the

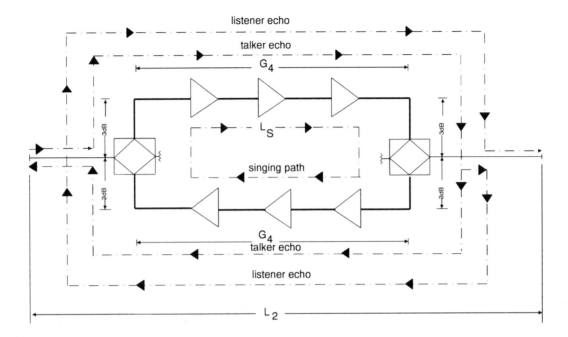

Figure 29.9 Four-wire circuit

two channels of the four-wire circuit. Thus, it is theoretically possible for a four-wire circuit to provide zero loss, or even gain, between its two-wire ends. However, in practice, line balances are not perfect, so the losses across the hybrid transformers are not infinite. If the trans-hybrid loss is too low, or the gain (G_4) in either direction is too high, the nett gain around the loop will be greater than zero and the circuit can still sing. In practice, there is a tolerance on G_4 and line balances cannot exactly match the two-wire lines. Consequently, the gains G_4 must be set to provide an adequate stability margin to cater for these variations. As a result, there is usually an overall loss (L_2), typically 3dB, between the two-wire ends (Hills, 1973).

Even if a four-wire circuit is stable, it still impairs transmission if its trans-hybrid losses are non-infinite. As shown in Figure 29.9, a signal from one two-wire line can return to it (attenuated and delayed) after traversing the four-wire circuit in each direction. This is called talker echo. This signal can then be transmitted again over the four-wire line to produce listener echo. In each case, the echo follows the direct signal after a delay equal to twice the one-way propagation time of the 4-wire circuit. This is known as the round-trip delay. For the listener, echo reduces the intelligibility of the conversation. For the speaker, it can actually interrupt his speech and is thus even more troublesome. It is therefore necessary to ensure that echoes are attenuated sufficiently to make these effects unobjectionable.

29.4.3 Trunk transmission plans

A complete connection through a trunk network consists of several four-wire circuits connected in tandem at exchanges. The exchanges may use either 2-wire switching or 4-wire switching. If 2-wire switching is used, 4-wire circuits must be terminated at every switching node, as shown in Figure 29.10(a). If each 4-wire circuit is lined up to provide, say, a loss of 3dB (to provide an adequate

stability margin) and each exchange introduces a loss of, say, 1dB, a connection of n tandem links will have a loss of 4ndB. The number of links that can be connected in tandem is thus severely limited. In the BT analogue trunk network, GSCs used 2-wire switching, as shown in Figure 29.7. Consequently, connections between GSCs which did not use the transit network could be routed through only one other intermediate GSC (Tobin, 1960).

If 4-wire switching is used, terminating sets are required only at the ends of the connection, as shown in Figure 29.10(b). This avoids 3dB loss for every intermediate switching node. Consequently, modern trunk networks use 4-wire switching and are able to provide connections having more links in tandem. For example, the BT trunk transit network shown in Figure 29.7 provided connections with up to five links in tandem and the North American toll network shown in Figure 29.6 connects up to seven links in tandem.

When 4-wire links are connected in tandem as shown in Figure 29.10(b), their variation in overall loss is, of course, greater than for the single 4-wire circuit shown in Figure 29.9. It is therefore necessary for the complete circuit to have a greater overall loss to obtain the same stability margin. This may be achieved either by arranging for the end links in the connection to have more than 3dB loss and operating the intervening links at zero loss. Alternatively, every link may have a small loss, typically 0.5dB. The former policy was used in the BT analogue trunk network shown in Figure 29.7 and the latter policy in the North American network (Andrews, 1971) shown in Figure 29.6 and the international network (Munday, 1967) shown in Figure 29.8.

The annoying effect of echo increases with its delay. The longer the distance, the greater the round-trip delay and so the greater the echo attenuation required. This can be achieved by making the overall loss increase with distance, as shown in Figures 29.6 and 29.8. However, there is a limit to the extent to which echo can be controlled by increasing overall loss. This is usually reached when the round-trip delay is about 40ms. This delay is exceeded on long

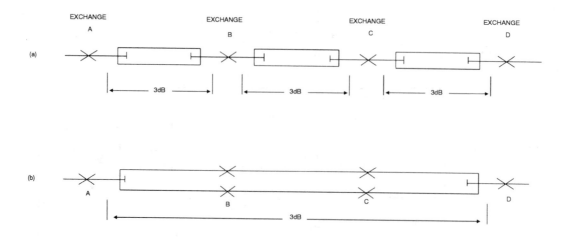

Figure 29.10 Switching of four-wire circuits: (a) 2-wire switching; (b) 4-wire switching

trans-continental and inter-continental circuits, particularly if these use satellite links. It is then impossible to obtain both an adequately low transmission loss and an adequately high echo attenuation. On such circuits, it is necessary to control echo by fitting echo suppressors or echo cancellers. Figure 29.6 shows these between regional centres in the North American network.

29.4.4 Digital transmission

If digital transmission is used for telephony (see Chapter 28), there are impairments due to quantisation noise and the noise and jitter on transmission links; however, these are normally negligible. The attenuation of each transmission link is zero with zero tolerance. Thus, the number of links connected in tandem does not affect the overall loss or its variation, as in the case of analogue circuits considered above. Only the digital error rate accumulates with the number of links in tandem.

In an integrated digital network, as described in Section 29.5, the subscribers' lines at the two ends of the connection are the only cause of variation of loss between different connections. This eliminates the wide variation of losses encountered in analogue networks and enables every connection to have a loudness rating within the preferred range.

29.5 Integrated digital networks

Since the analogue networks shown in Figures 29.6 and 29.7 were designed in the 1960s, there have been great reductions in the per-circuit cost of long-distance transmission because of the development of high-capacity transmission systems using coaxial cables, microwave radio and optical fibres. Modern systems using these transmission media now employ digital transmission using time-division multiplexing (TDM) instead of analogue transmission using frequency-division multiplexing (FDM). Pulse-code modulation (PCM) is now the preferred transmission technique both for junction and trunk routes.

During the same period, electronic digital time-division switching systems (Redmill, 1990) have been developed to supersede electromechanical analogue space-division switching systems. If space-di-

vision switching is employed to interconnect circuits provided by transmission systems using FDM or TDM, it is necessary to install channelling equipment at each end of every link in order to demultiplex every channel to audio frequencies before switching it and, after switching, to multiplex it again for transmission over the next link in the connection. If both the transmission systems and the switching systems employ digital time-division multiplexing, the need for channelling equipment at the end of each line is eliminated, since channels are both switched and transmitted in PCM frames. The cost saving is very large.

When electromechanical space-division switching is used, apparatus individual to each incoming and outgoing circuit is needed to transmit and receive signalling information associated with it. This is known as channel-associated signalling. Modern digital exchanges use stored-program control (SPC); the information required for controlling connections is handled by their central processors. Thus, for a tandem connection between SPC exchanges, signalling information can be exchanged between their central processors by means of data links connecting them directly. This is known as common-channel signalling. No signalling apparatus is required to be associated with individual circuits and this produces a further cost saving. It has been estimated that the cost of providing inter-exchange signalling by means of common-channel signalling is only about 5% of the cost of channel-associated signalling.

A network having compatible digital transmission and switching is called an integrated digital network (IDN). The cost savings mentioned above make it economic to use many more direct routes between trunk exchanges and to require fewer tandem routings. This enables the hierarchy to use fewer levels. It also makes it economic for an exchange to have routes to two or more switching centres at the next higher level, instead of the single backbone route used in analogue networks. This increases the security of the network. If one of these routes breaks down, traffic can still use the other.

Since the introduction of digital exchanges has reduced the per-line cost of switching, quite a high proportion of the cost of an exchange is due to its central processors. This makes it desirable for a digital local exchange to have more subscribers' lines than an analogue exchange and so serve a larger area. Increasing the size of exchange areas favours the use of remote concentrators. Analogue circuits from subscribers' premises are terminated at a concentrator which only requires two PCM systems to connect it to the main exchange. In addition to reducing the per-line cost of call processing, having larger local exchanges reduces the number of exchanges in an area and so reduces the cost of junction plant and tandem switching. Having fewer local exchanges also reduces the costs of operation and maintenance.

The final stage of this evolution is to extend digital transmission to subscribers' premises. Since a stream of digits is suitable for the transmission of high-speed data in addition to speech, this enables an IDN to evolve into an integrated services digital network (ISDN), whereby many different subscribers' services are provided over the same plant. This development is discussed in Chapter 44.

The IDN of BT (Muir, 1987) is shown in Figure 29.11. Local areas are served by digital cell centre exchanges (DCCEs). Subscribers obtain access to a DCCE to process their calls via a remote concentrator (RCU) unless they are situated very close to the DCCE. The concentrator is connected to the main exchange by two low-capacity digital transmission systems, usually operating at 2Mbit/s or 8Mbit/sec. These are diversely routed in order to provide against failures. Concentrators parented on about 400 DCCEs will replace over 6000 local exchanges.

The trunk network contains only one level of switching centres. These exchanges are called digital main switching units (DMSUs) and are fully interconnected. The digital trunk network contains

only 60 DMSUs, whereas the analogue network contained over 400 GSCs. Each DCCE has junction routes to two DMSUs. Thus, it is still able to connect trunk calls to and from its subscribers in the event of the breakdown of one route or its DSMU.

The data links used for common-channel signalling between digital exchanges in the PSTN form a separate self-contained network, as shown in Figure 29.12. However, this signalling network uses channels in the basic digital transmission bearer network, just as does the PSTN. In order to maintain synchronism of the PCM frames in all the digital transmission links and exchanges, it is necessary to distribute synchronising signals from a national reference clock source. This results in a synchronising network linking it to all the digital exchanges. Finally, centres remote from exchanges have been introduced to collect bulk data (e.g. traffic statistics, billing, etc.) from exchanges and to provide man-machine interfaces for maintenance and making software changes (Waliji, 1980). Management centres receive real-time information on traffic flows and allow traffic to be re-routed to minimise congestion (Bealby, 1990). These require an administration data network connecting the remote centres to the nodes of the PSTN. It is thus seen that a complete IDN contains four separate networks, as shown in Figure 29.12. However, all of these use channels in the basic digital transmission network, making five networks in all.

It has been shown in section 29.4.1. that an analogue network cannot provide a satisfactory transmission performance between

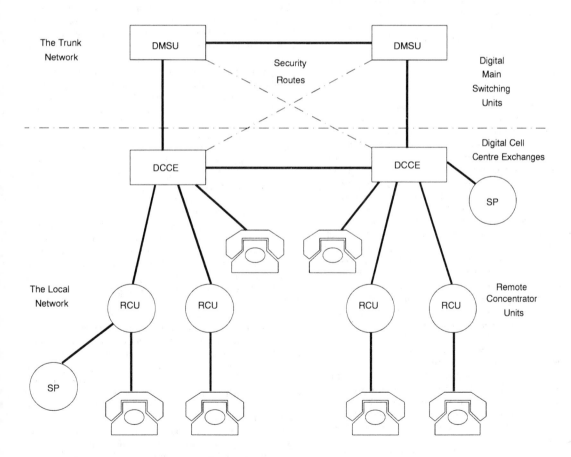

Figure 29.11 BT (British Telecom) digital network

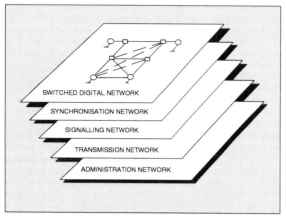

INTEGRATED DIGITAL NETWORK

Figure 29.12 Component networks of IDN

every possible combination of subscribers. However, digital transmission links have zero loss; thus, this will apply to any connection of links set up in an integrated digital network. The only variation in overall attenuation between different connections is that due to differences in the lengths of the subscribers' lines. This represents an enormous improvement and can ensure that all calls through the network have a loudness rating within the preferred range.

29.6 Network services

The chief service provided by the PSTN is to make connections for communication between its subscribers. A call is made by the calling subscriber dialling the directory number of the required destination. For a local call, only the local number need be dialled. For a trunk call, the number dialled is the subscriber's national number; this consists of an area code, followed by an exchange code and the number of the subscriber on that exchange. Subscribers must therefore obtain access to other services in the same way.

When services are provided locally (e.g. emergency services, operator assistance, etc.) the subscriber need only dial a local number. If a service is provided remotely, an area code is required. In the BT network, these additional services are provided by the derived services network (Roberts, 1985; Roberts, 1987). This can be considered as an additional level in the trunk hierarchy. Although service providers may share a common code of the same form as an 'area' code, they may be anywhere in the country and the call is routed there via the derived services network. This caters for calls where the call is charged to the called customer instead of the calling customer (Freephone, 0800) or where the caller is charged at a premium rate for the call (e.g. message services).

In countries where the telecommunications service is 'liberalised', there are several competing PTOs; thus, a subscriber on one network must be able to obtain access to subscribers on other networks. In the UK, other PTOs have 'area' codes and BT provides access to them via this derived services network. For example, calls are routed to the two competing cellular radio mobile systems (Cellnet and Vodafone).

In the case of a call to a mobile-radio subscriber, the number dialled represents the identity of the subscriber rather than his location (which may be anywhere in the country). Ideally, this should apply to all subscribers. It would avoid abortive calls when subscribers are away and the cost and inconvenience of subscribers having to change their numbers when moving to another town. In order to cater for this, an 'intelligent' network would be required. Every exchange would need to access a complete national data base to determine the location of a called subscriber instead of merely routing the call according to the area code dialled. As shown in Figure 29.13, the BT derived services network has been provided with an 'intelligent' network data base (INDB) to provide its exchanges with call-routing and charging information, together with management information for both the network operator and the service providers (Webster, 1989)

29.7 Numbering and charging

29.7.1 National schemes

In order to establish a connection through a network, it is necessary for a caller to inform the switching centre of the required address of the subscriber being called, i.e. the called subscriber's directory number. This determines both the route for the call and the charging rate. Thus, a numbering plan is required to allocate a unique number to each subscriber connected to the network. At first, each numbering scheme applied only to a single exchange and exchanges were identified by the names of their towns. Later, linked number schemes (Flood, 1975) were applied to multi-exchange areas.

In a linked numbering scheme, the 'local' numbering scheme covers a number of exchanges in the area, so that a call from any exchange in the area uses the same number to reach a particular subscriber. Thus, the first part of a subscriber's directory number is an exchange code and the remainder is the subscriber's number on the exchange. For example, a 5-digit linked numbering scheme has a theoretical capacity for ten 4-digit exchanges or 100 3-digit exchanges, or a combination.

The subsequent introduction of subscriber trunk dialling (STD) for long-distance calls required the development of national numbering plans (Barron, 1959; Francis 1959; Clarke, 1952; Nunn, 1952). Later, the introduction of international subscriber dialling (ISD) made it necessary for national numbering plans to conform to an international numbering plan.

Numbering plans may be either 'open' or 'closed'. An open numbering plan has no fixed number of digits. Such a numbering plan resulted from networks containing only step-by-step exchanges without registers; the number of digits to be dialled for each call was determined by the number of switching stages it was routed through. A closed numbering plan has a fixed number of digits to be dialled for all calls, regardless of the geographical positions in the network of the calling and called subscribers. The need to use a fixed number of digits arose from the introduction of register-controlled switching systems. The registers had a limited digit-storage capacity and relied on this being full to indicate that sufficient information had been received to enable a call to be set up and the register released. Modern switching systems can cater for numbers of varying length. Many national numbering schemes therefore contain numbers having several different lengths, up to a given maximum number of digits.

There must always be an upper limit to the maximum number of digits in a national number to comply with international requirements. The CCITT has recommended (CCITT, 1989a) that the maximum number of digits for an international call shall be 11. The maximum number of digits in a national number is thus 11-N, where

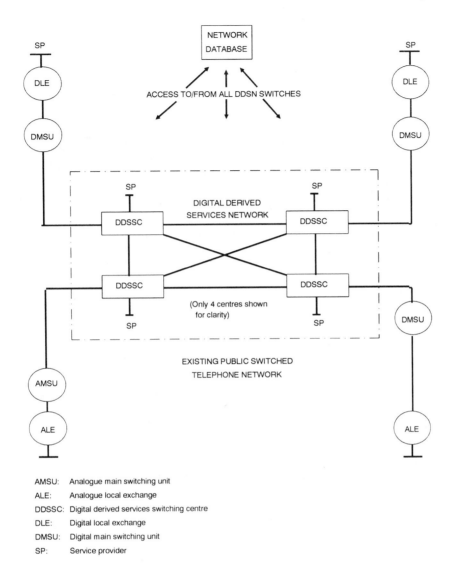

AMSU: Analogue main switching unit
ALE: Analogue local exchange
DDSSC: Digital derived services switching centre
DLE: Digital local exchange
DMSU: Digital main switching unit
SP: Service provider

Figure 29.13   Derived services network

N is the number of digits of the country's code in the world numbering plan.

Since each subscriber has a directory number in his own exchange, a unique national number can be obtained by adding to this number a code identifying the exchange. These codes could be allocated in a purely arbitrary manner. This has the advantage of being able to accommodate the largest possible number of exchanges and makes it easy to cater for unseen developments. It has the disadvantage that each originating trunk exchange must be able to identify the code of every local exchange in the country to determine the routings and charges for calls. Instead, the country is usually divided into geographical areas, each having a separate code and containing a number of local exchanges. The originating trunk exchange then only requires to identify the area code to determine the routing and charging rate for each call.

In general, a national number comprises three parts:

1. An area code.
2. An exchange code.
3. The subscriber's local-exchange number.

In addition to dividing the country into numbering areas (each with an area code) and determining a local numbering plan for each area, it is necessary to determine appropriate dialling procedures for both trunk and local calls. The use of a single dialling procedure (i.e. the full national number is dialled for both trunk and local calls) is only justified if trunk traffic represents a high proportion of the total traffic or if the country is sufficiently small for national numbers to contain few digits. Otherwise, it is preferable to use two procedures, whereby local calls are obtained by dialling the local number and other calls by dialling the national number. The local exchange must be able to differentiate between them. This is usually done by means of a trunk prefix digit. In the UK, this digit is '0'. Recognition of the prefix causes the local exchange to route the call to the trunk exchange.

An additional prefix can also be used to differentiate between trunk calls and international calls. In the UK, the international prefix is '010'. The first digit (0) routes the call to the trunk exchange. The next two digits (10) cause the call to be switched to the international gateway exchange. This three-digit prefix is followed by the international code for the required country and the national number of the called subscriber in that country.

The UK numbering plan is illustrated in Table 29.1. Six of the largest cities are director areas. These have a uniform 7-digit numbering scheme, consisting of a 3-digit exchange code and 4-digit subscriber's number. These areas are identified by 2-digit area codes. Other areas have 3-digit codes and have numbering schemes with uniform 6-digit numbers or mixed schemes not exceeding six

Table 29.1 Typical UK national numbers

Type of area	Prefix	Area code	Exchange code	Subscriber's number	Total number of digits
Director area	0	X1	XXX	XXXX	10
Non-director area	0	XXX	XX	XXXX	10
	0	XXX	XXX	XXX	10
	0	XXX	X	XXX	9
	0	XXX	XX	XXX	9

digits. The total number of dialled digits, excluding the trunk prefix, thus varies between seven and nine. This complies with the CCITT recommendation that national numbers (excluding prefix digits) shall not exceed 11 digits minus the country code (for the UK, the country code is 44 and 11-2=9). The long-term objective is to have a national number of fixed length with 6-digit or 7-digit local numbers (McLeod, 1990).

A national numbering scheme must make a generous allowance for growth in the number of subscribers for up to 50 years ahead. However, growth is not uniform and the numbering schemes in some areas become exhausted before the others. For example, the London area, which previously had a single numbering code (01) has had to be split into two (Banerjee,1989), 071 for inner London and 081 for outer London. Similar changes have been made in a number of American cities. In France, the entire country has been divided into two numbering zones: L'Isle de France covering the region around Paris and La Province covering the rest of France.

The capacity of national numbering schemes is reduced by the need to avoid use of the trunk prefix as the initial digit of any local-exchange code to avoid ambiguity. Similarly, the international prefix must not form the initial part of any area code. There is also a need to reserve codes for accessing various services. For example, in the UK the code '999' is used for emergency services, '100' is used to obtain operator assistance, '192' for directory enquiries, and so on. Thus, the digits '0', '1' and '9' are not available as initial digits for local numbers. This reduces the capacity of the numbering schemes of all local areas. The numbering capacity of local areas is also reduced by the need to provide direct dialling in (DDI) to PABXs. This requires each extension to have a number within the scheme for the area. Thus, a PABX uses a large block of numbers instead of a single number. The advent of the integrated services digital network (ISDN) also has an impact. It may be necessary for

a basic-access subscriber to have up to eight numbers in order to receive calls through the PSTN.

In countries where the telecommunications service is 'liberalised', codes must be reserved to enable subscribers to obtain access to different competing networks. In the USA, different trunk prefixes are used to enable subscribers to choose different carriers for their long-distance calls. In the UK, area codes may not use the initial digit '8', since this provides access to the BT derived services network (Roberts, 1985; Roberts, 1987). This network caters both for charging the call to the called subscriber instead of the caller (Freephone service, 0800) and for charging the caller at a premium rate (e.g. message services). Access is also provided to other networks, e.g. the cellular radio networks of Cellnet and Vodafone. Thus, '0836' might appear to be an area code, but '0836XXXXXX' would be the number of a cellular telephone which could be anywhere in the UK.

The introduction of mobile services had led to numbers being associated with individual subscribers, rather than geographical locations as in the fixed PSTN. Ideally, this would apply to everybody. There would be no need for abortive calls when subscribers are away and no need for subscribers to have their numbers changed if they move to another town. This would require every exchange to identify complete subscribers' numbers for distant subscribers (instead of only area codes) and to access a complete national database to determine the routing for every such call (Webster, 1989).

29.7.2 International numbering

The introduction of international subscriber dialling made it necessary for every subscriber's station in the world to have a unique number. In the CCITT world numbering plan each subscriber's number consists of a country code followed by the subscriber's national number (CCITT, 1989a).

For numbering purposes, the world is divided into zones, each

Table 29.2 World numbering zones

Code	Zone
1	North America (including Hawaii and Caribbean islands, except Cuba)
2	Africa
3 & 4	Europe
5	South America and Cuba
6	South Pacific (Australasia)
7	USSR
8	North Pacific (Eastern Asia)
9	Far East and Middle East
0	Spare code

given a single-digit code. Each country within a zone has the zone number as the first digit of its country code. However, the European numbering zone has been allocated two codes because of the large number of country codes required within this zone. The codes for the world numbering zones are listed in Table 29.2.

Within each zone, every country has been allotted a single 2- or 3-digit code number. For example, within zone 3 (Europe) Holland has the code '31' and Albania has '355'. The 3-digit codes have been allocated to smaller countries, having fewer digits in their national numbering plans, to minimise the total number of digits in subscribers' international numbers. Exceptions occur where an integrated numbering plan covers an entire zone; countries in these zones require only a single-digit code. Thus, '1' is the country code for all countries in the North-American numbering plan (Nunn, 1952) and the country code for the USSR is '7'. Some examples of international numbers are given in Table 29.3.

The existence of a world numbering plan places restrictions on the national numbering plan of each country to enable subscribers in other countries to make international calls into its national network. The restrictions are:

1. The number of digits in a subscriber's world number is limited to an absolute maximum of 12. In practice, with a few exceptions, world numbers are limited to 11 digits. The number of digits available for a national numbering plan is thus 11-N, where N is the number of digits in the country code.
2. National numbers must consist of all numbers and no letters. Countries which used letters on telephone dials chose different ways of allocating the 26 letters of the alphabet among the 10 decimal-number characters. Thus, exchange codes containing letters could have been dialled as different numbers by subscribers calling from outside the country.
3. National numbering plans must include international prefix codes to avoid ambiguity when national and international numbers have the same initial digits.

Table 29.3 Examples of typical international numbers

Zone	Country	Country code	No. of digits in national number	Total no. of digits
1	USA	1	10	11
1	Canada	1	10	11
2	Egypt	20	8	10
2	Liberia	231	6	9
3	France	33	8	10
3	Portugal	351	7 or 8	10 or 11
4	UK	44	8 or 9	10 or 11
4	Switzerland	41	8	10
5	Brazil	55	9	11
5	Ecuador	593	7	9

29.7.3 Numbering plans for the ISDN era

In 1984, the CCITT made recommendations for an international numbering plan to cover integrated services digital networks (ISDNs) (CCITT, 1989b). This extends the existing numbering plans for PSTNs. Thus, a subscriber's ISDN access will normally be indistinguishable from PSTN access and will be provided by the same local exchange.

The maximum length of international numbers is extended to 15 digits. The area code becomes a network destination code (NDC). This arises from the present situation whereby some 'area' codes have been used for access to mobile networks and special services

(which are non-geographic). An international exchange will analyse six digits to determine a route. These can therefore include digits within the NDC in addition to the country code, in order to route a call to the appropriate network in the destination country.

It is intended that provision will also be made for sub-addressing. This will use additional digits following a subscriber's national number, which will be transmitted to the destination for use on the subscriber's premises. These can select the appropriate terminal for an ISDN connection or provide DDI on a PBX without using up numbers in the area numbering scheme. The sub-address field can range from four digits for simple applications up to 40 digits for use in open systems interconnection (OSI). For OSI, a global scheme for the identification of network service access points has been developed by the International Standards Organisation (ISO).

The CCITT has recommended (CCITT, 1989c) the full implementation of this plan by the end of 1996. It is hoped that, by that date, stored-program-controlled digital exchanges will have penetrated all countries so that they can handle 15-digit international numbers and the increased number of digits to be analysed.

29.7.4 Public data networks

For public switched data networks (CCITT, 1989d), an international number consists of two parts: the data network identification code (DNIC) of four digits and the network terminal number (NTN) of 10 digits. Thus, the complete number has 14 digits. The DNIC consists of a data country code (DCC) of three digits followed by a 'network' digit. By this means, a single country can have up to 10 different data networks. Furthermore, a country can have more than one DCC. The UK has been allocated codes '234' to '237'; thus it can ultimately have up to 40 different public data networks.

The format used for the 10-digit NTN can be determined by the network operator, since only the DNIC needs to be analysed to route the call into that network from another country. However, the CCITT recommends that the last two digits shall be a sub-address for use by the subscriber. In the BT packet-switched service (PSS), the first three digits of the NTN serve as a routing code to identify the packet-switching exchange and the next five digits identify the network terminating point serving the subscriber. The final two digits correspond to a sub-address for use within the subscriber's own system.

29.8 Routing

National networks are hierarchical, as shown in Figure 29.5. The minimum configuration of star-connected exchanges is usually augmented by direct routes inter-connecting those exchanges where a high community of interest results in sufficient traffic. There is thus a backbone route joining each switching centre to the highest level via intermediate centres, together with transverse branches between some centres at the same level. There may also be some other direct routes between centres at different levels which violate this pattern.

If it is assumed that a country is already divided into local-exchange areas and the locations of their exchanges have already been decided, a routing plan should be developed to determine:

1. Which exchanges should be interconnected by direct junctions, and which connections made indirectly via tandem switching centres.
2. The number and location of tandem switching centres.
3. The number of levels of tandem switching to be used in the network.

4. Whether automatic alternative routing is to be used and, if so, under what conditions.

The routing plan must be consistent with the plans for numbering, charging, transmission and signalling.

Large groups of circuits are more efficient than small groups because of their higher occupancy (i.e. traffic per circuit), as explained earlier. If there is a large amount of traffic between two exchanges, it is economic to provide a direct route between them. If there is little traffic between two exchanges, it is more economic to combine this with traffic to other destinations to produce a large amount of traffic over a common route to a tandem switching centre. The correct solution obviously depends on the cost of the circuits as well as the amount of traffic. If circuits are cheap it is less expensive for them to be lightly loaded than to incur the cost of switching equipment in a tandem exchange. Thus, many direct routes are provided between local exchanges in a small area with a high subscriber density but not to more distant exchanges.

In some networks, automatic alternative routing is used (Clos, 1954). Direct routes are under-provided with circuits; when all circuits on a direct route are busy, traffic overflows to a fully-provided tandem route through a switching centre at a higher level in the hierarchy. An under-provided direct route is called a high-usage route and the fully-provided indirect route to which its traffic finally overflows is called a final route. Only a small proportion of calls use the complete backbone of final routes, since transverse routes are used whenever these are free.

The traffic levels at which direct routes, tandem routing and automatic alternative routing should be used depend on the relative costs of direct and tandem routes (including associated switching and signalling equipment). Low traffic and high-cost direct routes indicate tandem working. High traffic and low-cost direct routes

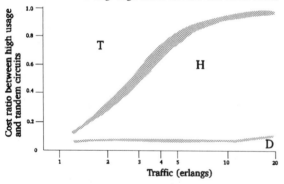

Figure 29.14 Domains for employment of tandem (T), high usage (H), and direct circuits (D)

indicate direct connection. Intermediate situations favour automatic alternative routing, as shown in Figure 29.14, due to Rapp (1964).

Automatic alternative routing is applicable in private networks as well as in PSTNs. A PABX in a private network may be programmed so that, when all private circuits to another PABX in the network are busy, the traffic then overflows onto the PSTN.

Variations of the basic automatic alternative routing scheme have been introduced. In dynamic alternative routing (Stacey 1989), if a call is successful on a given routing then that current choice is retained. If instead the call fails on the current choice, then a new choice is selected for the next one. The introduction of common-channel signalling between exchanges, together with exchanges

having routes to more than one centre at the next-higher level, makes possible complex alternative routing schemes. Thus, if a call encounters congestion at a higher level in the hierarchy, it is possible to 'crank back' to an exchange at a lower level and choose a different outgoing route there.

Automatic alternative routing will re-route calls away from a high-usage route whenever it is unable to carry traffic. This can happen if there is a breakdown instead of high traffic. This is beneficial, since traffic can still reach its destination, whereas it could not if there were only the direct route. However, the large amount of additional traffic offered to the backbone route can cause severe congestion resulting in the loss of calls to destinations served only by that route (which could be to most other exchanges in the network). A solution to this difficulty is trunk reservation (Ingham, 1989; Katzschner, 1973). A proportion of the circuits on the final route is reserved for calls which can only take that route. Thus, these calls still obtain a reasonable grade of service when the overflow traffic offered to the route is abnormally large.

Sophisticated automatic alternative routing can cause congestion originating at one part of the network to spread as traffic overflows to other routes. This is obviously undesirable, so network management (Macurdy, 1973; IEEE, 1988) is being introduced. A central management centre can monitor the traffic on different routes and, if necessary, it can reduce or entirely cut off traffic originating from switching centres to prevent the overload from spreading.

Network management can also provide economies if the busy hours in different parts of a network do not coincide. Calls which would normally be routed through part of the network which is busy can be routed instead through another part of the network which is less busy. Thus, overall, fewer circuits are required to carry the total traffic. In the USA, there is a time difference of three hours between the East and West coasts with a corresponding difference between the busy hours. Thus, it is economic to route long-distance calls between North and South either via the East or the West of the country at different times in the day.

29.9 Dimensioning

It is uneconomic for a telecommunication network to have sufficient circuits for all subscribers to make calls simultaneously. Instead, sufficient circuits are provided to make the probability of a subscriber finding congestion (i.e. all circuits are busy) on the required route to be acceptably small in the busy hour. This probability is called the grade of service (GOS). Thus, a high grade of service corresponds to a poor service and vice versa. In a circuit-switched network, if a call encounters congestion, the call is lost. In a message-switching or packet-switching network, if a call encounters congestion, it enters a queue and so is delayed. The problem of dimensioning a route is thus to determine from the traffic forecast the number of circuits required to provide the grade of service specified by the network operator (Farr, 1982).

It can be shown that, for a circuit-switched route, the grade of service (i.e. the probability of a lost call) is given by (Bear, 1988) Erlang's equation (Equation 29.1) where A is the traffic offered (in erlangs) and N is the number of trunks on the route.

$$E_{1,N}(A) = \frac{\dfrac{A^N}{N!}}{\displaystyle\sum_{k=0}^{N}\dfrac{A^k}{k!}} \tag{29.1}$$

For a queuing system, provided that the probability of delay is small, it is approximately given by Equation 29.2.

$$E_{2,N}(A) = \frac{N}{N-A} E_{1,N}(A) \qquad (29.2)$$

The assumptions made in deriving the above formulae include full availability, random (Poisson) call arrivals, and a negative exponential distribution of holding times. Full availability means that any call can use any trunk on the route, provided that it is free.

Equation 29.1 is well suited to calculate the GOS, given A and N. However, the dimensioning problem is: given A and the GOS, determine N. Equation 29.1 is ill-suited for this. Fortunately, tables are available giving the traffic capacity of different numbers of trunks for various grades of service. An example (Bear, 1988) is shown in Table 4. By looking down the column for the specified grade of service until the required traffic is exceeded, one can read across to determine the number of trunks that is needed. For example, to handle 20 erlangs of traffic with one lost call in 100, the table shows that 30 trunks are required. Table 29.4 applies to lost-call system. Tables are also published for queuing systems (Hunter, 1988).

Specifying a grade of service is, ultimately, a matter of judgement. It should be sufficiently large to make the provision of trunks economical, but not so large as to cause undue customer dissatisfaction. In practice, grades of service may vary between 0.001 for trunks within an exchange to 0.1 for expensive long-distance and international circuits.

Equations 29.1 and 29.2 and the traffic tables relate to the busy-hour traffic. At other times of the day, the probability of loss will be much smaller. Moreover, routes are dimensioned to cater for the traffic forecast at the end of a planning period for which plant is provided. Thus, if traffic grows in accordance with the forecast, the GOS will initially be much better than the specified value and increase towards it over the provisioning period. However, if traffic grows more quickly than was forecast, the specified GOS will be reached during the provisioning period and towards the end of it the GOS will be much worse than that specified. This situation has occurred often, since telecommunications has expanded so rapidly in recent years.

Of course, a subscriber is interested in the grade of service of a complete connection which often consists of several routes connected in tandem, whereas Equations 29.1 and 29.2 give the grade of service for a single link in such a connection. However, if a

Table 29.4   Traffic capacity table for full availability groups (continued on next page)

Number of trunks	1 lost call in				Number of trunks	1 call lost in			
	50 (0.02) E	100 (0.10) E	200 (0.005) E	1000 (0.001) E,		50 (0.02) E	100 (0.01) E	200 (0.005) E	1000 (0.001) E
1	0.020	0.010	0.005	0.001	24	16.6	15.3	14.2	12.2
2	0.22	0.15	0.015	0.046	25	17.5	16.1	15.0	13.0
3	0.60	0.46	0.35	0.19	26	18.4	17.0	15.8	13.7
4	1.1	0.9	0.7	0.44	27	19.3	17.8	16.6	14.4
5	1.7	1.4	1.1	0.8	28	20.2	18.6	17.4	15.2
6	2.3	1.9	1.6	1.1	29	21.0	19.5	18.2	15.9
7	2.9	2.5	2.2	1.6	30	21.9	20.3	19.0	16.7
8	3.6	3.1	2.7	2.1	31	22.8	21.2	19.9	17.4
9	4.3	3.8	3.3	2.6	32	23.7	22.0	20.7	18.2
10	5.1	4.5	4.0	3.1	33	24.6	22.9	21.5	19.0
11	5.8	5.2	4.6	3.6	34	25.5	23.8	22.3	19.7
12	6.6	5.9	5.3	4.2	35	26.4	24.6	23.2	20.5
13	7.4	6.6	6.0	4.8	36	27.3	25.5	24.0	21.3
14	8.2	7.4	6.7	5.4	37	28.3	26.4	24.8	22.1
15	9.0	8.1	7.4	6.1	38	29.2	27.3	25.7	22.9
16	9.8	8.9	8.1	6.7	39	30.1	28.1	26.5	23.7
17	10.7	9.6	8.8	7.4	40	31.0	29.0	27.4	24.4
18	11.5	10.4	9.6	8.0	41	31.9	29.9	28.2	25.2
19	12.3	11.2	10.3	8.7	42	32.8	30.8	29.1	26.0
20	13.2	12.0	11.1	9.4	43	33.8	31.7	29.9	26.8
21	14.0	12.8	11.9	10.1	44	34.7	32.5	30.8	27.6
22	14.9	13.7	12.6	10.8	45	35.6	33.4	31.7	28.4
23	15.8	14.5	13.4	11.5	46	36.5	34.3	32.5	29.3

Table 29.4 (continued) Traffic capacity table (continued from previous page)

Number of trunks	1 lost call in				Number of trunks	1 lost call in			
	50 (0.02) E	100 (0.10) E	200 (0.005) E	1000 (0.001) E,		50 (0.02) E	100 (0.10) E	200 (0.005) E	1000 (0.001) E
47	37.5	35.2	33.4	30.1	74	62.9	59.8	57.3	52.7
48	38.4	36.1	34.2	30.9	75	63.9	60.7	58.2	53.5
49	39.3	37.0	35.1	31.7	76	64.9	61.7	59.1	54.4
50	40.3	37.9	36.0	32.5	77	65.8	62.6	60.0	55.2
51	41.2	38.8	36.9	33.3	78	66.8	63.5	60.9	56.1
52	42.1	39.7	37,7	34.2	79	67.7	64.4	61.8	57.0
53	43.1	40.6	38.6	35.0	80	68.7	65.4	62.7	57.8
54	44.0	41.5	39.5	35.8	81	69.6	66.3	63.6	58.7
55	44.9	42.4	40.4	36.6	82	70.6	67.2	64.5	59.5
56	45.9	43.3	41.2	37.5	83	71.6	68.2	65.4	60.4
57	46.8	44.2	42.1	38.3	84	72.5	69.1	66.3	61.3
58	47.8	45.1	43.0	39.1	85	73.5	70.0	67.2	62.1
59	48.7	46.0	43.9	40.0	86	74.5	70.9	68.1	63.0
60	49.6	46.9	44.8	40.8	87	75.4	71.9	69.0	63.9
61	50.6	47.9	45.6	41.6	88	76.4	72.8	69.9	64.7
62	51.5	48.8	46.5	42.5	89	77.3	73.7	70.8	65.6
63	52.5	49.7	47.4	43.3	90	78.3	74.7	71.8	66.5
64	53.4	50.6	48.3	44.2	91	79.3	75.6	72.7	67.4
65	54.4	51.5	49.2	45.0	92	80.2	76.7	73.6	68.2
66	55.3	52.4	50.1	45.8	93	81.2	77.5	74.5	69.1
67	56.3	53.4	51,0	46.7	94	82.2	78.4	75.4	70.0
68	57.2	54.3	51.9	47.5	95	83.1	79.4	76.3	70.9
69	58.2	55.2	52.8	48.4	96	84.1	80.3	77.2	71.7
70	59.1	56.1	53.7	49.2	97	85.1	81.2	78.2	72.6
71	60.1	57.0	54.6	50.1	98	86.0	82.2	79.1	73.5
72	61.0	58.0	55.5	50.9	99	87.0	83.1	80.0	74.4
73	62.0	58.9	56.4	51.8	100	88.0	84.1	80.9	75.2

connection contains n links with GOS given by B_1, B_2,..., B_n, the overall loss probability is given by Equation 29.3.

$$B = B_1 + B_2 (1 - B_1) + ... + B_n \prod_{k=1}^{n-1} (1 - B_k) \qquad (29.3)$$

Thus, if the losses are small (which they should be) then B is given approximately by Equation 29.4.

$$B = B_1 + B_2 + B_3 + ... + B_n \qquad (29.4)$$

Grades of service are specified for the busy-hour traffic. Thus, if the busy hours of the links are non-coincident, the loss probabilities of some links may be very low when those of others are high. The overall loss is then mainly determined by the links which are busiest at the time considered.

It has been noted that large groups of trunks are more efficient than small groups, since each trunk can have a higher occupancy for a given grade of service. In the example shown in Figure 29.15, trunks in a group of five each carry less than 0.2E of traffic, whereas those in a group of 40 each carry over 0.6E with the same grade of service. The price paid for the greater efficiency of a large group of trunks is greater susceptibility to overload. For the same example, Figure 29.16 shows that an increase in traffic of 10% increases the loss probability for a group of 5 trunks by 45%, but for a group of 100 trunks it increases by 550%.

For this reason, it is common practice to specify two grades of service: one for the specified traffic and a higher value for a given

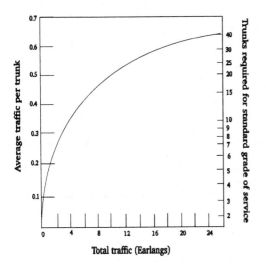

Figure 29.15 Trunk occupancy for full availability groups of various sizes (groups designed to give same grade of service

overload. For small groups of trunks the former criterion determines the number required, whereas the latter criterion determines the number of trunks when the traffic is high and the number of trunks large. For example, if it is specified that the grade of service shall be 0.002 but not deteriorate beyond 0.01 when the traffic increases by 10%, then Figure 29.16 shows that the former criterion is the more stringent when the number of trunks is less than 70 but the overload criterion applies far more than 70 trunks. Many public network operators therefore use traffic tables based on such dual criteria. BT adopted tables based on three criteria. If the permitted GOS is B when the normal traffic is offered, it shall not exceed 2.5B for a 10% overload or 6.25B for a 20% overload.

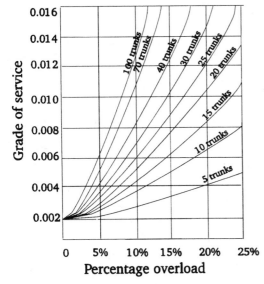

Figure 29.16 Effect of overload on grade of service

If automatic alternative routing is used, the traffic which overflows from a high usage route to the tandem route consists only of the peaks of the traffic which is offered to the high-usage route. At times when the number of calls is less than the number of trunks on the high-usage route, the overflow traffic is zero. Consequently, the overflow traffic is non-poissonian; it is 'peaky'. Equation 29.1 and traffic tables based on it should not be applied. It is necessary to take into account the variance of the traffic as well as its mean value. Methods for determining the numbers of high-usage and tandem circuits required have been developed (Wilkinson, 1956; Wallstrom, 1969; Rapp, 1964).

Results obtained from analytical formulae may be inaccurate in practical cases, particularly when complex alternative-routing schemes are involved, because the assumptions have been oversimplified. The alternative is to obtain results by means of a computer simulation of the system under study (Bear, 1988). Public network operators have extensive computer programs for this purpose. Other programs, which may be used in planning private networks are available commercially.

29.10 References

Andrews, F.T. and Hatch, R.W. (1971) National Telephone Network Transmission Planning in the American Telephone and Telegraph Company, *Trans. IEEE* **COM-19**, p. 302.

Banerjee, V., Rabundrakumar, K., and Szczech, B.J. (1989) London Code Change, *Brit. Telecommun. Eng.* **8**, (3), p.134.

Barron, D.A. (1959) Subscriber Trunk Dialling, *Proc. IEE* **106B**, p. 341.

Bealby, A.G. (1990) Network Administration Implementation Programme, *Brit. Telecom. Eng.* **8** (4) p. 212.

Bear, D. (1988) *Principles of Telecommunication Traffic Engineering*, Peter Peregrinus.

CCITT (1989a) *Recommendation E163, Numbering Plan for the International Telephone Service*, Blue Book, (9th Plenary Assembly).

CCITT (1989b) *Recommendation E164, Numbering for the ISDN Era*, Blue Book (9th Plenary Assembly).

CCITT (1989c) *Recommendation E165, Timetable for co-ordinated implementation of the full capability of the numbering plan for the ISDN era*, Blue Book (9th Plenary Assembly).

CCITT (1989d) *Recommendation X121, International numbering plan for Public Data Networks*, Blue Book (9th Plenary Assembly).

Clarke, A.B. and Osborne, H.S. (1952) Automatic Switching for Nationwide Telephone Service, *Bell Syst. Tech. J.* **31** p. 823.

Clos, C. (1954) Automatic Alternate Routing of Telephone Traffic, *Bell Lab. Rec.* **32**, p. 51.

Farr, R.E. (1988) *Telecommunications Traffic, Tariffs and Costs*, Peter Peregrinus.

Flood, J.E. (ed.) (1975) *Telecommunication Networks*, Peter Peregrinus.

Francis, H.E. (1959) The General Plan for Subscriber Trunk Dialling, *Post Off. Electr. Eng. J.* (January), **51**, p. 258.

Hills, M.T. and Evans, B.G. (1973) *Transmission Systems*, Allen and Unwin.

Hunter, J.M., Lawrie, N. and Peterson, N. (1988) *Tariffs, Traffic and Performance*, Com. Ed. Publishing.

IEEE (1988) *Journ. on Selected Areas in Communications*, **SA6**, (4), (Papers on Telecommunications Network Operations and Management).

Ingham, A.R. and Elvidge, A.M. (1989) Trunk Reservation with Automatic Alternative Routing, *In Sixth UK Teletraffic Symposium*.

Katzschner, L. (1973) Service Protection for Direct Final Traffic in DDD Networks, *In 3rd Int. Teletraffic Congress, Stockholm*.

Macurdy, W.B. (1973) Network Management in the United States - Problems and Progress, *In Proc. 7th Teletraffic Congress, Pt. 2*, p. 621/1.

McLeod, N.A.C. (1990) Numbering in Telecommunications, *Brit. Telecom. Eng* **8**, (4), p. 225.

Muir, A. and Hart, G. (1987) The Conversion of a Telecommunications Network from Analogue to Digital Operation, *In IEE National Conf. on Telecommunications Networks*, London.

Munday, S. (1967) New international switching and transmission plan recommended by the CCITT for public telephony, *Proc. IEE* **114**, (5) p. 619.

Nunn, W.H. Nationwide Numbering Plan, *Bell Syst. Tech. J.* **31** p. 851.

Rapp, Y. (1964) Planning of a Junction Network in a Multiexchange Area, *Ericsson Tech.* **20**, p. 77.

Redmill, F.J. and Valdar, A.R. (1990) *SPC Digital Telephone Exchanges*, Peter Peregrinus.

Richards, D.L. (1973) *Telecommunication by Speech*, Butterworth.

Roberts, G.J. and Brutnell, R.F. (1985) An Introduction to the Analogue Derived Services Network, *Brit. Telecom. Eng.* **4**, (3), p. 129.

Roberts, G.J. (1987) The Digital Derived Services Network, *Brit. Telecom. Eng.* **6**, p. 105.

Stacey, R.R. and Songhurst, D.J. (1989) Dynamic Routing in British Telecom Network, *In International Switching Symposium*, Phoenix, Arizona.

Tobin, W.J.E. and Stratton, J. (1960) A New Switching and Transmission Plan for the Inland Trunk Network, *Post Office Elec. Engrs. Journ.* **53** (1) p. 75.

Waliji, A.A. (1980) Architecture of System X: the Local Administration Centre, *P.O. Elec. Engrs. Jour.* **73** (1) p. 36.

Wallstrom, B. (1969) Methods for Optimising Alternative Routing Networks, *Ericsson Tech.* **25**, p. 3.

Webster, S. (1989) The Digital Derived Services Intelligent Network, *Brit. Telecom. Eng.* **8**, (3), p.144.

Welch, S. (1981) *Signalling in Telecommunication Networks,* Peter Peregrinus.

Wilkinson, R.I. (1956) Theories for Toll Traffic Engineering in the USA, *Bell Syst. Tech. J.* **35**, p. 421.

30

Transmission planning

G J Cook
BSc (Eng) CEng MIEE
BT plc

Contents

30.1 Introduction

Transmission planning is concerned with the transfer of signals across a telecommunications network with the minimum loss of information. Such a transfer will always result in some impairment to the transmitted signal due to technical and economic considerations. Distortionless transmission is not generally technically possible and near-distortionless transmission may not be economically viable. The role of the transmission planner is to work within the technical and economic constraints to control the impairments introduced by the network. The objective is to ensure that the end to end performance meets the customer requirements for the services in question.

The key steps in the process are:

1. Understanding the customer service requirement.
2. Relating these requirements to the relevant end to end transmission impairments.
3. Understanding the factors determining end to end performance.
4. Developing a transmission plan.

30.2 Purpose of a transmission plan

The transmission plan is the means of controlling the end to end transmission impairments accumulated on any connection through the network. The plan should state the end to end limiting values and show the apportionment of these values to the constituent parts of what may be a complex network. For example Figure 30.1 shows a possible analogue network structure with transmission loss apportioned across the network. The maximum overall transmission loss (point A to point B in this figure) is 42.5dB.

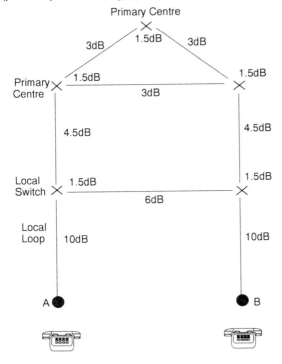

Figure 30.1 Example of analogue transmission loss plan

Such a plan shows the possible routeing arrangements and the transmission loss apportioned to each component of the network e.g. the switches and transmission systems. Individual components of the network can then be considered separately for design purposes. Providing the loss introduced by that component does not exceed the transmission plan limit allocated, the component designer need not know the exact network structure. The transmission plan can therefore be considered as the budget, in this case, for transmission loss.

Similar budgets can be drawn up for the other essential transmission parameters. In all cases these budgets provide the information on the relevant performance limit for the individual network component and can be used by the component specifier or designer.

30.3 Typical service groups

A transmission parameter requires an apportionment or budget where it affects the end to end performance of the service in question, hence the parameters need to be service based. The relation between service requirements and network performance requirements is being studied within CCITT (1989a).

To illustrate the approach adopted the three most common service groups are used:

1. Analogue telephony.
2. Voiceband data.
3. Digital services.

30.3.1 Analogue telephony

The key customer requirement is for clarity and adequate volume of received speech together with acceptable noise levels. The relation between this customer view of quality and the relevant transmission characteristics is not straightforward (Richards, 1973). It is necessary to consider a range of parameters including transmission loss, noise, distortion, echo and delay and loss/frequency distortion, and, in general it is important to have a plan for the apportionment of each of these parameters.

30.3.2 Voiceband data

Sometimes called modem data, these services involve the transmission of data over the same nominal 3kHz bandwidth path as for analogue telephony. The performance of this path is characterised by similar impairments as for analogue telephony. Modern high speed modems (see Chapter 39) employ adaptive techniques to provide equalisation of the transmission path hence the modems can work over a wide range of path characteristics. However adaptive techniques are generally not able to work well over paths with significant non-linearity or with characteristics that have significant short term variations e.g. gain and phase hits.

Non linearities are generally introduced by the use of lower rate encoding systems and some form of overall apportionment is required as for telephony. However the time variant characteristics e.g. phase jitter, are generally not important for telephony and in practice are not specified for switched network transmission equipment. There is therefore always a potential problem in telephony networks supporting higher speed modem services as the telephony network performance specification tend not to include the parameters important for these services.

30.3.3 Digital services

This class covers the range of services that would be provided over ISDN networks i.e. networks providing end to end 64kbit/s paths. The potential degradations introduced by the network will include errors in the bit stream and possible timing inaccuracies. The permitted end to end impairment needs to take into account the information being carried on the network. For example encoded voice signals are relatively tolerant of errors whereas the throughput of digital data services can be drastically reduced by error bursts.

30.3.4 Impact on transmission plan

It is important for the transmission planner to know what services will be carried on the network and the allowable end to end performance for those services. Ideally the transmission planner would take the most demanding service requirement for each parameters, derive an appropriate limit and develop a plan for a network capable of supporting all services.

In practice however the transmission plan tends to be developed for the majority use service i.e. telephony. The approach adopted to date by the majority of network operators is to develop a list of parameters required for the support of telephony and then consider the impact of the choice on voiceband data transmission.

In general analogue transmission plans are not developed for parameters only of relevance to voiceband data services. However, for the ISDN the approach has been to consider the requirements of the most demanding digital service and develop an appropriate error performance plan. Such a plan has generally proved adequate for the support of telephony services using digital telephones.

30.4 End to end requirements

Adopting the approach outlined in the previous section, i.e. developing a list of parameters for telephony and digital services, we arrive at the following list of key parameters:

1. Transmission loss.
2. Noise/interference.
3. Loss/frequency distortion.
4. Non-linear distortion including quantising distortion.
5. Propagation delay.
6. Talker-echo.
7. Listener-echo.
8. Stability.
9. Error performance.
10. Sidetone.
11. Crosstalk.

These are the essential parameters to be considered for any transmission plan for an evolving network capable of supporting telephony and digital services. Such a network is also likely to be able to support the majority of voiceband data services. Required end to end values for these parameters are given in the following sections.

30.4.1 Transmission loss and loudness rating

The exact definition of transmission loss depends on the service offered. In the case of telephony where telephone instruments are included in the service offering then the end to end transmission loss is the ratio of the acoustic power at the telephone microphone to the

resultant acoustic power at the output of the telephone receiver. If the service offering does not include the telephone instrument then the end to end loss will be defined in terms of a ratio of electrical power in, to electrical power out, and be expressed in decibels (dB).

Loudness ratings are a convenient method of expressing the end to end loudness loss (the acoustic to acoustic loss) in a form that can be related to customer opinion. Loudness ratings provide the transmission planner with a single value that indicates the overall loss of a particular connection. In practice it is convenient to divide overall loudness rating into the sum of send, receive and circuit loudness ratings as shown in Figure 30.2 and given by Equation 30.1.

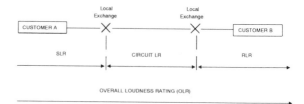

Figure 30.2 Overall Loudness Rating (OLR)

$$OLR = SLR + CIRCUIT\ LR + RLR\ (\ in\ dB\ ) \tag{30.1}$$

There are agreed methods of defining and measuring loudness ratings, detailed in CCITT recommendations in the P Series (P76, P78, P79) (CCITT, 1989b). Readers may also see Reference Equivalents and Corrected Reference Equivalents used in earlier CCITT documentation and the transmission plans of some countries. In outline these were similar to loudness ratings but had some disadvantages and have now virtually been replaced by loudness ratings. If approximate conversion factors are required these can be found in Annex A to CCITT Recommendation G111 (CCITT, 1989c).

Subjective tests carried out in a number of administrations indicate the values of loudness rating that are preferred by customers and also the values that are considered to be too loud or too quiet. Examples of typical results are shown in Figure 30.3 where it can be seen that there is an optimum range for loudness rating on an overall connection, usually called the overall loudness rating or OLR. CCITT recommend in G.111 that the long term objective value of OLR is in the range 10dB to 12dB and the maximum value should not exceed 29dB for an average sized country. This informa-

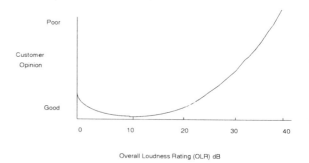

Figure 30.3 Customer opinion against OLR

tion is of key importance to transmission planners as it sets the bounds for overall loss planning.

30.4.2 Noise and interference

Noise in telephone systems has a major impact on customer opinion. Noise is characterised by its spectrum, amplitude distribution and absolute power level. It is generally measured using an instrument called a psophometer which includes a frequency weighting function to take account of the sensitivity of the human ear to different frequencies. Measurements made with a psophometer are generally expressed in dBmp where the 'p' indicates the use of the psophometric weighting function.

Subjective tests have indicated that for telephones on average lines the noise values need to be less than –65dBmp to have a negligible effect on customer opinion. As the overall noise value increases there is a worsening in customer opinion although the rate of worsening depends on the overall loudness rating of the connection. Supplement 3 to the CCITT P series Recommendations (CCITT, 1989b) shows typical results for combinations of noise and OLR.

30.4.3 Loss/frequency distortion

Loss/frequency distortion is determined by the transmission loss at frequencies other than the reference frequency of 1000Hz. In modern networks the main contributors to loss/frequency distortion are the telephone set characteristics, 2-wire local lines and the anti-aliasing filters in PCM coders.

Overall distortion now tends to be less than the values that were common when the majority of long distance transmission systems used FDM techniques where the channel filters introduced significant distortion. For this reason it is not common to include overall loss/frequency distortion planning as part of the transmission plan. However techniques for such planning exist and are documented in Annex B to Recommendation P.11.

30.4.4 Non linear distortion and quantising distortion

Non linear distortion results from systems where the output signal is not exactly proportional to the input signal and harmonics or intermodulation products are generated. The impairment is introduced by the analogue part of transmission and switching systems and needs to be considered in the specification of the performance of the individual network components. However the levels of distortion encountered are such that it is rarely necessary to consider the distortion on an end to end basis.

Quantising distortion is introduced by analogue to digital coding techniques where an input signal is sampled and encoded into a finite set of values. The quantising distortion results from the difference between the recovered analogue signal and the original analogue input.

Quantising distortion from tandem analogue to digital codes, for example PCM systems interconnected through analogue interfaces, is cumulative and can have a significant effect on customer opinion. It is one of the essential components of the transmission plan of a modern network.

End to end planning for quantising distortion has been simplified by the introduction of the quantising distortion unit (qdu).

The quantising distortion introduced by a single 8 bit A-law or μ-law PCM system is taken as being 1qdu. Subjective tests have shown that the distortion equivalent to 14qdu represents the upper limit for acceptable transmission and this is used as the basis for the end to planning rule as detailed in CCITT Recommendation G.113. Tests have been done to assign values of qdu to a number of different coding or digit processing systems e.g. 32kbit/s ADPCM and digital pads hence the transmission planner can add the various qdu contributions to check compliance with the overall limit.

At the present time there is some uncertainty as to whether the qdu approach can be applied to the more advanced low rate encoding systems e.g. 8kbit/s coders where the distortion is not quantising distortion in its true sense. However it is important to have a planning measure for the distortion introduced by these systems as they can have a significant effect on the quality seen by customers and the qdu approach is generally used.

30.4.5 Propagation delay

Propagation delay (sometimes called absolute delay) is introduced by all the transmission components of an overall connection. The principal contributors in modern networks are long terrestrial co-axial cable or fibre systems, digital switches, satellite and radio systems and low rate encoders. Delay has two principal effects on communication; it increases the subjective disturbance due to the presence of an echo signal, and high values of delay can disrupt conversational fluency.

CCITT Recommendations G.114 covers recommended limits for end to end propagation delay where it is recommended that one-way delays should not exceed 400ms. Delays of less than 400ms may be acceptable if appropriate echo control is provided.

Delay planning is essential but needs to be done in association with echo control planning.

30.4.6 Talker echo

As its name implies, talker echo is concerned with echo perceived by the talker. It occurs when the talker's speech is returned with sufficient delay to worsen customer opinion. Figure 30.4 illustrates a typical talker echo path, from a connection through a digital network, where signals are reflected from the distant 2-wire to 4-wire conversion unit.

The subjective effect of the talker echo is a function of the acoustic to acoustic loss of the echo path and the delay of the echo path, sometimes called the round-trip delay. The acoustic to acoustic loss of the talker echo path can be expressed in terms similar to those used for end to end transmission loss i.e. overall loudness ratings. For the example shown in Figure 30.5 the overall loudness rating of the talker echo path (usually called talker echo loudness rating (TELR), can be estimated from the send and receive loudness ratings and the echo loss at the 2- wire to 4-wire conversion unit.

The echo loss is a weighted average of the power loss at frequencies in the voice frequency band and is defined in Recommendation G.122 (CCITT, 1989c). The values of TELR required to give satisfactory performance to customers are a function of the round trip delay of the talker path. For a given TELR value, increasing the delay will worsen customer opinion.

Recommendation G.131 gives an estimate of the recommended value of TELR required for a given probability of objectionable echo. Figure 30.6 is taken from Recommendation G.131 and shows values of TELR required for a range of one-way delays. In this figure percentages refer to the probability of encountering objectionable echo and OLR refers to the overall loudness rating of the talker echo path, approximately equal to TELR. It should be noted that large values of TELR are required for one-way delays of for

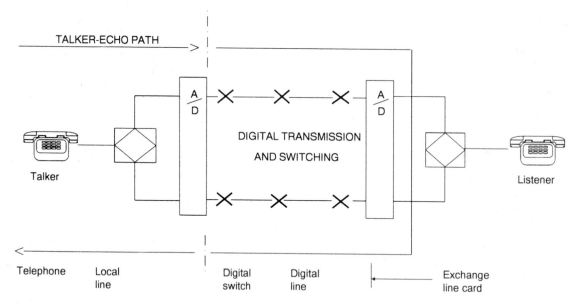

Figure 30.4 Talker echo path

example 250ms. In general these high values of TELR can only be achieved by the use of separate devices such as echo cancellers or echo suppressors. Application rules for such echo control devices are included in Recommendation G.131.

In summary, there is no single objective value for end to end talker echo. The procedure is to calculate TELR, round trip delay and to then calculate the resultant probability of encountering objectionable echo. G.131 recommends that this calculated probability should not exceed 1%.

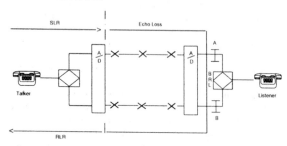

Figure 30.5 Talker Echo Loudness Rating (TELR)

30.4.7 Listener echo

Whereas talker echo is a result of a single reflection in the network, listener echo is caused by a further reflection of the echo signal. The listener then hears the wanted signal together with a delayed, attenuated version of the original signal, as shown in Figure 30.7. As for talker echo the subjective effect is a function of the level of the listener-echo and, to a lesser extent its delay. From Figure 30.7 it can be seen that if listener echo is present then talker echo will also be encountered and this talker echo is likely to be the most demanding requirement. Required values for listener echo are given in Supplement 3 to CCITT Volume V (CCITT, 1989d). Listener echo

has a more significant effect on voice band data services than on speech transmission. Recommendation G.122 (CCITT, 1989c) includes information on required signal to listener echo ratios for voiceband data modems operating at a range of speeds.

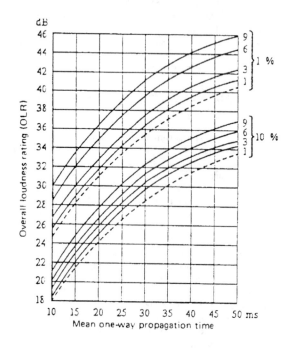

Figure 30.6 Echo tolerance curves. (Source: CCITT Recommendation G.131.) Solid lines indicate analogue circuits, with indication of number of 4-wire circuits. Dotted lines indicate fully digital connections

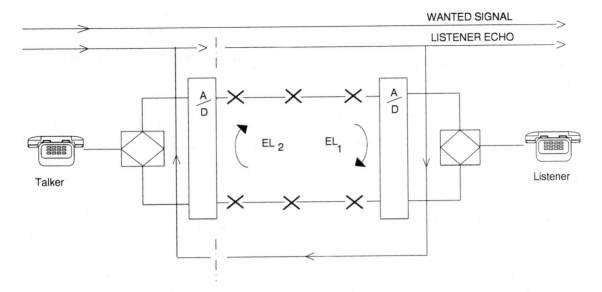

Figure 30.7   Signal to listener echo path and ratio

30.4.8   Stability

The signal to listener echo ratio referred to in Section 30.4.7 is commonly expressed in terms of a weighted power average across the frequency band of interest. The minimum value of this ratio at any one frequency gives the margin against instability or oscillation. From Figure 30.7 it can be seen that a signal to listener echo ratio approaching zero dB at some frequency will result in oscillation of the 4 wire circuit at that frequency. Stability is of most importance during the set up and clear down phases of a call when there is the likelihood of the 2-wire to 4-wire converters being terminated with virtual open circuit or short circuit impedances, thus minimising the trans-hybrid loss.

Stability is commonly specified under worst case terminating conditions and Recommendation G.122 provides the international planning guidance in this area.

30.4.9   Sidetone

Sidetone, i.e. the transmission of sound from the microphone to receiver of the same telephone is not strictly an end to end impairment as it is primarily determined by the telephone set and local line characteristics at each end of the connection. The two customers may therefore see quite different sidetone conditions at their respective ends.

Sidetone has a number of effects on the telephone users. High levels of returned signal may be disturbing to the talker who will automatically reduce his talking level hence worsening the performance as seen by the distant customer. Room noise will also be picked up by the microphone and returned to the receiver via the sidetone path. If this sidetone path has a low loss then the room noise at the receiver will tend to mask the incoming speech and the customers may complain of faint transmission. The problem however is not one of low levels of incoming speech but high levels of noise.

Sidetone is quantified using an approach similar to that used for loudness rating i.e. a weighted value of the acoustic to acoustic loss.

Sidetone Masking Rating (STMR) is used to describe the talking effects of sidetone and Listener Sidetone Rating (LSTR) for the room noise sidetone effect.

Both STMR and LSTR are defined in Recommendations P.76 and P.79 (CCITT, 1989b).

Subjective tests have shown that the preferred range for STMR values is 7dB to 12dB (Recommendations G.122). Values of less than 7dB (i.e. louder sidetone) will result in a reduction in talker level and values significantly greater than 12dB will give the impression of the telephone being 'dead' or inactive.

From the above it can be seen that sidetone has some similarities to talker echo. In practice the only significant difference is the delay of the reflected signal. For delays in the order of up to two or three milliseconds the effect is considered as sidetone; for longer delays when it may be possible to perceive a distinct echo, the reflection is considered as talker-echo.

30.4.10   Crosstalk

Customers expect telephony systems to provide some security in terms of freedom from overhearing. Overhearing other conversations clearly undermines a listener's confidence that his conversation is not being overheard. The intelligibility of the crosstalk is the key factor and this is influenced by talker levels, acuity of hearing, noise on the line and the degree of coupling between connections.

Recommendation P.16 gives details of crosstalk intelligibility thresholds and methods for calculating the probability of interference.

30.4.11   Digital impairments

The major digital impairment is error performance i.e. the received bits not being the same as the transmitted bits. Errors may be contributed by any digital component in a connection hence there is a need for end to end transmission planning of error performance. The difficulty is that, unlike the previous parameters where it is generally possible to predict the performance on a connection, error performance is impossible to predict on a short term basis. Errors can be caused by a variety of mechanisms even on well designed equipment.

Lightning, man-made electrostatic discharges, climatic effects on radio systems all may generate errors. Systems tend to run error-free for long periods of time with errors coming in unpredictable bursts.

CCITT attempt to describe the long term error characteristics of reference connections in Recommendation G.821 using the concept of error free seconds, (EFS) severely errored seconds (SES) and degraded minutes (DM).

Table 30.1 gives the error performance objectives for a long international reference circuit averaged over a period of one month. If periods of less than one month are used then there will be increased uncertainty in the values quoted.

Table 30.1 G.821 objectives for error performance of a 64kbit/s reference connection

Performance classification	Objective
Degraded minutes	<10% of 1 minute intervals to have a bit error ratio $>1.10^{-6}$
Severely errored seconds	<0.2% of 1 second intervals to have a bit error ratio $>1.10^{-3}$
Errored seconds	<8% of 1 second intervals to have any errors (>92% to be error free)

It is clearly difficult therefore to accurately predict the performance of a switched digital connection with a holding time of a few minutes.

The other digital impairment that may be seen on some types of services is slips i.e. the deletion or repetition of one bit, or a number of consecutive bits. Recommendation G.822 (CCITT 1989d) gives slip rate objectives for international connections.

30.5 Meeting end to end requirements

The previous section outlined typical objectives for end to end values of the key transmission parameters. The next step for the transmission planner is to identify the main drivers in this process. End to end performance is a function of a number of variables within the network and these variables need to be identified and their effect on end to end performance quantified. Only when this step has been done can the planner claim to 'control the levers' of the transmission plan and begin to specify requirements for the parts of the network.

30.5.1 Economic aspects

Transmission planning cannot be divorced from the economic realities of telecommunication networks. Broadly, it is necessary for the transmission planner to demonstrate that the solutions he proposes will contribute to providing the required return on investment.

The financial aspects are covered in more detail later. For the purposes of this section it will be assumed that the financial aspects

have been adequately covered and their impact on, for example network structure, already taken into account.

30.5.2 General factors influencing end to end performance

To illustrate principles consider a digital network connecting together 2-wire local lines when the structure of the digital network has already been agreed in outline and is shown in Figure 30.8. This network structure is representative of a significant number of typical digital networks either in operation or being planned.

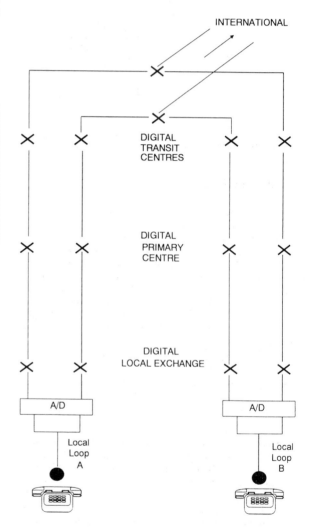

Figure 30.8 Example of a digital network structure

From Figure 30.8 it is clear that the end to end performance of any connection is a function of the individual system performances together with the actual routing through the network. For example the end to end transmission loss of any connection would be dependent on the individual transmission losses of all the individual systems in that connection i.e. the telephone instrument, 2 wire local line, digital local exchange and any digital attenuation introduced.

However the impedances presented by the transmission systems are also important as the resulting mismatch losses could have a significant impact on end to end losses. This impedance aspect can be considered as an interface requirement that also needs considering in any requirements document.

In summary the end to end performance for any parameter is determined by the following aspects:

1. Network structure and routeing rules.
2. Performance of the individual network systems.
3. System interface requirements.

Successful end to end planning therefore requires an understanding of how these aspects apply to the transmission parameters under study.

30.6 Key influences on end to end performance

Section 30.4 identified the major end to end parameters together with CCITT recommended limits. Section 30.5 illustrated the need to identify the factors contributing to end to end performance for each parameter.

This process is outlined below and concludes with a table summarising the key dependencies.

30.6.1 Transmission loss

Key factors influencing transmission loss are:

1. Transmission loss of individual network components.
2. Mismatch losses introduced at analogue interconnection points.

The mismatch losses are determined by the impedance at the various points of the connection. Calculation of overall transmission loss is best carried out using a transmission and calculation programme of the type outlined in Supplement 3 to Vol. V (CCITT 1989b)

Use of such a programme will enable the end to end losses to be calculated for routeings through the intended network structure.

Such a programme is also used to calculate loudness ratings (SLR, RLR and OLR) of a connection from the characteristics of the telephone sets and any local lines. In many cases it is convenient to calculate SLR and RLR to the first switching point in the connection which may well be a digital highway. Although this point is not analogue, the digital code represents encoded analogue signals and a high quality digital to analogue converter would be used to determine the equivalent analogue level.

30.6.2 Noise and interference

The value of noise seen at the output of a connection is the sum of the noise generated by the individual network components. Calculation of the total noise is not straightforward as the various noise sources are attenuated by different amounts as they traverse the connection. A suitable calculation procedure is outlined in Annex A to Recommendation G.103. Where digital systems are used in the connection an additional source of noise (errors) is introduced, which is decoded as analogue noise.

As error distributions tend to be non uniform the resultant noise can appear impulsive in nature.

Noise can be injected or induced into connections by crosstalk mechanisms from adjacent systems, non linearities in cable joints and also lack of immunity from external interference. Such interference is minimised by controlling impedance balance about earth of the nominally balanced 2-wire parts of the connection.

30.6.3 Loss frequency distortion

The influences on end to end distortion are similar to those for transmission loss, i.e. the distortion introduced by systems together with mismatch losses at the interface points. In this case the mismatch losses may be more significant as the values are likely to vary with frequency.

30.6.4 Non linear distortion and quantising distortion

Calculation of overall non-linear distortion is generally not undertaken as any calculation requires an exact knowledge of the non-linear characteristic.

For the specific case of quantising distortion it is possible to estimate the total quantising distortion using the quantising distortion unit approach (qdu) outlined in Section 30.4.4.

It has been found that such an approach is reasonably accurate for coding systems with bit rates of 32kbit/s and above. The accuracy for lower rate systems is under study within CCITT.

30.6.5 Propagation delay

Calculation of overall propagation delay is straightforward providing the delays contributed by the component parts are known. Information on typical planning delays is given in Recommendation G.114. Overall delays for any connection can be calculated by addition of the delays of the component parts.

30.6.6 Talker-echo

From Figure 30.5 the loudness rating of the talker echo path TELR is given by Equation 30.2

$$TELR = SLR + RLR + Echo\ loss\quad (in\ dB)$$
$$\approx SLR + RLR + Balance\ Return\ Loss + (A + B) \qquad (3.2)$$

The Sound and Receive Loudness Rating (SLR and RLR) of the local end are determined as outlined in Section 30.6.1. The echo loss is a function of the nominal 2-wire to 4-wire losses together with the balance return loss of the 2-wire to 4-wire converter. (Balance return loss is the contribution to echo loss from the degree of match between the hybrid balance impedance and the impedance presented by the 2-wire local access circuit.)

Control of talker echo therefore requires adequate specification of a number of transmission characteristics i.e. loss, impedance and delay.

30.6.7 Listener echo

To a first approximation, the signal to listener echo ratio is given by the sum of the two echo losses as shown in Figure 30.7 and Equation 30.3.

$$Signal\ Listener\ Echo\ Ratio \approx EL_1 + EL_2 \quad (\ in\ dB\ ) \tag{30.3}$$

A more accurate calculation would need to take into account multiple transmission around the loop but this is generally not needed as typical signal to listener echo ratios are in the order of 20dB or better. The second reflection is therefore 40dB lower and can be neglected.

30.6.8 Stability

As outlined in Section 30.4.8, the margin against instability is indicated by the worst case signal to listener echo ratio i.e. under worst case terminating conditions and at the frequency giving the lowest ratio. Combinations of open circuit and short circuit are commonly used as test conditions although it is necessary to check what conditions are actually encountered in practice. An additional factor to be considered is the switching characteristics of the exchanges. In some cases the transmission path is not complete at the time of application of worst case conditions such as open circuits hence no loop path is present. For example when the calling customer replaces his telephone handset the digital exchange detects the on-hook condition and breaks the 4-wire switch path thus removing any chance of instability.

30.6.9 Sidetone

The sidetone masking rating (STMR) is a function of the telephone set characteristics and the impedance presented by the local connection as shown in Figure 30.9. In Recommendation G.111 expression given in Equation 30.4 is developed, where Am is a weighted sidetone balance return loss.

$$STMR = SLR_{set} + RLR_{set} + (Am - 1) \quad (\ in\ dB\ ) \tag{30.4}$$

From Figure 30.9 the impedance presented to the telephone is a function of the characteristic impedance of the local cable and the impedance presented by the 2-wire interface of the digital exchange. Again, the use of a transmission calculation programme simplifies the evaluation of STMR for any given connection.

The Listener Sidetone LSTR is given by Equation 30.5, where D is a constant which reflects the sensitivity of the telephone set to room noise.

$$LSTR = STMR + D \quad (\ in\ dB\ ) \tag{30.5}$$

Values of D are determined by the acoustics of the handset and the type of microphone used as indicated in Recommendation G.111.

30.6.10 Crosstalk

Recommendation P.16 gives a detailed description of the factors influencing the intelligibility of any crosstalk. These are:

1. Loudness ratings of telephone sets.
2. Circuit noise (including telephone noise).
3. Room noise.
4. Crosstalk coupling between circuits.

The crosstalk coupling between circuits in multi-channel equipment e.g. exchanges and line systems, generally forms part of the specification of that equipment and can be suitably controlled. However crosstalk coupling between 2-wire local circuits in the same cable is more complex. Achieving adequate coupling requires that the balance about earth of both the cable and the termination is well controlled. For example poor termination balance about earth can result in crosstalk between the pairs of a perfectly balanced cable ITU (1976).

30.6.11 Digital impairments

In Section 30.5.2. it was shown that end to end performance was a function of:

1. Network Structure and routeing rules.
2. Performance of individual systems.
3. System interface requirements.

This approach is especially useful for the complex situation of digital impairments.

For example end to end error performance is a function of the error contribution of the individual line systems and exchanges in the connection. However a straightforward addition of the contributions may not be accurate as errors may be generated by interface problems. The jitter and wander requirements at interfaces are particularly important. If the input port of one equipment is unable

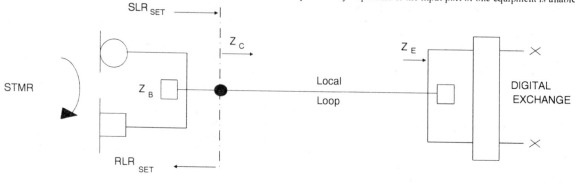

Figure 30.9 Sidetone influences

to tolerate the output jitter and wander from the output of the previous equipment then errors may be introduced.

Jitter and wander guidance is given in Recommendation G.823 (CCITT, 1989d). The network structure is important in determining end to end performance but the structure and operation of the network synchronisation system can also have an effect on end to end performance. Timing inaccuracies may result in slips within the network which appear as error bursts on end to end performance.

Digital transmission and switching systems are considered in more detail in other sections of this book. It should be appreciated that the interaction of these digital network systems and the resultant effect on end to end performance is not straightforward. The best available guidance on the issues is included in the CCITT G series. Recommendations in particular:

1. G.821 Error performance.
2. G.822 Slip rate objectives.
3. G.823 Control of jitter and wander within digital networks.
4. G.811 Timing requirements at the outputs of reference clocks and network nodes.

30.7 Summary of interactions

The previous section has shown that adequate control of end to end performance requires controlling the performance of many of the network elements. In many cases the performance of a single element can influence several end to end performance parameters. To show these interactions the end to end performance of the connection given in Figure 30.4 is considered. For the principal connection elements the main analogue transmission parameters are identified in Table 30.2. From the discussion in Section 30.6 the impact of each of these parameters on the main end to end performance can be summarised. Table 30.3 shows these and whether they have any impact on the key end to end analogue parameters. For clarity the Table does not include crosstalk, non-linear distortion and qd, and delay although a similar approach can be adopted for these par-

Table 30.2 Main analogue transmission parameters

Telephone	Local line	Digital switch	Digital line	Exchange line card
SLR/RLR	Loss	Delay	Delay	Loss
Loss/frequency	Noise		Errors	Noise
Impedance	Impedance			Impedance
Noise	Balance about Earth			Impedance balance about Earth
				Quantising distortion

ameters. The use of the term 'all' is intended to cover those network components where the parameter is relevant. For example loss/frequency distortion would not be relevant to a digital line system.

Table 30.3 is the basis of a transmission plan as it identifies the network component parameters that determine end to end performance.

30.8 Example transmission plan

This section illustrates the basic steps required in developing a transmission plan for the hypothetical network given in Figure 30.8 where the network structure has already been determined. It is also assumed that the telephone instruments are provided by the network operator.

Table 30.3 Effect of network component performance on end to end performance

Parameter	Network component	End to end performance					
		End to end loss	Loss/frequency	Noise	Sidetone	Talker echo	Listener echo/stability
Loss(LR)	All	*		*	*	*	*
Loss/frequency	All	*	*			*	*
Input impedance	Telephone	*	*			*	*
	Local line	*	*		*	*	*
	Linecard	*	*		*	*	*
Balance impedance	Telephone				*		
	Linecard					*	*
Noise	All			*			
Balance about Earth	All			*			
Delay	All					*	

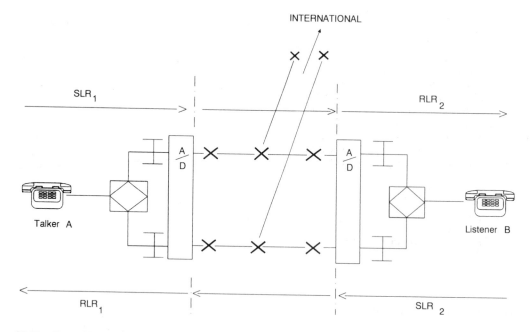

Figure 30.10 Overall Loudness Rating (OLR)

The objectives of the plan are to provide the end to end performance to support a telephony service covering both national and international calls.

The recommended steps are as in the following sections.

30.8.1 Stage 1: Provisional loudness rating values

A telephony service is the main aim therefore planning will be in terms of loudness rating. For this digital network the loudness ratings will be determined by the local ends as shown in Figure 30.10 and Equations 30.6 and 30.7. Assuming transparent 64kbit/s paths between local exchanges then the range of values for SLR and RLR will determine the values for OLR.

$$OLR_{A-B} = SLR_1 + RLR_2 \quad (in\ dB) \qquad (30.6)$$

$$OLR_{B-A} = SLR_2 + RLR_1 \quad (in\ dB) \qquad (30.7)$$

At this stage preliminary objectives for minimum, maximum and median values of SLR and RLR should be identified. These should be based on the SLR and RLR Recommendations in G.111 and the traffic weighted mean value of OLR should lie in the CCITT preferred range of 8dB to 12dB.

30.8.2 Stage 2: Delay assessment

Ideally a distribution of the delays introduced on routeings between the digital local exchanges should be calculated from a knowledge of the geographical location of the exchanges, the routeing structure and the propagation delays of the switching and transmission equipment. In practice this assessment may take too long and only limiting case scenarios may be investigated. This will give an indication of the maximum delay expected for routeing both within the network and also on access routes to other networks. This maximum delay value is now used to make a preliminary assessment of talker echo performance in Section 30.8.4.

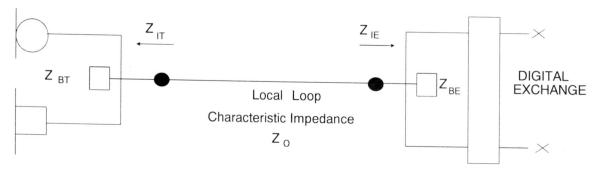

Figure 30.11 Local impedance strategy

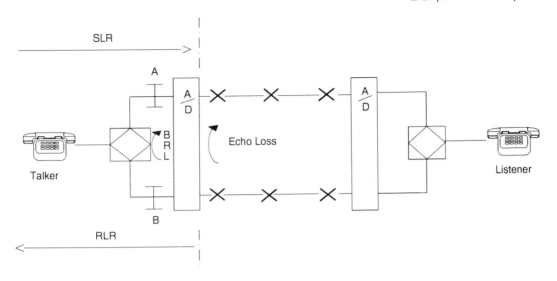

Figure 30.12 Exchange line card losses

30.8.3 Stage 3: Impedance strategy

From Table 30.3 it can be seen that the impedances associated with telephones, local lines and digital exchanges affect a number of parameters including echo, sidetone and loss. The main impedances are shown in Figure 30.11 where it can be seen that for the case of telephone instruments the optimum conditions will be encountered when $Z_{BT} = Z_{IT} = Z_{IE} = Z_{BE} =$ cable characteristic impedance Z_O.

Such an arrangement will give optimum sidetone performance and minimum reflected levels at the exchange 2-wire to 4-wire converter thus minimising talker and listener echo signals. However in practice it is unlikely that all telephone instruments will have the same nominal impedance, and 2-wire local lines are unlikely to all have identical values of Z_O therefore the ideal impedance match cannot be achieved. In this case it will be necessary to calculate distributions of values for STMR using the known characteristics of the telephone set and local lines. At the same time, distributions for values of balance return loss at the exchange hybrid can be calculated. STMR values can then be compared with the sidetone objectives given in Section 30.4.10 and the balance return loss distribution used later for echo assessment.

30.8.4 Stage 4: Loss apportionment and echo assessment.

This stage involves an interactive process. The objective is to assign values to the exchange interface losses A and B in Figure 30.12 such that:

1. SLR and RLR meet Section 30.8.1 limits.
2. A and B result in a sufficiently high echo loss value to meet the talker echo objective.

The two requirements tend to be conflicting as meeting SLR and RLR objectives require low values of A and B whereas echo performance is improved by increasing A and B. SLR/RLR can be calculated with transmission data on telephone instruments and local lines using either a computer model or the approximate method outlined in G.111.

Calculation of talker echo requires:

1. SLR and RLR values.
2. BRL values from 30.8.3.
3. Delay values from 30.8.2.

The method is outlined in G.131 and leads to values for the probability of customers encountering objectionable echo.

Calculations according to G.131 will demonstrate whether adequate echo performance can be obtained for the chosen values of loudness and impedances, taking into account the delays on the connections. If a suitable compromise cannot be achieved then the use of echo control devices such as echo cancellers may need to be considered.

Guidance on the use of echo cancellers is given in G.131 which covers aspects such as preferred location and interworking with other echo control devices such as echo suppressors. To date it has generally only been large countries such as U.S.A. and Canada that have needed echo control devices on national calls not involving satellites. However increased use of signal processing devices is tending to increase connection delays whilst end to end losses are being reduced by the use of digital transmission and switching. There will therefore be an increasing risk of encountering echo problems in situations where echo has not previously been noticeable.

30.8.5 Stage 5: Review

Stages 1 to 4 above are the most complicated as a number of compromises may be required to meet acceptable values for loudness rating, sidetone, talker echo and listener echo. The complexity arises because the losses and impedances of the telephone, exchange and local area all interact to influence several end to end parameters as shown in Table 30.3.

The remaining parameters to be covered are loss/frequency distortion, noise, balance about earth, crosstalk, errors, non-linear distortion and quantising distortion (qd).

30.8.6 Stage 6: Remaining parameters

Some simplification is possible for the chosen example. The network structure does not incorporate multiple analogue to digital conversions with their associated non-linear and loss/frequency distortion. In addition noise sources are limited to the exchange interface, local line and telephone instrument. Providing values in line with the relevant CCITT equipment recommendations (CCITT, 1989d; CCITT, 1989e) are adopted then the end to end values will be significantly inside the Section 30.4 objectives and detailed calculations are not required.

The chosen example covers the telephony service which is relatively tolerant of the digital impairments such as error performance. The error contributions potentially come from the digital line systems, multiplexors and switches. Compliance with the appropriate CCITT values is likely to result in acceptable end to end performance for telephony as the additional noise contribution due to errors will not be significant.

30.8.7 Stage 7: Additional areas

Stages 1 to 6 have addressed the relevant end to end parameters and indicated a procedure for arriving at a plan. There are a few additional areas which, if not considered, may have an effect on performance i.e.:

1. DC current feed. The digital exchange must supply the appropriate minimum DC current on the highest resistance local loop. This ensures correct operation of the telephone instrument and appropriate values of SLR and RLR.
2. Power loading. Codecs have a limited dynamic range as defined in G.711 for 8 bit PCM systems. SLR values in line with the CCITT recommended ranges should adequately limit the speech power to prevent codec overload. If digital attenuators are used then care needs to be taken to prevent codec overload.
3. Synchronisation. Covered in 30.6.11. An inadequate synchronisation scheme will lead to slips in the digital circuits resulting in additional noise at the analogue output.

30.9 Future network trends

The example case considered above covered an all-digital switching network with analogue 2-wire access to customers. The major difficulty in the transmission plan exercise was finding an acceptable compromise between loss and echo performance for the propagation delays in question. This problem will increase in the future, even for this network configuration, as the majority of customers will still be served by analogue copper access for many years. Meanwhile there will be pressure for the switched network to incorporate new techniques such as ATM, and such techniques will increase propagation delays.

Over the next ten years a rapidly increasing number of customers will be served by digital exchange lines where the network boundary is at a digital interface. In this case the network operator will be providing a switched network path at, for example, 64kbit/s. If no analogue transmission is involved then the network transmission plan will just involve the digital impairments together with propagation delay. The end to end analogue performance as seen by users will be wholly dependent on the characteristics of the customer equipment e.g. PBXs and digital telephones. It is particularly important that the designers of such equipment appreciate the end to end transmission issues and the significance of the terminal equipment performance.

The use of end to end digital connections will also affect the present thinking on the use of echo control devices on long delay circuits such as provided by satellites. At present the echo control device will be associated with the international part of the connection for economic reasons. However echo control devices are, by definition, signal processing devices which destroy bit integrity therefore they could not be used on circuits where a 64kbit/s transparent path was required. Any telephony service over a satellite system without echo control is likely to give major problems hence the user would not be able to use his transparent 64kbit/s path for speech. The solution to this problem is to migrate the echo control to the terminal equipment which is consistent with the G.131 objective of locating echo control devices close to the point of reflection. It seems possible therefore that future digital terminal equipment will need to incorporate an echo control function in the same way as is proposed for the European digital cellular system GSM. Such an arrangement would minimise the problems of incorporating new technologies like point to multipoint radio access systems and ATM switching, both of which result in increased delay.

30.10 References

CCITT(1989a) *General aspects of quality of service and network performance in digital networks, including ISDN,* CCITT Recommendation I.350. Blue Book Fascicle 111-8. Geneva.

CCITT (1989b) *Telephone Transmission Quality,* CCITT Series P Recommendations. Blue Book Fascicle V. Geneva.

CCITT (1989c) *General Characteristics of International Telephone Connections and Circuits,* CCITT Series G.100. Recommendations Blue Book fascicle 111-1. Geneva.

CCITT (1989d) *Digital Networks, Transmission Systems and Multiplexing Equipment,* CCITT Series G.700-G.956 Recommendations Fascicle 111-3. Geneva.

CCITT (1989e) *Digital Local, Transit, Combined and International Exchanges in Integrated Digital Networks and Mixed Analogue-Digital Networks,* CCITT Series Q.500 - Q.554. Recommendations Fascicle V1.5. Geneva.

ITU (1976) *Transmission Planning of Switched Telephone Networks,* International Telecommunication Union. Geneva Annex 3 P4.

Richards, D.L. (1973) *Telecommunications by Speech,* Butterworth Heinemann, London.

31

Principles of switching systems

Eur Ing S F Smith
BSc (Eng) CEng FIEE
Northern Telecom Europe

D G Bryan
DFH CEng FIEE
Telecommunication Consultant

Contents

31.1 Introduction

The simplest form of telephone system consists of two terminations and a metallic connection between them. However, this arrangement is clearly not viable for more than a very small number of terminals and the concept of switching is introduced, whereby each terminal is connected to a central location (exchange) where means is provided to interconnect any two of the total population of terminations.

Within an exchange, more than one connection will be required at any one time but not all terminations will be wanting service at the same time. Practical systems are designed to provide a number of links which is less than the number of terminations determined on a statistical basis. Figure 31.1 shows such an arrangement, based on a matrix of crosspoints where each crosspoint is some form of on/off switch such as a manually operated key, an electromechanical relay or a transistor.

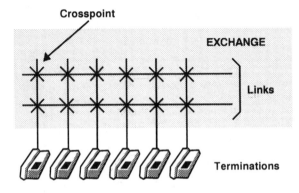

Figure 31.1   Switching principle

This simple example can be regarded as a single node network with all connections passing through one single exchange. This is clearly unreasonable on a global scale and in a practical network, as the number of terminations increases, so must the number of nodes or exchanges, normally on a geographical basis. There is then a need to provide interconnections (junctions) between the different exchanges. Each exchange must be able to handle connections between its own terminations and between them and the external junctions. In large networks it is usual to transit switch calls between

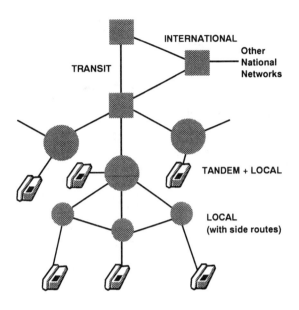

Figure 31.2   Exchange hierarchy

other exchanges and some exchanges exist solely for this purpose and have no terminations of their own. This leads to a hierarchical arrangement of exchanges as shown in Figure 31.2.

The various types of call routing are shown in Figure 31.3 and traffic is not usually evenly divided over these types of call. Only a small proportion (5% to 15%) of the traffic is normally between customer terminations (subscribers) on the same exchange. The remainder is divided between incoming and outgoing calls. Services such as emergency, speaking clock etc. are usually centralised at one exchange in an area, so that the outgoing traffic at other exchanges normally exceeds the incoming traffic. The proportion of transit (tandem) traffic varies from zero at small rural exchanges to 100% at exchanges provided solely for this purpose.

A network must, therefore, consist of terminations provided at the customers' premises, a transmission medium to connect them to the local exchange and a means of signalling between the termination and the exchange. As well as the telephone customers, there is an increasing requirement for the connection of teleprinters and other

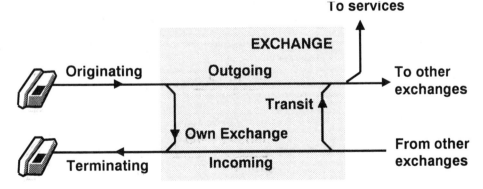

Figure 31.3   Call routing

data terminals and the public switched telephone network (PSTN), which was originally established to carry voice traffic, is increasingly being used to carry data traffic and to provide a variety of services beyond plain old telephone service (POTS).

31.2 Structure of telephone systems

31.2.1 Telephone instrument

The speech transmission elements of a telephone instrument, Figure 31.4, consist of a receiver and transmitter (microphone) usually assembled in a common mounting to form a handset and connected to the line through an anti-sidetone induction coil (hybrid transformer) or an equivalent electronic circuit. The complete instrument also incorporates signalling elements, the exact form of which depends upon the type of exchange with which it is designed to interwork. Generally they comprise a dial or push buttons and associated gravity switch for signalling to the exchange and a ringer (bell) or an electronic detection circuit and sound transducer for receiving calling (ringing) signals from the exchange.

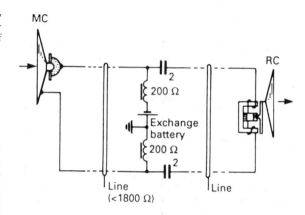

Figure 31.5 Principle of transmission bridge

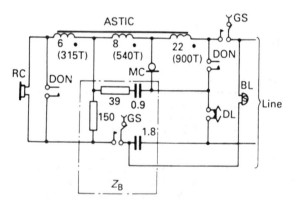

Figure 31.4 Typical telephone instrument circuit

31.2.1.1 *Transmitter*

Most instruments employ a carbon microphone. Sound waves cause the diaphragm to vibrate, varying the pressure exerted on the carbon granules. This produces corresponding variations in the electrical resistance between the granules and hence in the current flowing through them when connected to a d.c. supply.

Power may be derived from a battery or other d.c. supply locally at the instrument but in public systems it is now the universal practice for a single central battery to provide a supply to all lines on the exchange. The a.c. component of the line current produced in this way is known as the speech current and the d.c. component derived from the battery is the microphone feed current (transmitter feed) or polarising current.

The feed to each line is decoupled by individual inductors, often in the form of relay coils, and speech is coupled from one line to another through the exchange switching apparatus by means of capacitors as shown in Figure 31.5 or through a transformer. The

combination of d.c. feed, battery decoupling and speech coupling components is known as a transmission bridge or feeding bridge. The relays providing the battery decoupling also serve to detect line signals to control the holding and releasing of the connection.

The microphone resistance is nonlinear and is subject to wide variations due to temperature, movement of granules and, of course, the effects of sound. Typically it is between 40 and 400 ohms under normal working conditions.

Some telephone instruments employ other types of microphone (e.g. moving coil) which do not themselves require a d.c. feed. Such microphones, however, lack the inherent amplification of the carbon microphone. They are usually supported by a transistor amplifier driven by the line current and designed to operate with similar feeding bridge conditions to carbon microphone instruments.

31.2.1.2 *Receiver*

Most types of receiver operate on the moving-iron principle employed by Alexander Graham Bell for both transmitting and receiving in his original telephone in 1876. In some cases the diaphragm is operated on directly by the magnets but a more efficient arrangement is shown in Figure 31.5 in which the design of armature and diaphragm can each be optimised for its own purpose without conflict of mechanical-acoustic and magnetic requirements. A permanent magnet is included in the simple receiver to prevent frequency doubling due to the diaphragm being pulled on both the positive and the negative half cycle. In the rocking armature arrangement shown in Figure 31.5, no movement of the armature would occur at all without the permanent magnet.

Unlike the carbon microphone, the moving iron receiver requires no direct current for its operation and is usually protected against possible depolarisation by a series capacitor.

31.2.1.3 *Anti-sidetone induction coil (ASTIC)*

This is a hybrid transformer which performs the dual function of matching the receiver and transmitter to the line and controlling sidetone.

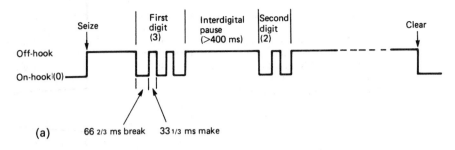

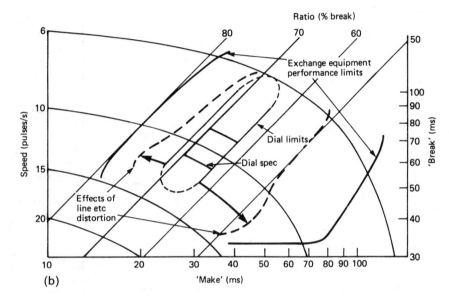

Figure 31.6 Telephone subscriber's line signalling: (a) waveform; (b) performance curves

Sidetone is the reproduction at the receiver of sound picked up by the transmitter of the same instrument. It occurs because the transmitter and receiver are both coupled to the same two-wire line. The most comfortable conditions for the user are found to be when he hears his own voice in the receiver at about the same loudness as he would hear it through the air in normal conversation. Too much sidetone causes the talker to lower his voice, reduces his subsequent listening ability and increases the interfering effect of local room noise at the receiving end. The complete absence of sidetone, however, makes the telephone seem to be 'dead'.

The use of a hybrid transformer divides the transmitter output between the line and a corresponding balance impedance. If this impedance exactly balanced that of the line there would be no resultant power transferred to the receiver. In practice there is some transfer to produce an acceptable level of sidetone.

31.2.1.4 *Gravity switch (switch hook)*

To operate and release relays at the exchange and thus indicate calling and clearing conditions, a contact is provided to interrupt the line current. This contact is open when the handset is on the rest and closes (makes) when the handset is lifted. Because it is operated by the weight of the handset it is known as the gravity switch. It is also known as a switch hook contact and the terms off-hook and on-hook

are often used to describe signalling conditions corresponding to the contact closed or open respectively.

31.2.1.5 *Dial*

This is a spring-operated mechanical device with a centrifugal governor to control the speed of return. Pulses are generated on the return motion only, the number of pulses up to ten depending upon how far round the finger plate is pulled.

The pulses consist of interruptions (breaks) in the line current produced by cam-operated pulsing contacts. A set of off-normal contacts operate when the finger plate is moved and are used to disable the speech elements of the telephone during dialling. These dial pulses are usually specified in terms of speed and ratio and the standard values of these parameters are designed to match the performance of electromechanical exchange switching equipment. Figure 31.6.

31.2.1.6 *Push-button keypad*

For use with exchanges designed for dial pulse signalling there are telephones in which a numerical keypad is used to input numbers to an l.s.i. circuit which then simulates the action of a dial. The output device for signalling to line is usually a relay, typically, a mercury-wetted relay.

For electronic exchanges and some types of electromechanical exchange, a faster method of signalling known as multifrequency (MF) can be used. In this, a 12-button keypad is provided with oscillators having frequencies as shown in Figure 31.7. Pressing any button causes a pair of frequencies to be generated, one from each band.

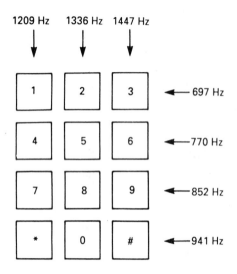

Figure 31.7   Push-button (multifrequency) dialling

31.2.1.7   Ringer (bell)

In the idle state, the handset is on its rest, the gravity switch is open and no direct current flows in the line. The ringer is, therefore, designed to operate on alternating current. This is connected from a common supply at typically 75V r.m.s. and 25 Hz connected through a 500 ohm resistance at the exchange.

31.2.2   Types of customer (subscriber) installation

Telephones are installed at customers' (subscribers') own premises or made available to the general public at call offices (paystations) with coin collecting boxes (CCB) or card reading devices. Each of these installations is normally connected to a local exchange by a pair of wires but in isolated locations radio links may be used and optical fibres are now being used increasingly for at least the part of the connection nearest to the exchange. In some cases more than one customer's instrument may be connected to the same line which is then described as a party line. In some countries a party line, especially in remote rural areas, may serve as many as 20 customers with a system of coded ringing signals. In the UK the only party lines are those serving two customers on a system known as shared service. The case of one customer per line is known as exclusive service.

At the customer's premises there can be more than one telephone. Residential and small business users often have two or more instruments with one of several simple methods of interconnection known as extension plans. Larger businesses generally have private branch exchanges (PBX) on their premises providing connection between their extensions either under control of a switchboard operator (private manual branch exchange, PMBX) or by dialling (private automatic branch exchange, PABX).

These private exchanges are connected to their local exchange by a group of exchange lines and the public exchange selects a free line within the group (PBX hunting) when a caller dials the first line of the group.

In some cases calls incoming to the PABX are routed to an operator (attendant) who makes the connection to the required line (extension). Direct Dialling In (DDI) may also be provided so that the caller is able to dial the required extension. A PABX can also be provided as a virtual group within the public exchange, a system known as Centrex.

31.2.3   Hierarchy of exchanges

Each local public exchange provides the means for setting up calls between its own customers' lines. It is normally also connected to other local exchanges in the same area (e.g. the same town) by junctions. For calls outside this area, junctions are provided to trunk (toll) exchanges which are in turn interconnected by trunk lines, enabling calls to be established to customers in other areas. Trunk lines are also provided to one or more international exchanges which enable calls to be established to customers in the national networks of other countries.

A single exchange can sometimes combine two or more of these functions and the larger national networks have more than one level of trunk exchange in their hierarchy (e.g. three levels in the UK, four in the USA). A trunk call in the UK, therefore, passes through up to six trunk exchanges in addition to the local exchanges at each end.

In large areas, some local exchanges may be interconnected only by having calls switched through another local exchange, a technique known as tandem switching which can be independent of the trunk switching hierarchy used for calls outside the area. (See Figure 31.2.)

31.2.4   Exchange structure

The most elementary form of switching network consists of a single square switch, where connection can be made between any one inlet and any one outlet by connecting the associated horizontal and vertical circuits at the point where they cross. However, to provide an exchange capable of serving say 10,000 customers, it would not be economic either to construct a single large switch or simply to gang a large number of smaller switches to form a square matrix of 10,000 x 10,000 crosspoints. A more practical arrangement is to connect the switches in two or more stages. To illustrate this Figure 31.8 shows first a single square matrix of 81 crosspoints providing for nine paths between nine inlets and nine outlets and then how to meet the same requirement with only 54 crosspoints. The advantage of this approach is even greater with larger numbers of circuits and practical switches having typically 10 x 20 crosspoints or more, rather than only 3 x 3 as shown in the example.

This simple example provides only for the distribution of calls from the inlets to an equal number of outlets through the same number of links. In practical exchanges, it is only necessary to provide as many paths through the switching network as the number of calls which are expected to be in progress at one time. The

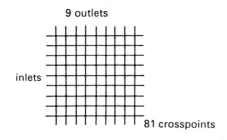

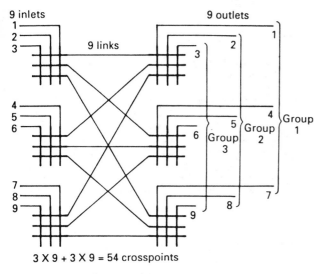

Figure 31.8 Trunking principle of distribution stage for crossbar and electronic exchanges

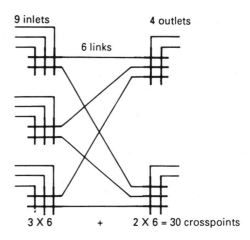

Figure 31.9 Trunking principle of concentration stage for crossbar and electronic exchanges

31.2.5 Types of exchanges

The early exchanges were all manually operated and many are still in service around the world. The exchange equipment consists of a switchboard at which an operator (telephonist) connects calls on demand.

The term 'automatic' is used to describe exchanges where the switching is carried out by machine under the remote control of the caller who could be either a customer or an operator.

The first public automatic exchange opened in 1892 at La Porte, Indiana (USA), and used rotary switches invented in 1891 by Almon

concentration of lines on to a smaller number of paths or trunks can be achieved using the principle illustrated by another simple example in Figure 31.9.

A complete local exchange then consists of a combination of a distribution (group selection) stage and one or more line concentration units, as shown in Figure 31.10.

The separate switches are interconnected through yet another switching stage which does not provide concentration or expansion, i.e. a square switch as shown in Figure 31.8. This group switching (distribution) stage can also be used to make connections to other exchanges. (See also Section 31.4.3.)

To complete the exchange, two other functional blocks are needed. The call connection (and disconnection) instructions have to pass between the terminations and the exchange and also between exchanges for interexchange (junction) calls. These supervisory messages are conveyed by the exchange signalling systems which may transmit the relevant data over the same paths as the calls they control or they may use separate links for the purpose. Also needed is a control system for interpreting these instructions to enable appropriate paths to be set through the switches.

The operation and design of exchange switching systems can be conveniently separated into these three separate, but interdependent, functions: switching, signalling and control. In practical terms, the choice of switching technology is very dependent upon the transmission methods used in the network concerned and this in turn influences the choice of signalling and control methods.

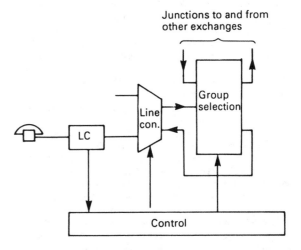

Figure 31.10 Generalised architecture of a complete crossbar or electronic exchange

B. Strowger, an undertaker in Kansas City, after whom the system is named. Since then several systems have been developed. The most successful of these employ mechanical devices called crossbar switches or arrays of reed relays. Modern versions of these systems use stored program control (spc) in which the operations to set up each call are determined by software in the exchange processors (computers).

The new generation (digital) systems employ totally solid-state switching as well as stored program control.

31.2.6 Types of transmission

Transmission may be either analogue, in which the electrical signal represents directly the speech signal, or digital, in which speech or data are coded in pulses. At present, telephone instruments and customers' lines are generally analogue, but the trunk and junction network is increasingly digital.

The essential feature of digital transmission, as opposed to analogue, is regeneration. The digital signals consist of a sequence of digits (or symbols) each of which have a few recognised levels (typically four or less) and occupy equal periods of time known as digit (or symbol) periods. Transmission systems are designed so that corruption of the digits, due to noise, interference or distortion, does not cause the signal level in each digit period to become indeterminate. A regenerator measures the level in each digit period and generates a new digit of the original amplitude. This means that noise and corruption of the signal do not accumulate through a series of regenerators. Only two types of impairment are left. Digital errors occur when excessive noise and corruption cause a regenerator to make wrong decisions about the level and jitter, which is displacement of the digit periods from their ideal positions. Time is essentially analogue in digital transmission and so is subject to analogue types of distortion.

31.2.7 Signalling

To connect calls through a network of exchanges, it is necessary to send data referring to the call between the exchanges concerned. In the simplest case, this consists of loop/disconnect signalling similar to that used on customers' lines. Each speech circuit consists of a pair of copper wires which have direct current flowing when in use on a call and this current is interrupted to form a train of break pulses for each digit corresponding to those produced by the telephone dial. When the called party answers, the called exchange sends back an 'answer' signal to the calling exchange by reversing the direction of the current flow.

Longer circuits are unsuitable for direct current signalling e.g. due to the use of amplifiers, multiplexing equipment or radio links. Voice frequency (VF) signalling is then used in which pulses of alternating current are used at frequencies and levels compatible with circuits designed for handling speech currents (typically 600, 750, 2280 and 2400 Hz). This use of frequencies within the speech band (300-3400 Hz) is termed in- band signalling.

An alternative is the use of out-of-band (outband) signalling, in which a signalling frequency (e.g. 3825 Hz) outside the speech band is separately modulated onto the carrier in a frequency division transmission system. In digital transmission systems, the signals are digitally encoded and certain time slot(s) are reserved for this purpose separate from the speech time slot(s).

These are all channel associated signalling systems, in which the signalling is physically and permanently associated with the individual speech channel even though no signalling information is transmitted during the greater part of the call. The use of stored program control has given rise to a more efficient signalling means, known as common channel signalling. In this, one signalling channel serves a large number of speech channels and consists of a direct data link between the control processors (computers) in the exchanges concerned. Each new item of information relating to a call is sent as a digital message containing an address label identifying the circuit to which it is to be applied.

31.3 Teletraffic

31.3.1 Grade of service

It would be uneconomic to provide switching equipment in quantities sufficient for all customers to be simultaneously engaged on calls. In practice, systems are engineered to provide an acceptable service under normal peak (i.e. busy hour) conditions. For this purpose, a measure called the grade of service (g.o.s.) is defined as the proportion of call attempts made in the busy hour which fail to mature due to the equipment concerned being already engaged on other calls. A typical value would be 0.005 (one lost call in 200) for a single switching stage. To avoid the possibility of serious deterioration of service under sudden abnormal traffic it is also usual to specify grades of service to be met under selected overload conditions.

31.3.2 Traffic units

Traffic is measured in terms of a unit of traffic intensity called the Erlang (formerly known as the traffic unit or TU) which may be defined as the number of call hours per hour (usually, but not necessarily, the busy hour), or call seconds per second, etc. This is a dimensionless unit which expresses the rate of flow of calls and, for a group of circuits, is numerically equal to the average number of simultaneous calls. It also equates on a single circuit to the proportion of time for which that circuit is engaged and consequently to the probability of finding that circuit engaged (i.e. the grade of service on that circuit). The traffic on one circuit can, of course, never be greater than one Erlang. Typically a single selector or junction circuit would carry about 0.6 Erlang and customers' lines vary from about 0.05 or less for residential lines to 0.5 Erlang or more for some business lines.

It follows from the definition that C calls of average duration t seconds occurring in a period of T seconds constitute a traffic of A Erlangs given by Equation 31.1.

$$A = C \frac{t}{T} \qquad (31.1)$$

An alternative unit of traffic sometimes used is the c.c.s. (call cent second) defined as hundreds of call seconds per hour (36 c.c.s. = 1 Erlang).

31.3.3 Erlang's full availability formula

Full availability means that all inlets to a switching stage have access to all the outlets of that stage. Trunking arrangements, in which some of the outlets are accessible from only some of the inlets, are said to have limited availability.

For a full availability group of N circuits offered a traffic of A Erlangs, the grade of service B is given by Equation 31.2.

$$B = \frac{\dfrac{A!}{N}}{1 + A + \dfrac{A^2}{2!} + \dots + \dfrac{A^N}{N!}} \qquad (31.2)$$

This formula assumes pure chance traffic and that all calls originating when all trunks are busy are lost and have zero duration.

31.3.4 Busy hour call attempts

An important parameter in the design of stored program control systems, in particular, and common control systems in general, is the number of attempts to be processed, usually expressed in busy hour call attempts (BHCA). Typically a 10,000 line local exchange might require a processing capacity of up to 80,000 BHCA.

31.3.5 Blocking

If two free trunks cannot be connected together because all suitable links are already engaged the call is said to be blocked. In Figure 31.8, if one call has already been set up from inlet 1 to outlet 1, an attempted call from inlet 2 to outlet 2 will be blocked. The effects of the blocking are reduced here by allocation of the outlets to the three routes.

Blocking can be reduced by connecting certain outlets permanently to the inlet side of the network to permit a blocked call to seek a new path. Alternatively, a third stage of switching may be provided.

It is possible to design a network having an odd number of switching stages in which blocking never occurs. Non-blocking arrays need more crosspoints than acceptable blocking networks and are uneconomic for most commercial telephone switching applications.

31.3.6 Network routing

Telephone networks are normally based on a hierachical arrangement and the higher levels are often fully interconnected, e.g. the UK transit network. Dimensioning is simplified by the use of fixed routing but the overall Grade of Service is sensitive to faults and overloads on individual links. All routes must, therefore, be dimensioned to overload conditions.

It is possible to use Automatic Alternative Routing based on overflow, although the dimensioning is more difficult since the overflow traffic is not random and, therefore, Erlangs loss formula does not apply.

If unlimited overflow is allowed, there is a danger of affecting the performance of traffic which normally uses the secondary route.

A method sometimes used in spc systems is known as Trunk Reservation, whereby the overflowing traffic is only given access to the secondary route if more than a set level of circuits are free, while the traffic normally using this route always has access to it.

31.3.7 Queuing

A queuing system provides facilities for storing calls in order until the server is available. The number of calls which can be held in a queue at any one time must be limited and, therefore, dimensioning must take account of the loss probability as well as delay conditions.

Many practical systems involve multiple queues dependent on the service required and this results effectively in a queuing network which can be quite complex to analyse.

31.4 Analogue switching

31.4.1 The manual exchange

The first telephone exchanges were operated by hand. Instructions were passed verbally between the subscriber and the operator (telephonist). Similar principles were used on early telegraph exchanges. As the network grew and the operators were expected to handle increasing volumes of traffic, the signalling and control elements were developed, which formed the basis of the first automatic systems.

In its more common form, the manual switchboard has subscribers' (customers') terminations connected to jacks (sockets). The "links" consist of a pair of plugs on flexible cords (wires) which can be used to interconnect any pair of jacks. Signalling consists of calling indicators (e.g. relays and lamps) associated with the jacks and clearing indicators associated with the cords and plugs. Call routing instructions are passed verbally.

The simplest type is the magneto board on which the caller gains the attention of the operator by using a hand generator to send an a.c. signal which is detected by an electromechanical indicator at the switchboard. An improved design is the central battery (CB) board which uses gravity switch contacts at the telephone to operate a relay at the exchange to light a lamp at the switchboard. In both cases the caller then tells the operator verbally what call he wants to make.

The great strength of the system is that the 'control' is human and, therefore, intelligent and the variety of connections that can be made is virtually unlimited. Services such as advice of duration and charge, transfer of calls when absent, wake up calls etc., which are so complex to provide automatically, present no problem at all on manual exchanges.

The weakness of the manual exchange, which has led to its almost complete disappearance, was essentially its slowness. Unless operators could set up calls faster it would have been impossible to find enough operators to handle the volume of traffic on the modern network.

31.4.2 Step by step

Ratchet driven switches, remotely controlled directly by pulses from the calling telephone, are used to simulate the operator's actions on a plug and cord switchboard. The wipers (moving contacts) are connected by short flexible cords and perform a similar function to the switchboard plugs. The place of the jack field is taken by a bank of fixed contacts and the wipers are moved one step from each contact to the next for each pulse, as in Figure 31.11, by means of a ratchet and pawl mechanism.

In early Strowger exchanges, each customer was provided with his own 100-outlet two-motion selector. The expense of providing one large switch or selector is now avoided by using a stage of smaller cheaper uniselectors to connect the callers to the selectors as and when they require them. Expansion of the exchange beyond 100 lines is by adding further stages of selectors as shown in Figure 31.12.

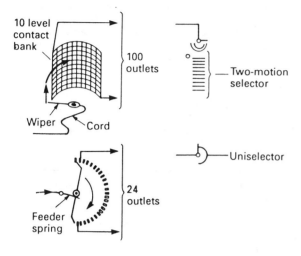

Figure 31.11 Strowger (step-by-step) selectors

The setting up of a call progresses through the exchange stage by stage. Each selector connects the call to a free selector in the next stage in time for the train of pulses to set that selector. The wipers step vertically to the required level under dial pulse control at 10 pulses per second then rotate automatically at 33 steps per second to select a free outlet by examining the potential on each contact. This is step-by-step operation and, when used with Strowger selectors, it needs only simple control circuits which can be provided economically at each selector.

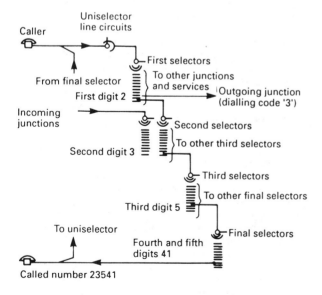

Figure 31.12 Strowger (non-director) exchange trunking

Concentration is provided at the uniselectors. In this example there are then three stages of group selectors to provide the "distribution" function. The final two digits of the number are used to position the final selector (connector) wipers to the contacts connected to the required line, thus providing the expansion function.

The final selectors also contain the circuit element known as the 'transmission bridge' which provides current to the calling and called telephones from the central supply (battery) at the exchange. It is here that 'answer' and 'clear' conditions are detected to control charging (metering) and release of the connection.

A large city often has a large number of exchanges with overlapping service areas where it would be unacceptable for callers to have to consult a different list of dialling codes according to which exchange the telephone they happen to be using is connected. To

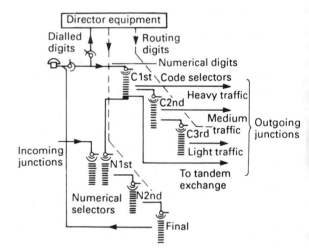

Figure 31.13 Strowger director exchange trunking

allow the same list of codes to be used anywhere in the area, director equipment is provided, Figure 31.13, which translates the code dialled by the caller into the actual routing digits required.

Even with the addition of the director, the step-by-step system lacks flexibility. The convention of ten finger holes in a dial, means that the switching network branches in a decadic fashion. Each switch requires a decadic ability and is mechanically designed accordingly. If, however, traffic is unevenly distributed throughout the exchange numbering range, some parts of this capability will be under-used. The relative slowness of the switches also makes it impractical to attempt rerouting for call transfer or to by-pass congestion in the network. The mechanical complexity of the switches themselves presents reliability problems and requires expensive maintenance.

Even on these systems there are some calls which customers either cannot or will not set up for themselves. To provide for these, numbers are allocated (e.g. 100) which can be dialled for assistance. Such calls are connected through the automatic exchange to a switchboard where the operator can establish the required connec-

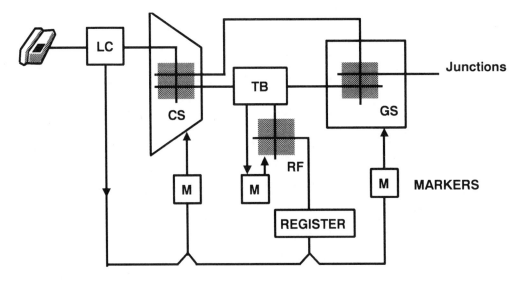

Figure 31.14 Crossbar exchange

tion also through the automatic equipment. These switchboards are called automanual exchanges.

31.4.3 Register control (Crossbar)

In crossbar and analogue electronic systems, the equipment operates at high speed, it functions on an end-to-end instead of the step-by-step basis used by Strowger exchanges and the trunking pattern does not conform with the decimal notation used by the telephone dial. For these reasons, it is necessary to interpose some equipment during the setting up process which will convert the customers' dialling signals into information which can be used by the switching equipment. When a call is originated, therefore, the control sets crosspoints to connect the calling line to a register which has functions broadly similar to those of an operator. The register detects and stores the dial (or MF key) pulses and signals them to the control. The control, which is duplicated or sectioned in some way for security, see Section 31.7, analyses the digits received and sets the appropriate crosspoints to establish the call. Being common, the control equipment can be used to set up only one connection at a time but operates so quickly that this restriction is not noticeable to customers.

The director, as used in the Strowger system, is an example of register control. Some of the disadvantages of the Strowger switches have been overcome with other designs of mechanical switch but they are generally unsuitable for direct control from the customer's dial. Register control provides a way of using such switches.

The most successful register controlled systems are based on the crossbar switch which is mechanically simpler than the rotary switches of the Strowger system and can be designed for greater reliability and smaller size. Translation facilities like those provided by the director system, but not limited by considerations of mechanical switch sizes, are readily obtained because there is no inherent relationship between number allocation and particular switch outlets.

The Crossbar switch mechanism consists of a rectangular array of contact sets or crosspoints, which can be selected by energising the electromagnets corresponding to their vertical and horizontal coor-

dinates. Typical mechanisms contain 200 or more crosspoints per switch. The switches are generally used in combinations to form a group selection (distribution) stage and a combined concentration/expansion stage, as shown in Figure 31.14. Additional crossbar switches may be used for establishing other connections necessary for the operation of the exchange e.g. RF, which connects registers, as required, to callers via the concentration stage CS.

Fig 31.15 shows a much simplified diagram of a single crosspoint and a general view of a complete switch. The flexible selecting

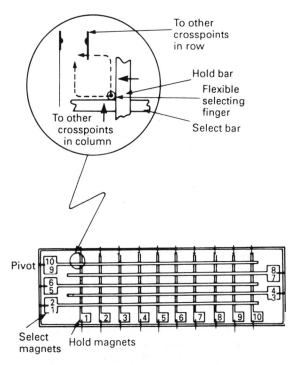

Figure 31.15 Crossbar switch

finger should be thought of as a stiff piece of wire sticking up out of the paper. The horizontal (select) and vertical (hold) bars move in the direction shown by the arrows when their associated coils are energised. It can be seen that the crosspoint contact will be operated only when the horizontal bar 'selects' before the vertical bar operates. Once operated, the contact remains held by the vertical bar which traps the finger and holds it even when the horizontal bar has been restored. The horizontal bar can be used again to select another crosspoint in the row without disturbing those already in use.

In the most usual form of construction, the movement of the bars is produced by a slight rotation about the pivot in a manner similar to the armature of a telephone relay. The spring finger is attached to the select bar and swings across when the bar rotates.

The function of the register is to receive the caller's instructions in the form of dialled digits and convert them into the appropriate signals for route selection. Operation of the relevant magnets in the required crossbar switches in the concentration stage (CS) and the group selection stage (GS) is carried out by the markers.

Each marker is directly associated with a set of crossbar switches which it serves exclusively. The registers are available in a common pool and are assigned as required to incoming calls.

The subscriber's line circuit (LC) detects the calling condition and signals to the relevant marker which causes CS to connect the calling line to a free transmission bridge (TB). This in turn cooperates with another marker to set a connection through the Register Finder (RF) to seize a free register.

Unlike the Strowger system, the number of switching stages need not be related to the exchange numbering scheme.

31.4.4 Central control (Reed systems)

The use of registers represents one application of 'common control' where one control circuit (e.g. a marker or a register) is shared by several switches.

Greater centralisation of the control, however, offers some further operational advantages. When numbering changes are made during the life of the exchange, for example, it may be possible to avoid the need to change a large number of circuits such as registers. It is also possible to employ more effective search patterns to find free paths, thus making economies possible in switch provision. For example, in register systems, the register chosen initially for the call does not necessarily have an unrestricted choice of switch paths for the forward connection of the call. It may have access only to some of the switches at the next stage and it cannot govern the choice of free switches beyond that. Although suitable free paths may exist the exchange may be unable to allocate them and the customer may fail to get his call.

In any block of switches under one control, it is only possible to set one call at a time. To extend the control across a whole exchange needs faster switches and a control speed to match. Although some central control has been used with crossbar switches, it has been more widely applied to reed relay exchanges in the public network and later to fully electronic exchanges.

The reed relays consist of sealed contact units inside an operating coil. They are interconnected to form switch matrices, similar to Figure 31.1, in which each crosspoint has its own reed relay. Being sealed and having no moving parts, they are more reliable than crossbar switches.

A typical arrangement for a reed relay exchange with central control is shown in Figure 31.16. This is the system known as TXE4 which is further described in Chapter 32.

This system shows a return to the concepts of the simple manual exchange. All terminations on the exchange are connected to the

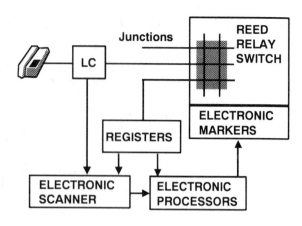

Figure 31.16   Reed electronic exchange

same set of switches and the complete operation of setting up a path is controlled by a processor, which corresponds to an operator and can observe directly the state of the whole exchange. Several processors are provided per exchange and they work independently of one another, as did the operators on a multiple position switchboard, sharing only common directory information and operating rules. Provided the processors are made powerful enough, the systems organised in this way have again begun to acquire the power and flexibility associated with an operator-controlled manual exchange.

31.4.5 Distributed control

In the Strowger system, control elements are associated with each element of the switch so that control is distributed with no centralisation. Communication between control elements is minimal, instructions being received directly from the subscriber at the relatively slow rate of ten pulses per second.

Although centralisation of the control brought many benefits it also has its problems. Exchanges grow to meet traffic demand during their 'life' and their processing power requirements grow with them. This is not easy to achieve economically if all the processing power resides in one central processor. Also, it is usual to provide at least two central processors to guard against failure yet doubling the capacity in this way is wasteful.

Various architectures have, therefore, been devised which retain the essential functional centralisation of processing while allowing decentralisation of the processors themselves. This facilitates growth and permits a more economical replication strategy.

31.5 Digital switching

31.5.1 Space division and time division switching

Analogue exchanges such as Strowger, crossbar and reed relay systems employ space division switching in which a separate physical path is provided for each call and is held continuously for the exclusive use of that call for its whole duration.

Digital and other pulse modulated systems employ time division switching in which each call is provided with a path only during its allocated time slot in a continuous cycle. Each switching element or

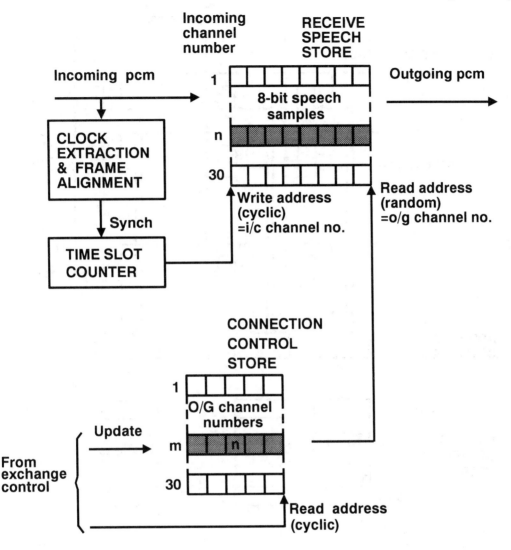

Figure 31.17 Simple time switch

crosspoint is shared by several simultaneous calls, each occupying a single time slot, in which a sample of the speech is transmitted. This sample may be a single pulse as in pulse amplitude modulated systems or a group of pulses as in pulse code modulated (pcm) systems.

Speech itself is analogue and so too are most telephones. Analogue to digital (A/D) conversion (modulation) is, therefore, necessary at some point in each connection if digital switching is to be employed. For customers connected to existing analogue local exchanges this occurs when the call first encounters a pcm transmission trunk on leaving the exchange. For customers connected to a digital local exchange it is necessary to provide the A/D conversion on each line. The cost of this conversion constitutes a major part of the exchange cost but is amply compensated for by the overall economy of digital switching and the performance advantages in the transmission network.

The European standard is for speech encoded in 8 bit bytes at 64kbit/s. The US standard is 7 bit coding at 56kbit/s.

31.5.2 Digital tandem (transit) exchange

This interconnects transmission systems which are multiplexed in groups usually of 24 or 30 speech channels on each link. The tandem exchange has to be able to connect an incoming channel in one pcm link to an outgoing channel in another PCM link. Received speech samples must, therefore, be switched in space to the appropriate link and translated in time to the required channel time slot.

A simple time switch is shown in Figure 31.17, which provides for time slot interchange between the 30 channels of an incoming pcm circuit and the 30 channels of an outgoing circuit.

Each successive byte corresponding to a channel is written cyclically into the appropriate location in a 30 x 8 bit RAM under the control of a time slot counter synchronised with the incoming circuit clock. The contents of the store are read out to the outgoing circuit under the control of a connection store. The words in the store, which is itself addressed cyclically, identify which address in the speech store is to be addressed. If the incoming time slot counter

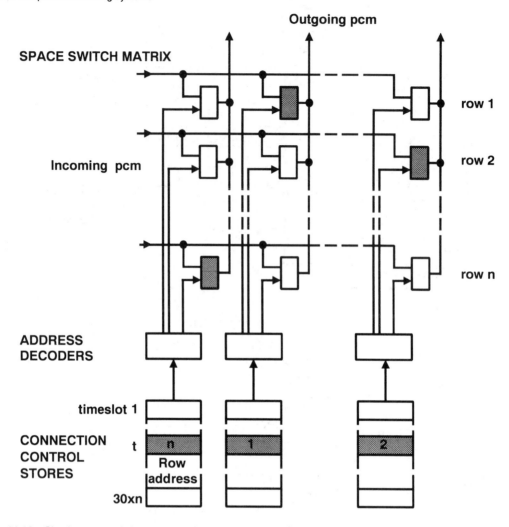

Figure 31.18 Simple space switch

and connection store run in synchronism, the outgoing circuit carries a similar multiplex to the incoming circuit but with the timeslots in a different order as determined by the contents of the connection store. In practice, the connection store may have a different speed or a different number of channels (words) from the incoming circuit.

Practical PCM systems employ additional channels for signalling and framing purposes. These can be extracted for use by the exchange control by providing additional RAM addresses from which they are read out on to a circuit connected to the exchange control processor. Each incoming circuit, therefore, requires 32 x 8 bit RAM addresses.

For large exchanges, each time switch serves a group of say 32 incoming circuits using 1024 RAM addresses. The connection store then runs at 32 times the incoming multiplex data rate to interleave all 30 x 32 speech channels on a single high speed highway to the next switching stage in the exchange.

A simple TDM space switch is shown in Figure 31.18 consisting of a matrix in which the crosspoints are electronic gates controlled by a connection store. Each incoming timeslot on each incoming circuit is switched individually to the appropriate outgoing circuit,

in accordance with the addresses stored in the space switch connection store.

A complete tandem exchange might use a time switch, like Figure 31.17, to connect each incoming circuit to a row in a matrix, like Figure 31.18. The verticals of the matrix could be the outgoing circuits but are more usually highways connected to a time switch associated with each outgoing trunk group. This arrangement is shown in Figure 31.19 and is known as time-space-time (TST) switching.

If the internal exchange bit rate is high enough to interleave all the incoming channels on to a single highway, no space switch is required. Each cross-office timeslot corresponds to a unique outgoing circuit/timeslot combination so no outgoing time switch is required either. Allocation of highway timeslots to outgoing channels is achieved by gating on a fixed pattern of strobe clock pulses. This is sometimes known as TS switching, the output gating being regarded as a 'space' (S) switching stage. It is also sometimes called memory switching. The size of exchange is limited by the available technology since RAM size and speed requirements are proportional to the number of channels provided across the exchange. The

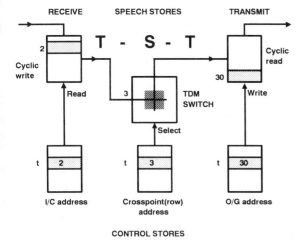

Figure 31.19 T - S - T switch

continuous evolution of l.s.i. performance makes this technique increasingly attractive. Larger exchanges can be constructed by interconnecting separate TS stages.

One other possible configuration is space-time-space (STS). This was used for some early designs when the only available time switching technology was to insert expensive time delay elements in the speech path.

The arrangements described above carry speech in one direction only. All 'receive' channels are connected to one side of the switch, regardless of whether the circuits are incoming or outgoing in the traffic sense and all 'transmit' channels are connected to the other side. Each call requires transmission in each direction and these two paths can occupy the same crosspoint in the space switch but at different time slots, usually 180 degrees out of phase. Separate time switches must be provided in each direction of transmission.

31.5.3   Digital local exchange

The switching networks in Section 31.5.2 provide only for the distribution of calls from the inlets to an equal number of outlets through the same number of links. In practical exchanges, it is only necessary to provide as many paths through the switching network as the number of calls which are expected to be in progress at one time. (See also Section 31.3.)

The concentration of lines on to a smaller number of paths or trunks is provided in the form of an additional time switching stage. The number of available time slots to the main switch is less than the total number of input time slots and store locations in the concentrator speech stores they serve. This might consist typically of up to 16 groups of 256 lines, each written cyclically into a 256 word store but with only 256 timeslots available for allocation to the acyclic read out from all these stores.

Telephone customers' lines are generally on individual pairs employing analogue transmission. The interface to the analogue customer's line includes certain functions which require voltage and power levels incompatible with the digital concentrator switch and which, therefore, have to be provided at the individual line circuit (line card). The line interface functions are generally referred to as the Borscht functions:

Battery feed to line.
Overvoltage protection.
Ringing current injection and ring trip detection.
Supervision (on-hook/off-hook detection).
Codec for analogue to digital conversion.
Hybrid for two-wire to four-wire conversion.
Test access to line and associated line circuit.

The connection between the concentration stage and the main switching stage is a pcm multiplex and very suitable for connection over an external transmission line. This is not true of analogue exchanges where the connection consists of a pair of wires per link (channel).

Digital exchanges are, therefore, particularly suited to provision as a single large central switch serving a number of remote concentrators.

31.6   Stored program control

31.6.1   Processors

The functions of a digital exchange switch, described above, need processor control to interpret the connections required in terms of signals received and connection store contents to be maintained.

One advantage of central control by processors, is that facility changes may be effected by changes to a few processors instead of many registers. This advantage is further increased if the processors are based on 'software' programs. This method of operation is known as stored program control (spc) and the exchange shown in Figure 31.16 has a large part of its logic contained in stored program. It is possible, in the limit, to convert into processor software almost all of the logical functions of the exchange, including signalling.

The advantages are that the variety of hardware may be minimised, so easing production and stocking problems, and that facility changes may be readily accomplished. Disadvantages are that software development can be exceedingly complex and that real time problems may occur.

31.6.2   Software

The essence of spc is that it is software driven. The functionality of the exchange control processors can be changed to suit different hardware configurations (number and type of lines, traffic etc.) for different installations and growth during the life of the system. The features offered can also develop as requirements change over time (e.g. tariff structures, dialling codes) without major hardware replacements.

This software must, of course, meet the same standards of reliability and availability as those demanded of the switch and processor hardware. Software does not wear out like hardware. Failures can only occur due to design faults (bugs) which have not been detected during the design and development phase. The number of combinations of external inputs and system states in programs of this size makes it impossible to guarantee the complete absence of such bugs.

To provide some degree of fault tolerance, it is first necessary to design the software in discrete modules with defined interfaces between them. This enables more comprehensive testing of possible combinations within each module than would be possible on the complete system. It also allows checks to be applied to input and output conditions at the interfaces. These checks can either be used to trigger the hardware changeover mechanism or to reinitialise the software module to an acceptable state.

The modular design of software also facilitates the evolution of features during the life of the system and the implementation of distributed control.

The primary function of the software is to set up and clear down calls on demand. Calls arise concurrently in real time and in a random manner. In addition, the software is required to carry out diagnostic checks on the hardware, provide statistical data on traffic and performance and provide call records for billing purposes. Separate modules are provided for each of the functions in the applications software. The operating system schedules the use of the hardware resources by these application programs, storing the status of all registers etc. when a program is deactivated and restoring the same state when it is reactivated. This multiprogramming technique enables high priority tasks (e.g. call set up) to be given precedence over lower priority tasks (e.g. statistics).

Figure 31.20 shows in simplified form a typical modular break down of the software in an spc exchange. The line scan program continuously updates a tabular store of the state of each line termination (e.g. free, busy, calling etc.) and alerts the central call routing software to connection requests. The latter validates the request against a pre-determined class of service for the termination and receives called number data from the line scanner or the signalling software, depending on the type of termination. The received digits are compared with the stored routing data (translation table) to enable the switch to be controlled via the connection control stores (Figures 31.17 to 31.19). Exchange staff can interrogate the status of the processor and update the routing and class of service tables through the Man Machine Interface (MMI).

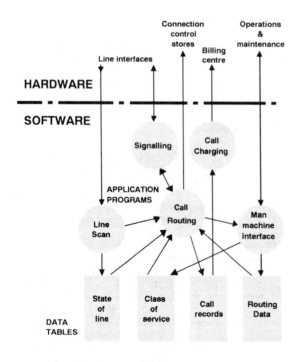

Figure 31.20 SPC software structure

31.6.3 Network aspects

The introduction of spc has enabled electronic exchanges to provide customer and administration features not readily available with earlier control systems. Examples include the ability to transfer calls at will and allow calls to wait on a busy line. Where new features are self contained within an exchange they can be introduced by installing a new build of software. If the operation of a feature requires identical operation at all exchanges, the practical problems of modifying them all at once become immense.

One solution is to download new programs, routing data etc. remotely via data links and to site the operations and maintenance terminals at a central location to serve a group of exchanges. Central access to the databases and processors of all the exchanges permits short term as well as long term changes to be made to facilities and routing. This is known as Network Management and enables plant failures to be identified, located and traffic to be re-routed around congestion bottlenecks. A further development of the centralised control principle is the concept of the Intelligent Network in which individual exchange processors interrogate a remote database for instructions on how to process particular types of call, or route such calls to a central service provider.

31.7 Operational security

Unlike many other systems which can plan for regular downtime for maintenance, telephone switching systems are required to provide virtually uninterrupted service 24 hours a day, seven days a week, year in – year out, to tens of thousands of customers (and junctions). At the same time they must be adaptable to growth and operational requirements. Occasional faults are, of course, inevitable and the system design must allow for this, so that a fault does not result in loss of service to any significant number of customers. It is better for a fault to temporarily reduce the grade of service to all customers rather than to deny service entirely to a smaller number. As a result, various system architectures have evolved.

In electromechanical systems, each call follows a path wholly exclusive to itself, sufficient paths being provided to carry the predicted traffic. Failure in any path, therefore, reduces the grade of service to all terminations normally having access to it, but since other paths are available, service is not wholly cut off to any one. Electromechanical systems are, therefore, inherently fault-tolerant as regards path switching and, for example, Strowger type selectors incorporate their own local control which reacts to loop-disconnect signalling over the path concerned.

In electronic (common control) systems, security is achieved by building in redundancy and by the use of inbuilt check circuits and fault detection which will both route calls round a faulty condition and also indicate the presence of the fault so that maintenance action can correct it.

In the switching area, security is normally provided by giving any termination access to multiple paths through the network. A particular example of this is the use of sectionalisation where the switching network is divided into planes of switching, operating in parallel and all accessible to all terminations. Thus a fault affecting any one plane of switching will not cause loss of service to any terminations, the traffic being carried by the remaining planes, albeit at a slightly reduced grade of service.

In the control area, security is normally provided by replication. In its simplest form this would mean a single duplicated control unit. The two units can operate:

1. In parallel with a fault cutting out the defective unit.
2. As worker and spare with automatic changeover in the event of a fault.
3. Alternatively under the control of a time cycle.

However, except in very small systems, a single duplicated control is unlikely to be adequate and a number of alternative options are available:

1. Triplication, where three identical units are used in parallel with majority decision equipment on the outputs.
2. One-in-N Sparing, where a number of similar equipments are involved and one (or more) spares are provided such that, in the event of a fault, one of the spares may be switched into service in place of the faulty equipment.
3. Load sharing, where a number of similar equipments operate in parallel each carrying a proportion of the traffic. In the event of a fault, the equipment concerned is taken out of service with the traffic being carried by the remainder at a reduced grade of service.

In practice, some combination of these options is often used with the overall control area being sub-divided dependent on the function to be performed.

In the case of traffic dependent equipment such as registers, these are normally dimensioned to carry the predicted busy hour traffic at the required grade of service in the presence of one or more faults, depending on the predicted fault rate.

Whichever method is employed to provide the operational security, it is essential that adequate check circuits and routines are provided to detect the faults together with appropriate means for reporting them (e.g. lamp display, audible alarm or print out) such that the fault can be remedied within the mean time between failures (MTBF) for the equipment concerned.

31.8 Bibliography

Atkinson, J. (1950) *Telephony*, Pitman.

Bear, D. (1988) *Principles of Telecommunication Traffic Engineering*, Peter Peregrinus.

Berkeley, G.S. (1949) *Traffic and Trunking Principles in Automatic Telephony*, Benn.

Briley, B.E. (1983) *Telephone Switching*, Addison Wesley.

Hills, M.T. and Kano, S. (1976) *Programming electronic switching systems*, Peter Peregrinus.

Hughes, C.J. (1986) Switching — State of the art, *British Telecom Tech.*, **4**, (1) and (2).

Redmill, F.J. and Valdar, A.R. (1990) *SPC digital telephone exchanges*, Peter Peregrinus.

Smith, S.F. (1978) *Telephony and Telegraphy*, 3rd edn, Oxford University Press.

Takamura, S. et. al. (1979) *Software design for electronic switching systems*, Peter Peregrinus.

32

Telephone exchanges

D G Bryan
DFH CEng FIEE
Telecommunications Consultant
(Sections 32.2 - 32.4)

Kjell Persson
Ericsson Ltd
(Sections 32.8 - 32.10)

Eur. Ing. S F Smith
BSc (Eng) CEng FIEE
Northern Telecom
(Sections 32.2 - 32.4, 32.11 - 32.19)

M Smouts
Alcatel Bell Telephone
(Sections 32.5 - 32.7)

Contents

32.1 Introduction

Chapter 31 introduced the principles of switching systems. There are currently many switches being used throughout the world. A large number of these are analogue, although they are gradually being converted over to digital switching systems.

In this chapter some of the switches in current use are described. It is not the intention to provide a comprehensive description of these switches, but rather to cover their architecture, and show how they implement the basic switching functions. Because of space limitations only a few of the many major switches are described. These are the TXE analogue switch from STC, part of Northern Telecom; the System 12 switch, originally from ITT but now being developed by Alcatel Bell; the AXE switch from Ericsson; and the DMS switch from Northern Telecom.

32.2 TXE analogue exchanges

The TXE2 and TXE4 analogue exchanges are used in the U.K. for small and large exchanges respectively. These systems employ a switching matrix having a similar structure to crossbar systems but using reed relays for the crosspoints. These have the advantage of being sealed against corrosion and dirt and operate in only about 2ms, making them more amenable to electronic control than Strowger or crossbar switches. They also have a separate operating coil for each crosspoint enabling switch sizes to be optimised for system requirements.

The higher speed of operation and the use of electronic control permits greater use of self checking features to improve reliability and quality of service. The greater use of electronics enables these systems to benefit from advancing technology in that field, in terms of size and versatility in the provision of customer facilities.

32.3 The TXE2 system

TXE2 is designed for use as a small local exchange. Its capacity is limited basically by the number of busy hour calls it can handle. The theoretical maximum capacity of a TXE2 unit is 240 erlangs of total traffic (i.e. originating, terminating and tandem) and the multiple is determined by the total traffic per line; typically a single unit of TXE2 can serve from two to three thousand lines. The lower limit is basically an economic one and could be about 200 lines in circumstances where the growth rate is fairly large.

Normally a TXE2 will be installed as a single unit within the stated capacities for lines and traffic. Should either of these grow beyond the capacity of the single unit, a second unit may be coupled to the first to double the exchange capacity. In exceptional circumstances, growth beyond the capacity of two exchange units could be met by using unit switching equipment to combine three or more exchange units.

The TXE2 system may be divided into three main areas:

1. The switching area comprising three stages A, B and C in the outward direction and four stages D, C, B and A in the inward direction.
2. The supervisory and register area comprising outgoing junction, incoming junction and local supervisory relay sets, together with a common pool of registers serving all three types.
3. The control area comprising calling number identification, called number marker and call control equipment.

32.3.1 The switching area

The switching network is a general purpose network as shown in simplified form in Figure 32.1. The sizes of the various switches can be varied to meet differing requirements of lines and traffic but are

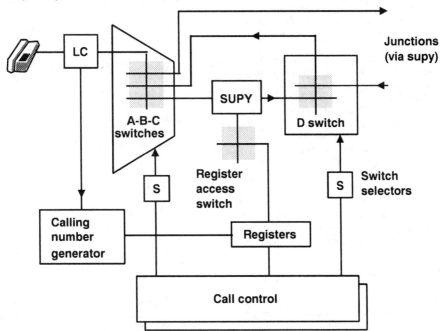

Figure 32.1 TXE2 system (Compare this with Figure 31.14)

multiples of a standard switching module comprising 25 crosspoints arranged in a 5 x 5 reed relay matrix. The A switch serves to concentrate customers' lines onto B switch inlets and the number may be varied to ensure optimum loading. The B and C switches are interconnected to obtain full accessibility between every B switch inlet and every C switch outlet. The D switch is provided to ensure a good grade of service on terminating calls without upsetting the modular construction of the A, B and C switches. All crosspoints have four reed inserts.

32.3.2 The supervisory and register area

Only three basic types of supervisory are needed although variations may be introduced to meet particular requirements. Each type contains a transmission and signalling bridge and appropriate logic circuits.

The outgoing supervisories provide facilities for routing dial pulse signals to a register, for onward transmission to other exchanges, for the receipt of called subscriber answer signals and service tones. They also generate metering signals in response to answering or, where appropriate, repeat metering from the called exchange.

The incoming and local supervisories are also arranged to receive dial pulse signals and to route these to a register. Provision is made for ringing the called subscriber's bell, the transmission of ringing tone to the caller and detecting the answer signal.

The registers associated with the supervisories are general purpose registers. Access is obtained via a register access switch (reed relay). The registers may be arranged to receive and store either dial pulse signals or multi-frequency coded push button signals.

32.3.3 The control area

The control apparatus is common to the exchange and is shown in block schematic form in Figure 32.1. It is duplicated to ensure continuous service in the event of faults. The two controls are independent and are used alternately with a periodic changeover to ensure that both controls are exercised and that faults will not go undetected for long periods.

When a customer or incoming junction originates a demand for access to a register, this demand is first routed to a calling number generator which identifies the calling line or junction and stores this number in a free register. The register then takes over and applies for access to call control to set up a connection from the calling line or junction to itself. The register marks all free supervisories of the first choice route and, simultaneously, sends the calling line's number to the called line marker. This decodes the number and marks the line concerned. The path selection apparatus now selects and establishes a path between the calling line and a free supervisory with access to the register already allotted.

This method of control greatly improves flexibility in use, since it takes advantage of the high speed of the system and permits originating calls to be released and set up again to a different point within the inter-digital pause and without the knowledge of the caller.

32.3.4 System operation

Each customer's line is connected via the MDF to a line circuit providing the exchange line termination. Junctions are terminated on supervisory equipments. Each line circuit or incoming supervisory is given an identifying code known as the equipment number (EN) which indicates its location on the equipment racks.

To originate a call, the customer loops his line and causes his directory number (DN) to be inserted in a free register. If there are no free registers, the customer receives equipment engaged tone (EET) and is required to make another attempt later.

The allotted register applies to the call control for the selection of a free supervisory which, when found, causes the register to be connected via the register access switch, the chosen supervisory and the C, B and A switches to the calling line.

Initially, the allotted supervisory may be either an O/G junction supervisory or an O/E supervisory, depending on the facilities required and the distribution of traffic. For example, if the majority of the traffic is to the local tandem exchange, an O/G supervisory on this route will be the first choice. If there are no free supervisories on this route, a second O/G group or O/E supervisory is allotted instead.

When the register sets up the initial connection, it determines from the class of service signal received if any special facilities are required, for example if the call is from a public call box. When the facilities have been provided, dial tone is returned and dialling can proceed.

From the digits received, the register determines whether the call is:

1. An own exchange call.
2. A local call to or through the tandem exchange.
3. A long distance (trunk) call.

Assuming the tandem route is the first choice, in case 1, the register proceeds after the first digit or, in the case of a linked numbering scheme, a later digit to release the initial set up, to call in a free O/E supervisory and to reset the call, all during the inter-digital pause. The calling customer is not affected.

In case 2, as soon as sufficient digits have been received to indicate that the call is to the tandem exchange, the register is released and dialling continues over the already established path.

In case 3, the call will be released and reset to a supervisory in the trunk route.

Because all calls are connected from a supervisory to a customer's line, terminating calls are set up in a manner broadly similar to originating calls. Typically when a call arrives on an I/C supervisory, its terminal identifying number is generated by the calling number generator and placed in a free register which then proceeds to connect itself to the indicated supervisory. When the wanted number has been received by the register it applies to the decoder to set up an equivalent EN marking. Connection from the incoming supervisory then proceeds, as already described, except that an additional stage of switching (the D stage) is involved.

32.4 The TXE4 system

TXE4 is designed for local exchanges ranging from 2000 to 40000 lines and with calling rates from 0.02 to 0.35 erlangs per line. The system is readily extensible up to an overall limit of approximately 10000 erlangs of bothway traffic.

The system uses a reed relay switching network with electronic stored program control. The fundamental concept underlying the design is that it should consist of an assembly of a limited number of types of sub-system, hardware or software, arranged so that the exchange capacity in terms of connections, traffic or facilities can be extended by simple addition of similar subsystems. This arrangement illustrated in Figure 32.2 also ensures that exchange security is safeguarded in the event of failure of any subsystem without the

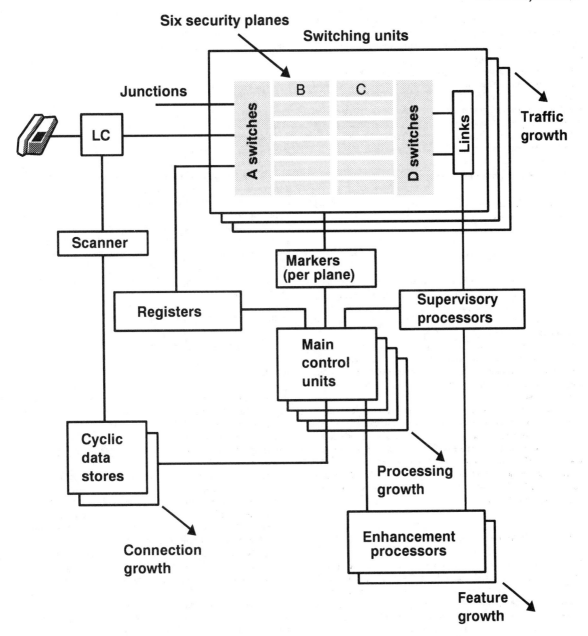

Figure 32.2 TXE4 system (Compare this with Figure 31.16)

need for interchange of information or external monitoring of the working of each subsystem.

32.4.1 The switching network

The switching network consists of a number of separate but identical units up to a maximum of 48. Each unit handles a fixed amount of bothway traffic and the number of units provided for any particular application is, therefore, determined by the total traffic (originating, terminating and tandem) to be handled. The network is arranged as a three stage link system folded upon itself via an additional switching stage, so that connection between any two terminations can be completed by the operation of seven crosspoints.

The BC stages of each switching unit are sectionalised to provide a number of identical sub-units (6 or 8) which can be considered as being in planes on top of one another. This concept of sectionalisation provides security in the switching network, since a fault affecting any one sub-unit will not mean the loss of service to any customers but only a slightly reduced grade of service.

Customers, junctions and other circuits are connected to the network via A switches, separate switches being provided for customers and junctions. The traffic concentration within the A switch can be adjusted to match the calling rate of the terminations to the fixed capacity of the switching unit. On the opposite side of the BC networks, interconnection is achieved by means of a fourth stage (D) of switching and groups of link circuits which provide local supervision where necessary.

The adoption of a general purpose switching network, as described, avoids the need for auxiliary switches for the connection of registers and other circuits. All such peripheral circuits are terminated on the general purpose network via junction A switches. Any peripheral may be associated with any termination by a path (or paths) through the network. This principle leads to the concept of serial connection of switching paths known as serial trunking.

32.4.2   The control equipment

The control equipment supervises the setting up of all calls through the switching network.

32.4.2.1   *Cyclic data store and scanning*

The data stores provide common central storage for the exchange data relating to customers, junctions, code translations and routing information etc. The stores consist of read only shift registers which continuously circulate data and present this on common highways to all main control units.

Associated with the data store is scanning equipment, including additional storage for maintaining a record of the state-of-line information for customers. This is synchronised with the main data store so that all information relating to a particular termination is available simultaneously.

The basic store module provides for 5760 customers and a proportion of incoming and outgoing circuits. Up to seven data stores can be provided in an exchange giving a maximum size of over 40000 lines. For security, the complete shift register data files are duplicated and parity coding is used to enable single errors to be detected and corrected without any effect on exchange operation. A complete backup store is also provided on magnetic tape and this can be used to reload the data files.

32.4.2.2   *Main control units and registers*

The main control units are special purpose processors employing stored program control techniques. Up to 20 of these units may be provided dependent on the number of calls to be handled. The processors operate simultaneously but independently in a load sharing mode so that, in the event of a fault, the processor concerned is busied out and the traffic is distributed over the remaining processors at only a slightly reduced grade of service.

The overall operation of the main control processor and the manipulation of the information within it is controlled by a stored program held on read only memories. The use of non-volatile memory for program storage gives complete security against malicious or accidental corruption of the program. Changes are not required in service since the essential variable parameters are located in the data store with keyboard access.

Registers are processed in groups by the main control units, so that dialled digits from the calling termination, which are detected by the register, are stored in a common working store within the main processor. The register itself contains only the limited amount of equipment required to count the dial pulses under microprocessor control and to supervise the call during set up. Both 10 pps dial pulses and MF key signals can be accepted. The registers are

connected to the periphery of the network via junction A switches, so that all registers are fully available to all customers and a standard setting up procedure can be used.

32.4.2.3   *Interrogator markers and supervisory processors*

Interrogators and markers are provided for each sub-unit of the switching network, although each marker can control up to five interrogators on the same plane. When path selection is required, the main control unit signals to all interrogators through their controlling markers and the free paths available are identified. The main control unit then selects the most appropriate route available and instructs the particular markers to operate the crosspoints within the selected sub-units and also to allocate the required type of link circuit for the connection.

The supervisory processor controls both the bridge link used for supervising local and terminating calls and also the outgoing junction circuit used for supervising outgoing calls. Each supervisory processor is triplicated for security and can control over 6000 connections at a time, serving 16 switching units. Data is obtained by monitoring the highways between the main control unit and the markers. The supervisory processor is program controlled using reprogrammable read only memories.

32.4.3   System operation

32.4.3.1   *Connection to a register*

When a call is originated either from a customer or an incoming junction, the calling condition is detected via the scanning by one of the main control units (MCU) which has been pre-allotted. At the same time, the equipment number, directory number and class of service relating to the calling line, available on the cyclic store highways, are stored in the MCU.

Under the control of its program, the MCU analyses the class of service of the calling line to determine if any special requirements apply, such as calls barred. If the call is to proceed, the MCU initiates a search over all registers available to it on the cyclic store highways. A free register is selected and its equipment number stored by the MCU in readiness for setting up the connection.

The MCU then seizes the common highways to the interrogator markers when these become free, thus busying them against seizure by other MCU. The equipment numbers of the calling line and register are then sent to all interrogators to identify free paths through the switching network. Interrogators with no free paths available release. Each of the others identifies the optimum path through its own sub-unit and signals this to the MCU which selects one of these for the actual connection. The appropriate markers are then instructed to set up a path. The register will signal to the MCU that the path has been completed and the MCU can then release. Should this path not be completed successfully, a second attempt is made automatically and the identity of the faulty path is printed out.

When sufficient information has been received by the register, the MCU is recalled and examines the dialled information to establish the destination of the call.

32.4.3.2   *Local call*

For a local call, the MCU stores the directory number of the called line. It then inspects the output of the cyclic store highways until by comparison it sees the same digits that it has stored.

At the same time, the state-of-line information indicates whether the wanted line is free or busy. If it is free its equipment number and class of service are stored by the MCU, which will then apply with the equipment numbers of both calling and called lines to the interrogator markers for final path selection. This is done in the same way as for the connection from calling line to register. Again, the successful completion of the path will be detected by the register, after which the original path between calling line and register is released.

Should the called line appear busy when it is scanned, the MCU immediately hunts for a free tone circuit and connects this to the calling line via the network to return busy tone.

32.4.3.3   *Outgoing call*

When the MCU examines the dialled digits received by the register and identifies that the call is outgoing from the exchange, it will, where appropriate, apply with the initial digits to the cyclic store for a code translation and will store any routing digits which may be returned together with the identity of the route and, where required, the number length.

The MCU then carries out a further search over the cyclic stores to identify a free junction within the required route and when this is found by comparison, its identify is stored within the MCU. Two paths are now set up in sequence in the same way as already described, one between the sending side of the register and the selected outgoing junction, and the other between the calling line and the outgoing junction, the latter path having a split function in the link circuit. The MCU then instructs the register to send the appropriate routing digits over the junction, followed by the numerical digits identifying the wanted customer. When this has been done, the split is removed from the final conversation path and the connections between the calling customer and the register and the register and the outgoing junction are released.

32.4.3.4   *Supervision*

Once a connection has been set up, the MCU is released for the setting up of other calls and the established connection is monitored and supervised by the supervisory processing unit (SPU) in conjunction with either a bridge link circuit for locally terminating calls or an outgoing junction circuit for outgoing calls. The bridge link circuits apply the necessary ringing current and tones required.

32.4.3.5   *Feature evolution*

The TXE4 system provides service to some eight million lines, approximately a third of the U.K. network and it has been necessary over the years to enhance the features provided to match those provided by the newer digital systems. This has been achieved by the addition of specific functional processors interconnected by an Ethernet local area network and connected to the TXE4 MCU and SPU.

This arrangement provides call logging facilities including both bulk and itemised billing; fast call set up using Common Channel Signalling System No.7 to other TXE4 or digital exchanges; and centralised management of the operation and maintenance features of the exchange. It also permits the provision of supplementary subscriber services, both exchange and network based, and including the possibility of digital access to voice and data services. This

enhancement process, which will make TXE4 exchanges almost indistinguishable to customers from fully digital systems, is still in progress and is likely to continue for the life of the system which is expected to continue well into the twenty-first century.

32.5   System 12 overview

32.5.1   Introduction

The System 12 functions are concentrated in different module types which are connected to a digital switching network. Each modular function is controlled by its own processor. Therefore the System 12 switching system is a modular system with fully distributed control, using the latest microprocessor technology and large memory capacities. The switching network control functions in System 12 are dispersed throughout the network. This results in an end-controlled network arrangement in which the several individual control elements (microprocessors) associated with different network ports are able to set up digital paths through the network simultaneously without a need for some central network controller.

The distributed control implementation in System 12 results in a number of system characteristics representing direct benefits to both network operators and users, e.g. robustness against total system failure, capability for smooth incremental growth both in traffic and control capacity, high degree of system uniformity leading to the need for only a very limited set of printed board types to build up an exchange. All these aspects make System 12 an outstanding product in the world of telecommunications.

Finally, good indications exist that for the next major evolutionary step in switching, the so called Broadband ISDN, fully distributed control systems based on end-controlled switching networks are the obvious solution. In this sense, System 12 is already prepared for this transition.

32.5.2   System 12 evolution

The studies, which lead to the System 12 configuration, were based on two main premises:

1. Digital systems should from the start be designed not just for voice traffic but also for an ISDN environment.
2. New semiconductor technology (LSI, VLSI) became available during the 1980s providing ample computing power and massive memory storage capability.

During this period also the end controlled digital switching network (DSN) was conceived and its basic LSI component (switch port) designed.

By the end of 1981 a first system was installed in the Belgian network and the next year 4 additional System 12 exchanges were installed in Germany.

Subsequently, System 12 product versions were quickly introduced in several countries in parallel, first in various Alcatel n.v. home markets, then in export. The System 12's novel attractive architecture aroused interest with many telephone companies and administrations throughout the world. By 1991 over 15 million equivalent lines of System 12 awards have been accumulated from 22 countries.

System 12's distributed architecture allows it to cover a very broad spectrum of exchange applications with respect to both size and network hierarchical level. Its expandable digital switching network and distributed control provide economical solutions for exchanges ranging from a few hundred of lines up to over 100000 lines. For transit exchanges up to 60000 trunks may be handled. With respect to network levels, System 12 may be applied as local, tandem, national and international transit exchange. Also combined local transit exchanges are possible.

The list of individual exchange sites clearly shows the variety of applications: from small and large locals via numerous transits and combined exchanges up to several international transit exchanges including the highest possible level.

32.5.3 Developments and future

The digital switching System 12 has the flexibility that is necessary to allow economic extension in terms of the number of lines and new services. It also offers high fault tolerance and rapid isolation and identification of faults.

Since the initial introduction of System 12 in public telephone networks, the range of its features and facilities has been significantly expanded:

1. To extend the application range to very small sizes as required for rural networks, a Remote Subscriber Unit (RSU) was developed.
2. For national and international transit exchanges, a fully featured Operator Position System called 12SO, was developed.
3. As required for several advanced features and in view of the quickly approaching ISDN in many networks, the CCITT No.7 common channel signalling system was introduced in System 12.
4. A further enhancement was the development of a centralised operations and maintenance facility for System 12 networks, called the Network Service Centre (NSC). The NSC greatly benefits from System 12's CCITT No.7 capability since the No.7 links provide the basic means of communication between the System 12 exchanges and the NSC.

Additional proof of System 12's flexibility is its application in various specialised configurations or entire specialised networks as used by governments and large institutions. Examples are exchanges which deal specifically with freephone service, signal transfer points for CCITT No.7 Common Channel Signalling, wideband System 12 exchanges handling up to 30 x 64kbit/s connections and cellular radio switching applications (also called mobilophone system).

Development of ISDN feature capability for System 12 was started some years ago and already System 12 ISDN field trials were held in a number of countries.

A feature which has recently been gaining importance in Europe is Centrex (see Chapter 35). A combined ISDN/Centrex package is seen as particularly attractive for business customers. ISDN Centrex features for System 12 are presently under development and the initial Centrex installations are already serving analogue subscribers.

Along with the System 12 ISDN product version, a combined ISDN/ Centrex package will be available.

32.6 System 12 architecture

The System 12 flexible architecture, which allows extensions and new services to be introduced as required, can be used for the entire range of exchange applications:

1. Rural areas: remote subscriber units and small exchange configurations: up to 488 lines.
2. Urban and metropolitan areas: medium to large scale local exchanges: 512 to over 100000 lines.
3. Toll exchanges: up to 60000 trunk terminations.
4. Transit applications: tandem, toll, international, and inter-continental exchanges.
5. Network Service Centres (NSCs).

All exchanges throughout the range provide a full set of modern services and features to subscribers and network operators.

System 12 independent exchanges are designed to cover both individual and multi-exchange network applications. They provide a full range of maintenance and administrative features including the possibility of remoting man machine communication terminals or connecting the exchange to a Network Service Centre (NSC). Figure 32.3 shows the modular structure of System 12.

32.6.1 System 12 hardware configuration

A System 12 exchange comprises a Digital Switching Network (DSN) and a range of modules and Auxiliary Control Elements (ACEs) which perform all the exchange control and signal processing.

Each module comprises a standard Terminal Control Element (TCE) and a terminal which is specific to the function of the module.

Figure 32.4 illustrates the Terminal interface configuration.

32.6.1.1 *Digital Switching Network (DSN)*

The DSN is a combined time and space switching network that provides time and space selection at each of this switching nodes.

The DSN comprises standard Digital Switching Elements (DSEs), which are used for all stages of switching.

32.6.1.2 *Control Elements (CE)*

All CEs have similar hardware comprising a microprocessor, with associated memory and a Terminal Interface (TI).

Most important hardware modules are described in the following sections.

32.6.1.3 *Analogue Subscriber Module (ASM)*

The ASM, which can be equipped as a paired module, provides the interface for up to 128 subscriber lines which are terminated by line circuits.

The module is controlled of two TCEs which are connected in a dual controlled pair configuration (also called the crossover mode).

32.6.1.4 *Digital Trunk Module (DTM)*

The Digital Trunk Module (DTM), performs the preprocessing and control for a single 30 or 31 channel PCM trunk.

The DTM converts the various PCM formats which can be used on a digital trunk to the standard format used in System 12 exchanges.

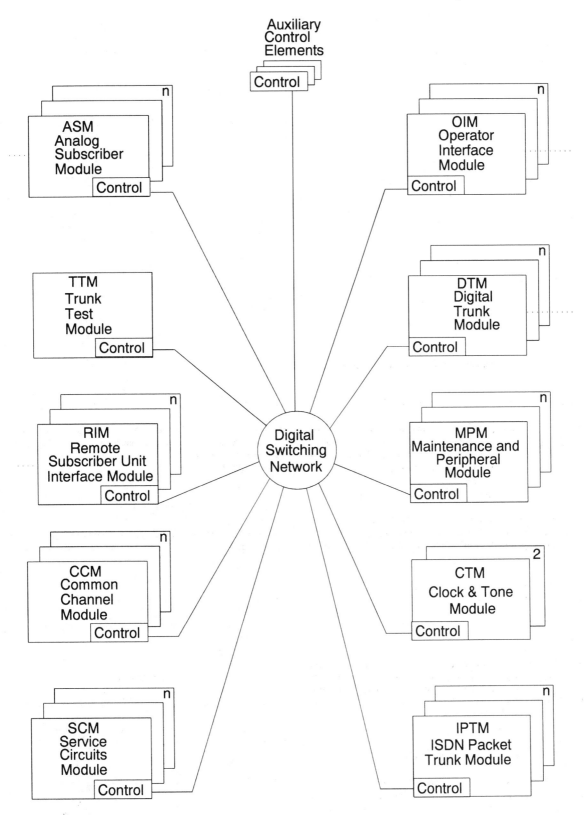

Figure 32.3 System 12 modules

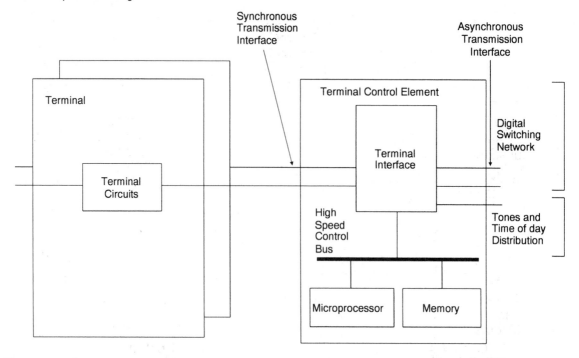

Figure 32.4 General structure of a Terminal Module

32.6.1.5 *ISDN Remote Interface Module (IRIM)*

The IRIM, which is equipped as a paired module, is similar to the DTM but is used to control Remote Subscriber Units (RSUs) and to interface them (singly or in multi-drop) to a host System 12 exchange. The lines can be analogue or ISDN lines.

32.6.1.6 *Support and Peripherals Modules (SPM)*

An SPM, comprises a Support Module (SUM) and a Computer Peripherals Module (CPM), each of which has a TCE and a terminal. Each SPM is duplicated for reliability. There are two types of SPM:

1. Maintenance SPM.
2. Administration SPM.

32.6.1.7 *Clock and Tones Module (CTM)*

The CTM, generates a clock timing signal, a range of PCM encoded audio tones and the TOD signal for distribution throughout the exchange. The outputs of the CTM, which are duplicated for reliability, are distributed to the TCEs, ACEs and DSEs via a Clock and Tones distribution (CLTD) subsystem.

32.6.1.8 *Service Circuits Module (SCM)*

The SCM, provides tone handling facilities for subscribers with push-button telephone sets and also for exchanges that use multifrequency (MF) senders and receivers for inter-exchanges signalling. Optionally, a conference call facility can be included.

32.6.1.9 *Common Channel Module (CCM)*

The Common Channel Module (CCM), performs signal processing for CCITT Number 7 Common Channel Signalling (CCS) systems. The module can be used either for purely common channel signalling or for ISDN environments.

32.6.1.10 *ISDN Subscriber Module (ISM)*

The ISDN Subscriber Module (ISM), Provides up to 64 basic access (BA) connections for ISDN subscribers or ISDN PABXs and control the handling of related ISDN calls.

32.6.1.11 *ISDN Packet Trunk Module (IPTM)*

The IPTM can perform several functions always combined with the trunk module function.
  Those functions are:

1. MTP functions for CCITT N7 signalling.
2. PRA interface.
3. X.25 DCE functions for connection to the Network Service Centre.
4. Frame handler functions for D-channel multiplexing.
5. Packet Handler interface.

32.6.1.12 *Trunk Test Module (TTM)*

The TTM provides facilities for automatic, semi-automatic and manual testing of trunk devices.

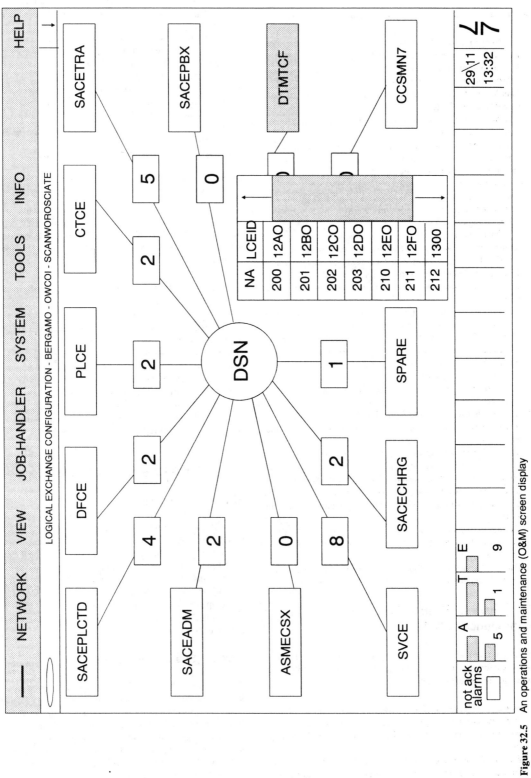

Figure 32.5 An operations and maintenance (O&M) screen display

32.6.2 System 12 general software configuration

The system 12 on-line software contains the following main areas:

1. Operating system and network handler, managing all exchange resources and control the SW in each CE.
2. Input/output software, interfaces between the application (user) software and the peripheral devices.
3. Man Machine (MMC) software provides a part of the interface between the MMC devices and the applications software.
4. Database software allows central management of data, common to a number of software modules.
5. The load and initialisation software provides initialisation and loading of software modules into all control elements during the start up or restart phase, initialisation and/or loading control of disc systems.
6. The maintenance software handles the processing of any exchange hardware and software faults to ensure the continuity of call handling operations.
7. The status and alarm software controls the status condition of terminal processors, records and displays alarm situations.
8. The Clock and Tone, calendar software contains the Clock and Tone device handler software, the associated diagnostic and routine tests, calendar scheduler handler and interactive control software.
9. The Line and Trunk Testing software gives test and maintenance facilities for subscriber and trunk lines.
10. The Call Handling and Facilities software interfaces with the other exchange to control the set up and connection of a call, through the exchange, to its destination.
11. The Signalling handling software provides an interface between the signalling systems and the call handling and facilities software.
12. The Telephonic Device and Signalling Adaption software provides the interface between the telephonic devices and the Signalling Handling software.
13. The Call Services software supports the Call Handling and Facilities software, manages the allocation of telephonic resources and it interfaces with the Database software (recalling data for prefix handling and routeing information).
14. The charging software performs call charging and accounting functions.
15. The administration software allows measurements, statistical and network management functions to be performed in an exchange.
16. Hardware and Software Extensions software enable extensions on hardware devices and updates of software functions.

32.7 System 12 operation and maintenance (O&M)

Operations and maintenance is the key to ensuring a high level of service quality. System 12 O&M facilities provide the following advantages for an administration:

1. Simple procedures for daily operations, such as line additions, trunk additions, trunk group assignments, changes, etc.
2. An effective charging system, for accurate and prompt billing, etc.
3. Easy exchange expansion or modification to satisfy increased traffic handling requirements or changing network conditions.

4. Measurement and Data collect procedures using simple Man Machine Command (MMC).
5. Efficient diagnostics and repair procedures, normally involving the replacement of a printed board assembly (PBA), which gives a low mean time to repair.
6. Minimum physical contact with the equipment, made possible by the use of the MMC facility. This facility is used to provide most of the O&M related functions, e.g. subscriber administration, corrective maintenance.
7. Easy modification of exchange data (routeing tables etc.) by the use of MMC commands. Modified tables etc. are automatically stored in back up mass memory (e.g. disc) to ensure that an updated copy of the data is loaded into the memory of a processor if a reload is done.

New systems were developed to ease O&M tasks, as follows.

32.7.1 The Network Service Centre

It can be directly integrated with a System 12 exchange or used in a standalone mode. It is constructed from standard System 12 modules, CCITT No.7 signalling modules, and X.25 packet interface modules. Generally a network service centre is connected to a number of exchanges via CCITT No.7 links.

32.7.2 Advanced Terminal for Operation and Maintenance (ATOM)

A user friendly man machine interface has been provided by means of PC programmes called ATOM.

This terminal provides functional screens representing parts of the system functions like e.g. system diagram, trunking diagram, floor plan etc. which allow by clicking of the mouse to instruct the system which function has to be performed.

Also for an easier overview of the exchange performance, post processing function are performed to display information like statistics, received error reports, alarms etc. (see Figure 32.5).

32.8 The AXE system concept

32.8.1 Introduction

The AXE system from Ericsson is widely deployed throughout the world. Today, AXE exchanges are in service in local, long distance, international and cellular mobile networks in some 80 countries.

AXE supports a complete range of telecommunication network applications. It is fully digital and designed to minimise overall network and handling costs. Stored Programme Control provides for an open ended supply of new features and services.

A unique modularity structure is the corner-stone of the AXE system concept.

32.8.2 System structure

The philosophy behind AXE is embodied in one word — modularity. Modularity means easy handling and ability to adapt to the changing world of telecommunications. Throughout the system, in both hardware and software, modularity is the guiding principle. This facilitates software and hardware design, system upgrades, system extensions and multi-functionality in network applications.

The AXE architecture is a five level hierarchy, each level made up of specific modules, as in Figure 32.6.

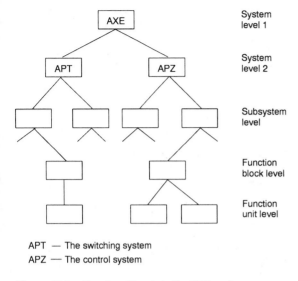

APT — The switching system
APZ — The control system

Figure 32.6 Functional levels in the AXE system

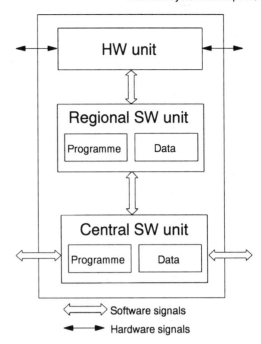

⇔ Software signals
◄—► Hardware signals

Figure 32.7 Functional block structure

32.8.3 Functional modularity

Rapid developments in electronics technologies and of telecommunication networks have imposed specific requirements on switching systems. Functional modularity is a prerequisite if the system is to be introduced easily and effectively in a variety of different and changing environments. AXE is defined in terms of functions; what they do rather than how they are to be implemented. Functions will not change in the future; implementation techniques may.

The entire AXE system is a set of specified functions, implemented in modules, or function blocks. These function blocks are grouped in subsystems. Each function block and subsystem is considered as a 'black box' at its specific level in the system hierarchy, and has a defined interface to other function blocks and subsystems. Since each function block is defined by its interface with other functions, it is of minor significance how the function is implemented, in hardware and/or software.

The heart of the AXE system structure is the function block with its function units. The function units are located within each function block. Here, the distinction between hardware and software becomes evident. A typical function block consists of a hardware unit, a regional software unit and a central software unit (see Figure 32.7).

The interwork between function blocks and function units is carried out by means of software signals. Software signals are a set of data which precisely define the interface between the 'black boxes'. The use of software signals permits design modifications with minimum overall system impact, that is, without affecting other function blocks. A typical AXE telephone exchange is built up of 400 – 500 function blocks.

32.8.4 Software modularity

Each software unit is programmed independently of all the others. Interaction between software units is by means of software signals and each software unit can only work with its own data. Consequently, a programme fault in one software unit can not mutilate

data belonging to other software units. In other words AXE provides inherent software security.

Hardware units normally exist in numbers of identical devices with the exchange. In a similar manner, regional software units are repeated in regional processors controlling a certain type of hardware unit. The central software units are stored in the central processor.

Figure 32.8 illustrates the internal structure of a central software unit. The software unit consists of a programme part, which contains the logic and the ability to receive and transmit software signals, and a data part, which contains the stored information of the unit. This information may be common or can be individual for the controlled hardware units. In the latter case, the current data record is addressed by a pointer.

To obtain software security and ease of handling, the control system supports this functional structure with:

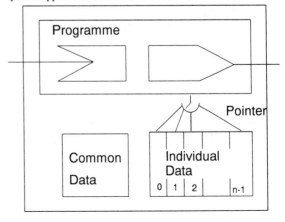

Figure 32.8 Central software unit structure

1. Special microprogrammed machine instructions used to transmit software signals between central software units.
2. Protection against data access to data of other software units. In addition, all absolute address calculations are performed automatically by microprogrammes.
3. Relocatable central software units; as the programme and data parts of a software unit can be stored in any free area of the programme and data store, each software unit can be handled separately, when faulty software units are replaced, or when new functions are introduced to the system.

Each function block in an exchange is assigned a unique function block number. Only when the function block number register (one of the programme control registers) contains the function block number for a certain block, access can be obtained to the programme and data.

Access to data which is only permitted within the function block uses a base address method, in which every separate piece of data is given its own base address. The base address is found in the reference store. This base address contains all the information about the location of the data in the data store and how addressing is carried out. In this way address calculations are made in hardware and not in software, which simplifies programming considerably. By using this base address method, all data in the data store is completely relocatable, that is, it can be placed in or moved to any idle area in the data store.

The programme for a function block forms a continuous area in the programme store. The start address to this area is also found by means of the reference store. The machine instruction list does not contain any operations which refer to an absolute address in the stores. Thus the programme part of a function block is also relocatable.

Each software signal to a function block is defined by a unique symbolic number. In the software signal operation the block number for the receiving function block and the signal number in question must be given in order to access a specific programme sequence, (See Figure 32.9). First the function block number register is loaded with the block number. The function block start address is then extracted from the reference store and finally the symbolic signal number is used to obtain the entry address to the task sequence from a signal distribution table located in the beginning of the programme. In this way, programme changes made in a function block do not affect other function blocks as long as the software signal interfaces are maintained.

The major part, i.e. all central software units, of the programmes for AXE are written in a high level language, PLEX (Programming Language for Telephone Exchanges) that takes the modularity attributes, function blocks and software signals into account.

32.8.5 Hardware modularity

AXE hardware is composed of magazines, mechanical frames holding printed board assemblies, which are housed in cabinets. Hardware units can be added, modified or deleted while the AXE system is operational. All connections between frames are made by plug in cables. The AXE hardware structure is shown in Figure 32.10.

From the smallest component on the printed board assembly up to the cabinets containing full equipment, a building block philosophy is applied.

32.8.6 Technological modularity

Technological modularity, in turn, permits the adoption of improved technical components within the framework of the system.

New technology, e.g. new components, may be introduced, making possible a continuous development of the system. AXE therefore always represents state of the art technology.

32.9 AXE implementation

One system for all applications is achieved through specified functions, grouped together to form subsystems. These may be combined to suit different applications. An AXE exchange is a combination of switching subsystems and control subsystems.

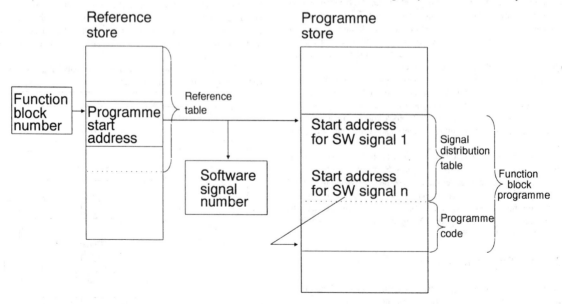

Figure 32.9 Addressing principle

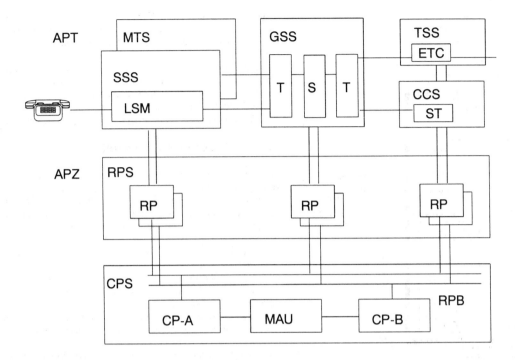

APT Switching System
MTS Mobile Telephony Subsystem
SSS Subscriber Switching Subsystem
GSS Group Switch Subsystem
TSS Trunk and Signalling Subsystem
CCS Common Channel Signalling Sub.
LSM Line Switch Module
ETC Exchange Terminal Circuit

APZ Control System
RPS Regional Processor Subsystem
CPS Central Processor Subsystem
RP Regional Processor
CP Central Processor
MAU Maintenance Unit
ST Signalling Terminal

Figure 32.10 AXE hardware structure

32.9.1 Switching system APT

The switching system APT performs traffic handling functions and also operation and maintenance functions related to traffic handling.

The division of APT into subsystems is determined by conditions and requirements that arise from traffic handling and operation and maintenance functions. These subsystems are implemented both in hardware and software.

In the following sections the basic APT subsystems are described.

32.9.1.1 *APT subsystems*

The subscriber Switching Subsystem, SSS, supervises the state of connected subscriber lines, sets up and releases connections in the subscriber switching network and sends and receives signals to and from subscribers. SSS is a mandatory subsystem in local exchange applications.

The SSS hardware, the digital subscriber switching stage, consists of a number of Line Switch Modules (LSM) each of which contains line circuits for 128 analogue subscriber lines or alternatively 64 digital subscriber lines (2B+D). Special LSMs also exists for alter-

native accesses to the subscriber network, such as ISDN 30B+D. A hardware block diagram of the digital subscriber switching stage for analogue accesses is shown in Figure 32.11.

LICs, KRD and JTC/ETCs are connected to a time switch (TS). The time switch is non-blocking and has full availability. Thus any channel in the JTC/ETC within an LSM can be reached from any LIC within the same LSM. Via a time switch bus (TSB) any channel in other JTC/ETCs can also be reached. Consequently, the access switch is completely insensitive to unequally distributed loading (mixture of high and low traffic subscribers).

When the subscriber switching stage is remotely located, built in emergency functions are activated in case of a break in the communication towards the host exchange. These functions allow the subscriber to make internal calls with reduced facility level. It is also possible to connect one of the subscriber lines to an emergency centre in order to maintain '999' service.

The Group Switch Subsystem, GSS, is used to set up speech paths between connected devices.

The Digital Group Switch has a T-S-T (time-space-time) structure. It is built up of a number of time switching modules and a number of space switching modules. Time switching is performed

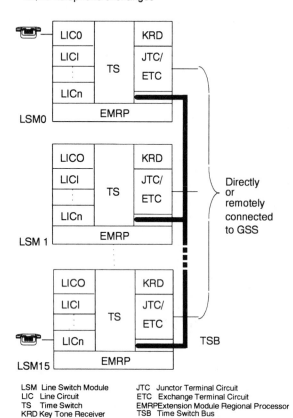

LSM   Line Switch Module
LIC   Line Circuit
TS   Time Switch
KRD   Key Tone Receiver

JTC   Junctor Terminal Circuit
ETC   Exchange Terminal Circuit
EMRP Extension Module Regional Processor
TSB   Time Switch Bus

Figure 32.11   The digital subscriber switching stage

by buffer memories and space switching by electronic crosspoint matrices. The switching part of the group switch is duplicated in two planes and all calls are established in both planes. The active plane is determined on a per call basis.

The timing in the digital group switch is performed by a triplicated clock module. Synchronisation is implemented by means of a software algorithm that can accommodate alternative network synchronisation methods.

The Trunk and Signalling Subsystem, TSS, supervises the state of trunks to and from other exchanges. For analogue and analogue to digital conversion trunks, the signalling is extracted and inserted in the trunk before entering the switch. Multi frequency signalling is handled via the group switch using code senders and code receivers.

The Common Channel Signalling Subsystem, CCS, implements the Message Transfer Part (MTP) of the CCITT signalling system No.7.

Signalling system No.7, as specified by CCITT, is built up of two parts, namely User Parts (UPs) and a common Message Transfer Part (MTP). The task of the MTP is to transfer information reliably between UPs in different switches. The user parts belong to the Trunk and Signalling Subsystem, TSS.

The Traffic Control Subsystem, TCS, controls and supervises the set up of all calls. TCS stores and analyses digits received directly from subscribers or via trunks and based on stored information (analysis data) decides how the call is to be handled.

The Charging Subsystem, CHS, performs the task of charging calls or at least to collect raw data needed for charging purposes. The charging system can be used for either pulse metering, itemised billing or both.

The Operation and Maintenance Subsystem, OMS, is equipped with a wide range of functions for supervision, fault locating, statistics and administration. AXE is designed to work without any external support system but necessary interfaces to interwork with centralised operation and maintenance systems are also provided.

32.9.2   The control system APZ

The control system architecture, with a central processor and a varying number of regional processors, is optimised for real time data processing. The real time environment imposes high demands on the control system: calls appear in an irregular manner; a variety of call models must be supported; very short response times are required; and overload situations must be handled.

All the specific requirements and demands of real time data processing are efficiently handled by the AXE distributed control solution; an expandable front end line up of small but fast processors, controlled and co-ordinated by a central processor.

Frequent call processing functions such as scanning operations and signal processing present stringent real time requirements. In AXE these functions have been assigned to special purpose regional processors. The central processor is free to handle the higher level processing functions. The two processor levels are shown in Figure 32.10.

32.9.2.1   APZ subsystems

The Central Processor Subsystem, CPS, consists of a duplicated central processor (CP). The APT central software units are stored and executed in the central processor.

The two processor sides work in a synchronous parallel mode. Permanent or temporary (intermittent) hardware faults can affect only one side at a time, data mutilation occurs in that side only. The intact side automatically continues traffic handling with correct data while the faulty side is taken out of traffic. This process is sufficiently fast to make corrective software actions unnecessary. Thus, in the majority of cases hardware recovery will not affect switch operation. The synchronous duplication model in fact guarantees that central processor hardware faults will not cause software failures. In addition, comparison between the two processor sides is an effective diagnostic tool for locating a faulty hardware sub-unit. The ability to separate the system without affecting its operation is also a valuable aid during major extensions or substantial software modifications.

Error correcting techniques in the memories mean that most memory faults are corrected without affecting the application software.

AXE can be equipped with either of two alternative central processors that are fully compatible on target code level, towards RPs and I/O peripherals and may be changed or modified, even in service. One is aimed for low cost, small physical volume and high reliability whereas the other is aimed at high capacity requirement applications. They have a similar logical and physical structure. Each processor stores software in three logical stores. Programme Store (PS), Data Store (DS) and Reference Store (RS).

The operating system is structured to be largely hardware independent. It has functions for job monitoring, loading, function change, automatic re-loading, storage allocation, size alteration of data files, programme correction, programme test, processor statistics and handling of regional processors.

The Regional Processor Subsystem, RPS, consists of a dimensionable number of regional processors (RPs). The APT regional software units are stored and executed by RPS. The interwork between the central processor and the regional processors take place via a duplicated regional processor bus, RPB.

The Maintenance Subsystem, MAS, supervises the proper operation of APZ and takes appropriate action should faults occur. The MAS functions can be divided as follows:

1. Supervision for detection of occurred faults.
2. Tasks after fault detection to limit the effect of a fault and to localise it.
3. Repairs, including methods and aids to execute repairs with minimum disturbance.
4. Support for CP hardware extension.

Finally there are four subsystems designated for input/output functions. To relieve the central processor, input/output functions are carried out by a support processing system connected to the central processor.

The Support Processor Subsystem, SPS, contains the above mentioned support processing system. It is built up of one or several general purpose type processors that can be configured in a modular way, from small to large configurations, depending on capacity and reliability requirements.

The Data Communication Subsystem, DCS, consists of support processor software for data communication. It provides various kinds of data communication facilities supporting remote operation and maintenance, transfer of charging and accounting data to a remote or local facility etc.

The File Management Subsystem, FMS, comprises of support processor software for advanced file management. FMS supports various file structures such as direct, keyed or sequential access. Files may also be transferred to a data link via DCS. File transfer normally takes place via hard disc, which function as a backup for the data link.

The Man Machine Communication Subsystem, MMS, consists of central and support processor software, and hardware devices for alphanumeric input/output. Man machine communication in AXE is performed via alphanumeric terminals and alarm displays. The man machine language is consistent with the recommendations of CCITT. Terminals can be placed locally or remotely and remote subscriber stages can also be fitted with transportable terminals when needed. Unauthorised access is prohibited by a number of security systems, e.g. authority checks, passwords and identity cards.

32.9.3 Packaging structure

The AXE packaging structure has been developed to meet the requirements of a modern switching system. From both mechanical and electrical viewpoint, the packaging offers a very high degree of flexibility.

The basic unit is the magazine. Each magazine corresponds to a function of the AXE switching system. At the factory the magazines are fitted with their printed boards assemblies. Then they are tested as functional units, either as single magazines or as complete cabinets. Accordingly, a complete switch may be pretested in the factory thus reducing on-site activities to a minimum.

The packaging system contributes to easy handling all the way: during design, manufacture, installation and operation/maintenance.

32.10 AXE applications and features

The concept of AXE is to provide one system for all network applications through a system wide concept of open ended modularity.

Telecom operators request services to be tailored to their individual needs and require some degree of control over the services. The opportunities for creating new sources of revenue for operators seems tremendous. Successful exploitation of these new opportunities will depend on getting new services to market very quickly.

32.10.1 The residential network

In the residential network AXE can be used for:

1. Local exchanges for metropolitan areas, towns and rural areas.
2. Remote subscriber switches.
3. Local (tandem) and national transit exchanges.

AXE local exchanges comprise a variety of subscriber services. Typical services are abbreviated dialling and hot line, multi party conference, call transfer, call barring etc.

32.10.2 The business communication network

The different activities within large organisations are normally distributed between several widespread locations nationally and internationally. In fact, structures with increasing geographic distribution can be envisaged, such as offices located remotely or even in the home. By applying a combination of soft (additional software to already installed local exchanges) and hard (new switches) network overlay principles, all locations within a company can be interconnected via a Virtual Private Network (VPN).

AXE provides a complete business communication package with Centrex type services which combines all the functions required by the demanding business subscriber: implementation in any network application; both mobile and wired access; provisioning of both voice and data services; service to both large and small companies; coverage of single site as well as multi site companies.

AXE comprises a full set of ISDN services in accordance with the ETSI Memorandum of Understanding. ISDN accesses can also be incorporated within the business groups.

The first generation of AXE broadband switches will be based on pre-B-ISDN offerings, such as Local Area Network (LAN) interconnect and virtual leased line services for High Speed Data Communication (HSDC).

32.10.3 International gateways

International telephony involves many special demands: high traffic load day and night, demands for secure charging and accounting, demands for sophisticated maintenance functions, advanced operator services, and a full range of national and international signalling systems. AXE offers a complete international exchange system, including large trunk switching capacity, a powerful central processor, all international signalling systems, advanced charging and accounting functions, and an operator system.

32.10.4 The operator system

The operator system contains functions for operator handling of manually assisted calls. It can provide services for national and international switching centres and also for directory inquiry service centres, message service centres, alarm collection centres, etc. An operator position can be used for all types of traffic, thus allowing for an integration of operator assisted services.

The operator system includes automatic demand and delay ticket handling; automatic charging and accounting, same as in the overall concept; automatic call distribution functions, based on queues and priority levels, resulting in a maximum utilisation of the system in all situations.

The operator terminal system is based on standard personal computers and the terminals can be clustered by means of a Local Area Network (LAN). The operator terminals can be freely located in large or small office areas or even in the home environment. Through the LAN, operators may access a wide range of data bases.

32.10.5 Mobile networks

AXE can be equipped as a mobile switch for both European and North American standards for both analogue and digital mobile telephony. All the major analogue standards, NMT 450, NMT 900, TACS and AMPS, are supported by AXE as well as the digital standards for the pan-European GSM and the North American ADC networks.

In a mobile network the AXE switch can be used in the following applications:

1. As Base Station Controller (BSC).
2. As Mobile Switching Centre (MSC).
3. As Visitor Location Register (VLR).
4. As a transit switch interconnecting the MSCs and to provide access to the fixed network.
5. As a Service Control Point (SCP) for IN (Intelligent Network) functionality (the service control functionality can also be integrated on the MSC or transit layer).
6. As an operator exchange for manually assisted calls.

The mobile applications covered by AXE also encompasses functionality for Personal Communication Networks (PCN).

32.10.6 Intelligent Network (IN)

The AXE/IN architecture consists of six functional levels:

1. Basic switching.
2. Service switching.
3. Service control.
4. Network management.
5. Service management.
6. Service creation.

The first three layers are implemented in AXE. The last three in a specially tailored Service Management System (SMAS).

The central processor in AXE is by nature a real time, high availability computing system, optimised for use within telecommunications networks. It fits with the intelligent network application as it meets the highest transaction rate and short response time requirements.

As the AXE can be configured both as Service Switching Points (SSPs) and as Service Control Points (SCPs), the possibility to make combined Service Switching and Control Points (SSCPs) also exists. This approach allows for the service execution to migrate from a central service control point (SCP) into the local network (SSCP) once a service has become established and widespread.

The AXE/IN implementation has a built in software platform, the service script interpreter, which is generic, or service independent, across a range of services. This allows the telecom operator to design and develop new service software in the form of service scripts. The Service Management System provides the tool for service creation, and it also allows for service management and end user control of service data.

32.10.7 New switching techniques

In the transport network, the use of a wider range of switching techniques will be implemented in order to permit a more flexible allocation of bandwidth. Traditional circuit switching will be supplemented by Asynchronous Transfer Mode (ATM) techniques for services such as LAN (Local Area Network) interconnect and other high speed data communication services, finally forming the new infrastructure of the Broadband ISDN (B-ISDN).

32.10.8 AXE development

AXE has been continuously further developed since the first exchange was brought into service in 1977, but the ever changing telecommunication arena constantly provides new demands. Table 32.1 gives some examples of already ongoing changes, including the possibility of digital access to voice and data services.

Table 32.1 Changes in telecommunication requirements

From	To
Node defined switching	Network wide services
Copper bandwidth	Fibre bandwidth
Node intelligence	Intelligence diffused through the entire network
In band signalling	Common channel signalling
Standard services	Customised services
Wire access	Wire and radio access
Local/regional standardisation	Global standardisation
Monopolistic regulation	Competitive markets
Circuit switching	A mix of circuit and packet switching
Narrowband services	A mix of narrowband, wideband and broadband services
Calling defined locations	Calling personal numbers
Plesiochronous transmission	Synchronous transmission

32.11   DMS system

The DMS (Digital Multiplex System) family of digital switches manufactured by Northern Telecom has variants designed to meet the requirements of all levels in the network hierarchy (Figure 31.2), e.g. DMS-100 for local exchanges of 1000 to 100000 lines, DMS-200 for tandem exchanges of up to 60000 trunks or junctions and DMS-300 for international gateways up to 27000 trunks.

Through the use of highly modular architecture, for hardware and software, Centrex, combined local/tandem, mobile telephone, military and PABX (DMS Meridian) versions are also available. This modular architecture also enables the Intelligent Network applications to be integrated with the DMS-100, DMS-200 or DMS-300 applications as appropriate.

The modular architecture permits customisation to meet local needs and DMS is in service in many countries world-wide including the USA, Canada, Europe and Japan. In the U.K., DMS exchanges form the basis of the Mercury network and provide advanced services in the BT network.

Members of the DMS family are characterised by their ability to meet new application and reliability requirements, and to incorporate new technology in their design. New technology in turn provides increased capability and reliability at reduced cost.

The DMS family can evolve because modular design techniques are used in the development of both its software and its hardware. Modularity may be thought of as the implementation of a complex system through a set of functional units or modules connected by well defined interfaces. As a result of proper module and interface design, the various units can be connected, disconnected, modified, or improved, without affecting either the operation of other modules in the system or the system as a whole.

There are two generations of DMS. The second generation is known as DMS SuperNode and provides increased processing and call handling capacity at reduced size and with improved reliability. This is the current product and, except where otherwise stated, the following description refers to DMS SuperNode. The first generation (NT-40) is, however, in widespread use so its principal features are also mentioned.

An overview of the DMS system architecture is shown in Figure 32.12. In the first generation system the speech links are 4 wire copper at 2.56Mbit/s in DS30 format comprising 30 digital speech channels plus parity and supervision. Second generation systems employ a mixture of DS30 and DS512 optical fibre links (equivalent to sixteen DS30 links each). Similarly, the message links are either DS30 or DS512 but with all channels used for message data.

32.12   The DMS switching network

The switching network provides two way digital speech and messaging connections between the Peripheral Modules (PM), interfacing both originating and terminating lines and junctions. Security of each network connection is achieved by providing two separate speech paths (Planes 0 and 1) for every call.

The first generation employs a Junctored Network (J-net) comprising a series of interlinked Network Modules (NM). Each NM provides one stage of time switching to route each call from one PM via a junctor link to another NM which routes the call to the required terminating PM. There can be up to 32 NM, each interfacing 64 DS30 links giving a network capacity of 64K channels.

The second generation network which is now being used for all new work is known as the Enhanced Network (E-net) and comprises a single stage junctor-less non-blocking switching matrix of up to 128K channels, as shown in Figure 32.13. The crosspoint cards comprising the matrix each contain four 16K (in) by 4K (out) time switches combined to form a 16K by 16K matrix. The entire E-net is housed in two cabinets, one for each plane.

Each shelf of crosspoint cards is controlled by its own processor communicating with the DMS-Core over a DS512 message link.

Referring to Figure 32.13, it can be seen that four incoming DS512 pcm signals, or an equivalent number of DS30 streams, are multiplexed into a single 2K (2048 channel) stream by each speech link interface card. The 2K pcm stream from each interface card is passed to the crosspoint card positioned directly in front of it and also distributed by a vertical bus (V bus) to the corresponding crosspoint cards mounted on the other three shelves. Each crosspoint card thus receives four 2K pcm streams, one from its own interface and three more from the interface cards above and below on the other three shelves, a total of 8K channels. In addition, the vertical buses are mated in odd/even pairs so that each card also receives a further 8K channels from the adjacent mated bus. This gives a total of 16K channels multiplied over 8 cards comprising an odd/even pair on all four shelves.

With up to 16 (8 pairs) crosspoint cards per shelf, this gives the total of 128K channels in eight streams of 16K.

Each incoming call will appear on eight of the crosspoint cards, serving the 16K stream within which it originates. One of these cards switches the call to one of the pair of horizontal buses (H-bus) available on its shelf. The call is then switched by the appropriate card on the same shelf and the same H-bus serving the 16K stream containing the destination port. Since any incoming call appears on both the odd and even card on each shelf via the mated V-bus arrays, it may be switched to any other crosspoint card via the appropriate H-bus. The second crosspoint card simply passes the incoming 2K stream from the H-bus to the speech link interface for demultiplexing into four separate DS512 speech link ports. A call between two channels in the same 16K stream is switched twice on the same crosspoint card.

In terms of the definitions of time and space switching, given in Chapter 31, this network can only be described as a time switch. There is no separation of time and space switching functions and the whole network can be regarded as a space switch having time switches as its crosspoints. Each call is connected via two time switches but the network itself is not divided into separate stages.

It will be seen that this switching network corresponds to the Group Selection stage of Figure 31.10. The line concentration is provided in the relevant Peripheral Module (PM).

32.13   DMS Peripheral Modules (PM)

A range of different PM is provided to interface the Switching Network to all external facilities. Four typical ones are shown in Figure 32.12 and these are described in the following sections.

32.13.1   Line Concentrating Modules (LCM)

There is a variety of these PMs which may be housed either at the Central Office (host site) or at a location closer to the customer premises being served (remote site). They support analogue lines and provide low level functions like line scanning and ringing.

A maximum of 640 lines can be connected to each LCM. Each LCM consists of two shelves, known as Line Concentrating Arrays (LCA). There can be up to 320 lines connected to each LCA.

A group of LCM connects to a Line Group Controller (LGC), a Line Trunk Controller (LTC), or a Remote Cluster Controller (RCC), which in turn connects to the Switching Network. There are

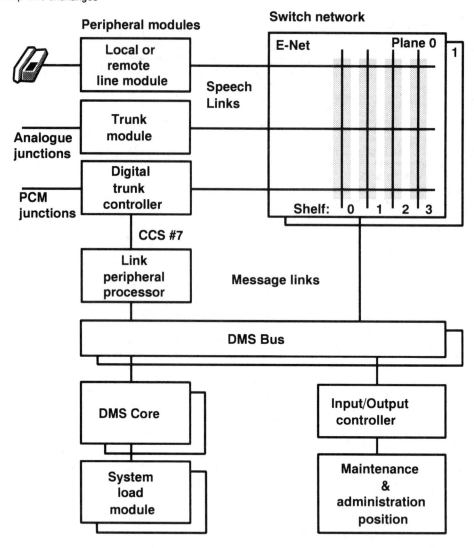

Figure 32.12 DMS (SuperNode) system

a maximum of three DS30 links per LCA and a maximum of six DS30 links per LCM.

For reliability, each Line Concentrating Array is capable of taking over the lines of the mate LCA. The LCAs are connected by a serial data link that allows one LCA to checkpoint its data with the mate LCA. The data for each call in progress is sent to the mate LCA over this link. If a fault occurs in one LCA, the mate LCA can take over the calls in progress.

Between the two LCA, there can be one or more speech links (DS30). If all channels on an LCA are busy, but the mate LCA has free channels, a call originating on the busy LCA can be routed over one of the inter-LCA speech links to a free channel on the mate LCA. This capability provides access for all lines to all six DS30 links for traffic engineering purposes.

The LGC performs high level functions, such as call coordination and the provision of the different tones required. It is equipped with duplicated processors operating in hot worker/standby mode.

As Figure 32.14 illustrates, there is usually some concentration of lines, depending on the engineering of the particular exchange. The concentration can occur in two places: in the LCM or in the LGC.

Each LGC has a maximum of ten LCM and, therefore, a maximum of 6400 (10 x 640) lines. The LGC has a maximum of 20 ports available for DS30 links from the LCM and, therefore, also has a maximum of 600 (20 x 30) speech links from the LCM.

There are up to 480 (16 x 30) speech links between the Switching Network and the LGC.

Line concentration can be lessened either by reducing the number of Line Concentrating Modules or the number of lines per LCM.

Remote line modules can provide a limited local switching service should the remote site become isolated from the host.

32.13.2 Digital trunk controller

This is used for 30 channel PCM connections to DMS. The PCM30 Digital Trunk Controller (PDTC) interfaces up to 16 2Mbit/s carrier

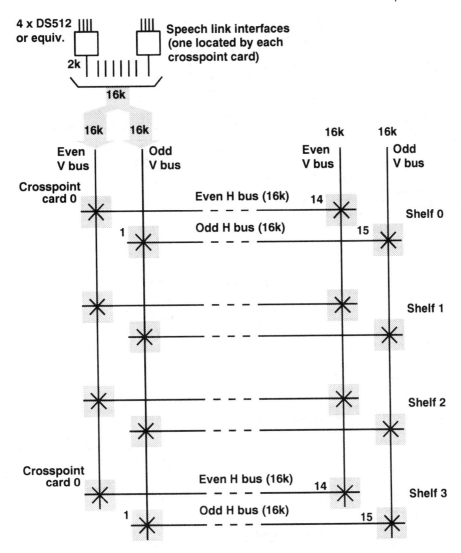

4 x DS512 or equiv.

Speech link interfaces (one located by each crosspoint card)

2k

16k

16k | 16k

Even V bus | **Odd V bus**

16k | 16k

Even V bus | **Odd V bus**

Crosspoint card 0

Even H bus (16k)   14   **Shelf 0**

1   Odd H bus (16k)   15

Shelf 1

Shelf 2

Crosspoint card 0

Even H bus (16k)   14   **Shelf 3**

1   Odd H bus (16k)   15

Figure 32.13 DMS switch network (E Net)

systems via 16 DS30 speech links to the network (i.e. a total of 480 channels per PDTC). Its two processors operate in hot worker/standby mode.

32.13.3 Trunk Module

Trunk Modules (TM) are used for analogue trunk or junction connections to DMS. The TM encodes and multiplexes incoming speech from a maximum of 30 analogue circuits into a digital format incorporating the line supervisory and control signals. Outgoing speech and signals are demultiplexed and decoded into their respective speech and signalling information on each circuit. A range of different analogue signalling systems may be supported by selecting different interface circuit packs.

A variation on the TM is the Maintenance Trunk Module (MTM) which has all the functions of a TM card and interfaces a maximum of 28 service circuits (tones, alarms, etc.) and test equipments.

32.13.4 Link Peripheral Processor

A Link Peripheral Processor (LPP) consists of a number of Link Interface Units (LIU) which are connected to DMS- Bus via a Link Interface Module (LIM). Each LIM consists of a pair of Local Message Switches each serving a maximum of 36 LIU.

An LIU configured for No.7 signalling is known as an LIU7. Each LIU7 will provide message discrimination, routing and distribution for one No.7 signalling link. The signalling link enters the LIU7 as a 64 kbit/s (single channel) link which may have been derived from a multiplexer connected to a PDTC or directly from the PDTC as a DS0 (digital speech – no channels) link.

The LPP may be used to support Signalling Transfer Point (STP) working.

It is the architecture of the LPP which not only provides the capabilities for advanced features and services of the future, but also the ability to process the large volume of intelligent messaging

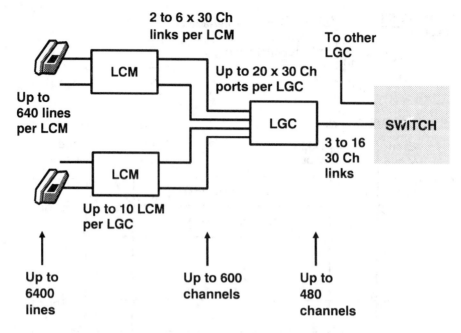

Figure 32.14 DMS line concentration

required whilst maintaining the necessary firewalls to ensure total network integrity.

In first generation systems, No.7 signalling is supported by Message Switching Buffers and associated Signalling Terminals performing a similar function to the LPP.

32.14 DMS-Core

DMS SuperNode employs a distributed processing architecture. Real time functions associated with a particular facility or periphe-

ral are delegated to local processors in the relevant sub system. A central control (DMS-Core) co-ordinates call processing including the interactions between the Switching Network and the Peripheral Modules. (See Figure 32.15.)

There are two Central Processing Units (CPU) based on 32-bit microprocessors operating in parallel, simultaneously executing the same instructions with the same data. They are linked by a Mate Exchange Bus (MEB) for fault detection and maintenance purposes. Each has its own integrated Program and Data store, data changes in the active CPU data store being copied to the inactive one across the MEB.

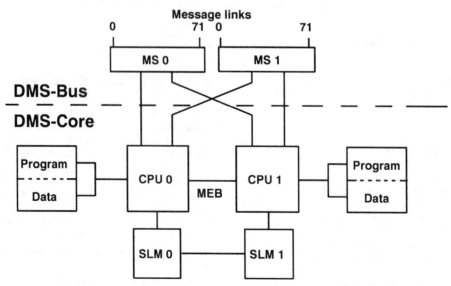

Figure 32.15 DMS central control

Directly associated with each CPU is a System Load Module (SLM) incorporating a Winchester disk for software loads and a magnetic tape cartridge drive for archiving. This allows more rapid loading and saving of software than via the Input/Output Controller. Crossover buses are provided to allow either CPU to be loaded by either SLM. Periodic back-ups of the contents of Program and Data Stores (Office Image) are taken on the disks and are constantly made available to the system for use in the event of a major system failure. Reloading and full recovery after a total system failure (e.g. after power supply failure) is fully automatic.

The first generation systems are generally similar but use 16-bit microprocessors, separate stores for Data and Program and are not provided with SLM.

32.15 DMS-Bus

DMS-Bus is perhaps the key architectural innovation in DMS SuperNode. It connects all system components in a uniform manner to give flexibility for future evolution. Because all sub-systems are connected directly or indirectly to ports on DMS-Bus they can communicate freely with one another by having DMS-Bus switch messages between its input and output ports. A sub-system wishing to communicate simply creates a message and sends it in the appropriate format to DMS-Bus which then routes it to the required destination.

Assuming an average message length of 64 bytes, one fully duplicated DMS-Bus module is capable of handling about 125K messages per second.

The DMS-Bus comprises two Message Switches (MS), each having its own processor with associated memory and software. A copy of the MS load forms part of the Office Image. The two MS operate in load sharing mode but either is capable of handling all the message traffic if the other is removed from service (e.g. for maintenance or under failure conditions).

Links to the MS can be either DS30 or DS512 and messages are transmitted internally over four parallel 4Mbit/s synchronous buses.

The MS also provide the master clock facilities for the whole system.

In first generation systems, communication between the CPU and other subsystems is via Central Message Controllers, each providing up to 70 DS30 ports to the Switching Network and Input/Output Controller.

32.16 DMS software

The control component software system provides the software necessary for the basic call processing decision functions; it also provides extensive software for the administration and maintenance of the DMS-100 hardware and connecting facilities. There are several thousand software modules consisting of several million lines of program code. In order to manage the design and production of reliable software on this scale, the system has the following characteristics:

1. Programming in a high level language.
2. Programming modularity.
3. Programming structure.
4. Programming portability.

Both the Central Control CPU (first generation) and the DMS SuperNode CPU are programmed in PROTEL (PRocedure Oriented Type Enforcing Language), a high level language developed at BNR. PROTEL is a block structured, type enforcing language that enables extensive type checking on the source code at compile time.

In both generations of the DMS, multitasking in real time is based on processes that use messages to communicate with one another. These messages can be exchanged by processes within the control component; they can also be exchanged by control component processes and processes in the Switching Network or in the Peripheral Modules.

The software is structured in functional layers so that each layer provides a set of services that are available to the software layers above it. As one moves up through the hierarchy, the software provides more advanced levels of operation.

For example, at the bottom of the hierarchy is the layer which provides the basic tools required by the Support Operating System (SOS) and thus provides a set of services for all the layers above it. The top layer of the hierarchy contains the various features, such as the Traffic Operator Position System (TOPS). TOPS is an integrated operator call handling system that operates in conjunction with a DMS-100.

In addition to this functional layering, the software is also organised into a hierarchy of modules in four layers:

1. Area; a product line.
2. Subsystem; a unit of software delivery.
3. Module; a unit of loading.
4. Section; a unit of compilation.

Most of the control software created for the first generation system did not need to be modified for DMS SuperNode except to remove processor dependencies and to introduce new features to take advantage of the new processor. A proprietary Operating System (SOS) mediates between the application software and the hardware vehicle and a sophisticated compiler has been developed for re-targeting the software. Consequently, DMS SuperNode can be upgraded in future to take advantage of any new high performance processors that become available.

32.17 DMS-Link

The greater part of one of DMS SuperNode key elements, DMS-Link, is implemented in software. Essentially a software and protocol structure for use on the signalling links between DMS SuperNode applications and network nodes, DMS-Link delivers specific capabilities to end users on the telephony network to suit a variety of requirements. DMS-Link also includes a standard set of application and base interfaces for use in Custom Programming.

DMS-Link consists of sets of communicating applications and protocol stacks where the applications are software programs that provide end-to-end functions and services to the user and the protocol stacks provide the means of communication between the programs. These protocols include ISDN Access (Q.921 and Q.931) the Network Operations Protocols (NOP and X.400) X25 for packet switched communication and Common Channel Signalling System Number 7 (SS7).

Application programs, which can be services or utilities, interface with the top layers of the protocol stacks, and by using special software interfaces, customers can add their own applications to the system as appropriate. The standard software application set currently includes call processing, OA&M processing databases and Custom Programming. Many new applications can, however, be added as desired, because of the flexibility of DMS-Link and the DMS SuperNode architecture.

The hardware for DMS-Link is based on that of DMS SuperNode and DMS SuperNode's distributed operating system controls communication between the various processors in the system. When a single application is spread across multiple processors, the operating system allows the various elements of that application to communicate. When several similar functions are integrated across a number of switching nodes, they are said to be networking.

Networking with DMS-Link provides a seamless view of a function, whether it is the transportation of the calling number from originating to terminating node, or the transmission of a traffic summary for a given Centrex customer to multiple nodes. This seamlessness is achieved through DMS-Link's use of protocols (comparable to languages) and applications (comparable to semantics) which together help create a suitable environment for 'conversions' between nodal functions. This environment, which disassociates the customer's logical network from any specific physical implementation, creates a platform for launching new services.

32.18   DMS OA&M

The maintenance and administration area consists of all the Input/Output Devices and their controllers used to support the operation and maintenance of the switch. These may include a selection of disk drives, tape drives, printers, terminals, modems, PCs and data link controllers. They may be interfaced onto the DMS-Bus either directly via Input Output Controllers (IOC) or via Ethernet Interface Units supporting Local Area Networks (LANs). A minimum of two IOC are always provided to guarantee terminal and modem access to the system at all times.

The maintenance and administration workstations on DMS switches are known as MAP, Maintenance and Administration Positions. These consist of a terminal VDU and keyboard (the man machine interface), audio visual alarm panel (providing Minor, Major and Critical alarm indications), headset or keyset telephone system (for voice circuit monitoring) and integrated test jacks (for using non-standard external test equipment).

The MAP may be used, subject to terminal and user security screening, to access a variety of maintenance and administration software environments. These include:

1. General exchange maintenance.
2. Network management.
3. Service analysis.
4. Operational and traffic measurements.
5. Trunk testing.
6. Line testing.
7. Data modification and service orders.

Full screen displays are used to provide a 'live' picture of overall system and subsystem status as well as menu driven command prompting for maintenance, testing and data modification.

IOC are interfaced onto the DMS-Bus via two DS30 message links (one to each Message Switch). Each IOC consists of a firmware Message Processor Card and up to nine Device Controller cards, each with four ports.

Devices connected to Local Area Networks (LANs) may access the DMS-100 system through Ethernet Interface Units (EIUs). These are housed in peripheral modules called Link Peripheral Processors.

32.19   Further evolution with DMS

DMS SuperNode architecture is now not only providing a firm foundation for other switching products to build on, but its enhanced functionality is making advanced features and sophisticated services happen. Furthermore, the Intelligent Network is one step nearer since common channel signalling started using DMS Super-Node based Signal Transfer Points to bring to the domestic subscriber a type of service previously only available on large private business exchanges.

33

Structured cabling systems and voice distribution frames

Derek Kingaby
BTech CEng
Reichle De Massari (UK) Ltd
(Sections 33.1 - 33.8, 33.10 - 33.11)

Graham Hewitt
ISICAD (UK) Ltd
(Section 33.9)

Contents

33.1 Introduction

Rewiring a house or even fitting an extra power socket requires a large amount of effort. Multiply that by the range of voice and data services, and the number of outlets required in a modern office building, and the scale of the problem increases exponentially.

Add to that the fact that the modern office is likely to have a new tenant every few years and the needs of these tenants will change. Also the wiring records are likely to be either out of date or lost.

The answer to this chaos is a structured cabling system! In the following paragraphs some of the considerations of office cabling systems and their data networks are described. This is followed by a definition of a structured cabling system and the way in which various networks are implemented in structured cabling systems. The chapter concludes with a description of computer aided cable layout techniques.

33.2 Structured cabling

In the past, most offices were wired to suit the installed computer system. That is, the cable was specified by the data equipment manufacturer. The building then had a variety of cable types to suit the range of data systems installed.

Changing the computer system would result in changing the cable and hence rewiring the building.

Table 33.1 illustrates the type of cable required for various computer systems.

In the past the power and influence of the major computer companies and the absence of any alternative allowed them to force users to install the cable they specified. This restricted the users' choice when changing their computer system.

However, the extent and variety of communications in the modern office and the introduction of standards has changed the emphasis.

Today the user can install cables which meet internationally recognised standards and the equipment manufacturers can design equipment to conform with the same standard. All manufacturers equipment will run over the medias defined in the standard. It is the advent of standards like EIA/TIA 568, IEEE 802.3i 10BaseT and the more general acceptance of twisted pair cables that has made this approach possible.

A vendor independent cabling system uses cables of internationally recognised standards to carry a wide range of voice and data services. This is the key to a structured cabling system.

A structured cabling system is an ordered building voice and data wiring system which uses internationally recognised media in vertical riser backbones and in horizontal floor distribution. Wiring closets are located at the interception of the floors with the risers. Patch panels in the Information Technology (IT) room and the wiring closets provide flexibility to route any signal from the IT room to any workplace on any floor. The medias - usually fibre in the riser and UTP in the horizontal - are used to carry a wide range of services with capacity for future services.

Table 33.1 Services handled by structured cabling systems (NA = Not applicable)

Manufacturer	Service	Cable	Ohms Z_0	Data rate (Mb/s)
IBM	34 36 38	Beldon 9207	100	1
IBM	AS400	Twinax	110	1
Wang OIS/VS	Wangnet	Twinax RG59/u	75	4.27
Ethernet	Thicknet (10base5)	Beldon 9880	75	10
Ethernet	Thinnet (10base2)	Beldon 9907	50	10
Ethernet	Cheapnet (10baseT)	Twisted Pair	100	10
Burroughs	TDI	Beldon 9272	78	
IBM	516588+2462048	Beldon 9463	78	
Wang	928	Twinax	110	4.275
IBM	3270	RG62A/U Coax	93	2.36
IBM	Token Ring	4MHz Type 1 IBM	150	4
IBM	Token Ring	16MHz Type 1 IBM	150	16
APPLE	Appletalk/Localtalk	Twinax Beldon 9999	120	
Several	RS232/V24 Synchronous	Multicore	100	0.0192
Several	RS422/V11 Asynchronous	UTP	100	0.0192
Several	Telephone Analogue	UTP	100	0.004
Several	ISDN TIA	UTP	100	2.064
Several	FDDI	Fibre optic	NA	100
Several	TPDDI	UTP	100	NA
Several	ISDN	UTP	100	1.544

When a building is first wired, the tenant and his voice and data needs are generally not known. To ensure there are suitable outlets at every possible location, the office floor area is laid out in a 6 metre grid. Locating a floor box in the middle of each 6 metre square, containing two voice and two data outlets, will provide adequate communications cover. Wiring all of these outlets back to the patch panel(s) on that floor will provide "flood wiring".

Modern buildings are designed for a life of about 50 years, while the computers and PABX equipment is bought to last between 3 and 10 years.

It is reasonable to plan for a major refurbishment every 12 to 15 years. It is important that the cabling system is geared to the building elements and not to the installed communications system.

It is also important that minor changes can be performed quickly and efficiently. To get this flexibility the initial installation cost will be higher but the system will last longer and changes will be less expensive.

33.2.1 Wiring closet location

The most basic limitation on the positioning of telecommunications closets is the need to keep the lengths of cables within the limits set by the structured cabling scheme that will ultimately be used. Most can provide 100 metres and this is the limit given in the emerging Electronic Industries Association (EIA) standard. This distance is sufficient for most uses of the main proprietary cabling schemes. There is a fire regulation which requires a fire exit to be within 90 metres of the workplace. The building risers are generally located near fire escape stairways.

Four factors combine to reduce the office area that can be served from a single closet below that of a circle of 90m radius. They are:

1. The use of 'street and avenue' horizontal cable routes
2. The need to route cables around obstacles such as service cores.
3. The need to avoid congestion in the areas where the cables approach and enter the closets. These areas are often densely packed with other services as well.
4. The need to allow some cable length at the patch panel, and sometimes, from the service space to the presentation.

The area that can be served is further reduced when the shape of the building is considered. This often leads to the location of a telecommunications closet near a corner of the space to be served.

In practice, it is quite difficult to serve areas of more than 1,000m^2 (lettable) space from a single closet; an area of 500m^2 is a better guideline. If the design team wishes to support a larger area from a single closet, it should ensure all services can be satisfactorily distributed. This may involve increasing the floor void depth from 120mm to 150mm or 200mm.

33.3 System components

The major system components are:

1. Distribution frame/patch panel in IT room.
2. Riser cable - fibre or multicore copper.
3. Active hub technology equipment - multiplexer, MAU, etc.
4. Patch panel per wiring closet.
5. UTP horizontal cabling.
6. Socket outlets.

There is a choice of seven basic cable types shown in Table 33.2 with the data rates currently being used on them.

Unshielded twisted pair (UTP) is a number of individually twisted pairs in a common outer sheath. The laylength of the twists are arranged to be different between each pair to reduce the crosstalk between pairs. The term laylength is a measure of the length along the wire taken by one complete twist.

Unshielded twisted pair with an overall screen is of a similar construction but with an overall foil shield. This often has a larger overall diameter to compensate for the detrimental effect of the shield on crosstalk.

Shielded twisted pair (STP) is made up from individually screened pairs in a common outer sheath which often includes an overall shield.

The outer diameter of the cable is an important consideration in structured cabling systems. The packing density of the cable is dependent on the diameter. This is one of the advantages of PVC insulated UTP cable.

Low smoke zero halogen fire resistant cables should also be considered because of the PVC fire hazard.

The electrical and transmission characteristics of the commonly used data cables are shown in Table 33.3.

A cable is defined by the characteristics: near end crosstalk; attenuation; characteristic impedance; conductor resistance; insulation resistance; velocity factor; and mutual capacitance.

The characteristics of the link between the wiring closet and the floorbox outlet must meet the most stringent standard required by the services to be carried. This is usually the service with the highest data rate. The link includes the patch panel, plugs, sockets, fly leads and 100 metres of cable to make the connection.

Table 33.2 Data transmission rates. (@ = under evaluation. # = used in broadcast industry.)

Media level number	Media type	Data rate (Mb/s)					
		.004	.02	1	10	20	100
1	Telephone cables	*	*				
2	Traditional UTP	*	*	*			
3	High quality UTP	*	*	*	*	*	
4	UTP with overall shield	*	*	*	*	*	@
5	STP (shielded pairs)	*	*	*	*	*	@
6	Coax	*	*	*	*	#	#
7	Fibre optics	*	*	*	*	*	*

This series connection is often referred to as the simplex link. The specification for this link is defined by the IEEE 802.3i standard.

Table 33.3 Typical 16MHz voice and data cable characteristics (UTP)

Parameter	Value/Type
Insulation	PVC or LSZH
Velocity factor	0.50
Conductor type	Solid copper
Capacitance	46nF/km
Insulation resistance	50 Mohms/km
DC resistance	93 ohms/km
Insertion loss	24dB/km @ 1MHz
Character impedance	100 ohms @ 1MHz
	100 ohms @ 10MHz
	100 ohms @ 20MHz
Attenuation	2.1dB/100m @ 1MHz
	3.6dB/100m @ 4MHz
	5.6dB/100m @ 8MHz
	6.3dB/100m @ 10MHz
	9.1dB/100m @ 16MHz
NE Crosstalk	50dB/100m @ 1MHz
	40dB/100m @ 16MHz
Outer Diameter	6mm
Conductor Diameter	0.5mm

33.3.1 Baluns

Baluns are impedance matching and circuit balancing devices primarily consisting of a ferrite toroidal transformer. They provide the interface between one cable media and another but present the characteristic impedance of the original media to the transmitting and receiving equipment. For example, if an office has been wired in unshielded twisted pair (UTP) but the tenant requires to run a coax service, a balun at both ends of the UTP line will give it characteristics similar to coax.

The word BAL-UN is an amalgamation of the abbreviations BALanced and UNbalanced. Baluns are fitted at both ends of the UTP cable, at the equipment end and terminal end. There are a range of baluns to correct for each type of media.

At the terminal end there are three options to where baluns are located:

1. Baluns in adaptors at terminal end.
2. Baluns in leads.
3. Balun in adaptor at socket end.

Considering the socket outlet end the balun/adaptor can be located at the terminal or socket outlet end of the terminal lead.

The advantage of putting it at the terminal end is that it uses the same lead irrespective of the type of terminal, coax, twinax, etc. The lead is then part of the structured cabling system.

However, when one introduces voice into the system, telephones tend to have fixed leads and require a Line Jack Unit (LJU) floor socket. Locating the adaptor at the socket outlet provides the most general solution.

At the modem/data concentrator end, the choices are very similar. Locating the balun at the patch panel provides a neater installation but requires the lead to be specific, i.e. coax, twinax.

33.3.2 Media filters

Some systems which have been designed for coax or screened cable of a similar impedance to UTP can operate over UTP without the use of baluns.

However, to cope with the additional noise picked up by the unshielded cable, media filters must be fitted at the ends of the UTP cable.

33.3.3 Transformers

Impedance matching transformers use the effect of mutual inductance between two or more windings on a ferrite toroid core.

In its simplest form there are two windings where the impedance are as in equation 33.1.

$$Z_1 = \left(\frac{n_1}{n_2} \right)^2 Z_2 \tag{33.1}$$

where Z_1 is the impedance of the first winding
n_1 is the number of turns on the first winding
Z_2 is the impedance of the second winding
n_2 is the number of turns on the second winding

More complex impedance matching can be achieved by wiring additional windings in series with these windings so that their mutual inductance adds to or substracts from the total inductance.

The equations of the resultant inductance formed by connecting two mutually coupled windings in series are shown in Equations 33.2 and 33.3, where the mutual inductances add in one case and oppose in the other.

$$L = L_1 + L_2 + 2M \qquad series\ aiding \tag{33.2}$$

$$L = L_1 + L_2 - 2M \qquad series\ opposing \tag{33.3}$$

Where L is the resultant inductance
L_1 is the inductance of winding 1
L_2 is the inductance of winding 2
M is the mutual inductance between the two winding.

33.4 Network topology

The topology of a network is its physical layout or shape.

There are four basic topologies: bus, ring, star and tree.

The star has the advantage that one end of each cable comes back to a common point. This enables changes to be made at one place. By linking the legs of the star together, bus, tree and ringlike structures can be created.

Structured cabling systems have a star topology while the network that is to be implemented can be bus, ring, star or tree. The solution is to make the network into a local star. That is, the last 100 metres from the desk is a star. This is achieved with patch panels plus the devices given in Table 33.4 depending on the basic network being used:

Table 33.4 Network topology, services and conversion

Network	Service	Conversion device
Bus	Ethernet	Multiport transciever/hub unit
Daisy Chain	Twinax	Loop wire concentrator
Ring	Token	Multiple access unit
Star	Ethernet	Multiport transceiver/hub unit
Tree	Ethernet	Multiport transceiver/hub unit

33.4.1 Patch panels

Patch panels give flexibility to the structured cabling system. They allow any service to be routed along any cable to any desk. Patch panels ar used for two functions:

1. Horizontal patching, which allows re-routing of services between desks.
2. Vertical patching, which allows re-routing of services between floors.

Patch panels fall into four categories:

1. Wire patching, where linking is performed by individual wires.
2. Cable patching, where linking is performed by 2,4,6, or 8-core patch leads with plugs on both ends.
3. Soft patching, where linking is performed by software configured, electronic equipment.
4. Fibre patching, where linking is performed by fibre patching leads.

The length of patch leads is an important issue. The flexible patching leads have to be limited to a maximum length (i.e. 6 metres) as they tend to have worse high frequency characteristics than the solid conductor cable used for the fixed installation. This places a restriction on the patching panel size and hence the number of outlets a single patch panel can serve.

33.4.2 Implementation

Using the structured cabling system, there are two areas where a computer/communications system may have to be adapted to operate over an SCS. These are the media and the topology.

Media conversion is achieved by baluns and filters. Topology conversion is achieved with patch panels, loop wiring concentrators, multi access units and multiport hub units.

UTP provides a cost effective solution for the horizontal part of a structured cabling system. However, where these all meet at the hub/wiring closet and travel down the riser, there is a heavy concentration of data which can be carried over multi-core UTP or, alternatively, it can be multiplexed.

In the preceding sections, the data rates carried by the UTP cable have been listed and the limits of this type of media have been shown. The data rates required are achieved by UTP cable but there is minimal spare bandwidth for combining on copper.

Fibre optic multiplexing provides a solution for the data concentrations in the riser (vertical) part of the structured cabling system.

There are two approaches to the fibre multiplexed backbone. One is to have independent fibres for each service and the second is to combine them into a common fibre system such as FDDI (Fibre Distributed Data Interface).

The two main issues are the cost of the fibres against the cost of the equipment to combine different services onto the same network. The simpler, cheaper and most robust solution today is to provide independent fibres for each service. Although a common system with one network management system does have its benefits.

Fibre backbones are generally based on a fibre patching system with fibre to copper interface devices in wiring closets and 50/125 or 62.5/125 multimode graded index vertical fibres. The first figure is the core size and the second is the outer cladding thickness in microns.

For overlay services or general future use, fibre can be extended to the desk using a combination copper/fibre cable and terminated in the floor box cassette.

33.5 Services

Overlay services are often specified by the client and use data rates that far exceed the capabilities of the UTP. They are usually carried in coax or fibre. For example, some banking, insurance, video conference, satellite and international information and new services can be handled as overlay services.

Examples of these services are: REUTERS, TOPICS, CHAPS, BACS, MegaStream links, KiloStream links, TV, video and teletext.

Table 33.1 shows the range of cable types which are recommended by the computer manufacturers. A structured cabling system replaces these with a common UTP cable type.

The characteristic impedance (Z_o) of a cable is the ratio of the applied voltage and resultant current at the same point. Because of the capacitive and inductive effects within the cable, the characteristic impedance varies with frequency. Changes in characteristic impedance along a cable length will give rise to signal distortion and reflection.

Table 33.1 shows the characteristic impedance of the cables recommended to suit the various computer systems. The use of baluns and media filters enables any of these services to operate over 100 ohm UTP cable.

Recent technological improvements in cables and communication equipment has led to an increase in the data rates carried by copper cable. Table 33.1 gives an indication of the data rates carried by structured cabling systems. At the low end the analogue voice systems have a data rate of 4Kbps (bits per second) while at the high end token ring has a bit rate of 4Mb/s or 16Mb/s.

Higher data rates of 20, 32, 64 and even 100Mb/s over UTP cable are being evaluated, although at these high data rates an overall shielding cable is used. Table 33.2 shows a data rate comparison between various media.

33.6 System performance

Structured cabling systems are provided with a system performance specification, which defines the services, data rates, and distances that the system can handle. This performance is effectively a combination of the cable, the equipment and how they are installed.

System performance specifications usually come in two parts; a general performance guarantee and a list of service specific limitations. This is shown in Table 33.5.

Table 33.5 Performance guarantee

Service	Distance (meters)	At Mb/s
General performance	100	16
Token Ring	100	16
Ethernet	140	10
Token Ring	150	4
IBM 3270	300	2.34
IBM AS400	250	1
RS232	400	0.0096

33.6.1   Installation specification

The installation specification for a structured cabling system ensures that the equipment is installed in a professional manner which will avoid sources of interference.

It would include statements such as:

1. Cable runs to be more than 3.5m from fluorescent lamps, shredders and lift motors.
2. That they should not run in parallel and adjacent to power cables and must cross at 90°.
3. That the installation of the cable shall be such that noise induced in the link should not exceed the following when measured in accordance with IEEE 802.3i Section 14. Namely, Impulse Noise above 264mV should not occur more frequently than one every 5 seconds; Crosstalk Noise should be below 264mV.
4. That the wires are terminated in accordance with the IEE 803.3i standard defining which colours are connected to each connector pin.

33.6.2   Earthing

This is one area often overlooked by building cabling systems. Most equipment requires some earthing at the terminal, in the wiring closet and at the equipment room.

Where earthed socket outlets are provided on a structured cabling system it is important that the adjacent socket earths are not connected together but wired back to their source. Socket outlet earths which are connected together provide a path for earth loops between networks. For example between two different computer systems.

This same isolation issue applies at the patch panel where screened cable is used. Screened patch panels should conduct the screen through from inlet to outlet cable without cross coupling between circuits. Cross connection between screens can lead to earth loop problems if more than one computer system is being handled by that patch panel. The best solution is to provide a selectable facility so that screen coupling between sockets can be made if appropriate for that installation.

Installation rules must be adhered to to minimise interference from power cables, shredders, fluorescent lamps, lift motors and telephone ringing and dialling signals.

Equally as important to noise induced into the system is the issue of noise emission from the system that could interfere with other equipment. This is covered by an EEC standard No. EEC 89/336 Electromagnetic Compatibility and part 15 of FCC Rules.

33.7   Testing

Because of the future proof/flood wire nature of a structured cabling system only part of it will be used at the time of installation. The installed equipment cannot be used for testing as this only uses some of the system's capacity. A total system test is required, encompassing every pair throughout the system.

There are a number of automatic test units on the market which will do this very efficiently. Some test equipment used on UTP was developed for voice wiring and adapted to cover data cables, while others have been developed for Ethernet and Token Ring installation.

The way in which the test equipment connects into the system is an important consideration. A quick connection method encompassing several circuits can save a lot of testing time.

Some automatic systems sequence through the pairs, others send a unique signal down each wire. Most require a piece of equipment at each end of the wire to test all possible types of faults, although capacitive and resistive tests can be performed from one end.

For telephone line testing traditionally a 1 pair plus earth line test would be sufficient. It is becoming more common to test all 3 pairs in the line jack unit (LJU). There are a number of continuity, resistance and capacitance tests which can be performed to establish the type and location of faults.

Table 33.6 shows some of the possible faults on pairs of wire, their symptoms and whether capacitive (C) or resistive (R) tests are used to detect them. The distance to a short can be determined by the resistance, given that the conductor resistance per metre is known. The distance to an open circuit can be determined by the capacitance to earth between the pair.

Table 33.6   UTP fault systoms

Fault	Test type	Symptom
Pair cross	R	Works
Leg cross, split	C	Capacitance imbalance, low mutual capacitance
B leg to earth	R	Works but attenuated signal and line permanently in recall mode
A leg to earth	R	Voice signal lost
A to B short	R	Voice signal lost
Open circuit A	C	Capacitance imbalance
Open circuit B	C	Capacitance imbalance

Unshielded twisted pair cable has a relationship between the mutual capacitance between pairs and each line capacitance to earth. The capacitance to earth is generally 1.5 times the mutual capacitance. This applies provided the cable has an earthed shield or is laid in an earthed environment, tray, soil or damp duct etc. This property can be used to analyse some otherwise difficult faults.

Voice communications between the two ends of the pair is important for fast and efficient testing. This can be achieved by radio or some test equipment makes use of the pair under test.

There are more sophisticated pieces of test equipment, for example Time Domain Reflectometer (TDR). This works on an echo sounder or radar principle of timing the echo from the other end of the cable or from any breaks, joints or changes in capacitance along the length of the cable. This time delay is then displayed as a distance from the test point to joints, breaks or interference points.

Some TDR instruments include a CRT oscilloscope type of display which shows the amplitude and shape of the reflected signal against time. The distance along the x axis indicates the time delay for the reflection(s) and hence the distance(s) the cause of the reflection is away from the instrument. By moving a cursor to the reflections an LCD display indicates the distance in metres. The instrument must be set up with the velocity factor for the cable under test. The shape of the echo gives an indication of the cause, which could be a short circuit, open circuit or joint, etc.

The velocity factor or velocity of propagation is a measure of the speed at which a signal travels along the cable as compared with free air.

The velocity of a signal in a cable is a function of that cable depending mainly on the type of dielectric material and construction. Commonly used dielectric materials such as polyethylene, polyvinylchloride, polypropylene. polythene, cellular polythene, all slow the progress of the signal by various amounts. Table 33.7 shows the velocity factors associated with these materials.

Table 33.7 Effect of dielectric on velocity of propagation

Dielectric material	Velocity factor	Velocity of propagation
Free air	1.00	100%
Semi polythene	0.84	84%
Polythene	0.78	78%
Polyethylene	0.66	66%
Polyvinylchloride	0.50	50%

When using TDR's the velocity factor must be entered into the instrument if it is known or can be measured using a known length of good cable with an open end.

The shape of a reflection as displayed on a TDR CRT screen will indicate the cause of the reflection. Some modern TDR's can analyse the signal and indicate the cause in words on a liquid crystal display. For example "short circuit at 25 metres".

33.8 Voice distribution frames

33.8.1 Main Distribution Frame

The Main Distribution Frame (MDF) is located at the interface between the external PTT cable and the PTT switching equipment. Its purpose is to provide the following:

1. Cross connection flexibility point.
2. Termination point for cable.
3. Overvoltage protection.

4. Interface between external and internal cable.
5. Test point.
6. Isolation point.

Many designs of MDF's exist ranging from the basic angle iron frames dating back to 1893, to the more modern modular frames seen today. With modern electronic exchanges the frame has, in many cases, become the largest single unit within the PTT switching equipment. Because of this, considerable work is taking place with a view to reducing the overall size conducive with the practicalities of working with the number of circuits involved.

The advent of optical fibres has led to the arrival of very compact optical mainframes which can handle around 100 fibres per 3U of 19" standard framing. The future could be that as fibre is used more into the local distribution network as well as the trunk network much of the size and space problems associated with the MDF will disappear.

Today insulation displacement connection, IDC, is used most extensively as the connection method for all joints: incoming cable termination; both ends of the jumper; and the equipment termination. Traditional solder or wirewrap techniques are rarely used today.

33.8.2 Building distribution frame

The Building Distribution Frame (BDF) is the interface between the private (automatic) business exchange PABX and the building wiring network.

The BDF is analogous to the vertical distribution frame in the structured cabling system. It provides:

1. Cross connection flexibility point.
2. Termination point for cable.
3. Interface between PABX and building wiring.

With the building distribution frame many of the space and size problems exist in the same way as with the PTT MDF's. In the voice area, the use of fibre optics is some way off but may be hastened when legalisation allows voice and data in one cable sheath.

In the case of a small PABX handling 200-300 extensions and their associated incoming lines from the PTT, size is not a problem with the use of the modern IDC connectors available. As the installation increases in size to 10,000 extensions, which is not unusual, the same problems as with MDF's exist.

Another demand on the BDF is that on one side the cables are terminated from a structured or flooded cable scheme with a planned life of many years (future proof). On the other the PABX wiring to a switch which will have an expected service life of often only a few years. This is owing to the rate of technical advancement and the need for business users to maximise their voice installation efficiently. These differing requirements often mean that a separate frame directly associated with the switch is provided and changed when the switch is changed. This means that the BDF must be able to facilitate the teeing of the old and new switches to the building wiring, and facilitate the ready removal of the old PABX wiring without breaking service. Some of the more modern IDC connect systems and frames tackle this need.

33.9 Computer aided cable layout

Over the past two years the use of computers to assist in the design and management of cabling schemes has become commonplace.

This application of technology has been brought about by two factors:

1. The wider use of structured cabling schemes which provides more flexibility than traditional cabling schemes.
2. The acceptance that buildings have to accommodate increasing technology.

The main influence on this application of technology is the dependence that companies have placed upon it and the chaos that ensues when a change in the organisation occurs. Most office workers today use a computer terminal, and the predictions are that by the middle of the decade every office-bound worker will have an intelligent terminal on their desk. (Butler-Cox Plc, 1989, Information Technology and Building Design, London, 1.01). Therefore everyone will need at least two cable based services to their work space, data and voice, in addition to the power supply.

In order to accommodate this requirement the designer of the building has to take into account any number of furniture and organisational configurations. This means that there has to be the capability to connect a variety of cables to distribution points from virtually anywhere in the building. This requirement has brought about the use of structured cabling.

Structured cabling reduces the number of cables required to support an organisation but increases the number of possible interconnections within the network. In order to ensure that all configurations are accounted for in both a structured and non-structured environment an accurate design and documentation method is required. This is best achieved using Computer Aided Design (CAD) systems that produce drawings and related information electronically and much more accurately than manual methods ever can. They also allow the user to view a number of options and all the relevant information at one time and on the same drawing.

Drawings from the architect can be merged electronically with the services layout or the space planning drawings. Modern computer aided cable design systems also provide intelligent tools which enable the designer to check their designs and produce bills of material for a complete project.

CAD became popular in the 1960s to assist in the layout of microelectronic components on printed circuit boards and the design of microchips. Since then it has been used by people as diverse as car designers and architects. There are a number of CAD systems available, each with their own special features and applications in specific areas. It is possible to exchange data between the various systems so that a variety of professionals can transmit drawings electronically and make the best use of the technology available to them.

Some CAD systems available offer a range of applications which use the same core software and powerful networking technology. An example of this is 'Workgroup CAD', jointly developed by ISICAD and Novell. This enables designers to communicate with each other and immediately see what changes have been made by other members of the design team.

The most readily available form of drawing transfer is DXF (direct exchange format) developed by Autodesk, authors of the AutoCAD^{TM} software package. Most CAD systems will convert drawings to and from the DXF which means that data can be exchanged between systems. This transfer is only available for graphic information; any associated intelligence is normally lost during the transfer. Before attempting transfers the user must liaise with the vendors of the system and test the transfer thoroughly.

There are two types of Cable Design and Management systems, one using a database only and the more popular system combining CAD and database technologies. In both systems the database is used to store and maintain all relevant data on the cabling infrastructure. This can be anything from a description of components to costings and material lists which are generated automatically as the cables are routed on the floor plan. The CAD drawing is used to represent the database information and to input data to the database in a very fast and efficient manner.

The CAD based system requires more training and will need more sophisticated equipment on which to run. However its greater capacity to assimilate data makes it more productive than a database only system.

33.9.1 Using Computer Aided Cable Layout

Once the designer has the floor-plan available, the layout of IT components is planned. Various conventions exist to determine where layer or overlay information is stored. For example on a CAD drawing which has 256 layers available, layer number 155 may be reserved for floor outlets. The user can then view only the items needed. This means the architectural shell and furniture layout could be viewed in conjunction with the floor outlets although the drawing may contain much more information such as the electrical cabling and the HVAC services.

A Computer Aided Cable Design system will allow the designer to define a variety of symbols to represent a number of types of equipment. These can range from floor boxes to terminals, from patch panels to computers and from multiplexers to MAU's. These are, in most cases, not just graphical representations but can also contain considerable non-graphic data relating to the details of the equipment, such as number of sockets and cost. The information can be maintained with each symbol, or pointers associated with the symbol will allow the user access to the relevant information in a database.

Symbols stored in libraries on the computer can be re-used on a number of different projects. It is therefore useful to create a master library of components for use on all projects undertaken. These should not only be the graphical representation of the component but should also contain non-graphic information such as part number and cost.

Most CAD based cable design and management systems will allow the user to specify the type of equipment to be installed and the grid spacing on the floor. The system will automatically place the components on the floor plan in an array. It is important to ensure that the layout of components such as floor boxes is consistent with the floor tiles or the access to the under floor void. This is where the ability to exchange data with other consultants is important. The architect, building services engineer, interior planner and IT designer all need to agree the parameters to which they are all going to work during the course of a project, and communicate any changes. This is better co-ordinated if they are all using compatible CAD systems to exchange data and review what the other is doing.

The cable ways, which could be trays or ducts, can then be located on the drawing. The majority of CAD based computer aided cable layout systems will not record the route of the cables graphically because there are normally far too many and the graphics would become too cluttered and slow. Instead they record the routes through which the cables pass. These could be cable trays, trunking, or just painted lines on the floor. These routes are displayed as a pair of lines connecting nodes. The nodes denote a change in direction, or a meeting of more than one cable way. The route a cable takes is recorded in the database by listing the segments or nodes through which a cable passes.

In some cases the computer aided cable design and management system will record the maximum capacity of a cableway in terms of volume and weight. As cables are placed within a tray, the system monitors how much of that capacity is used up and warns the user when maximum capacity is reached. The designer will then be able to re-size the tray or re-route the cable. The maximum capacity may not equal the theoretical capacity; allowances must be made for cables crossing over within the tray which will occupy more space than the sum of the cross-sectional areas of cables.

33.9.2   Computer Aided Cable Management

There are two reasons for using computer aided cable design systems. Firstly, they will automate the process of material take-offs and will generate the drawings needed for the installer and the client. The second reason is that they provide an accurate record of the installed cabling scheme to pass to the client. This is important as there will inevitably be a number of changes to the cabling scheme once it comes into use. There will also be a number of faults which will occur, and an accurate record of where everything is will assist greatly in locating the cause of problems.

What should be recorded on a computer aided cable layout system? Obviously all cables should be recorded but this is not of much value on its own; the user will also want to know what they are connected to. The system should therefore record the items which connect to the cables, i.e. all kinds of IT and telecoms equipment. These items should also be identified on the layout as they are useful in assisting with the task of managing the IT infrastructure.

It is important that the cabling infrastructure is maintained in an orderly and operational manner. In order to effect this it is vital that when the project is handed over to the client it is well documented and a procedure is in place to ensure that every change is assessed properly and recorded on the cable management system. It is easy to do this if a computerised system is used for the design. All the designer need do is pass the as-built information to the client in electronic format when the project is complete.

The system on which the design is completed should therefore have tools available to assist the manager of a cabling scheme. Typically these include the ability to determine usage of cabling and equipment, and record where in the building spare connections or specific items of equipment are located.

As well as reporting functions, the management system should provide the ability to evaluate the cost of a particular action and, once an option is selected, produce the work orders for the work to be completed.

In adopting a computerised approach to cable design and management, the design of cabling schemes will become more efficient and management will improve dramatically, thus reducing the problem of over-crowded cable ways and 'lost' cables. The use of some form of computerised documentation system may soon become mandatory for most cabling installations and designing the cabling on the system will ensure the accurate registration of the cables as installed.

33.10   References

Butler Cox (1990) *Information Technology & Buildings: A Practical Guide for Designers.*

McKenzie, Smith and Hosie, K.T. (1972) *Basic Electrical Engineering Science*, Longman.

33.11   Relevant standards

Regulatory body	Number	Subject
ANSI/ICEA	S-80-576-1988	Cable specification
REA	PE-71	Cable specification
IEEE	802.1 Part B	Protocols by which different objects can be managed
IEEE	802.1 Part D	LAN bridges
Bell	48007	Cable specification
IEEE	802.3i	10BaseT Ethernet over UTP
EIA	PN2072(CSA T530)	Building standards for Telecom Media
EIA/TIA	568	Commercial building wiring std
IBM	Type 3	Cabling system
AT&T	DIW	Systemax
BT OSCA	CW1700	Cable specification
FCC	Part 15	Rules & Regulations Sub Part J for Class A Computing Devices
BT	CW1308B	Cable specification
BT	CW1700	Cable specification
BT	CW1704	Patch lead specification
BS3573	3573	Cable specification
BS	4808	Cable specification
BS	6701 Part 2	Installation of switching apparatus for analogue telecoms
BS	6301	Safety requirements for equipment connected to BT network
BS	9055	Gas discharge tubes
CCITT	K12	Gas discharge tubes
BS CECC	42201	Varistors
OFTEL	NS/G/1235/M/10 0009	Apparatus approval
IEE	15th edition	Wiring regulations
TCP/IP	SNMP	Simple network management protocol
EEC	89/336	Electo-magnetic compatibility

34

PABX and key systems

Steve Berrisford
Northern Telecom
(Section 34.1)

David M Davidson
Northern Telecom
(Sections 34.2–34.7)

Fred Howett
Northern Telecom
(Section 34.8)

Contents

34.1 Purpose of key systems and PABXs

Prior to the existence of key systems and PABXs (also referred to as PBX) a company would have a separate telephone line from the public exchange for each employee requiring a telephone. If a call came in to the wrong telephone then either the caller would have to call back to the correct telephone or the correct person would have to physically come to the called telephone. Also, the company would have to pay the rental charge for every telephone line used.

With a key system or PABX, incoming calls can be answered by one person and then the call transferred to the correct person. The number of telephone lines from the public exchange is now determined by the expected maximum number of simultaneous calls (i.e. traffic) rather than the required number of telephones. Key systems and PABXs pay for themselves by the reduction in exchange line rental costs, the increased convenience to callers, and the increased productivity of employees.

Early key systems and PABXs were distinguished mainly by how they answered and made external calls. Key systems were (and still are) mainly used in smaller locations without a centralised answering position. Incoming calls ring several telephones and employees have a collective responsibility to answer calls and transfer calls to the correct person. PABXs usually do have a centralised answering position where the prime responsibility is to answer incoming calls and transfer them to the appropriate person. Key systems usually have a visual appearance for each exchange line showing whether it is use or not. To make an outgoing call, a free exchange line is manually selected and the required number dialled. PABXs usually pool exchange lines together and require an access code to be dialled to seize an outgoing exchange line. After dialling the access code, the receipt of dial tone indicates that an exchange line has been successfully seized while busy tone indicates that there are no free exchange lines at that time.

In recent years, the differences between key systems and PABXs have become blurred. Key systems now offer centralised answering positions and access codes to exchange lines while PABXs offer many features traditionally only available on key systems. Many manufacturers now refer to their products as hybrid PBX key systems.

Figure 34.1 shows the main elements of a PABX or key system.

34.1.1 Control system

In very early equipment, the number of services supported were very small. There would be an ability to recognise off-hook states, provide dial tone, recognise dialled digits, route calls, and ring telephones, but not much else. The control system was more of a concept than a physical reality. Each part of the system controlled the functionality of that part of the system. In modern day terms, this would be referred to as distributed processing.

As technology changed, the architecture changed to consolidate the major control elements in one part of the system. The technology used in this changed from relays to wired logic to microprocessors, but the fundamental principle has remained the same.

As microprocessor technology has evolved and become more cost effective, there is now a trend to move back towards more of a distributed processing environment. Processors in various parts of the overall system off load tasks from the central processing unit, and hence improve the overall performance of the system. Individual products have different architectures in terms of what tasks to perform locally and what tasks to perform centrally, but the fundamental principle of a hierarchical structure of processors communicating with each other, and with the rest of the system, is now common.

34.1.2 Switching matrix

This is the part of the system which connects one peripheral device to another. In step by step (Strowger) technology, the switching matrix consisted of a series of line finders, group selectors and final selectors which, under the control of the dialled digits, routed a call to its final destination. Physical movement caused one pair of wires to be connected to one of a number of other pairs of wires depending on the destination of the call. The number of elements (e.g. group selectors) in the matrix was determined by the expected number of simultaneous calls (traffic) through that part of the matrix. Higher than expected traffic levels would cause calls to be blocked and hence not reach their final destination. Since the call was routed through the matrix in a step by step manner under the control of the dialled digits, there was no opportunity to try alternate routes through the matrix.

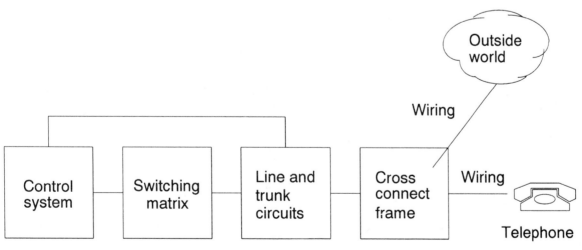

Figure 34.1 Main elements of a PABX or key system

Crossbar technology (Figure 34.2) used relays to make connections between wires in a physical matrix. Rather than responding to individual digits, all the all the required digits would be sent to the control system which would then find a possible route through the switching matrix. While calculating the required number of matrix elements was still required, this method of operation was more efficient since all possible paths through the matrix could be tried. The other major advantage of this method was that routeing information could be different to the dialled number information. This made it much easier to achieve the goal of one telephone number regardless of where the call originated from.

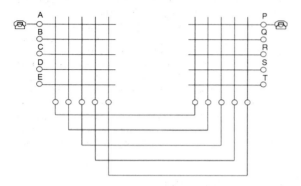

Figure 34.2   Simple crossbar matrix

Silicon controlled rectifier (thyristor) technology simply replaced the crossbar matrix with an electronic equivalent. However the cost effectiveness of this technology allowed non blocking matrices to be produced, thus reducing, or even eliminating, the need for matrix engineering.

All the above switching matrices are referred to as analogue systems. That is, once the human voice is converted into an analogue electrical waveform, it remains in that form until converted back to sound in the telephone receiver.

The next major technology change was to digital systems. In a digital system, the analogue electrical waveform is sampled, and the samples converted into a digital code. At the far end of the call, this digital code is converted back into an analogue sample. The series of samples are then filtered to convert back to an analogue waveform. The most common digital encoding scheme is called Pulse Code Modulation (PCM). In PCM, the analogue waveform is sampled 8000 times a second, and each sample is converted into an 8 bit digital code. The bandwidth of PCM is therefore 64000 bits per second (64kbit/s).

Digital systems use Time Division Multiplex (TDM) to interleave digitally encoded telephone calls onto a common highway. The management of this highway (or highways) in effect creates a switching matrix.

34.1.3   Cross connect frame

The control system and switching matrix are all normally located in one part of the customer's building. The telephone instruments on the other hand are distributed throughout the customer's building. The cross connect frame is therefore used to connect pairs of wires from individual telephones to individual circuits in the system peripheral equipment. Similarly, the cross connect frame is used to connect circuits from the outside world to the peripheral equipment.

34.1.4   Telephones

Telephones perform a number of fundamental purposes. On receipt of a signal from the telephone system indicating an incoming call (ringing), the telephone is expected to deliver an audible and/or visual signal to alert the called person. When the called person answers the call (goes off-hook), the telephone must signal the telephone system to remove the ringing signal and cut through the transmission path. The receiver in the telephone converts electrical energy representing the caller's voice into acoustical energy. The transmitter in the telephone converts acoustical energy into electrical energy. A part of the telephone circuitry sends some of the electrical energy from the transmitter to the receiver so that the user can hear their own voice. This is called sidetone. When the called person disconnects the call (goes on-hook), the telephone must signal the telephone system to this effect.

On an outgoing call, the telephone must request service from the telephone system (by going off-hook). The telephone system usually returns dial tone to the caller at this point. The telephone must now indicate to the telephone system the number of the called person. Early telephones disconnected and reconnected the circuit to the telephone system to send pulses (dial pulses) to indicate the number dialled. More modern telephones send bursts of tones (DTMF) to achieve the same end. The transmitter and receiver perform the same functions as for incoming calls, and a disconnect signal is sent at the end of the call.

PABXs and key systems require the telephone to perform more than the above fundamental purposes.

In order to perform functions such as transfer and conference, a recall signal must be sent from the telephone to the telephone system. Two types of recall signal are in common use. The first creates a temporary disconnect in the circuit, similar to a dial pulse. The second connects an earth (ground) to the circuit.

For PABX and key systems operation, the technology available on standard dial pulse and DTMF telephones became a limiting factor. Special telephones were developed for use with particular telephone systems. To begin with, multi-pair cables were used between these telephones and the associated telephone system to transmit the various signals required to perform additional functions. Later, electronic circuitry was used to transmit these various signals over a single pair of wires using some kind of digital code. At that time, the electrical energy representing the persons voice was still transmitted between the telephone and telephone system in an analogue format, and hence these telephones were still classified as analogue telephones despite the fact that the signalling was now in a digital format. The next stage in telephone set evolution was to move the conversion from analogue to digital voice (codec) from the telephone system to the telephone itself. Telephones with a codec built into them are classified as digital telephones.

Using the techniques of Time Compression Multiplex (TCM), a digital telephone is able to multiplex the digitalised voice and digital signals onto a single pair of wires.

34.2   PABX architecture

Figure 34.3 shows a more detailed block diagram of a PABX. The trunk circuits provide the basic access to and from the public network and can be analogue or digital connections. A variety of signalling systems are in operation ranging from basic loop disconnect signalling to common channel signalling on a 64kbit/s channel of a 2Mbit/s 30 channel trunk circuit.

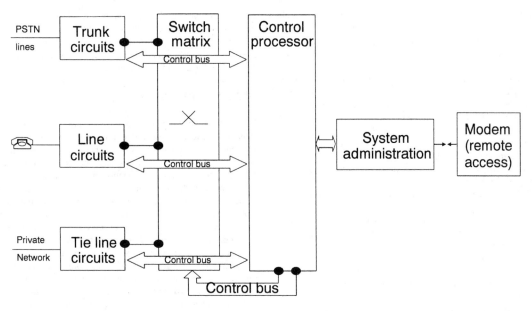

Figure 34.3 PABX block diagram

Tie line circuits provide access to the private network interconnecting a number of PABXs directly or indirectly via tandem private exchanges. The signalling on these circuits range from basic E&M through the spectrum to common channel signalling carrying DPNSS or Qsig signalling, with feature rich inter-PABX functions transferred over the signalling channels during call set up and during the conversation phase of the call. Line circuits provide the basic BORSCHT functions for analogue telephones.

Special proprietary analogue line circuits are in use for multifunctional terminals and digital multifunctional telephones, with data transmission on either the D-channel or the 2nd B-channel. The switching matrix can be either CMOS analogue switches for the smaller systems and digital switching is the most cost effective on nearly all other designs. The system control provides all the operational software/control functions to interconnect the various functions.

34.3 Trunk circuits

Trunk circuits provide the interface to the PSTN and use a number of different signalling systems to interact with the network.

34.3.1 Loop calling

This form of trunk circuit is the simplest interface which mimics that of the basic telephone interface to the public network. The circuit is a 2-wire connection to the public exchange with the basic elements shown in Figure 34.4. In the idle condition the public exchange presents a negative d.c. voltage on one wire and either an exchange earth on the other or the positive side of the exchange battery on the other wire, depending on whether the exchange has a floating battery or a battery connected to ground.

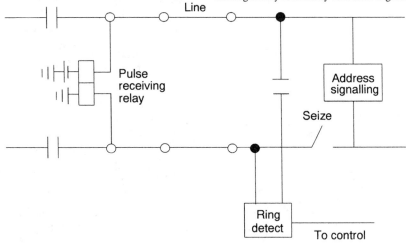

Figure 34.4 Loop calling

The PABX circuit presents the off-hook impedance of the ring detect circuit to the exchange. Incoming calls from the exchange to the PABX are ringing current superimposed on the d.c. of the exchange battery. The capacitor in the ringing detector circuit blocks the d.c. exchange battery and the a.c. ringing signal is presented to the ring detector circuit, which generally consists of an opto coupler which isolates the line from the low level electronic circuits. The a.c. ringing activates the opto coupler and the signal is presented to the system. It is normally the system software which performs the persistency checking on the signal and timers are set to monitor the on and off periods of the ringing signals.

As no common international standards exist for ringing signal cadences, different public exchanges provide different ringing signals depending on the individual operator's specification, so the PABX circuit must be flexible enough to cater for different requirements.

The problem that can arise with loop calling lines is call collision due to the line seizure being applied by the public exchange before the ringing signal is available at the PABX. This condition arises from the nature of ringing signals as they are bursts of a.c. signals followed by a silent period. It is during this silent period that the exchange line may be seized simultaneously by the public exchange and the PABX trunk circuit.

To initiate a call the PABX trunk circuit will seize the exchange circuit by closing a contact and looping the line. The public exchange will respond by returning dial tone superimposed on the d.c. exchange battery feed within a specified period of time depending upon the network specification. At this point the PABX can go into the addressing phase which can be either loop disconnect signals at 10pps or DTMF signals. In either case the out pulsing of digits is controlled not by the users telephone but by the system software of the PABX so that features such as short code dialling etc. can be implemented in the PABX. The address signalling is therefore regenerative signalling and PABX can have 10 pps, DTMF, or proprietary signalling from the PABX telephones to the PABX and then the address signalling is regenerated as required towards the public exchange.

A call can be cleared by either the distant end or the PABX removing the loop from the line giving a disconnect clear. The main problem for the PABX is knowing when the distant end has cleared as the disconnect clear signal is not normally transmitted from one end of the network to the other and in some cases dial tone may be returned to the PABX while the PABX still has the line seized. The system relies on both parties clearing. For this reason, and the call collision mentioned earlier, high traffic PABX trunk circuits use earth calling or ground start signalling.

34.3.2 Earth calling

Earth calling signalling (also known as ground start) was introduced when automatic direct outward dialling from the PABX extensions was introduced and the telephone operator was removed from monitoring the progress of the call and hence the disconnect signal. The major reason for the introduction of this signalling system was to prevent call collision during the silent period of the ringing signal.

The principle of operation of the earth calling signalling is shown in Figure 34.5. To request service the PABX applies local earth via a relay contact to one leg of the pair from the public exchange. The exchange detects current flowing in this wire and responds by applying the exchange battery across the pair with dial tone superimposed. The PABX can then go into the addressing state like loop calling and send the digits to the exchange in either 10pps loop disconnect or DTMF signals. On an incoming call to the PABX the public exchange applies an earth potential to one leg of the pair (the opposite leg to that used by the PABX to call the exchange) and the PABX detects this signal as a calling signal.

Ringing is also applied by the network but is now of less importance and the PABX does not need to wait for the ringing signal during the silent period before acting on the incoming call signal. Either end can disconnect the call by breaking the loop, but the PABX is required to run a timeout and maintain the PABX trunk busy to all other PABX users until the public exchange has had time to clear the call down and return the line to its idle condition.

34.3.3 Meter pulse detection

On any of the 2-wire analogue signalling systems the PABX may also be required to detect meter pulses sent from the exchange. These are normally only used on systems where it is necessary to provide accurate call accounting within the PABX e.g. in a hotel applications or where the PABX is in a multi-tenant environment

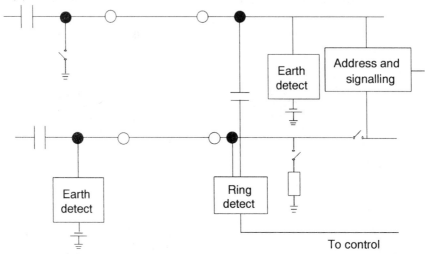

Figure 34.5 Earth calling

and the PABX owner charges for the use of the system on a timed basis related to the meter pulses received from the public exchange.

Two signalling systems are in use for meter pulse detection and both use out of band signalling as it is necessary to send the meter pulses to the PABX during the conversation phase of the call and the talkers should not be able to detect the pulses. 50Hz longitudinal pulses are applied to the speech pair and the trunk circuit of the PABX must therefore be equipped with a detector which senses the meter pulses and then passes them onto the system controller for assimilation with the call record. The other method uses 12kHz or 16kHz signals.

34.3.4   2Mbit/s digital access

2Mbit/s digital access is presented to the PABX as a coaxial circuit carrying 30 channels for voice or data, a synchronisation channel on timeslot 0 and a signalling channel on timeslot 16. In the UK DASS2 is the signalling system employed on the primary rate ISDN service. The signalling system is based on the ISO 7 layer reference model with Layer 1 using a CCITT G.703 2.048Mbit/s interface utilising HDB3 line coding. The PABX must be designated as the slave as far as synchronising to the network is concerned and this is achieved via timeslot 0.

The messaging between the PABX and the public exchange is via timeslot 16 using Link Access Protocol D (LAPD) which is designed for end-to-end signalling over ISDN and is an extension of the ISO High Level Data Link (HDLC) control procedure.

LAPD is a frame orientated protocol with the information it carries consisting of messages that are delimited by flags. Error correction of information frames is by re-transmission until correct or until a timeout expires. The next frame is not transmitted until the last is correctly acknowledged.

Within DASS2 there are three types of call identified:

1. Category 1 calls, which are calls that require end-to-end digital paths e.g. a data call. In this type of call no in band tones or announcements are given by the network.
2. Category 2 calls, which are calls for which an end-to-end digital path is not essential and if a non-digital path is encountered then a 'not suitable for data' message is sent back to the PABX.
3. Telephony, which cannot be used for data and the swap facility in the system cannot be used, nor can the user-to-user supplementary data services.

The public network offers 5 services to the DASS2 PABX user as follows:

1. User to user signalling, which allows several blocks of 32 bytes of data to be transmitted between the calling and the called PABXs. There is also the option to configure one or more DASS2 speech paths as tie lines, to permit transmission of large amounts of data end-to-end from user to user.
2. Closed user group facility enables a logical grouping of users within the public network. Connected party identities can be displayed on the PABX feature phones. Each group is identified by a number and the network places restrictions upon calls into and out of the group. Most of the functionality is provided by the network and the PABX has to provide the appropriate call set up and acknowledgement messages.
3. Calling line identification provides the PABX with the identity of the calling customer and apart from displaying the calling line number on the operator's position on a PABX, it can also be made use of in ACD applications where the customer's line

number can be used as an additional check when accessing a data base via a CSTA link.
4. Call charge indication is an attractive feature for PABX applications in hotels. It provides information on customer originated calls and, in the basic PABX, an input to the call management packages. At the end of each call the network reports the number of units used and the cost of the call.
5. Network address extension is only available on category 1 calls and enables a destination code to be appended to the PSTN number. The feature can be used to access a specific device on a LAN connected to the PABX.

34.4   Private networking

Many PABXs are interconnected by private networks carrying both voice and data traffic. Access to these networks is provided by tie line circuits in the PABX which provide the signalling and interconnection between the PABX and the transmission network of the private system. Some private networks are not point to point and the PABX must then act as a tandem exchange interconnecting the tie line circuits and providing a digit translation facility, to enable the user to dial the least number of digits to get from one point to the other.

With the deregulation of telecommunication services the PABX operator is able to offer 'break out' facilities over the private network. When the user dials a PSTN number, the PABX will interpret this number. If it is more economical to send it over the private network, the call will be routed to the nearest geographical point in the private network to the required PSTN number, normally within the local call charging area. It will then 'break out' into the public network via a normal PSTN trunk circuit.

These types of facilities require intelligent tie line signalling systems and like the PSTN signalling, tie line signalling comes in varying degrees of complexity depending on the application within the private network.

34.4.1   E&M signalling

E&M signalling is the simplest form of tie line signalling and has been borrowed for PABX usage from the public network where it has been used to interface public switching systems with the long distance transmission line signalling systems. The signalling scheme can be applied to both 2-wire transmission circuits and 4-wire transmission circuits as the signalling is carried on an additional two wires between the PABX and the distant end, or the intermediate transmission or multiplexing equipment.

The E&M signalling system derives its name from the historical designations of the signalling leads between the PSTN trunk circuits and the transmission equipment which tended to be housed in different parts of the building of a public exchange. The E&M signalling circuits use one lead for each direction of transmission and a common earth return which makes them more prone to noise than a balanced 2-wire system.

The E-lead has an earth potential applied from a contact and the receiving equipment has a battery connected relay as the receiving circuit. The same circuit is used in the opposite direction on the M-lead but in reverse, as in Figure 34.6. The impedance between sending and receiving ends is thus limited to about 140 ohms.

In the UK the E&M signalling system is called SSDC5 and is now only used between equipment in the same building. The relay contact is pulsed at 10pps from the PABX control system to send digits into the private network. It is possible to use the E&M circuit

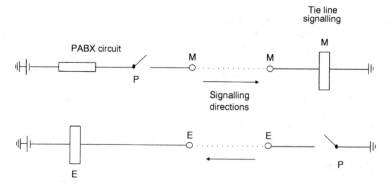

Figure 34.6   E&M signalling

only for line seizure and release signals and use MF inter register signalling for address signalling.

34.4.2   Double current signalling

With double current signalling a polarised relay is used which is very sensitive and the signals are transmitted as opposite directions of current flow as in Figure 34.7. The use of double current signalling also minimises the effect of line capacitance by continually reversing the current in the line. The limitation of double current signalling is that the address signalling can only be sent at 10pps and a physical pair is required between the PABXs.

34.4.3   Single frequency signalling

Single frequency a.c. signalling has been developed for use on 4-wire amplified circuits between PABXs enabling line and address signalling to be sent over the amplified circuits on unlimited distances for the PABX user. The signalling system was derived from the signalling circuits used in the 4-wire amplified circuits between the public exchange and the long distance transmission systems.

An important requirement was the choice of tone for line signalling to avoid imitation of the signalling tone by the voice signal. This was achieved by selecting a tone high enough in the speech band such that the power within the voice signal was at its lowest level. The tone selected was 2280Hz.

In the UK the signalling system is SSAC15 and is similar to CEPT L1 which makes it suitable for international use. The system operates on a forward and backward signalling basis, as in Figure 34.8, with both directions of signalling separated. Signals are sent as either the application of the 2280Hz frequency (tone on) or removal of the frequency (tone off).

The system operates on a link by link basis and signals are contained within each link. Forward and backward signals may be passed simultaneously and in some cases when speech is present but the primary use is for call set up and clear down. The system allows for address signals to be sent at 10pps.

Like E&M signalling on physical wires this signalling system allows the use of multifrequency inter-register signalling for address signalling and the 2280Hz for the line signalling.

34.4.4   Inter-register signalling

Inter-register signalling, like its counterpart in the public network, is intended to provide the PABX private network user with fast call set up and the use of a set of supplementary services across the network, similar to those available between the the telephone users on the same PABX.

The signalling system is based on CCITT R2 signalling using multifrequency signalling on either 2-wire or 4-wire circuits between PABXs. The signalling system requires a supporting line signalling system on each link, such as E&M or SSAC15, to control seizing, answering and clearing signals.

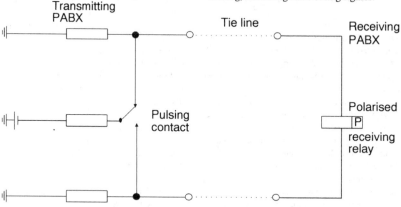

Figure 34.7   Double current signalling

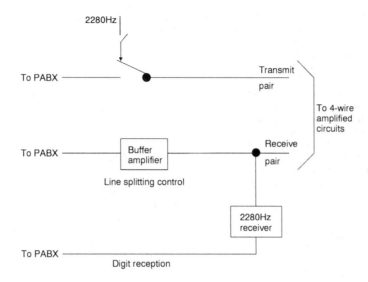

Figure 34.8 Single frequency signalling

The signalling system operates on an end to end basis with the signalling path being progressively extended as the call progresses through the private network tandem switches. It is a compelled system i.e. a forward signal once sent remains on the line until a response is received from the distant end. Once the forward removal signal has been detected at the distant end this causes the removal of the acknowledgement signal and completes the compelled signalling cycle.

Twelve frequencies are used, divided into upper and lower bands for signalling in the forward and reverse direction respectively. Each frequency is spaced 120Hz apart starting at 540Hz and going through the range to 1980Hz. The frequencies are sent as 2 out of 6 combinations giving 15 discrete combinations in each direction.

The system is further extended by reserving some of the combinations as shift functions so that the basic combinations can have up to 3 meanings. The later is used to add features between PABXs such as three party conference, executive intrusion, call offering etc.

The main use within PABX private network operation is to provide fast call set up and the basic set of signals is defined for the sending of routing digits between registers.

34.4.5 Dual Tone Multi Frequency

As PABXs were modernised and took advantage of DTMF telephones on the extensions, the need for fast call set up over private circuits became very apparent and the post dialling delays on tie lines using 10pps E&M or AC15 signals was not adequate for the modern business needs. R2 signalling was used to overcome this problem but only the larger PABX systems could afford the cost of implementing the full R2 system with its forward and backward signalling. The smaller PABX manufacturer found that he had to provide DTMF receivers for interpreting the address signals from DTMF extension telephones. When public exchange DTMF lines became available DTMF senders also had to be provided for the regeneration of signals and the pulsing out of short code dialling stores. This meant that the PABX had all the elements within the system for fast call set up using DTMF signalling over the private network and it was merely a software task to reorganise the PABX to make better use of these existing facilities.

Fast call set up over AC15 tie lines was then possible by using the AC15 for line signalling seize, release, and answer. The AC15 10pps address signalling was then suppressed and the sending PABX connected a DTMF sender to the tie line; the distant end on seizure connected a DTMF receiver to detect the incoming DTMF signals.

On the simpler PABXs where no restrictions were placed on dialling or where the routing digits required by the private network were minimal, the PABX user's telephone was directly connected to the tie line and the DTMF pulses dialled directly into the distant PABX. The frequencies used in this form of signalling are identical to those of the basic telephone.

34.4.6 Digital private network signalling

In the early 1980s 2Mbit/s private circuits became available for use in private networks and this led the need for an inter-PABX signalling system that would maximise the benefits of the all digital network. In the absence of any international standards developments in this area UK manufacturers and BT formed a working party to create an open standard so that PABXs from different manufacturers could interwork freely within a network for at least the simple call set up process, but also capable of implementation of advanced features as the need arose in the customer's network. Not all PABXs in the network needed to be capable of implementing the advanced features such was the flexibility built into the specification.

Digital Private Network Signalling System No 1 was first published by the working party in May 1983 and has since been revised and extended as customers' needs grew. DPNSS is a common channel signalling system on 2Mbit/s links using CCITT G.703 interface with the signalling information carried on a common 64Kbit/s channel in timeslot 16 for the 30 voice or data channels. Synchronisation is provided by the one remaining channel in timeslot 0.

DPNSS extends the facilities normally only available between extensions on a single PABX to all extensions on all PABXs that are connected together in the DPNSS private network. It specifies the signalling for a wide range of facilities for voice and circuit switched data calls.

DPNSS is organised on the ISO 7 layer reference model with the Physical Layer 1 and the Link Access Layer 2 virtually identical to the DASS2 equivalent layers. Layer 3 provides the basic messaging for DPNSS between the PABXs and these messages are implemented entirely in the software of the PABX.

Messages can be transmitted transparently through a PABX in the network if the destination address points to a PABX not linked directly to the PABX originating the call. When a call is set up on DPNSS the originating PABX sends an initial service request message (ISRM) with information on who the caller is (OLI), category of the calling line (CLC), a service indicator code (SIC) and the destination address (DA). This is transmitted over timeslot 16 to the distant PABX which responds with a number acknowledgement message (NAM), the called line category (CLC) and the called line identity (CLI) if the called line is free. If the called line is busy the distant PABX responds with a clear request message and busy indication. (See Figure 34.9.)

Channel 16 is divided to permit virtual and real messages to be transferred, where the real messages are used to set up calls for normal voice activity and the virtual channels can be used to pass supplementary information to enhance the interconnection of the PABXs. Within the PABX network DPNSS has had to define specific functions of a PABX. A transit function interconnects a call between two DPNSS channels. The call may be the initial set up via a new channel or a supplementary service call over an existing channel.

An end function interconnects a DPNSS channel to an extension telephone, a non voice terminal, a route to another signalling system or a conference bridge. The end function may be provided by an originating PABX, a gateway to another signalling system, a gateway from another signalling system, a terminating PABX, or a conference PABX. A branching function may occur when some supplementary services result in a new (related) call sharing a channel on part of its path from the originating PABX with the existing call. Branching functions may occur at the originating, terminating, transit, or gateways. As far as each call is concerned the branching function is always accompanied by either an END or a Transit function.

The DPNSS specification is divided into a number of sections with 1 through to 6 covering the basic call set up and mandatory interworking requirements. Sections 7 to 39 define supplementary services and it is these that make the networking of PABXs a very powerful, feature rich system.

34.4.7 Analogue private network signalling

As the PABX private networks are places of high innovation and largely free from bureaucratic restrictions the users have found a need to re-use their existing analogue tie line private circuits, but with enhanced features that came with DPNSS. Providing 2Mbit/s links to all PABXs on a network with 30 voice or data channels was an overkill for all applications, particularly if the network had a number of branch offices with a small number of tie lines connecting them to the main network. If a user wanted the same features available at the small branch office as was available on the main network then a signalling system as comprehensive as DPNSS but which would operate over existing tie lines would be required.

This problem was solved by PABX manufacturers by re-using all the software that had been developed for DPNSS and redirecting this over a data link between the two PABXs. Each PABX is equipped with an asynchronous signalling circuit which converts the PABX processor bus into a serial signalling output that can be connected to a modem. The modem is used to convert the digital signals from the PABX into analogue signals to run on the analogue tie line between the PABXs. It is selected to run at a low speed 1200, 2400 baud etc. depending upon the private circuit available between

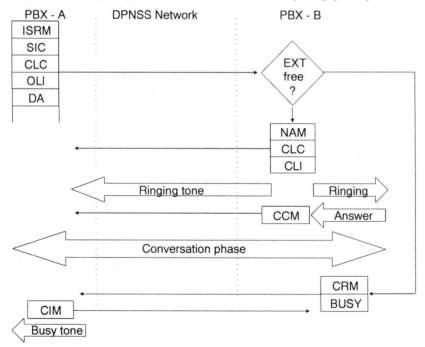

Figure 34.9 DPNSS call set up messages

the two PABXs and the expected message traffic for the number of speech channels between the PABXs.

The voice traffic is carried on separate private circuit tie lines that do not have any signalling system and are kept open at all times. Availability of circuits and feature transfer is controlled on the inter-PABX signalling channel via the modems with messages identical to those used in DPNSS.

34.5 Line circuits

34.5.1 Analogue line circuits

Analogue PABX line circuits are very similar to those of public exchanges providing the same functionality for connection of the plain ordinary telephone.

The PABX line circuit needs to provide the BORSCHT functions but the specification can be less severe in some areas, as the line length of the average PABX line is under 1km.

34.5.2 Key system line circuits

In key telephone systems the line circuits differ from that of a PABX in that additional signalling information needs to be transmitted to and from the telephone to provide the functionality of a key system. No standards exist for these signalling systems and they are all proprietary to the individual key system manufacturer. However the principle is the same in all the systems even if the physical and logical implementations may differ.

The key telephone and the line circuit have a bi-directional data circuit that connects the processor in the telephone with the processor in the key system. A message is sent from the the key telephone to the system requesting service and this is acknowledged by the system returning a message to light a lamp or change the indication on the telephone display. Messages are sent between the telephone and the system until the call is completed. The system may require to send messages to idle or busy telephones on the system, depending on the system configuration, informing each telephone of the status of all the other telephones, the status of tie lines, or trunk lines. As the system size increases so does the need for more messages on the line.

In this form of system the telephone is normally analogue and similar to an ordinary telephone but the signalling can be digital or analogue on a separate pair of wires from the system to the telephone, depending upon the individual designs.

34.5.3 Digital line circuits

Digital line circuits take many forms depending upon the transmission system employed between the telephone and the line circuit and within the PABX and key system environment many of the systems are proprietary, being designed for the most cost effective arrangement. If the system is 4-wire then one pair will be used for transmit and one for receive and the circuits at either end are connected with transformers. CCITT have now defined a system that works on a 4-wire basis between the terminal and the line circuit (in CCITT I.420/430) which operates to the S reference point standard at 144kbit/s with 2B+D channels.

In 2-wire systems the line interface is more complex and two line systems are common, burst mode or echo cancellation. Echo cancellation is much more complex to implement in silicon and PABX line circuits have tended to use the simpler burst mode technique. Echo cancelling is a full duplex solution in that it transmits data continuously in both directions at the same time. In burst mode operation the line circuit transmits a burst of data to the terminal, the line is switched off for a guard period and then a burst of data is transmitted from the terminal to the line circuit. The line transmission rate in burst mode systems is therefore much higher than in echo cancellation systems for the same rate of information transfer between the terminal and the line circuit. The technique is based on the fact that duplex transmission can be achieved on a single pair of wires by increasing the line transmission rate by some factor greater than 2 such that the transmit and receive signals at each end are compressed in time and never overlap, as in Figure 34.10.

Transmission rates of 384kbit/s on cable up to 1000 ohm loops are possible. A typical transmission system would have the following key parameters: 4kHz burst repetition rate; 2 PCM characters (16 bits); 1 data word (16 bits); signal/aux channel (4 bits); total bits/burst (36 bits); 384kbit/s line transmission; scrambled AMI pulse transmission.

Figure 34.11 shows how the voice and data are combined on the one pair of wires, then separated at the line circuit end to be switched through the system.

34.6 Control and administration

In the modern PABX the system is under software control, running on either a single processor for the smaller systems or with the functions divided between processors in the larger systems. In any case the particular architecture is governed by the system designer's

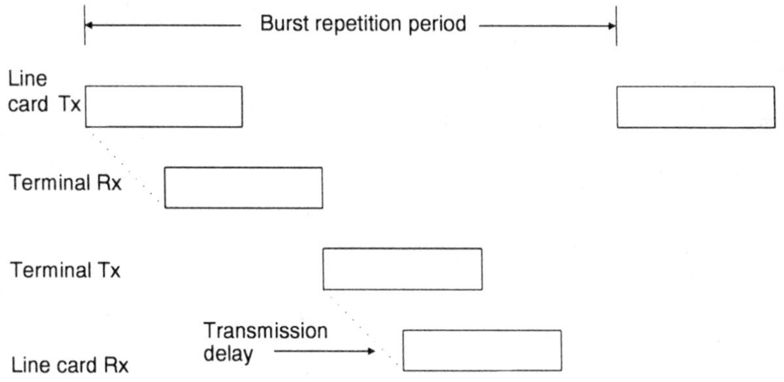

Figure 34.10 Burst mode transmission

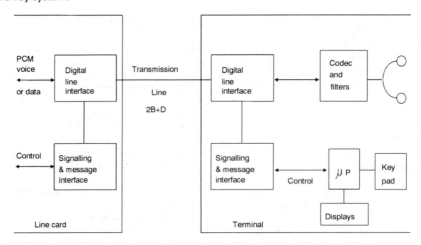

Figure 34.11 Voice and data over one wire pair

needs to balance cost against the functionality specified. In most systems, like any computer system, the software runs on a processor(s) with an operating system handling the basic low level functions and then the application layer interacting with the operating system.

All the call control software operates in real time and only peripheral facilities, like call statistics and database administration, operate in non real time mode. Control of a PABX is all centred round the software, which can be visualised as a number of concentric rings with the real time multitasking operating system in the centre surrounded by the hardware drivers e.g. the Layers 1 and 2 functions of the OSI 7 layer model. The database for the system is then the application software. It is in the application software that all the logical functionality of the switch resides and this is the most dynamic area of the software, which is required to evolve with the users' needs.

Access to the database is of prime importance to the PABX user, as this needs to be regularly updated to keep pace with the changing needs of the business. Early designs of PABX software were complicated to use and relied on the system manager understanding not only the business requirements but also how the PABX database bit pattern was organised, since changes to the database involved laboriously entering bit patterns at the appropriate points to re-programme the system. This led to the development, particularly in the US, of off line PC controlled database management systems, which had a more friendly user interface. This was used to program the new requirements off line and then up load this onto the PABX during a quiet traffic period. PABX suppliers have in the main now developed menu driven database management software that is resident as a set of application programs in the PABX and allows online changes to be made to the database without the need for out of hours working by the system manager. The application software is the most complex and handles a number of functional areas such as telephone or terminal interface, incoming call disposition, outgoing call handling trunk or tie line, database administration, system statistics and interfacing to other peripheral equipment.

34.6.1 Telephone or terminal software

Telephone or terminal software interprets the commands and functions invoked from the telephone or multifunctional terminal. Apart from receiving the dialled digits validating them, and passing them onto the outgoing call handling software, the telephone or terminal handling software controls all the user features.

On a basic PABX telephone, with only DTMF signalling, access to features is restricted to dialling special codes, which usually means that any call in progress needs to be put on hold before a feature such as conference another party, or dial ahead to determine if a colleague is free or busy. This limited signalling system and the absence of visual feedback for confirmation of feature invocation, has led to the development of multifunctional terminals with displays and arrays of keys to enable easy feature activation.

Typical features on the modern PABX would be:

1. Discriminating ringing, where internal and external calls had a different ring cadence to alert the called party to the type of call waiting to be answered.
2. Intrusion on a call already set up, unless any of the attempted intruding parties had secure statue to block intrusion.
3. Manager-secretary facilities, which enabled call filtering by the secretary, but with manager able to contact the secretary and automatic switch through to the manager when secretary is absent. Voice calling by secretary or manager and possibly auto answer by either if handsfree telephones are in use. One key calling of either manager or secretary. Visual indication of either manager or secretaries' line by either one.
4. Private line working, where a special line can be directed to a senior manager for undisturbed confidential calls.
5. Account coding of calls, either forced by the user on initiation of a call (useful in situations where consultants/partners must charge all clients for calls) or account coding at will, where the user can enter an account code during either an incoming or outgoing call to charge the client.
6. Broker's call, where the telephone user can hold two calls and shuttle between each call with secrecy on each line.
7. Callback on busy and call back on no answer, are all useful everyday features for the general telephone user.
8. Call pick up, which enables a user to pick up a colleague's ringing telephone from his/her own telephone.
9. Diversion of calls at various stages is helpful for efficient office organisation, as most can be preprogrammed so as to divert on busy i.e. when the called telephone is busy calls are diverted to an alternative telephone. Divert on no answer enables the user to divert calls on no answer to perhaps an alternative telephone

than the divert on busy one. Divert all calls ensures that when a telephone is completely unattended e.g. out of office hours, all incoming calls are diverted to either another telephone, a voice mail system or a message centre.

10. Multiple party conference is a desirable feature to enable more than two parties to be engaged in a conversation. The ability to dynamically alter the number of parties engaged in the conference during the call makes the feature much more useful in the business environment.

34.6.2 Outgoing call handling

Outgoing call handling used to be relatively simple on a PABX; the software was required to check if the originator of the call was permitted to dial that specific type of number e.g. national, international etc. and then place the call with a free trunk handling software module and permit out dialing to commence. If the PABX had central speed dialling stores then these could also be handled by the outgoing call handling software and frequently the user would be permitted to speed dial international or national numbers but not make any other calls of this category.

Recent years has seen dramatic changes in the way outgoing call handling software has had to be structured. The software now needs to decide which carrier to use e.g. in the UK the user has the choice of BT or Mercury or his own private network, with breakout at the nearest point to the destination on the PSTN. The number dialled by the PABX user can bear absolutely no relationship to the addressing sent by the outgoing call handling software. If the call is via Mercury for all national calls then the outgoing call handling software is required to check the look up tables built into the PABX to determine if Mercury service is available and appropriate, then to send the Mercury access code to the trunk handler, then send the Mercury PIN, and then the routing digits.

The software of the outgoing call handler is made even more complicated if an automatic route selection (ARS) or least cost routing (LCR) suite of software is included in the PABX, as this software contains numerous algorithms for routing calls based on the time of day, the load on the private network, and the charges being applied to the calls by the main carriers at that particular time. An outgoing call request has to weave its way through all this software before the digits can be dialled out from the PABX to place the call.

The outgoing call handling has a further subdivision to cater for private networking and access the data base with the private network numbering schemes and routing plans. For example banks use easily remembered numbers to access other banks and as all banks have a unique sort code then the PABX must be capable of translating between the sort code dialled and the routing information via the private network.

34.6.3 Incoming call handling

Incoming call handling software caters for a number of features just like the outgoing call handling. In the traditional PABX an incoming call signal was presented to the incoming call handling software and the software placed the call in a queue waiting for a telephone operator to answer the call before presenting it to the telephone or terminal handling software. Although this basic function still remains the software is required to handle much more complex tasks. The call may be a DDI call and therefore routed directly to the users telephone, or this may be a group of telephones, such as a service desk, where a number of users may be programmed to accept the

calls. Only if the call is not answered will it be routed back to the telephone operator. The system may have a voice response attached to the PABX or as an integral feature of the PABX. In any case the call will first be placed with the voice response unit to answer, and provide the caller with the initial greeting, before either placing the call with the operator for onward processing or accepting DTMF signals from the caller to route the call to a particular port on the system.

The PABX may be a multi-tenant system and the operator may handle the calls for more than one company, in which case the incoming call handling software will be required to place the call in the appropriate company's queue for the operator to answer and flag the operator with the company name at the time the call is presented.

In many business applications the need for automatic call distribution (ACD) working is essential. This facility originally required specially designed high traffic non-blocking systems with specialised control to route calls to agents who handled calls depending up the particular distribution selected by the business management. The ACD system could comprise a high traffic PABX front ended by a call sequencer and a management system that displayed the calls waiting in the queues on special screens. As PABX are now nearly all digital and non-blocking the PABX incoming call handling software has evolved to provide the functions of the ACD and call sequencing system as part of the incoming call handling task. The software is required to accept the incoming call request, route the call to a voice announcement, keep track of the time the caller is listening to announcement and switch the call onto a more appropriate announcement depending upon the time spent in the queue or the status of the agents.

The software is also required to interact with the telephone handling software to determine when agents become free to handle the next call and then force feed the call onto the agent's headset without the need for the application of ringing tone. The incoming call handling software is also required to interface with the real time call statistics software, which is a feature of ACD operation. The status of all calls in the queue, the number of calls lost, how quickly the calls are being answered, the mean time of individual agents to deal with customers, are presented as management information for the ACD supervisor to adjust the staffing levels of the system and therefore dynamically change the incoming call handling parameters of the system.

34.6.4 System reports and logging software

The software described so far has all had to operate in real time, but there are a few areas within the PABX where the operation is not time critical and therefore the tasks can be allocated a lower priority. These tasks are mainly concerned with logging of calls, generating reports on the status of the system etc. An important part of any PABX is the measurement of the traffic that it handles and the call logging software does this. Generally call logging software will monitor the start of any call, who originated the call, where the call was destined i.e. the dialled digits, the duration of the call and the date and time of either the start or finish of the call.

The PABX will normally only provide a cyclical buffer memory of a few calls, as it is normally anticipated that the user will attach a printer or, more usefully, some form of external storage medium to record all the calls made in a given time period and then analyse them off line on a PC. The same logging software is also used for incoming calls but unless the incoming line is DASS2 with calling number identification then the log is restricted to the called extension. This can give time to answer by the extension, as well as the follow on call. That is, the extension transfers the call to another extension plus the call duration and time and date of the call.

System reports are varied but the software will be expected to generate an equipment map showing the location of all the circuits within the system and whether the circuit is in service or has been taken out of service. The software will also be expected to log all the problems encountered and generate trouble reports e.g. that a particular circuit has been seized numerous times but released immediately without call completion, indicating a faulty circuit which may be, for instance, the private tie line. This indication can be used to pass messages to the outgoing call handling software to remove the circuit from service and raise an alarm.

34.7 Data transmission

The PABX is not the ideal mechanism for data transmission as it is designed around the speech bandwidth of 4kHz and in digital switching uses circuit switched digital signals at 64kbit/s, which is not the ideal medium for LANs running at 10Mbit/s or FDDI at 100Mbit/s. However, for the occasional data user, where small amounts of data are transferred from one point to the other, it can make an economical medium. PABXs have therefore concentrated in this area of the data switching market, providing such facilities such as modem pools on the PABX to which users can have dial up access, and calls set up over the PSTN with the modem.

In PABXs which have digital transmission two types of data facility can be provided. 64kbit/s switched connections, where the data circuit is normally of a slower speed and is rate adapted by a terminal adaptor using either an ECMA or proprietary rate adaption technique, which converts the data terminal output into the 64kbit/s bit stream. D channel packet switching is available on some ISDN PABXs, particularly French designs, where low speed data in packet format is supported on all basic rate ISDN lines and makes a very simple and cheap way to access packet network services.

34.8 Cordless PABX and key systems

A cordless PABX (or key system) may be simplistically regarded as a PABX (or key system) where some or all of the terminals are connected to the central switching system by cordless means instead of by hard wiring. Such a definition encompasses the situation where individual wired terminals connected to a conventional PABX are replaced by individual cordless telephones, and thus requires further qualification.

The additional requirement is that there should be some integration or interaction between the normal PABX functions and the cordless functions, in order to provide additional benefits or advantages. Such advantages might include smaller PABX switch requirements due to concentration within the cordless sub-system, or terminal mobility.

The cordless link may be provided by ultrasonic, infrared, or radio techniques using either analogue or digital modulation methods, but in order to meet the wide range of user requirements, digital radio techniques are almost invariably employed. The main advantages of cordless systems over their wired counterparts are:

1. Mobility, where a user is able to make or receive calls anywhere within the overall coverage area.
2. Reduced cost of ownership, due to simpler installation and ease of moving system users.

34.8.1 Requirements

The main requirements for the cordless sub-system to support the essential cordless PABX features are:

1. Support for high user densities.
2. Good subjective speech performance.
3. High reliability and grade of service.
4. Data capability.
5. High security.
6. Support for user mobility.
7. Self adjusting frequency allocation and re-use.

In environments such as city business centres with adjacent multi-storey buildings, fully equipped with cordless business systems, traffic densities of the order of 10000 Erlang per square kilometre per floor are required. Good subjective speech quality comparable to that of wired terminals is required at the cordless terminals, and the performance of the trunk network is often used as the yardstick.

Cordless business systems must be designed so as to provide acceptable grade of service (GoS) with respect to both call set up and forced call curtailment. Call set up GoS is a blocking phenomena as in conventional switches, whereas forced call curtailment GOS is a phenomena of cordless systems only due to interference of adjacent apparatus, and is subjectively the more important of the two.

Most modern PABXs and key systems are digital in nature and therefore inherently capable of providing both voice and data services. Cordless business systems must be capable of supporting the same range of voice and non-voice services. High integrity authentication procedures and mechanisms are required in order to provide secure access to the cordless system and provide confidentiality of the information transmitted over the cordless link.

A major feature of cordless systems is the provision of mobility both within a system and between systems, and specific mechanisms and protocols must be defined to support this important feature.

Wide area coverage systems such as cellular radio require central control and allocation of the channels available to each transmitter, to optimise channel re-use in order to maximise spectrum usage. This central control is not possible in the cordless business system area where a multiplicity of unrelated systems installed by numerous service providers must coexist. Cordless business systems must use dynamic channel allocation techniques to be self adjusting to changing local conditions.

34.8.2 Implementation

Although cordless PABXs and key systems are in their infancy, current designs are invariably based on radio links using digital modulation. The permitted radio spectrum bandwidth is shared amongst a number of users, with multiple access by the use of frequency division and/or time division techniques. In order to help achieve the high user densities required, a picocellular base station arrangement is used with cell radii ranging from about 10 up to 200 metres. Since all channels are available to all base stations by the use of dynamic channel allocation techniques, the traffic handling capacity of the system can be increased simply by adding extra base stations.

The radio performance in such systems is limited by the interference levels rather than by noise performance, so as the base station density increases, the interference levels from surrounding

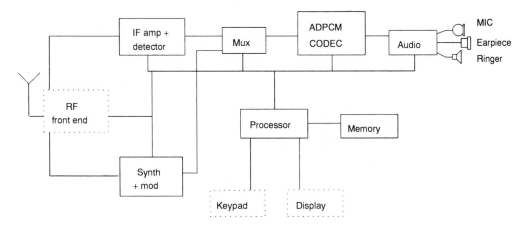

Figure 34.12 Block diagram of a typical CT2 handset

cells increase, and the usable cell size, which is determined by the carrier to interference ratio, automatically reduces.

Another possible method for sharing spectrum among a multiplicity of users is by the use of code division (spread spectrum) techniques. In CDMA systems the available bandwidth is not divided into separate channels. Each user has a unique code known to both handset and base station, which is used to spread the voice signal over the whole available bandwidth at the transmitter and to reassemble the transmitted signal at the receiving end. Although such cordless systems are complex compared with analogue systems, the low powers used, and the extensive use of digital techniques lead to highly integrated products. A block diagram of a typical CT2 handset is shown in Figure 34.12.

34.8.3 Standards

Commercial pressures towards open standards lead to the adoption of common air interface standards to encourage competition and facilitate roaming and public access services. The first two common air interface standards for cordless systems are CT2 and DECT and are both European in origin.

CT2 (second generation cordless telephone) and DECT (Digital European Cordless Telephony) both provide cordless speech bearers by using 32kbit/s ADPCM (adaptive differential pulse code modulation) to the CCITT G.721 standard developed for transmission on the trunk telephone network. The ADPCM coding takes the 64kbit/s PCM bit stream comprising 8-bit samples at the 8kHz rate, and reduces the 8-bit samples to 4 bits.

CT2 uses a 4.0MHz block of radio spectrum between 864MHz and 868MHz to provide 40 duplex channels, and DECT uses the 20MHz from 1880MHz to 1900MHz to provide 120 duplex channels. Average power levels are around 10 milliwatts per channel for both systems, and both systems employ dynamic channel allocation.

There are substantial differences in the frame structures of the two systems as shown in Figures 34.13 and 34.14. CT2 is a frequency division multiple access, time division duplex (FDMA/TDD) system arranged as 40 frequencies spaced at 100kHz intervals, with one duplex channel per frequency, using time division to carry the traffic in both directions. In order to interleave the transmit and receive bursts and maintain the overall bearer capacity, the transmitted bit rate must be at least twice the overall data rate. For CT2 the transmitted bit rate is 72kbit/s.

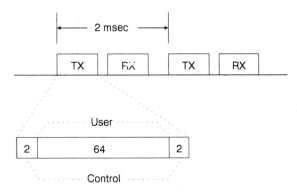

Figure 34.13 CT2 frame structure

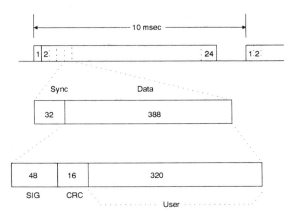

Figure 34.14 DECT frame structure

DECT is a multiple carrier, time division multiple access (MC/TDMA) system which uses ten channels at 1.728MHz intervals, with 12 duplex channels multiplexed on to each carrier and a transmitted bit rate of 1152kbit/s. Within a DECT base station each time slot may be transmitted on any of the ten carrier frequencies,

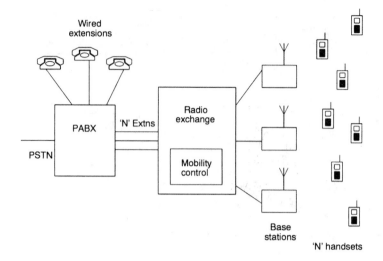

Figure 34.15 A basic cordless PABX arrangement

and a single base station may operate with up to 12 handsets simultaneously. In both systems a transmit or receive burst comprises a number of ADPCM samples together with control and signalling data.

The use of time division techniques introduces delay in the speech paths which may require additional echo control to provide acceptable subjective performance, particularly in DECT systems with their longer framing delay.

Both CT2 and DECT specifications have adopted a layered approach based upon Layers 1 to 3 of the ISO open systems interconnect 7 layer model. These cover the physical aspects such as carrier frequencies, power levels, modulation characteristics, multiplexing of user and signalling information, channel assignment, link set up and control, and network layer protocols for managing calls between the portables and the central system and external networks. In addition the requirements for speech transmission performance over the air interface are also specified.

34.8.4 Possible configurations

Figure 34.15 shows a simple cordless PABX structure where N standard PABX extensions are assigned to N cordless handsets. The radio exchange links the PABX extensions to the radio base stations and also handles handover and location updating functions. The PABX provides the normal services. This configuration may be added to most existing types of PABX.

Figure 34.16 shows a more complex structure where the radio exchange incorporates additional common control and switching functions to improve roaming and to provide concentration. The connection between the radio exchange and the PABX may be by a multi-channel digital link, such as ISDN primary rate access. The normal services are still provided by the PABX. The radio exchange and the PABX may be built as a single integrated system or as separate unit.

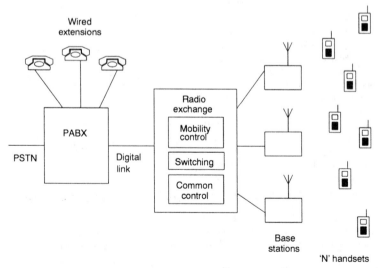

Figure 34.16 An improved cordless PABX arrangement

35

Centrex

Kanagendra
B Tec MBA CDipAF
Northern Telecom Europe

Contents

35.1   Introduction

Centrex is a service offered by telephone companies which gives their customers the capabilities of a sophisticated voice and data Private Branch Exchange (PBX) without the need to purchase and maintain on-premises switching equipment.

A modern digital PBX is a specialised real-time computer which routes calls and provides calling features such as call forwarding and handles data transmission for a customer's business site. Lines connect each individual telephone and data terminal to the PBX. The PBX is connected to the Public Telephone Network Operator's (PTO) main exchange (called the Central Office switch) by voice and data channels called trunks. Voice and data traffic to and from the public network travels over these trunks, while traffic internal to a customer's site is routed by the PBX. Traditionally, trunks do not provide any features.

Centrex is an alternative for businesses which do not wish to buy and run their own private telecommunications system. As the name implies its is a Central Office Exchange, with the lines from individual telephones and data terminals connected directly to the PTO's exchange rather than a PBX. This exchange is also used for the public telephone service. The software resident in the central office switch is partitioned and programmed to create a virtual PBX that delivers voice and data services comparable to those on any modern digital PBX. Numerous virtual PBXs can exist on on any one central office switch, all sharing the same processing resources.

Centrex is attractive to corporations, particularly the larger ones, who increasingly find that telecommunications is using up considerable resource, financial and human. This coincides with these organisations seeking to create strategic advantage in their core business activity using sophisticated telecommunications. In the UK this has resulted in a proliferation of private networks and large departments to manage the telecommunications service. An alternative service from the public network which fulfils the same requirements allows these organisations to outsource their telecommunications and concentrate on their core, revenue generating, activities. An additional benefit for multi-sited corporations is that their various sites can be linked together over a public telephone network based on sophisticated central office exchanges such as the Northern Telecom DMS range, to form a 'virtual private network' (VPN). This gives a simpler internal dialling plan as well as network wide use of features such as call forwarding, ring again and call waiting.

Centrex is also attractive to business that do not have enough lines to justify the purchase of a PBX, yet need the sophisticated voice and data services an expensive PBX can offer, such as Automatic Call Distribution (ACD), and integrated Voice Mail (IVM).

35.2   Centrex services

The network and PBX approaches offer comparable features and benefits. When both options are available, as in North America, hybrid networks are frequently found, with a vast majority of Centrex users using a PBX somewhere in their network. However, PTOs can offer integrated access to a much wider range of service with Centrex, for example ACD, advanced data switching such as Frame Relay for LAN to LAN interconnection, and private leased lines. A typical deployment of Centrex and hybrid networking on the Northern Telecom DMS is shown in Figure 35.1.

35.2.1   Featured voice

Centrex has voice features which help ensure that calls are answered quickly and routed appropriately and cost effectively within the network. Features provided by typical advanced digital Centrex include direct dialling inward (DDI), flexible intercept, hunting, night service and security provisions. Advanced business sets with user programmable feature keys enhance access to a range of features. The addition of displays on these sets provides calling information such as the called or calling party's name and number, reasons for redirected calls, and digits dialled during call origination or while activating system features.

The system offers further facilities, including ACD with sophisticated management and centralised message service. A simplified console enables operators to concentrate on incoming calls.

35.2.1.1   *User terminals*

Northern Telecom's terminals support three access interface technologies, namely:

1. Analogue, for plain old telephone service, or POTS.
2. Business set, for network-wide featured voice services.
3. ISDN, for network-wide interworking of voice and data capabilities.

These technologies complement each other to meet both the user's and the PTO's requirements for service and ease of deployment. The ISDN interface is an enhancement to the business set interface, which in turn offers an improvement in functionality over the POTS interface.

The attraction of the POTS interface stems from its historical standardisation and simple implementation at both the subscriber and central office ends of the loop. The limitations of the interface result from its single analogue channel. Consequently, multiple line appearances require a key system at the customer premises. Limitations of the interface also make access to most Centrex features difficult; the user has to use 'feature' codes, for example, "*74" is used to invoke call forward. With the more advanced sets users can take advantage of assignable feature keys, which eliminate the need to remember the feature access codes. Some terminals also offer the user hands-free capability, message waiting features, line status monitoring and visual ringing. However, these features are dependent on what the terminal can support.

The POTS interface can transmit data only with a modem at limited data rates. It is, however, the most cost-effective interface for basic telephone service.

The second access technology, the business set interface, offers significant advantages over the POTS interface. The benefits result from an out of band signalling channel which carries the feature control signalling information independently of the voice call over the same pair of wires.

This capability to carry both voice and signalling information allows multiple line appearance on the terminal and provides users with easier access to advanced Centrex voice features. The out-of-band signalling capability also allows the switch to constantly update the terminal on the status of the line or any feature being invoked.

This technology was first introduced by Northern Telecom in the early 1980s. One of the most recent additions is the M5000 series of

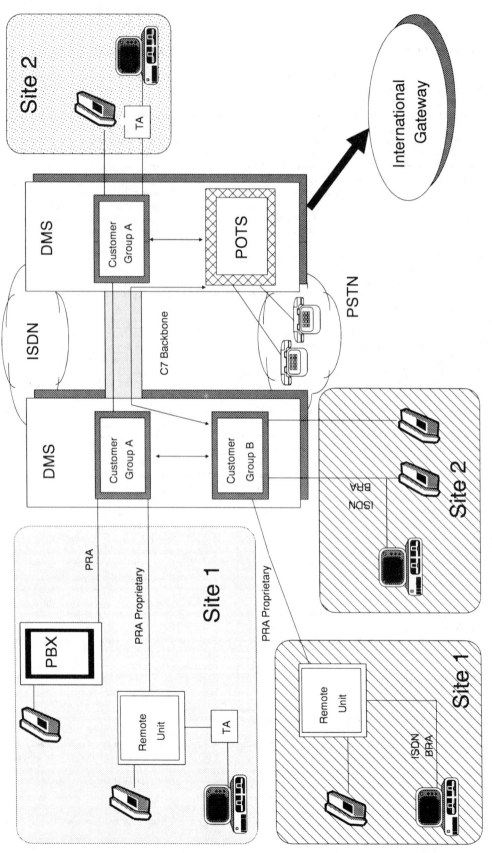

Figure 35.1 Typical Centrex architecture

advanced business sets, offering single key access to DMS digital Centrex features such as ring again and three-way calling. User response from US and Canadian field trials has been extremely positive, particularly in the areas of audio quality, functionality of the display and ease of use.

Most of the functionality of these sets resides in the DMS-100 software. The sets themselves transmit messages corresponding to key depressions to the switch, and receive indicator messages from the switch. Because the terminals are unaware of the feature actually invoked, new features can be added and old ones upgraded without changing the installed base of terminal hardware or firmware.

The introduction of liquid crystal displays (LCDs) on some of the business sets further improves the user interface by enabling, where available, the caller's number and name to be displayed. There are also other reasons for the display, such as allowing the user to see why a call has been forwarded, and from whom.

It is frequently postulated that most people in a business environment only use about four features on their telephone system, mainly because access to these features is inconvenient. The M5000 series makes it much simpler to use many features available on the DMS Centrex, thus allowing normal users to realise the benefits these features have to offer.

35.2.2   Automatic call distribution

Automatic Call Distribution (ACD) is a powerful business feature which can be readily implemented in Centrex. It distributes large numbers of incoming calls equally among a designated group of answering positions, presenting the first incoming call to the position which has been idle longest. If all 'agents' i.e. answering positions, are busy, later calls are queued and answered in order of arrival. Comprehensive information on the incoming calls, such as time to answer, number of callers who abandoned while in the queue are all available from a management information system.

Current DMS systems will deliver a full ACD feature set regardless of line size, whether to a 2000-line sales or reservation system or a 10-line group medical practice. This extends the benefits of ACD to small and medium sized businesses which would find the cost of a PBX-based solution prohibitive.

The DMS also allows network wide distribution of ACD groups. A service organisation e.g. motor insurance, could publish one directory number for inquiries, but incoming calls would be passed to an agent group located closest to the caller, reducing the cost of the call. It also allows calls to overflow to other groups if the first group is busy.

Using the calling line information passed with each call, sophisticated applications can be developed e.g. for telemarketing or information services. This is done via a Switch to Computer Applications Interface (SCAI), which allows the DMS to be linked to business computers. These services can be used to generate extra revenue (e.g. mail-order) or save on operating expenditure (e.g. outbound calling to check customers are at home before sending out service engineers). Further sophistication can be added by using an Interactive Voice Response system, with the ACD, to provide interactive routing, such as determining if the caller wants sales or service departments before queuing the call. Credit card validation systems also use the same technology, which can, for example, be provided on the NT Meridian Mail system.

35.2.3   High speed digital data

Convergence of voice and data in digital networks is an accomplished fact. A recent US survey of Fortune 1500 companies showed that despite the continued dominance of voice traffic in terms of volume, data is the dynamic service requirement and driving force behind new applications. Local Area Networks (LANs) solved immediate data handling requirements at working group level. Local integration of voice and data at site level through a PBX delivered greater interconnection options. The use of private leased lines to interconnect sites created wide area data networks.

Digital Centrex brings the flexibility, capacity and resilience of the public network to wide area data networks as well as Integrated Service Digital Network (ISDN) capabilities.

Major offerings available from data services implemented on Northern Telecom DMS digital public switches are:

1. Datapath services provide completely digital synchronous and asynchronous data transmission with automatic rate adaptation and handshaking protocols, freeing the user from the need to get transmission parameters for each call. Datapath will also work into analogue data transmission systems through a DMS-based modem pool.

2. DataSpan, an integrated Frame Relay, based on standards recommended by the CCITT. Frame Relay is a wide area 'fast' packet switching technology that offers an intelligent alternative to private lines for data interconnection. It uses less error checking than packet switching, optimising on the high quality of transmission on digital networks. This makes it more efficient for applications such as LAN interconnection. Existing solutions for connecting several data sites require leased or dedicated lines of fixed bandwidth in a complicated mesh. With DataSpan the public network becomes a viable alternative, eliminating the need for multiple connections; each location now links to the other through a single access line to the Frame Relay network.

3. ISDN services which realise the full potential of data management by Centrex. Standard features are being implemented on the DMS as they are defined. The Basic Rate Interface (BRI) carries two 64kbit/s B-channels plus one 16kbit/s signalling channel and delivers voice, circuit and packet switched data to as many as eight terminals on one pair of telephone wires. The Primary Rate Interface (PRI) offers 30 B-channels plus one 64kbit/s signalling channel, and can form the ISDN link between a central office switch, digital PBXs, and host computers.

Since all DMS data services provide switched access, terminals can reach multiple hosts as quickly and easily as dialling a normal phone call. Digital Centrex provides a range of calling features as well as a range of security features, such as defined customer groups, closed user groups, and direct inward system access authorisation codes, to guard against accidental or deliberate breaches of security.

The DMS also has the capability to support existing simple data networks based on drop and insert multiplexors utilising spare capacity on private leased lines for voice networking. Changing the voice network over from a PBX to Centrex will not call for an immediate re-appraisal of the overlay data network.

A key benefit resulting from taking the Centrex route to ISDN is future-proofing of the corporate network. New ISDN features are continually being defined and are likely to force expensive upgrades on PBXs. In contrast, upgrades by the PTO to central office switches are immediately available to all users.

35.2.4 Network management

The existence of a virtual private network means that the telephone company is able to offer customers advanced network management features. The user specifies the features required and retains direct control over their use. In addition, the operator can provide central monitoring, measurement and control, allowing more sophisticated management than possible on a network of PBXs. The management systems will capture comprehensive details of every call, which can be sent to the customer with the regular bill or transmitted on a data link directly to the customer.

35.3 Development of the Centrex market

By the 1960s AT&T, the North American PTO, had achieved universal POTs service. They then looked for new market opportunities and Centrex was born. First generation analogue Centrex services were highly acceptable by the standards of the day, and, by the start of the 1970s, 20% of the business market used Centrex. This then slumped as AT&T chose to focus on the PBX business to protect its position in anticipation of divestiture. Centrex recovered sharply following the divestiture of AT&T and the introduction of more highly featured digital Centrex such as that on the Northern Telecom DMS. Today, every Bell Operating Company has experienced growth in Centrex services, which once again handles close on 20% of North American business telecommunications.

In Europe Centrex is emerging as a result of liberalisation, with the first European digital Centrex service launched in the UK by Mercury Communications in 1987. Mercury regards Centrex as a technique for adding value to its public network services, while simultaneously delivering competitive advantage to customers.

The market's initial perception of Centrex as expensive led to some customer resistance. However, in 1989 Peat Marwick, the accounting and management consultants, compared the total costs of Centrex with PBXs and concluded that in four UK company models calling for between 100 and 1500 extension lines, over seven years Centrex turned out to be the economic choice, with the greatest savings made through operating efficiency.

Mercury's initial service was limited to customers directly connected to their central London optical fibre network. In four years, features have been enhanced to make sure that the service continues to meet or exceed leading PBX offerings and tariff reductions have made the service even more competitive against PBXs. Early users included members of the London financial community, who saw customer benefits as:

1. Speed of installation and service; less than 4 months from signing of lease to full operation in a new building.
2. Financial flexibility; the equivalent of a £2M installation without capital outlay.
3. Operational flexibility; the ability to add or alter functions, and to cope with expansion and possible office moves.
4. Maintenance; 24 hour monitoring and support.

The next logical step is wide area Centrex. This makes it possible for the user to configure a highly featured wide area virtual private network while retaining an exceptional level of flexibility. Wide area Centrex draws on a database of users, identifying their location, and privileges, giving them the full range of Centrex business services at all sites. It amounts to a virtual private managed network operated by the telephone company retaining the availability possible only on the PSTN.

The telecommunications revolution has so far served the business user within the office environment. Extension of the wide area Centrex concept through intelligent networks brings the networked office environment into the home and also brings the home worker into the mainstream business community through shared facilities. Any user, wherever he or she is, can have access to the range of services which would previously have been available only in the office environment on the corporate network.

The advantages of Centrex for the business and domestic consumer are clear, such as variety of features, low investment, protection against obsolescence, reliability and flexibility to meet change positively. In addition, it greatly strengthens the position of the telephone company as a one-stop service provider. The basic telephone network is unique in its ubiquity and vast resources. Centrex enables numerous services to be added, or deleted according to business volume and type of activity. Given this range of service flexibility, the traditional understanding of the term Centrex is limiting. The DMS allows telephone companies to deliver Network Based Services thereby positioning themselves as a responsive business supplier rather than a commodity service provider.

36

Call Management

Jean R Oliphant
Rockwell International

Contents

36.1 Introduction

Call management began as the recording of basic call information by sampling signalling activity on voice trunk circuits carrying calls into and from a call centre. The information provided circuit usage, but not an identification of who placed the call and to where it was placed. The information may have been derived by equipment at the facility or from the public phone office providing service to the facility. Analog printers, magnetic tape recording devices, or mini computers were used to perform the recording. The carrier may have collected and charged for the information on a request basis, with the customer responsible for processing the data. Basic reports of not much more than call by call activity were created from this information. Visual scanning of the reports for exceptions and other management information was then performed.

Call management has continued to grow in many dimensions from its humble beginnings. Competition among switch vendors, the advent of the PC, plus demand from call managers for more information, more quickly, are all contributing to new systems and management capabilities. This chapter covers voice call management in its current dimensions and looks at trends for the future.

36.2 Why call management?

The desired goal of effective call management is almost always to reduce costs and to increase the profit for the call centre. The switch hardware, the carrier services and connections, plus the user calling habits are the major areas which affect the costs and profit. The ways in which the goals are achieved can depend on the type of call centre and the type of call management used. The call management approach, with the investments in systems and services to be used, should be carefully considered against the types of call centre and the management goals in the short and long term.

The payback for investments in call management systems, software, and personnel can be cost justified on one or more elements to be optimised. The method for optimisation to produce the greatest profit is dependent on the application. In an application providing help for product service related calls, the goal would be to keep all calls as brief as possible so time sensitive trunk circuits are used less. In another application which provides consultation and advice, and bills callers based on time, the goal could be to encourage continuing the conversations, since the longer the call the more the profit. In other applications the goals may be to reduce the number of calls or to allow more calls to be made. The reduction of excessive calls, elimination of under utilised extensions and trunk circuits, plus improvements in service are other goals useful as cost justification elements.

A common approach used in cost justification of an ACD (Automatic Call Distributor) to be used for high volume inbound call applications is to assign a cost or profit value to each call, or even to each second in time of call duration. The investment in the completely stand alone ACD can be proven just by using the improvement in answering time, compared to other alternatives. For example, if the application is moved from a PABX group to the ACD, the ACD can answer each call and connect it to a service person faster than the PABX. The expected payback period is the result of dividing the cost of the ACD by the product of the difference in seconds of answering time, the number of calls per second and the value per second. If the payback period is short enough, then the cost is justified for the call management benefits the ACD will provide.

36.3 Special needs

Under the general call management sphere exist individual environments which are generally defined by the type of call application. Each environment has special call management requirements. In high call traffic inbound and outbound telemarketing applications, management of the trunk circuits and call servers is as important as handling the calls.

The stand alone ACD system, and to a lesser extent, the ACD option packages in PABX systems, are specifically designed for these high traffic applications. In other applications, multiple environments are being addressed by common hardware and software programs which are tailored to the application by adding options. Several of the major environments will be considered in detail.

36.3.1 Corporate environment

In the corporate environment (refer to Figure 36.1 for a general representation of this environment) call management is directed at several distinct areas of interest. The most prominent area consists of PABXs providing internal communications and connections to non-corporate systems. The call traffic is basically intracompany and intercompany business calls, plus the non-business related calls. The next areas are those groups dependent on call traffic, providing service and generating revenue to the corporation. These areas are PABX attendants, ACD groups within the PABXs, and stand alone ACD systems. The final area appears when the corporation occupies multiple distant locations. This area connects the PABXs and ACDs at the multisite locations by a company private network of tandem switches or by virtual private network interfaces. Each area in this corporate environment can be addressed by separate call management systems, reports and management approaches.

Call management in the corporate environment PABX area should first be directed at controlling calls before they are made. This is accomplished by providing employees with phone books covering good calling practices and listing restricted numbers, letting them police themselves, and then by using internal call restriction tables in the PABX to catch or block all violations. The internal call restriction tables would contain specific and partially specified phone numbers. For example, one partially specified restriction may be for all numbers in an entire country code, another for a selected city within a country, and another a specific number within a city. The restrictions, depending on the PABX, are specified as either the numbers allowed or not allowed to be dialled. If the PABX can assign a class level to the users, then the restrictions could be applied to all, or selected class levels. Such restrictions are sometimes based on date and time. The PABX would use the day of week and time of day to map to a specific table to be used from a set of restriction tables. The restrictions might also be based on the trunk circuit type for which usage or special service charges would be incurred.

Information on the number of attempts to restricted numbers can provide valuable information. Network modifications and removal of restrictions may be required if legitimate attempts are being blocked, but are being completed by other methods at a higher cost. The call restriction tables should be easily changeable and should be regularly reviewed to reflect current requirements and call management goals.

Calls which pass the restriction tables should be analysed for traffic patterns, call durations, and other parameters useful to call management. This information is derived from the call detail records produced by the CDR (Call Detail Recording) or SMDR (Station Message Detail Recording) features of the PABX. The PABX either produces the information in report form directly,

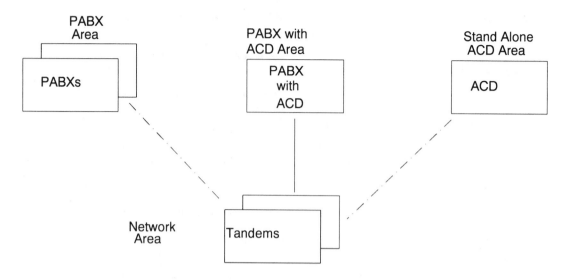

Figure 36.1   Corporate environment with areas of call management

provides the detail to a storage media for off-line processing, or outputs the detail to an external reporting system through a V.24 interface. All of these alternatives and the reports produced from the call detail are covered in more depth later in this chapter.

While the PABX typically provides detailed information for out-bound calls, it can be very useful to capture detailed information for inbound calls also. This is sometimes available as a special service, usually called AMA (Automatic Message Accounting), from the carrier providing calls to the PABX. This information can indicate a need to add more trunk circuits in some areas to reduce blocking, and to remove trunk circuits in other areas because of low usage. It can also be used to find abuses, such as excessive calls to selected extensions.

Call management in the corporate environment network area is directed at reducing the costs for the network facilities and the costs per call. Privately owned network facilities, leased, public and common carrier services may all be used at times, with changes made to obtain the lowest overall cost based on the tariffs for the call volumes offered to the network. The other area for call management attention is to reduce employee abuse and eliminate non-employee usage of the network.

Calls are offered to the network area from directly connected PABXs and ACDs, plus from public and common carrier networks. Direct access to the network may also be provided from carrier networks so that employees on travel or at home may perform business transactions. Such access must be protected from misuse by unauthorised users and non-employees. In the most common forms of protection, the network access numbers are disclosed only to authorised users, and individual employee identification numbers are assigned which must be dialled with each call. The access numbers are changed periodically as a further preventative step.

The tandem switches in the network should validate identification numbers before access is allowed, then provide automatic least cost routing for approved calls according to the caller's privileges on the network. The alternate route choices are ordered and automatically tried by increasing cost for the time of day and day of week. The caller identification, the route choice, plus other call information is entered in the call detail record. From the call detail and circuit

utilisation information produced by the tandem switch the call management decisions must be made.

In the corporate environment, high volume service and revenue producing call traffic is handled most efficiently by ACD functions. The ACD functions are provided by optional add-on features in the PABXs or by stand alone ACDs. Call management in the ACD is directed at the equipment, trunk circuits, call handling staff, application groups, and software controls on call handling. The management decisions are made from real time display information and from detailed reports produced directly by the ACD. Often the decisions must be made and actions taken very quickly to react to quickly changing traffic patterns. Longer term decisions can be made from the daily, weekly, monthly, yearly and call detail reports produced by the ACD.

Basic ACD design is founded on the management of queues. Incoming calls enter a queue and wait if servers are not available. If servers are available but there are no incoming calls, then the servers wait in queue. A very typical goal is to connect 85% of all incoming calls to servers within 20 seconds. Real time display information and reports produced every 15 - 60 minutes show management how close to this goal actual performance is. If performance is better than 85%, then staff may be re-assigned to other functions. If performance is less than the goal, then additional staff may be required.

Call management in the ACD is often divided between staff managers and a network manager. The staff managers have to use the alternatives available to adjust the staff levels to meet the performance goals under the current traffic load. Reassigning staff between applications, from less busy to more busy, may be the first alternative. This should not require hardware changes, but it must be possible by software commands to the configuration database. A resource pool of part time employees who are willing to work flexible hours as needed, is another alternative. Another choice may be to let an interactive call response unit record caller information with the intent of the servers calling back as soon as the current traffic peak passes.

Managers in applications using more than one ACD may have another alternative to balance traffic. The ACDs may be able to automatically transfer a portion of the calls waiting for service to each other to balance the traffic loads. This is especially effective when the ACDs are in different time zones with peak traffic somewhat time dependent. In this manner the ACDs work to provide better individual performance and better performance over all the network. The network manager determines the most effective ways to move the calls between the ACDs.

If staff adjustments or other alternatives cannot be made, then management may attempt to limit calls coming into the system. A queue limit or waiting time for service can be established. When the limit is exceeded an announcement is played to the caller indicating the expected wait time and alternatives they may have, such as calling back later, leaving a message, or transferring to another department. A more definitive action may also be taken in that if the established queue limit is reached, then any new calls beyond the limit receive a timed period of busy or re-order tone and are then disconnected. If callers immediately call back, then this alternative may actually be counter productive.

An external call management system may be connected to the ACD for staff scheduling and forecasting of staff and trunk circuit requirements processing. ACD applications commonly operate full time every day with full and part time staff. Scheduling and forecasting for this staff becomes a formidable task requiring the special system, especially as the ACD grows to the thousand or more positions supported by the current stand alone ACDs.

Call traffic patterns and staffing requirements for an ACD can be forecast based upon past history information with expected growth and management performance goals. The scheduling and forecasting management systems can provide information to know how many trunk circuits are needed, expected total call volumes, and what staffing levels are needed for future periods. A period can be even to the half hour detail. When connected directly to the ACD with a V.24 interface, actual performance information can be used to track and produce new forecasts.

The call detail information from the ACD can have special significance for both management decisions and for customer service billing. Information may be collected on both inbound and outbound calls. Answer supervision, either provided by signalling or by hardware detection of voice energy, is important to determine whether an outbound call is answered and call duration is correct.

36.3.2 Lodging environment

Call management in the lodging environment is directed primarily at appropriate sizing of trunk circuit groups and accurate answer detection for outbound calls. While inbound calls may follow a uniform distribution, outbound call attempts may often experience extreme peaks during the evening registration period and following the closing of large meetings. General guest dissatisfaction can occur if it is consistently difficult to get an outside line and often necessary to go somewhere else to make calls. If guests are billed for outside calls, then it is important to know whether calls are only attempts or are completions. Making the determination based solely on call duration is an inaccurate approach, which opens the way for the guests to contest phone charges on individual calls. Answer detection performed with a high degree of accuracy by the PABX, or by an attached call management system monitoring the trunk circuits, becomes important to the hotel and guests.

With an interface to the front desk and direct connection to the PABX, excessive phone charges can be controlled. At registration an established credit limit for phone charges can be entered into the system. As calls are made, this limit is checked. When the limit is exceeded, the call accounting system informs the PABX to block further calls.

36.3.3 Hospital/University environment

The hospital and university environment also requires very accurate call billing information since users pay for individual toll calls. This environment and the corporate environment share the same call management requirements for least cost routing alternatives when large campus installations are created using multiple PABXs connected in a network.

Call restriction capability is less important, however, than in the corporate environment simply because the PABX is a revenue producer.

36.3.4 Client environment

The client environment is that segment of business where calls are to be billed to a client or account rather than to the person making the calls. The caller enters the account or billing code for the call along with the destination number. The PABX enters the code into the call detail information.

PABX attendants may also perform a similar operation if an outcall cannot be placed directly, but only by way of the attendant. Billing reports for this environment should provide separate reports organised by the code.

36.3.5 Shared tenant environment

In the shared tenant environment the call centre is a revenue producer, since users are billed for the calls they make in addition to basic services. Call management has to be directed at providing good service while keeping overhead costs low.

Circuit trunk group sizes, the optimum number of attendants, and optional services, such as voice mail, all have to be considered under shared and non-shared operation. In this environment the call centre and any call accounting systems that are used require shared tenant reporting capability.

36.4 Call accounting

Call management in the various application environments is heavily dependent on call accounting information. In order for the information to be useful, however, the large volume of information must be organised and summarised into manageable reports and displays. If the switching systems cannot perform this function directly, then there are many choices available for add on call accounting systems and outside services.

The add on call accounting systems and service bureaux compete for customers by offering a wide range of reports, formats, data selection methods, and display outputs. If the user wants a report which currently does not exist, then the system may provide online report creation capability, or the vendor may offer this as an optional service.

The standard list of report choices include: call by call detail by time, by extension and by trunk circuit, busy hour, plus summaries by extension, department, account code, trunk circuit, and trunk group. These same reports are offered in a weekly, bimonthly, monthly and yearly version. Bar, pie and line graphic charts, and histograms are common alternative formats to the standard analytical printed reports. Colour is often used with the graphic reports and displays. Rather than printing reports, the output may be written to magnetic media or retained on the system for manual scanning and selected report printing.

Call cost information may be included in the reports with the cost calculated from a current tariff database using V&H co-ordinates. The report may be used directly for billing or for comparison of used facilities versus the alternative tariffed facility.

Exception reports, if available, can provide very beneficial information. Exception reports can list those calls with call durations longer than a specified length or greater than a specified cost. Exceptions can also show those extensions where more calls than a specified amount were made, plus the total calls made to specified numbers. The reports can be used to detect misuse, high or low volume traffic patterns to areas which may require network reconfiguration and facility changes. Exception reports can also indicate switching hardware and trunk circuit problems. Trunk circuits which consistently carry many calls with very short durations, or very few calls but very long durations when compared to other circuits in the group, are indications of problems in the switch hardware or trunk circuit.

36.4.1 Service bureau

Service bureaux process call detail information into a finished product for return to the customer. The call detail information is typically provided to the service bureau on magnetic media, either tape or diskette, on a weekly or monthly basis. A more direct and timely interface may be available by daily polling from the service bureau to call buffer units at the user's switches to receive the information. The finished product is dependent upon the service bureau. Printed reports are almost standard. Magnetic media containing reports to be printed or modified by the user for additional information before printing is another alternative.

The advantages of service bureaux are that they provide the processing hardware, supporting staff, and can offer reports customisation services. Since the staff is dedicated and familiar with the product, new reports can be developed very quickly. The service bureau is also not affected by real time call traffic rates, since the data is processed off-line. Distribution of product to individual customer departments can occur directly from the service bureau.

The disadvantages of the service bureau are that flexibility and control may be lost. The customer is now dependent upon the service bureau's schedules, product revisions, and cost structure changes.

36.4.2 User owned systems

The alternative to the service bureau is for the user to own, or lease, the call accounting system. The hardware and software may be acquired from the same vendor; however, most PC-based software systems are sold independently. The user may also choose to perform the software development.

The advantages of the user owned system are that reporting alternatives are just as available as provided by the service bureau. The software vendor may offer alternative packages, or the package may allow report selection and creation online.

Reports can be produced more frequently, such as daily or on demand for selected call tracing. The user may also be able to add other software packages, such as front desk, attendant directory service, and PABX moves and changes to the same hardware.

The user must determine the type of hardware, the operating system, and the call management software to use, plus any other application software packages to be integrated. Assurance must be made that the operating system and application packages allow seamless integration so there are no conflicts which allow only one or the other to execute.

The user has to decide whether a PC-based system can handle the call volume and peak traffic periods, plus provide the reliability, or whether a mini or mainframe will be needed. From history or by estimates, a determination has to be made of how many call records will be created per reporting period(s) and the call rate during the peak traffic periods.

The user must decide whether the system will be directly connected to the call centre or whether it will interface through a polling unit. If polling is used, then the frequency of polling and the call rate will determine the requirements for the size of the call buffers.

There are other questions which have to be answered. Will the system be dedicated to one call centre or will it be connected to many call centres at remote locations? If there are many centres, then is there good cost justification for not using a service bureau? If online access will be allowed for report manipulation and perusal, then how many terminals should be provided? Will the terminals be directly connected, remotely located, or interface by LAN or WAN? Again, can a PC handle these requirements, or will a mini or mainframe be required?

All these requirements should be put in the procurement specifications. The vendor should be required to demonstrate performance against the specifications as one criteria for acceptance of the system.

36.5 System interfaces

Call management systems currently on the market almost universally expect to connect to the switch by a V.24 port. The port is an RS-232-C physical interface. The call management system can be co-located with the switch or remoted using modems. The older method of connecting to the trunk circuits may still be an available alternative to the V.24 port, but offers less information and flexibility to automatically handle trunk configuration changes.

If full time call management information is critical, then interface failure detection processes should be provided between the switch and call management system. Since producing call management information may be a minor objective for the switch, failure detection becomes the responsibility of the call management system. An alarm, either audible or visual can be generated if call information, or keep alive data, is not received as expected within a specified time period. If the detection is based on receiving call records, then the process should adjust to lack of records that may naturally occur during some times in the day.

The data buffer capacity in the switch and call management system should be considered, for this becomes an important factor during out of service periods. Standard buffer and optional expansion increments should be considered against the requirements. If buffer capacity is 10,000 records, the switch produces one call detail record per call, and the call rate is one call per second, then the buffer can hold call records for 2 hours, 46 minutes and 40 seconds. If the requirement is to support an out of service period of 4 hours, then a buffer capacity of 14,400 records is required.

Depending on the switch, call detail information is provided either as a single record containing all the information at the end of the call, or as a series of records which are produced as phases of the call occur. In the latter case the switch assigns an unique sequence number to each call. All the records pertaining to the call contain the sequence number. The call management system then must use the sequence number to locate and accumulate all the records for each call.

The call detail information may be provided in ASCII, binary, or a combination of both formats. The switch usually produces only one format. The user is not given a choice. The ASCII format offers the advantage of being directly printable for verification of the record contents produced. A binary format typically offers the advantage of encoding more information into fewer characters.

There are no official or de facto standards established for call detail record formats or the data contents. The current record is typically a common set of information elements with additional elements provided depending on the switch. The common set includes: the date and time the call was placed, the call duration, the called number, the extension placing the call, and the outbound circuit used. Additional elements include: an accounting or billing code, attendant or directly dialled indicator, identification of any shared switch hardware that was used, a reason why the call was attempted but not completed, and indicators that transmission of data occurred. If inbound calls are also recorded, then additional elements include: inbound circuit, caller identification by ANI and ISDN information.

The call detail interface described so far is a one-way flow from the switch to the call management system. The newer call management systems, which offer integrated switch management service, require a two-way interface to get information back into the switch. The information moves and changes the switch configuration database as made by the switch administrator, or as the result of an attendant making directory service changes. The information can also be status values and alarms input from sensors monitoring facility environmental and security conditions.

A very low protocol form may be used with one-direction interfaces. The call management system may connect as if it were a printer with only request to send (RTS), clear to send (CTS) or XON and XOFF flow control capability. With two-way interfaces, a more complex protocol, such as Bisync, SDLC or X.25 may be used.

Call management requirements for ACD systems are more complex than for PABXs, due to the real time critical operating conditions. Management information for control of the queuing functions within the ACD is typically provided by the ACD. Agent force scheduling and forecasting is typically handled by a separate force management system. The information required by the force management system is manually input or provided through a V.24 port from the ACD. Entering the information manually might be used when one force management system is shared by multiple ACD sites; however, this can be impractical as the size of the work force and number of ACD systems grow.

Depending on the ACD, multiple choices for interfaces to call detail information may be available. Examples are a V.24 port with one-way or two-way direction, with one or more protocol choices. Magnetic medium may also be available.

Call management information from an ACD can be extensive. Performance reports may be produced every 15, 30 or 60 minutes all day, every day. On very large ACD systems, the information can be for a thousand servers and proportionate number of trunk circuits, with call detail information for every inbound and outbound call produced at call rates up to 9 calls per second.

36.6 Call management trends

A clear trend is to merge call centre systems. Individual specialised systems which have addressed separate functions in the call centre are being merged into the same processing equipment providing call management reports. Modularity in the software, multi-tasking operating systems, and better adherence to OSI standards make this possible. Within the PABX environment, directory service and call accounting can be logically combined because they both need extension number and user name database information. The PABX equipment inventory and configuration information is another logical addition when the processing system is physically located near the PABX. Other additions can include property management systems, security monitoring, cable/wire management, reservations, message centres, hotel/motel features such as front-desk management, plus data network interfaces and reports.

Multi-site interface capabilities are becoming more commonplace as vendors attempt to provide more cost effective systems with new features. The call accounting systems will be able to join call detail records of calls passing through multiple switches for complete network path analysis and maintenance call tracing. With the evolution of more powerful processors, these capabilities will be extended to the PC-based systems.

On-line report modification and creation capabilities are being extended. Relational databases are being used with direct SOL query allowed. The user will be able to create special reports easily without returning to the vendor. User screens will be friendly and database information will be easy to load. Direct interfaces to spreadsheet programmes will be provided so special analysis can be performed and graphic display forms with colour selections can be used.

Availability and usage of ISDN will continue to expand, with a corresponding upgrade in systems to address the new requirements. Additional call information, hardware interfaces, circuit requirements forecasting, network control strategies, and maintenance specific information will be provided in reports and real time displays.

Better call accounting reports will be provided directly from the PABX and ACD systems. Shift scheduling and forecasting will be integrated into the ACD. Actual staff adherence to the shift schedules will be shown in real time by exception on supervisor screen displays and in system reports. These advances can be accomplished by improving the standard reports produced by the ACD and through marketing agreements which will allow integration of the add on system into the ACD. Such total integration provides a major benefit to the customer, since the add on call management system(s), procurement process, integration testing, and support issues can be eliminated as a result.

Strong competition among switch, software and service bureau vendors continues to result in new products and services. With the advent of the PC, the call management systems markets have been opened wide to many small entrepreneurial companies presenting new approaches. Requirements from call managers for more information presented more ways, even more quickly, and at lower cost are also contributing to the trends in call management. The continuing trend is to provide better and more cost effective call management systems and services to help people manage their call centres better.

36.7 References

(1990) Advanced Traffic Control Methods for Circuit Switched Telecommunications Networks, *IEEE Communications*, **28** (10) (October).

(1990) Counting Call Costs, *Communications*, (October).

(1989) Making Sense of Call Statistics, *Communications Management*, (November).

Berman, C. (1990) Call Management: Moving Towards OSI Standards, *Communicate*, pp. 32-7, (March).

Borthick, Sandra L. (1989) Old Habits Stifle Telemanagement Software Market, *Business Communications Review,* pp. 46-49, (August).

Brown, Barbara, (1990) Paperless Call Accounting, *Teleconnect,* (October).

Cummins, Michael and Stonebraker, Everett (1989) Total Quality Management of Telecommunications, *Business Communications Review,* pp. 36-41 (December)

Fermazin, Tom (1991) Call Centre Managers: Rethinking Your Business Strategy to Take Advantage of Modern Tools, *Voice Processing Magazine,* (January).

Fross, Alan (1988) The ACD Market Comes of Age, *Business Communications Review,* pp. 74-77, (November- December).

Gordon, James. Klenke, Maggie and Camp, Kathey (1990) Centrex System Management Tools, *Business Communications Review,* pp. 35-39, (April).

Hayes, Robert and Harrison, Karen (1989) Chasing ACD Phantom Calls, *Business Communications Review,* pp. 26-29, (September- October).

Horton, Venetia (1990) Call Management Stops Telephone Abusers, *Office Equipment News* pp. 24-7, (October).

Huffadine, Roger (1990) Trends in Call Management Technology, *Telecommunications* (International Edition) **24,** (12) pp. 57-8, 71 (December).

MacPherson, Gordon (1989) How Staffing Affects ACD Trunking Requirements, *Business Communications Review,* pp. 36-39, (February).

Middleton, Peter (1989) Managing Your Calls, *Communications* (July).

Mikol, Thomas (1991) The IRS Collects With ACDs, *Inbound/Outbound Magazine,* pp. 16-18, (April).

Sanchez, Robert (1988) Buffers and Borders: The Zenith Call Accounting Project, *Business Communications Review,* pp. 43-48, (November-December).

Stusser, Daniel (1989) Call Accounting: Not Just a Numbers Game, *Business Communications Review,* pp. 51-54, (August).

Tucker, Tracey (1990) Call Accounting Update, *Teleconnect,* (October).

Wilson, Kim (1991) Call Centre Automation: Enhancing TSRs with New Technologies, *Voice Processing Magazine* (February).

37

Voice processing

John Holdsworth
Newbridge Networks Ltd.

Contents

37.1 The voice processing market

37.1.1 Introduction

Voice processing is the term used for the technologies of storing and replaying speech, compressing and decompressing speech, the technologies of speech recognition and text to speech conversion.

While voice processing can be used in industrial process control and military applications to allow hands free operations of plant or equipment, the industry is increasingly focused on telephone callers accessing the voice processing equipment. What follows addresses these telephony oriented applications.

Voice processing products can be split into the following types:

1. Audiotex.
2. Voice response.
3. Voice mail.
4. Automated attendant.

Analysts value the European voice processing for 1994 at £300M. This clearly shows dramatic uptake in the European voice processing equipment over the next three years, and to a large extent mirrors the growth in the US that has occurred already.

37.1.2 Audiotex systems

Audiotex systems are used to publish spoken information to callers. Callers can interact with audiotex systems using DTMF tones, dial pulses, by speech power detection (grunt detection), or in more advanced systems by using Speech Recognition.

Many applications are currently available ranging from weather forecasts, games and contests, medical advice.

These services can be accessed by the public using special telephone numbers. These numbers are tariffed at a premium over normal call rates; hence the term 'premium rate services'. The revenue from these calls is split between the PTT and the Audiotex service provider.

As an enhancement to basic Audiotex services, caller details can be recorded. This is used in games to identify the winner, or can be used for telemarketing purposes. A typical telemarketing use would be to automate the collection, collation and transcription of names and addresses of callers responding to a television advert.

Here the Audiotex system can be used to collect large numbers of caller details (e.g. names, address and telephone numbers). These details are then transcribed by data entry operators from the voice processing system into computer databases.

The benefit of collecting of names and addresses this way is that the peaks of traffic caused by media advertisements are accommodated 24 hours a day, 365 days a year and can be dealt with when convenient.

For example, a TV advertisement will generate a peak of traffic immediately it is shown. To reach the maximum audience, these adverts will be shown at peak viewing times in the evening, which is probably one of the most difficult times to employ staff to answer the calls.

37.1.3 Voice response

Voice response systems are used to allow callers access to databases using a telephone. These systems require the callers to specify the data they are looking for, and so intrinsically are interactive services requiring the use of DTMF or voice recognition techniques. Historically these systems have used DTMF telephones, but increasingly in Europe are using speech recognition technology for caller interactions. The services offered by a voice response unit are usually limited to one or two and the voice storage capacity on disk as a consequence is very limited. The range of telephone line sizes of voice response units commonly found is between 4 and 30 lines.

Traditionally the voice response system interfaces to the computer containing the database by emulating a terminal. A common form of terminal emulation used is IBM 3274 / 3278 SNA. The voice service 'reads' data from the terminal emulation 'screen' and speaks this information to the caller. The caller can select the information to be spoken and the screen being used. The DTMF commands sent by the caller are translated into 'key pushes' on the emulated keyboard.

Other systems use directly interpreted data, especially formatted for the application. This data is sent by any of the traditional data communications protocols. However X.25 is a particularly popular technique due to the flexible nature of the data communications network and the software support in mainframe computers. Typically used in home banking applications, this technique allows simpler systems to be realised.

More advanced systems in the IBM system environment use LU 6.2 and distributed database enquiries based on Standard Query Language (SQL) techniques.

Voice response systems have to readily speak numbers to callers. In order to facilitate this, and because of the limited vocabulary needed, the speech may be stored in the voice processing systems semiconductor memory (RAM). The words are brought out of memory by using a microprocessor and presented to digital to analogue converters. This reduces the load on the system compared with taking such speech from disk and hence makes the concatenation of numbers easier to achieve without recourse to specialist disk controller hardware and software.

As an adjunct to this feature, some voice response systems have text-to-speech capability. For example this is used to speak item descriptions to callers from a stock list. It is considered impractical to individually record each part description when there may be many thousands, or even millions of distinct descriptions.

Whilst not directly being part of a voice processing system there is a growing use of fax response systems. These allow the caller to select information using voice processing techniques and then send out a fax of the required information to the caller.

In many cases it would be difficult to speak the information to callers, and there is considerable benefit in a fax message being sent.

37.1.4 Fax responses

Fax response systems, when incorporated within a voice processing system, have two basic modes of operation; store and forward on demand and the on line transmission of information constructed for the particular caller from a database. The first mode is used to make a standard document, such as a map, available to a large number of callers. The second is used to allow caller relevant details to be put in to a fax and be sent. Typical applications include faxing of bank statements, inventory status etc.

The fax information sent is chosen during a normal telephone call to the voice processing system. During this call their fax machine number is entered by the caller. When the desired information has been selected, the system automatically dials up the identified fax machine and sends the information.

The problem with this approach is that the owner of the system pays for the call. It is not surprising therefore that many of the applications of this technology involve closed user groups (such as bank account holders), which allows a charge to be readily levied for this service.

However, according to industry sources approximately 80% of the installed base of fax machines support the reverse polling mode of operation. Here the fax response system would simulate a fax machine already loaded with a document. The caller could then make his fax dial up the system and it would send him the document. This feature is not widely used at present.

37.1.5 Voice Mail

Voice mail was one of the first voice processing applications developed during the late 1960s. Voice mail, as the name suggests, allows callers to leave voice messages for other users of the system. Typically connected to a PABX via a few analogue telephony interfaces, these systems are widely used in North America where the large penetration of DTMF phones facilitates its use.

The voice messages are usually short reminders or enquiries. The person intended to receive the message is notified by a message waiting lamp on his/her telephone, or by a different dial tone when the recipient uses their phone. Sometimes a radio pager is used to alert the recipient of new voice mail.

Inexpensive telephones with message waiting lamps are not as readily available in Europe as they are in the USA. The other alerting systems are generally thought of as unsatisfactory or too expensive for widespread use.

One popular use of voice mail is as an adjunct cellular telephones. Since cellular phones may be switched off for substantial periods the use of a voice mail box offers many advantages in business situations.

Within the UK voice mail competes directly with telephone answering machines and has not been as successful as in North America.

With the advent of GSN cellular telephones and the concept of a personal number for life associated with GSN, the need for large call delivery oriented voice mail systems will increase and probably become an accepted facet of business life within the European business community. The Pan-European GSN standard will considerably facilitate the take up of these services.

Voice mail systems can be stand alone or units can be networked to provide a seamless but geographically separated system. The interface protocols between voice mail systems have been proprietary until recently. Now there are the AMIS standards for voice mail systems. One is a digital standard based on the CCITT recommendation X.400, which is a wide ranging messaging standard based on OSI principles. The other is an analogue standard using DTMF control tones associated with the analogue transmission of the voice files. The widespread adoption of these standards is not happening as rapidly as was expected.

The X.400 system is split into two main parts; the User Agent (UA) and the Message Transfer Agent (MTA). On top of these two standard parts is the particular manufacturer's user interface. The user interface interacts with the UA to set parameters such as destination address. Once the necessary parts are complete, the message and UA details are passed to the MTA for delivery to the destination. This can be by a number of data communications protocols such as X.25, but this detail is hidden and made irrelevant to the user. X.400 is currently used by electronic mail systems. A number of voice mail suppliers have it as an available option.

The destination address can be selected using a CCITT recommendation X.500 directory service. This can allow users to select destinations using database search techniques. These standards will potentially allow different manufacturers' systems to inter-work and users to be able to use just one set of command structures.

However, the transmission of messages between voice mail systems by these techniques is at best only moderately faster than real time. For this reason geographically distributed voice mail systems are generally used only where necessary, such as in the transatlantic situation. The great majority of voice mail systems at present are not distributed, but work by having users connect to them using private or public telephone facilities. In the US the majority of sales are for systems of 4 lines upwards.

There are many features in the currently available voice mail systems. They use DTMF tones to control the addressing and selection of menu options. DTMF tones are also used to identify the caller. This means that usually only business users in the U.K. can take advantage of these systems.

However a limited number of systems support speaker dependent recognition technology to receive commands from callers. This is very suited to voice mail systems since inherently the user has to identify himself to the system initially by using a password. The speech recognition templates for that particular caller can then be recalled and used. Command words can therefore be chosen to suit customers on an individual basis.

One important aspect of a voice mail system is the management of the users, mail and system. When selecting a voice mail system these features should play an important part of the decision.

Guide lines for the size of a voice mail system are difficult to define, since the number of lines and disk size depends on the usage of the system by users. However, for example, in a medium use environment one voice mail system port for 30 users and a 3 minute voice storage capacity per user could be a reasonable starting point when sizing the system.

37.1.6 Automated attendant

This voice processing application is usually used as an overflow mechanism in conjunction with switchboard operators. In North America, automated attendants are used with the callers DTMF phone to reach extensions directly (so called simulated DDI). The caller is prompted for the required extension or department by the system. If the person being called is busy or doesn't answer, a voice mail application is usually made available to the caller so that an appropriate message can be left.

The use of automated call handling is becoming important for large corporations striving to reduce costs, make their services available 24 hours a day and improve their image. Here the concept is to handle caller queries as comprehensively as possible and not involve an operator if at all possible. Customer care is an important public relations issue. There is a reluctance to accept this technology in Europe because of the perception of talking to a machine as being undesirable. Since caller sessions can be more interactive than in the case of talking to an answering machine, this barrier is being overcome.

Links to databases and diversion to live operators can be used to enhance the capabilities and usefulness of automated attendant.

37.1.6.1 *Links to PABX/ADC*

In many cases the voice processing system is installed behind a PABX or ACD. This allows calls to be handled automatically or by live operators. Callers can be readily transferred from voice processing system to live operator or vice versa. However, in many situations the maximum benefit can be gained by having the caller screened by the voice processing system first; details obtained and then the caller being transferred to a live operator only if necessary. The details obtained by the voice processing system are shown on the operators VDU prior to the call being transferred.

There are many problems associated with achieving this functionality, centred around the lack of integration between PABX/ACD, host database and voice processing system. In an ACD for example the call is presented to a number of operators. The first operator to accept it gets the call. The information about which operator took the call may not be available to the host computer to present the relevant details on the correct VDU. Also the call may be put through before the VDU screen is presented. There is a wide variation in ACD/PABX functionality between manufacturers.

While there are many proprietary standards available from individual manufacturers there is no clear de facto standard emerging in this area of Computer Supported Telephony Applications (CSTA). ECMA and ANSI standards are being formulated but are not available yet.

37.2 Anatomy of a voice processing system

In order to understand some of the issues involved in the many applications of voice processing let us examine a generic voice processing system. This description is not intended to relate to any particular manufacturer or model.

The diagram above is intended to depict a general voice processing system. In the real world keen attention is payed to the number of lines supported, the amount of disk storage available and the speech recognition capabilities of the system. Architecture, software and hardware, and modularity are also key issues.

The basic subsystems of the voice processing system are linked by two buses. The speech bus conveys caller speech to the various speech processing elements and voice from the system to the caller. In advanced systems a degree of configuration of these speech paths is possible using digital cross connection switches.

The computer bus links the subsystems to the voice service applications processor for monitoring and control purposes. This bus is also used to deliver speech information to and from the voice compression/ decompression module. If the subsystems are intelligent, then they are down loaded with software using this bus.

The system functions by recording and replaying compressed speech from disk under the control of the voice service applications processor. There are two basic architectures; those based on PCs and those that are proprietary. PC base products, in general, address the low end of the market in terms of line size and usually focus on just one application area; proprietary architectured products on the other hardware suited to more general purpose use with higher performance and more line ports and disk storage. There are many PC based products in the market place. One of the benefits claimed for the PC products is the 'openness' of the platform. This openness is usually only effectively available to companies with experienced programmers. Also, because of the limitations of the platform for voice processing applications, it may be difficult to incorporate a wide range of features and applications in the same PC.

The callers access the system via the telephone network interfaces. There are two main types of telephone network connection: analogue and digital. The trend is increasingly towards digital network connection. This is because of the improved quality, the

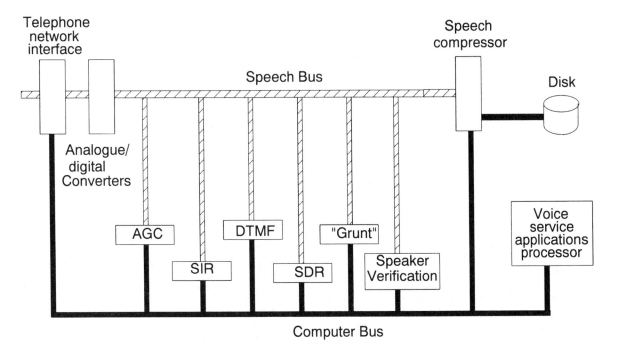

Figure 37.1 Generic voice processing system architecture

convenience of the physical network connection and the increased functionality and reliability possible.

37.2.1 Analogue network connections

There are four types of analogue network connections: direct dial inwards, normal telephone, Centrex and E&M.

37.2.1.1 *Direct Dial Inwards (DDI)*

This type is widely used by the Audiotex service providers and is currently offered in the UK by BT using the Derived Services Network (DSN) and Mercury using their normal network. The BT DSN has been dimensioned to cope with the large volumes of traffic that can be associated with Audiotex applications. The telephone network forwards the last 2 or 3 digits dialled by the caller to the voice processing system. These digits select the opening service given to the caller. This circuit type only supports incoming calls. It has been used with PABX systems in the past to allow callers to dial straight into a particular extension telephone on the PABX from the public telephone network.

The service access digits are sent by decadic dial pulsing from the telephone exchange to the voice processing system. When the digits have been completed (detected by a quiet interval significantly longer than the inter-digit pause) the voice processing system validates the access code and returns number unobtainable, engaged or ringing tone to the caller, depending on the availability of the service.

Two or three bursts of ringing tone are given before the caller is connected to the selected voice service. (In a PABX environment the ringing would continue until the extension was answered.)

At this point call charging is initiated by the voice processing system reversing the polarity of the battery voltage it supplies to the telephone exchange. This means that call charging is initiated by the equipment, not the telephone network. As can be imagined this results in the rigorous testing of the equipment before it is approved for connection to the public network.

37.2.1.2 *Normal telephone type*

The voice processing system mimics a normal telephone. This kind of connection is used for information update lines or when the voice processing system is placed behind a PABX. The telephone exchange sends ringing current cadences to the voice processing system. After two or three bursts the voice processing system answers the call and thus stops the ringing current from the telephone exchange by looping the circuit. The caller is also then connected through to the voice service. Since there is no pre-selection of the service (cf. DDI), the caller may have to interact with the voice processing system to then select the service required. Caller charging commences as soon as the voice processing system answers the call.

The call may be terminated by the exchange temporarily removing the battery from the circuit, or in some exchanges by the voice processing system un-looping the line. This type of connection can support both incoming and outgoing calls.

There is a problem for this kind of connection associated with detecting the release of the call by the calling party. There may be no firm indication to the equipment that the caller has released from the telephone network. For example, some PABX systems may give dial tone when the caller releases, some may give silence.

Whereas normal human-to-human conversations naturally terminate in the face of silence, human machine conversations do not. Unless the machine has a clear indication from the telephone network that the caller has gone, it will continue trying to interact with the caller. The procedure usually adopted to overcome this is for the voice processing system to give short fixed length messages, or for it to prompt the caller for an interaction (DTMF, Grunt etc). If the caller does not reply the system drops the call so as to be ready for new callers. Alternatively, if the network / PABX returns dial tone to the voice processing system when the caller hags up, a dial tone detector can be used. However to be effective the dial tone detector must reliably detect dial tone in the face of the voice processing system replaying speech. Digital signal processors are suitable for the filtering and detection function in this case.

37.2.1.3 *Centrex type*

This is a variant of the normal telephone type. The more popular large capacity PABXs support the connection of voice mail systems through interfaces of this kind. Whilst not being described as Centrex, the interface is very similar. These interfaces differ from normal extension ports in that DTMF tones identifying the calling party (if its an internal call) are sent by the PABX as soon as the call is answered by the voice processing system. Centrex features offered by the telephone exchange are intended to replace those offered by on-site PABXs.

Service selection digits (dialled by the caller) are sent immediately after the call is answered by the voice processing system from the telephone exchange. As in the case of DDI, these digits correspond to the last 2 or 3 digits dialled by the caller. However, these are sent by DTMF tones to the voice processing system.

Once the call is established a recall indication can be sent from the voice processing system to the exchange. This takes the form of a timed loop break (100ms) or an earth applied to one leg of the telephone cable pair.

The telephone exchange then sends a dial tone to the voice processing system as an indication that it can dial out the number using DTMF tones and invoke features such as three party conference calls.

When the original calling party or the voice processing system terminates the call all parties are usually released from the connection.

37.2.1.4 *E&M type*

Sometimes referred to as DC5 or DC10 signalling systems the Ear and Mouth telephone interfaces are used by VPSs when connecting to ACDs or PABXs.

There are many types of E&M interfaces, depending on region and PABX. E&M can be configured to support both incoming and/or outgoing calls. The E&M interface is designed to avoid incoming and outgoing call collisions by operating a simple signalling protocol. These interfaces are falling out of use in voice processing applications. This is because in many applications it is desirable to be able to connect the caller to a live operator. To do this using E&M interfaces would require the voice processing system to route the caller out on another circuit back to the PABX (so-called tromboning). The voice processing systems call handling capacity is reduced because it is associated with the call for its complete duration. Also, twice the numbers of ports are required both on the PABX and the voice processing system compared with using normal or Centrex type PABX ports equipped with the recall and dial out feature. Using the voice processing system in this way may make it "Call Routing Apparatus" in regulatory terms, adding significantly to the regulatory approval issues and to installation and on going support standards. Most voice processing equipment manufacturers have therefore not taken the step of becoming call routing apparatus.

37.2.2 Digital network connection

There are two main standards for digital connections: T1 (24 channels) in the US and Japan and E1 (30 channels) in the rest of the world. T1 standards are set by ANSI; E1 standards are set by CEPT. T1 has a clock rate of 1.544Mbit/s and E1 2.048Mbit/s. T1 signalling is carried within each telephone channel; E1 signalling is carried in time slot 16.

37.2.2.1 *Channel Associated Signalling (CAS)*

In the E1 version of CAS the E1 framing structure is used to transmit 4 bits of information per channel during 16 E1 frames. For historic reasons the 4 bits are termed the A,B,C and D bits. Each E1 frame consists of 32 timeslots of which 30 can be used to carry one voice conversation each. Timeslot 0 and 16 in the E1 link are reserved for signalling use. Two channels' information is sent in each E1 frame in timeslot 16. Timeslot 0 is used for other purposes such as frame synchronisation signalling. The sixteen E1 frames are termed a superframe. Each channel's signalling bits are pre-allocated into a particular frame in this scheme. Whether it is necessary or not, new signalling bits are sent in each superframe for each channel. The signalling bit rate for each timeslot is 4kbit/s, which is adequate for most telephony applications. The bits are used to mimic line states, such as battery presented etc. and dialled digits. The dialled digits are represented by simply sampling the dialling waveform and transmitting its state in the relevant bit and frame within the superframe.

In the T1 case a similar system is used, but the bits are hidden in the caller timeslot bits. Every 6th frame, bit 8 of the caller timeslot is replaced by a signalling bit. This is termed robbed bit signalling. A multi-frame structure is identified by the use of a spare bit at the end of each T1 frame (bit 193). By this means up to 4 (but usually 2, the A and B bits) bits per channel are transmitted. The bits are used in a similar way to the E1 case. There are many variants of the use of the CAS bits.

37.2.2.2 *Common Channel Signalling (CCS)*

In common channel signalling systems a more complex and flexible protocol is used. These systems are not at all common in the T1 system because robbed bit signalling is unsuitable for this application. In E1 systems timeslot 16 in the E1 frame is used to carry HDLC formatted data. Any caller timeslot of the frame can have signalling data inserted in timeslot 16 at any time. There is no pre-allocation of bits within the superframe to timeslots. Signalling information is only sent when necessary.

When primary rate ISDN protocols become available they will use a CCS system as described above. Currently DPNSS and DASS2 CCS schemes are widely used in the UK. DASS2 is currently the only way to interface at E1 rates to the BT public Network. Mercury support DASS2 and a CAS scheme at the moment for public network access at E1 rates.

37.2.3 Signalling information extraction/insertion

Usually in voice processing systems signalling information sent from the telephone exchange is extracted to select the opening service. Information can be sent by decadic dial pulsing loop disconnect signalling or DTMF tone and/or digital signalling in E1 or T1 connections. In more advanced E1 and T1 systems, signalling information can be sent as HDLC framed data such as in ISDN (CCITT), DMI(AT&T), DASS2 and DPNSS signalling schemes. These allow the calling party to be identified if this information is provided by the PTT. In the USA this feature, known as Automatic Number Identification (ANI) is widely supported. Most current US systems currently use DTMF techniques to receive this data from the network. In the UK regulatory and legislative issues may prevent its widespread availability. The feature of providing this information within the UK is known as Calling Line Identity (CLI).

Outbound signalling can be performed using a new circuit or the same circuit used for the incoming call once the exchange has been notified by a recall signal, by any of the above methods.

37.2.4 Analogue to digital conversion

In the case of analogue network connections the caller's speech needs to be digitised before it can be used. In the case of digital connections the digitalisation process is usually carried out in the callers local telephone exchange. A-Law (European) and μ-Law (USA and Japan) are companding rules used to enhance signal quality. Companding is the term used to describe the non-linear allocation of the 256 levels in the 8 bit timeslot sample to analogue signal levels. Usually the digitalisation process creates 8 bit quantised values. This gives adequate audio quality for telephone network use.

Either before or after the digitisation process the caller's speech is processed to detect tones, to amplify it to a reference level etc. (e.g. DTMF tone detection, automatic gain control, etc.). In advanced systems these processes are carried out by Digital Signal Processes (DSPs). These are special purpose microprocessors with an instruction set specially for these purposes. In early voice processing systems these functions were carried out in the analogue domain using op-amps etc. These, by comparison, are difficult to manufacture and modify in service. Analogue systems using tightly toleranced components also have a tendency to degrade with time due to component ageing and are inflexible, difficult to modify and perform field upgrades. On the other hand DSP software can be altered at will to modify and enhance functionality and no degradation over time is usually experienced.

DSPs use the digital representations of analogue waveforms obtained from analogue to digital conversion and manipulate them using software. All the usual analogue filtering techniques can be realised and many more, such as adaptive filtering, correlation and convolution, delay lines, matched filtering, Fourier analysis and echo cancellation.

37.2.5 Speech compression

In order to maximise the effective size of the speech storage in the voice processing system caller prompts and inputs are usually compressed before storage and decompressed during replay. Traditionally achieved by using many simple special purpose chips, the speech compression technology has gone full circle. DSPs can be and are used for compression algorithms. However, the expense and bulk of this approach for voice processing systems with many lines has caused the introduction of special ADPCM chipsets which can compress/decompress 60 channels of speech into 30 channels space. These chipsets are widely used in telecommunications transmission equipment for compression purposes.

Currently Continually Variable Slope Digitalisation (CVSD) and Adaptive Differential Pulse Code Modulation are the preferred methods. CVSD is used at a rate between 20kbit/s and 32kbit/s, ADPCM at 24kbit/s or 32kbit/s (i.e. 3:8 or 2:1 compression).

ADPCM at 32kbit/s introduces negligible distortions and is generally considered superior to CVSD, although it is more complex and expensive to realise. ADPCM has become the preferred compression technique.

More advanced compression algorithms yielding 8:1 compression ratios are available, but either the quality is poor or the hardware cost and complexity is too great for application in multi-channel voice processing system.

37.2.6   Text to speech conversion

This capability is used to convert computer based text (held in a database or disk files) into speech for transmission to the caller. Normally the caller hears pre-recorded and replayed speech. However, using this technique to speak the contents of a database may be impractical because of the huge repertoire involved.

There are two main parts of the text to speech conversion process. The text is analysed and converted to phonetic equivalents. The phonetic equivalents are then spoken to the caller by a formant voice synthesiser. This device mimics the resonant cavities of the human vocal tract by using variable filters (usually realised in DSPs) and simple impulse excitation of these filters. To complete this filter arrangement the fricative (hissing) part of the speech output is formed from a filtered and amplitude controlled noise generator.

There are usually five formant filters which model the human voice tract and as few as three can be varied and still achieve reasonable speech quality.

The process of translating from text into a phonetic representation is well developed. Some text-to-speech converters are capable for pronouncing over 100,000 words correctly, and can use the context of the words to derive the correct pronunciation.

Subsequent prosodic processing of these phonetic representations, introduces the intonations, inflexions and the rise and fall of the volume of the speech to make the output more acceptable.

However, to date the output quality achieved by this process still has a pronounced robot like quality, and as a result this capability is not widely substituted for replaying pre-recorded speech.

37.2.7   Speech recognition

It is this capability that will alleviate the current lack of DTMF telephones in Europe and allow voice processing technology to reach its full potential. There are two main variants; Speaker Dependent Recognition (SDR) and Speaker Independent Recognition (SIR).

Speaker dependent recognition systems need training to individual callers' voices, whereas speaker independent systems don't. Because of this SDR systems are falling out of favour due to the training chore, even taking into account the considerably increased complexity and cost of SIR systems.

Speaker independent recognition systems analyse the caller's speech and, in parallel for all the available words, match certain qualities of the speech against templates corresponding to the words to be recognised.

These templates are generated by taking many samples of the words desired from the range of accents likely to be encountered. These samples are usually processed off-line to create the templates. Typically between 100 and 200 different speakers are required to construct the templates.

The quality of speech examined is usually the frequency content of the spoken word. This extracted information typically corresponds to the syllables of the spoken words.

Commonly only isolated words can be recognised. However, there are other speech recognition products being introduced capable of connected word recognition. This can separate and recognise a series of words spoken without significant pauses. For example, connected word recognition systems allow the caller to speak a string of digits to the system. The speech recognition system then has to separate the individual digits in order to recognise them.

Even if the SIR system has a recognition performance in the high 90% region individual digits, the length of string that should be attempted is practically limited by the overall recognition accuracy that may be achieved. For example, if a recognition accuracy greater than 80% is desired and the single word performance is 95%, then a 4 digit string would have a 81% probability of being accurate.

It is also quite difficult to identify which spoken digit is incorrect and then prompt for that digit's re-utterance by the caller. For these reasons connected digit recognition systems are usually programmed to prompt the caller to speak a large number a few (3 or 4) digits at a time.

37.2.8   Word spotting

Word spotting systems continually examine callers' speech in an attempt to recognise an embedded word. This approach has the advantage that it may be able to find one of the words in an unstructured reply by the caller to a prompt. For example, the system might prompt the caller to say "yes" or "no". If the caller replies "Well, yes, then". a normal speech recogniser would not find the embedded "yes", whereas a word spotting system would.

37.2.9   Speaker verification (voice printing)

This is a system where the voice print of a caller is taken in an enrolment session and subsequently used to authenticate the caller's identity. The caller is prompted to speak a word or phrase which is then compared with the samples taken during the enrolment session.

Speaker verification system performance is classified in two ways. The percentage of false acceptances and the percentage of false rejections. The system is usually biased to reject rather than accept people. Systems with a performance of a few per cent false rejections, and a fraction of a per cent false acceptances are available. Obviously any change in the caller's voice due to a cold or stress can increase the false rejections made.

When perfected this feature will enable many over the telephone financial transactions to be completed securely. It is envisaged that these systems will be used in conjunction with a limited number of live operators who will help people who have failed the security check.

37.3   Future directions

There is an continuing trend towards the miniaturisation of equipment; increasing amounts of voice storage and easy to use voice service programming tools. To fully reach the potential that this technology has to reduce costs, it will need to be more closely integrated with the corporate I.T. infrastructure. The technology of voice processing, through advanced system software, needs to be made more available to end users.

One of the key technology breakthroughs will be comprehensive speech recognition technology capable of recognising many thousands of words and also capable of understanding the contextual issues within speech. The ability to recognise a few words is with us today. The incremental improvement to recognise a few tens of words is in sight. However, the step of being able to interact with the machine as if with a human is not clearly visible (except on Star Trek!).

In order to enable voice processing to leave behind the stigma of the answering machine and reach its full potential, the ability to hold natural and non-deterministic dialogues is key. Simply programming the machine with a tree of responses and menus is not good enough. The human-machine dialogue should be natural, allow interruptions and leave people with some doubt as to whether or not it is a machine they are talking to. This may well need advances in artificial intelligence beyond current technology. Some how the machine must be programmed with an 'opinion' so that the thread of the conversation with the caller can be maintained.

The future for voice processing technology is bright. The ability to use the telephone as a cheap terminal device, able to access data and allowing callers to command and control systems has not yet been fully explored. The challenge to go beyond the current talking computers can and will be met.

37.4 Bibliography

Frost & Sullivan (1990) *The European Market for Voice Processing Systems*, Frost & Sullivan Ltd., London.

Tetschner, W. (1991) *Voice Processing*, Artec House, Norwood, ISBN 089006 468 7.

Walters, R.E. (1991) *Voice Information Systems*, NCC, Oxford, ISBN 1 85554 075 4.

38

Electronic data interchange

Paul W Bizzell
AT&T EasyLink Services

Contents

38.1 Fundamentals of EDI

Electronic Data Interchange (EDI) is a subset of the messaging marketplace. A working definition of EDI is the computer to computer transmission of documents using agreed formats and protocools.

It is rarely mentioned but often assumed that EDI refers to interchanges between businesses. Whilst this may be largely true, in practise intra company exchanges are not precluded and large companies may see many benefits in adopting EDI standards for internal use.

There are two good reasons to introduce EDI into a business: firstly to reduce the overheads of running a business and secondly to enable the provision of improved service to customers.

The tangible benefits of EDI include:

1. Less manual data entry leading to an increased accuracy.
2. Reduced clerical overheads resulting in a lower cost base.
3. Faster delivery of data allowing shorter lead times and even enabling lower stock levels with consequent cost savings.

38.2 EDI in the messaging marketplace

The marketplace for EDI goods and services has been operating for some time but it is only since November 1990 that a complete OSI standard for moving EDI messages over the OSI stack has been fully ratified. To understand how this standard, X.435, was arrived at a brief history of the messaging marketplace is included with an outline of the X.400 standard used for inter personal messaging (IPM).

The area of messaging has been the most active area for standards work over the past couple of years. This may well be because it takes about six years from the recognition of a business need to the provision of standards based products to fit the requirement. The time lag is due to the four year cycle of the international standards body, the CCITT, and then the two years it may take to develop and bring a standards conformant product to market.

The messaging marketplace used to have a black and white split into EDI and Electronic Mail, however recent trends are creating many shades of grey and it is the standards process which is allowing a much richer range of integrated services to become available from the major service providers. As the marketplace becomes more sophisticated the ability to deliver a range of messaging products down a single pipeline, thus simplifying the underlying network, is becoming a key differentiator in the messaging marketplace.

38.3 Messaging standards

Much standards work has previously been done in the messaging arena, however the standards fell into two broad categories which may be summarised as follows:

1. The 'movement' standards, building on the previous work which established the OSI seven layer model and defined the lower levels up to transport (Level 4), these now take the model to the application layer, Level 7.
2. The 'message' standards, work done to define the content, layout and data sets which are then moved over the above. This is the traditional realm of EDI and leads to definitions of EDI

such as 'The use of computers to exchange documents using agreed formats and protocols'. Examples of the 'movement' standards relating to messaging are X.400, FTAM and OFTP. These standards place the minimum of constraints on the content of the message but concentrate on the delivery mechanisms.

Whilst X.400 and FTAM have been driven centrally by the CCITT, message standards have tended to be community specific. The message standards, such as the American ANSI X12 and EDIFACT consist of two parts:

1. A language or rule set for constructing an interchange,
2. Building blocks; a hierarchy of parts to which the rules are applied to build up an interchange.

The building blocks start with data elements, which map onto familiar data items such as part number.

These are combined to form segments which are groups of related elements e.g. name and address. Some syntaxes allow compound elements and compound segments.

Segments are used to build EDI messages (also known as transaction sets in ANSI X12). A message is analogous to a document such as a purchase order.

Finally messages are grouped together in batches for transmission and this is known as an interchange.

Interchanges for all the main EDI standards include the concept of a header containing special segments to pass control information about the sender, recipient, date/time and a reference number.

Whilst many data elements are alike in the three main EDI standards (EDIFACT, ANSI X12, TRADACOMS), the main differences lie in the characters used to separate fields, the definitions of segments and messages.

As mentioned above the process of defining specific messages has been community, even industry, driven. So whilst EDI messages may conform to an international standard such as Edifact for the syntax of the message the actual data set used is often industry specific.

The situation is further confused in as much as there are several national and industry standards bodies, e.g. ANSI, SMMT, who have defined widely implemented standards ahead of the ISO/UN-EDIFACT work becoming internationally adopted. Worse yet much of the EDI marketplace relies on proprietary communications rather than OSI.

Recently however the two strands have begun to converge with the emergence of standards which relate to both, messages and movement and also addressing i.e. X.435 and X.500. A major current activity of the service providers, such as AT&T EasyLink, is offering a bridge between the older and the newer systems so that previous investment can be protected but access and connectivity can be provided to those new entrants to the community wishing to conform to the latest standards.

This explains the apparent paradox between a six year lag after standards are formed and there being an established EDI community. A six year wait is clearly unacceptable if a business edge is sought so a means of making new technology more immediately available is clearly required.

To achieve such a target it is necessary to distinguish between the principles involved and the actual protocols.

Historically the U.K. EDI marketplace has been dominated by the use of VANS with a high degree of added value on the network. The added value has taken the form of verification of the data set, security and trading relationship checking, translation services be-

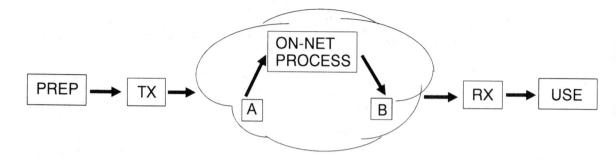

Figure 38.1   Network value added

tween data sets and to some extent communications protocol conversion.

The communications prevalent have been proprietary or at best de facto, either IBM protocols or OFTP (albeit over X.25). Whilst the Edifact syntax is standardised the number of registered international standard messages is relatively small. Most recognised messages relate to smaller industry groups and are awaiting international ratification.

To fully understand the emergence of OSI standards for EDI it is necessary to take a brief look at the electronic mail marketplace.

E-mail has had one characteristic which has made a significant difference to its development. Whilst EDI is primarily used for inter company communication E-mail has tended to be intra company. Therefore the early E-mail marketplace showed a host of proprietary systems, often incompatible. As companies sought to combine internal systems a standard was required and X.400 was born.

The U.S. EDI marketplace initially followed a different standard to Europe, ANSI X12 instead of EDIFACT. However a larger number of messages were defined in ANSI X12 and the existence of these messages enabled a different solution. More generalised premises based software was possible and the marketplace which evolved reflected this. The value added by the network was less, the off net processing correspondingly higher.

However for E-mail there was little difference in the standards U.K. to U.S. so the same profile evolved, i.e. a large number of proprietary systems. The market for E-mail on both continents is however a little further advanced than EDI in as much as E-mail was

seen as the ideal vehicle to further the completion of the OSI model, perhaps as it was a fairly easy concept to grasp.

So the second wave of E-mail products were able to convert the principles of the proprietary systems into the 1984 X.400 protocols to give an OSI solution to the E-mail requirement. This is now being refined to the 1988 X.400 model which gives a much closer match to the 7 layer model. This is because it splits the application down and actually uses layers 5 and 6 properly instead of being a complete application (layers 5, 6 and 7 in one) sitting on layer 4 as the 1984 implementation did.

The U.K. EDI marketplace, as the E-mail before it, is now taking advantage of the second generation of thinking. Premises based software is now being produced to move the processing off net, with the resulting requirement for a simpler value added service and a corresponding cheaper and simpler pricing structure from the service providers (Figures 38.1 and 38.2)

The network also provides extra delivery mechanisms, both in terms of the devices which may be used and the protocols used to reach them.

These changes enable smaller players to enter the market, extending the accessibility of EDI to the next tranche of customers who were previously priced out.

The connectivity, translation and other services are achieved by means of gateways on the service. Each gateway provides a specific service. This means that a new service can be easily added or revised so that as a standard emerges in a particular area the gateway can be enhanced to meet the protocol requirements without changing the principle behind the service offering.

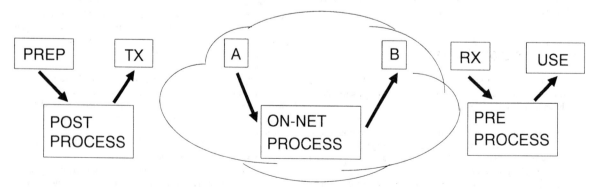

Figure 38.2   Premises based processing

VANS will continue to play a key role in the transition from proprietary network protocols to OSI transport through their translation facilities. By offering translation it releases the individual company from the need to harmonise its network offerings and change procedures to those of all its trading partners.

38.4 Technical infrastructure

X.400 is generally used to refer to a series of recommendations which provide an international standard for structuring and transmitting electronic mail messages. So far there have been two iterations of the four year cycle, yielding the 1984 and 1988 version of the standards.

Since the early days it has been recognised that the base standards were suitable for transmitting other types of messages other than IPM so the 1990 standard for P_{cdi} built on the earlier work to define a complete ISO stack for EDI. However, industry could not wait for the 1990 standard so work was done in America and Europe to adapt the 1984 X.400 standard for EDI.

The key elements of the 1984 standard are the message transfer agent (MTA), the user agent (UA). These are processes (composed of software and hardware) which provide services for moving messages from site to site and enabling users to send and receive messages. Figure 38.3 illustrates these concepts. Note that human users are explicitly included in the model!

There are other key concepts in X.400 as follows:

1. MHS — message handling system

2. ADMD — administrative domain, a public service provider
3. PRMD — private domain, a company's internal service
4. ORName — the originator/recipient name, a specific form of address required by X.400
5. P1 — the protocol between MTAs, equivalent to the envelope
6. P2 — the protocol between UAs for IPM, equivalent to the structure of a memo with header and body
7. DNs — delivery notifications, confirmation of receipt

As well as some refinements and extensions to the 1984 standard (e.g. P2 was enhanced and became P22), another key concept was introduced in 1988, that of the message store (MS). A MS allows a MTA to store a message it cannot immediately deliver to a UA e.g. when the UA is implemented on a PC which is periodically turned off.

Whilst in practice the MS is extremely useful its use is optional. For the sake of clarity in the following discussion the MS is conveniently omitted.

An X.400 message consists of an envelope (P1) and content (P2 for IPM). A P2 content has a header and a body, as in Figure 38.4. In adapting X.400 1984 for EDI two approaches were possible. The first, adopted in Europe on the recommendation of the CEC, is to put the EDI message into the P2 body part. A copy of the originator and recipient from the EDI message header are put into the P2 heading.

The second approach, standardised by NIST in the U.S., is to create a new content type, PO, for the EDI message. The EDI message goes directly into the P1 envelope as an 'undefined' content type.

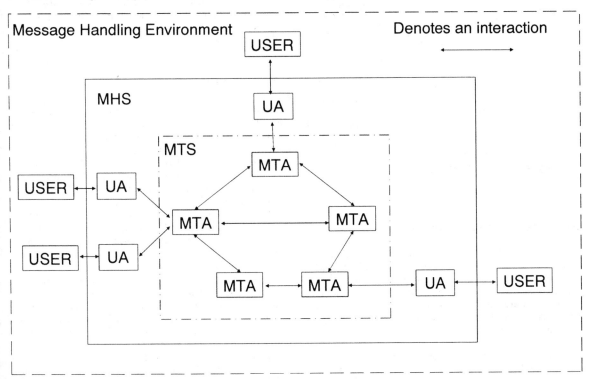

Figure 38.3 Functional view of MHS model

Envelope P1

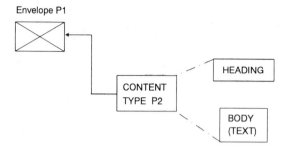

Figure 38.4 Structure of an X.400 I.P.M.

Note that it is not possible to interchange messages of different types between software that supports one type or the other.

The 1988 P_{cdi} protocol provides an X.400 message specifically for EDI: the EDIM. A P1 envelope is still used but it has a content type called the 'EDI message type'. X.435 defines a user agent for EDIMs. In contrast to IPM an X.435 user agent does not have a human user but the 'EDI user' is another process, i.e. the computer systems that generate or use EDI data.

The concept of EDI notifications is also supported in 1988 P_{cdi} as in Figure 38.5.

Envelope P1

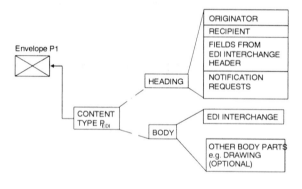

Figure 38.5 P_{edi} and EDIM structures

38.5   Internal topologies

The one thing the X.400 and X.435 standards do not specify is how they should be implemented. This leads to a variety of possible solutions, each best suited to a particular business scenario.

Five possible models are listed below but this is by no means an exhaustive list and many combinations of scenarios may be applicable to larger firms. The P_{cdi} protocol contains elements in support of all the following:

1. The EDI UA is linked to a single EDI application
2. The EDI UA is a 'corporate gateway', i.e. a sophisticated piece of software capable of audit trails, translations of data format and may onward transmit via proprietary protocols. In this case the gateway may take responsibility for returning notifications of delivery.

3. As above but no responsibility is taken for notification. This will be handled by the final recipient UA.
4. The EDI UA uses a VAN for its MTA services. In this case the VAN would support the MS
5. EDI UA and MTA are co-located entirely on a VAN service. Here the VAN would most likely be supplying not only store and forward services but also protocol translations.

38.6   X.500 directory services

As the use of X.400 increases the need for an automated directory service grows. This was recognised quite soon in the process of X.400 definition and in 1988 a standard for electronic directory services was published and this is X.500.

X.500 will be particularly useful for EDI since it will allow EDI processes to obtain both ORAddresses of EDI applications on trading partners machines and the specific attributes and capabilities of those applications. This will ensure (if the directory is accurate!) that data can be sent in an appropriate format to an address that is known to be able to handle it.

The structure of X.500 is similar to X.400 in as much as it consists of two key elements: the directory services agent (DSA) and the directory user agent (DUA). A DUA and a DSA converse in a defined protocol called directory access protocol (DAP).

A typical implementation in the EDI scenario is that the DUA will run in the same machine as the EDI UA and requests for information will be passed from the EDI UA to the DUA. The DUA will then extract the information using DAP from a remote directory, perhaps maintained centrally by a VAN (in X.500 terms an ADDMD — administrative directory management domain). The DUA will then pass the information back to the EDI UA which can then format and address the message correctly.

38.7   Security

Security is a major consideration in EDI since much of the data moved using EDI can be termed 'mission critical'. Security is used as a blanket term to cover many different needs according to the type of data and use to which it is being put.

Three types of security are available with P_{cdi}. These can be classified as authentication, data integrity and confidentiality.

A fourth threat to any network is of course availability, however this is generally left to lower level protocols to handle.

Much thought has been given to security in P_{cdi}, and indeed X.400 1988 is also much improved in this area. The concept of different levels of security in a network is allowed for and specific elements of the protocol allow a message to be configured for the particular type of security required.

Security in EDI is obtained by the use of keys and encryption. Keys can be of two types, symmetric where the same key is used at both ends and asymmetric where the key used to unlock is different from the key used to lock but has exactly the same effect. One type of asymmetric key algorithm (the RSA) is given in annex to the X.509 standard.

Authentication is about ensuring that the message originates from who it purports to. This is essential where instructions for payment are being issued.

Authentication relies on the application to a message of an asymmetric private key known only to the sender. It works in the following manner.

The message being sent is put through a hashing function and encrypted i.e. locked with the secret key. Both the hashed message and the original message are passed to the receiver who uses his different key to unlock (decrypt) the hashed message.

The unhashed message is compared to the original message. If the results are the same then the message must have come from the originator since he is the only one who could have created the locked message as his key is private.

Data integrity can also be achieved using the above method, but may also be achieved using symmetric keys. Note that symmetric keys can guarantee data integrity but since by definition they are known by at least two people they cannot guarantee authenticity.

Confidentiality can be achieved simply by encrypting the contents of the P1 envelope. The standards do not specify any particular encryption method, which is left free to the implementors of the end systems.

Further security features are typically provided by the VANS. These include audit trails and notifications, both positive and negative.

Full support for notifications is not mandatory, however compliant systems which do not support the accepting of responsibility for a message must forward that responsibility to the next system in the network.

P_{edi} also contains mechanisms to provide proof of content received and non repuditable proof of content received.

Proof of content received is equivalent to returning a copy of the original content to the sender on receipt of a message.

Non repuditable proof allows the originator of a message to be sure the receiver cannot say it was never received. It is similar in concept to the above but the copy sent back can be considered to be notarised as a certificate of origin is passed between the parties.

38.8   Global VAN topologies

With the trend to global marketplaces and global networks three styles of global VAN are evident.

In the first case a VAN operates its processing in a single location but uses a network to transport data to it via long lines from all over the world. This approach is the simplest for the VAN but the lack of local processing can make traffic between endpoints in the same remote country uneconomic.

To address this the idea of franchising the service was created. This meant in-country operations and local presence, but international traffic is essentially inter-VAN traffic and often subject to surcharges.

A more up to date method, in line with current trends in distributed processing, is to run a single global service with distributed, co-operating nodes. This is an expensive approach, out of reach for all but the largest players, but it does have significant benefits.

Instead of franchising the service so that each node is an island or long-lining into a single central point the distributed nodes all co-operate. This means that each node may host mailboxes and processing for another to facilitate load balancing or disaster recovery and only a single registration is required for an account to be directly accessible via any node world wide. This allows the global management of a multi-national company's account from the most appropriate regional centre.

The global distributed approach matches both the structure of the standards bodies and the trends in computing which are driving the development of standards such as X.400 and X.500.

38.9   Future trends

The current round of standards work concerns the integration of standards, and this is reflected in current developments. In the EDI world this is the emergence of X.435 as the standard for EDI over X.400. This will allow an organisation to utilise a single physical (OSI) connection to carry all its text messaging whether structured or unstructured. The X.500 directory services will allow the off-net processes to address and route the data to the correct endpoint.

Further work is being done in the area of office document architecture (ODA). This will further integrate the messaging media as it allows a separation of the content of a document from the layout and formatting of the content. Thus it is possible not only to transmit the content of a document but instructions for its presentation. It also allows for multimedia documents so a document which includes a picture can be sent in a single transmission and interpreted correctly at the far end.

In assessing future trends in the VANS we must look at services under development today. Clearly there are three thrusts for the future. These all concern the shift of focus up the OSI stack towards the abstract user orientated functionality. This will protect users' current investment decisions rather than past.

The first is the consolidation of vital translation facilities, with the focus moving from the lower levels to the higher.

The second is an extension of the media used to include such things as voice, video etc.

The third is the provision of higher level services. These will be such things as document conversion, directory services and on-net library services where whole document layouts are held on the service but only the content is transmitted.

39 Modems

T J Egginton
BEng (Sheffield University)
Gandalf Digital Communications Ltd

Contents

39.1 Introduction

With a long and illustrious history behind them, one might be forgiven for thinking that the humble modem should be firmly consigned to the electronic scrap heap. Indeed, it was not so long ago that the majority of industry pundits believed that ISDN would eventually finish off the modem for good. But the modem is a survivor and in the 1990s, some twenty years after its first appearance, those same pundits agree that far from being finished, the modem is still firmly fighting back and looking forward to another decade of life.

This renewed enthusiasm is based on two fundamental reasons:

1. The introduction of ISDN, the Integrated Services Digital Network. The hype of the eighties delivered little in the way of actual service, so that towards the end of that decade it was viewed with an increasing amount of cynicism and scepticism. Now, ISDN has turned the corner and is a key element in the strategies of networking companies, but although BT are rolling out 90,000 Basic Rate or ISDN2 circuits (2x64kbit/s bearer channels plus 1x16kbit/s signalling channel), it is still a drop in the ocean compared to some 24 million analogue lines installed in the U.K. While reasonably priced switched digital circuits are hard to come by, there remain many applications for which the modem will be eminently suited, and areas where ISDN will never be available.
2. The modem's resilience and stability as a product. The modem has benefited from the same advances in microelectronics as the rest of the computing industry. This has allowed it to change

radically but remain reliable enough to more than keep pace with alternative transmission systems.

When the CCITT Telecommunications Standards Organisation introduced the V.32 standard in 1986 for operation at 9000 bit/s, it was hailed as the last, great modem standard. By February 1991 the CCITT had approved the V.32bis standard and has a study group working on an even faster standard called appropriately, V.fast. Whilst this quest for sheer performance continues apace, shipments of V.22bis modems operating at a stately 2.4kbit/s expect to top 2.5 million in 1994, roughly two and a half times that of V.32 product.

With faster operation, greater functionality and reducing prices, the outlook, for the consumer at least, is rosy indeed.

39.2 Principles of operation

The principles of modem operation were fashioned by the limitations of the telephone network for which they were originally designed (Figure 39.1). The telephone circuits of the Public Switched Telephone Network (PSTN) are designed to reproduce speech of a quality that is reliably understandable to the human ear. Most of the intelligible sound generated by vocal chords can be contained in a frequency range of 300Hz to 3400Hz, although generating sounds both higher and lower in frequency. The restriction of frequencies to this range also eliminates a lot of interference and extraneous noise.

In order to provide a constant response to sounds within this range, telephone circuits are 'loaded' with extra inductance to offset the

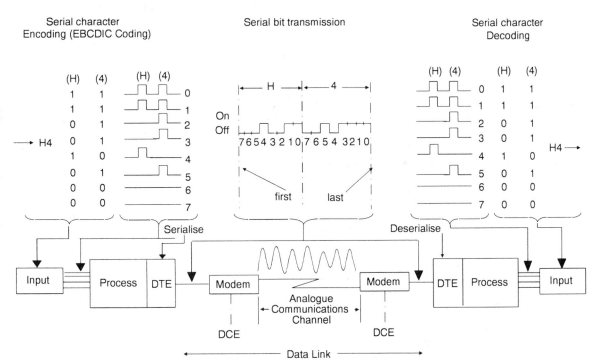

Figure 39.1 A complete end to end data communication system using a modem link

cables natural capacitance. Add to this the effect of switching and the variation in route from call to call and it can be readily appreciated that it is not an environment conducive to digital transmission, where acceptable bit error rates are typically less than one in a million.

The humble dial up modem must deal with all of this, but is limited as a result to a maximum speed of around 30kbit/s for today's dial up line according to Shannon's Law. Contrast this with a digital KiloStream circuit delivering 64kbit/s and digital MegaStream circuits delivering 2.048Mbit/s.

An analogue signal has an amplitude, a frequency and a phase. Each can be varied to modulate the waveform (Figures 39.2 to 39.4). In practice, simple amplitude modulation is not used on its own because of its sensitivity to noise. Crackles on the line may not impair the ability of a human ear to understand speech, but they certainly impair a computers' ability to understand a digital signal if it is corrupted by them during transmission. Frequency modulation changes the frequency of the basic carrier wave (unmodulated signal) according to the state of the digital signal generated by the computing or terminal equipment.

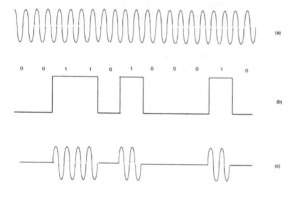

Figure 39.2 Amplitude modulation: (a) carrier; (b) modulating waveform; (c) modulated waveform

All the signals or tones generated remain in-band. In phase modulation, the carrier frequency remains constant, but the phase can be shifted in increments over a complete cycle of the waveform. Dibit Phase Shift Keying for example allows two bits of information to be represented by a single cycle. The rate of the waveform is called the baud rate. The information rate in bits per second, is twice the baud rate, since each signal level represents two bits.

Other modulation techniques provide for far greater throughput. Quadrature Amplitude Modulation for example, combines amplitude modulation with phase modulation to generate 16 different signal combinations, so that each signal element transmitted on the line represents a 4 bit digital sequence. The CCITT V.29 standard uses this modulation technique over 4 wire lines at a baud rate of 2400. Since each baud represents 4bit/s, the resulting speed of operation is rated at 4x2400 or 9600bits/s.

Having outlined how a digital signal can be encoded into a signal suitable for transmission over the telephone line, what happens when the modem has used its dial up telephony capabilities to establish a transmission path? (Figure 39.5; Scott, 1980). The digital equipment originating the call uses the interface signals presented to it by the modem to raise the Request To Send (RTS) signal. If the

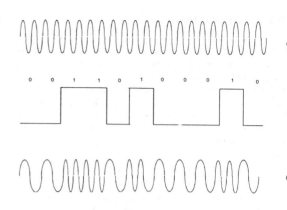

Figure 39.3 Frequency modulation: (a) carrier; (b) modulating waveform; (c) modulated waveform

modem is ready, it responds with Clear To Send (CTS) and turns on its Data Carrier Detect (DCD).

Having raised CTS, transmit data is applied to the encoder where the modulation of the carrier wave we have previously described takes place. The modulated wave is filtered to eliminate unnecessary frequencies and the level of transmission is adjusted to suit the line before it is actually transmitted. When transmission has been completed, the RTS signal is turned off by the digital equipment. At the destination end, the signal is filtered again to remove unwanted frequencies generated as the signal propagates along the line, before being applied to an amplitude and delay equaliser.

Although speech circuits are "loaded" to give an even response to in-band frequencies, distortion does take place. Private leased lines can be conditioned or fine tuned to reduce this distortion, but dial up circuits can deliver a different path, quality and response on each connection. The faster the modem operates, the more complex this becomes.

From the equaliser an automatic gain control amplifier compensates for different levels of received signal before the analogue signal is demodulated to reconstruct the original digital signal. In the example of Dibit Phase Shift Keying used earlier, the demodulator measures the phase of the incoming signal and the correspond-

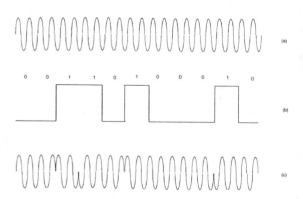

Figure 39.4 Phase modulation: (a) carrier; (b) modulating waveform; (c) modulated waveform

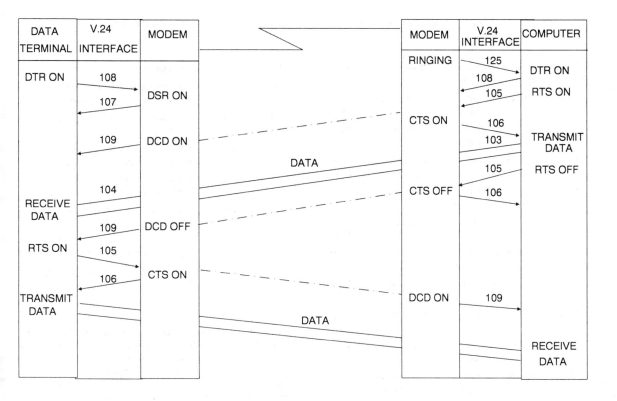

Figure 39.5 Simplified timings for data transmission between a data terminal and a remote computer over the telephone network. The terminal initiates a PSTN call to the computer which responds to set up a two way dialogue

ing 2 bit digital signal is output at the Receive Data (RD) line at the modem interface to the receiving digital equipment.

So far data has been serially transmitted from source to destination. But data only went one way, and while the source transmitted the destination listened. This is half duplex operation and is inefficient since the line has to clear before transmission in the opposite direction can take place, limiting the speed of operation. The use of four wire lines, instead of two, reduces the turnaround time. Modems that operate full duplex permit simultaneous operation in both directions and is accomplished by using four wire lines or much more commonly by dividing the bandwidth of two wire lines using different transmit signals frequencies. CCITT V.32 echo cancellation techniques broke new ground by providing full duplex operation over two wires with the full bandwidth available in each direction.

The patterns of 1's and 0's of course have to be arranged in a way that makes sense to the digital equipment. Modems operating asynchronously do this by sending a start bit. The modem can then count off the required number of bits that make up a byte or character, including a parity and stop bit before sending the next start bit. Synchronous modems on the other hand, solve this timing problem by synchronising their clocks. Instead of having to re-synchronise after each character, synchronous modems send timing information along with the data in a continuous sequence. A protocol is used to define these synchronising sequences, block sizes and formatting

characters. The extra circuitry and logic to achieve this provides greater throughput but at a price premium compared to asynchronous modes.

39.3 Modem standards

Standardisation in modem operation is important to guarantee that a user can connect to a modem attached to the same link or network (Tables 39.1 to 39.3).

This is particularly important in the dial up environment where the modem model operating at the distant end may not even be known. At one time, high speed modems would only operate at peak performance when talking to another modem of the same type, typically operating a proprietary transmission standard. When connected to a different modem, they would have to accept the lowest common level of operation, often significantly less than their individual optimum performance.

The main force for standards in Europe and increasingly more in the United States is the CCITT. Over the years they have developed standards from the 300bit/s V.21 operation of the early 1970s to the recently agreed 14400bit/s V.32bis standard and beyond. Digital signal processing technology now delivers chip sets covering multiple standards in an attempt to provide universal connectivity. Since optimum performance of links may depend not only on a

Table 39.1 CCITT V Series transmission standards

Standard	Transmission rate	Duplex capability	Mode	Media
V.21	300bit/s	Full duplex	Asynchronous	2 wire PSTN
V.22	1200bit/s	Full duplex	Asynchronous	2 wire PSTN
V.22 bis	2400bit/s	Full duplex	Asynchronous/ synchronous	2 wire PSTN
V.23	1200/ 75bit/s	Full duplex	Asynchronous	4 wire leased
		Half duplex	Asynchronous	2 wire PSTN
V.26 bis	2400bit/s	Full duplex	Synchronous	2 wire leased
		Half duplex	Synchronous	2 wire PSTN
V.27 ter	4800bit/s	Half duplex	Synchronous	2 wire PSTN
V.29	9600bit/s	Full duplex	Synchronous	4 wire leased
V.32	9600bit/s	Full duplex	Asynchronous/ synchronous	2 wire PSTN
V.32 bis	14400bit/s	Full duplex	Asynchronous/ synchronous	2 wire PSTN
V.33	14400bit/s	Full duplex	Synchronous	4 wire leased

common transmission standard but a common error correction and data compression standard, connecting modems must undergo a sequential negotiation before actual transmission can take place.

The V.32 transmission standard introduced 5 years ago, pushed full duplex operation over 2 wires up to 9600bit/s. The first to use a technique called echo cancellation, it was made possible only because of the development of Digital Signal Processing (DSP) tech-

Table 39.2 Error correction standards

Standard		Description
CCITT	V.42	Standard for error correcting protocols including LAP/M and MNP4
MNP	Level 1	Error correcting/Throughput reduced to 70%
	Level 2	Error correcting/Throughput reduced to 84%
	Level 3	Error correcting/Throughput up to 108%
	Level 4	Error correcting/Throughput up to 120%

Table 39.3 Data compression standards

Standard		Description
CCITT	V.42bis	Standard for data compression using BTLZ for throughput up to 400%
MNP	Level 5	Data compression/Throughput up to 200%
	Level 6	Data compression with V.29 technology/Throughput up to 200%
	Level 7	Predictive data compression/ Throughput up to 300%
	Level 8	Predictive data compression with V.29/Throughput up to 300%
	Level 9	Predictive data compression with V.32/Throughput up to 300%
	Level 10	Enhanced Level 9/Throughput up to 300%

nology. Previously, full duplex operation required the available bandwidth to be split into two frequency bands so that simultaneous transmission in both directions was possible. Echo cancellation made the full bandwidth available in both directions by allowing the transmitting modem to detect its own signal mixed in with the received signal of the distant modem and remove it.

V.32 also uses a second technique called Trellis encoding which uses an extra bit to help identify and correct errors. This extra bit, added to those multiple bit per baud sequences for improving throughput described earlier, do not carry information. Although this appears as a simple signal overhead, their presence can actually further increase throughput.

A V.32 signal space diagram, or constellation, shows pictorially all the 32 signalling combinations possible from a 5 bit digital sequence (Figures 39.6 and 39.7). To show how this relates in performance terms, the baud rate for V.22bis is 600bit/s. Each baud

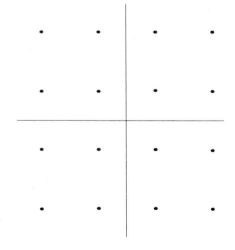

Figure 39.6 A signal space diagram (or constellation for V.22 bis modems

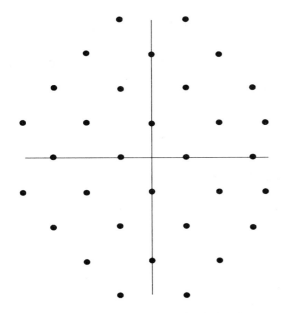

Figure 39.7 A signal space diagram for V.32 modems

Table 39.4 Interface standards

	Electrical Signals Interface	Mechanical Interface	Functional Protocols	Procedure Protocols
RS-232-C	*	*	*	*
(V.24)			*	*
(V.28)	*			
(ISO-2110)		*		
(X.21bis)		*	*	*
X.24			*	
X.21		*	*	*
(ISO 4903)		*		
RS-422-A	*			
(V.11/X.27)	*			
(ISO 4902)		*		
(V.24)			*	*
(V.54)				*
RS-423-A	*			
(V.10/X.26)	*			
V.35	*		*	*
(ISO 2593)		*		

contains a 4 bit digital code (or 16 combinations), 600 baud x 4 bits equals 2400bit/s. The baud rate for V.32 is much higher i.e. 2400bit/s. Four of the five bit V.32 code is used for information, the fifth for Trellis encoding. 2400 baud x 4 bits equals 9600bit/s performance.

The recently ratified V.32bis standard builds on V.32 by using a 7 bit digital sequence per baud. With six bits for information and a similar baud rate, V.32bis performance is pushed up to 14400bit/s over 2 wires.

Standards must equally be applied to the DTE-DCE boundary (Table 39.4; Enslow, 1988). Although perceived as a mundane subject, specifications and standards are in a continual state of flux and merit some discussion. On the simplest level, an interface consists of three parts, a protocol, an electrical specification and a mechanical connector. The protocol describes the logical attributes which typically include the meaning of the electrical signals on each pin, the interrelationship between the signals and the means to exchange information.

The electrical and mechanical specification in turn specify the physical attributes of the electrical signals on the pins and the dimensions and construction of the connector itself. A successful connection is dependent on the combination of all three. The best known of these is the ubiquitous Electronic Industries Association (EIA) RS232C specification which formed the basis of the CCITT V.24 recommendation. Whereas RS232C described both physical and logical attributes, V.24 describes only the logical and is supplemented by recommendations V.28 and ISO2110 for electrical and mechanical characteristics.

The use of the term V.24 popularly implies the use of the other two. Specified for operation up to 20kbit/s via a 25 way D type connector it provides a set of unbalanced (one leg goes to ground potential), double current (current may flow in either the go or return path depending on voltage polarity) interchange circuits. Unbalanced circuits are susceptible to crosstalk and other interference. The operating distance is capacitance limited to 2500pF

but, when the specification was written, cable technology imposed a limit of about 50 feet.

Improvements made since can deliver four times that distance without exceeding the capacitance limit, although V.28 sets no such limitation. The second interface in common usage is the V.35 recommendation supplied via a 34 way connector, its electrical characteristics providing for balanced (carrying equal and opposite voltages) interchange circuits. Neither lead is at ground potential.

Balanced circuits provide a cancellation effect which bestows higher immunity to interference and, due to lower capacitance, allows extended transmission distances in comparison to RS232C. Originally specified at 48kbit/s operation, it is common to find U.S. developed equipment rated at up to MegaStream speeds. Later standards developed for higher rates and operating distances originated initially as EIA RS423 and RS422 which were subsequently adopted by the CCITT as recommendations V.10 and V.11 respectively. Because their electrical characteristics were suitable for public data network interfaces they have also been assigned as X.26 and X.27 respectively.

The potential for confusion increased when EIA released RS449 to cover the non electrical aspects, as well as updating RS232C. RS449 was designed to overcome limitations in RS232C but because it arrived late and specified pins for ten additional circuits it has not become widely adopted. V.10 delivers an unbalanced interface, with maximum ratings of 100kbit/s and 1000 metres and V.11 a balanced interface with maximum ratings of 10Mbit/s and 1000 metres. Maximum distance and speed are mutually exclusive. V.11 electrical interface signals are commonly combined with a 15 way

D type connector in common use as the method of connection to BT's KiloStream service.

The goal for the future is to reduce the number and size of these interfaces, ideally to an universal DTE/DCE standard, so a DTE would not care if it were connected to a DCE or another DTE. Various issues of control signal pass through and timing are the principle problems.

Supremacy in error connection and data compression standards is currently a straight two horse race between CCITT international standards, and proprietary standards developed by Microcom called the Microcom Networking Protocol MNP (TM). CCITT recommendations specify a negotiation process that attempts error correction using the V.42 standard or Link Access Protocol for Modems (LAPM).

If LAPM (Clark, 1991) is not available in both devices attempting communication, MNP class 4 is attempted. MNP up to level 4 is included as an addendum to this international standard owing to the large installed base of modems using it, but higher levels will not be included in further developments. If neither is acceptable, simple asynchronous operation is used.

Once error correction is established, modems operating CCITT standards will attempt to instigate compression using V.42bis. Failing this, the fallback is to MNP level 5 (2:1 compression) and from there to uncompressed operation. V.42bis uses a technique called the Lempel-Ziv algorithm (Section 39.3.1). This like other techniques, builds dictionaries of code words for recurring characters in the data stream. The code words are abbreviations, so that it takes less bits to transmit, thereby increasing throughput and lowering cost over dial up lines.

Unlike other techniques, Lempel-Ziv develops these dictionaries dynamically as it goes along and stores them in Random Access Memory in both modems. Providing up to a fourfold performance increase, its choice as the CCITT adopted international standard was due to efficient use of both memory and processing power and perhaps more importantly its ability to shut the compression algorithm down when incompressible scrambled, encrypted or random data is presented to it.

Figure 39.8 shows examples of compression ratios possible for various applications. From a commercial viewpoint, V.42bis is an expensive proposition for vendors. Three companies, BT, IBM and the Unisys Corporation all patented their contributions to it and charge licence fees.

39.3.1 The V42.bis algorithm

In order to compress data, the V.42bis algorithm must first identify recurring strings of characters in the data stream. These code words are used to compile dictionaries which are duplicated at both ends of the transmission link and are accessed by a common synchronised index system.

This process is dynamic and the dictionaries are constantly being updated and modified. As data is transferred to the modem for transmission, a complex string matching or 'parsing' process must take place requiring an extensive dictionary search. It is easy to see how less efficient compression techniques could consume large amounts of memory and why it is necessary to disable the algorithm when presented with incompressible or encrypted data.

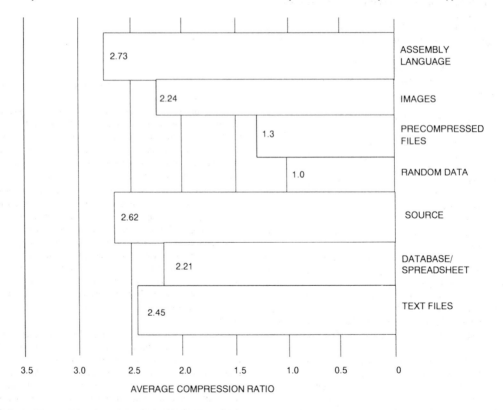

Figure 39.8 Examples of compression on files using V.42 bis

V.42bis dictionaries do not search from start to finish but use a 'tree' type data structure somewhat similar to a telephone directory. In that way the same information will be identically stored whenever it is placed in either the encoding or decoding dictionaries.

V.42bis uses the concepts of nodes to store information. The initial character is stored as a 'root' node which has 'leaf' nodes associated with it on paths radiating out from the root. Suppose the modem tries to find the code word 'STRING'. The initial character S is read and the entry located. T, the next character is read and a search started amongst the immediate offshoots or 'leaves' of the root node (see Figure 39.9). If found, the location is recorded and the next character read. This is repeated until the 'I' character when this particular root node has been exhausted. At this time the compressed index value of the location for 'STR' is transmitted, the algorithm adds an 'I' leaf node to the string 'STR' and starts afresh to look for a new root node associated with 'I' which may be elsewhere in the dictionary.

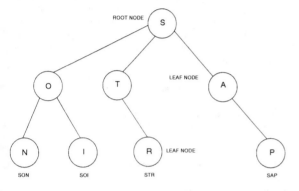

Figure 39.9   V.42 bis dictionary tree

Implementing this concept into a memory structure is shown in Figure 39.10. V.42bis devices commonly use a method called the 'trie', which uses both a character and three pointers to identify information by location. Starting again with our initial character 'S', the right hand pointer designates the alternative characters at the second level, 'T', 'A' and 'O'. These are the dependent characters of the parent character 'S'. Similarly 'N' and 'I' are dependent characters of the 'SO' string.

Since the index value built up by the pointer locations are unique, the far end modem can use the transmitted, compressed, index value to locate the entry in its own dictionary, with the parent (upward facing pointer) used to locate the preceding entry. By following the pointers backwards to the root the whole string is reconstructed in its uncompressed form. To maintain synchronisation of information the encoding dictionary updates are delayed by one string to allow the decoder to store new index values before attempting to decode them. In our example, the first time the index value for 'STRI' is transmitted, it is not recognised. The new index value is stored for subsequent use by the decoder and instead decodes the index value already stored for 'STR'.

39.4   Types of modem

When modems first appeared providing terminal to mainframe computer connection over the PSTN, the definition of a modem was clear. The modem was required to take the computers digital binary

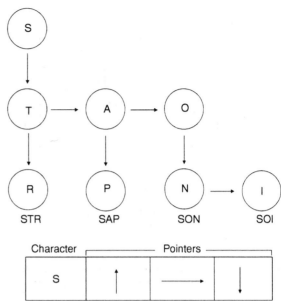

Figure 39.10   V.42 bis data structure

signals and use them to modulate an analogue signal capable of being transmitted down a telephone line, where another modem could demodulate the analogue signal and reproduce the computer's original digital signal faithfully. The modem took its name from this MODulating and DEModulating process.

Today there are a number of devices called modems that do not modulate or demodulate a carrier signal in the same way as the original dial up modem. In order to classify devices, we have to consider the type of line they use, the mode of transmission and the distances over which they operate.

The most commonly used medium is still the telephone network. Links are made by dialling over the PSTN or by using private point to point circuits leased from the telephone company. Dial up and leased line modems using these voice grade circuits, sometimes collectively referred to as long haul modems, must compensate for the frequency limitations and the variable quality of the transmission media. Distance however is unlimited.

Baseband modems are not 'true' modems, because they do not modulate signals in the normally accepted sense of the word. Baseband signals contain frequencies outside the normal 300-3400Hz voice grade circuits going right down to DC. Voice grade circuits are loaded so that performance for speech is optimised. Baseband modems therefore cannot use them, because they act like low pass filters, eliminating the higher baseband frequencies. Instead they use unloaded cable where they have the entire bandwidth at their disposal, but are subject to the linear relationship between frequency and attenuation which limits the operating distance. The baseband modem takes the digital signal it is presented with and either transmits it directly or in a slightly modified form to the line. In Figure 39.11 each time cell represents one information bit. The first half represents the complement of the bit value, the second half the bit value. By ensuring a signal change half way through each cell, synchronisation is maintained without separate synchronisation signals.

End users can provide their own unloaded circuits by laying twisted pair cable within the confines of private property or lease

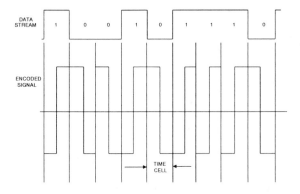

Figure 39.11 Baseband signalling (Manchester encoding)

from carriers like BT. Unloaded circuits are restricted to local exchange areas which means a maximum distance of approximately 7 miles. Short haul modems and local data sets are two popular terms for devices using baseband techniques over short distance unloaded lines, providing both synchronous and asychronous operation up to 19.2kbit/s, and up to 64kbit/s in special applications. The maximum operating speed is usually distance dependent.

Limited distance modems are hybrid devices. Some offer the same performance as CCITT standard modems over shorter distances by using less sophisticated, non standard modulation and equalisation techniques. Indeed some U.S. developed modems converted for the U.K. market provide nationwide operation over dedicated and wire leased lines at speeds up to 19.2kbit/s. From the U.S. perspective, coverage of the U.K. would constitute a limited distance! Some modems, described as limited distance devices, use the baseband technique and are subsequently limited to the local exchange operating restrictions.

The types of modem so far have dealt exclusively with digital data using baseband techniques that carry one channel per line. Broadband signalling has its origins in the cable television industry and carries many channels per cable (Minoli, 1991). A 300MHz broadband system can handle seventy five thousand 4kHz voice channels, but can also carry data, text and image. Using a two cable implementation to link devices to the network, the interface is provided by a radio frequency transmitter/receiver called an RF modem. Radio modems are now being developed for data transmission over cellular links and packet radio. Packet radio accommodates asynchronous and synchronous data transmission at 9.6kbit/s over mobile land channels and is set to foster a new generation of wireless local area networks.

39.5 Typical modem features

The years have seen a tremendous change in modem features and functionality. Although quite adequate at the time, the 300 baud modem of the early 70s is a far cry from the sophisticated and powerful, multi transmission standard, error correcting and data compressing products of today. Techniques like multi layer printed circuit boards, surface mount technology and DSP (digital signal processing) have combined increasing functionality with decreasing physical size.

The range of options, once available only in hardware, can now be programmed by software, and each year brings a new diversity

of applications and a relentless downward trend in pricing. Features can be categorised into three groups. Some enhance the basic group's modem performance itself. Some actually restrict performance in order to better accomplish a specialised task, whilst others aid user operation independent of performance. The features emphasise dial up modems since they incorporate such a wide range of functionality.

39.5.1 Transmission

The most common standards are those of the CCITT. The CCITT transmission standards are covered by the V series, the code designation for data transmission over the telephone network. Digital signal processors now deliver multiple transmission standard capability in a single chipset.

Two of the most popular combinations today are the low speed 'quad' combination covering V.22bis, V.22, V.23 and V.21 and the high speed 'quin', V.32. V.22bis, V.22, V.23 and V.21. Although demanding ever more powerful processing to be able to provide and negotiate the inter modem communication for this automatic multi standard capability, the user benefits of universal connectivity are a powerful selling point.

39.5.2 Operating modes

A modem will typically offer a range of operating modes over a variety of lines, as described in following sections.

39.5.2.1 *Half duplex vs full duplex*

A train travelling on a single track illustrates half duplex operation over two wire circuits, because while it is travelling in one direction, travel in the other direction is not possible. The train would have to be removed from the track at its destination before another could be sent in the opposite direction. Half duplex operation on four wire circuits can also be illustrated using the same analogy if we now have a second track, so there is one for each direction, but one train is not allowed to start before the other is finished.

Continuing with two parallel tracks, full duplex operation is equivalent to the trains being able to operate independently of each other on their own track. In practice, full-duplex operation is provided over four wire lines where the outward and inward 'tracks' are physically separate or over two wires where either the modem splits the physical circuit into two channels of different frequency or uses echo cancellation.

39.5.2.2 *Dial up vs leased lines*

Calls over the PSTN are routed by tone or pulse signals generated by the modem which duplicate those of an ordinary telephone. The advantages are that one modem can connect to any other modem on the same network no matter where it is and charges are based on distance and connection time, not the amount of data transmitted. Disadvantages are that the line quality varies because the circuits are switched through exchanges which introduce transmission loss and noise. Even if the same destination is dialled, the route may be different, so the line cannot be "tuned" for better quality.

Leased lines or private lines obtained from telephone companies are permanent connections between two points. Because the quality of the line is constant and the route is fixed, it can be fine tuned or conditioned to carry high volumes of data, at higher speeds than dial up lines and with lower error rates. Most of today's sophisticated dial up modems incorporate 2 or 4 leased line operation as standard.

39.5.2.3 *Synchronous or asychronous*

Controlled by the transmission standard invoked on call set up, typically both asynchronous and synchronous operation is provided within a single unit. Synchronous operation is usually protocol transparent, whereas asynchronous operation will be possible over a variety of character lengths, parity and stop bit combinations under software programme control.

39.5.2.4 *Equalisation*

Equalisation circuitry compensates for the distortion caused as different frequencies travel at different rates down a transmission line changing the shape of the signal waveform. Fixed equalisers used in lower speed modems are designed to compensate for average line conditions, which include frequency response and envelope delay. For higher speed operation, automatic adaptive equalisers are used which continually re-adjust for changes in line quality, especially useful in dial up operation.

39.5.2.5 *Error correction*

As speeds of operation increase, modem links become more prone to errors, because a line disturbance that corrupts one bit at 300bit/s corrupts thirty two at 9.6kbit/s. At higher speeds, errors may less obviously be generated by communications software or lower quality cables.

Error correction need not necessarily take place in the modem. In fact, most dial up modems have an operating mode where error correction is disabled. For example, if a workstation or computer uses a built in synchronous error control protocol like that used by an X.25 Packet Assembler/Disassembler (PAD), data is presented to the modem and just transmitted. Further error correction from the modem would simply increase the overhead and degrade throughput.

Where error correction does occur in the modem, the most basic form is the parity bit where an extra bit, either 1 or 0, is added to each character so that the sum of the bits is always odd or even. When bits are corrupted during transmission, the receiving modem can detect it and ask for a retransmission. This is known as Automatic Retransmission Request (ARQ). Because its ability to detect errors is limited (two compensating errors within a single character would go undetected) the next stage is to incorporate a checksum. Here a number of characters are grouped together into a frame and certain bits of it are combined together according to a mathematical algorithm to generate a checksum, often called a Cyclical Redundancy Check (CRC). This is then transmitted with the frame. The receiver does the same computation on the transmitted frame and compares its own checksum with that transmitted to it. Depending on the result it sends an acknowledgement or a retransmission request back to the originating modem.

Although a typical 16 bit checksum is far more efficient at detecting errors it cannot detect all. As the move towards standards has been consolidated these techniques have been incorporated into standards. The two major players are the international CCITT V.42 standard and the Microcom Networking Protocol. V.42 uses a 32 bit CRC option.

39.5.2.6 *Data compression*

Data compression schemes are a way of increasing throughput as it gets increasingly difficult to improve the modem's basic operating speed as upper limits of performance over analogue telephone lines are approached.

Data compression relies on encoding recurring sequences more efficiently. If more information can be represented by fewer bits, the faster it can be transmitted. Although vendors data sheets always quote the maximum compression rates, they vary with the type of data being transmitted and the quality of line being used. The two standards battling it out in the market-place are again the V.42bis and the MNP standard, currently at level 10.

39.5.2.7 *Call control*

Originally dial up operations could only be performed by a telephone attached directly into the modem, the use of internal relays preventing the phone from disturbing the data call, once it was in progress, as well as allowing normal phone operation at all other times. It is now common to find manual call control possible by using front panel buttons which initiate a call stored in internal registers. Automatic calling can be programmed through the connected terminal, PC or workstation so that a number, or sequence of numbers, is dialled on a typed command.

For even simpler usage, some can initiate dialling to a stored number location on power up, typically by raising the DSR signal on the V.24 modem interface. Varying with available memory, storage is typically between 10 to 20 fourteen digit numbers, although up to 100 is available. For dialling behind a PABX, a pause function in the dialling sequence is often still required, to allow the public line to be accessed. Both the pulse dialling of the older Strowger telephone exchanges and the dual tone multifrequency signalling of the new generation are standard features. Software programming can limit the modem to originating calls only. Standards for automatic dialling include the proprietary Hayes 'AT' protocol, specifically designed for asynchronous personal computers communications, or the CCITT's V.25bis command set covering both asynchronous and synchronous environments. Vendors are finding it necessary to include both these, to satisfy user demands on connectivity.

39.5.2.8 *Auto answer*

When a modem requires an operator to receive a call and switch from voice to data it is called attended operation. Unattended operation is when the modem turns on its associated equipment and commences operation from a distance, especially useful in overnight data collection by a central computer from geographically dispersed locations.

39.5.2.9 *Auto call back and line restoral*

For the leased line application, transferring large amounts of data between two points, a PSTN link can be used as a back up in the event of the leased line failure. Dial up to one or more destinations can be initiated automatically by the modem keeping the network on line. Leased line restoral is either attempted after the expiry of a simple time out function when the back up line is inactive, or the modem incorporates active circuitry that monitors and tests the leased line continuously and restores at the first available opportunity.

The second method is far superior, because it eliminates switching back to a faulty line and avoids using the back up circuit any longer than necessary. Ideally a visual indication of this back up mode is desirable to avoid excessive call charges generated by a consistently poor leased line service.

39.5.2.10   *Speed conversion flow control*

Increasingly included in the feature list is the ability to automatically cater for communicating devices operating at different speeds, essential for modem pool applications where a host computer running at a fixed speed is accessed by a multi speed environment.

39.5.2.11   *Visual audio indications*

To allow a simple and instantaneous check on status, front panel indications are typically provided for transmit, receive, carrier detect, terminal ready, off hook and power on signals. This is increasingly complemented by an internal speaker which monitors the call set up tones.

The introduction of sophisticated liquid crystal displays has spawned a new generation of intelligent front panels which can be used to programme both local and remotely connected units without the need to attach a separate programming terminal via a console port. This is a boon in the synchronous environment allowing in situ reprogramming and diagnostics.

39.5.2.12   *Diagnostics*

Once proprietary but now conforming increasingly to the CCITT V.54 standard, diagnostic tests typically include the local analogue and digital loop, and remote digital loop often with a test pattern generator and decoder to simplify both the initial installation and subsequent fault isolation.

39.5.2.13   *Timing*

To allow for both synchronous and asynchronous operation, modems must be capable of being driven by a range of clock sources.

Asynchronous operation uses the clock internal to the modem. Synchronous operation, which requires timing information to be passed with the data, uses a combination of internal, system and external clock sources. A synchronous link requires a master clock source, either generated internally by the modem or externally by data terminal equipment at one end. At the remote end the modem uses the system clock option to synchronise its received and transmitted data to the master.

39.5.2.14   *Management*

Essential for the corporate network running business critical applications, modem management is sold as either a software package or a complete hardware and software solution. Typically locally attached to a centrally sited racking system and driven by a personal computer, management packages offer port traffic monitoring and statics coupled with local and remote diagnostics and configuration. A management system monitor displays information either textually or as dynamic graphical information, whilst hard copy output tends to be limited and textual only. Largely proprietary, these systems lag behind in terms of open systems standards compliance as vendors development budgets focus on local area network management.

39.5.2.15   *Security*

A rapidly developing market as companies provide increasing access to their networks from either the high street outlet or direct to the customer, modem security is typically delivered as a basic password system which can be optionally combined with a dialback facility. On connection the called modem requests a password. If the password is validated by the modems directory, it will disconnect the line and redial outwards to the telephone number associated with it in memory. Once reconnected, the password is again requested. If successful the user is connected to the service. Modem security is often integrated within a management system and may be supplemented by modem identification codes.

39.6   Applications

The future of modem applications depends on a variety of tariffing, technological, business and political factors operating at both national and international level and the extent to which any one of them can dominate.

The short haul modem suffers the least from pressures like public network digitisation and tariffing. Technologically it is characterised by a level of miniaturisation and cost reduction that further development would be hard pressed to improve, where medium speed, limited distance interoffice and on premise intersite connectivity is required. Commercially it is firmly established as a commodity product and is becoming an integrated part of structured cabling systems. The only real threat to its existence is the demand on bandwidth to the desktop of new computing and workstation applications.

By contrast, the long haul dial up and leased line modem suffers more, reflected by the effort put into its technological advancement. The last few years have seen an upsurge in dial up applications, triggered by the introduction of 2 wire V.32 technology coupled with echo cancellation, trellis encoding, error correction and data compression techniques.

Satisfying a user need for faster, less error prone communications and underpinned by cost savings achieved in switching from 4 wire leased circuits to 2 wire dial up circuits, the upper modem limit of 30kbit/s imposed by the copper loop is however rapidly being reached. Compensating for this are a number of new emerging markets. At the low speed V.22bis commodity end where ISDN, for the time being at least, is less of a threat, a new market place has developed for the portable, laptop and now palm top computer. Miniaturised battery powered and increasingly integrated modems are being used to connect the business traveller from the home, hotel or even the car to the office for data transfer. These will inevitably be looking to upgrade to V.32 technology and beyond.

In the high speed modem sector, the 15 million Group 111 analogue fax terminals installed world-wide represent a major opportunity (Braue, 1991). Currently using V.29 and V.27 technology they are expected to upgrade to V.32 and V.32bis within one year. Some vendors have already grasped the facsimile opportunity by building these facilities onto battery powered, pocket size, V.22bis modems with a view to keeping the mobile business man in constant touch.

New standards are being developed by the CCITT for transferring digital data over Group 111 analogue connections and improvements in both speed and error correcting capability have been recommended. CCITT study groups are currently looking at connectivity between digital Group 1V fax and Group 111 fax, a sure sign of a healthy market.

Apart from the fax boom, other applications, which improvements in dial up technology have made possible, include local area network interconnection. Formerly the sole province of analogue or digital leased lines, dial up technology now provides for Internet Protocol (IP) addressing over switched circuits. The continuing viability of this trend from leased circuit to dial up circuit, typically for back up applications, is the speed with which ISDN can erode this technological advance.

Increasingly there will be a choice to be made between high speed modems over switched analogue lines and ISDN over switched digital lines, as PTTs fulfil their promises on basic rate ISDN availability. For the moment, costing up analogue switched, digital leased and ISDN alternatives is easy but potentially misleading. Connecting and installing ISDN is expensive, whereas the call charges are identical to analogue dial up lines, being based on distance and time but independent of the volume. By comparison with analogue voice lines, they offer considerably more bandwidth, the quality of end to end digital connections and practically instantaneous call set up. So in reality it is not a like for like comparison.

Based purely on today's tariffs, and compared with a V.32 alternative, ISDN can only be justified by substantial use, where its greater bandwidth can reduce call charges to recoup the much higher initial outlay. By comparison, used on a single location for more than three hours a day, it could well be cheaper to use digital leased lines like KiloStream. For a genuine comparison, the nature of the application, the expected traffic, connection and equipment charges must all be carefully considered. If the 30kbit/s limit on modems is achieved and can successfully be combined with compression techniques operating a 4:1 reduction in line transmission requirements, potential throughputs of 120kbit/s will provide modems with ISDN basic rate performance. The question is, will they need to?

Already products are having to be developed to help computer serial communications ports keep up with current modem performance as users fall into the speed trap of assuming their desk top equipment can run fast enough to make full use of it. Significantly those vendors who have a foot in both the modem and ISDN camps still believe there is a lot of mileage left in the modem. Their future is not in trying to match ISDN in terms of performance, but providing innovative, added functionality, for increasingly cost effective communications.

39.7   References

Braue, J. (1991) The state of the modem. *Data Communications International*.

Clark, A. (1991) Error control and modem communications, *Communication and Computer News*. May.

Dennis, T. (1990) Dial up modems. *Datacom*. June.

Doll, D. (1978) *Data Communications; Facilities, Networks and System Design*. John Wiley & Sons.

Enslow, P. (1988) *The OSI Reference Model and Network Architectures*. Frost & Sullivan, London.

Minoli, D. (1991) *Telecommunications Technology Handbook*. Artech House, Boston.

Scott P.R.D. (1980) *Modems in Data Communication*. NCC Publications, Manchester.

40

Multiplexers

J Hoolan
Dowty Communications Ltd

Contents

40.1 Introduction

The multiplexer is one of the most important components in communications networking. Its central function, from the network managers viewpoint, is to concentrate many users (or information channels) on to a single transmission channel in order to maximise the efficiency of that channel: it is used in almost every aspect of networking digital data, voice and video. This section will describe the advantages and disadvantages of different data multiplexing techniques, why these different techniques evolved to solve particular network engineering problems and how they fit in to modern networks.

Figure 40.1 shows the basic theoretical model for a multiplexer with the composite line speed exactly equal to the aggregate speed of the inputs.

Given a transmission channel, there are two ways the available bandwidth can be used: firstly by dividing the available bandwidth frequency spectrum into a subset of frequencies, each of which can then simultaneously use the transmission channel and allocate each frequency band to an input channel that needs to be multiplexed; or secondly, allocate all the available bandwidth to each channel for a fixed discrete time period. The first of these methods would be Frequency Division Multiplexing (FDM) and the latter Time Division Multiplexing (TDM). FDM is used primarily as an analogue solution to multiplexing and, for example, has been used extensively in telephony; indeed many of the FDM standards and techniques such as the multiplexing ratios dictated by the early designs of telephone exchange multiplexers (such as 24:1) are still in evidence in some of the latter digital exchanges.

This chapter is concerned however with the use and applications of latter type of multiplexing technique, Time Division Multiplexing which can be used in one of two modes, deterministic or non-deterministic. Deterministic TDM (which is the more commonly known just as TDM) allocates the available transmission channel bandwidth of a fixed regular basis to the input channels, whether they have data to send or not. Non-deterministic TDM or statistical TDM (which is more commonly just statistical multiplexing) allocates the available bandwidth to input channels only on demand when data is present.

40.2 Time Division Multiplexers

40.2.1 Principles

Time division multiplexing is the earliest and simplest form of digital multiplexing. It was developed to solve the communications problem created by the growth in remote computer processing during the 1960s. Computer terminals (or consoles) were locally attached in early computers but as computers became multi-user, so the need grew for more users gaining remote access over a single transmission line. Single users could gain access by simply attaching their terminal to a modem that converted the digital information by modulation into a voice frequency that could then be transmitted down a telephone to a modem at the receiving end that demodulated the signals back into digital form and hence onto the computer. However the need for groups of co-located users to gain access to computing resource meant that multiplexing techniques had to be applied to maximise the utilisation of rented PTT lease line circuits or costly dial up calls.

The early forms of multiplexers, which evolved to meet this growth in computing power, were designed for use with asynchronous data as this was the most commonly available type of terminal and printer. Typically running at speeds of up to 1200bit/s and with code formats of 5 and 7 bits (Baudot and ASCII respectively). As computer manufacturers moved to synchronous data, as a more efficient form of communications, so the design of multiplexers was adapted for handling this type of traffic. It was in this period that many of the design techniques to overcome specific engineering and networking problems evolved.

In common with all multiplexing techniques the primary requirement was for the two multiplexers to have some form of synchronisation procedure whereby they could calculate the location of each channel. This was done by defining a fixed length composite frame format, as in Figure 40.2, that had a unique synchronisation code at the start. When the link was first started the multiplexers would enter into a 'training' period, with only empty frames plus the synchronisation 'header' code being sent to each other to determine the frame boundaries. The composite overhead or bandwidth needed could be taken by reducing the available aggregate from the input channels.

Starting with the first commercially available asynchronous multiplexers the initial multiplexing technique was bit interleaved. In this method, the incoming data on each channel is sampled bit by bit and stored in a transitory central buffer before being assembled on to a composite. This is the simplest technique that can be employed as it only requires that the multiplexer recognises the bit boundaries of the incoming data. Providing that the sequence of data bits is then forwarded to the remote end and demultiplexed without losing integrity, then any type of data format can be handled. However, as this meant sending all data bits for an asynchronous character including the stop, start and parity bits, the multiplexing technique adopted quickly moved to byte interleaved. In this method the ancillary bits could be stripped off and only the data sent. At the receiving end they could be reconstituted. The byte was

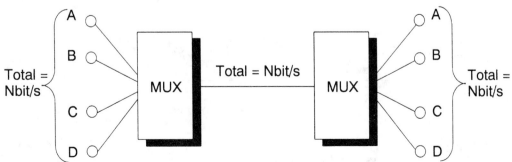

Figure 40.1 Basic model for a multiplexer

Sync. pattern

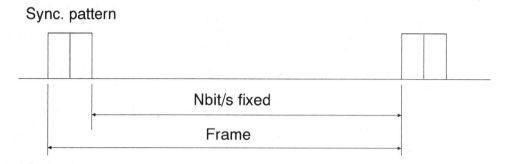

Figure 40.2   The basic operation of framing

8 bits with data requiring 7 bits and the 8th bit in each byte indicating whether data or controls were being sent. Although it meant that 5 bit data such as Baudot had 2 bits per byte wasted and that 8 bit codes could not be sent, as the majority of traffic was based on 7 bit code (ASCII), the overall gains made it worthwhile.

As stated above, the original design was for handling asynchronous traffic and the only rules for configuration would involve working out the total aggregate input and formulating the best 'scanning' method to cater for all the different speeds, so that they could mapped on to the available composite bandwidth. According to the design of the multiplexer a small percentage of the bandwidth had to be allocated for the synchronisation pattern, or sequence, so the general design rule was to limit the overhead to around 1% or 2 bits in a 200 bit frame. In addition, if the status of the V.24 (RS232) control lines such as Data Terminal Ready (circuit 108/1 or 2) or Request to Send (circuit 105), then this had to be allocated bandwidth as if it were data. As an example, if a half duplex circuit is being employed, which means that the data and control signals have to be kept contiguous, then the control information could require as much bandwidth as the data. The result is that the bandwidth actually available for data could be less than the theoretical maximum by up to 50%. The technique developed to overcome this problem is to use multi-frames with two types of controls, high and low priority. High priority is dealt with as described above. Low priority control information is sent every N frames, where N could be from 4 to 64 depending on the frame size and speed of the composite.

Figure 40.3 shows the ideal model of time division multiplexing operation, where all eight channels are being efficiently multiplexed onto a composite line. At any one instant in time there is always one of the channels using the available bandwidth. Figure 40.4 shows the realistic utilisation of the line. Note that only channels 1, 2 and 6 have any data to send. However, time slots in the form of bandwidth still have to be allocated since the TDM cannot recognise the absence of real data; this is the trade-off against data transparency and speed.

To summarise, the technique of sending asynchronous data by TDM is to use a frame synchronised, byte interleaved method with facilities for control information using a redundant bits.

The advantage is transparency to data format; any format of asynchronous data can be sent, at any speed.

The disadvantages are:

1. Fixed speeds; it was usually difficult to change any speeds without completely re-programming the multiplexers.
2. Poor efficiency; input channels always have a fixed allocation of composite bandwidth, whether they have data to send or not. As asynchronous data is by definition 'bursty' interactive type traffic, there will almost certainly be long periods of inactivity which still has bandwidth being allocated to it.
3. Prone to errors; in the process of being transmitted, any errors generated on the composite circuit are passed to the receiving end without any indication to the end device (in fact the parity recovery method makes this worse as it hides dual bit errors).

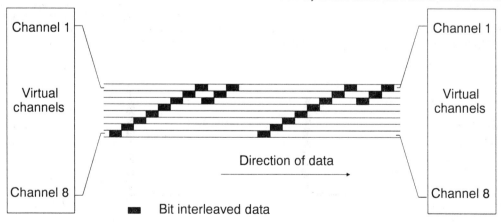

Figure 40.3   Ideal model of a TDM

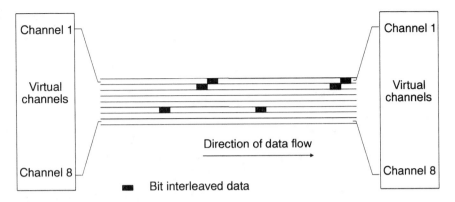

Figure 40.4 Line utilisation in a typical TDM

Unless the link synchronisation actually fails the remote end has no indication that there is a problem on the line.

40.2.2 Synchronous TDM

As synchronous protocols evolved the need to multiplex them grew; networks with remote sites that had a mix of asynchronous and synchronous terminals needed to connect them to the central site computing resource.

For synchronous TDMs, the bit-interleaved method was adopted as the most superior technique. The main difference from asynchronous multiplexing being that as well as keeping data integrity, the multiplexers had to keep the associated clock timing synchronisation so that the demultiplexed recovered data could have a re-generated clock associated with it. This point will be referred to later as it imposes major restrictions on the design and operation of networks and techniques have been developed to solve the problem. Apart from timing considerations, the synchronisation header in the composite frame has to be included in the overall bandwidth calculation.

In asynchronous data the actual speed of transmission can vary, according to the manufacturer's specification, by up to ±15%, therefore devices running overspeed were a particular problem. Synchronous data has a much tighter specification and may only vary by 0.1%, as recommended by CCITT V.28. This is particularly important for synchronous modems which cannot tolerate any deviation from the specified speed.

The technique of 'robbing' the low speed input channels and allocating it to the composite was normally only applied within these constraints. Two alternatives were:

1. To designate one of the input channels as a 'vari-speed' input which may be attached to non-critical devices. This approach, for obvious reasons, has to be handled with caution.

2. By the preferred technique used by latter designs to permanently allocate a synchronisation overhead.

A mixture of bit and byte interleaving with a fixed synchronisation header was also adopted by some high order multiplexers, where multiple voice channels needed to be multiplexed after being digitally encoded; the US Bell D1 system for example. The basic technique employed is for an analogue sample of the voice signal to be converted into an 8 bit code word, after being manipulated through a compander circuit operating on a logarithmic law to reduce the signal to noise level. The Bell D2 system used bit robbing for signalling purposes. The standards which has been adopted for this type of high order multiplexing are discussed later in this Chapter e.g. the CCITT standard G.711 for pulse code modulation.

From the viewpoint of line efficiency between two point to point multiplexers, the advantages and disadvantages of synchronous TDM compared to asynchronous TDM are almost identical. The main exception is that error detection and correction is not an issue with a synchronous data, as it will be enveloped in its own protocol independent from the multiplexer and therefore will have its own error recovery mechanisms via retransmission. However, from a networking viewpoint, the network timing recovery mechanisms and the methods by which the nodes in a network can be synchronised together, is a major issue.

Figure 40.5 shows a more realistic model of a multiplexer, with the overheads taken into account, that results in a composite that

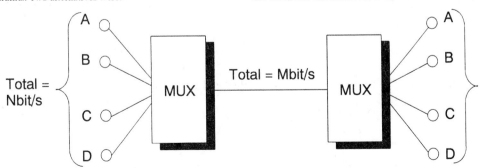

Figure 40.5 Model of a multiplexer with overheads considered

must be faster than the input aggregate. The value of M is given by Equation 40.5, therefore M > N.

$$M = A + B + C + C$$
$$+ synchronisation\ header + control\ information \qquad (40.1)$$

In summary it can be stated that time division multiplexing has established itself as the most efficient technique for handling synchronous protocols and data at different speeds, even though it suffered from the fact that bandwidth is always wasted. It is not however very effective at handing asynchronous data due to the inflexibility and lack of error detection and correction. It is from this major disadvantage that the use of statistical multiplexers evolved.

40.3   Statistical time division multiplexing

40.3.1   Principle of Operation

Caught between the exponential growth of computing power and the use of asynchronous terminals as a cheap and convenient way of accessing computers, the statistical TDM was developed. It was first formulated in the early 1970s and in particular on the Arpanet network in the USA from which the X.25 packet switch standard evolved (Davis, 1973).

As stated above, the main problems with using TDM techniques on asynchronous data were lack of error detection and correction, and poor efficiency on the composite line, especially since the average asynchronous device is only active for 5 to 10% of the time.

The solution for asynchronous multiplexers was to use a formal protocol between the multiplexer nodes which could concentrate the data and provide the means of detecting and recovering from errors on the line. The protocol invariably chosen was based on a High Level Data Link Control (HDLC) which in turn had been derived from the IBM's SDLC protocol. This protocol had several design advantages over previous synchronous protocols such as IBM's 3270, as follows:

1. It was solely concerned with the maintenance of the data link and did not have to get involved with device control.
2. It had one common frame format for data, control and supervision with a unique flag indentifier for synchronisation.
3. It was bit oriented and therefore inherently transparent to data structures. However, it used byte aligned boundaries to permit byte interleaving, if required.
4. It had a Frame Check Sequence (FCS), in the form of a Cyclic Redundancy Check sum (CRC), that allowed error checking of the complete contents of all frames and thereby providing a mechanism for error recovery.

5. It was being considered as an international standard.

There were still drawbacks however, in that early versions of HDLC only allowed one virtual circuit (or user) per frame, and therefore modifications were made by many manufacturers to allow several users to share the same frame. In addition the multiplexers needed to pass not just data but also various other types of information such as:

1. The status conditions of the V.24 (RS232) interface controls.
2. Test information, such as setting a specific remote channel into loopback for testing purposes.
3. Information for validation of a channel connection, to check that it is working end to end.
4. A SPACE condition for so many milliseconds.
5. Information to set remote buffers into an XOFF state so that no more data should be sent until further notification.

It also had to allow the input channels to locally emulate some asynchronous polled protocols e.g. HP3000, so that polling could be locally acknowledged rather than end-to-end. The link need only carry a poll count and report polling exceptions.

The standard HDLC format has no inherent mechanism for allowing these facilities as it was designed purely to control the link level functions. It is up to the designer to implement this in the information (data) fields in order to make the product as flexible as possible.

Figure 40.6 shows a basic HDLC Information frame with the unique flag identifier 7E (hexadecimal), the address field and the control field, which in this case is indicating that the frame contains data.

Figure 40.7 shows a modified HDLC information frame format, used by a proprietary STDM manufactured by Dowty Case, other manufacturers using different encoding techniques. Here the information frame does not require an address field. It does, however, require a mapping field for each block of 4 bytes for a given channel, which indicates whether the following bytes are data or control and timing codes e.g. DTR dropped, set channel loopbacks, set SPACE condition for 100mS.

Given the mechanisms of a link protocol it was a small step to design a multiplexer that only transmitted data when there was data to sent. By scanning the input channels for activity and placing any data present into a common buffer pool, a frame could be assembled with data from different channels, plus any control information, and transmitted to the multiplexer at the other end of the link for demultiplexing.

Since HDLC uses a go-back-N frame sequencing count, any errors on the line due to a bad CRC or out of sequence frame would be detected and a request for the frame to be retransmitted issued from the remote end (also known as Automatic Repeat Request or ARQ). At that time, no standards existed for describing how the

Flag	Address	Control	128 bytes of user data	CRC	CRC	Flag

Figure 40.6   Basic HDLC information frame

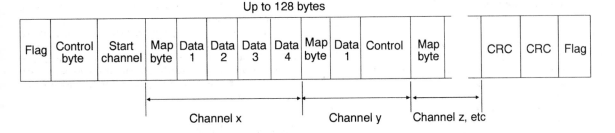

Figure 40.7 Proprietary HDLC information frame format (Dowty Case Communications Ltd.)

frames should be constructed for multiple users and interface control information, so every manufacturer developed their own proprietary standard, compared to the present development of LAPD which overcomes these restrictions. The outcome of this was to see a generation of proprietary statistical multiplexers before the establishment of X.25.

Figure 40.8 shows the simplified operation of a statistical multiplexer which operates by scanning the input buffers for data presence (indicated by the flag). Data is transferred into a buffer queue waiting to be assembled and transmitted as a frame.

40.3.2 Features

By definition, statistical multiplexers have to concentrate many input channels onto a composite link, where the aggregate input speeds may temporarily exceed the available composite bandwidth. In this situation it is essential that the multiplexer has the facility to flow control the data input, either by use of XON/XOFF or V.24 control signals such as DTR or CTS. The decisions by which the network designer decided how to size a network with the mix of input speeds and output speeds were assisted by queuing theory.

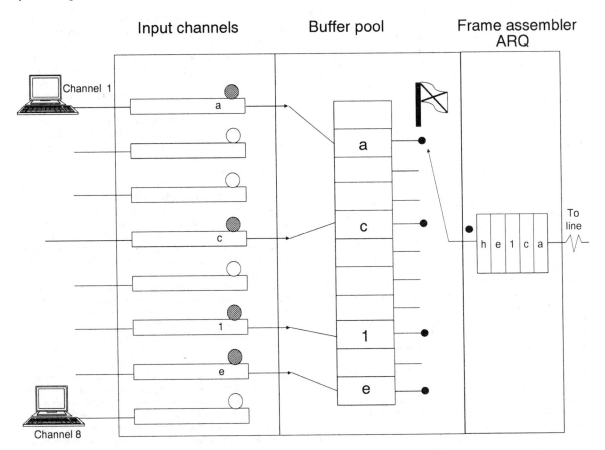

Figure 40.8 Simplified operation of a statistical multiplexer

In summary, statistical time division multiplexers offer asynchronous users the advantages of:

1. Better use of the composite line by only allocating bandwidth when sending data.
2. Techniques for encoding additional control and timing information to make the system more flexible.
3. Speed translation end to end.
4. Intelligent interaction to allow some asynchronous protocols to be emulated locally rather than over the whole link.

However some of the disadvantages are:

1. Only asynchronous data was practical. Synchronous protocols could be handled in the same manner as some asynchronous protocols in that local emulation of the host end and terminal end would result in only the actual data being transmitted over the link and the majority of the control information could be handled locally.

40.3.3 Networking

Only point to point multiplexers have been considered so far, as they illustrate the basic principles of multiplexing. However, a major development in the mid 1970s was to give a user on a terminal the facility to select more than one destination. The requirement grew out of the development in computing power, which meant that many companies were expanding on the number of computers they used and were perhaps dropping the mainframes in favour of distributed minis. To allow these to be accessible the users required the multiplexers to become networked. In effect rather than let the computer switch the user to an application it was left to the network.

40.4 High order multiplexing

40.4.1 Standards

The term, high order multiplexing, is used to describe the technique for multiplexing multiplexers. By successively taking input channels of fixed speed and creating a hierarchy of 'groups' of multiplexers, a final high speed output composite is produced, that is logically structured to contain all the input channels in a defined sequence.

High order multiplexers were originally developed as described above to allow voice circuits to be multiplexed. This simple statement is the underlying design principle for all the decisions that have been made on PTT digital speeds and frame structures throughout the world in the past 20 years. Although today they can be used for any type of digitally encoded data, including fax and video, these are the result of data communications manufacturers, and lately PTTs, 'highjacking' the circuits developed for digitised voice and using them for pure data.

The lowest input speed for high order multiplexing contained within CCITT is 64kbit/s. This is the speed arrived at from encoding voice, with a maximum frequency of 3.4kHz, at 8000 samples a second (which is above the Nyquist sampling rate) and then converting each sample into an 8 bit word or byte. The original technique used by the PTTs was to use frequency division multiplexing with 12 or 24 voice channels being frequency multiplied. For example, in the CCITT 960 channel system, channel 1 would be frequency translated to 62kHz in the first group and then to 420kHz in the second or supergroup.

At present the three principal hierarchical systems in existence, are from Europe, US and Japan.

From Table 40.1 (based on CCITT G.702) it can be seen that each system, from a base speed of 64kbit/s, multiplexes in fixed, discrete bands, up to the Gigahertz bands, suitable for transmission over microwave and satellite carriers.

Table 40.1 High order systems

Multiplex level	Europe (kbit/s)	USA (kbit/s)	Japan (kbit/s)
0	64	64	64
1	2048	1544	1544
2	8448	6312	7876
3	34368	44736	32064
4	139264	274176	97728
5	565148		397200

The underlying system employed is bit interleaved, although the framing structure is byte oriented. Analysis of the framing structures gives more detail on how they were used as general purpose data multiplexers. In general the input channels were constructed in frames, each consisting of 12, 24 or 30 voice channels or 'timeslots' depending on the system. This gave the first hierarchical grouping. Within this group the frames could be assembled together in superframes to contain signalling and control information.

The early US systems need to be examined separately as they used a technique that was completely alien to pure data use. The original Bell D1 system had an input rate of 56kbit/s (7 times 8000 samples per second) because the timeslots used a 'bit robbing' technique whereby the 8th bit in every slot was used for maintaining timing information on the line. By always setting the 8th bit to zero and inverting the PCM data sample so that it was normally set to all 1's i.e. no speech signal, the line signal could be guaranteed to have data transitions which kept the timing content. When the D2 system was introduced using HDB3 (high density bipolar 3) line encoding, this allowed 8 bits per slot. However, the system used part of the old standard in that it again allowed the same 'bit robbing' to take place in the same way but only every 6th frame and in this case it was used for passing control and signalling information. For speech purpose this did not impose an reduction in the quality of service as the human ear did not detect this impairment, but for pure data it introduced an unacceptable error rate.

The speeds which became standard offerings were derived in the following ways. US Bell system D2 (usually known as T1) used a frame made of 24 timeslots (or input channels) at 8 bits each i.e. 192 bits: an additional bit was added on to each of the frames for synchronisation purposes giving 193 bits per frame. The 'sweep' rate or number of frames per second was 8000 (the voice encoding, or codec, sampling rate) giving an overall speed of 1.544Mbit/s.

In the version adopted by the CCITT the frame consisted of 32 timeslots, of which 30 were for voice and two for synchronisation and signalling information, giving a total of 256 bits. At a sweep rate of 8000 frames per second this gives a speed of 2.048Mbit/s.

All digital exchanges and the space/time switches used these speeds at the core of their design.

As with all synchronous TDM networks timing is a major consideration in all network design. Simply put, in order to maintain data integrity, the whole network must run off a single clock or timing source, with every node 'slaved' to that clock designated the 'master'. Failure to do so results in 'bit slippage' in the frames, with data loss. On a small network, geographically spread over a small area, this may not present a serious implementation problem. On a national network it requires careful planning with contingency back up clocks available automatically if the master fails. International networks resolve the problem by clocking parts of the network independently or plesiochronously, that is off a clock that is so stable (1 part in 10^{-12}) that the slippages are low enough to be acceptable.

40.4.2 Synchronous Digital Hierarchy (SDH)

In an attempt to reconcile the different high order multiplexers a new set of G. standards have been proposed which can support the US and European variants. CCITT have initially proposed G.708, G.708, and G.709 to offer a ultra high speed Synchronous TDM system based on the US SONET. (See Chapter 42.)

40.5 Multiplexing and packet switching

The evolution of multiplexing over the past 20 years has seen the generalisation of the original design techniques into two distinct types: circuit switching and packet switching.

Circuit switching has developed out of the synchronous digital techniques and, as its name implies, supports network source to destination connections as a single, end-to-end circuit. Bandwidth over the network links is permanently allocated for the duration of the call. It is then set aside whether information is being sent or not. In this it is analogous to a telephone connection.

Circuit switching is implemented using space-time switches that move the timeslots from one frame to another. Timeslots access is through multiplexers which operate in 'drop and insert' mode. This works by taking a timeslot that terminates on one channel, and therefore becomes free, and allowing another channel to use that timeslot for sending data back out. It can be seen that no method to dynamically allocate bandwidth is available.

Figure 40.9 shows how circuit switching is implemented using space-time switches that route the timeslots in high-speed T1/E1 frames around a network.

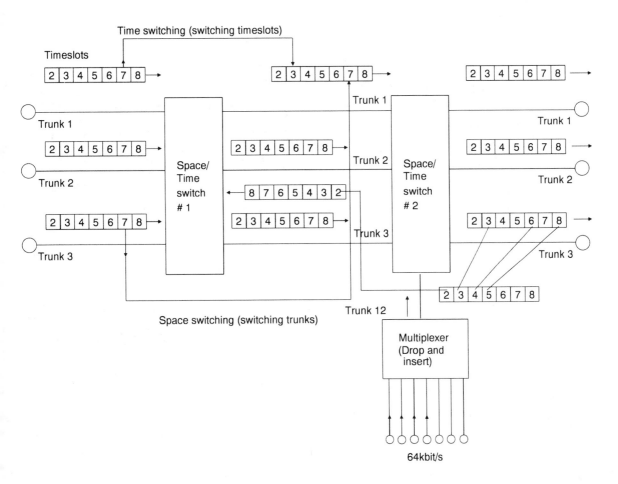

Figure 40.9 Circuit switching used to route frames

Packet switching, on the other hand, does not require permanent bandwidth to be allocated. Data is sent through the network in discrete packets, each packet only demanding bandwidth on any specific link for the time it is being transmitted. In this it is similar to statistical multiplexing. There are, however, two ways in which packet switch connections can be tracked through a network for the duration of a call or session. These are Connection (CON) and Connectionless (CLNS) oriented. The differences between these two methods are so important to networking that they will be explained in detail here.

The first method (CON) requires that the destination address only be sent in the first packet, when the call is first set up. The network merely has to assign virtual links to that call so that subsequent packets have a route assigned to them through the network. CLNS packets, on the other hand, have the destination address in every packet, and as such do not require a virtual network path to be set up in advance. In fact each packet can take a different route through the network, even arriving out of sequence at the far end and relying on the protocol to reassemble them in the correct sequence. Connection oriented networks such as X.25 packet switching derive their design methodology from telephony techniques, while connectionless techniques, which are now widely used on LANs, were derived from Ethernet radio broadcast systems, such as the Aloha system developed by the University of Hawaii.

Today the single most important multiplexing technique is packet switching as defined in the CCITT X.25 world wide accepted standard. From 1976 when it was first ratified it has become a fundamental part of the Open Systems Interconnection model as one of the primary standards in layer three, the network layer.

In its basic form, as an independent networking standard, it is designed to allow asynchronous devices to make and clear network connections by a defined calling procedure. It uses the CCITT standards for defining how the asynchronous device should interface (X.3); how to interpret network messages (X.28); the numbering system for setting up international calls (X.121); and negotiation parameters for end to end session compliance (X.29).

The strength of X.25 lies in the fact that it relies on other standards for interfacing into the lower layers. It resolves the logical and physical link connection problems by utilising an HDLC format LAPB and an X.21bis physical interface.

In order to use X.25 in a packet switch network two components are required: a Packet Switch Exchange (PSE) and a Packet Assembler/Disassembler (PAD). The former takes in X.25 formatted packets and, after reading the addressing information in the header, routes it to its destination down the appropriate link. Terminals gain access onto the network through the PAD which may typically handle up to 32 terminals or other devices (the upper limit is restricted only by physical constraints). Figure 40.10 shows the basic components of a packet switch network.

X.3 is the terminal profile standard that helps to define exactly how the asynchronous device (printer or terminal) should communicate with the PAD. There are a range of parameters that must be set, such as speed, flow control, how to edit and when to wrap around the screen. The parameters were originally designed to include the totally 'dumb' terminal (such as an electromechanical Teletype) so that to a modern device they appear unnecessary. However, in an international context, such a device may still be in use and connected to the network in some remote region of the world. The X.28 set of commands and messages are essential for controlling and monitoring the PAD functions.

40.6 X.25 and OSI

X.25 goes a long way towards being OSI compatible and is a recognised standard. Figure 40.11 shows how X.25 and its associated layers fits into the OSI model. The physical layers of both X.25 and the OSI reference model are similar though X.21 and X.21bis only cater for point to point full duplex links. These physical layer standards, which are common to other forms of multiplexing, are described in a later section.

The data link layers are very close with minor differences. The most significant difference is that X.25 link layer only deals with full duplex single links. This has been mostly remedied by the 1984 version of X.25 which caters for multiple links, though X.25 still does not cater for multi-point connections.

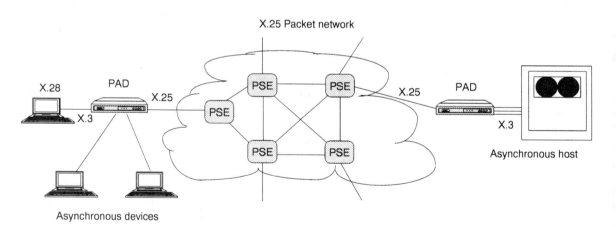

Figure 40.10 A packet switch network

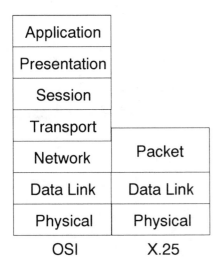

OSI	X.25
Application	
Presentation	
Session	
Transport	
Network	Packet
Data Link	Data Link
Physical	Physical

Figure 40.11   X.25 and the OSI model

The X.25 packet layer provides the majority of the functions specified in the OSI network layer and some of the functions specified in the OSI transport layer. The network layer functions which are not provided are routing and switching. This is because X.25 is a network interface specification and not an internal network specification as mentioned previously. The transport layer function provided for in the X.25 packet layer is end to end data acknowledgement.

40.6.1   The benefits of X.25

The advantages of using X.25 are as follows:

1. Flexibility. A user can make and break communication sessions with many destinations.
2. Economical. A user only pays for the resources used. It is possible for a user to establish many concurrent communication sessions with the same or different destinations over one physical connection to the network. A network administration can produce a cost reduced system because not every user wishes to communicate at the same time, or continually.
3. Reliability. The probability of a fault occurring on a relatively short leased line is far less than for a long distance line. If an inter-node link fails within the network the communication sessions can be re-routed and data recovered with little or no inconvenience to the end users.
4. Maintainability. The node or network is intelligent and can provide statistical and diagnostic information to aid fault tracing.
5. OSI Compatible. X.25 is part of the OSI model and as such can be used as part of an OSI networking strategy.

The disadvantages of X.25 are:

1. Network Delay. Although networks can provide the same (or very close) throughput figures to private wires, there is always a finite delay caused as packets are routed (stored and forwarded) through the network. This is a product of the number of nodes in the route across the network, the traffic load on different parts of the network and various other factors.

2. Poor efficiency with interactive traffic. Because of the way in which packets are built up with the data from a single user per packet, X.25 tends to become inefficient with network bandwidth if a predominance of single character enquiry traffic is being sent. (Compare this with the statistical multiplexer frame with multiple users per frame). However X.25 becomes very efficient for file transfer type applications where the packets can be filled to a maximum. It should be pointed out that in OSI, the layer 4 functionality does include the facility for enveloping multiple channels into a single packet.
3. Network Congestion. It is not economically viable for a network administration to run a network sized to provide enough bandwidth for the worse case traffic load. Therefore at peak times network congestion conditions occur causing existing sessions to slow down and preventing new sessions from starting. This is analogous to the public telephone networks i.e. "All lines to Cityville are engaged please try later".
4. Wrong Numbers. Expensive as generally all outgoing calls are billed.
5. Network Variance. Not all networks obey the protocol in the same way. This is due to grey areas in the CCITT X.25 Recommendations and to individual manufacturer's interpretations on how to handle exception conditions.
6. Bureaucracy. Most PTTs insist that X.25 products must pass a set of certification or conformance tests in order to gain permission to connect to their network. This can take a considerable period of time and money. This problem will be resolved to a certain degree in EC countries as the NETs attachment testing regime becomes law.

40.6.2   Using X.25

X.25 can be used in many different way for communication. Figure 40.12 shows how an X.25 based network can operate with different components such as:

1. Asynchronous terminals and hosts communicating via PADs.
2. X.25 based devices connected directly to the network.
3. Synchronous devices communicating via protocol converts.
4. Gateways to non-X.25 based networks.
5. Connection to international networks using the X.75 protocol.

Note that all devices can communicate through using X.25 as the common carrier.

X.25 networks can be bolted on to other X.25 networks simply by making one look like an X.25 terminal or by using the X.75 protocol (a protocol similar to X.25). X.25 networks can be connected to non-X.25 networks via a gateway or router which is just a type of protocol converter. Some of the larger public networks offer an integrated PAD service. A large PAD is resident at the node and subscribers rent stop/start lines to the PAD (dial-up or modem link). In this configuration the X.25 interface is actually within the network and not available to the subscribers.

Another method of accessing an X.25 network is via a high speed leased line link, such as KiloStream in the UK. KiloStream operates at speeds of up to 64kbit/s (but only 48kbit/s when connecting to the PSS X.25 network).

40.6.3   Services provided by X.25

Recommendation X.25 defines three types of data transmission services for use with PDNs: leased circuit, circuit switched, packet switched. The packet switched service is primarily considered here.

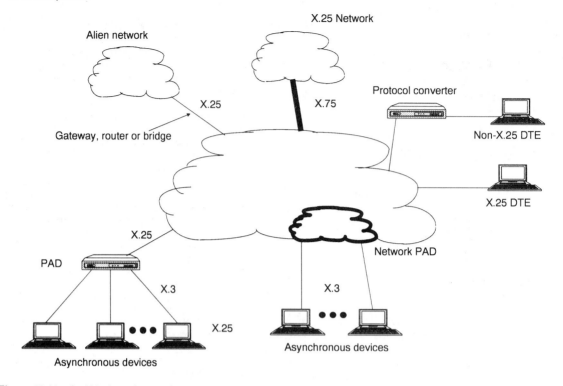

Figure 40.12 An X.25 based network

The packet switched service is subdivided into three services: Permanent Virtual Circuits (PVCs), Switched Virtual Circuits (SVCs) and Datagrams. PVCs and SVCs are essential services i.e. all networks should provide them (although not all provide PVC services). Datagrams are now being made obsolete within connection oriented (CON) X.25 and will be replaced by a connectionless (CLNS) version of X.25.

Recommendations X.25 defines the user facilities for each of the three types of data transmission services. These facilities provide capabilities beyond the basic service, a few examples are: reverse charging, preventing incoming calls and call re-direction.

40.6.3.1   *Virtual circuits*

The packet level interface comprises a set of logical channels, each with a unique identifier. Each logical channel can be associated with a single virtual circuit. A virtual circuit provides a connection based service similar to that of circuit switched services but with the added advantage of statistical multiplexing.

For every physical link, the number of possible logical channels is given by sixteen groups of two hundred and fifty six channels. The relevant group and channel number are contained in each packet header. There is a one to one correspondence between DTE and DCE channel numbers.

Each virtual circuit can support at least one communication session, so in the most extreme (but unrealistic) case a single DTE/DCE link can support 4095 concurrent virtual circuits. The available virtual circuits are utilised to offer two facilities, namely the Permanent Virtual Circuit (PVC) and the Virtual Call (VC) or Switched Virtual Circuit (SVC).

40.6.3.2   *Switched virtual circuits*

Switched virtual circuits, or virtual calls, must be dynamically established between DTEs at extreme ends of a network by the exchange of command packets between the two DTEs and the network.

A virtual call is a temporary association between two DTEs. It is initiated by a DTE sending a Call Request packet to the network on a free logical channel. The logical channel should be the highest free channel available. A Call Request packet must contain either the destination address or a reference to it.

When a Call Request packet is received by a network it will send the called DTE an Incoming call packet on the lowest free logical channel number available at that interface. The called DTE then has the option of accepting or refusing the call.

The calling DTE will subsequently receive a response indicating whether or not the called DTE has accepted the call. If the call is accepted the virtual circuit is established and enters the data transfer mode. At this point either DTE can send packets containing data, via the network, to the other DTE. If however a virtual call cannot be established the network will return a call clearing packet to the calling DTE to indicate that the virtual circuit has not been established. Either DTE can clear an established call.

40.6.3.3   *Permanent virtual circuit*

A permanent virtual circuit is a logical connection between two DTEs at extreme ends of a network which is constant for an agreed period of time. When the lower levels of X.25 are operational, either DTE can send packets containing data via the network to the other

DTE without the need for the Virtual Call establishment procedures mentioned above.

40.6.3.4 *Virtual circuit services*

A virtual circuit service (connection oriented) is considered superior to a connection-less service for handling long messages. Virtual circuits are analogous to the telephone service in that messages are delivered in the order in which they are sent. The full destination and source network addresses as well as the information required in order to deliver a packet, are only required to establish a circuit.

Once a virtual circuit has been established the logical channel numbers allow either of the DTEs on the virtual circuit to send data to the other. Network congestion is controlled by limiting the inputs to a virtual circuit (or controlling the flow of data) rather than by discarding packets.

Individual packets on a virtual circuit are rarely autonomous, generally they are only part of a message.

40.7 Physical layer standards

There are two standards applicable to the physical layer X.21 and X.21 bis. X.21 allows the user to access the network via a high speed serial interface. X.21 bis allows the user to access the network using a lower speed (<20000bit/s) serial interface. X.21bis is the most common method of connection to an X.25 network.

The full X.21 protocol provides all the services of the first three layers: physical, data link, and network services. X.25 only uses the X.21 physical interface specifications.

40.7.1 X.21 bis

X.21 bis is based upon CCITT Recommendations V.24/V.28 where V.24 specifies the control signals such as Request to Send (RTS circuit 104) and Clear to Send (CTS circuit 105). V.28 specifies the electrical interface in terms of voltage levels, impedances and the rise and fall times of the signals. It is suitable for speeds up to 19200bits/s. Higher speeds can be achieved using the V.35 and V.36 interfaces which were specifically designed for that purpose. The EIA RS232-C and D standards are almost identical to the V.24/V.28 standard but also include the connector specifications which is a 25 way D-Type.

40.7.2 V.35

The V.35 interface provides for speeds up to 48000bits/s at a distance of up to 1 kilometre incorporating a partially balanced interface to give a higher noise immunity. The V.35 connector is significantly different from the D type V.28 connector. It has a square profile with a staggered pin layout to prevent it being coupled incorrectly and is known as the MRAC connector. V.35 uses a balanced interface for TxD, RxD and the clocks but not the control signals. V.35 is however no longer recommended by CCITT who suggest using V.36 in its place for all new developments.

40.7.3 V.36

The V.36 (similar to RS-449) interface provides for speeds up to 72kbit/s at a distance of 1 kilometre. All control, data and clock

signals have balanced interfaces which gives greater noise immunity. V.36 uses the 37 pin D type connector.

40.7.4 X.21

X.21 operates over eight interchange circuits, and this is shown in Table 40.2.

Table 40.2 X.21 interchange circuits

Circuit		Direction to DCE	Direction to DTE
G	Signal Ground		
Ga	DTE Common Return		
T	Transmit	***	
R	Receive		***
C	Control	***	
I	Indication		***
S	Signal Element Timing		***
B	Byte Timing		***

The circuits function is defined in CCITT Recommendations X.24 and their electrical characteristics are defined in CCITT Recommendations X.27 for DCE and X.26 for DTE.

Signal Element Timing provides bit timing. Byte Timing is optional and therefore not always supplied. All timing is provided by the DCE.

The DTE uses the Transmit and Receive circuits to exchange data and control messages with the DCE. Unlike the V.24 and RS232-C/D standards X.21 specifies that control information be exchanged using characters transferred on the interchange circuits, rather than using circuit states.

The Control and Indication circuits are used in conjunction with the Transmit and Receive circuits to indicate the state of the DTE or DCE respectively. No characters are transmitted or received on these circuits; they are simply turned ON or OFF to indicate their current state.

The Byte Timing circuit provides information pertaining to the grouping of bits into characters. When the byte timing circuit is not available a synchronising character is inserted before each string of characters. Byte timing and SYNC characters are only required when exchanging physical layer control characters. When the physical layer is being used to transmit link layer information on the transmit and receive circuits byte timing and synchronising characters are not used.

40.7.5 Physical interface

The X.21 physical interface is specified by V.11 and is basically a cut-down version of the V.36 interface. There are only two control signals (one in each direction) other than that the interface is the same. The physical interface for X.21 is the 15 pin D type connector.

40.8 Multiplexers in communications networks

This section will focus on the more practical aspects of network design giving attention to performance, configuration, routing, traffic requirements, expansion and topology. Some of these areas are interrelated and there is a degree of overlap in functionality.

40.8.1 Specification

The first consideration when specifying any data communications network is to establish the nature and rates of traffic which the network will be expected to support both in the short and the long term. This is crucial to all network design and is the starting point of all network decisions. If errors are made here, the network cannot be expanded to meet new (and possibly unexpected) requirements.

40.8.2 Traffic types

There are numerous different types of traffic, some of which are:

1. Stop-start traffic in the form of lots of short packets travelling in one direction often with slightly longer packets in the reverse direction. A characteristic of this type of traffic is that it is often associated with a requirement for very short turn-around and transit delays (e.g. word-processing). This is a classical form of asynchronous traffic.
2. 'Forms' traffic where a small amount of data travels in one direction on an ad hoc basis, but it is answered with a stream of traffic in the other direction (database enquiry).
3. Block mode traffic, where there is a stream of large full packets travelling in one direction with short packets travelling in the other (file transfer).
4. Transaction traffic where there are high numbers of calls with limited data transfer, often done with the Fast Select facility (e.g. credit card checks, holiday booking lounges).
5. Optimised traffic, where many users are sharing a single connection (often using a Transport connection). Optimisation is achieved by filling the packets as full as possible without degrading the class of service below the user requirements (OSI).
6. Priority traffic. This may be any of the traffic types described above but takes precedence over the normal data flowing in the network.
7. Management traffic, which is an overhead in any network.

A corporate or public data network would handle all these types of traffic (and more). Most small private networks will only have one or two types of traffic and are often designed and tuned to those specific requirements.

The list above is not intended to be conclusive, but to give an idea of the differing traffic types that exist.

40.8.3 Topology

The construction of a network is very dependent on the distribution of the users and the resources. In the past large organisations centralised computing centres to which the users were linked to using private communications circuits. Today, distributed processing has created the WAN/LAN topology network structure where the LANs provide high speed local connectivity between the users and the local computing resources such as file servers, local electronic mail servers, local computers, printers, etc. The wide area network provides connectivity and interoperability between the LANs and to centralised computing resources i.e. a centralised stock distribution system or an aircraft booking system.

Often the geographic distribution of the users and the information technology resources dictates the basic topology of the network which serves to interconnect them. A typical network topology comprises a set of very high speed low intelligence backbone switches, such as synchronous TDMs, which serve to interconnect lower speed high functionality packet switching nodes, or statistical multiplexers, to which LAN users are connected (via modems or kilostream links) through bridges.

40.8.4 Performance requirements

A common misconception is that performance is all about line rates. This is only a part of the equation. Hop counts, accumulative transit delays, turn around times, congestion level, congestion handling and the actual end systems all contribute to the performance of the network as a whole.

The performance requirements of a network depend on the types of traffic running over it, the time of day traffic requirements, the distribution of the traffic, the cost of the resources, the reliability requirements.

40.8.5 Traffic requirements

Obviously the different traffic types mentioned above place differing requirements on the network equipment.

A transaction system (such as a booking system) will require fast call establishment and termination, high call capacity, but not necessarily fast data throughput as it will only be the occasional screen.

A network with a large community of stop-start terminal applications (typically the CCITT triple X PAD) require fairly low transit delays and low hop counts, but again not necessarily high data performance.

Block mode traffic, such as file transfer or database enquiry systems, probably do not require low transit delays but do require high data performance.

Certainly, as technology progresses, users are becoming more and more aware of the different jobs that IT can do for them and consequently the dumb terminal is being replaced by the intelligent terminal which in turn is being replaced by the personal workstation.

Ultimately users will be transferring files, sending electronic mail, booking holidays, home banking, home shopping, paying bills and making directory enquiries all from the same (pocket) workstations!

40.8.6 Traffic variance

Traffic type and load can vary with the time of day. This must be considered when estimating the performance requirements of a system.

An example is that of a large company with many retail outlets. During the day the traffic is almost completely local to the individual retail outlets, as they process data onto the local processor with just a few interactive enquiries to head office. At the end of the day's business the local processors up load the stock requirements for the next day's trading to regional main frames, which arrange for the goods to be on the shelves for the following day's trading. This change in traffic conditions needs to be calculated in the overall network design.

40.8.7 Load balancing

The most basic (and most used) form of traffic balancing comes in the form of local load balancing across links connecting adjacent nodes within a network.

In the most basic form the traffic is evenly balanced across all the links connecting two devices. Some systems apply a weighting factor to the links based on the link speed. The next step is to dynamically adjust the weighting factor based on the real time performance of the link. This ensures that a link which is performing badly (perhaps due to noise on the line) is only allocated the amount of traffic that it can reasonably transfer.

The X.25 multi-link procedures can achieve a reasonable load balancing and can, depending on the implementation, provide dynamic load balancing.

The most basic requirement is that load balancing takes account of the link speed.

40.8.8 Hop counts and life times

Hop counts and life times are used to ensure that a particular traffic element does not spend too much time traversing the network. The hop count is set in a message when it enters a communications network, to a pre-defined value. Every time the message is switched (i.e. passes through a node) the hop counter is decreased. If the hop counter reaches zero the message is either cleared or discarded.

Life times are very similar. The message life time is set up when it enters the network and if it is not acknowledged within its lifetime the originator sends another via a different route.

Hop counts and lifetimes can be dynamically adjusted to suit the traffic Quality of Service requirements and the real time network characteristics.

40.8.9 Configuration

Configuration of a network is normally proportional to its size, although there are some aspects which seem to increase exponentially in complexity as a network grows. For large networks manual configuration becomes a major issue and in some cases out of the question. A widely distributed network can be a real headache in terms of manpower to manage and support without the complication of configuring links.

Configuration tends to fall into five categories:

1. Manual configuration using a locally attach terminal or push buttons.
2. Remote configuration via a virtual call.
3. Automatic configuration with remote configuration for fine tuning.
4. Off-line configuration (minimum downtime).
5. Online configuration (minimum disturbance).

40.8.10 Fault tracing

There are various tools which a networking product can supply to aid fault tracing. At the simplest level this would be statistical counts of all the frames and packets received and transmitted on each link and trunk. With the appropriate timing information this can be compiled into link utilisation and packet throughput statistics. This

information can be used to check the general well being of the network.

40.8.11 Error rate monitors

Errors can be assigned to alarms with various levels of significance from calls being incorrectly sent (users not entering data properly) to link failures.

40.8.12 Call tracing

One of the most common problems is often referred to as call tracing. This is rather like the PSTN namesake. If a user gets connected to a faulty port on a host computer which is connected to a PAD using a hunt group, it is very difficult to ascertain which is the offending port of the computer. This is because the logical channel identifier (LCIs) change throughout the network from one link to the next. A network has to provide constantly updated routing tables, which display this type of information to solve this problem.

40.8.13 Network management

Network management is one of the most important issues in networking today. A badly run network, or one which has been poorly designed so that management is difficult, can cost a company an enormous amount in money and labour to maintain it. The actual definition of network management varies according to the user perspective. A network operator will have a different list of priorities to the network manager and to the managing director. In OSI network management is being codified to give a common platform so that everyone plays by the same rules and uses the same terminology. Network management is described in Chapter 16.

40.8.14 Different multiplexer types in a network

Figure 40.13 shows how time division multiplexers and packet switch exchanges may be intermixed in a network. The multiplexers form a hierarchy from the LANs which are multiplexed on to medium speed 64kbit/s circuits and then on to the high speed 2Mbit/s trunks. Not shown on the diagram is the distance factor, normally the higher speed trunks are geographically much further apart, up to hundreds of miles, than the lower speed circuits.

40.8.15 Network expansion issues

There are various reasons to expand a network:

1. Geographic changes.
2. More users.
3. New facilities.
4. Higher traffic performance requirements.

Geographic changes, more users and new facilities tend to mean more connections and more or larger user access nodes. This normally means that the traffic requirements change i.e. the aggregate traffic levels per trunk increase.

Higher performance can be the result of more users; higher performance end user equipment; lower transit delay requirements; or that existing users are making more use of the network. Performance increases can be addressed by adding links between the nodes or by raising the speed of the existing links between nodes. It

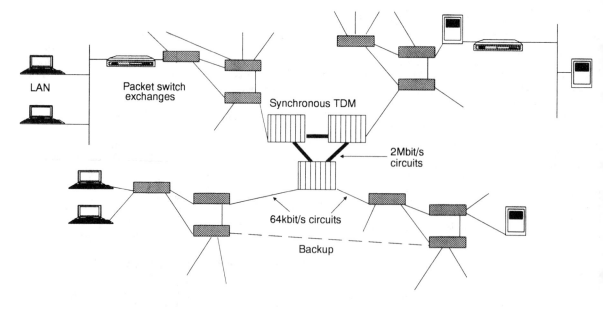

Figure 40.13   A network of TDMs and PSEs

is important to note that raising the link speed often means that the network node equipment will require upgrading.

40.8.16   Adding new links

When analysing the statistical information provided by a network it is important to take the historical information into account. A link running at a high utilisation may not necessarily be saturated. X.25 is designed to be more efficient when a link is heavily used. The first sign that a link is becoming overloaded is when network response times become erratic. X.25 will not lose data; as the network becomes busy it merely delays the transit of that data.

The next sign of overloading is when users cannot make new calls and are left with 'busy' messages. Normal network practice is to design a network for 30% to 40% theoretical usage, which leaves enough capacity to cope with fluctuations in traffic density. Note that this not only includes trunk bandwidth capacity but also the ability to set up and clear calls. Other factors which should be taken into account for sizing the network is that the majority of traffic

tends to be local, practical usage suggests that up to 90% of all data on a LAN is between local devices.

40.9   The future of multiplexing

40.9.1   Frame relay

The speeds required by networks increases every year to cope with the increase in computer processing power. Network transmission is being revolutionised by the availability of high speed fibre systems. Because of the inherent low loss and error free transmission capabilities of fibre a complete rethink on the multiplexing requirements has come about. Instead of relying on the multiplexer to provide an error free path it only need provide a basic routing path. This is the basis of frame relay. As can be seen form Figure 40.14, the routing path is part of the link layer and as such network addressing only works on a link by link basis. Each node will have

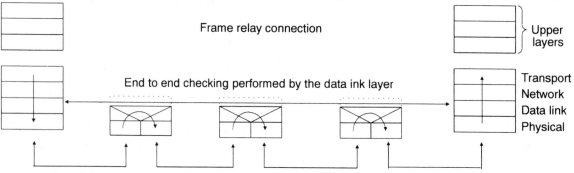

Figure 40.14   Layer model of frame relay

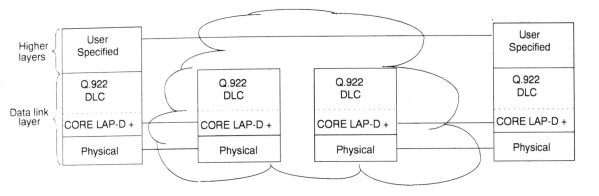

Figure 40.15 Frame relay standards

a routing table indicating where the frame should go but, having transmitted it does not have any mechanism for checking whether it arrived.

Figure 40.14 shows the layer model of frame relay. Note that it only operates in the lower half of the data link layer. Figure 40.15 shows the standards associated with frame relay and where they fit in the model and Figure 40.16 shows the utilisation on a frame relay circuit with different traffic types. Note that this is almost identical to the format of the statistical multiplexer shown in Figure 40.8. Frame relay, and other fast packet techniques, are covered in more detail in Chapter 55.

40.9.2 Synchronous Digital Hierarchy (SDH)

In an attempt to reconcile the three main variants of high order multiplexers a new set of G. standards have been defined, which can transport all types of synchronous traffic. These are G.707, G.708 and G.709 on frame structure; G.781, G.782 and G.783 on SDH multiplexing equipment; G.784 on SDH management; G.957 on SDH optical interfaces; and G.958 on SDH line systems. Other standards are being proposed for network management and digital cross-connect equipment. The underlying rationale for SDH is to provide a transparent 'bit pipe' for synchronous data.

SDH works on the principle of Virtual Containers (VCs) which contain the various services. These are assembled into Administrative Units (AUs) which can then be assembled as frames into Synchronous Transport Modules (STMs). There is a hierarchy of STMs from STM-1 which runs at 155Mbit/s to STM-16 at 2.488Gbit/s. Again it is the PTTs that are taking the initiative, and services based on this system are on offer in the US as SONET (Synchronous Optical Network).

One of the main benefits of SDH is that it allows plesiochronous networks to operate with relatively inaccurate (1 part in 10^{-4}) and therefore inexpensive, clocks. Another is that this service can then be used by other emerging technologies, such as Asynchronous Transfer Mode (ATM) which is the result of the CCITT work on the I.121 standard.

In ATM data can be transferred without reference to an underlying clock system. Frame relay is an example of an early form of this but ATM is more generally aligned with the switching and multiplexing techniques known as 'cell relay'. Unlike frame relay, which uses variable length frames, cell relay operates with fixed frames (called

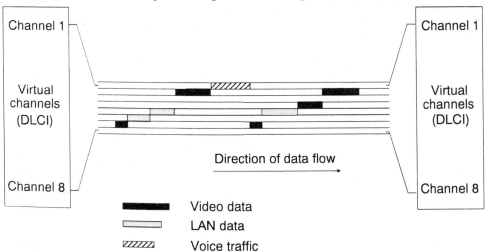

Figure 40.16 Frame relay utilisation when carrying a mix of traffic types

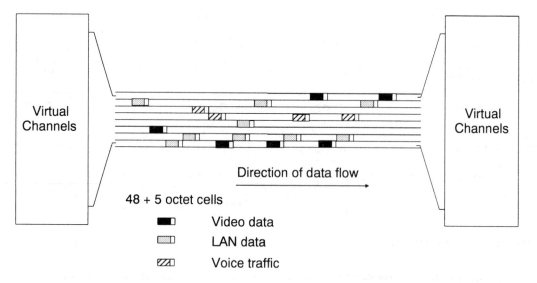

Direction of data flow

48 + 5 octet cells

▬▭ Video data

▭▭ LAN data

▨▭ Voice traffic

Figure 40.17 Use of fixed length cells for the transport of data (Compare with Figure 40.16)

cells) of 48 octets for the information field and 5 for the header. Because these cells are so simple in structure, they can be implemented in hardware rather than software (as for X.25 packets). This means gigabit speeds will be achievable.

Different data services such as computer data, video and voice, break up their data streams into the cells for transmission over the network where they are recovered at the remote end. As with frame relay, errors are not detected and recovered by the network but by the transport layers in the end systems (OSI layer 4) which initiate the data recovery mechanisms on a peer to peer basis across the network. Obviously such a technique relies on a very efficient high speed, low error transmission path for efficient throughput. This can be provided by fibre optic cables running at the speeds quoted above.

Figure 40.17 shows how fixed length cells, each carrying different types of data, are multiplexed down a link. The VPI/VCI is only assigned on a cell by cell basis. It is the address in the cell header that determines the route taken. This makes for a highly efficient use of bandwidth using the best of TDM and statistical multiplexing. ATM is described in more detail in Chapter 41, and SDH in Chapter 42.

40.10   References

Brewster, R.L. (1987) *Telecommunications Technology*, Ellis Horwood Ltd.

CCITT (1988) *Data Communications over the Telephone Network*, Series V Recommendations, Vol. VIII, Fascicle VIII.I.

CCITT (1988) *General Aspects of Digital Transmission Systems*, Recommendations G.700–G.795, Vol. III, Fascicle VIII.4.

CCITT (1990) *Draft proposals on B-ISDN*, Recommendations I.113, I.150, I.311, May.

Davis, D. and Barbar, D. (1973) *Communication Networks for Computers*, John Wiley and Sons.

Halsall, F. (1988) *Data Communications, Computer Networks and OSI*, Addison Wesley Publishing Co.

Ronayne, J. (1991) *Introduction to Digital Communications Switching*, Pitman Publishing.

Tanebaum, A.S. (1989) *Computer Networks*, Prentice Hall.

41

Asynchronous Transfer Mode

Mike Hillyard
BSc (Eng) CEng MIEE
BNR Europe Ltd

Contents

41.1 Overview and content

Current communications networks fall into discrete types dependant on the types of traffic being handled. Voice networks have been based on the use of circuit switching which offers guaranteed path availability and uniform delay during a connection. Network congestion results in the blocking of calls rather than delay. Data services often possess a very bursty traffic pattern and packet networks, with their flexible mechanism for interleaving traffic from different sources, offer an efficient solution. Variable delays, however, are introduced into the path as a result of queueing and these, though acceptable for data, would not be tolerable for voice and other constant bit-rate (CBR) services.

The increasing use of optical transmission and the general availability of large-scale integrated digital technology, offer the possibility of an integrated approach to handling all types of traffic source, including a range of new services, some, such as video-based services, requiring much broader channel capacities.

It is against the background of this Broadband Integrated Services Network (B-ISDN) that the technique known as ATM is being defined.

41.2 History

Circuit switched techniques such as those used for voice communications have been used in combination with STDM (synchronous time division multiplex) techniques. Here, the bandwidth on a link is divided into channels consisting of (typically) eight bits. The identity of a particular channel is defined by its relationship to a fixed frame reference. In contrast, in packet switching a block of data is associated with a 'header' which both defines its length and contains an address defining its identity.

'ATD' (asynchronous time division), arguably lies somewhere between STDM and packet switching and is intended for the transport of data, video and voice services. (Figure 41.1) Versions of the technique emerged in Europe in the 1980s in which a bitstream was sub-divided into short, fixed-length slots (32 bytes maximum) with each slot having an address field attached to it. The term 'cell' was used to describe the slot plus the address field and transmission links would carry a contiguous stream of fixed length cells.

The work on ATD was a major influence when CCITT Study Group XVIII commenced the definition of the target transfer mechanism for B-ISDN in 1988. This transfer mechanism was to be standardised for use at the User/Network interface for B-ISDN and to be used as the basis for switching and multiplexing within B-ISDN nodes.

Asynchronous Transfer Mode (ATM), the name used by SG XVIII to describe the chosen solution, owes much to the early ATD proposals but some features were also adopted from 'Fast Packet Switching' (FPS), a technique developed in the US aimed at reducing the end to end delays inherent in X.25 packet switching. FPS still used variable length packets but had much reduced protocol complexity to permit a high speed hardware implementation.

ATM employs fixed length cells having 48 information bytes and 5 header bytes which contain address information and other functions.

41.3 ATM basic principles

Asynchronous Transfer Mode is a specific packet oriented mechanism for the transfer of digital information based on the use of 'cells' which are of constant length, having a payload field and a 'header'. The cells are transmitted contiguously on a transmission link and

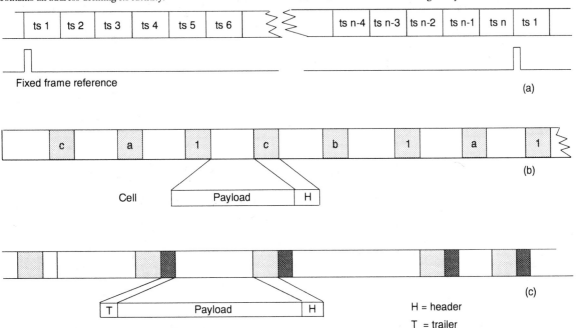

Figure 41.1 ATM compared with STDM and packet mode: (a) synchronous time division multiplex; (b) asynchronous transfer mode; (c) packet mode

are not identified by their position in relation to a fixed time reference but by means of address information in the header defining a 'virtual channel'. The technique is *asynchronous* in the sense that the cells carrying a particular address (i.e. within a particular virtual channel) may appear at irregular intervals within the cell-stream. The technique is connection oriented in that a 'virtual circuit' is established at call set-up time and this will associate the virtual channels used on a series of network links to form the end to end connection.

ATM offers a flexible transfer capability common to a broad range of services with widely varying traffic patterns and can be employed on various transmission media operating at widely varying rates. ATM adaptation functions are provided to accommodate the data formats and operating characteristics of specific services.

41.3.1   The ATM cell (Figure 41.2)

The cell consists of a header (label of 5 bytes) and a payload (information field of 48 bytes).

The header includes:

1.   Address field defining the virtual channel to which the cell is assigned, divided into two parts, a virtual path identifier (VPI), and a virtual channel identifier (VCI).
2.   Payload type identifier (PTI).

3.   8-bit CRC field for header error control (HEC). This field also supports the mechanism for cell delineation, i.e. the identification of the start of each cell within a serial bit stream.

The payload may be user information (voice, data, images, etc in digital form), signalling, or O&M messages (operations & maintenance).

The payload is transferred transparently from end point to end point across the network.

41.3.2   ATM multiplexing (Figure 41.3)

41.3.2.1   *Multiplexing mechanism*

Information from a particular user is assembled into cells as it becomes available. Cells from a number of such sources will be placed in a queue in their order of appearance and the cells on the queue output will be placed in order in contiguous slots on the transmission link. If the aggregate information rate from the set of sources being multiplexed exceeds the link capacity at a particular time, then the queue fill will become greater, increasing the delay in the system or even causing loss if the queue becomes full. If source activity is low, such that the queue becomes empty, then 'idle cells' are inserted on the link to maintain the contiguous cell flow.

The sequence of cells from a particular user or source all carry the same value in the header address field and this cell sequence

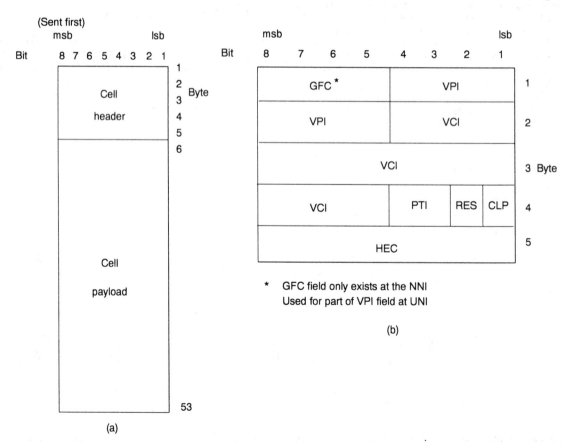

Figure 41.2 The ATM cell: (a) cell structure; (b) cell header structure

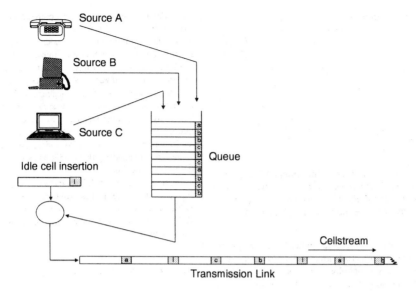

Figure 41.3 ATM multiplexing

constitutes a 'virtual channel': the rate of transmission of cells within the virtual channel can be variable, reflecting the source activity and resource availability and it is in this sense that the transfer mode is said to be asynchronous.

41.3.2.2 *Physical layer*

An ATM multiplex is capable of being supported on a range of possible physical media and mapped into a number of existing bit-stream structures. For B-ISDN two possibilities are envisaged at the User-Network interface (UNI): a cell-based interface where timing is derived from the cell-stream and OAM messages are carried in special OAM cells with a unique header; a Synchronous

Digital Hierarchy (SDH) based interface where the cell stream is mapped into the C-4 container and then packed into the VC-4 virtual container along with the VC-4 Path Overhead (POH). The ATM cell boundaries are aligned with the STM-1 octet boundaries and the H-4 pointer indicates the next occurrence of a cell boundary, offering a supplement to the HEC Cell delineation mechanism (Figure 41.4).

41.3.3 **ATM switching**

41.3.3.1 *Switch function*

The cell header address field is sub-divided into two parts: the virtual path identifier (VPI) and the virtual channel identifier (VCI,

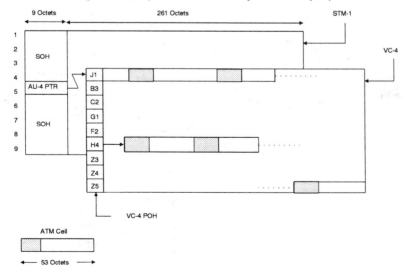

Figure 41.4 Mapping ATM cells into the SDH STM-1

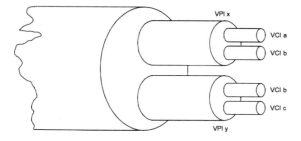

Figure 41.6 Virtual paths and virtual channels. VCIa and VCIb represent two of the possible values of VCI within the VP link with the value VPI x. Similarly VPI x and VPI y are values within the physical layer connection. (Based on Fig. 1/I.150)

as in Figure 41.5). The virtual path identifier field offers the possibility of establishing semi-permanent virtual paths. These would be established in cross-connects controlled via network management and may be used for private circuits, for access network paths to particular service providers or for semi-permanent virtual trunks. Each of these could carry a number of virtual channels which, in the case of semi-permanent end-end paths could support a set of user defined processes. In the case of access paths and trunks, the virtual channels would provide the basis of switched connections handled at switching nodes. (Figure 41.6).

41.3.3.2   Switch mechanism and characteristics

A switching node, whether it be a VP cross connect or a VC switch, will have a number of incoming and outgoing ATM multiplex streams and the function of the switch is to transfer cells with a particular address field code on a particular incoming multiplex, to a particular outgoing multiplex (space switching) whilst placing the appropriate code in the cells' address field for use at the next switching node (asynchronous time switching). This function is performed according to a translation stored at the switch control and maintained for the duration of the 'virtual connection' (Figure 41.7). Before cell switching can take place, cell delineation is performed on the incoming multiplex cell streams, to permit extraction of cells and analysis of their headers. The 'idle cells', inserted into the multiplex at times of low source activity, are now removed and it is an important feature of ATM switching that the matrix is not burdened with handling these cells: the switch handles only the real traffic from the links

The transit time of an ATM switch will depend in the main on the traffic levels on the queues providing access to the outgoing links and may vary considerably with time: the queues have to be dimensioned such that the probability of cell loss due to overflow is acceptably small.

41.3.3.3   Switch implementation

There are many possible implementation architectures for the internal structure of an ATM switch node, the choice being influenced by factors such as maximum capacity, growth and modularity requirements, connection types to be handled (point to multi-point connections present specific problems) and general performance issues. Specific architectural issues include:

1. The topology of the overall structure: ring, bus, single/multi-stage array etc.
2. The method of routing used within the switch matrix: Self-routing or translation table controlled.
3. The location of the buffer memories within the switching elements.

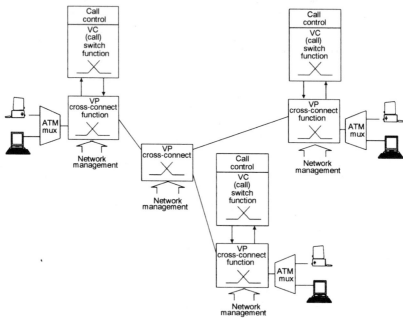

Figure 41.5   Example of a VP and VC switching hierarchy

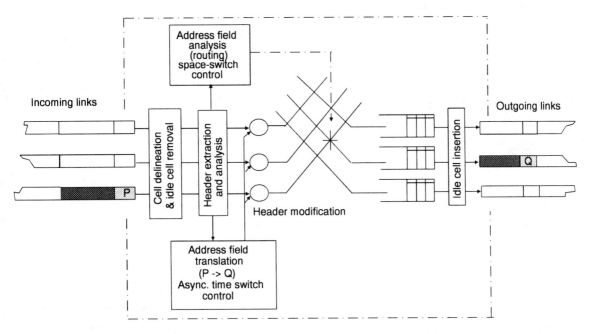

Figure 41.7 Functional representation of an ATM switch

41.3.3.4 *Topology*

Dependent on the required characteristics, an ATM switch can be implemented using a variety of possible topologies. There are two basic parts of the structure, the port and the interconnect, and topology is determined by the means of providing the interconnect between the ports. Some examples of topologies are:

1. Bus, ring: the simplest switching arrangement where a number of ports are 'hung' on a single bus and communicate using a defined protocol which may use slots or some form of contention resolution. Simple and easily expanded but limited in overall capacity by the throughput of the bus. A ring is in effect a closed bus offering the possibility of different access protocols but with generally similar limitations.
2. n x m matrix: an array of simple 'on/off' switch elements providing the possibility of many co-existent paths between n inputs and m outputs (analogous to the electro-mechanical crossbar switch). Avoids the capacity limitations of the bus and ring by spreading the traffic over a number of paths but expansion of the number of ports can result in very large cross-point matrices.
3. Multi-stage matrices: If switching elements with a p x q capability are used instead of the simple 'on/off' function, then more complex arrays may be constructed having a variety of possible characteristics. In general, such networks may be expanded by addition of stages to handle very large numbers of ports, but do not expand in total size as rapidly as the simple matrix when additional ports are added; also they usually offer a multiplicity of path possibilities between each pair of inputs and outputs and this offers advantages in connection with both traffic and security. The individual elements of such a matrix may themselves be implemented using topologies such as those described

above. Batcher-Banyan networks and Clos networks are examples of such multi-stage matrices.

41.3.3.5 *Routing*

Self-routing switches require only one translation at the matrix input and this results in the appending of a header prefix which is used for routing purposes by each of the matrix switching elements and discarded on exit from the switch. In translation table controlled switches the path is marked locally in translation tables within each switching stage, permitting routing to proceed on the basis of the original external header.

Routing through the switch matrix may be connection oriented i.e. cells always follow the same route through the switch and therefore remain in sequence. Alternatively, a connectionless approach to routing within the switch may be taken, the output port address being carried in the cell and individual cells being routed toward that port according to the local routing algorithm at the particular point in the switch matrix. With connectionless routing, cell sequence integrity across the matrix may not be maintained.

41.3.3.6 *Buffering*

Cell buffering in the switching elements can be organised on three possible bases:

1. Input buffering: One buffer dedicated to each switching element input. Contents can be switched to one (or several in point to multi-point operation) output.
2. Output buffering: One buffer dedicated to each switching element output, with no blocking of cells from any of the switching element inputs.

3. Central buffering: one common buffer memory block is provided for all cells in the switching element.

41.3.4 Traffic control and resource allocation

41.3.4.1 Admission control

It is anticipated that the ATM based B-ISDN will carry a mixture of traffic sources varying from uniform rate to very bursty, from very short to very long duration. When a new connection is requested it is necessary to ensure that capacity can be allocated on the network resources such that the new connection will provide the required Quality of Service (QOS) and that the QOS targets of existing services is still met. This is done by expressing each requested connection in terms of a set of Flow Enforcement Parameters (FEPs) and on each link through the network, an admission control algorithm decides whether or not to accept the connection. (FEPs could be based on estimates of the average and peak bit-rates and expressions of the burstiness.)

41.3.4.2 Flow conditioning

Having 'admitted' a connection, to ensure that actual cell flows conform to the parameters negotiated during connection admission, flow conditioning procedures are required. Without these, the QOS of other connections could be disrupted.

Flow conditioning has two components: flow enforcement (otherwise 'Police function' or 'Usage parameter control') which is mandatory and located just within the network periphery and flow throttling, which is optional and located between the source and the network boundary. (Figure 41.8, Andersen, 1990). Throttling is applied by the user to ensure that the source data flow conforms to the agreement. Enforcement discards cells which are in excess of the negotiated levels.

41.3.5 Key Advantages of ATM

The basic multiplexing and switching characteristics described above give rise to some of the most important advantages of ATM:

1. Flexibility.
2. Inherent adaptation between information flow rates and transport resources.

3. Ability to handle a range of user traffic source rates using the same technique and equipment.
4. Statistical multiplexing capability.
5. Flexibility in handling the mix of service demand.
6. Transport infrastructure is general purpose, being conceived to handle by adaptation, a very wide range of traffic/service types.
7. Possibility of service integration on the same medium, an important consideration for a broadband network where service types and demand are still ill-defined.

41.4 Standards for ATM

Standardisation of broadband started in CCITT during the 1985 – 1988 study period which, by its close had resulted in the choice of ATM as the transfer mode to be used at the broadband User/Network Interface (B-UNI) and as the basic switching mechanism for all B-ISDN services, this being defined in the first version of recommendation I.121.

A set of standards for Broadband ISDN is being established in CCITT within Study group XVIII during the current study period (1989 – 1992) under the I-series recommendations and 13 recommendations dealing with ATM parameters are being processed under accelerated procedures. Inputs to this process derive, amongst other sources, from the regional standardisation organisations (ETSI in Europe and T1 committee in North America) and from the major European Community communications R&D initiative known as RACE (Research in Advanced Communications technologies in Europe).

Other CCITT Study Groups are now becoming concerned with broadband, for example SG XI is active in considering the signalling requirements. However SG XVIII remains the main focus and the following sections outline the contents of the thirteen draft recommendations relevant to ATM, highlighting the key points and providing detail on the primary features (CCITT, 1990). The content is, of course, provisional and subject to change as the process of standardisation continues: many of the paragraphs are annotated 'for further study'.

The structure of the standards is shown in Figure 41.9. Under a top-level document giving an overview of B-ISDN, there are five groups of documents covering:

1. ATM functions.
2. Broadband services.

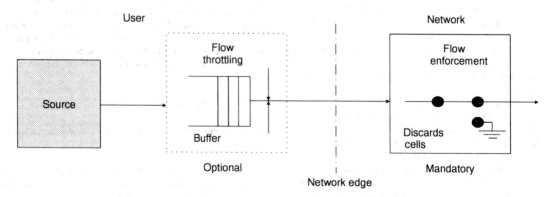

Figure 41.8 Flow conditioning functions

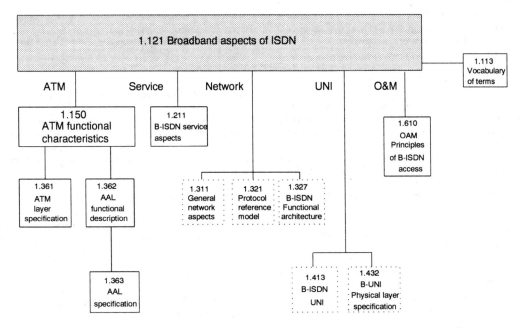

Figure 41.9 CCITT I-Series standards for B-ISDN

3. Network aspects.
4. User-network interface.
5. Operations and maintenance.

41.4.1 I.113: Vocabulary of terms for broadband aspects of ISDN.

Glossary of terms and definitions, organised under two headings: services; and interfaces, channels and transfer modes. These are kept updated to remain in line with the evolution of terminology used in the other recommendations in the series dealing with broadband.

41.4.2 Broadband aspects of ISDN

Statement of the basic principles of the broadband aspects of ISDN.
  Establishes ATM as the transfer mode for implementing B-ISDN and identifies certain specific advantages:

1. Flexibility of network access.
2. Dynamic bandwidth allocation on demand: fine degree of granularity.
3. Flexible bearer capability allocation; easy provision of semi-permanent connections.
4. Independence from the means of transport at the physical layer.

41.4.3 I.150: B-ISDN ATM functional characteristics

Describes the basic principles of ATM and addresses the functions of the ATM layer:

1. Describes how the physical layer connection can carry a number of *virtual paths* distinguished by the 'VPI' field: also how

each virtual path can carry a number of *virtual channels* distinguished by the 'VCI' field. (Figure 41.5.)

2. Defines a *virtual channel connection* (VCC) as a concatenation of *virtual channel* links that extends between two points where the adaptation layer is accessed. VCCs may be switched or semi-permanent, provide a Quality of service defined by parameters such as *cell loss ratio, cell delay variation* and preserve cell sequence integrity. VCC traffic parameters will require negotiation and VCC usage will be monitored. (Figure 41.10.)

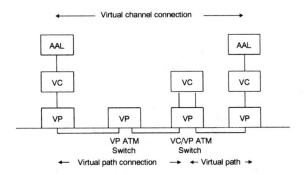

Figure 41.10 Types of ATM layer connection (Based on Fig. 2/I.150)

3. Describes how VCCs may be established and released citing four methods at the UNI: by subscription (semi-permanent connection set up by management); using a meta-signalling VC to establish a signalling VC; by using a signalling VC for user/network signalling; similarly for user/user signalling.
4. Defines a *virtual path connection* (VPC) as a concatenation of *virtual path links* that extends between the point where VCI

values are assigned/translated/removed. VPC characteristics are broadly as for VCCs except that VPCs are only set up on a semi-permanent basis via network management.

5. Defines a number of uses for pre-assigned VPIs.

It deals with the definition of the following:

1. Cell multiplexing and switching: The VC is the basic routing entity for switched services and is handled in VC multiplexers and switches. VCs are aggregated in VPCs which are routed through VP multiplexers and switches.
2. Quality of service related to VP and VC connections: particular QOS classes will be requested at call establishment for both VP and VC connections. A VPC will carry VCs of various different QOSs. The VPC must meet the most demanding QOS requirement of the VCs carried.
3. Quality of service related to cell loss priority (CLP): many variable bit rate (VBR) services will require a guarantee of some minimum capacity as well as a peak capacity. When congested, the network will need to know which cells may be discarded without violating (e.g.) the guaranteed minimum capacity. The CLP bit is set by the user or service provider to indicate such cells.
4. Payload types (user information/network information) and the payload type identifier field.
5. Generic flow control (GFC) mechanism for control of user information towards the network at the broadband user-network interface (UNI) in order to alleviate any short term overload conditions that may occur.

41.4.4   I.211: B-ISDN service aspects

Provides a general classification of the standardised services to be supported by a B-ISDN and gives guidance on important network aspects which need to be taken into account when supporting services for B-ISDN. In particular, gives consideration to video coding aspects in relation to ATM.

41.4.4.1   *Service classification*

The classification separates services into two main categories: interactive and distribution services. Interactive services are subdivided into:

1. Conversational, which permit bilateral communication with real-time, end-to-end information transfer from user to user.
2. Messaging, which permit user-to-user communication via storage units with store and forward, mailbox and/or message handling functions.
3. Retrieval, which permit retrieval of information stored in information centres (usually) provided for public use.

Distribution services are sub-divided into those:

1. Without user individual presentation control, and includes broadcast services. Continuous information flow from central source to authorised receivers attached to the network. User has no control over start and order of presentation.
2. With user individual presentation control, information from central source to large number of users, provided as sequence of information entities with cyclic repetition. User can control start and order of presentation.

The recommendation deals with each class in detail, describing the type of information, giving examples of the services and their possible applications and defining some of their attributes.

41.4.4.2   *B-ISDN aspects with an impact on services*

The recommendation also gives guidance concerning some important aspects which need to be taken into account when supporting and developing services for B-ISDN, and also provides an introduction to recommendations I.362 and I.363 dealing with the ATM adaptation layer.

Multimedia aspects:

Deals with the need to separate out connection control from call control so that one call can support several types of connection dealing with different (standardised) information types.

Quality of service aspects:

Deals with QOS negotiation and indication options also the need for the Cell Loss Priority indicator.

Service bit-rate aspects:

1. Constant bit-rate services: bit-rates negotiated at call set-up time to ensure resources are fully allocated for duration of call.
2. Variable bit-rate services: expressed by a number of parameters related to traffic characteristics (see Rec. I.311). Parameters negotiated at call set-up time are supported for duration of call.
3. Maximum service bit-rate supported by the 155 Mbit/s interface: UNI (SDH) payload = 155.52 x 260/270 = 149.760 Mbit/s. With ATM cell format, cell payloads carry 149.76 x 48/53 = 135.631 Mbit/s (= maximum possible service bit-rate). May in fact be less due to: transfer capacity required for OAM and signalling cells; ATM adaptation layer overheads; the time period associated with the 'structure' attribute for CBR services.
4. Maximum service bit-rate supported by the 622 Mbit/s interface: for further study.

Service timing/synchronisation aspects:

1. End-to-end methods: use of an adaptive clock; use of a synchronisataion pattern; and time stamping.
2. Network methods: mechanisms to be provided to support services with 8kHz integrity. Examples are network sourced time-stamped cells; timing information from the T-interface.

Connectionless data service aspects:

Can be supported in B-ISDN.

1. Indirectly via a B-ISDN connection-oriented service
2. Directly via a B-ISDN connectionless service (for further study).

Interworking aspects:

Services normally available from narrow-band interfaces will also be available from broadband interfaces.

Signalling aspects:

A number of service-based signalling capability requirements are listed.

41.4.4.3 *Video coding aspects*

The final section of the recommendation deals with video coding aspects and argues for coordination of video coding studies with B-ISDN studies in order to minimise the number of video terminals needed to access a range of interactive and distribution video and still image based services. Minimising the number of coding techniques and matching them to network characteristics is key to this aim. Constant bit-rate and variable bit-rate coding are discussed as are a layered approach to video coding for service integration and the impact of the ATM network on video coding. The recommendation concludes that layered coding combined with variable bit-rate coding has advantages for video service integration and for utilisation of ATM network capabilities and therefore recommends that studies should be concentrated on these methods.

41.4.5 I.311: B-ISDN general network aspects

Describes a number of separate network related aspects of B-ISDN: networking techniques, signalling principles and traffic control and resource management.

41.4.5.1 *Networking techniques*

This deals with the layering principles used in defining the B-ISDN and the hierarchical relationship between the physical layer, the ATM layer and the layers above.

It defines an ATM transport network as being structured in two layers: ATM layer and Physical Layer. The ATM layer has two sub-layers, the Virtual Path (VP) sub-layer and the Virtual Channel (VC) sub-layer. The physical layer transport functions are subdivided into three levels: transmission path, digital section and regenerator section levels.

I.311 takes further the VC and VP concepts introduced in I.150:

1. Virtual Channel (VC): a generic term to describe a unidirectional communication capability for ATM cells.
2. VC Link: VC between two consecutive ATM entities where the VC Identifier (VCI) value is translated. A specific value of VCI is assigned each time a VC is switched in the network.
3. VC routing: translation of VCI values between the incoming and outgoing links on a VC switch.
4. VC Connection (VCC): concatenation of VC links. Extends between two VCC endpoints (more than two for point to multipoint). Provided for user-user, user-network, network-network information transfer. Cell sequence integrity is preserved by the ATM layer within a VCC.
5. VCC endpoint: where cell information field is exchanged between the ATM layer and the user of the ATM Layer Service.
6. Virtual Path (VP): generic term for a bundle of virtual channel links. All VC links in the bundle have the same endpoints.
7. VP Link: unidirectional capability for transport of ATM cells between two consecutive ATM entities where the VP Identifier (VPI) value is translated. A specific value of VPI is assigned each time a VP is switched in the network.
8. VP routing: translation of VPI values between the incoming and outgoing links on a VP switch.

9. VP Connection (VPC): concatenation of VP links. Extends between two VPC endpoints (more than two for point to multipoint). Provided for user-user, user-network, network-network information transfer. Cell sequence integrity is preserved by the ATM layer within a VCC.
10. VPC endpoint: where VCIs are originated, translated or terminated. When VCs are switched the VPC supporting the incoming VC links must be terminated first and a new outgoing VPC created.

The Physical Layer is also explored:

1. Transmission path: extends between network elements that assemble/disassemble the payload of a transmission system. Cell delineation and Header Error Control are required at the end points.
2. Digital Section: extends between network elements which assemble/disassemble a continuous bit or byte stream.
3. Regenerator Section: a portion of a digital section.

Figures 1,2,3 and 4 of I.311 represent:

1. The relationship between VC, VP and Transmission Path (Figure 41.11).
2. The hierarchy of the ATM transport network (Figure 41.11).
3. The hierarchical layer to layer relationship (Figure 41.12).
4. VC and VP switching (Figures 41.13 and 41.14).

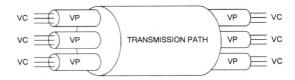

Higher layers		
ATM layer	Virtual channel level	
	Virtual path level	
Physical layer	Transmission path level	
	Digital section level	
	Regenerator section level	

Figure 41.11 Relationship between VC, VP transmission path (Fig. 1/I.311) and hierarchy of the ATM transport network (Fig. 2/I.311)

I.311 explores the identified applications of VCCs and VPCs, categorising each as user-user, user-network and network-network. In each application the connection end-points are localised and an indication of possible use given.

41.4.5.2 *Signalling principles*

This identifies the signalling capabilities required in B-ISDN to support a multiplicity of service types and covers the requirements

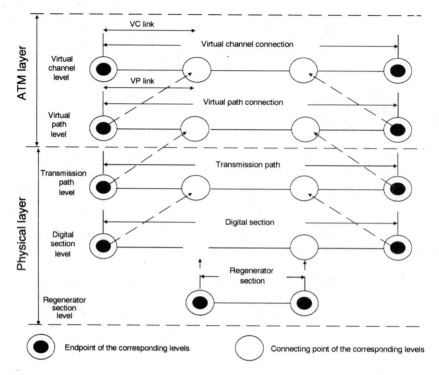

Figure 41.12 Hierarchical layer to layer relationship (Fig. 3/I.311)

for establishing signalling communication paths. It examines the capabilities required to control ATM VC and VP connections for information transfer and (implicitly acknowledging the distinction between connection and call) further examines the capabilities required to support simple multi-party and multi-connection calls. Capabilities include:

1. Establish, maintain and release VCCs and VPCs. May be on-demand, semi-permanent or permanent, but must comply with requested connection characteristics.
2. Support point-to-point, multipoint and broadcast configurations.
3. Negotiation of traffic characteristics at set-up and during calls.

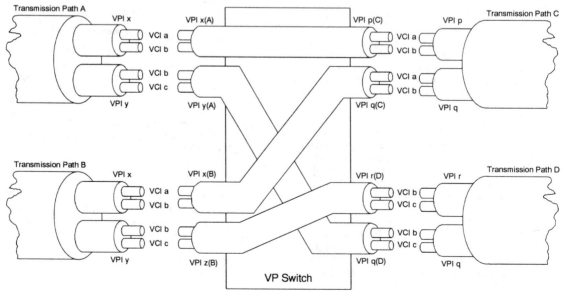

Figure 41.13 Representation of VP switching (an elaboration of Fig. 4/I.311)

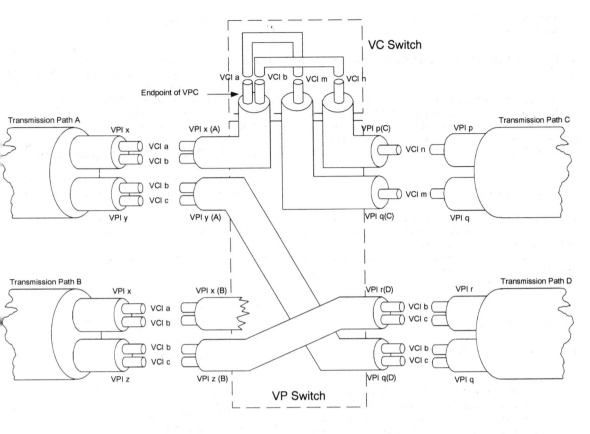

Figure 41.14 Representation of VP and VC switching (an elaboration of Fig. 4/I.311)

4. Support of symmetric and asymmetric calls.
5. Addition/removal/reconfiguration of connections and parties from multi-connection and multi-party calls.
6. Support interworking between different coding schemes and with non B-ISDN services.

Signalling principles also examines the requirements for signalling virtual channels on the user access and in the network and also the requirement for meta-signalling procedures to establish, check and release signalling virtual channel connections.

Three types of signalling virtual channel are considered at the user access (those in the network are for further study):

1. Point-to-point, one in each direction allocated to each signalling end-point.
2. Selective broadcast, one allocated to each service profile (relates to supplementary services: see CCITT Rec. Q.932). It can only apply in the network-user direction. A number of possible service profile configurations have been identified.
3. General broadcast, which is used for broadcast signalling independent of service profiles.

The meta-signalling is carried in a permanent virtual channel connection with a standardised VPI and VCI value.

I.311 illustrates some possible signalling configuration cases: each describes a possible provision of meta-signalling, signalling and information virtual channels and paths between the customer

equipment (CEQ) and local or transit connection related functions (CRFs) or exchanges.

41.4.5.3 *Traffic control and resource management*

This deals with the several levels of traffic control capabilities to be provided by the ATM-based B-ISDN:

1. Connection admission control, which are actions taken by the network during call set-up phase in order to establish whether the call should be accepted or rejected. Acceptance is on the basis that sufficient resources are available to establish the call (at the required QOS) across the whole network without impact on the QOS of existing calls.
2. Usage parameter control, which are actions taken by the network during the information transfer phase of a call to ensure that actual cell flows conform to the parameters negotiated during connection admission control, thus protecting the QOS of other calls on the network. (Also referred to as the flow enforcement or policing function.)
3. Priority control, which is the possibility for the user to assign different priorities to different traffic flows by using the cell loss priority bit.
4. Congestion control, which are mechanisms used by the network in the face of traffic overloads which prevent the network

from guaranteeing the negotiated QOS to the calls in progress in the network.

41.4.6 I.321 B-ISDN Protocol Reference Model (PRM)

This is based on the ISDN PRM defined in I.320. This recommendation takes into account the functionalities of B-ISDN and defines a B-ISDN PRM, reflecting the principles of layering of communications as defined in the Reference model of Open Systems Interconnection (CCITT Rec. X.200).

41.4.6.1 *Protocol reference model*

The B-ISDN PRM is represented as a cube with a number of horizontal layers and with three vertical planes: the user plane, the control plane and the management plane. (Figure 41.15.) The control plane and user plane are layered as follows: physical layer; ATM layer; ATM adaptation layer; higher layers. The Management Plane contains both layer related and plane related functions.

41.4.6.2 *PRM Layer Functions*

The basic functions in the PRM Layers are as follows:

1. Physical Layer:
   Physical medium sublayer; bit timing; physical medium.
   Transmission Convergence sublayer: cell rate decoupling; HEC header generation and verification; cell delineation; transmission frame adaptation; transmission frame generation and recovery.
2. ATM Layer: generic flow control; cell header generation and extraction; VPI/VCI translation; cell multiplexing and demultiplexing.
3. ATM Adaption Layer:
   AAL Segmentation and Re-assembly sublayer (SAR); CS PDU Segmentation; CS PDU Re-assembly.
   AAL Convergence sublayer: convergence (service dependent).

41.4.7 I.327 B-ISDN functional architecture

This provides a statement of the basic functional architecture of B-ISDN to complement that for ISDN given in I.324. The architecture model defines reference configurations for B-ISDN, breaking down these into connection elements such as private access, public access, national transit etc. and identifying the locations of reference points for interfaces. The way in which functional groups relate to the connection elements is defined.

41.4.8 I.361 B-ISDN ATM layer specification

This defines the cell structure and the coding of the fields of the ATM cell header, and also addresses the ATM protocol procedures. (Figure 41.2.)

The cell header fields at the UNI are defined in Table 41.1, and the cell header fields at the NNI are defined in Table 41.2.

Table 41.1 Cell header fields at the UNI

Header field	Number of bits
Generic Flow Control (GFC)	4
Virtual Path Indicator (VPI)	8
Virtual Channel Indicator (VCI)	16
Payload Type (PT)	2
Reserved (Res)	1
Cell Loss Priority (CLP)	1
Header Error Control (HEC)	8

The coding of the fields is as follows:

1. GFC field: 4 bits, UNI only. 0000 when not used. Coding for further study.
2. Routing field: At the UNI = 8 bits VPI + 16 bits VCI. Specific values are assigned for meta-signalling virtual channel identification and general broadcast signalling virtual channel identification. At the NNI = 12 bits VPI + 16 bits VCI. Specific

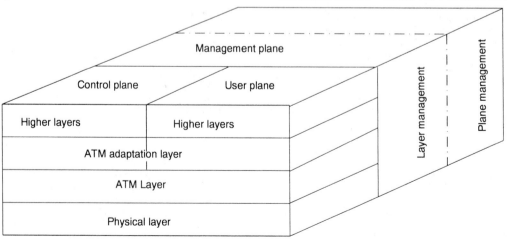

Figure 41.15 B-ISDN protocol reference model (Fig. 1/I.321)

Table 41.2 Cell header fields at the NNI

Header field	Number of bits
Virtual Path Indicator (VPI)	12
Virtual Channel Indicator (VCI)	16
Payload Type (PT)	2
Reserved (Res)	1
Cell Loss Priority (CLP)	1
Header Error Control (HEC)	8

Table 41.4 Examples of services

Class of service	Example of service
Class A	Circuit emulation
Class B	Variable bit rate video and audio
Class C	Connection oriented data transfer
Class D	Connectionless data transfer

values are assigned for idle cell identification, physical layer OAM cell identification, code for the use of the physical layer, unassigned cell identification.

3. Payload type field: 2 bits for payload type identification. User information = 00. Other values for further study.
4. Cell Loss Priority (bit): Value = 1: Cell is subject to discard depending on network conditions. Value = 0: cell has higher priority.
5. HEC field: operation described in I.432.
6. Reserved field: use not yet specified.

41.4.9 I.362 B-ISDN ATM Adaptation Layer (AAL) functional description

This classifies the services which may require AAL capabilities accessed through different Service Access Points (SAPs).

The organisation of the AAL into two sublayers is defined. These are the Segmentation and Re-assembly (SAR) sublayer and the Convergence (CS) sublayer.

The Service classification is based on three characteristics:

1. Timing relationship between source and destination, needed or not needed.
2. Bit rate, constant or variable.
3. Connection mode, connectionless or connection oriented.

Four classes are defined as given in Table 41.3. Examples of the

Table 41.3 Four classes of service

	Class A	Class B	Class C	Class D
Timing relationship between source and destination	Required		Not required	

services in the four classes are given in Table 41.4.

41.4.10 I.363 B-ISDN ATM Adaptation Layer (AAL) specification

This describes the interactions between the AAL and the next higher layer and between the AAL and the ATM layer, and also AAL peer to peer operations. It describes in detail the four types of AAL relating to the four classes of service defined in I.362, in each case addressing the functions which may be performed in the AAL to enhance the service provided by the ATM layer. In particular the SAR functions are addressed and the format of the SAR Protocol Data Unit (PDU) is defined for each type.

41.4.10.1 AAL Type 1

Services provided to higher layer:

1. Transfer/delivery of constant bit-rate 'service data units'.
2. Transfer of timing information.
3. Indication when information is errored or lost.

SAR Functions in AAL type 1 are:

1. Segmentation and re-assembly of user information.
2. Handling of cell delay variation.
3. Handling of lost/misinserted cells.
4. Source clock frequency recovery at receiver.
5. Monitoring for/ handling of AAL Protocol control information bit errors.
6. Monitoring for/ handling of user information field bit-errors.

Segmentation and re-assembly (SAR) Protocol Data Unit (PDU): Type 1 SAR-PDUs contain a header having a 4-bit sequence number field to detect lost or misinserted cells, also a 4-bit sequence number protection field.

41.4.10.2 AAL Type 2

Services provided to higher layer are:

1. Transfer of variable source bit-rate SDUs.
2. As for AAL type 1.
3. As for AAL type 1.

SAR Functions in AAL type 2: all as for AAL type 1, items 1 to 6.

Segmentation and re-assembly (SAR) Protocol Data Unit (PDU): Type 2 SAR-PDUs contain a header having a sequence number field to detect lost or misinserted cells and an information type field to indicate Beginning of Message (BOM), Continuation of Message (COM), End of Message (EOM); also a trailer containing a Length Indicator (LI) field and a CRC code field.

41.4.10.3   *AAL Type 3*

Services provided to higher layer are:

1. Message mode service: transports single AAL-SDUs in one or (optionally) more CS-PDUs.
2. Streaming mode service: transports one or more fixed size AAL-SDUs in one CS-PDU. The AAL-SDU is the atomic unit of data recognised by the application and is therefore delivered as a unit.

Both service modes may offer the following procedures:

1. Assured operations: flow control and re-transmission of corrupted/missing CS-PDUs ensures delivery of correct AAL-SDUs.
2. Non-assured operations: Integral AAL-SDUs may be lost/corrupted and will not be corrected. Options are delivery of corrupted AAL-SDUs and flow control on point-point ATM layer connections.

SAR sub-layer accepts variable length CS-PDUs from CS and generates SAR-PDUs with up to 44 octets of CS-PDU data. SAR Functions in AAL type 3 are:

1. Preservation of CS-PDU: achieved by identifying segment type and fill of SAR-PDUs.
2. Error detection: bit errors or lost/inserted SAR-PDUs.
3. Multiplexing/demultiplexing of multiple CS-PDUs concurrently from multiple AAL connections over a single ATM layer connection.

Segmentation and re-assembly (SAR) Protocol Data Unit (PDU): Type 3 SAR-PDUs contain a header having an information type (segment type) field e.g. BOM, COM, EOM, SSM (Single Segment

Message), a Sequence Number Field, and a Reserved Field; also a trailer containing a Length indicator field and a CRC code field.

41.4.10.4   *AAL Type 4*

Services provided to higher layer: transfer of the AAL-SDU for one AAL user to one or more AAL users through the ATM network. Message and streaming modes with assured/non-assured operation procedures are defined as for AAL type 3.
SAR Functions in AAL type 4: as for AAL type 3.
Segmentation and re-assembly (SAR) Protocol Data Unit (PDU): Type 4 SAR-PDUs are as for type 3, except that the reserved field is used for Multiplexing Identification, to assist in interleaving ATM-SDUs from different CS-PDUs.

41.4.11   I.413 B-ISDN User-Network interface

41.4.11.1   *Reference configuration*

This gives the reference configuration for the B-ISDN User/Network Interface (B-UNI), defining the functional groups and reference points which apply (Figure 41.16). These are essentially the same as for Narrow-Band ISDN as described in I.411. but to clearly identify the existence of broadband capabilities, the letter 'B' is used in the labelling of all reference points and functional groups.
Functional groups in the B-ISDN reference configuration are: B-NT1, B-NT2, B-TE1, TE2, B-TE2, B-TA. Reference points are: T_B, S_B, R.

41.4.11.2   *Physical realisation*

A limited set of examples of possible physical configurations are given. These cover configurations which could be supported by

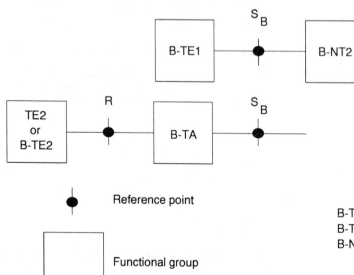

Figure 41.16   B-ISDN reference configurations (Fig. 1/I.413)

standardised interfaces at reference points S_B and T_B and also illustrate physical configurations for shared medium applications.

41.4.11.3 *Characteristics of interfaces at the T_B and S_B reference points*

The characteristics of the interfaces at the T_B and S_B reference points are described. There are two physical layer options at 155.52 Mbit/s: cell-based and SDH based. The options at 620 Mbit/s are for further study.

41.4.11.4 *B-ISDN model applied to functional groups*

A list of functions which might be included in each of the B-UNI functional groups is given, although these lists are not exhaustive:

1. B-NT1 functions: line transmission termination; transmission interface handling; OAM functions.
2. B-NT2 functions: adaptation functions for different media and topologies; functions of a distributed NT-2; cell delineation; concentration; buffering; multiplexing/demultiplexing; resource allocation; usage parameter control; adaptation layer functions for signalling (for internal traffic); interface handling (T_B and S_B); OAM functions; signalling protocol handling; switching of internal connections.
3. B-TE functions: user-user and user-machine dialogue and protocol; interface termination and other layer 1 functions; protocol handling for signalling; connection handling to other equipments; OAM functions.

41.4.11.5 *Physical layer information flows and interface functions*

Physical layer information flows between the physical medium (PM), the transmission convergence (TC) sublayer and their adjacent entities (ATM layer and management plane) are defined as are UNI related OAM functions.

41.4.12 I.432 B-ISDN User-Network interface, physical layer specification

This defines a limited set of Physical Layer interface structures to be applied to the S_B and T_B reference points. It also covers the physical medium and the transmission system structure that may be used at these interfaces and also addresses the implementation of UNI related OAM functions.

The main orientation of the recommendation is toward optical transmission since this is the preferred physical medium, however both optical and electrical interfaces are recommended. Implementations are to allow for terminal interchangeability. Maximum functional commonality between the UNI physical layer and that of the NNI is aimed at.

41.4.12.1 *Physical medium characteristics of the UNI*

Physical characteristics of the UNI at both 155.520Mbit/s and 622.080Mbit/s are considered, listing transmission media, interface range, electrical and optical parameters and connectors.

41.4.12.2 *Transmission convergence sublayer functions*

These are covered including the available information transfer rate, transmission frame adaptation functions (subdivided into 'Cell-based interface' and 'SDH based interface', and covering timing, interface structure and OAM implementation), header error control, idle (empty) cells and cell delineation and scrambling. From the ATM viewpoint, the mappings into SDH and the HEC field and cell delineation and scrambling algorithms are perhaps the most important.

1. Transmission frame adaptation functions: SDH based interface. The interface bit-stream is based on SDH as described in CCITT Rec. G.709. The ATM cell stream is mapped into the C-4 container and then packed into the VC-4 virtual container along with the VC-4 path overhead. The ATM cell boundaries are aligned with the STM-1 octet boundaries. The C-4 is not an integer multiple of the cell length so cells will cross C-4 boundaries. The H-4 will be set at the sending side to indicate the next occurrence of a cell boundary. This may be used optionally to supplement the mandatory HEC cell delineation mechanism. (Figure 41.4.)
2. HEC field and cell delineation. The HEC field of the cell header is calculated across the entire cell header and the code used is capable of single bit error correction and multiple bit error detection. The 8-bit HEC field is the remainder of the modulo 2 division by the generator polynomial $x^8 + x^2 + x + 1$ of the product x^8 multiplied by the content of the header excluding the HEC field. Cell delineation is performed by using the correlation between the header bits to be protected and the relevant control bits introduced into the header by the HEC. In the 'hunt' state the delineation process is performed by checking bit-by-bit whether the HEC coding law is respected (syndrome = zero) for the assumed header field. Once such an agreement is found, it is assumed to identify a cell boundary and the 'pre-sync' state is entered. In this state the process is confirmed several times before the 'synch' state is declared. In the 'synch' state, a certain number of incorrect recognitions of the coding law indicates loss of cell delineation causing transition to the 'hunt' state once more. (Figure 4.17.)
3. Scrambling will be used to improve the security and robustness of the HEC cell-delineation mechanism. In addition it helps

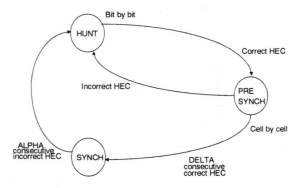

Figure 41.17 Cell delineation state diagaram (Fig. 5/I.432)

randomise the cell data for possible improvement of the transmission performance. The self-synchronising scrambler polynomial $x^{43} + 1$ has been chosen for the SDH-based physical layer. A Distributed Sample Scrambler (DSS) using the polynomial $x^{31} + x^{28} + 1$ appears the probable choice for the cell-based physical; layer. (ETSI, 1990)

41.4.13   I.610 OAM principles of the B-ISDN access

This covers the maintenance of the B-UNI and the B-ISDN subscriber access. It follows the maintenance principles defined in Rec. M.20 and describes the minimum functions needed to maintain the Physical layer and ATM layer of the customer access. Five phases have been assumed in specifying OAM functions for B-ISDN: performance monitoring, defect and failure detection, system protection, failure or performance information, fault localisation and the implementation of a Telecommunications Management Network (TMN) to support the operation of these phases is assumed.

OAM functions in the network are performed at five distinct levels of hierarchy associated with the ATM and Physical layers of the PRM. Corresponding bidirectional OAM data flows result, F1 corresponding to the regenerator section level, F2 to the digital section level, F3 to the transmission path level, F4 to the virtual path level and F5 corresponding to the virtual channel level. The physical layer contains F1, F2 and F3 whilst F4 and F5 lie in the ATM layer. (Figure 41.18.)

The mechanisms to handle OAM flows are described. For physical layer flows, these are considered for three separate types of transmission system: SDH based, Cell based and PDH based: use of SDH path and section overheads, maintenance cells for the physical layer and bit messages in PDH are described. For ATM layer flows, special cells dedicated to OAM functions are provided.

A tabulated approach is used to specify the OAM functions of the UNI and their related OAM flows. Tables are provided for the SDH-based physical layer, the cell-based physical layer and the ATM layer.

41.5   Quality of service performance requirements

Quality of Service (QoS) is a set of measures of service performance which determine the degree of satisfaction of a user of the specific service.

In an IBC network different services will have different QoS requirements. Voice traffic can tolerate only limited delay but can accept a moderate loss of cells. High speed data may be very sensitive to information loss but relatively insensitive to delay. In services using coding techniques in which cell loss may result in loss of synchronisation, the time interval between cell loss events may be more critical than the actual cell loss. Thus QoS requirements have to be stated in the context of the specific bearer service concerned. Further, the user-oriented QoS requirements have to be related to specific network related network performance (NP) requirements before the requirements of a particular QoS on the network can be parameterised.

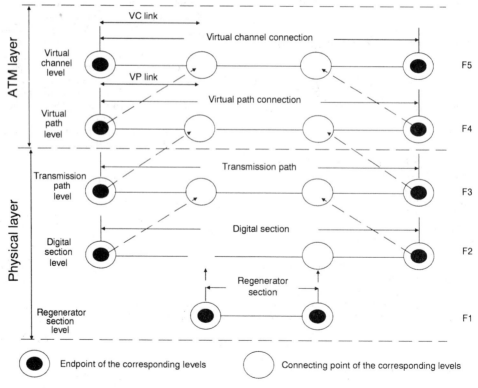

Figure 41.18   OAM hierarchical levels (Fig. 3/I.610)

Network performance parameter values are required to give network providers a view of the performance they must provide to meet the users' needs and to provide manufacturing industry with performance targets upon which to base equipment designs. They are defined against the following assumptions:

1. All ATM connections maintain cell sequence integrity.
2. Each teleservice is supported by a single ATM bearer service.
3. Each ATM bearer service is supported by one virtual circuit.
4. ATM bearer services are regarded as different if at least one of their attributes differs.

The QoS of an ATM Layer service can be characterised by a number of parameters: cell insertion rate due to header errors; cell loss rate due to header errors; cell loss rate due to buffer overflow; mean/maximum delay; delay dispersion/burst diffusion; connection set-up delay; reliability/availability; information field error-rate.

These correspond to the attribute network performance for connection types and in the following section definitions are given for a set of network performance parameters based on the CCITT attribute description method which characterises the requirements for a number of important and characteristic services. Some of the issues governing choice of parameter values are discussed and the values proposed for each bearer service are given in tabular form. (Tables 41.5 and 41.6.) This material is based on a literature survey and analysis made at the National Technical University of Athens as part of the RACE project 1014 'Atmospheric' (Anagnostou, 1991).

The network oriented QoS sub-attributes are sub-divided into two categories: information transfer related and call control related.

41.5.1 Information transfer parameters

These are as in the following sections.

41.5.1.1 *Bit Error Ratio*

This is the ratio of the number of bits incorrectly received to the total number of bits sent. In ATM it may be applied to the Cell information field only. It is expected to be no higher than the BER in present STM networks and will probably improve further with the introduction of optical transmission systems.

Table 41.5 Bearer services and applications

Bearer service	Application
64kbit/s 8kHz structured (CCITT Rec. I.231 196I.231.4)	Telephony; data; videotelephony
2x64kbit/s unrestricted, 8kHz structured (CCITT Rec. 1.231.5)	Videotelephony
< 64kbit/s	Access to server for connectionless services. These services include 'Remote process control'
64kbit/s	Interoffice signalling between signalling points in public networks or between two PABXs
384kbit/s unrestricted, 8kHz structured (CCITT Rec. 1.231.8)	Videotelephony/conferencing; data
1.92Mbit/s unrestricted, 8kHz structured	Videoconferencing; data
2.048Mbit/s	Circuit emulation (multiplex signal)
> 2Mbit/s up to < 130Mbit/s	Data; image; video
Approx. 1Mbit/s unidirectional	Stereo sound contribution
45–130Mbit/s unidirectional	TV contribution
8.448Mbit/s	Circuit emulation

41.5.1.2 *Cell Loss Ratio (CLR)*

This is the ratio of lost cells in a given VC to the total number of cells entering the VC. Cell loss may occur due to errors in the header of the cell (misrouted cells) or due to buffer overflow. CLR is a key performance parameters in an ATM network and is an ATM specific attribute. Cell loss can be detected using sequence numbering of

Table 41.6 Provisional QoS parameter values for bearer services

Bearer service	BER	CLR	CIR	End-to-end delay	Cell delay variation
64kbit/s	10^{-6}	10^{-4}	10^{-3}	400ms	20ms
2 x 64kbit/s				200ms	
Connectionless access interoffice signalling	10^{-6}	3×10^{-4}	10^{-3}	50ms	10ms
384kbit/s – 1.92Mbit/s	10^{-7}	10^{-5}	10^{-3}	200ms	20ms
> 2Mbit/s	10^{-7} with FEC(10^{-8} without FEC)	10^{-5} with FEC (10^{-9} without FEC)	10^{-3}	200ms	20ms
Stereo sound Broadcast TV	10^{-7} with FEC (10^{-8} without FEC)	10^{-5} with FEC (10^{-9} without FEC)	10^{-3}	500ms	20ms 10ms
8.448Mbit/s 34.368Mbit/s	10^{-7} with FEC(10^{-8} without FEC)	10^{-5} with FEC(10^{-9} without FEC)	10^{-3}	80ms	10ms

cells and this is regarded as the minimum adaptation layer functionality for all services. Cell header errors affecting the destination address field could lead to lost cells with potential violation of service privacy and security, therefore such errored cells are discarded. Discard, however, can also have a deleterious effect on some services, particularly video where some coding algorithms may give error extension to a complete video frame. In this context, CLRs of 10^{-11} might be required and this is a very demanding target in terms of buffer lengths in the ATM network. Signals of higher digital hierarchies, 8 Mbit/s and 34 Mbit/s, may lose synchronisation if a cell loss affects justification control bits. Thus for all the high bit-rate services a FEC in the terminals for bit errors and cell losses may be necessary.

41.5.1.3   *Cell Insertion Ratio (CIR)*

This is the ratio of inserted cells to total number of cells entering a VC. It results from header bit errors in the address field. Cell insertion is considered more serious than cell loss: for some services it may cause loss of terminal synchronisation. FEC, whilst dramatically improving CLR, can actually adversely affect CLR by converting an errored header to a valid one but with the wrong VCI value. This effect can be tolerated only because CIR values are much less than CLR values.

41.5.1.4   *Cell delay variation*

This is the difference between the values of the transit delay of cells belonging to the same VC during a pre-defined period of time (tentative definition). It is caused mainly by variations in cell delay in the network nodes, in particular in the queueing and cell rate adaptation buffers and can be augmented when asynchronous operation is used within the network node. Delay variation can be controlled at the receiving terminal at the expense of increased delay and provision of greater buffer space. With a level of compromise between the requirements on terminals and switching centres, a maximum peak to peak delay variation of 100 micro-seconds per ATM switching centre can be expected, resulting in a network end-end delay variation of a few milliseconds.

41.5.1.5   *End to end transfer delay*

This is the one way propagation time between two S/T interfaces. It excludes Cell assembly/disassembly time and is not applied to lost/misrouted cells. It is therefore confined to the delay caused by the transmission links and by the transit delays of the switches.

41.5.2   Call Control Parameters

These are as follows:

1.   Connection set-up delay, which is the interval between the event of the call set-up message transfer and receipt of its

acknowledgment. (Called user response time is not included.) Provisional target maxima based on the I.352 figures for 64 kBit/s ISDN are:

Mean connection set-up delay of 4500ms.
95% connection set-up delay of 8350ms.

2.   Connection release delay, which is the interval between the event of the call release message transfer and receipt of its acknowledgment. Provisional target maxima based on the I.352 figures for 64kbit/s ISDN are:

Mean connection release delay of 300ms.
95% connection release delay of 850ms.

41.6   References

Anagnostou, M.E., et. al. (1991) Quality of service requirements in ATM based B-ISDNs, *Computer Communications*, May.

Andersen, I., Sallberg, K., Stavenow, B. (1990) A resource allocation framework in B-ISDN. In *Proceedings of the X111 International Switching Symposium (ISS '90)*, 1, p.111.

Batcher, K.E. (1968) Sorting networks and their applications. In *Proceedings of AFIPS 1968 SJCC, 1968*, pp. 307-314.

CCITT (1990a) Study group XV111 report R.34, (Geneva Meeting May), *Recommendations drafted by Working party XV111/8 to be approved in 1990*.

CCITT (1990b) Study group XV111 report R.45, (Matsuyama Session, November), *Recommendations to be approved in 1991*.

Clos, C. (1953) A study of non-blocking switching networks, *Bell System Technical Journal*, **32** (2) pp. 406-424.

Daddis, G.E. et. al. (1989) A taxonomy for broadband integrated switching architectures, *IEEE Communications*, May.

Dupraz, J., DePrycker, M. (1990) Principles and benefits of the asynchronous transfer mode, *Electrical Communication*, **64** (2/3).

ETSI (1990) Sub technical committee NA5 (broadband networks). *Draft CCITT Contribution: Distributed Scrambler*, Report on rapporteurs meeting, Lannion 22-26 October, pp. 79-85.

Fisher, D.G., Tat, N., Berglund, A. (1990) A flexible network architecture for the introduction of ATM. In *Proceedings of the X111 International Switching Symposium (ISS '90)*, 1, p.105.

Gard, I., Rooth, J. (1990) An ATM switch implementation — technique and technology. In *Proceedings of the X111 International Switching Symposium (ISS '90)*, 4, p. 23.

Haduong, T., Stavenow, B., Dejean, J. (1990) Stratified reference model — an open architecture approach for B-ISDN. In *Proceedings of the X111 International Switching Symposium (ISS '90)*, 1, p. 105.

Hui, J. (1988) Resource allocation for broadband networks, *IEEE Journal on Selected Areas in Communications*, **6** (9) Dec.

Schaffer, B. (1990) ATM switching in the developing telecommunication networks. In *Proceedings of the X111 International Switching Symposium (ISS '90)* 1, p.105.

Wernik, M.R., Munter, E. (1990) Broadband public network and switch architecture. In *Proceedings of the X111 International Switching Symposium (ISS '90)*, 1, p.15.

42

The Synchronous Digital Hierarchy (SDH)

Mark Matthews
Northern Telecom Europe

Contents

42.1 Introduction

The Synchronous Digital Hierarchy (SDH) is a new standard for multiplexing together many low rate digital traffic channels into higher rate channels, in order that these low rate channels may be more efficiently transported around a telecommunications network. Viewed in this way, the SDH is merely a better alternative to the existing Plesiochronous Digital Hierarchy (PDH), which attempts to achieve more or less the same results. However, as we shall see later in this chapter, SDH has evolved to become much more than just the latest standard for combining and separating traffic channels. Due to the business pressures confronting the world's Public Telecommunications Operators (PTOs), SDH has developed into a comprehensive set of standards which address all aspects of a telecommunications transport network. The most important of these additional aspects concern the performance of traffic paths across the network, together with the automation of their management. The result of implementing the SDH standards is that a PTO now has a consistent mechanism for partitioning, monitoring and controlling the raw transport capacity of the whole network.

Nevertheless, without some sound business drivers, most PTOs would view a move from the current, well proven, PDH to the more advanced SDH as, at best, an interesting academic exercise, and at worst, a scandalous extravagance. To see why there is such frenetic activity to changeover to SDH it is necessary to briefly examine the business environment in which the world's more advanced PTOs are now operating.

The source of the problem is the PTOs' business customers. These are the customers from whom the PTOs derive a disproportionately large percentage of their profits, and who are becoming increasingly dependent on telecomms services for their very survival. Not surprisingly, business customers are looking to their use of telecomms to give them a competitive edge and thus, in addition to a straight reduction in tariffs, they are now demanding other things such as lower error rates and higher availability on their existing services, together with the bandwidth flexibility (i.e. channel capacity and routing capability) that enables the introduction of completely new services. In the past most PTOs operated as monopoly suppliers, and to some extent they could afford to resist these demands. Now, however, liberalisation and deregulation have introduced signifi-

cant competition into several of these former monopoly markets, especially in the USA, UK and Japan. This competition to supply high quality telecom services to business customers is forcing PTOs to re-examine the cost effectiveness of their existing transmission networks. In particular, they are looking to balance the quality of service delivered to their customers against the capital and operating costs of their networks. The objective of this balance is, of course, to maintain or increase profits.

The disturbing conclusion of most PTOs is that it is not possible to deliver the quality of service demanded by business customers, at the right price, if they continue to operate transmission networks based on the current PDH. Even more disturbing is the fact that this conclusion was reached with full awareness of the falling costs of raw bandwidth i.e. the effects of reduced costs for optical fibres, electro-optic devices and the Application Specific Integrated Circuits (ASICs), which are the heart of any piece of transmission hardware.

42.2 PDH deficiencies

In order to fully appreciate SDH, it is useful to briefly examine some of the limitations of the PDH. These limitations fall under three main headings:

1. Lack of flexibility. It is more difficult, using PDH based equipment, to drop and insert a low rate channel from a high rate channel, without the use of a 'multiplexer mountain'. The normal example given is that of dropping out a 2Mbit/s channel from a passing 140Mbit/s stream. (See Figure 42.1.) The cause of this particular problem lies in the amount of information processing necessary to locate and extract the required traffic channel. The basic PDH multiplexing process involves a bit interleaving operation which obscures knowledge of the individual byte boundaries, and thus leads to an inflexible system. This inflexibility extends beyond drop and insert functionality, to crossconnects. These become rather large and cumbersome because the PDH restricts them to use only space switching, as opposed to the much more efficient Time-Space-Time techniques that SDH allows.

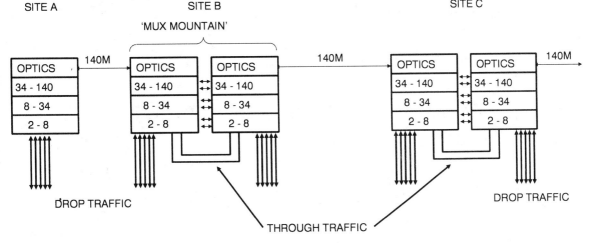

Figure 42.1 The difficulty of accessing a passing 2Mbit/s stream using PDH equipment

2. Lack of performance. The PDH does not currently have any internationally standardised ways of monitoring the performance of traffic channels at 8Mbits and above. Even at 2Mbit/s, where there is a mechanism (CRC4), it only works when the 2Mbit/s channel has a G.704 frame structure imposed on it. Furthermore, the PDH does not have any agreed management channels or protocol stacks etc. Although some of the spare bits in the frame alignment words can be, and already are, used to carry management information, the information capacity is somewhat limited (e.g.22kbit/s @ 34Mbit/s). Worse still, when operating at one of the higher order rates, the PDH makes it difficult to retrieve any management information associated with lower order channels, without a full demultiplexing operation. Finally, even at 2Mbit/s, there is no guarantee of any management information. The usual example here is that of the 2Mbit/s private circuit, leased to the customer as a clear channel i.e. the PTO imposes no G.704 frame structure and the customer has full control over the entire 2.048Mbit/s bandwidth. In this case, there is no room for the PTO to insert any monitoring or control information, hence it cannot tell when the performance of such a circuit drops out of specification. On the other hand, the customer has almost certainly imposed his own frame structure, and therefore can monitor the delivered performance with great accuracy.

3. Lack of 'Mid-Fibre Meet'. Although the PDH specifies the exact format of the bit stream at the aggregate port of any PDH multiplexer, it puts no such constraints on the bit stream on the line side of a line transmission terminal. (See Figure 42.2.) Consequently, every manufacturer has used his own proprietary line code and optical interface specification, making it impossible for a PTO to interconnect line terminals from two different manufacturers. This operational constraint is destined to because an increasing problem due to the progressive fragmentation of the erstwhile monopoly transmission networks into a patchwork of smaller operations, all of which need to interwork with each other. Without an agreed Mid-Fibre Meet standard, this interworking becomes rather clumsy, as both ends of an interconnecting line system have to be bought from the same manufacturer, and will probably need to be controlled as a pair, rather than independently by each operator. It is interesting to note that Mid-Fibre Meet was one of the original targets for the SDH standard, when it was first proposed in the US as part of the early work on SONET, back in 1984. (SONET, Synchronous Optical NETwork, is the North American counterpart to SDH. It preceded SDH by some years.)

Of the above three problem areas, it is reasonable to suppose that (3) and to some extent (2) could have been solved by extensions and modifications to the existing PDH standards. In the future, though, it is likely that the sheer quantity of management information needing to be transported around a network, will eventually pose an insoluble problem for even a modified/extended PDH, hence any solution to this problem would always be viewed as a stopgap measure.

The problem of traffic path inflexibility is much more difficult to overcome by modifying the PDH. It is tempting to suggest synchronising an entire PDH transmission network, as many PTOs have already done at the 2Mbit/s level. Unfortunately, as well as being progressively more difficult to do at the higher bit rates in the PDH, synchronisation alone does nothing to preserve the byte boundaries within each bit stream. Without any easy method of identifying these byte boundaries, the task of extracting both low order traffic and management channels has not been significantly simplified. As a final nail in the coffin, strict network synchronisation also entails the addition of 'wander' buffers at every multiplexer, in order to accommodate slow variations in the inherent delay of the transmission media (usually optical fibres these days). These buffers themselves give rise to further undesirable transmission delays, which could push some PTOs towards the otherwise

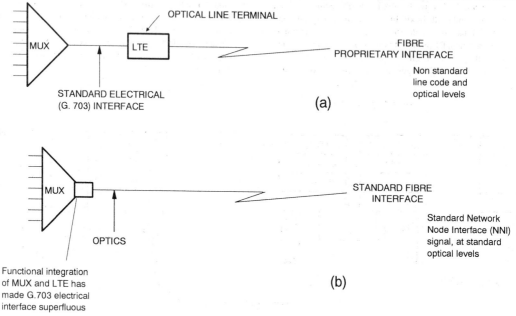

Figure 42.2 Comparison of interfaces needed in PDH and SDH environments: (a) current PDH; (b) SDH

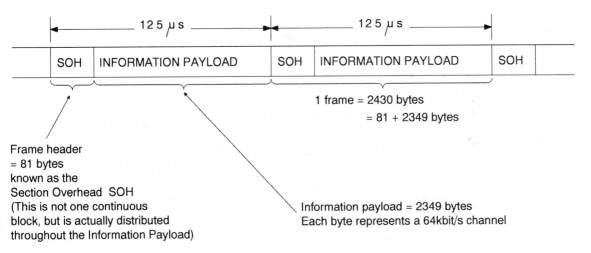

Figure header elements:

125 μs — 125 μs

| SOH | INFORMATION PAYLOAD | SOH | INFORMATION PAYLOAD | SOH | |

1 frame = 2430 bytes
= 81 + 2349 bytes

Frame header
= 81 bytes
known as the
Section Overhead SOH
(This is not one continuous
block, but is actually distributed
throughout the Information Payload)

Information payload = 2349 bytes
Each byte represents a 64kbit/s channel

Figure 42.3 The basis of SDH frame structure

unnecessary adoption of costly echo cancellers on 64kbit/s circuits throughout their networks.

42.3 The basis of SDH

Before investigating the SDH standards in detail, it is worth pausing for an overview of what SDH is designed to achieve, and the general way it goes about this task.

As with PDH, SDH is designed to transport isochronous traffic channels and is focused very much on layer one of the well known ISO seven layer OSI protocol hierarchy. Again, like PDH, SDH is based on a hierarchy of continuously repeating, fixed length frames. This contrasts with the majority of competing standards, almost all of which attempt to deliver more efficient use of both transmission and switching plant by employing some form of packetisation of the transported information. Usually, these packets are launched into the network asynchronously and arrive at their destinations with a non-deterministic delay. Consequently, they present something of a problem to delay sensitive voice circuits, which still constitute 80% of all traffic, in even the world's most advanced networks. SDH, on the other hand, was formulated on the premise that despite the pressure to support novel forms of business oriented services, it is of paramount importance to preserve a smooth interworking with the existing PDH networks, most of which were designed to serve the PSTN above all else. At the same time, it was also apparent that the increasingly widespread deployment of optical fibres would rapidly reduce the cost of raw transmission bandwidth, hence there was relatively little pressure to restrict the proportion of bandwidth devoted to multiplexing overheads, as opposed to the traffic payload. Beyond the transport of isochronous traffic channels, and smooth interworking with the existing PDH, the developers of SDH also addressed those weaknesses of the PDH that were identified above. They recognised that it was necessary to adopt not only a synchronous frame structure, but one which also preserved the byte boundaries in the various traffic bit-streams. The basic SDH frame structure is one that repeats at intervals of 125μs i.e. it is tailor made for the transport of 64kbit/s channels, or any higher rate channels which are an integer multiple of 64kbit/s. (See Figure 42.3.) In fact, with one rather important exception dealt with in Section 42.4, SDH currently focuses on the transport of 2.048 Mbit/s, 34Mbit/s and 140

Mbit/s circuits, plus their North American counterparts at 1.5Mbit/s, 6Mbit/s and 45Mbit/s.

The general way that any of these PDH rate circuits are transported by SDH is to map such a circuit into a 'Synchronous Container'. (See Figure 42.4.) A Synchronous Container can be viewed as a subdivision of the basic SDH frame structure, and it consists of a predefined number of 64kbit/s channels. The entire family of Synchronous Containers comprises only a few different types, each of which has been sized to accommodate one or more of the common plesiochronous transmission rates, without wasting too much bandwidth. The operation of mapping a plesiochronous circuit into such a Synchronous Container is very similar to the normal stuffing operation performed in a conventional PDH multiplexer. However, in this case, the plesiochronous channel is being synchronised not to the master oscillator in a PDH multiplexer, but to the frequency of the Synchronous Container, which is, in turn, synchronous to the basic SDH frame structure. (See Figure 42.5.)

Before examining the question of exactly what the SDH frame structure is synchronous with, it is worth digressing to discuss a further operation specified by SDH. This is the attachment of an Overhead, known as the Path Overhead (POH), to each Synchronous Container. (See Figure 42.4.) The idea is that once a plesiochronous circuit has been loaded into a Synchronous Container, this Container has a defined set of POH bytes appended to it, which remain completely unchanged until the Synchronous Container arrives at its destination. The combination of Synchronous Container plus POH is known as a Virtual Container (VC). The VC POH bytes allow a PTO to monitor several parameters, the most important of which is the error rate of the VC between the points at which it was loaded and unloaded with its plesiochronous payload. This provides a PTO with the much sought after end to end performance monitoring that was so difficult using conventional PDH techniques.

Most plesiochronous channels are bi-directional, hence there are usually two continuous streams of VCs travelling in opposite directions between the two end points at which the plesiochronous channel enters and leaves the SDH portion of a network. Viewed in this way, the job of an SDH based network is to load its VCs with (usually) convention PDH channels, and then transport these to their various destinations together with an accurate indication of the quality of the delivered VC payload.

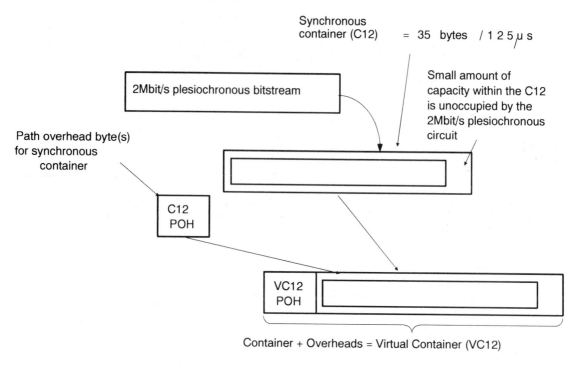

Figure 42.4 Example of the creation of a VC

This process of loading containers and then attaching POHs is repeated at several levels in SDH, resulting in the nesting of smaller VCs within larger ones. (See Figure 42.6.) The nesting hierarchy stops when the largest level of VC is loaded into the payload area of a Synchronous Transport Module (STM). These logical STM signals are seen at the interface between any two pieces of SDH equipment, where they can be presented either electrically or, more usually, optically. (See Fig 42.2.) Such an interface is referred to as a Network Node Interface (NNI), because it is usually confined to the internal interfaces within the network, rather than any interface presented to a network user. A User Network Interface (UNI) has also been defined, however, the way in which the payload information in a UNI is mapped into a standard NNI signal is not yet completely defined, and hence it is not widely used. Finally, the reason for the name Virtual Container is that unlike the STM signals that appear at the NNI, VC signals are never presented to the outside world. They exist only within pieces of SDH equipment or within STM signals, hence an SDH network element can have NNI and PDH interfaces, but never VC interfaces.

Returning to the question of exactly what is synchronised to what, the basic problem is that, as outlined in Section 42.2, it is very difficult to maintain a complete transmission network in rigid synchronisation for all time. Even if we could tolerate the delays introduced by the addition of the numerous 'wander buffers' necessary to accommodate the slow changes in transmission medium delay, there is no guarantee that different PTOs' networks would all be synchronised to the same master clock. For a network based on the SDH, this problem translates to that of how to synchronously multiplex and demultiplex many individual VCs, which, because they have been created in disparate parts of the same, or even different SDH networks, may have slightly different short term bit rates.

42.3.1 The concept of pointers

The solution adopted by SDH is to associate a pointer with each VC so that when it is multiplexed, along with others, into a larger VC, its phase offset in bytes can be identified relative to some reference point in this larger VC. (See Figure 42.7.) Furthermore, there is also a mechanism for allowing the value of this pointer to change if, for some reason, there is a loss of synchronisation, and the smaller capacity VC is running either slightly slower, or slightly faster than the larger VC. In fact, each of the smaller capacity VCs has its own pointer, which can change independently of any of the others. Although the use of these pointers still entails some input buffers, these are very much smaller than would be required if there were no mechanism for changing the phase of a small capacity VC within a larger one, hence the problem of excessive delays can be contained. We now have a picture of an SDH network as one in which the majority of VCs, both large and small, are well synchronised to each other, but, at the same time, there are a few which are not so well synchronised, and every so often, the increasing strain of their asynchronism has to be relieved by a byte sized slip relative to the majority of the other VCs in the network. Nevertheless, we retain our ability to locate the management and control information in the VC's POH bytes, because the pointer value associated with VC is recalculated whenever a slip occurs.

The pointer mechanism described above is at the very heart of the SDH standard. It is this mechanism that enables us to construct networks that are nearly, but not completely synchronous, and yet still allows us to easily locate each traffic channel (VC), together with its associated management and control information i.e. POH, but without incurring large penalties in transmission delay. It could be argued that SDH networks are not really synchronous at all, but are actually very tightly controlled asynchronous networks. How-

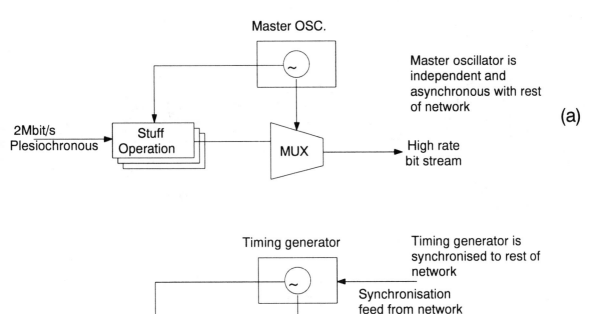

Master oscillator is independent and asynchronous with rest of network

(a)

Timing generator is synchronised to rest of network

Synchronisation feed from network

(b)

Figure 42.5   Difference in synchronisation between PDH and SDH: (a) PDH; (b) SDH

ever, the fact that we have quantised the slips due to this asynchronism means that it is now possible, at any time, to locate and route

any of the traffic paths within an SDH network. This, together with network management software, gives us the traffic routing flexi-

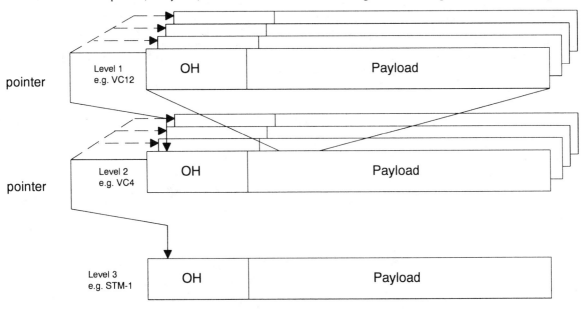

Figure 42.6   General representation of a 3 layer synchronous multiplexer structure

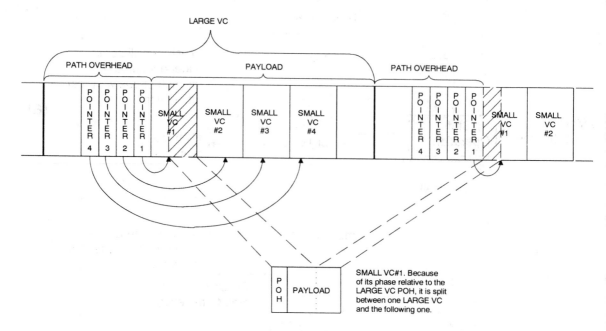

Figure 42.7   Pointers allow small VC to have arbitrary phase with respect to large VC

bility that was very difficult to achieve using PDH based equipment. In terms of actual network hardware, it opens the way to the production of economically viable drop and insert multiplexers and cross connects.

42.4   The SDH standards

There are now a dozen or more CCITT recommendations describing various aspects of SDH, but the centre-piece of the whole group is undoubtedly CCITT G.707/8/9. These three standards define the SDH multiplexing structure and the ways that non SDH traffic channels can be mapped into the SDH Virtual Containers. Other standards in the group deal with such things as the functionality of multiplexers (G.781/2/3), the management requirements of such equipment (G.784), and the equivalent recommendations for line systems (G.958). Optical interfaces for all types of SDH equipment are covered in G.957. Further standards (G.sdxc1/2/3, still in the draft stages) address the functionality of synchronous cross connects. Finally there are two more standards (G.sna1/2), which address the way that entire SDH based networks should be constructed in order that they can interwork successfully with other such networks and, even more importantly, so that the management of these networks can be brought under software control. Nevertheless, because of their central role in SDH, we shall concentrate mainly on explaining G.707/8 & 9.

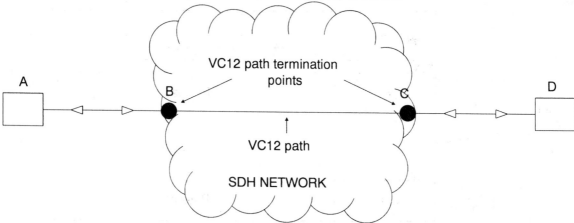

Figure 42.8   2Mbit/s plesiochronous circuit from A to D, which is transported by an SDH network for part of its journey

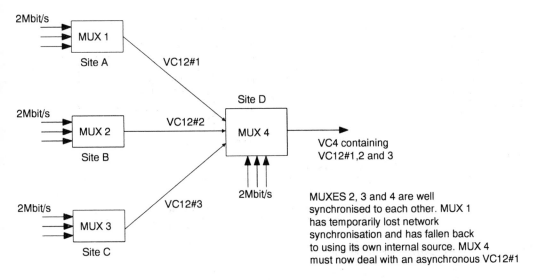

Figure 42.9 Synchronous multiplexing of VC12s into a VC4 when VC12s are created in various places

Bearing in mind the nesting of smaller VCs within larger ones, and thence into STMs, the best way to appreciate the details of the SDH multiplexing standards G707/8/9, is to follow the progress of a bi-directional 2Mbit/s plesiochronous circuit, which, for part of its journey, is transported across an SDH based network. (See Figure 42.8.) Such a 2Mbit/s circuit could be a channel between two PSTN switches, or it could be a private leased line which is connecting two PBXs. Although the 2Mbit/s circuit is bi-directional, the SDH operations are identical in both directions, hence we shall concentrate on just one direction of transmission, that from A to D.

At point B, where the 2Mbit/s circuit meets the SDH network, the first operation is to take the incoming plesiochronous bit stream and selectively add 'stuffing' bits in order to 'pad-out' this bit stream to the exact rate required to fill the appropriate Synchronous Container. In this case, the Synchronous Container size would be a C12, which is sufficiently large to accommodate a 2Mbit/s plesiochronous bit stream at the limits of its 50 ppm tolerance, together with some additional 'fixed stuffing' bytes. The stuffing of the plesiochronous bit stream should ideally be done relative to the clock to which the whole SDH network is beating, however, as discussed in Section 42.3, there is a chance that the SDH network element (e.g. multiplexer) which is performing the stuffing operation, is not quite synchronous with the rest of the network. In this case C12 which it creates is similarly asynchronous.

42.4.1   Path OverHead information

Having mapped the 2Mbit/s bit stream into the C12, the next operation is to generate and attach the Path Overhead byte (POH), which enables this C12 to be identified, monitored for errors and routed through the SDH network. The addition of this POH byte to the C12 creates a Virtual Container 12 (VC12). As mentioned in Section 42.3, the idea is that the POH stays attached to its C12 all the way from the point where it was generated, to the point at which the 2Mbit/s payload exits the SDH network. These two points are the 'Path Termination' points for this VC12, with the continuous stream of VCs between them being referred to as the Path. Between the two path termination points at B and C, there is no legitimate mechanism for altering any of the information in the POH, hence if

the receiving path termination detects any discrepancy between the POH and the content of the VC12 payload (i.e. the C12), this indicates that the VC12 payload has somehow become corrupted during its journey across the SDH network. Although path level monitoring is sufficient for a PTO to ascertain what error rate is being inflicted by the SDH network on his customers' 2Mbit/s circuit, it provides no information whatsoever on the source of the errors i.e. which network element has gone faulty. This task is dealt with by the addition of still further overhead information, which will be described shortly. Before this, it is necessary to examine the way in which several VC12s are multiplexed into a higher rate signal.

42.4.2   Multiplexing of Virtual Containers

The general principle of this multiplexing operation is fairly straight forward. Several VC12s, which should, hopefully, be synchronous with one another, are loaded into a larger Synchronous Container, which subsequently has its own POH added, thus creating a larger i.e. higher bit rate, VC. (See Figure 42.6.) In CEPT countries, this operation results in the creation of a VC4, which is large enough to accommodate up to 63 VC12s. Unfortunately, as discussed in Section 42.3, complications arise in this operation, because the network element that is performing this task, may not itself have created all the VC12s. (See Figure 42.9.) This leads to the possibility that not all the VC12s are completely synchronous with one another or, more importantly, with the VC4 into which they are being loaded.

The solution to this problem comes in two parts. Firstly, the internal structure of the VC4 has been purposely designed to allow each VC12 to run slightly faster, or slower, than the VC4 rate. This is done by designating certain bytes in the C4 as overflow bytes (one per VC12) to cope with a VC12 that is running too fast. On the other hand, when a VC12 is running slow, then occasionally, a VC12 byte can be repeated. Secondly, this (hopefully) infrequent change of phase of a VC12 relative to its VC4 is recorded by means of a pointer. A VC4 maintains one pointer for each of the VC12s within its payload, and each pointer registers the offset in bytes between the first byte of the VC4 and the POH byte of a particular VC12. Each pointer is located in a pre-defined position within the VC4, hence once the VC4 POH has been located, it is a simple matter of

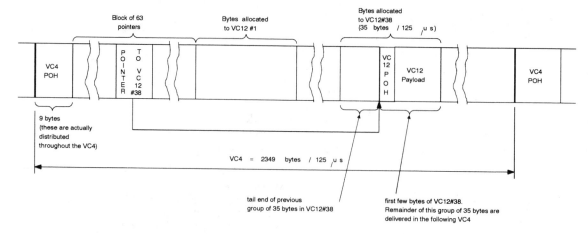

Figure 42.10 Fixed location of VC12 pointers within a VC4

counting bytes in order to locate each of the 63 pointers to the VC12s. (See Figure 42.10.)

The trigger for a rephasing of a VC12 relative to its VC4 is when the fill of the VC12 input buffer (into which the incoming VC12 is written prior to loading into the VC4) exceeds a pre-determined threshold. At this point, what appears to be a fairly conventional justification occurs, with either an extra VC12 byte being loaded into the VC4 (into the overflow position mentioned earlier) or,

conversely, one byte being repeated. (See Figure 42.11.) Either way, the resulting change of phase of VC12 relative to VC4 is tracked by a corresponding change in pointer value.

Because of the importance of pointers for locating low order VCs (VC12s) within high order VCs (VC4s), the combination of a low order VC plus its pointer is referred to as a Tributary Unit (TU). In this case, the combination of a VC12 plus its pointer constitutes a TU12.

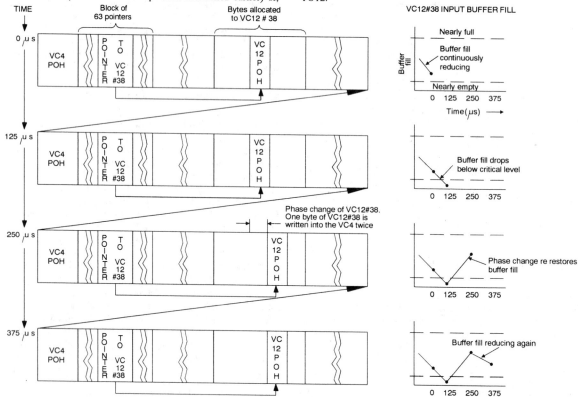

Figure 42.11 Pointer adjustment resulting from VC12#38 running slower than the VC4

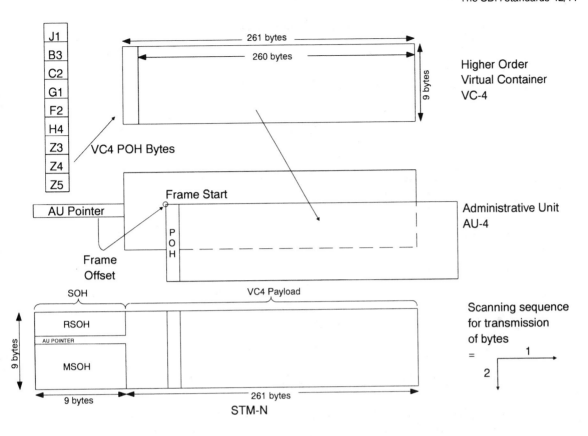

Figure 42.12 Representation of a VC4 as a block of 261 x 9 bytes together with its incorporation within an STM signal

42.4.3   Channels and Tributary Unit Groups

Having discussed the way in which up to 63 individual TU12s are multiplexed into a VC4, it is now necessary to examine more closely the internal structure of the VC4. For this purpose, it is helpful to consider a VC4 not as a linear string of bytes, but instead, as a two dimensional block of bytes which is arranged as 9 rows, each of 261 bytes. For transmission purposes, this block is serialised by scanning left to right, top to bottom. (See Figure 42.12.) With this structure, a TU12 can be seen to occupy 4, widely separated, 9 byte columns, rather than the contiguous block of bytes, as suggested by Figures 42.10 and 42.11. (See Figure 42.13.) Since a VC4 repeats every 125μs, this implies that a TU12 contains 36 bytes per 125μs i.e. rather more than the 32 bytes nominally required by a plesio-chronous 2.048 Mbit/s signal. This, however, is consistent with the need for a TU12 to include a pointer, overflow byte positions, VC12 overhead byte, plesiochronous stuffing etc. Each such group of four columns represents a separate channel within the VC4 and when a VC12 slips phase relative to the VC4 it slips within its own channel i.e. it does not overflow into another channel, as this would ob-viously corrupt the data in the other channel. As mentioned earlier, the position of the pointer within this channel is constant, only the VC12 part of the TU12 is allowed to wander in phase.

A group of three such TU12 channels within a VC4 is known as a Tributary Unit Group (TUG). As with the concept of a channel, a TUG is not a multiplexing level (such as a VC12) but a group of

defined byte positions within a VC4. Some of these positions are reserved for TU pointers, while the others are for the rest of the TUs i.e. the VCs. The reason for introducing the concept of a TUG, instead of sticking with that of a channel, is that, as mentioned in Section 42.3, a C12 and hence VC12, is not the only size of Synchronous Container which has been defined. (See Figure 42.14.) For example, there exists a C2 which is designed to accommodate the North American 6.3Mbit/s plesiochronous rate. In the event of a PTO needing to transport both 2Mbit/s circuits and 6.3Mbit/s ones, they can both be accommodated within the same VC4 by assigning some TUGs to carry groups of three TU12s while other TUGs are assigned to each carry a single TU2.

The TUG in this example is known as a TUG2, because at 12 columns of 9 bytes, it is large enough to accommodate a single TU2. Beyond this, a TUG3 has also been defined. This is slightly larger than 7 TUG2s, and designed to accommodate a single 45Mbit/s circuit, after this has been mapped into its appropriate Synchronous Container (in this case, a VC3). A 34Mbit/s signal can also be mapped into a VC3, in an operation that appears somewhat wasteful on bandwidth, as the C3 has been sized for a 45Mbit/s signal. It is interesting to note that, rather than use a more aptly sized container, this bandwidth sacrifice was agreed to by European PTOs in order to reduce the potential network control problem posed by a larger variety of VCs.

A TUG3 is one third of the payload capacity of a VC4, and together with the TUG2, it constitutes an extremely flexible mech-

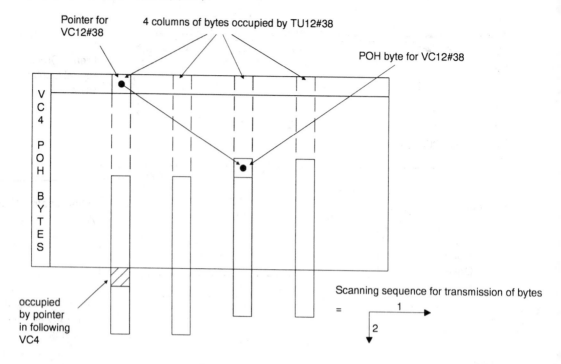

Figure 42.13 Internal structure of VC4 showing fixed pointer locations and distribution of a single TU12 over 4 separate columns

anism for partitioning the payload bandwidth of a VC4. The potentially complicated nature of this partitioning can be better understood by replacing the two dimensional representation of the VC4 payload structure by a three dimensional one. (See Figure 42.15.) For this representation, the order of transmission is left to right, front to back, top to bottom. Figure 42.15 not only shows TU12s and TU3s, as we have already discussed, but also, examples of other types of TUs, notably the TU11, which is the TU used to accommodate a 1.5Mbit/s (DS1) signal in North America. This payload flexibility extends to alternative mechanisms for constructing a VC4 payload in which, for instance, a normal 140Mbit/s signal is mapped directly into the C4, without any need for recourse to the notion of TUGs. Because of the variety of possible VC4 payloads, part of the VC4 overhead (i.e. the H4 byte) is reserved for indicating the exact structure of this payload. This ability of a single VC4 to carry a mixture of different sized VCs within its payload is considered to be especially useful in the Access portion of the network, where a PTO will not usually have the freedom to dedicate particular VC4s to carrying a single type of lower order VC.

42.4.4   VC4 into a Synchronous Transport Module

Although a VC4 can have its payload constructed in a variety of ways, its POH conforms to the same principles as those of a VC12 i.e. it is generated and attached at the point where the C4 is loaded, and remains unchanged until the C4 is unloaded at its destination. As with the VC12, the VC4 POH is capable of indicating that errors have been introduced into the VC4 payload during its journey, but it is not capable of identifying which network element was responsible. This problem is solved by the addition of yet another set of overhead bytes to the VC4, known as the Section Overhead bytes

(SOH). The combination of the SOH plus the VC4 is termed a Synchronous Transport Module (STM), but another way of looking at this structure is to regard the VC4 as fitting neatly into the payload area of the STM. (See Figure 42.12.) Like the VC4, the STM repeats every 125µs. In order to appreciate the structure of an STM, and particularly the SOH, it is best to revert to using the two dimensional representation of a block of bytes. Figure 42.12 shows the standard representation of the smallest STM, known as an STM-1, which has 9 rows of 270 bytes each. This produces a transmission rate of 155.520Mbit/s.

The significance of the STM SOH is that, unlike the VC4 POH, is it generated afresh by every network element that handles the VC4. This handling of the VC4 includes the operations of creating, multiplexing or routing within the network, even if such multiplexing or routing happens to be completely inflexible (e.g. hardwired). When a network element (i.e. line terminal, multiplexer or cross connect) receives an STM, it immediately examines the relevant bytes of the SOH to determine whether any errors have been introduced into the payload i.e. the VC4. Unless this particular network element happens to contain the VC4 path termination point, it subsequently calculates a new, replacement set of SOH bytes which are then attached to the VC4 for onward transmission to the next network element. (See Figure 42.16.)

This section by section monitoring gives the PTO a powerful tool for locating the source of any poor performance within his network, and compliments the capabilities of the VC POHs, which are solely concerned with end to end, rather than section by section (i.e. network element to network element) issues. It could be argued that the POH monitoring is redundant, because the end to end path performance could be synthesised from the individual section indications. However, not only would this be difficult to do, especially if the VC4 journey happened to traverse the networks of more than

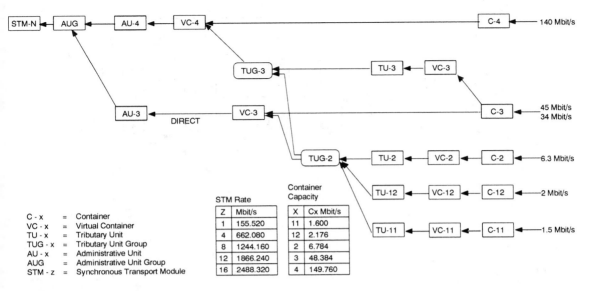

STM Rate			Container Capacity	
Z	Mbit/s		X	Cx Mbit/s
1	155.520		11	1.600
4	662.080		12	2.176
8	1244.160		2	6.784
12	1866.240		3	48.384
16	2488.320		4	149.760

C - x = Container
VC - x = Virtual Container
TU - x = Tributary Unit
TUG - x = Tributary Unit Group
AU - x = Administrative Unit
AUG = Administrative Unit Group
STM - z = Synchronous Transport Module

Figure 42.14 SDH multiplexing structure

one PTO, but it would not necessarily detect all the errors in the VC4, because it is quite possible for errors to be generated within the confines of a transited network element, i.e. within that portion of a network element between where the old SOH has been removed, and a new one has been added, e.g. between X and Y of the Mux at site C in Figure 42.16.

Although both the VC POHs and STM SOHs have other duties in addition to the performance monitoring described above, the SOHs shoulder by far the larger part of the burden, hence the reason for the much larger number of bytes in the SOH than, for instance, in a VC4 POH. (See Figure 42.12.) These additional duties include STM alignment function, the carriage of the network management chan-

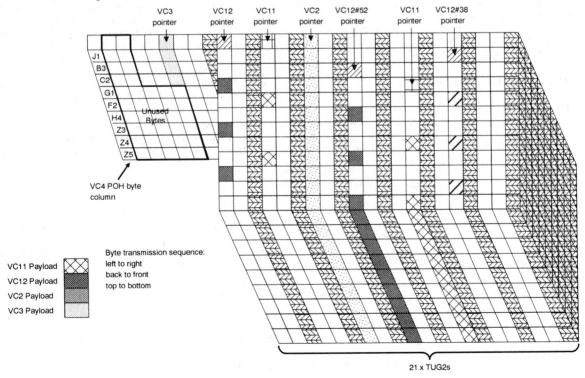

Figure 42.15 Partially filled VC4 with TU structured payload

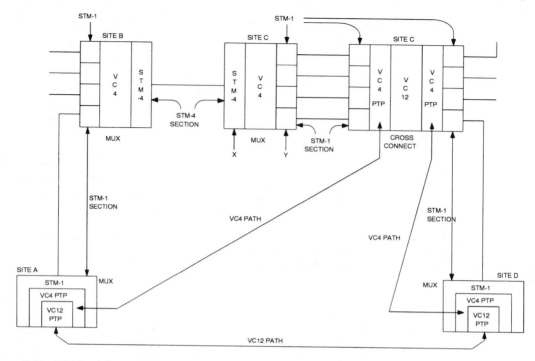

Figure 42.16 VC12 path between sites A and D, showing the VC4 and STM sections involved

nels, Engineer Orderwire channels, data channels reserved for the PTO and synchronisation signalling channels. Even when these have been accommodated, there is substantial unallocated capacity which is being kept in reserve, to service future network control requirements that have not yet been identified.

42.4.5 Further use of Pointers

The use of STMs and their associated SOHs entails a few additional complications beyond those discussed above. An STM may well be generated by a network element which did not have the privilege of also generating the particular VC4 that it is attempting to load. This

immediately introduces the possibility of a slight asynchronism between STM and VC4, and, as with the VC12, this problem is also solved by a slip mechanism plus pointer. The pointer bytes occupy defined positions within the SOH and indicate the offset, in bytes, between themselves and the first byte of the VC4 POH. The main difference between this and the VC12 pointer is that when a VC4 slips its phase relative to the STM SOH, it does so by three bytes at a time, rather than the single byte phase change experienced by the VC12.

A second difference between this case, and that of a VC12, is that the combination of a VC4 plus its pointer is known as an Administrative Unit 4 (AU4), rather than a TU4, when the pointer is located

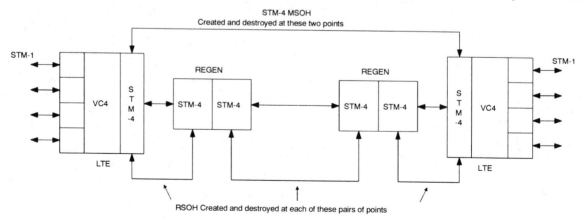

Figure 42.17 Line transmission system showing the multiplexer section overshea (MSOH) operating between LTEs, while only the regenerator section overhead (RSOH) is recalculated between each pair of regenerators

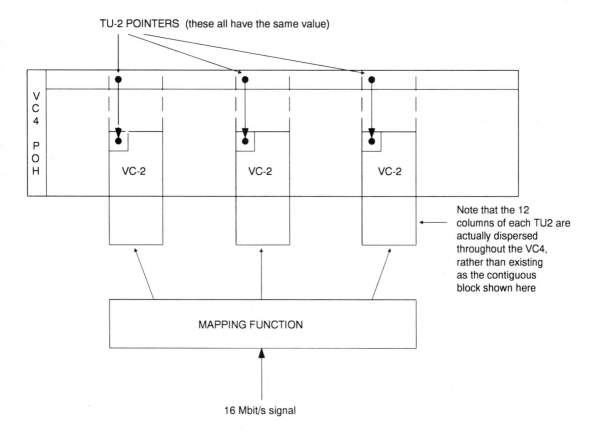

Figure 42.18 Loading of a hypothetical 16Mbit/s signal into 3 concatenated VC-2s (VC2 -3c) within a VC4

in an STM. The AU4 is used in all CEPT countries as the size of traffic block on which networks are planned and operated. There is also an AU3, which is used mainly in North America. This refers to an alternative construction of an STM, whereby the payload consists not of a single VC4, but instead, of a group of three VC3s, together with their associated pointers. A further difference between the STM SOH and a VC POH is that the SOH can be divided into two parts, known as the Multiplexer Section OverHead (MS OH) and the Regenerator Section OverHead (RSOH). (See Figure 42.12.) The reason for this is that on long line transmission systems the regenerators do not need to perform the rather costly, and in this case, unnecessary operation of generating and destroying the complete SOH. Instead, only a subset of a SOH is processed, leading to a reduction in gate count, power consumption etc., but still preserving the ability to detect traffic errors and access some management channels. On the other hand, the line terminal equipments process both the RSOH and MSOH. (See Figure 42.17.)

Finally, as with VCs, STMs come in various sizes. As mentioned earlier, the smallest size is termed an STM-1, and can accommodate a single VC4. However, larger sizes exist whose bit rates are integer multiples of the basic STM-1 rate. CCITT G.707 currently recognises the STM-4 and STM-16, but STM-12 based network elements are also being designed, and it is likely that STM-64 will become a de facto standard in the near future. For all these higher rate STMs, the construction mechanism is the same: The payload is produced by straight byte interleaving of the tributary VC4s, while the SOH

is constructed in a more complicated way, particularly in relation to the way the error checking bytes are calculated.

42.4.6 Other sizes of VCs and payloads

The above description of the loading of a 2Mbit/s circuit into a VC12, VC4 and thence into an STM-1, mentioned the existence of other sizes of VC. The complete family of VCs, together with their allowed multiplexing routes up to STM-1 are shown in Figure 42.14. So far mappings into these Synchronous Containers have been defined for all the common plesiochronous bit rates, together with few others, notably the 125Mbit/s FDDI signal. This latter mapping is somewhat wasteful of transmission bandwidth, as it loads the 125Mbit/s FDDI signal into a VC4 which has a payload capacity of around 149Mbit/s. It might be thought that this degree of inefficiency is more or less inevitable for any further type of signal whose bit rate does not correspond roughly with that of one of the existing Synchronous Containers. In fact, this is not necessarily so, because CCITT G.708 and G.709 contain provision for the concatenation of both TU2s and AU3s and AU4s.

As a hypothetical example, to illustrate the use of concatenated TU2s, an incoming service signal at, say 16Mbit/s, is mapped into a group of three VC2s, known collectively as a VC2-3c. (See Figure 42.18.) These three VC2s are loaded into the VC4 with identical pointer values, and are subsequently transported, as a group, across the entire SDH network. The best current example of the use of this technique is in the area of video transmission, where a TV signal is

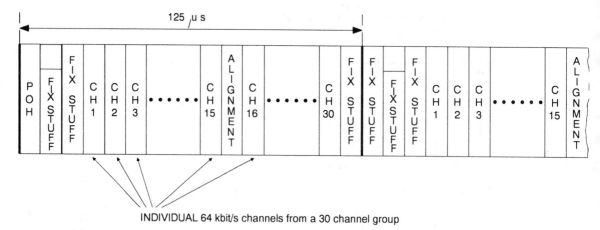

INDIVIDUAL 64 kbit/s channels from a 30 channel group

Figure 42.19 Byte synchronous mapping of a G.704 structured 2.048Mbit/s signal into a VC12, showing the fixed location of each of the 30 x 64kbit/s channels

digitally encoded at around 32Mbit/s, and subsequently loaded into a concatenated group of five VC2s (VC2-5c). This mapping allows up to four such video signals to be transported in a single VC4. If, instead, the normal mapping into a VC3 had been used, then only three video signals could have been accommodated within one VC4, hence a useful increase in efficiency by using concatenation.

So far, in this discussion, all the examples of a service rate signal being mapped into a Synchronous Container have assumed that the SDH network element makes no use of any structure that might be present in the service rate signal. In fact, this assumption is always true when the service rate signal is plesiochronous, however, because of the way the PSTN service is usually operated, with all of the switches running synchronously with one another, it was decided to endow SDH with a second class of mapping, known as byte synchronous mapping. Currently, the only byte synchronous mapping defined, is for a 2Mbit/s signal which has a G.704 frame structure (i.e. is byte orientated) and which is synchronous to the SDH network or, more precisely, synchronous with the network

element which is mapping it into a Synchronous Container. In the course of a byte synchronous mapping, the SDH network element locks onto the incoming G.704 frame alignment word, and subsequently proceeds to load this, and every other byte in the G.704 frame, into predefined positions in the C12. (See Figure 42.19.)

This results in a situation whereby any channel of a 30 channel group can be easily located once the location of the VC12 POH has been established. The advantage of this mapping becomes apparent when considering two PSTN switches which are interconnected by several groups of 30 channels, that are transported over an SDH network. (See Figure 42.20.) It is easy for such a PSTN switch to operate as part of the SDH network by generating and byte synchronously loading its own VC12s, because it already knows the location of all 30 channels. It obviously does not need to search for frame alignment, as this too is already known. At the receiving PSTN switch, because the VC12s were mapped byte synchronously, there is also no need for a frame alignment operation, because this follows automatically once the phase of the VC12 is known. The

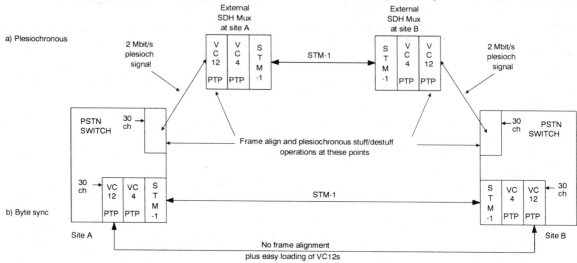

Figure 42.20 Comparison of plesiochronous and byte synchronous mappings of 30 channel groups between two PSTN switches

removal of the G.704 frame alignment process not only leads to a reduction in gate count (and hence cost), but also reduces the delay associated with this operation. These advantages apply not just to the PSTN example given above, but, in fact, to any network where visibility and routing of individual 64 kbit/s channels is required, hence they could also apply to networks of PBXs or 64 kbit/s cross connects.

42.4.7 SONET and SDH

Several mentions have been made of SONET as being both the forerunner and the North American equivalent of SDH. The SONET standards were designed around the need for efficient transport of the existing North American PDH rates, the most important of which are the 1.5Mbit/s and 45Mbit/s rates. This leads to a standard where a 45Mbit/s signal is loaded into the equivalent of a VC3, which, in turn, is loaded into the SONET counterpart of an STM, known as a Synchronous Transport Signal – 1 (STS-1), which runs at 51.84Mbit/s i.e. precisely one third of the STM-1 rate. As with SDH, there is also a concatenation mechanism for dealing with customer signals which do not easily fit inside any of the already defined VC payload areas. This mechanism is particularly useful for carrying rates such as 140Mbit/s, where the concatenation results in a SONET NNI signal known as an STS-3c, which has a bit rate that is identical to an STM-1, and an SOH and payload area of exactly the same size as well.

Other terminology within SONET is also different, in that SONET refers to Virtual Tributaries (VTs) rather than VCs, and the equivalent of the VC3, referred to above, is known as a Synchronous Payload Envelope (SPE). It also makes a distinction between the STS logical signal and its optical manifestation at an NNI, in which case it is referred to as an Optical Carrier (OC). North American transmission systems are usually referred to by their transmission rates in OCs e.g. OC3 or OC48.

42.4.8 NNI Optical Interface standardisation

Although recommendations G.707/8/9 have done an excellent job in standardising the logical signal presented at an NNI, this alone is not enough to ensure a Mid-Fibre Meet between equipment from two different manufacturers. G.957 recognises this problem and specifies the relevant physical parameters for a range of standard optical interfaces, at the preferred SDH rates of STM-1, STM-4 and STM-16. In addition, there is also an extension to the existing G.703 electrical interface specification to accommodate an electrical presentation of an STM-1 signal. Despite this, there is still no guarantee of anything beyond traffic path interworking, as the management channels that flow across the mid-fibre boundary may still be carrying information which is unintelligible to the network managers on the other side. This is an important area that the standards bodies are still addressing.

42.4.9 SDH network elements

Because traffic routing flexibility is one of the reasons for the existence of SDH, the simplest way of considering any SDH network element is as a group of transport termination functions (TTFs) surrounding a traffic path connectivity function (see Figure 42.21). The TTFs are essentially the conversion functions from the VC level to either the STM or plesiochronous signal levels, while the connectivity function allows VCs to be routed between the various TTFs. More than anything else, it is the size and flexibility

of the connectivity function that distinguishes one type of network element from another. For example, a crossconnect may have a large connectivity function, capable of simultaneously routing a large number of VCs of a given type between a large number of TTFs, with very few restrictions on this connectivity. This, of course, is consistent with the normal role of a crossconnect, as a major traffic routing node in a transport network, where electronically controllable traffic routing flexibility is its raison d'etre. At the other end of the scale come Line System Terminals (LTEs), which normally incorporate a multiplexer as well. The connectivity between tributaries and aggregate ports of such a multiplexer is normally hard wired, hence no flexibility whatsoever. Between these two extremes come drop and insert (Add/Drop) multiplexers, which attempt to strike a balance, that leads to adequate, rather than comprehensive routing flexibility, with an attendant reduction in equipment costs.

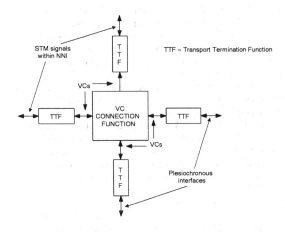

Figure 42.21 Generalised representation of the traffic paths through an SDH network element

All of the above mentioned types of network element normally assume that any interconnection will be based on optical fibres. It is, however, also possible to use other interconnection media, in particular radio transmission. The problem in using radio interconnection is that, unlike optical fibres, the available spectrum is finite, and in short supply. The liberal use of overhead capacity in SDH only exacerbates the already difficult problem of squeezing the traffic information into the existing arrangement of radio channel bandwidths. These problems are by no means insuperable, but they do tend to restrict radio interconnection of NNI signals to the lower end of the SDH range e.g. up to STM-2 at present. This inability to match the transmission capacity of optical fibres will progressively force radio based systems out of the core areas of transmission networks, and into the more peripheral areas. In particular, it is likely that radio based SDH equipment will be heavily used for access duties.

The reduction in cost that accompanies a network element with restricted connectivity results not only from simpler hardware, but also from simpler control software. This is somewhat surprising at first sight, as it has often been said that SDH does not really make economic sense without a large measure of software control over all the network element functionality and, in particular, that of routing flexibility. However, the complexity of even relatively simple SDH network elements leads to a situation where control of complete networks rapidly escalates unless some restrictions are put on the

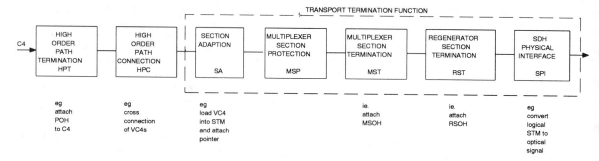

Figure 42.22 Fragment of an SDH network element showing how it is broken down into atomic functions acording to CCITT G.783

traffic routing complexity. In short, every additional piece of traffic routing flexibility is a potential network control headache.

The general problem of control of a whole SDH network, notwith-standing the traffic routing problem, is almost impossible if it is composed of network elements from different manufacturers, which do not have some form of common control interface. Before we can arrive at such a universal interface, we must first standardise, to a large extent, on the functions which each of the network elements actually perform. This is where the network element functional standards, CCITT G.781/2/3, come in. These are the recommendations which describe how the functionality of a network element can be decomposed into the basic 'atomic' elements of functionality, together with how such atomic functions may be combined and thereafter exchange both traffic and control information. (See Figure 42.22.)

The rules for combination of these atomic functions enable a variety of network elements to be synthesised, with differing traffic capacities and routing capabilities. Indeed, one of the current problems is the potentially large number of different ways a comformant network element can be constructed. It is rather difficult for software based control systems to cope with this variety and hence there are efforts in several standards fora (notably ETSI), to standardise on a more restricted range of network element functionalities. G.781/2/3 were created primarily to describe different types of drop and insert multiplexers, however, the general principles and indeed, much of the detail, are just as applicable to LTEs and large cross connects. Moreover, the formalism required to describe complete SDH networks was produced very much with this same functional decomposition in mind. We shall see, later, how these atomic functions may be paired between network elements on opposite sides of a network to produce a complete traffic path, that is sufficiently well defined for a computer to recognise.

42.5 Control and management

Control and management within any type of telecommunications network (not just an SDH one) can best be viewed in terms of a series of layers (See Figure 42.23). At the lowest level, there is internal control of an individual network element, which performs internal housekeeping functions and deals in alarm and control primitives. CCITT G.783 has rigorously defined a minimum set of control and alarm primitives for each of the SDH atomic functions, and these are the basis of all SDH management. However, beyond this CCITT G.784 describes how such primitive information should be processed and ordered to produce derived information such as error rates etc, which is stored in logs of defined duration, and

reported at set intervals, etc. At the lowest level, some of this information may look rather different to that specified in G.783/4 etc, however, the internal network element control system takes these and from them, synthesises the information that is required by the next level in the management hierarchy i.e. the element manager.

The element manager is a piece of software which can control many individual network elements (usually in the range 10-1000), but it can only control them as individual elements and does not have any view of the traffic relationships between them. Usually it is located remote from the elements it is controlling and more often than not, it runs on some form of workstation. The interface between the element manager and the network elements is an obvious area for standardisation, as without this there is little chance of a single element manager controlling network elements from more than one manufacturer. Despite the progress that has been made in rigorously describing the network element atomic functions, it has still proved very difficult to agree on a software description of them. The approach adopted in CCITT, ANSI, and ETSI has been to describe complete network elements as collections of 'objects' in line with the rules of 'object orientated' programming.

The idea is that an object is a software entity that has both attributes and behaviour. External stimulate (i.e. information, commands, etc.) trigger an object to behave in a certain way e.g. change its attributes, transmit information, commands etc. The claim is that a standardised object could be looked upon as the software equivalent of a hardware integrated circuit. One of the biggest areas of disagreement in generating an agreed standard set of SDH objects, is the questions of whether an object should represent a piece of

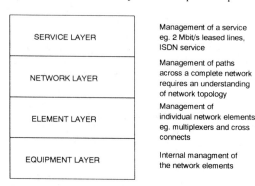

Figure 42.23 Network management layering for the control of telecoms networks and services

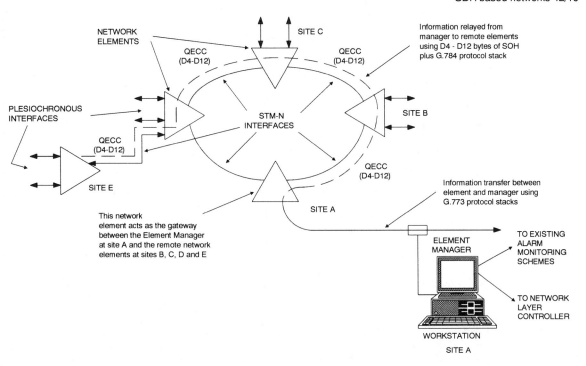

Figure 42.24 Control channels and protocols within a SDH entwork

functionality or whether an object should represent a (small) piece of hardware. Although CCITT G.783 functionally decomposes SDH equipment, its says almost nothing on the way such atomic functions are split or combined in any real hardware implementation. The current view within both CCITT and ETSI is that the set of objects (collectively known as the 'Information Model') should present both a functional and a physical view of the network element that they represent. ETSI, in particular, is making good progress in generating a model along these lines.

Not only is it necessary to have a standardised information model, so that the network element and element manager can understand one another, it is also necessary to have an agreed message set to go with it. Fortunately, this flows reasonably easily from the definition of the objects themselves. However, the existence of such a message set, then leads to the requirement for an agreed information protocol stack with which to transport it. For information transferred between a network element direct to its element manager, CCITT G.773 details several allowed protocol stacks, which split into two groups, those which have a full 7 layer structure and those which have a 'short stack', where layers 4, 5, and 6 are absent. Most observers favour the use of the heavier, but more flexible, seven layer protocol stacks for SDH networks, while the 'short' stacks are more appropriate for PDH equipment for which it is more difficult to justify the burden of the additional layers.

Not only are there defined protocol stacks for information transfer direct from element manager to network element, but there is also a defined protocol stack for information transfer between individual network elements. In general, the majority of information transfer between network elements is actually information arising from an element manager, which is being relayed by an intermediate network element to a more remote element. (See Figure 42.24). This flow of management information amongst network elements, ele-

ment managers and yet more managers at the network and service levels, gives rise to the concept of a Telecommunications Management Network (TMN).

The main recommendation concerning the TMN is CCITT M.30, which attempts to define a series of interfaces between different management entities in such a network. It is not confined purely to SDH networks, but SDH networks will probably be the first to implement an M.30 style TMN. (See Chapter 16.)

42.6 SDH based networks

An SDH based network can be viewed as the transmission bedrock which supports all other terrestrial telecommunications services. (See Figure 42.25.) As already mentioned, the main advantages of such a network are the ease and precision with which the available network bandwidth can be partitioned amongst the higher layer services, together with accurate monitoring of the quality of the transmission links. Despite this, the control and management of complete networks of the size operated by BT, France Telecom, or DBP is a difficult problem, which requires some degree of standardisation in the way such networks are functionally decomposed, in much the same way as the individual network elements have already been functionally decomposed into their atomic elements by CCITT G.783.

The basic idea behind the functional decomposition described in CCITT G.sna1 is that a transport network can be stratified into a number of layers. Each layer provides a service to the layer above it, and is, in turn, a client of the layer below it, in much the same way as the ISO seven layer information transfer model consists of layers which participate in client-server relationships with their vertical nearest neighbours. (See Figure 42.26.) This layering within

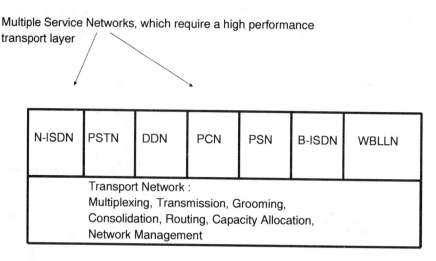

Figure 42.25 Managed transmission network; SDH network as a bearer for other services

an SDH network could be viewed as a subdivision of ISO layer 1. As an example of a non-SDH client-server relationship in a transport network, consider Figure 42.27, which shows a 64kbit/s circuit being a client of the 2Mbit/service layer i.e. the 2Mbit/s layer, which can be viewed as a 2Mbit/s network, transports the 64kbit/s circuit between its desired end points. In order to do this, the 2Mbit/s layer will probably call upon the services of the 8Mbit/s layer, and so on up to the 140Mbit/s layer. The SDH counterpart of this simple PDH

example is slightly more complicated in that the transport layers are divided between those concerned with end to end networking (i.e. the Path Layers) and those concerned with transport between each pair of SDH network elements along the route (i.e. the STM section layer). As an additional complication, there are two path layers, the lower order paths consisting of VC1s, VC2s or VC3s, and the higher order paths, which are VC4s in CEPT countries, but could also be VC3s. (See Figure 42.28.)

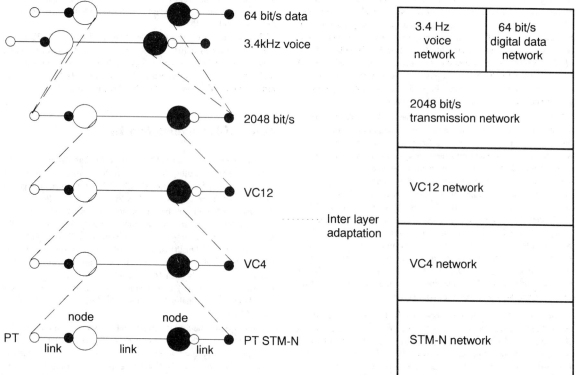

Figure 42.26 Layering and client server relationships between the layers of an SDH network

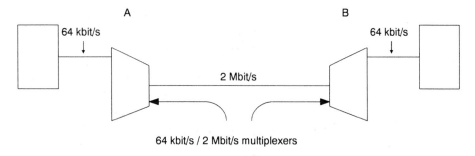

Figure 42.27   64kbit/s circuit making use of a 2Mbit/s service in order to get from A to B

Usually when a client layer makes use of a server, it is necessary to adapt the client signal to a form suitable for transport by the server layer. (See Figure 42.29.) Examples of this 'adaptation' function are the plesiochronous 'stuffing' which occurs when a 2Mbit/s channel is multiplexed into an 8Mbit/s one, or the progressive change in a VC12 pointer value to accommodate a small frequency mismatch with the VC4 into which it is being loaded. The adaptation function is only one of the network atomic functions that have been described in G.sna1, and it is indeed fortunate that G.sna1 has been developed in full recognition of the contents of G.782/783 because many of the equipment and network atomic functions are identical.

G.sna1, not only describes a series of vertical client-server relationships for an SDH transport network, it also gives a structure to each of the individual layers. Each layer can be viewed as a network in its own right, which can be partitioned into a series of subnetworks. (See Figure 42.30.) These subnetworks are connected together by 'link connections', and can, if necessary, be further subdivided into yet smaller subnetworks. The logical place to stop this process is where a whole subnetwork is completely contained within one network element. As an example consider a VC12 cross connect. The switching matrix (connectivity function) within this element could be considered as a subnetwork, which is capable of

making VC12 layer subnetwork connections from one port to another. (See Figure 42.31.)

To connect one of these VC12s to another cross connect, a link connection is now required, which will need to make use of the VC4 and STM layers. This concatenation of subnetwork and link connections across the VC12 path layer network begins and ends at the points where the VC12 is created and destroyed, namely the path termination points. It is at these points that the VC12 POH is added or removed, exposing only the C12 Synchronous Container. This same path termination function is recognised in both G.783 and G.sna1 and it is located immediately next to the adaptation function described above. On the assumption that the C12 in question is carrying a 2Mbit/s circuit, then the combination of adaptation functions, termination functions and the chain of subnetwork and link connections in the VC12 layer have succeeded in transporting this 2Mbit/s circuit between the two end points of a single 2Mbit/s link connection. (See Figure 42.31.) From this point, the above analysis can now be repeated in the 2Mbit/s layer, where the particular 2Mbit/s circuit cited above will probably be found to be serving as part of a link connection for a number of 64kbit/s circuit (see Figure 42.27).

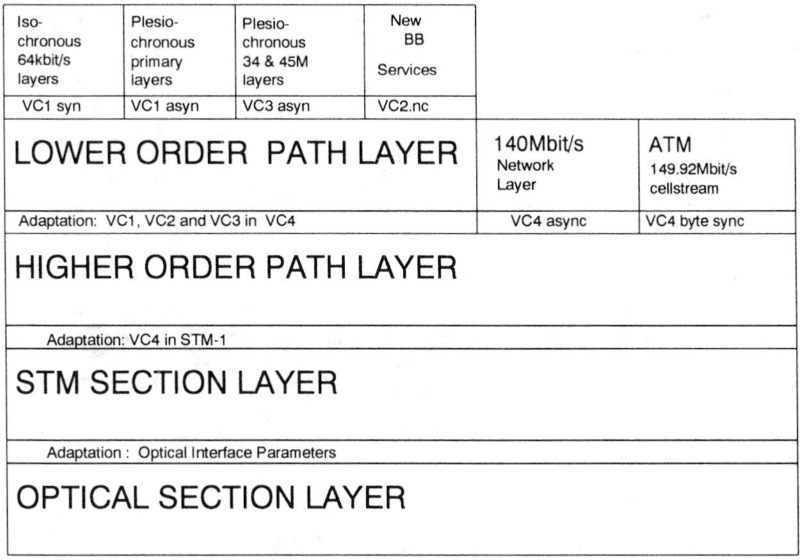

Iso-chronous 64kbit/s layers	Plesio-chronous primary layers	Plesio-chronous 34 & 45M layers	New BB Services		
VC1 syn	VC1 asyn	VC3 asyn	VC2.nc		
LOWER ORDER PATH LAYER			140Mbit/s Network Layer		ATM 149.92Mbit/s cellstream
Adaptation: VC1, VC2 and VC3 in VC4			VC4 async		VC4 byte sync
HIGHER ORDER PATH LAYER					
Adaptation: VC4 in STM-1					
STM SECTION LAYER					
Adaptation : Optical Interface Parameters					
OPTICAL SECTION LAYER					

Figure 42.28   Layering in an SDH transport network

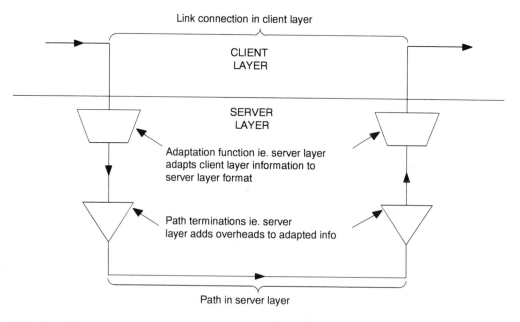

Figure 42.29   Handling a link connection in a client layer by a path in a server layer

This formal description of an SDH network opens up the prospect of real control and management of large networks consisting of network elements from several manufacturers. The pairing of path termination functions on opposite sides of a network, together with a similar operation on the same functions in the STM layer, allows a PTO to accurately monitor the service which the SDH network is delivering, and to pin-point those network elements responsible for any poor performance. Beyond that, the SDH network model greatly facilitates management of the all important traffic flexibility points i.e. those subnetworks which consist of an electronically controllable connectivity function.

42.6.1   SDH network topologies

Once again traffic routing flexibility, its control and physical distribution within an SDH network, is one of the most important

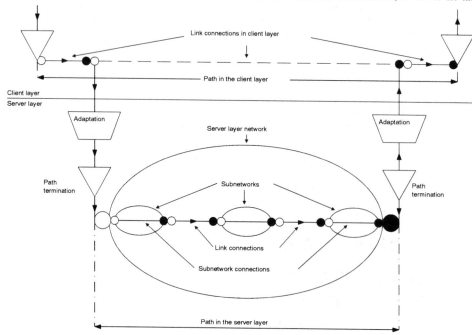

Figure 42.30   Partitioning of a transport layer network into a series of subnetworks

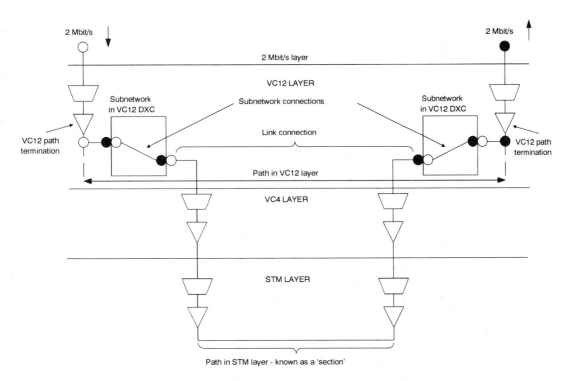

Figure 42.31   Use of two VC12 cross connects to produce a path within the VC12 layer

influences on the topologies proposed for the deployment of SDH equipment. The most obvious manifestations of this are the drop and insert ring topologies that are finding favour in the former junction areas of PTO networks. (See Figure 42.32.)

The idea behind a drop and insert ring is that the ring structure can give a high degree of protection against cable cuts etc. due to its potential for routing traffic either way round the ring. In fact, one of the biggest advantages, in control terms, of this topology is the limitation on the re-routeing possibilities for any traffic affected by a cable break. Anything more complicated than a simple clockwise/counter-clockwise routing decision requires up to date knowledge of a rather more extensive portion of an SDH network than just a simple ring. The nodes of such a ring are populated by drop and insert multiplexers which have a restricted traffic routing flexibility that is tailored to the requirements of a ring. This gives a relatively low cost ring implementation, which nevertheless, when viewed as

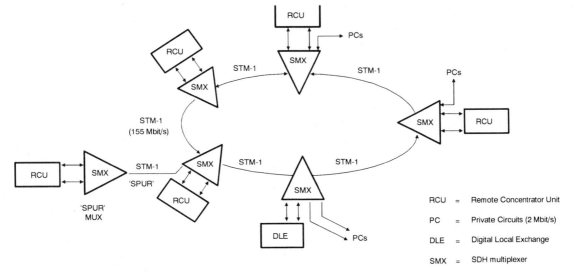

Figure 42.32   SDH multiplexers deployed in a drop and insert ring

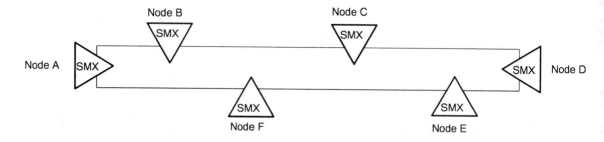

Figure 42.33 Drop and insert chain produced by 'flattening' a conventional drop and insert ring

a single entity, appears as a restricted form of a cross connect. The versatility of drop and insert rings also extends to drop and insert chains, which can be considered as a 'flattened' version of a conventional ring. (See Figure 42.33.) Beyond this, a ring can also be made from a chain of drop and insert multiplexers, whose ends have been joined by an SDH line system. The main problem with implementing this type of ring, at least in the junction area, is that the existing layout of cables and ducts usually takes the form of a star, which formerly linked the old analogue local exchanges to their district switching centre. In many cases, a partial physical ring can be created by a small extension of the existing cable pattern. This can be supplemented by creating a logical ring when existing cables are laid in a star arrangement, although this obviously affords less protection against cable breaks (See Figure 42.34.) Finally, it is sometimes possible to produce a physical ring by linking some of the ring nodes with microwave radio rather than optical fibre.

Outside of the former junction areas, i.e. within the transmission core of the average PTO network, the normal topology advocated is that of a mesh of cross connects, interconnected by point to point transmission systems. (See Figure 42.35.) For this application, the SDH transmission systems, like their PDH counterparts, require

almost no routing flexibility. This is more than compensated by the cross connects, which provide complete traffic routing flexibility at the VC4 and VC12 (and possibly other VCs as well), although not usually in the same network element. Used in this way, cross connects can be viewed as electronic replacements for the present day digital distribution frames. The benefits of this deployment of flexibility are alleged to be those of easier traffic path provisioning and a fast, efficient scheme for restoring failed paths which requires the absolute minimum of standby transmission capacity. This last benefit is heavily dependent on the control that is exercised over the cross connects, and here there are some potential problems.

The main problem is that of database integrity. With a network of meshed cross connects, when a transmission link fails, the path restoration action will usually involve re-routeing all the affected paths through several alternative cross connects. In order to do this efficiently the network control system must rapidly command simultaneous switching actions in all of these crossconnects, which usually implies that the control system has a pre-determined plan of action which is based on the spare bandwidth that is thought to be available on the relevant transmission links and cross connects. Unfortunately the integrity of the control systems database may

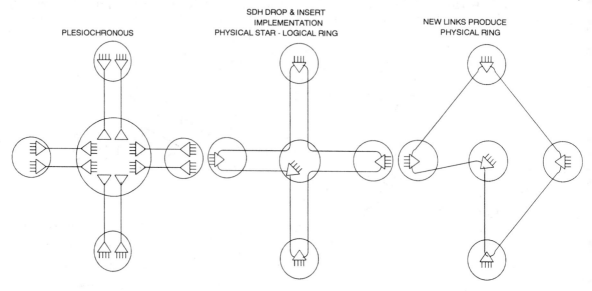

Figure 42.34 Comparison of topologies possible with PDH and SDH multiplexers

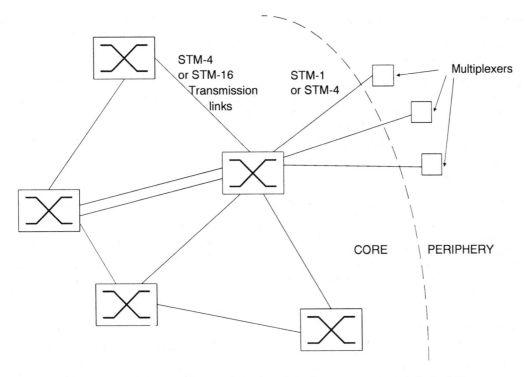

Figure 42.35 Example of core transmission network topology that relies on cross connects for flexibility

have been compromised because of other recent reconfiguration. This problem escalates rapidly as the number of cross connects in a network increases.

There are several potential solutions to this problem. One is to simply not use the cross connects for protection against transmission failures, and, instead rely on transmission systems having 1+1 or 1:N protection. In this case the cross connects are used solely for off-line management of the network's transmission capacity. This is often call 'Facilities Management' in North America. An alternative is to deploy the cross connects in a rather more bounded topology than the completely free mesh topology assumed above. A limiting case of this idea is to deploy them in a ring. The restriction on routing choices imposed by such a topology greatly eases the control problem, albeit with some significant increase in the standby line transmission capacity that must be available to allow a traffic re-route. Although the present day cost of such standby capacity is considerable, it has already been observed that raw point to point transmission capacity is the one thing that will continue to become cheaper, in real terms, for some time to come, hence this option may look increasingly attractive.

Finally, the most interesting possibility is to endow a network of cross connects with a signalling system that will allow it to dynamically set up and clear down paths, in much the same way as a PSTN sets up conventional 64kbit/s circuits. The idea is that the intelligence required for this type of operation resides, not in a single large network manager, but, like the PSTN, distributed throughout the whole network. This greatly reduces the data base integrity problem, and should operate quickly enough to meet the criteria for fast restoration of failed paths, as well as facilitating other operations such as rapid provision of bandwidth (i.e. bandwidth 'on demand') in response to requests from the client services of the SDH network.

42.6.2 Deployment strategies

There are three main strategies for the deployment of SDH equipment:

1. Synchronous islands.
2. 'Thin' overlay networks.
3. Ad hoc deployment dictated by traffic growth, etc.

Many PTOs are currently using the ad hoc approach and deploying the latest STM-16 (2.5 Gbit/s) transmission systems, not so much because they conform to the SDH standards, but because they offer higher transmission capacities than any available PDH systems. Even so, most PTOs which are doing this, are intending to eventually fill in the gaps between these ad hoc deployments so as to create an SDH overlay network.

The idea behind the 'thin overlay' strategy is to rapidly deploy a limited SDH capability across the whole of a PTO network so that a small nucleus of key business customers can be offered the benefits of SDH as soon as possible. This type of deployment is most appropriate to networks where the important communities of interest are geographically widely dispersed.

The synchronous 'island' deployment strategy assumes that the most important communities of interest are geographically concentrated, and that each one can start to benefit from SDH without necessarily having full SDH connectivity with similar communities of interest. The classic example here is that of the financial community in the City of London. With the passage of time, a synchronous island would normally increase in geographical size, so as to eventually coalesce with other islands. Long before this, they would probably be interconnected by an emerging SDH trunk network.

42.7 Impact of broadband standards

As an ISO layer 1 transport standard, intended for building the PTO's backbone transmission networks, SDH currently has no real rivals. The nearest thing to a competitor that has emerged so far is Asynchronous Transfer Mode (ATM), and its adoption was strongly favoured by several European PTOs. However, ATM, as with most of the other popular broadband standards comes under the heading of 'Fast Packet' technologies. As with all packet transfer techniques, it tends to be better at transporting bursts of traffic, rather than the largely constant traffic load presented by the PSTN. On top of this, ATM is a standard that is really aimed at the problem of rationalising the switching machines required for the complete range of telecom services, rather than producing a bedrock transport network. In theory, it is capable of doing this, but at present, commercial implementations of ATM switches are thought to be at least five years away. In the meantime, SDH equipment will be deployed to such an extent that it will be impossible to dislodge it from its position as the workhorse of all PTO transport networks. ATM switches, when they are introduced, will appear to the SDH network as yet one more client service which needs SDH transmission bandwidth allocated to it. As the operational problems of running a cell based service are progressively overcome, we can expect an increasingly proportion of the SDH transmission network capacity to be routed to these ATM switches.

Besides ATM, there are several other Fast Packet techniques that have been proposed, which are either already available, or promised soon. They are all aimed at satisfying the business communities requirements for wide area data transmission, and, in particular, the burgeoning requirement for LAN interconnect. In view of what was said in Section 42.1 about the needs of business customers driving PTOs to install SDH networks, it is essential to determine whether the introduction of these other techniques will render SDH superfluous.

42.7.1   Frame Relay

The current front runner in the Fast Packet standards is Frame Relay. This is actually a network access protocol which, like X.25, says nothing about the interfaces between internal nodes in the network i.e. it is only a UNI standard, and has no counterpart to the SDH NNI. The best way to view Frame Relay is as a supercharged version of X.25, which is designed to handle the high speed (i.e. up to 2Mbit/s and beyond) but bursty, LAN interconnect traffic that X.25 is far too slow for. The reason that a Frame Relay network can deliver much higher throughputs than an X.25 network is that it uses a very 'lightweight' protocol, which removes the majority of the X.25 processing burden from the network access nodes and, in all probability, in the internal nodes as well. In particular Frame Relay provides no end to end error recovery, but instead, leaves this function to the ISO transport layer protocols (layer 4), which are assumed to be installed in the customer's equipment, rather than the network access nodes. This makes a Frame Relay network heavily dependent on the quality, especially the error rate, of the underlying transport network, which is where SDH comes to the rescue. The high quality ISO layer 1 service provided by SDH is exactly what the lightweight layer 2 protocol of Frame Relay requires if it is to avoid excessive frame retransmissions from the CPE.

This symbiotic arrangement should, in theory, result in a peaceful coexistence, however, the issue is, as ever, clouded by that of tariffing. If a 2Mbit/s circuit, delivered by SDH, is tariffed sufficiently attractively, then, for many private networks, it may be cheaper to run multiple, point to point 2Mbit/s links, rather than

obtain the same connectivity from a Frame Relay network. However, experience to date with quasi Frame Relay networks in North America indicates that this will not be the case, and that Frame Relay and SDH will not compete directly, for business traffic.

42.7.2   Switched Multimegabit Data Service (SMDS)

Like Frame Relay, SMDS is another broadband wide area service aimed at achieving economies in transmission bandwidth by statistical multiplexing of bursty data traffic. Rather than being a standard in its own right, SMDS refers to a service which is delivered over a wide area network, which employs the DQDB standard for its access protocol. Originally it was targeted at rather higher bandwidths than Frame Relay i.e. 1.5Mbit/s to 45Mbit/s, but now, it too is being repositioned to serve the LAN interconnect market. SMDS encapsulates the customer's data in trains of fixed sized cells, which are then relayed, via the SMDS switches to their destinations. Like Frame Relay, SMDS needs a high quality layer 1 service, in order that the number of cell corruptions is kept to a minimum. Once again, there is a technical sybiosis between SMDS and SDH, and they will only be in direct conflict if there are inconsistencies in some tariff structures.

42.7.3   Fibre Distributed Data Interface (FDDI)

FDDI is a high speed LAN that was designed for private operators who were able to install their own cables. However, the extension of the original interface definitions to incorporate single mode, as well as multimode optical fibre has increased the maximum ring circumference to 100km. This potentially brings it into conflict with PTO provided MANs e.g. SMDS. This is even more likely now that there are proposed mappings of the full FDDI 125Mbit/s signal into a VC4, so that PTO transmission facilities can be used to bridge those spans where the private operator cannot run his own fibre. Unfortunately, there are some problems, relating to the maximum delay that an FDDI ring can withstand. As it is this minimum ring delay which limits the size of an FDDI ring, care must be taken in the routing of the VC4 in order that this extra delay does not significantly reduce the maximum ring size. In short, because of the self contained nature of the FDDI standard, together with its rather narrow targeting as a high-speed LAN, as opposed to MAN or WAN, we expect no competition at all between SDH and FDDI.

42.8   Future technologies

Equipment which implements the SDH standards will be strongly influenced by the capabilities and cost of the enabling technologies. This section reviews the impact on both equipment, and the standards themselves, of some of these developments.

42.8.1   Integrated circuits

The unrelenting trend to faster, smaller and cheaper traffic handling ICs (ASICs), obviously leads to cheaper network element hardware. This, in turn, will eventually lead to the introduction of SDH equipment onto the premises of business customers. The trend to higher functional integration will probably lead to changes in PTO premises design because of increased heat dissipation in a given volume of rack space.

42.8.2　Optical interfaces

Very low cost SDH optical interfaces are expected to produce the long awaited shift in PTO station cabling from coaxial copper to optical fibres. There are several advantages to optical interconnection e.g. relatively long range, no crosstalk, physically small calling volume. However, perhaps the biggest advantage is the future proofing which results from the fact that an optical interconnect cable can, within reasonable limits, carry any bit rate. Besides enabling the reuse of cables that would be difficult to reuse otherwise, it also reduces the problem of successive layers of interconnect cables physically preventing the withdrawal of the older, disused, cables that they are burying.

42.8.3　Optical amplifiers

Erbium doped fibre amplifier technology has made great strides in the last three years. By using such amplifiers at both ends of an optical link, it is possible to greatly increase the maximum distance between transmitter and receiver, with distances up to 300km being predicted for links that employ low loss optical fibre cables. (c.f. present day optical inks at 565Mbit/s which can typically span 40-70km). This great increase in span capability holds out the prospect of interconnecting the majority of large centres of population in Europe by unrepeatered line systems i.e. the line systems consist of two LTEs plus cable, without any intervening simple repeaters. (Drop and insert repeaters are a different case, as they are deployed to drop and insert traffic, rather than solely to boost the amplitude of the optical signals). The resulting extinction of conventional line system repeaters means that the SDH RSOH in the STMs will eventually become redundant for terrestrial systems.

In addition to this, there is also the future proofing that results from replacing a conventional, electronically regenerating repeater, with a repeater that merely amplifies the transiting optical signals. Optical amplifiers are largely bit rate independent, hence it should be possible to upgrade the capacity of a line system by merely changing the LTEs, and not the repeaters. This idea is particularly exciting for undersea line systems where a major part of the total system cost lies in the repeaters. Up till now, these have always been constrained to operate at a fixed bit rate.

42.8.4　Optical switching

The use of optical switching, together with various forms of Wavelength Division Multiplexing (WDM), will lead to a requirement for yet another layer in the SDH hierarchy beyond the STM section layer. Real high speed optical switching, together with wavelength

conversion is still some way in the future, hence there is no pressure to extend SDH at present.

42.8.5　Memory and processing power

As soon as it becomes economically feasible, more memory and processing power will be installed in individual SDH network elements. The use of this capability to support ever larger blocks of software will results in the average software download action transferring ever more bytes, thus putting a strain on the Embedded Communication Channels (ECCs) that are built into the STM S0Hs. There is also the chance that larger quantities of more sophisticated element control software will result in more management traffic between network elements and between elements and their controllers, further increasing the load on the existing ECCs. Thus, at some point in the future is very likely that the SDH standards will have to be altered to expand the capacity of the ECCs beyond their current rates of 192 and 576kbit/s.

42.9　Conclusion

SDH is here to stay as the dominant public network transmission standard of this decade. However, the effects of the full range of SDH standards will probably be felt over a much wider area of telecommunications, because of their general applicability. For example the mere existence of the SDH optical interface specifications will probably lead to their use in a variety of non-SDH applications, simply because there is a dearth of competing standards. Another example is that of the SDH network recommendations, G.SNA1/2, which, with relatively little modification, are applicable to a wide variety of non-SDH networks, in particular, plesiochronous networks.

42.10　References

Bellamy, John (1991) *Digital Telephony*, 2nd Edition, Wiley, ISBN 0 471 62056 4.

Flood, J.E. and Cockrane, P. (eds.)(1991) *Transmission Systems*, Peter Peregrinus, ISBN 0 86341 148 7.

Ferguson, S. (1991) A common demnominator for Broadband, *Telecommunications*, August.

Mathews, M.S. and Newbombe, P.J. (1991) The Synchronous Digital Hierarchy, *IEE Review*, May and June.

Sexton, M.J. (1990) New directions in Transport Networks, *Telecommunications*, October.

43

Signalling systems

Samuel Welch
OBE MSc (Eng.) CEng FIEE
Telecommunications Consultant
Formerly Head of Signalling, BT.

Contents

43.1 Analogue network signalling

The basic signalling on subscriber lines comprises the following:

1. Supervisory, the on-hook, off-hook conditions of the subscribers.
2. Address information from the caller which may be decadic dialled pulses or push-button signals.

These signalling functions are transferred over the switched network by signalling systems. Call processing can be performed by the above two functions. A further function 'operational' is necessary to enable the best use to be made of the network and to cater for system and operating organisation facilities.

The type of switching equipment, direct control or common control, and the type of transmission equipment have significant influence on the type of signalling system.

43.1.1 Type of switching system

Direct control switching systems, e.g. step-by-step, do not allow for separation of the supervisory and address signalling functions. The dialled address positions the switches directly, the numbering scheme controlling the routing of call connections. The supervisory and address signalling functions are combined in the network line signalling systems. The signalling limit tends to be limited by the permissible decadic address pulse distortion.

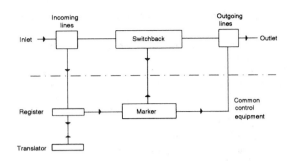

Figure 43.1 Generalised principle of common control switching

In common control switching (Figure 43.1), the common control equipment (register, translator, marker) deals with the call connection set-up through the switchblock, being released from a call on connection establishment to deal with other call connections. The marker controls the switching. The incoming line is the incoming mark at the switchblock. Address information inputs the register which refers to the translator. The resulting translation establishes the outgoing mark identifying the outgoing line. The marker switches the two marks together through the switchblock. The translation facility permits automatic alternative routing.

Common control switching permits separation of the supervisory (line) and address (selection) signalling functions over the network (Figure 43.2).

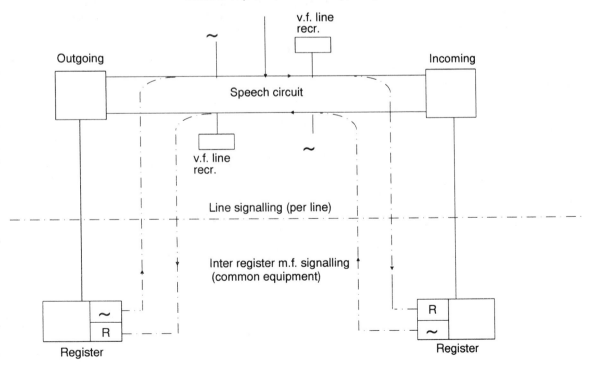

Figure 43.2 Line and interregister signalling

43.1.2 Influence of type of transmission system

Analogue network transmission plant varies in type: audio, FDM, point-to-point PCM. As analogue network signalling is on the call speech path, the type of transmission plant has influence on the signalling method.

A.C. signalling within the voice range (300Hz to 3400Hz) can be applied to any type of transmission media, but this application rationalisation is not economic since supervisory line signalling systems are equipped per line. Line signalling is of type (d.c., v.f. etc.) according to the type of line transmission.

A connection switched through an analogue exchange is supervised. A supervisory unit is equipped per line switched for this purpose. The unit incorporates a transmission bridge and detects supervisory signal conditions on the calling and called sides independently. Line units associated with external lines enable electrically independent signal conditions to be used in the exchanges and those on the external lines. The supervisory unit is then often combined with such line units.

43.1.3 D.C. line signalling

43.1.3.1 Short-haul d.c. line signalling systems

There are a number of different forms (Welch, 1979): loop disconnect d.c., loop reverse battery, single wire d.c., high/low resistance d.c., battery and earth pulsing. Loop disconnect d.c. signalling on 2-wire lines is the simplest and most widely used.

The basic signal repertoire is:

1. Forward; seizure, address information (when direct control switching), clear forward.
2. Backward; answer, clear back.

Figure 43.3 shows the principle of loop disconnect d.c. line signalling. Its operation is as follows:

1. Seizure. Relay A at A operates to the caller's off-hook loop.
2. Address. (Assuming direct control switching). Relay A at A responds to the caller's dialled pulses. When switched through exchange A, contact A1 loops the line to operate relay A at B. A1 loop disconnects the line, so transmitting the remaining dialled pulses to relay A at B.
3. Answer. Relay D at B operates to the called subscriber's off-hook loop. D1 and D2 reverse the line d.c. polarity to operate the rectified relay D at A (or a polarised relay as in the loop reverse battery d.c. system).
4. Clear back. The called subscriber's on-hook disconnect releases relay D at B, contacts D1 and D2 restoring releases relay D at A.
5. Clear forward. The caller's on-hook disconnect releases relay A at A. A1 releases relay A at B (assuming the more usual calling party release).

With common control switching, address signalling is inter-register and would not be conveyed by the line signalling system.

43.1.3.2 Long distance d.c. line signalling (LDDC)

LDDC is applied on lines beyond the limits of short-haul d.c. signalling when a metallic circuit is available (Welch, 1979). The phantom of the 4-wire circuit is used for signalling. The method extends the signalling limit by the use of sensitive polarised relays and the decadic address pulsing limit by a more efficient pulsing technique than loop disconnect.

With loop disconnect pulsing, the send end impedance varies during the decadic pulsing process (substantially zero on pulse make and infinite on pulse break). This variation results in asymme-

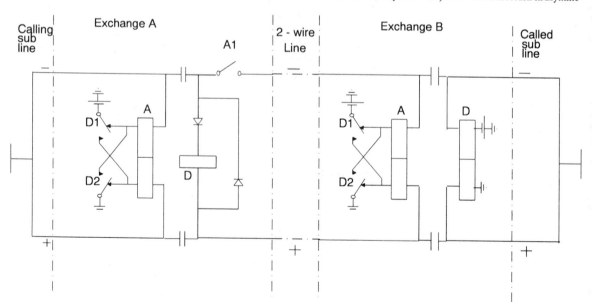

Figure 43.3 Principle of loop disconnect d.c. signalling

tric waveforms and thus to decadic pulse distortion on repetition. Further, the single current pulsing receive relay, with fixed operate and release current values, gives varying pulse distortion when operating on asymmetric waveforms.

LDDC necessitates symmetrical pulsing waveforms. To achieve this:

1. The send end impedance is equal during the pulse make and break periods.
2. The pulsing battery is at the send end (it is at the receive end in short-haul).
3. The polarised receive relay operates in one direction for the make, and in the other for the break pulses.

The above requires the provision of both outgoing and incoming line signalling terminals. Both terminals incorporate the transmission bridge.

There are different designs of LDDC systems. The use of polarised relays for signalling sensitivity and for bi-directional operation to minimise decadic address pulsing distortion is a common principle.

43.1.4   A.C. line signalling

43.1.4.1   *Low frequency a.c. signalling*

This uses a below the speech band signalling frequency. Signalling imitation by speech does not arise. Typical frequencies are 25, 50, 80, 135, 150 or 200Hz. D.C. signals are converted to a.c. for transmission, these being converted to d.c. at the distant end. The system may be applied to metallic circuits above the range of short-haul d.c., and to circuits isolated for d.c. when d.c. signalling is not possible. The more usual application is on 2-wire circuits, the

signals usually being pulsed since only one transmission path is available. The technique has declined in importance.

43.1.4.2   *Voice frequency (v.f.) line signalling*

The signalling frequency is inband, within the speech range of 300Hz to 3400Hz of f.d.m. transmission. The system is completely flexible in that it can operate on any circuit affording speech transmission. The signals are amplified by transmission system amplifiers. 4-wire operation is the more usual, the forward and backward signalling paths being separate, the duplex signalling being achieved by two simplex signalling paths (Figure 43.4).

In 4-wire operation, the v.f. receivers are permanently associated with the respective speech paths. As speech may contain the signalling frequency, the system is subject to signal imitation by speech and must incorporate features to safeguard against this.

A buffer amplifier of unit gain forward and some 60dB loss in the reverse direction protects the signal receiver from near-end interference from the switching equipment. The signalling is usually link-by-link on multi-link connections and an arrangement of line splits adopted to isolate the v.f. signal to the particular link. Signalling during speech is inadmissible.

Protection against signal imitation (false line splits or false signalling) relies on exploiting differences between speech and signal currents, e.g.:

1. Adoption of a signal frequency which is less liable to exist, or persist, and has less energy than other frequencies in speech. This indicates a reasonably high signal frequency, typically, U.K. 2280Hz, N. America 2600Hz.
2. Speech currents containing the signal frequency usually have other frequencies. The signal receiver has two elements:

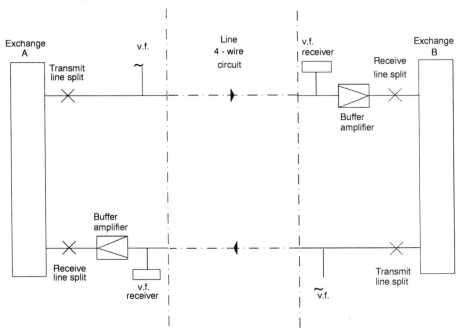

Figure43.4   General arrangement of v.f. line signalling system

(a) tuned to the signal frequency, and (b) responsive to other frequencies to oppose receiver operation to (a).

3. Signals made longer than the normal persistence of the signal frequency occurring in speech. At least 40ms longer for important signals such as release.

4. Signals of two frequencies compounded are less liable to occur, and persist, in speech than one frequency. 2 v.f. signalling systems are known, but 1 v.f. systems are more usual.

The v.f. signals may be continuous or pulse. Pulse signals of different lengths permit a greater signal repertoire. A continuous signal requires a continuous response to cease it.

43.1.4.3   *Outband signalling*

This is a.c. signalling within a 4kHz channel of FDM transmission. The channel bandwidth is divided into a speech channel (300Hz to 3400Hz) and a signalling channel by filtration. One frequency only is used, located approximately midway between two adjacent 4kHz channels. The forward and backward signalling paths are separate on the 4-wire circuit, the duplex signalling being achieved by the two simplex signalling paths. Signalling frequency 3700, 3825, or 3850Hz is typical; the CCITT recommends 3825Hz. E-lead and M-lead control applies for outband signalling.

Unlike inband v.f. signalling, outband signalling:

1. Is not subject to signal imitation by speech or other interference.

2. Eliminates the line splits.

3. Permits signalling during speech (e.g. meter pulse transmission).

On the other hand v.f. signalling can be applied to any type of transmission media, whereas outband signalling can only be applied to FDM channel circuits.

As outband signalling is independent of speech, there is virtually complete freedom in the choice of signalling mode with simple arrangements. The signalling may be:

1. 2-state continuous tone-on idle (off during speech).

2. Tone-off idle (on during speech), which however tends to overload the transmission system.

3. Semi-continuous, tone-off idle and off during speech (not preferred).

4. Pulse.

With the 2-state continuous signalling mode in each direction, outband signalling enables the basic loop d.c. signalling condition to be simulated far more easily compared with inband v.f. signall-

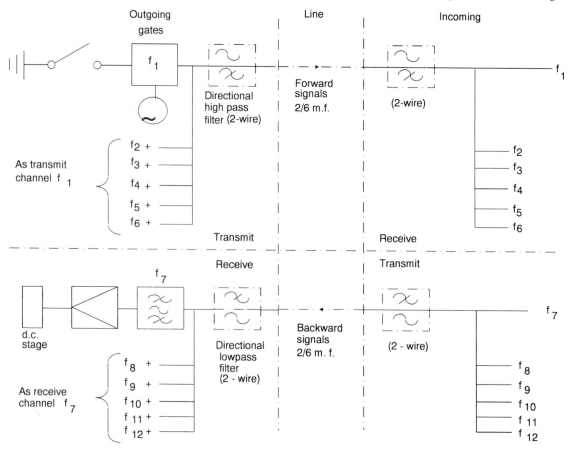

Figure 43.5   General arrangement of interregister i.f. signalling system

ing, making for much simpler signalling terminals. For the general application, tone-on idle (off during speech) is preferred.

43.1.5 PCM signalling

Applied when a PCM system is applied point-to-point in an analogue network. The CCITT specifies for two PCM systems: 30-channel (32 time slots) and 24-channel (24 time slots).

43.1.5.1 *30-channel PCM*

Time slot 16 is used for signalling for the 30 speech channels in each direction. A 16-frame multiframe technique gives 16 (0 to 15) appearances of time slot 16. The 8 bits of time slot 16 of frames 1 to 15 of the multiframe are divided into two groups of 4 bits each. Thus, in every 2ms (the multiframe time) 4 out-slot signalling bits are available for each speech channel. The coding gives 15 signal possibilities for each speech channel (code pattern 0000 is not used). This is ample for line signalling requirement. Should inband interregister m.f. signalling apply, the PCM system deals with this as for speech.

The logic behind the approach was that time slot 16 would be the 64kbit/s bearer for common channel signalling in the future integrated digital networks. The PCM system would be retained in service, but with signalling change.

43.1.5.2 *24-channel PCM*

This is the N. American system. In the pioneer D1 version, bit 8 of the octet in each time slot is used for in-slot signalling, the speech bits being reduced to 7. This only gives two signal conditions (0000 --- and 1111 ---) in each direction, a very limited repertoire.

The later D2 version adopts a 12-frame multiframe. Bit 8 of the time slots in every sixth frame (called signalling frames) is used for signalling, giving two in-slot signalling bits per time slot. This slows the signalling relative to D1, reduces the speech bits in the signalling frame time slots to 7, but increases the signal repertoire.

43.1.5.3 *Interregister signalling*

Applied with common control switching, the signalling terminals being associated with the registers (CCITT, 1988a; Miller, 1971). The system deals primarily with address signalling and is separate from line signalling systems (Figure 43.2).

The address signalling may be decadic d.c. pulsing, but is more usually 2-out-of-6 multifrequency (2/6mf), giving potential for 15 signals in each direction (Figure 43.5). The signalling is non-decadic, the 2/6mf combination giving the address digit value. This contributes to fast signalling. On 2-wire lines, the two simplex signalling paths are obtained by filtered bandwidth separation.

Subscriber and system facilities often require network signalling. The increased signal repertoire of 2/6mf compared with decadic interregister signalling enables the network to be exploited for facilities.

The 2/6mf signals may be pulse or continuous (compelled). In compelled, a continuous acknowledgement backward signal ceases the forward information signal, which cessation ceases the acknowledgement.

A number of different detail 2/6mf signalling systems exist, but are the same in principle. The CCITT R2 system is based on:

1. Continuous compelled signalling.
2. Forward signals 120Hz spaced in the band 1380Hz to 1980Hz, backward signals 120Hz spaced in the band 1140Hz to 540Hz.
3. To increase the signal repertoire if required, both the forward and backward 2/6 frequency combinations have primary and secondary meanings by a shift condition.

43.2 Common channel signalling

Stored programme control (s.p.c.) of switching prompted a reappraisal of the network signalling technique. Processor control makes possible the concentration of signalling logic for a large number of traffic circuits. With s.p.c. it is inefficient for the processor, which works in the digital mode, to deal with on-traffic-circuit analogue signalling. A much more efficient way of transferring information between s.p.c. exchanges is to provide a bi-directional high speed data link between the two processors over which they transfer signals in digital form by coded bit fields. A group of traffic circuits (many hundreds) would thus share a common channel signalling (c.c.s.) link. All c.c.s. signalling is link-by-link.

C.c.s. gives rise to the following requirements which do not arise with signalling on traffic circuit systems:

1. High order error rate performance.
2. Signalling backup to maintain service on failure or unacceptable performance.
3. Assurance of traffic circuit continuity as, unlike on-traffic-circuit signalling, c.c.s. does not establish traffic path integrity.
4. Circuit label included in the signal messages to give traffic circuit identity.

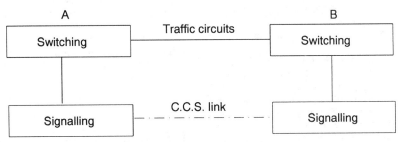

Figure 43.6 Example of associated c.c.s. between A and B

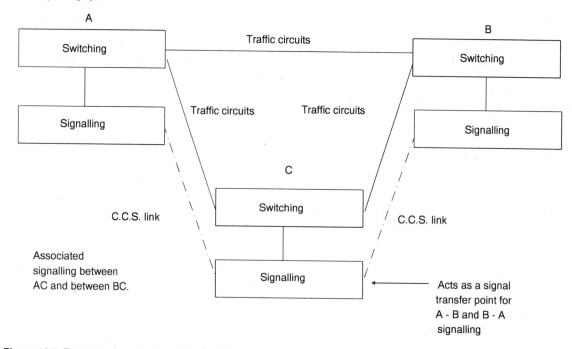

Figure 43.7 Example of quasi-associated signalling between A and B and between B and A

C.C.S. may be associated or quasi-associated signalling. In associated (Figure 43.6) the c.c.s. link is between the same locations as the traffic circuits served.

In Figure 43.7, associated signalling applies AC and CB. The signalling for traffic circuits AB is routed ACB (and BCA) in the quasi-associated mode, C being a signal transfer point. Should associated c.c.s. be equipped AB, on failure of any one of the associated signalling links AB, AC or BC, backup quasi-associated signalling ACB, ABC or BAC may apply to maintain service; C, B or A acting as signal transfer points.

43.2.1 CCITT No.6 c.c.s. system

This was the pioneer c.c.s. system (Welch, 1979; CCITT, 1988; Dahlbom, 1972). Its main features are:

1. Signalling bit rates 2.4kbit/s (analogue link), 4kbit/s and 56kbit/s (digital link). Other rates as required.
2. Error control; error detection by redundant coding and error correction by retransmission.
3. Signal units (SUs) 28 bits each of which the last 8 bits are error check bits.
4. SUs grouped into blocks of 12, the 12th and last SU of each block being an acknowledgement, i.e. the number of the block in the other direction being acknowledged and the error control acknowledgements, positive that the relevant SU has been received error free; negative indicating error detected and thus a request for a re-transmission of that SU.
5. Blocks are numbered sequentially, but individual message SUs in the block are not, being identified by their position in the block.

The later requirement for ISDN indicated the need for a more advanced c.c.s. system than No.6. This resulted in the CCITT No.7 c.c.s. system (see Section 43.3.1.)

43.3 Digital network signalling

Digital transmission and s.p.c. digital switching systems in telephone networks form Integrated Digital Networks (IDN). The logical evolution of IDN is to Integrated Services Digital Networks (ISDN). This is achieved by extending the IDN to the user by providing Integrated Digital Access (IDA). Present ISDN is narrowband (N-ISDN), based on the 64kbit/s channel capacity of the digital networks. Figure 43.8 identifies the signalling requirements for N-ISDN.

43.3.1 CCITT No.7 inter-exchange c.c.s. system

The pioneer CCITT No.6 c.c.s. system was produced primarily for the analogue environment, the digital versions being produced by subsequent study, but retained the basic features of the analogue system (Welch, 1979). In the result, No.6 has limitations for ISDN. The No.7 system is optimised for the ISDN. The CCITT No.7 international specification is framed as a common vehicle, admitting variants for national application. The signalling bit rate is 64kbit/s time slot 16 30-channel p.c.m. Figure 43.9 shows the No.7 general arrangement.

43.3.1.1 User parts

No.7 adopts a functional concept (Figure 43.9), allowing change to a function without significant impact on others (CCITT, 1988c). User parts (telephony TUP, data DUP, etc.) are service dependent parts of the signalling system controlling message requirements for

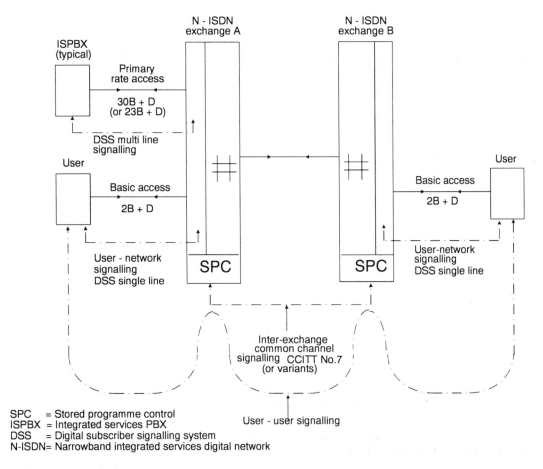

Figure 43.8 N-ISDN signalling requirements

particular services. This allows system evolution for additional services by additional User Parts, permitting the s.p.c. processor to be a common utility from the signalling aspect. Appropriate coding of a bit field in the signal messages indicate the service.

43.3.1.2 *No.7 formatting principles*

The signal messages are HDLC octet byte variable bit length signal units (SUs) with opening and closing flag delimiters coded 01111110 (CCITT, 1988d). The circuit label includes the originating and destination exchanges point codes, plus the circuit identification of the traffic circuit directly connecting the originating and destination points.

H0 codings identify the various signal groups (address signals, call supervision signals, etc.). H1 codings identify particular signal messages in a relevant H0 group; e.g. answer signal (H1 coding) in the call supervision group (H0 coding).

43.3.1.3 *No.7 error control*

The basic error control is error detection by redundant coding (CRC) and error correction by re-transmission (CCITT, 1988e). This requires positive and negative acknowledgement signals to be returned from the receive end. The former clears the signal message from the retransmission store at the transmit end on correct receipt; the latter causes the signal message and all other signal messages which may be in the retransmission store to be retransmitted. The signal messages are sequence numbered.

Idle (fill-in) SUs are transmitted when no message SUs are available for transmission. Idle SUs, not deposited in the re-transmission store and not retransmitted on error detected, are CRC error checked; this being a form of preventative maintenance.

A variant of the above basic error control is adopted for long propagation time signalling links (e.g. satellite). In this case the whole content of the retransmission store is retransmitted repeatedly when there are no new signal messages to be sent (so called preventive cyclic retransmission). This is a form of forward error correction.

Receive end monitors measure the error rate, automatic changeover to the backup signalling facility being initiated on unacceptable performance. The backup may be associated or quasi-associated signalling. Figure 43.10 shows a typical associated signalling backup. The up-to-four signalling links, but at least two, are signalling load shared. Assuming a four link signalling module, in normal operation each signalling link serves, typically, 1000 traffic circuits. In extreme error conditions the one remaining c.c.s. link carries the total signalling load for 4000 traffic circuits.

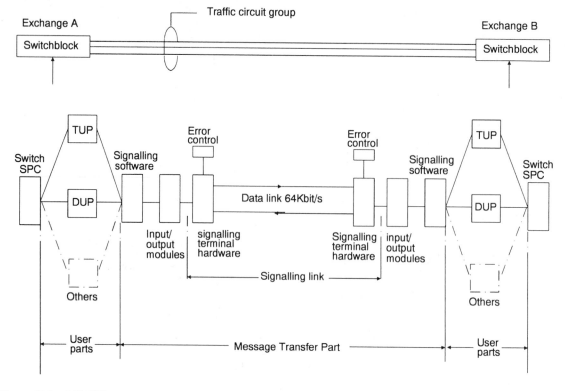

Figure 43.9 CCITT No. 7 c.c.s. system generalised arrangement

The polynomial for the error check is given by expression 43.1. The CRC (sometimes called FCS, frame check sequence) is a 16 bit field.

$$x^{16} + x^{12} + x^5 + 1 \qquad (43.1)$$

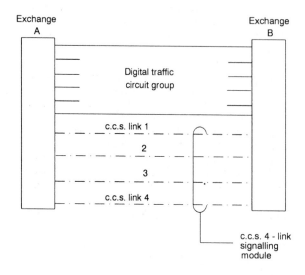

Figure 43.10 Common channel signalling module principle

43.3.2 User-network signalling

Digital Subscriber Signalling No.1 (DSS 1 is the CCITT name for the N-ISDN access protocols.

In N-ISDN, the network is extended down to the user's location, terminating in a Network Termination (NT). The NT forms the interface between the user's Terminal Equipment (TE) signalling and the network signalling and performs the signalling conversion. The CCITT regulates for a concept of S and T reference points at the interface (CCITT, 1988f).

The main types of user-network capabilities recommended by the CCITT are (CCITT, 1988g):

1. Basic access 2B + D.
2. Primary rate access 30B + D (30-channel PCM networks) or 23B + D (24-channel PCM networks).

B is a 64kbit/s traffic channel; D the signalling channel (16kbit/s in basic access, 64kbit/s in primary rate access).

43.3.2.1 *Basic access signalling*

Information TE-NT and NT-TE is transferred in 48 bit 250 microsecond frames in each direction (CCITT, 1988h; CCITT, 1988i). Each frame contains four traffic octets (two B1 and 2 B2), four outslot D signalling bits giving the 16kbit/s signalling channel, plus other information. 4-wire operation applies on a passive bus.

The signalling in the two directions NT-ISDN exchange, which may be on a 2-wire user access line, adopts the HDLC protocol with opening and closing flag delimiters and error check by a CRC bit field.

A command and response technique is recommended, a command signal message being discarded if checked as error. The command signal is transmitted continuously within a certain time period and ceased by receipt of an error free response. CCITT, 1988j gives the detail of the various signal messages.

43.3.2.2   *Primary rate access signalling*

Here, the ISPEX (or LAN etc.) incorporates the NT function, the access being 4-wire to the N-ISDN exchange. The D signalling channel is 64kbit/s time slot 16 in 30-channel PCM (time slot 24 in 24-channel PCM). Common channel signalling is adopted, the system serving the 30 B traffic channels (23 B in 24-channel PCM). The signal messages, CRC checked, are in sequence numbered HDLC frames delimited by opening and closing flags. Frames may be retransmitted continuously until an error free acknowledgement of correct reception is received from the other end of the access link.

CCITT, 1988k, gives the detail of the various signal messages.

43.3.3   User-to-user signalling

This facility may be used to exchange information between two N-ISDN users, the information transferred being, for example, data or keypad/display. The user-to-user signalling may be performed:

1. Over the circuit switched B traffic path connection between the two users.
2. Over an end-to-end signalling connection between the two users (Figure 43.8).

The user-to-user information is carried transparently, and is not interpreted, by the network.

The network is informed by the calling user that the user-to-user signalling facility is a requirement. This requirement is included in the call set-up message from the caller.

43.4   References

CCITT (1988a) *Specifications of signalling system R2*, Blue Book Vol.VI Fasc. VI.4, Recomms. Q.350 – Q.368, ITU, Geneva.

CCITT (1988b) *Specifications of signalling system No.6*, Blue Book Vol.VI, Fasc. VI.3, Recomms. Q.251 – Q.300, ITU, Geneva.

CCITT (1988c) *Introduction to CCITT signalling system No.7*, Blue Book Vol. VI. Fasc. VI.7, Recomms. Q.700, ITU, Geneva.

CCITT (1988d) *No.7 functions and codes of the signal unit fields*, Recomms. Q.703, item 2.3.

CCITT (1988e) *No.7 error control*, Recomms. Q.703 items 4-6.

CCITT (1988f) *ISDN user-network interface — reference configurations*, Blue Book, Vol.111 Fasc. 111.8, Recomms. I. 411, ITU, Geneva.

CCITT (1988g) *ISDN user-network interfaces, — interface structures and access capabilities*, Recomms. I. 412.

CCITT (1988h) *Basic user-network interface*, Recomms. I. 430.

CCITT (1988i) *Primary rate user-network interface*, Recomms. I. 431.

CCITT (1988j) *Digital access signalling system, data link layer*, Blue Book, Vol. VI Fasc. VI.10, Recomms. Q921, ITU, Geneva.

CCITT (1988k) *Digital access signalling system, network layer*, Recomms. Q931.

Dahlbom, C.A. (1972) Common channel signalling, — a new flexible interoffice signalling technique, *IEEE International Switching Symposium Record*, Boston, U.S.A.

Miller, C.B. and Murray, W.J. (1971) Trunk transit network signalling systems — multifrequency interregister signalling, *Post Off. Electr. Eng. J.*, **63** Pt.1. 43-48.

Welch, S. (1979) *Signalling in Telecommunications Networks*, IEE Telecommunications Series 6, Peter Peregrinus Ltd., London.

44

The Integrated Services Digital Network

Richard A Boulter
BSc (Hons) CEng FIEE
BT

Contents

44.1   Introduction

The main features of any network can be categorised into the transmission, switching, signalling and control capabilities of the network. All three of these areas in the Public Switched Telephone Network have evolved in different stages and at different rates. However, they have evolved in such a manner as to enable them to converge towards an Integrated Services Digital Network (ISDN) at minimal cost.

Until fairly recently the whole of the Public Switched Telephone Network (PSTN) was based upon analogue transmission and switching techniques. The telephone converts the acoustic waves of the speaker into an electrical signal occupying a bandwidth of the order of 4kHz (300Hz to 3400Hz). This is transmitted over the telephone network in this form to a remote telephone which then reconverts the electrical signals back to acoustic waves. The electrical signals are carried over a copper pair in the local network to a switching node.

Switching at the local exchange used space division techniques, originally Strowger and later crossbar and reed relay, on the baseband signal in order to concentrate traffic onto junction routes to main network switching centres which were again of the space switching type. Trunk routes then interconnected these main network switching centres and it is on these high capacity routes that we first saw the introduction of Frequency Division Multiplexing (FDM) techniques which required separate go and return channels.

During the late 60's and early 70's digital techniques began to emerge to replace the analogue techniques. First we saw the introduction of digital transmission to carry the analogue telephony signal. The 4kHz analogue signal is sampled at 8kHz and the resulting samples quantised into 256 levels according to the A law logarithmic code and encoded into 8 bit bytes to produce a rate of 64kbit/s. Thirty of these channels are then assembled, along with a 64kbit/s signalling channel and a 64kbit/s framing channel, into a 2048kbit/s system. Digital transmission has gradually become more cost effective to such an extent that a higher order TDM structure has been established at rates up to and above 565Mbit/s and it is now the normal method of provision.

In the same way that technology had made the use of digital techniques in the transmission field more attractive, so digital exchanges became cheaper to implement and maintain. These digital exchanges are designed to handle the 64kbit/s transmission channels transparently using both space and time division digital switches. These digital main network exchanges together with the digital transmission form what is known as the Integrated Digital Network (IDN). In the U.K. the first digital exchanges were put into the main network in 1980 and now all the main network exchanges are digital and fully interconnected by digital transmission routes and by the middle of 1991 half of the local exchanges were digital.

The introduction of digital transmission and digital exchanges was complemented by the introduction of common channel message based signalling systems, where messages relating to different connections are statistically interleaved on a common channel. CCITT signalling system No 7 is the system defined for use between switching nodes.

The conversion from the analogue signal produced by the standard telephone to a digital signal occupying 64kbit/s is now occurring at the front of the local exchange. Therefore connections across the main network between local exchanges are able to provide:

1.   A completely transparent 64kbit/s channel.
2.   A powerful digital signalling capability.
3.   The flexibility provided by stored program control exchanges.

These facilities have been provided in order to support telephony in the most economical way possible. They have, however, set the scene for the development of what has become known as the ISDN, Integrated Services Digital Network.

44.2   International standards for ISDN

The principles guiding the evolution of the public telephone network from the analogue to the digital environment were established within CCITT in the 1970's. However towards the end of this decade CCITT recognised the high level of interest in evolving this network further to establish the concept of an Integrated Services Digital Network (ISDN). An initial series of recommendations, the I-Series, were first agreed and published at the end of the 1980- 84 plenary period. These were further enhanced during the 1984-88 plenary period resulting in a full set of recommendations being published in the Blue Book and during this plenary period further enhancements have been made and published in 1992.

The CCITT I series recommendations are structured so that new recommendations can easily be included in the appropriate sections. The structure is shown in Figure 44.1 and described in detail in Recommendation I.110. It comprises six main parts as follows :

1.   Part I - General Structure; I.100 series.
2.   Part II - Service Capabilities; I.200 series.
3.   Part III - Overall Network Aspects and Functions; I.300 series.
4.   Part IV - ISDN User/Network Interfaces; I.400 series.
5.   Part V - Internetwork Interfaces; I.500 series.
6.   Part VI - Maintenance Principles; I.600 series.

The recommendations state that ISDNs will be based on the concepts developed for telephony IDNs and may evolve by progressively incorporating additional functions and network features, including those of any other dedicated networks such as circuit switching and packet switching for data, so as to provide for existing and new services. As far as practicable, new services introduced into ISDN should be arranged to be compatible with the 64kbit/s switched digital connections, although later enhancements may include bit rates higher and lower than this, this also includes an element of packet switching. The network will contain intelligence for the purpose of providing service features, maintenance and network management functions. The I 100 series recommendations therefore describes the general structure of the recommendations, a vocabulary and a description of ISDNs which include the framework for providing additional packet mode bearer services.

The majority of the current I series recommendations are on what is called narrowband ISDN based upon 64kbit/s rates; however during the last few years a lot attention has been given to what is called a Broadband ISDN. In Part I of the recommendations there is also a recommendation (I.121) which describes the Broadband aspects of an ISDN, giving significant details of the main parameters of such a network which will be based upon asynchronous transfer mode (ATM) techniques. These aspects will be discussed in more detail later.

44.3   ISDN services aspects

When we refer to services in the ISDN context what is meant are the telecommunication services offered by a network operator, or service provider, and which are accessed by users either at an ISDN interface or within a terminal connected to the ISDN. The telecom-

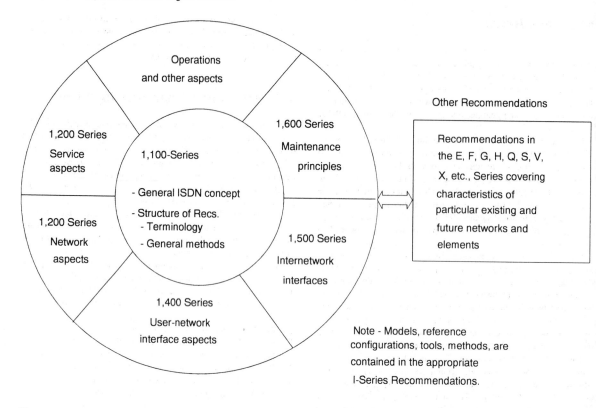

Figure 44.1 Structure of CCITT I. Series Recommendations

munication services are the products which are supported by the ISDN as such and there are various categories of telecommunication services supported by the ISDN.

The CCITT Recommendations on telecommunication services to be offered by an ISDN appear in the I.200 series of Recommendations, and the first of these, Recommendation I.210 defines the general principles and categorisation of services. The CCITT has developed a hierarchical structure for the definition of services in the ISDN because of the wide range of services likely to be offered. There are two main categories of telecommunication services, bearer and teleservices, to both of which can be added a third category of supplementary services.

44.3.1 Bearer services

Bearer Services supported by an ISDN provide the capability for transferring information between ISDN user-network interfaces and involve only low-layer functions (layers 1 to 3 in the protocol stack). Customers may choose any set of high-layer protocols for their communications and the ISDN does not necessarily ascertain compatibility at these layers between customers. An example of a bearer service is a switched 64kbit/s circuit mode unrestricted service.

Bearer services are characterised by a set of low-layer attributes and these are classified into three categories:

1. Information transfer attributes.
2. Access attributes.
3. General attributes, including operation and commercial attributes.

The following circuit-mode bearer services have been defined in the 1988 recommendations :

1. 64kbit/s unrestricted, 8kHz structured.
2. 64kbit/s, 8kHz structured, usable for speech information transfer.
3. 64kbit/s, 8kHz structured, usable for 3.1kHz audio information transfer.
4. Alternate speech, 64kbit/s unrestricted, 8kHz structured.
5. 2 x 64kbit/s unrestricted, 8 kHz structured.
6. 384 kbit/s unrestricted, 8 kHz structured.
7. 1536 kbit/s unrestricted, 8 kHz structured.
8. 1920 kbit/s unrestricted, 8 kHz structured.

The following packet-mode bearer services have been identified:

1. Virtual call and permanent virtual circuit.
2. Connectionless (for further study).
3. User signalling (for further study).

44.3.2 Teleservices

Teleservices provide the full capability for communication by means of terminals, network functions and possibly functions provided by dedicated centres. They involve the standardisation of the higher layer function (layer 4 to 7 in the protocol stack). Examples of teleservices are telephony, teletex, videotex and message handling. Teleservices are characterised by a set of low layer attributes, a set of high layer attributes and operational and commercial attributes.

44.3.3 Supplementary services

The two categories of services that have been described above are referred to as "basic services". The basic service is what the customer gets when he asks for a communication capability. A supplementary service modifies or supplements a basic telecommunication service, for example redirection of calls to another number. Consequently the supplementary service cannot be offered to a customer as a standalone service, and must be offered in association with a basic telecommunication service. It is possible for the same supplementary service to be common to a number of telecommunication services. The technique for describing supplementary services also uses the attribute method. However, because of the complexity of these supplementary services, the description technique has now been widened. The following categories of supplementary service have currently been standardised:

1. Number identification supplementary services; (Recommendation I.251).
2. Call offering supplementary services; (Recommendation I.252).
3. Call completion supplementary services; (Recommendation I.253).
4. Multiparty supplementary services; (Recommendation I.254).
5. 'Community of interest' supplementary services; (Recommendation I.255).
6. Charging supplementary services; (Recommendation I.256).
7. Additional information transfer supplementary services; (Recommendation I.257).

44.4 Network aspects

44.4.1 Network capabilities

The ISDN functional description defines a set of network capabilities which enable bearer services and teleservices to be offered to customers. The services require two different levels of ISDN capabilities: low layer which relate to bearer services and high layer which, together with low layer capabilities, relate to teleservices. By the network capabilities it means all the technology and techniques which are available in the ISDN to support the telecommunication services. This involves the transmission, switching, signalling and control procedures which will exist in various parts of the network, or interconnected networks, involved in supporting a call end-to-end. These network capabilities are described by various "connection types", which use the attribute method for this description and are described in Recommendation I.130.

An ISDN connection is a connection established between reference points; thus, it is the physical or logical realisation of an ISDN connection type. Each ISDN connection can be categorised as belonging to a connection type depending on its attributes of information transfer rate, signalling access protocol and performance which are all examples of ISDN connection type attributes. An ISDN connection is composed of connection elements as shown in Figure 44.2, and these concepts provide the basis of a very powerful tool for defining network capability in a rigorous manner to enable interworking, quality of service and performance and routing studies to continue.

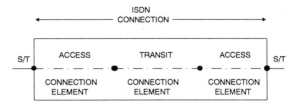

Figure 44.2 Example of connection elements forming an ISDN connection

Recommendation I.320 describes a protocol reference model for ISDN. It is based on the general principles of layering given in the X.200 series of Recommendations and has been developed to model the information flows, including user information and control information flows to and through an ISDN, and to take into account the separate channel signalling nature of the ISDN. In order to construct the ISDN protocol reference model, a fundamental generic protocol block has been identified and is shown in Figure 44.3.

In particular, the model has been designed so that protocols in an ISDN can be studied in a structured and uniform way with account being taken of the wide range of communication modes and capabilities that can be achieved in the ISDN. For example:

1. Circuit-switched connection under the control of common-channel signalling.
2. Packet-switched communication via the circuit-switched or packet channel.
3. Signalling between users and network-based facilities.
4. End-to-end signalling
5. Combinations of above in multimedia communications.

44.4.2 ISDN numbering

ISDN numbering and addressing principles are detailed in Recommendation I.330, and Recommendation I.331 (E.164) describes the numbering plan for the ISDN era. It has been agreed that the ISDN numbering plan should be based on and evolve from the existing telephony numbering plan, and therefore the telephony country code is used to identify a particular country. The principles relating to an ISDN number in relation to the user/network reference configuration are that an ISDN number shall be able unambiguously to identify a particular:

1. Physical or virtual interface at reference point T, including multiple interfaces.
2. Physical or virtual interfaces at reference point S, including multiple interfaces, for point-to-point configuration.
3. Interfaces at reference point S for multipoint configurations (for example, passive bus).

The ISDN numbering plan, Recommendation I.331, indicates that the international ISDN numbering shall consist of three parts the country code, the national destination number and the subscriber's number. The country code is used to select the destination country (or geographical area) and varies in length as outlined in Recommendation E.163. The national (significant) number is used to select the destination subscriber. In selecting the destination subscriber, however, it may be necessary to select the destination network. To accomplish this selection, the national (significant) number code field can be seen as comprising a national destination code (NDC)

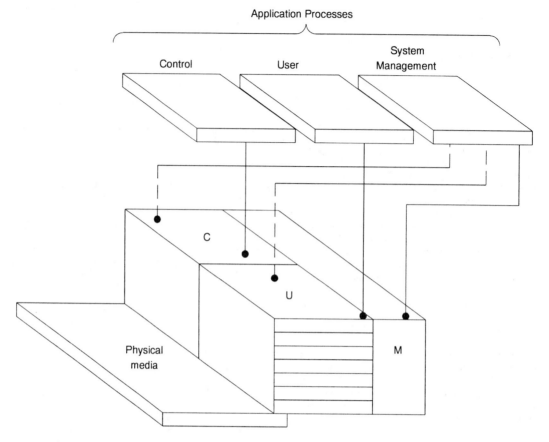

Figure 44.3   Generic protocol block

followed by a subscriber's number. The NDC code field will be variable in length dependent upon the requirements of the destination address. It can be used to select a destination network serving the destination subscriber or used in a trunk code format to route the call over the destination network in the called country. The ISDN address can be further expanded by the addition of an ISDN sub-address but this is not part of the network numbering plan. The full structure of the ISDN address is shown in Figure 44.4.

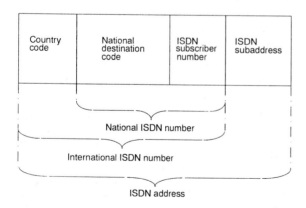

Figure 44.4   Structure of ISDN address

44.5   User/network interfaces

From a user's perspective, an ISDN is completely characterised by the attributes that can be observed at an ISDN user-network interface, including physical, electromagnetic, protocol, service capability, maintenance and operation and performance characteristics. Recommendation I.410 lists the requirements of the user-network interface and outlines the scope to be covered in defining the interface characteristics and capabilities. A key objective in the definition of ISDN has been that a small set of compatible user/network interfaces can economically support a wide range of user applications, equipment and configurations. To assist the definition of ISDN user/network interfaces, the CCITT has produced a reference model for user/network terminal arrangements, shown in Figure 44.5, which is described in Recommendation I.411.

44.5.1   Reference model

The ISDN user/network interface Recommendations apply to physical interfaces at reference points S and T. At reference point R, physical interfaces in accordance with existing CCITT Recommendations (for example, X-series and V-series) or physical interfaces not included in CCITT Recommendations may be used. There is no reference point assigned to the transmission line to the local exchange since an ISDN user/network interface was not envisaged at this location.

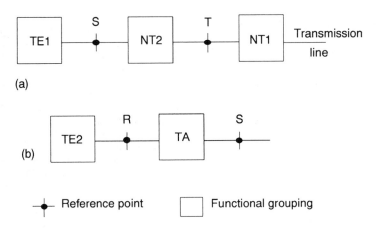

Figure 44.5 Reference configuration for the ISDN interfaces: (a) S and T; (b) R and S

In the reference model the NT1 functional grouping includes functions equivalent to layer 1 of the Open Systems Interconnection (OSI) Reference Model and are associated with the proper physical and electromagnetic termination of the network.

The NT2 functional group includes functions equivalent to layer 1 and higher layers of the OSI Reference Model. PABXs, local area networks and terminal controllers are examples of equipment or combinations of equipment that provide NT2 functions.

The terminal equipment (TE) functional grouping includes functions equivalent to layer 1 and higher layers of the OSI Reference Model. Digital telephones, data terminal equipment and integrated work stations are examples of equipment or combinations of equipment which provide TE functions.

Two types of TE have been categorised:

1. TE1 is an ISDN terminal equipment with an interface that complies with the ISDN user/network interface.
2. TE2 is a terminal equipment with an interface that complies with non-ISDN interface Recommendations (for example, the CCITT X-series and V-series interfaces) or interfaces not included in CCITT Recommendations.

The terminal adapter (TA) functional grouping includes functions equivalent to layer 1 and higher layers of the OSI Reference Model that allow a TE2 terminal to be served by an ISDN user/network interface.

44.5.2 Interface structures

Structures and access capabilities of the ISDN interface are described in Recommendation I.412. A set of channel types has been defined for the ISDN user/network interface. The main types of channels recommended by CCITT are as follows:

1. B channel. This is a 64kbit/s channel. It carries user information such as voice encoded at 64kbit/s (with 8kHz sampling), or wideband voice, or data information.
2. D channel. This is either 16kbit/s or 64kbit/s. It is primarily intended to carry signalling information for circuit switching by the ISDN. In addition to signalling it may also be used to carry packet-switched data. It uses a layered protocol in accordance with the CCITT Recommendations I.440, I.441, I.450 and I.451.

3. H channel. This is currently defined at 384kbit/s (the H_0 channel), 1536kbit/s (the H_{11} channel) and 1920kbit/s (the H_{12} channel). The H channel is intended to carry user information for services requiring high information throughput (e.g. fast facsimile, videoconferencing).

Two main interface structures are currently defined at the T & S reference points, a basic rate interface and a primary rate interface. The basic interface structure is composed of two B channels and one D channel, 2B+D. The B channels can be used independently, that is, in different connections at the same time. With the basic interface structure, two B channels and one D channel are always present at the ISDN user/network interface, but one or both B channels, however, may not be supported by the network.

The primary rate interface structures correspond to the primary rate of 1544kbit/s and 2048kbit/s. At the 2048kbit/s primary rate, the interface structure is 30B + D, although one or more of the B channels may not be supported by the network. Channel types at rates higher than 64kbit/s have been defined such as 384kbit/s, 1536kbit/s and 1920kbit/s, and these will also be supported by this interface.

The CCITT 'brand' name for the basic access interface is I.420 and for the primary rate interface I.421. These recommendations then call up I430 and I431 respectively for the layer 1 descriptions, and common recommendations for layer 2 in I440/1 and layer 3 in I450/1. The relationship between these recommendations is illustrated in Figure 44.6. The characteristics of these recommendations will now be described in a more detail since they represent an important aspect of the ISDN.

44.5.3 Layer 1 — Basic rate access

The ISDN terminates in the Network Termination 1 (NT1) and the socket in the NT1 is the regulatory boundary between the Public Telephone Operator's (PTO) network and the liberalised customers' premises environment in Europe. (In the United States the local loop pair is the regulatory boundary and the NT1 is part of this customers premises equipment). It provides the layer 1 interface between the local loop transmission system and the ISDN interface layer 1. Into this socket is plugged the four wire bus often known as the S or T bus because it is at the S and T reference points in the CCITT reference model. This Bus can operate in 2 modes, point to point or point to multipoint. In the point to point mode one Terminal Equip-

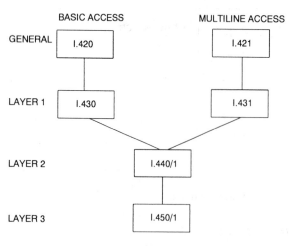

Figure 44.6 Relationship between CCITT Interface Recommendations

ment (TE) is connected at the end of up to about 1km of cable. In the point to multipoint mode up to 8 terminals can be connected in parallel anywhere along the bus, but the bus length is now limited to 200 metres.

Over this bus passes the two B channels, which are transparent 64kbit/s user channels, as well as the D channel, which is the 16kbit/s signalling channel, and other bits used for miscellaneous purposes such as frame synchronisation. The B channels contain the

user data which is switched by the network to provide an end to end transmission service. B channel paths are established by signalling messages in the D channel. In a multi-terminal situation all terminals have access to the D channel by the use of an access procedure, but each B channel is allocated to a particular terminal during call set-up and is not capable of being shared between terminals.

The line coding used is Alternate Mark Inversion (AMI), with the binary ones encoded as high impedance and the binary zeros as full width pulses. Violations of the coding mark the beginning and end of the layer 1 frames. The physical connection across the interface consists of eight wires, 2 balanced pairs being used for transmission of the layer 1 signals to and from the network and 2 pairs for power feeding which are optional. Power feeding is also possible over the transmit and receive pairs via the phantom, and may be used to provide power from the network to the terminal in order, for example, to maintain a basic telephone service in the event of local power failure. However to save power fed from the local exchange, both in the local network and the NT1, an activation/deactivation procedure is defined. Deactivation is also provided to reduce electromagnetic radiation.

A connect/disconnect indication is used by Layer 2 to determine if a terminal is plugged into the bus. This is necessary as each terminal is given a random, unique identity (its TEI value) by the network. If disconnected the terminal must forget its original identity to prevent duplication when reconnected. The connect/disconnect indication is achieved by monitoring the presence of DC power on the bus.

The layer 1 structure for supporting these functions is shown in Figure 44.7. The dots demarcate those parts of the frame that are independently d.c. balanced. The frame is 48 bits long and lasts

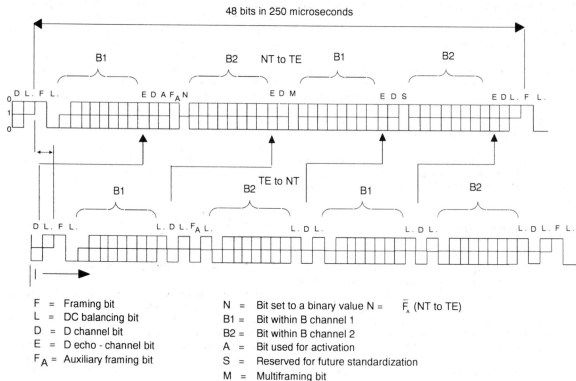

F = Framing bit
L = DC balancing bit
D = D channel bit
E = D echo - channel bit
F_A = Auxiliary framing bit

N = Bit set to a binary value N = $\bar{F}_A$ (NT to TE)
B1 = Bit within B channel 1
B2 = Bit within B channel 2
A = Bit used for activation
S = Reserved for future standardization
M = Multiframing bit

Figure 44.7 Basic access interface. Layer 1 frame structure

250µs resulting in a bit rate of 192kbit/s with each bit approximately 5.2µs long. Figure 44.8 shows that there is a 2 bit offset between transmit and receive frames. This is the delay between a frame start at the receiver of a terminal and the frame start of the transmitted signal. It also shows a 10 bit offset between the D channel leaving a terminal, travelling to the NT and being echoed back in the E channel. This 10 bit delay is made up of bus and transmission delays in the NT. A frame contains several L bits, which are balanced bits to prevent a build up of DC on the line.

FLAG 01111110	ADDRESS	CONTROL	VARIABLE LENGTH INFORMATION FIELD	FRAME CHECK SEQUENCE	FLAG 01111110
8 BITS	16 BITS	8/16 BITS	MULTIPLE OF 8 BITS	16 BITS	8 BITS

Figure 44.8 Layer 2 structure

44.5.4   Layer 1 — Primary rate access

The primary rate access is contained in Recommendation I.431 and is based on existing primary rate PCM multiplex structures, and therefore reflects the two alternate standards of 1544kbit/s and 2048kbit/s. In Europe the 2048kbit/s standard contains 30 B channels, one D channel and a 64kbit/s synchronisation channel. The primary rate access is permanently activated and operates in a point to point manner and therefore does not require any activation/deactivation procedures. An HDB3 line code is used over coaxial or screened balanced pairs and it has a reach capability restricted to 6dB loss.

44.5.5   Layer 2

The layer 2 structure and features are based upon the High Level Data Link Control (HDLC) procedures shown in Figure 44.8 and has the following fields.

1. The flag acts as a unique delimiter and additional circuitry ensures that the flag pattern never occurs in the bits in the rest of the frame.
2. The address field is used to indicate whether the message is a command or a response, a signalling or maintenance message and to which channel it refers.
3. The control field is one or two octets depending on the frame type and carries information that identifies the frame and the Layer 2 sequence numbers used for link control.
4. The information field contains the signalling or level 3 message.
5. The Cyclic Redundancy Check (CRC) bits enable the receiver to determine whether any errors have been incurred during transmission.

In more detail the address field enables layer 2 multiplexing to be achieved by employing a separate Layer 2 address for each LAP in the system. To carry the LAP identity the address field is two octets long and contains a service identifier (SAPI), a terminal identifier (TEI) and a command/response bit. This address identifies the intended receiver of a command frame and the transmitter of a response frame. The address has only local significance and is known only to the two end points using the LAP. No use can be

made of the address by the network for routeing purposes and no information about its value will be held outside the Layer 2 entity.

The Service Access Point Identifier (SAPI) is used to identify the service that the signalling frame is intended for. Consider the case of I.420 telephones sharing a passive bus with packet terminals. The two terminal types will be accessing different services and possibly different networks. It is possible to identify the service being invoked by using a different SAPI for each service. This gives the network the option of handling the signalling associated with different services in separate modules. In a multi-network ISDN it allows Layer 2 routeing to the appropriate network. The value of the SAPI is therefore fixed for a given service.

The Terminal Endpoint Identifier (TEI) takes a range of values that are associated with terminals on the customer's line. In the simplest case each terminal will have a single unique TEI value. It is important that no two TEIs are the same and therefore the network has a special TEI management entity which allocates TEIs on request and ensures their correct use. The values that TEIs can take fall into the ranges:

1. 0 - 63 for automatic assignment TEIs which are selected by the user.
2. 64 - 126 for automatic assignment TEIs selected by the network on request.
3. 127 for a global TEI which is used to broadcast information to all terminals within a given SAPI.

The combination of TEI and SAPI identify the LAP and provide a unique Layer 2 address. A terminal will use its Layer 2 address in all transmitted frames and only frames received carrying the correct address will be processed.

In practice a frame originating from telephony call control has a SAPI that identifies the frame as "telephony" and all telephone equipment will examine this frame. Only the terminal whose TEI agrees with that carried by the frame will pass it to the Layer 2 and Layer 3 entities for processing.

44.5.6   Layer 3

The general structure of the layer 3 signalling messages is shown in Figure 44.9. The first octet contains a protocol discriminator which gives the D channel the capability of simultaneously supporting additional communications protocols in the future.

The call reference value in the third octet is used to identify the call with which a particular message is to be associated. Thus a call can be identified independently of the communications channel on which it is supported. This feature is particularly important in connection with incoming call offering procedures on a passive bus arrangement since the channel is only allocated to the called terminal after answer.

The message type code in the fourth octet describes the intention of the message (e.g. a SETUP message to request call establishment). A number of other information elements may be included following the message type code in the fourth octet. The exact contents of a message is dependent on the message type, however the coding rules are open ended and in principle it is a simple matter to include additional information elements to satisfy any requirement which may be identified in the future.

In order to make an outgoing call request, a user must send all of the necessary call information (i.e. called party number and supplementary service requests) to the network. Furthermore the user must specify the particular bearer service required for the call (i.e. speech, 64kbit/s unrestricted or 3.1kHz audio) and any terminal

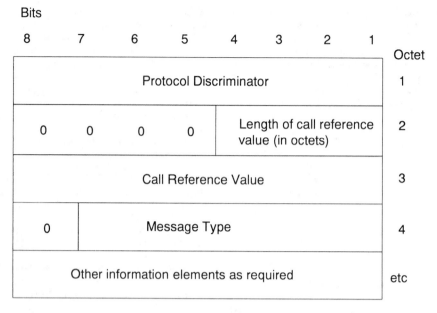

Figure 44.9 Signalling message structure

compatibility information which must be checked at the destination. This information element may also be used to specify low layer terminal characteristics such as data rate. Where applicable the non-voice application to be used on the call may be specified via the High Layer Compatibility information element (i.e. Group 4 FAX, teletex, videotex or slow scan video).

As well as bearer services and teleservices the ISDN is able to support a range of supplementary services similar to those that are available on PABXs and private networks today. Two generic layer 3 signalling protocols have been specified for the control of supplementary services, namely stimulus and functional signalling procedures.

In stimulus procedures, the terminal is not required to have knowledge of the supplementary service invoked. No records of the supplementary service call state are held by the terminal and layer 3 messages are generated as a result of human action (e.g. pressing a button on the keypad). The operation of the terminal (e.g. display of messages, lighting of lamps etc.,) is controlled by the network via layer 3 messages. The network response to facility requests will be generally in the form of a sequence of IA5 characters in a DISPLAY information element or an in-band tone or announcement. The arrangement of IA5 characters within a DISPLAY information element follows similar rules to the coding of facility requests. Use is made of the separators "*" and "#" so that sequences are machine readable and suitable for display to a human operator.

There are 2 types of stimulus procedures defined, the Keypad Protocol and the Feature Key Management Protocol. Both procedures use the basic call control layer 3 messages, particularly the INFORMATION message, as the transport mechanism for conveying the information between the terminals and the network. In the Keypad Protocol the user invokes a service by keying in the appropriate sequence of digits delimited by "*" and "#". Only the generic procedure has been specified and the sequence and digits for any given supplementary service is network dependent.

The feature key management protocol requires the network to hold a terminal or service profile for a given terminal. A given terminal is allocated a feature number which is invoked by the terminal signalling that number to the network. This mechanism is very similar to that currently offered on PABXs where the PABX terminals have feature keys which can be programmed to correspond to a particular supplementary service.

In functional signalling, the terminal must have knowledge of the supplementary service being invoked and have the associated signalling protocol implemented. Both the terminal and the network then hold records of the supplementary service call state. The functional protocol is based on using the facility information element conveyed in the basic call control messages if the supplementary service is invoked during call establishment or call clearing and in the FACILITY message otherwise. For the control of supplementary services which are independent of the active call, the REGISTER message is used. In addition, specific layer 3 messages have also been defined for the function of holding and retrieving a call.

44.6 ISDN developments in the U.K.

In common with most telecommunications administrations, BT wished to fully exploit the features of its emerging Integrated Digital Network (IDN) in order to extend the range of services offered to its customers. BT saw the early introduction of an ISDN pilot service as a means of gaining practical experience of developing and operating an ISDN and stimulating customer interest, and planning for this was started in 1979. In June of 1985 an ISDN pilot service was opened in the U.K., based on a System X local exchange in the City of London, under the marketing name IDA (Integrated Digital Access). Early in 1986 it was extended to three further System X exchanges located in Birmingham, Manchester and London, which were fully interconnected via their respective digital main network switching centres with digital transmission links using CCITT No. 7 (BT) signalling. This was further extended to more than 200 additional exchange areas in the major centres of population.

This pilot service offered two new types of customer access, a single-line access and a multi-line access which were structured as follows:

1. Single-line IDA: a 64kbit/s channel for speech or data; an 8kbit/s channel for data only; an 8kbit/s channel for signalling only. Total 80kbit/s plus additional framing information.
2. Multi-line IDA: 30 x 64kbit/s channels for speech or data; 1 x 64kbit/s channel for signalling; 1 x64 kbit/s channel for framing and alarms. Total 2048kbit/s as for the PCM primary multiplex structure.

During the period in which BT was specifying and developing equipment for its pilot ISDN, work began in earnest within CCITT to define a set of recommendations relating to ISDN. At quite an early stage in the CCITT studies it became apparent that the emerging standards for signalling in an ISDN would be significantly different from BT's initial ISDN access arrangements. The notable differences arose from the CCITT requirement to support two 64kbit/s B channels and a 16kbit/s D channels for signalling and for the interface to support a passive bus arrangement which enabled up to eight terminals to compete for access to either B channel.

BT were anxious to gain experience of the CCITT standard interface at the earliest opportunity. Consequently, following the publication of the CCITT Red Book in 1984, BT began to specify an ISDN basic rate access arrangement using the I-Series interface described by recommendation I.420. BT placed a contract for the development of a multiplexer and a network termination which supported the I.420 interface. Although initially based on the 1984 Red Book recommendations the interface specification was kept in alignment with changes made to the recommendations. The multiplexer had to interface to the exchange via an existing 2048kbit/s interface. The multiplexer was therefore required to convert the protocols of the I.420 interface to those developed for the pilot ISDN as well as provide a transmission system capable of supporting 144kbit/s over the local loop. Further contracts were placed for the multiplexer so that by the middle of 1991 BT had 90,000 lines available throughout the country for service.

In order to introduce these new services a number of new developments were required and these included:

1. Digital transmission system for the local network.
2. Message based digital customer-network signalling.
3. New types of customer's Network Terminating Equipment with standardised interfaces for the connection of data terminals.

44.6.1 Local network transmission

A cable network has already been established in the local area to provide telephony to customers and this represents a large proportion of any PTO's capital assets. Although this cable has been installed to carry telephony with a bandwidth of less than 4kHz, it can be exploited to carry the wider bandwidth digital signals of and ISDN basic access link. The bandwidths for the single line access will be of the order of 100kHz to 200kHz depending upon the digital information rate and the modulation technique employed and as a consequence will be subjected to much greater attenuation (up to 60dB) than the telephony signal (a maximum of 10dB or 15dB). Notwithstanding these high attenuations it is still feasible to provide full duplex transmission over the single telephony pair of wires by the adoption of suitable modulation techniques.

Two main techniques are used for providing digital transmission over the local network, the burst mode technique and a more complex echo cancelling technique.

44.6.1.1 *Burst-mode technique*

In its pilot service BT adopted the burst mode technique operating at 80kbit/s because of its simplicity. In this technique illustrated in Figures 44.10 and 44.11, the 80kbit/s input data is loaded into a buffer and then clocked out into the cable pair in bursts of 22 bits (20 information bits and 2 marker bits) at an increased rate of 256kbit/s. The interval between the bursts of data, 250µs, is such that there is ample time to receive bursts of data from the remote transmitter. Full duplex transmission is therefore achieved without having to identify a low level receive signal in the presence of a high level transmit signal.

When the transmit bursts of a number of systems in the same cable are synchronised the problems of near end crosstalk are also avoided. However, if systems on pairs with a long reach are mixed in cables with a short reach this advantage is to a certain extent nullified. A WAL$_2$ line code is used which ensures there is sufficient timing information present and that no equalisation of the characteristic distortion of the line is required at the receiver. The system is therefore relatively simple and therefore cheap to implement. The disadvantage of the system is that because of the higher frequency at which it operates it suffers high attenuation. This burst-mode system has a maximum loss of 34dB and will give a range of approximately 2.5km over 0.4mm copper pairs enabling 78% of BT's customers to be connected directly to their local exchange.

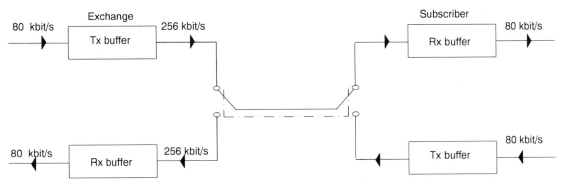

Figure 44.10 Two wire duplex: burst mode transmission

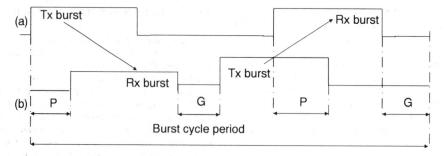

Figure 44.11 Cycle for burst mode transmission: (a) exchange; (b) subscriber

44.6.1.2   Echo cancelling technique

The echo cancelling technique is now recognised as the standard technique by most PTOs and is used by BT in its National ISDN Service launched in 1991. Using this technique it is possible to transmit and receive simultaneously. Figure 44.12 illustrates the principles of the more complex echo cancellation system. A hybrid with a compromise balance provides some initial reduction of the transmit signal passing into the receiver, but inevitably the transmit signal will still be much larger than the receive signal on the longer lines. An adaptive network therefore models the echo path response between the transmitter and receiver which results from the imperfect hybrid and the reflections on the line. The signal generated is then subtracted from the receiver input to leave the true receive line signal. The adaptive network derives its signal by minimising the residual echo components on the wanted receive signal, hence the system's name.

44.6.2   Signalling

The introduction of a pilot ISDN in the U.K. required the specification of a new digital signalling system since no CCITT recommendations on digital access signalling protocols were available at the time. A new signalling system DASS (Digital Access Signalling System) was therefore defined. As with the current CCITT recommendations the structure of DASS is based upon the levels of the ISO (International Standards Organization) model for OSI (Open Systems Interconnection). The main differences being that at layer

2, although based upon the HDLC structure the use of the address and control fields was different. Similarly the structure of the layer 3 messages and their defined sequences was different.

The introduction of DASS for multi-line access to PABXs, the development of digital PABXs and the use of digital leased circuits to form digital private networks, led to a need for a digital inter-PABX signalling system. BT and a number of U.K. PABX manufacturers therefore collaborated on the definition of a signalling system based upon DASS but which was enhanced to meet the inter-PABX signalling requirement. This has been called the Digital Private Network Signalling System (DPNSS).

During the definition of DPNSS it became apparent that it was desirable to align more closely certain of the messages at level 3 of DASS with those of DPNSS. At the same time proposals were being made to enhance the repertoire of messages at level 3 in order to provide more facilities to the user. An enhanced version of DASS No. 1 was therefore defined, called DASS No. 2, which would enable PABXs to have a common type of signalling system for both inter-PABX and PABX to network signalling. The common features of DPNSS and DASS enable them to be interleaved on a common signalling link such as time-slot 16 in a 2048kbit/s multiplex structure.

The use of DASS 2 has now been superseded by the new I.440/1 and I.450/1 recommendations (Q921 and Q931) on the basic rate ISDN service. However because of the maturity of the DASS and DPNSS specifications they continue to be used on the primary rate service in the U.K. for a number of years. It is expected that a new

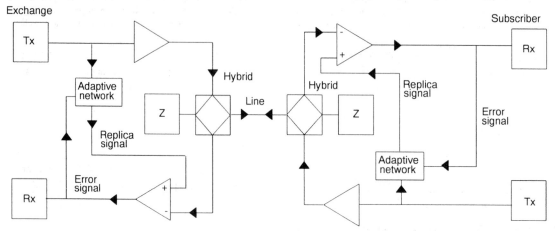

Figure 44.12 Echo cancellation

primary rate service based on the CCITT recommendations will be introduced by the end of 1993.

44.6.3 Network terminal equipment

For BT's pilot service a network terminal was developed with two X.21 ports supporting both circuit switched and leased circuit variants for synchronous data rates up to 64kbit/s. They also incorporated a V.24 port for use only for facility programming. In order to facilitate interworking to V-series terminals and to provide a telephony capability, a range of terminal adapters were made available to connect onto the X.21 port of the network terminal. The new national ISDN service based upon the CCITT recommendations required a new network terminal (NT1) which has been developed to support the I.420 interface directly. A range of customer premises terminal equipment is now being developed on the open market which includes Terminal Adapters (TA), PC plug in cards, Group 4 facsimile machines etc. Before these can be connected to the network however they have to go through a formal approval procedure and be approved against a European Commission standard Net 3.

44.7 ISDN applications

The extension of the 64kbit/s digital capability of the network together with the provision of a much more powerful signalling capability to the customer opens up the opportunity for new services and applications together with an improvement in the performance of some existing services.

44.7.1 Digital telephones

A complete digital transmission path will mean that voice quality transmission should be much better with little or no noise and interference from extraneous sources. 64kbit/s transmission will also give the opportunity for using different encoding techniques which provide a wider bandwidth, such as 7kHz speech transmission. Alternatively other techniques could be used to carry more than one voice channel provided they are all destined for the same remote customer. Customers will also see the benefits of digital signalling with fast call set-up and a range of advanced supplementary services. New digital telephones are therefore being developed which will take advantage of these features in particular the supplementary features such as calling line identity.

44.7.2 Videophone

Video compression techniques now enable video and speech signals to be compressed into 128kbit/s either using one 64kbit/s channel for speech and one for video or other combinations that add up to 128kbit/s. Videophone terminals are currently becoming available throughout the world initially in Japan in 1991 and in Europe and elsewhere during 1992. Although still expensive they are in their early days as regard development and prices can be expected to fall in the future.

44.7.3 Video conferencing terminals

Video conferencing units are already available which support this service at a number of different rates. Originally developed for use

at 2Mbit/s they are now in use at 384kbit/s and 128kbit/s and therefore can be supported on a standard ISDN basic access interface.

44.7.4 Facsimile terminals

Current analogue facsimile terminals conforming to the Group 3 standard can take between 1 and 3 minutes to transmit an A4 size page. A new Group 4 standard has been agreed that can exploit the 64kbit/s capability of the ISDN and these terminals are now coming onto the market. They feature high definition pictures with various options and are able to transmit an A4 size document in 4 to 5 seconds over a 64kbit/s channel.

44.7.5 Terminal adapters

Terminals with non-ISDN standard interfaces will continue to exist for some time. Terminal adapters which support the I.420 interface on the network side and a range of non-ISDN standard interfaces on the terminal side are therefore becoming widely available. They support such interfaces as the standard analogue telephony interface, the V.24 asynchronous interface, various versions of the X.21 interface and the V.35 leased line interface.

44.7.6 PC Terminals

Personal Computers (PC) are currently being enhanced to support access to the ISDN via I.420 interface cards. These are seen as one of the main sources of ISDN terminals because of their ability to support a wide range of different software applications. Cards are therefore becoming available for most makes of PC. Some of the applications that are becoming available are :

1. Telesurveillance, which is a slow scan TV (SSTV) surveillance application, often with the ability to display images from a number of remote cameras. The refresh time for a slow-scan TV frame on ISDN is 3 to 4 seconds. This speed of picture replenishment makes SSTV viable for remote security surveillance and for medical diagnostic purposes.
2. Image database, which is a video image application which provides the means to store scanned and photographed colour images on a central database which can then be accessed via an ISDN link and PC. An initial application is for use by estate agents and travel agents for showing pictures of properties and resorts.
3. File transfer, these applications allowing files to be transferred from one PC to another via ISDN. Conferencing can also take place between the two users on the file and updates provided to the files in virtually real time. Other conferencing applications can involve speech, text, and or graphical information from a light pen.
4. PC videophone, which is a future application that is becoming available on a PC similar to the standard videophone terminal. The picture is now displayed on a standard PC screen just as any other application in the windows environment.

44.8 Broadband ISDN

The specification of a Broadband Integrated Services Digital Network (B-ISDN) is actively being pursued in international standards bodies, such as CCITT who adopted accelerated procedures for a number of recommendations in 1990. In Europe this activity is being led by the European Technical Standards Institute (ETSI) whilst in the USA, the American National Standards Institute (ANSI) is the driving force. (Similar standards bodies in Australia, Japan etc. are also contributing to the debate.) Also in Europe the European Commission are supporting a collaborative research programme called RACE (Research into Advanced Communications in Europe) to work towards an Integrated Broadband Communications Network.

The rationales in Europe and the USA in pressing for these standards has been fundamentally different. In the USA pressure has arisen for B-ISDN standards because of the perceived need for high speed local area network (LAN) interconnect to form wide area networks (WANs). As a consequence contributions to these standards are heavily influenced by LAN and WAN procedures. In Europe on the other hand, B-ISDN is seen as an integrated network capable of supporting all services from a few bit/s up to the bandwidths required for high definition TV.

44.8.1 Services

The main need for a broadband network capability comes from two main areas, those services requiring high quality video and those requiring the exchange of large amounts of data such as certain computer automated design applications and the interconnection of high-speed local area networks. In CCITT two main service categories have been defined in recommendation I.211, interactive services and distributive services. The interactive services are subdivided into conversational services, message services, and retrieval services.

Conversational services are generally bi-directional, although in some circumstances they can be unidirectional and in real time between users, or between a user and a host. Examples include videotelephony, video conferencing, and high speed data transmission. Message services will offer communication via storage units such as mailbox or message handling functions which not only include speech but also moving pictures and high resolution images. Retrieval services offer user access to information stored centrally and accessed on demand. Examples of these services include film and high resolution images together with audio.

The distributive services are differentiated between those services without individual user presentation control such as the broadcast services for TV and radio, and those with individual user control. The latter includes centrally based services which broadcast cyclical stored information and as a result the user is presented with the information at the beginning of a cycle.

The availability of high bandwidth will enable a number of different types of information to be supported by one service resulting in the development of multimedia services. For example, video telephony will include audio and video, and also possibly text and graphics. Discussions are now being held to try and establish a limited set of information types and how they may be assembled to provide multi media services, given that each information type will have different characteristics and require different network performance characteristics.

The emergence of multi media terminals supporting a number of types of communicating information with a wide variety of bandwidths therefore make it desirable that a switching and transmission technique (the transfer mode) is chosen that is able to carry all services efficiently and in a cost effective manner.

44.8.2 Transfer mode

In the 1988 CCITT Recommendations it was agreed that the most effective technique for handling broadband services and yet still be capable of handling all the narrowband-ISDN services should be a network based upon Asynchronous Transfer Mode (ATM) techniques. This decision therefore influences the standardisation of not only switches and interfaces but of the digital hierarchies and multiplexing structures. The technique is relatively new and immature although research centres have been investigating it for the last decade in various forms. It can be thought of as a technique that is between the pure circuit switching technique used for the B channel of N-ISDN (which can be called a Synchronous Transfer Mode (STM)) and the packet switching technique of a datagram packet network (conforming to X.25 Datagram Protocols).

In circuit switching a connection is established for the duration of the call between the two end users, usually providing a transparent path between the two, the connection being established by means of signalling messages at the start of the call. This is called a connection oriented service. Although information may not be sent all the time the connection is held and the user is paying for it until the connection is cleared (unless a leased line is being used). This happens in narrowband ISDN and the exact structure of the information carried over the connection is of little interest to the carrier. In the X.25 datagram protocol, information to be carried to the remote user is assembled into packets of varying length and the routeing information for each packet is contained within it. A connection is therefore not established, making it a connectionless service. A series of packets to the same destination could therefore go over different routes. Since the routeing information is carried at layer 3, at each switch the layer 2 protocols have to be terminated and layer 3 interrogated. Potentially this can cause long and variable delays in the transmission of the signal, possibly making it unacceptable for real time services such as speech.

A technique was therefore needed that avoids the under utilisation of the circuit switch channel when carrying sporadic information and the time consuming processing of the X.25 type service. The chosen technique was the ATM technique. This requires the information to be assembled into fixed length packets or cells as they are now called. Each cell comprises a 5 byte header and a 48 byte information field as shown in Figure 44.13. The main purpose of the header is to identify cells belonging to the same call, since calls are allocated virtual channels over the network when a number of them are multiplexed onto a single bearer. The technique is connection oriented since effectively a virtual connection across the network is established at the start of the call by the use of special signalling cells. Each cell in the call is then routed over this virtual channel by

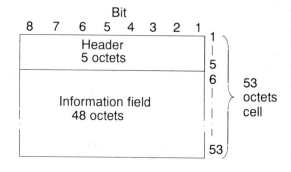

Figure 44.13 ATM cell structure

referring the information in the header to a look-up table in the exchange.

The advantage of the ATM technique is that it is able to multiplex services requiring different cell throughput rates from a few cells per second up to perhaps several hundred thousand cells per second in any combination on a 150Mbit/s circuit. The services don't have to produce information at a constant rate either, which will be more efficient when transmitting interactive data or using video coding techniques where only changes in picture content has to be transmitted. It is for these reasons that ATM is seen as an ideal candidate for an integrated broadband network.

44.8.3 Reference models

For B-ISDN a reference model similar to that for the narrowband ISDN has been adopted in CCITT with the reference points being labelled S_B and T_B instead of S and T as shown in Figure 44.5. As with N-ISDN the functions of B-NT1 are to terminate the transmission systems in the local line plant and support the interface to the B-NT2. In Europe this function is seen as part of the public network and also provides maintenance features for use by the network operator. The B-NT2 contains a local switching element equivalent to the narrowband PABX or LAN.

One of the issues currently being debated is the relationship between the interfaces at the T_B and S_B reference points and whether these interfaces should be point-to-point or point-to-multipoint. It is desirable that the two interfaces are compatible to ensure terminal portability between the large business customers and the small domestic customer who may not need an NT2. However it is imperative that the interface at S_B, which may be in the majority, is of minimum cost. The cost of any additional features required at the interface at T_B should therefore not have to be borne by the interface at S_B.

Another issue is centred on the number of interfaces that need to be defined, in particular at S_B. Since different terminals will support different services and applications, the throughput across the interface will vary considerably. This could be from the few bit/s of a telemetry service, through the tens of kbit/s required for telephony, to the hundreds of Mbit/s required for high definition visual services. However with the flexibility provided by an ATM interface, multi-service and multi-media terminals supporting various combinations of services and applications should emerge.

44.8.4 Customer's access connection

The customer's access connection between the B-NT1 and the first switching node in the network, often referred to as the "U" reference point may take many forms. It may be a copper pair, coaxial cable, optical fibre cable, satellite or cellular radio. The transmission equipment may use existing plesiochronous multiplex or the new synchronous digital hierarchy standards. It could be a network employing passive optical devices with time-diversion multiple access (TDMA) equipment, or in the future a cellular radio network with a restricted throughput.

The B-NT1 will provide the interworking between this range of media, rates, transmission standards supported by the network operators and a common interface for all terminal equipment and customer premise networks. This will ensure portability of CPE across the whole range of satellite, cellular and terrestrial networks. The functions that therefore could be performed by the B-NT1 in addition to the standard transmission conversion may also include rate conversion from the standard interface rate to a wide range of rates

supported by the access network, which would then identify a need for flow control across the interface.

44.8.5 The user/network interface

The narrowband ISDN presents two well defined network interfaces to the customer that are able to support a range of services up to 64 kbit/s, in the same way B-ISDN must present a minimum set of well defined interfaces that supports all services up to 150 Mbit/s. Well defined stable interfaces are necessary to enable customer premise equipment to evolve to support new applications independently of the public networks. In Europe the interface at the T_B reference point also provides the regulatory boundary between the liberalised customer premise equipment and the public network as for narrowband ISDN. Considerable effort has therefore gone into the definition of this interface.

44.8.5.1 *Physical layer*

Two interfaces are to be defined at both the reference points at T_B and S_B and the bit rates have been standardised at 155.52Mbit/s and 622.08Mbit/s by CCITT (although the use of 622.08Mbit/s at the S_B reference point is for further study). These rates were chosen to align with the synchronous digital hierarchy (SDH) rates at levels 1 and 4 (STM-1 and 4 x STM-1) and at the same time provide sufficient capacity for carrying encoded HDTV channels. However the whole of these bit rates are not available to the user; of the 155Mbit/s a maximum of only 135Mbit/s can be used due to the maintenance overheads and the ATM header.

Several different types of media can be considered for the physical layer, but only coaxial cable and optical fibres are serious contenders since they will both satisfy the performance requirements for both interfaces. In the short term it can be shown that two coaxial cables are more cost effective for the 155Mbit/s interface giving a reach of up to 100m. However the cost of optical transmission components is expected to fall and it is anticipated that an optical interface will become economic in the future if current cost trends continue and this could give a reach of up to 2km.

As well as the physical media the physical layer also includes the framing structure. Two alternatives have currently been identified, the cell based structure and the SDH based structure. The first consists of a continuous stream of cells each containing 53 octets; in the second the stream of cells are mapped into the payload of an STM-1 frame of the SDH as shown in Figure 44.14. Maintenance messages are contained within the section and path overheads of the SDH frame in the latter case, but special operation and maintenance cells have been defined for inclusion in the former such that they can easily be recognised at the physical layer from a unique pattern in the header.

44.8.5.2 *ATM layer*

This layer specifically addresses the ATM cell structure and coding. As mentioned in Section 44.8.2 and shown in Figure 44.14 the cell is composed of a 5 octet header and a 48 octet information field. The primary role of the header is to identify cells belonging to the same virtual channel in the ATM stream. To do this the header contains a routeing field comprising a Virtual Channel Identifier (VCI) and a virtual path identifier (VPI). A virtual channel is fully defined at the interface by the combination of VCI and VPI, since two different virtual channels in different virtual paths may have the same VCI.

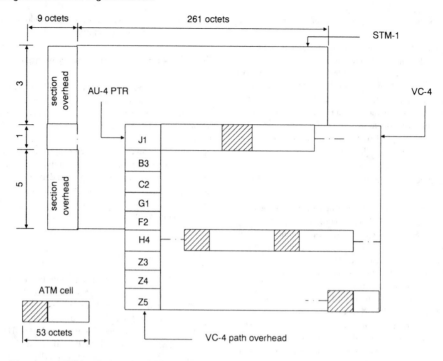

Figure 44.14 Mapping of ATM cells into the STM-1 frame

The header also contains a Generic Flow Control (GFC) field, which is used to control traffic flow during short term overload conditions, a Payload Type (PT) field, used to indicate whether the information field contains user or network information, a Cell Loss Priority (CLP) field to indicate whether the cell has a lower priority and therefore can be discarded during overload conditions and a Header Error Control (HEC) field which covers the entire header. The structure of the header is shown in Figure 44.15.

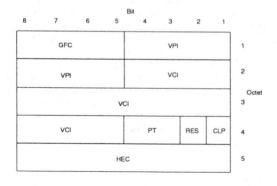

Figure 44.15 ATM header structure

44.8.5.3 *ATM Adaptation Layer*

As the name implies this layer adapts or maps the functions or services supported by the higher layers onto a common ATM bearer service. Different services therefore require different ATM Adaptation Layer (AAL) protocols if the carriage of each service is to be

optimised. However it is hoped that a minimum of AAL protocols need be derived with only minimal degradation to some of the services. Currently four classes of service have been defined based on the timing relation between source and destination, the bit rate (constant or variable) and the connection mode (connection oriented or connectionless) and these are shown in Figure 44.16.

Two sub-layers have been defined in the adaptation layer, these are the Segmentation and Reassembly sublayer (SAR) and the Convergence Sub-layer (CS). The SAR divides the information to be carried by the ATM layer into segments suitable for carrying in the 48 octet information field of the ATM cell and vice versa. Other functions such as handling cell delays variation, cell loss, timing and error monitoring and control are handled by the service dependent CS.

44.8.5.4 *Higher layers*

The higher layers in the user, signalling and management information are all supported on a common ATM bearer service with specific service dependent adaptation layers adapting the features of the higher layers of these services. Each service or application in the user plane for example will have differently specified higher layers, whilst the higher layers of the signalling in the control plane may be different again. For example signalling may be based upon the narrowband ISDN signalling with layer 3 signalling messages and protocols defined in I.450/1 (Q.930/1). In which case decisions will need to be taken as to whether they should still be supported by the layer 2 specification (I.440/1) or whether these functions can be performed by the adaptation layer.

Signalling is established via a signalling circuit which is implemented by assigning two virtual channels, one for each direction, across the interfaces. Any number of signalling circuits can be

	Class A	Class B	Class C	Class D
Timing relation between source and destination	Required		Not required	
Bit rate	Constant	Variable		
Connection mode	Connection-oriented			Connection-less

Figure 44.16 Service classification for adaption layer

established. These Signalling Virtual Channels (SVC) are identified by Signalling Virtual Channel Identifiers (SVCI) and are only assigned when required. To assign, check and remove these SVC a meta-signalling protocol has been defined which is carried in a meta-signalling virtual circuit with a predefined VCI and which is always present.

Discussions are still proceeding on the specification of the signalling protocols. A short term solution may be to base these on the narrowband ISDN signalling protocols defined in 1.450/1 (Q.930/1), however a longer term solution may to define a new signalling protocols suitable for use both in the access network and main network.

44.8.6 Broadband standards

The standards and specifications for a broadband ISDN are now beginning to emerge. In Europe the European Commission is assisting this process through its RACE programme. The RACE programme began in 1988 with 50% funding of some 50 collaborative projects aimed at establishing the standards, technology and applications for Integrated Broadband Communications in Europe and now has nearly 100 projects due for completion by the end of 1992. A further stage of this programme is now being planned to extend the work until 1994. In CCITT work is continuing with the enhancement and addition of new recommendations on Broadband ISDN with a further set of recommendations being issued in 1992.

Whilst these standards are being developed various companies and administrations are involved in a variety of different field trials exploring not only the technology but the new broadband services and applications that will be required by users. Specification work is progressing very quickly and it is expected that pilot broadband networks conforming to international standards will begin to emerge towards the end of the decade.

44.9 Bibliography

Bonnati, Casali and Popple (1991) *Integrated Broadband Communications: Views from RACE* , North Holland.

CCITT (1988) *Blue Book - Fascicle III.7 to II.9*, CCITT/ITU.

Clark, M.P. (1991) *Networks and Telecoms*, Wiley.

Griffiths, J.M. (1990) *ISDN Explained*, Wiley.

Griffiths, J.M. (1986) *Local Telecommunications 2 - Into the digital era*, Peter Peregrinus Ltd.

Marsden, B.W. (1988) *Communication Network Protocols*, Chartwell Bratt.

NCC (1983) *Handbook of Data Communications*, NCC Publications, England.

Purser, M. (1987) *Computers and Telecommunication Networks*, Blackwell Scientific Pub.

Redmill, F.J, and Valdar, A.R. (1990) *SPC Digital Telephone Exchanges*, Peter Peregrimus Ltd.

Rutkowski, A.M. (1985) *Integrated Services Digital Network*, Artech House Inc.

45 Radio paging

Richard J Mumford
C Eng MIEE
Multitone Electronics plc

Contents

45.1 Introduction

Radiopaging is a cost effective solution for staff location, alerting personnel and transmitting one way messages or data. Compared to land mobile radio, and cellular radio, radio pagers or 'bleepers' as they are known in hospitals, are much smaller and less expensive. They are also less expensive then CT2 or DECT handsets and are not limited in range as are these systems. With two notable system exceptions, however, the communication is only one way and without acknowledgement. Each pager has its own address and when the paging caller sends a coded transmission it alerts the bearer by means of an audible tone, a light and/or a vibration.

Paging systems fall into two classes called wide area and on site. The wide area user rents a paging receiver on a public service provider's network, while the on site user purchases his own private transmission system and paging receivers.

45.2 Markets

In Europe the industry has developed from single on site systems, the first of these being an inductive loop system installed in St. Thomas's hospital by Multitone Electronics in 1956. Transmissions were in the range 30kHz to 50kHz and each receiver was tuned to its own unique individual frequency. Loop current of 100mA around 200m to 500m length horizontal loops were driven by 5W to 10W drivers. Paging sensitivities of 100μA ft. sq. turn were typical. For a narrow tall building a vertical loop was used successfully. Many such systems are still in use, but the cost of installing the loop cable tends to be prohibitive.

National wide area systems in Europe, started by the Netherlands PTT in 1964, were followed by public member operator licences being granted to private consortia. In North America, however, the concept of private subscriber local wide area systems was developed early in the 1970's and by 1988 there were more than 600 radio common units and 40 telephone companies providing services to 1.5 million subscribers.

45.3 Frequency allocations

Frequencies for on site and wide area paging vary from country to country. The following is not exhaustive, but is indicative of the challenge facing the design engineers.

45.3.1 UK

45.3.1.1 *On site*

26.2375MHz to 26.8655MHz.
26.978MHZ to 27.262MHz; 31.725MHz; 31.75MHz; 31.775MHz (special allocation).
49.0MHz to 49.4875MHz.
49.425MHz; 49.4375MHz; 49.45MHZ; 49.4625MHz; 49.475MHz (speech permitted).
161.00MHz to 161.10MHz. Return speech (emergency/special licence only).
459.125MHz to 459.45 and 495.475MHz. (Shared with local communication systems.)
161.0MHz to 161.10 and 161.1125MHz. Return speech. (Shared with local communication systems.)

45.3.1.2 *Wide area*

V.H.F.

National and public systems exist on frequencies 138MHz to 141MHz and 153MHz to 153.5MHz. Private wide area schemes are assigned 'to manufacturers' preferred frequencies' in the 153MHz band. Additionally, the ERMES system occupies the band 169.425MHz to 169.80MHz. 'Overlay' and emergency systems are possible in conjunction with mobile radio systems, which cover the band 138MHz to 174MHz.

U.H.F.

Private wide area schemes are concentrated in the band 454.0125MHz to 454.825MHz. The 'Europage' (pan-European) scheme has been assigned to 466.075MHz. Again it is possible to have overlay systems in the mobile bands 450MHz to 470MHz.

45.3.2 Germany

45.3.2.1 *On site*

27.51MHz; 40.76MHz and 40.68MHz. 20kHz channel spacing.
40.665MHz to 40.695MHz. 10kHz channel spacing.
468.35MHz; 468.375MHz; 468.4MHz to 469.150MHz.
Talkback 151.07MHz; 160.49MHz to 160.55MHz; 170.55MHZ to 170.79MHz.

45.3.2.2 *Wide area*

Cityruf scheme 465.97MHz; 466.070MHz; 466.23MHz.
Private wide area, proposed frequency band 440MHz to 450MHz; 12.5kHz.

45.3.3 France

45.3.3.1 *On site*

26.635MHz; 26.695MHz; 26.745MHz.
446.475MHz to 446.525MHz.
Talkback 152.0125MHz and 445.50MHz.
All frequencies are narrow channel (10/12.5kHz).

45.3.3.2 *Wide area*

31.30 MHz.
Pan-European 466.075MHz. Other overlay/emergency services schemes are operating across all the mobile bands.

45.3.4 Holland

45.3.4.1 *On site*

26.5, 26.6, 26.7, 26.8, 26.9MHz. (Low power systems.)
26.15MHz to 27.85MHz. (Excluding the above frequencies.)
39MHz to 40MHz.

Talkback 156MHz to 174MHz.
450MHz to 470MHz.

45.3.4.2   *Wide area*

PTT Semafoon scheme 154.9875MHz and 164.35MHz (Benelux). Emergency services etc. across the mobile bands.

45.3.5   Italy

45.3.5.1   *On site*

26.20MHz; 26.35MHz and 26.50MHz.
459.65MHz and 469.65MHz.
Talkback 161MHz to 161.10MHz.

45.3.5.2   *Wide area*

A proposal was put forward for a PTT scheme on 161.175MHz, but this has been overtaken by the pan-European scheme on u.h.f.

45.3.6   Belgium

45.3.6.1   *On site*

Frequencies centred on 26MHz and 40MHz, and on 440MHz to 470MHz.

45.3.6.2   *Wide area*

PTT Semaphoon scheme 147.25MHz (national) and 164.35MHz (Benelux).
Overlay and emergency schemes on mobile frequencies.

45.3.7   Denmark

45.3.7.1   *On site*

29MHz to 31.42MHz h.f.
445.9MHz to 445.975MHz u.h.f.
Talkback frequencies at 146MHz, 161MHz and 422MHz.

45.3.7.2   *Wide area*

Public system (OPS) 469.5MHz; 469.65MHz and 469.95MHz.

45.3.8   Sweden

45.3.8.1   *On site*

26.1MHz to 26.958MHz.
Talkback 160MHz.

45.3.8.2   *Wide area*

169.425MHz to 170.0375MHz Public Regional Paging Service (MiniCall).

Overlay and emergency services etc. in the PMR bands at v.h.f. and u.h.f. 138MHz to 174MHz and 410MHz to 470MHz.

45.3.9   USA and Canada

The manner of frequency allocations in these countries is according to end user category, rather than any specific frequency bands. This means that the whole mobile spectrum is encompassed. To cover both countries, pager manufacturers have to provide for 27MHz to 50 MHz h.f.; 138MHz to 174MHz v.h.f.; 445MHz to 470MHz u.h.f.. 900 MHz is also popular in these countries. None of the bands is divided into on site or wide area categories. 931MHz is used for satellite paging.

45.4   Paging receiver types

There are three types of paging receivers. The first and simplest is a tone receiver, which can have a number of different audible tone patterns (usually four or eight) to alert the bearer, but it does not display numbers or messages. The bearer takes a predetermined action e.g. telephone a given number, or proceed to a location. Since there can be up to eight tones others can indicate alternative actions or degree of urgency.

The numeric pager has a display of typically 12 or 24 digits thereby enabling the caller to send a telephone number that he wishes the bearer to contact. By prior arrangement the numbers sent can represent a message. The pager is usually able to store these numeric messages in a memory.

The third type of pager is the alphanumeric, which has a display of 16, 32, or 80 characters. Between 500 and 5000 characters of message can be stored in the memory and can be read by scrolling. Unlike the tone and numeric pagers which can be called directly by telephone, the sender must use an alpha keyboard to send alpha messages. Generally wide area paging users send alpha messages via an operator at a bureaux service while on site users receive alpha messages from the local paging system operator.

45.5   On site paging

45.5.1   Applications

On site paging systems are intended for the coverage of a premises or a local site completely within the user's control. These systems are usually owned and licensed by the user and vary from a single low power transmitter/control unit operating with 5 pagers to large high power, multi-site, multi-access systems with 1000 or more pagers.

All three types of pager can be used in on site applications but, because speech messages are also permitted, tone alert and numeric systems have generally satisfied the needs of staff location and one way message transmissions.

By preprogramming a series of fixed alpha messages into the receiver's memory, which are displayed on receipt of predetermined number sequences dialled by the calling party, a numeric pager provides many on site alpha numeric functions at low cost. With the growing demand for the transmission of data in the health care market and process industries, the on site alpha pager is becoming more in demand.

Sites vary from large warehouse areas with few personnel, where travelling time is saved by updating requirements from stores office to fork lift truck driver, to densely populated sites such as hospitals where emergency calls for groups of staff (cardiac arrest teams) can be summoned as a unit by the group call facility. A waitress, with a tone pager, can be notified by the chef when her next order is ready, and a broker can be continuously updated of selected stock prices when a few miles from his office, by using an alphanumeric pager on a private wide area system.

45.5.2 Code formats

There have been many different on site paging system manufacturers since 1956, and each has been free to devise its own code format. Early proprietary formats used sequential audio tone modulation using two inductor coils 2cm x 1.3cm x 1.3cm in the range of 500Hz to 3.4kHz. For example a tone of 640Hz had a coil of inductance 11.7H and a Q of 10. Vibrating mechanical reeds were also used to achieve higher Q's and more frequencies, thereby increasing system capacity, but at the expense of mechanical robustness. These were ultimately replaced by active filters which could then be made smaller with high Q and high stability by using hybrid thick film circuits.

By this time the EIA (Electronic Industries Association) had standardised on two tone and five tone sequential tone formats in the 67.0Hz to 1687.2Hz frequency range. Since such a two tone code can have a user capacity of over 3000 this format could be adapted for speech and was suitable for even the largest on site systems.

As the market demanded more features and facilities and even smaller receiver size, digital code formats were devised. Unfortunately the benefits, such as the narrow noise bandwidths of the two tone systems, meant a sensitivity loss, when using digital formats of 4dB to 6dB. A modern on site digital proprietary code format specification is shown in Table 45.1.

45.5.3 Small systems

A small modern paging system will probably consist of a transcoder and five tone or numeric pagers. The transcoder is a combined digital paging encoder consisting of a keyboard and a 10 digit display, and a small 1W transmitter incorporating an integral microphone. In the 25MHz to 54Mhz h.f. band a standalone base loaded whip aerial would be provided, but at u.h.f. a flexible stub antenna is connected directly into the encoder.

1W is sufficient r.f. power to provide good coverage in the office building environment, or 200 metres to 300 metres in a hotel block, and up to 8Km. on an open site. Range varies due to attenuation of buildings especially if steel reinforced structures or sun reflective windows are used. Attenuations at different frequencies can be encountered as shown in Table 45.2, which give average relative levels in dB. It has been found that, when walking with a pager, peak to trough variations of 30dB can be encountered due to Rayleigh fading effects, so this table is only a guide.

Table 45.2 Attenuation at different frequencies

	30MHz dB	150MHz dB	450MHz dB	850MHz dB
Urban	+35	+20	+10	+12
Suburban	+20	+10	0	+2
Rural	+6	0	−10	−8

At h.f., r.f. noise from electrical machinery, lighting, power lines and motor vehicles is prevalent. U.h.f. has marked benefits, in penetration of modern buildings and cellars. Some particularly r.f. noisy equipment used in hospitals e.g. diathermy units, are avoided for safety reasons by special frequency allocations for paging.

45.5.4 Telephone coupling

For many users, with say 20 to 100 pager wearers, passing messages through a paging controller, who may well also be the switchboard operator, is inconvenient and direct paging access by the caller's own telephone extension is desirable. A telephone coupled encoder may be installed via one of the PABX extensions to satisfy this requirement. The units can have call transfer or absence registration programmed via the telephone for a limited number of pagers (e.g. 10). The system will be capable of sending tone, numeric messages, followed by up to 120 seconds of speech, but this is limited to 30 seconds speech transmission by regulations in the UK.

A 'meet me' facility is available via the PABX whereby the caller pages the person he wishes to contact, holds, and is connected directly through the PABX when the person dials the 'meet me' number.

Fig.45.1 shows the block diagram of a telephone coupled encoder which, via a telephone extension, decodes over dialled DTMF tones

Table 45.1 A typical digital proprietary format

Code capacity addresses	10 000 x 4 systems
Paging rate (call/sec)	Max 13 c/s tone alerts preamble. 40ch. 0.38 c/s. 80ch. 0.25 c/s
Data rate	512bit/s
Message rate	512bit/s
Radio channel	25kHz
Modulation	±4.5kHz FM FSK
Transmission mode	Manchester or NRZ
Multiple transmitter conditions	Quasi-Sync or sequential
Line transmission	Data modems 1200bit/s
Absolute line delay	0.25ms + 0.195ms from transmitter. Telegraph distortion ≤10% Isochronous
Error correcting potential	2 errors in 12 bits preamble. 2 bits in 32 non-message codewords. 1 bit in 32 message code words
Battery economy	Yes. Variable unframed
Message capability	No limit

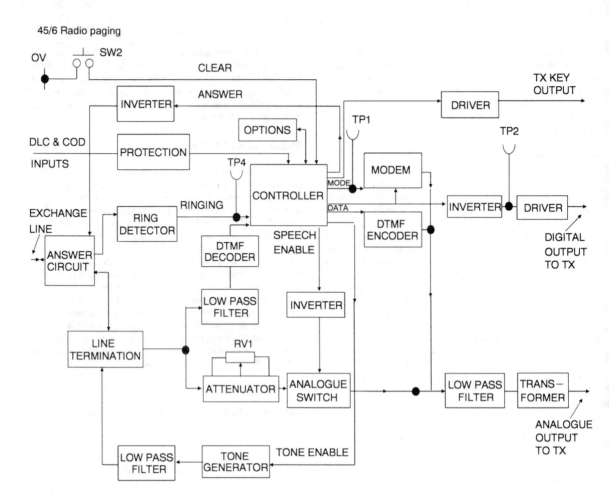

Figure 45.1 Block diagram of a telephone coupled encoder

to generate paging calls. Programmed software is stored in a 8K EPROM. Two isolation barriers are provided, one to connect to a PABX and the other for a dedicated line. All 16 DTMF tones are decoded and encoded. Provision for different line levels has also to be made, e.g. −10dBm to −20dBm (600Ω) on the incoming telephone line, and attenuated to −13dBm (600Ω) out to the private wire.

45.5.5 Regulating authority requirements

Duration of the speech part of paging messages is limited by many European countries to 30 seconds only. In France this is limited to 10 seconds. While the usual compliance with and approval to radio regulations are required, telephone coupling equipment will also have to be approved by telephone line and safety authorities. In the UK BABT (British Approvals Board for Telecommunications) is responsible for type approval of telephone line connection equipment and for safety compliance to BS6301. In Germany the line approval is undertaken by ZZF. In the USA FCC has responsibility as does the Department of Communications in Canada.

45.5.6 Talk back paging

Portable units comprising a paging receiver and a transmitter capable of speech acknowledgement are used on about 10% of all on

site systems. Such systems allow 2-way speech and 2-way signalling in any combination provided that CTCSS (Continuous Tone Controlled Squelch System) or selective calling are used in both directions. A base receiver is required fitted with a matching CTCSS or selective calling squelch.

In the UK this system is licensed as local communications and pairs of frequencies are allocated with the receivers in the 459MHz band, and transmitters in the 161MHz band. Typical specifications of a range of talkback pagers which are required for different European markets are shown in Table 45.3. In France talkback paging is at 445.5MHz with a channel spacing of 12.5kHz and maximum ERP of 50mW.

An additional feature is that the control station can be switched to talkthrough, so that one receiver can talk direct to another. This is a useful facility for first aid teams or security guards.

The European Selective Paging Association (ESPA) are currently considering putting forward proposals to ETSI to replace the cross band talkback frequencies by 10 additional frequencies at u.h.f.

45.6 Large on site systems

Figure 45.2 is an example of a large on site paging scheme and is fully featured. It has a remotely linked section of the system as would be found on a two sited hospital complex or a large brewery.

Table 45.3 Typical talkback pager specification

Receiver frequency range	25MHz to 54MHz	406MHz to 490MHz
Channel spacing	10, 12.5, 20, 25kHz	20kHz to 25kHz
Sensitivity (typical call)	20μV/m	15μV/m
Speech (12dB Sinad)	40μV/m	30μV/m
Adjacent channel select (typical)	65dB	70dB
Spurious response (typical)	50dB	60dB
Spurious emissions (max.)	2nW	2nW
Transmitter frequency range	146MHz to 174MHz	
Channel spacing	10, 12.5, 20, or 25kHz	
Output power (typical)	20mW ERP	
Talkback time limits	Unrestricted/restricted according to regulations	
Audio distortion	≤ 5%	
Spurious emissions (max.)	0.25μW	
CTCSS (optional)	To EIA standards	
RS220 frequencies	103.5, 114.8, 151.4, 167.9, 225.7, 250.3Hz etc.	

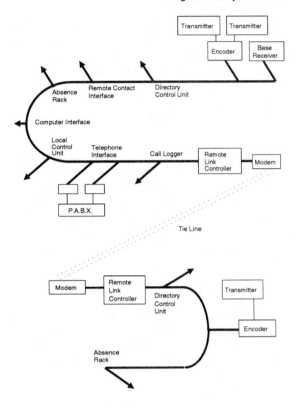

Figure 45.2 A fully featured on site paging system

Modular systems such as these may have as few as 15 or as many as 1500 pagers. The common bus connecting these units forms a local area network with a bus cable length of up to 1km. The bus cable is 8 way, with one pair of data lines (RS485 standard), 1 pair outgoing speech, 1 pair return speech and the remainder used for earth connection. The data rate is 19.2kbit/s and digital data voltages are 0 and +5V. For the speech pairs frequency band is 300Hz to 3kHz at a line level of –13dBm.

The master/slave architecture, where one module is used as the master and the rest of the modules are treated as slave devices, operates a communications protocol using a token passing scheme. This scheme gives permission for slave devices to use the system data bus on command of the master. The master also holds a device parameter table, which stores the initialisation parameters for every module on its bus.

Operators can send paging calls and enter and update information by means of small local control units, or larger alpha numeric control units and, if on a large site connected by private wire, operation can also be made by remote control unit via a gateway module.

The telephone interface units shown are via interface cards, which provide a direct hard wired link between the paging system and PTT or other approved private lines, selector level circuits, extension circuits or tie line type circuits. The cards provide the correct electrical signal conditioning and safety requirements of such connections.

For direct machine driven paging calls, or push button driven paging calls, a remote contact interface is used. Typical uses are for callers who require entry to a locked building patrolled by a security guard carrying a pager, or by process engineers who are supervising many pieces of continuous running equipment, and need to be notified of faults, or important machine parameter changes.

Connection to a standard computer by RS232c line is shown. The computer operator could also page by directory viewing if this software is entered into computer memory.

The call logging facility provides a record of times and user numbers actually called on the system, which is useful when reviewing system usage.

Absence rack units automatically register the user as absent, when he places his pager in one of the slots. Subsequent callers will be informed that he is unavailable or the call may be transferred to an alternative pager. These are usually sited at staff exits and usually contain a charging facility to recharge pagers overnight.

The remote link controller allows the system data bus to be extended via any RS232c compatible link. For examples modems and telephone lines, KiloStream, MegaStream, or data networks can all be used to carry the link.

The system has a large data base containing user, remote contact interface and team records. This provides comprehensive data processing and organising functions for these records and the memory is protected against power supply failure by battery backup. The memory allows all records to be sent to a dedicated printer for a hard copy.

Through this unit, a pager's identity can be transferred to another pager, if the first pager is withdrawn from service for repair. If a user is going off site, for example, or if the user is on holiday, he can have his calls transferred to another user's pager, by entering the relevant data and identity into the data base. New teams of users can be constructed readily by the operator, for group calling purposes.

Figure 45.2 shows paging transmitters from each of the two sites and also a base receiver, to enable talkback paging to be used.

45.6.1 On site transmitters

On small systems 0.5W at u.h.f. and 1.0W at h.f., are sufficient transmitter r.f. powers to satisfy the small site application, and these can be integral with the encoder. For larger sites, higher powers are required with appropriately sited antennas. A limit of 5W ERP is generally imposed by regulation in Europe, (limit is 2W in Belgium) so it often becomes necessary to install more than one transmitter on the large area sites and campus (100 sq. km). Table 45.4 shows typical on site transmitter specifications. Greater r.f. powers, up to 25W or 100W depending on the system, are allowed in North America.

Since a variety of proprietary analogue and digital code formats, as well as speech, have to be transmitted, modulation techniques differ. FM is suitable for many applications but for non return to zero codes (Figure 45.3) such as CCIR RPC1 (POCSAG), FSK modulation is also required. Although POCSAG is a large capacity code not supporting speech, it can be used on site. Mixed paging

code formats, both analogue and digital, can be found on large on site systems.

45.6.2 Transmitter synchronisation

On large sites, or in areas of difficult propagation, it is often necessary to use multiple transmitters to give adequate radio coverage. Sequential polling is the obvious solution for those on site systems where speech is not used. When both paging calling and speech is used either quasi synchronisation or full synchronisation may be used. The former requires transmitters of high inherent stability, $\pm 2 \times 10^8$ over -10^oC to $+50^oC$, and hence is expensive for on site use. Full synchronisation can give poorer radio performance in that a fixed standing wave pattern is set up, leading to fixed null areas. The cost is however less for small systems and thus line synchronisation units are used as one method of fully synchronising transmitters.

Transmitters in both the h.f. and u.h.f. bands will probably use phase locked techniques with a crystal reference oscillator as the frequency determining element. An audio signal in the 2.8kHz to 3.0kHZ range, derived by dividing this oscillator, may be sent down a telephone line. At the slave transmitter, the crystal oscillator, divided to the same frequency, can be fed to a phase detector with the filtered signal from the line. The resultant error signal then controls the slave oscillator frequency using varactor diodes.

Table 45.4 Typical on site transmitter specifications

Frequency range	25 to 54MHz		390 - 490MHz	
Frequency stability	± 10ppm from -10 to $+55^oC$		5ppm from -10 to $+55^oC$	
Output power	5 watts nominal		5 watts nominal	
RF load	50Ω nominal impedance, VSWR better than 2.1		50Ω nominal impedance, VSWR better than 2.1	
Channel spacing	10/12.5/20/25kHz		20/25kHz, 12.5kHz	
Modulation type	FM	FM with FSK	FM	FM with FSK
Modulation system	Data F2D; Speech F3E	Data F2D, F1D; Speech F3E	Data F2D; Speech F3E	Data F2D, F1D; Speech F3E
Spurious emissions	Better than 73dB (250nW) below carrier. 100kHz to 2GHz (excluding wanted and two adjacent channels)			
Line input	-33dBm to -13dBm 600Ω balanced line			
Mains input	100V to 240V a.c. nominal 50/60Hz			
External transmitter control	-13dBm 600Ω speech and data outputs for modulation/control of a second transmitter			
Back channel input	TTL compatible for line transmission of data			
Line synchronisation (P211 only)	Input/output for future installation of optional modules			
Master-slave	Connectors provided for optional			
D.C. output	13.5V d.c. 50mA maximum for ancillary equipment			
Panel display (7 segments)	Standby transmitter keyed and transmitter failed			
Internal LED indictors	Phase-lock fail high reverse power and line sync fail			
Alarm outputs	Open-collector logic outputs for transmitter keyed (on/off) and r.f. output (absent/present)			

The telephone line interfaces from the master and to the slave will be required to meet the national standard of the country in which the equipment is used. Some degradation in the S/N ratio (modulation on/modulation off) will occur from noise on the synchronisation line. Since the effective multiplication of the controlled crystal is much greater in the h.f. band than in the u.h.f. band, a specification of signal to noise ratio of 40dB at u.h.f. requires a much better signal to noise of the crystal oscillator itself, than is needed to meet 40dB in the lower frequency h.f. case. It should be such that noise on the line will not interfere with normal working with a 20dB signal to noise ratio at the slave end of the line. Noise bursts however will temporarily unlock the synchronisation.

A guide to a specification is that the slave must synchronise correctly with noise bursts of maximum duration of 1 second, at an amplitude equal to the synchronising signal. Frequency of the master oscillator, may drift by up 40ppm at h.f. and ±10ppm at u.h.f. over worst conditions of temperature and/or time. Acquisition of lock and synchronisation of performance should be met over the whole of these ranges.

Speech signals may be passed down the synchronisation line, in which case a low pass filter will be used to attenuate speech frequencies above 2.5kHz. This leaves the range 2.8kHz to 3.0kHz to be available for the control signal.

45.7   Wide area paging

45.7.1   Tone code formats

City wide paging was developed by US BELL in the early 1960's, followed by the Dutch PTT who opened their national Semafoon network at v.h.f. using Motorola EIA 5 Tone signalling. This had an address capacity of 100,000 with a calling rate of 5 calls per second. Tone duration was 33mS and tone frequency relationship was an arithmetic progression. The first pan-European system, Eurosignal, commenced in 1967, uses 6 tone sequential system and has a capacity of over one million, with a calling rate of 1.25 calls per second. Tone duration is 100mS and tone frequency relationship is a geometric progression.

45.7.2   Digital code formats

Bell Canada introduced its wide area digital paging system in 1970. Compared to sequential tone formats, digital formats can provide greater system address capacities, much greater battery economy and thereby use smaller power cells, faster call rates, pager size reduction by integration, additional functions such as storage of calls and messages in memory, multiple addresses and many other features. Sweden inaugurated its national digital paging service using a subcarrier on the national broadcast system in 1970 and Japan, already up to 600,000 on a tone system opened the NTT digital system in 1978. Meanwhile in North America the majority of systems supplied since 1973 were based on the Golay code format.

In 1978 in the UK the British Post Office announced and agreed a common digital paging system, POCSAG (Post Office Code Standardisation Advisory Group). This was the result of 2 years work by the British Post Office and representatives from 16 major pager manufacturers under the chairmanship of Mr R Tridgell. This standard was adopted by the CCIR as Radio Paging Code RPC No.1. In 1980 the advisory group met again with world wide

Table 45.5   Comparison of digital code formats

Parameter	GSC	POCSAG	NTT
Code type	Golay 32.12	BCH 32.21	BCH 31.16
Address capacity	1 x 4 address	2 x 4 address	30k x 2 address
Tone call rate	5 call/s	15 call/s at 512 baud	5.7 call/s
Message call rate	2.5 call/s 12 CH; 0.45 call/s 80 CH	5 call/s 10 CH; 0.52 call/s 80 CH	
Transmission rate	300/600	512 or 1200	200 units
Decoder type	asynchronous	Bit synchronisation and word framing	
Random errors: Detection	6	5	6
Random errors: Correction	3	2	3
Burst errors: Detection	11	11	15
Burst errors: Correction	5	5	7

representation, and minimum standards for numeric and alpha numeric messaging were agreed.

Table 45.5 compares the basis parameters of three of the most significant digital paging code formats used to date.

45.7.3   POCSAG

An outline of the POCSAG format is shown in Figure 45.3. A transmission sequence starts with a series of alternate digits, 101010..... as a preamble to awaken the paging receiver to obtain synchronisation. This lasts for at least 576 bits which is equal to the duration of one batch plus one codeword. A synchronisation code word is then followed by eight frames, each two code words long. Each pager is allocated an address in one of the eight frames and having gained synchronisation it need not turn fully on until that frame's time period, thereby saving battery power.

If there is a message for a pager then it immediately follows the address code word. It can be any number of consecutive code words and may continue for more than one batch, but the synchronisation code word remains at the front of every batch. The message end is always followed by the next address code word or an idle word.

The receiver distinguishes address from message code words by reading the first bit (F) which is a flag bit, equal to zero for an address code word and equal to one for a message code word.

Address code words consist of 21 bits the 18 most significant of which determine the address. The three least significant are not transmitted, but are used to identify the frame in which the address code word is transmitted. Bits 20 and 21 are two function bits which serve to indicate which of the 4 addresses of the pager is being called. Both address and message code words have a final bit chosen to give even parity following the parity check bits.

For numeric messages only a 4 bit per character format is used, restricting messages to decimal numerals, U (urgency indicator), space, hyphen, opening and closing brackets and a spare symbol. This format saves air time, but for full alphanumeric messages a full 150 7-bit character set is used.

When using the numeric only format the pager address with the message will have its function bits set to 00. When the 7 bits per character format is used the pager address has its function bits set to 11.

45.7.4 Wide area transmission

Transmitters of typically 100W/250W are used to cover wide area paging zones, but there are many exceptions of much higher powers being used across the world depending on local terrain. The coverage area for the system is generally divided into zones. These zones vary considerably in size from 256 sq. km to 25,600 sq. km depending on service that is being provided. The principle however is the same, in that the paging subscriber pays for the use of his pager in chosen zones.

All paging calls are usually sent to a control centre where they are dispatched to the relevant zones transmitter controller. The paging calls are stored, batched and then transmitted. Some systems transmit calls twice or even three times depending on service provider.

Transmission in these zones can be sequential or simultaneous. Often only one frequency is employed but BT, who claim to cover 97% of the UK population with an estimated half a million subscribers, have 2 frequency channels and 40 zones. Since zones are adjacent, with varying degrees of signal overlap and co channel interference, calls are transmitted in time slots. Zones are allocated a time slot such that overlap is minimised. Time slots can be varied in length depending on the paging population in each zone.

For the RPC No.1. code format sequential transmission can also be used within a zone, but where traffic is heavy simultaneous transmission must be employed. Since the transmitters are not locked together they run in a quasi synchronous mode, and therefore require higher stability with temperature and ageing (2×10^8 over -10°C to $+50^{\circ}$C and 0.5 ppm /year) than a transmitter used for sequential transmission. They must have a maximum line delay differential no greater than 250µs and isochronous distortion no greater than 10%.

It is possible in zone overlap areas or with time slotting, to receive the same paging call twice, albeit one of the calls is at a much lower signal strength level than the other. Many pagers have memory configured such that they reject the second identical call.

45.7.4.1 *Digital modulation*

To modulate the digital signal phase modulation is unsuitable, and therefore Frequency Shift Keying (FSK) is used. For the particular characteristics of POCSAG and similar formats, non return to zero FSK is used. This means that the modulation frequency is either +4.5kHz or –4.5kHz and the modulation does not diminish to zero during the change. Three common types of digital modulation for a binary number are shown in Figure 45.4. In NRZ level a one is represented by one level and a zero by the other level. In NRZ mark, a one is represented by a change in level and a zero by no change in level. In biphase level a one and a zero are represented by a positive/negative pulse sequence, each pulse being half a symbol wide.

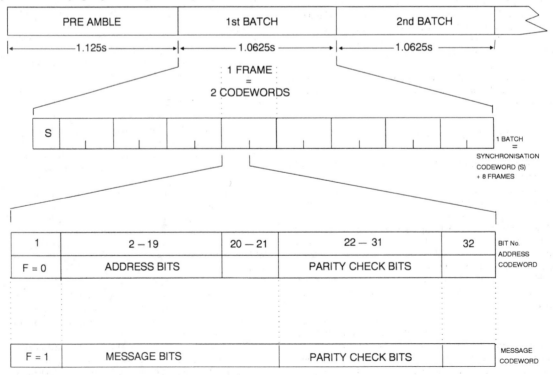

Figure 45.3 RPC no. 1 POCSAG code format

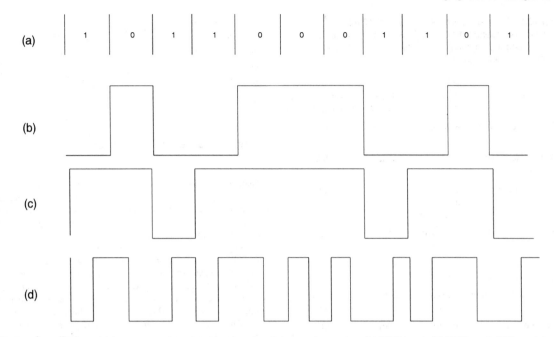

Figure 45.4 Three common types of modulation used for digital paging codes: (a) NRZ level; (b) NRZ mark (differential encoding); (c) Bi-Phase level (Manchester code)

45.7.5 Swedish Mobilsoekring system (MBS)

This nation wide system was launched by the Swedish PTT in late 1978 and uses the existing broadcast FM infrastructure. It is a cost effective system for thinly populated countries; 8 million people in 449,750 sq. km. Use is made of one of the stereo broadcast programmes in the 87MHz to 104MHz band, which covers most of Sweden and some of Norway and Denmark.

Transmission is by the differentially coded binary information modulating a 1.187 kHz (±0.1Hz) tone which itself modulates a 57kHz (±6Hz) sub-carrier with maximum deviation of ±3kHz. This 57kHz signal is transmitted as a sub-carrier with the FM programme signal. The sub-carrier is phase locked to the 19kHz stereo multiplexed pilot signal.

Because the programme operates in different areas on different frequencies the receiver scans the 87MHz to 104MHz band every 10 seconds looking for an MBS system identification code. The caller dials a four digit entry code, a subscriber 6 digit number and further digits for options, such as a privacy code which is used to prevent unauthorised callers paging the subscriber. A 52 bit paging code is sent which consists of two blocks of 16 information bits and 10 parity check bits.

45.8 Paging receiver design

The challenge to the paging receiver designer is always to package more facilities into a smaller unit without losing radio performance. In 1970 a typical size was 13cm x 6cm x 2cm but today wide area tone units can be 5cm x 4cm x 1.5cm, or 5cm x 1.5cm x 1.5cm depending on the type of battery used. A numeric pager the size of a fountain pen has been used for several years, and a pager in a wrist watch has now been launched. Credit card style pagers 7.5cm x 0.5cm x 5cm are currently available on the Hong Kong national network at 280MHz and use a 1.4v zinc air cell of 700mAh capacity. Many of these more ambitious physical formats have compromised sensitivity when actually worn on the body.

Paging receiver designs must match world wide requirements in the range 25MHz to 900MHz.

45.8.1 Receiver specifications

Typical receiver specifications are shown in Table 45.6. Each country has its own regulations set by its type approval authorities (PTT's, FCC etc.) and they usually differ. Under the European Community Directives, harmonisation of specifications will occur and if a paging equipment is awarded the CE mark then it will be approved for sale in any EEC market. This will save the costs of multiple approvals and reduce time delays from the manufacturers.

The regulations appertaining to paging receivers both in Europe and North America will be restricted to EMC interference from the receiver and, in Europe, immunity from external interference to the receiver. The European regulation also specifies a minimum immunity to electrostatic discharge. The actual specification and limits of the new common European standard are due to be announced in 1992. Operators of wide area systems will however still determine their own more comprehensive minimum performance requirements specification, which the manufacturer's equipment will have to meet if he wishes to sell to them.

45.8.2 Receiver architecture

The receiver architectures that are usually employed are single superhet, double superhet and direct conversion. The latter lends itself to a high degree of integration to two or even a single multi chip circuit, plus supporting circuitry of voltage multipliers, integral antenna, alerter transducer and battery. This arrangement makes for a very small pager especially if a button cell is used as the battery.

Table 45.6 Typical receiver specifications. On body sensitivity is dependent on code format and pager usage whilst co-channel rejection depends on code, speech and measurement techniques

Parameter	25 to 49MHz	138 to 174MHz	406 to 470MHz
On body sensitivity: face-on	8μV/m	5μV/m	8V/m
On body sensitivity: 8 pos.ave	12μV/m	8μV/m	10μV/m
Channel spacing	10/12.5kHz or 20/25kHz	25kHz	20/25kHz or 12.5kHz
Adjacent channel selectivity	>50dB or >60dB	>65dB	>65dB
Spurious emissions up to 1GHz	2nW	2nW	2nW
Co-channel rejection	−2dB to -10dB	−2dB to −10dB	−2dB to −10dB
Inter modulation rejection	>45dB	>50dB	>50dB

Initially it was found to be vulnerable to interference from nearby high power transmitters due to poor AM rejection, but now there are several techniques for minimising this affect.

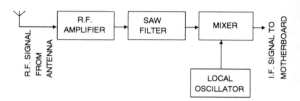

Figure 45.5 Superhet r.f. block diagram

Analogue processed speech is not possible using direct conversion thus it is only suitable for wide area applications. Typical single superhet and direct conversion block diagrams are shown in Figure 45.5 and Figure 45.6. Figure 45.7 shows the block diagram of the decoder and audio sections. A wide area decoder would omit the audio amplifier section. Speech is shown outputting to a speaker but it may also be simply channelled through the beep transducer.

The latter allows a smaller on site pager but many customers insist on better quality and louder speech than is possible from the small beep transducer, whose audio characteristic will have a substantial resonant peak in the 2.5kHz to 3kHz band. This peak is necessary to gain maximum loudness from the transducer at the beep frequency. Transducer beep output is often a requirement in the operator's specification, usually in the range 75dB to 85dB SPL measured in an anechoic chamber facing the transducer output, and at a point 30cm away.

The front end r.f. noise factor using the very low voltage supply rail and minimum current, is a very important factor in the S/N ratio which finally enters the decoder, but the inefficient antennae that have to be employed largely determine the overall sensitivity.

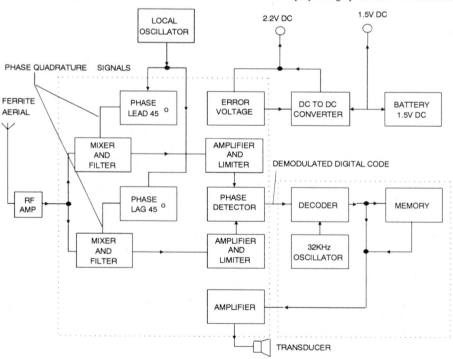

Figure 45.6 Direct conversion receivers

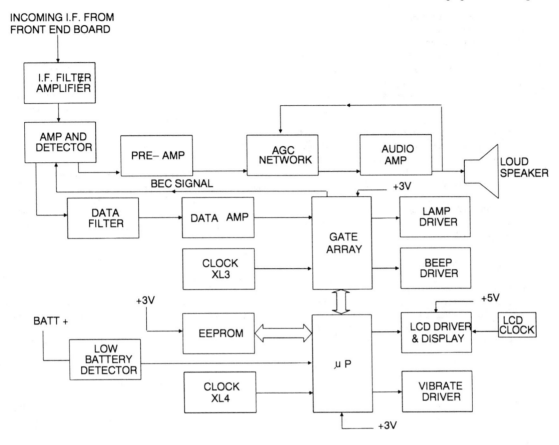

INCOMING I.F. FROM
FRONT END BOARD

Figure 45.7 Decoder and audio block diagram

45.8.3 Antennas

Ferrite antennas are usually used for 25MHz to 54MHz band receivers and sometimes in the 137MHz to 174MHz band, and are wound with flat copper strip. For the 430MHz to 490MHz band antennas can be a helical coil, discontinuous directional ring radiator, etc. Unfortunately, because of the limited space within the pager and close proximity of other components and earth tracks, u.h.f. antennas are not able to operate at their optimum. While antennas may result in good calling sensitivity (e.g. 5μV/m) measured in an open field attached to a pole or on a strip line in the lab, performance maybe considerably reduced when worn by the user due to the effect of the body.

45.8.4 Performance measurement methods

There are two particular difficulties in performing measurements on the paging receiver:

1. The calling signal must be the pager's digitally modulated address.
2. The integral antenna prevents direct connection from the signal generator.

Not withstanding the difficulties, the measurement method which has been the most commonly used is to set the signal generator

below the level of calling and increase this level in 0.5dB stages, sending the pager's address 5 times at each stage. The generator level, at which 5 successful calls out of 5 calls are sent, is deemed to be the sensitivity. This can be shown to be related to a theoretical 87% probability of calling.

Another method, from IEC No. 49, and mandatory for pagers, when determining the sensitivity of equipment used on the German Cityruf system, is as follows. The signal generator level is adjusted so that less than 10% of the tone only calls are successful. The signal is continuously repeated so as to ascertain each time whether a tone only call is successful or not. The level is increased by 1dB until three successive calls are successful. The level is then noted. The level is reduced by 1dB and the new level noted. The signal is then sent 20 times. The level of the signal:

1. Remains the same if a tone only call is successful.
2. Is increased by 1dB, and the new level noted if a tone only call is not successful.
3. Is reduced by 1dB and the new level noted if 3 successive tone only calls are successful.

The pager sensitivity is deemed to be the arithmetic mean of the noted levels.

As direct line connection of the modulated call is not possible, the pager must be placed in a uniform field strength capable of being varied. Three methods are commonly used:

1. The pager is strapped to a wooden pole facing the transmitting antenna 1.5m up from the ground in an open field, and is sent a signal from a calibrated antenna 30 metres away. It is important that the area is clear of trees and nearby buildings, to avoid reflections distorting the uniform electromagnetic field.
2. The pager may be placed in the centre of a strip line.
3. The pager is placed in a TEM (Transverse ElectroMagnetic) cell.

The first method provides an absolute result directly, but due to the nature of the calling process, several results should be averaged. Although the strip line and TEM cell fields may be calculated, it is usual to take the portable TEM cell out to the free field site, and correlate the face-on level determined on pole, directly to the required TEM cell level.

The second and third methods require a radio noise free environment which, along with portability, is the main advantage of using a TEM cell as in the third method.

45.8.5   Free field sensitivity

Because, in practice, transmissions may arrive at a receiver from any angle, the sensitivity specification is very often expressed in terms of the free field 8 position log average. For this purpose the pager on pole is rotated and measured every $45°$ starting with E1. The sensitivity is said to be E_m, given by Equation 45.1.

$$E_m = \left(\frac{8}{\dfrac{1}{E_1{}^2} + \dfrac{1}{E_2{}^2} + \dots + \dfrac{1}{E_8{}^2}} \right)^{\frac{1}{2}} \qquad (45.1)$$

The relationship between face-on free field sensitivity and the 8 position average is fixed for a given receiver design, but needs to be determined by field measurement (a loop aerial will have significant nulls at $90°$ and $270°$ with respect to face-on, whereas a helical mono-pole will have a much more circular polar diagram). Thus a correlation factor between the 8 position free field sensitivity and the face-on figure in the TEM cell can also be established.

For some public wide area operator's specifications, pager on pole measurements are called up. Others specify pager worn on body measurements in free field. While different antennas are affected in different ways by the body, those favoured are those whose performance is enhanced by the body. Since different bodies affect the same antenna to different degrees, in order to establish a claim for on body sensitivity, measurements of sensitivity of the same pager on 30–50 different people are required. However, there appears to be no obvious correlation between height or weight of the wearer and the sensitivity measured. It has been found that sensitivity measurements made on various pager designs, each worn by 40 people, can have standard deviations of approximately $4.0\mu V/m$.

45.8.6   Power sources

To meet world wide markets the pager must be designed with easily available primary cells because, with the exception of on site systems with more than 20 to 40 pagers, the user generally does not wish to purchase a charger. This considerably restricts the choice of cell since suitable button cells are not freely available outside N. America and major European countries. As a battery life of 800 to 900 hours or about 2 to 3 months, depending on paging receiver and system usage, is required then the AA cell is widely used. With improvements in circuit techniques and world wide availability, the

AAA cell with renewal periods of 1 to 2 months is now often used. Rechargeable AA cells of 500 mAHrs capacity may be employed and single or multiway charging racks are available. Non rechargeable cells, such as zinc, alkaline, manganese dioxide, start life with 1.5V and slowly decrease to around 0.9V. Rechargeable cells only start at approximately 1.25V but maintain this level, then rapidly collapse when discharged. The paging circuitry has to take account of these different characteristics especially at the lowest working temperature of $-10°C$.

45.8.7   Battery economy

To provide acceptable primary cell life times suitable paging code formats and receiver designs are required. Referring to Figure 45.8 and assuming the code is POCSAG, then the decoder circuit always has power on, but only switches on the radio circuit every 0.4 to 1 second (depending on data rate) to search for preamble. If preamble is detected a sync word search commences while power is still maintained to the receiver.

When a sync word is found the pager synchronises with the incoming data stream and immediately turns off the radio circuits until the pager's own time frame in the batch of 8 is approaching. The radio is then turned on for say 10ms settling period followed by a 64 bit period to read the address code words. If its address is found then a tone pager will beep and flash, and a numeric or alpha pager will decode and display and/or store the message, before the radio section is once again switched off.

45.8.8   Receiver programming

Each receiver needs to be programmed with its individual address or addresses and with its feature options. This is carried out by a programming unit which can be used to programme the receiver by the manufacturer, and to reprogramme it by the customer service engineer if desired. Each pager has a type of plug in programmable memory. In the early 1980's this may well have been a bipolar array such as an 8 x 4 diode matrix with fusible links. Programming would take place by passing currents of 1A through these links for a period of 10ms to form an open circuit. The disadvantage with this type of memory was that to change the programme a new memory had to be used to replace the old one. The design of the programmer unit had to ensure that the current and time for breaking the links was carefully controlled otherwise it was possible for the fused links to reform. The operator programmed the pager by means of a keypad on the programmer unit.

As personal computers became less expensive and more readily available, field programmers for service work stations were designed using a simple driver interface between the PC and the pager memory. As EEPROMs became available these were used as the programmable pager memory. Early versions of 128 bits had sufficient memory for pagers with 2 addresses 31 bits long, and a series of programmable options. These were programmed by a PC controlled device but needed 15 volts to satisfactorily programme the EEPROM. Later versions of the EEPROM with 4K of memory and 3 volts read/write capability superseded the earlier types and made possible the storage of precoded alpha text, different language texts and customised characters. These options are incorporated in the pager memory and are called up by transmitting a numeric code. For alphanumeric pagers which require greater memory storage for received messages, static RAMs working from 5 volts and capable of storing 6000 characters are used, the disadvantage with these devices is that they need separate battery backup. For numeric pagers which are only required to store short numeric messages the

RAM of the microprocessor can be used without battery backup. The advantage of 3 volt read/write EEPROM is that off air programming is possible where the pager receives reprogramming information transmitted to it from the base station. The low voltage means it can rewrite its own memory.

45.9 Private wide area paging

45.9.1 Overlay paging

Overlay paging is a system where paging addresses are sent over a PMR two way vehicular radio system to directly alert the driver, who has temporarily left his vehicle, to the fact that a message awaits his attention. Such additions to PMR schemes are permitted, though in the UK they are subject to the following conditions:

1. The number of mobile paging receivers must not exceed the number of mobiles in a system and each paging receiver must be used only in conjunction with a particular mobile station.
2. The normal base station transmitter power may not be increased.
3. The use of additional stations cannot be licensed solely on the grounds that they are necessary for overlay paging.
4. The paging system must use the same type of modulation as that of the mobile system in which it is employed.

45.9.2 Revertive paging or secondary calling

Revertive paging, or secondary calling, is an addition to PMR systems where paging addresses originating at the base station are received by the vehicle radio and retransmitted to a paging receiver carried by the driver.

45.9.3 Private off site paging

These are non public subscriber large area (up to 10 sq. miles) systems. To avoid interference between neighbouring small on site systems, alternative frequencies are chosen where available. In the UK, in order to minimise interference, manufacturers who are members of the Radio Paging Association, determine the appropriate channel by entering the ordnance survey coordinates of the transmitter location into a data base of existing systems. It is possible though, for a group of adjacent sites to timeshare the same channel frequency. In the UK specific time slots of 15 seconds in a 60 second cycle are allocated to a site to transmit its paging calls. Code formats are proprietary and speech is not allowed. In the UK 5 frequencies of 25kHz channels in the band 153.375MHz to 153.475MHz are allocated and maximum transmitter ERP of 25W is allowed.

45.9.4 German POSP system

A new u.h.f. private off site paging system (POSP) has been proposed in Germany and the specification has been published. This is not an ETSI initiative, and currently only applies to Germany. Each site's transmitter is allocated a specific permanent 6 second slot in a 60 second cycle. The time slot sequence is standardised (Numbered 1 - 10) and begins with time slot No. 1. at the start of each new minute. The allocation of the time slot is carried out by the Deutches Bundesposte, when the licence is issued. The use of more than one 15W transmitter synchronised to the same time slot is allowed, in order to improve transmission distance within a system. A sequence of time slots can be allocated to one user where the system has a high call rate. The ZZF issue a range of address codes to the manufacturer upon equipment approval.

45.10 Pan-European systems

45.10.1 Euromessage

This system (Table 45.7) opened late 1989 and is now operational in major towns and industrial regions in France and West Germany, in the UK in London and Home Counties, and some parts of Italy. Full messaging is possible in each individual country and the common specification is shown below. Additional features are added according to the National Operator's requirements.

Table 45.7 CCIR radiopaging code no. 1

Parameter	Value
Frequency	466.075MHz ±50Hz (frequency offsets max. ±1800Hz allowable)
Deviation	±4.0 or ±4.5kHz depending on country
Channel spacing	20 or 25kHz depending on country
Transmission rate	1200 ±10 Baud
Signal rise time	≤275µs
Character set	Special characters e.g. umlaut ($\ddot{a}$, $\ddot{o}$) are both possible and permitted and will be specified by each country involved

The disadvantage of this system is that since it utilises existing paging networks in each country, it is only possible to call a pager somewhere in Europe through its own national base.

45.10.1.1 *Transmission*

Time slotting of transmitters is used to ensure decoupling of adjacent simulcast areas. One, two or a maximum of three simulcast areas form a paging zone depending on traffic and country. The duration of the time slot cycle can be adjusted to conform to traffic requirements and the differences are shown below. In the case of Germany the fixed figure refers to the standard Cityruf system and the range allows the possibility of expansion for Euromessage as traffic increases.

The methods of filling a time slot with idle words under low traffic level varies between the 4 operators (Table 45.8) as does the total length of time slots.

45.10.1.2 *Euromessage receiver*

Numeric receivers must be capable of receiving at least 15 characters per call and alphanumeric radio paging receivers at least 80 characters per call. The remaining basic specification for the receiver is as in Table 45.9.

Table 45.8 Methods used for Euromessage

Country	Germany	U.K.	France	Italy
Preamble length in bits	576	608	576	576
Synchronisation codeword	RPC1	RPC1	RPC1	RPC1
Idle codeword	RPC1	RPC1	RPC1	RPC1
Max batches between preambles	24 (or 42-96)	61	25	25
Transmission cycle time in seconds	84 (or 66-141)	30	11.8	12
Number of timeslots	3 or 1	1	1	1
Longest timeslot in seconds	28 (or 22-47)	30	11.8	12 or 24

Table 45.9 Euromessage receiver specification

Parameter	Value
Minimum sensitivity: On body tone only (salty man)	≤ 29µV/m
Minimum sensitivity: tone only free field	≤ 32µV/m
Adjacent channel selectivity	≥ 60dB
Co-channel rejection	≥ −8dB
Intermodulation response	≥ 50dB
Spurious response rejection: image, above or below 47-60MHz 87-108MHz 174-230MHz or 470-862Mhz	≥ 50dB
All other cases	≥ 60dB

45.10.2 ERMES

This new European Radio Messaging Service is due to start in December 1992. The standards are the result of an ETSI Working Group, and are awaiting approval by individual countries before being fully approved by ETSI. All operators will use the channels within the 16 allocated, and the same protocol, so that one operator's pager will work on another operator's system.

Operators in 16 European countries including the UK, France, Germany and Italy, signed a Memorandum of Understanding, to provide a system that allows international roaming, and would serve each of their capital cities and 25% of total service population (90 million people) by December 1993. The pager will scan 16 v.h.f. paging channels, many of which are already used in these countries for other services.

45.10.2.1 *Type of service and specification*

Services to be provided are: tone, numeric, alpha numeric and transparent data. Additional optional features are related to: paging acknowledgement, call destination, three levels of priority, charging services, protection against inadvertent message loss, call privacy and bureau services.

The specification for ERMES is given in Table 45.10.

Table 45.10 Specification for ERMES

Parameter	Value
Frequency range	169.4125MHz to 169.8125MHz
Channels	16 channels 25kHz spacing
Modulation	4 level (4-PAM/FM) ±4687.5 and ±1562.5Hz
Data rate	6.25Kbit/s
Symbol rate	3.125kbaud
Error correction	2 bits (30, 18) shortened cyclic code
Interleaving to provide burst error correction	Message only to a depth of 9 code words

45.10.2.2 *Code format*

The construction of the transmitted code is shown in Figure 45.8. A sixty minute sequence is shown, of which a 1 minute cycle and then a 12 second subsequence is detailed. Batch I is expanded into its synchronisation, systems information, pager addresses block, and pager messages block of code words.

Battery economy is built into the format at various levels, and to assist current saving, addresses and system information is not interleaved. The pager will be addressed in only one of the sixteen batches (A-P) in a subsequence, enabling it to ignore each of the other fifteen. Once a pager has been addressed within its batch, the corresponding message may be in any of the following batches of that subsequence, or in the following subsequence, up to a point 12 seconds from the start of the batch containing the initial address. The addressed pager must therefore monitor all the subsequent batches until it finds one with its own address appended, or it times out after 12 seconds. Battery economy is also possible in other ways, but the process becomes complicated.

In multi-frequency networks the paging receiver will be informed on which channel to expect its messages. This is accomplished with a combination of the frequency subset indicator transmitted in the system information partition, and the frequency subset number stored in the receiver. (See Figure 45.9.) Each pager will be assigned a frequency subset number (FSN) between 0 and 15. This identifies a unique subset of five frequency subset indicators (FSI). Each FSI defines the unique subset of FSNs to which the message may be directed. The FSI broadcast on a paging channel indicates that messages will be transmitted for pagers with an FSN in that FSIs subset. For example, when the FSI on a channel equals 27, only messages for receivers with FSNs of 12, 13, 14 or 15 will be carried. Conversely a receiver with FSN equals 12 should look for its

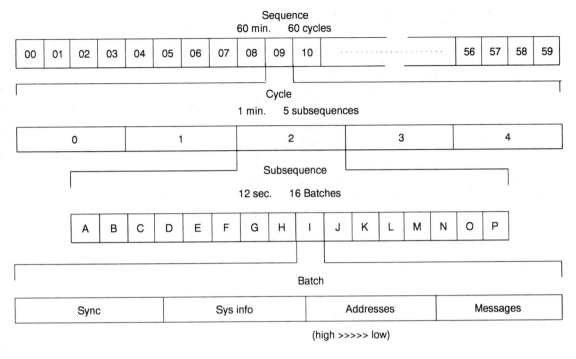

Figure 45.8 ERMES protocol timing

messages only on channels broadcasting FSI values of 12, 22, 27, 29, or 30. The FSNs do not correspond to frequency channel numbers.

45.10.2.3 *Transmission*

Several hundred 100/250W transmitter base stations per country will initially be employed in quasi-synchronous operation. The modulation of adjacent base stations must be synchronised such that no more than 50ms differential delay is measured at the receiver. Zoning is employed and the 12 seconds, 16 batch sub-sequences (Figure 45.9) are allocated to a zone.

45.11 Indirect satellite paging

The SkyTel service in the US uses a geostationary satellite, West Star IV, to communicate with a satellite up-link station operating in C-band using spread spectrum modulation in California, and satel-

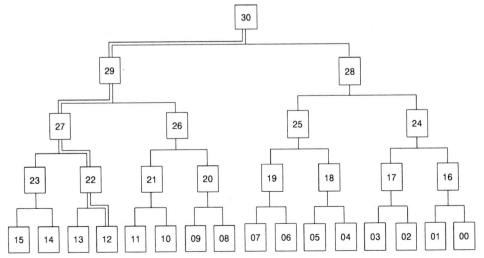

Figure 45.9 ERMES frequency subset indicators

lite down-link stations across the US. The caller uses the PSTN to make a toll free call from anywhere in the US to the central paging computer in Washington D.C. which then passes its calls to the up-link station in California. Selected paging calls are then transmitted via the normal local zone transmitters. The total transmission time is approximately 20 seconds and it is claimed to have 85% coverage of the US population. Redundancy is built into the system by having a second satellite which operates in the Ku-band. The bit error rate of the system is approximately one error in ten million bits sent. The system can be accessed from the UK by telephoning the Washington number and the u.h.f. pager can be hired in the UK or the US.

The ground transmitter frequency used is 931MHz and this frequency has also been allocated or reserved in Canada, Singapore, Malaysia, Shanghai, Bolivia, Brazil, Uruguay, Ecuador, Peru, Sri Lanka and Venezuela.

45.12 Bibliography

BT (1980) *A standard code for radio paging*, report of the Post Office Code Standardisation Advisory Group (POCSAG), June 1978 and November 1980.

BT (1986) *The book of the CCIR Radio Paging Code No. 1*, Radiopaging Code Standards Group.

French, R.C. (1984) A high technology v.h.f. radio paging receiver, *IEE 1984 Conference on Mobile Radio Systems, September.*

IEC (1987) No. 489, Part 6, 2nd Ed.

Komura, M. et. al. (1977) New radio paging systems, *Japan Telecom Review*, **19**, July.

Makitalo, O. and Fremin, G. (1970) New system for radio paging over the FM broadcasting network, *TELE (English Ed.)* **XXII**, (2).

Okumura, Y. et. al. (1968) Field strength and its variability in v.h.f. and u.h.f. land mobile radio service, *Review of the Electrical Communications Laboratory*, **16**, *(9 and 10), September/October.*

Sandvos, J.L. (1982) A comparison of binary paging codes, *IEEE Vehic. Tech. Conference*, May.

Tridgell, R.H. (1982) The CCIR radio paging code no. 1, a new world standard, *IEEE Vehic. Tech. Soc. Conference*, May.

Tridgell, R.H. and Denman, D. (1984) Experience of CCIR radio-paging code no. 1 (POCSAG) for message display paging, *IEE 1984 Conference on Mobile Radio Systems*, September.

46

PMR and trunked radio systems

C Lorek
BSc (Hons) AMIEE
South Midlands Communications Ltd

Contents

46.1 Private Mobile Radio

Private Mobile radio, or PMR, has developed substantially over the years, from simplex AM communication on a single channel employing crystal controlled equipment, to that of today's multiple channel systems employing synthesised transceivers operating under microprocessor control, often with intelligent channel allocation from off-air received signalling.

46.1.1 Spectrum usage

The majority of PMR services employ sub-bands within the frequency range 30MHz to 960MHz, these being periodically agreed internationally in the World Administration Radio Conference. It must be noted however that the use of these bands are not common throughout the world, as the radio regulatory bodies of individual countries often administer the use of the v.h.f. and u.h.f. spectrum to their own needs, based upon a 'non-interference' operation with other countries. A typical case is that of the Band III range of 174MHz to 225MHz, which is used in the U.K. for trunked PMR but in the neighbouring country of France for Television Broadcast services.

46.1.2 Equipment

Spectrum conservation techniques in mobile radio equipment used under digital agile frequency control combined with digital signalling have thus made standard the use of LSI control circuitry, with resultant sophisticated two way communications equipment becoming relatively smaller each year.

46.1.2.1 *Frequency generation and signal processing*

Single IC frequency synthesisers with internal u.h.f. prescalers are commonly used, whereas previously these were comprised of a separate ECL prescalar, programmable divider, reference divider, and phase comparator/loop filter. The use of a relatively high first IF (Intermediate Frequency) with advanced filtering methods allows the use of lesser filtering stages in the r.f. front end stages to obtain the required band selectivity, thus minimising the physical size of the receiver circuits. Digital filtering at the second IF, typically 455kHz, may be used to allow the selection of IF selectivity under software control, to allow interchangeability of equipment between 25kHz, 20kHz, 15kHz and 12.5kHz r.f. channel spacings. Digital control of transmitter processing and resultant frequency deviation may be performed using a single IC as opposed to manual potentiometer adjustments.

46.1.2.2 *Tuned circuits*

Varicap controlled tuned filters under software control may be used in combination with D/A converters in the r.f. stages, to allow automatic factory alignment to be performed by digital means. The parameters for each channel or frequency range are stored in the transceiver's memory circuitry and are retrieved according to the channel selected. This may be coupled with active tuning of transmit stages to provide efficient operation with minimal generation of spurious signals, thus further reducing the size and power consumption of transceivers.

46.1.2.3 *Battery requirements for portable equipment*

In the case of portable equipment, the rechargeable battery source is often the limit in the equipment's overall size and hence portability. Developments in reducing portable equipment size are likely to concentrate in this area. Nickel hydrogen cells are being investigated as an alternative to nickel cadmium, the charge/discharge voltage gradient of these being similar to that of nickel cadmium thus allowing retrospective fitment. Nickel hydrogen offers approximately twice the capacity/volume ratio and four times the capacity/weight ratio of nickel cadmium. Lithium cells are commonly used in the limited number of cases where rechargeable capability is not required, these cells also having a significantly higher capacity ratio compared with nickel cadmium cells.

46.2 PMR systems

46.2.1 Simplex

The simplest form of personal mobile communication is the use of a single 'open' frequency for both transmission and reception, this normally being termed a 'simplex' channel communication method. Here all parties to the communication use a common frequency, with all users within range having communication ability, as shown in Figure 46.1.

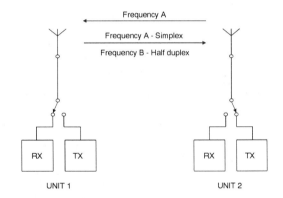

Figure 46.1 Simplex operation

46.2.2 Half duplex

Progressing from this, with transmit/receive switching in use at both stations, a 'half duplex' mode occurs where personal or mobile units communicate using a different transmission frequency to that used for reception. The central radio base station uses the reverse pair of these frequencies to thus enable communication between itself and all mobile outstations. Although at first this may seem inefficient use of the spectrum, by suitable frequency management linked with geographical base station planning, more efficient use in fact may be made due to planned frequency re-use in adjacent areas.

46.2.3 Full duplex

Where simultaneous reception and transmission is required, this may be achieved in split frequency duplex mode by suitable filter circuits comprised within or external to the radio units, as shown in

Figure 46.2. This increases the physical size of the equipment somewhat due to the high-Q resonant filters required, the size of these normally being in proportion to the isolation required and in an inverse proportion to the frequency range used (DTI, 1987).

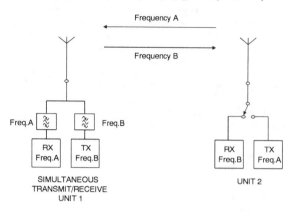

Figure 46.2 Full duplex operation employs simultaneous reception and transmission by the use of suitable r.f. filtering

It is common practice in personal radio communication usage for the base station unit to operate in full duplex mode (DTI, 1981a), with mobile outstations operating in half duplex mode. This method allows the base to control communication, by disallowing uncoordinated portable to portable communication and allowing users with emergency messages to interrupt the communication. By coupling the received audio from the base station receiver to the base station transmitter modulator, 'talkthrough' operation may be achieved. Here the base station transmitter with its normally advantageous site over the portable/mobile stations is used to significantly extend the range of communication to a defined coverage area. Figure 46.3 shows this concept, where receive audio is linked to the transmitter for re-transmission under manual or automatic signalling control. Simplified PABX and PSTN telephone interconnect is also feasible with this system, with the portable unit controlling dialling and call clear down through analogue or digital signalling.

46.2.4 Remote base station

To achieve a controlled radio coverage range in the v.h.f./u.h.f. spectrum used, a defined aerial site is normally required which may be significantly at variance with the physical location of the base station operator's console. In the case of an exclusive or shared channel allocation, a leased landline may be used to control a remotely sited base station transmitter/receiver, alternatively a point to point u.h.f. or s.h.f. radio link may be used where geographical and propagation limitations allow.

46.2.5 Communal base stations

A progression from the remotely sited base is a 'Communal Base Station' (DTI, 1988a). This operates in an automatic talkthrough mode in full duplex on a shared user basis. Several groups of users, each having inter-communication within their own fleet, employ the facilities of the remotely mounted equipment in a time shared mode. To ensure privacy between fleets, analogue or digital selective signalling is employed. This mode of operation is based upon the

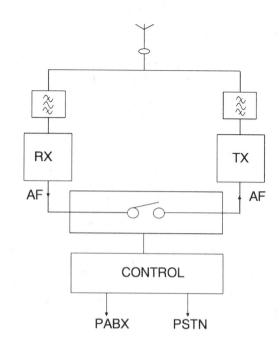

Figure 46.3 Talkthrough operation. Receive audio is linked to the transmitter for re-transmission under manual or automatic signalling control

radio usage of each fleet occupying only a small percentage of available air time on the channel.

To prevent waiting users from other fleets being denied access for unreasonably long time periods, an electronically controlled time out timer is normally employed. Circuitry controlling this is fitted both to the mobile transmitter circuitry to limit the maximum length of user transmission, and to the remote base station to limit the length of air time for a given user fleet in the time slot provided.

46.2.6 Quasi-synchronous operation

An area or nationwide system using quasi-synchronous operation may be employed using cellular coverage on a single given channel, often combined with base station receivers having voting circuitry fitted to continuously detect and transmit received signal strength indications to the central control switch. Each transmitter is operated at a small but accurately controlled frequency offset from that of its neighbour, to combat the effects of phase cancellation in received signals at mobile unit locations (Philips, 1980). This frequency offset is typically 5Hz to 6Hz in a v.h.f. system operating with 12.5kHz channel separation, and 3Hz on u.h.f. systems. In areas where two base station transmitter signals overlap, a beat note of this frequency will be present if both signals are within the capture effect range of the mobile receiver. The probability of a complete null occurring diminishes where three or more signals overlap. Figure 46.4 gives an example of a typical coverage system.

Using these techniques, a wide coverage system based on cellular coverage techniques may be achieved without the need for a relatively advanced central processing switch, nor the use of frequency agile mobile or terminal units. Channel re-use may be achieved through the use of selective base transmitter operation dependent upon voting signal levels received from individual base station receivers.

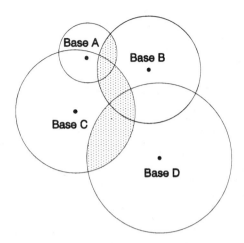

Figure 46.4 Quasi-synchronous operation employs stable transmitters operating at a small frequency offset. Signal overlap produces received signal phase additions and cancellations

46.3 Trunked mobile radio

46.3.1 Spectrum re-use

Over the years several improvements in spectrum conservation in PMR bands have been made in an effort to use available frequencies to the maximum benefit possible. In many developed countries, severe overcrowding of available PMR channels is encountered, especially in urban areas, and progress is continually being made towards better channel utilisation. This overcrowding has frequently led to the use of shared radio channels in a given area, with selective signalling methods used to allow a degree of communication to occur between users without an unacceptable lack of privacy.

In some cities, e.g. London in the U.K., the entire v.h.f. private mobile radio allocation has been already filled to capacity with no further channels being available for new users, and the U.K. System 4 v.h.f. radiophone system some time ago was terminated due to overcrowding. Other frequency bands such as u.h.f. as used for private mobile radio communication also suffer from congestion to varying degrees, and in some countries further u.h.f. allocations such as 900MHz are used to supplement existing 450MHz allocations for PMR use.

46.3.2 Trunked systems

A trunking system typically used for mobile communication employs similar basic principles to landline telephony trunking, where several radio channels are used to allow more efficient use of the available spectrum by sharing a 'pool' of channels with other users. This is the basis for most current analogue radio trunking systems in use. The application of Erlang C may be used (Erlang, 1918) to provide approximate performance figures and hence grade of service (DTI, 1986), as in Equation 46.1, where P_d is probability of delay, C are the number of trunked channels, and A is the traffic load in Erlangs.

$$P_d = \frac{A^C}{A^C + C!\left(1 - \dfrac{A}{C}\right)\displaystyle\sum_{k=0}^{k=C-1}\frac{A^k}{k!}} \qquad (46.1)$$

Table 46.1 gives indications for typical 5, 10, and 20 channel mobile systems. In typical usage on a large system a dedicated 'control' channel is permanently enabled, this carries signalling information, the protocol being dependent upon the system employed, for reception by frequency scanning mobile units. In small usage systems the control channel may also be used as a traffic channel when required. This improves channel utilisation at the expense of losing instantaneous call processing signalling during peak traffic periods.

Table 46.1 Mobile trunked system performance

No. of Channels	Grade of Service	Traffic (Erlang) Per channel	Traffic (Erlang) Total	No. of Mobiles Per channel	No. of Mobiles Total	Mean waiting time(s)
	%	a	A			,
5	5	0.645	3.22	116	580	3.3
	10	0.719	3.59	129	645	5.8
	30	0.846	4.23	152	760	16.8
10	5	0.793	7.93	143	1430	3.8
	10	0.839	8.39	151	1510	6.2
	30	0.914	9.14	165	1645	16.5
15	5	0.853	12.79	153	2300	4.1
	10	0.886	13.29	159	2390	6.5
	30	0.939	14.09	169	2535	16.4
20	5	0.885	17.70	159	3185	4.3
	10	0.911	18.22	164	3280	6.7
	30	0.953	19.06	172	3430	16.4

46.3.3 Trunked area coverage

Trunking may usefully be combined with area coverage techniques for use with frequency agile radio units under synthesiser control. Here the required area coverage is sectored, with adjacent sectors being allocated different frequencies rather than the previously described quasi-synchronous coverage method operating on a single frequency. From carefully tailored planning of individual cell coverage patterns, frequency re-use may be employed due to capture effect performance of mobile receivers together with sufficient geographical separation of cells operating on the same frequency. Due to the tailored coverage required, either v.h.f. for wide area coverage, or u.h.f. for more closely defined coverage, is utilised.

46.3.4 Cell clusters

A regular polygon shape for a given cell coverage is convenient for use when planning u.h.f. trunked systems, with clusters of adjacent cells thus easily modelled for frequency re-use strategies. It must be borne in mind that local geography may radically alter this coverage shape in practical cases, however the commonly used hexagon will be used for the purposes of demonstration.

This hexagon will allow a wide degree of cluster sizes which fit together in a repeating pattern. The integer number of cells in each cluster may be given by Equation 46.2, where a and b are any positive integers and a ≥ b (Parsons, 1989).

$$C = a^2 + ab + b^2 \qquad (46.2)$$

This yields typically used cell clusters of 3, 7, and 12 cells as shown. Where a given number of channels are available for use in a dedicated trunked system, these may be divided for use in repeating numbers of cell clusters, the number of cells within each cluster depending upon the number of channels available together with acceptable degradation requirements between each cluster. This strategy is also dependent upon signal propagation, communication bandwidth, and signalling methods used. Different numbers of cells per cluster may be combined also in a typical wide area system where urban coverage is required together with rural coverage, each cell thus being tailored to the required parameters.

46.3.5 Base station coverage

Although mobile units often effectively have an omnidirectional aerial radiation pattern, efficiencies may be achieved in the overall number of base station sites required by the use of directional aerials. V.h.f systems are often used with omnidirectional or slightly tailored radiation patterns where local topography dictates to provide wide area coverage with a minimum number of base station sites, whilst those operating on u.h.f. (typically 450MHz and 900MHz systems) commonly use controlled aerial radiation patterns to give multiple cell clusters from a single base station site.

On elevated aerial sites in urban environments a degree of beam down-tilt is normally required on u.h.f. for effective coverage at ground level. This practice may also be usefully employed in achieving maximum frequency re-use with closely defined coverage in a given urban area supplementing that in rural and semi-rural areas.

46.3.6 Mobile roaming

Mobile units may roam throughout the area covered by the network of the trunked radio system base station sites, the mobile receivers being commanded to hunt for a control channel with sufficient signal strength in the area of operation. An RSSI (Radio Signal Strength Indicator) circuit in the mobile unit constantly monitors the strength of the permanently enabled control channel base transmitter, alternatively or also a bit error check is performed on received data, to establish a usable control channel.

An optional variation in a regional cellular trunked system for more efficient utilisation of a limited number of channels for combined control and traffic utilisation is that of a 'time shared' control channel. Here a dedicated signalling channel is time shared amongst a number of control transmitters operated in a cyclic manner, mobiles thus respond to the individual base transmitter giving adequate reception strength for their area.

Semi-duplex or full duplex operation is used, the base transmitter control channel being termed the Forward Control Channel (FOCC) and the corresponding mobile transmit channel being termed the Reverse Control Channel (RECC).

46.3.7 Control channel recognition

Once a signalling channel has been identified, the signalling information is examined by the mobile and a check performed to ensure the correct system, control category, and area or zone information is present, dependent upon the mobile unit's individual network personalisation.

If the received data is valid, the mobile locks on to this channel and, dependent upon the system being used, sends a registration identification to the relevant base station. This updates the system records on the presence and area of operation of the mobile unit. If the unit is not registered onto the system being received, the mobile relinquishes that channel and commences a further control signalling channel search.

46.3.8 Handoff usage

On moving away from the recognised base control transmitter, a low RSSI indication or a high bit error rate in the mobile unit causes the mobile to hunt for other acceptable control channels (Bye, 1989). The roaming mobile unit thus re-registers as required onto different base transmitter areas when moving from area to area. The system network switch updates its records to store the traffic area and channel the mobile is currently active on, hence routing incoming call indications to the mobile on the appropriate site and channel being used.

46.3.9 Communication

Once a call set up has been made, further signalling continues either on the control channel until the called party answers, alternatively a traffic channel is allocated for further call processing dependent upon the system being used. During communication, speech combined with supervisory signalling is employed.

Where a mobile is travelling from one cell coverage area to another, a 'handoff' action may occur where the base station signals the mobile to move its operational channel to that used by the neighbouring cell. Here the base station in use polls adjacent cell sites to examine the signal strength being received from the mobile, and if traffic channels are available on the relevant cell site the mobile is instructed to handoff accordingly. During the communication, periodic 'maintenance messages' may also be processed to ensure correct channel utilisation and communication takes place.

46.4 Band III

46.4.1 Interface specification

Commonly called 'Band III' due to its intrinsic use in the U.K. trunked PMR system operating in the 174MHz to 225MHz Band III (HMSO, 1984) range of the spectrum, the MPT1327 signalling specification (DTI, 1988b) for trunked mobile use chosen as the mandatory protocol is also currently in use by several countries operating on Band III and other v.h.f./u.h.f. bands. Although subject to intellectual property rights, an agreement has been achieved for the specification's use by CEPT manufacturers together with its use by system operators (Pascoe, 1989). The MPT1327 protocol is currently used in the 165MHz, 200MHz, 450MHz and 900MHz bands.

46.4.2   Systems

Together with public access national systems currently in use (Oliver, 1989), these based upon cellular coverage techniques combined with FDMA trunking use, public regional systems are in operation covering major cities. Large private users, e.g. airport authorities (Armstrong, 1989), employ this protocol for efficient usage of a limited number of radio channels on dedicated networks which may also use multi-site operation for area coverage requirements.

The system allows:

1. Wide area coverage with handoff capability.
2. Individual calls.
3. Fleet and sub-fleet calls.
4. Inter-fleet calls.
5. PABX interconnection
6. PSTN interconnection.
7. Off-air call set up.
8. Automatic call queuing.
9. Off-air call progress tones from digital signalling received.
10. Emergency and priority call modification.
11. Status messages.
12. Short and long data messages.
13. Call diversion.
14. Queuing of calls for automatic callback.
15. Indication of calling party identification.
16. Receiver co-channel interference protection.

46.4.3   Half/full duplex

Base station control channels operate either on a dedicated channel basis, on a rotating channel basis with 'Move' commands instructing mobiles to change channel accordingly, on a time shared basis where a channel is cycled between multiple transmitter sites, or with a combination of these dependent upon system requirements. Base stations for both control and traffic channel purposes operate on a full duplex basis, mobile units operate using half duplex with 1200bit/s FFSK signalling and FFSK data communication.

46.4.4   Control channel

A Control Channel System Codeword (CCSC) is continuously transmitted, giving details of the system's network, area, zone, control category etc. Mobile units scan the available channels stored in a programmed 'preferential hunt list', followed by an optional 'comprehensive hunt', until the correct control channel matching the unit's personalisation is confirmed.

The CCSC operates on a 'Slotted Aloha' basis, with Aloha messages inviting mobile units to register and/or send message requests, indicating the number of available message 'slots' available. Mobiles transmit randomly timed messages using FFSK to coincide with the available slots, in an effort to overcome data collisions. Upon receipt, the base station sends an acknowledgement to the calling mobile thus confirming correct reception.

A queuing system is used where the network operates on a 'first in, first out' basis together with call time limitation thus ensuring

short waiting times for communication using a traffic channel. Dynamic timing is also possible using control channel 'Broadcast' messages which internally set mobile unit call timers dependent upon the traffic density at any particular time. If a user completes his allocated maximum communication period before reaching the end of the desired message, further traffic channel time is possible by entering the queue again.

Appendix A46.1 gives a selection of available MPT1327 messages thus indicating the flexibility of the network compared with alternative systems, Figure 46.5 showing the address codeword structure.

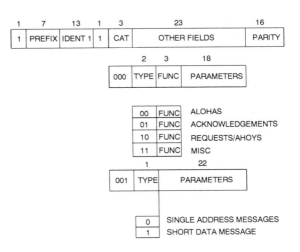

Figure 46.5   Sample MPT1327 trunking system address codeword structure

46.4.5   Call processing

Once a successful RQS has been made, the called party is polled with an AHY message on the control channel the called mobile is active on at any time. An ACK from the mobile indicates it will accept calls, otherwise alternative messages, such as ACKB indicating the call will be queued in the mobile memory for callback, are sent for information to the calling party. The called party is then either alerted for subscriber availability status, or queued for traffic channel availability, both parties receiving a GTC message when a traffic channel at each site is available. PABX originated calls may be made with a dedicated link between the user PABX and the Trunking System Controller (TSC), likewise with PSTN calls.

Once the mobile is present on the traffic channel, periodic FFSK maintenance messages from both the mobile and base may be processed, indicating user pressed 'on', 'off', and mobile identifications. An AHYC message requests the mobile to transmit an FFSK data message containing the unit identity and its individual Electronic Security Number (ESN), a non-registered or incorrect user receiving a CLEAR message from the TSC. Throughout communication on the channel, periodic identification fields from the base may be sent, an incorrect field received causing the mobile to clear. This ensures the required privacy from other users during co-channel reception from other cells' areas.

46.4.6   Data messaging on Band III

Status messages (SDM1) and short data messages (SDM2) employ use of the control channel only, the ACK protocol combined with automatic data re-transmission providing integrity of transmitted data reception. SDM1 may be linked for automatic status transmission of vehicle activity for fleet communication (GEC, 1990), and/or rapid digital messaging for fleet communication. 32 RQQ status codes are provided for, with RQQ (00000) and RQQ (11111) used for 'off hook' and 'on hook' status signalling.

SDM2 may be used for dispatcher originated short data messages entered via. a terminal, such as delivery and order details. Mobile usage of SDM2 typically employs a bar code reader for work progress and parts ordering/updating.

Traffic channel data transfer is possible following either manual or automatic call set up, an error correcting protocol such as an X.25 derivative is commonly used to prevent data corruption from periodic maintenance messages. Otherwise, no defined protocols are required as an open channel is available as in the case of analogue cellular, thus base computer interrogation may be performed with added security through data encryption techniques.

46.5   The use of troposcatter

46.5.1   Introduction

With the use of high transmission power combined with high gain aerials, it is possible for v.h.f./u.h.f. signals to propagate beyond the normal 'line of sight' range. This method makes use of the availability of random irregularities in the refractive index structure of the tropospheric layer, where the refractive index differs from that of the surrounding area.

A 'common scattering volume' as shown in Figure 46.6, is used where a faint signal illumination occurs at the reception end of the path. The title of 'troposcatter' is also more commonly known in commercial fields as 'forward scatter'.

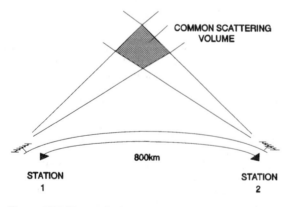

Figure 46.6 Tropospheric scatter

46.5.2   Equipment requirements

The propagation medium involving the forward scattering volume involves a large transmission loss, and it becomes necessary to use high gain, narrow beamwidth aerials for both transmission and reception. The effect of the scatter angle between the receiving and transmitting beam is significant and is kept as small as possible by choosing transmitting and receiving sites so as to have an unobstructed view of the horizon.

As such, tropospheric scatter is normally limited to point to point links for medium to long distance communication. A common use is that over a sea path between a land based station on a cliff top and an offshore platform to provide telephony and other communications services.

46.5.3   Signal levels

The troposcatter signal received at the distant fixed point may continuously vary in signal level due to the presence of the randomly varying parameters involved in the scatter process. Variations in signal level may reach 20dB with monthly, daily, and hourly variations often being encountered (Orr, 1987).

Providing sufficient effective radiated power output exists from the transmitter, the maximum attainable communication range is in the order of 800km. This is limited by the maximum height of the useful common scattering volume in the troposphere. Although no critical frequency is involved with the scattering mechanism, the intensity of the scattered reflections decreases with increasing frequency, thus aerial gain and transmitter power must be correspondingly increased with increase of frequency.

46.5.4   Tropospheric ducting

Tropospheric ducting of v.h.f./u.h.f. signals leads to extended communication range over a given geographical path. Ducting is the result of the variation of the refractive index of the atmosphere found at the periphery of air masses of differing temperatures. A temperature inversion promoting tropospheric ducting occurs when a mass of cold air is overrun by a mass of warm air, and this periphery may extend in excess of 1000km to 2000km along a stationary weather front.

Temperature inversions frequently occur along coastal areas bordering large bodies of water, due to the natural onshore movement of cool, humid air shortly after sunset when the ground air cools more quickly than upper air layers. The same action may take place in the morning when the rising sun heats the upper air layers. Ducting over water has produced v.h.f. communication in excess of 4500km.

46.5.5   Limitations to PMR and trunked systems

Unlike troposcatter, tropospheric ducting cannot normally be controlled, but its presence should be borne in mind when planning PMR services. Disruption to local community repeater and trunking services may occur due to strong received signals on the same channel frequency from users in other areas, and along the South and East coasts of the U.K. this phenomenon is often experienced by PMR users on both v.h.f. and u.h.f.. Careful frequency planning together with suitable digital or analogue selective signalling techniques may be used to lessen disruption to communication services.

46.6   Transmission standards

Under the Telecommunications Convention, classes of emission are designated by groups of a minimum of three characters. Currently the majority of PMR services on v.h.f./u.h.f. employ narrowband FM telephony (F3E) as the principal modulation method. AM telephony (A3E) is used in some cases, often to retain compatibility with existing systems but also for emergency services where it is advantageous for the base station control operator to be aware of a weaker mobile station attempting to establish communication whilst the channel is occupied by a stronger signal.

Single sideband telephony (J3E) is used in some cases in an effort to attain greater usage of available frequency spectrum, some systems employing pilot carrier SSB to aid frequency synchronisation between the transmitter and remote receivers. These modes of communication are extensively documented elsewhere.

A variety of signalling methods are used in addition to the speech modulation to provide control of the communication.

46.7 Analogue signalling

46.7.1 DTMF

Dual Tone Medium Frequency signalling, which is comprehensively documented elsewhere in this handbook, is commonly used for simple numerical signalling from the mobile unit in commanding the base either to route calls to a required PABX or PSTN number, or in a more limited number of cases to selectively address other mobile units for alert indications to be given. In a Rayleigh fading propagation environment, DTMF signalling becomes prone to errors caused by signal loss, e.g. by a single DTMF digit being decoded as a repeated digit during a signal fade with resultant incorrect signalling.

46.7.2 CTCSS

The Continuous Tone Controlled Squelch System (DTI, 1978) is a basic form of selective signalling which is extensively used throughout the private mobile radio field. (Figure 46.7) In typical usage a single 'sub-audible' tone frequency is transmitted at 10% to 15% of

In normal personal communication use this tone is used in addition to the carrier or noise squelch system inherent in personal receivers to control the loudspeaker muting circuitry. Thus if a signal is received with either no tone or an incorrect tone, the user's receiver remains muted to allow privacy between users of a shared radio channel in a given geographical area.

For telephone interconnection or communal base station operation, through a given dedicated or common base station, this tone is used to control line/talkthrough seizure together with user authorisation, billing and time limitation switching. Mobile units may optionally have circuitry present to also inhibit transmission whilst receiving an incorrect tone, thus preventing interference to other users of a shared channel. An internationally used set of sub-tones are given in Table 46.2.

Table 46.2 CTCSS frequencies

67.0	107.2	167.9
71.9	110.9	173.8
74.4	114.8	179.9
77.0	118.8	186.2
79.7	123.0	192.8
82.5	127.3	203.5
85.4	131.8	210.7
88.5	136.5	218.1
91.5	141.3	225.7
94.8	146.2	233.6
97.4	151.4	241.8
100.0	156.7	250.3
103.5	162.2	

46.7.3 Sequential tone

To overcome the effects of Rayleigh fading in a mobile environment, sequential tone signalling may be used (DTI, 1981b). Here a unique single tone corresponding to each digit is sequentially transmitted, together with a unique 'repeat' tone in place of the digit tone in the case of repeated digits. Strings of repeated digits are thus sent in the manner digit, repeat, digit, repeat etc. as shown in Figure 46.8.

The tones are sent with a defined signalling interval, this varying between 40mS and 100ms dependent upon the system being used. Thus if a tone is missed due to signal fade, the sequence is recognised as invalid and is thus re-transmitted by the mobile unit rather than being received incorrectly.

A 'transpond' system is commonly used where inter-unit dialling and status indication is performed. Here the base interrogates the mobile user, this unit acknowledges by automatically transmitting a pre-set status number to indicate availability etc. This operation may be performed automatically on a periodic basis under computer control, with the base console display being updated as required.

Alternatively the mobile unit may manually send a status update in a short time slot by entering relevant digits on the personal unit fascia, one such code normally being a request for a speech channel

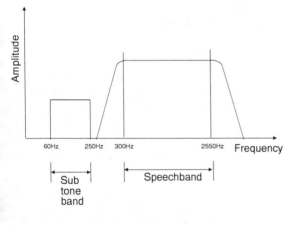

Figure 46.7 Continuous tone controlled signalling system employs tone frequencies below 300Hz

the maximum system FM deviation, along with the user's speech at 100% system FM deviation, to control a tone decoder at the distant receiver. The audio output of the receiver is bandwidth filtered to typically pass frequencies above 300Hz only, thus suppressing the received tone from the user.

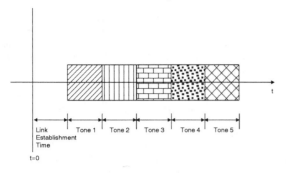

Figure 46.8 Sequential tone signalling uses a tone sequence at commencement of transmission. A link establishment time period is required for simplex half duplex systems

or telephone interconnection followed by the required number being sent by sequential tone signalling.

Table 46.3 tabulates internationally agreed tones from the EEA (Electronic Engineering Association), CCIR (Committee Consultatif International radio Communication), ZVEI (Zurerein der Elec-

Table 46.3 Sequential tone signalling frequencies

Standard	EEA	ZVEI	DZVEI	CCIR	CCITT
Digit 1	1124	1060	970	1124	697
Digit 2	1197	1160	1060	1197	770
Digit 3	1275	1270	1160	1275	852
Digit 4	1358	1400	1270	1358	941
Digit 5	1446	1530	1400	1446	1209
Digit 6	1540	1670	1530	1540	1335
Digit 7	1647	1830	1670	1640	1477
Digit 8	1747	2000	1830	1747	1633
Digit 9	1860	2200	2000	1860	1800
Digit 0	1981	2400	2200	1981	400
Repeat	2110	2600	2400	2110	2300
Tone length (ms)	40	70	70	100	100

tronissches Industrie) and CCITT (International Telegraph and Telephone Consultative Committee). To conform with 12.5kHz channel spacing where audio transmission is tailored to a 2.55kHz maximum frequency, a modified form of ZVEI, named 'Depressed' or DZVEI, is used.

46.7.4 FFSK digital selective signalling

Fast Frequency Shift Keying is now commonly used on v.h.f. and u.h.f. systems to achieve data addressing and unit identification. A

modulation rate generally used is 1200 bits/sec, with a binary '1' corresponding to 1 cycle of 1200Hz, a binary '0' corresponding to 1.5 cycles of 1800Hz, with NRZ coding, as illustrated in Figure 46.9. The first bit of each message commences with either phase 0 degree or 180 degrees thus ensuring phase continuity (DTI, 1981c).

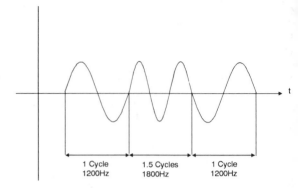

Figure 46.9 Fast frequency shift keying employs phase continuity between digits

Systems are generally capable of providing a data stream as shown, with a minimum transmission length of 96 bits. Transmissions commence with a preamble of at least 16 bit reversals such that the receiver demodulator can acquire bit synchronisation. This preamble is normally sufficient for transmissions where the r.f. carrier is already present, although the preamble may be continued as required to allow link establishment time in the case of simplex or half duplex operations. The following code word carries the user's identity together with address data and parity check bits to ensure correct reception, the message being re-transmitted as required in case of corruption due to Rayleigh fading.

46.8   Data transmission

46.8.1   Characteristics

Digital signalling is commonly operated in land mobile radio systems, for example data messaging on Band III systems as previously detailed. The logical progression from this is the transmission of other or longer data messages over any radio system. Typical applications include status messaging, vehicle location, pre-programmed messages e.g. of 'bar code' information, progressing up to portable and mobile data terminals employing printers and visual display screens.

A format for the transmission of digital information over land mobile radio systems has been documented in the MPT1317 code of practice (DTI, 1981c), and common usage of this employs 1200 baud FFSK using phase continuous 1200Hz (binary 1) and 1800Hz (binary 0).

The data stream is in the format shown in Figure 46.10, with a minimum length of transmission of 96 bits. A preamble for remote receiver decoder bit synchronisation is used, consisting of a minimum of 16 bit reversals, i.e. 1010...10, to be sent once the transmitter has been enabled and is transmitting power.

The length of the preamble may be extended to allow for link establishment, the preamble always ending in a logic '0'. Each message then commences with a 16 bit synchronising word as

PREAMBLE	SYNC WORD	ADDRESS CODE WORD	OPTIONAL DATA CODE WORDS

Figure 46.10 MPT1317 digital code format for data over PMR

shown in Figure 46.11, to enable the decoder to establish code word forming.

Messages are transmitted in 64 bit code words, each message may occupy one or more code words as determined by the message length. Each code word contains 48 information bits and 16 check bits which are used for error detection and data code words. There are two types of code word, address code words and data code words.

BIT NO.	1	2	3	4	5	6	7	8	9	10	11	12	13	14	15	16
BIT VALUE	1	1	0	0	0	1	0	0	1	1	0	1	0	1	1	1

Figure 46.11 MPT1317 synchronisation frame

46.8.2 Address code word

The first code word of every message is an address code word as shown in Figure 46.12. Bit 1 is always binary 1 to distinguish the word from a data code word, bits 2 to 8 inclusive specify the user's identity, bits 9 to 48 inclusive may be assigned to represent addresses and data, and bits 49 to 64 inclusive are check bits. Within the data field, the recommended practice is for bits 9 to 20 to specify the addressee's identity, bits 21 to 32 to specify the addressor's identity, and bits 33 to 48 to be used for data.

BIT NO.	1	2	8	9	48	49	64
NO. of BITS	1	7		40		16	
	'1'	USER's ID		ADDRESS AND DATA		CHECK BITS	

Figure 46.12 MPT1317 address code word structure

46.8.3 Data code word

An arbitrary number of data code words as shown in Figure 46.13, may follow an address code word, as required to accommodate the message.

Bit 1 is always binary 0 to distinguish the word from an address code word, bits 2 to 48 are used for the data, and bits 49 to 64 are used as check bits.

Several messages may be sent in one transmission as shown in Figure 46.14, i.e. concatenated messages. In this case it is not necessary to send the preamble at the start of every message.

BIT NO.	1	2	48	49	64
NO. of BITS	1	47		16	
	'0'	DATA		CHECK BITS	

Figure 46.13 MPT1317 data code word structure

46.8.4 Encoding and error checking

The 16 check bits are calculated in three stages. Firstly, 15 check bits are appended to the 48 information bits by encoding them in a (63,48) cyclic code. For encoding, the information bits 1 to 48 may be considered to be the coefficients of a polynomial having terms from X^{62} down to X^{15}. This polynomial is divided by modulo 2 by the generating polynomial as in Equation 46.3.

$$X^{15} + X^{14} + X^{13} + X^{11} + X^{4} + X^{2} + X^{1} \qquad (46.3)$$

The 15 check bits, code word bits 49 to 63, correspond to the coefficients of the terms from X^{14} to X^{0} in the remainder polynomial found at the completion of the division. The (63,48) cyclic code has a minimum distance of 5 and so guarantees detection of up to 4 bit errors in one code word.

Secondly, the final check bit of the (63,48) cyclic code (code word bit 63) is inverted to protect against misframing in the decoder.

Thirdly, one bit is appended to the 63 bit block to provide an even bit parity check of the whole 64 bit code word. The overall parity bit ensures that all odd numbers of errors can be detected, so that the overall 64 bit code guarantees that up to 5 bit errors can be detected.

At the receiver, each code word can be checked for errors by recalculating the check bits for the received information bits. Any differences between the received check bits and the recalculated check bits indicates that the received code word contains errors.

46.8.5 Packet data communication

Data communication networks employing error correcting protocols have been used non-commercially for some time now, and are currently starting to become employed for data transmission over PMR systems. Packetised data with automatic requests for re-transmission may be used to overcome effects encountered in typical PMR usage such as Rayleigh fading in a mobile environment, as well as allowing the shared use of a single r.f. channel. Interconnected packet nodes may be linked to radio base stations operating on h.f., v.h.f., u.h.f. and s.h.f. to form an international network for data store and forward operations, using both terrestrial routing and orbiting digital communications satellites for inter-continental message routing.

AX.25 (Arrl, 1984) a derivative of X.25, is commonly used together with level 2, 3, and 4 node systems.

User access employs 1200 baud FFSK operation using either Bell 202 tones or MPT1317 tones modulating an FM carrier, with operating frequencies on v.h.f. and u.h.f.. TDMA is used with terminal node controllers automatically re-transmitting packets of between 32 and 255 bytes when an ACK is not received within a given time.

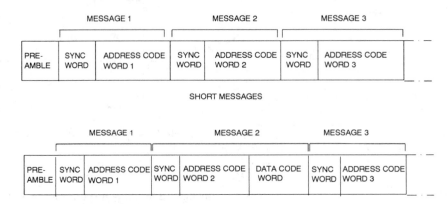

Figure 46.14 MPT1317 concatenated messages

Inter-node routing and satellite uplink/downlinking commonly uses 9600 baud FSK with Manchester coding (Miller, 1988) with operating frequencies in the u.h.f. regions. Coverage in many areas is such that hand portable data terminals may be successfully used, the automatic retry protocol linked to suitable packet data lengths for the intended use combating signal fading to a large degree.

46.8.6 Frame format

Link layer packet transmissions are sent in a number of frames, each frame subdivided into fields as in Figure 46.15. The transmission of a frame is preceded by 16 bit reversals, followed by the start flag, address field, control field, a network protocol identifier (PID), information field, frame check sequence (FCS) and an end flag.

The information field may be of a variable length, this may be set to any integral number of octets of information up to a maximum of 256. This allows the length of the transmitted packets to be controlled, thus allowing customisation to account for interpolation with other overhead messages such as the periodic maintenance messages found on MPT1327 systems. Together with a six unit alphanumeric identifier string, a seventh identifier, the SSID (Secondary Station Identifier) may be used to allow up to sixteen streams of individual data connections to be conducted from a given ID.

Commercial packet network usage is now commencing using proprietary protocols linked to data encryption for security, e.g. in the U.K. a small number of such systems are licensed for national coverage, employing nodes interlinked via. landlines. Uses of similar systems for Electronic Funds Transfer are also in hand.

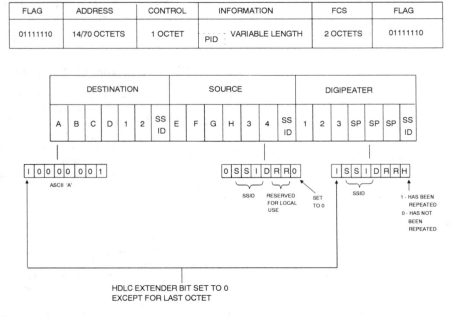

Figure 46.15 AX25 packet frame format

46.8.7 Satellite land mobile data communication

Low Earth orbiting satellites (Clark, 1988) allow the use of store and forward data communication to be achievable using low power transportable and mobile mounted equipment on v.h.f. and u.h.f. employing omni-direction aerials (AMSAT, 1991).

As well as one to one AX.25 usage, a 'broadcast' protocol may also be employed from the satellite where continuous bulletin information is transmitted for reception by permanently installed land terminals linked to computer controlled disk based storage, with individual repeat request messages only being transmitted by the ground station to complete 'holes' in the received packetised data.

46.9 Applications

Private Mobile Radio is identified thus to distinguish it from PAMR, Public Access Mobile Radio. PMR normally is used by individual fleets of users with inter-fleet communication, whereas PAMR covers public access communication such as those with PSTN access, e.g. Cellular, CT2 etc. A degree of overlap occurs however, with many PMR systems having 'private' PABX and PSTN access facilities from within their own systems, together with trunked PMR offering intra-fleet communication and PABX/PSTN access facilities, dependent upon the system in use.

46.9.1 Business use

PMR is thus generally used within a business environment for inter-unit communication within the business fleet, e.g. for rapid dispatcher to delivery vehicle communication. Through the use of carefully tailored base station aerial sites, communication may be usefully achieved within an area where public access systems are unable to provide a service, for example within an office or building site environment, or on a larger scale along a dedicated network of permanent ways such as the British Railways trunked PMR system now in use.

Due to the one to one communication scenario, PMR is generally considered unsuitable for private citizen use where PSTN access, either one way or two way, is often required. Here, cellular telephony, CT2, and PCN are likely to be of greater benefit. Fees levied by national cellular system operators for network calls however often make this unsuitable for users with frequent but often short calls, e.g. taxi and delivery firms operating in a given locality, where PMR normally offers a more economic solution if frequency assignments exist for this.

46.9.2 PMR growth

The usage of PMR is continuing to increase rather than decrease in the U.K. (Radiocom, 1990), indicating that public access systems are complimenting rather than replacing PMR systems. The extra frequency spectrum needed must thus be used to the best possible effect in congested areas, with trunked PMR becoming more prevalent. Frequency sharing between users is under control in many countries by co-ordination work performed by national regulatory bodies, and this must be considered and complied with to ensure the continued usefulness of PMR.

46.10 Appendix 46.1

MPT1327 sample command structure

46.10.1 Channel allocation

GTC - Go To Channel

46.10.2 Aloha invitations

ALH - General
ALHS - Standard Data Excluded
ALHD - 'Simple' Calls excluded
ALHE - Emergency only
ALHR - Registration or Emergency

46.10.3 Acknowledgements

ACK - General
ACKI - Intermediate
ACKQ - Call queued
ACKX - Message rejected
ACKV - Called Unit unavailable
ACKE - Emergency
ACKB - Call-back

46.10.4 Radio unit requests

RQS - Simple
RQD - Data
RQT - Divert
RQE - Emergency
RQR - Registration
RQQ - Status
RQC - Short Data

46.10.5 TSC Ahoys

AHY - General availability check
AHYQ - Status message
AHYC - Short Data Invitation

46.11 References

ARRL (1984) *Packet Radio Link Layer protocol, AX25*, December.

Armstrong, W. (1989) Trunked PMR in British Airways, *IBC Trunked Private Mobile Radio Conference*, November.

Bye, K.J. (1989) Handover criteria and control in cellular and microcellular systems, *IEE Fifth International Conference on Mobile Radio and Personal Communications*, December.

Clark, T. (1988) AMSAT's Microsat/pacsat Program, *7th ARRL Computer Networking Conference*, Columbia U.S.A., October.

AMSAT (1991) SatelLife - Healthnet satellite communications using transportable Earth terminals, *AMSAT-U.K. Colloquium*, University of Surrey, July.

DTI (1981c) *Code of practice for the transmission of digital information over land mobile radio systems*, Department of Trade and Industry, London, MPT1317, April.

DTI (1986) *Engineering memorandum for trunked systems in the land mobile radio service*, Department of Trade and Industry, London, MPT1318, February.

DTI (1988a) *Code of practice for repeater operation at communal sites*, Department of Trade and Industry, London, MPT1351, June.

DTI (1978) *Performance specification for continuous tone controlled signalling (CTCSS) for use in the land mobile services*, Department of Trade and Industry, London, MPT1306, January.

DTI (1981a) *Code of practice, requirements for duplex operation in the land mobile services*, Department of Trade and Industry, London, MPT1315, March.

DTI (1981b) *Code of practice for selective signalling for use in the private mobile radio services*, Department of Trade and Industry, London, MPT1316, January.

DTI (1987) *Code of practice for radio site engineering*, Department of Trade and Industry, London, MPT1331, April.

DTI (1988b) *A signalling standard for trunked private land mobile radio systems*, Department of Trade and Industry, London, MPT1327, January.

Erlang, A.K. (1918) Solution of some problems in the theory of probabilities of significance in automatic telephone exchanges, *Post Office Electrical Engineers Journal*, January.

GEC (1990) *Data services for fleet managers*, GEC National One.

HMSO (1984) *Bands 1 and 111, A consultative document*, May.

Hobeche R.J. (1985) *Land Mobile Radio Systems*, Peter Peregrinus.

Lee, W.C. (1982) *Mobile Communications Engineering*, McGraw Hill, New York.

Miller, J. (1988) 9600 baud packet radio modem design, *7th Computer Networking Conference*, Columbia U.S.A., October.

Oliver, B. (1989) U.K. national network services, *IBC Trunked Private Mobile Radio Conference*, November.

Orr, W.I. (1987) *Radio Handbook*, 23rd Edition, Sama.

Parsons, J.D. and Gardiner, J.G. (1989) *Mobile Communications Systems, 1st Edition*, Blackie and Sons Ltd., Glasgow and London.

Pascoe, R. (1989) The manufacturer's viewpoint, *IBC Trunked Private Mobile Radio Conference*, November.

Philips (1980) *Quasi-synchronous operation of two or more transmitters*, Philips Radio Communications Systems Ltd. publication ref. TSP361/2, April.

Radiocom. (1990) *Mobile Radio*, U.K. Radiocommunications Agency, Annual Report 1990-1991, pp. 30-31.

47

Cellular radio systems

Malcolm Appleby
MA
Cellnet
(Sections 47.1–47.4, 47.6)

Fred Harrison
BSc CEng MIEE
Cellnet
(Sections 47.3, 47.5, 47.7)

Contents

47.1 Introduction

Cellular radio systems are by far the most common of all public mobile telephone networks, the earlier (pre-cellular) networks now all being in decline. The basic principles of cellular systems were established by Bell Laboratories in 1949, but it was not until the early 1980s that technology allowed real commercial networks to be built and service offered to the public.

Systems were developed at different times in different countries and subject to a variety of different constraints such as frequency band, channel spacing etc. As a result, a number of different and incompatible cellular standards are in use throughout the world, and the more important standards are summarised later in this chapter.

Work is already well in hand to specify and develop second generation cellular systems, for which the opportunity is being taken to develop common standards and systems across several countries. One such notable system, GSM, has been developed in Europe, and is described in some detail later in this chapter.

47.2 Principles of operation

47.2.1 Network configuration

In a cellular radio system, the area to be covered is divided up into a number of small areas called cells, with one radio base station (BS) positioned to give radio coverage of each cell. Each base station is connected by a fixed link to a mobile services switching centre (MSC), which is generally a digital telephone exchange with special software to handle the mobility aspects of its users. Most cellular networks consist of a number of MSCs each with their own BSs, and interconnected by means of fixed links. The MSCs interconnect to the public switched telephone network (PSTN) for both outgoing calls to, and incoming calls from fixed telephones. Figure 47.1 shows a typical network arrangement.

A cellular network will be allocated a number of radio frequencies, or channels, for use across its coverage area, this number being dependent upon the amount of spectrum made available by the licensing authority and the channel spacing of the technical standard used by the network. The radio channels are grouped together into a number of channel sets, and these sets are then allocated to the cells, one set per cell, on a regular basis across the whole coverage area. Each channel will therefore be re-used many times by the network. The method of radio planning and allocation of channels to the cells is described later in this chapter.

47.2.2 Signalling

Generally, one radio channel is set aside in each cell to carry signalling information between the network and mobile stations. In the land to mobile (L-M) direction, overhead information about the operating parameters of the network, including an area identifier code, is broadcast to all mobiles located in the cell's coverage area. In addition specific commands are transmitted to individual mobiles in order to control call setup and mobiles' location updating.

In the mobile to land (M-L) direction, the signalling channel is used by the mobiles to carry location updating information, mobile originated call setup requests, and responses to land originated call setup requests.

47.2.3 Location registration

When a mobile is not engaged in a call, it tunes to the signalling channel of the cell in which it is located and monitors the L-M signalling information. As the mobile moves around the network, from time to time it will need to retune to the signalling channel of another cell when the signal from the current cell falls below an acceptable threshold.

When the mobile retunes in this way, it reads the overhead information broadcast by the new cell and updates the operating parameters as necessary. It also checks the location information being

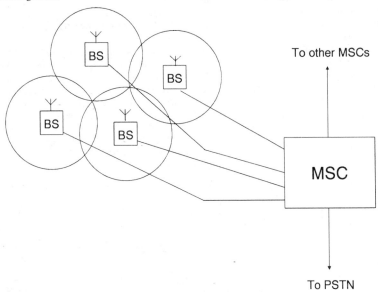

Figure 47.1   Cellular network configuration

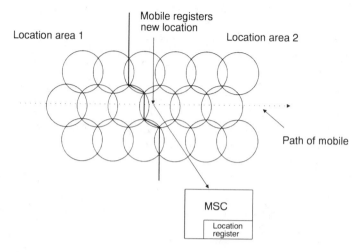

Figure 47.2 Mobile location registration

broadcast by the new cell and, if this differs from the previous cell, the mobile automatically informs the network of its new location by means of an interchange on the signalling channel (Figure 47.2). By means of this location registration procedure, the network is able to keep updated a database of the location area of all mobiles. This information is used in the call setup procedure for land to mobile calls.

47.2.4　Call set up

The signalling procedures for mobile to land (M-L) and land to mobile (L-M) call set up depend upon the technical standard of the particular network. However the general procedure described below holds true for many networks. When the user wishes to make a call, the telephone number to be called is entered followed by a 'call initiation' key (eg pressing the SEND button).

The mobile will transmit an access request to the network on the M-L signalling channel; this may be preceded by the mobile rescanning to ensure it is operating on the signalling channel of the nearest base station. If the network can process the call the base station will send a voice channel allocation message which commands the mobile to switch to a designated voice channel, namely one of the channels allocated to that cell. The mobile retunes to the channel indicated and the network proceeds to set up the call to the desired

number. As part of the call set up procedure, the network will validate the mobile requesting the call to ensure that it is a legitimate customer. Many networks incorporate specific security features to carry out this validation.

When the network receives a call for a mobile (eg from the PSTN) it will first check the location database to determine in which location area the mobile last registered. Paging calls to the mobile are transmitted on the L-M signalling channels of all the base stations in the identified location area and a response from the mobile awaited. If the mobile is turned on and receives the paging call it will acknowledge to its nearest base station on the M-L signalling channel. The base station receiving the acknowledgement sends a voice channel allocation message to the mobile and informs the network so that the two halves of the call can be connected.

47.2.5　In-call handover

At all times during a call (whether L-M or M-L) the base station currently serving the mobile monitors the signal (strength and/or quality) from the mobile. If the signal falls below a predesignated threshold, the network will command neighbouring base stations to measure the signal from the mobile (Figure 47.3(a)). If another base station is receiving the mobile with a stronger signal than the current

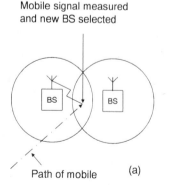

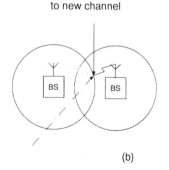

Figure 47.3　In-call handover

base station, a signalling message is sent to the mobile on the voice channel from the current base station commanding the mobile to a new voice channel, namely a free voice channel from those allocated to the neighbouring cell. The mobile changes frequency (and thereby the serving base station) and simultaneously the network connects the call to the new base station (Figure 47.3(b)).

The measuring process and new cell selection may take several seconds, but the user will only be aware of a brief break in transmission as the mobile tunes to the new voice channel.

47.2.6 Power control

Since the size of a cell may be anything from one kilometre to tens of kilometres across, it is not necessary for a mobile to transmit on full power at all times in order to maintain a satisfactory signal level at the base station's receiver. Most cellular standards therefore incorporate mobile power control, the base station commanding the mobile to transmit at one of a number of power levels. As the mobile moves closer to or further from the base station, further commands are issued to keep the received signal level to prescribed limits. By reducing the average mobile power level, co-channel interference is reduced, improving overall system quality.

47.3 Radio planning

As previously described, cellular radio re-uses the same radio channels in different cells and because of this re-use, two mobiles using the same channel in different cells may interfere with each other, a phenomenon known as co-channel interference. The key objective of planning a cellular radio system is to design the cell repeat pattern and frequency allocation in order to maximise the capacity of the system whilst controlling co-channel interference to within acceptable limits.

47.3.1 Cell repeat patterns

The cell plan has to be chosen such that the number of channel sets (N) fit together in a regular fashion without gaps or overlaps. Only certain values of N achieve this, and typical arrangements of interest to cellular radio are N = 4, 7 and 12 as shown in Figure 47.4. The value of N has a major effect on the capacity of the cellular system.

As the number of channels sets is decreased, the number of channels per cell increases, hence the system capacity increases. For example, if there are a total of 140 channels available, a 4 cell repeat pattern would provide 35 channels per cell, whilst a 7 cell would provide 20 channels per cell.

On this basis, the smallest possible value of N seems desirable. However, as N decreases, so the distance between cells using the same channels reduces, which in turn increases the level of co-channel interference.

The repeat distance D and the cell radius R are both related by the geometry of the cell pattern. These are shown in Figure 47.5 and Equation 47.1.

$$Re\text{-}use\ ratio\ D/R = \sqrt{3\,N} \qquad (47.1)$$

In practice, in a real network, it is not possible to achieve a regular cell pattern. This is because radio propagation at the frequencies

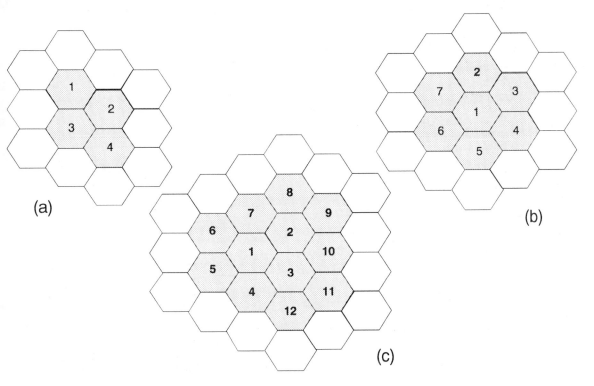

Figure 47.4   Cell repeat patterns: (a) four cell repeat; (b) seven cell repeat; (c) twelve cell repeat

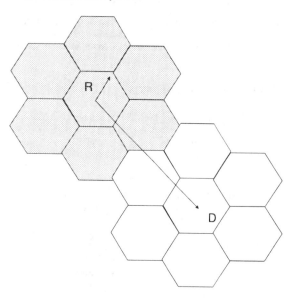

Figure 47.5   Frequency re-use – D/R ratio

used by cellular radio systems is affected by the terrain and by buildings, trees and other features of the landscape.

47.3.2   Co-channel interference

Generally, a mobile will receive a wanted carrier signal (C) from the base station serving the cell in which it is located, and in addition, interfering signals (I) from other cells. The carrier to interference ratio C/I is related to the re-use ratio D/R. Cellular radio systems are designed to tolerate a certain amount of interference, but beyond this, speech quality will be severely degraded. The TACS cellular system, for example, will work with a C/I down to around 17dB. This lower limit on C/I effectively sets the minimum D/R ratio that can be used.

The two key factors in ensuring that good quality transmission can occur between a mobile and base station are that the wanted signal strength is sufficiently large, that is, above the receiver threshold sensitivity, and that the interference level is low enough to give an adequate C/I ratio. Both of these factors depend on the radio propagation between the mobile and base stations.

47.3.3   Radio propagation

There are a number of elements which contribute to the received signal strength at a mobile. Firstly, for a line of sight path, there is a free space path loss which is related to the radial distance between base station and mobile.

In addition to this loss, where there is no direct line of sight path, there will be a diffraction loss resulting from obstructions in the path. In general there will also be an effect due to multiple signals arriving at the mobile due to reflections from buildings and other terrain features. This multi-path effect will result in signals either adding constructively or destructively.

As a mobile moves around within a cell it will experience varying signal, as shown in Figure 47.6, due to these factors. Fast fading is caused by the multipath effect, and occurs with only a small movement of the mobile. This is also known as Rayleigh fading. Slow

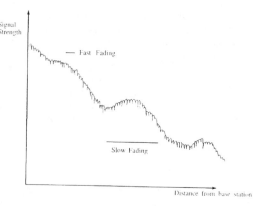

Figure 47.6   Fading effects

fading is mainly caused by terrain features and occurs over large distances of hundreds of metres.

In addition, the path loss is also dependent upon the type of terrain, for example, urban with dense buildings, or rural with trees, or even over water. The height of the mobile and base station above ground level also affects the propagation, although the mobile height is not usually a variable.

Predicting path loss is an essential part of radio planning, and because of the large number of contributing factors, empirically based formulae are used. The most widely used formula is the Hata model (Hata, 1980) which is based on the propagation measurement results of Okumura et al. (1968).

Hata's basic formula for the total path loss, Lp, is given by Equation 47.2 where f_c is the carrier frequency in MHz, h_b is the base station antenna height, h_m is the mobile antenna height, R is the radial distance in kilometres, and $a(h_m)$ is the mobile antenna height correction factor.

$$Lp\,(dB) = 69.55 + 26.16 \log(f_c) - 13.82 \log(h_b)$$
$$- a(h_m) + (44.9 - 6.55 \log(h_b)) \log R \qquad (47.2)$$

Correction factors can be used to take into account the type of terrain.

47.3.4   Practical radio planning

Armed with a propagation model it is possible to calculate both the wanted signal strength and the interference level for all locations in a cell. Generally this is done using a computer based tool which can draw upon a database of cell site information and terrain data. Some advanced tools can also take account of diffraction losses. For practical purposes a planner will aim to achieve the required signal strength and C/I ratio over 90% of the cell coverage area, by varying antenna heights, transmitter powers, frequency allocations and other factors as appropriate.

To simplify calculations, an allowance for Rayleigh fading and shadow fading is usually made within the system power budget. A typical power budget is shown in Table 47.1.

47.3.5   Adding capacity

Once a cellular network has been planned to provide overall coverage, there are a number of ways of adding additional capacity. A

Table 47.1 Typical power budget (TACS)
(1 = Key planning parameters)

Signal strength budget	Downlink	Uplink
Transmitter power (EIRP)	50dBm	39dBm
Receiver sensitivity (including antenna gain)	106dBm	113dBm
Fade margin (90% of area)	4dB	4dB
Required receiver level[1]	102dBm	109dBm
Maximum path loss (allowing for fading)	152dBm	148dBm
Interference budget		
C/I threshold	17dB	17dB
Target C/I for planning (90% of area)[1]	25dB	25dB

simple and cost effective option is to allocate further radio channels to existing cells. However, this can only be done by an extension band, for example the ETACS allocation in the UK. Other alternatives involve rearranging the cellular plan, either by cell splitting or by sectorisation.

Cell splitting is achieved by dividing an existing cell up into a number of smaller cells, by adding additional base stations as shown in Figure 47.7; it is then necessary to reallocate the radio channels. By repeatedly splitting cells; the cell size, and hence the system capacity, can be tailored to meet the traffic capacity requirements demanded by customer behaviour in all areas.

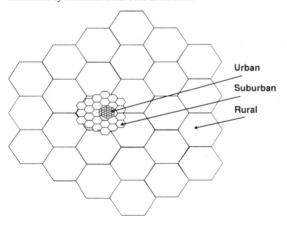

Figure 47.7 Cell splitting

In rural areas, cells may be 20km to 30km in radius. In practice, as cell sizes decrease, propagation effects, particularly in city areas, cause an increase in co-channel interference, even if the repeat pattern is maintained. Also, as cell sizes decrease, it becomes increasingly difficult to find suitable base station sites, which need to be accurately positioned in order to keep to a regular pattern.

The cost of providing and maintaining a large number of individual base stations is also a factor, such that in addition to cell splitting, sectorisation of cells is commonly used in urban areas.

In a regular cellular layout, co-channel interference will be received from six surrounding cells which all use the same channel set. One way of cutting significantly the level of interference is to use several directional antennas at the base stations, with each antenna illuminating a sector of the cell, and with a separate channel set allocated to each sector.

There are two commonly used methods of sectorisation, using three 120 degree sectors or six 60 degree sectors as shown in Figure 47.8, both of which reduce the number of prime interference sources to one. This is because, of the six surrounding co-channel cells, only one will be directed at the wanted cell.

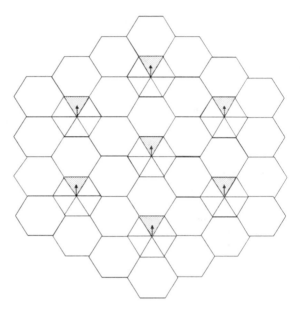

Figure 47.8 Sectorisation

A disadvantage of sectorisation is that the channel sets are divided between the sectors such that there are fewer channels per sector, and thus a reduction in trunking efficiency. This means that the total traffic which can be carried for a given level of blocking is reduced. However, this effect is offset by the ability to use smaller cells, such that the end result is a significant increase in total capacity.

47.4 Overview of systems

Cellular networks have been developed and deployed at various times and places in many countries across the world. In several cases, the local telecommunications authority or company was central to the specification and development of the standard with which the network complied. Since frequency allocations and other basic parameters (such as channel spacing) have often been set at national level and not co-ordinated between countries, these local factors resulted in different standards being adopted by different countries.

In addition, in cases where the development of a standard has started later, the opportunity has been taken to introduce new features made possible by advances in technology, further increasing the diversity between standards.

From this wide range of differing system standards, four have become largely dominant and have been adopted in many countries, albeit still with some variations. These four are AMPS, TACS, NMT

Table 47.2 Comparison of system parameters

	AMPS	TACS	NMT 450	NMT 900	C-450
Frequency band	800MHz	900MHz	450MHz	900MHz	450MHz
Channel spacing	30kHz	25kHz	25kHz	12.5kHz	20kHz
Speech modulation	FM	FM	FM	FM	FM
Deviation	12kHz	9.5kHz	5.0kHz	5.0kHz	4.0kHz
Signalling	Direct FSK	Direct FSK	Audio FFSK	Audio FFSK	Direct FSK
Signalling bit rate	10kbit/s	8kbit/s	1200bit/s	1200bit/s	5280bit/s
'Overlay' signalling	NO	NO	NO	NO	YES

(both NMT 450 and NMT 900) and C450, and their basic system parameters are shown in Table 47.2. Each of these is described in outline below, but in addition special mention must be made of the European designed GSM system which is set to become the dominant standard for Europe in the mid to late 1990's.

47.4.1 AMPS

AMPS stands for Advanced Mobile Phone System and was developed in the USA primarily by Bell Laboratories as a successor for the heavily congested IMTS (Improved Mobile Telephone System). Being designed for the north American market, AMPS uses the 800MHz band allocated to mobile services in ITU Region 2 (the Americas), with 30kHz channel spacing in common with established PMR practice.

AMPS uses analogue FM for speech transmission, but with a wider frequency deviation (12kHz) than is the norm for a 30kHz channelling system. By adopting the wide deviation, the dynamic range of the speech channel is extended and protection against co-channel interference is increased. This, together with the use of speech compression/expansion (companders) yields a high quality voice circuit with the capability to maintain performance in a high capacity (poor interference ratio) configuration.

Signalling between mobile and base station is at 10kbit/s, with Manchester encoding applied taking the bit rate to 20kbit/s. The data is modulated onto the radio carrier by direct frequency shift keying (FSK). Error control is achieved by multiple repetition (5 or 11 times) of each signalling word, with majority voting applied at the receiver to correct errors. A BCH block code is also applied to detect any uncorrected errors.

Whilst a call is in progress, the base station transmits a low level supervisory audio tone (SAT) in the region of 6kHz. Three different SAT frequencies are used by the network, and are allocated to the base stations so that the nearest co-channel base stations (i.e. those most likely to cause interference) have a different SAT from the wanted base station. The mobile continuously monitors the received SAT and also transponds the signal back to the base station. If the mobile (or the base station) detects a difference between the received SAT and that expected, the audio path is muted to prevent the interfering signal from being overhead. If the condition persists, the call is aborted.

AMPS underwent a long development period, and an extended trial (technical and commercial) which not only fixed the system parameters but also contributed to the basic planning rules which hold true for all cellular systems. The system design was comprehensively described in 1979 (Bell, 1979), but it was not until 1983

that operating licences were issued and true commercial exploitation of the system commenced.

AMPS is in operation extensively across the north American continent (USA and Canada). Due to the regulatory conditions in force in the USA, deployment has been in the form of a patchwork of largely independent standalone systems, with two competing systems operating in each licence area. Although commercial roaming agreements exist to allow customers of one operating company to obtain service from another when they are in a different part of the country, a seamless nationwide service is, as yet, not available to the customer.

AMPS is now also used in a number of a number of central and south American countries, in Australia and some far east countries. World-wide it is the dominant standard in terms of installed customer base.

AMPS is being further developed to incorporate digital speech encoding, with TDMA techniques to give three digital voice channels per one radio channel. Digital AMPS (DAMPS) has the same basic architecture and signalling protocol as AMPS and is therefore more evolutionary than revolutionary (as is GSM in Europe).

47.4.2 TACS

TACS stands for Total Access Communications System, and was adapted from the AMPS standard by the UK when cellular radio was licensed for operation from 1985. The adaptation was necessary to suit European frequency allocations which were at 900MHz, with 25kHz channel spacing. This meant a reduction in frequency deviation and signalling speed was necessary (BS, 1990).

The signalling scheme of AMPS was retained largely unchanged, but some enhancements were introduced, particularly in the procedures for location registration, to make the standard more suitable for deployment in systems offering contiguous nationwide coverage. The opportunity was also taken to introduce extra features, such as signalling of charge rate information (e.g. for payphones).

TACS was originally specified to use the full 1000 channels (2 x 25MHz) allocated to mobile services in Europe. However in the UK, only 600 channels (2 x 15MHz) were released by the licensing authority, the remainder being reserved for GSM. Subsequently an additional allocation of channels below the existing TACS channels was made, namely the Extended TACS (ETACS) channels, and the standard was modified accordingly.

TACS equipment availability and cost have both benefitted from the standard's similarity to AMPS, and TACS systems have been adopted by several European countries (UK, Eire, Spain, Italy, Austria and Malta), in the middle east (Kuwait, UAE and Bahrain) and the far east (Hong Kong, Singapore, Malaysia and China). In

Europe, TACS is on an equal footing with NMT in terms of installed customer base. A variant of TACS (called J-TACS) has also been adopted in Japan.

47.4.3 NMT

NMT stands for Nordic Mobile Telephone (system), and was developed jointly by the PTTs of Sweden, Norway, Denmark and Finland during the late 1970's/early 1980's. The system was designed to operate in the 450MHz band, and was later adapted to also use the 900MHz band. Although NMT was developed after AMPS, it saw commercial service before it, opening in late 1981.

NMT450 uses a channel spacing of 25kHz, speech modulation being analogue FM with a peak frequency deviation of 5kHz, the same as standard PMR practice. NMT900 also uses a frequency deviation of 5kHz, but with a 12.5kHz channel spacing to double the number of available channels, albeit with a degraded adjacent channel rejection performance which must be taken into account during frequency planning. Signalling is at 1200 bit/s using audio fast frequency shift keying (FFSK). Error protection of the signalling information is by means of a Hagelbarger convolutional forward error correcting code.

NMT was designed from the outset to support international roaming and was first implemented with full four nation roaming in the four participating countries (Norway, Sweden, Finland and Denmark). Since then NMT450 has been deployed in many other European countries (Austria, Spain, Netherlands, Belgium, Luxembourg, France, Iceland, Faroe Is., Turkey and Hungary) but due to differences in the frequency allocations in the 450MHz band between countries, not all networks are fully compatible to allow roaming.

NMT900 was developed as a necessity as capacity became exhausted on the NMT450 networks, and has been deployed since 1987 as an overlay network in several countries, and in Switzerland as their main network.

47.4.4 C450

C450 (also known as Netz-C) was developed by Siemens during the early 1980's under the direction of the (West) German PTT, Deutsche Bundespost. Commercial service opened in 1985 following a trial period.

C450 has a channel spacing of 20kHz, in common with other mobile services in Germany at 450MHz and speech modulation is analogue FM with a frequency deviation of 4.0kHz. Signalling for call control is transmitted at 5.28kbit/s by direct FSK. Error protection of the signalling is by bit interleaving with a BCH block code backed by an acknowledgement protocol.

In addition, C450 uses continuous signalling between base station and mobile during a call, achieved by time compressing the speech in bursts of 12.5ms, each burst being compressed into 11.4ms. This process opens up slots of 1.1ms duration every 12.5ms and the signalling data is inserted into these slots and extracted by the receiver which also time expands the speech back to its original form.

This continuous signalling serves several purposes:

1. It allows the base station to send power control and handover messages to the mobile without disturbing the voice channel.
2. The data is checked for jitter, and thereby the quality of the channel can be determined in order to indicate the need for a handover.

3. The time delay between a base station transmitting a data burst and receiving the response from the mobile is measured at the base station and used to calculate the distance between them. This distance is also taken into account in handover determination.
4. The data is used as a timing reference by the mobile to lock its internal clocks.

C450 contains a number of advanced features made possible by the application of current developments in technology. Although speech transmission is analogue, it can be regarded as a hybrid technology system, and several of its characteristics such as time slotted signalling channels and continuous signalling during call have been carried through into the GSM system design.

Coming later to the European scene, C450 has chiefly only served the German market, although systems are also operating in Portugal and South Africa.

47.4.5 GSM

The GSM standard was developed as a joint initiative by the members of the Conference of European Posts and Telecommunications administrations (CEPT) with the eventual aim of building a unified pan-European network, giving the user a near uniform service throughout all European countries. An added bonus of a common standard should be lower terminal equipment prices through economies of scale.

Work on the standard started in 1982, and by 1987 all the basic architectural features were decided. The full Phase 1 specification was completed in 1990, but work continues on further phases incorporating new features and services. In 1987, the majority of operators participating in GSM signed a Memorandum of Understanding (MoU) committing them to make GSM a reality by installing networks and opening commercial service by 1991. Since that time further operators have signed the MoU, bringing the total to date to 25.

The GSM technical standard makes full use of currently available levels of technology, incorporating features such as low bit rate speech, convolutional channel coding with bit interleaving and frequency hopping. The standard is intended to endure for many years to come.

47.5 Detailed description of GSM

47.5.1 GSM architecture

The basic architecture of GSM is not dissimilar to other cellular radio systems and comprises base transceiver stations (BTS), Base Station Controllers (BSC), Mobile Switching Centres (MSC), a variety of registers and a network management system, as shown in Figure 47.9. The mobile station comprises a mobile equipment and a subscriber identity module (SIM). In addition to these functional entities, GSM also defines several interfaces, the Radio Interface (Um), the interface between the MSC and BSC (A interface) and the signalling interface which allows roaming between networks. This is based on the CCITT No.7 signalling standard and is defined as a Mobile Application Part (MAP).

The BTS and BSC together form the Base Station Subsystem (BSS) and carry out all the functions related to the radio channel management. This includes the management of the radio channel configurations, allocating radio channels for speech, data and sig-

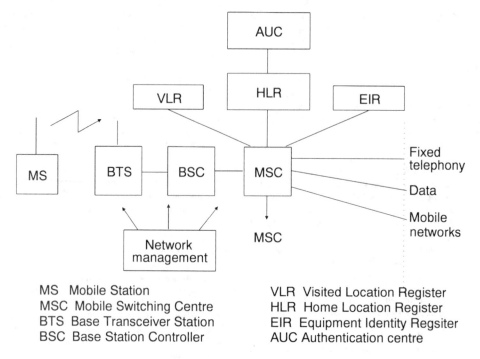

MS   Mobile Station
MSC Mobile Switching Centre
BTS Base Transceiver Station
BSC Base Station Controller

VLR Visited Location Register
HLR Home Location Register
EIR Equipment Identity Regsiter
AUC Authentication centre

Figure 47.9   GSM architecture

nalling purposes, and controlling frequency hopping and power control. The BSS also includes, as does the MS, the speech encoding and decoding, and channel coding and decoding.

The MSC, VLR and HLR are concerned with mobility management functions. These include authentication and registration of the mobile customer, location updating, and call set up and release. The HLR is the master subscriber database and carries information about individual subscribers numbers, subscription levels, call restrictions, supplementary services and the current location (or most recent location) of subscribers. The VLR acts as a temporary subscriber database for all subscribers within its coverage area, and contains similar information to that in the HLR. The provision of a VLR means that the MSC does not need to access the HLR for every transaction.

The authentication centre (AUC) works closely with the HLR and provides information to authenticate all calls in order to guard against fraud. The equipment identity register (EIR) is used for equipment security and validation of different types of mobile equipment. This information can be used to screen mobile types from accessing the system, for example if a mobile equipment is stolen, not type approved, or has a fault which could disturb the network.

Network management is used to monitor and control the major elements of the GSM network. In particular, it monitors and reports faults and performance data. It can also be used to re-configure the network.

47.5.2   Air interface

The GSM Air Interface (Um) provides the physical link between the mobile and the network. Some of the key characteristics of the air interface are given in Table 47.3. As already described, GSM is a digital system employing time division multiple access (TDMA)

techniques and operating in the 900MHz band. The CEPT have made available two frequency bands to be used throughout Europe by the GSM system, namely;
1. 890MHz to 915MHz for the mobile to base station (uplink) direction.
2. 935MHz to 960MHz for the base station to mobile (downlink) direction.

These 25MHz bands are divided into 124 pairs of carriers spaced by 200kHz. In addition, consideration is now being given to specifying additional carriers in a pair of extension bands 872MHz to 888MHz and 917MHz to 933MHz. Each of the carriers is divided up into eight TDMA timeslots of length 0.577ms such that the frame length is 4.615ms. The recurrence of each timeslot makes up one

Table 47.3   GSM air interface parameters

Frequency band mobile – base	890 – 915MHz
Frequency band base – mobile	935 – 960MHz
124 radio carriers spaced by 200kHz	
TDMA structure with 8 timeslots per radio carrier	
Gaussian Minimum Shift Keying (GMSK) Modulation with BT = 0.3	
Slow frequency hopping at 217 hops per second	
Block and convolutional channel coding with interleaving	
Downlink and uplink power control	
Discontinuous transmission and reception	

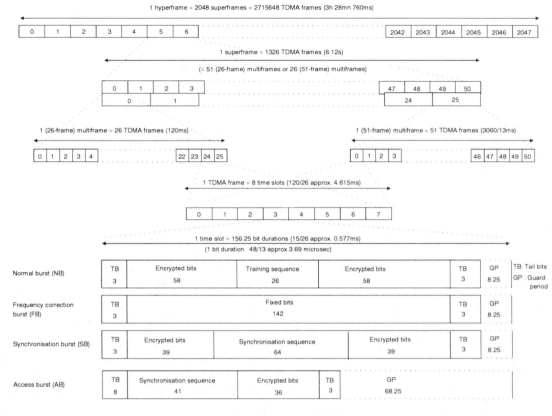

Figure 47.10 GSM timeframes, timeslots and bursts (Extract from GSM Recommendation 05.01)

physical channel, such that each carrier can support eight physical channels, in both the uplink and downlink directions.

The timeslot allocation in either direction is staggered so that the mobile station does not need to transmit and receive at the same time. Data is transmitted in bursts within the timeslots and a number of different types of burst can be carried as shown in Figure 47.10. The normal burst has a data structure as shown. It consists of 148 bits of which 114 are available for data transmission, 26 are used for a training sequence which allows the receiver to estimate the radio propagation characteristics and to set up a dispersion equaliser, 6 bits as tail bits, and two stealing flags. These physical channels therefore provide a data throughput of 114 bits every 4.615ms or 24.7kbit/s.

The bursts modulate one of the RF carriers using Gaussian Minimum Shift Keying (GMSK) modulation with a BT index of 0.3. The allocation of the carrier can be such that frequency hopping is achieved, i.e consecutive bursts of a physical channel will be carried by differing RF carriers. This "hopping" is performed every TDMA frame, or every 4.615ms and provides extra protection against channel fading and co-channel interference.

A number of logical channels can be carried by the physical channels described above. These are summarised in Table 47.4.

There are two categories of traffic channels; speech, whether full rate using 22.8kbit/s or half rate using 11.4kbit/s, and data, providing a variety of data rates. There are four basic categories of control channels, known as the broadcast control channel (BCCH), the common control channel (CCCH), the standalone dedicated control channel (SDCCH) and the associated control channel (ACCH).

These are further divided into channels with specific purposes and for a detailed description of these channels the reader is referred to the GSM Recommendations published by ETSI.

Each of these logical channels is mapped onto the physical channels, using the appropriate burst type as shown in Figure 47.10.

TDMA frames are built up into 26 or 51 frame multiframes, such that individual timeslots can use either of the multiframe types, and then into superframes and hyperframes as shown in Figure 47.10. The TCH and the associated ACCH uses the 26 frame structure, whilst the BCCH and CCCH use the 51 frame structure. The SDCCH may occupy one physical channel, providing 8 SDCCH, or may share a physical channel with the BCCH/CCCH. Typical arrangements for allocating the 8 physical channels could be:

1. 7 channels TCH and SACCH + 1 channel BCCH/CCCH/SDCCH
2. 6 channels TCH and SACCH + 1 channel BCCH/CCCH + 1 channel SDCCH.

Each cell must have at least one physical channel assigned to the BCCH/CCCH, where there are 2 or more carriers per cell, the non-BCCH carriers may have all 8 channels allocated to TCH.

47.5.3 Speech coding and channel coding

The speech coder is a regular pulse excited linear predictive coder (RPE-LPC) with long term prediction. This provides a net bit rate of 13kbit/s. It is a block based coder where the input samples are

Table 47.4   GSM logical channels

Traffic Channels (TCH)		Control Channels (CCH)			
Speech	Data	Broadcast CCH (BCCH)	Common CCH (CCCH)	Standalone Dedicated CCH (SDCCH)	Associated CCH (ACCH)
Full rate TCH/F	TCH/F9.6	Frequency Correction	Paging Channel		Fast (FACCH)
	TCH/F4.8	(FCCH)	(PCH)		
	TCH/F2.4	Synchronisation	Random Access		Slow (SACCH)
		(SCH)	(RACH)		
Half rate TCH/H	TCH/H4.8		Access Grant		
	TCH/H2.4		(AGCH)		

analysed in blocks with a 20ms duration. Work is also being carried out to specify a half rate speech coder which will effectively double the system capacity of GSM.

Before being assembled into the timeslots and frames, the digital speech and signalling data is encoded and interleaved. The speech coder output is divided up into three classes of bits and the most sensitive bits are encoded by adding parity check bits followed by a convolutional coder. Signalling data is encoded using a FIRE code. A process of interleaving is then used to spread the data blocks over a number of bursts.

For speech, an interleaving degree of 8 is used, i.e the speech block is spread over 8 bursts, whilst an interleaving degree of 4 is used for signalling. This overall process is shown in Figure 47.11,

and the combined use of coding and interleaving provides good protection of channel data from the fading, dispersion and interference effects on the radio path. With the addition of frequency hopping and diversity techniques, the GSM air interface is particularly robust.

One of the penalties to be paid for this is the overall transmission delay. The speech coder contributes about 25ms and the channel coding and interleaving a further 37ms. The rest of the transmission delay budget allows for analogue to digital conversions, 16kbit/s transmission and switching in various parts of the network. The overall one way transmission delay thus amounts to around 90ms. Such a delay means that echo control is necessary even on short national calls.

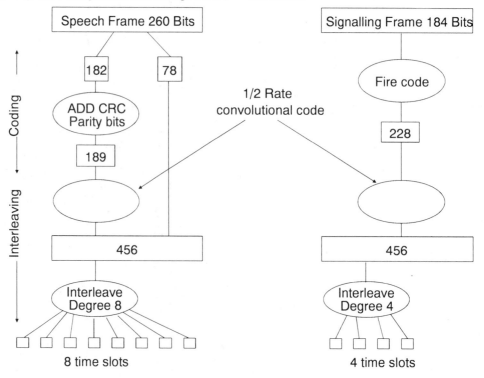

Figure 47.11   GSM channel coding and interleaving

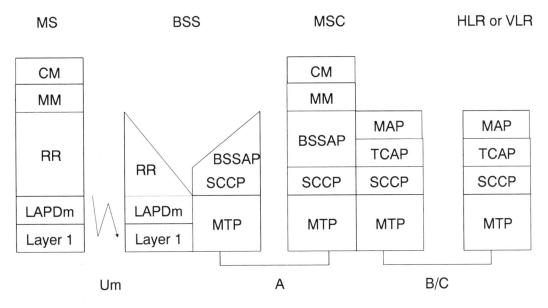

Figure 47.12 GSM signalling model

47.5.4 GSM signalling

Figure 47.12 shows the overall signalling model. The Air Interface uses LAPDm Layer 2 signalling protocol and this is also used for the A-bis, BTS to BSC interface.

The layer 3 protocol consists of three sublayers, dealing with radio resource management (RR), mobility management (MM), and connection management (CM). Radio resource management is concerned with managing the logical channels, including paging, channel assignments, handover, measurement reporting, and other functions.

The mobility management layer contains functions necessary to support the mobility of the user which include authentication, location updating, attach and detach of IMSI (International Mobile Subscriber Identity), and registration. The connection management layer is concerned with call control, establishing and clearing circuits, management of supplementary services and the short message service.

The BSC to MSC A-interface, and the various MSC to Register interfaces employ CCITT No.7 signalling using the Message Transfer Part (MTP), Signalling Connection Control Part (SCCP), Transaction Capabilities Part (TCAP) and Mobile Application Part (MAP).

An example of the signalling messaging for establishing a mobile originated call is shown in Figure 47.13. The key events are:

1. Request and assignment of a channel, between MS and BSS.
2. A service request procedure which accesses the VLR.
3. An authentication and ciphering exchange which validates the mobile user and sets the encryption cipher.
4. Call set up which includes sending of dialled digits and establishing the connection.

Location updating is shown in Figure 47.14 An update request is indicated by the mobile and passed to the VLR in the new location area. The new VLR requests the IMSI from the old VLR and then signals the new location to the HLR. The HLR provides the sub-scriber data to the new VLR and cancels the subscriber entry in the old VLR. Finally a confirmation message is set back to the mobile.

There are, of course, many other signalling exchanges, dealing with mobile terminating calls, supplementary services, and short message service. There is not space in this chapter to deal with the detailed signalling for these cases; the examples above describe the general principle and illustrate the roles of the MS, BSS, MSC, VLR and HLR.

47.5.5 Security features

The information on the air interface needs to be protected, to provide user data (including speech) confidentiality and to prevent fraudulent use of subscriber and mobile identities. The basic mechanisms employed are user authentication and user data encryption.

Each mobile user is provided with a Subscriber Identity Module (SIM) which contains the IMSI, the individual subscriber authentication key (Ki) and the authentication algorithm (A3). After the mobile user has made an access and service request, the network checks the identity of the user by sending a random number (RAND) to the mobile. The mobile uses the RAND, Ki and A3 algorithm to produce a signed response SRES. This response is compared with a similar response calculated by the network, and access only continues if the two responses match.

The SIM also contains a cipher key generating algorithm (A8). The MS uses the RAND and A8 to calculate a ciphering key (Kc) which is used to encrypt and decrypt signalling and user data information.

The authentication centre (AUC) is responsible for all security aspects and its function is closely linked with the HLR. The AUC generates the Ki's and associates them with IMSIs, and provides the HLR with sets of RAND, SRES and Kc for each IMSI. The HLR then provides the appropriate VLR with these sets and it is the VLR which carries out the authentication check. Authentication of mobile users can be carried out on call set up, both mobile originated and mobile terminated, on location updating, and on activation of

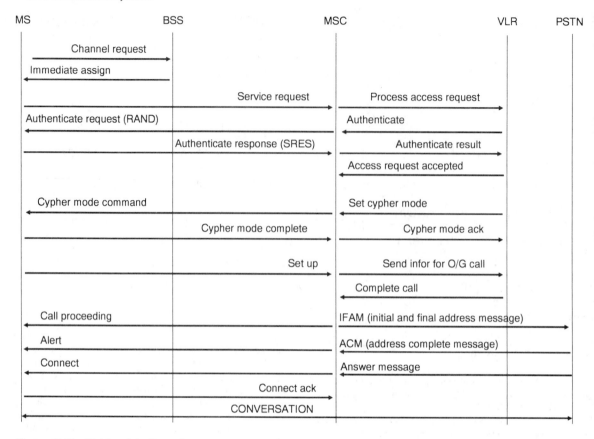

Figure 47.13 Mobile originating call

supplementary services. As the authentication sets are used up in the VLR, further sets are requested from the HLR.

An additional security feature of GSM is the equipment identity register (EIR). This enables monitoring of the mobile equipment IMEI (International Mobile Equipment Identity) which is used to validate mobile equipments thus preventing non-approved, faulty or stolen equipment from using the system. This range of security features provide a high degree of protection to the user and the network operator.

47.5.6 GSM services and features

In addition to speech, GSM offers a wide range of data bearer services up to 9.6kbit/s suitable for connection to circuit switched or packet switched data networks. GSM also supports Group III facsimile as a data service by use of an appropriate convertor.

A comprehensive range of supplementary services are offered by GSM, including call forwarding, call barring, multi-party service, advice of charge and others. A full description is provided in the GSM Recommendations, and further detail of cellular services is provided later in this chapter.

An important feature of GSM is the short message service (SMS). This allows transmission of alphanumeric messages of up to 160 characters to or from a mobile via a service centre. If the message cannot be delivered due to mobile being switched off, or outside of the coverage area, the message is stored at a service centre and re-transmitted when the mobile registers again. Received messages

can be displayed on the mobile and stored in the SIM for future reference. A related service is cell broadcast which allows messages of up to 93 characters to be sent to all mobiles within a specific geographical area, for example to deliver traffic or weather reports.

47.5.7 Roaming

Naturally, with a pan-European system, roaming of subscribers between networks is specified by GSM. When a mobile first switches on in a foreign PLMN (Public Land Mobile Network), the local MSC/VLR will determine the identity of the home PLMN from the mobile network code which is part of the IMSI. The home HLR will be interrogated to establish whether roaming is permitted and for authentication. The home HLR then passes the subscriber data to the local (foreign) VLR and registers the foreign location of the mobile. Calls to and from the roamed mobile can then take place.

47.6 Services

The primary purpose of all cellular radio networks is to offer speech telephony service to its customers. In addition most networks offer a range of supplementary and value added services to enhance the basic product.

In analogue systems, basic telephony is provided directly by the audio path between mobile and network. Other than some linear speech processing to increase the channel's signal to noise perfor-

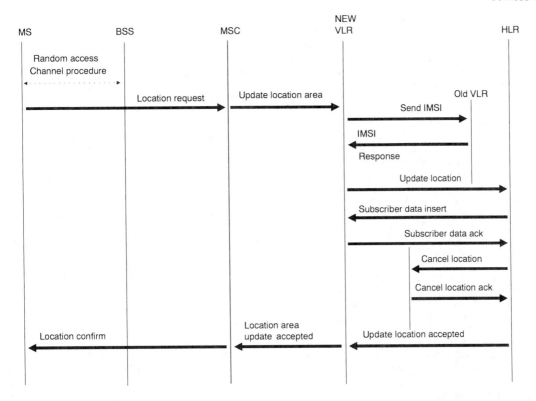

Figure 47.14 Location updating

mance, the audio path is transparent across the speech band, allowing other sounds (tones, non-voice signals etc) to pass through undistorted. By contrast GSM (and other digital systems) use a speech coder tailored to voice characteristics. They therefore provide a fully acceptable telephony service, but non-voice signals can suffer distortion across the non-audio transparent path.

47.6.1 Supplementary services

Supplementary services are provided by means of enhancements to the basic call processing software in the MSCs. Many of these services have specific relevance to the cellular radio user, and in the main they parallel services which are becoming increasingly available on the fixed telephone networks (such as BT's Star Services in the UK).

Typical services are as follows:

1. Call divert, where all calls are diverted to the specified number, which may be another mobile or a termination on another network. This is of use if the user wishes to make calls but not receive them.
2. Divert on no answer, where calls are diverted to the specified number when the user does not answer within (for instance) 20 seconds. This is of use if a mobile is left switched on in an unattended vehicle.
3. Divert on mobile unavailable, where calls are diverted to the specified number if the network cannot contact the mobile owing to its being turned off or out of range. This is of particular use in a cellular system where, in general, users are not available at all times, and where coverage is not universal. This

service is often combined with the "divert on no answer" service.
4. Divert on busy, where calls are diverted to the specified number when the mobile is already engaged on a call. As an alternative, networks also provide call waiting.
5. Call waiting, where if a call is received when the mobile is already engaged on a call, the user is informed that a second call is waiting, and can choose to place the first call on hold whilst dealing with the second caller.
6. Three party calling, where the mobile user may set up calls to two other parties and connect them in a three way conference. This service can also be used to make enquiry calls whilst holding the original call.

47.6.2 Value added services

Value added services are normally provided by means of peripheral units attached to the cellular network, or to the fixed network with which to cellular network interconnects. In some countries, the prevailing regulatory regime will influence what services may be offered and in what manner, however, the following are typical.

47.6.2.1 *Messaging services*

Voice messaging is commonly available in association with cellular networks. Used in conjunction with the call divert supplementary services, the messaging service can pick up calls when the user cannot, and the caller can leave a message for later retrieval by the user. Some services allow the user to be alerted to the receipt of messages by means of a radiopaging service, or in some cases by a ringback on the cellular network itself.

In addition to voice messaging, GSM networks will incorporate the 'Short Message Service' which effectively turns a GSM mobile into a two way alphanumeric pager with forced message delivery and message delivery confirmation.

47.6.2.2 *Information services*

Voice information services are commonly available on fixed networks, normally carrying some premium call charge. Some services (such as travel and weather information) are of particular value to a mobile user and some networks make these more readily accessible, for instance by using the mobile's current location to select the appropriate information for that area.

47.6.2.3 *Private interconnect*

A large user of cellular can often gain economies by leasing a direct connection between the cellular network and their company's private network, thus bypassing the PSTN. Call charges for such direct connections are tariffed by the cellular operator at a level substantially less than that for PSTN calls. An extra benefit of private interconnect are that calls can be delivered direct to extensions on a company's network without having to be handled by the switchboard operator, saving time and labour.

47.6.3 Data services

In analogue cellular systems, the transparent audio path between the network and mobile can be used not only for voice communication, but also for non-voice communication such as data using in-band modems, and facsimile. In order to be used in conjunction with a mobile, data modems and fax machines which are designed for PSTN use have to be adapted for connection to the mobile by means of a special interface. Such interfaces are available for a range of mobiles, and often permit automatic call establishment and clear down under the control of the modem or fax machine.

The data rate achievable over a cellular radio channel will often be less than that over a direct PSTN path, mainly due to the more limited frequency response of the channel, and the delay spread characteristic which is affected by the audio processing in both mobile and base station. However data transmission at 1200bit/s (using CCITT V.22) and 4800bit/s (using V32) can be achieved quite commonly on cellular networks, as well as fax up to 7200 or 9600bit/s.

The radio link between a cellular network's base stations and a mobile station is a notoriously hostile environment for data transmission. Disturbance and interruptions come from a variety of sources, such as variability of the radio signal strength, noise and interference, and 'intentional' breaks due to signalling interchanges between base station and mobile for handover and power control. In order to transmit data reliably over such a path, error control of some form is essential.

The simplest form of error control is a layer 2 protocol, and the emergence of the CCITT V.42 standard has led to error correcting modems becoming readily available. Although V.42 (which contains two protocols, the 'open' LAP-M and 'proprietary' MNP4) was designed for fixed PSTN use, it has proved to perform sufficiently well over cellular paths, particularly to static mobiles, for the user to receive good service.

Many proprietary protocols have been specifically developed to cope with the errors experienced over cellular radio channels. One such protocol is called Cellular Data Link Control (CDLC), and was developed in the UK by Racal Vodata. CDLC uses two levels of error correction with dynamic switching, and techniques such as forward error correction, bit interleaving and BCH block coding with a basic HDLC protocol to give a highly robust data transmission path, even over poor quality channels.

Facsimile transmission over cellular has benefitted by the increasingly widespread adoption of Group 3 error correcting (ECM) fax machines and the availability of portable machines suitable for vehicle use.

The GSM system does not provide a transparent audio path due to the voice coding techniques used, so data transmission in GSM is dealt with differently. When the data mode is selected, the speech coder is replaced by a rate adaptor and channel coder which apply forward error correction to the data bits, and the resulting bit stream is then transmitted across the radio path in the same burst structure as for voice transmission. At the receive end the bit stream is extracted and errors are corrected up to the limit of the forward error correction scheme. If there are any errors remaining, a higher layer protocol is needed to detect and correct them.

GSM has defined two families of data services, termed transparent and non-transparent. The transparent service applies only forward error correction as described above, and the user application must be able to cope with the residual error rate. The characteristics of the transparent service are constant delay and throughput but variable error rate. The transparent service is of particular use in synchronous applications (eg X.25, IBM SDLC) where the higher layer protocol inherent in the application will correct the errors. Asynchronous applications may also use the transparent service, particularly at low bit rates where the forward error correction applied by GSM is stronger.

The non-transparent service applies a GSM specific layer 2 protocol between the mobile and the network in order to correct all residual errors, resulting in a near zero error rate. The penalty, however, is variable throughput and delay, dependent upon the prevailing radio conditions. The non-transparent service is of particular application to simple asynchronous terminals, although provision in the standards is also made for protocol conversion to allow X.25 packets to be carried.

Facsimile transmission over GSM is complicated by the use in the Group 3 standard of a number of data transmission rates and modem types (V.21, V.29, V.27). In order to carry the fax signals, GSM mobiles need a special adaptor to convert the multiple standards into a synchronous bit stream for transmission between mobile and network. A similar converter in the network then converts the signal back into the Group 3 protocol to interwork with fax machines in the fixed network.

47.7 Future developments

The technology of cellular radio systems continues to develop very rapidly. The early 1980s saw the introduction of the first commercial analogue systems and by the end of the decade trials of second generation digital systems were already under way. Systems such as GSM are now entering into service and work is already starting on the specification of a third generation world wide standard system.

These developments are not introducing technology for its own sake, but are aimed at improving the quality, capacity, and availability, and reducing the cost of mobile communications. In addition to these step changes in 'generations' of system there are technical advances which are applicable to current systems. These include techniques such as microcellular and intelligent networks.

47.7.1 Microcells

As the capacity of cellular systems has increased, cell sizes have decreased, in some networks to as small as 0.5km radius, such that controlling co-channel interface becomes a major problem. The use of microcells, that is, very small cells, is a way of increasing capacity still further. In a microcellular layout, base station antennas are placed below the building height in urban areas, and low power is used such that the propagation characteristics between base station and mobile are dominated by the street layout. Interference from adjacent cells is blocked by buildings.

Microcellular techniques allow significantly higher traffic densities to be achieved, and also enable smaller, lower power mobiles to be used. The use of microcells requires improved handover techniques, which allow for fast and reliable handoff, for example when turning a street corner. One way of easing handover problems is to employ an 'umbrella cell' arrangement using conventional cells overlaying the microcells such that handover can be made into the umbrella cell where no suitable adjacent microcell can be identified. This also avoids the need to plan a contiguous coverage of microcells in an urban area.

New technology is now enabling the use of more compact and cheaper base stations. Conventional base sites have generally required a purpose built building, or rented space within an existing building for installation of base station racks of equipment. Now, base stations can be housed in small roadside or roof top mounted cabinets, and further reductions in size can be expected. Small base station equipment, and antennas, are essential to enable microcells to be built cost effectively.

47.7.2 Intelligent networks

Intelligent Network techniques (IN), are not, of course unique to cellular systems and have already become well established in fixed networks for the provision of 'free fone' or 'toll-free' type services, for example. However, the ability of an IN architecture to provide customised services is particularly valuable to a mobile user, who can have improved control over the handling of incoming calls. IN techniques also provide the ability to create a wide variety of advanced services.

Second generation cellular systems such as GSM are already designed around an architecture which can support IN type applications. In particular, the HLR function is closely related to the IN service control point. We can expect further developments in the near future which will bring a range of IN features to both the mobile user and the service provider.

47.7.3 Personal communications

The term PCN, Personal Communications Network, is used widely in the UK, whilst PCS, Personal Communications Services is used in the USA. Both aim at the same objective of serving the mass consumer market with mobile communications. The key challenge is to provide a very high capacity network to support a large number of users at low cost. Microcellular techniques will certainly be needed, and in order to keep costs down, the concept of regional service, and local access to the PSTN is being considered. IN techniques may offer personal numbering across a variety of networks.

PCN is dealt with in detail in Chapter 48. The standard in Europe, known as DCS1800 is based on the GSM standard but operating at 1800MHz. There is therefore unlikely to be a significant technical difference between Cellular GSM and PCN, with microcellular techniques being equally applicable to either system.

In the USA, the use of CDMA, code division multiple access, is being trialled for PCS. CDMA works on the principle of transmitting unique (orthogonal) codes to identify different users. Detection of signals is achieved by using correlating receivers such that other users appear as pseudonoise. CDMA thus allows a large number of users to share the same (wideband) radio channel.

There is considerable debate about the advantages and disadvantages of CDMA, in particular how to control near/far user interference; the extent to which this can be achieved is crucial to the ultimate capacity of CDMA. One of the key benefits of CDMA is the potential to share spectrum with other users, for example fixed links, and for this reason it is particularly attractive where additional spectrum for mobile systems cannot be made available.

47.8 Conclusion

Cellular radio is a comparatively young technology. Networks employing analogue systems have developed rapidly and now provide high quality service and excellent coverage in many of the developed countries. Technology developments are now increasing the potential network capacity, reducing the size of mobiles, and bringing advanced features and services to the mobile user. The decade ahead with the opportunity to introduce new digital systems and create a world-wide land mobile standard looks particularly exciting.

47.9 References

Bell (1979) Special issue on Advanced Mobile Phone Service, *Bell System Technical Journal*, January.

BS (1990) Total Access Communication System (TACS) *BS6940 Parts 1 & 2*.

Hansen, S. (1988) Voice Activity Detection (VAD) and the Operation of Discontinuous Transmission (DTX) in the GSM System. In *Proceedings of the Digital Cellular Radio Conference*, October 12–14, Hagen, Germany.

Hata, M. (1980) Empirical Formula for Propagation Loss in Land Mobile Radio Services, *IEEE Transactions*, **VT- 29**, (3), August.

Hodges, M.R.L. (1990) The GSM Radio Interface, *Br Telecom Technology Journal*, **8**, (1).

Mallinder, B.J.T. (1988) An Overview of the GSM System. In *Proceedings of the Digital Cellular Radio Conference*, October 12–14, Hagen, Germany.

Okumura, Y. et al. (1968) Field Strength and its Variability in u.h.f. and v.h.f. Land Mobile Radio Service, *Review of the Electrical Communication Laboratory*, (6).

Oschner, H (1988) Overview of the Radio Subsystem. In *Proceedings of the Digital Cellular Radio Conference*, October 12–14, Hagen, Germany.

Van der Arend, P.C.J. (1988) Security aspects and the implementation in the GSM System. In *Proceedings of the Digital Cellular Radio Conference*, October 12–14, Hagen, Germany.

Vary, P. (1988) GSM Speech Codec. In *Proceedings of the Digital Cellular Radio Conference*, October 12–14, Hagen, Germany.

48

Personal communications networks

P J Marnick
BSc (Hons) CEng MIEE
Hutchison Microtel Ltd

R G Russell
BSc (Hons)CEng MIEE
Hutchison Microtel Ltd

Contents

48.1 Introduction

Personal Communications Networks or PCN is a unique concept in that a commercial requirement has driven the development of a telecommunications standard. This commercial requirement has resulted in the development of a standard within 18 months. Contrast this with ISDN where standards have been evolving for 10 years and only now are networks being introduced.

This chapter will explain what PCN is and why it came about.

48.2 History

The United Kingdom was one of the first countries to consider introducing PCN type services when its Department of Trade and Industry outlined the concept of Personal Communications Networks in its paper 'Phones on the Move' in January 1989. This paper expressed the government's intention to allocate Radio Spectrum within the range 1.7GHz to 2.3GHz. The government held the idea that 'telephones should be for people and not places', whereby small personal communicators would allow access to the telecommunications network wherever that person should be.

As the Department of Trade required that any personal communications network should conform to a publicly available technical standard and as an early introduction was required using up-to-date technology, the view was expressed that pan-European Digital Cellular Technology would be a strong contender offering the following advantages:

1. Early implementation in line with pan-European digital systems.
2. Cost benefits arising from economies of scale.
3. The possibility of having customers' equipment which can operate on both PCN and pan-European Systems.
4. Staying in the mainstream of European developments and standards.

'Phones on the Move' concluded by seeking views on the following questions, which are relevant to wherever PCN type services are being introduced, as in North America:

1. Whether the market within the country will be able to support more public mobile radio operators?
2. Whether improvements could be made over today's networks with the advent of the pocket radio telephone?
3. The date by which new Personal Communication Networks could/should be implemented?
4. The most effective frequency. For example in Europe is the combination of 1.7GHz to 2.3GHz frequency channels and pan-European digital cellular radio technology the most effective solution for the early to mid 1990s?
5. How much bandwidth is needed for each operator in order to build up and maintain a viable subscriber base?
6. Should handover be a feature for a Personal Communications Network?
7. Should an immediate move to seize market opportunities be given priority over waiting to see where future international allocations for mobile services will be located?

Following the expression of views, the government allocated PCN licences to three consortia: Microtel, Unitel and Mercury PCN. All three companies decided to introduce PCN networks based on the ESTI GSM standard and expressed their intention to bring in service during 1992.

48.3 PCN definition

PCN is a system which provides the ability for customers to make and receive telephone calls from their pocket radio telephone: anytime, anywhere in the country. The system is based upon GSM, but operates within the 1.8GHz frequency band. It provides all the services you would expect from a modern digital telephone network. People can use the service in the car, or on the train, in fact anywhere they want to. It will offer ISDN-type services such as calling number identification, diversion, call back when free, call waiting, etc.

48.3.1 PCN and GSM

The personal communications networks which are to be introduced into the UK will be based upon GSM, but operating at 1.8GHz.

ESTI GSM was tasked with developing a version of GSM for operation in the 1.8GHz range. The series of recommendations became DCS1800 (Digital Cellular System at 1800MHz).

ESTI agreed to produce DCS1800 in two phases:

1. Phase 1 by January 1991 establishes the generic differences between GSM 900 and DCS1800.
2. Phase 2 establishes a common framework for both PCN and GSM.

For Phase 1 the changes to the GSM900 standards were:

1. Increase in bandwidth from 25MHz to 75MHz in each direction. This has impacts on the signalling and some RF aspects.
2. RF link definition to account for the translation from 900MHz to 1800MHz and to reflect the low power handsets.

So that the networks could be rolled out quickly, giving faster geographic coverage, the notion of National Roaming was introduced. This would allow a number of network operators to share infrastructure.

To allow the RF parameters for DCS1800 to be calculated, six scenarios were examined:

1. Single MS (mobile station), single BTS (base transceiver station).
2. Multiple MS and BTS where operation of BTS's is co-ordinated (single operator).
3. Multiple MS and BTS where operation of BTS's is uncoordinated (multiple operator).
4. Collected MS.
5. Collocated BTS.
6. Collocation with other systems.

The impact of each of the above on radio performance was assessed. Practical worst case conditions were assumed. One critical parameter that had to be determined was the mobile station power class. This is derived from:

1. Maximum range for a single MS and single BTS.
2. Handset, cost, size, weight and battery life.

Two power classes for PCN were set 250mW and 1W peak power. This is compared with GSM900's five power classes from 800mW to 20W peak.

To derive RF performance requirements such as blocking, output RF spectrum and spurious omissions, it was necessary to define the worst case of MS-BTS coupling. This was achieved by considering the worst case of coupling between the BTS-MS, i.e. uncoordinated environment (located close to a non servicing base station antenna and located 30m away). From this a value of 65dB for the worst case coupling was agreed.

48.4   Overview of the PCN network

Figure 48.1 shows the main network elements within a PCN Network. The key elements are as follows:

48.4.1   Base transceiver station (BTS)

The BTS essentially provides the radio coverage and as such provides the air interface to the customer. (The air interface will be described in more detail later). The BTS also provides a number of 1.8GHz channels dependent upon the predicted traffic demand of the particular location. The size of the cell depends upon a number of factors, namely, terrain, traffic density, quality and local clutter. Within the PCN, system cells are expected to vary in size from a few decades of metres to several kilometres. Functions within the BTS include radio transceiver, channel coding, radio signalling, frequency hopping, paging control, access detection, measurements, encryption, radio channels.

48.4.2   Base station controller (BSC)

The BSC provides all the necessary local radio control features, i.e. intra-BSC handover, power control and channel allocation. The

BSC also acts as a concentration site for traffic, signalling and OA & M information. As such the BSC allows flexibility in radio subsystem development strategies to provide a balance between cost and quality.

48.4.3   Mobile switching centre (MSC)

The MSC is the 'telephone exchange' of the network and provides call routeing and control, handover, service interworking, interconnection to other networks and echo control. Collocated with the MSC is the Visitor Location Register (VLR) which provides location update, location area information, local database and encryption key generation.

48.4.4   Home location register (HLR)

The HLR is the network's main database, and contains all the subscriber's information, e.g. what services the customer has subscribed to.

The specific functions of the HLR are: number translation, course location, customer profile, and charging.

48.5   Call set up

Consider the simplified network in Figure 48.2. 'A' is a customer on the PCN who wishes to make a call to 'C', a customer on the PSTN.

'A' is registered on the PCN. 'A' dials 'C'. The call is passed from the BTS to the MSC via the BSC. The MSC recognises that it is a call destined to the PSTN and selects an outgoing route. The route to the PSTN must include an echo canceller (EC). The PSTN routes the call to 'C'. 'C' answers and conversation commences.

The echo canceller is required due to the long delay in the radio subsystem, and as the call will be going to a two wire PSTN, customer echo would be introduced.

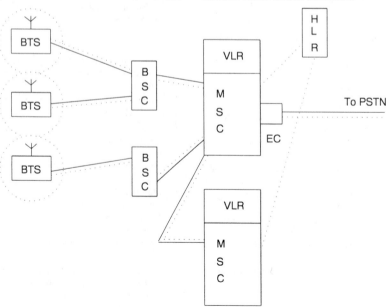

Figure 48.1   Main elements within a PCN network

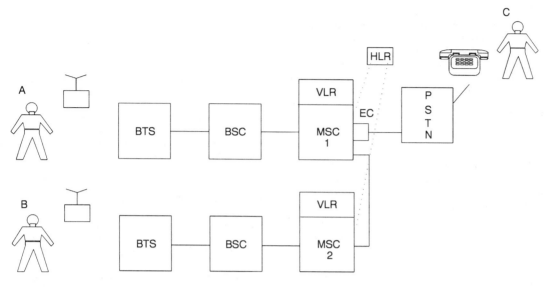

Figure 48.2   Simplified PCN network

Now consider the situation where 'A'(customer on PCN) wishes to call 'B', also a customer on the PCN.

'A' dials 'B'. The call is passed to the MSC via the BSC. The MSC recognises that it is a call destined to B. The PCN sends a query to the HLR to find the location of B. The MSC is advised that B is registered on VLR at MSC 2 and is given B's routeing number. MSC 1 routes the call to MSC 2, MSC 2 VLR identifies B as being a particular location area. MSC 2 pages that location area. B answers, conversation begins.

48.6   Planning a PCN

When planning a PCN, it is necessary to consider a number of areas, including the services to be offered. The definition of services will determine the selection of infrastructure suppliers, signalling systems to be used, as well as allowing operators to develop traffic plans.

48.6.1   Physical network realisation

The development of the physical network implementation requires answers to:

1.   What geographical coverage is required?
2.   What is the traffic density per area?
3.   What is the guaranteed service level, i.e. at street level or in buildings?

With this information, it is possible to plan the radio network and deploy BTS with sufficient transceivers to service demand. This then provides the customer interface.

Next the BSC's must be deployed to control the radio subsystem. Their function is to control the BTS. The location of the BSC is based upon a number of considerations:

1.   How many BTS's does the BSC control?
2.   What is the traffic handling capacity of the BSC?

3.   Are there any other limiting factors?

Given the above, the BSC allows the network operator to optimise the BSC location in order to reduce local transmission costs.

48.6.1.1   *BSC support of BTS's*

The number of BTS's supported by a BSC depends upon several considerations: traffic, type of BTS and BSC, local area cost determination. The answer can range between 1 and 128 BTS's, or even higher. However, it is important to decide, when planning the network, which BTS's will be parented on to which BSC. There are three main means of connecting BTS's to BSC's: star, ring and a combination of the two.

Typical star configuration.

Figure 48.3 shows a star configuration. This is simple to implement and, subject to traffic, consists of a minimum of one 2Mbit/s path between each BTS and BSC. The main advantage of this type of

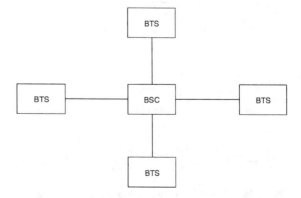

Figure 48.3   Star configuration of BTS's

configuration is that it is easy to augment routes. Growth at one particular site has no particular impact on growth at other sites.

However, the main disadvantages are:

1. Cost. It may not be possible to achieve line of sight between each BTS and the BSC and therefore it would be necessary to rent capacity, which is more expensive.
2. Reliability. Only one route exists between each BTS and the BSC which means that if we lose the link, we lose the BTS.

Ring configuration

Figure 48.4 shows a ring configuration. This has the main advantage in that each BTS has two routes to the BSC, thus giving an increase in reliability. However, as demand increases, unsuspected hot spots may develop.

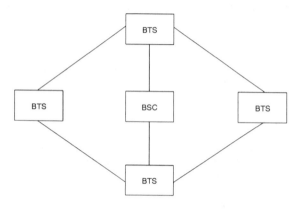

Figure 48.4 Ring configuration of BTS's

Ring — star combination

To produce a general method of linking BTS to BSC, a mixture of the star and ring methods should be used, as in Figure 48.5. To allow control of capacity, it has been proposed that Digital Cross Connect (DCX) equipment is used to re-route traffic when necessary.

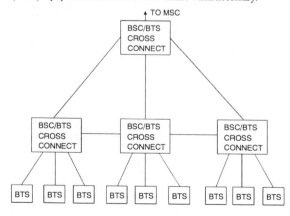

Figure 48.5 Star BTS's within a ring of cross connects and BSC's

48.6.1.2 *BSC —MSC connection*

The connection of BSC's to MSC presents interesting opportunities for network optimisation. As one of the functions of the BSC is to provide concentration of traffic, it can be envisaged that the utilisation of possible hubbing methods in linking BTS to BSC will ensure that traffic volumes between the BSC's and MSC's will be very high.

Given the high volume of traffic and the distances involved, protected high capacity microwave links or leased capacity will be used. However, given the economics involved, it can be expected that route diversity will need to be utilised.

48.6.2 Cost savings

The voice encoder used in the PCN operates at a data rate of 13kbit/s. Therefore prior to interworking with the ISDN/PSTN, the digitised voice signal must be converted to 64kbit/s A law. This is achieved via a transcoder.

The PCN architecture allows the network operator the option of positioning the transcoder at the BTS, BSC or even at the MSC. If one positions the transcoder at the MSC, this enables traffic to be carried through the radio subsystem on 16kbit/s channels.

48.6.3 Trunk network

The Trunk network is utilised for carrying inter-MSC traffic and for interconnecting the PCN to other networks, e.g. the national PSTN/ISDN. The interconnection of MSC's, given the distances involved, will be achieved by using high capacity bearers.

Routeing schemes are put in place to ensure that costs are optimised whilst maintaining the required quality of service.

48.6.3.1 *Location of MSC*

The location of the MSC is dependent upon the regulatory regime under which the PCN is being operated. For example, some countries might consider the MSC to be an adjunct to the ISDN/PSTN whereas in the UK, PCN operators are seen as independent networks. For this reason MSC's are situated in locations which achieve both on-net and off-net traffic routeing optimisation.

48.6.3.2 *BTS —BSC —MSC connection optimisation*

Notwithstanding the connection methods suggested above, it is necessary to ensure that location updating and handovers are optimised. This is achieved by parenting, and re- parenting BTS on BSC and BSC on MSC based upon predicted or measured traffic flows. For example, one would not have a location area boundary through the centre of Oxford Street or Times Square, nor would one have 2 BTS's in these areas parented on different BSC's.

48.6.3.3 *MSC —MSC routes*

Standard telecommunication practices are used to develop routeing rules for inter-MSC routes and to ensure a reasonable grade of service.

48.6.4 Numbering

One of the important considerations when developing the network routeing strategy for both customer traffic and signalling information, is to develop a detailed numbering plan.

Numbering plays an important part in PCN's, and the PCN companies are pressing for the introduction of a ten digit numbering scheme which will ensure that sufficient numbers are available, for both the proposed and future telecommunications services.

There are various types of numbers used within a PCN, as described in the following sections.

48.6.4.1 *International mobile subscriber identity (IMSI)*

The IMSI is associated with the PCN customer by being utilised on the Subscriber Identity Module (SIM). This is the plug card which, when combined with the handset, forms the mobile station.

The IMSI is the number which the network uses to identify the mobile.

48.6.4.2 *Mobile station ISDN number (MSISDN)*

The MSISDN is the 'telephone number' of the customer. This number conforms to CCITT recommendation E.164 (E.163), e.g. +44 71 492 2426 for international and 071 492 2426 for national.

The HLR provides a mapping between the MSISDN and IMSI.

48.6.4.3 *Roaming number*

This is used when it is necessary to route a call to a customer within a different service area. For instance where the customer has moved to another network, the HLR would provide a roaming number to allow the network to route the call to the customer.

48.6.4.4 *Global title*

This is s number conforming to CCITT recommendation E.214 and is utilised to route MAP SCCP information to appropriate nodes.

48.6.4.5 *Point codes*

This is used within C7 signalling networks. Point codes are used to allow signalling information to be routed through the signalling network.

48.7 Mobility

The philosophy behind the PCN service is 'Phones for people not places'. One must assume that the customer will move around with his telephone, unlike the fixed network where the telephone is always at the end of the line. If customers can move, the network must always have information concerning the location of the customer to enable calls to be delivered. Furthermore the customer must also be able to change location when engaged in a call.

For the purpose of mobility, the network can be considered as depicted in Figure 48.6. The network is split into a number of location areas (LA1 to LA8). The size of these areas is dependent upon the balance of signalling load; if the location area is small then the amount of location updating will be high. However, if the location area is large then the number of cells that have to be paged over to find the mobile will be high. RSS is the radio subsystem and incorporates BTS and BCS.

48.7.1 Location updating

Each PCN cell has a Broadcast Common Control Channel (BCCH) on which the location area is broadcast. The mobile monitors the BCCH channel which it can receive. When the mobile receives a

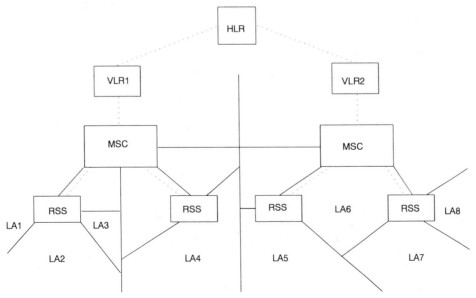

Figure 48.6 PCN network representation to illustrate mobility

new location area identification, it will send a location update request. This information updates the information stored on the VLR. If the MS enters a new VLR area, then the VLR informs the HLR. This is illustrated in Figure 48.8. Note:

1. If the mobile passes from LA2 to LA3, VLR1 information is updated.
2. If mobile passes from LA4 to LA5, VLR2 is advised, which then advises the HLR.

Once the location of the mobile has been determined, the call needs to be routed to the customer. Consider a call coming from the PSTN. The call is received at the gateway MSC which interrogates the HLR to find the MS. The HLR advises which VLR the mobile is registered on. The call is routed to the appropriate MSC. The VLR advises which LA the mobile is in and the MSC pages for the MS across the location area. The MS responds, and the call is answered and connected.

48.7.2 Handover

As already mentioned, people with mobile phones might want to move around when engaged in a call. It is therefore necessary for the network to maintain the call even if the customer moves between cells.

Within DCS1800 there are 4 types of handover specified:

1. Intra-BTS, a handover from one channel on a BTS to another on the same BTS.
2. Inter-BTS, Intra-BSC, a handover from a channel on one BTS to a channel on another BTS with both BTS's parented on the same BSC.
3. Inter-BSC, Intra-MSC, a handover between BTS's on different BSC's which are parented on the same MSC.
4. Inter-MSC, a handover between BTS's on different BSC's which are parented on different MSC's.

The network overhead in terms of signalling messages increases as the type of handover moves from (1) to (4). With this in mind, inter switch and inter BSC handovers should be kept to a minimum. Thus the network must be planned to achieve this.

Handover can be initiated by either the mobile or the network. The mobile will request handover as a result of radio channel measurements indicating low signal or excessive interference. The network will initiate handover for reasons such as:

1. Mobile causing interference.
2. Network management action.
3. For maintenance purposes.

48.8 Radio channel coding

The PCN air interface utilises TDMA techniques to conserve bandwidth. A TDMA frame consists of eight timeslots of 577ns duration. Within the PCN system, each RF channel provides eight physical channels. These physical channels can be classified into either traffic channels or control channels.

48.8.1 Traffic channels

These channels are intended to carry speech or data and two forms are defined:

1. Speech channels. Full rate speech channels are defined and the algorithm is specified. However, the half rate algorithm is at present being specified.
2. Data channels. The following data rates are specified: 300, 1200, 1200/75, 2400, 4800, 9600 bits per second.

48.8.2 Control channels

The control channels carry signalling and synchronisation data between the handset and the network. Three types of control channels are specified, as in the following sections.

48.8.2.1 Broadcast channel

This channel is used to broadcast information to the mobile station; the channel is downlink only. There are three broadcast channels defined:

1. Frequency Correction Channel (FCCH), for mobile station frequency correction.
2. Synchronisation Channel (SCH), for frame synchronisation of the mobile and BTS identification.
3. Broadcast Control Channel (BCCH), for the broadcast of general information on an individual basis.

48.8.2.2 Common Control Channel

The Common Control Channel (CCCH) is used during the establishment of a connection before dedicated control channel is assigned. There are three downlink-only channels which are used for paging, access grant and cell broadcast.

The single uplink-only channel is used for random access attempts.

48.8.2.3 Dedicated Control Channel

The Dedicated Control Channel is split into three types:

1. Standalone Dedicated Control Channel (SDCCH) carrying signalling information following mobile to network connection establishment and channel assignment.
2. Slow Associated Control Channel (SACCH) is always associated with a traffic channel or a SDCCH and maps on to the same physical channel. The SACCH carries general information from the mobile to the network such as details of current and neighbouring cell signal strengths.
3. Fast Associated Control Channel (FACCH). This channel carries the same signalling data as the SDCCH. A FACCH is assigned when a SDCCH has not been assigned and obtains access to the physical resource by 'stealing' frames from the traffic channel with which it has been assigned.

48.8.3 Speech coding

The PCN system uses the regular excited linear predictive coder (PRE-LPC) with long term pitch prediction. The code is block based, with blocks of 20ms, and the net bit rate is 13kbit/s. Thus one frame consists of 260kbit/s.

Following subjective tests, 182 of the 260 bits have been found to be more sensitive to bit errors and these have been called 'Class 1'

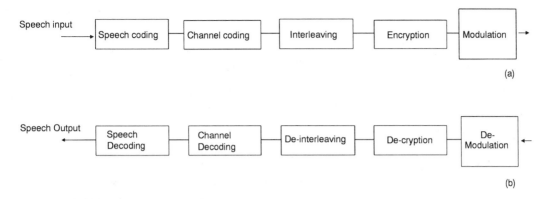

Figure 48.7 PCN speech coding and decoding process: (a) coding; (b) decoding

bits whilst the remaining 78 bits, being robust to error, are called 'Class 2' bits.

The PCN speech coding and decoding processes are indicated in Figure 48.7. The speech coder produces the 260 bits which make up one 20ms frame. The bits are delivered to the channel coder in descending order of importance. The first 50 Class 1 bits have 3 party bits added, generated by a cyclic redundancy code. The purpose of the party bits is to detect errors.

The 182 Class 1 bits and the 3 check bits are then reordered into even bits at the start, check bits in the middle, and odd bits at the end. 4 zero tail bits are then added to give $(182 + 3 + 4) = 189$ bits.

The 189 bits are encoded using a convolutional code. This produces an output of 378 bits.

The 78 Class 2 bits are added giving $378 + 78 = 456$. This gives a gross coded bit rate of 22.8kbit/s.

As errors in mobile radio systems are predominantly due to fading, it is possible in practice to have fades lasting a whole TDMA burst. The 456 coded bits are reordered and interleaved over 8 TDMA frames. During the interleaving process, bits are stolen for signalling purposes, i.e. the FACCH data.

Encryption is a very important feature of a mobile telecommunications service as it enables the confidentiality of conversations to be maintained. The PCN system uses inherent encryption by the authentication key Ki which is stored with the IMSI on the PCN SIM card. This information is also stored in the HLR.

48.8.4 Echo control

The speech channel coding introduces a one way delay in the order of 90ms. In the case of on-net calls, as separate go and return channels are used, the delay does not cause any particular problems. However, in the case of calls between the PCN and PSTN, calls will mature on analogue telephones. This means that a 2 to 4 wire hybrid will be encountered, which will introduce echo. This echo, with a delay of 90ms, could cause annoyance to customers. Therefore, it is necessary to include an echo canceller at the point of interconnection with the PSTN to cancel the echo.

48.9 PCN base station design

48.9.1 Development from GSM 900

PCN base stations are logically similar to those used for GSM 900 systems, with a number of physical enhancements to tailor them to the unique requirements of smaller cells. The main differences between GSM 900 and PCN 1800 base stations are:

1. RF channels at 1800MHz instead of 900MHz.
2. Smaller physical equipment size.
3. Design optimised around large numbers of small cells, each carrying less traffic than a GSM 900 cell.

The limited number of GSM 900 technical specifications that had to be changed for 1800MHz, were released by ETSI in the DCS1800 specification in January 1991.

48.9.2 Base station structure

The Base Station Subsystem (BSS) is the part of the PCN network which connects the Mobile Station (MS) to the switch (MSC) where calls are routed to the network. Essentially, the BSS acts as a transparent bearer between the two, so that most of the enhanced services offered by PCN are provided by the MSC and not the BSS. However the 1800MHz PCN BSS is probably the most advanced cellular bearer available, and allows greater quality and quantity of traffic to be carried to the MSC than any alternative network could achieve.

The BSS consists of two network elements: the Base Station Controller (BSC), and the Base Transceiver Station (BTS) as in Figure 48.8. The BTS and BSC communicate with each other over an internal 'A-bis' interface which is represented physically by either a 64kbit/s data link or (more commonly) a 2Mbit/s data link. The connection to the MSC is via the 'A' interface, which will normally be a 2Mbit/s datalink.

In practice, a number of BTS's will be connected to each BSC. The exact number will be limited by a number of factors:

1. The number of BTS ports available on the BSC.
2. The amount of traffic generated by the BTS's (the maximum that a BSC can handle is typically around 500 Erlangs).
3. The number of transceivers (TRX) used at each BTS. Typically, a BSC cannot handle more than 100 TRX altogether.
4. The physical distance from the BTS's to the BSC. If microwave links are used, it can prove difficult to find line of sight paths to more than 20 BTS's, or even less in hilly rural areas.

To the rest of the network, the BSS looks like a single entity. The breakdown of functions between the two units is allocated in the following manner:

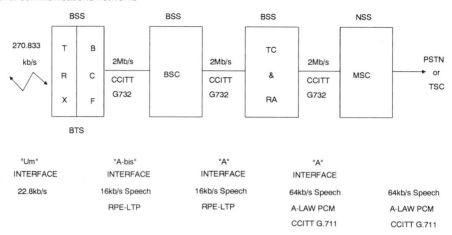

Figure 48.8 BSS interfaces

1. Base Transceiver Station functions: interface to Mobile Stations at 1800MHz; encryption; channel coding and interleaving; frequency hopping execution; random access detection; provision of control channels; transcoding/rate adaptation; uplink measurements, including timing advance; observation and reporting of idle channels.
2. Base Station Controller functions: channel allocation; radio channel management; frequency hopping management; access grant; processing of measurements; power control; handover; paging.

Traffic channels are set up between the Mobile Station and the MSC. Speech from the handset is encoded digitally using an efficient algorithm ('RPE-LTP') which reduces the analogue speech to 16kbit/s datastream. This 16kbit/s undergoes coding to improve the error protection, and is carried through the network as follows:

1. MS to BTS (the Um interface). Each voice channel from a mobile consists of a TDMA timeslot with a gross bit rate of 22.8kbit/s. On each RF carrier at the BTS, 8 TDMA timeslots are available.
2. BTS to BSC (the A-bis interface). Each voice channel consists of a 16kbit/s data stream. Typically, this will be carried on a 2Mbit/s datalink, with four 16kbit/s voice circuits being multiplexed onto each 64kbit/s slot.
3. BSC to MSC (the 'A' interface). Each voice channel will have been 'transcoded' from 16kbit/s to 64kbit/s A-Law PCM for connection to the MSC and onwards to the network. This transcoding will normally take place at the MSC end of the BSC to MSC link.

48.9.3 Radio frequency characteristics of PCN

The PCN BTS transmits and receives in the 1800MHz band. In the UK the following frequency allocations have been licensed:

1. Sub Band A. Ch 563 to 636. BTS Receive 1720.4MHz to 1735.0MHz. BTS Transmit 1815.4MHz to 1830.0MHz.
2. Sub Band B. Ch 671 to 744. BTS Receive 1742.0MHz to 1756.6MHz. BTS Transmit 1837.0MHz to 1851.6MHz.
3. Sub Band C. Ch 811 to 884. BTS Receive 1770.0MHz to 1784.6MHz. BTS Transmit 1865.0MHz to 1879.6MHz.

The channel spacing is 200kHz, and the transmitted signals are approximately 120kHz wide. The modulation method is GMSK with a BT product of 0.3 (i.e. the baseband data is filtered in a Gaussian filter with a bandwidth of 0.3 times the bit rate). This allows baseband data to be transmitted at 270.833kbit/s using only 120kHz of spectrum. The specifications for receiver dynamic range, transmitter spurious emissions and intermodulation products are particularly stringent to ensure satisfactory operation in a dense traffic environment.

The highest power class for PCN Base Stations is 20W, measured at the output of the transmitter. However, before this 20W reaches the antenna, it must pass through a power combining network which couples all the transceivers in the BTS to the same antenna connector. The choice of the correct combining method is crucial to avoid unnecessary losses.

Two methods exist: hybrid combining, and tuned cavity combining. Hybrids have the advantage of small size, low cost, and broadband operation, but the losses incurred become excessive when more than 4 transmitters are to be combined. Tuned cavity filters have the advantage of low loss, regardless of the number of transmitters to be combined, but they are large, expensive, and require some method of remote retuning. Generally, hybrids will tend to dominate because PCN networks will probably have no more than 4 transceivers at the majority of sites, and the slightly higher losses will be offset by the fact that retuning is not necessary.

48.9.3.1 *Diversity*

PCN base stations typically offer receiver space diversity. The method of combining is different from vendor to vendor, but will at least require separate receivers and two separate receive antennas. The gain on the uplink is typically 4dB or so. There is no downlink gain.

48.9.3.2 *Frequency hopping*

Frequency hopping can be implemented on PCN base stations. On each successive frame, the MS and BTS can change frequency giving a maximum of 216 hops per second. This gives two advantages: the exposure to interference on any one frequency is reduced, and the possibility of being in a fading null is eliminated.

The benefits of frequency hopping are mainly noticed on the downlink, as the uplink will normally have space diversity which already provides a similar effect. Frequency hopping on its own may improve the path by 3dB, but if space diversity is already in use the nett improvement may be as low as 1dB.

There are two different methods of implementing frequency hopping at the base station. The most straightforward is to provide a separate transceiver for each frequency in the hopping sequence (6 is about the minimum to obtain any worthwhile benefit). Then each user's voice frames will be sent successively on different transceivers. The disadvantage of this method is that in the PCN environment only 2 or 3 transceivers are typically necessary to support a cell's traffic, and to provide 6 represents a major investment when applied across the whole network.

PCN networks will tend to use a more difficult approach, which is to actually switch the frequency of the transceiver between successive timeslots. This fast switching speed (less than 30μs) is difficult to achieve, but allows hopping to be implemented with the 2 or 3 transceivers in a typical BTS.

48.9.3.3 *Discontinuous transmission*

To reduce the effects of interference, PCN mobiles and base stations usually support discontinuous transmission (DTX). This involves turning off the radio transmitter when speech is not present (which may be up to 50% of the time), using a Voice Activity Detection (VAD) algorithm in the speech coder. 'Comfort noise' is inserted by the receiving end to mask the silences that arise. This reduction in interference is particularly important in the PCN environment of small cells and high traffic density. It also has the desirable advantage of increasing the battery of the MS.

48.9.3.4 *Discontinuous reception*

The MS need not have its receiver continuously turned on, provided it wakes up periodically to look for paging requests or short messages. This 'sleep mode' can improve the MS battery life quite significantly.

48.9.3.5 *Dynamic power control*

A further technique for reducing interference is to allow the mobile station to use only just enough RF power to maintain acceptable quality. The power radiated by the MS can be reduced by command from the BS in 13 steps of 2dB each. The reduction is one step at a time. The decision to reduce the MS power is based on measurements of the signal level (RXLEV) and bit error rate (RXQUAL) which are made by the MS and reported to the BS.

48.9.3.6 *Multipath equalisation*

Very high bit rates are used over the air interface between the handset and the base station. When a signal is reflected from a building, it may arrive at the receiver slightly after the direct wave, and cause interference. The time delay may be small (up to 10μs or so) but the bit period of the baseband data is also very short (3.7μs), so multipath equalisation is needed to demodulate the signal

properly. This is achieved by transmitting a fixed bit pattern (the Training Sequence) in the middle of each time slot. Knowing this sequence, the receiver can estimate the transfer function in the time domain between the transmitter and receiver by means of a correlation process implemented in a Viterbi equaliser.

48.9.3.7 *Handover*

Handovers are used to maintain the link to the MS as it moves from cell to cell. The algorithms used in PCN networks are similar to GSM, but are tailored to the small cell environment. The two basic methods used are:

1. The 'Most Suitable Connection' method, where the mobile is always connected to the BS which provides the best path budget.
2. The 'Minimum Acceptable Performance' method where the MS is only handed over if the quality of the link drops below a certain threshold.

48.10 Microcells

The term microcell is often used to describe very small cells, particularly as used in PCN networks. The definition of a microcell is open to interpretation, but will generally apply to any of the following types of cell:

1. Cells with antennas positioned below rooftop or clutter height.
2. Cells with antennas inside a building (sometimes referred to as a picocell).
3. Cells covering a specific, restricted area with a typical range of less than 400m.

There are a number of significant problems associated with microcells which PCN manufacturers and operators have taken care to minimise:

1. Range. Because of the low range, large numbers of microcells are needed to provide area coverage.
2. Handover. Handover between microcells can be difficult to achieve, due to the short elapsed time required to move from one to another. Also, problems arise due to the 'street corner effect', where turning a corner may take the MS out of one cell into another with almost no overlap in which a handover can be set up.
3. Co-channel interference. Placing a large number of microcells in one area may ultimately lead to difficulties with frequency re-use. It becomes much more difficult to predict the carrier to interference ratio when the coverage is dominated by buildings rather than distance, and hence the maximum microcell density is not easy to forecast.
4. Network loading. The increased number of handovers inherent in the microcell environment lead to a greater requirement for signalling capacity in the network.

Solutions to these problems exist, and are being developed by PCN operators and manufacturers. Only when microcells are widely implemented will the advantages of PCN be fully apparent.

48.11   Bibliography

Balston, D.M. (1989) Pan-European cellular radio: or 1991 and all that, *Electronics and Communications Eng. J.*, January/February.

Cox, D.C. (1987) Universal digital portable radio communications, *Proc. IEEE*, April.

Gaskell, P.S. (1991) Elaboration of the DGS1800 standard for PCN service. IEE Colloquium *GSM and PCN Enhanced Mobile Services*, IEE Digest no. 1991/023.

HMSO (1989) *Phones on The Move*, UK Department of Industry.

Jakes, W.C.Jr. (Ed.) *Microwave Mobile Communications*, Wiley-Interscience.

Knight, P. (1991) Network planning using GSM and GSM based standards. IEE Colloquium *GSM and PCN Enhanced Mobile Services*, IEE Digest no. 1991/023.

Lindell, F., Swerup, J. and Uddenfeldt, J. (1987) Digital cellular radio for the future, *Ericsson Review*, (3).

Macaris, R.C.V. (1991) *Personal and Mobile Radio Systems*, Peter Peregrinus Ltd.

Marnick, P.J. (1991) Transmission network issues involved in the introduction of a PCN. IEE Coloquium *GSM and PCN Enhanced Mobile Services*, IEE Digest no. 1991/023.

Martin, P.C. *Networks and Telecommunications Design and Operation*, John Wiley and Sons.

Mischa, S. (1988) *Telecommunications Networks Protocols, Modelling and Analysis*, Addison-Wesley Publishing Co.

Vincent, G. (1990) Personal communication: the dream and the reality, *IEE Review*, **36**, (8), September.

William, C.Y.L. (1986) *Mobile Communications Design Fundamentals*, Sams.

49

Cordless telecommunications

R S Swain
C Eng MIEE
BT Laboratories

Contents

49.1 Introduction

Cordless telephone products first appeared as a low cost option for the home in North America during the late 1970's. Technically it was a radio extension telephone that operated at low power, to conserve operating time between battery charges, and frequencies of 1.7MHz (base to handset) and 49MHz (handset to base). The chosen technology was analogue frequency modulation which resulted in prices around $100 for a residential unit. Although range around the home was limited, typically covering an apartment or a house and gardens, the combination of low cost and freedom of use made the idea an instant success; they sold in their millions and still do.

The success was exported to Europe by way of illegal imports into the UK, France, Germany, Holland, etc. These imports infringed local telecommunications law and practice. In the UK, for example, the frequencies chosen for North American were allocated to maritime and the then broadcast television service. Furthermore their transmission characteristics gave unsatisfactory speech performance when they were connected to European public telecommunications networks. Nevertheless the quantity of illegal imports demonstrated that a market existed for such a product and consequently the European PTT's reacted by adopting appropriate standards for Europe. From this beginning the present cordless market is now on the verge of making a significant breakthrough as a natural telephone terminal apparatus in both the home, office and manufacturing environments.

49.1.1 Analogue technology

Two families of analogue CT have been standardised; that based on the original North American standard (h.f./v.h.f.) and a later higher capacity European development operating in the 900 MHz band.

49.1.2 H.f./v.h.f. analogue CT

In order to compete on equal price terms with the import of illegal North American standard product, many countries chose to adopt the same standard with or without technical design changes. In Europe the UK and France followed this course, making changes to the design that avoided radio frequency allocation and transmission quality problems, but did not significantly increase the basic production cost.

One major change was to incorporate some form of dialling and incoming call security that ensured only the legitimate handset was able to open up and receive a call from its associated base station. This stopped the accidental, or sometimes deliberate, practice of long distance calls being dialled over a neighbour's cordless terminal with consequent misdirection of the call charge. The basic technical characteristics of the UK version of this analogue CT are as follows:

1. Eight analogue FM channel pairs operating around 1.7MHz and 47.5MHz.
2. Radiated power limited to 10mW maximum.
3. Choice of channel pair is set at manufacture but random at time and place of purchase. Line access and incoming call security by a handshake process involving at least 60000 randomly selected binary codes.

Products to this enhanced specification have been freely available in the UK since 1983. In France different frequencies were adopted

(21MHz and 46MHz). More recently the North American market has concentrated both directions of transmission in the region of 49MHz in order to give more transmission channels and hence more transmission capacity. The technology, however, is basically the same and retains the very attractive low production cost.

49.1.3 European 900MHz analogue standard

Another body of opinion in Europe took a somewhat longer view of the potential of cordlessness, in terms of its potential demand on radio spectrum when the number of cordless terminals exceeded about 10% of normal wired terminals. This vision resulted in the following standard, that has been adopted in most CEPT affiliated countries, with the exception of the UK and France who chose the h.f/v.h.f. option that offered a significantly lower production cost. The CEPT standard has the following general characteristics:

1. Analogue FM operation.
2. Forty 25kHz duplex channels in the frequency bands 914–915MHz paired with 959–960MHz.
3. Radiated power limited to 10mW.
4. Dynamic channel selection (DCS) on call set up.

This last feature sets apart this standard from the earlier technology. On call set up either from a base (incoming call) or handset (outgoing call) all forty channels are scanned in order to select a vacant radio channel, or one where the co-channel interference is acceptable low, on which to set up the telephone call.

This feature has a complexity burden but results in all users being able to use any available radio channel. Therefore spectrum efficiency in terms of traffic carried per megahertz per square kilometre is very much increased compared to a factory set single channel system of the type considered in the last section. The benefits of DCS shows when the total cordless traffic demand in a localised area is such that co-channel interference from other users becomes the dominating factor in terms of speech quality and range of operation.

Technically the CEPT standard is a major step forward in cordless product design but is consequently more expensive than the far simpler h.f./v.h.f. analogue design. It has, therefore, not achieved the degree of market penetration throughout Europe as its proposers had originally predicted.

49.2 Digital technology

The analogue cordless telephone has succeeded in opening up the market for localised mobility around the home or place of work, without incurring the costs and regulation associated with a fully mobile cellular radio service. However, its analogue nature and, in its more successful form, limited traffic carrying capabilities severely limited its full development potential. What was needed was a ubiquitous technology that could be exploited widely in the home, office and factory, in such numbers that all could benefit from the economies of scale that mass uniform production can provide. The new generation needed the characteristics as in the following sections.

49.2.1 Areas of application

1. Residential, private use in houses and apartments.
2. Small CT systems for office use.

3. Large CT systems, multi-cell private switch telephony based building mobile systems with roaming and in-call handover between cells (the so-called cordless business communications system, CBCS).
4. Radio access to local public and other telecommunications networks, e.g. telepoint systems.

The CBCS opens the opportunity towards the cordless office with greater freedom to rearrange office space as work demands. This is a result of reduced telecommunications wiring needs and costs. However radio coverage over the entire service area must be good enough to ensure that the probability of a call being set up exceeds 99% otherwise users expectations, based on the performance of wired telephones, will not be met.

Telepoint is a service provided to cordless handset owners from cordless base stations located in public places, e.g. railway stations, shopping precincts, fast-food restaurants etc. This is a basic public communication service for the less migratory more localised sector of the travelling market and thus does not compete directly with the wide roaming mobile cellular network. Hence a handset purchased for use in the home and/or work place can also be used to gain access to a telepoint service whilst the user is in transit between them.

49.2.2 Main service principles

1. The system must make provision for voice and non-voice transmission.
2. All radio channels are available to all users and applications, hence channel licensing and regulation is not needed.
3. The air interface between the handset and base has a common specification for telephony so that a common handset design can be used in all applications.
4. Speech quality equivalent to that of a wired telephone.

49.2.3 Traffic capacity

Research has shown (Swain, 1985) that a modest CT penetration of 7% of all telephone terminals in a city centre could produce mean traffic densities in excess of 800 Erlangs per square km. (Note an Erlang is the amount of traffic carried by one line operating for 100% of the time. See Chapter 5). Other studies (ETSI, 1992a) indicate the following traffic densities by application:

1. Residential suburban house, 150E per sq. km at 0.05E per telephone and cordless penetration of 30%.
2. Residential apartment block, 200E per sq. km at 0.05E per telephone and cordless penetration of 30%.
3. Cordless business system, 10000 E per sq. km per floor at 0.2E per terminal and cordless penetration of 100%.
4. Telepoint service (examples of railway stations and airports), 900 – 5500E per sq. km.

49.2.4 Digital cordless standards

The foregoing requirements clearly point towards a new digital cordless telecommunications standard and as early as 1981 studies were in progress to identify the technical options. Since that time two digital standards have been developed within Europe to the status of interim European Telecommunications Standards by the European Telecommunications Standards Institute (ETSI), as follows:

1. CT2/CAI; which translates to second generation CT with a Common Air Interface (ETSI, 1991).
2. DECT; which means Digital European Cordless Telecommunications (ETSI, 1992b).

The key factor in both standards, however, is that they offer a common air interface specification. This means that each can support a public access voice service in which the handset and base station may be manufactured by different companies and yet still signal and communicate to each other to establish the call. This is not a feature of the earlier analogue standards.

These two ETSI standards are considered by many to be complementary in terms of the market expected to be served and the entry time to that market. CT2/CAI has been optimised to serve the residential and small (business) cordless markets with potential to open up the high capacity business market. DECT, however, has been designed from the outset to meet the demands of the very high capacity cordless office with roaming and in-call handover as standard features of the specification. It also has the capability to be appropriately configured for the residential markets. Both have telepoint capability.

49.3 CT2/CAI digital specification

These specifications are described in Swain (1990), Holmes and Swain (1990) and Evans (1990). The FDMA/TDD principle of operation of CT2/CAI is shown in Figure 49.1. Duplex transmission is provided by transmitting in time interleaved burst mode on the

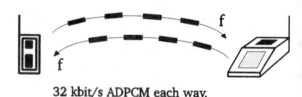

32 kbit/s ADPCM each way.
Channel bandwidth = 100kHz

Figure 49.1 Single-carrier burst-mode duplex system

same carrier frequency for both directions. This technique was appropriate for a low cost instrument since both ends are identical. Furthermore the technique only required a single block of radio spectrum rather than the duplex bands favoured by other mobile radio systems. Hence the band 864–868MHz was allocated to the service to support forty 100kHz duplex channels.

By adopting the CCITT standard 32kbit/s ADPCM speech coding algorithm it was possible to contain the transmitted symbol rate to 72kbit/s with some allowance for framing and signalling bits. In practice the corresponding B-channel capacity is 32kbit/s and that for the D-channel 1kbit/s or 2kbit/s depending on manufacturer's choice.

By adopting a common air interface the radio interface is standardised in terms of:

1. Physical parameters of the radio link e.g. modulation, frame rate, data rate.
2. System and user signalling.
3. Speech transmission.

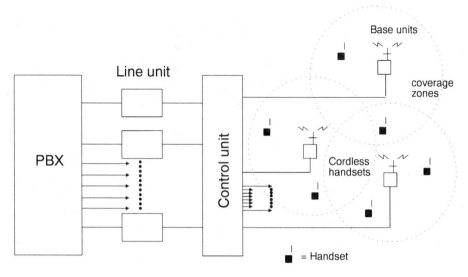

Figure 49.2 Wireless PBX system using antennas

49.3.1 Radio aspects

With only forty channels available to support the high traffic demands it was clear that the benefit of dynamic channel selection would be needed. Thus both handset and base are required to operate on any of the forty channel pairs through selection of the channel with the lowest co-channel and/or adjacent channel interference. This technique is more than adequate to meet the traffic capacity needs of residential and small business operations, but other techniques need to be exercised to raise the effective capacity to meet the requirements of larger business systems.

To increase the frequency re-use ability of the system in large buildings cordless business systems will need to use the multi-cell coverage techniques employed by cellular mobile systems. However, in a building the cells will be used on each floor consequently the cell structure has three dimensions to it and allowance must be made for signals passing through the floors as well horizontally through the walls of the building.

To ensure good and even coverage both antennae and radiating cables may be used to provide service in a large building complex as in Figures 49.2 and 49.3 (Holmes and Swain, 1990).

A typical example for CT2/CAI coverage from an antenna is shown in Figure 49.4 (Swain, 1984) where measured signal levels and computed bit error ratios are indicated.

The detail parameters of the radio interface are given in ETSI (1991) but it specifies two level frequency shift keying with Gaussian filter shaping and a frequency deviation of 14.4kHz to 25.2kHz above carrier frequency to represent a binary 1 and equal shifts below the carrier frequency for binary 0. This represents a modulation index range of 0.4 to 0.7. As previously noted time division duplex transmission is used with 1ms for each transmit and receive packet. A dead time between transmit and receive bursts has been created to allow transmitters to ramp up and ramp down their power in a way designed to limit spectral splatter across adjacent channels. This period also permits oscillators to settle between bursts.

49.3.2 Frame multiplex structure

When a call is being initiated there is no synchronisation between the handset and base, and both parts will be scanning across the forty radio channels. In order for a call to be set up and maintained CT2/CAI employs three multiplex structures during the course of a call.

Multiplex 1 is used during the normal handset to base communication phase when synchronisation and call set up have been achieved and the call is in progress. The structure is shown in Figure 49.5 (Evans, 1990) where it can be seen that two channels are supported.

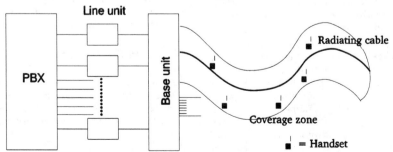

Figure 49.3 Wireless PBX system using radiating cable

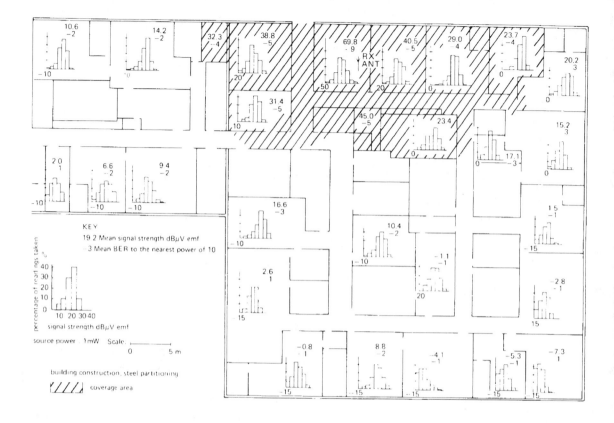

Figure 49.4 Typical example for CT2/CIA coverage with an antenna

The B-channel conveys the 32kbit/s speech signal (or perhaps 32kbit/s data) and the base and handset identities are conveyed through the D-channel. While D-channel errors are detected and corrected by requesting a re-transmission there is no error detection on the B-channel. The observed performance of the D-channel can be used to determine B-channel performance and if appropriate instigate a radio channel change to a better quality channel during the speech. Generally the channel change will be quick and go undetected by the user.

Figure 49.5 shows that the D-channel capacity can either be 1kbit/s or 2kbit/s according to manufacturer's choice, but this choice must be signalled between the base and handset at call set up. Clearly a public telepoint base station must be able to support both. It should be noted that the error corrected rates for each possibility is about half the basic throughput.

Multiplex 2 is used only when the base station is setting up a link with its associated handset. At this stage the B-channel is not active but the base needs to transmit its identity to the required handset via the D-channel and synchronise that handset to its frame using the SYN-channel. The format is shown in Figure 49.6 (Evans, 1990). In this format the D-channel has a 16kbit/s capacity, the preamble consists of 1,0,1,0,1...reversals for bit timing, and the channel marker word (CHM) is used to set up frame synchronisation. Successful synchronisation is marked by the transmission of the SYNC word from the handset at which point it is able to transmit the same frame structure and forward its identification code in the D-channel.

If the handset needs to set up a call then a different frame structure, multiplex 3, is initially used by the handset in order to synchronise with the base unit. This is important because in multiplex 1 and 2 operation the base and handset terminals alternately transmit and receive and it is necessary to avoid unsuccessful call set up due to, for example, both units transmitting at the same time. In multiplex 3 the handset repeatedly transmits a sequence of preamble bits, D-channel identity information and channel markers for a period of 10ms. This is followed by a 4ms receive period in which a response from the base unit is listened for. This process is repeated for up to 5 seconds after which call set up is abandoned. This frame structure is designed to ensure that the base station, which is operating in the 1ms transmit and 1ms receive mode, has a maximum chance of intercepting the initially un-synchronous handset transmission. After synchronisation call set up proceeds using multiplex 2.

49.3.3 Protocol structure

Signalling in CT2/CAI is similar in form to that adopted in Layers 1, 2 and 3 of the Open Systems Interconnection (OSI) model. Layer 1 ensures that communication channels can be established and maintained. To achieve this three channels types are needed:

1. B-channel for speech or data.
2. D-channel for signalling and control.
3. SYN-channel for bit and burst synchronisation.

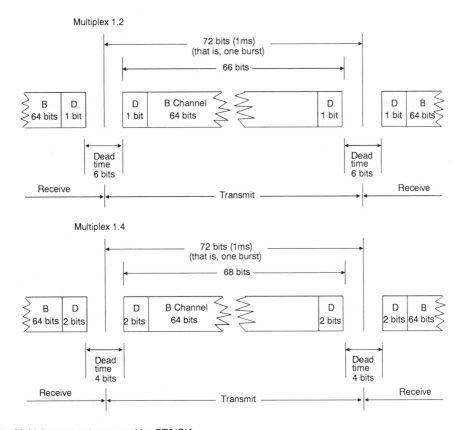

Figure 49.5 Multiplexer structures used by CT2/CIA

At various stages of a call set up these three are conveyed by the above mentioned multiplexes.

Layer 2 supports the ability of CT2/CAI to communicate messages between end points of the link. Such messages include those associated with the D-channel error detection and correction, message acknowledgement, call set up and clear down messages etc. A Layer 2 message package consists of up to six words each formed from eight 8-bit bytes. The first word is the address code word and the remainder are data code words. Messages may be formed from a number of message packages.

Layer 3 messages are the information elements delivered error free by layer 2 to the end of the CT2/CAI radio link. These elements have meaning and can be translated into specific responses. For example keyed digits 0–9, star and square, handset display elements and many other messages that a manufacturer may wish to employ in his product.

49.3.4   Transmission plan and digital codec

To meet the European standard objectives it is necessary to define the transmission characteristics of both the handset and base unit.

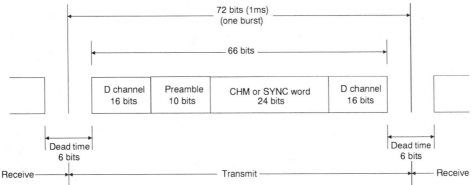

Figure 49.6 Format used for multiplexer 2 of Figure 49.5

For interworking with digital networks the requirements of ETSI draft recommendation NET33 are met. In the case of analogue network interconnection, for historical reasons, the requirements change from country to country throughout Europe. So to ensure a common handset specification, particularly for telepoint application, any necessary country specific corrections to the overall speech transmission characteristic is built in to the base unit. To avoid problems arising from terminal speech echo in the transmission network the loop delay imposed on a CT2/CAI link has been set to less than 5ms.

The digital speech codec algorithm used by CT2/CAI has been taken from the CCITT Recommendation G.721 (Blue Book) which defines a 32kbit/s adaptive differential pulse code modulation codec. Some, strictly controlled, licence is given to manufacturers to simplify the resulting codec in order to limit power requirements and complexity.

49.3.5 Implementation

The basic principles of CT2/CAI operation offer significant opportunities to minimise the inherent cost of the basic digital link. For example the 100kHz channelling does not require time dispersion equalisation even when operating in a multipath environment with no line-of-sight signal component. Furthermore there is no need for a radio frequency duplexer and less carrier frequency sources are

required. From a speech transmission point of view the moderate processing delays involved do not require echo control circuitry or raise absolute network delay issues. With these benefits the radio circuit design is simplified and the complexity of implementation is concentrated at baseband which can made using low power consumption, large scale integration CMOS technology.

Figure 49.7 is an example of the degree of integration that is possible and which leads towards a common set of components to support all applications. This is a key objective in realising the benefits of large volume production in terms of minimised component costs.

49.4 DECT digital specification

Around the mid 1980's a number of companies under the auspices of the European Conference of Telecommunications Manufacturers (ECTEL) started to define and specify a digital cordless telecommunication standard for business system use. It adopted many concepts previously exploited in European CT standards but by implementing multi-carrier time division multiple access it considerably increased the potential for cordless operation particularly in a business environment. Eventually this work led to the ETSI standard that is now know as Digital European Cordless Telecom-

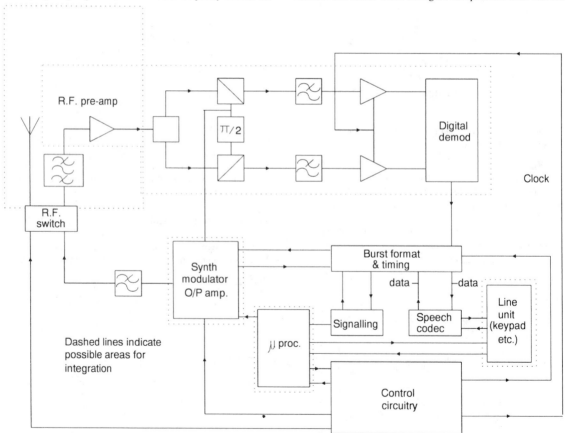

Figure 49.7 Possible integration of CT2

munications, or DECT for short. (ETSI, 1992b; Ochsner, 1990; ETSI, 1992c.)

The DECT specification has two levels of standardisation.

1. The Common Interface (CI) specification that enables conforming equipment from different manufacturers to successfully communicate in a public access service (e.g. telepoint).
2. The coexistence interface specification that allows proprietary, non-CI, standard equipment to coexist in the common spectrum resource.

Thus DECT is able to support both public access requirements and the proprietary needs of the manufacturers, particularly those interested in exploiting the considerable potential of cordlessness in the business environment. This is shown in Figure 49.8 (ETSI, 1992b), the layers being described in the next section.

The application areas of DECT are somewhat wider than those identified in Section 49.3. For example the system is expected to support radio access to office voice and data networks at information bit rates considerably in excess of the 32kbit/s foreseen for speech transmission. Indeed data transmission has figured significantly in the preparation of the specification. DECT, therefore, offers bearers that are well matched to the needs of teleservices.

For ISDN-based applications a continuous 144kbit/s full duplex bearer is available. Even this is not sufficient for other uses associated with data transmission in real time and/or short bursts. Such requirements are indicated in Table 49.1 (ETSI, 1992b). For data applications, variable transaction times 100ms to 10 seconds are anticipated and transmission is anticipated to be predominantly one way. Fast link establishment time, under 50ms (not including Portable Part verification) is required. Variable rate communications is required. Note that these applications demand rapid access to bearer channel and since radio channels must be released between bursts of information (to conserve spectrum for other users) then the result is a requirement for rapid radio channel acquisition algorithms capable of seizing a channel in less than 50ms.

Although the above has been written in terms of DECT as a piece of cordless terminal equipment, it was made plain during its development that the technology can also be used as an access technology to other communication networks both public and private. For example, provision has been made in the design of DECT to enable it to be developed as another access technique able to use the GSM digital cellular fixed network. This means that DECT must in due course be able to access and use the roaming and location intelligence built in to the GSM system. Similar provisions are being made to ensure the capability to interwork with evolving public intelligent telecommunication networks. Thus DECT is not just another cordless telephone peripheral to telephone networks, it also has the capability to become an access technology that is integrated with the network.

Table 49.1 Data requirements in DECT

Application	Access latency	Transaction duration at full rate	Full rate (without errors)
Remote terminal			
Text	50ms	100ms – 5 secs	10 – 20kbit/s
Graphics	50ms	500ms – 10 secs	24 – 128kbit/s
Batch file transfer			
Light	1 – 5 secs	1 – 30 secs	32kbit/s
Heavy	1 – 30 secs	5 – 1000 secs	64kbit/s
Real time file access			
Slices	50ms	200ms – 2 secs	64 – 256kbit/s
Chunks	500ms	1 – 10 secs	64 – 256kbit/s

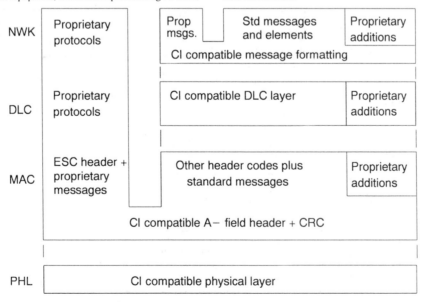

Figure 49.8 Structures of escape routes within the Common Interface

49.4.1 DECT protocol architecture

The DECT protocol (ETSI, 1992b) is based on the principles of the OSI model. The complete common interface relevant to public access applications is defined in terms of the three lowest layers modified to account for the specific requirements of radio transmission and in-call handover. The structure is shown in Figure 49.9 where four DECT layers are identified. The OSI layers are indicated for reference. The Physical Layer (PHL) has the task of modulation and demodulation, acquire bit and burst synchronisation, control synchronisation and independent burst collision detection and measure the received signal strengths.

The Medium Access Control Layer (MAC) performs two main functions:

1. It selects the radio channels and then establishes and releases the communication link.
2. It multiplexes and demultiplexes all information into burst packages.

These two functions are used to create three services; a broadcast service, a connection orientated service (e.g. for telephony) and a connectionless service (e.g. for packet-like transmission).

The broadcast service is always transmitted from every base in a reserved data field (A field) on at least one physical channel. This beacon transmission allows portable parts (PP) to quickly identify and lock on to any suitable base (fixed part, FP) without requiring PP transmissions. The Data Link Control Layer (DLC) is largely responsible for providing very reliable data links to the network layer. This layer has two operational planes. The C-plane is concerned mainly with the fully error controlled transmission of internal control and signalling information. The U-plane offers a similar function in support of the specific requirements of the services being conveyed. For example the transparent unprotected service used for speech transmission.

Finally the Network Layer (NWK) is the main signalling layer of the protocol. It functions by exchanging messages between peer entities in support of, for example, establishment, maintenance and release of calls. Many additional messages support a range of independent capabilities and services. One group contains the necessary procedures that support cordless mobility which includes FP and PP authentication and location registration.

The lower layer management entity is concerned with procedures that involve more than one layer and yet are often only of local significance. Consequently they are only defined in general terms.

49.4.2 Interworking Units (IWU)

The transmission of information to end users beyond the DECT link requires additional protocols that are outside the DECT specification. Thus to interface a DECT link with, say, a GSM fixed part will require an appropriate IWU to establish proper unambiguous message transfer and in the process influence the service standard to be offered. Clearly the IWU concept will play a very important role in the full exploitation of the DECT specification.

49.4.3 Spectrum resource

Throughout Europe the band 1880MHz to 1900MHz has been set aside for use by the DECT system. This 20MHz of spectrum must however be used efficiently and flexibly if it is to meet the requirements of high capacity business systems. It is the main purpose of the Physical Layer to bring this about by ensuring that adequate capacity radio channels are created in a manner that permits high orders of radio channel re-use. The DECT spectrum resource has been distributed in space, frequency and time.

Spatial distribution is brought about because DECT supports the use of the well-known concept of cellular radio channel re-use. In this process the area to be served is covered by a number of base stations, each of which provides radio coverage over a limited radius. This radius is typically of the order 20–50 metres depending partly on the construction nature of the building being served but more likely on the density of telecommunications traffic to be catered for. In this latter case each small cell is able to offer a certain

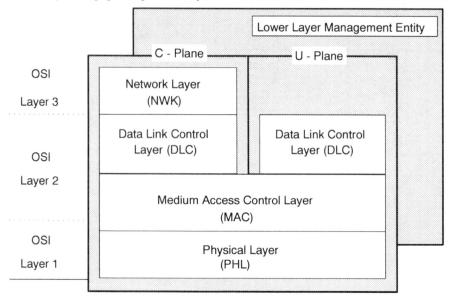

Figure 49.9 DECT structure in relation to the OSI model

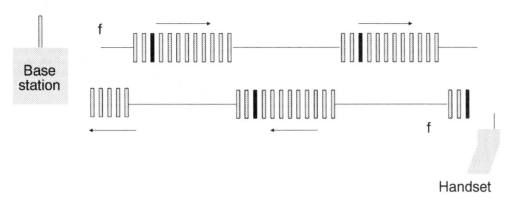

Figure 49.10 DECT system. Each one of 10 carriers can serve up to 12 handsets or terminals

number of radio channels and the smaller the cell the shorter the distance away the same channels can be re-used with acceptable co-channel interference ratio. This is the classical cellular frequency re-use concept that gives very high orders of spectrum efficiency, expressed in terms of Erlangs per MHz per sq. km.

Frequency distribution is achieved by segmenting the available band into ten carrier frequencies from 1881.792MHz to 1897.344MHz and separated by 1728kHz.

Time distribution has been achieved by employing time division multiple access (TDMA) coupled with time division duplex transmission (TDD) to provide two-way communication on the same carrier frequency.

49.4.4   Detail radio aspects

The above applications place a number of requirements on the basic design of the radio system. The following are indicative of this process:

1. Ability to handover between channels on the same base station and between channels on different base stations without disturbance to speech or data.

2. Ability to offer variable bit rate channels to data and ISDN options.
3. Ability to cater for the traffic requirements of high capacity business communications systems.

The result of putting all these requirements into practice, including those of Section 49.2, produced an FDMA/TDMA/TDD system having ten carriers each conveying 12 time division duplex 32kbit/s channels, (see Figures 49.10 and 49.11. To achieve the variable bit rate capability DECT is able to concatenate individual 32kbit/s timeslots to build up larger capacities. These concatenated timeslots need not be adjacent or on the same carrier frequency. Potentially the maximum throughput is, therefore, 12 x 32 = 384kbit/s bothway. Handover is another key specified feature of DECT and has been designed to support handovers in 10ms to 15ms.

Other radio parameters are given in Table 49.2.

Each frame consists of 5ms alternate periods of transmission and reception and it is a general requirement that all base and portable terminals shall be able to operate on all timeslots.

This technical specification indicates that in cluttered, multi-path, environments outside buildings time dispersion may be a problem.

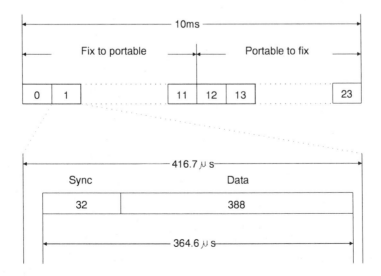

Figure 49.11   DECT frame format

Table 49.2   DECT radio parameters

Parameter	Value
Frequency band	1880 – 1900MHz
Radio channel spacing	1.728MHz
Transmitted symbol rate	1.152Mbit/s
R.F. carriers	10
Peak transmit power	250mW
Modulation	Gaussian FSK (B.T. = c0.5)
Nominal peak deviation	288kHz
Duplex channels per frame	12
Frame period	10ms
System loop delay	c25ms
Bits per timeslot	480
Bits per burst	420
Guard time bits	56
Net channel rates (traffic)	32kbit/s per slot (B field)

Antenna diversity located at the base station is considered the first line of defence in such instances.

49.4.5   Radio operational features

The fixed part (FP) has an active channel for paging and synchronisation. An incoming call is paged on all FP and the PP responds on a channel chosen by the PP.

If channel quality deteriorates, PP moves out of range or due to increased interference, then handover is initiated to a more appropriate FP. A base controller synchronises this re-routeing of calls. PP periodically scan all channels to update their list of free channels to ease handover.

Link quality is assessed from channel bit error ratios and received signal strength.

For handover the PP requests a second channel (perhaps on another FP) to be modulated with the wanted signal. The PP then decides when to switch channels and then informs the controller which channel to release.

49.4.6   Frame structure

Figure 49.12 (ETSI, 1992b) shows the multiplex burst as it would appear for a normal telephony call and shows also the relationship between the PHL and MAC layer responsibilities. The 48 bits of the A field support the associated signalling channel requirements (C), the broadcast beacon transmission (Q) and the paging channel (P). The remaining 16 bits of the A field is a cyclic redundancy code (CRC) check used to protect the data.

The B field is used to transport the traffic information (I) and offers 320 bits per burst which is equivalent to 32kbit/s. The four X bits (which optionally can be extended to eight) are provided to detect collisions between bursts emanating from independent, and hence un-synchronised, systems. It should be noted of course that other multiplex structures are used in DECT particularly in the channel set up phase.

49.4.7   Transmission plan and digital codec

DECT is subject to the same constraints as applied to CT2/CAI in terms of transmission performance. It is notable that both use the same codec standard and hence offer the same basic speech quality level. However, since DECT employs TDMA working the inevitable consequence is that DECT loop delay amounts to about 25ms. Such a delay cannot be tolerated in the local public network in the presence of speech echoes from the DECT handset. At present two approaches are being taken towards the amelioration of this effect:

1.   By designing handset with virtually zero echo return. This calls for high orders of acoustic coupling loss between handset ear and mouth pieces approaching 46dB.
2.   A combination of good handset design combined with the use of acoustic echo cancellation or control.

The latter seems to be preferred. Unfortunately the problem of echo cancellation and control in terminal equipment is not an independent design exercise as care needs to be taken to ensure that there are no unfavourable reactions with similar devices already in place on long distance connections, e.g. over a satellite link.

49.4.8   Implementation

To achieve success the basic production cost of DECT must be low. Thus the same objectives that were seen to be important to CT2/CAI's cost basis are equally applicable to DECT, i.e. the

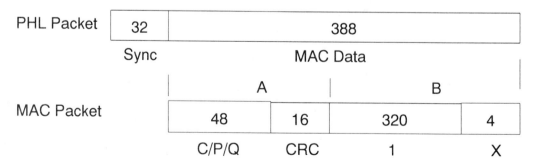

Figure 49.12   PHL and MAC Layer responsibilities

adoption of common components and large scale production to achieve the full cost benefits of scale.

Furthermore, equipment installation practices must be developed that can guarantee standards of communication quality that the customer has come to expect from the more conventional wired terminal equipment.

49.5 References

ETSI (1991) *Common Air Interface Specification to be used for Interworking between Cordless Telephone Apparatus in the Frequency Band 864.1MHz to 868.1MHz, Including Public Access Services. (prI-ETS 300 131)*.

ETSI (1992a) *DECT Services and Facilities Requirements Specification* ETSI Technical Report.

ETSI (1992b) *Digital European Cordless Telecommunications Common Interface. (prETS 300 175-1 to 9)*.

ETSI (1992c) Digital European Cordless Telecommunications Reference Document, ETSI Technical Report.

Evans, M. W. (1990) CT2 Common Air Interface, *British Telecom Technical Journal*, **9**, (2), pp. 103–111.

Holmes, D. W. J. and Swain, R. S. (1990) The Digital Cordless Telecommunications Common Air Interface, *British Telecom Technical Journal*, **8**, (1), pp. 12–18.

Ochsner, H. (1990) Radio Aspects of DECT. In *Proceedings of the Fourth Nordic Seminar on Digital Mobile Radio Communications (DMR IV)*, 26th–28th June, Oslo, Norway.

Swain, R. S. (1985) Cordless Telecommunications in the UK, *British Telecom Technical Journal*, **3**, (2).

Swain, R. S. (1990) Digital Cordless Telecommunications — CT2, *British Telecommunications Engineering*, **9**, (2), pp. 98–102.

Swain, R. S. (1984) Cordless Telecommunications in the UK. In *Proceedings of the National Communications Forum XXXIII*, Chicago, USA, Sept.

50 Line of sight radio systems

Jim Giacobazzi
TeleSciences Transmission Systems

Contents

50.1 Microwave system path design considerations

A thorough understanding of the principles of microwave path design is essential in the planning and engineering activities for a microwave system. The operator of a microwave system should also understand these principles if he is to evaluate the work of an engineering organisation designing his system.

50.1.1 Path clearance

Microwave energy tends to travel in a straight line between microwave stations — hopefully, most of the time. Unfortunately, the system designer is faced with the unavoidable fact that we live on a round earth. Thus, the curvature of the earth's surface between adjacent microwave stations must be taken into account when determining the antenna heights. The formula for calculating earth curvature is as in Equation 50.1 where h is the earth's curvature in feet, d_1 and d_2 in miles, and K is a constant.

$$h = \frac{d_1 d_2}{1.5 K} \tag{50.1}$$

In this equation d_1 and d_2 are the distances from the path location in question to either end of the microwave hop.

As may be seen from Figure 50.1, earth curvature has its greatest effect upon path clearance at the centre of the path. However, when calculating the total path clearance required using additional formulas to be described later, the earth curvature must always be included regardless of the location along the path.

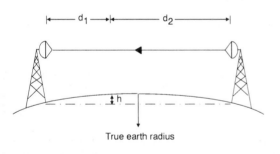

Figure 50.1 Effect of earth curvature on path clearance

The K factor in Equation 50.1 is a constant whose value depends upon the actual propagation of the microwave energy along the path. Various values of K are used to describe propagation that differs from a straight line, and an understanding of these 'K factors', as they are called, is important.

Microwave energy, due to its very high frequency (and corresponding short wavelength) tends to behave much like visible light. Microwave energy can be focused, reflected, and refracted (or bent) by the atmosphere. To describe an atmospheric effect that bends the microwave energy away from a straight line, the K factor that appears in the earth curvature formula is changed. The K factor used to describe straight line microwave propagation is 1.0.

Because the atmospheric density decreases as the height above the earth increases, the lower part of the wavefront of the microwave signal tends to travel slightly slower than the upper part of the wavefront. This results in a slight downward curvature of the signal (Figure 50.2). For this case a K factor of 4/3 is used, meaning that if the microwave path is drawn as a straight line, the earth will appear flatter than normal, or will have a radius greater than normal. A path design using 4/3 as the K factor would result in less lower height on each end of the path. However, a conservative design approach will use a normal K factor of 1.0.

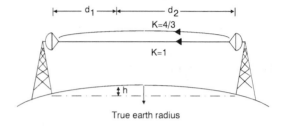

Figure 50.2 'Normal' 4/3 propagation

The possibility of abnormal propagation must also be considered. An effect known as earth bulge occurs more often than a system designer would like, especially in humid coastal areas. An atmospheric condition such as an inversion layer, with atmospheric density increasing with elevation will cause a bending of the microwave signal opposite to the curvature of the earth and, if the inverse bending is severe, the microwave signal will be diverted into the earth (Figure 50.3). The term 'earth bulge' arises from the apparent bulging of the earth sufficiently to block the microwave signal. The K factor most often used to protect against outage due to earth bulge is 2/3, although very conservative designs may use factors as low as 1/2.

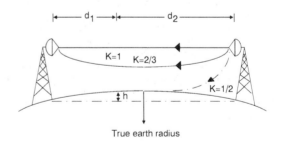

Figure 50.3 Earth bulge effect

Other propagation anomalies may occur from time to time. These include ducting i.e. steering of the microwave signal away from the receiving antenna by atmospheric ducts, Figure 50.4; super refractive effects which direct the signal into the earth, Figure 50.5; decoupling effects which cause the signal at the receiving antenna to arrive outside the main lobe of the antenna pattern and reflective effects from atmospheric 'sheets' causing cancellation of the main microwave signal. It is beyond the scope of this discussion to elaborate on these effects which, although relatively rare, should interest the serious microwave designer.

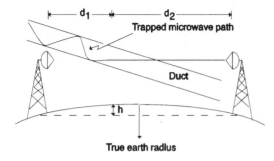

Figure 50.4 Atmospheric duct effect

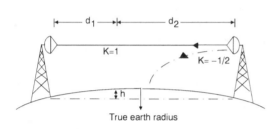

Figure 50.5 Super refractive effect

At this point the reader might be tempted to conclude that as long as earth curvature is taken into account, or as long as line of sight exists between the two ends of a microwave path, that the path clearance is satisfactory. This is not the case.

As microwave energy propagates from the transmitting antenna, an expanding wavefront is created. Looking at the wavefront on a cross-section basis, it may be seen to consist of a series of concentric areas around the path line as shown in Figure 50.6. These areas are numbered beginning with the area immediately around the path line. The signal at the receiving antenna will be affected if a portion of the wavefront is blocked, or if a portion of the wavefront is reflected from an obstruction along the path.

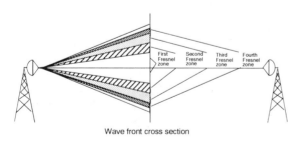

Figure 50.6 Fresnel zone concept

The first Fresnel zone consists of the first area around the path line. A path designed so that only this area is not blocked by any obstructions below the path would be described as having a first Fresnel zone clearance above the earth.

Another important consideration is the nature of the earth along the path. A reflective surface such as water may actually result in partial or complete cancellation of the desired signal. For example if the earth is perfectly reflective (R = −1.0), the desired signal will be cancelled with a path clearance equal to 2F as in Figure 50.7. Even with a less reflective earth (and a typical reflection coefficient is − 0.3) a partial cancellation may occur if the clearance is equal to any even Fresnel zone number and the obstruction is reflective. 'More is better' is not necessarily the case with path clearance.

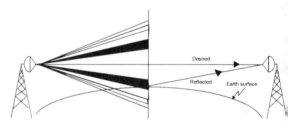

Figure 50.7 Effect of second Fresnel zone clearance

The formula for calculating Fresnel zone clearance is as Equation 50.2 where F_1 is the distance in feet from the path line to the edge of the first Fresnel zone; d_1 and d_2 are the distances in miles from the point in question to each end of the path; D is the total path length in miles; and f is the frequency in GHz.

$$F_1 = 72.2 \left(\frac{d_1 d_2}{D f} \right)^{1/2} \tag{50.2}$$

Fresnel zone clearances greater than F_1 may be calculated by Equation 50.3 where N is the Fresnel zone number.

$$F_N = F_1 \sqrt{N} \tag{50.3}$$

Propagation anomalies that alter the path line will obviously change the clearance above obstructions. It is possible that received signal variations may occur due to the clearance equalling an even numbered Fresnel zone clearance. This, in combination with a highly reflective surface, could cause a deep fade in the received signal.

It is worth noting that if earth bulge using a K = ²⁄₃ is considered, many path designers allow a zero Fresnel zone clearance (also called grazing).

50.1.2 Path profiles

The first step in planning a microwave path is to examine topographic maps along the path line for potential obstruction points. Obstructions to the sides of the path line such as cliffs or buildings should also be noted, especially if they can be considered reflective. A path profile may then be plotted showing the elevations of the path ends as well as elevations of points along the path.

Several methods of plotting this information have been used. Figure 50.8 illustrates these methods. Use of a curved base line to

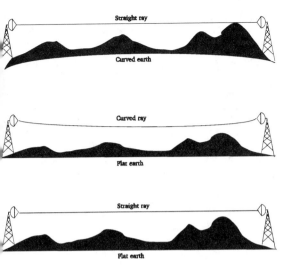

Figure 50.8 Three methods of drawing path profiles

represent each curvature or use of a curved template to draw the path line over a flat earth base line are two methods. With the advent of the modern scientific calculator, the easiest method is to use a straight earth line and a straight path line with the necessary clearance over each obstruction calculated and shown by a symbol. Both the earth curvature and the desired Fresnel clearance must be calculated and added in order to plot the clearance target above each obstruction.

50.1.3 Field path survey

In most cases, the path design derived from the map study must be confirmed by a field survey. Investigation of the potential microwave sites is usually necessary, and information on man-made obstructions as well as confirmation of natural obstructions should be obtained. Potential reflection points may also be determined.

A microwave path designed and installed without the benefit of a field survey is a high risk except for the obvious types of paths where the path characteristics are obvious and the path is short. A typical microwave survey report generated by the survey contractor will contain most of the site and path data needed for FCC licence applications and FAA approval in the case of towers near an airport.

In the case of potential reflection points observed along the path, it is possible to design a path so as to minimise the possibility of signal cancellation by a reflected signal. Calculation of the potential reflection areas that would cause cancellation may be made in advance of the actual field work, minimising the need for extensive field investigation along the path.

50.1.4 Propagation

Once the physical characteristics of a microwave path have been determined we can turn our attention to the determination of antenna systems and propagation availability (reliability) that might be expected.

Calculation of the path loss, or attenuation of the microwave signal between the ends of the path is the first step. In order to make the formula as generally applicable as possible, the path loss calculation assumes the use of a theoretical point-source or isotropic

antenna at each end of the path. With this concept the microwave energy is radiated uniformly in all directions at the transmitting end and the receiving antenna provides no directivity. The loss formula is given by Equation 50.4 where loss is expressed in dB; f is the frequency in GHz; D is the path length in miles. For example the path loss at 6.7GHz for a 25 mile path would be 141dB.

$$Loss = 96.6 + 20 \log_{10} f + 20 \log_{10} D \qquad (50.4)$$

Fortunately, microwave energy can be focused and reflected using a parabolic antenna at each end of the path. The gain or focusing effect of a typical antenna is 25dB to 45dB over an isotropic antenna, depending on the size of the antenna and the operating frequency. Thus with reasonable transmitter power and receiver sensitivity, satisfactory transmission may be achieved.

We may now determine the signal at the microwave receiver input for a typical path. Figure 50.9 is a graphical representation of the factors to be considered in this calculation. At the left side of the figure, the transmitter output power is shown. The loss of the transmission line is shown as a decreasing signal between the transmitter output and the input to the antenna. The antenna provides a gain, shown as a signal increase. The path loss, representing the largest single contributor, is shown as a decreasing signal as the path is traversed.

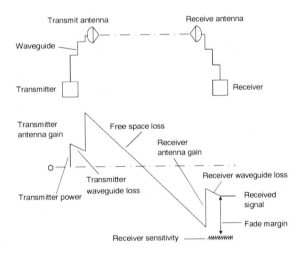

Figure 50.9 Path calculations

Similarly, the antenna gain and transmission line loss are shown at the receiver site. Notice that the signal at the receiver input is significantly higher than the receiver sensitivity, or minimum acceptable receiver input signal. This is intentional and the difference may be as large as 40dB or 50dB. The difference is known as fade margin.

Microwave signals, even under normal atmospheric conditions where none of the previously mentioned phenomena such as earth bulge, ducting, reflections, etc., occur, may still be subject to variation due to an effect called multipath fading. Multipath fading occurs when the microwave energy is diffracted or scattered along the path so that part of the signal arrives at the receiving antenna out of phase with the desired signal. Figure 50.10 shows this effect with the phases of the main and scattered signals compared.

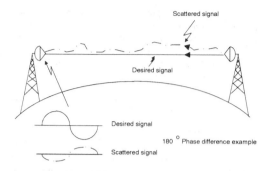

Figure 50.10 Multipath effect

Mathematically, multipath fading is described by the Rayleigh distribution function. Figure 50.11 shows this relationship. Notice that as the permissible fade depth is increased, the probability of cancellation decreases.

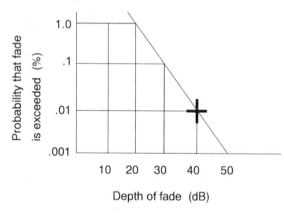

Figure 50.11 Raleigh fading

Now the reason for fade margin should be apparent. With a path designed for a 40dB fade margin, the probability of a fade deep enough to reach the receiver sensitivity point and cause the receiver to squelch is 0.01%. This corresponds to a path availability (or reliability) of 99.99%, or an outage time of 53 minutes per year. For a system consisting of a single microwave hop, this may seem acceptable. Consider, however, a system of 20 tandem hops, each with a 53 minute outage per year. Murphy's law says that no two paths will fade simultaneously so that a propagation outage time of 20 times 53 minutes per year, or 17.67 hours per year, might be expected. This would be unacceptable to most system users.

About 20 years ago W.T. Barnett and A. Vigants of Bell Telephone Laboratories developed new methods of calculating propagation unavailability based upon extensive experimental and theoretical work. These methods take into account the frequency and path length as well as climate and topographic factors. The formula for propagation unavailability (outage) is given as in Equation 50.5.

$$U = (a)(b)(2.5 \times 10^{-6})(f)(D^3)(10^{-F/10}) \quad (50.5)$$

U is the unavailability in decimal form. a is a topographic factor and equals: 4 for very smooth terrain including water; 1 for average terrain with some roughness; 0.25 for mountains, rough or very dry terrain. b is a climate factor and equals: 0.5 for Gulf coast or other hot humid locations; 0.25 for temperate or northern areas; 0.125 for mountainous or very dry areas. f is the frequency in GHz. D is the path length in miles. F is the fade margin in dB.

The formula assumes, of course, that the path has been designed for adequate clearance and does not take into account effects such as earth bulge, ducting, reflections, etc. The decimal form of U may be converted into time by multiplying by the number of minutes (or seconds or hours) per year. This formula and the unavailability formulas following apply to one-way propagation outages. The unavailability time should be doubled for a complete two-way path, since a conservative design would assume that outages in both directions do not occur simultaneously.

Figure 50.12 illustrates the propagation unavailability for several typical length 6GHz paths as compared to the Rayleigh distribution function.

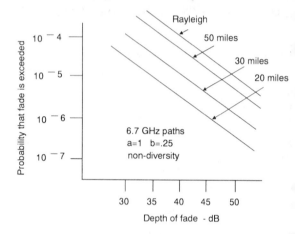

Figure 50.12 Propagation unavailability

At this point it may seem that the system designer, if faced with an unacceptable outage time for the path, must consider increasing fade margin, changing to a lower frequency microwave band or shortening the path in order to decrease the propagation outage time. Another solution is available.

Consider the situation shown in Figure 50.13. A single transmitting antenna is used, and the two receiving antennas are usually spaced vertically 30 to 60 feet. Each receiving antenna is connected to a separate receiver and the receiver baseband outputs are then connected to provide a combined signal (Figure 50.14). The desired microwave signal is received by both antennas, but should a cancellation at one antenna occur due to multipath or a reflected signal, a simultaneous cancellation on the other antenna is not likely, due to the different path length of the reflected signal. The formula for calculating the improvement to be expected by using space diversity is as in Equation 50.6, where I_{SD} is in decimal form; S is the vertical antenna spacing in feet; F is the lower fade margin associated with the receiving antenna with the longer transmission line.

$$I_{SD} = \frac{(7 \times 10^{-5})(f)(S^2)(10^{F/10})}{D} \quad (50.6)$$

Typical values of I_{SD} are in the range of 100 to 500.

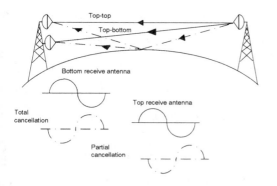

Figure 50.13 Space diversity

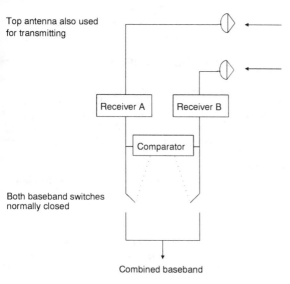

Figure 50.14 Space diversity receivers

The formulas for U and I_{SD} may be combined to provide an unavailability formula for the space diversity case as in Equation 50.7 where U_{SD} is the unavailability in decimal form for space diversity. The other factors are as defined previously.

$$U_{SD} = \frac{(a)(b)(3.6 \times 10^{-2})(D^4)(10^{-2F/10})}{S^2} \quad (50.7)$$

Notice that for U_{SD}, the frequency does not appear in the formula. This indicates that the old 'rule of thumb' requiring greater antenna spacing at lower frequencies is not the case.

Experience indicates that antenna spacing between 30 and 60 feet provide the best compromise between improvement in propagation reliability and increase in cost due to increased tower height. It should be remembered that both the top-to-top antenna path and the top-to-bottom path must meet the necessary path clearance criteria, however.

While it is theoretically possible to achieve some improvement in propagation availability by mounting the receive antennas 'edge to edge' where space is limited, little experience is available to demonstrate that the formulas are valid for small spacings. The general feeling is that such a configuration would provide an improvement over non diversity operation, however.

As stated, space diversity is an effective method of improving propagation reliability where multipath or reflective type of fading is expected. Diversity will not provide improvement where earth bulge, ducting, or similar effects that block or steer the signal away from the receiving antenna are present.

50.2 Short haul and millimetre path design

Microwave path design at 18GHz and higher follows a very similar procedure to path design at 2GHz and 6GHz. However, due to the high frequencies involved, some of the parameters evaluated along the way may be quite different than at the lower frequencies. To demonstrate this we have selected a few path design topics and evaluate their significance at 18GHz and 23GHz.

50.2.1 Fresnel zones and obstructions

One of the considerations in microwave path design is the effect of reflections and obstructions of the microwave path.

The effects of reflections and obstructions usually get sufficient attention at the lower frequencies since the paths are much longer and clearances are costly to achieve. It will be noted that the Fresnel zones are larger at the lower frequencies.

At the higher frequencies such as 18GHz and 23GHz the paths are much shorter and it is much simpler to establish line of sight since both ends of the paths usually can be seen.

Figure 50.15 shows a polar plot of an antenna pattern. The main lobe and the side lobes are shown. The beamwidth is shown at the 70 percent voltage point which corresponds to the half power point. The beamwidth is given in degrees. It will be noted that as the wavefront gets farther from the antenna, the dimensions of the wavefront get larger at the half power point. The effects of this will be shown in an example later.

A pictorial of the Fresnel zones is shown in Figure 50.16. Figure 50.16(a) is a cross section of Figure 50.16(b) taken through the

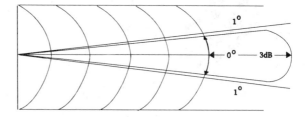

Figure 50.15 Antenna beam width

beam axis. The rings (shaded and non-shaded) are known as the Fresnel zones. The distance from T to a point on the circle to R is longer by some multiple of an half wavelength than the main beam. This difference in length is the cause of the Fresnel interference phenomenon.

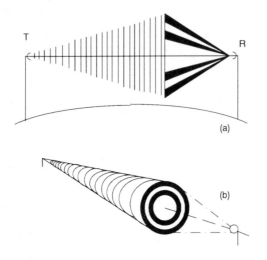

Figure 50.16 Pictorial of Fresnel zones: (a) cross-section of (b) through the beam axis

The effects at the receiving antenna of having multiple unobstructed Fresnel zones are shown in Figure 50.17. It will be noted that the nulls correspond to the even numbered zones while the peaks correspond to odd numbered zones. It can be seen that with a large number of zones unobstructed and a low reflective surface in the path that the path attenuation is equivalent to free space loss.

As an indication of what happens when various zones are blocked refer to Figures 50.16(a) and 50.17. If the towers of Figure 50.16(a)

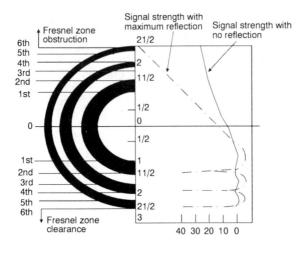

Figure 50.17 DB from free space

are lowered, portions of the wavefront will be obstructed by the earth's curvature or an obstacle in the path. As cancelling zones are obstructed the signal will increase and as phase zones are obstructed the signal will decrease. When the obstruction reaches the edge of the first Fresnel zone, the signal will be twice that in free space. Raising or lowering the towers at this point will decrease the signal.

The peaks and valleys will depend on the type of obstruction. A highly reflective obstacle will give deep nulls. If the towers are high enough to clear many zones then an obstacle in the right place can cause deep cancellations.

Some possible solutions to the cancellation problem are:

1. The Fresnel zones are closely spaced. This indicates that a slight increase or decrease in the antenna heights will remove the cancellation. This can be done if the reflection point is constant and does not change.
2. If the antenna is increased in size the midpoint illumination is decreased. With a narrower beam antenna the power drops off sharply.
3. Another method of reducing the amount of reflection is to tilt each antenna up. This can be done if the loss in power can be tolerated.

In conclusion, it can be seen that 23GHz paths may not always be simply 'aim and shoot'. The design of these paths should be done as carefully as the lower frequency paths. Fresnel zones and reflection point should be carefully considered.

50.2.2   Outage considerations

The main reason for being concerned with path design to begin with is to be sure the path availability will meet the requirements placed on the overall system. Assuming the path has been designed for the proper Fresnel clearance etc. the main contributors to outage become multipath fading and rain induced fading. For analog radios above 10GHz the predominant effect is due to rain induced fading. However, due to the high data rates used, digital radios at these frequencies may be limited by dispersion caused by multipath fades.

50.2.2.1   *Dispersive fading*

One mechanism that causes multipath fading is refraction in the atmosphere. Certain atmospheric conditions cause the received signal to arrive via many separate paths. Figure 50.18 is a simplified

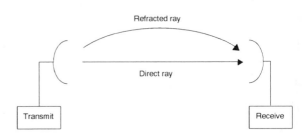

Figure 50.18 Multipath fading

representation of multipath fading where only two rays are shown. Since the two rays follow different paths, the distance travelled is different and the two signals may be out of phase. The result is a frequency dependent attenuation characteristic like that in Figure 50.19. For this reason multipath fading is often referred to as frequency selective, or dispersive fading.

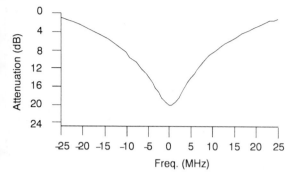

Figure 50.19 Selective fading attenuation characteristic (20dB notch)

The exact shape of the attenuation notch depends on the relative delay and attenuation of the two paths. The difference in level between the two rays determines how deep the notch is while the difference in phase determines the frequency where the notch occurs.

In addition to causing a notch in the attenuation characteristic, multipath causes distortion in the differential delay characteristic. When the delayed ray's amplitude is smaller than the main ray's, a notch in the differential delay occurs. This is referred to as a minimum phase fade. A non-minimum phase fade occurs when the amplitude of the delayed ray is larger than that of the main ray. In this case a 'bump' occurs in the differential delay characteristic while the attenuation characteristic still has a notch in it.

50.2.2.2 *Signature curves and DFM*

To determine the effect of dispersive fading on a digital radio, a multipath notch must be simulated. A test system like that of Figure 50.20 is often used for the simulation. The relative attenuation of the two paths, and therefore the notch depth, is set by the variable attenuators. The phase, and therefore the notch location, is set with the variable phase shifter. The fixed delay determines the width of the notch and is normally set at 6.3ns. The 6.3ns delay is considered statistically representative of most multipath fades.

The measurement is performed by setting the centre frequency of the notch somewhere in the r.f. channel of the particular radio system under test. The notch depth is adjusted until the Bit Error Ratio (BER) of the radio degrades to 10^{-3}. The phase shifter is then adjusted so that the notch appears at a different frequency and again the notch depth is adjusted for a 10^{-3} BER. This process is repeated

at a number of frequencies resulting in a curve like that in Figure 50.21, known as a signature curve. The signature curve shows the depth of notch required, at a particular frequency relative to the centre of the r.f. channel, to cause the BER to degrade to 10^{-3}.

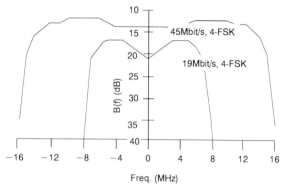

Figure 50.21 Signature curve

Two signature curves are shown in Figure 50.21, one for a 45Mbit/s radio and one for a 19Mbit/s radio, both using the same type of modulation. Note that the notch depth at the centre of the r.f. channel does not have to be as deep to degrade the 45Mbit/s radio as it does for the 19Mbit/s case. Also, the 45Mbit/s radio is affected by notches as far away as 15MHz while the 19Mbit/s radio is affected over a much narrower frequency range.

A signature curve should be taken for both minimum and non minimum phase fades. Only one is shown for each of the data rates in Figure 50.21 because the minimum and non minimum signatures are nearly identical for the particular system measured.

Originally the signature curve was used to directly calculate the outage time due to selective fading. More recently an intermediate step has been added. First the signature curve is used to calculate the Dispersive Fade Margin (DFM), which is then used to estimate outage time due to selective fading for the particular path under consideration.

The concept of DFM allows one to calculate outage time due to selective fading simply by substituting DFM for Fade Margin in the equation normally used to calculate the outage time of analog radios due to fading. This allowed existing path design programmes to be easily modified for use on digital radio paths. In addition, it allows

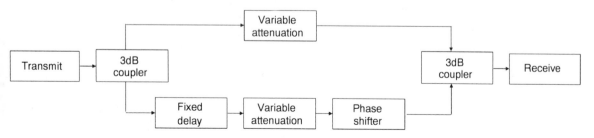

Figure 50.20 Simulation of a multipath notch

the susceptibility to selective fading of different radios to be compared on a one number basis instead of an entire signature curve.

Dispersive Fade Margin is calculated using Equations 50.8 and 50.9 from a Bellcore Technical Advisory, where $B_m(f_i)$ and $B_n(f_i)$ represent the minimum and non minimum phase signature curves respectively, and N is the number of f wide segments into which the curve is divided, in order to calculate its area.

$$DMF = 17.6 - 10 \log \left(\frac{S_W}{158.4} \right) \quad dB \tag{50.8}$$

$$S_W = \sum_{i=1}^{N} \left(e^{-B_n(f_i)/3.8} + e^{-B_m(f_i)/3.8} \right) \Delta f \tag{50.19}$$

For example, if the signature curve of Figure 50.21 for the 45Mbit/s radio is broken into 33, 1-MHz wide segments the result is as in expression 50.10

$$\sum_{i=1}^{33} e^{-B_n(f_i)/3.8} = 0.938 \tag{50.10}$$

Since the minimum and non minimum phase signatures are the same, S_W is twice this value, 1.876. Putting this into Equation 50.8 results in DFM = 36.9dB.

50.2.2.3   *Composite fade margin*

The significance of DFM depends on its value relative to the normal system fade margin which is often referred to as Flat Fade Margin (FFM). To see this, DFM and FFM are combined into a single term known as Composite Fade Margin (CFM) using Equation 50.11.

$$CFM = -10 \log \left(10^{-FFM/10} + 10^{-DFM/10} \right) \tag{50.11}$$

A plot of CFM vs. FFM for DFM = 30 and 40dB is shown in Figure 50.22. Note that when FFM = DFM the Composite Fade Margin is 3dB less than FFM or DFM. Also note that increasing FFM beyond DFM + 6dB results in very little further improvement in CFM.

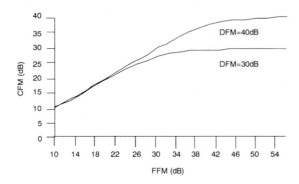

Figure 50.22   CFM vs. FFM

The Composite Fade Margin may now be substituted for Fade Margin in the equation for Fractional Annual Outage Probability as in Equation 50.12.

$$P = c \times b \times 2.5 \times 10^{-6} \times f \times D^3 \times 10^{-CFM/10} \tag{50.12}$$

For example, with CFM = 35dB, average terrain (c=1), average climate conditions (b=0.25), f=18.5GHz, and a path length of 10 miles, the resulting Outage Probability is, P=3.66x10⁻⁶. This is equivalent to 115 seconds per year. This outage time is due to the combined effects of Flat and Dispersive fading because we used CFM in the calculation.

50.2.2.4   *Conclusions about DFM*

When designing 18 and 23GHz paths, Dispersive Fading may dominate when using the highest data rate radios (DS3, 45Mbit/s), with r.f. frequencies in the 18GHz band, in areas of the country that are particularly dry (low rain rates).

At intermediate data rates, 19Mbit/s for example, in the same dry climate at 18GHz, the dispersive outage may be about the same as the rain outage. At the lower data rates (DS1, DS2) rain outages should dominate in all climates.

It also appears that rain outage will still be the largest factor in all 23GHz paths. When Dispersive Fading is dominant, increasing FFM beyond 6dB above DFM will not significantly improve outage time. When Rain Fading is dominant, increasing FFM beyond this point will improve outage time.

In summary, the Dispersive Fade Margin and specification is not as significant at 18 and 23GHz as it is at 2 and 6GHz because a typical path's outage time is still dominated by rain fading at the higher frequencies.

50.3   Digital and analogue microwave systems

Though it is in everyday use in the Common Carrier Services, digital microwave and multiplex is beginning to replace analogue microwave and multiplex in the Private Operational Fixed Microwave Services. The Private user, however, may question the need to replace his analogue system or to acquire a new digital system. There are system cost differences and system performance differences. This section will address mainly the system performance differences.

Hybrid systems transmitting data on analogue voice channels on analogue microwave are not uncommon. Another type of hybrid system is formed by the use of T-1 baseband modems, which permit the transmission of DS-1 signal over analogue microwave facilities. Certain of these configurations will also be considered.

50.3.1   Noise

The distance over which one hop of microwave radio can provide reliable communications is limited essentially by line-of-sight distance, i.e. the antennas of the two stations must be within visible range of each other. Within this limitation, the distance is further limited by multipath fading due to atmospheric effects which becomes rapidly more severe as the path length increases, and is worse for higher frequencies. For even higher microwave frequencies the phenomenon of rain attenuation becomes more important than multipath fading.

In short, the typical microwave path is relatively short, shorter than line-of-sight, and is designed for the desired path availability (these topics have been analysed in earlier sections). Thus, in order to extend a communications system to reasonable sizes, multiple hops, or relays, of microwave are required.

The concept of cumulative noise in analogue systems is well known. For analogue microwave/multiplex systems, the basic noise level is determined by the Frequency Division Multiplex channel equipment, and the microwave radios over which the channel is conducted adds to this noise. The noise of each microwave hop adds to what is already present, thus, the longer or larger the system, the worse the signal-to-noise ratio becomes. There is no easy way to avoid this phenomenon or to remove the accumulated noise and distortion.

It is commonly assumed that one of the great advantages of digital microwave/multiplex (and digital communications systems, in general) is that, unlike analogue systems, noise does not accumulate. Within limits, this is true, however, digital microwave/multiplex systems will be shown to have other noise phenomenon to consider.

Noise phenomena may be used to compare analogue and digital microwave systems on a static basis which is the 'normal' operating condition, and also on a dynamic basis where microwave signal fading reduces system availability.

50.3.2 Voice

Either analogue or digital microwave may be used to transmit voice communications effectively. However, the technical jargon used to describe system performance differs somewhat for analogue and digital microwave systems, thus tending to make comparisons based on voice communications difficult.

In this chapter, we will use the concept of Average Voice Power-To-Noise ratio as a common parameter to compare the voice channel performance of analogue and digital equipment.

50.3.3 General comparisons of analogue and digital performance

It is informative to note that in the digital microwave/multiplex system, both voice and data channels are affected similarly by microwave signal fading to the receiver threshold below which performance is unsatisfactory (see Figure 50.23). This is in contrast

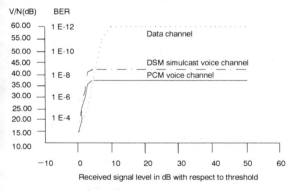

Figure 50.23 Average voice-to-noise and data channel BER vs. received level on a digital microwave system

to the difference in voice channel and data channel performance in an analogue system, where voice channel performance remains usable (above 15dB Average Voice-To-Noise) when the received signal level has faded below the level which will cause data channel outage. Figure 50.24 illustrates this for a 32 QAM 12Kbit/s data channel which occupies a voice channel on an analogue microwave system.

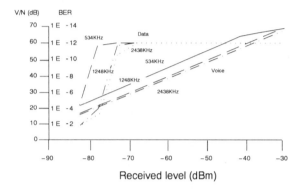

Figure 50.24 Average Voice-To-Noise and 32 QAM data channel BER vs. received level on a 600 channel analog FM system (with emphasis)

The digital system equivalent to baseband frequency slot allocation is time slot allocation, which makes absolutely no difference in channel performance, unlike the analogue FM system where the highest baseband frequency slot usually has the worst noise. In the analogue system, serious consideration must be given to the assignment of baseband frequencies, especially when assigning such sensitive devices as the 256 QAM T-1 baseband modem. This type of baseband modem may begin to make bit errors for received levels as much as 20dB above the analogue microwave FM receiver threshold, unless it is assigned to the low end of the baseband spectrum.

50.3.4 System performance vs. size

Further insight may be gained by comparing digital and analogue multi-hop systems. Table 50.1 shows the estimated Average Voice-To-Noise ratio of a voice channel on a hypothetical multi-hop analogue FM microwave system for various numbers of hops and parameters given in Table 50.2. The Average Voice-To-Noise ratio on a digital system, however, is limited by the A/D conversion technique used in the channel equipment; for companded PCM this is about 37dB. In this example, the number of hops where the analogue system Average Voice-To-Noise ratio has diminished to 37dB due to accumulating noise is 13. Where this crossover point occurs is very strongly affected by the NPR per hop assumed, as will be explained below; therefore, the number 13 should only be used as a rough generalisation.

It would appear that system performance of the hypothetical 13 hop analogue and digital systems are quite similar even when one of the hops experiences signal fading. This is because the Average Voice-To-Noise ratio of the analogue system will remain relatively unchanged, until the system noise level is overcome by the noise of the fading hop. This is illustrated in Figure 50.25, for the worst channel of the analogue system. For larger systems, the all digital

Table 50.1 Voice channel performance on analogue microwave

N (hops)	S/N (μW)	S/N (Total)	Average voice/noise (dB)
1	66.11	64.62	49.62
3	60.38	59.93	44.93
5	57.72	57.47	42.47
7	55.97	55.80	40.80
9	54.66	54.53	39.53
11	53.61	53.51	38.51
13	52.74	52.66	37.66
15	51.99	51.93	36.93
17	51.34	51.28	36.28
19	50.76	50.71	35.71
21	50.24	50.19	35.19
23	49.77	49.73	34.73
25	49.33	49.29	34.29
27	48.93	48.90	33.90
29	48.56	48.53	33.53
31	48.21	48.18	33.18
33	47.88	47.86	32.86
35	47.58	47.55	32.55
37	47.29	47.27	32.27
39	47.01	46.99	31.99
41	46.75	46.73	31.73

Table 50.2 Parameters for Table 50.1

Parameter	Value
No. of Channels	600.00
NLR	12.78dB
BWR	28.89dB
S/N — NPR	16.11dB
Nmux	18.00dBrncO
NPR1hop	50.00dB
S/N1hop	66.11dB

approach seems to be equal to or superior to the analogue for voice channel usage.

For a voice channel data modem, and using the same 13 hop system comparison, with one hop fading, the analogue microwave system seems to offer better performance than the digital. In part, this is because the analogue microwave hops used in the comparison have about 10dB lower (better) microwave receiver thresholds than those of the digital hops. Also as might be expected, performance of

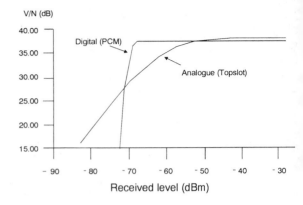

Figure 50.25 Voice-To-Noise performance with one hop fading in a hypothetical 13 hop system. Digital is a PCM channel on DS-3 microwave. Analogue is 2438kHz voice channel of 600 channel FM microwave

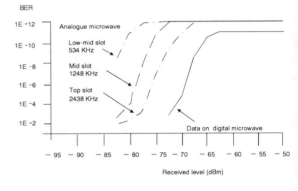

Figure 50.26 Low speed data channel performance on analogue vs. digital microwave. One hop fading in 13 hop system. Digital microwave = DS-3, 10MHz BW. Data channel on analogue = 32 QAM, 12kBit/s. Analogue microwave = 600 channel, FM, 10MHz BW

a data modem on the analogue system improves further if lower frequency baseband slots are used (see Figure 50.26).

For high speed data, however, the situation is different. The performance of a 256 QAM T-1 baseband modem is almost always worse than the performance of a T-1 on digital microwave, unless it is located in the low frequency end of the analogue baseband, in which case it may have equivalent performance (see Figure 50.27).

The 13 hop figure used in the above comparison must be accepted only as a typical system size, above which, the digital microwave/multiplex system provides performance advantages, and below which the analogue microwave/multiplex provides performance advantages. As mentioned above, this number is influenced very strongly by certain assumptions regarding the system design, in particular, by the NPR of the analogue microwave hop, as is shown in Figure 50.28. For example, if the NPR per hop is 53dB, the number becomes 26 hops. It also assumes that the majority of the communications traffic is voice.

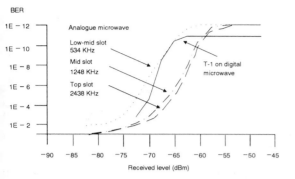

Figure 50.27 High speed data (T-1) performance on analogue vs. digital microwave. 1 hop fading in a 13 hop system. Digital microwave = DS-3, 10MHz BW. T-1 on analogue = 256 QAM modem. Analogue microwave = 600 channel, FM, 10MHz BW

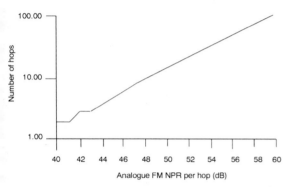

Figure 50.28 An estimate of system size above which TDM/DS-3 digital multiplex/microwave offers potential voice channel performance advantages over analogue FDM/600 channel FM multiplex/microwave

In general, it may be said that there is some system size limit, above which a digital microwave/multiplex system begins to offer significant performance advantages, even for the voice channel users.

50.3.5 Channel capacity comparisons

In the previous examples, DS-3 digital microwave of 10MHz bandwidth was compared with 600 channel FM analogue microwave because the voice channel capacities are similar. However, the data capacities of these types are not similar.

For example, the data channel modems assumed for the analogue examples were 32 QAM, which is used for transmitting 12kbit/s data on a voice channel. Since the microwave system under consideration has a voice channel capacity of 600, it might be said to have a data capacity of 12kbit/s x 600 = 7200kbit/s. However, even higher data rate types of data modems may operate at 19.2kbit/s. Therefore, the 600 channel microwave system might also be said to have a maximum data capacity of 19.2kbit/s x 600 = 11520kbit/s. ADS-3 digital microwave system has a capacity of just over

45000kbit/s, or 4 to 6 times the raw bit per second capacity of the analogue FM microwave system. This comparison is shown in Table 50.3.

Table 50.3 Comparison of approximately the same bandwidth and voice capacity analogue and digital microwave

	600 channel FM analogue	64 QAM/81 QPRS digital
Bandwidth	10MHz	10MHz
Voice Chan Cap	600	672
Max Data Cap	11.52MBit/s	45.3MBit/s
T-1 Capacity	10DS-1s	28DS-1s
System Gain	110.4dB	103.5 (or 104dB)

In this table the digital microwave voice capacity is based on PCM voice channels. The analogue microwave data capacity is based on 19.2kbit/s per voice channel. The analogue microwave T-1 capacity is based on 1 DS-1 per Supergroup.

Another comparison of data capacity might be done on a T-1 basis. In that case, the 600 channel analogue microwave system has a capacity of 10 DS-1s, since each DS-1 occupies a minimum of one Supergroup or 60 voice channels. The digital microwave system used in the comparison had a DS-3 capacity, which is the same as 28 T-1 capacity. The digital system thus has 2.8 times the T-1 capacity of the analogue system. This comparison of capacity is also given in Table 50.3.

For this case (similar bandwidth and voice channel capacity), the digital microwave system appears to be vastly superior in data or T-1 capacity over the analogue FM system.

In the preceding examples, the bandwidth and the voice channel capacity of the analogue FM and digital microwave systems were similar. It might also be reasonable to compare analogue FM and digital microwave microwave systems of similar data rate or T-1 capacity. An analogue FM system with a maximum data rate capacity of 11.52mbit/s or a T-1 capacity of 10 DS-1s, can be compared to a digital microwave system having a capacity of about 12.75Mbit/s and a T-1 capacity of 8 DS-1. (See Table 50.4. The same conditions as Table 50.3 apply.)

In this case the bandwidths are not comparable, the digital microwave system is much more efficient since it requires only 5 or 3.5MHz of microwave bandwidth vs. the analogue FM requirement of 10MHz. However, the digital system has PCM voice channel

Table 50.4 Comparison of approximately the same data capacity analogue and digital microwave

	600 channel FM analogue	16 QAM/49 QPRS digital
Bandwidth	10MHz	5(or 3.5) MHz
Voice Chan Cap	600	192
Max Data Cap	11.52MBit/s	12.75Mbit/s
T-1 Capacity	10DS-1s	8DS-1s
System Gain	110.4dB	114.5 (or 113dB)

capacity of only 192 vs. the 600 channel capacity of the analogue system.

For this case (similar data or T-1 capacity) the digital microwave system appears to be superior in terms of bandwidth usage efficiency if primarily data or DS-1s are to be transmitted. However, if primarily voice is to be transmitted, the analogue FM system has a clear capacity advantage.

50.3.6 System gain comparisons

Another significant way to compare analogue microwave and digital microwave systems is in terms of System Gain, i.e. the transmitter power to receiver sensitivity ratio in dB. Higher System Gain is generally viewed as a desirable characteristic of microwave radio equipment, since it is related to the ability of the system to withstand undesirable microwave propagation effects (multipath fading or selective fading, rain attenuation, ducting, etc.). In Tables 50.3 and 50.4 already referred to in the capacity comparison section above, System Gain was also listed for typical microwave radios of the various types.

In the case of the similar bandwidth, similar voice channel capacity comparison (Table 50.3), the System Gain of the analogue FM type is shown to be superior. This is due to the poorer microwave receiver threshold of the bandwidth efficient digital microwave system. This bandwidth efficiency was necessary for the digital microwave system to achieve a similar voice channel capacity and bandwidth.

In the case of the similar data or T-1 capacity comparison, the System Gain of the digital microwave type is slightly superior. This is because the digital microwave is a more efficient mode for transmitting high speed data, and requires less bandwidth for a similar data rate. Less bandwidth equates to less noise in the passband of the digital microwave receiver, and a relatively good receiver threshold.

Table 50.5 adds a new comparison, where similar System Gain

Table 50.5 Comparison of approximately the same System Gain analogue and digital microwave (for the same conditions as Table 50.3)

	600 channel FM analogue	16QAM digital
Bandwidth	10MHz	10MHz
Voice Chan Cap	600	384
Max Data Cap	11.52MBit/s	25Mbit/s
T-1 Capacity	10DS-1s	16DS-1s
System Gain	110.4dB	111.5dB

analogue FM and digital microwave are compared. In this case, the digital system is superior in terms of data or T-1 capacity (by up to two times), but the analogue FM system is superior by about the same factor (up to two times) in terms of voice channel capacity. The bandwidths are similar or the same.

50.3.7 Summary

Advantages of digital microwave are:

1. No difference between voice and data threshold to consider.

2. No baseband slot allocation difference to consider.
3. Performance advantage for voice users in large systems and for high speed (T-1) data.
4. Given similar bandwidth and voice channel capacity: much high data or T-1 capacity.
5. Given similar data or T-1 capacity: much more bandwidth efficient for data or T-1 transmission.
6. Given similar System Gain and bandwidth: higher data or T-1 capacity.

Advantages of analogue microwave:

1. In small to medium sized systems: superior voice channel performance.
2. For most system sizes: performance advantage for voice channel data modem users.
3. Given similar bandwidth and voice channel capacity: much higher System Gain.
4. Given similar System Gain and bandwidth: higher voice channel capacity.

Though rare exceptions may be found to these conclusions, the summary of advantages above will be found to be applicable given the bandwidth restrictions and the traffic requirements of the Private Operational Fixed Microwave Services.

50.4 System specification and equipment design

50.4.1 The role of microwave in systems

For the owner/user of a microwave system, performance and reliability are of utmost importance. The usual function of a microwave system is to serve as an interconnecting medium for other equipment which is considered the 'real' communications system. For example, microwave is commonly used to convey multiple telephone conversations from one location to another, possibly via one or more intermediate locations or sites. The telephone users do not expect to hear crosstalk from other telephone conversations sharing the same microwave system. Other sources of noise or interference due to the microwave system should also be imperceptible. To the user, the fact that microwave is being used is irrelevant, and normal landline telephone quality is the minimum expected.

Another example is where microwave is used to interconnect data devices (computer terminals, keyboards, CRT displays, etc.) with control and monitoring devices at remotely located sites along a pipeline. If the microwave interconnection somehow caused data errors in outbound transmission, the terminal operator's controlling commands could be misinterpreted at the remote site resulting in a wrong and possibly costly erroneous action taking place (such as opening or closing the wrong valve, etc.). Similarly, if the operator received erroneous gauge or meter readings due to a characteristic of the microwave system, he might be encouraged to take an erroneous action.

For the user, the microwave interconnection should be a transparent portion of his total system. This is the objective of the microwave equipment designer and the microwave system designer. In order to achieve system transparency:

1. The equipment specifications must be consistent with transparency in the system.

2. The equipment must meet or exceed its technical performance specifications.
3. The microwave system must be designed to make effective use of the equipment's performance.

50.4.2 Important system specifications or characteristics

One of the most important system characteristics affecting both performance and reliability is the area of coverage. This is true because the length and number of the microwave hops in the system has a direct effect on other desired system specifications such as signal-to-noise ratio and distortion in a voice channel, or Bit Error in a data channel.

The length and number of microwave hops has a strong influence on system availability due to probability of system outage from microwave propagation phenomenon.

Also, the area of coverage determines the amount of microwave equipment required which, since no equipment is perfectly reliable, strongly affects the system availability due to outages from equipment failure.

All of the above, i.e., signal-to-noise ratio, distortion, Bit Error Rate, and system availability are components of transparency, which, as previously discussed, is the most desirable overall characteristic of the microwave portion of a system. These components are determined by the microwave equipment specifications, and just as importantly, by microwave system design.

50.4.3 Important equipment specifications

Many microwave equipment specifications are interrelated, as far as their effects on system performance are concerned, and most of them are of importance. The most important of the equipment specifications, if any can be so identified, is System Gain. System Gain's importance is that it is a major controlling factor in system design, system performance, system availability and system cost, i.e. almost everything of interest.

Prior to defining System Gain and delving deeper into the subject, the equipment specification referred to as NPR must be listed as the next most important. Equipment NPR affects all of the system characteristics mentioned for System Gain, with the exception of system availability. Like System Gain, the definition of NPR will be given later and the subject examined further.

Let it be said at this point that improvements in both System Gain and NPR are highly sought by both the system designer and the equipment designer. Thus, the system requirements influence progress in equipment design; yet, the status of the equipment design determines the system characteristics. Improvements in both have been allowed mainly by advances in microwave semiconductor technology.

50.4.4 System gain

The microwave equipment performance parameters of transmitter power output and receiver sensitivity have been combined into a single specification — System Gain. System Gain is the decibel difference between transmitter power and receiver sensitivity. Thus higher transmitter power, improved receiver sensitivity, or both, will give a higher System Gain figure. High System Gain is considered beneficial for the following reasons:

1. It may allow longer hops.

2. It may allow smaller antennas.
3. It may allow improved S/N ratio.
4. It may allow less frequent outage due to multipath fading.
5. A combination of 1, 2, 3 and 4 may be obtained.

The well known inverse-square relationship between free-space path loss and path length expressed in decibels is as in Equation 50.13 or 50.14.

$$Path\ loss\ (in\ db) = 36.6 + 20 \log d\ (in\ miles) \\ + 20 \log f\ (in\ MHz) \tag{50.13}$$

$$Path\ loss\ \alpha\ d^2 \tag{50.14}$$

A microwave receiver requires a minimum received level, thus increased System Gain may be used to allow longer hops. This may seem obvious, but what is not so obvious is that longer hops can result in less microwave equipment required to cover a given distance, and that less equipment results in higher reliability. The inherent and unavoidable failure rates of cascaded equipment adds. The Mean Time Between Failure (MTBF) of the basic multi-hop microwave system is the inverse of this total failure rate as in Equations 50.15 to 50.17 where n is the number of similar microwave radios in series.

$$\lambda_T = \lambda_1 + \lambda_2 + \lambda_3 + ... + \lambda_n = n\lambda_i \tag{50.15}$$

$$MTBF_T = \frac{1}{\lambda_T} = \frac{1}{n\lambda_i} \tag{50.16}$$

$$MTBF_T\ \alpha\ \frac{1}{n} \tag{50.17}$$

If longer hops are not needed or desired, it may be possible to use smaller antennas. In the USA the FCC, however, places a limit on the smallest antenna that can be used. A commonly used formula for dish antenna gain is as in Equation 50.18 or 50.19.

$$G\ (in\ dB) = 20 \log f\ (in\ MHz) \\ + 20 \log D\ (in\ feet) - 52.6 \tag{50.18}$$

$$Antenna\ gain\ \alpha\ D^2 \tag{50.19}$$

Thus it can be seen that high System Gain may allow the use of the minimum size (diameter) dish antenna. This antenna not only costs less, but decreases stress due to wind loading on the supporting structure. In this manner, System Gain can reduce system cost and increase system reliability.

Given a path length and antenna size, increased System Gain will increase the level of the signal arriving at the microwave receiver. For the f.m. microwave receiver, this may improve the S/N ratio in a voice channel, or the BER in a data channel, if the intrinsic noise of the radio is not yet the limiting factor. This can be seen from the relationship between received level and S/N for an f.m. receiver, as in Equation 50.20, where C is the received level. 139 = (–KTB) in dBm in a 3kHz bandwidth. F is the receiver noise figure. d_{rms} is the test tone deviation. f_{mod} is the test tone frequency.

$$S/N\ (dB) = C\ (dBm) + 139 \\ - F\ (dB) + 20 \log \frac{d_{rms}}{f_{mod}} \tag{50.20}$$

Improved outage due to multipath fading can be the result of increased received signal level.

It should be apparent that System Gain is an extremely important equipment specification. Yet it is possible to have too much System Gain at some point and actually begin to harm system performance, reliability, or cost. For example, high transmitter power may be neither desirable nor beneficial as shall be shown in the following section.

50.4.5 Transmitter power output

On the subject of transmitter power output, it should first be realised that microwave transmitter power output has a direct and strong impact on all of the parameters of concern, namely equipment cost, system cost, reliability and performance. In addition, though the technology of generating transmitter power has changed and generally improved, the amount of transmitter power has not significantly increased. One interpretation of this is that transmitter power is still very costly, there has been no great need for increased transmitter power, and that system gain improvements, as we shall see later, have been made by relatively inexpensive improvements in receiver sensitivity.

The predicted increase in transmitter power output in the future may occur due to the fact that there is very little further improvement in receiver sensitivity to be had. The exact technology that will be used remains to be determined, but GaAs FET amplifier technology looks most promising. Unfortunately, it seems to be a law of nature that along with the benefits possible from increased transmitter power there are also severe penalties in cost and reliability. The thrust of new technology is generally to reduce those penalties.

Presently, the cost for transmitter power is strongly dependent on microwave frequency, i.e. power costs much more at higher frequencies.

In many systems, present microwave transmitter output power is already more than adequate, and in some cases is sufficient to degrade system performance by severely overloading the microwave receivers. Often the excess transmitter power is thrown away by using power attenuators. In these cases, the potential benefits to be gained by using low power are not realised. Not only is low power significantly less costly, but also the associated decreased equipment temperature, decreased parts count, and decreased d.c. load can yield improved equipment reliability.

For example: a typical solid-state power amplifier (either 2GHz or 6GHz) consists of several stages internally, and may have an MTBF[3] of 100,000 hours. A typical microwave installation might not require the power amplifier at all, but may require transmitter power output of no more than 10 to 100 milliwatts. If the MTBF of the transmitter, including the power amplifier, is known, the MTBF of the transmitter without the power amplifier can be estimated using Equation 50.21 as in Equation 50.22 for $MTBF_{XMTR\ W/PA}$ equal to 26000 hours or approximately three years.

$$MTBF_{XMTR\ W/O\ P.A.} = \frac{1}{\dfrac{1}{MTBF_{XMTR\ W/PA}} - \dfrac{1}{MTBF_{PA}}} \quad (50.21)$$

$$MTBF_{XMTR\ W/O\ P.A.} = \frac{1}{\dfrac{1}{26000} - \dfrac{1}{100000}} \quad (50.22)$$

Thus, a low power transmitter, capable of only 10 milliwatts or so should be preferred over a high power transmitter (1 watt or more)

followed by a power attenuator, when the system characteristics (path length, frequency, antenna gain etc.) permit.

50.4.6 Receiver characteristics

The receiver characteristic normally considered is sensitivity, i.e. weak signal performance. System Gain has been improved through the years by improving receiver sensitivity. Unlike transmitter power output, improved receiver sensitivity is relatively cheap. Today's low noise preamplifier transistors are actually cheaper and better performing than the devices of the past (tunnel diode preamplifiers, parametric amplifiers, low noise mixers, etc.). Unlike transmitter power output, there is a law of nature limitation on receiver sensitivity: this is the random noise (KTB noise) that, for a given bandwidth, is only dependent on temperature. It represents the '0dB Noise Figure' limitation, which in turn directly determines the best achievable receiver sensitivity.

Today's receivers are only perhaps 2 to 3dB from this limit in their preamplifiers, and also have further unavoidable limitations due to preselector filtering losses. In recent years, the Noise Figure of typical microwave communications receivers has followed the curve of Figure 50.29. This also shows the curve extended in the future towards the approachable, but unachievable limitations presented by KTB noise and filter losses.

Due to possible future improvements in both transmitter power

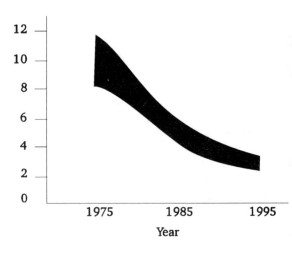

Figure 50.29 Receiver noise figure trends

output and receiver sensitivity, only 5 to 6dB increase in System Gain is anticipated. This improvement in System Gain may be used for worthwhile improvements in system characteristics by any of the means discussed earlier.

It should be noted, however, that barring unforeseen technological breakthroughs, it is not and probably will not be wise to design systems for significantly higher received levels than specified for the equipment. This is because, not only do the S/N improvements level out at the intrinsic limitations of the transmitter and receiver, but also NPR (of which S/N and distortion are components) may actually degrade due to receiver overload or saturation. Generally speaking, older receivers are worse in this regard, but receiver overload characteristics are seldom specified even today.

50.4.7 Noise Power Ratio (NPR)

Some references to NPR were made previously; this section will define the term and examine the subject in some detail. NPR is one of the most important microwave equipment specifications. NPR is a major controlling factor in system design, system performance, and system cost. NPR is expressed in decibels and a larger number is better. It is somewhat a function of System Gain in that it is partly determined by the level of the received microwave signal. Improved NPR primarily allows improved S/N and lower distortion in a voice multiplex channel on a microwave system. High NPR is necessary for low Bit Error Rates on data channels. NPR, therefore, is a prime factor in determining the desired transparency of the microwave portion of a system.

NPR stands for Noise Power Ratio. This is indicative of the test procedure performed in making the measurement. The basis for the measurement of NPR is that microwave systems carry many independent communications channels simultaneously. All of these channels not only are affected by the noise floor of the transmitter and receiver, but also create noise-like interference above this level by the creation of harmonic and intermodulation distortion due to phase and amplitude non linearities of the microwave system. I.e., harmonics of each channel are produced, and most importantly, each channel intermodulates with every other channel creating sum and difference frequencies.

In the NPR test, the multiple channel baseband signal is represented by a noise generator adjusted for the equivalent power level and frequency spectrum (see Figure 50.30). At the system output the

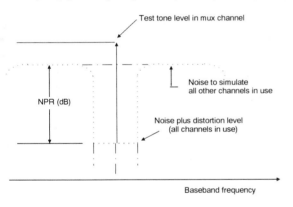

Figure 50.30 NPR test

power of this noise is measured in the channel under test. The noise generator spectrum is then notched at the frequency of the channel under test. At the system output, the residual noise power is measured in the channel under test. The ratio of these two readings is the Noise Power Ratio. An ideal, noiseless, distortionless system would have an infinite NPR.

Due to the nature of NPR, all sources of channel degradation are included. The microwave radio specification includes transmitter idle noise, receiver idle noise, receiver thermal noise, transmitter distortion, and receiver distortion. It is measured from baseband input jack to baseband output jack of a transmitter-receiver pair.

Signal-to-noise ratio limited by idle and thermal noise could be improved by increasing the baseband signal level. Normally, this cannot be done without exceeding the authorised bandwidth of the microwave transmitter, unless the entire baseband channel capacity of the microwave system is not going to be used.

Unfortunately, raising the baseband signal level also increases the distortion level which tends to degrade NPR. Therefore, there is an optimum baseband level which is sufficiently high to gain the maximum improvement over intrinsic and thermal noise without creating an excessive amount of distortion. This situation is represented by the 'Bucket Curve' (see Figure 50.31), and very likely the recommended level given by the equipment manufacturer is at or near the optimum level.

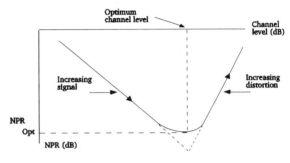

Figure 50.31 The bucket curve

If the received microwave signal level could be increased above 'normal' level perhaps due to increased transmitter power, the receiver thermal noise contribution could be decreased. Equivalently, improved receiver sensitivity, given a fixed received level, would also decrease the receiver thermal noise contribution and result in improved NPR. This improvement could be achieved if NPR is not already significantly limited by idle and intermodulation distortion noise. Thus, it can be seen that System Gain may somewhat control NPR.

It should not be forgotten that in the actual system, there are yet more noise contributors, namely co-channel and adjacent channel interference, and echo distortion. These will not be discussed here, but are mentioned as a reminder that system NPR is partly in the hands of the system designer.

It is interesting to note also that if idle and intermodulation could be entirely eliminated by clever design, and given that baseband levels are fixed at their current levels by bandwidth considerations, and given that received levels remain essentially at the current levels due to receiver overload considerations, the typical NPR could improve several decibels.

51

Communication satellites and systems

S C Pascall
BSc PhD CEng MIEE
Commission of the European Communities

Contents

51.1 Background

In 1883, Konstantin E Tsiolkovsky, a Russian schoolmaster explained the principles of rocket flight in space. Twelve years later, he mentioned the possibilities of artificial satellites circling the earth outside its atmosphere. Half a century later, Arthur C Clarke wrote of orbiting radio relay stations (Clarke, 1945) and identified many of the advantages which satellite communication would have over terrestrial systems for long distance communication and broadcasting. Above all he pointed to the unique value of geostationary satellites.

Sputnik 1, the first man-made satellite, was put into low orbit (227km x 941km x 65.1°) in October 1957 and stimulated many other tests and demonstrations of practical applications for artificial satellites in the following years, above all for telecommunications. By 1962 the Telstar 1 (Dickieson, 1963) and Relay 1 (NASA, 1968) satellites had demonstrated long distance telephone links between fixed earth stations. By 1964 an experimental satellite, Syncom III, had been placed in an accurate geostationary orbit. In the same year INTELSAT, an international consortium having the objective of setting up a global satellite network for fixed telecommunications, came into being. By July 1965 the 'Early Bird' satellite, taken over by INTELSAT and later to be renamed INTELSAT I F1, was in operation, relaying telephone calls between Europe and North America.

Much has happened since 1965. Satellites provide a major medium for linking together terrestrial telecommunications networks, province by province and country by country, using earth stations at fixed locations, typically with high gain antennas. INTELSAT has developed very extensively (Hall and Moss, 1978; Sachdev, 1990). INTERSPUTNIK became a second global system. Several regional systems, such as EUTELSAT, PALAPA and ARABSAT and many national networks are now in operation.

These systems have also become an important medium for the distribution of television programme material, to terrestrial broadcasting stations and more recently direct to home. In direct to the home television these satellites are competing, not only with terrestrial radio and cable broadcasting but also with newly emerging high power broadcasting satellites. And a substantial market has developed in the supply of satellite relay facilities for linking together networks of small, low cost earth stations on the users' premises.

There were early experiments with mobile earth stations as part of the NASA Applications Technology Satellite programme in the second half of the 1960s. The MARISAT system was set up by the Communications Satellite Corporation, starting in 1976, to provide telephone and data services by satellite to merchant ships. The internationally owned INMARSAT consortium took over that function in 1982. More recently there has been widespread interest in satellite communication for airliners and for various kinds of mobile station on land; INMARSAT and a number of national systems are developing new facilities to meet these needs, often coupled with position finding aids.

51.2 International regulations

51.2.1 Frequency bands

Of the bands allocated for satellite links between fixed earth stations (ITU, 1990a), the fixed-satellite service, those given in Table 51.1 are the ones which are already used, or are likely to be used soon,

Table 51.1 Frequency allocations for the fixed satellite service

Up-links (GHz)	Down-links (GHz)
5.85 – 6.425	3.625 – 4.2
6.725 – 7.025[a]	4.5 – 4.8[a]
12.75 – 13.25	10.7 – 10.95 and 11.2 – 11.45[a]
14.0 – 14.5	10.95 – 11.2 and 11.45 – 11.7 11.7 – 12.2[b] 12.5 – 12.75[c]
27.5 – 29.5	17.7 – 19.7
29.5 – 30.0[d]	19.7 – 20.2[d]

for commercial systems on a substantial scale. The following notes apply to this table:

a. These bands are to be used in accordance with a frequency and orbital slot allotment plan agreed in 1987.
b. ITU Region 2 only (North and South America). In Canada, Mexico and USA, the fixed satellite service has higher allocation status than any of the other services with which the band is shared. (ITU, 1990c.)
c. Not in ITU Region 2. This band is allocated exclusively for the fixed satellite service in many countries in ITU Regions 1 and 3.
d. These bands are allocated exclusively for the fixed satellite and mobile satellite services in most countries.

These bands are also allocated for terrestrial radio systems except where otherwise indicated, and some bands are also allocated, partly or wholly, for other kinds of space system.

There are certain other bands, relatively narrow in bandwidth, also allocated for the fixed satellite service, in particular around 2.6GHz, 3.6GHz and 6.6GHz, and there are wide bands above 30GHz, but none of these bands is used much at present.

The frequency bands allocated for links between satellites (ITU, 1990a) and mobile stations (the mobile-satellite services) on land, by sea or in the air and already used for commercial systems, are shown in Table 51.2. The following notes apply to this table:

a. Not in ITU Region 1 (Europe, Africa, Asia west of the Persian Gulf and the whole of the USSR). Use for mobile satellite systems is subject to protection of terrestrial systems for which the band is also allocated. (ITU, 1990d,e.)
b. ITU Region 3 only (Australasia and Asia, excluding USSR and countries west of the Persian Gulf). Otherwise as note a.
c. Land vehicles may use these bands for low bit rate data systems provided that they do not interfere with use by ships. (ITU, 1990f.)

The links, called feeder links, between these satellites and stations at fixed locations on the ground are operated in bands allocated to the fixed-satellite service (Table 51.1). It is already evident that the bandwidth allocated for satellite to mobile station links will not be sufficient for rapidly growing systems and prospective new systems, particularly for service to land vehicles, and the allocation of additional spectrum will be considered at an ITU conference in 1992.

Table 51.2 Frequency allocations for mobile satellite services

Up-links (MHz)	Down-links (MHz)	Direction unspecified (MHz)	Limitations on use
		806 – 890[a]	Not aircraft
		942 – 960[b]	Not aircraft
1626.5 – 1631.5			Ships only [c]
1631.5 – 1634.5	1530 – 1533		Not aircraft
1634.5 – 1645.5	1533 – 1544		Ships only [c]
1645.5 – 1646.5	1544 – 1545		Distress and safety only
1646.5 – 1656.5	1545 – 1555		Aircraft only
1656.5 – 1660.5	1555 – 1559		Land vehicles only

The frequency bands allocated for down-links from broadcasting satellites (the broadcasting satellite service) and currently being taken into use, albeit slowly, for television are as in Table 51.3

Table 51.3 Frequency bands allocated for down-links from broadcasting satellites

Region	Frequency band
ITU region 1 (Europe Africa Asia west of the Persian Gulf and the whole of the USSR)	11.7 – 12.5 GHz
ITU region 2 (North and South America)	12.2 – 12.7 GHz
ITU region 3 (Australasia and Asia excluding USSR and countries west of the Persian Gulf)	11.7 – 12.2 GHz

Frequency and orbital slot assignment plans have been drawn up for these bands (ITU, 1990g). The feeder links which carry programme signals up to these satellites may be assigned frequencies in bands allocated to the fixed satellite service for up-links. However, other frequency bands, not to be used for fixed satellite systems, have been set aside especially for these feeder links and assignment plans have been drawn up. The plans are in the bands given in Table 51.4 (ITU, 1990h).

Various other bands have been allocated for satellite broadcasting (down-links), in particular around 42GHz and 85GHz, but there is little sign at present of these allocations being taken into use.

Finally, frequency bands have been allocated (ITU, 1990a) for assignments to inter-satellite links, used for any kind of satellite system. The main bands below 100GHz are:22.55GHz–23.55GHz; 32.0GHz–33.0GHz; 54.25GHz–58.2GHz; 59GHz–64GHz.

Table 51.4 Frequency bands allocated for feeder links used in broadcast satellite services

Region	Frequency band
Regions 1 and 3	14.5 – 14.8 GHz and 17.3 – 18.1 GHz
Region 2	17.3 – 17.8 GHz

51.2.2 Constraints on frequency assignments

Satellite systems share the frequency spectrum with other satellite systems and, in most frequency bands, with terrestrial radio systems also. Consequently interference arises. In order to keep the interference down to acceptable levels, constraints on the characteristics of systems which determine their liability to cause and suffer interference have been agreed. Also, assignments are registered internationally; a new user of a frequency defers to a registered established user under the jurisdiction of another country where there is no international agreement to the contrary. It is assumed that interference problems between systems falling within the jurisdiction of the same country will be resolved by the government of that country. The constraints and agreements vary from service to service and from band to band; the more important provisions are as follows.

In the frequency bands at 12GHz in which frequency assignment plans have been agreed for satellite broadcasting (ITU, 1990g) and in the bands at 14.5GHz and18 GHz where there are corresponding feeder link assignment plans (ITU, 1990h), limits have been agreed for all of the satellite and earth station characteristics and all of the emission and orbital parameters which significantly affect the level of interference that these systems can cause to one another. With very minor exceptions, the radio stations of other services which also have allocations in these bands are not permitted to cause significant interference to satellite broadcasting, and they must accept any interference which they receive from authorised satellite broadcasting.

In the frequency bands at 4.5, 7.0, 10.8, 11.3 and 13GHz, which were used in drawing up the frequency and orbital slot allotment plan which provides for one fixed satellite system per country (ITU, 1990b), constraints were placed on equipment characteristics and emission and orbital parameters in more flexible ways than were used for satellite broadcasting at 12GHz. There are also procedures to be used when systems are set up, using these allotments, to ensure that these systems do not interfere with one another. However, these frequency bands are also allocated for terrestrial radio services and the measures outlined below to limit interference between terrestrial and satellite systems in bands which have not been planned for the satellite service apply in the allotment plan bands also.

These two sets of frequency plans for satellite systems are limited to geostationary satellites. Most communication satellites operating in other bands are also geostationary, but a few use other orbits. Satellites in non-geostationary equatorial orbits would present a persistent interference hazard for geostationary satellites. Non-geostationary satellites in orbits inclined to the equator, which pass through the equatorial plane twice in every orbit, could cause and suffer intermittent interference. Since it is agreed that the geostationary satellite orbit is the most important, especially for the fixed satellite service, there is a regulation (RR 2613) that requires systems using non-geostationary satellites using fixed satellite allocations must cease operation whenever this is necessary to prevent interference to a geostationary satellite system (ITU, 1990i).

There are also agreed procedures, implemented under the supervision of the ITU, to ensure that the owners of proposed new geostationary satellite systems, and the national administrations under whose jurisdiction they fall, will meet with corresponding representatives of established geostationary systems belonging to other countries, to make sure that interference problems will not arise; this is called frequency co-ordination (ITU, 1990j). When frequency co-ordination has been successfully completed and the new system has been brought into operation, frequencies assigned to the satellite can be registered in the Master International Frequency Register, maintained by the ITU. Procedures intended to deal systematically with the risk of interference between non-geostationary satellites have not yet been developed.

To keep within acceptable limits the interference which satellite transmitters cause at the receiving stations of terrestrial radio links, upper limits have been placed on the spectral power flux density (PFD) which satellites, regardless of orbit, may set up at the Earth's surface in frequency bands shared with terrestrial services (ITU, 1990k). These limits vary with frequency and with the angle of elevation at which the satellite signal reaches the ground. However, a limit of -145dB relative to 1 watt per m^2 in a sampling bandwidth of 4kHz is typical for frequency bands below 15GHz. Corresponding limits apply to the power of terrestrial transmitters operating in bands in which satellite receivers operate.

Finally there is the problem of interference between earth stations operating with satellites and the transmitting and receiving stations of terrestrial radio systems. As usual, national governments must resolve problems arising between stations under their jurisdiction. However, if a new earth station could suffer unacceptable interference from a foreign terrestrial transmitter or vice versa, the extent of the problem must be determined and solutions found where necessary before frequency assignments made to the earth station may be registered internationally (ITU, 1990l).

51.3 Spacecraft technology

51.3.1 Orbits

By far the most useful orbit for communication satellites is the geostationary satellite orbit. This is a direct equatorial orbit about 35800km above the ground, the period of which is the same as the length of the sidereal day, about 23 hours 56 minutes. A satellite in this orbit, moving in the same direction as the Earth's rotation, remains stationary as seen from points on the Earth's surface. A geostationary satellite has line of sight coverage of a great area of the Earth and, as Clarke noted in 1945, three of them suitably located around the Equator could cover almost all the Earth's surface. Figure 51.1 shows, for example, the coverage provided by satellites located at 30°W, 150°W and 90°E longitude.

There are, however, other orbits of interest for satellite communication. The USSR, with a territory which has an exceptionally wide span in longitude at high latitudes, found 12-hour elliptical orbits inclined at about 63° to the equatorial plane to be preferable for its domestic ORBITA network. These satellites are operated for periods of about eight hours when they are close to their apogee, about 40000km high above Siberia, but three satellites are required to provide continuous coverage.

Satellites in geostationary and 12-hour elliptical orbits are at great distances from the surface of the Earth and the transmission loss is very high; at 1.6GHz, for example, the free space loss is about

188dB. This loss has particularly serious consequences for satellite communication with mobile earth stations and in particular for hand portable and vehicle mounted stations, which typically have little antenna gain. Links with satellites in low orbits would have significantly less loss; for example, for an orbit only 1500km above the ground the loss would be about 28dB less, which would make a great difference to the weight of batteries required in a pocket radio telephone. For reasons such as these, low orbits are being seriously considered for this application.

51.3.2 Launchers and launching

The classic procedure for launching a geostationary satellite falls into three phases. In the first phase (boost phase) a powerful two stage liquid propellant rocket (the booster) places the satellite and the necessary upstage rockets in an orbit about 200km above the ground. This orbit, called the 'parking' orbit, has a period of about 100 minutes, it is direct (that is, the satellite revolves in the direction in which the Earth rotates), it is approximately circular and the plane of the orbit is inclined to the plane of the equator unless it happens that the launching site is located on the equator. The booster will have been jettisoned before this parking orbit is attained and the second stage rocket may be detached in the parking orbit.

In the second phase, as the satellite is passing through the equatorial plane, another rocket, called the 'perigee motor', is fired to accelerate the satellite out of the parking orbit and into the elliptical 'transfer' orbit. This orbit has a period of about 11 hours, and the same inclination to the equatorial plane as the parking orbit. The perigee motor casing is then discarded. Close to its apogee and about 35800km above the ground, this transfer orbit passes through the equatorial plane.

In the third phase, at a time when the satellite is close to its apogee and about to pass through the equatorial plane, the firing of the final stage rocket, called the 'apogee motor', accelerates the satellite to a velocity of about 3kp/s and removes the inclination of its orbit. This change of velocity and direction causes the orbit to become roughly circular and equatorial and its period becomes roughly equal to one sidereal day; it will, in fact, be approximately geostationary. Low-energy thrusters incorporated in the satellite itself, typically fuelled with hydrazine, are then used to move the satellite to the point in longitude at which it is to operate and to correct any remaining errors in circularity, period or orbital inclination.

The United States Space Transportation System (Space Shuttle) enables the first phase of launching to be carried out by reusable rockets, although this facility has not been available for commercial launching since 1986. Other reusable launch and upper stage systems are under development. However, all other launch vehicles in current use are expendable.

The classic procedure described above can be varied to take advantage of the capabilities of particular launch vehicles. 'Strap-on' solid propellant rockets are usually added to the booster to increase the payload mass which it can launch. The second stage rocket may also perform the functions of the perigee motor, allowing the first and second phases of the launch procedure to be fused into one phase. A single liquid propellant rocket may combine the functions of apogee motor and perigee motor. This, in fact, is the procedure that is most commonly used today; it is illustrated in Figures 51.2 and 51.3. Despite such variants, however, the principles of the classic procedure are generally applicable for all geostationary launchings and may also be used, with appropriate changes, for launching satellites which are not to be geostationary.

Launching facilities are available from a number of providers, government and commercial, in USA, USSR, France, Japan and

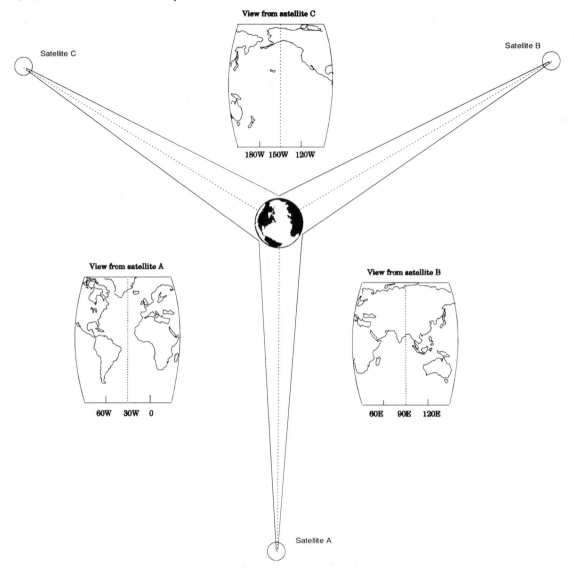

Figure 51.1 The concept of a world-wide geostationary satellite system

China. The mass which these launch vehicle systems can deliver into, for example, the geostationary satellite orbit ranges from 350kg to 4000kg, and the more powerful systems can also be used to deliver several light weight satellites into the same, or similar, orbits. A comparison between the payload capabilities of major communication satellite launchers is shown in Table 51.5.

51.3.3 Orbital perturbations and their correction

In time, natural forces change the orbits into which satellites are initially put. These perturbations are most significant and most thoroughly characterised for geostationary satellites.

Non-uniformity of the gravitational field of the Earth causes the period of a geostationary satellite, initially exactly equal to one sidereal day, to increase or decrease so as to accelerate the satellite towards either of two stable points, at 77° east longitude or 108° west longitude. In many parts of the orbit a significant drift in location, due to this cause, accumulates within a few weeks if not corrected.

The gravitational fields of the Sun and the Moon cause the orbital plane of a geostationary satellite, initially co-incident with the equatorial plane, to become inclined to it. The inclination grows at about 0.86° per annum if not corrected, causing daily excursions of the satellite north and south of its nominal position.

The pressure of solar radiation and solar wind on a geostationary satellite cause the orbit, initially circular, to become somewhat elliptical. The effect is seasonal, a build up of ellipticity at one time of year being neutralised by a change in the contrary sense at another time of year. Ellipticity causes the satellite to seem to oscillate daily east and west of its nominal position. The effect increases with the area of cross-section of the satellite and it is big enough to be significant if the satellite is large.

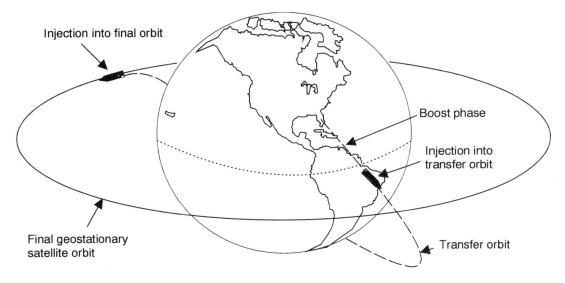

Figure 51.2 Flight profile to the goestationary satellite orbit

Significant movement of a satellite, east or west of its nominal position, is likely to cause interference to or from another network operating in the same frequency band and using a neighbouring satellite. Drifts due to the Earth's gravitational field can be corrected throughout the life of a satellite by means of the same Hydrazine thrusters as were used for the final adjustment of the orbit during the launch procedure; the amount of fuel required for this is relatively small. The ITU Radio Regulations require geostationary satellites using frequency bands allocated to the fixed satellite service to be maintained within $0.1°$ of their nominal orbital longitude, if an

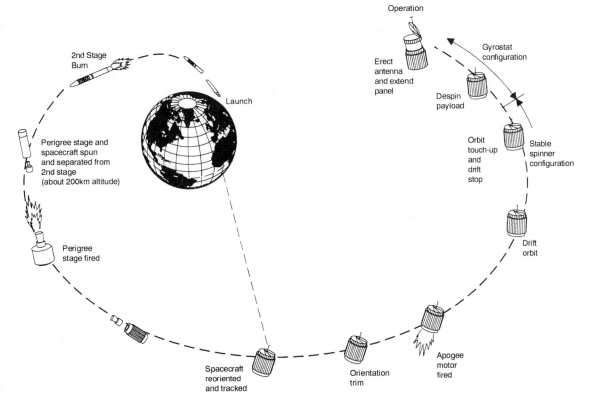

Figure 51.3 Launch sequence of a Hughes spin stabilised geostationary communications satellite using a Delta 3910 expendable launcher

Table 51.5 Characteristics of the major communication satellite launchers

	Space shuttle	*H-1*	*Atlas 2*	*Delta II*	*Proton 4*	*Ariane 4*	*Long March 3*	*Titan IV*
Country	USA	Japan	USA	USA	USSR	Europe	China	USA
Developer	NASA/ Rockwell International	NASDA/ Mitsubishi	General Dynamics	McDonnell Douglas	Glancosmos	ESA/CVES	CAST Ministry of Machines	Martin Marietta
Length × diameter (m)	56.1 × 23.79	35.35 × 2.44	475. × 3.05	38.4 × 2.44	44.3 × 7.4	57.1 × 3.8	43.83 × 3.35	60 × 3.05
Mass (kg)	2040815	135000	187560	228100	700000	243000	202000	800000
Capability	Due East launch from Cape Canaveral. Maximum payload into low earth orbit 29478kg	350kg geostationary orbit	6780kg to low earth orbit; 2740kg to geostationary transfer orbit	539kg to 28.7° 185km; 3819kg to 90° 185km. Uses upper stages for higher orbits	Using 4th stage block DM 2120ks to geostationary transfer orbit	1900kg to geostationary transfer orbit; 4600 to low earth orbit	1400kg to 31° 200-35500km geostationary transfer orbit	1770 to 28.6° low earth orbit. Use Centaur or ISU for geostationary transfer orbit or geostationary orbit
Year entering service	1981	1986	1991	1991	1967	1989	1984	1989

east-west perturbation would cause unacceptable interference to another system (ITU, 1990m). The constraint is eased to 0.5° for experimental satellites and satellites which do not use fixed satellite frequency bands (ITU, 1990n). A further relaxation, to 1.0°, applies to certain old satellites, launched before 1987 (ITU, 1990o). Constraints on broadcasting satellites operating at 12GHz are at least as severe, and they are unconditional (ITU, 1990g).

North-south excursions of satellites due to inclination of the orbital plane can also be corrected by the on board thrusters, but the amount of fuel that is required to maintain low inclination is quite significant; for a 10-year lifetime the mass of hydrazine required for this purpose is about 20% of the total mass of the satellite at start of life. For this reason, bi-propellant thruster systems and electrically powered ion engines which use less payload mass are coming into use (Hayn, et al., 1978; Free, 1980). No regulatory limit is applied to excursions north and south of the equatorial plane, but satellites with inclinations of more than 5° have not been regarded as geostationary for regulatory purposes.

51.3.4 Attitude stabilisation

Stabilisation of a communication satellite's attitude relative to the Earth is necessary, in order that the gain of directive satellite antennas may be used to use satellite power efficiently and to permit geographical re-use of spectrum. Spinning body stabilisation has been widely used in the past but three axis body stabilisation is in general use now.

In a spinning body satellite the satellite body rotates at 30rpm to 100rpm about the axis which is perpendicular to the plane of the orbit. Antennas are usually mounted on a rotatable platform which is 'de-spun' relative to the Earth and is, accordingly, stabilised in all three axes. A reference to enable the on board control system to keep the antenna platform continually pointing towards the Earth is

usually obtained from infra red Earth sensors, supplemented by Sun sensors. Antenna pointing accuracy of +_0.2° or better is obtained with such systems. The thrusters which are used for east-west orbit adjustment are usually mounted on the rotating body of the satellite, and these thrusters accordingly must be operated in a pulsed mode, synchronised with the rotation of the body.

Body stabilised designs generally employ an internal momentum wheel with its axis perpendicular to the plane of the orbit. Control of attitude about the pitch axis is obtained by varying the speed of rotation of the wheel. Hydrazine thrusters are used occasionally to dump momentum from the wheel, so avoiding an unacceptable build up of rate of rotation. Control about the yaw and roll axes may be obtained by gimbaling the wheel or by the use of hydrazine thrusters. Figure 51.4 shows INTELSAT V, a typical large body stabilised satellite (Fuenzalida et al., 1977).

The ITU Radio Regulations require geostationary satellites in general to be capable of maintaining their antenna beams within 10% of the half power beamwidth, or ±0.3°, of the nominal direction, whichever requirement is less stringent (ITU, 1990p). The frequency assignment plans for satellite broadcasting at 12GHz require beam pointing within ±0.1° (ITU, 1990g).

51.3.5 Electrical power supply in space

Silicon solar cells are used as the primary satellite power source in normal operation. When the Sun, for the satellite, is eclipsed by the Earth, power is maintained by nickel cadmium or nickel hydrogen secondary batteries. Full shadow eclipse for geostationary satellites occurs on 44 nights in spring and 44 nights in the autumn, the longest eclipses occurring at the equinoxes and giving 65 minutes of full shadow. Research on new types of storage cell, such as the silver hydrogen cell, seeking longer life, lower mass and higher efficiency, is in progress. ·

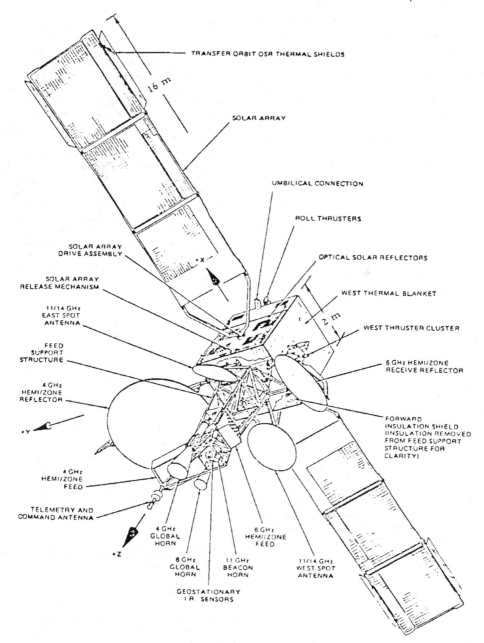

Figure 51.4 INTELSAT V satellite configuration

Spinning body satellites have body mounted arrays of solar cells, typically producing about 10 watts per kilogram of solar array mass. Body stabilised satellites using extendable arrays, which can be rotated so that they always face the Sun, deliver up to 23W/kg. Current research is aimed at increasing the dimensions of deployable solar panels and reducing their mass. Values are reaching 50 to 60 watts per kilogram and a few tens of kilowatts per panel. High efficiency solar cells now being developed could cut substantially the mass and size of arrays.

One disadvantage of deployed arrays is the limited amount of power available before the array can be deployed, that is, while the satellite is still in its transfer orbit.

51.3.6 Telemetry, tracking and command

Telemetry, tracking and command (TT&C) facilities are needed, in the launch phase and in normal operation of communication satellites, for a variety of purposes. Telemetry is used to monitor and evaluate the performance and behaviour of the satellite and to provide the ground control station with data for the diagnosis of fault conditions that may arise. Tracking facilities, used in conjunction with the command system, enable the location, velocity and orbit of the satellite to be determined, enabling the orbit and the nominal location in orbit to be set up initially, then maintained throughout the satellite's operating life. Command facilities are required for the initiation of all the manoeuvres which cannot be automated for on board control and which are required of the satellite as a vehicle and as a complicated piece of communications equipment.

The signal channels between satellite and control earth stations required for these functions are carried by two radio subsystems. One subsystem operates at low microwave frequencies allocated to the space operations service, using low gain satellite antennas; this subsystem is used during the launch phase, when TT&C may be required, for example between the launch site and the satellite and the attitude of the satellite is not normal. The other subsystem operates in a narrow band within the frequency bands appropriate to the mission of the satellite and uses the mission satellite antennas, often of high gain; this subsystem is used during the normal operation of the satellite.

51.4 The communication chain

51.4.1 The chain in outline

Figure 51.5 represents the communication chain in satellite communication in its simplest form. At one earth station, signals from a source modulate a carrier (M), the carrier is up-converted (U/C) to a radio frequency suitably for the up-link, amplified in a transmitter (Te) and radiated to the satellite receiving antenna. At the satellite, the received carrier is amplified (Rs), changed to the down-link frequency (F/C), amplified in a transmitter (Ts) and radiated to another earth station; this assembly of equipment in the satellite is called a transponder. At that second earth station the down-link carrier is received and amplified (Re), down-converted (D/C) and demodulated (D) so that the signal can be passed to its destination.

In practical systems the communication path is often duplex, the return signal channel usually being transmitted through the same

satellite transponder. A carrier transmitted from one earth station may be received at many earth stations. There may be several or many other pairs of earth stations passing carriers through the same satellite transponder simultaneously or in sequence, which is called multiple access. There may be other transponders in the satellite, isolated from one another by frequency separation, satellite antenna directivity or polarisation discrimination and relaying different groups of carriers. The techniques which allow satellite communication to be used in these various ways are reviewed later in this chapter.

The optimum choice of orbit for a satellite depends primarily on the mission. The geostationary satellite orbit (GSO) has several important advantages over other orbits that might be used for communication systems. A geostationary satellite, being stationary in the sky as seen from the Earth, is constantly in sight of a fixed earth station. The variation with time of the transmission delay is zero for an ideal geostationary satellite and it is small where good standards of satellite station keeping are maintained. Satellites in other orbits, such as those illustrated in Figure 51.6, move across the sky, so earth station antennas, if they are directional, must track the satellite movement.

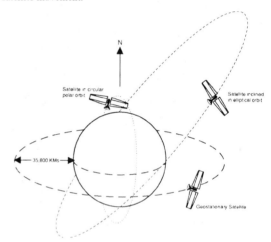

Figure 51.6 Some typical communication satellite orbits (not strictly to scale)

Most non-geostationary satellites periodically disappear below the horizon; if unbroken operation is required, several or many satellites must be deployed in suitable configured orbits and the communication links between earth stations must be transferred from one satellite to another at intervals ranging from several times per day down to several times per hour. Furthermore the motion of these satellites, relative to the earth stations, causes the earth station to earth station transmission time to vary with time, leading to synchronisation problems with high speed digital systems and doppler shift of signal frequencies in analogue systems.

However, the GSO has two serious disadvantages, which it shares with some elliptical orbits. The free space transmission loss between a satellite and an earth station and the transmission delay, earth station to earth station, are both very large. Figure 51.7 shows how these quantities vary with the altitude of the satellite above the Earth's surface (the transmission loss also varies with carrier frequency and the figure shows values for 10GHz).

Lower transmission loss for low altitude offers big advantages for some applications.

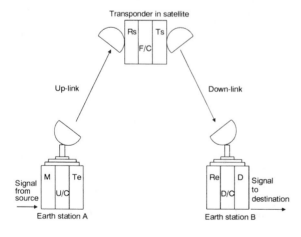

Figure 51.5 The basic satellite communication chain

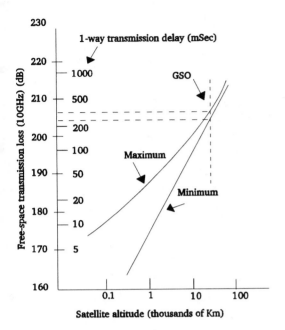

Figure 51.7 Transmission loss and delay as a function of satellite altitude

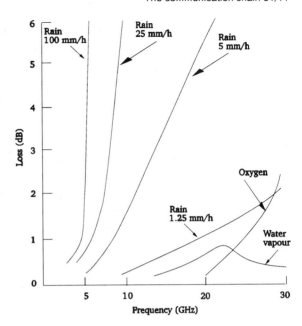

Figure 51.8 An approximate indication of tropospheric absorption on space-earth paths

51.4.2 Space-earth Propagation

In the early years of satellite communication the cost per watt of radio frequency power from a satellite transmitter was very high. Technical developments have reduced that cost, but economy in the use of satellite power remains a factor that dominates system design. Thus, the power of the carrier wave that is intended to reach an earth station receiver is determined rather precisely, to provide an adequate carrier to noise ratio for a sufficiently high proportion of the time, but no more.

The free space transmission loss from a geostationary satellite to an earth station is very much bigger than the corresponding loss for any terrestrial line of sight path. Figure 51.7 shows that a typical value for this loss is 204dB at 10GHz; this falls to 196dB at 4GHz and rises to 214dB at 30GHz. This loss is the principal factor determining what the satellite power level will be. However, a margin of power must be provided in addition to ensure that channel performance targets are reached. This margin provides in part for under achievement of equipment performance and operating targets and in part for propagation loss, due to absorption in the troposphere, which is additional to the free space value.

The principal cause of tropospheric loss at frequencies in use or in prospect of use for satellite communication is absorption in rain. Molecular resonance in water vapour begins to be significant as the frequency rises above 20GHz. The extent of the loss due to rain varies greatly, with frequency and climate but also with the angle of elevation of the satellite as seen from the earth station, and Figure 51.8 can give no more than a very general indication of how these losses vary with frequency under given weather conditions.

The margin of satellite carrier power that must be allowed, to protect link performance against the effects of rain, depends significantly on the percentage of the time during which deterioration of link performance can be accepted.

In reading Figure 51.8, it may be noted that a rainfall rate of 10mm/hour can be expected in many temperate climates for 0.1% of the time and that rates of 65mm/hour are found for 0.1% of the time in tropical high rainfall areas.

Significant depolarisation of signals arises in heavy rain, and it may be necessary to use adaptive compensation for this at earth stations in rainy climates which depend on a large measure of polarisation discrimination.

51.4.3 The transponders

The first INTELSAT IV satellite was launched in January 1971 but the design plan of the transponders for these satellites was highly innovative (Jilg, 1972) and it has remained a basic model for most satellites that have followed. The satellite used the 6GHz band for up-links and the 4GHz band for down-links. Figure 51.9 shows the basic elements.

Signals in the band 5.932GHz to 6.418GHz from the receive antenna were first amplified in a 6GHz tunnel diode amplifier (TDA) and then frequency translated by 2225MHz for further broadband amplification in a 4GHz TDA and a low level travelling wave tube (TWT). This part of the system had fourfold redundancy to achieve high reliability and long life. The signals were then split by a filter dividing network into 12 channels, each 36MHz wide and 40MHz spacing between centre frequencies. Each channel had its own redundant high level TWT amplifier rated at 6 watts single carrier saturated output power. The gain of the amplifiers for channels 1 to 8 was controllable in eight 3.6dB steps; for channels 9 to 12 there were four steps. The outputs of all of these amplifiers, after bandpass filtration to remove out of band distortion products, could be connected to one of two horn antennas covering the whole visible disc of the Earth. Alternatively, any or all of channels 1, 3, 5 and 7 could be connected by telecommand to spot beam antenna number 1 (half power beamwidth 4.5°) and similarly channels 2, 4, 6 and 8 had optional access to spot beam antenna number 2.

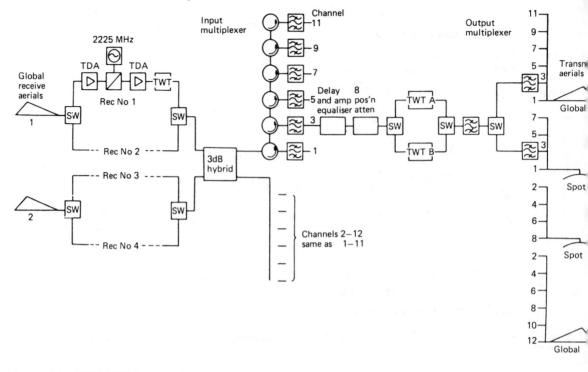

Figure 51.9 INTELSAT IV transponder

The principal characteristics of the transponder and antenna sub-systems were as follows:

1. Receive system gain to noise temperature ratio (G/T) equal to −17.6dB/K.
2. Up-link power flux density at receive antenna for output TWT saturation equal to −73.7dBW/m^2 to −55.7dBW/m^2.
3. Transmit e.i.r.p. at single-carrier saturation: global beam equal to 22dBW per channel; spot beam equal to 33.7dBW channel.
4. The receive antennas were LH circularly polarised and the transmit antennas were RH circularly polarised.

By way of contrast, the EUTELSAT II design is very new, the first being launched in 1991. The 14GHz band is used for up-links and the 11GHz and 12GHz band for down-links. The system employs 'frequency re-use' by dual linear polarisation, providing up to 1GHz of usable bandwidth, some accessed by narrow band (36MHz) transponders and some by wide band (72MHz) transponders. All transponders have redundant TWT amplifiers rated at 50 watts single carrier saturated output.

Where the demand for satellite services is high it is economically advantageous to maximise the bandwidth that is available for signals. Many satellites, like EUTELSAT II, obtain two fold frequency re-use by dual polarisation. Many satellites are equipped to operate in more than one pair of frequency bands, typically having some transponders operating at 6GHz and 4GHz and others operating at 14GHz and 11/12GHz. In satellites serving extensive geographical areas, the transponder capacity may be enhanced by frequency re-use between non-overlapping spot beams. Thus, applying all of these frequency use techniques, the INTELSAT VI satellites have 38 transponders which use the 6 and 4 GHz bands 8 times over, plus 10 transponders which use the 14 and 11/12 GHz bands twice over.

At the sub-unit level, major changes are taking place. Solid state amplifiers have largely replaced TWTs in power amplifiers at

4GHz. There is a trend away from transponder power to bandwidth ratios appropriate to high performance earth stations and towards more powerful transponders suitable for small antenna earth stations. Most radically, transponders and on board signal path switching systems are becoming optimised for digital transmission systems. On multi-beam satellites, in addition to long term flexibility switches which enable signal paths to be set up on a semi-permanent basis between a specified up-link beam and a specified down-link beam within a given frequency band, switch matrixes capable of reconfiguring beam to beam connections from millisecond to millisecond are now being taken into use for on-board switched time division multiple access systems (Watt, 1986). Development work is also in progress on on-board signal processing equipment which can demodulate up-linked digital signals, regenerate the digital waveform and assemble the signals in appropriate time division multiplex streams for more economical transmission back to Earth (Evans, 1986).

51.4.4 Satellite antennas and footprints

A circular beam 17.5° wide is just sufficient to cover the whole disc of the Earth visible from a geostationary satellite. Such a beam has a beam edge gain of about 16dBi and it is generally provided by a horn antenna.

For most purposes, coverage of the whole visible Earth is not necessary, in which case it is also not desirable. Antennas with higher gain which, nevertheless, cover the required service area can provide much greater transmission capacity for given transponder power than global coverage antennas. Furthermore, frequency co-ordination of such satellites with others operating in the same frequency band is made easier, and the possibility may arise for frequency re-use within the satellite network if beams do not overlap.

The basic high gain antenna is an offset fed reflector, generating an approximately circular beam. The beam edge gain of such an antenna is given approximately by Equation 51.1 where D is the half power beamwidth in degrees.

$$Gain = 41 - 20 \log_{10} D \quad dBi \qquad (51.1)$$

However, it is so important to obtain the highest feasible gain from a satellite antenna that it is usual to adopt a more complex antenna design, producing a pattern of illumination on the Earth's surface (called the 'footprint') which matches closely the geographical area which is to be served. Thus, for example, INTELSAT V has six antennas for access to and from the transponders and two of them, optimised to generate beams from a mid-Atlantic orbital location which serve areas on both sides of the Atlantic Ocean where large amounts of traffic originate, take the form of front fed reflectors with an array of 88 carefully phased feed horns at their offset foci. (See Figure 51.10.) The corresponding feed horn arrays on INTEL-SAT VI antennas have 146 elements.

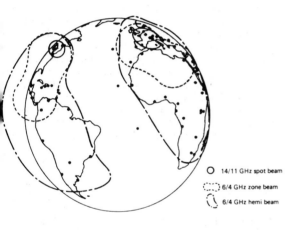

○ 14/11 GHz spot beam

⋯ 6/4 GHz zone beam

⌒ 6/4 GHz hemi beam

Figure 51.10 Approximate aerial beam coverage of INTELSAT V spacecraft for the Atlantic Ocean region

51.4.5 Modulation techniques

Up to the present time the choice of modulation technique for use in satellite communication has been greatly influenced by the cost of carrier power reaching the receiving antenna. This cost is tending to fall, in particular as satellites with higher antenna gain come into use, but another limitation on down-link power levels is likely to remain as long as most spectrum allocated for space services is shared with terrestrial radio services which have equal allocation status. Despite the low receiver noise levels obtainable with even low cost earth station receivers, modulation techniques must be suitable for operation at relatively low carrier to noise ratios. Amplitude modulation is never used for analogue signals and the use of high order phase shift and hybrid modulation for digital signals is rare. However, modulation techniques which tolerate lower pre-demodulator carrier to noise ratios (C/N) tend to need wider bandwidth for a given information capacity. Thus the modulation parameters should be optimised for each situation, to ensure that the best use is made of transponder capacity.

Frequency modulation is most commonly used for signals which are radiated in analogue form and a relatively high index of modulation is typical. Ideally, the index of modulation, and therefore the bandwidth occupied before demodulation, and the carrier power level are chosen so that:

1. The threshold of the demodulator under clear sky conditions (that is, in the absence of signal absorption in the troposphere) will be exceeded by a few decibels (related to the required rain and implementation margins) and the necessary post demodulator signal to noise ratio (S/N) will be attained for the specified proportion of the time.
2. The power and bandwidth available from the transponder for the carrier, and any other carriers that the transponder may be relaying, will be occupied when the transponder is fully loaded.

The choice involves consideration of many of the characteristics of the satellite network, the most important of which is probably the figure of merit (G/T) of the antenna and receiver combinations of the various earth stations involved.

Wide deviation FM is widely used for analogue television signals and frequency division multiplex (FDM) multi-channel telephone baseband aggregates. When used for single speech channels, a valuable saving in power can be obtained by suppressing the carrier when the speaker is silent. The concentration of spectral energy in the neighbourhood of the carrier frequency of an FM signal may necessitate the application of a carrier energy dispersal waveform to the baseband of a television emission or a high capacity FDM telephone emission, to meet the PFD constraint referred to earlier, if the down-link frequency allocation is shared with terrestrial radio services.

For digital signals, phase shift keying (PSK) is most commonly used, 2-phase or 4-phase. For 2-phase PSK a clear sky C/N ratio of 8.4dB, plus a small rain and implementation margin, is sufficient and for 4-phase PSK the ratio should be 3dB larger. However, some form of forward error correction (FEC) is often used, especially where the G/T of the earth station receivers is low and this permits satisfactory operation with a significantly lower C/N ratio. Such emissions carry all kinds of digital signals, ranging from single speech channels, through time division multiplex (TDM) multi-channel telephone aggregates and data systems of a wide range of information rates to digital television signals, although the last mentioned are usually subjected to some form of bit rate reduction video signal processing.

Wide band digital emissions may exhibit strong spectral lines under idle circuit conditions, and it may be necessary to add to the modulating signal at the transmitting earth station a pseudo-random sequence, to be subtracted at the receiving earth station, to disperse these lines if the down-link frequency allocation is shared with terrestrial radio services. When the G/T of receiving earth stations is very small, as it may be with some very small aperture terminal (VSAT) networks, it may be preferable to disperse the spectral energy of the carrier by using frequency hopping spread spectrum modulation.

51.4.6 Multiple access methods

Communication satellites are designed to relay several, or more usually many, signals simultaneously. In some cases there may be a separate transponder for each carrier; this is typical of broadcasting satellites and of satellites used for distributing television signals to terrestrial broadcasting stations. More usually, each transponder will relay, not one carrier, but several or many. This is called 'multiple access'. There are three basic techniques for achieving multiple access without unacceptable interference between the various signals involved.

In frequency division multiple access (FDMA) the carriers that will be relayed by a transponder are assigned carrier frequencies within the transmission band of the transponder, the frequency separation between assigned frequencies being sufficient to avoid overlap of emission spectra. The travelling wave tube (TWT) and solid state power amplifiers which are used in transponders have relatively constant gain characteristics within a certain range of drive levels, but they become non-linear, then saturate, as an upper limit is approached. Therefore the output of the transponder will contain the input carriers, amplified, plus distortion products, such as harmonics of the carriers and the products of intermodulation between them, the level of which will be high if the input carrier aggregate is powerful enough to drive the amplifier close to saturation (Westcott, 1972; Chitre and Fuenzalida, 1972).

For a transponder operating in the FDMA mode, the power level of each up-link carrier reaching the satellite must be set with two objectives. The first is to obtain at the output of the amplifier the optimum ratio between useful carrier power and noise due to the distortion products in the vicinity of the carriers. This involves backing-off the aggregate input level from the point where the amplifier would be driven to maximum total output, in order to obtain a larger reduction in distortion products. The output backoff necessary for TWTs is typically in the range 6dB to 10dB, although the available useful power output can be increased above that level by optimising the assignment of frequencies to carriers and by the use of TWT linearising networks. The second objective is to divide the available output carrier power between the carriers in accordance with their down-link transmission needs.

FDMA may be used for groups of carriers which have been modulated in any way, analogue or digital. Some of the carriers assigned frequencies in an FDMA system may themselves be multiple access systems, using time division multiple access (TDMA). Furthermore, if the C/N ratio in the output of the transponder is not too high, it may be feasible to overlay the FDMA signals with spread spectrum signals, forming, in effect, a code division multiple access (CDMA) system.

A time division multiple access (TDMA) system, operating alone in a transponder, allows the full power to the transponder to be used, that is, no backoff is required. This is because only one carrier is present in the transponder at any instant in time. Each earth station in the system transmits its signals in turn, in bursts, in assigned time slots, typically using PSK modulation, a brief guard time being assigned between each pair of burst slots to ensure that the bursts do not overlap even if small timing errors arise. Figure 51.11 illustrates the frame structure of a high capacity TDMA system.

Signals which are to be transmitted over a TDMA system must be digital. Bits within a frame are stored at the transmitting earth station, then assembled into a burst with the necessary preamble bits and transmitted at high speed at the appropriate time. At the receiver the reverse process puts the signal bits into store, then reads them out at the appropriate lower speed, frame by frame. The characteristics of TDMA systems vary over a wide range because the principle can be applied in many different circumstances, ranging from the transmission of low information rate monitoring or control signals with an aggregate bit rate of a few kbit/s, probably transmitted on a frequency assigned within a FDMA system, to the high capacity international telecommunications network TDMA systems operating at 120Mbit/s in the INTELSAT and EUTELSAT systems (INTELSAT, 1972; Eutelsat, 1981; Hills and Evans, 1973).

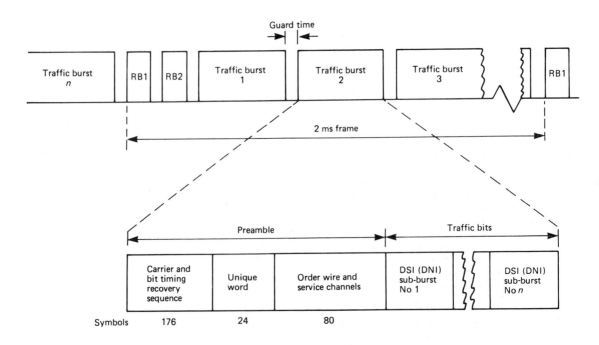

Figure 51.11 Frame and burst format of the INTELSAT TDMA system. RB1 and RB2 are the reference bursts from reference stations 1 and 2 respectively. The drawing is not to scale

On board switched TDMA has become feasible in multi-beam satellites like INTELSAT VI, using switch matrices which can operate within the TDMA frame to route one burst to down-link beam A and the next burst to another down-link beam, B.

The functioning of TDMA systems which make efficient use of the time dimension demands precise timing and complex control of access. Such systems may be costly. Where the traffic flowing through the system is light, much simpler systems which use principles first explored within the ALOHA system may provide adequate availability. In these, the transmission path is normally open and an earth station with information to send verifies that no down-link burst from another earth station is in progress; it then transmits its burst. However, several hundreds of milliseconds elapse before the start of a signal from an earth station, sent via a geostationary satellite, can be received at another earth station. Two earth stations may therefore inadvertently transmit overlapping bursts, causing both messages to be mutilated. If this happens, they are both retransmitted automatically.

CDMA systems do not structure their use of transponders either in frequency or time. Earth stations transmit spread spectrum signals which can be identified, after re-transmission by the satellite, by the coding which the signal elements carry.

These various multiple access systems differ in the effectiveness with which they use the facilities provided by a transponder. Figure 51.12 provides a measure of the capacity of a transponder having a bandwidth of 36MHz, using various multiple access and modula-

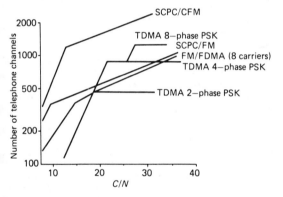

Figure 51.12 Telephone channel capacity in 36 MHz channel

tion techniques, as a function of the C/N ratio at the earth stations. Methods for calculating transponder performance are given in Hills and Evans, 1973, and in Bargellini, 1972.

51.5 Applications

Satellites can be used for virtually any kind of telecommunication system. They provide a very flexible transmission medium; once a satellite is available in orbit, many kinds of earth station, for many kinds of use, can be put in place and set into operation very quickly. Satellite networks also offer high reliability. However, the costs of satellite systems fall quite differently when compared with the costs of terrestrial radio and cable systems where these are capable of providing equivalent facilities.

In some circumstances there are major differences between the demands which satellite and terrestrial radio systems make on another resource which is in short supply, namely the frequency

spectrum. When these two factors, cost and spectrum availability, have been taken into account there are four main areas of application where satellite communication is already established or is becoming established and is likely to remain in significant use:

1. Trunk telecommunications. The global trunk network, linking fixed points at national centres and provincial centres all over the world, carrying massive amounts of telephone, data and video channels and all the other kinds of telecommunication facilities that can be conveyed by such channels, is routed mainly by terrestrial and submarine cable (increasingly optical fibre) and terrestrial radio relay systems. Such systems are very competitive in cost, relative to the satellite medium, for short distances. However, the distance between link terminals is sometimes large, and for these long links the satellite medium, the costs of which are little affected by distance, may be lower than those of terrestrial media.

2. Thin-route telecommunications. The economies of scale which make terrestrial transmission media so competitive for high capacity, short and medium distance links between pairs of fixed points do not necessarily apply in some other circumstances. Public telecommunications facilities may be provided economically by satellite over relatively short distances when the level of demand is low, especially where the intervening terrain is underdeveloped and rugged. Private telecommunications networks covering extensive geographical areas and requiring flexibility or non-standard facilities (such as high speed data and point to multipoint communication) are another area of application which is already important in some countries.

3. Communication with mobile stations. There is no terrestrial transmission medium for communication with ships and aircraft when far out of sight of land, which can be regarded nowadays as satisfactory. Satellite communication for ships is well established as the medium of choice. The use of satellites for communication with air liners on ocean crossings has begun, and it is likely to be extended soon to air traffic control and other aeronautical communication services. Finally, while both cost and limitations of radio spectrum availability seem certain to ensure that most communication with land mobile stations, such as car and hand portable cellular radiotelephones, will be served by terrestrial radio systems, it is likely that satellite communication will extend the availability of such facilities into areas which would not be economically attractive for the establishment of terrestrial systems.

4. Broadcasting. Three transmission media, namely terrestrial radio, cable and satellite, are competing for domestic, standard definition, television broadcasting at present and each seems to be identifying markets where it can dominate. Studies are well advanced on two additional broadcasting services for the satellite medium, namely high definition television and high quality sound broadcasting suitable for reception on motor cars.

These four areas of application are considered further in the next section.

51.6 Satellite systems

51.6.1 Trunk telecommunications

The International Telecommunication Satellite Organisation (INTELSAT) is controlled in matters of policy by the many governments that are parties to the agreement that set it up and it is owned by the telecommunications undertakings that those governments have designated for the purpose. The INTELSAT system exhibits well the characteristics of a trunk telecommunications satellite system. The satellites, all geostationary, are located in three groups, for the Atlantic, Pacific and Indian Ocean regions. Some of the transponders are leased for domestic networks but the larger part of the system provides facilities for an international network linking earth stations owned by national telecommunications operating organisations. It is characteristic of this global network that the total required capacity is very large; that large numbers of national earth stations need access to it; that most of those earth stations need to be able to communicate directly with many of the other earth stations having access and that these country to country links vary greatly in scale, some requiring only one circuit but others requiring thousands of circuits (Hall and Moss, 1978; Alper and Pelton, 1984).

It would be ideal for INTELSAT users if a single satellite in each ocean region had enough fully interconnected capacity to carry all of the traffic that the region requires. Successive series of INTEL-SAT satellites have had larger capacities, satellite antenna beams have been kept wide to maximise connectivity and the required figure of merit (G/T) of earth station antennas has been kept high to maximise per-satellite capacity. However, demand per region has outpaced capacity per satellite consistently since 1967. There are currently 13 operational satellites, of the INTELSAT V, VA and VI series, seven of them serving the Atlantic Ocean alone. In each ocean region, one satellite is designated as the Primary Satellite and every country is allocated some capacity in it, so that earth stations with a relatively light total traffic flow can get access to all the routes of interest to them within their own ocean region without using more than one antenna. If the capacity required between two earth stations is large, it will usually be carried by one of the other satellites serving the region, called a Major Path Satellite.

All current INTELSAT satellite series have transponders operating in both the 6GHz and 4GHz and the 14GHz and 11–12GHz bands. High gain spot beam dish antennas, steerable from the ground, are used for the transponders operating in the higher frequency band pair. For the lower band pair, some transponders use dual polar horn antennas covering the whole Earth visible from the satellite whilst other transponders use higher gain reconfigurable dual polar multi feed reflector antennas to cover smaller areas, the footprints being shaped to fit the geographical configuration of important service areas (see Figure 51.10). Both travelling wave tube and solid state power amplifiers are used with single carrier saturated output power ratings up to 20 watts, and transponder bandwidths ranging between 36MHz and 112MHz.

Earth station antennas having access to INTELSAT satellites for the global network are required to have high performance, to ensure that bandwidth and satellite power can be used efficiently. Until recently the standard receiving Figure of Merit (G/T) was 40.7dB/K at 4GHz and 39dB/K at 11GHz, requiring antennas with primary reflectors about 32 metres and 18 metres in diameter respectively. Many antennas now in service meet these requirements, but the minimum G/T requirements for new all purpose antenna has been reduced to 37dB/K (1GHz) and 35dB/K (11GHz). Much lower performance is acceptable for some limited applications (INTEL-SAT, 1977; Thompson and Buchsbaum, 1985).

The high gain antennas must use active satellite tracking techniques to avoid loss of performance due to satellite orbital perturbations; typically earth station beam pointing errors are detected by observing the effect on the level of the telemetry beacon radiated by the satellite of small deliberate movements of the beam.

Both time division and frequency division multiple access methods are used in the INTELSAT global network for the transmission of narrow band channels which are designed primarily for telephony but which are, of course, also used for other narrow band telecommunications services. It is usual for the earth station to combine the telephone channels it transmits to many destinations onto one or a few multiplexed carriers; conversely, a typical earth station receives multiplex carriers from many other earth stations, extracting from the multiplexes only those channels which are its concern.

The INTELSAT TDMA systems operate at an information rate of 120.832Mb/s, using 4-phase PSK modulation and coherent demodulation, with transponders of 72MHz bandwidth ((INTELSAT, 1972). Digital speech interpolation (DSI) is used to increase the capacity of the system for telephone traffic (Campanella, 1978). Satellite switched TDMA is available with INTELSAT VI satellites to enable up-beam or down-beam connectivity to be optimised.

However, most INTELSAT transponders are operated in the FDMA mode, with various modulation method, analogue and digital. Multiplexed analogue systems use FM and FDM, with standardised basebands of various capacities, the structure of the baseband being related to the CCIR and CCITT standards for analogue radio relay system basebands. The deviation and power level of the carriers are optimised to give channels which attain their performance objectives with economical use of transponder power and modulator allotments of bandwidth. Most digital systems use TDM and 4-phase PSK, with channels 8-bit encoded, although single channel PSK systems are also used.

Another important function of the INTELSAT global network is to provide temporary, brief wide band links for the transmission of news, in the form of television pictures, from the scene of origin to all parts of the world, for re-broadcasting. A transponder is reserved for this purpose in each Primary Satellite and frequency modulation by an analogue video signal, which may contain a digitalised sound signal, time division multiplexed amongst the synchronising pulses, is usual.

Wide band low noise first stage amplifiers, typically parametric amplifiers, are used to compliment the high receiving gain of the big earth station antennas, and these amplifiers are usually thermo-electrically cooled (Peltier effect) at 4GHz. High power is often required from the output stages of earth station transmitters, involving hundreds of watts output and sometimes several kilowatts, more especially when the station will be transmitting television signals to a global coverage transponder or where large numbers of telephone channels are to be transmitted on several carriers. These high power amplifier stages may consist of wide band travelling wave tubes, or groups of klystrons operating in parallel through frequency selective combining networks. In other respects the equipment of an earth station accessing the INTELSAT global network is similar, in principle, to that of a major radio relay station.

The INTELSAT system is by far the biggest provider of satellite facilities for trunk telecommunications but the EUTELSAT system provides digital international links with Europe, closely resembling the TDMA system operated by INTELSAT and using very similar satellite and earth station equipment (EUTELSAT, 1981). Similar configurations also arise in some of the North American domestic satellite networks. Recent satellite designs, like EUTELSAT II, tend to have transponders with higher output power, and a single carrier saturation rating of 50 watts if often found now.

For systems which are used in this way, the gain of transponders and such earth station emission parameters as carrier power and (for FM) carrier deviation are typically determined so that the CCIR and CCITT channel noise and bit error ratio (BER) objectives for international telephone, data and other channels will be met (CCIR, 1980a; CCIR, 1980b; CCIR, 1980c). Foreseeable levels of interference from other satellite networks are allowed for, and a margin is left for interference from terrestrial radio systems operating in the same frequency bands. The more important of these criteria are as follows:

1. For analogue telephone channels, the total noise, including interference reckoned as noise, psophometrically weighted, at a point of zero relative level in the telephone network, shall not exceed 10000pW for more than 20% of the month. Nor shall this noise exceed 50000pW for more than 0.3% of any month.
2. Within (1), the margins allowed for interference from terrestrial radio systems are 1000pW for 20% of any month and 50000pW for 0.03% of any month (CCIR, 1980d).
3. For 64kbit/s digital channels which are to form part of an Integrated Services Digital Network (ISDN), the BER should not exceed one in 10^7 for more than 10% of any month. For 2% and 0.03% of any month, the BER should not exceed one in 10^6 and one in 10^3 respectively.
4. For a video signal the objective is for a weighted signal to noise ratio of not worse than 53dB, for 99% of any month, measured in a baseband 0.01MHz to 5.0MHz.

51.6.2   Thin route telecommunications

INTELSAT and EUTELSAT transponders which are not required for trunk telecommunications may be leased to telecommunications operating organisations for national networks and for onward leasing to users for their private networks. A considerable number of other organisations have brought satellites into operation primarily to provide for national networks and private networks, and many more satellites are currently in the planning stage or under construction, their frequency assignments and orbital locations being co-ordinated with those of other satellites which are already in operation. These national satellites are broadly similar to those of INTELSAT and EUTELSAT. They use the same frequency bands, although there is a growing tendency to concentrate on the frequency bands which are allocated exclusively to the fixed satellite service (see Table 51.1) in order to avoid constraints arising from sharing spectrum with terrestrial radio systems. Their transponders are typically 36MHz in bandwidth and with a single carrier saturated power rating between 6 and 20 watts. They differ mainly in their use of antennas with higher gain and footprints which are limited, more or less, to national boundaries.

With few exceptions the earth stations which use these satellite facilities are simple and relatively low in cost. Some have antennas of substantial size, up to 10 metres in diameter and requiring active satellite tracking but most antennas are less than 5 metres in diameter, making them less environmentally objectionable, and their relatively broad beams do not need to track actively a satellite which is in an accurately maintained geostationary orbit.

These points of similarity apart, these earth stations and the facilities that they provide show considerable variety. The following can perhaps be taken to cover the majority of cases:

1. In a number of large countries where high quality terrestrial communication facilities do not link all centres of population, satellite networks have been set up to provide trunk connections between provincial centres. Elsewhere, where the population is sparsely distributed over inaccessible terrain, amongst mountains or across archipelagos, satellites may provide reliable communications to isolated communities. The trunk network configuration will usually resemble the INTELSAT global network, although on a smaller scale, using FDMA and with analogue telephone channels in frequency division multiplexed basebands frequency modulating the radio carriers, or digital channels in time division multiplexes phase shift modulating the carriers. Networks serving isolated communities are likely to use voice switched carriers for single telephone channels, analogue or digital.

2. Big corporations operating in well separated localities have found it worth while to lease satellite transponders for private telecommunications networks linking their establishments. In principle these networks resemble the national trunk networks described in (1) above, but they may be more flexible in their configuration, being designed to cater for needs such as teleconferencing and high speed data transfer which are not well supplied at present by the public telecommunications networks.

3. The largest single use of satellite transponders in the fixed satellite service, at present, is for the distribution of television programme signals to terrestrial radio broadcasting stations and the head ends of cable broadcasting networks.

4. In recent years extensive use has developed, in particular in the USA, of very low cost earth stations for data networks. These earth stations use very small antennas, typically less than 2.5 metres in diameter; they are the so called Very Small Aperture Terminals (VSATs). Their use may become more widespread in the future.

51.6.3   Satellite communication for mobile stations

An important advantage of satellite communication over all other media for long distance communication is its ability to operate with mobile terminals. Indeed, satellites provide the only feasible way of providing reliable communication with ships and aircraft which are far out of sight of land. The microwave frequencies which are used for communication between satellites and fixed earth stations are, however, unsuitable for use with mobile stations. Lower frequencies provide a better trade off between the satellite carrier power required and the cost of mobile earth station antennas. As shown in Table 51.2, frequency bands have been allocated for satellite mobile services around 1.6GHz and, in some parts of the world, at 800MHz. However, the 1.6GHz bands are narrow and the 800MHz bands are crowded by terrestrial services.

The first commercial satellite communication service for ships was provided in 1976 by the MARISAT satellites, owned by Comsat Corporation (Lipke et al., 1987). These satellites covered most significant sea areas, although with some gaps in arctic and antarctic waters. In 1982 the International Maritime Satellite Organisation, a global consortium similar to INTELSAT, took over and expanded this service. The INMARSAT system initially used the MARISAT satellites leased from COMSAT, some transponders which had been added for the purpose to three INTELSAT V satellites and two MARECS satellites on loan from the European Space Agency. All of these satellites operated their ship satellite links at 1.6GHz and their feeder links with earth stations ashore at 6GHz and 4GHz. Their transponders had bandwidths of a few Megahertz and the saturated output power of their transmitters was rated at a few tens of watts. All satellite antennas had footprints which covered the whole earth visible from the satellite.

The standard INMARSAT ship earth station antenna in the receive mode has a Figure of Merit (G/T) of −4dB/K, typically achieved by an antenna gain of 23dBi from a 1.2 metre dish and a receiver with a system noise temperature of 500K. Such an antenna has a −3dB beamwidth of about 10° and a simple beam stabilising and control system is sufficient to compensate for the movement of the ship and slow changes in the direction of the satellite as the ship changes its location. Single channels of narrow bandwidth analogue telephony signals frequency modulate voice switched carriers, and the transponder power per channel requirement is further reduced by companding. A low speed TDMA system provides many channels of telex, for use with all equipped ships. A second TDMA system as used for signalling and order wire purposes to control both telephone and telex facilities.

A second generation of INMARSAT satellites is in the process of deployment, replacing the various satellites that brought the system into being (Berlin, 1986). These satellites operate in the same frequency bands as did their predecessors but the transponder bandwidth has been increased to 16MHz and the available down-link power is also considerably increased.

With the additional capacity that the second generation of satellites will bring to the INMARSAT system, it will be possible to provide for growth of maritime use but it also becomes possible to consider opening up new services. In 1987 the INMARSAT Convention was amended to permit the organisation to offer service to aircraft and a start has been made in offering connections to the public telephone network to passengers on some aircraft on trans-Atlantic flights. INMARSAT is also offering telex service to road vehicles.

Various other satellite systems are also being set up to provide communication services to mobile stations and in particular to road vehicles. Some of these will operate in the same frequency bands as INMARSAT. Others, and particularly some that are emerging in North America, will use the frequency allocations at 800MHz to 960 MHz.

51.6.4 Satellite broadcasting

Subject to various constraints to protect terrestrial radio services, and in particular terrestrial television broadcasting, which make extensive use of the same band and has superior allocation status, paragraph 693 of the ITU Radio Regulations permits satellite broadcasting to be done in the band 620GHz to 790GHz. The USSR has been using EKRAN satellites to broadcast FM TV in this band for a number of years, providing signals that can be received over a wide area. However, there seems to be little prospect that satellite broadcasting will expand in this band.

The main frequency bands foreseen for satellite broadcasting are at 12GHz. Frequency assignment plans for broadcasting down-links in these bands, and the corresponding feeder links in other bands at 18GHz and 15GHz, were agreed at various administrative conferences of the ITU between 1977 and 1988. These plans define the ways in which the band is to be used in some considerable detail, but in essence:

1. With few exceptions, down-link footprints may not exceed national boundaries;
2. With allowances made for the climate of the country concerned, the power flux density at the ground at the edge of the coverage area should be $-103dB(W/m^2)$ for ITU Regions 1 and 3; $-107dB(W/m^2)$ for Region 2.
3. Every country has been assigned a share of the channels that the plan can provide. In Region 1 the shares are equal, every country being assigned 5 channels, except where the country is so large that provision must be made for extra channels to enable each time zone to have its own programmes.

These plans have been ratified by national governments, providing strong protection against cross frontier interference. Several countries had experimented with satellite broadcasting at 12 GHz before the plans were finalised (Siocos, 1978; Roscoe, 1980; Ishida et al., 1979). Others have launched satellites more recently to make use of the planned assignments, including TV-SAT, TDF-1 and Marco Polo for France, Germany and the United Kingdom, respectively. However, in general the take up of these planned assignments has been slow. The specified power flux density requires satellite transmitter output powers of several hundreds of watts for the larger countries, which causes capital costs to be high and it is arguable that recent advances in the design of low cost satellite broadcasting receivers has made such a high power flux density unnecessary. Furthermore, the limiting of coverage to national boundaries is no longer attractive in, for example, Western Europe. The general public is tending to get its satellite broadcasting signals from other sources.

Many satellites of the fixed satellite service, in particular domestic systems of the USA, are used to distribute substantial numbers of TV programme channels to terrestrial radio stations, cable network head ends, hotels and so on. However, members of the public also set up domestic antennas to receive these transmissions for their own enjoyment. This process has spread, for example, to Europe, and account has now been taken of it in the design of satellites. Thus, the ASTRA satellites of SES and the EUTELSAT II series, both transmitting in the 10.7GHz to 11.7GHz band, have relatively large beam footprints for international coverage and are used, for example, to distribute programmes to designated fixed earth stations for onward distribution to the public. However, the transponders of these satellites, being equipped with 50 watt transmitters, provide a signal strength on the ground which is not so very much less than the objective set for high power satellites in the planned 12GHz bands; in consequence these satellites tend to be seen by the public as broadcasting satellites and large numbers of homes treat them as such.

51.7 Future developments

For communication by satellite between fixed earth stations the distant future lies in a struggle, technical and economic, with terrestrial systems, cabled or by radio relay system. How fast will the public telecommunications network become converted to a universally available, omni-purpose, global, integrated, synchronised, digital network? To what degree will satellites provide special communication facilities that the world is going to want and which are not available at an acceptable price from that integrated global network?

Who can tell? It seems likely, however, that in the nearer future the use of satellites for main links in the public telecommunications network will grow, as the world economy grows, but perhaps at a slower rate than hitherto and under strong pressure to minimise costs. On the other hand, there may well be considerable growth in the use of powerful satellites and small earth stations for a variety of other purposes. Thin route public network systems will bring modern telecommunications facilities to sparsely populated and under developed areas. Private networks using VSATs may provide cost effective data transmission in some circumstances. Above all, use will be found for satellites for limited access multi-destination transmissions, 'narrow casting' as it is sometimes called, for conference television and for other situations where wide bandwidth is required for short periods. Indeed the indications are that the use of satellites for purpose of this kind may be limited, for the developed regions of the World, not by shortage of demand but by difficulties of supply, arising from increasing congestion in the geostationary satellite orbit. These difficulties will, no doubt, lead to the use of the frequency bands allocated to the fixed satellite service around 20GHz and 30GHz (see Table 51.1) for applications where the additional cost of operating in these bands can be absorbed.

It is clear that there will be strong growth in demand for the use of satellites for communication with mobile stations, and in particular with road vehicles in sparsely populated regions. There will also be a considerable demand for communication by satellite with aircraft, to provide telephone services for passengers and probably also for air traffic control purposes. Major growth could not be supplied without an increase in the bandwidth allocated for these purposes in a technically suitable part of the spectrum, and an administrative conference of the ITU, meeting in February 1992, considered proposals for making such an increase. These proposals include provision for low orbiting satellites, which would have advantages for service to road vehicles and in particular to hand portable radio telephones.

Development of high definition television (HDTV) is in progress in many countries. Most of the systems that have been announced so far require much more information to be transmitted than is needed for standard definition TV. In consequence there are no ready means, terrestrial or satellite, of distributing such signals widely and there is interest in securing a new frequency allocation for satellite broadcasting of HDTV, probably around 20GHz. A second broadcasting development looks towards multi channel sound broadcasting of 'CD-quality' that could be received in motor cars; for this purpose another new frequency allocation is being sought, but this would have to be much lower in the spectrum, probably below 3GHz. The ITU Conference in 1992 will consider proposals for both of these developments.

51.8 Acknowledgements

The author wishes to thank the Commission of the European Communities for making this work possible and Mr D Withers for his assistance.

51.9 References

Alper, J. and Pelton, J. N. eds. (1984) The INTELSAT Global Satellite system, Progress in Astronautics and Aeronautics series Vol 93, *American Institute of Aeronautics and Astronautics Inc.*.

Bargellini, P.L. (1972) The INTELSAT IV communication system, *COMSAT Tech. Rev.*, 2 **2** p. 437.

Berlin, P. (1986) INMARSAT's second-generation satellites, *Proc. IEE*, **133**, Part F. (4) p. 317.

Campanella, S. J. (1978) Digital speech interpolation techniques, *1978 National Telecommunications Conf.*, Birmingham, Al, USA, Conf. Record of the IEEE, 14.1/1.5 December.

CCIR (1980a) *Allowable noise power in the hypothetical reference circuit for frequency division multiplex telephony in the fixed-satellite service*, CCIR Rec. 353, ITU, Geneva.

CCIR (1980b) *Single value of the signal-to-noise ratiio of all television systems*, CCIR Rec. 558, ITU, Geneva.

CCIR (1980c) *Allowable bit error ratios at the output of the hypothetical digital reference path for systems of the fixed-satellite service using pulse code modulation for telephony*, CCIR Rec. 522, ITU Geneva.

CCIR (1980d) *Maximum allowable values of interference from line-of-sight radio relay systems in a telephone channel of a system in the fixed satellite service employing frequency modulation, when the same frequency bands are shared by both systems*, CCIR Rec. 356, ITU Geneva.

Chitre, N.K.M. and Fuenzalida, J.C. (1972) Baseband distortion caused by intermodulation in multicarrier FM systems, *COMSAT Tech. Rev*, 2, **1** p. 147.

Clarke, A.C. (1945) Extra-terrestrial relays, *Wireless World*, p. 305.

Dickieson, A.C. (1963) The TELSTAR experiment, *Bell Syst. Tech. J*, **42** p. 739, (and associated papers).

EUTELSAT (1981) TDMA/DSI system specification, *EUTELSAT Document ESC/C-11-17 Rev 1*, September.

Evans, B.G. et al. (1986) Baseband switches and transmultiplexers for use in an on-board processing mobile/business satellite system, *Proc. IEE*, Part F, p. 356.

Free, B.A. (1980) North-south station keeping with electric propulsion using on-board battery power, 1980 *JANNUF Propulsion Meeting*, **5** p. 217.

Fuenzalida, J.C. Rivalan, P. and Weiss H.J. (1977) Summary of the INTELSAT V communications performance specifications, *COMSAT Tech. Rev.* **7** No.1 p. 311.

Hall, G.C. and Moss P.R. (1978) A review of the development of the INTELSAT system, *Post Office Elect. Eng. J*, **71** p. 155.

Hayn, D., Braitinger, M. and Schmucker, R.H. (1978) Performance prediction of power augmented electrothermal hydrazine thrusters, *Technische Universitaet Lehrstuhl fur Raumfahrttechik*, Munich, W. Germany.

Hills, M.T. and Evans B.G. (1973) *Telecommunications System Design*, Vol.1 Transmission Systems, pp. 176-198, George Allanand Unwin.

INTELSAT (1972) TDMA/DSI system specification (TDMA/DSI Traffic terminals), *INTELSAT Document BG 42/65 (Rev1)* June 1981.

INTELSAT (1977) *Standard A performance characteristics of earth stations in the INTELSAT IV, IVA and V systems having a G/T of 40.7dB/K (6.4GHz frequency bands)*, INTELSAT document BG 28/72, 75, August.

Ishida, et al. (1979) Present situation of Japanese satellite broadcasting for experimental purposes, *IEEE Trans*, **BC-25**, (5) p. 105.

ITU (1990a), Article 8, *Radio Regulations*, International Telecommunication Union, Geneva.

ITU (1990b) Appendix 30B, *Radio Regulations*.

ITU (1990c) Para. 837, *Radio Regulations*.

ITU (1990d) Para. 700, *Radio Regulations*.

ITU (1990e) Para. 701, *Radio Regulations*.

ITU (1990f) Para. 726B, *Radio Regulations*.

ITU (1990g) Appendix 30, *Radio Regulations*.

ITU (1990h) Appendix 30A, *Radio Regulations*.

ITU (1990i) Para. 2613, *Radio Regulations*.

ITU (1990j) Articles 11 and 13 and Appendix 29, *Radio Regulations*.

ITU (1990k) Paras. 2552 – 2585, *Radio Regulations*.

ITU (1990l) Articles 11, 12 and 13 and Appendix 28, *Radio Regulations*.

ITU (1990m) Paras. 2615 – 2617 and 2619, *Radio Regulations*.

ITU (1990n) Paras. 2618 and 2620 – 2623, *Radio Regulations*.

ITU (1990o) Paras. 2624 – 2627, *Radio Regulations*.

ITU (1990p) Paras. 2628 – 2630, *Radio Regulations*.

Jilg, E.T. (1972) The INTELSAT IV Spacecraft, *COMSAT Tech. Rev.*, **2** No.2, p. 271.

Lipke, D.W. et al., (1987) MARISAT — a maritime satellite communications system, *COMSAT Tech. Rev.* **7**, (2) p. 351.

NASA (1968) *Relay program final report*, NASA special publication SP-151.

Roscoe, O.S. (1980) Direct broadcasting satellites — the Canadian experience, *Satell. Commun*, (USA) **4** (8) p. 22.

Sachdev, D.K. (1990) Historical overview of the INTELSAT system, *J. Br. Interplanet. Soc.* **43**, p. 331, August.

Siocos, C.A. (1978) Broadcasting satellite reception experiment in Canada using high power satellite HERMES, IBC-78, *IEE Conf. Publ.*, (UK) **166**, p. 197.

Thompson, P.T. and Buchsbaum. L.M. (1985) INTELSAT earth-station standards — A new look to an old theme, *International Journal of Satellite Communications*, **3**, p. 259.

Watt, N. (1986) Multibeam SS-TDMA design considerations relating to the Olympus Specialised Services Payload, *Proc. IEE* **133**, Part F, **4** p. 317.

Westcott, R.J. (1972) Investigation of multiple FM/FDM carriers through a satellite TWT operating near to saturation, *Proc. IEEE*, 114, **6** p. 726.

51.10   Bibliography

Al-Mashat, A. (1985) Arabsat system: regional telecommunications programme for the Arab States, *Telecom J.*, pp. 52-11.

Almond, J. (1981) Commercial communication satellite systems in Canada, *IEEE Commun. Mag.* (USA), **19**, (1) p. 10.

AUSSAT (1986), *Australia's National Satellite System — Network Designer's Guide.*

Briskman, R.D. (1977) The COMSTAR program, *COMSAT Tech. Rev.* **7**, (1) p. 1.

Chan, K.K., et al. (1980) ANIK-C Antenna system, *1980 Int. Symp. Digest, Antennas and Propagation*, Quebec, Canada, 2–6 June 1980, p. 89.

Chayes, A. et al. (1973) *Satellite Broadcasting*, Oxford University Press, Oxford.

Dalgleish, D.I. (1989) *An introduction to satellite communications*, Peter Peregrinus, London.

Feher, K. (1981) *Digital communications satellite/earth station engineering*, Prentice-Hall, Englewood Cliffs, N.J.

Fischer, C. (1974) Satellite communication systems ORBITA-2, *Radio Fernbehen Elektron* (Germany) 23, **17** p. 548.

Fleury, L. Guenin, J.P. and Ramat, P. (1980) The TELECOM 1 system, *Echo Rech.* (France) **101**, p. 11.

Gothe, G. (1980) The ANIK-B slim TDMA pilot project, NTC-80, miIEEE 1980 National Telecommunications Conference, Houston, Texas, USA, 71.4/1.9.

Grenier, J. et al. (1979) Telecom 1, a national satellite for domestic and business services, *ICC-79, 1979 Int. Conf. on Communications*, Boston, MA (USA) 10–14 June, 49.5/1.

Hogwood, P. (1977) PALAPA — Indonesia to the fore, *J. Br Interplanet, Soc.* (GB) **30**, (4) p. 127.

ITU (1985) *India Satellite System*, Handbook on satellite communications, Fixed Satellite Services, Geneva.

Kantor, L.Y., Polukhin, U.A. and Takyzin, N.V. (1978) New relay stations of the ORBITA-2 satellite communications system, *Elektrosvyas (USSR)* **27**, (5) p. 1.

Keigler J.E. (1978) RCA SATCOM; an example of weight of optimised satellite design for maximum communications capacity, *Acta Astronautica*, **5** p. 219.

Love, A.W. (ed) (1978) *Reflector antennas*, IEEE Press, New York.

Maral, G. and Bousquet, M. (1986) *Satellite Communications Systems*, John Wiley, New York.

Martin, J. (1978) *Communications Satellite Systems*, Prentice-Hall, Englewood Cliffs, NJ.

Miya, K. (ed). (1975) *Satellite Communications Engineering*, Lattice Co. Tokyo.

Pelton, J.N. and Snow, M.S. (1977) *Economic and policy problems in satellite communications* (Economic and political issues of the first decade of INTELSAT), Praeger Publications.

Pritchard, W.L. and Sciulli, J.A. (1986) *Satellite communication systems engineering*, Prentice-Hall, Englewood Cliffs, NJ.

Rainger, P. et. al. (1985) *Satellite Broadcasting*, John Wiley, Chichester.

Schmidt, W.G. and Lavean, G.E. (1976) *Communication satellite development technology*, American Institute of Aeronautics.

Schneider, P. (1979) WESTAR today and tomorrow (satellite communications), *Signal* (USA), **34**, (3) p. 43.

Slater, J.N. and Trinogga, L.A. (1985) *Satellite broadcasting systems planning and design*, Ellis Horwood, Chichester.

Soewandi, K. and Soedarmadi, P. (1976) Telecommunications in Indonesia, (mi)IEEE Trans, Commun, (USA), COM-24, **7** p. 687.

Spilker, J. (1977) *Digital communication by satellite*, Prentice-Hall, Englewood Cliffs, NJ.

Tengker, J.S. (1976) Indonesian domestic satellite system, EASCON 76, *Proc. of Eastern Electronics Conf.*, Washington DC, (USA), pp. 11-A to 11-U.

Unger, J.H.W. (1976) *Literature survey of Communication Satellite Systems and Technology*, IEEE Press, New York.

Van Trees, H.L. (1979) *Satellite communications*, IEEE Press, New York.

Verma, S.N. (1975) US domestic communication system using WESTAR satellites, *World Telecommunication Forum, Technical Symp.*, Geneva, 6–8 October, 1975, 2.4.3/1.6.

Weischdale, G.M. and Koury, A. (1979) SBS terminals demand advanced design, *Microwave Syst. News*, (USA) **9** (4) p. 70.

Westwood, D.H. (1979) Customer premises RF terminals for the SBS system, *ICC-79 INT. Conf. on Communications*, 6.3/1.5.

Whittaker, P.N. (1980) Satellite Business Systems (SBS) — A concept for the 80s, *Policy implications of Data Network Development in the OECD*, p. 35.

52

Point to multipoint urban and rural radio

S A Mohamed
BSc MSc PhD CEng MIEE
BT Laboratories

Contents

52.1 Introduction

Radio systems have the following advantages over other transmission media such as coaxial and optical cables:

1. Radio systems can be installed relatively quickly for permanent or temporary applications.
2. Equipment can be recovered and re-used elsewhere.
3. Ideal for use in hostile environment e.g. marshes, hilly terrain, over water paths etc.
4. Radio is more attractive to use when the demand for a new service is not certain or difficult to forecast.
5. Radio can provide media diversity to cable systems on routes requiring highly reliable communication.

The disadvantages of radio are as follows:

1. Generally line-of-sight is required between terminals.
2. Radio signals distort and/or attenuate due to the weather.

Point-to-point radio systems are suitable for relatively large transmission capacity. However, for kilobit rate services it is difficult to provide spectrally efficient point-to-point systems at microwave frequencies for two reasons: it is difficult to make low loss filters with extremely narrow bandwidths, and power source instabilities could result in a relatively significant transmission bandwidth requirement. These disadvantages are overcome by using point-to-multipoint systems. There are two types of multipoint systems, one designed for urban use and the other for rural applications.

52.2 Urban multipoint systems

For urban applications such as data and integrated services digital network (ISDN) access, multipoint systems are usually required to operate over relatively short hops of up to 7km to 10km. This requirement, coupled with the general non-availability of spectrum below about 10GHz (this spectrum is often used for high capacity trunk radio systems) and the desirability to use small, compact, lightweight and unobtrusive roof top mounted equipment has led to the development of a number of multipoint systems in the 10.5GHz to 26GHz bands (Mohamed, 1985; Nakayama, 1985; Omiveit, 1989; Shindo, 1983; and others).

The higher frequencies permit the use of small compact antennas with high gains, and production of highly integrated low cost transceivers. To produce systems with a high spectral efficiency it is essential to use extremely stable but costly oscillators. Thus cost considerations rather than spectral efficiency appear to be the important influencing factors in the system design. Rainfall attenuation becomes significant above about 10GHz and therefore the range and non-availability of these systems are affected by this factor.

52.2.1 System operation

The system comprises a central station (CS) and a number of subscriber outstations (OS) which are usually roof mounted and have line of sight (LOS) paths to the CS. A block diagram of an urban multipoint system is shown in Figure 52.1. The CS would normally be located on a tall building with cable connections to a nearby exchange or central office.

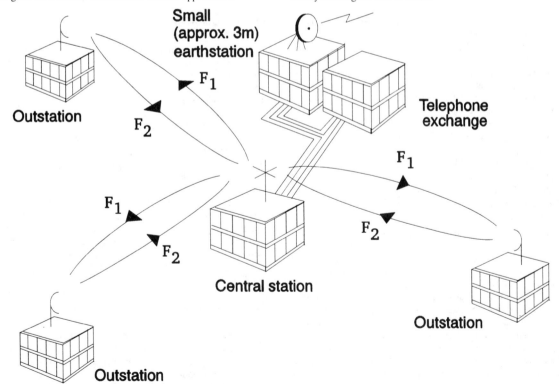

Figure 52.1 Urban multipoint system operation

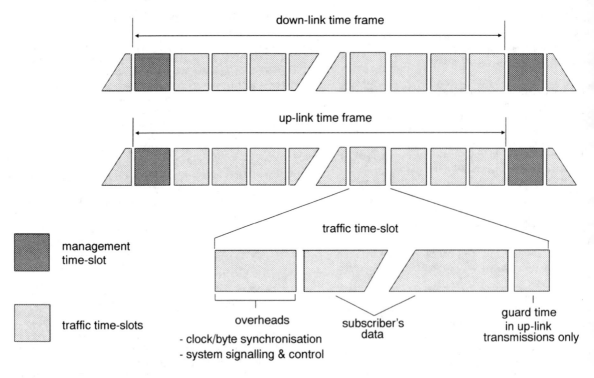

Figure 52.2 Typical frame periods and traffic time slots for TDM/TDMA systems

At the CS, low bit rate circuits are time division multiplexed (TDM) into a relatively high aggregate data stream which is then transmitted as a modulated signal at one frequency F_1 in a continuous mode from a wide beamwidth sector antenna. Each roof top radio terminal (or outstation), equipped with a directional paraboloid or cassegrain antenna, receives this signal and extracts from it the data addressed to it. Return transmissions from all identical OSs occur at a second frequency F_2. Low bit rate customer data are formatted at the same aggregate data rate of the CS for transmission at regular intervals as interleaved bursts with adequate guard time between adjacent bursts. Thus the OSs access the CS in a time division multiple access (TDMA) mode.

The down-link (CS to OSs) modulated signal carries data continuously at the system aggregate rate. In the up-link direction (OSs to CS) burst transmissions are repeated periodically once every 'time frame' period.

Figure 52.2 shows an example of the up-link and down-link time frames for a system designed to operate at 19GHz (Ballance, 1984). Each time slot includes a system overhead such as carrier recovery, symbol timing recovery, signalling, error checking and unique byte identification. This is essential since all the OSs have sources operating at nominally the same frequency F_2. Since the overhead bits for each time slot remains constant, the frame efficiency (i.e. the ratio of total time for subscriber data to the frame time) can be improved by increasing the ratio of useful data to the overhead data. This can be achieved by increasing the frame period in the up-link direction. A very long time frame period can result in excessive transport delay which may be unacceptable to meet network requirements for speech communication. The choice of time frame period is a compromise between the frame efficiency, system capacity and ease of system implementation.

52.2.2 Channel access

A management or control time slot in the up-link and down-link frame periods (named time slot zero, for instance, in Ballance, 1984) is generally used for tasks such as time slot request/allocation, ranging, error messages and system updates. The number of time slots determines the number of connections possible at any one time. For private wire or leased circuits, the time slot allocation is fixed or pre-assigned. On the other hand, time slots may be assigned as and when they are required on demand. In this case two methods of channel access are generally in use, polling and slotted ALOHA random request (see Chapter 13). In polling method, the CS continuously polls each OS to determine if a time slot allocation is required. Where a large number of OSs is involved, such a technique requires an unacceptably long time for polling. In ALOHA, time slot allocation requests are again made during the control time slot period (which may be sub-divided into a number of signalling channels). If the signalling bursts from two or more OSs collide, no acknowledgement is given in the down-link path. Requests are therefore repeated after a random delay duration in order to decrease the probability of further collisions.

52.2.3 Ranging

The burst transmissions from all the OSs, located at various distances, must arrive at the CS as non-overlapping bursts. A small guard time is generally allowed between adjacent bursts in order to cater for slight timing differences occurring in the OSs. When an OS is first installed, it acquires a timing reference from the CS and subsequently determines the time by which its transmission must be adjusted. In one system (Ballance, 1984), when an OS is first

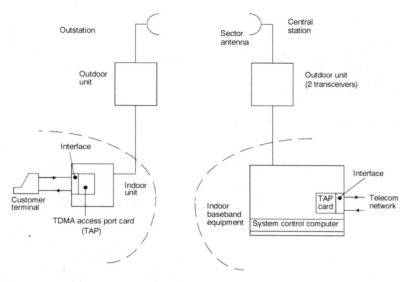

Figure 52.3　A simplified block diagram of a multipoint system

installed, it acquires a timing reference signal from the CS, and when commanded by it, the OS transmits a burst in the up-link control time slot. The CS determines its range and instructs the OS to retard its transmissions suitably to correspond to that of an OS located at a maximum distance from it.

Figure 52.4　A 19GHz roof mounted outstation

52.2.4　System details

A simplified block diagram of an urban multipoint system is shown in Figure 52.3. The r.f. equipment at both the CS and OSs is generally located outdoors with power and baseband (or intermediate frequency, i.f.) signals carried between it and the indoor baseband equipment. Figure 52.4 shows a roof mounted OS designed for 19GHz system (Hewitt, 1984; Bailey, 1987). The antenna is an offset parabola of 355mm diameter at the back of which is housed the r.f./i.f. unit and power supplies.

A number of multipoint systems have been designed at frequencies between 10.5GHz and 26GHz employing binary or 4-level modulation schemes (Table 52.1). The system aggregate rates vary between 2Mbit/s and 16Mbit/s. These systems are usually used over relatively short hops (up to 7km to 10km), and therefore the dominant impairment mechanism is rainfall attenuation rather than atmospheric multipath fading.

Link budgets for such systems are illustrated in Table 52.2 with an example (Scott, 1984). The receiver sensitivity (–85dBm) is for a

Table 52.1　Urban point-to-multipoint radio systems

	System			
	10.5GHz	*19GHz*	*23GHz*	*26GHz*
Aggregate bit rate (Mbits/s)	2.048	8.192	0.832	16.384
Modulation	QPSK	2 FSK	2 ASK	FSK (CS to OS); DFSK (OS to CS)
Frame period (ms)	5	7	0.125 (CS to OS) 5 (OS to CS)	1

carrier to noise (C/N) ratio of 11dB since, for binary FSK, the total noise power is the sum of the receiver noise figure (8dB) and thermal noise of –104dBm in a noise bandwidth of 10MHz.

The system fade margin determines the outage due to rainfall. For instance, in the U.K., for a maximum non-availability of 0.01% of an average year, fade margins of 14.2dB and 17.0dB are respectively required at 17.7GHz and 19.7GHz (CCIR, 1990).

Table 52.2   Link budget for a multipoint system (Scott, 1984)

	Direction of transmission	
	OSs to CS	*CS to OSs*
Frequency (GHz)	17.7	19.7
(a) Transmitted power (dBm)	21	27
(b) Transmit antenna gain (dBi)	17.5	35.5
(c) Receive antenna gain (dBi)	34.5	18.5
(d) Fixed losses: feeder; filters; radome etc. (dB)	–2	–2
(e) Receiver sensitivity (dBm) for 1 in 1000 bit error ratio	–85	–82
(f) System gain in dB (a)+(b)+(c)+(d)-(e)	156	161
(g) Path loss in dB for 10km	137.9	139.3
(h) System fade margin in dB (f)-(g)	18.1	21.7

The path loss is the sum of the free space loss given by Equation 52.1 and the loss due to atmospheric water vapour absorption (CCIR, 1990a).

$$Path\ loss\ =\ 20\log_{10}\left(\frac{4\pi\ hop\ length}{free\ space\ wavelength}\right) \qquad (52.1)$$

52.2.5   Modulation/demodulation methods

Spectral efficiency, ease of implementation and resistance to interference are some of the considerations which can influence the choice of modulation methods. At frequencies above about 10GHz microwave source stability consideration is important in the selection of a suitable modulation method. For instance, for dielectric resonator stabilised microwave oscillators, stabilities of 10^{-4} (temperature range of 5°C to 60°C) around 26GHz have been reported (Ogawa, 1984a). In one system employing binary frequency shift keying (FSK) modulation, the resulting d.c. offset at the CS demodulator has been used to convey a measure of the frequency offset information back to the OS so that the transmit oscillator frequency can be corrected, thus providing a closed loop for fine frequency tuning (Hewitt, 1984; Mohamed, 1985).

Burst transmissions arriving at a CS from all the OSs are nominally at the same frequency. At the CS the carrier phase has to be recovered from the preamble associated with each burst. However, differential demodulation does not require carrier recovery and although it requires a higher C/N ratio, its implementation in the up-link direction is often preferred. The source stability considerations have led to earlier implementations of binary (ASK) ampli-

tude shift keying (Shindo, 1981; Shindo, 1983a; Marchand, 1986). Transmitter power control have also been used to minimise received power variation. However, measurements have shown that ASK requires about 7dB more C/N ratio than for differential frequency shift keyed (DFSK) modulation.

52.2.6   Channel plans

Channel plans are generally different for various systems designed over a frequency range of 10.5GHz to 26GHz (CCIR, 1990b). These are influenced to some extent by the modulation method selected, source frequency variations and the general desirability of avoiding the use of RF filters with extremely narrow fractional bandwidths.

52.2.7   Frequency re-use

The CS antenna is usually a sector antenna with 90 degrees, 120 degrees or 180 degrees coverage. The antenna patterns are generally shaped to ensure that adequate signal is available at OSs which are located at heights much lower (or higher) than the CS (Scott, 1984; Murakami, 1983). In order to increase coverage, other systems at different frequencies may be employed.

Figure 52.5 shows as an example a frequency re-use pattern using 8 frequencies, 90 degrees sector antennas and 4 cell clusters

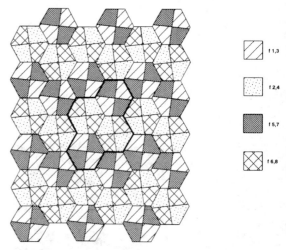

f 1,3
f 2,4
f 5,7
f 6,8

Figure 52.5   One example of a frequency re-use pattern using 90 degree sector antennas

(Shindo, 1981; Mohamed, 1985). In practice, the locations of the systems will inevitably depend on the locations of population centres. Furthermore, the terrain features can have a significant effect on frequency re-use distance. The re-use plan should therefore be used as a guide in determining the frequencies of systems which are widely separated geographically when there is a possibility of using similar systems subsequently in the intervening terrain.

Further variations of the frequency plan are possible by considering the use of both horizontal and vertical polarisations in different sectors/cells (Murakami, 1983). Interference calculations must allow for co-channel interference from geographically distant systems under differential rainfall fading conditions.

An important consideration in the use of multipoint systems in built up areas is often the non-availability of LOS paths between a subscriber building and a CS. Studies have therefore been carried out in estimating the number of CSs necessary to provide service to a certain percentage of customers in a large city (Ogawa, 1984b). These rely on the availability of actual building density and height distribution information from which the probability of obtaining LOS paths is calculated statistically.

The effect of building reflections has also been examined but it has been shown that a very small percentage of subscribers are likely to be affected from these (Ogawa, 1984b; Rhese, 1986). Other studies (Yoshida, 1984; Dupuis, 1983) have estimated the coverage area for high frequency systems requiring LOS paths between transceivers e.g. as a function of antenna heights.

52.2.8   Applications

The urban multipoint systems are generally used for serving the needs of business customers (e.g. financial and banking community) over relatively short distances in built up cities (Rhese, 1986). Applications include low bit rate data transmission and facsimile. Other applications include access to ISDN and videoconferencing at various bit rates. The use of high capacity radio systems has been studied for emergency use in situations where, for instance, an exchange serving several thousand subscribers is destroyed by fire or other disasters (Nakayama, 1985).

52.3   Rural multipoint systems

For rural applications, telephony is the main requirement and systems are generally required to operate over long distances, often over hostile, mountainous or marshy terrain. Consequently several systems have been designed to operate in the 1.5GHz to 2.5GHz

bands. More recently, following the FCC's authorisation in the U.S.A. of the use of v.h.f. and u.h.f. bands (150MHz, 450MHz and 800MHz) for basic exchange telecommunications radio service (BETRS), 'basic exchange radio' (BEXR) systems (Bellcore, 1989) have been designed for 450MHz band (McGuire, 1989; Mullen, 1989; Lin, 1990). For rural systems hop lengths can be up to 30km to 50km depending on the terrain and the frequency of operation. However, by using synchronised repeaters, the range can be increased further to more than 300km. Designs of these systems have been influenced by the following factors:

1. Systems are required to operate over hostile terrain with poor road access.
2. Inadequacy of primary power supplies makes solar powered system operation highly desirable.
3. Equipment maintenance must be simplified.
4. Equipment must have high reliability.
5. Equipment cost must be low.

52.3.1   System operation

The operation of a typical rural TDM/TDMA system is illustrated in Figure 52.6. Its operation is similar to that of an urban multipoint system. The system comprises a central station (CS) with a wide beamwidth antenna (e.g. omni-directional antenna), and a number of subscriber outstations (OSs) which have directional horn or yagi antennas.

The CS is generally located at or near a telephone exchange. The OSs, with line of sight (LOS) paths to the CS, are usually pole mounted and serve a number of subscribers over a distance of a few kilometres via overhead or buried cable pairs.

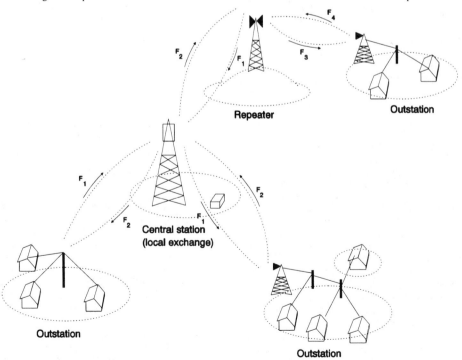

Figure 52.6   Rural multipoint system operation (James, 1990)

For telephony, the system effectively provides a transparent path between the telephone exchange and a telephone instrument at a subscriber's premises. Typically the telephony signals from the exchange are encoded in PCM format (A or μ law) by the CS, and these are then time division multiplexed (TDM) before being transmitted in the down-link direction as a modulated signal at one frequency F_1 in a broadcast mode. From this received signal, each OS extracts a timing reference and the data intended for telephony subscribers served by that OS.

In the up-link direction, the telephony signals at each OS are similarly encoded in PCM format, and subsequently suitably formatted for short periodic burst transmission at a second frequency F_2. Thus the OSs access the CS in time division multiple access (TDMA) mode. Although most systems operate in a TDM/TDMA mode, the use of TDMA technique in both directions has also been used (Bonnerot, 1987). This allows the system to operate in a power saving mode at the expense of introducing further time delay.

For most rural applications, the systems are generally designed to operate over considerably longer distances by employing one or more synchronised repeaters in cascade as illustrated in Figure 52.6. The radio hop between a repeater and an outstation (or repeater) requires a further pair of frequencies in order to minimise co-channel interference.

52.3.2 Additional features

The rural multipoint systems generally provide transparent 2-wire analogue telephony connections between telephone instruments and an exchange, although traffic is usually concentrated and de-concentrated digitally over the radio path. The two wire connection gives maximum flexibility but is expensive in terms of line card costs. Therefore consideration has been given to provision of 1.5Mbit/s or 2Mbit/s interfaces from the CS to the exchange (Chas, 1986). At the CS end 2Mbit/s links between radio and telephony sections have also been used to provide flexibility in siting the radio section remote from the telephony section (De Couesnongle, 1987).

The system design generally permits extension of 2-wire analogue lines a few kilometres from an OS. Some of the systems have additional facilities such as intra-call and automatic ring back mode (Beaupre, 1984). In systems with intra-call facility there is intelligence in an OS to recognise when an outgoing and the corresponding incoming call involve two subscribers who are served by the same OS.

Once the call is established via the exchange, the signalling/metering connection to it via the CS is retained over the management or control time slot, but the OS connects the two subscribers directly, thereby freeing two trunks or time slots for other traffic. This facility increases the traffic carrying capacity.

It is also possible to have intra-call facility even when the link to the CS is temporarily unavailable. Information on local calls during this period may be stored for a limited time and transferred to the CS when the link is restored. In systems with automatic ring back facility, a subscriber attempting to make a call when all the circuits on the radio system are in use, is notified of this fact. Subsequently, the subscriber is offered the opportunity to make a call as soon as a free circuit is available, thereby reducing outgoing lost calls.

Some of the systems designed for rural and urban applications also allow access to ISDN (Bonnerot, 1987; Le-Ngoc, 1989) at 144kbit/s (2B+D). These connections can be at U or S interface in the CS and OSs. Within the radio system, the entire capacity of 144kbit/s per call is not necessarily allocated all the time to the subscribers. Instead the B and D channels may be processed separately so as to use the radio capacity more efficiently, providing B

channels as and when needed. Naturally the whole process is transparent to the subscriber.

52.3.3 Channel access and ranging

In urban multipoint systems the path distances are relatively short so that the free space round trip propagation delay (3.3μsec/km) is short enough to enable ranging to be performed automatically by instructing an OS to transmit within the up-link control time slot, for instance, and estimating its distance from the CS. For rural multipoint systems, the use of synchronised repeaters enables one to cover much longer distances which results in a large round trip propagation delay. Consequently in some systems it is necessary to know the locations of OSs within a few kilometres range from the CS so that the OSs can be ranged automatically (Berndt, 1986; Hart, 1988). In some systems multi-carrier narrowband TDMA systems have been used (Saunders, 1988; Mullen, 1989) so that channel access, still via a control channel, uses a combination of frequency division multiple access (FDMA) and TDMA techniques.

52.3.4 Traffic capacity/grade of service

In a demand assigned system some of the calls will be lost or delayed. The probability of this occurring represents the grade of service (GoS) of the system. The GoS depends on the number of available timeslots or trunks and the offered traffic in Erlangs (E) per subscriber. Traffic intensity is a dimensionless quantity expressed in Erlangs. If a timeslot is occupied all the time its maximum capacity is 1E. The loss probability, p, of a system is given by the Erlang loss formula, Equation 52.2, where y is the offered traffic in Erlangs and n is the total number of circuits.

$$p = \frac{\dfrac{y^n}{n!}}{1 + \dfrac{y}{1} + \dfrac{y^2}{2!} + \dots + \dfrac{y^n}{n!}} \tag{52.2}$$

This is tabulated, for instance, in CCITT, 1989a. Further information on loss probability for network connections is given in CCITT (1989a).

As an example, for a typical busy hour offered traffic per subscriber of 0.07E, the GoS for a system with 15 trunks and 116 subscribers from equation 1 is equal to 0.01.

52.3.5 Channel plans

Most of the rural multipoint systems above 1GHz are designed to operate in the frequency band 1427MHz to 1525MHz, and use an inter-leaved frequency plan. The channel spacing between adjacent channels on the same polarisation depends on the channel bit rate and the modulation method used. CCIR, (1990) gives channel arrangements for systems operating in 2.3GHz to 2.5GHz band. For rural multi-carrier FDMA/TDMA BEXR systems in the 150MHz and 450MHz bands, channel spacings of 30kHz and 25kHz respectively have been specified (Bellcore, 1989).

52.3.6 System details

Table 52.3 shows details of some of the multipoint systems currently on the market or under development. These systems use either binary or four level modulation, and system aggregate rates vary

Table 52.3 Examples of multipoint systems

System	150MHz 450MHz 800MHz	450MHz	1.5GHz 2.5GHz	500MHz 1.5GHz	1.5GHz 1.8GHz 2.4GHz	800MHz 1.5GHz	1.5GHz 2.5GHz	1.5GHz	1.5GHz 2.5GHz	1.4GHz 2.7GHz	2.3GHz 2.7GHz	1.5GHz
Number of trunks	26 x 4 16kbit/s channels	6 x 64kbit/s or 12 x 32 kbit/s	10 x 64kbit/s	15 x 32kbit/s	15	15 x 64kbit/s	28 x 64kbit/s	30 x 64kbit/s	30 x 64kbit/s	60 x 64kbit/s	60 x 64kbit/s	60 x 64kbit/s
Aggregate bit rate (kbit/s)	64 (x26)	—	832	704	—	1152	2176	2432	2304	4864	4000	4608
Frame period down-link (ms) up-link (ms)	TDMA/ FDMA	FDMA	0.125 5.5	4 4	0.125 0.125	0.125 0.5	4 4	0.125 12	1 8	4 8	4 4	1 1
Modulation	16 level DPSK	8 QAM or 32 QAM	MSK (modulation index 0.5)	2-FSK (modulation index 0.5)	PPM-FM	2-FSK	QPSK	QPSK	QPSK	OOQPSK	QPSK	QPSK
Number of customers	> 500	24	128 max	128 (or 256)	94 max	128 max	up to 250	256	480	512 (or 1024)	512 (or 1024)	512 or 480 (2Mbit/s links)
Number of customers per outstation	1 x 64kbit/s or 2 x 32kbit/s	1 x 64kbit/s or 2 x 32kbit/s	8, 16, 32, 96	3 (extendable to 67)	1 or 6, 12 ... 25	up to 6	up to 24	24 (steps of 8)	32, 48, 128 (ISDN 12 max 160 kbit/s)	16 256 (rack mounted)	8 to 32 (expandable to 80)	6 (increase in steps of 6)
Transmit power (Watts)	—	0.1 min 0.8 max	0.3 or 1	3	4 (1.5GHz) 3 (1.8GHz) 2 (2.4GHz)	0.2/2 (800 MHz) 0.2/1 (1.5 GHz)	2.5	0.5	0.1 or 1	5 (1.5GHz) 1 (1.7– 2.7GHz)	1	0.5
Threshold (dBm) BER	—	$-111\ 10^{-3}$ (8QAM) $-110\ 10^{-3}$ (32QAM)	$-96\ 10^{-4}$ (1.5GHz) $-94\ 10^{-4}$ (2.5GHz)	$-94\ 10^{-4}$	Analogue – 87	$-97\ 10^{-4}$	$-91\ 10^{-3}$	$-92\ 10^{-3}$	$-93\ 10^{-4}$	$-91\ 10^{-4}$	$-92\ 10^{-3}$	—

from just below 1Mbit/s to below 5Mbit/s. The number of trunks or time slots varies between 10 and 60. The smaller systems tend to employ polling technique for accessing time slots, whereas random request slotted ALOHA is used for larger systems (Le-Ngoc, 1985).

The systems are designed for operation in remote locations and consequently low power consumption through use of VLSI and high system reliability are their main features. Figure 52.7 shows a typical solar powered outstation. The outstations can be generally mains powered with battery back up or solar powered. Figure 52.8 shows a pole mounted outstation with a power and junction pack.

Figure 52.8 A solar powered outstation showing the antenna, solar panels and equipment box (Photo courtsey of TRT, France)

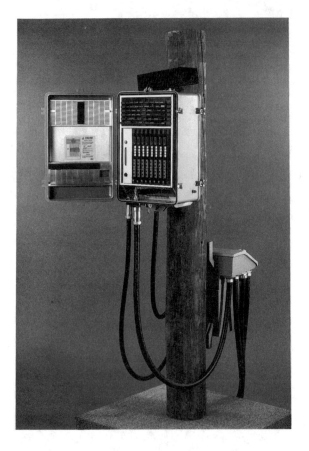

Figure 52.7 A typical pole mounted outstation with power and junction pack, shown on the bottom left (Photo courtsey of SR Telecom Inc. Canada)

Two wire telephony, and low bit rate data interfaces are generally provided at the CS and the OSs. At the CS critical circuits such as transceivers are duplicated for increased reliability.

A typical link budget for such systems is given in Table 52.4. At the relatively low operating frequency, rainfall attenuation is less significant. However, the hop lengths can be long (up to about 50km) and therefore atmospheric multipath propagation becomes significant. Since these systems have relatively low bandwidths the narrow bandwidth fading model (CCIR, 1990a) has generally been used to calculate the worst month outage.

The system fade margin, M, is used to determine the non-availability of the system due to propagation effects. The probability (P) that fading exceeds a given margin, M, is given by Equation 52.3, where D is path length (km), and F is frequency (GHz).

$$ P = K Q F^B D^C 10 \exp\left(-\frac{M}{10} \right) \tag{52.3} $$

As an example, the parameters K (climatic factor), Q, B and C for North-West Europe are given by K = 1.4 x 10^{-8}, Q = 1, B = 1 and C = 3.5. For this example, P = 1.4 x 10^{-8} x 1.5 x $24^{3.5}$ x $10^{-21.5/10}$, or the availability is given by [(1-P) x 100] or 99.999% for a path of 24km.

The error performance and availability objectives for digital radio systems used in the local grade portion (between the subscriber and the local exchange) of an ISDN connection is given in CCITT Recommendation G.821 (CCIR, 1990b). For a 64kbit/s circuit, the bit error ratio (BER) should not exceed 1x10^{-6} during more than 1.5% of any month, and 1x10^{-3} during 0.015% of any month. Furthermore, the total errored seconds should not exceed 1.2% of any month.

The unavailability allowance is generally divided between equipment failure and propagation effects (rainfall for systems above about 10GHz and multipath for lower frequencies). The relationship between errored seconds objectives at 64kbit/s and at the system aggregate rate is given in CCIR (1987).

Table 52.3   Link budget for a 1.5GHz multipoint system

Item	Value
Transmission direction	CS to OSs
Frequency (GHz)	1.5
(a) Transmitter power (dBm)	30
(b) Transmitter antenna gain: omni-directional (dBi)	10
(c) Receiver antenna gain yagi (dBi)	16
(d) Fixed losses in dB (transmit/receive end feeders filters etc.)	−5
(e) Receiver sensitivity for 1 in 1000 bit error ratio (dBm)	−94
(f) System gain dB (a)+(b)+(c)+(d)−(e)	145
(g) Path loss in dB for 24km hop	123.5
(h) System fade margin M dB (f)−(g)	21.5

52.3.7   Modulation/demodulation methods

Although pulse width modulation of speech channel followed by frequency modulation has been used in an earlier system, most systems employ binary frequency shift keying, binary phase shift keying or quarternary phase shift keying methods (Table 52.3). At the CS, the phase of the carrier from each OS burst has to be established rapidly. To facilitate this, the OS burst has a preamble for carrier recovery. However, when differential demodulation is used, it is not necessary to recover the carrier. This consideration has led to the use in some systems of differential demodulation at the CS, while coherent demodulation is generally used at the OSs.

Recent BEXR systems have used 16 level differential phase shift keying modulation (Saunders, 1988; Mullen, 1989). Others designed for similar applications have also used 4-, 8-, and 32-level quadrature amplitude modulation in narrower channels of 25kHz (Hampton, 1989; McGuire, 1989).

52.3.8   Power

In a rural environment lack of primary source of power is quite a dominant feature. When power is available it may be subject to interruptions. Therefore subscriber radio systems are designed with the aim of minimising power consumption so that, for instance, solar power operation is possible. The radio equipment generally requires either a.c. power or solar cell arrays with a nominal 12V (or 48V) d.c., the operational voltages being derived by d.c./d.c. converters. Power consumption has been minimised by using, for instance, efficient d.c./d.c. converters, FET amplifiers, low power consuming CMOS arrays and surface mount components (Bonnerot, 1987). In some systems, burst mode transmission is also used in the down-link direction (depending on the frame activity) in order to save power.

52.3.9   Frequency re-use

Frequency planning is a complex exercise (Lawson, 1986). In considering the use of multipoint systems, it is essential to take account of the following:

1. Interference to and from existing systems in the frequency band.
2. A cellular re-use plan must allow for future system growth.
3. The use of repeaters must be considered.

The available channel frequencies may be allocated to form a cellular pattern of 3,4,7,9,12 ... cells (Cox, 1982), with perhaps a smaller number of channels forming an overlap pattern for extra capacity. In addition a frequency re-use pattern may also be established for repeaters.

The frequency re-use pattern is generally based on geometric pattern. However, in practice it is essential to evaluate worst case co-channel interference from cells using similar frequencies in various clusters. Examples of frequency re-use patterns are given in CCIR, 1990b.

52.3.10   Applications

The primary application of these systems is in providing telephony service, often in isolated mountainous villages, deserts or off-shore islands for the very first time. Therefore they are designed to operate in harsh environments over a wide range of temperatures (e.g. −25°C to 55°C). They have found applications in desert areas to provide connections to remote drilling sites with transportable solar powered OSs.

Transportable OSs have also found applications in providing temporary telephony, facsimile and telex services at important events and shows (Holm, 1988). Other applications include emergency service restoration, provision of SCADA (supervisory control and data acquisition), and data services in rural areas. The more recently developed systems offer facilities for connecting subscribers to ISDN. With the higher capacity systems, the OSs are capable of serving a large (> 100) number of subscribers. Therefore, it is possible to consider the advantages of installing a multipoint OS rather than a small exchange (Blake, 1989). Combined with an intra-call option, the OS then behaves effectively as a small exchange.

52.4   Economics of urban and rural systems

Generally, urban systems can potentially be high revenue earning systems since they would be used for serving the needs of business subscribers. On the other hand, rural systems give a poor return on investment, and the decision to employ them is often a political one.

The cost per circuit depends on the system configuration which, in turn, depends on subscriber distribution and terrain features requiring possible use of repeaters to overcome LOS path problems. In general, the initial cost of the system is significant when only a few circuits are provided and the cost of the CS predominates. Subsequently, however, the cost per circuit decreases as more circuits are added in a flexible manner as the demand grows. Generally, the cost per circuit is low when a large number of circuits are provided from an outstation, since the cost of the common hardware (e.g. RF transceiver) is shared (Figure 52.9).

In general, the cost of a circuit provided by radio is constant as a function of distance. On the other hand, cable costs generally increase with distance. However, cost comparison with alternative media such as fibre or coaxial cable depends on the extent of existing telecommunications infrastructure and the operational environment (CCITT/CCIR, 1976).

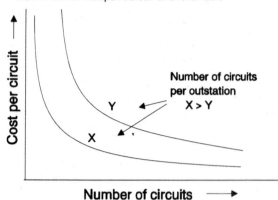

Figure 52.9 Cost per circuit as a function of number of circuits

52.4.1 Transport delay considerations

Point-to-multipoint systems introduce group delay due to the packetised nature of the system. Thus the round trip delay of a system is the sum of the up-link and down-link frame periods plus additional processing delay which could be 10% to 30% of the frame delays. In addition, where synchronised repeaters are used to increase the system range, the propagation delay of about 3.3 microseconds per kilometre also becomes significant since the maximum delay corresponds to that of an outstation located at a maximum distance from the CS. A combination of excessive delay and mismatches from a far end 2 to 4 wire hybrid can give rise to echo which can hinder communication unless echo control devices are introduced in the network.

CCITT (1989b) give guidance on the use of echo control devices for telephony when the one way group delay exceeds 25 milliseconds. In addition to this, in a national network, consideration has to be given to the use of echo control devices at gateway international switching centres, and the possible consequences of using echo control devices in cascade. In a national network, where two or more Public Telecommunications Operators provide service, the delay limits may preclude the use of the systems which introduce large group delays, unless suitable echo control devices are permitted without affecting the telephony performance significantly.

52.4.2 Future trends

In future systems, three issues are likely to be important: cost, spectrum efficiency and delay associated with multipoint systems. The use of higher level modulation schemes (e.g. 16 QAM) would lead to an increase in spectral efficiency and potential reduction in delay. However, counter measure techniques now commonly used on trunk radio systems would then need to be carefully adapted to increase the system range and reduce costs.

TDM/TDMA techniques are also being employed in fibre systems for application in the local loop (Oakley, 1988; Hoppitt, 1989). In such systems, the use of passive splitters ensures that no electronics is used between the exchange and the subscribers' premises. There are advantages in making the TDM/TDMA sub-systems for providing telephony over passive optical networks (TPON) such that they can be readily employed for radio use. This provides additional flexibility in employing the most appropriate medium (radio or fibre) in different circumstances whilst using common TDM/TDMA sub-systems and network interfaces.

Cellular radio systems at 450MHz and 900MHz have proved to be popular in Europe. Although such systems do not provide speech quality as good as that over fixed radio or cable, their popularity is likely to grow rapidly since they offer additional roaming facility. Their use in fixed network (Stern, 1987) may be hindered by lack of spectrum, regulatory constraints and higher infrastructure costs resulting in higher charges than for fixed service.

In Europe the establishment of personal communications networks (PCN) over the next few years in the 1.7GHz to 1.9GHz band may well pose a challenge to multipoint radio systems providing fixed services. The envisaged mass markets for these networks will inevitably lead to hardware price reductions and reflect in lower telecommunications costs to the subscribers. Manufacturers of multipoint systems may adapt the cheaper hardware, for instance, to provide complete exchange to subscriber premises radio solutions.

To date, most multipoint radio systems have aggregate rates of less than 20Mbit/s. The synchronous digital hierarchy (SDH) multiplexer offers flexible 1.5Mbit/s or 2Mbit/s drop and insert facility together with maintenance/management protocols at 155.22Mbit/s (STM-1) bit stream (see Chapter 42). Therefore designs of multipoint radio systems with STM-1 aggregate data rate may well become attractive in future (Richman, 1990).

The role of satellites in rural communications is mentioned in passing. Interest in this has increased with the recent announcement of plans for Iridium, a digital voice/data system in the 1GHz to 2GHz range providing global coverage via 77 low orbiting, networked satellites (Satellite Communications, 1990). In such a system a LOS path would be possible to every point on the earth's surface. However, it will be late nineties before service commences from such a system.

The search for ways of decreasing radio system power consumption, increasing its reliability and reducing its costs (such as with the widespread use of monolithic microwave integrated circuits) will no doubt continue.

52.5 References

Bailey, V.L. (1986) A multipoint radio for local networks, *European Conference on Radio Relay Systems, ECRR*, Munich, West Germany, pp. 276-283.

Bailey, V.L. and Ogborne, J. (1987) A multipoint radio for local networks, *IEEE International Conference on Communications, ICC'87*, Seattle, U.S.A., pp. 332-335.

Ballance, J.W. (1984) A low cost TDM/TDMA subsystem for point-to-multipoint radio applications, *Br Telecom Technol J.*, **2**, (2), pp. 19–24.

Bannister, G. and Capewell, C. (1988) The Australian digital radio concentrator system — DRCS *IEE International Conference on Rural Telecommunications*, London, U.K., Conference Publication No.286, pp. 56-62.

Battistig, G. et. al. (1985) A simple point-to-multipoint subscriber radio system in the 1.5GHz band, *IEEE International Conference on Communications, ICC'85*, Chicago, U.S.A., pp. 23.3.

Battistig, G. Marczy, A. and Rona, P. (1986) IER, a subscriber radio system in the 1.5GHz band, *Proceedings of the Eighth Colloquium on Microwave Communications*, Budapest, Hungary, pp. 19-20.

Beaupre, D.M. (1983) Five years of TDMA subscriber radio *IEEE International Conference on Communications, ICC'83*, Boston, U.S.A. pp. 375-379.

Beaupre, D.M. Le-Ngoc, T. and Zavitz, H.J. (1984) A new point-to-multipoint microwave radio system, *6th International Sympo-*

sium on Subscriber Loops and Services, ISSLS'84, Nice, France, (1) pp. 47-51.

Bellcore (1989) Generic requirements for Basic Exchange Radio Systems *Technical Advisory TA-TSY-000911* Issue 2, July 1989. Further details from Bellcore Document Registrar, 445 South Street, P.O. Box 1910, Morristown, New Jersey, 07960-1910, U.S.A.

Berceli, T. Frigyes, O.I. and Varady-Szabo, M. (1984) Some development results in rural radio systems, *IEEE International Conference on Communications, ICC'84*, Amsterdam, Netherlands, (2) pp. 965-9.

Berndt, A. (1986) RURTEL — A point-to-multipoint digital radio relay system for local subscriber links in rural areas, *European Conference on Radio Relay*, ECRR, Munich, Germany, pp. 268-275.

Blake, R.G. (1989) The role of radio for fixed local access, *Br Telecom Technol J.*, **7** (2) pp. 123-135.

Bonnerot, G. Floury, G. and Tanguy, R. (1987) IRT 2000 A versatile multipurpose radio system for subscribers, *IEEE/IECE Global Telecommunications Conference, Globcom'87*, Tokyo, Japan, pp. 169-173.

CCIR (1990a) *Recommendations of the CCIR, XVIIth Plenary Assembly*, Dusseldorf, 1986, Vol V — Propagation in non-ionized media. See also Annex to Vol V — Reports of the CCIR, 1990.

CCIR (1990b) *Recommendations of the CCIR, 1990, XVIIIth Plenary Assembly*, Dusseldorf, 1990, Vol IX, Part 1 — Fixed Service using radio-relay systems. See also Annex to Vol IX, Part 1 — Reprots of the CCIR, 1990.

CCIR (1987) Conclusions of the Interim Meeting of Study Group 9, Part 1 (Fixed service using radio relay systems) Geneva, Nov/Dec.

CCITT (1989a) Telephone Network and ISDN. Quality of Service, Network Management and Traffic Engineering, Blue Book Vol II — Fascicle II.3, *Recommendations E.401-E.880*. Geneva.

CCITT (1989b) General characteristics of International Telephone Connections and Circuits, Blue Book Vol III — Fascicle III.1 *Recommendations G.101-G.181*, Geneva.

CCITT/CCIR (1976) *GAS-3 Economic and technical aspects of the choice of transmission systems*, Geneva.

Chas, P.L. et. al. (1986) A new generation of TDMA point to multipoint systems: Architecture and concepts, *European Conference on Radio Relay, ECRR*, Munich, West Germany, pp. 260-267.

Chas, P.L. and Jimenez, J. (1987) Applications and perspectives of ISDN multiaccess systems for rural and urban applications — a view from Spain, *IEEE/IECE Global Telecommunications Conference, Globcom'87*, Tokyo, Japan, pp. 174-177.

Cox, D.C. (1982) Co-channel interference considerations in frequency re-use small coverage area radio systems, *IEEE Trans. Comms*, **COM-30**, (1).

Daboual, H. Floury, G. and Garnier, C. (1981) IRT 1500 Rural telephony system, *Commutation and Transmission*, **3**, (3) pp. 39-53.

De Couesnongle, M. and Garnier, C. (1983) IRT 1500 Integrated rural telephony system, *Philips Telecommunications Review*, **41**, (2).

De Couesnongle, M. Floury, G. and Tanguy, R. (1987) IRT 2000 subscriber multiple access radio system, *Commutation and Transmission*, pp.15-18.

Dupuis, P. et. al. (1983) Millimetre wave subscriber loops, *IEEE Journal on Selected Areas of Communications*, **SAC-1** (4) pp. 623-632.

Fichaut, J., et. al. (1985) New services for the IRT 1500 subscriber connection system, *Commutation and Transmission*, **2**, pp. 25-38.

Forestier, A. (1985) UDS 10-64 — An urban data transmission system on TDMA microwave radio, *IEE Conference Publication No. 246*, pp. 97-100.

Garnier, C.R. and Chabert, J.L. (1981) The IRT 1500, a digital system serving rural zone subscribers by TDMA radio, *International Switching Symposium – ISS'81*, Montreal, Canada. (4) pp. 41C6/1-5.

Hampton, W.R. (1989) Applications and economics of the new exchange radios for basic exchange telecommunications radio service (BETR), *IEEE Global Telecommunications Conference, Globecom'89*, Dallas, U.S.A. pp.1045-8.

Hart, P. (1988) A point-to-multipoint digital radio system for rural subscriber areas, *IEE International Conference on Rural Telecommunications*, London, U.K., Conference publication No.286, pp. 80-83.

Hewitt, M.T. Scott, R.P. and Ballance, J.W. (1984) A cost effective 19GHz digital multipoint radio system for local distribution applications, *IEEE International Conference on Communications*, ICC'84, Amsterdam, Netherlands, pp. 31.4.

Hiyama, T. et. al. (1985) Digital Radio Concentrator System *NEC Res. and Develop.*, (76) pp. 24-35.

Hiyama, T. et. al. (1986) 1.5GHz transmitter-receiver for Digital Radio Concentrator System (DRCS), *NEC Res. and Develop.*, (81) pp. 86-91.

Holm, V. (1988) Point to multipoint microwave in spanning the globe, *Global Communications*, Second Quarter, pp. 20–23.

Hoppitt, C.E. and Clarke, D.E.A. (1989) The provision of telephony over passive optical networks, *Br Telecom Technol J.*, **7** (2) pp. 100-113.

James, S.W., Hooppell, A.R. and Mohamed, S.A. (1990) Point-to-multipoint radio in the British Telecom network, *Second IEE International Conference on Rural Telecommunications*, London, UK, Conference Publication no. 328, pp. 85–90.

Latorre, M.A. Tellado, A. and Chas, P.L. (1987) SMD 30/1'5: An advanced P.M.P. TDMA radio system with powerful operation and maintenance facilities, *IEEE International Conference on Communications, ICC'87*, Seattle, U.S.A. (1) pp. 10.3.1-5.

Lawson, I.C. and Ellershaw, J.C. (1986) Co-channel interference in a cellular rural radio telephone system, *IEEE International Conference on Communications, ICC'86*, Toronto, Canada, pp. 55.1.

Le-Ngoc, T. (1985) A random-request demand-assigned multiple access protocol for point-to-multipoint radio systems, *IEEE International Conference on Communications, ICC'85*, Chicago, U.S.A., pp.744-748.

Le-Ngoc, T. and Zavitz, H.J. (1985) A point-to-multipoint microwave radio system with a random-request demand-assignment time division multiple-access (RR-DA-TDMA) scheme, *IEE Conference Publication No. 246*, London, U.K. pp. 93-96.

Le-Ngoc, T. (1986) SR500 — A point-to-multipoint digital radio system, *IEEE International Conference on Communications, ICC'86*, Toronto, Canada, pp. 55.2.

Le-Ngoc, T. Stashin, M. and El Kateeb, A. (1989) ISDN signalling and packet data support on point-to-multipoint subscriber radio systems, *IEEE International Conference on Communications, ICC'89*, Boston, U.S.A. pp. 1314-1318.

Lin, S.H. and Wolff, R.S. (1990) Basic exchange radio — from concept to reality, *IEEE International Conference on Communications, ICC'90*, Atlanta, U.S.A. pp. 206.2.1-206.2.7.

Manichaikul, Y. Silverman, D. and Szeliga, J.J. (1983) RAPAC — a point-to-multipoint digital radio system for local distribution, *IEEE International Conference on Communications, ICC'83*, Boston, U.S.A., pp. 1013-16.

Marchand, P. (1986) 23GHz digital transmission system DTS 10-64 *European Communications on Radio Relay*, Munich, West Germany, pp. 284-290.

McGuire, R.J. (1989) Exchange radio technology *IEEE Global Telecommunications Conference, Globecom'89*, Dallas, U.S.A. pp. 29.A.4.

Mohamed, S.A. and Ballance, J.W. (1985) 19GHz digital point-to-multipoint radio system for local distribution, *IEEE International Conference on Communications, ICC'85*, Chicago, U.S.A., pp. 735-739.

Moris, M.J. and Zavitz, H.J. (1988) A new high capacity TDMA radio system, *IEE International Conference on Rural Telecommunications, Conference Publication No. 286*, pp. 74-79.

Mullen, J.F. (1989) Wireless digital access, *IEEE Global Telecommunications Conference, Globecom'89*, Dallas, U.S.A. pp. 1036-1044.

Murakumi, M. et. al. (1983) A multiple access digital microwave radio system for local subscribers, *IEEE International Conference on Communications, ICC'83*, Boston, U.S.A., Vol.1, pp. 380-6.

Nakayama, H. Yoshida, T. and Tanaka, K. (1985) 26GHz band digital subscriber radio system (26SS-D1) for high speed digital communications, *IEEE International Conference on Communications, ICC'85*, Chicago, U.S.A., pp. 729-734.

Oakley, K.A., Taylor, C.G. and Stern, J.R. (1988) Passive fibre loop for telephony with broadband upgrade, *Proceedings of the International Symposium on Subscriber Loop and Services, ISSLS'88*, Boston, U.S.A. pp. 179-183.

Ogawa, H. Yamamoto, K. and Imai, N. (1984a) A 26GHz high performance MIC transmitter/receiver for digital radio subscriber systems, *IEEE Transactions on Microwave Theory and Techniques*, **MIT-32**, (12) pp. 1551-1555.

Ogawa, E. and Satoh, A. (1984b) Radio zone design using visibility estimation for local distribution systems in metropolitan areas, *IEEE International Conference on Communications, ICC'84*, Amsterdam, Netherlands, pp. 946-950.

Okubo, H. Miura, S. and Nagasawa, S. (1988) Building block design of large capacity PCM-TDMA subscriber system and direct digital interface to digital exchange, *IEE International Conference on Rural Telecommunications*, London, U.K., Conference Publication No. 286, pp. 69-73.

Omtveit, O. (1989) Development of a radio network, *Communications Engineering International*, **10**, (10), pp. 46-48.

Raju, G.S. and Prasad, K.V.K.K. (1990) A TDMA point to multipoint rural radio system for trunking and local loop applications, *Second International Conference on Rural Telecommunications*, London, U.K., Conference Publication No. 328, pp. 91-5.

Rhese, J.K. (1986) The logical first/last mile digital termination system, *IEEE International Conference on Communications, Icc'86*, Toronto, Canada.

Richman, G.D. Chisholm, J.A. and Smith, P.C. (1990) Transmission of synchronous digital hierarchy signals by radio, *IEEE International Conference on Communications, SuperComm/ICC'90*, Atlanta, U.S.A.

Sasaki, S. et. al. (1983) 2GHz multi-direction time division multiplex radio equipment, *IEEE International Conference on Communications, ICC'83*, Boston, U.S.A. (1) B2.2.1-5.

Satellite Communications (1990) Motorola plans to marry satellite and cellular; Inks deals with Inmarsat, AMSC and TMI, August, pp.11.

Saunders, R.G. (1989) Ultraphone — wireless digital loop carrier system, *Proceeding of National Communications Forum*, **42**, (2) pp. 1860-6.

Scott, R.P. (1984) A low cost 19GHz radio sub-system for point-to-multipoint radio applications, *Br Telecom Technol J.* **2**, (3) pp. 50-57.

Shindo, S. Kurita, O. and Akaike, M. (1981) Radio subscriber loop system for high speed digital communications, *IEEE International Conference on Communications, ICC'81*, Denver, U.S.A., pp. 66.1.1-5.

Shindo, S. et. al. (1983a) TDMA for local distribution system, *IEEE International Conference on Communications, ICC'83*, Boston, U.S.A., pp. 370-374.

Shindo, S. et. al. (1983b) Radio local distribution system for high speed digital communications, *IEEE Journal on Selected Areas in Communications, SAC-1, (4), pp.609-615*.

Stern, M. (1987) Cellular technology — revisited for rural service, *Communications International*, Oct., pp. 96-100.

Takada, M. (1983) A multidirection time division multiplex system for point-to-multipoint communication, *NEC Res. and Develop.*, (71) pp. 9-19.

Yamada, T. Tajima, K. and Aikawa M. (1986) High capacity subscriber radio, *IEEE International Conference on Communications, ICC'86*, Toronto, Canada, **3** pp. 1758-1762.

Yoshida, T. (1984) Digital subscriber radio system in the 26GHz band, *Japan Telecom. Rev.*, **26**, (3), pp. 188-194.

52.6 Bibliography

CCITT (1970) *GAS-4, Primary sources of energy*, Geneva.

CCITT (1989) *GAS-7, Vol II, Training Handbook of Rural Telecommunications*, Geneva.

CCITT/CCIR (1979) *Rural Telecommunications*, Geneva.

53

Fibre optic communications

Takis Hadjifotiou
Bell Northern Research
(Sections 53.1–53.6)

John McFarlane
Northern Telecom
(Section 53.7)

Contents

53.1 Principles of light transmission

53.1.1 Basics of optical fibre transmission

The propagation of light is governed by Maxwell's equations but a good insight of the propagation in dielectric material can be gained through Snell's law on refraction and reflection.

Consider two media I and II with refractive indices, n_1 and n_2 respectively. Then according to Snell's law the incident and refracted light rays satisfy Equation 53.1, and in general there is also a reflected ray which propagates in medium I.

$$n_1 \sin \varphi_1 = n_2 \sin \varphi_2 \qquad (53.1)$$

Consider now the case where $n_1 < n_2$, as in Figure 53.1. Then as the angle φ_1 approaches a critical value φ_{cr} the refracted ray approach the extreme angle of $\pi/2$ and at this point transmission of

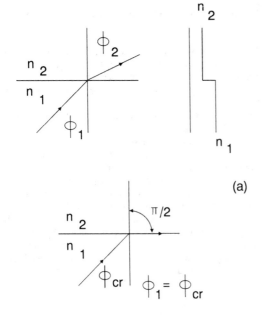

(a)

(b)

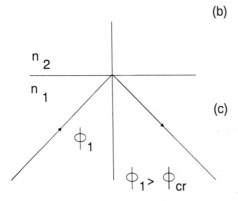

(c)

Figure 53.1 Principles of light guiding: (a) light refraction; (b) the critical angle φ_{cr} for the limiting case of zero refraction; (c) total internal reflection for $\varphi_1 > \varphi_{cr}$

light into medium II ceases completely. This critical angle is given by Equation 53.2.

$$\sin \varphi_{cr} = \frac{n_2}{n_1} \qquad (53.2)$$

When the incident angle $\varphi_1 > \varphi_{cr}$ no light propagates into medium II and all the incident light is reflected back into medium I. This basic behaviour at the interface of media I and II with $n_1 > n_2$ can be used to guide the propagation of light.

The most practical structure for the propagation of light over long distances has been the optical fibre, shown in Figure 53.2. The optical fibre is a cylindrical structure with a central region, called the core, and a surrounding external cylinder, called the cladding, with the refractive index of the core being higher than that of the cladding. If now a light ray is incident at the interface between core and cladding at an angle greater than φ_{cr} then the light will propagate along the fibre through a series of consecutive total reflections. This description of the propagation of light assumes ideal interface conditions and any departure from them will lead to both reflection and refraction and the light ray will lose energy as it is guided by the fibre.

Since the fibre guides light, one of the basic features is the ability to collect light from an optical source. This parameter is known as the numerical aperture of the fibre, NA, and in physical terms is half the apex angle of the light acceptance cone, as shown in Figure 53.3. It is given by Equation 53.3, where Δn is the difference in refractive index between core and cladding.

$$NA = n_o \sin \pi_a$$

$$= \left(n_1^2 - n_2^2 \right)^{1/2} \approx n_1 (2 \Delta n)^{1/2} \qquad (53.3)$$

For instance if $\Delta n = 1\%$ and $n_1 = 1.5$ then $NA = 0.212$ and the light acceptance cone has an apex angle of $24.5°$.

The propagation of light in a fibre can be understood at least qualitatively through the concepts of mode and that of the normalised frequency. An optical wave propagating by internal reflection can be represented as a bundle of rays, called modes, which is a concept of geometric optics. The concept of normalised frequency belongs to the formal analysis of the light propagation in fibre and is defined as in Equation 53.4.

$$V = \frac{2 \pi}{\lambda} a \left(n_1^2 - n_2^2 \right)^{1/2}$$

$$= \frac{2 \pi}{\lambda} a n_1 (2 \Delta n)^{1/2} \qquad (53.4)$$

Now the combination of the concepts of mode and normalised frequency enable us to derive a fundamental characteristic of light propagation in fibre. It was stated earlier that the fibre will accept and propagate all the rays entering the acceptance cone. The question now arises as to how many modes of propagation can be supported by the fibre. Assuming that the refractive index of the core is uniform then the number of modes is given by Equation 53.5.

$$M_{si} = 0.5 \left(\frac{2 V}{\pi} \right)^2 \qquad (53.5)$$

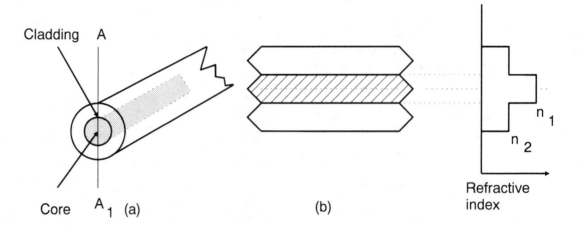

Figure 53.2 The geometry of a fibre waveguide: (a) physical shape; (b) the fibre internal geometry along the axis AA_1

For example with $\Delta = 0.1$, $n_1 = 1.5$ and $a = 25\mu m$ the number of modes at $0.85\mu m$ is 311 and 936 at $1.55\mu m$. This regime of propagation is known as multimode propagation and implies that a number of rays propagate simultaneously. The alternative to multimode is single mode or monomode propagation, that is $M = 1$. The condition for single mode propagation is given by Equation 53.6.

$$V = \frac{2\pi a \left(n_1^2 - n_2^2 \right)^{1/2}}{\lambda} < 2.045 \qquad (53.6)$$

The parameter which must change, other things being equal, to make a multimode fibre single mode is the fibre radius. For the multimode fibre discussed above and for single mode propagation at $0.85\mu m$ the fibre radius should be reduced to $4.85\mu m$. However, this only shows the size of dimensions involved.

Usually the wavelength of operation is decided from other considerations and the single mode propagation conditions are satisfied by changing either Δn or a or both. Since very small Δn leads to high bend losses both parameters are used in designing for single mode propagation.

In order to preserve the mechanical strength of the fibre, the core diameter is reduced to around $8–10\mu m$ but the cladding is maintained at $60–125\mu m$. Since the standard multimode fibre has a core diameter of $50\mu m$ but a cladding diameter of $125\mu m$ it is not possible to identify the propagation conditions from a visual inspection of the fibre. One other restriction imposed by single mode propagation is that since only one mode propagates the optical source which excites the fibre must also be single mode.

It was assumed up to now that the refractive index of the fibre changes in a step-like way at the core-cladding boundary, as in Figure 53.4(a). This fibre is known as step index fibre and it is easy to make and is widely used. However, as it will be seen later, the information bandwidth of the step index multimode fibre can be

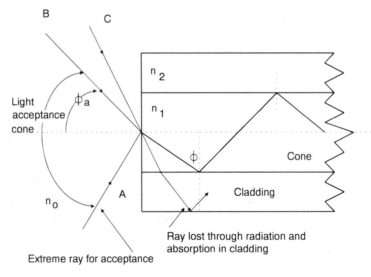

Figure 53.3 The light acceptance cone geometry

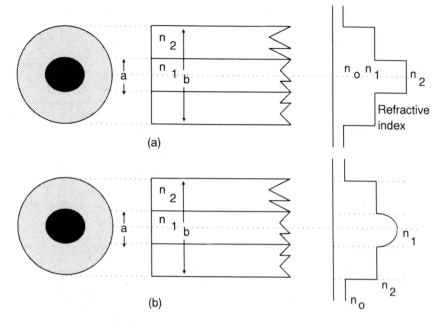

Figure 53.4 Fibre types: (a) step index profile; (b) graded index parabolic profile

improved if the refractive index of the core is graded with the maximum value at the centre of the core, as in Figure 53.4(b).

Using axial symmetry in general the index variation can be written as in Equation 53.7, where α is the profile parameter.

$$n(r) = n_1 (1 - 2\Delta n (r/a)^\alpha)^{1/2} \quad r < a \quad (core)$$

$$n_2 = n_1 (1 - 2\Delta n)^{1/2} \quad r \geq a \quad (cladding) \tag{53.7}$$

From the performance and manufacturing view point a very attractive profile is the one with $\alpha = 2$ known appropriately as the parabolic profile, shown in Figure 53.4(a). The change of refractive index affects the number of modes and for a parabolic profile the number of propagating modes is given by Equation 53.8.

$$M_{pp} = 0.5 \left(\sqrt{2} \frac{V}{\pi} \right)^2 \tag{53.8}$$

The number of modes therefore is halved. Single mode fibre are usually step index fibre because graded index single mode fibres do not offer any significant advantages.

The single and multimode fibres just outlined are made of silica or multicomponent glass compounds and dominate the communication market where performance is the prime consideration. For low bandwidth applications multimode plastic clad fibre or all plastic fibre can be used with significant cost reduction. The plastic clad fibre has plastic cladding but the core is silica. The all plastic fibre is of even lower cost but its performance is also lower.

53.1.2 Optical fibre characteristics

In order to use the fibre in communication systems the potential user needs to know their optical, electrical and mechanical charac-

teristics. From the transmission point of view these can be reduced to essentially two: attenuation (loss) and dispersion (bandwidth).

The total loss in an optical fibre consists of two elements: intrinsic losses due to the fundamental properties of the materials used to make the fibre and extrinsic losses which are attributed to the actual fibre and the details of the usage.

The intrinsic losses are essentially two: absorption and scattering. Absorption is a property of the material and in optical wavelength it takes place when the energy of the incident optical radiation is absorbed by electronic transitions and dissipated through non-radiative processes. Fibre used in optical communications is made from glasses with high silica content doped with various oxides. For these glasses there are two absorption resonances. One is the ultraviolet and one in the infrared. At the ultraviolet part of the spectrum the loss is 1dB/km at 0.62μm but falls rapidly at longer wavelengths and at 1240nm it reaches 0.02dB/km. The infrared loss is around 0.03dB/km at 1500nm and 0.5dB/km at 1700nm.

If one assumes that 0.5dB/km loss is a reasonable one then there is a 1.5μm window between the two absorption edges. However, at this point scattering enters the picture. The scattering, known as Rayleigh scattering, is the result of microscopic material inhomogeneities. The inhomogeneities arise both from the glass and the various dopants which are used to produce the index difference, Δn, between core and cladding. Rayleigh scattering is sensitive to wavelength because it varies as λ^{-4}. Because of that scattering is insignificant at long wavelenths. Figure 53.5 shows the total loss of single mode fibre and it is interesting to notice that the global loss minimum of silica fibre is at 1550nm where the loss attains the minimum value of 0.18dB/km.

The extrinsic fibre losses owe their presence to the practical difficulties in making and using fibres. Extrinsic losses include scattering due to the departure from perfect core-cladding interface, bending losses, losses due to the permanent joining of fibre (splicing), loss of connectors and coupling losses at the input and output. The scattering at the core-cladding interface results in both mode

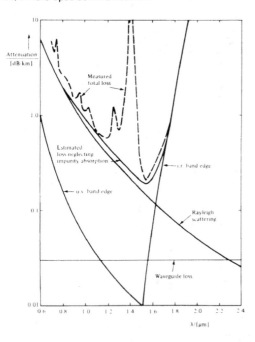

Figure 53.5 State of the art loss of single mode fibre

conversion and radiation loss. This loss can be controlled by increasing the radius of the core and the index difference, Δn. Bending loss depends on the size of the core and the bend radius. The bending loss can be represented as in Equation 53.9.

$$\alpha_{bl} = C e^{-R/R_c} \tag{53.9}$$

R is the radius of curvature of the bend and R_c the critical curvature given by Equation 53.10, with a being the fibre radius.

$$R_c \approx \frac{3 n_1^2 \lambda}{4 \pi \left(n_1^2 - n_2^2 \right)^{3/2}}$$

$$\approx \frac{a}{2 n_1 \Delta n} = \frac{a}{N A^2} \tag{53.10}$$

Looking at the equation for R_c the approach to minimising α_{bl} is to use the largest possible Δn and operate at the shortest possible wavelength. This implies that operation at long wavelengths, that is around 1550nm, will possibly lead to higher bend losses.

The physical cause of bend losses is the loss by radiation of the energy, since a tight bend forces the radiation to propagate into the cladding. The bending losses introduced and discussed up to now were due to gross fibre bends introduced by the user. However, there are bending losses introduced randomly along the waveguide, with each of them introducing a very small loss but the aggregate loss can be quite high. This is known as microbending loss and it can be caused by pressure exerted by other fibre within a fibre cable.

One additional form of loss is the result of the small variation in the core diameter of a fibre arising during the manufacturing phase.

The physical mechanism is similar and the loss is known as waveguide loss.

Fibre can be pulled in lengths between a few metres to a few kilometres and since system length range from a few kilometres to tens of kilometres, permanent joint techniques are required. The permanent jointing fibre is known as splicing. Two broad categories of splicing techniques have emerged: fusion splicing (welding) and mechanised splicing.

Fusion splicing is accomplished by the fusion of two pre-aligned fibres by the application of heat. The heat can be generated by an electric arc or flame, and the technique is easy to apply and yields remarkable low losses in the field. For example fusion splicing yields routinely 0.2dB loss per splice. One drawback of fusion splicing is the reduction of the tensile strength of the fibre in the vicinity of the fused splice because of the heating of the fibre. For this reason fusion splices are packaged with the aim of reducing the tensile load in the vicinity of the splice.

Mechanical splicing, before the introduction of fusion splicing, was the only way of permanently joining two fibres. The basic idea behind this mechanical splicing is the alignment of two fibre ends and then through the use of a transparent adhesive with refractive index which matched that of the fibre, the joint is made permanent. The alignment of the fibre and the mechanical strength are achieved by using capillaries or a V-groove. The performance obtained with mechanical splicing is in the range of 0.2dB to 0.3dB. Which splicing technology is used depends on the application but fusion is simpler to use and it is very popular.

In optics the term dispersion is used to indicate the dependence of the refractive index of the material on the wavelenght of the radiation. This dependence is a basic characteristic of the material. The effect of dispersion on a pulse of light propagating in the fibre is to increase the width of the pulse and the understanding of dispersion and its effects is fundamental in understanding optical fibre transmission.

Optical energy propagates along the waveguide with a velocity known as the group velocity, u_g, given by Equation 53.11 where, in this equation, the denominator is known as the group index.

$$u_g = \frac{c}{n_1 - \lambda \left(\dfrac{d n_1}{d \lambda} \right)} \tag{53.11}$$

Clearly if $\dfrac{d n_1}{d \lambda} = 0$ then the group velocity is independent of wavelength and is equal to the phase velocity. An optical pulse consists of a number of wavelengths (frequencies) and since each of them propagates with different group velocity they arrive at the end of a fibre of length L each delayed by τ_g given by Equation 53.12.

$$\tau_g = \frac{L}{u_g} \tag{53.12}$$

For normal dispersion the higher frequencies are delayed more than the lower ones, with the result that the pulse width increases. Assuming linear operation and that the output pulse emerging from the waveguide is Gaussian of standard deviation (r.m.s. value) σ then the 3dB optical bandwidth is given by Equation 53.13.

$$B W_{opt} = \frac{0.1874}{\sigma} \tag{53.13}$$

The 3dB electrical bandwidth is defined as the frequency at which the optical power is down to 0.707 of that at zero frequency, as in Equation 53.14.

$$B W_{elc} = \frac{0.1325}{\sigma} \qquad (53.14)$$

After this brief introduction to the concept and impact of dispersion we proceed to examine the effect of dispersion in single and multimode fibres.

53.1.2.1 Dispersion

The dispersion of a fibre of arbitrary parameters can be separated into two elements, intramodal and intermodal. The intramodal dispersion is the dispersion whose origin lies in the interaction of the material of the waveguide and of the waveguide itself with the optical signal. It consists of two main components, material or chromatic dispersion and waveguide dispersion. The origin of the intramodal dispersion, known also as chromatic dispersion, is the finite spectral width of the optical source and its interaction with the waveguide material properties (material dispersion) and the structure (waveguide dispersion).

Intermodal dispersion, also referred to as modal dispersion, is the result of the propagation delay between modes in a multimode fibre. Both types of dispersion are present in a multimode fibre because each mode is subject to intramodal dispersion but as should be clear by now only intramodal dispersion is present in a single mode fibre. Since intramodal dispersion is more fundamental we examine it first.

Consider a pulse of near monochromatic radiation of average wavelength propagating in a single mode fibre of length L. Then combining Equations 53.11 and 53.12 the pulse delay due to the material dispersion is given by Equation 53.15.

$$\tau_d = \frac{L}{u_g} = \left(\frac{L}{c} \right)\left(n_1 - \lambda \left(\frac{d n_1}{d \lambda} \right) \right) \qquad (53.15)$$

Assuming that the r.m.s. spectral width of the radiation is σ_s then the pulse broadening due to the material dispersion is given by Equation 53.16.

$$\sigma_m = -\left(\frac{L \sigma_s}{c} \right)\left(\lambda \frac{d^2 n_1}{d \lambda^2} \right) \qquad (53.16)$$

The material dispersion parameter, $D(\lambda)$ is usually defined as in Equation 53.17, which gives Equation 53.18.

$$D(\lambda) = -\left(\frac{\lambda}{c} \right)\left(\frac{d^2 n_1}{d \lambda^2} \right) \quad ps/nm.km \qquad (53.17)$$

$$\sigma_m = \sigma_s D(\lambda) L \qquad (53.18)$$

The physical origin of waveguide dispersion is the non-linear dependence of the propagation constant of the waveguide on the optical frequency. This is the irreducible minimum dispersion and it is present in the waveguide even for zero material dispersion. The waveguide dispersion can be approximated by Equation 53.19.

$$\Delta \tau_w = \frac{L}{c} n_1 \Delta n \, V \frac{d^2(V b)}{d V^2} \frac{\Delta \lambda}{\lambda} \qquad (53.19)$$

For V in the range 1.5 < V < 2.4 the parameter b can be approximated by Equation 53.20.

$$b = \left(1.428 - \frac{0.996}{V} \right)^2 \qquad (53.20)$$

Since for single mode transmission 2.0 < V < 2.4 and $d^2(Vb)/dV^2$ is of the order 0.1 to 0.2. At short wavelengths, that is around 1μm, both waveguide and chromatic dispersion have the same sign and they are added.

As it was stated above the material dispersion for silica decreases to zero around 1.28μm. At wavelengths longer than that the waveguide and material dispersion are of opposite sign and as a result the wavelenght of zero dispersion moves to longer wavelengths. In general waveguide dispersion is small and by itself a second order effect, but by a suitable choice of fibre parameters it can be made to cancel the material dispersion yielding a fibre with zero dispersion at longer wavelength than the natural zero dispersion of the silica. It is particularly important that the dispersion zero can be moved to 1550nm to coincide with the global loss minimum of the silica fibre.

The total dispersion of a single mode fibre is shown in Figure 53.6.

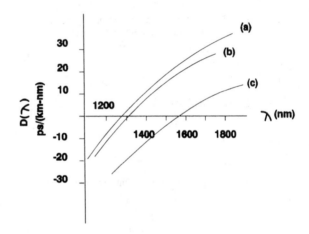

Figure 53.6   The dispersion for single mode fibre: (a) pure silica; (b) non-dispersion shifted fibre (NDSF); (c) dispersion shifted fibre (DSF)

The dispersion of a multimode fibre consists of the material and waveguide dispersion of a single mode fibre and of the intermodal dispersion. The nature of the intermodal dispersion can be understood by considering a step index multimode fibre.

The light launched into this fibre can propagate in the extremes along two paths as in Figure 53.7(a). The first is along the axis of the fibre and along this path the pulse will be subjected to the minimum delay, ΔT_{min}, given by Equation 53.21.

$$\Delta T_{min} = \frac{L}{c / n_1} \qquad (53.21)$$

The second is the extreme meridional ray which will experience the maximum delay, given by Equation 53.22.

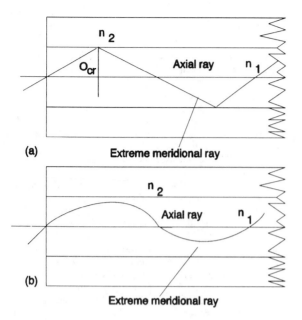

Figure 53.7 Propagation of extreme rays: (a) in step index fibre; (b) in parabolic refractive index fibre

$$\Delta T_{max} = \frac{L / \cos \theta}{c / n_1} = \frac{L n_1}{c \cos \theta} \qquad (53.22)$$

Using Snell's law of refraction gives Equation 53.23.

$$\Delta T_{max} = \frac{L n_1^2}{c n_2} \qquad (53.23)$$

The delay difference $\Delta \tau_d$ between the two rays is given by Equation 53.24.

$$\Delta \tau_d = \Delta \tau_{max} - \Delta \tau_{min} = \frac{L n_1^2}{c n_2} \left(\frac{n_1 - n_2}{n_1} \right)$$

$$= \frac{L n_1}{c} \Delta n \qquad (53.24)$$

Using the numerical aperture of the fibre gives Equation 53.25.

$$\Delta \tau_d = \frac{L (NA)^2}{2 c n_1} \qquad (53.25)$$

Using $n_1 = 1.5$ and $\Delta n = 0.01$ we obtain $\Delta \tau_d = 50\text{ps/km}$. Comparing this to the material dispersion of a single mode fibre around 1.3μm the difference is substantial and the question is as to whether or not the dispersion of a multimode fibre can be reduced. Before we discuss this issue it will be very important to see what happens in practice.

The maximum dispersion (see Equation 52.25) is usually reduced in practice through a number of mechanisms. The first and obvious one is that high order modes, that is those with the maximum delay,

exhibit higher losses because they penetrate deep in the cladding. The second and not so obvious is mode mixing. Because of the irregularities at the core-cladding interface of an actual fibre energy is transferred from slower to faster modes and vice versa, with the result that in a long fibre the intermodal dispersion is reduced. With mode coupling between all guided modes the dispersion is given by Equation 53.26, where L_m is the characteristic length for mode mixing.

$$\Delta \tau_s = \frac{n_1 \Delta n}{c} (L L_m)^{1/2} \qquad (53.26)$$

In practice L_m is established by measurements.

In spite of the effect of mode mixing in reducing intermodal dispersion the most successful approach in reducing the dispersion of multimode fibres is by grading the refractive index of the core. The most popular grading profile is the parabolic which yield a dispersion given by Equation 53.27.

$$\Delta \tau_s = \frac{L n_1 \Delta n^2}{8 c} \qquad (53.27)$$

The pulse broadening given by Equation 53.26 or 53.27 corresponds to the maximum value and if used in system design it gives the worst case. Since in practice the value obtained is smaller but depends on a number of random parameters it is acceptable to use the root mean square value of the pulse broadening. Assuming that the light is launched into the fibre uniformly over the cone of acceptance the r.m.s. pulse broadening for step index and parabolic graded index fibre is given by Equation 53.28.

$$\sigma_{si} \approx \frac{L (NA)^2}{4 \sqrt{3} n_1 c} = \frac{L n_1 \Delta}{2 \sqrt{3} c}$$

$$\sigma_{gi} = \frac{L n_1 \Delta n^2}{20 \sqrt{3} c} \qquad (53.28)$$

The total dispersion of the multimode fibre is given by the sum of the intramodal and intermodal dispersion but in the mean square sense. The reason for this lies in the independence of the physical effects that cause the pulse broadening. The total dispersion, σ_t, is given by Equation 53.29, where σ_m and σ_d are the chromatic (intramodal) and intermodal pulse broadening respectively.

$$\sigma_t = (\sigma_m^2 + \sigma_d^2)^{1/2} \qquad (53.29)$$

The total fibre dispersion can be used to establish an important figure of merit for a fibre, the bandwidth-length product, $B_{opt}L$. This is given by Equation 53.30, where σ_t refers to the dispersion per unit length, usually the kilometre.

$$B_{opt}L = \frac{0.187}{\sigma_t} \approx \frac{0.2}{\sigma_t} \qquad (53.30)$$

The performance of a state of the art single mode fibre regarding losses and dispersion is summarised in Figures 53.5 and 53.6. The loss in a state of the art multimode fibre is similar to that of a single mode with 2.0dB/km to 2.5 dB/km at 850nm and 0.55dB/km to 0.6 dB/km at 1300nm. The difference of course lies in bandwidth. The bandwidth of graded index 50/125μm multimode fibre is around 600MHz.km and 1500MHz.km at 850nm and 1300nm respectively. The equivalent r.m.s. dispersion is 333.3ps/km and 125ps/km respectively and it is easy to see the advantage of single mode transmission.

53.2 Optical sources

53.2.1 The basics of light generation

Matter absorbs or emits radiation by electron transitions between energy levels which characterise the material. According to quantum mechanics this interaction takes place only in discrete quantities of energy. That is assuming that two energy levels E_1 and E_2 exist with $E_2 > E_1$ then the minimum energy which can be absorbed or emitted is E_g (where $E_g = E_2 - E_1$) which corresponds to a characteristic wavelength λ_c given by Equation 53.31, where h is Planck's constant (6.6261 X 10^{-34}Js), c is the speed of light (2.999 X 10^8m/s) and λ the wavelength of the radiation.

$$\lambda_c = \frac{h\,c}{E_g} = \frac{1.24}{E_g\,(eV)} \quad (\mu m) \qquad (53.31)$$

There are three ways in which absorption or emission can take place. Consider again the two level system, shown in Figure 53.8, but with electrons at level E_2. Then without external light irradiating the material the electrons will drop spontaneously to level E_1 emitting photons of energy E_g. This emission is completely random and without any triggering mechanics being involved.

Consider now that the material is irradiated with light of wavelength λ_o close to λ_c. Then the incoming photons will be absorbed by the material and electrons will now appear at level E_2. The electrons stay at E_2 for a time interval $\Delta\tau$ whose duration is a characteristic of the material. If now the external irradiance is removed the electrons will delay to level E_1 through spontaneous emission and eventually the level E_2 will be empty.

The third possibility is the most important. Consider again the two level system but this time there are electrons at level E_2 and the material is irradiated. Then the electrons at level E_2 interact with the radiation, drop to level E_1 and photons are released in phase with those of the input light. This phenomena is called stimulated emission and under certain conditions can lead to light amplifica-

tion. This is a fundamental concept and its understanding is invaluable in understanding the operation of optical sources.

Consider again the two level system with a total number of atoms N of which n_1 are at E_1 and n_2 at E_2. Under thermal equilibrium the number of atoms at level E_2 is given by Equation 53.32, where k is Boltzmann's constant (1.38 X 10^{-23}JK^{-1}) and T the absolute temperature in Kelvin.

$$n_2 = n_1 \exp\left(\frac{-h f_o}{k\,T}\right) \qquad (53.32)$$

Since $T > 0$ then $n_1 > n_2$. If now external light irradiates the material the probabilities of absorption ($E_1 \rightarrow E_2$) or emission ($E_2 \rightarrow E_1$) are proportional to the intensity of light and the number of atoms at levels E_1 and E_2, that is, the probability of absorption is approximately equal to In_1 and the probability of emission is approximately equal to In_2.

Since $n_1 > n_2$ the material absorbs the radiation. Now consider that somehow $n_2 > n_1$ but since the probability of absorption is as before emission predominates and we have achieved Light Amplification by Stimulated Emission of Radiation (Laser). The condition that leads to laser action is known as population inversion.

Using the basic mechanisms of matter radiation interaction two classes of optical sources have emerged. Devices using spontaneous emission (Light Emitting Diodes or LEDs) and devices using light amplification (lasers). The details of their operation depend on the material systems used and we briefly discuss this important issue.

Spontaneous emission and laser action has been observed in a large number of material systems ranging from glasses to crystals to semiconductors. Which material system is used depends on a number of requirements imposed by the application and for fibre communications the indisputable choice is that of semiconductor materials. Optical sources made of semiconductors offers excellent performance both optical and electronic, small size, reliability and perhaps what may be the most important feature for future evolution the possibility of integrating optical sources with the electronic functions using the same material system.

Since the emitted frequency is a function of the energy bandgap a number of semiconductor material systems have evolved to satisfy the transmission requirements. The first system to be developed was the ternary $Ga_{1-x}Al_xAs/GaAs$ ($0 \leq x \leq 1$). The subscript x is referred to as the mole fraction and by varying it one varies the wavelength at which the device operates. The extremes of operation are obtained with x = 0, $\lambda = 0.9\mu m$ and with x = 0.4, $\lambda =$

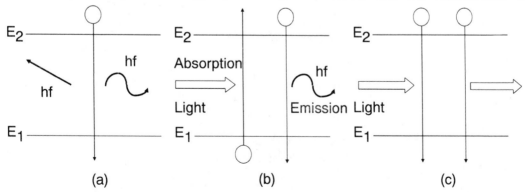

Figure 53.8 The intreaction of radiation and matter: (a) random emission; (b) absorption and random emission; (c) stimulated emission and amplification

0.65*mm*. The GaAlAs system therefore covers the 0.8μm fibre window, the first optical window to be used. A study of the fibre loss verses wavelengths will highlight the simple fact that operation of 0.8μm is not the optimum. The silica fibre has the zero dispersion of around 1.3μm and the global loss minimum at 1.55μm. To operate at these two windows a quarternary compound semiconductor has been developed, $In_x Ga_{1-x} As_y P_{1-y}$. Now there are two mole parameters and the bandgap energy corresponds to wavelength ranging from 0.92μm to 1.65μm. This material therefore covers both the 1.3μm and 1.55μm windows. Other materials have been investigated but they have never reached the maturity of the two outlined above.

53.2.2 Light emitting diodes and lasers

The operation of LED and lasers is based on the same principle, that of population inversion (negative temperature), but the structures used are radically different.

Population inversion is obtained in a semiconductor p-n junction by heavily doping both types of the material. This leads to a degenerative p-n junction which means that at equilibrium this Fermi level lies within the valence and conduction bands and the state between the Fermi level and the end of the band are filled.

With strong forward bias there exist at the depletion layer a region which is doubly degenerate, that is contain degenerate electron and holes. This corresponds directly to the population inversion condition. In this region, called the active region, electrons are available for either spontaneous or stimulated emission. Which of the two predominates depend on the structure.

An LED relies on the spontaneous emission for operation and the structure of typical devices are shown in Figures 53.9 and 53.10. The device consists of three layer two $Al_x Ga_{1-x} As$ and one GaAs (x=0). Since the bandgap of AlGaAs is larger than that of GaAs the spontaneous emission generated in the active layer (GaAs) is not absorbed and it is available for collection and launching into a fibre. This structure is known as double heterojunction because of the p-p and p-n junction.

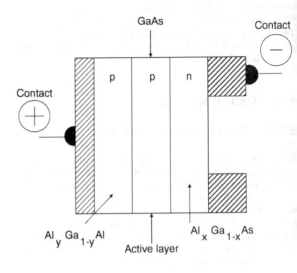

Figure 53.9 Double heterojunction LED

Devices operating on the principle of stimulated emission require, in addition to population inversion, the presence of radiation. In a laser this 'radiation' is obtained through optical feedback. Optical feedback is established by embedding the active material into a cavity whose walls are mirrors, (Figure 53.11). Then the operation is like that of any other oscillator. When heavy forward bias is applied the population is inverted and spontaneous emission follows. Some of the photons of the spontaneous emission are reflected from the end mirrors and playing the role of the radiation are irradiating the active material. Due to the stimulated emission effect the reflected radiation is amplified and laser action commences.

From both the theoretical and practical points it is extremely important to know the optical wavelength (frequency) at which

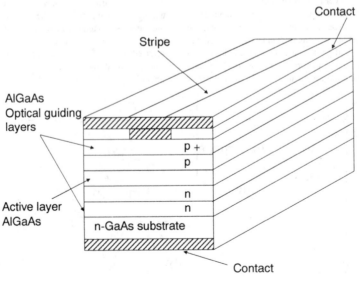

Figure 53.10 Structure of an edge emitting LED

Active layer

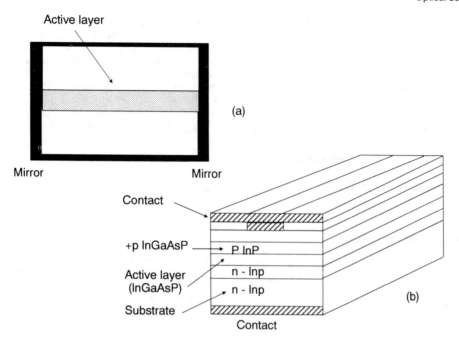

Mirror · Mirror

(a)

Contact

+p InGaAsP —— P InP

Active layer
(InGaAsP)

Substrate

n - Inp

n - Inp

(b)

Contact

Figure 53.11   Principles of optical feedback: (a) schematic of a laser; (b) structure of a long wavelength laser

LEDs and lasers radiate. With LED the situation is simple. The emitted radiation corresponds to the spontaneous emission. This can be quite broad 30µm to 50µm and it is centred at the λ_c. For the laser the situation is very different. Being an oscillator there are two conditions for operation: internal gain to overcome losses in the resonator and positive feedback.

The gain, which corresponds to the range over which the material will amplify is characteristic of the material. The cavity however imposes additional conditions through the feedback mechanism and selects the frequencies at which the device oscillates. Figure 53.12 shows the basics of the operation. The device gain is $g(\lambda)$. The frequencies at which the device can potentially oscillate are those for which there is positive feedback. These wavelengths are called the longitudinal modes of the cavity. The spacing of the modes is given by Equation 53.33, where n the refractive index of the material and L the length of the device.

$$\Delta\lambda = \frac{\lambda^2}{2nL} \qquad (53.33)$$

The number of the longitudinal modes which can be supported by the cavity is given by Equation 53.34.

$$M_{lg} = 2n\frac{L}{\lambda} \qquad (53.34)$$

For example at $\lambda = 0.850\mu m$ for GaAs with n = 3.5 and device length, L, of say 200µm the number of modes is 1647. However, only those modes for which the device has gain can oscillate and, in contrast to an LED spectrum, which is continuous the laser spectrum is discrete. For the device used in the example, the mode spacing is $\Delta\lambda = 0.516nm$. Depending on the design and driving conditions the number of laser modes range from one (single mode) to many (multimode). 'Many' usually implies 5 to 10 modes.

In semiconductor lasers the mirrors are made by simply cleaving the device to the required length and leaving the facet un-coated. The laser devices that depend for feedback on two mirrors on the facets of the active layer is known as a Fabry Perot laser. This is the simplest possible laser structure and naturally it has a number of disadvantages especially mode instability. To cure this problem advanced laser structures, such as distributed feedback lasers (DFB), are being introduced. The optical feedback for these devices is provided not by mirrors at the end of the cavity but by a grating built into the laser which provides continues feedback along the whole length of the device, as in Figure 53.13. The result is virtual single mode lasers because the other modes are 25–30dB below the fundamental.

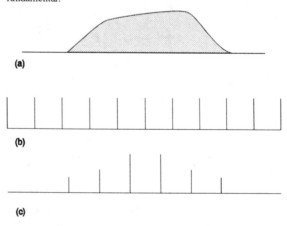

(a)

(b)

(c)

Figure 53.12   The generation of the discrete laser spectrum: (a) device gain; (b) cavity modes; (c) laser spectrum

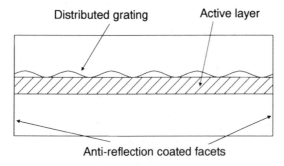

Figure 53.13 Schematic of DFB laser

53.2.3 Device characteristics

The characteristics required to describe the operation of optical sources depend on the application. For fibre communication applications a minimum set of parameters which can describe the device operation satisfactory is as follows:

> **LEDs**: light output vs current, spectral density, information bandwidth.
> **Lasers**: light current characteristics, spectral density, turn on delay, relaxation oscillation, spectral broadening under modulation, partition noise and information bandwidth.

The light current characteristics of a LED is shown in Figure 53.14 for three device structures. Notice that for the surface and edge emitting LEDs the device exhibits a linear characteristic for low currents with the edge emitting device being linear for a substantial part of the characteristic. The spectral density of a LED

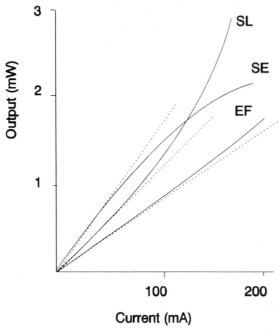

Figure 53.14 The light/current characteristic of LEDs

is continuous, Gaussian shaped and quite broad. Depending on the details of the structure it ranges from 25nm to 40nm for the 850nm window and from 50nm to 120nm for the 1.2μm to 1.7μm range. The spectral width quoted applies for the surface emitting (SE) structure. The spectral width of an edge emitting (EE) device is 0.6 that of a SE and that of a superluminence (SL) about 0.25 of the SE spectral width.

The information bandwidth of LEDs is given by Equation 53.35, where the constant τ is the total carrier lifetime.

$$P(\omega) = \frac{P(O)}{\left(1 + (\omega\tau)^2\right)^{(1/2)}} \tag{53.35}$$

The modulation bandwidth, f, is given by Equation 53.36.

$$\Delta f_{LED} = \frac{\Delta\omega}{2\pi} = \frac{1}{2\pi\tau} \tag{53.36}$$

Since the lifetime depends on the current density the bandwidth is a function of the bias of the device and it drops as the power increases.

There is are fair number of LED device but the typical parameters of devices suitable for fibre communications are summarised in

Table 53.1 Typical LED performance parameters with multimode fibre tail (50/120μm)

λ_p (nm)	$\Delta\lambda$ (nm)	P_o (μW)	BW (MHz)	t_{rf} (ns)	C_t (pF)	V_F (V)	I_b (mA)
865	45	80	200	10	220	2.0	100
1300	80	20	400	2	300	1.5	100
1550	125	20	—	3	—	1.8	150

Table 53.1. As one can see from this table the output power into a standard multimode fibre tail is of the order of a few tens of microwatts only in spite of the fact that the power from the facet of the device is of the order of 5mW to 15mW. The reason for this difference is the broad far field radiation pattern of the LEDs and the relatively small NA of the standard multimode telecommunication fibre.

The light current characteristic of a laser is shown in Figure 53.15. In contrast to the same curve for LEDs there is now a sharp 'knee'. The current corresponding to the knee is the threshold current, I_{th}, and it is an important parameter of the device. At currents below I_{th} the laser behaves like an LED, that is, the radiation is spontaneous and the power low. Above I_{th} the power rises very rapidly and now the device operates in the regime of stimulated emission. The spectral density of the laser is now very different from that of an LED. It is narrow and consists of a number of spectral lines under an envelope that is nearly Gaussian. The spectral density depends on the driving conditions of the device especially with large digital or analogue signals.

One special feature of the laser is the turn on delay. With the device biased at an arbitrary current level, I_b, below threshold, the time taken by the optical radiation to rise as a result of an applied pulse is the turn on delay t_d as shown in Figure 53.16, and is given by Equation 53.37, where τ is the recombination time constant and I the applied signal current.

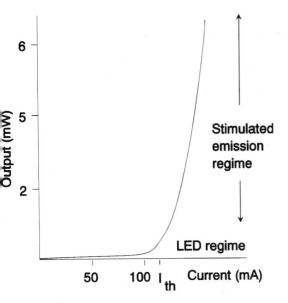

Figure 53.15 The light-current characteristic of a laser

$$t_d = \tau \ln \left(\frac{I - I_b}{I - I_{th}} \right) \tag{53.37}$$

For $I_b \to I_{th}$, $t_d \to 0$ with the maximum of t_d obtained for $I_b = 0$. Biasing the device at or above threshold, the turn on delay is zero. This implies that for high bit rate systems pre-bias is mandatory, otherwise there will be a pattern effect. In addition to the turn on delay a laser driven by a digital signal exhibits relaxation oscillations. Clearly the period of the relaxation oscillations should be less

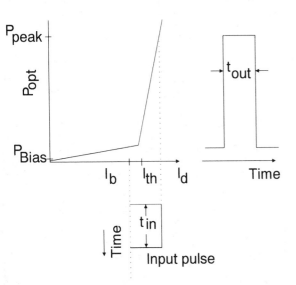

Figure 53.16 The concept of turn on delay in semiconductor lasers: $t_{out} < t_{in}$ for $I_b < I_{th}$

than the width of the pulse otherwise there will be again a pattern effect.

It was mentioned above that the spectral density of a laser depends on the modulation. This leads to two related phenomena, spectrum broadening and partition noise. Spectral broadening manifest itself with the appearance of new spectral lines which where not there under CW driving conditions. The cause of partition noise is the variability of the energy of each laser mode as the device is modulated. Now, assuming that the pulse propagates over a dispersive medium, each mode suffers different delay and at the receiver the pulse amplitude fluctuates, suggesting the existence of noise process in operation. The information bandwidth of lasers range for a few megahertz to gigahertz with current experimental devices reaching 20GHz. The theoretical bandwidth relation is as in Equation 53.38.

$$P(\omega) = P(O) \frac{\omega_o^2}{(\omega_o^2 - \omega^2) + j\beta\omega} \tag{53.38}$$

In this equation ω and $\beta\omega$ are given by Equations 53.39 and 53.40, and τ_{sp} and τ_{ph} are the spontaneous recombination time and mean photon lifetime respectively, as in Figure 53.17. Again as in LEDs the bandwidth depends on bias current.

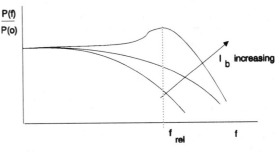

Figure 53.17 Small signal frequency response of semiconductor lasers

$$\omega_o^2 = \frac{(I_o - I_{th})}{\tau_{sp}\tau_{pt}I_{th}} \tag{53.39}$$

$$\beta = \frac{I_o}{\tau_{sp}I_{th}} \tag{53.40}$$

At $\omega = \omega_o$ the device exhibits a resonance which corresponds to the relaxation oscillation frequency.

It was mentioned above that multimode lasers are subject to spectral problems. The solution to these problems lie in operating the device in a single longitudinal mode. Fabry Perot devices cannot generally operate in a stable single mode. As was mentioned earlier a successful single mode device is the Distributed Feedback laser (DFB). These devices are used in all long haul systems operating at 1550nm with or without dispersion shifted fibre. However, even these devices are not free of imperfections. They suffer from chirping, that is the small change of wavelength during the duration of the current pulse corresponding to a digital '1' symbol.

Table 53.2 Typical laser performance parameters with single and multimode fibre tails for digital applications
(1) corrresponds to DFB laser

λ_{peak} (nm)	I_{th} (mA)	P_{out} (mW)	$\Delta\lambda$ (nm)	t_r (ns)	t_f (ns)	Device class	Fibre tail
(nm)	(mA)	(mW)	(nm)	(ns)	(ns)	Class	Tail
1550	20	1.3	see(1)	0.1	0.1	DFB	S/M
1300	20	2.0	see(1)	0.1	0.1	DFB	S/M
1550	30	2.0	4.0	0.5	0.7	F-P	S/M
1300	40	1.5	5.0	1.0	1.0	F-P	S/M
850	16	4.0	3.0	0.4	0.4	F-P	M/M
1300	20	3.0	8.0	0.3	0.3	F-P	M/M

The power from the facet of lasers designed for fibre communication is around 5mW to 10mW but the power available from the fibre tail is of the order at 1mW to 2mW. This again is due to the rather broad and asymmetric far field of the lasers.

The performance of lasers varies depending on the application but for fibre communications Table 53.2 summarises the characteristics of some typical state of the art lasers.

The performance of state of the art lasers for analogue modulation is summarised in Table 53.3.

These tables contain but a fraction of what is available on semiconductor lasers and the interested reader is advised to consult manufacturer's catalogues for further information.

53.3 Optical detectors

53.3.1 The basics of optical detection

The function of an optical detector is to recover the information which was imposed on the optical carrier. There are many effects which can be used for optical detection but in terms of performance detectors based on the photoelectric effects and using semiconductor material outperform all others, at least in the field of fibre communication, and we will concentrate on them.

The principle of photodetection is simple. Photons are absorbed by the material and electron from the valence band are raised in the conduction band leaving behind holes. If an electric field is applied across the device both electrons and holes are swept out of the device creating the photocurrent.

Since the generated photocurrent is proportional to the intensity of the irradiance, that is the square of the optical field, the detection process is also known as direct detection and is the most widely used form of optical detection. Mathematically it is stated as in Equation 53.41, where R is a constant to be discussed later.

$$i_{ph}(t) = Re(t)^2 = RP(t) \qquad (53.41)$$

The most successful detector structure has been the p-i-n photodetector, shown in Figure 53.18. The device consists of three layers. Two heavily doped layers, p$^+$ and n$^+$, and a lightly doped n$^-$ layer sandwiched between the two. The n$^-$ layer is so lightly doped that it is virtually an intrinsic semiconductor. Hence the name p-i-n.

In order to minimise the capacitance, the device operates reversed biased. The operation is very simple. The radiation penetrates the thin p$^+$layer with minimum absorption and it is totally, or nearly totally, absorbed in the i layer. The threshold wavelength for absorption is given by the Equation 53.42, which is the same equation met in the interaction of radiation with matter, in the section on optical sources.

$$\lambda_{th} = h\frac{c}{E_g} = \frac{1.24}{E_g\,(eV)} \quad (\mu m) \qquad (53.42)$$

Photodetectors are transducers in the sense that they convert optical power (photons) into electrical power (electrons). A critical parameter of a detector is the efficiency with which it performs this conversion. This parameter is known as the quantum efficiency and is defined as in Equation 53.43.

$$m_q = \frac{electrons\ collected}{electrons\ available} = \left(\frac{I_{ph}/e}{P_{opt}/hf}\right) \qquad (53.43)$$

The value of n_q with wavelength depends on the detector material and is a function of wavelength. Figure 53.19 shows the absorption of some typical detector materials and for fibre communications Si, Ge and the quarternary/ternary InGaAsP cover the wavelength range of interest. Using Equation 53.41 the photocurrent can now

Table 53.3 Typical laser performance parameters with single and multimode fibre tails for analogue applications
(1) is in dBc units

λ_{peak} (nm)	I_{th} (mA)	P_{out} (mW)	$\Delta\lambda$ (nm)	BW (GHz)	2nd H. Dist. (dbm)	3rd Or. Int. (dbm)	Fibre tail
1300	20	2.0	8	15.0	−15	−30	M/M
1300 1550	25	2.0	7.0	1.5	−40[(1)]	−50[(1)]	M/M
1310 1550	20	4	—	0.6	−60[(1)]	−65[(1)]	S/M

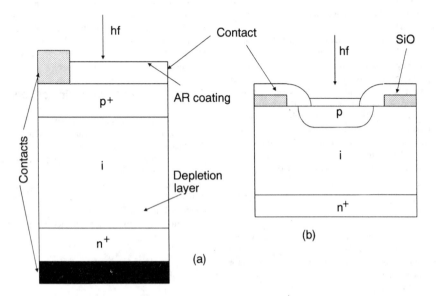

Figure 53.18 The p-i-n photodetector: (a) the schematic of a p-i-n; (b) silicon p-i-n photodetector

be written as in Equation 53.44, where e is the electronic charge and R the device responsivity in [A/W].

$$i_{ph}(t) = n_q e \frac{P(t)}{hf} = RP(t)$$ (53.44)

The principle of the operation of the p-i-n photodetector is that in the limit as $n_q \rightarrow 1$ one photon produces one electron-hole pair. However, for reasons which will become apparent in the section on receivers, if the device could yield for each photon many electron-holes pairs then the impact of the noise of the electronic amplifiers

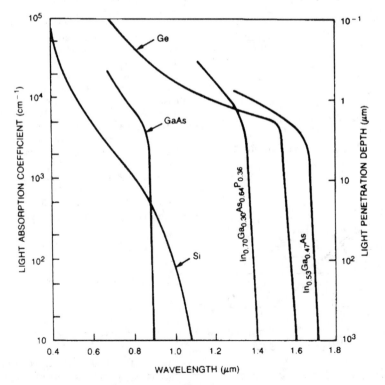

Figure 53.19 The optical absorption coefficient for some materials used in fibre optic communications

following the detector on the total (S/N) ratio will be minimised. Such devices, known as Avalanche Photodetectors (APDs), make possible the design of high sensitivity optical receivers.

In an APD, electron-hole pairs released by the primary photoelectron effect are accelerated to velocities capable of initiating impact ionisation. The secondary pairs, who owe their presence to ionisation, in their turn generate other pairs and the final current is many times larger than primary photocurrent. The APD designs are more complex than those for p-i-n detectors but essentially a p-i-n detector can function as an APD with the i-layer both absorbing the photons and accelerating the photoelectrons and holes. Of course such a device is not as good as could be made and special designs have evolved for APDs. The current in the output of an APD is given by Equation 53.45 where M is the current gain of the device.

$$I_{apd}(t) = i(t)_{ph} M = n_q \frac{P_{opt}(t)}{h\upsilon} M \qquad (53.45)$$

Clearly for M=1 the output current equals the photocurrent as in a p-i-n detector. The maximum usable value of M depends on the material, the device structure and the quality of the semiconductor processes used to produce the device.

Typical Si and InGaAsP designs as shown in Figure 53.20. The Si device, known as reach through APD, offers good quantum effi-

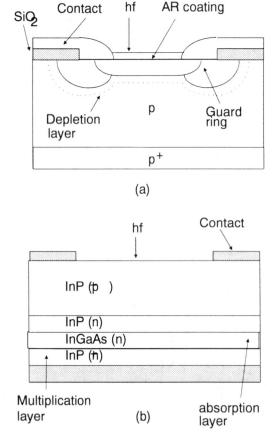

(a)

Multiplication
layer   (b)   absorption
                                             layer

Figure 53.20 Some typical APD device structures: (a) silicon (b) InGaAsP

ciency down to 850nm in spite the fact that the Si absorption starts tailing off. The InGaAsP device is specially designed for long wavelengths in the sense that the absorption and multiplication do not take place in the same layer. Such devices, known as separate absorption and multiplication detectors (SAMs for short), aim at minimising the multiplication noise.

53.3.2 The characteristics of optical detectors

The device parameters of a p-i-n detector relevant to the design of an optical receiver are the quantum efficiency n_q, or responsivity R, the capacitance C_d, the series resistance R_s, the dark current I_d and the device bandwidth. The n_q or R depend on the material and the device design. For well designed devices n_q of the order of 80% to 95% is possible. Since p-i-n detectors operate reversed biased the device capacitance can be approximated to that of a plane capacitor, given by Equation 53.46 where ε_o is the free space permittivity, εr the relative permittivity, A_d the device junction area and w the width of the i-layer.

$$C_d = \varepsilon_o \varepsilon_r \frac{A_d}{w} \qquad (53.46)$$

The value of C_d depends on the material (ε_r), the device area (A_d) and the width of the i-layer width. For fast devices with 50μm diameter the capacitance can be as low as 0.5pF. The series resistance is the resistance of the material and of the contact bonding. In well designed detectors the series resistance is of the order of 5 to 20 ohms.

The dark current of the device is the current flowing in the circuit with bias applied but without light. This current is small because the device is reversed biased but it depends on temperature, device structure and material quality. In general devices for long wavelengths (because of the smaller band gap) have larger dark currents than those for short wavelength devices. For example Si p-i-n have much lower I_d that both Ge and InGaAsP, pAs rather that nAs. The device operates reversed biased and consequently the device resistance, that is the resistance of the junction, is large and is usually ignored in designs. The equivalent small signal circuit for normally biased photodiodes is shown in Figure 53.21.

The bandwidth of the p-i-n detector is dictated by the transit time of the carrier across the i-layer and the circuit time constant established by C_o and any other external capacitance and the total resistive load.

The bandwidth due to the transit time effect is given by Equation 53.47 where w the depletion layer of the device, usually equal to the width of the i-layer, and v_{sat} the carrier velocity corresponding to the reverse bias. Usually this is the carrier saturation velocity.

$$\Delta f_{tr} = \frac{0.44}{w} v_{sat} \qquad (53.47)$$

The bandwidth imposed by the circuit time constant is given by Equation 53.48 where C_t the total capacitance.

$$\Delta f_{CR} = \frac{1}{2\pi R C_t} \qquad (53.48)$$

C_t consists of the diode capacitance, the parasitic circuit capacitance and any other capacitance external to the detector. Therefore for high bandwidth all these capacitances must be as small as permitted by the technology used. Usually inequality 53.49 applies.

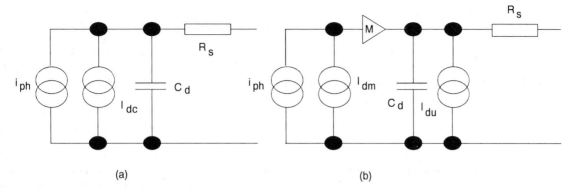

Figure 53.21 Equivalent circuit for p-i-n and APD detectors: (a) p-i-n; (b) APD

However for very high bandwidth, that is in excess of 3GHz to 5GHz, the transit time starts limiting the device bandwidth and as a result the width of the i-layer is reduced with a subsequent reduction in n_q.

$$\Delta f_{tr} \gg \Delta f_{CR} \tag{53.49}$$

The noise of the p-i-n detector is due to the flow of current, shot noise, and due to thermal effects primary in R_s. The shot noise consists of two contributions; shot noise due to the dark current, given as usual by Equation 53.50, and shot noise due to the signal photocurrent itself, given by Equation 53.51.

$$<i_{dc}^2> = 2 e I_{dc} \Delta f \tag{53.50}$$

$$<i_{sig}^2> = 2 e I_{ph} \Delta f \tag{53.51}$$

The total p-i-n noise is given by Equation 53.52.

$$<i_{pin}^2> = 2 e (I_{ph} + I_{dc}) \Delta f \tag{53.52}$$

It should be clear now that even if the dark current is zero there will always be a noise component due to the signal. This noise-in-signal component establishes the performance limit of an optical receiver.

Because of the random nature of the impact ionisation process there is a fundamental difference between the noise of a p-i-n and that of an APD. The APD noise is given by Equation 53.53 where I_{dcm} is the part of the dark current subject to multiplication, I_{dcu} the un-multiplied dark current and F the excess noise factor.

$$<i_{apd}^2> = 2 e (I_{ph} + I_{dcm}) M^2 F \Delta f + 2 e I_{dcu} \Delta f \tag{53.53}$$

Had the ionisation process been deterministic then F = 1. In terms of gain, the excess noise factor can be expressed as in Equation 53.54.

$$F = M^x \tag{53.54}$$

The exponent x depends on the material and the design of the APD and for a well designed and used detector $0 < x < 1$.

The bandwidth of an APD depends on the circuit time constant but also on the gain-bandwidth product of the device, as given by Equation 53.55, where τ_{av} is the average transit time.

$$Gain - Bandwidth = \frac{3}{2 \pi \tau_{av}} \tag{53.55}$$

The C_d of APDs is usually larger than that of p-i-n detectors because of the complexity of the devices. The state of the art of available p-i-n detectors is summarised in Table 53.4 and that of the

Table 53.4 Parameters for p-i-n detectors

Diameter (mm)	R (A/W)	I_d (nA)	C_d (pF)	Rise time (ns)	BW (MHz)	Material
0.24	0.8	0.5	1.5	1.0		Si
0.40	0.8	3.0	3.0	—	200.0	Si
0.08	0.8	5.0	1.0	—	1000	InGaAs
0.05	0.8	2.0	0.6	—	1000	InGaAs

APD in Table 53.5. Because of the superior performance of In-GaAsP devices these tables do not include data on Ge detectors.

These detectors were selected as being suitable for communications. There are available even faster detectors but there are used mainly in optical measurements.

Table 53.5 Parameters for avalanche photodetectors

Material	Diameter (μm)	R (A/W)	C_d (pF)	x	I_{dm} (nA)	BW (MHz)
Si	300	0.8	2.0	0.3	0.025	700
InGaAs	80	0.75	0.7	0.7	5.0	1200
InGaAs	50	0.75	0.4	0.7	4.0	2500

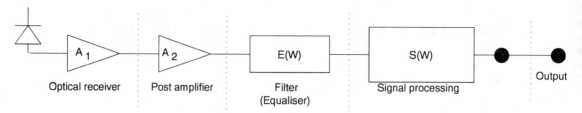

Figure 53.22   Analogue optical reveiver

53.4   Optical receivers and transmitters

The function of the optical receiver is to recover the information imparted on one of the parameters of the optical carrier and in our case this means the intensity of the carrier. An optical receiver consists of an optical detector (the transducer) and a low noise electronic amplifier which raises the signal level to a value where further signal processing is possible without deterioration of the S/N ratio. After the low noise amplifier the details of the receiver depend on the application. An analogue receiver will include stages of amplification, filtering, electronic signal detection (whose function depends on the modulation format) and some additional signal processing such as filtering, and only after this is the information available to the user, as in Figure 53.22.

A digital receiver will include some more amplification, filtering, detection, clock recovery circuits, and finally the regenerator, after which the information is available to the user as in Figure 53.23. A combination is possible by using digital modulation on a subcarrier. In such a situation the subcarrier is first processed by an analogue receiver which recovers the digital information, but in analogue form, and this is then processed by a digital receiver now minus the optical front end.

The measure of performance used in the design of optical receivers depends on the application. For analogue receivers the signal to noise ratio (SNR) is in widespread use. For digital receivers the bit error rate (BER) is used more or less universally.

The design of a complete receiver is a complex task and the purpose of this section is to concentrate on the design of the optical front end which consists of the detector and the low noise amplifier.

53.4.1   Receiver architecture

There are basically three classes of optical receivers; resistive load input, high input impedance or integrating receivers and low input impedance. The resistive load input optical receiver is the simplest possible, as shown in Figure 53.24. The detector is terminated on a

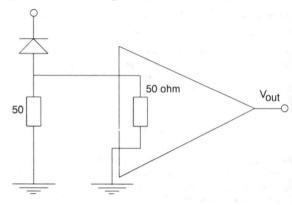

Figure 53.24   Resistive input optical receiver

resistor and the voltage developed across it is applied to the amplifier. The bandwidth is limited by the detector bandwidth, the bandwidth of the input circuit and the bandwidth of the amplifier itself. With a 50 ohm load the bandwidth can be very large. For example with a total capacitance of 1pF, a 50 ohms load and a 50 ohms amplifier input impedance the bandwidth is about 6.35GHz. Higher bandwidth can be obtained if the load is reduced and since commercially available amplifiers have bandwidths of the order of 15GHz to 20GHz optical receivers with bandwidths of similar order are feasible. The difficulty with this approach lies in the high noise the resistive load input receiver yields compared to the other approaches. For this reason optical receivers designed for communication systems do not use the resistive load input configuration.

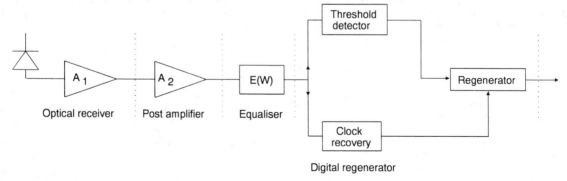

Figure 53.23   Digital optical receiver

In a high input impedance or integrating receiver the photodetector is feeding directly a high to very high ohmic load, as in Figure 53.25. The signal developed across this resistor is fed to an active device of high input impedance such as a FET which acts as a voltage amplifier. After the first device there is subsequent amplification using amplifiers, with or without feedback according to requirements. The low frequency gain of the receiver is given by Equation 53.56 where A_{ampl} is the low frequency voltage gain of the amplifier.

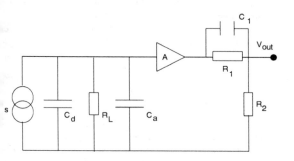

Figure 53.25 High input impedance optical receiver

$$A_{hi} = A_{ampl} R_L R P_{opt} \qquad (53.56)$$

The receiver bandwidth is established by the first time constant at the input and it is given by Equation 53.57 where C_T is the total input capacitance.

$$f_1 = \frac{1}{2 \pi R_L C_T} \qquad (53.57)$$

The bandwidth is usually insufficient and some equalisation is required. The simplest approach is to cancel the pole by a zero using a RC network, as in Figure 53.25. The transfer function of this network is given by Equation 53.58 with the frequencies f_1 and f_2 given by Equations 53.59 and 53.60.

$$\frac{V_{out}}{V_{in}} = \frac{R_2}{R_1 + R_2} \frac{1 + j \frac{f}{f_1}}{1 + j \frac{f}{f_2}} \qquad (53.58)$$

$$f_1 = \frac{1}{2 \pi R_1 C_1} \qquad (53.59)$$

$$f_2 = \frac{R_1 + R_2}{2 \pi R_1 R_2 C_1} \qquad (53.60)$$

The bandwidth of the integrating receivers is very small because the first pole is established by the high value load resistor and the input capacitance. This is of the order of 300kHz to 500kHz. However the bandwidth can be very large if the first pole is cancelled by a zero. With this approach bandwidths of the order of 10GHz to 15GHz are possible, provided the first pole is at a few MHz making the compensation easy. Integrating receivers with

very large loads are used in low capacity systems such as 140MBit/s and below.

The low input impedance receivers use parallel input feedback at the point where the detector drives the amplifier, as in Figure 53.26, and they are also known as transimpedance receivers. In principle there is no need for high value resistive loads and the bandwidth of the receiver can be large. The receiver transfer function is given by Equation 53.61, with the bandwidth given by Equation 53.62.

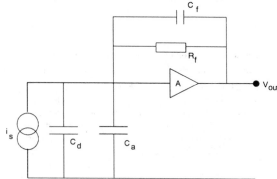

Figure 53.26 Transimpedance optical receiver

$$\frac{v_o}{i_s} = \frac{-R_f}{1 + j 2 \pi R_f (C_f + C_T / A) f} \qquad (53.61)$$

$$f_{BW} = \frac{A}{2 \pi (C_T + A C_f) R_f} \qquad (53.62)$$

Depending on the technology, bandwidths up to 5GHz are possible. Above that transimpedance receivers are not used because the use of feedback may lead to stability problems. For larger bandwidths the receivers are designed with input impedances corresponding to that of the active devices, which are relative high but nowhere near the megaohm range used by truly integrating receivers. Equalisation is still necessary but the first pole is in the megahertz rather than the kilohertz range.

The main reason for using an integrating receiver is the capability of these receivers to deliver very low noise operation because the thermal noise is very small. If an APD is available then the reason for using them is marginal. Their main disadvantage is that the very low bandwidth before equalisation requires the use of coding with small digital sum variation, (DSV). As the bit rate increases coding becomes progressively difficult. The use of integrating receivers is expected to be further reduced with the introduction of signal formats with nearly uncontrollable DSV. Transimpedance receivers do not impose limits on the signal DSV and in spite of the fact that the noise performance with a p-i-n detector is inferior they dominate above 140MBit/s.

53.4.2 Analogue optical receivers

The SNR of an analogue receiver can be interpreted as either the SNR directly applicable to the information being received or as the carrier to noise ratio (CNR) which should then be used as the input SNR to the demodulator suitable for the modulation scheme employed. For example in a FM subcarrier modulation scheme the FM SNR can be obtain from the CNR by standard FM detection analysis. The SNR or the CNR is given by Equation 53.63 in which m is the modulation index, $< i_{na}^2 >$ is the amplifier mean square noise and Δf is the receiver bandwidth.

$$SNR = \frac{1}{2} \frac{(m R M < P_{opt} >)^2}{[2 e (I_{dm} + R < P_{opt} >) M^2 F + 2 e I_{um}] \Delta f + < i_{na}^2 >}$$

(53.63)

The meaning of the other parameters can be found in the section on detectors. The details of the $< i_{na}^2 >$ depend on the representation of the amplifier noise. For optical receivers the best approach is to represent the amplifier, being a single device or a multistage amplifier, by two independent noise sources with white spectral density, a current source i_n and a voltage source e_n. The detailed equations for these noise sources depends on the class of active devices used. For a FET amplifier they are given by Equations 53.64 and 53.65.

$$\frac{d < i_n^2 >_{fet}}{d f} = 2 e I_{gate}$$

(53.64)

$$\frac{d < e_n^2 >}{d f} = \frac{4 k T \Gamma}{g_m}$$

(53.65)

Γ is a numerical constant with a typical value of 0.7 for silicon FETs, 1.75 for GaAs MESFETs and 1.0 for short channel silicon MOSFETs. Then the noise spectral density referred to the input of the receiver is given by Equation 53.66 where R is either the load of the detector for high impedance input or the feedback resistor of a transimpedance amplifier.

$$\frac{d < n^2 (f) >_{fet}}{d f} = \frac{4 k T}{R}$$
$$+ 2 e I_{gate} + \frac{4 k T \Gamma}{g_m} (2 \pi C_t)^2 f^2$$

(53.66)

C_t is the total input capacitance, which consists of the detector and input parasitic capacitance, the gate-source and gate-drain FET capacitances and the parasitic capacitance of the load resistor R. The value of $< e_{na}^2 >$ is obtained by integrating Equation 53.66 over the bandwidth of the receiver. For a bipolar transistor amplifier noise spectral density is given by Equation 53.67.

$$\frac{d < n^2 (f) >_{bip}}{d f} = \frac{4 k T}{R} + 2 e I_b + \frac{2 e I_c}{g_m} (e \pi C_t)^2 f^2$$
$$+ 4 k T r_{bb} (2 \pi C_{sf})^2 f^2$$

(53.67)

The capacitances C_T and C_{df} are given by Equations 53.68 and 53.69, where C_d is the parasitic detector capacitance and C_π and C_μ are the hybrid-π model capacitances.

$$C_T = C_{df} + C_\pi + C_\mu + C_f$$

(53.68)

$$C_{df} = C_{df} + C_f$$

(53.69)

53.4.3 Digital optical receivers

The design of a digital optical receiver is more complicated because first the performance index is the BER and secondly the receiver bandwidth depends both on the transmitted pulse and of receiver output pulse. The BER of a binary digital optical receiver is given by Equation 53.70, where the parameter Q is related to the signal to noise ratio.

$$BER = \frac{1}{\sqrt{2 \pi}} \int_Q^\infty \exp\left(-\frac{x^2}{2}\right) dx$$

(53.70)

For Gausssina statistics and equal noise power for both ones and zeros, 2Q is the peak SNR required for a given BER. For large SNR a good approximation of the error integral is based on the asymptotic expansion, as in Equation 53.71 and for a BER of 10^{-9} Q=6.

$$BER = \frac{1}{\sqrt{2 \pi}} \frac{\exp\left(-\frac{Q^2}{2}\right)}{Q}$$

(53.71)

Now in terms of Q the required optical power $< P_{opt} >$ for a p-i-n receiver is given by Equation 53.72.

$$< P_{opt} > = Q \frac{h f}{N_q e} (i_{na}^2)^{1/2}$$

(53.72)

The value of the reviver noise depends on the front end device. For a FET amplifier it is given by Equation 53.73, where I_2 and I_3 are the values of the Personic integrals that are depended on the shapes of the incident and out pulses and B the bit rate.

$$< is_{na}^2 > = 4 k \frac{T}{R} B I_2 + 2 e (I_d + I_g) B I_2$$
$$+ 4 k \frac{T}{g_m} (2 \pi C_T)^2 B^3 I_3$$

(53.73)

With an incident non-return to zero (NRZ) pulse and a full raised cosine output pulse, $I_2 = 0.562$ and $I_3 = 0.0868$. With a return to zero (RZ) pulse, $I_2 = 0.403$ and $I_3 = 0.0984$. It is clear that since the optical power depends on the cube of the bit rate the receiver design should minimise the C_T. With a bipolar front end receiver Equation 53.74 is obtained.

$$< i_{na}^2 >_{bip} = 4 k \frac{T}{R} B I_2 + 2 e I_b B I_2$$
$$+ 2 e \frac{I_c}{g_m} (2 \pi C_t)^2 B^3 I_3 + 4 k T r_{bb} 2 \pi C_{sf}$$

(53.74)

The receiver sensitivity equation for an APD detector is given by Equation 53.75, where the un-multiplied dark current was assumed to have negligible effect on the sensitivity and I_1 the value of another

Personick integral which equals 0.5 for both NRZ and RZ pulse formats.

$$<P_{opt}> = Q \frac{hf}{n_q e} \left[\left(\frac{<i_{na}^2>}{M^2} + 2 I_{dm} F B I_2 \right)^{1/2} \right.$$

$$\left. + e F B I_1 Q \right] \qquad (53.75)$$

The details of the design of optical receivers depend on the applications but as a general guideline low noise operation is achieved by minimising the input capacitance of the receiver.

Because of the importance of the optical receivers, there has been a large number of designs aiming at particular requirements. However, since the main use of optical receivers is in the trunk and junction network, where the information capacity is standardised, receivers corresponding to these rates have been introduced. Table 53.6 summarises the current performance of optical receivers using p-i-n detectors and operating in the 1300nm to 1600nm range. APD

Table 53.6 Sensitivity of optical receivers using p-i-n detectors. (All parameters are at BER = 10^{-9}; all the receivers are with multimode fibre tails)

Bit rate	Sensitivity (dBm)	
	Min	Typ
2Mbit/s	−56.5	−58.5
16Mbit/s	−52.0	−54.0
45Mbit/s	−49.0	−51.0
90Mbit/s	−46.0	−48.0
160Mbit/s	−43.0	−45.5
565Mbit/s	−36.0	−38.0
680Mbit/s	−34.0	−35.5
1200Mbit/s	−31.0	−33.0
1600Mbit/s	−29.0	−31.0
2400Mbit/s	−28.0	−29.0

receivers tend to be in house products and the improvement depends on the details of the design but on average 5db of improvement is expected.

Some of the bit rates are not within the digital hierarchy, but in a fast evolving field some of the applications require special bit rates.

53.4.4 Optical transmitters

The configuration of an optical transmitter depends first on the signal format and second on the class of the device (LED or laser).

The simplest modulation format is that of intensity modulation. In this format the information carrying current is injected into the optical source and consequence the intensity, that is the square of the field, is modulated.

For analogue modulation the optical source is biased at a given point and the modulation current is superimposed on it. Figure 53.27 shows a driver which can be used for analogue modulation.

The modulation waveforms vary depending on whether the optical device is a LED or a laser, as shown in Figures 53.28 and 53.29. Clearly there are issues of linearity as with any analogue system

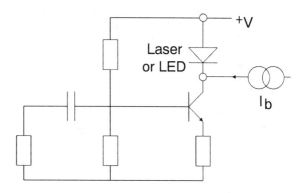

Figure 53.27   Driver for analogue modulation

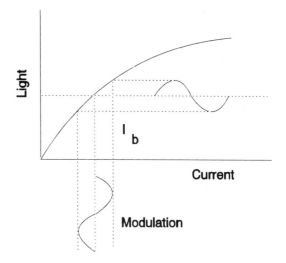

Figure 53.28   Analogue LED modulation

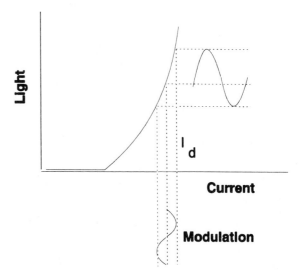

Figure 53.29   Analogue laser modulation

which has to be resolved. The usual techniques of feedback and pre-distortion can be used but improved device performance is the critical issue in analogue modulation.

For digital modulation the device is based either around zero (LEDs) or at threshold (lasers). If lasers are biased at zero current then there is significant turn on delay, which impairs the performance at high bit rates. The typical high speed digital modulator is current mode logic otherwise known as the emitter coupled switch, shown in Figure 53.30. The advantage of this configuration is the large bandwidth available and the ability to control the modulation

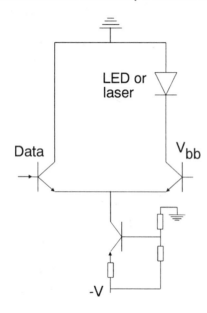

Figure 53.30 Digital modulator for LEDs and lasers

current through the constant current source at the tail of the switch.

In addition to the actual modulator an optical transmitter is required to maintain a constant output optical power. This is far more important for lasers which are very sensitive to temperature. A

typical arrangement to maintain the output power constant is shown in Figure 53.31.

The photodiode monitors the power at the back facet of the laser and produces a signal proportional to the average optical power. This signal is then compared with a reference and the controller adjusts the laser bias current accordingly. This control scheme cannot control the level of 'ones' and 'zeros' individually and for some advanced applications, such as long haul systems, more elaborate schemes are used which control the level of 'ones' and 'zeros'.

53.5 Optical system design

The design of optical systems follows the same approach as any other communication system. The approach can be summarised in a number of steps as follows;

1. The required performance against an agreed performance index is established.
2. The basic system parameters are selected.
3. The performance of suitable subsystems is established.
4. Allocations are made for the implementation penalties of subsystems.
5. The impact of environmental factors is assessed in terms of performance impairment.
6. The system operational margins are introduced.
7. On the basis of (3) to (6) the expected performance is estimated and compared to the required one from (1).
8. If the requirements are not satisfied then a design iteration begins, covering steps (2) to (7).

The design therefore is in both principle and practice an iterative process and some of the parameters entering the iteration depend on existing practices and understanding rather than scientific principles. This particularly applies to steps (4) and (6) above.

A methodology of system design as summarised in steps (1) to (8) can be treated completely in the abstract in terms of system theory, but it will be far easier to describe system design by analysing a concrete case. Since the approach applies to both analogue and digital systems only digital system shall be discussed. However,

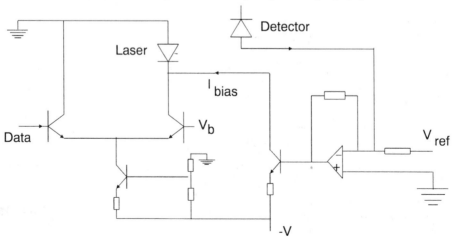

Figure 53.31 Mean optical power controller

efore system design examples are discussed it is important to examine the question of coding in optical fibre systems.

53.5.1 Coding in optical fibre systems

The coding of the transmitted information has been used in coaxial systems to reduce the bandwidth and make it possible to increase the section length and as a result minimise the number of repeaters in a system. This was at the expense of increased terminal complexity, but overall it yielded cost effective systems. With the advent of fibre communications the issue of bandwidth lost its importance because the bandwidth of single mode fibre is very large. For this reason, in the initial stages of the introduction of fibre communications, coding was used to ensure that the transmitted signal had sufficient clock content so that low Q clock extraction circuits could be used. In principle of course that was not necessary.

The requirement for a code to perform a function of primary importance emerged with the use of integrating optical receivers. Since the dynamic range of an integrating receiver is limited there is the need for codes with small digital sum variation (DSV). Such codes turn out to be invariably block codes. In a block code a number of information digits, say N, are mapped through deterministic rules into M output digits with M > N. This will lead to a slight increase of the bit rate in the fibre and in error extension, but the small penalty in receiver sensitivity is worth paying. Block codes such as 5B6B and 7B8B have been used in optical systems up to 565MBit/s.

As the information capacity increased it became progressively more difficult to design such coding schemes because of the limitations in the speed of the electronics. In addition the requirements for information transparency forced the design of optical receivers capable of handling signal formats with very high DSV. These receivers offer sufficient sensitivity to make possible cost effective systems even if their sensitivity is not as good as that of the integrating receivers. Taking into consideration all these factors, state of the art fibre systems used codes of very low redundancy for data management purposes. These low redundancy data sequences are scrambled to minimise the requirements on the clock extraction subsystem in the receiver. Block codes are not error correction codes and in principle error correction can be used in optical systems especially where an error floor is introduced. Again, the complexity and speed requirements of the electronics are such that error correction at the fibre bit rate is hardly used. Error correction is used at the low capacity tributary channels where, due to the relative low speed, high levels of integration are possible.

53.5.2 Design of multimode systems

Consider as the design target the maximisation of the section length of a digital system operating at 140Mbit/s and using a directly modulated laser with 1mW (0dB) output power and a spectral width under modulation of 3nm.

Since we want to maximise the length the obvious choice of wavelength is the 1550nm window. At 1550nm the fibre loss is around 0.3dB/km with an intermodal dispersion of 120ps/km and a intramodal dispersion of 17ps/nm.km. With a 3nm spectral width the total dispersion is 130ps/km. Assuming that 1dB dispersion penalty can be tolerated the maximum dispersion limited section length for a quarter of a bit duration dispersion is 13.7km. This length corresponds to a fibre loss of 4.1dB and the system is dispersion limited. Because of that one can design a receiver with reduced sensitivity using a p-i-n detector. For the example discussed here let us assume that the theoretical receiver sensitivity is –

30dBm. The various impairments and margins introduced reflect current practice and they are expected to change as better understanding is achieved. The system power budget is summarised in Table 53.7.

Table 53.7 System power budget

Transmitter output (dBm)		–3.0
Receiver sensitivity (dBm)		–30.0
Available section loss capability (dBm)		27.0
Transmitter penalties		
Implementation penalties (dB)	0.5	
Temperature effects (dB)	1.0	
Ageing effects (dB)	0.5	
Total transmitter penalty (dB)		2.5
Receiver penalties		
Implementation (dB)	1.5	
Temperature effects (dB)	1.0	
Digital regenerator (dB)	1.5	
Ageing (dB)	0.5	
Total receiver penalty (dB)		4.5
System margins		
Operating margin (dB)	3.0	
Connectors (pair) (dB)	1.0	
Cable repairs (dB)	2.0	
Dispersion penalty (dB)	1.0	
Total system margin (dB)		7.0
Section loss capability (dB)		13
Section loss (dB)		4.1
Additional system margin (dB)		8.9

The additional system margin can be used in a variety of ways. For example if the dispersion penalty increases to 3dB the dispersion limited section length increases to 19.2km. This represents an additional total loss of 3.65dB reducing the margin to 5.25dB.

This example indicates the limitations of multimode transmission for high bit rates and low loss fibre. Had the dispersion been negligible the section loss capability would have been equivalent to 46.6km and this big difference is the fundamental reason for the introduction of single mode transmission.

53.5.3 Design of single mode systems

As a design example for a single mode system consider the problem of maximising the section length of a 2.4Gbit/s system. Again the optimum wavelength window is around 1550nm where top quality single mode fibre has a loss of 0.2dB/km. The dispersion at 1550nm depends on the class of the fibre. Fibre designed for zero dispersion at 1300nm has 16 to 18ps/km.nm dispersion at 1550nm. On the other hand fibre designed for zero dispersion at 1550nm is usually specified as having a window within which the dispersion is less than a given number. A usual number for this tolerance is 3ps/km.nm.

In the design of high capacity single mode systems using non-dispersion shifted fibre one of the problems is laser chirping. Chirping takes place because in directly modulated lasers the injection of the modulation current forces a small but nevertheless crucial wavelength shift in the single longitudinal mode of the device. For well designed DFB lasers the chirping is of the order of 0.1nm to 0.3nm.

In spite this small value chirping imposes a significant limitation on the section length. For example with conventional fibre of 16ps/km.nm dispersion and a 0.2nm chirp the 1db dispersion penalty corresponds to 32km. Again the system is dispersion limited but this time not exclusively due to dispersion but also to the interaction of laser dynamics (chirp) with dispersion. With a DSF the 1dB dispersion penalty corresponds to 173km.

The dispersion penalty for $(LD(\lambda)\Delta\lambda <) t_c$, where t_c is half the period of the laser relaxation oscillations, is given by Equation 53.76, and for $LD(\lambda)\Delta\lambda > t_c$ by Equation 53.77.

$$Penalty\,(dB) = 10\log\left(\frac{1}{1 - 4\,LD(\lambda)\,B\,\Delta\lambda}\right) \quad (53.76)$$

$$Penalty\,(dB) = 10\log\left(\frac{1}{1 - 4\,B\,t_c}\right) \quad (53.77)$$

For example assume that $t_c = 80$ps. Then with $\Delta\lambda = 0.15$nm the maximum $LD(\lambda)$ product is 0.533ns/nm. For $LD(\lambda) = 0.5$ the penalty is 5.53 at 2.4Gbit/s.

The obvious solution to the chirp problem with directly modulated lasers is to use DSF. However, the use of external modulators such as LiNbO or electro-optic absorption devices offers possible alternatives if the use of DSF is not possible. This is particularly important in upgrading installed NDSF fibre. The design of a single mode system is similar to that of a multimode system outlined earlier.

53.6 Applications of fibre optic communications

The basic characteristics of fibre optic communications are the low loss and large bandwidth of the channel (the fibre), the high performance, compactness and reliability of the components (sources and detectors) and the high performance subsystems possible (optical receivers and transmitters). These features, combined with the rapid progress made in integrated electronics, has ensured fibre optic penetration into virtually all the communication applications ranging from submarine systems to data buses for avionics. Considering that it was only twenty years ago when it became clear that it was possible to realise the potential of fibre transmission this rapid and virtually complete acceptance of the new technology is quite unusual. The impact of fibre optic communications lies not so much in that they can do better than other technologies but they have altered the way the communication issues of the next century will be approached.

53.6.1 Submarine fibre optic systems

The impact of fibre communications in submarine communications has been greater than that on terrestrial applications. In submarine applications not only the medium has changed, from coaxial cable

to fibre, but also the transmission format, the system configuration and the long term prospects of submarine communications. The key to this change is the high reliability of the electro-optics components. Submarine systems are planned and designed for 25 years service with a maximum of three repairs, because repairs of these systems are time consuming and expensive operations.

The first submarine system was the Transatlantic telephone cable (TAT-8) connecting the USA with the UK and France. The distance is about 6000km and the information capacity of the system was 560Mbit/s realised with 2 x 280Mbit/s channels. The loss and dispersion requirements were satisfied by operating single mode at 1300nm with a chromatic dispersion of less that 2ps/km.nm, Fabry-Perot laser and a InGaAsP p-i-n detector followed by an integrated Si transimpedance receiver. The receiver sensitivity was –31dBm, –2dBm optical power and with 6dB total margin the available section loss was 23dB including the splice losses. With 0.45dB/km loss the section length was 50km.

The system was commissioned in 1988 and its success encouraged the installation of other systems such as the Trans Pacific Cable TPC-3 (2 x 280Mbit/s; 1988) the California to Hawaii HAW 1 (2 x 280 Mbit/s; 1988), the Private Transatlantic Cable PTAP-1 (2 x 420 Mbit/s; 1989), the North Pacific Cable NPC (3 x 565 Mbit/s; 1990) and the TAT-9 system (2 x 560 Mbit/s; 1991). TAT-9 is the most complex of the submarine systems designed. At the American end there are two spurs. One from Canada (220 km) and one from the USA (1320 km). They combine in an undersea branching multiplexer/demultiplexer. Then there are 4600km across the North Atlantic to another undersea multiplexer/demultiplexer out of which there are three spurs. One to UK (530km), one to France (302km) and one to Spain (1390km). This system is the first to use the 1550nm window with DFB lasers, p-i-n detectors and integrated silicon bipolar receivers. The section length is 120km using NDSF.

53.6.2 Terrestrial fibre optic systems

The first application of fibre optic communications were in terrestrial systems. The first systems were operating at 850nm using multimode transmission but the advances made in the performance of the fibre at the 1300nm window and of the electro-optics forced the migration of the applications to this wavelength.

Bit rates of 140MBit/s and above are used in the trunk network and those below in the junction network. Trunk systems use lasers and high sensitivity p-i-n/FET or APD receivers and because the aim is to maximise section length, single mode fibres are used. Junction systems usually use LEDs and multimode fibre because the dispersion penalty is negligible.

The length of trunk system varies and depends on the distribution of population. System length can be as short as 50km but as long as 1000km. In Europe and some areas of the USA system lengths are of the order of 100km to 150km. The length of junction systems is around 2km to 25km. Therefore the benefits of using fibre in long haul transmission are not apparent in the junction network. Nevertheless, fibre optic systems are used in the junction network because they are able to operate without repeaters in the congested environment of the urban areas.

The majority of optical systems currently in operation use the 1300nm window but the requirements for higher capacity, that is 2.4Gbit/s and higher, and the trend for un-repeatered transmission ensured that future systems will operate at 1550nm. The technology needed for this migration is DFB lasers and long wavelength APDs. They are both beginning to be available in volume and at prices which will lead to cost effective systems.

3.7 The future of fibre networks

ι the early 1980's an attempt was made in North America to
ddress the shortcomings of the asynchronous multiplexing struc-
re then in use. The main task was to try and avoid the multiplexed
gnal 'hiding' its contents amongst control and stuffing bits. The
nly way to extract information in this format was to completely
emultiplex the signal to extract a single channel. A standard called
yntran was the result of this work supported primarily by Bellcore
3ell Communications Research). Syntran, however, as its name
ıggests, required a synchronous environment in order to permit
ccess to any low order signal within the multiplexed high order
gnal without having to demultiplex the whole thing.

Needing a synchronous network is not a bad idea, in fact it is the
hole basis of the new Synchronous Digital Hierarchy transmission
andards (known as SONET in North America), however, at the
me Syntran was introduced the benefits of using it did not over-
ɔme the difficulties of implementing it. Consequently, Syntran saw
ery little application in the North American network.

At about the same time that Syntran was being developed there
as an emerging need in the fibre optic network to develop mid span
ıeet standards. That is, a standard that would allow different
ıanufacturers products on each end of a fibre to communicate. At
ıe time each vendor used proprietary methods of encoding infor-
ıation into an optical signal; the only common interface being at
ιe electrical asynchronous ports.

As a result of this need for easy access to low order signals and
ıid span meet on fibres the new SONET (Synchronous Optical
etwork) standard was developed in North America. Before the

standard was completed there was significant interest expressed by
the CCITT standards body, resulting in a modification to SONET to
make it adaptable to CCITT plesiochronous bit rates. The standard
issued by CCITT became known as SDH (Synchronous Digital
Hierarchy).

53.7.1 Basics of SONET/SDH

The principle behind the standard is to create a synchronous fibre
optic network that can accept asynchronous electrical tributary
signals and carry them through the network in payloads, the payload
being of a higher bandwidth than the tributary (See chapter 42). The
tributary is allowed to 'float' around within the payload due to the
difference in clock rates between the synchronous fibre network and
the asynchronous electrical network. As the tributary floats around
it is necessary to know exactly where it is should it need to be
extracted for termination at its destination in the network. This is
done through the use of pointer tables that are attached to a payload
as overhead bytes. The pointer table identifies where within the
payload the first byte of the tributary is located.

The lowest rate SDH signal is called STM1 (Synchronous Transport Module) and is defined at 155.52mbit/s, including payload and
overhead. Higher rate signals are exact multiples of the STM1
signal. Each of these signals has the same structure; floating payloads of tributary traffic and an overhead carrying pointers. The
overhead actually carries other information besides the pointers. It
carries information channels that allow the SDH products to communicate with each other throughout the network. They can exchange maintenance information (alarms, error rates, protection

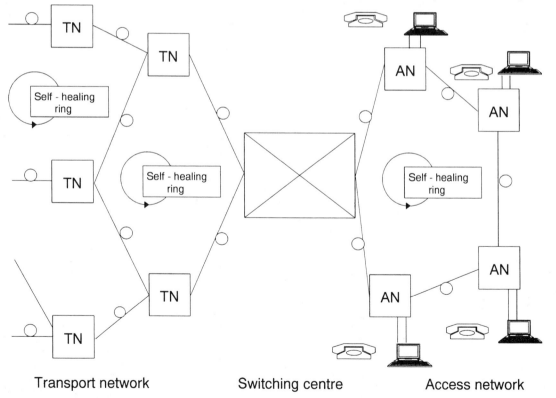

Transport network   Switching centre   Access network

Figjure 53.32 Typical end to end Sonet/SDH network with integral OAM&P

switching etc.) that permits widespread network management and control from a single point.

Compared to plesiochronous (or asynchronous in North America), SDH brings five major benefits to the network that make deployment very worthwhile:

1. Multi-vendor. There is now a standard allowing for the mixing of products from a variety of vendors without having to be concerned about interfaces. In fact this history of interface issues forced the structure of the telephone network into categories of switching and transmission with well defined boundaries at which interface problems were dealt with. This need no longer be true.

2. Flexibility. As SDH now allows us to reach in to any multiplexed signal and extract only the information we need it frees the network designer from a cost problem. The problem used to be that back to back multiplexers had to be used to perform this add/drop function which was very costly. As a result this tended to be avoided or centralised to reduce costs, either of which led to difficult engineering rules that limited service responsiveness to the end user.

3. Control. Combined with the flexibility inherent in the SDH network, the control available through the overhead maintenance channels gives the telephone company the ability to respond to customer service needs immediately. The software intensive design of these new generation products also means that the telephone company will be able to dialogue with individual terminals and obtain status reports on performance.

4. Reliability. SDH will have an overall effect of simplifying the network. An SDH terminal performs several levels of multiplexing and optical conversion all in one unit thus reducing the number of network elements required. A simpler network combined with sophisticated control capability and the intelligence in each terminal to report on its health (and correct it if necessary) results in a very reliable network.

5. Transmission capacity. Because SDH is a standard for fibre transmission it brings all the benefits of the bandwidth of fibre to the network. An STM16 product has a 2.4Gbit/s capacity, far greater than todays plesiochronous products. And this is not the limit since the standard could support up to 9.6Gbit/s on conventional single mode fibre cable! Now the network need not be service restricted due to bandwidth bottlenecks.

A typical SDH based network is shown in Figure 53.32.

The fibre optic cable can be directly connected to the switch, since all of the SDH based bandwidth can now be managed by software control. As fibres enter the central office there would be no need for patch panels or cross-connects as all bandwidth assignment and capacity grooming will be performed throughout the network at each network element. Nor will it be necessary to segregate traffic in the central office for management based on type of service. All fibres will connect to one switch capable of handling all service whether analog or digital; voice, data or video; narrowband, wide band or broadband; connection oriented or connectionless.

Traffic needing to go on into the network will do so on very high capacity fibres again configured as rings for survivability. Service provisioning now becomes a keyboard entry that is interpreted and transmitted to all network elements immediately, providing rapid response to the end user.

54 Packet switching

Jim Costello
Telecommunications Consultant

Paul Dyer
Northern Telecom

David L Jeanes
Bell Northern Research

Contents

54.1 History and underlying concepts

Packet switching is a mature, secure method of transferring data across a network. It divides data into segments, each of which is wrapped in an envelope to form a packet; a typical message comprises one or more packets. Each packet contains the actual user data plus information helpful to its movement across the network, such as addressing, sequencing and error control.

A tried and tested, robust technique, packet switching attracts a large and growing installed base. It is ideal for transaction-oriented applications such as banking, point-of-sale retail and electronic mail. Investment in packet switching continues to grow at over 25% per annum, largely in the private sector, while most industrialised countries offer at least one public data network based on the technology.

The driving force behind the development of packet switching was the need in the late 1960s for asynchronous terminals to access numerous remote hosts. Its rapid acceptance owes much to the wide implementation of the X.25 international standard interface to packet switched networks (PSNs).

While private leased lines offer fixed bandwidth, security and protocol transparency, data transfer speed is limited by the capability of the attached modems, re-routeing is impossible, unused bandwidth is unavailable to other users and a charge is levied for the line irrespective of use.

Circuit switching, as found in a conventional telephone network, provides a dedicated circuit for the duration of the call and charges according to time and distance. However, public voice networks are optimised for voice, prone to data-corrupting noise and are normally without security, such as call screening, for dial-up access to a host computer.

As networks have grown in size and importance, functions such as routeing, error correction and flow control have also become essential.

Packet switching therefore evolved to distribute these components throughout a network. It is a subset of traditional message switching, in which data is transmitted in blocks, stored by the first switching node it meets in the network and forwarded to the next and subsequent downstream nodes until it reaches the destination.

At its heart is the concept of the virtual circuit: a fixed path through the network from sender to destination is defined at the beginning of the session or call. The path remains unchanged for the duration of the connection. (Figure 54.1).

The idea owes much to statistical multiplexing, in which many switched circuits can be active on a single physical link – an efficient use of a circuit's available bandwidth. Extending the idea beyond statistical multiplexing, however, packet switching offers the following advantages:

1. Each terminal in a group sharing the same physical circuit may be connected to a totally different destination. This versatility is one of the major strengths of packet switching. (Figure 54.2).

2. Unlike message switching, packet switching has a block size limit, usually 128 bytes or 256 bytes, but up to 4096 bytes on some networks, thereby reducing storage demands or buffering in the nodes, as well as delay at each node.

3. No single user or large data block can tie up circuit or node resources indefinitely, making it well suited for interactive traffic.

4. Data protection against corruption or loss; errors are corrected by retransmission.

5. Users can select different destinations for each virtual call, overcoming the inflexibility of point-to-point dedicated networks.

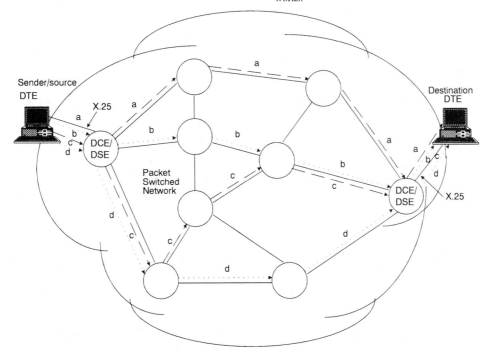

Figure 54.1 The virtual circuit concept: multiple paths

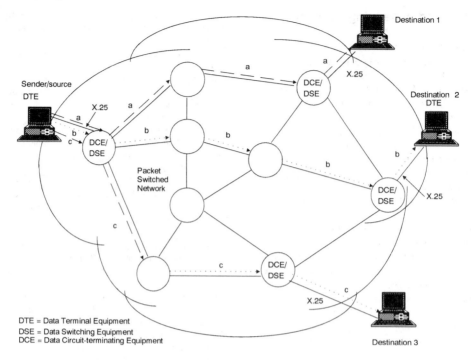

Figure 54.2 The virtual circuit concept: multiple destinations

6. Simultaneous calls allow PC users to access multiple windows to different remote applications.
7. Since many users can share transmission resources efficiently, the cost of intermittent data communications is reduced.
8. New calls can be added and old ones disconnected without affecting other users.

While suppliers have increased the number and sophistication of switch functions over the years, supporting a myriad of terminal and host protocols, the X.25 specification of an interface to PSNs remains standard and non-proprietary, offering users flexibility in equipment choice.

The first recommendations for a standard PSN interface were laid down in 1976 by a subcommittee of the CCITT (International Telephone and Telegraph Consultative Committee). They have evolved into the X.25 international standard, approved by the International Standards Organisation in 1984 (ISO 8208), for accessing a host over a wide area network.

Geographically scattered standalone LANs can be interconnected to form a single logical LAN using X.25 over WAN links, taking advantage of its shareable, protocol independent data transport mechanism. Built under the Open Systems Interconnection framework, the network can be upgraded to take advantage of new developments, leaving the software affecting the upper layers in place.

Significantly, the recommendations say nothing about the internal protocols and algorithms needed to run a PSN but describe the interface between Data Terminal Equipment (DTE) and Data Circuit-terminating Equipment (DCE) for devices designed to run in packet mode. Rather than being a protocol in itself, the X.25 specification describes an interface using individual protocols at the three lowest layers of the OSI model.

54.2 Packet switched call

Each call on a PSN is made up of several steps (Figure 54.3), similar in their progression to a switched telephone call. A terminal user enters a command for connection to the network, then the numeric network address of the destination.

On hitting the Enter key, a specially formatted call request packet is generated and sent across the network; it holds the network address of both the source and destination. If the call is unacceptable, the destination host may reject the call and disconnect. If the call is accepted, a call connected packet is returned to the sender, indicating that an end-to-end switched virtual circuit (SVC) has been established for the duration of the call.

To either end, the terminal and host, the SVC looks like a circuit switched connection, but because packets can take any route in the network, call set-up time is less, often measured in tenths of a second compared to several seconds.

Typically, the first PSE in the chain determines to which particular link the call request packet will be forwarded and sends it to the next PSE along that route. This continues until the data reaches its destination.

Once connection is made, the data transfer begins: electronic mail, updates to databases and so on. It is the network's responsibility to ensure fast, error-free data delivery, transparently between the two end points.

Network operations at this stage include sorting the packets into the correct sequence at the destination, flow control (ensuring data input rates match delivery rates) and signalling, i.e. notifying the source or destination of any unusual network events.

The final phase of a packet call is disconnection or call clearing, by either the source or destination. A unique packet notifies the network and the opposite end that the call is to be cleared and the SVC freed.

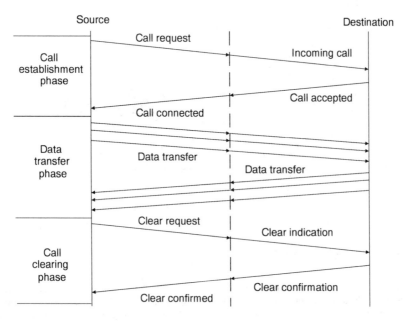

Figure 54.3 Phases of a PSN call

Each user-originated call over the network demands its own virtual circuit, whether a SVC, emulating the PSTN, or permanent link, such as a leased line. For a permanent-circuit, the DTEs are permanently connected, obviating the need for a call set-up phase.

54.3   The packet switched network

A DTE is a generic term for any equipment designed to manipulate packets that is attached to the network (Figure 54.4). It could be an end-user terminal or a standalone minicomputer running X.25 soft-

ware and offering an X.25 port, for example. It could also be a Packet Assembler/Disassembler (PAD), converting data between X.25 and other communications protocols, allowing devices unable to support X.25, such as ASCII terminals, to access an X.25 based PSN.

The term PAD is often applied too widely, covering any device allowing non-X.25 devices to communicate over an X.25 based network, such as devices supporting SNA to X.25 conversion.

A PAD assembles packets as data arrives from attached users in asynchronous, character by character, form. It assigns relevant addresses and error correction data and forwards the packets on to the

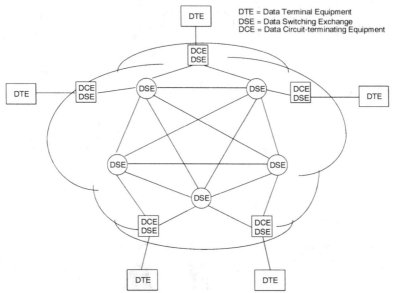

Figure 54.4 PSN mesh topology

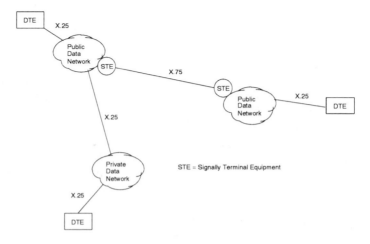

Figure 54.5   Interworking PSNs via X.25 and X.75

switch. Conversely, it sorts data arriving from the switch in packets, converting the packets into a character stream again for onward passage to the recipient computer.

PADs are most widely used for asynchronous display terminals but can support printers, terminals servers and other devices. There need not be a PAD at both ends of the call – one end may be a PAD tackling a terminal's asynchronous signals, the other might be a mainframe host with a direct connection through an X.25 port.

PADs invariably support three CCITT standards: X.3, X.28 and X.29, allowing each PAD port to match the requirements of incoming terminals and remote host computers. X.3 defines PAD parameters, such as whether or not it echoes keystrokes back to the screen; X.28 and X.29 control how those parameters are installed, X.28 from terminal to PAD via a keyboard command and X.29 from host to PAD via a so-called qualifier bit in a data packet.

Each X.25 port in the network and all the devices associated with it such as modems and cables, constitute a DCE.

No CCITT specification exists for DCE-to-DCE communications, so data must pass through an intermediate device known as a Data or Packet Switching Exchange (PSE), either at an intermediate or at a destination point on the network. PSEs are usually linked in a mesh topology, providing at least two circuits to each node, their bandwidth determined by traffic demand. (Figure 54.5).

While the CCITT standards offer guidance for access to a PSN, what goes on inside it is left entirely to the network suppliers and PSE manufacturers such as Northern Telecom. The internal protocol usually resembles X.25 but adds functionality such as flow control, network management and accounting.

Internetworking between discrete PSNs is increasingly important, such as between private and public networks. It takes place via virtual circuits through gateways. The CCITT X.75 recommendation supports X.25 to provide such a gateway in special nodes known as signalling terminal equipment (STE).(Figure 54.5). They provide connectivity services but operate at the first three OSI

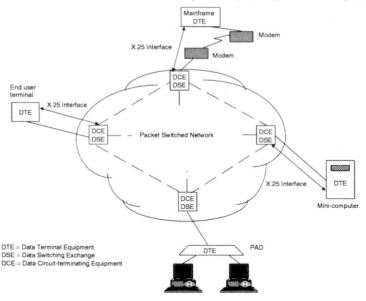

Figure 54.6   Inside and outside the X.25 cloud

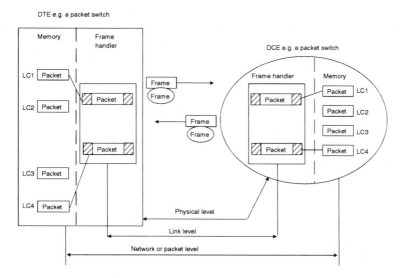

Figure 54.7 X.25 packet switch recommendation for PSN access

layers in contrast to a full OSI gateway that employs all seven layers.(Figure 54.6).

54.4 Packet switching and the OSI model

At the Physical, Data Link and Network layers of the OSI seven layer model, equipment at customer premises or in the network must share a compatible set of interfaces and signalling conventions to comply with the X.25 standard.

Each level or layer is responsible for one aspect of the total X.25 based communication. It is functionally independent from the other layers, interacting with them in clearly defined areas, providing a service to the level above and receiving a service from any lower level. Corresponding levels on the other side of the link, a level's peer, communicate via a peer protocol, co-ordinating the exchange of information between peer levels across the interface. (Figure 54.7).

The higher layers proposed by the ISO, through which data passes before reaching the packet switching layers, have not been fully laid out, though their overall aims are well defined. Once at the X.25 level, communication can be established between an end point device and the corresponding X.25 level of the local DCE. Having passed the local DTE/DCE interface, a conversion to the network protocol takes place for transport through intermediate nodes in the network. (Figure 54.8).

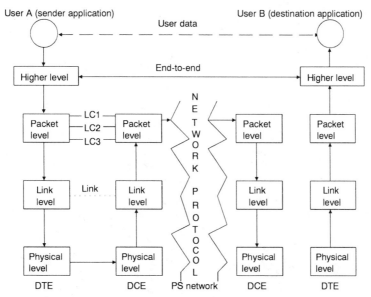

Figure 54.8 PSN transportation through the OSI layers

At the destination DCE, conversion back to the X.25 protocol takes place for transporting the message across the DCE/DTE interface, the data then moving up each of the seven layers until it reaches the final application at the destination end point device.

54.4.1 Packet switching at the Physical Layer

The Physical Layer describes the physical connection — the electrical interface and procedures involved in establishing a communication path. The connection outside the X.25 cloud is between an end point device, such as a user terminal, and a PSE on the network. Within the cloud, connections are between the PSEs themselves as they make up the network.

Each network link will have different characteristics, chosen according to many parameters such as the maximum acceptable error rate, minimum rate of transfer and the distance over which the circuit must run.

The most common medium for DTE to DCE connection is copper via a leased line to a public data network, but fibre links are becoming increasingly cost effective. Depending on the electrical signalling, devices may be connected directly, otherwise line drivers or modems are necessary to carry the signals over long distances.

Up to about one million bits per second over distances below about one kilometre, twisted pair (ordinary telephone wire) is normally adequate. Beyond this fibre optic cable, which is insensitive to electrical noise, may be required to ensure the error rate on the link is not so high that the error detection and correction at layer 3 is rendered ineffective.

The CCITT chose the X.21 specification as the physical interface between a DTE and DCE for X.25, despite the prevalence of the Electrical Industries Association's RS-232-C standard for computer-modem connections. There are only minor differences, however, with X.21 geared eventually to delivering a digital signal to customer premises, replacing the analogue circuit switched network with ISDN.

Prior to ISDN, the CCITT approved an interim standard, X.21bis, which is practically identical to the ubiquitous RS-232-C. It specifies a leased line connection, but dial-up is feasible.

Information passing across the interface at this level comprises three signal types:

1. Data signals transfer the higher level information between the two devices, a signal carrying data in one direction and another in the other direction.
2. Clock signals, in conjunction with data signals, reconstruct transmitted information at the destination.
3. Where devices are connected directly via an X.25 port, software handles flow control (which monitors the amount of traffic on the circuit) automatically as part of the protocol functions. Asynchronous traffic, however, makes use of control

signals to manage the link traffic volumes and to decide whether the circuit is in an acceptable condition.

In-band or software flow control involves special control characters or bit patterns sent by the receiver, such as a terminal or a PAD, which are embedded in the normal data stream to tell the transmitter to slow down its data output.

After a receiving device has submitted a clear-to-send signal, it has the option of dropping the command at any time if traffic becomes too heavy, a process known as out-of-band or hardware flow control. This method in effect stretches the function of an RS-232 command originally intended for modem control. The whole subject of flow control outside of software based controls, though, is the subject of complex debate.

Within X.25, much of the responsibility for flow control is given to layers 2 and 3. It should be remembered, too, that the Physical Layer takes no account of line transmission quality. It passes valid and corrupted data with equal enthusiasm along the circuit; its job is only to hide the nature of the physical media from the Data Link Layer above.

54.4.2 Packet switching at the Data Link Layer

The aim of the Data Link Layer is to ensure that data passing between devices is error free and in the correct order. Given the global influence of the X.25 standard, it is no surprise that the most important PSN link layer in use is X.25 layer 2, although there are other variations of layer 2 implementation that achieve the same objective.

Link layer information is passed between the two end point devices in frames. The most common protocol used for encapsulating data into frames is the ISO's High-Level Data Link Control (HDLC) dating back to the mid-1970s. Its origins lie in work done by IBM seeking to replace older Binary Synchronous Communications with its Synchronous Data Link Control protocol.

Unlike previous protocols, HDLC, SDLC and their peers, such as ANSI's Advanced Data Communications Control Procedure, are bit oriented rather than character oriented. Frame length in a bit oriented protocol is an arbitrary number of bits rather than a fixed multiple of a selected character size. This makes life simpler by reducing the number of necessary framing and control characters. The CCITT adopted HDLC largely intact, producing the Link Access Procedure Balanced (LAPB).

54.4.2.1   *The make-up of a frame*

A basic X.25 level 2 or HDLC (Figure 54.9) frame opens and closes with a flag, a specific pattern of bits transmitted on the link to act as reference points for frame synchronisation. When there are no

Flag 01111110	Address field	Control field	Information field	Frame check sequence	Flag 01111110
8 bits	8 bits	8 bits	N bits	16 bits	8 bits

Figure 54.9   An X.25 level 2 frame: HDLC structure

frames to transmit on a circuit, flags are sent continuously to fill in time and maintain synchronisation between the two end points.

When a recipient detects a flag, it examines the data stream for an eight bit address field or area, used to identify to which direction of transfer the frame belongs. A control field specifies what the frame contains and carries frame sequence numbers, acknowledgements, retransmission requests and other control information.

Next comes the information field, containing the actual user data, followed by a frame check sequence (FCS) of bits by which the receiver determines, by reference to a checksum, whether or not frames have been received correctly.

A final or trailing flag marks the end of the frame and indicates to the receiver that the preceding 16 bits should be interpreted as the FCS field. The recipient processes the data stream, compiles its own FCS and compares the result with the FCS received in the frame. If they match, the data is correct, otherwise the frame is discarded and the receiver issues a retransmission request.

HDLC and LAPB contain three types of frame, each built up from the building blocks outlined above:

1. Unnumbered frames carry no send or receive sequence numbers and simply offer additional data link control functions such as circuit initialisation and disconnection, helping to set up and later close down or reset links.
2. Supervisory frames control information flow, request retransmissions and acknowledgement frames. They contain commands such as Receive Ready from a DTE or DCE or a temporary busy condition, for example.
3. Information frames are the only frames to transport data across the link.

To establish the link under LAPB, either end of the DTE/DCE link can begin link initialisation by sending out the relevant command, known as the Set Asynchronous Balanced Mode (SABM). Acceptance of the SABM is confirmed by the other end when it issues an Unnumbered Acknowledgement response. Once this process is complete, I-frames can begin to flow.

54.4.2.2   *Error correction and flow control*

As mentioned above, the Data Link Layer is responsible for error correction and flow control of I-frames. The most common technique is known as positive acknowledgement. A recipient must acknowledge that a frame has been received correctly. Alternatively, but less common, the receiver may only respond to a received frame if it is not received correctly: negative acknowledgement.

At its most basic, the transmission process works as follows. A sender transmits a frame then waits for an acknowledgement from the recipient. If the checksum is correct, the frame is regarded by the receiver as correctly received and the receiver sends back an acknowledgement. If the checksum is incorrect, the frame is regarded as corrupted. The receiver discards that frame and simply waits.

If the sender successfully receives an acknowledgement, it assumes the frame has been correctly transferred and can send the next. If nothing arrives within a set acknowledgement period, it assumes the frame was not correctly received and re-transmits, waiting again for a response. If this is repeated a set number of times, the sender assumes the link is faulty.

There are, however, complications such as frame corruption, an incorrectly received acknowledgement and even the appearance of false frames due to electrical interference. To help identify one frame from another, each information frame is assigned a pair of sequence numbers, carried for X.25 level 2 in the control field, operating in both the send and receive directions.

The initial frame carries a sequence number in a three bit field. The receiver, maintaining a count of error free frames received, sends an acknowledgement carrying the sequence number of that first frame then adds one to the sequence number, which is the anticipated number of the next frame. The sender receives the acknowledgement, adds one to the sequence number, attaches it to the next frame and repeats the process, which is known as a Modulo-8 or Modulo-N frame level window.

If, therefore, a receiver's reply is corrupted, the transmitter can ignore the frame and wait for the acknowledgement time to expire. It then sends the original frame again: as the receiver has successfully received the frame on the sender's first attempt, it will be expecting a frame marked with the next sequence number along. It can conclude that the sender did not receive a correct acknowledgement, discard the repeated frame and resend the original acknowledgement.

Sequence numbers range from zero to seven, avoiding the problem of large numbers taking up valuable frame space. It could work with just two numbers: in the example above, the initial frame could be labelled 0 and the faulty acknowledgement 1. The receiver will be sent the retransmitted frame, still numbered 0 and can see immediately what has happened.

To avoid the sender having to wait for an acknowledgement before transmitting the next frame, thereby limiting throughput due to the time taken to transmit, check and process frames, X.25 level 2 adopts a window size of seven. This means the sender can transmit up to seven frames before an acknowledgement is required, allowing the receiver to be relatively slow and utilising the circuit more efficiently.

As data will normally flow in both directions on a link simultaneously (full duplex operation) different sequence numbers are allotted for each direction. A device will therefore transmit and receive a mixture of information frames and acknowledgement frames.

Some packet switch protocols, including X.25 level 2, can piggyback an I-frame with an acknowledgement frame that acknowledges a I-frame from the other direction. Although often difficult to implement, it reduces the total number of frames transmitted and received.

The Modulo-N or window-N system of sequence numbering enables the Data Link Layer to detect and correct corrupted frames. The limited window size plus the numbering provides flow control.

Should a receiver be unable to process frames as fast as is necessary at any one point in the communication, it simply stops acknowledging frames it is receiving. The sender transmits as many frames as are allowed before it needs an acknowledgement, then stops and waits, giving the receiver a chance to catch up.

A DTE or DCE can suspend transmission by issuing a disconnect command, acknowledged by the receiver through a UA response as for set-up, after which the link can be closed.

The LAPB protocol also contains a complex variety of commands and responses indicating reasons for retransmission, frame reject responses and so on.

Within the Data Link Layer mandate to ensure error free transmission, the CCITT X.25 1984 recommendation added a service known as the Multilink Procedure (MLP). The function of MLP is to distribute packets from layer 3 across multiple physical links (Figure 54.10). It is most associated with expensive international rather than national links.

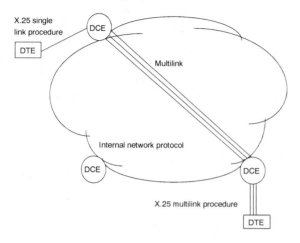

Figure 54.10 Multilink procedure within a PSN

Although packets carried along the same virtual circuit may travel on different physical paths, to the Network Layer, these different physical links appear as one logical circuit. MLP manages any number of Single Link Procedures, each of which is an orthodox LAPB circuit. It carries out resequencing for all received frames over different physical links, adding a multilink control field and an information field to each frame

MLP offers several advantages:

1. Load sharing or balancing is an inherent strength within MLP.

2. Improved reliability and resilience against link failure as packets flow via different physical paths.
3. Additional bandwidth to support increased traffic can be added incrementally without affecting or disrupting existing physical connections.

Packet switch links over satellite are subject to far longer transit delays than normal, around 250ms one way, making X.25 inefficient if used with Modulo-8 windows. The sender will be idle for relatively long periods waiting for acknowledgements.

ISO and the CCITT therefore produced Modulo-128, within LAPB, allowing up to 127 frames to remain outstanding before an acknowledgement is needed. Currently available only within some public PSNs, it is accessed through an extended SABM command. A future development is likely to be some form of hot keying between Modulo 8 and Modulo 128 modes.

54.4.3 Packet switching at the Network Layer

While the Data Link Layer sorted out an error free link between two connected devices, the Network Layer provides communications between devices that are not necessarily connected together they will have a network in between them.

Network Layer terminology talks of information in packets rather than in their Data Link equivalent, frames. A Network Layer for an X.25 PSN is connection oriented. A connection is established between two end point devices via a virtual circuit, and making that connection is a major function of this layer.

Much of layer 3's work is transparent to end users, such as multiplexing simultaneous calls over a single physical connection.

Routeing, relaying, packet sequencing and flow control are also functions of the Network Layer, plus providing services to the Transport Layer and higher layers, such as addressing and data transfer.

To make a normal telephone call, it is necessary to know the number at the other end. In the same way, Network Layer connections rely on a system of reference that provides a unique address to locate each device attached to the network. Two methods predominate in providing end point addressing for PSN attached devices.

Depending on the size and complexity of the network, each device can be given a unique address that remains valid throughout the network. From anywhere on the network, the device can be contacted via that address and the address remains the same at all times.

Alternatively, the route taken to reach a device is used to build up the address, so that the address differs according to the route taken and, naturally, also depends on the starting point on the network. A device's address is an outline of the route the data will take to reach it.

In Figure 54.11 the network links are numbered from one to nine. An end point device at A sending data to end point device B could

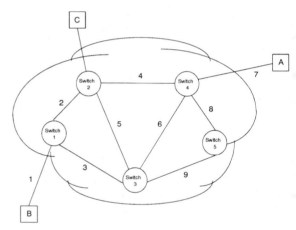

Figure 54.11 Addressing example

take a route along circuit seven to six, six to three, three to one and out to B. From A's viewpoint, B's address would be 7631 along this particular route. For C to send data to B, the shortest route would be via circuit two followed by one. B's address from C's viewpoint would be just 21.

Known as a route addressing system, a feature of this method is that the address of any end point device will vary according to who is sending data, in contrast to the global addressing system in which an end point's address remains the same irrespective of wherever it is being sent data.

A typical call set-up in Figure 54.11 would occur as follows. Device A establishes a virtual call on a virtual circuit to device B by sending a call request packet down its link to packet switch 4. A call request packet requests a communications path be established to the called device. It contains the address of that called device and often the address of the calling device, too, so that the recipient knows where the call has originated.

Packet switch 4 looks at its routeing table to decide over which link the call request should be passed en route to its destination. It decides to pass the request to packet switch 2 which carries out the same process and sends it to switch 1 which passes the request to the destination device.

If B decides to accept the call request, it returns a call accepted packet along the route set up by A's request. The communications path is now successfully established, the virtual call created, between devices A and B and end-to-end information can now be transferred.

Should B reject the call, it sends a clear request packet to tell A that the call is unacceptable. At the end of the virtual call, a clear request packet is also sent by one of the parties and acknowledged with a clear confirmation packet.

54.4.3.1   *Logical Channel Numbering*

The network layer can support multiplexing, sustaining many active virtual calls simultaneously. For example, it can set up virtual calls to devices B and C from device A at the same time. As a result, a mechanism has to exist to identify the relevant virtual call along which packets are transmitted and received.

A unique Logical Channel Number is therefore assigned to each virtual call and used to refer to that virtual call for the lifetime of the call. Each packet contains the LCN of the logical call to which it refers at its start, followed by a packet type field explaining the packet's function and any additional information that may be needed depending on the packet type.

For device A to set up a call to B, it assigns a unique LCN to the virtual call, carried in the call request packet. The LCN indicates to packet switch 4 that all other packets transferred between switch 4 and A for this virtual call must carry the same LCN.

The call request packet is then routed across the network to packet switch 1, the most appropriate to device B. Switch 1 then assigns a unique LCN for the for the circuit to device B and sends the call request packet to B using this new LCN, which means all other packets for this virtual call must carry this LCN.

Usually, as in the above example, the LCNs at each end of the virtual call will be different. Furthermore, the LCN is only significant between an end point device and the packet switch to which it is connected.

It is important to remember that within the PSN, internal network links may be subject to different, often enhanced, protocols from those affecting the link between a switch and its attached end-point devices.

Just as in a conventional telephone system, a normal subscriber is plugged into the network via standard circuitry, whereas sophisticated communications equipment comes into play, from fibre optics to satellites, beyond that subscriber interface. At the other end, of course, will probably be another conventional telephone.

The role of X.25 as a standard interface to and from PSNs is paramount in presenting a common face to a user, to whom the complexities and richness of the internal PSN are transparent, and to an end-point device from the attached packet switch.

54.4.3.2   *Network Layer flow control*

Clearly, the sequence of information transfer at the Network or packet level is similar to that of the Data Link Layer. Error detection and correction are by and large left to layer 2, but the Network Layer does impose its own flow control mechanisms. Layer 2 flow control affects all traffic on the link; Network Layer flow control operates only on the information relating to a single virtual call running over a link which may be supporting numerous other virtual calls.

If the Data Link Layer is flow controlled and data is temporarily blocked from running over the circuit, then no Network Layer packets can be transferred. If the Data Link Layer is not flow controlled, but an individual virtual call is being blocked, other virtual calls can operate normally, unaffected by the temporary blocking of that single virtual call.

Flow control at layer 3 is governed, as at layer 2, by the window N system, typified by the X.25 level 3 protocol. The standard sequence number for data transfer in each direction takes up three bits in the packet, with possible sequence numbers running from zero to seven. The maximum window size is therefore seven packets before acknowledgement is needed.

Changing the window size in the Network Layer has a similar effect to changing it in the Data Link Layer, only more so. In a virtual call from device A to B, every packet from A has to pass through packet switches 4, 2 and 1 before reaching B. In other words, the packet on this route must pass across four different links.

Each link adds delay (transit time) before the data gets through. For each packet a network layer acknowledgement must follow down the same tortuous path in the opposite direction to reach device A.

If, for instance, each link in the virtual circuit above imposes a delay of 10ms, ignoring for this example any delay within the switches themselves, the four links used between end point devices A and B amount to an imposed delay of 40ms on each packet travelling one way, and double including the obligatory acknowledgement. But the delay is proportional to packet length and the acknowledgement is usually short, unless piggy-backed.

A window size of one means device A only transmits one packet every 80ms: a maximum packet rate of 12.5 packets every second.

A window size of two makes a dramatic difference. Device A sends the first packet then another 10ms later, the minimum delay time. (Figure 54.12). It takes 40ms for the first packet to reach B, for which B sends an acknowledgement. The second packet arrives 10ms later and is also acknowledged. Acknowledgement of the first packet arrives at device A after 80ms, time taken for the round trip. A then sends a third packet, receives acknowledgement of second packet 10ms after the arrival of the first acknowledgement and is then able to send a fourth packet into the network.

In other words, device A sends two packets in every 80ms period: 25 packets a second to B, twice the rate of a window size of one. If a window size of seven was imposed, device A could send seven packets before the first could feasibly be acknowledged and achieve a packet rate of 87.5 each second.

It may seem odd, then, that the most common window size used in PSNs with the most common interface, X.25, is only two, so that the maximum number of packets that can remain unacknowledged at any one time in each direction is two. Cynics have pointed out that X.25 equipment is usually delivered with the window size set to two and is never altered, but a significant factor is also the storage buffer needed to support a larger window.

At any time, any device may be called upon to buffer the entire window size: all packets sent inside the window of a virtual call. Moreover, that packet switch or end point device may be supporting numerous virtual calls simultaneously, putting considerable potential pressure on its buffer space. If the buffer fills, the device has to resort to emergency action which may mean taking down some calls to retain others.

The Network Layer in some PSNs allows for different window sizes depending on the nature of the virtual call, mainly those calls that need maximum throughput. It will depend on the delay time imposed by different links and packet switches en route between the end point devices. The optimum window size will vary according to

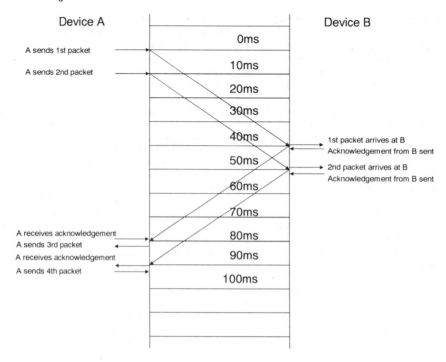

Figure 54.12 Illustration of a window size of two

the end device being called. In other circumstances, an average or compromise window size is chosen to accommodate most calls.

54.5   Datagram networks

An alternative to the concept of the Switched Virtual Circuit or virtual call in providing communications between end point devices over a PSN is a datagram network.

The phases of call set up, information transfer and call clearance are not needed in a datagram network. Each packet is simply launched into the PSN, leaving it up to the PSN to route the packet to its destination. Without call set-up there is no need for LCNs in the Network Layer, but each packet must therefore contain its source and end point destination addresses.

Communicating devices in a datagram network are not connected to each other as in a virtual circuit, so the packet switches do not have to keep records of active calls and can therefore be kept both simple and fast.

If the amount of data to be sent can be confined to a single datagram packet transferred between devices, it can also be very efficient. As call set-up of a virtual call is one of the most time consuming operations for such networks, if the call period is only short, but set-up rates are high, the PSN performance can be seriously impaired.

Described as a lean and mean method of shifting data, datagram bearer networks place responsibility for error correction, resequencing packets on delivery and lost packets from the PSN to the end point node or user device. In terms of the OSI model, these functions are left to the Transport Layer, one above X.25.

Data is broadcast into the network and left to fend for itself, sometimes described as spray and pray, bringing with it some disadvantages:

1. There is no flow control mechanism in a datagram network comparable to that of a virtual call network.
2. As each datagram packet contains its explicit addresses and the network contains no record of connections, every packet switch en route has to look up the specific address in its routeing table to find out where it should switch that packet. This can prove slower than having a LCN identify a route, as happens in a virtual call network.
3. There is no formal acknowledgement system. In circumstances in which errors may be among the data stream due to adverse line quality and so on, a sender cannot be sure the datagram packet was successfully received.

After much controversy and changes of mind, the CCITT X.25 1984 recommendation removed any support for the connectionless datagram method. For many network managers it is comforting to be able to track data to its destination.

Datagrams, however, can still be effective internal network protocols. The idea is to combine the speed and simplicity of datagram packet switches with the advantages of a virtual call network, producing a topology in which the domain outside the cloud is connection oriented, but inside is connectionless. Perhaps the largest example is the US Department of Defence's military oriented research network, Arpanet.

54.6   Routeing over packet switched networks

A packet entering a PSN cloud from an end point device has to be routed to its destination device by the packet switches within the network according to various techniques, each with their own advantages and drawbacks. The choice is usually a balance between

the complexity of the solution and the breadth of routeing function-
lity provided.

The most common PSN architecture is an irregular mesh, reflect-
ng the gradual, if not actually haphazard growth of any large PSN
iming to meet changing user demands. A routeing strategy must be
flexible enough to cope with a different topology as the need arises.

Switch manufacturers provide many different routeing solutions;
researchers have produced literally dozens of routeing algorithms or
ules such as 'hot potato', 'selective flooding' and 'delay-based,
single-path distributed adaptive per-packet' routeing. They are all
decision making processes for deciding which output link is most
appropriate for a given data packet, each allied to a type of routeing.

54.6.1 Fixed or static routeing

The most common overall routeing choice is between fixed, sometimes called static or directory routeing, and dynamic routeing, with
some variations between the two.

The simplest and least expensive strategy is fixed routeing, in
which the network's packet switches are provided with routeing
tables containing all the information they might need to route
packets over that network. It is fairly common among X.25 PSNs to
have fixed routeing.

A routeing table for a packet switch comprises entries for each end
point device connected to the network. In Figure 54.13 there are six,

Table 54.1 Routeing table for switch 2 of the example given in Figure 54.13

End point device 2 address	Link
A	3
B	3
C	4
D	1
E	2
F	2

Table 54.2 Routeing table for switch 3 of the example given in Figure 54.13

End point device 3 address	Link
A	3
B	3
C	3
D	4
E	2
F	1

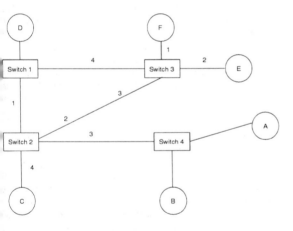

Figure 54.13 Routeing example

so the routeing table for switch 2 in this example (Table 54.1), has
six entries, each showing the address of the end point device (see
also Figure 54.11) and the immediate link down which packets
intended for each device should be routed.

A routeing table for switch 3 (Table 54.2) reveals a different
picture because it looks at the end point devices from a different
perspective within the network.

Packets for more than one end point device can be routed down
the same link. For switch 2 this is true for end point devices A, B
and E, F, in which case, there will be at least one more switch en
route to those destination devices.

A prerequisite of fixed routeing is the construction of routeing
tables which are then loaded into the network switches, usually
when the network is first configured. Adding a new end point device

to the network means updating the table in each switch, a potentially
burdensome task for managers of medium to large networks.

Fixed routeing is straightforward, but depends on manual building
and upkeep of the tables, for which a detailed knowledge of the
network topology and traffic loadings is necessary. Software table
building programmes are available to ease this task.

Not all PSN links necessarily have the same capacity and an
understanding of the particular network usage can be essential for
efficient communications. For example, in Figure 54.13 there are
two routes between switch 2 and switch 3, one direct, the other
indirect through switch 1. The direct circuit may, in fact, be slower
than the alternative or the traffic may be heavy enough to warrant
splitting it between the two routes. Traffic for device E through
switch 2 might best travel directly, while traffic for F should take
the indirect route.

A move in the direction of dynamic routeing is domain addressing,
in which end point device addresses contain some routeing information. In a network of four switches, each switch can be regarded
as a separate domain, from one to four. Addresses of end point
devices linked to each might have a digit referring to their immediate domain, followed by digits identifying them individually within
that domain, such as 101 (number one device linked to packet
switch 1,) or 304 (number three device linked to switch 4).

Routeing tables in domain addressing are kept to a minimum; not
every end point device need be recorded as many may share the
same link to a domain. The switch needs to know only where the
domains are to be found, rather than every device within those
domains. Instead of updating every routeing table on attaching a
new device, only the table of the switch to which the device is
directly linked needs to be altered.

Also, table search time is reduced when a call request packet
arrives and a virtual call path needs to be set up. Alternatively, in a

datagram network, as each datagram packet has to be routed individually, any routeing time saved is particularly significant.

Large PSNs even create sub-domains within domains, just as the digits in an orthodox international telephone number can be subdivided into national, regional and individual areas. As a packet switch only needs routeing information about its immediate domain, the domain addressing technique can be practical for large PSNs without the burden of enormous routeing tables.

However, static routeing is poorly equipped to cope with line failures. As the routeing tables are fixed, the link will remain unavailable until it is restored. Even though there might physically appear to be more than one route from A to B, packets and virtual calls cannot suddenly re-routed if the normal route fails.

As a result, network management systems capable of informing managers of any untoward events as soon as possible are of paramount importance, as manual intervention to alter the routeing tables is the only option.

In practice, load sharing between multiple routes is often a partial answer, with automatic fall backs in the case of a network failure. Alternatively, switches can refer to secondary and even tertiary routeing tables if the primary options become unavailable, although it demands more skill on the part of the network administrators.

Fixed routeing with some degree of dynamic alteration in the event of node failure is generally common in commercial networking environments.

54.6.2 Dynamic routeing

Dynamic routeing is a complex solution favoured in academic or networks such as Arpanet in which security or the lack of commercial demands favour more esoteric methods.

Rather than refer to predetermined routeing tables, packet switches capable of dynamic routeing make their own routeing decisions based on prevailing network conditions. Network managers and installers therefore do not need such a detailed knowledge of the live network; the implementation looks after itself to a degree.

The algorithms involved are capable of recognising both predictable network changes, such as time of day variations in network traffic and unforeseen alterations, such as intermittent circuit problems or a power outage. They are able to compute the optimum path through the network under prevailing conditions, even if it applies for only a short period, such as to relieve congestion at a particular switch.

A switch can time stamp delays on a link, for example, by sending packets known as ping packets to neighbouring nodes and measuring the time needed for the ping packet to complete a round trip.

Where circuit availability between user devices is paramount, dynamic routeing offers immediate alternative routeing between end points in the event of a line or switch failure. Also, load sharing of traffic between routes is more easily obtained, maximising circuit usage and minimising packet transit delay, if decisions can be made by the switches on a packet-by-packet basis.

If some links in the network belong to one or more public PSNs, load sharing through dynamic routeing can ensure that circuits paid for according to traffic load are optimised for maximum cost effectiveness.

54.6.3 Distributed adaptive routeing

A version of dynamic routeing assigns a cost value to each circuit based on available bandwidth, link loading, transit delay and throughput. The number of links or hops in the route is also assigned a value. The optimum path provides the overall lowest cost between

end devices on that specific occasion; congestion at a node, for instance, may well increase the cost so that a cheaper route is found for the rest of the virtual call.

Packet switches can exchange route status information at regular intervals with adjacent or more distant nodes to build up a picture of current network conditions a capability known as distributed adaptive routeing. Arpanet, for instance, employs this form of routeing and is able to circulate information regarding link availability and route loading estimates to end point devices.

Routeing tables in these type of switches contain an entry for each end point device attached to the network. When the network is first installed, these entries contain only estimates of route loadings to the end devices.

The network's aim is always to make use of the optimum route between communicating end point devices: a route in which the transit delay is as low as possible. Once in action, the network estimates the delay of any one route by combining its own information regarding the size of the packet queue with data from the switches to which it is directly connected.

At defined intervals a switch sends a delay table to every switch to which it is directly connected. This contains an entry for every end point device on the network. On receipt of a delay table, a switch combines it with its own current routeing table, producing a new table.

For each end point device, each switch compares the delay in its routeing table with that indicated in the received delay table, adjusted for the effects of the link on which it was received. If the new delay is shorter than that for the route currently in use, the routeing table entry for that end point device is updated to show a better route has been found.

The result of this operation is that advice of alterations in network loading can be transmitted automatically through the PSN. As the size of each routeing table is itself dynamic, any new end point devices added to the network automatically appear in the switch tables soon after initial connection. The location of every end point device linked to the network is therefore available at any time within the network.

Any new circuit added to the network will automatically be taken into account in computations where using it results in shorter packet transit delays.

The overall ability of a PSN with dynamic routeing to alter itself dynamically to changing fortunes and topology gives it remarkable operational independence and strength. Monitoring devices whose location and status is known at all times is straightforward. As no manual changes are involved when expanding the network, extra links or end devices can be added easily.

Delay table transmission between switches can be fixed according to line speed. Most of the time, nothing has changed, so that large networks can generate a considerable transmission overhead, wasting switch and circuit capacity. A solution is to send delay tables only when events deem it necessary: when something in the network has changed.

A new route, a new active end point device, increased delay time on a route, could all constitute an event in such a strategy. A stable, constant network, will therefore not be burdened with unnecessary delay table transmissions.

Datagram PSNs are particularly suitable for DAR as no information about virtual calls needs to be kept within the switches and the volume of network related information on the move is therefore manageable. In contrast, the data necessary to decide how and when to switch packets is found within the switches on the route of a virtual call; if packets are to take a different route, the virtual call information also has to be moved.

DAR for a virtual circuit network is best provided by running the virtual call protocol above the datagrams. The datagrams convey the virtual call information between end point devices, while only the end point devices need to know anything about the virtual call protocol. BT's international data network operates in this way.

4.7   Packet switching equipment

An example of a successful packet switching system is DPN-100 from Northern Telecom. As well as private corporate networks over 10 PTT's have installed DPN networks as the basis of their national X.25 services. DPN switches are modular, so that they can be purchased to match the capacity requirements of the network, and subsequently grow with future needs. In addition to X.25, a variety of access protocols, (all major international and most de facto standards such as SNA) are supported, enabling the support of a multi-vendor data processing environment. Trunks can be directly attached to the DPN-100 at speeds of up to 1.544Mbit/s (US T1) or 2.048Mbit/s (UK MegaStream and equivalent). Enhancements to the DPN range include the support of Frame Relay as an access protocol.

A major advantage of the DPN-100 range is its conformance to international and industry networking standards including X.25 as an interface to packet mode devices, X.31 for access to ISDN packet-mode services, X.32 for PSTN and circuit-switched public data networks accessed by X.25 devices, X.75 gateways and X.3, X.28 and X.29 for asynchronous devices.

The range also provides transparent communications between otherwise incompatible protocols and devices, enabling users to choose equipment from multiple vendors, unrestricted by proprietary vendor protocols. The protocols at either end of a resulting DPN-100 network do not have to be the same to communicate. Examples include SNA/SDLC, 3270 display system protocol for IBM 3270 bisynchronous terminals, and asynchronous polled interface (API) for relevant point-of-sale terminals.

The switch and network architecture focuses on users' need for transparent access to applications, shielding them from control and security mechanisms necessary to maintain the integrity of the data passing across the network.

The DPN-100 range gives the network controller the ability to define network service targets based on user needs: fast application access, no interruptions during application processing and fast system response. There is also an emphasis on secure information flow through the establishment of Closed User Groups and Network User Identifiers, plus passwords as desired. It also highlights the importance of comprehensive network management, providing a real time network control system with dynamic updates of switch and overall network performance at configurable central, regional and local levels.

55

Fast packet switching

K L Moran
B Sc (Hons) CEng MIEE
Sprint International

Contents

55.1 Introduction

The telecommunications industry is currently being driven by switching technology which is changing at an ever increasing pace. The demand for high capacity systems is becoming increasingly important for providing both sophisticated networking applications and offering flexible new services.

Today's carrier systems, E1 (2.048Mb/s) in Europe and T1 (1.5Mb/s) in the United States, provide a popular choice for networking voice traffic and data employing Time Division Multiplexing (TDM) techniques. This is due mainly to the functionality and cost savings that intelligent TDMs offer, and the fact that there have not been any other alternatives; that is until Fast Packet Switching came onto the scene.

In today's corporate networks voice traffic often represents around 80% of a network's capacity while data is only about 20%. However, many data applications are growing at 30% to 40% per year, while voice applications are growing at only 5%. This change in focus means that a communications network must meet today's heavy voice demands, yet be able to adapt to increasing data demands. For example, with the introduction of Local Area Network (LAN) applications and ever more powerful client/server workstations, the large amounts of data which must be transferred will become a critical issue in a company's overall communications network.

Fast Packet Switching is sometimes regarded as similar to CCITT X.25 packet switching, but the two techniques must not be confused, despite having a common name. Both methods take transmissions from user devices, partition them into packets and route them over a backbone of network switches until they arrive at the right destination. However, due to its protocol transparent nature a Fast Packet Switch (FPS) approach uses technology which can handle all types of transmission, not just data; as well as providing much higher transmission speeds within the 150 to 600 megabits per second range. Now, applications that depend on high bandwidth can co-exist on the same network, as well as the low speed (64kb/s and less) data applications addressed by traditional packet switched networks.

Fast Packet Switching is a new digital communications approach that is revolutionising communications networking strategies, and proprietary FPS implementations are already widely used in the US and gaining momentum internationally. There is however some confusion surrounding the term 'Fast Packet Switching'. It is usually taken as a concept covering Frame Relay and Cell Relay technologies, as illustrated in Figure 55.1.

Frame Relay uses a variable length frame, and as such creates variable delays across the network. It is a data-link layer approach (level 2 of OSI) and as such depends on the end systems supporting the Frame Relay protocol. These properties make Frame Relay best suited to non-delay-sensitive information transfer, such as data communications or still image.

Cell Relay on the other hand uses a fixed length frame or packet to carry information, and as such does not create variable delays across the network. It is a physical layer approach and consequently is protocol independent. These properties make Cell Relay suitable for transfer of delay sensitive information such as live speech.

55.2 Frame Relay

CCITT recommendation I.122 — 'Framework for providing additional Packet Mode Bearer Services', describes the architectural framework for two types of Frame Relay service. The frames are based on Recommendation I.441. Frame Relay is proving to be the

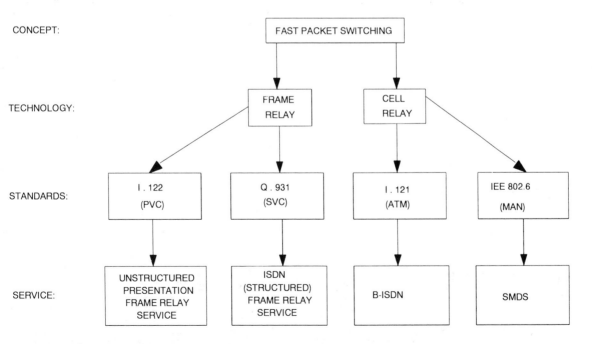

Figure 55.1 Fast Packet overview

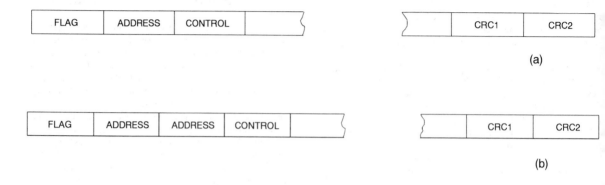

Figure 55.2 Frame Relay format: (a) standard LAPB frame; (b) LAPD frame as for Frame Relay

most popular of the additional packet mode bearer services defined. It also is the most simple.

The development of ISDN Frame Relay services is a packet mode interface to narrowband and broadband ISDN networks, and is designed to provide high speed packet transmission, minimal network delay, and efficient use of network bandwidth.

The basic aim of Frame Relay is to exploit the similarity of the OSI layer 2 function (data link control) between X.25 packet switched networks, IBM's SNA signalling protocol (LAPD), the IEEE 802 LAN protocols, and MAP/TOP. The standard (LAPB) frame and the LAPD frame are illustrated in Figure 55.2.

Figure 55.3 shows the frame relay communication paths relative to the OSI seven layer model. It is only at layer 3 that these protocols begin to look substantially different.

IBM originated what we now think of as the layer 2 or link layer function with its SNA SDLC protocol, and submitted it to various bodies for standardisation. SDLC emerged from ANSI as Advanced Data Communications Control Protocol (ADCCP), from ISO as HDLC and from CCITT as LAP (the link access procedure for X.25). LAP evolved into LAPB for X.25 and into LAPD for ISDN. HDLC was adapted to the IEEE 802.2 Logical Link Control (LLC) for LANs, which also became the link layer for MAP/TOP.

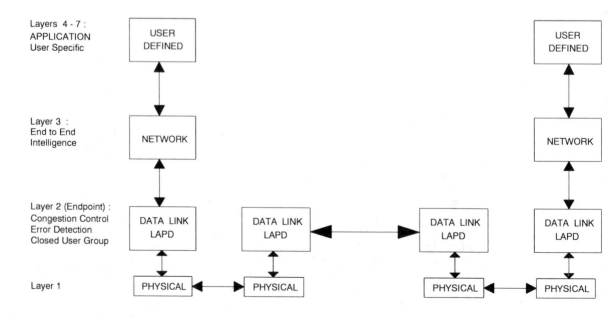

Figure 55.3 Frame Relay communications path

In simpler terms, the object is to use a Frame Relay (level 2 routing) interface to connect between different types of communications networks because the link layers of these networks are already similar. The potential impact on corporate networking is significant, because the approach is relatively straightforward to implement compared to a layer 3 approach, and existing hardware can be utilised.

This idea is by no means a new one. It was suggested back in 1975 during the formative stages of the CCITT X.25 recommendation for the packet switch network interface, that a simpler protocol would have many attractions. However the suggestion was rejected because of the proliferation of error-prone analogue transmission facilities still in existence at the time, requiring added complexity for error recovery. Digital transmission facilities are now widespread enough for a simplified protocol with error detection only, to be a viable option.

55.2.1 Frame Relay Networks

Frame Relay has been proposed to the CCITT as an adaption layer protocol for connection to ATM networks. Although it is possible to implement Frame Relay interfaces on time division multiplexers (TDM) and packet switches to produce so called Frame Relay switches, Cell Relay platforms are by far the most efficient and flexible partner for the Frame Relay interface.

Some vendors implement a frame relay to X.25 interface on their packet switches, which only gives the performance of a traditional packet switched network. Time Division Multiplexers with Frame Relay interfaces have the disadvantages outlined below. A packet switch with a different software load removing the level 3 functions in the switch and creating fixed packet sizes on the switch trunks effectively achieves Cell Relay functionality for data traffic. There are also proprietary ATM multiplexers available which handle voice and data traffic, although standard ATM platforms are evolving (See Section 55.3 and Chapter 41). For the benefit of the following discussion, such platforms will be regarded as 'Frame Relay Switches'.

Instead of transferring bits between fixed locations like a circuit, a Frame Relay network acts like a wide area LAN. A sending device places an addressed frame into the network and it arrives quickly at its destination.

To achieve these objectives, the network simply 'relays' the packet, or frame, to a destination indicated by the layer 2 address field of the packet. The Frame Relay switch performs the core layer 2 functions, of frame separation with flags, zero bit insertion, frame multiplexing via the address field, and CRC error detection to enable frames with errors to be discarded. The switch does not acknowledge or request re-transmission. This and all other protocol functions (layer 3 and up) are implemented end-to-end through the network, rather than by it.

Simplifying the protocol functions allows the network to operate cost effectively at high speeds and low delays. Instead of connecting switches at 64kb/s, it is done at N x 64kb/s (V.35 or X.21 interfaces) or with narrowband ISDN at 2Mb/s or 1.5Mb/s. Packets, instead of being processed at intermediate switches (as would be the case with conventional packet switches), are relayed directly from the originating switch to the destination switch. The result is that the delay incurred in relaying a packet is much less than the delay incurred in switching (software processing) a packet.

With the implementation of Frame Relay on a Cell Relay backbone, network bandwidth is used more efficiently. The pool of

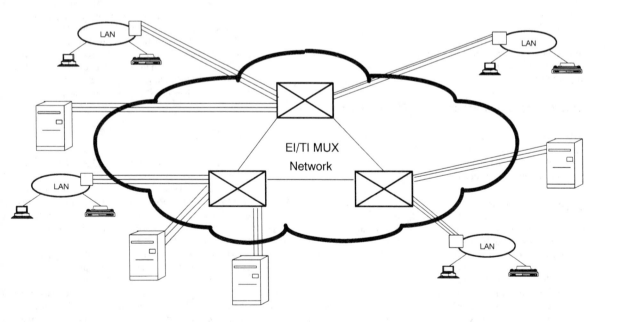

Figure 55.4 Conventional network without Frame Relay

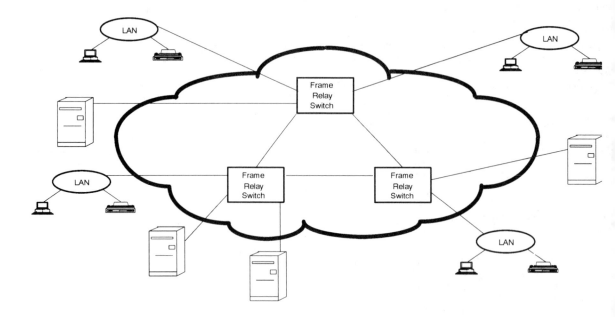

Figure 55.5 Network with Frame Relay

available bandwidth is shared among all applications (data, voice etc.). Bursty, high speed Frame Relay connections, can access the entire network trunk bandwidth for very short intervals, and then release it for other applications. This unique property of Cell Relay switching makes high performance, bursty frame relay connections affordable because bandwidth does not have to be dedicated to those connections (as would be the case using a time division multiplexing backbone).

55.2.2   Benefits Available with Frame Relay

LAN/WAN integration is by far the most popular application for Frame Relay services, although LAN to Host and still-image transfer are also possible.

Together Cell Relay switching and Frame Relay provide:

1. Savings on Hardware. Only one port is needed with Frame Relay, since frames contain their destination addresses this effectively splits the physical connection into multiple logical connections to different destinations. This replaces the TDM interface requirement of dedicating one port for each destination. The result is reduced hardware costs, especially in large networks. Figures 55.4 and 55.5 illustrate this.
2. Bandwidth savings. Cell Relay switch handling of bursty data, when used with the Frame Relay interface provides continuous savings on line costs by offering more efficient management of bandwidth. Idle data is not transmitted over the network as it is with TDM platforms. Bandwidth is instantaneously used for bursts of data when necessary, and is then instantaneously freed for usage by other traffic. Bursts from multiple sources are interleaved on the same available bandwidth.
3. Better performance. Cell Relay switching together with Frame Relay offers better performance than TDMs with Frame Relay. The Frame Relay interface can operate at much higher speeds without wasting bandwidth on the backbone. This results in lower delay and higher network performance. Because the Frame Relay interface provides full interconnectivity, every device is directly connected to every other device. This eliminates delay caused by routing traffic through intermediary (end system) nodes, such as LAN routers or front end processors.

55.3   Cell Relay

Cell Relay platforms transmit all information, including voice, data, video, and signalling in a single packet format. They provide truly integrated transmission over a single high-speed digital line. Unlike traditional packet switches, Cell Relay switches use short, fixed length packets (cells), and, using a hardware-based switching technique, switch them at very high speeds (100,000 to 1,000,000 packets per second), as in Figure 55.6.

Because Cell Relay networks have very high throughput and low delays, they can be used for all kinds of communication traffic: voice, synchronous data and video, as well as the low speed data applications that are being serviced by conventional packet networks to date. The use of a common packet format for transport of all network traffic, results in simple packet routing and multiplexing.

All packets are of the same length, use the same number of address bits, and are transported through the network using common switching, queuing, and transmission techniques, no matter what the connection type or its bandwidth requirements. Other than control

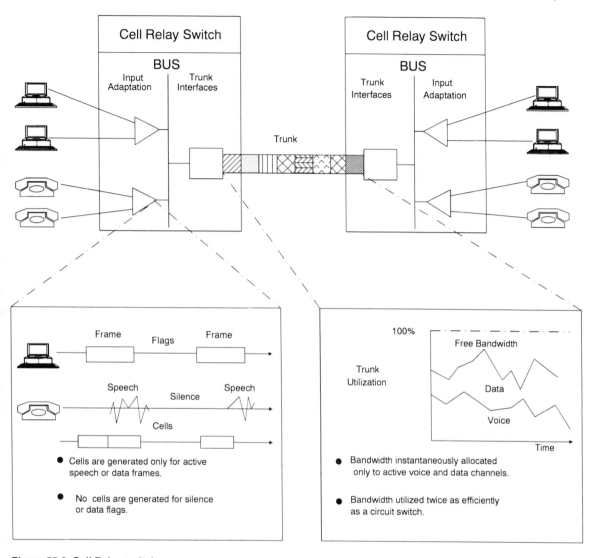

Figure 55.6 Cell Relay switch

information, the only real differences between packets are content and destination. Packets or cells are only generated on the trunk when actual information is present, therefore genuine bandwidth on demand is provided.

Comparing TDMs and packet switching with Cell Relay, the main benefits of traditional packet switching networks are lower costs, due to statistical multiplexing techniques, and higher reliability, due to the self-routing nature of individually addressed packets. The main benefit of TDMs is that dedicating bandwidth provides the high throughput and low delays needed for voice, video and high speed data communication. Cell Relay switching delivers the best of both worlds by bringing the economy and reliability of packet switching to traditional TDM applications, such as voice, and the high throughput and low delays of TDMs to packet applications.

Some manufacturers have introduced hybrid TDM and packet switched platforms as an attempt to capture the benefits of both technologies in one product, as in Figure 55.7.

Hybrid switching attempts to provide both circuit and packet switching features by dividing the slots on a TDM frame between voice channels and data channels. Since the voice slots are time division multiplexed, and the data slots are packet switched, voice and data traffic must be separated to different sections of the switch.

With the simplest scheme, the voice/data boundary and frame length are fixed. This fixed boundary is inefficient because voice and data slots cannot be interchanged to accommodate statistical fluctuations in voice and data traffic. For more efficiency, the voice/data boundary can be designed to be movable, and the frame length dynamic, but not without complicated network analysis and increased complexity of switching architecture.

Hybrid switching is not really an integrated solution because not only are two different switches built, but a bandwidth management system is required that can deal with two separate types of data. In effect, there are two separate networks piggybacked onto one trunk. The product can cost twice as much as a truly integrated Cell Relay

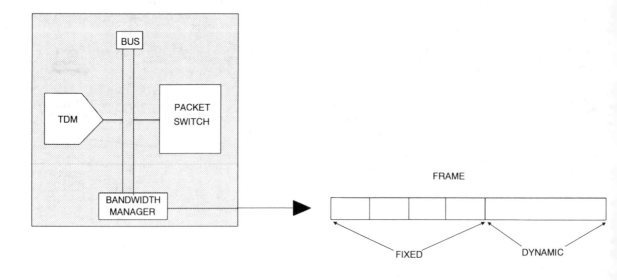

Figure 55.7 Hybrid switch

approach, with less of the simplicity and bandwidth economies to show for it.

There are two recognised branches of Cell Relay technology, Asynchronous Transfer Mode (ATM) and Distributed Queue Dual Bus (or Queued Packet Synchronous Exchange). Let us deal with these each in turn.

55.3.1 Asynchronous Transfer Mode

CCITT recommendation I.121 Asynchronous Transfer Mode (ATM), is one of two approaches defined in Broadband ISDN. The other is Synchronous Transfer Mode (STM), which is an extension of traditional TDM principles providing fixed bandwidth channels

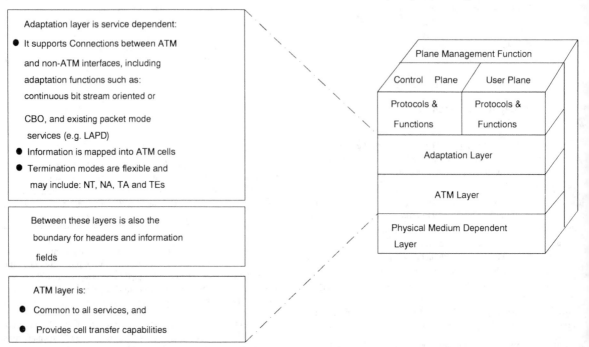

Figure 55.8 B-ISDN protocol model for ATM

and a packet switched signalling mechanism. ATM is a Cell Relay technology and offers the major advantage of flexibility over STM.

For ATM, standards bodies ANSI and CCITT have agreed to use a 53 byte cell, consisting of a 5 byte header and 48 byte information field. The momentum to converge to ATM standards is evident in the adoption of a 53 byte cell format by the IEEE 802.6 committee for Metropolitan Area Networks (see below).

ATM is a wide area networking approach which is why it is more suited to B-ISDN. The network platforms using ATM will be in the form of switching multiplexers or digital cross-connect switches. The intention is that ATM networks will act as the backbone for LAN, MAN and other existing networks, consequently there are adaption layer protocols being defined to provide the necessary re-formatting of frames and packets to the ATM Cell format.

Figure 55.8 shows the Broadband ISDN protocol model for ATM.

True standards based ATM networks are not anticipated to be available until well after Frame Relay and MAN approaches. Major vendors world-wide are developing ATM switches with a close eye on standards. Those with proprietary switches are developing modifications to meet the standards. The major force driving B- ISDN in Europe is the Deutshe Bundespost which is due to end a Broadband ISDN applications trial (Berkhom project) in 1992. The platforms used for the trial are STM and proprietary ATM switches. In the United States AT&T has had a 160Mb/s proprietary switch on trial for over a year. Public services are not expected to be available until 1994/5. However private networks are already available using proprietary ATM approaches and standards compliant private ATM networks are expected in 1993.

For further information on ATM see Chapter 41.

55.3.2 DQDB Metropolitan Area Networks

MANs are based on ring or bus topologies and are intended to provide city-wide networking, to interconnect LANs and to carry digital voice and video. MANs are also seen as a means of accessing Broadband ISDN (ATM) networks in the longer term, hence the alignment between MAN and ATM Cell formats, (i.e. 53 byte cells).

The standard IEEE 802.6 Distributed Queue Dual Bus MAN comprises two contra-directional data buses up to 150Km long running up to 140Mb/s, as shown in Figure 55.9.

The bus may be looped into a ring format to give a much more resilient topology than LAN ring approaches. The ring is not closed, in the way a token ring LAN is. It is configured such that information terminates at the loop closure point on each side of the 'opening'. If a node or cable segment fails the logical opening is moved to the physical outage, and operation continues without degradation.

DQDB MAN technology is used in the Switched Multimegabit Data Service (SMDS) currently being used in the United States by some of the Regional Bell Operating Companies (RBOCs). SMDS is designed for access speeds of 1.544Mb/s and 45Mb/s. In Europe ETSI is developing standards for a similar service and some PTTs have already installed MANs.

Although SMDS is based on MAN technology, it will be possible to link the MANs together later using T3 lines to create Wide Area Networking. SMDS is a connectionless network unlike ATM which will be connection oriented.

55.4 Conclusions

It is generally accepted that the network of the 1990s will be some kind of extremely fast and completely integrated network, combining voice, video, image, data, signalling and high speed LAN transfers onto one backbone. The fast packet concept addresses these applications and uses the next generation communication technologies for future integrated broadband communications networks, which will be capable of handling all narrowband and broadband services.

In the U.S. Frame Relay services have already been announced by major carriers to provide an alternative to traditional leased lines and some will be offering a commercial service by the end of 1991. These virtual leased lines will offer bandwidth in the way bursty applications require it, and charge for usage in a similar way to X.25 services. However all the benefits of Frame Relay will apply. Existing physical interfaces (e.g. V.35) are to be used initially, with standard ISDN interfaces following on later. Private Frame Relay networks are also in use.

Although MANs, in the form of SMDS, are very visibly supported in the U.S. by Bellcore and the Regional Bell Operating Companies (RBOCs) in terms of market development and technology life cycle, MANs are at a much earlier stage than Frame Relay. While the

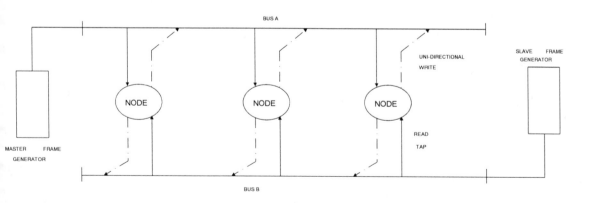

Figure 55.9 DQDB architecture

RBOCs are pushing SMDS for city-wide networking, standards have not been defined for interconnection of these networks to form wide area networking. In addition, SMDS requires hardware changes to existing CPE equipment. It is most likely that SMDS will not be viable as a public service until sometime late in 1992 or into 1993. As if in confirmation of this the RBOCS are also actively engaged in Frame Relay trials.

International standards bodies have concluded that Asynchronous Transfer Mode provides the only effective backbone technology for bursty broadband communications over a wide area, such as LAN to LAN connectivity and digitised video/image distribution. Developments to date have underwritten this.

It now remains to be seen how existing networks, LANs with Frame Relay, MANs and ATM approaches compete for precedence and how each will relate to the other.

LAN routers with Frame Relay interfaces connecting into an ATM backbone (B-ISDN) along with voice services (VPN/ISDN) is one model for a private network. Another is LANs connecting into MANs, which are in turn linked by dedicated high speed WAN circuits or again into an ATM backbone with voice services on the MAN or on the ATM backbone. Maybe it will be a mix of all these, who knows!

55.5 References

ANSI (1990) *TI.606, Frame Relaying Bearer Service — Architectural Framework and service description.* ANSI Inc.

CCITT (1988a) *Recommendation I.122, Framework for providing additional packet mode bearer services.* Blue book, ITU Geneva.

CCITT (1988b) *Recommendation I.121, Broadband aspects of ISDN.* Blue book, ITU, Geneva.

Hullet, John L. and Evans, Peter (1988) New proposal extends the reach of MANs. *Datacommunications* (February)

Kanzow, Jurgen (1991) *The Berkhom Project.* IEE Review (March)

Modahl, Mary A. and McClean, Karyn P. *Frame Relay's Impact* Forrester Research Inc. Network Strategy Report.

Mollenauer, Jim (1989) The Global LAN is getting closer. *Data communications International* (December)

Moran, K.L. (1990) Fast Packet and Frame Relay. *Communication Magazine* (September)

56

Local and Wide Area Networking

Hubert A J Whyte
Newbridge Networks Ltd

Contents

56.1 Introduction

Incredible though it may seem, a four-fold increase in data traffic is predicted by the year 2000, the beginning of the 21st Century. Yet it is conceivable that this may be an underestimate when one consider the range of new multimedia services potentially available in the next few years, the ever growing power of computing resources and the continual imagination of business and residential applications in combining computer and communications as a single platform for services.

This chapter examines Local Area Networking (LAN) and Wide Area Networking (WAN), developments from the early 1960s, the phenomenal leaps of technology recorded during its development, the issues concerning implementing such a network today and the future role of such networks for business and residential communities.

56.2 Network development

In 1960 the term wide and local area networks was as foreign as MacDonalds. The wide area network was principally the transmission network implemented by the dominant monopolitic PTT/Telco, which was analogue based, with copper reaching to the subscriber and the backbone network pulled together by Frequency Division Multiplexing (FDM). (See Figure 56.1 and Chapter 20.)

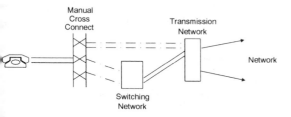

Figure 56.1   Analogue Wide Area Network of the 1960s

The network was designed to carry analogue voice telephony, in the 300Hz to 3.4kHz frequency range. This arose out of the conversion of voice into an electrical signal and is still the vital component for all voice telephony. Frequency Division Multiplexing provided the means of grouping a number of 300kHz to 3.4kHz signals into single group by multiplexing them on to a higher and higher frequency carrier.

It allowed PTTs to build multiple groups of analogue circuits throughout their network with immediate consolidation of the raw transport mechanism, which at the time on the trunk network was coaxial cable.

In the late 1960s users began to build computer systems to assist in the management of their business. Initially these systems were centralised into one facility with clusters of user terminals and peripherals located around a large mainframe system such as IBM 3000 range. The benefits of computing applications were realised by such businesses as airlines, banking and insurance companies, so the pressure to remotely connect some of the user community from the mainframe became paramount.

The availability of modem technology allowed the mainframe applications to be distributed into remote sites over the analogue PTT network. (See Figure 56.2.)

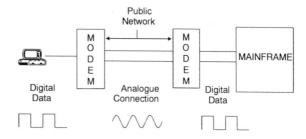

Figure 56.2   Remote mainframe applications over an analogue network

Modem as the name suggests modulates and demodulates from analogue tone into digital data and vice versa. (See Chapter 39.) In practice it allowed digital data from a remote terminal to be converted into analogue signals for its onward connection into the restrictive (300kHz to 3.4kHz) analogue public network.

Earlier modems such as V22 (1200 baud) and V22 bis (2400 baud) offered, in comparison to modern modem, slow speeds. Nevertheless, these served to provide the initial revolution of Wide Area Networking. Major analogue networks soon appeared as the platform for companies to distribute their centralised computing resources. Based principally around IBM's SNA environment they become the workhorse of many corporate organisations. (See Figure 56.3)

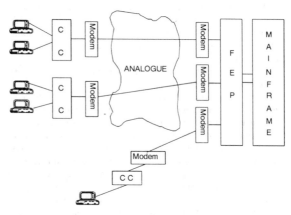

Figure 56.3   Distributed computing over an analogue network. (CC = Cluster controller; FEP = Front end processor.)

The heart of the service were analogue leased lines, as supplied by the monopolistic PTTs. As these networks increased and expanded better technology was developed to improve the speed at which data could be transmitted, with more sophisticated modems such as V.29 and now V.32 and V.42, and to optimise the manner in which the analogue service was presented using such techniques as multidrop and multiport. These had two goals, speed of information to the user, and to attempt to save money from the high PTT tariffing cost associated with such networks.

Throughout this period of growth other means were developed for the delivery of computer sources to the user which at first seemed a good alternative to the large analogue based networks.

The most notable was the introduction of X.25 networks. These networks combined leased services to the user at a local network with switched data services withn the network. (See Figure 56.4.)

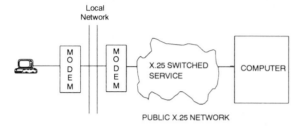

Local
Network

X.25 SWITCHED
SERVICE

COMPUTER

PUBLIC X.25 NETWORK

Figure 56.4   Remote computer access over the X.25 network

Unfortunately the earlier PTT X.25 services had some drawbacks:-

1. Tariffing based on a number of data packets, so high usage was more expensive than leased services.
2. Slow speeds, where new modem technology was now offering faster speeds.
3. Delays across large networks which did not suit SNA networks.

Nevertheless, X.25 services could be considered as an alternative to Wide Area Networking and would have important benefits for many network business applications. These included a wide connectivity capability, unlike leased services the switched capability enabled a one to many connection rather than a one to one. The ability to handle protocol conversion in its simplest form, such as different speeds, and a more robust networking service, since it was based on the PTT core service.

Modem networks grew phenomenally during the 1970s both domestically and internationally. The SNA networks offered efficient data connection based on synchronous data connection, however, many computer systems also adopted different protocols for communication, including asynchronous type connections. Synchronous connections essentially rely on the accurate timing of the two elements trying to communicate. This allows fast exchange of information, given that both elements are synchronised.

Asynchronous connection on the other hand assumed poor timing between the elements. Therefore data was surrounded by error and start/stop information so enabling its accuracy when received.

Synchronous connection is much more efficient than asynchronous since large amounts of data can be transmitted faster. To improve the efficiency of asynchronous connections statistical multiplexing methods were developed during the late 1970s, both for local and wide area connectivity.

The principles of statistical multiplexing was to take advantage of slow data connections associated with asynchronous connections. This allowed a number of asynchronous devices to utilise one circuit for onward connection. (See Figure 56.5 and Chapter 21.)

The statistical multiplexer's role is to handle the inward, and in reverse the outward, connections using buffering and retransmission techniques. This simple process provided incredible improvement in the efficiency of the time and combined with modem

devices became the work horse for many asynchronous based analogue networks.

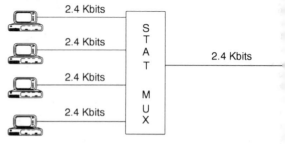

2.4 Kbits

2.4 Kbits

2.4 Kbits

2.4 Kbits

S
T
A
T

M
U
X

2.4 Kbits

Figure 56.5   The user of statistical multiplexing

Voice services remained within the PSTN, although some international applications and large corporate networks were developed around analogue leased services. This is very true of North America and the UK. However, private voice networks were separate from data networks and restrictive in their application because of the poor network technology and the monopolistic control of the PTT.

The arrival of digital networks brought a new ear of communications. During the 1960s more progressive PTTs had started to build digital infrastructures to replace the analogue networks and in the 1970s this was dramatically accelerated.

Digital networks offer benefits to the PTT which caused this accelerated implementation. These included:

1. Better quality.
2. More efficient use of the infrastructure.
3. Lower cost.
4. Higher speeds.
5. The ability to manage the network efficiently.

This implementation is still occurring throughout the world-wide PTT networks, nevertheless, in many countries the bulk of the infrastructure is now based on digital connections both leased and switching.

Wide Area Network users realised the same benefits as PTTs in digital connections and in the earlier 1980s the first service became available from PTTs for digital leased services. AT&T, the deregulated long distance carrier offered T1 services to Government offices in North America.

56.3   Digital networks

The early 1980s T1 services were the start of an explosion in growth of T1 services throughout North America, with 11 million digital connections in place today. In Europe a different standard for digital connection was offered by British Telecom in the mid 1980s called 2Mbit/s or E1.

Both T1 and E1 utilise the same basic building blocks, but are constructed in a different way. The building block for T1/E1 is 64kbit/s, which is arrived at for historical reasons by the manner a which analogue voice connections are converted to a digital stream. In the 1930s, Standard Telephones and Cables Ltd. (STC), developed a technique for converting analogue voice to a digital stream called Pulse Code Modulation (see Chapter 19). This technique was adopted as standard by CCITT as G712. The concept is s follows. The analogue network had been characterised to operate t 300Hz to 3400Hz (or 0 to 4kHz), this frequency range essentially nabling acceptable voice communication across a telecommunication infrastructure. The frequency range of 4kHz therefore requires a sample rate of twice its value in order to provide accurate reproduction.

Given this sampling rate, there was need to code the representation of the waveform. Two forms of representation were adopted, one North American called μ-law and one European called A-law. The sampling rate and the subsequent code provide an 8Kbit code which represented therefore a 64Kbit signal.

The foundation of digital conversion was therefore adopted, and its development was based on the earlier restrictions within the analogue network. The 64kbit building block was in turn used to form the basis of T1 (North American) and E1 (European) digital services. T1 is 24 x 64kbit/s circuits combined to form 1.536kbit/s service which is expanded by 8kbit/s to 1.544kbit/s. The 8kbit/s is used for PTT service information. (See Figure 56.6.) The signalling information is either transported as a rob bit in each channel (called imeslot) for channel associated signalling or as a complete channel (timeslot 24) for common channel signalling.

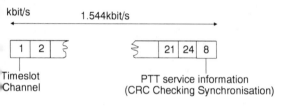

Figure 56.6 T1 transmission frame

E1 on the other hand is 30 (32) x 64kbit/s combined to form 2.048Kbit service. (See Figure 56.7.)

In this arrangement timeslots 1 to 15 and 17 to 31 are the 30 user usable channels. Timeslot 0 is for PTT service information, whereas timeslot 16 was preserved for signalling information either Common Channel or Channel Associated.

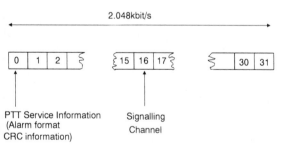

Figure 56.7 E1 transmission frame

In due course PTTs offered lower speed digital services. In North America this was because of Digital Data Services (DDS) which offered 64Kbit and below connectivity. This was followed in the late 1990s by Fractional T1 services, which simply is a full T1 delivered to the user but only a fraction of it, as desired, is utilised.

In Europe, BT was once again the first to provide 64Kbit and below service under the banner of KiloStream. Now throughout Europe one is able, dependent on the PTT, to receive digital speeds below 64kbit/s, or N x 64kbit/s service (where N = 1 to 30) or 2Mbit/s (E1) or indeed Fractional E1 the equivalent to North America.

The arrival of T1 and E1 services, although initially tariffed high in the early 1980s provided the means for users to save cost; to improve quality of service; to meet the growing demands of service; and lastly to consider their network as a single point of integration for voice, data, video and image. The means to achieve these goals were originally thought to be the new modern PBX, but this was quickly thrown aside by a new generation of sophisticated multiplexer, the digital data multiplexer. (See Chapter 40.)

It was designed by new entrants who adopted their own proprietary techniques of sending growing user data demands into T1 on E1 digital pipes. The multiplexers needed unstructured T1 or E1 pipes to capitalise on their proprietary techniques of sending data effectively through the network. Initially designed as point to point devices they effectively adapted into full networking platforms. (See Figure 56.8.)

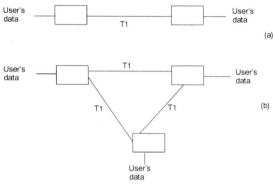

Figure 56.8 Use of multiplexers within a network: (a) point to point; (b) delta network

It was not until the mid 1980s that the user realised the weakness of these 1st and 2nd generation multiplexers, whose design was principally restricted to data and proprietary in technique.

A third generation of multiplexers then appeared in the late 1980s and early 1990s, these were characterised by:

1. The ability to integrate any form of service, be it voice, data, image, video and LAN. Connectivity would be the issue for the 1990s.
2. Robust, evolving, flexible architecture. Adoption of new technology would be required in the 1990s.
3. Totally software driven. The ability to offer complete management capability.
4. International in design using a balance of standard and proprietary technology, i.e. Global networking.
5. A greater reach. The ability to network the smallest to the largest office from a 3 node network to a 10,000 node network.
6. Hybrid in design. The ability to operate in the PTT network or private network or both, as a single product.

Today's multiplexers adopt these basic principles and have become the main solution for wide area networking.

The features and benefits realised by such networking capabilities together with the growing reduction of digital service tariffs and their availability means their continual adoption by corporate clients into their networking connection solutions.

Today multiplexers incorporate a rich set of features to allow efficient management of the digital services.

56.3.1 Connectivity

The need to deliver a number of different services into a single integrated network requires a range of connectivity solutions, such as:

1. Voice, the ability to connect digitally from a modern PBX, but also to connect analogue devices such as E&M circuits (the original analogue private wire), telephone lines and telephone exchanges.
2. Data, the ability to handle the range of data speeds both asynchronous and synchronous from as low as 1.2kbit/s through to 1920kbit/s (and eventually to 34Mbit/s).
3. Video, the ability to handle video at rates from 64kbit/s through to 1920kbit/s.
4. Image, the ability to handle services from CAD devices with minimal delay across a network.
5. LAN, the ability to incorporate LAN interconnection devices both routers and bridges in an integrated manner.

56.3.2 Compression

Compression techniques both for voice and data offer advantages in optimising the digital service. Data compression can offer effectiveness of 8 to 1 using such techniques as statistical multiplexing.

Voice compression development however, has been more pronounced and on international circuits can realise enormous cost saving.

The compression technique adopted by the original multiplexer vendors was proprietary, called CVSD (Continuous Variable-Slope Delta Modulation).

This offers compression successfully down to 24kbit/s (nearly 3 to 1 over PCM) but is plagued by bad quality and high delays.

A technique which became standard within CCITT G.721, called ADPCM (Adaptive Differential Pulse Code Modulation) was therefore integrated on to the earlier multiplexers and became a standard for all new generations. This offered 32kbit/s (2 to 1 compression), was of acceptable quality and minimal delay. Its quality also allowed fax to be sent across 32kbit/s unlike CVSD.

Most recently new techniques have been adapted, the most prominent being Code Excited Linear Prediction (CELP). This offers excellent quality, and with new Digital Signal Processor components, minimal delay, and will shortly be recorded as the standard for 16kbit/s voice compression by CCITT. Using this technique 8Kbit voice compression offers excellent quality and the ability to pass fax signals.

56.3.3 Network robustness

As the networks have grown so have their importance to the corporate business. To this end the multiplexer has developed techniques to protect the users' connections against failures within a network, be they the multiplexer itself or the network links. The techniques include channel re-routeing (many channels from a failed link to a

working link), channel priority (nominating in order of priority the most important channels to remain in operation when limited services are available), channel down speeding (maintain a channel connection even at lower speed when resources become limited), parameter routing (to define the manner in which channels route through a network) and resilience of both multiplexer, network management and links.

This robustness is a combination of the intelligence within a networking node and within the network management platform.

56.3.4 Family

Networks grow and change and it is therefore extremely important to support a family of product to meet different network sizes and with the inherent ability to change. To this end multiplexers are not single product categories, indeed 'the network is the product'. Within the same multiplexer family one can range from a single network connection right through 256 x E1 network connection, from a two multiplexer network to a 10,000 node network, and from delta (triangle) topology through to a complete mesh topology. With all these variation of network design and size, it is essential that a consistent view of the network is maintained with the same 'look and feel' no matter what the size of the multiplexer or network. Users demand a single tightly coupled view of their network not one that has a core network surrounded by alternative or even OEM access products. The reach of the network must at least have the capability to extend digitally to the smallest office in an organisation at a competitive price. This should even extend to the desk of the user, giving full management control to the network management system. Features within the multiplexer will also include:

1. Multidrop capability to mirror analogue IBM multidrop environments.
2. Integration into umbrella management systems such as IBM Netview, AT&T UNMA, DEC Enterprise Management Architecture, CCITT Telephone Management Network, and of course OSI management environment.
3. The ability to migrate to ISDN technology.
4. Support of such capabilities as PCM bridging, and conference and virtual channel capability.

The development of digital Wide Area Networking based on the multiplexer platform is a reality of corporate private service. Its role is now either being enhanced or under threat, depending on the point of view, due to the sudden growth of Local Area Networks.

56.4 Development of Local Area Networks (LANs)

56.4.1 Proliferation of personal computers

In the early 1980s Personal Computers (PC) infiltrated the office environment on a large scale. PCs were purchased either as replacements for larger, and subsequently out-dated systems or as part of an office automation program.

The replacement of older, (i.e., mainframe/mini) systems was the result of innovative technology that placed tremendous processing power in a small desktop device. Users who required pure computing power, but not necessarily access to remote information, benefited directly from this migration to PCs.

PCs were also purchased in an effort to improve productivity by automating manual processes, such as word processing, filing and accounting.

At this point in time, the vast majority of PCs were installed as stand alone devices. That is to say, they were not attached to any other devices, except perhaps a printer. External communications, such as to other PCs within the same work area did not exist. However, as the computing power of the PC increased, and the need to make use of, and share the information on PCs also increased connectivity, or networking, became a necessity.

56.4.2 Evolution of Local Area Networks

The requirement for computer connectivity led to the development of the modern day Local Area Network (LAN).

The first LANs to appear on the market in the early 1980s were represented by many different proprietary networking schemes from a multitude of vendors. Most of these products featured low speed, (under 1 Mbit/s), bus or serial connections between computers, with little if any software control of the network. As such, these early networks were complicated and difficult to use.

The market today is very different. Vendors such as Novell, Banyan and Microsoft have produced software-driven network operating systems that can function over a multitude of standards-based LANs. Standards such as IEEE 802.3 (Ethernet), and IEEE 802.5 (Token Ring), have provided reliable and functional methods

for interconnecting PCs. In addition, many LANs also connect mainframe and mini computer systems.

56.4.3 LAN applications

Local Area Networks can be utilised to provide any or all of the following facilities (see Figure 56.9):

1. The interconnection of all computers, terminals, PCs and other workstations within a department or building.
2. The effective communication between all devices attached to the network, regardless of their vendor.
3. The sharing of expensive peripheral resources attached to the network such as disks, printers and plotters, central processors, and databases.
4. The standardisation of wiring, hardware and software required for communication and applications.
5. The establishment of a foundation for continued growth and the expansion of a distributed computing environment.

56.4.4 LAN characteristics

The key characteristics of a LAN are:

1. Transmission medium.
2. Signalling technique.

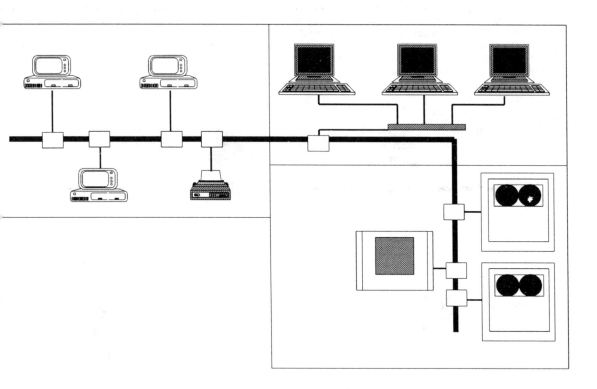

Figure 56.9 Example of a typical LAN application

3. Access method.
4. Network topology.

56.4.4.1   *Transmission media*

The transmission medium is the physical entity used to convey data over the LAN and includes any active hardware, such as amplifiers, required to regenerate the signal on the medium, and any passive hardware, such as taps and connectors, required to provide access to the medium.

The most common types of installed media are (see also Chapter 15):

1. Broadband coaxial cable.
2. Baseband coaxial cable.
3. Twisted pair wire.

In addition, optical fibre is emerging as an increasingly important transmission medium. (See Chapter 53.)

56.4.4.2   *Signalling techniques*

LAN signalling techniques can be divided into baseband and broadband transmission.

Baseband transmission utilises direct encoding to convey digital information in its digital form, to the transmission medium. In baseband transmission, only one channel is available to all network users, therefore only one signal can survive on the transmission medium at any one time.

Broadband transmission utilises radio frequency modems to convey data signals over the transmission medium. Because the avail-

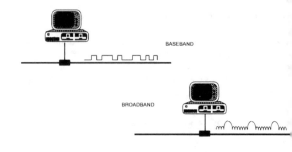

Figure 56.10   Signalling techniques on LANs

able bandwidth is divided into separate channels, the use of frequency division multiplexing (FDM) allows several 'conversations' to coexist on the LAN simultaneously.

Baseband LANs are generally less expensive and easier to install than broadband LANs. (See Figure 56.10.)

56.4.4.3   *Access methods*

The method of access to the LAN permits all the devices attached to the transmission medium to share that medium in a controlled fashion.

The two most common access methods are Carrier Sense Multiple Access with Collision Detection (CSMA/CD) and Token Passing (See Figure 56.11 and Chapter 13.)

CSMA/CD

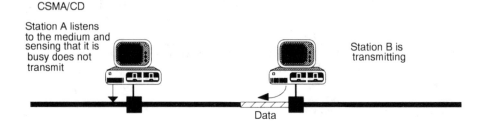

Station A listens to the medium and sensing that it is busy does not transmit

Station B is transmitting

Data

TOKEN PASSING

Station A is awaiting receipt of the Token so it can transmit.

Station B has completed its transmission and has released the Token.

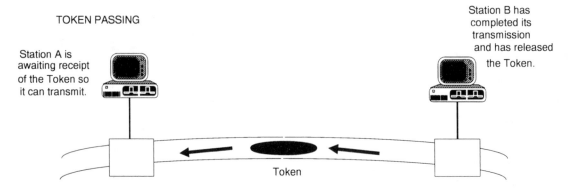

Token

Figure 56.11   LAN access methods

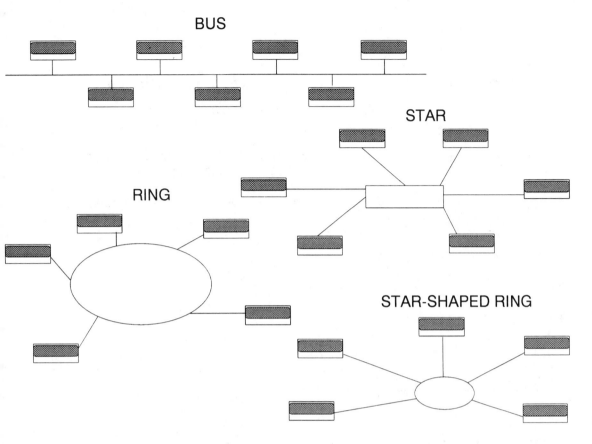

Figure 56.12 Network topology

CSMA/CD permits any device attached to the medium to transmit on that medium (multiple access), if it senses that the medium is free (carrier sense). Occasionally two or more devices simultaneously sense that the medium is free and begin to transmit. This creates a collision which is detected by the sending device and the data is retransmitted after a set random time.

Token Passing permits each device on the LAN to control the medium for a predetermined maximum time while it is in possession of a message packet (token). The token is passed from workstation to workstation on the LAN until the one wishing to transmit receives it. When the workstation has finished transmitting, the token is passed to the next device in a predetermined sequence.

56.4.4.4   Network topology

Several network topologies, (physical layout), can be used to design a Local Area Network, the most common being Bus, Ring, Star and Star-Shaped Ring. (See Figure 56.12.):

1. Bus network is the most prevalent LAN configuration, used in both Ethernet (CSMA/CD) and Token Passing Bus. All devices connect to the bus by means of a tap, (transceiver).
2. In Ring topologies, all networked devices are connected in a closed loop.
3. For Star topologies the networked devices are connected directly to a central network device, which is usually active.

4. Star-Shaped Ring networks use dedicated cabling to each workstation, which converges together in a wiring closet.

56.4.4.5   LAN standards

Because the first LAN systems were based on vendor specific technology, customers were forced to deal with single suppliers. In order to allow users the freedom to purchase and interconnect equipment from multiple vendors, it was clear that equipment standardisation was required.

The two most influential bodies in determining LAN standards are the Institute of Electrical and Electronic Engineers, (IEEE), and the International Standards Organisation, (ISO).

The IEEE Local Network Standards Committee, (Project 802), is developing LAN access standards and protocols in a layered approach similar to the ISO's Open Systems Interconnection (OSI) Reference Model.

The OSI Reference Model (see Chapter 12) represents the relationship between a network and the services it can support by a hierarchy of seven protocol layers. Each layer uses the services of the lower layers in conjunction with its own functions to create new services which are then made available to the higher layers. (See Figure 56.13.)

Sub groups within the IEEE 802 Committee are producing the following LAN standards:

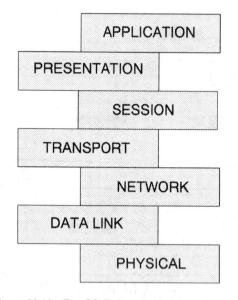

APPLICATION	Includes user programmes
PRESENTATION	Data formatting and compression
SESSION	Establishment/termination of transport connections
TRANSPORT	Provides end to end service between layers 1-3 and the higher layers
NETWORK	Includes routing and switching functions
DATA LINK	Includes synchronisation and lower layer error control
PHYSICAL	Includes signal transmission

Figure 56.13 The OSI Reference Model

1. IEEE 802.1, covering architecture, addressing, internetworking and management.
2. IEEE 802.2, Logical Link Control (LLC) Protocol, common to the various types of media implementation.
3. IEEE 802.3, Carrier Sense Multiple Access and Collision Detect.
4. IEEE 802.4, Token Passing Bus.
5. IEEE 802.5, Token Passing Ring.
6. IEEE 802.6, Metropolitan Networks.

The ISO has adopted the IEEE standards as ISO 8802 and relates the IEEE model to its own. (See Figure 56.14.)

The IEEE 802 series are standards covering access methods and as such are applicable over several types of media, such as coaxial cable, twisted pair wiring and optical fibre. The IEEE has developed a classification system which groups local area networks according to speed, signalling technique and segment length.

For example, the most popular type of 802.3/ Ethernet LAN is 10 Base 5. This refers to LANs over the common, thick, yellow coaxial cable, (YE-50). The speed at which data can theoretically travel over this medium is 10Mbit/s, the signalling technique is baseband and the maximum segment length without signal regeneration is 500 metres, hence 10 Base 5. This particular standard requires the special 'thick' Ethernet cable, most often yellow or bright orange in colour, with multiple layers of shielding.

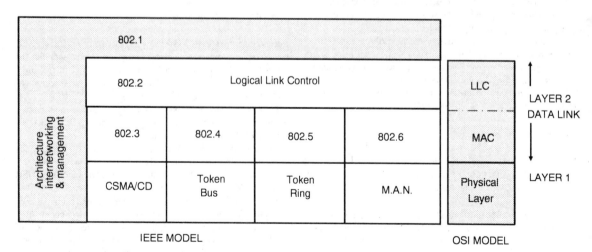

Figure 56.14 IEEE and OSI Models

Other 802.3 LAN standards include:

1. 10 Base 2, also known as Thinnet or Cheapernet.
2. 1 Base 5, the original standard for the AT&T StarLan™
3. 10 Base T, applicable to LANs over twisted pair wiring.
4. 10 Base F, applicable to LANs over an optical fibre.
5. 10 Broad 36, CSMA/CD using broadband signalling techniques.

IEEE 802.5 has standards governing nine types of physical media, including shielded and unshielded twisted pair at 1, 4, and 16Mbit/s. Table 56.1 shows the characteristics of some popular LANs.

Table 56.1 Characteristics of some popular LANs

Signalling technique	Access method			Transmission medium	Network topology
	802.3	802.4	803		
Broadband	Yes	Yes	No	Coax	Bus
	Yes	Yes	No	Coax	Bus/Tree
Baseband	Yes	No	No	Coax	Bus
	Yes	No	No	Twisted Pair	Bus
	Yes	No	No	Multi-Wire	Bus
	Yes	No	No	Coax	Bus/Star
	Yes	No	No	Fibre Optic	Bus/Star
	Yes	No	No	Coax	Star
	Yes	No	No	Twisted Pair	Star
	No	No	Yes	Coax	Ring
	No	No	Yes	Twisted Pair	Ring
	No	No	Yes	Fibre	Ring

56.5 Internetworking devices

Although local area networks have been in existence in one form or another for many years, the unprecedented growth of LANs during the latter half of the 1980s made network users increasingly aware of the limitations of their installed networks, and refocused attention on ways to overcome them.

The first problems realised were those concerned with the physical distance of the network. A typical 10 Base 5 coaxial Ethernet, for example, has a maximum segment length of 500 metres and may only accommodate up to 100 'taps' per segment.

The requirement to extend the length of the network led to the development of what is commonly acknowledged as the first inter-network device, the repeater.

56.5.1 The repeater

The repeater is the simplest form of internetworking device and evolved first in conjunction with CSMA/CD-type networks in the mid 1970s. It operates at the lowest layer of the ISO Reference Model, i.e., the Physical Layer. (See Figure 56.15.)

Figure 56.15 OSI model of a repeater

Repeaters can extend the physical range of a LAN by collecting the stream of electrical impulses on one LAN and repeating that signal on to another identical LAN. Repeaters, however are limited in their ability to extend LANs. This is because LAN architectures incorporate certain assumptions regarding propagation delays, and as repeaters are added to networks, propagation delays eventually increase beyond tolerable thresholds. In addition, use of repeaters often requires careful and detailed network design and planning. (See Figure 56.16.)

Since they operate at the Physical Layer, repeaters perform independently of the higher-level processing required in more complex networks. Therefore, they can effectively operate at the same speeds as the extended network. This, however, also means that repeaters are only capable of interconnecting LANs with similar protocol formats.

A further advantage to the deployment of repeaters in extending a LAN is that they can effectively isolate cable faults to a single segment of the extended LAN. On the other hand, indiscriminate use of repeaters can create problems with network performance and station-to-station accessibility.

56.5.2 Bridges

As more and more devices become attached to the LAN, the utilisation increases. As the amount of traffic on the network approaches the prescribed operating limits of the LAN, network efficiency begins to decrease.

For example, on a non-contention LAN, such as an IEEE 802.5 Token Passing Ring, the station must wait a finite time before the token makes its way around the ring to it, thereby enabling it to transmit. This minimum time to transmission increases with the number of attached devices. Similarly, on a contention LAN, such as an IEEE 802.3 CSMA/CD, as the number of devices contending for control of the medium increases, the number of collisions on the network also rises, thereby reducing its overall performance.

Analysis of the nature of traffic on the LAN, in most cases, led to the conclusion that effectively segmenting the network into two or more separate LANs could increase overall network performance.

This would certainly be the case when the network could be segmented into heavy users, (e.g. CAD/CAM users, computer rooms), and light users, (e.g. word processing). (See Figure 56.17.)

A further advantage of such segmentation is that failures on a particular segment of the LAN can be contained within that segment.

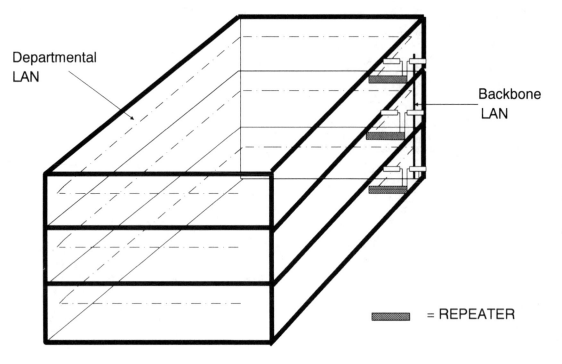

Figure 56.16   Repeater application within a building

The solution to the congestion problem led to the development of the bridge, or to be more precise, the local bridge.

Since a local bridge could be used to create two networks out of a single network, it followed that it could also be employed to create one logical extended network out of two, (or more), locally dispersed LANs.

56.5.2.1   *Local bridges*

Bridges operate at the Data Link Layer, (Layer 2), of the OSI Model, or more specifically at the Media Access Control, (MAC), sublayer. (See Figure 56.18.)

Upon receipt of a data packet, bridges examine the source and destination address of the data packet. If the destination device is on a network other than that of the source device, then the bridge will 'FORWARD' the packet onto the extended network. If the destination device address is on the same network segment as the source device, then the bridge will not forward the packet; instead it will block its path onto the extended network effectively keeping it local. In this way the bridge acts as a 'FILTER' of data packets.

By means of 'Filtering and Forwarding' bridges can create one single logically unified network out of several locally discrete LANs, while at the same time limiting the flow of unnecessary traffic between them.

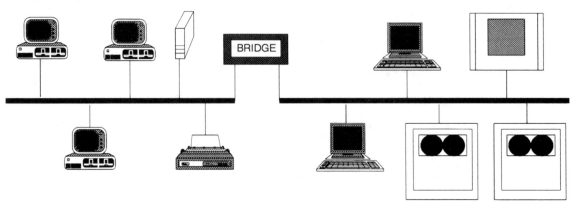

Figure 56.17   LAN interconnection using a local bridge

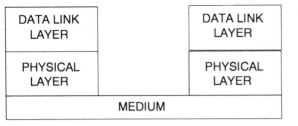

Figure 56.18 OSI model of a bridge

Organisations that had local area networks within their geographically dispersed operating sites soon began to express a desire to interconnect all their remote LANs together, to effectively build a single organisation-wide area network, irrespective of geography.

Manufacturers responded to this requirement with two types of solutions, remote bridges and routers.

Manufacturers offered as a simple, 'transparent' solution, bridges that incorporated wide area interfaces to provide access to different types of media, such as leased or switched analog telephone lines, 48, 56, 64kbit/s lines, or E-1 or T-1 lines.

This led to the development of the remote bridge which performed exactly the same functions as a local bridge, with the exception that it could now be used to build a single logical network, unrestricted by geography. Since this type of bridge had wide area interfaces the user typically had to have two identical bridges at either end of the communications link. Thus, remote bridges were often referred to as 'half bridges'. (See Figure 56.19.)

56.5.3 Routers

The second solution to the problem of interconnecting LANs over unlimited geographical distances was the router.

This device operates at the Network Layer of the OSI Model, (Layer 3). Routers essentially offer selective routing of individual packets over multiple communications paths. (See Figure 56.20.)

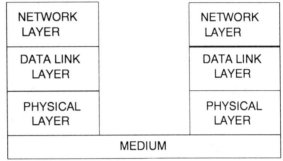

Figure 56.20 OSI model of a router

Routers have the capability to transmit data packets over different paths in an extended network depending on the network user's priorities, such as the least costly, fastest, or most direct route.

Because they operate at a higher layer in the OSI Model than bridges, routers have a greater level of 'understanding' of the data

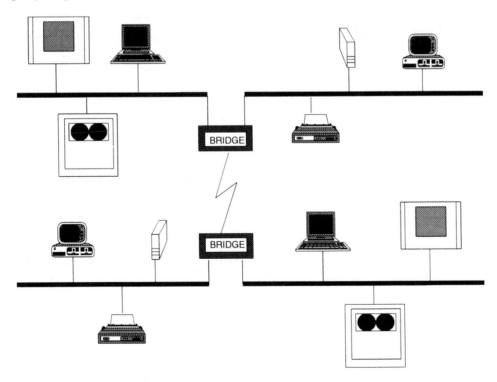

Figure 56.19 LAN interconncetion using remote bridges

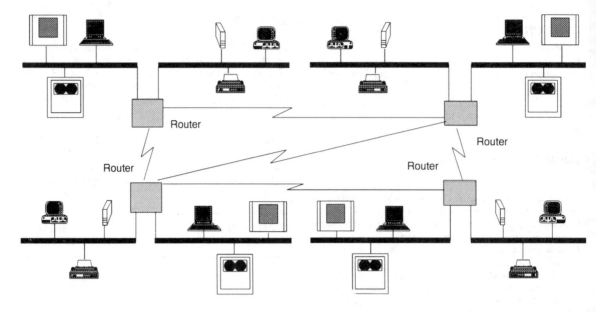

Figure 56.21 An example of an extended network using routers

passing on the LAN. This allows routers to create a logically extended network comprised of separate subnetworks, in contrast to the single logically unified network constructed by bridges. (See Figure 56.21.)

The extra processing required by routers to manipulate data packets, however, impacts upon throughput performance. Typically, conventional routers introduce longer delays in getting packets from source node to destination node, resulting in slower response times or require more processing power to provide the same response times. As Network Layer connectors, routers are protocol specific; indeed the earliest routers could only connect LANs with identical Network Layer protocols.

56.5.4   Gateways

Network users who want to connect two totally dissimilar LANs together use a 'gateway'. There is still some confusion regarding the use of this term. Many people still refer to routers as gateways. The following definitions are now more widely accepted:

1. Router: a device that operates at Layer 3 of the OSI Model.
2. Gateway: a device that operates at Layers 4, 5, 6 and 7, (i.e. the Transport, Session, Presentation and Application Layers) of the OSI Model.

Gateways effectively provide a protocol conversion service, at each of the higher layers of the OSI Model for the interconnection of LANs. Therefore, LANs with separate protocol formats such as NetBios and SNA can communicate through a gateway.

Similarly, gateways permit different machine types to communicate. For example, IBM PCs and asynchronous terminals can communicate with IBM hosts through gateways via protocol emulation.

Gateways operating at the Session, Presentation and Application Layers allow diverse architectures such as SNA or DECnet to communicate. Such gateways may make use of common 'lower layer' network facilities such as X.25 packet networks. (See Figure 56.22.) Operating at the Application Layer, gateways can enable specific applications, such as different electronic mail systems to communicate.

Gateways were primarily designed for specific environment-to-environment connectivity and not particularly for the high speeds common to LAN communications. Since they operate at the highest layers of the OSI Model, gateways are required to perform substan-

APPLICATION LAYER		APPLICATION LAYER
PRESENTATION LAYER		PRESENTATION LAYER
SESSION LAYER		SESSION LAYER
TRANSPORT LAYER		TRANSPORT LAYER
NETWORK LAYER		NETWORK LAYER
DATA LINK LAYER		DATA LINK LAYER
PHYSICAL LAYER		PHYSICAL LAYER
MEDIUM		

Figure 56.22 OSI model of a gateway

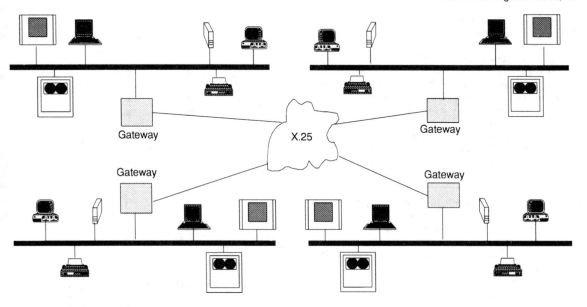

Figure 56.23 Example of an extended network using gateways

tially more data processing than the other internetworking devices. They are, therefore, slower, less transparent, less flexible and perhaps the most network specific of all the LAN interconnectivity devices. (See Figure 56.23.)

Because both repeaters and gateways are network specific, bridges and routers emerged as the most popular solutions to internetworking problems.

Nevertheless, considerable confusion remains as to when it is best to bridge and when it is best to route. This confusion has been compounded by several factors. Firstly, conventional bridge functionality has expanded into the territory originally monopolised by routers. Secondly, routers are now performing at speeds traditionally associated with bridges, and thirdly the developments in both bridge and router technology have been accompanied by a host of totally new hybrid internetworking products.

56.5.5 Developments in bridging technology

The first major development in bridging was the addition of 'learning'. Learning enabled bridges to automatically track the source addresses of data packets received by the bridge in order to build up a learned address table of locally attached devices. This capability enabled the bridge to automatically and dynamically filter local segment traffic from the rest of the network.

A network management capability has been added on more intelligent bridging devices to provide extended network management performance statistics and remote configuration of bridges.

One of the problems of implementing bridges in complex network topologies, particularly networks that involve looped data paths, is the likelihood of a 'broadcast storm'. That is, certain types of packets could be perpetually circulated around the extended network causing a degradation of throughput performance and eventually bringing the network down. To overcome this problem, many bridges now implement the IEEE 802.1(D) Spanning Tree algorithm.

The Spanning Tree algorithm decides which bridge in the network is to become the 'root bridge', based upon the number and speed of the paths between the bridges. The bridge deemed to be the root bridge is allocated the highest priority of all the bridges in the network and the network is then configured and routes determined.

Effectively, the bridges automatically disable selected routes within the extended network to create a 'loop-free' network. This in effect changes a looped or 'mesh' network into a tree structure for which there is one and only one active path from one station to any and every other station. However, the Spanning Tree algorithm carries the disadvantage that alternate paths, and in many cases, expensive wide area network bandwidth, remain unused and become active only when other paths fail.

The latest bridges are now capable of automatically configuring themselves upon insertion into a network, and have become true 'plug and play' devices.

56.5.6 Developments in router technology

While developments in bridge technology were occurring, router technology was also advancing.

Conventional routers only supported the interconnection of local area networks that had identical characteristics (e.g. Ethernet networks). Similarly, these routers only operated for a single routing protocol over the extended network, such as TCP/IP or DECnet.

The latest generation of routers, however, now supports a variety of LAN types and concurrently supports more than one routing protocol.

The speeds at which routers process data have also increased, and in some cases performance now almost matches that of a straightforward bridging device.

56.5.7 Hybrid interconnection devices

The concurrent developments in bridging and routing technology led to the emergence of hybrid interconnection products such as the router bridge, sometimes referred to as bridge/routers, or brouters.

These devices are capable of operating at both layers 2 and 3, (Data Link and Network respectively), of the OSI model.

A router/bridge can provide a Network Layer (routing) service to one or more protocols that it has been programmed to support, while at the same time offering a Data Link Layer (bridging) service to protocols that it does not recognise. Therefore, a router/bridge can simultaneously route the DECnet protocol and bridge the DEC LAT protocol, (which cannot be routed) over the same link.

The term brouter is also commonly applied to a bridge (Layer 2) device, which rather than using the standards based Spanning Tree algorithm, uses a proprietary scheme for avoiding the problems introduced by mesh or 'looped' topologies, while at the same time taking advantage of multiple and alternate paths. (See Figure 56.24.)

56.6 LAN/WAN challenge for the 1990s

Following the wide scale adoption of LANs in the 1980s, bridges became and remain, popular due mainly to their simplicity, ease of installation, and low cost. A bridging solution performs well in small-to-medium-sized departmental environments.

However, as networking continues to evolve, so does the requirement for effective management of the extended network. Bridges are only capable of building one logically extended network, unlike routers which can establish independently managed networks, (or sub-networks), within the extended network.

Router/bridges attempt to provide the best of both technologies, offering the simplicity and performance of bridging and the network control capabilities of routing, to help resolve the ever increasing complexities of LAN-to-LAN communications.

In the last two sections we covered the development of two discrete network technologies, WAN and LAN.

The Wide Area Network, initially based on analogue modem connectivity, developed to a sophisticated digital networking infrastructure. Local Area Networks have rapidly been introduced in the networking environment, first as discreet networks and then as interconnection into the analogue or digital infrastructure.

The 1990s and into the next century is set to see an expansion of both technologies, both as separate networking solutions, but most importantly as single network solution under the apt name 'All Area Networking' (AAN).

The traditional wide area supplier has quickly realised the importance of integrating LAN interconnect as a unified product within his overall product line. Unified product means not only the capability to be managed under the same network platform, but to operate with the same physical attributes as all his existing connectivity elements.

The rising local area interconnection suppliers have attempted to brush aside the issue relating to other forms of networking, but concentrate on improving the LAN capability. This under the belief that all private networking will be dominated by the needs of LANs rather than voice, video, traditional data service and image. This is not an assumption but a realisation that if tariffed correctly all these other services can be either replaced by LANs or in the case of voice or video replaced by the existing but improved public switched network (be that in an ISDN form).

In some respects this was a real threat, since it was clear that routing LAN traffic via a multiplexer have no real benefits. This was true until the emergence of a new standard called Frame Relay. Frame Relay (see Chapter 55) which is based on CCITT I.120 standards provides an effective method of handling multiple LANs into a single or multisystem wide area network. As has been the case previously, the most reasonable platform for this type of network would be a multiplexer. Frame Relay efficiency handles the packet

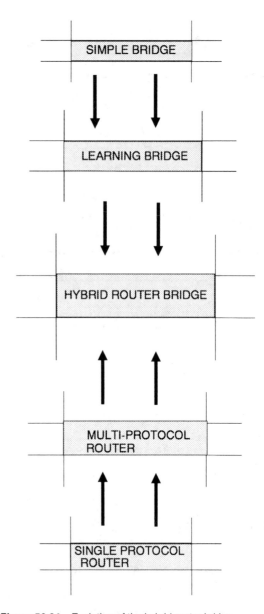

Figure 56.24 Evolution of the hybrid router bridge

type connectivity of LAN by optimising the infrastructure to meet the dramatic demand for LAN traffic.

A network of the very near future will combine all the traditional attributes of digital multiplexers together with the ability to handle LAN interconnection, either as part of the multiplexer or as a separate access device on the network, but all under a single management environment.

Yet the challenge of the 1990s are not yet over with the arrival of new standard transmission techniques based on Synchronous Digital Hierarchy (SDH) or as it is called in North America SONET. (See Chapter 42.) These allow transmission planners to construct networks on single building blocks, with higher bandwidth using fibre error free connection, as a standard product from many vendors and most importantly the ability to integrate into the existing

efficient and proprietary networks they have developed. This is
allowed by a new network switching infrastructure called (see
chapter 41) Asynchronous Transport Mode (ATM), which caters
or the growing demand of higher switching connectivity and packet
mode of both LAN, voice, video and image. Also included is the
arrival of management architectures based on OSI standard and with
the ability to separate/partition services and function from this
single management architecture.

The changes within the network during 1990s and early next
century will see an ever demanding role for WAN and LAN networking, which will ultimately be under the same networking
banner AAN, all working to the goal 'the network is the product'.

56.7 Acknowledgement

Acknowledgement to Steve Gerrard, Marketing Manager for local
and wide area integration, with Newbridge Networks, who practically wrote the LAN section.

57

Video transmission

Pat Hawker
Formerly IBA Engineering Division
(Sections 57.1–57.2)

J R Fox
MA (Cantab) MSc PhD MIEE CEng MSCTE
BT Laboratories
(Section 57.3)

D G Morrison
MA
BT Laboratories
(Section 57.4)

Ian Corbett
BSc CEng MIEE
BT Laboratories
(Section 57.5)

Contents

57.1 Principles of video transmission

The development of electronic television in the mid 1930s, for the first time, presented communications engineers with the need to handle signals having a base bandwidth measured in MHz rather than the kHz required for the early multi channel telephony systems. For the original UK black and white television broadcast standard of 405 line, 2:1 interlace, 50 fields (25 frames) per second, the video bandwidth was of the order of zero to 3MHz in all sections of the programme chain from camera to transmitter, and similarly for the video amplifier in the receiver. This stimulated the development of broadband, linear circuitry and transmission systems which soon found application also for multiplexed telephony transmission.

Within the television broadcasting environment, communication links include the routeing systems within the studio complex, linking cameras with mixers (switchers) and between mixers and a central apparatus room etc., often involving hundreds of metres of cabling; contribution links from OB (remote) venues to the studio centre or for incoming 'live' programmes from distant studio centres or overseas broadcasters; distribution links from studio centres to transmitters, including the inter city links required for network operation, inter country, inter continental links for programme exchanges. Short range microwave links may also be used for portable radio cameras used in ENG (electronic news gathering), sportscasting etc., linking the camera with a mobile control room or portable video recorder.

The original broadband video/sound links were concerned with analogue signals of black and white video; the later introduction of analogue composite (encoded) waveforms for colour television required significantly more stringent performance standards in order to minimise picture degradations resulting primarily from differential gain and differential phase. Over many years, radio relay links have used frequency modulated carriers to convey analogue video waveforms, but from the 1970s onwards increasing use is being made of digital video, digital audio and digital data signals within parts of the programme chain with a corresponding gradual introduction of digitally modulated carriers for terrestrial radio relay and optical fibre links and also, to some degree, for satellite links in accordance with ISDN hierarchial levels.

Video signals conveyed over relatively short distances of coaxial cable in studio routeing systems are normally transmitted directly at video frequency. When the cable path exceeds about 100m the distribution amplifiers may provide passive equalisation to offset the distortions caused by the attenuation and delay characteristics of the cable. For cable systems extending beyond about 500m, the video signal modulates a carrier frequency between about 20MHz to 70MHz, using either double sideband or vestigial sideband amplitude modulation, suitable for distances up to a few km without intermediate amplifiers.

A re-broadcasting link (RBL) is a commonly used method of feeding programme information from a main transmitter to its low power gap filling relay transmitters. The key component of an RBL is a high grade re-broadcasting receiver (RBR). RBLs may also be used to link high power main transmitters forming a regional network. Incoming signals presented to the RBR are usually not demodulated at gap filling relays but converted to an intermediate frequency (e.g. 70MHz) and then re-converted to the required channel (frequency translation).

Signals coded in digital form are more resistant to the effects of noise and distortion in transmission links, although vulnerable to multipath distortion, and can be regenerated without loss of fidelity. The quality of the pictures and sound is determined primarily by the coding. Telecommunications practice is tending towards digital links and networks designed to carry a flexible mixture of television, telephony and data services. The European standard ISDN levels are: 64kbit/s, 2048kbit/s, 8448kbit/s, 34.368Mbit/s and 139.264Mbit/s. The last two of these levels are of particular interest in television broadcasting, and are usually referred to as 34Mbit/s and 140Mbit/s respectively.

Straightforward PCM coding of 625 line PAL generates a digital signal with a bit rate of about 100Mbit/s. The CCIR component digital standard (Rec. 601, 4:2:2) for YUV components generates a source signal of 216Mbit/s. Recently developed video bit rate reduction techniques can reduce the bit rate by a factor of about 8 to 10 times; feasibility studies, using computer simulation, suggest that it may be possible to reduce video bit rates by a factor between about 20 and 40, permitting digital broadcasting to the home of 625 line composite or component video within the bandwidth of terrestrial TV channels. An example of such studies is the Eureka 625 project VADIS (Video Audio Digital Interactive System) aimed at multiplexing video, audio and data information for transmission in high speed LANs and future broadband telecommunications networks.

Video bit rate reduction involves the use of such techniques as sample rate reduction, differential coding (DPCM), transform coding, variable length coding and vector quantisation, or a combination of these. The channel bandwidth of a digital signal depends on both the bit rate and the modulation process. It should however be noted that where digital video has been subjected to appreciable bit rate reduction, or is in composite rather than component form, it cannot be further processed or manipulated within the production process; the requirements of a contribution link may thus differ from that of distribution links.

Direct to home digital broadcasting from terrestrial transmitters would permit a very significant reduction of transmitter power and might permit the use of the so called 'taboo channels' denied to terrestrial broadcasters on account of co-channel and/or adjacent channel interference. Multipath leading to inter symbol distortion and consequent high bit error rates can be minimised by the use of special modulation techniques such as Orthogonal Frequency Digital Modulation (OFDM) of a large number of spaced carriers.

57.2 Television transmission

57.2.1 Fundamentals and standards

All television systems are based on translating a scene into a series of small points, termed picture elements (pixels), by methodically tracing out or scanning the picture, and then conveying the intensity (light value) of each picture element in an agreed sequence. At the receiver, a reproduction of the image is built up by means of an identical and synchronised scanning sequence (Figure 57.1). The display screen glows with an intensity dependent upon the light value of the pixels, with a degree of integration (memory) in both camera and display. This, combined with the persistence of vision of the eye, gives the viewer the impression that the display is presenting a complete series of pictures with a resolution depending on the total number of pixels in each frame; if subsequent frames follow sufficiently rapidly the illusion of natural movement, as in a cinematograph film, is provided.

A series of images presented to the eye at a rate above about 10 per second (10Hz) gives an illusion of continuous motion but accompanied by a pronounced flicker. If the rate is increased to 25Hz to 30Hz the flicker is much reduced but still just noticeable, particularly when the images are bright. A repetition rate of 50Hz

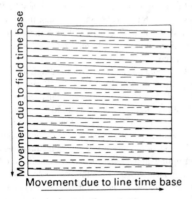

Figure 57.1 Simplified representation of sequential scanning

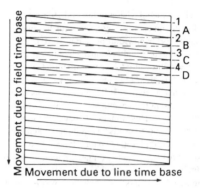

Figure 57.2 Simplified representation of double intrlaced scanning

provides motion virtually without flicker although for some very bright pictures 60Hz or even higher may be desirable. The rate at which video images (frames) follow one another is called the frame rate.

To transmit a series of sequentially scanned pictures at a frame rate of 50Hz or 60Hz would require an excessively large bandwidth if the line resolution is more than about 300 lines. An alternative technique, universally adopted for broadcast transmission, is termed interlacing; instead of transmitting each adjacent horizontal line in sequence, alternate lines are scanned first, to form a field, with the missing lines traced out subsequently as a second field, the two fields forming one complete frame. Since the eye hardly perceives individual lines of a single frame, the effect is to provide 50 (60) 'images' per second, although transmitting only 25 (30) frames per second, at the cost only of introducing a small degree of interline flicker at the 25Hz (30Hz) rate. It has also been shown that with digital memory in the receiver, it is possible to display an interlaced picture with sequential (progressive) scanning. With interlaced scanning the final line of the first field and the first line of the second

field are half lines, the line starting at the centre of the top line with a similar half line at the bottom of the picture, as in Figure 57.2.

Since the scanning process has to be carried out synchronously in the studio and in the receiver, it is necessary to provide synchronising signals that accurately define the start of the field scans and each line scan. Conventionally, this is achieved by transmitting two sets of timing pulses which are used by the receiver to lock its horizontal and frame timebases, although it is feasible, using digital technology, to provide only one set of pulses from which both rates can be derived by counting techniques.

The way in which 625 line video signals are combined with line sync pulses is shown in Figure 57.3.

Colour television requires the transmission of additional information which, in practice, takes the form of two chrominance signals, which together with the black and white (luminance) signal defines the picture in terms of the three primary colours, red (R), green (G) and blue (B).

Any colour can be defined by three characteristics: its brightness (luminance); its hue (dominant electromagnetic wavelength/fre-

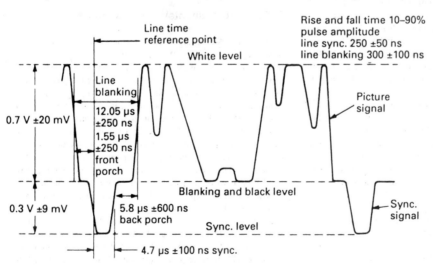

Figure 57.3 The waveform of a typical line showing synchronising signals

Table 57.1 International standards for television broadcasting. (*Amplitude modulated sound.)

System line/fields		Channel width (MHz)	Video width (MHz)	VSB width (MHz)	Polarity vision modulation	Sound/vision carrier spacing (MHz)
B	625/50	7	5	0.75	Negative	5.5
D, K	625/50	8	6	0.75	Negative	6.5
G	625/50	8	5	0.75	Negative	5.5
H	625/50	8	5	1.25	Negative	5.5
I	625/50	8	5.5	1.25	Negative	6.0
K1	625/50	8	6	1.25	Negative	6.5
L	625/50	8	6	1.25	Positive	6.5*
M	525/60	6	4.2	0.75	Negative	4.5
N	625/50	6	4.2	0.75	Negative	4.5

uency); and its intensity (saturation) which corresponds to its colourfulness.

In colour television systems, chrominance information defines the ue and saturation of the pixels independently of the luminance, so hat theoretically any distortion of the chrominance information oes not affect the detail of the picture. A system designed to satisfy his condition is termed a constant luminance system, although in ractice some departure from this ideal is to be found in systems urrently in use.

It was recognised that to achieve wide acceptability of colour in n era when black and white television had achieved popularity, a olour system needed to be compatible, that is the colour trans-nissions should be receivable as black and white pictures on a black nd white only receiver, and should also have reverse compatibility /hereby black and white transmissions should be receivable as lack and white pictures on a colour receiver.

The standard adopted to define whiteness is the colour tempera-ure (which determines the amount of blue or green in peak white). 'he standard adopted in Europe is Illuminant D corresponding to 500K.

To define completely the luminance and chrominance informa-ion, a colour source, such as a camera, analyses the light from the cene in terms of its red (R), green (G) and blue (B) components by neans of optical filters and then gamma corrects these to take into ccount differences between source and display tube characteristics. iamma corrected signals are termed R', G', B' signals which are rocessed to provide the basic luminance signal (Y). The green and ed signals contribute more to luminance than blue and in practice

a matrixing network is designed such that Equation 57.1 is satisfied.

$$Y' = 0.3\,R' + 0.6\,G' + 0.1\,B' \tag{57.1}$$

Since the four signals Y', R', G' and B' are related mathematically it is unnecessary to transmit all four. Since for compatibility a Y' signal is needed, this is transmitted with two (chrominance) signals obtained by taking the red and blue signals and subtracting from them Y', that is (R' - Y') and (B' - Y'). (G' - Y') can be derived within the receiver by matrixing. The transmitted signals are thus Y', as in Equation 57.1 and (R' - Y') and (B' - Y'). These three signals allow Y', R', G' and B' to be recovered in the receiver.

Tables 57.1 to 57.3 provide an overview of the international standards and the countries using them. Detailed information on the international standards for television broadcasting is given in CCIR Report 624 (ITU Sales Service, Place des Nations, CH-1211, Geneva 20, Switzerland).

57.2.2 Bandwidth

The maximum upper frequency of a video signal is governed by the picture content and the scanning standard being used. For the UK System I this is normally taken as 5.5MHz.

Were conventional double sideband AM to be used, this would imply a maximum vision bandwidth of 2 x 5.5 = 11MHz. In addition, further bandwidth would be required for the sound signal. In view of the restricted frequency spectrum at v.h.f. and u.h.f., it

Table 57.2 Composite colour video signals in terrestrial systems (simplified)

System	Chrominance	Chrominance subcarrier (MHz)	Chrominance subcarrier modulation
PAL	E_U, E_V	Approx. 4.43 (3.58 for M/PAL)	Suppressed carrier AM of two subcarriers in quadrature
NTSC	E_I, E_Q	Approx. 3.58	Suppressed carrier AM of two subcarriers in quadrature
SECAM	D_R, D_B (line sequential)	Approx. 4.41(D_R) Approx. 4.25 (D_B)	Frequency modulation alternating one line D_R one line D_B

Table 57.3 Television systems by country. (* V.h.f. band only)

System	Country
I/PAL	Angola* Botswana Hong Kong Ireland Lesotho South Africa UK
B G/PAL	Albania Algeria Australia Austria Bahrain Bangladesh* Belgium Brunei Darussalam* Cameroon Denmark Equatorial Guinea* Ethiopia Finland Germany (FRG) Ghana Gibraltar Iceland India* Indonesia* Israel Italy Jordan Kenya Kuwait Liberia* Luxembourg Malawi Malaysia Maldives* Malta* Monaco Mozambique Netherlands New Zealand Nigeria* Norway Oman Pakistan Papua New Guinea Portugal Qatar Sierra Leone Singapore Spain Sri Lanka* Sudan* Sweden Switzerland Syria Tanzania* Thailand Tunisia Turkey Uganda* United Arab Emirates Yemen (AR)* Yemen (PDR)* Yugoslavia Zambia* Zimbabwe*
N/PAL	Argentina* Paraguay* Uruguay
D/PAL	China
M/PAL	Brazil
D K/PAL	Korea (DPR) Romania
B G/SECAM	Cyprus Egypt Germany Greece Iran Iraq* Lebanon Libya* Mali* Mauritania* Mauritius* Morocco Saudi Arabia Tunisia
D K/SECAM	Afghanistan* Bulgaria Czechoslovakia Hungary Mongolia* Poland USSR Viet Nam
K1/SECAM	Benin Burkina Faso Burundi Central African Republic Chad Congo Cote d'Ivoire (Ivory Coast) Djibouti* Gabon Guinea Madagascar Niger Senegal Togo Zaire
L/SECAM	France Luxembourg Monaco
M/NTSC	Bermuda* Bolivia British Virgin Islands* Burma* Canada Chile Colombia Costa Rica Cuba Dominican Republic* Ecuador* Guatemala* Haiti* Honduras* Jamaica* Japan Korea (Republic of) Mexico Montserrat* Netherlands Antilles* Nicaragua* Panama Peru Philippines* St. Christopher & Nevis* Suriname* USA Venezuela

has for many years been the practice to reduce the bandwidth of one of the two sidebands to produce vestigial sideband or asymmetric sideband vision transmission. In System I the full upper sidebands to 5.5MHz are transmitted but the bandwidth of the lower sideband is restricted to 1.25MHz (in 625 line System G as used in many countries the lower sideband is restricted even more to 0.75MHz).

This means that for System I the total vision bandwidth is 1.25 + 5.5 or 6.75MHz and a gap of 0.5MHz is left before the sound carrier, which is thus 6MHz above the vision carrier, as shown in Figure 57.4

For both Systems I and G in the European region the agreed international u.h.f. channels occupy 8MHz; in System I the vision carrier is always +1.25MHz from the lower end of the channel; the FM sound carrier +7.25MHz. Figure 57.4 shows the vision response curve of System I as related to the video signal, the r.f. channel, and the standard BREMA receiver i.f. channel. The FM sound is transmitted with a maximum a.f. signal of 15kHz and with a peak carrier deviation (corresponding to a 400Hz tone at a level of +8dBm at the modulator input) of ±50kHz. The pre-emphasis time constant is 50µs.

The use of an asymmetric sideband vision signal results in a degree of quadrature distortion when the signal is envelope demodulated: this form of distortion (which can usually be detected only with some difficulty, even on a test card) can be eliminated by the use of synchronous demodulation.

Although the chrominance signals generated in the colour camera occupy the full range of video frequencies, it is only the luminance signal that requires to be transmitted to this degree of resolution. The ability to resolve fine detail depends on visual acuity, and our ability to resolve colour in small details of a picture is inferior to that for corresponding black and white or grey pictures. Since the human eye does not resolve colour in small areas there is no need to reproduce this, even for high quality television pictures (Figure 57.5). This influences many aspects of colour television, not least the ability to limit the bandwidth of chrominance information relative to that required for the luminance signal. In practice chrominance information in a 625 line system can begin to roll off at about 1.3MHz. The restriction of chrominance bandwidth makes possible inband transmission of chrominance information, although this technique gives rise to some loss of compatibility (dots and crawl being seen on a monochrome display) and also cross colour effects on colour reproduction (flaring of patterned jackets is a common example), due to luminance signals appearing in the colour channels.

Basically the information in a monochrome signal is distributed in a series of packets separated by the line frequency, with only little spectrum energy in the gaps between as shown in Figure 57.6. By choosing a colour subcarrier frequency that is accurately placed between multiples of the line frequency, and noting that chrominance modulation energy is similarly in the form of packets it is possible to interleave the basic energy spectra of the luminance and chrominance signals for 625 line transmission the colour subcarrier frequency is maintained very precisely at 4433618.75Hz ±1Hz with a maximum rate of change of subcarrier frequency not exceeding 0.1Hz/s.

The relationship between subcarrier and line frequency is given by Equation 57.2 where f_h is the line frequency and f_v is the field frequency.

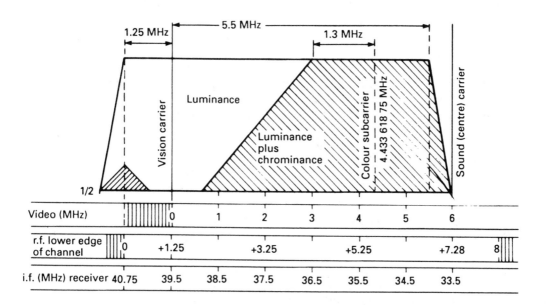

Figure 57.4 The frequency bands occupied by colour picture components and sound signal from an ideal 625 line System 1 transmitter as related to video, vision, and the i.f. of a receiver (BREMA standard i.f.)

$$f_{sc} = \left(284 - \frac{1}{4}\right)f_h + \frac{1}{2}f_v \quad Hz \qquad (57.2)$$

The way in which colour information is transmitted in the PAL System 1 standard is shown in Figures 57.7 to 57.10.

57.2.3 Analogue component hybrid systems

The picture impairments inherent where the colour information is encoded within the luminance signal ('mixed highs') for PAL, NTSC and SECAM can be eliminated by maintaining the three fundamental component signals representing red (R), green (G) and blue (B) or, more practically, by separation of the luminance (Y) and colour difference (U, V, or I, Q) chrominance signals. However, if the RGB or YUV signals are maintained within the studios, and as far as the transmitter, it is impractical to transmit a frequency multiplex of such component signals within the channels available in Bands I, III, IV, V or the 12GHz DBS/FM bands. Additionally, component signals would not be compatible with existing black and white, PAL, SECAM or NTSC receivers. There would also be great difficulty in retaining accurate timing (phasing) of separate analogue component signals during routeing or over distribution links.

A digitally based system that permits the time division multiplexing of YUV analogue signals into a form suitable for DBS/FM transmission within the 27MHz channels (19MHz carrier separation) was developed initially by the IBA and subsequently adopted for DBS in Europe in the early 1980s. This system (now comprising a family of systems) is termed Multiplexed Analogue Components (MAC), with the separate YUV signals digitally time compressed and then time division multiplexed to occupy the active line periods of the 625 line standard. Digital sound/data signals are inserted into the video channel during the line sync periods and then frequency

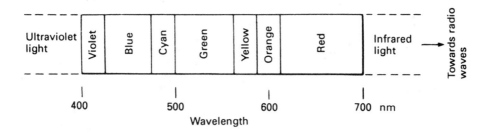

Figure 57.5 The electromagnetic spectrum of visible light. Short wavelengths such as these may be quoted in Angstrom units (10^{-10} m)

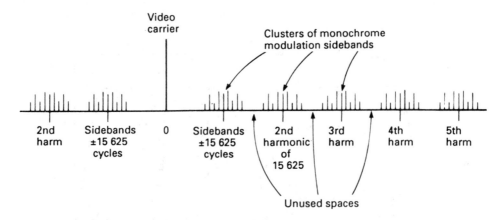

Figure 57.6 In a monochrome television transmission the sidebands are in groups around harmonics of 15625Hz leaving spaces in which colour information may be inserted

modulated with the video signals on a single carrier. Although digitally processed, the video signals are thus transmitted in analogue form. The receiver decoder demultiplexes the signal, restoring the YUV signals to their original parallel relationship, making them suitable for display as conventional 625 line YUV signals.

A number of MAC systems have been developed not only for DBS applications but also for use as a multiplexed signal within studios or for OB contribution links, electronic/satellite news gathering, etc. There are also several different standards relating to the way in which the digital audio/data signals are transmitted:

1. B-MAC. This system developed by Scientific-Atlanta for satellite cable distribution links or DBS can carry six digital audio channels as baseband data symbols and is designed for minimum complexity in its data multiplex, requiring only 15 000 gates in the decoder IC. It is a fixed format system (i.e. not individually addressed 'packets').
2. C-MAC/packet transmits up to eight digital high quality audio channels directly modulated on to the carrier during the line

blanking periods using binary phase shift keying. Data bit rate 20.25MHz.

3. D-MAC/packet has the same data rate as C-MAC but with the data signal in duobinary form inserted on to the baseband signal as part of the multiplex rather than directly modulating the carrier.
4. D2-MAC/packet has a format similar to D-MAC but the data rate is half that of D-MAC (i.e. 10.125Mbit/s). It can thus carry four high quality audio channels or eight medium quality channels.

The 625 line D-MAC/packet system was adopted as the UK DBS standard. The baseband video waveform of a D-MAC television line is shown in Figure 57.11.

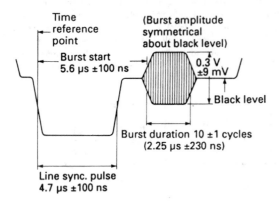

Figure 57.7 The colour burst on a standard level signal (700mV white level)

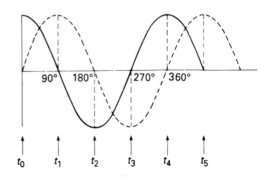

Figure 57.8 The principle of synchronous demodulation of quadrature modulated signals. Two carrier waves are shown of the same frequency but in quadrature. If each is amplitude modulated by different information and if two demodulators, one synchronised with each carrier, sample the waves only at the times when one is at a peak and the other at null, then the two sets of information can be separately retrieved at the receiver. The solid line waveform is sampled at times t_0, t_1, t_4, etc. and the dashed line curve at times t_1, t_3, t_5, etc.

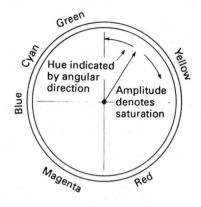

Figure 57.9 In the NTSC and PAL systems any hue can be represented by a phasor having a specific phase angle and an amplitude representing the degree of saturation

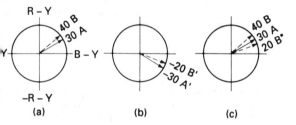

Figure 57.10 Principle of PAL automatic line correction by averaging: (a) hue A transmitted with a positive (R–Y) component; recieved as B because of a phase shift; (b) same hue transmitted with negative (R–Y) component A'; received as B' due to a phase error equivalent to that at (a); (c) after reversing the polarity of (b) the two received signals B and B' represent B and B'' which when averaged give the correct hue A

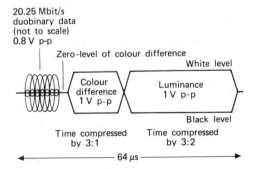

Figure 57.11 Baseband video waveform of a D-MAC television line. The duobinary data burst conveys 206 bits and is followed by time compressed vision signals

Each line of luminance information is digitally compressed by a factor of 3:2 (52μs to about 35μs). the U and V colour difference signals are reduced by a factor of 3:1 (52μs to about 17.5μs). This has the effect of increasing the maximum baseband video frequency from about 5.7MHz to about 8.5MHz. The remaining 10μs periods carry 20.25Mbit/s duobinary data, which take the form shown in Figure 57.12, inserted on to the baseband signal. Each line period thus has 206 data bits with a mean data capacity of about 3Mbit/s.

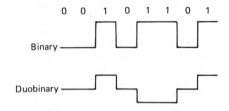

Figure 57.12 Comparison of binary and duobinary coding. After low pass filtering, the three level duobinary data signal is time division multiplexed with the time compressed vision signal

Line 625 carries only data, with duobinary data inserted onto the baseband signal with a capacity of 1296 bits. The use of duobinary coding means that both vision and data signals are contained within a baseband of about 8.5MHz. The digital data are organized into 'packets' of 751 bits with 164 packets in each 625 line frame (4100 packets/s). The basic structure of a D-MAC packet frame is illustrated on Figure 57.13, having, for example, up to eight 15kHz audio channels with 32kHz sampling and NICAM companding of 14 bits/sample to 10 bits/sample, or up to sixteen 7kHz 'commentary' audio channels. The total data capacity is optionally available for

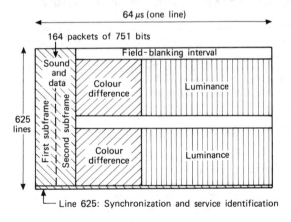

Figure 57.13 Simplified structure of D-MAC packet frame showing the distribution of vision and 20.25Mbit/s duobinary data. Organising the data into two sub-frames allows easy transcoding of one sub-frame into D2-MAC

any mix of teletext data, high quality stereo audio, mono/stereo 'commentary' channels, or for utilisation in part for the provision of analogue wide screen (16:9 aspect ratio) video information in various MAC enhanced modes or for the use of digitally assisted (DATV) vector motion enhancement.

All MAC systems facilitate the use of 'conditional access' encryption systems offering a high level of security for subscription television channels. One possibility is the use of 'double cut' component rotation, with the decoding key transmitted in the digital packets, addressed to individual receivers or groups of receivers.

The digital channel capacities of MAC/packet systems while analogue vision signals are present are: C-MAC and D-MAC 3.04Mbit/s; D2-MAC 1.52Mbit/s. In the absence of vision signals, the full channel capacity of a D-MAC channel can be used.

Within an analogue component area, MAC techniques can be used for routeing, contribution, ENG links, etc. T-MAC for studio interconnection, etc. retains the multiplexed analogue video component portion (4-2-0) of the MAC family of transmission formats, but dispenses with the packet data portion, substituting in its place a line repetitive sync pulse and sampling frequency reference burst. T-MAC signals are capable of conveying component originated video signals and an accompanying sound in sync audio signal over networks conforming to CCIR Recommendations 567 and 965. If the SNR set out in these Recommendations is exceeded, the subjective performance of T-MAC is better than PAL. Below this minimum SNR, the noise is more noticeable in T-MAC than in PAL, but the pictures may still appear better because cross colour effects are absent.

T-MAC was originally conceived as a means of transmitting the signals available from analogue component ENG equipment to studio centres, using existing transmission circuits. The following MAC luminance and chrominance compression ratios apply to routeing and contribution links, etc.:

S-MAC	component 4:2:2 signals	Y 13:6 R-Y/B-Y	13:3
ACLE	component 4:1:1 signals	Y 14:9 R-Y/B-Y	56:9
T-MAC	component 4:2:0 signals	Y 3:2 R-Y/B-Y	3:1
—	component 3:1:0 signals	Y 4:3 R-Y/B-Y	4:1

57.2.4 Enhanced and high definition systems

During the past decade, much research and development work has been devoted to the study of electronic television systems capable of providing wide screen, flicker free pictures of a resolution comparable with that of 35mm cinematograph film. Such high definition TV systems (HDTV) are seen as being suitable for broadcast transmission, wideband cable distribution, electronic cinematography, for the production of master tapes for videocassettes and videodiscs, and for various applications in electronic graphics and printing. Efforts are being made to:

1. Establish worldwide production standards for 50Hz or 60Hz areas, or preferably for both.
2. Develop bandwidth compression techniques for broadcast, cable, contribution and distribution links and studio routeing systems capable of carrying HDTV signals with minimum loss of quality.
3. Develop display systems that could do justice to HDTV pictures at prices within consumer budgets.

Target areas for the development of HDTV and Advanced TV(ATV) systems include:

1. Image quality directly comparable with that of film.
2. Elimination of large area and interline flicker present with 50Hz and, to a lesser extent, 60Hz interfaced TV systems.
3. Elimination of the cross colour defects inherent in composite coded colour systems.

4. Wide screen displays with an aspect ratio of at least 16:9.
5. Economic conversion of material from tape to film and from film to tape, without noticeable degradation of picture quality.
6. Transmission systems compatible with existing receivers.
7. Sufficient flexibility for an HDTV standard to permit advantage to be taken of continuing improvements in display systems, digital signal processing, etc.

While it is feasible that future fibre optic cables may permit, at least theoretically, the distribution direct to the home of HDTV RGB component signals with a bit rate of the order of 1Gbit/s, in practical terms an HDTV signal should be amenable to digital bandwidth compression (bit rate reduction) techniques to the ISDN level of 140Mbit/s.

It has been shown that, as in the cinema, a wide screen display, viewed at a distance of about three or four times picture height, has significantly more impact than pictures with the standard aspect ratio of 4:3 (width/height). For domestic viewing, market research tends to confirm that wide screen pictures, even of conventional resolution, are preferred by the great majority of viewers. This has led to increased interest in various techniques, including the MAC family, that can provide improved quality, wide screen pictures without increasing the basic scanning rates of conventional systems and are fully compatible with those systems. Some of these 'enhanced' or 'advanced' systems are suitable for transmission on terrestrial as well as satellite channels.

57.2.4.1 HD-MAC

A European Eureka EU-95 project in which a large number of organisations have co-operated is to develop a compatible HDTV satellite transmission and will make proposals to the CCIR for HDTV production and transmission standards. The project, initiated in 1986, concerns all aspects of HDTV, from programme production, recording and distribution to broadcasting, consumer equipment and display processing. The aim is to give the viewer a more realistic viewing experience by doubling the vertical and horizontal resolution, suitable for viewing on a 40 inch display that can be seen from the same distance as a conventional 625 line display but with an aspect ratio of 16:9.

The EU-95 project is proposing a production standard of 1250 lines, 50 frames/s in a sequential format, with 1920 pixels per line. Such a standard would permit high quality conversion to other standards, including both 625/50 and 525/60. A secondary production standard, for use within 50Hz areas, would use 1250 lines, 50 fields, 2:1 interlace.

HD-MAC transmission proposals are intended for broadcast DBS transmission within a standard 12GHz channel. Since the bandwidth of its HDTV material is about four times that available, the signals need to be compressed by about four times. It is a project requirement that the compressed HD-MAC signals should give an acceptable 4:3 aspect ratio picture when received on a DBS receiver with a standard MAC decoder. This requirement inhibits the use of all digital techniques, although it is recognized that a 12GHz channel could support digital transmission of HDTV pictures at bit rates of the order of 140Mbit/s, which has been shown to be a practical bit rate for the distribution of HDTV pictures/sound.

A complete HD-MAC system, shown in Figure 57.14 uses three basic techniques to reduce the bandwidth of the channels while retaining as much of the original image quality as possible.

1. Diagonal filtering which can reduce the bandwidth by a factor of two with very little reduction in subjective picture quality.

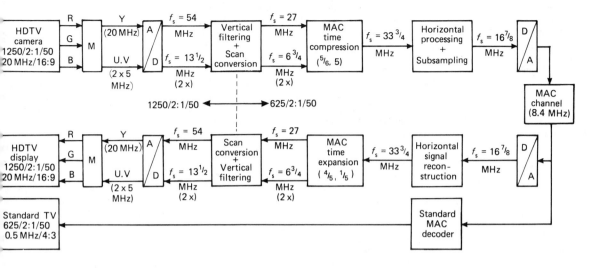

Figure 57.14 Complete HD-MAC system

2. The exchange of spatial and temporal resolution.
3. Motion compensated temporal resolution.

Technique (2) is used in conjunction with (3). A digital signal of about 1Mbit/s is added to the digital sound/data channel to provide the digitally assisted television (DATV) information needed to assist the receiver decoder. A bandwidth reduction of another factor of about two can be achieved by the exchange of spatial and temporal filtering with motion compensated information of the DATV channels used to minimise subjective effects.

For contribution links, where post production editing is required, the source bit rate of the active lines at roughly 1Gbit/s can be compressed to the 560Mbit/s ISDN level by the use of differential pulse code modulation (DPCM).

57.2.4.2   *Hi Vision*

The NHK broadcasting organisation, in collaboration with Japanese industry, has developed and widely demonstrated an HDTV system capable of excellent quality on closed circuit. The system was originally proposed as a world studio production standard, for which purpose it has gained support primarily in 60Hz areas. It was not developed as a compatible system, but subsequently a number of bandwidth reduction systems – MUSE (Multiple Sub-Nyquist-Sampling Encoding) family – have been developed that permit the 1125 line material to be transmitted on terrestrial channels.

The original MUSE system permits the broadcasting of 1125/60/2:1 HDTV programmes in a single 12GHz DBS satellite channel, compressing the signal into a base bandwidth of 8.1MHz by multiple sub sampling and includes techniques for motion compensation, quasi constant luminance principles and non linear emphasis with a four field cycle. MUSE-T is a related system for the distribution of HDTV programmes to broadcasters via communication satellites, employing 2 field cycle sub sampling for motion resolution improvement. It has a 16.2MHz signal bandwidth requiring an FM channel of approximately 50MHz. NHK has also pro-

posed MUSE systems that would permit the transmission of NTSC compatible ADTV wide screen pictures on terrestrial AM channels: MUSE-9 in 9MHz channels: MUSE-6 in 6MHz channels.

57.2.4.3   *All digital systems*

In 1990, the USA began to investigate and compare a number of proposed all digital (transmission) systems capable of being introduced alongside ('simulcasting') the existing 525 line broadcasts and suitable for either terrestrial or satellite or cable distribution, using digital techniques for both source coding and channel coding. Proposed systems of bit rate production have been claimed to permit 525 line broadcast TV at bit rates from about 5Mbit/s to 10Mbit/s and HDTV at between 30Mbit/s to 50Mbit/s. All the proposed digital systems use video bandwidth compression after basic analogue to digital conversion including interlace scanning, removal of source redundancy, making full use of human perception limitations, three dimensional processing (time as third dimension) and entropy coding.

Because a digital system could be transmitted at much lower transmitter power for equal coverage than conventional analogue AM systems, the possibility of using existing 'taboo' (adjacent channels etc.) terrestrial channels for additional 525/625 line channels is also under investigation.

Bit rate reduction for the distribution of digital TV (broadcast, and intercity/satellite distribution) is being investigated for both contribution and distribution circuits and possibly for broadcast distribution. Techniques include: sample rate reduction (reducing the sample rate to the minimum value possible within the quality objective); discrete cosine transform (DCT) which is similar to the discrete Fourier transform with a block of N samples transformed to give N coefficients, representing the amplitude of specific patterns within the block and subsequently transformed back in the decoder to give the original N samples (effective because the majority of coefficients have an amplitude close to zero); variable length coding in which the number of bits assigned to a given quantised value depends on its probability; temporal prediction modes which take advantage of the similarity of one picture to another; video framing in which all the information relevant to the video signal is multiplexed together before being written into a buffer store.

Although DCT based coding techniques represent the most popular approach, it is possible that sub-band coding, based on splitting the picture into different two dimensional frequency bands (sub-bands) and encoding each one separately may give slightly better quality than equivalent DCT schemes, particularly for multi resolution applications such as HDTV broadcasting.

57.2.4.4 *PAL plus*

The possibility of developing for terrestrial and satellite broadcasting an enhanced, compatible wide screen (16:9 aspect ratio) version of 625 line PAL came under investigation in Europe in the early 1990s by a consortium of major receiver manufacturers and a number of broadcaster research organisations. Objectives include: 16:9 aspect ratio; freedom from PAL cross effects; improved resolution; compatibility with normal PAL and recordable on standard VCRs; a display compatible with HD-MAC/HDTV. Various methods of meeting all these targets are considered technically feasible, although it is recognised that 'compatibility' must be a relative term since reception of PAL plus in either 'letter box' or 'side panel' formats would involve some loss to viewers with standard PAL receivers. Cross effects could be removed or minimised by degrees of band segregation or phase segregation; increased resolution by the use of spectral folding. System specification (based on letter-box format) was agreed in late 1991.

57.2.5 Digital and component systems

Since the early 1970s, digital techniques in video/audio processing and transmission have been under intensive investigation and implementation. This work has led to the first worldwide production standard (CCIR Recommendation 601 of 1982), the implementation of a few experimental and operational all digital studios, the widespread use of 'stand alone' digital studio equipment for special effects, noise reduction, standards conversion, etc., and the Nicam 728 dual channel digital system for television sound.

Initially, the introduction of digital processing was applied to encoded 'composite' waveforms with input and output from each unit in analogue form. However, it was soon appreciated that digital processing offered an opportunity to improve picture quality by eliminating the degradations inherent in the PAL, NTSC and SECAM colour encoding systems due to 'mixed highs' (frequency multiplex) insertion of chrominance information within the luminance baseband. Attention was therefore turned to use of 'component' signals with luminance and chrominance signals kept separate, although this involves an extension of the baseband of the analogue signals and consequently higher digital bit rates.

Advantages of handling signals in digital form include the more rugged nature of a digital signal, which requires a much lower signal to noise ratio, and its greater immunity to many forms of phase and amplitude distortion and interference. The ability to make use of picture redundancy and complex coding strategies can provide very large degrees of bit rate reduction without excessively increasing the harmful effects of bit errors. However, once large bit rate reduction has been applied, it becomes impracticable to use such production techniques as chroma keying 'downstream' of the bit rate reduction.

By 1987 digital cassette broadcast videotape recorders, based on the EBU/SMPTE D1 digital component format, had reached the market place, making possible all digital production centres. Such machines can produce more than 20 generations of tape without noticeable degradation, but represent a relatively high cost system applicable primarily to studios converted for component working. Digital cassette recorders for use on composite signals (D2 format) have also appeared. The increased packing density of metal particle videotapes has led to the successful development of lower cost analogue component cassette recorders using half inch tape formats (M.II and Betacam-SP) suitable for both studio and field operation.

During 1989, a further digital composite digital tape format (D3) was announced by Panasonic Broadcast (Matsushita) based on a half inch wide metal particle tape with a tape thickness of 10μm using M.II (VHS) type cassettes but with thinner tape. The cassettes are substantially smaller than those of D1 or D2 for equal running time. In all three formats there are four digital (PCM) audio channels plus analogue tracks for cueing and time code.

An analogue signal can be converted to digital form, processed and then reconverted to analogue form several times in tandem with little visible degradation. However, if this tandem chain is extended too far it will tend to lead to a marked increase in the quantisation noise caused by the use of a restricted number of amplitude levels. Other impairments in digital video may be due to aliasing, clock jitter, error rates and the impossibility of transmitting perfect pulses. Digital video signals may also call for added complexity for monitoring and measuring the impairments, and some still uncertain cost factors in equipment and maintenance.

The advantages of digital transmission include freedom from the ill effects of differential phase and differential gain and the ability to regenerate an exact replica of the input data stream at any point in the chain, thus avoiding cumulative signal to noise degradation. It was Shannon's communication theory that first underlined mathematically the outstanding efficiency of digitally encoded transmission systems.

However it is important to realise that digits do not eliminate all problems. From the earliest days of manual and machine cable telegraphy it has been recognised that the transmission of high speed pulses within a channel of restricted bandwidth can present severe practical problems, including inter symbol interference and susceptibility of the error rate to all forms of 'echoes' and multipath propagation.

Digital systems are inevitably subject to quantising noise, which depends upon the number and arrangement of the levels at which the original analogue signal is digitised, and also to aliasing foldover distortion. Aliasing represents spectral components, arising from the process of sampling, not in the original signal; when these fall within the spectrum of the sampled signal they result in foldover distortion. Aliasing can be minimised by effective filtering, although the ease and cost with which such filtering can be accomplished is very much a factor of the sampling rate.

The increasing use of digital equipment based on the CCIR Recommendation 601 (1982) as given in Table 57.4 created the need to interconnect equipments with outputs in either digital or analogue form. With the introduction of digital equipment it is easier to build a completely new centre rather than modify an existing complex.

CCIR Recommendation 656 (1986) provides interface standards for digital parallel working at 27Mbit/s and serial working at 243Mbit/s in fully digital areas.

Experience with digital video processing has shown that 8 bit PCM is not considered by some manufacturers as adequate for all intermediate interconnections within a processing chain. One result is that a de facto standard of 10 bits exists, which makes use of the

Table 57.4   Major parameters of the digital component standard CCIR Recommendation 601 (1982): 4:2:2 standard

	Luminance (Y)	Colour difference signals	
		(R-Y)	(B-Y)
Sampling frequency (MHz)	13.5	6.75	6.75
Bandwidth (analogue) (MHz)	5.75 (±0.1 depending on sampling filters)	2.75 (+0, −1 depending on sampling filters)	2.75
Form of coding	Uniformly quantized PCM	8 bits per sample for Y, R–Y and B–Y	
Coded signals representing	Y	R–Y	B–Y
Samples per total line:			
625-50 systems	864	432	432
525-60 systems	858	429	429
Samples per active line:			
625-50 systems	720	360	360
525-60 systems	720	360	360
Quantized signal levels:			
Lowest level	16(black)	16	16
Highest level	235(white)	240	240
Zero chrominance level		128	128
SNR peak to peak r.m.s. unweighted (dB)	56	56	56
Sample structure	Orthogonal, line, field and picture repetitive. R–Y and B–Y samples co-sited with odd (1st, 3rd, 5th, etc.) Y samples in each line		

spare contacts in the 656 (parallel) interface. A studio standard for GBR component working, rather than the colour difference (Y, Cb, Cr) of the 4:2:2 standard has been proposed.

The introduction of the D2-PAL/625 and D2-NTSC/525 digital composite standard into existing or new composite areas has led to operational VTR cassettes, VTRs and computer controlled 'cart' machines. Additionally, equipment for conversion between D1 and D2 digital formats, conversion from analogue composite, and between various combinations of digital interface has been developed. For D2, sampling frequencies, phased to the colour sub carrier reference burst and at four times the subcarrier frequency, are approximately 17.73MHz for 625/PAL and 14.32MHz for 525/NTSC. Digital composite recording is not practical for SECAM working, and in SECAM environments the signal must first be decoded back into Y, D_R, D_B and then re-encoded into PAL or else processed in component form.

In converting an RGB signal to digital YUV, (see Figure 57.15) the signal is matrixed, filtered, clamped and digitized.

It has been noted that this may introduce a number of possible signal impairments including:

1. Lift errors (clamp, low frequency or digitizing problems).
2. Delay inequalities (filter or path length differences).
3. Phase response differences (filter differences).
4. Non linearities (digitizing problems).
5. Quantization noise (digitizing effect).

Such impairments can affect component more than composite signals, since the effects on the separate paths of the interconnec-

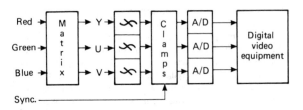

Figure 57.15   RGB to digital YUV interface

tions can be differential, and relatively small defects can significantly affect the colour balance of a picture. Differential delays within or without analogue component equipment can produce significantly more visible impairments than with a single composite signal. The visibility of some effects depends on the actual luminance and colour values of the picture.

CCIR Recommendation 656 (1986): 'Interfaces for digital component video signals in 525 line and 625 line television systems', Part I covers common signal format of the interfaces and Part II covers bit parallel interfaces, including a table of contact assignments, as in Table 57.5.

Any spare pairs connected to contacts 11,24 or 12,25 are reserved for bits of lower significance than those carried on contacts 10,23. Parallel interfaces comprise 8 x 27Mbit/s pairs.

Part III covers bit serial interface, including the recommendation that the 8 bit data words are encoded for transmission in 9 bit words in a specified form, set out in a detailed encoding table. The least

Table 57.5 CCITT Recommendation 656 table contact assignments

Contact	Signal line	Contact	Signal line
1	Clock A	14	Clock B
2	System ground	15	System ground
3	Data 7A(MSB)	16	Data 7B
4	Data 6A	17	Data 6B
5	Data 5A	18	Data 5B
6	Data 4A	19	Data 4B
7	Data 3A	20	Data 3B
8	Data 2A	21	Data 2B
9	Data 1A	22	Data 1B
10	Data OA	23	Data OB
11	Spare A–A	24	Spare A–B
12	Spare B–A	25	Spare B–B
13	Cable shield		

significant bit of each 9 bit word should be transmitted first. The signal should be conveyed in NRZ (non return to zero) form with the bit stream carried on either coaxial cable or fibre optic bearer. Peak to peak signal amplitude should lie between 400mV and 700mV measured across a 75Ω resistive load connected directly to the output terminals without any transmission line.

57.2.6 Digital transmission (links)

Digital transmission of video and/or audio programme channels over well engineered links is capable of offering a performance that is virtually independent of distance or of the number of regenerating, multiplexing or switching stages involved. Overall, quality is determined by the parameters chosen for the encoding of the signal and the performance of the encoders/decoders (codecs). Multiplexed digital signals can be transmitted without significant mutual interference (crosstalk). Digital links offer flexibility in their ability to carry video, audio, data facsimile and telephony signals with equal facility, and to carry such services without requiring a long 'lead time' to set up. Digital transmission is well suited to the use of optical fibre links with widely spaced regenerators.

It is foreseen that eventually intercity links for both television and sound radio will use digital transmission within the ISDN hierarchy.

The economics of digital distribution and contribution circuits is less certain. The introduction by telecommunications carriers of, for example, digital stereo links for outside broadcasts has tended to be accompanied by higher costs, leading to increasing use of satellite links for outside broadcast of sound radio.

The serial bit rate of digital video to the CCIR Recommendation 601 (4:2:2) standard within studio centres is 243Mbit/s (216Mbit/s of video data). However, once the requirement for editorial processing has been completed, the bit rate can be significantly reduced without noticeable loss of quality. For intercity links, the bit rate will normally be reduced to meet the 140 or 70Mbit/s ISDN hierarchy levels. For international transmission via satellite or for satellite news gathering bit rate reduction can be to the 35Mbit/s level. A rate of 30Mbit/s to 45Mbit/s is practical for international TV links since two TV programmes, of better quality than with FM transmission,

can be transmitted through a 36MHz transponder. If necessary, for satellite distribution to cable networks, it is possible that four programmes at 15Mbit/s of NTSC/525 can be transmitted through a single transponder, although picture quality will be significantly degraded unless sophisticated bit-reduction systems are used.

Where the highest quality digital transmission of CCIR Recommendation 601 (4:2:2) digital signals is required, 140Mbit/s (or more precisely 139.264Mbit/s) represents the European standard fourth order digital transmission level chosen to provide 30 x 4 x 4 x 4 = 1920 telephone channels each of 64kbit/s, after taking into account the necessary housekeeping overheads incurred at each multiplexing stage.

For a typical 140Mbit/s system, 5Mbit/s are allotted for audio, asynchronous multiplexing and other system housekeeping, leaving about 134Mbit/s for the coded video signal. Removal of the line blanking periods from 4:2:2 digital component video results in 175.5Mbit/s representing the active line periods. This provides a theoretical bit rate reduction of 18% at the cost of some buffer storage and digital line sync data. A further 8% reduction could be achieved by the removal of the field blanking intervals, although this would require significantly more buffer storage. With about 134Mbit/s available for digital video, the effective average data word length must still be reduced from its initial 8 bits to an average of not more than 6.11 bits. There are a number of ways in which this modest degree of reduction can be implemented. For example, an experimental system developed by the IBA investigated two main approaches. The first involved discarding alternate samples with sub Nyquist sampling and the second used differential pulse code modulation (DPCM). Variations and combinations of these two basic techniques were simulated.

In sub Nyquist sampling, advantage is taken of the two dimensional sampling nature of the digitized video signal to maintain horizontal and vertical spatial frequency response at the expense of some small loss of resolution and the introduction of some aliasing in diagonal frequencies. DPCM removes some of the redundancy in a typical TV signal by transmitting only difference information between samples within some areas of the picture.

Excellent results were achieved with hybrid (H) DPCM, in which every fourth word in a line quincunx structure remained an an unmodified 8 bit linear PCM sample. The pattern of these data words was then used as the basis of two dimensional predictor/interpolators for the intervening words, which were non linearly coded 5 bit differences. This HDPCM 8-5-5-5 mode results in an average word length of 5.75bits, reducing the 175.5Mbit/s data to just over 126Mbit/s with virtually no perceptible loss of quality.

57.2.7 Teletext transmission

During the 1970s, a data transmission system riding 'piggy-back' on conventional television transmission was developed in the UK and introduced under the service designations Ceefax (BBC) and Oracle (IBA-ITV). An agreed technical specification was introduced in 1974. Teletext transmission systems have since been introduced in a number of countries, and basically similar systems but with rather different technical specifications have also been developed in some countries. Teletext (Figure 57.16) uses the broadcast television signal to carry extra information. These extra signals do not interfere with the transmission and reception of normal programmes. A teletext receiver, a television receiver with additional circuits, is capable of reconstructing written information and displaying it on the screen. The system allows the transmission of very many bulletins of information, and the viewer can choose any one by selecting a three figure number on a set of controls, usually push buttons.

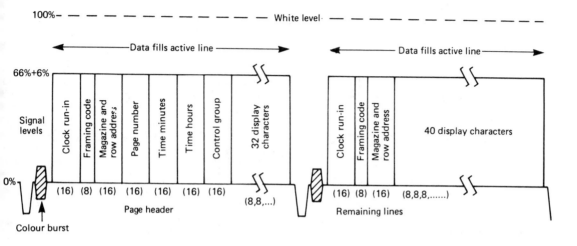

Figure 57.16 Teletext data organisation. (The figures in brackets are the number of binary digits)

After a short interval the information appears and remains for as long as it is needed.

A major use of teletext is as an information service, but it can also supplement normal television programmes with subtitles or linked pages. The entire signal is accommodated within the existing 625 line television allocation, and so costs nothing in terms of radio frequency spectrum space. It was, effectively, the first broadcasting system to transmit information in digital form.

Teletext pages look rather like pages of typescript, except that they can also include large sized letters and simple drawings. The standard sized words can use upper or lower case, and be in any one of six colours, red, green, blue, yellow, cyan and magenta or white. The shape of the characters is usually based on a 7 x 5 dot matrix, with a refinement known as character rounding. As many as 24 rows of the standard sized characters can be fitted on a page, and each row can have up to 40 characters. Each page can carry about 150 to 200 words.

The specification also allows the option of characters of twice the height of standard characters. Larger sized characters and also drawings are made by assembling small illuminated rectangles, each one sixth the size of the space occupied by a standard character, and these too can be in any of the six colours or in white. Part or all of each page can be made to flash on and off (usually once per second), to emphasise any particular item.

The page background is usually black, although the specification allows the editor to define different background colours for part or all of the screen. Also, at the teletext editor's discretion, text can be enclosed in a black window and cut into the normal picture. Furthermore, certain receiver designs allow the whole page (sometimes in white only) to be superimposed upon the picture.

It is potentially possible for the system to carry up to 800 single pages but, because of the way the pages are transmitted, this could mean an appreciable waiting time between page selections. So for the moment not all 800 pages are used at any one time.

Additional circuits are needed in a television receiver to decode teletext. First, data extraction and recognition circuits examine the incoming 'conveyer belt' of teletext data lines, and extract those signals which make up the page which has been selected. The data from these lines is then stored, usually in a semiconductor memory, so that the page can be displayed at the same rate as a normal picture. The binary number codes are then translated to their corresponding characters or graphics patterns. Finally a video raster scan representation of the page is switched onto the screen.

57.2.8 Digital audio standards

A number of different sampling rates have emerged for digital audio systems:

1. Broadcast audio distribution is based on a sampling rate of 32kHz to provide a 15kHz audio bandwidth, with 14 bit linear (uniform) coding.
2. Professional recording studios use a sampling rate of 48kHz equivalent to 1920 audio samples per video frame (625 line, 25Hz frames) or 2000 audio samples per frame for 24fps film, with 16 or 20 bit coding.
3. Compact disc records (masters) have a sampling rate of 44.1kHz (CD/EIAJ/RDAT replay only, 14 or 16 bits).

It is generally accepted that 16 bit/sample coding offers satisfactory quality, but for signals prior to level control, or combined signals having a very wide dynamic range, longer data words are required of 20 bits or more per sample.

Interface units permit conversion between sampling rates of 32kHz, 44.1kHz and 48kHz. Rate conversion between 44.1kHz and 48kHz is rather more difficult than 32kHz to 48kHz. Cascading a number of sample rate converters (SRCs) tends to degrade the signal. Mixing consumer and professional digital audio equipment can result in balance, level and impedance differences in routeing. Amplitude levels rather than reflections tend to cause the most problems. Digital audio synchronisation at mixing (switching) points represents a new requirement.

For the distribution of 48kHz digital audio, the EBU/AES/IEC system (see Figure 57.17) uses bi-phase Mark coding which has the effect of shifting the required frequency spectrum to between 1.5MHz and 3MHz rather than to 1.5MHz.

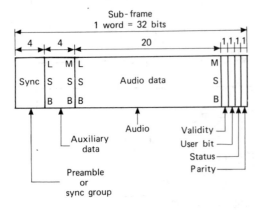

Figure 57.17 AES/EBU audio interface

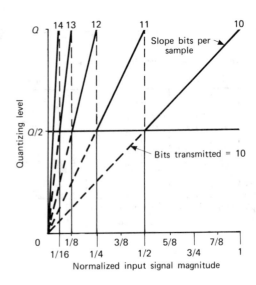

Figure 57.18 NICAM-3 near instantaneous companding law

This system has 32 bit data words, 24 bits for audio data, sandwiched between a 4 bit sync/preamble and 4 bit parity and selection messages. Since this standard is not error corrected, it needs clean distribution (low bit error rate). With a 48kHz sampling frequency, the audio bandwidth is 20Hz to 20kHz (±0.5dB, depending on sampling filters) and quantization provides 16 bits/sample linear (standard mode) and up to 20 bits/sample (high fidelity mode), giving a dynamic range of more than 90dB.

57.2.9 Audio digital companding

For the distribution of high quality (15kHz) audio signals in digital form, a sampling rate of 32kHz and a quantizing level signal to noise ratio of about 75dB is desirable. The required SNR can be achieved in the initial digitisation with 13 bit linear PCM. This has a theoretical SNR of 83dB and is reduced to 81.5dB by the addition of a dither signal to remove 'granular' distortion on critical low level material. The dither signal can be at half sampling frequency and have an amplitude equal to half a quantising step together with white noise at a level of 4dB below the inherent quantising noise. In practice for point to point links, a single parity check digit is added to each 13 bit sample word.

A 13 channel PCM sound distribution system introduced by BBC Radio in 1972 had a transmission bit rate of 6.336Mbit/s. This has been progressively superseded by a 6 channel system with near instantaneous companding (NICAM-3) (see Figure 57.18) with a total transmission bit rate of 2.048Mbit/s (676Kbit/s for each stereo pair).

High quality audio links are more vulnerable to bit errors than digital video. Without error protection, 'just perceptible' impairment can be detected with a BER of the order of $1:10^7$. With protection of the five most significant bits (MSBs), an equivalent impairment would need a BER of $1:10^5$.

With instantaneous companding, a limited number of digits is transmitted per sample word together with a scale factor indicating the significance (weight) of the transmitted word. For near instantaneous companding, the scale factor is transmitted less frequency (for example, once every 32 samples), its value being determined by the peak signal level during the complete group of 32 samples.

NICAM-3 encodes the audio samples to 14 bits, placing each block of 32 samples (one millisecond) into one of five ranges, determined by the largest value sample within the block. By discarding leading zeroes and MSBs according to the range, this compresses the samples to 10 bits for transmission. This has the effect that the lowest level samples are encoded to 14 bit accuracy with the highest level samples to 10 bit accuracy. The range codes for three blocks of 32 samples are combined into a 7 bit code and four Hamming code protection bits are added. The five MSBs in each sample word are protected by parity checks, enabling error concealment by interpolation at the decoder.

57.2.10 Multichannel sound systems

Although the monaural sound channel of conventional television broadcasting is capable of providing high fidelity (15kHz) audio, this has seldom been reflected in the design of domestic receivers. Increasing consumer awareness of the fidelity provided by other media, including FM stereo radio, stereo cassette tapes and digital CD records, has led to the development of systems for dual channel and multi channel audio for television capable of providing sufficient separation to permit simultaneous dual language broadcasting.

The desirable requirements include: general improvement of sound quality; possibility of receiving stereo sound programmes in mono (direct compatibility); possibility of receiving mono programmes on stereo receivers (reverse compatibility); no discernible interference between picture and audio channels; possibility of transmitting either a stereo or two or more separate high quality mono channels; maximum possible technological compatibility with existing systems and equipment, and receiver decoder cost compatible with perceived benefits to the viewer. For (L + R)/(L − R) stereo a separation of 25dB to 30dB is considered sufficient. For bilingual transmission, separation of the order of at least 55dB is required.

57.2.10.1 *One carrier systems (with FM subcarriers)*

The Japanese FM/FM system (1978) in which the subcarrier is locked to the second harmonic of the line frequency (31.5kHz for 525 line systems) with a switching (AM) subcarrier at 55kHz.

The American BTSC/MTS system (Broadcast Television Systems Committee/Multichannel Television Sound) is derived from the pilot tone FM stereo system used in radio broadcasting but with a pilot frequency (15.734kHz) locked to the video line frequency and with 'dBx' noise reduction. There is provision for a 15kHz stereo quadrature channel plus a 10kHz monophonic 'second audio channel' (sap) on a low level subcarrier at five times the vision line frequency and, where required, an engineer's order wire ('professional channel') on a subcarrier at six times the vision line frequency.

57.2.10.2   *Two carrier systems*

The German dual channel system for stereo or bilingual sound transmission has (for System G) a separate carrier located .742MHz above the vision carrier at –20dB in addition to the normal sound carrier at 5.5MHz above the vision carrier at –13dB. The 242kHz difference between the sound carrier is an odd harmonic of the vision line frequency. The usual sound FM carrier is modulated with (L + R)/2, and the second carrier with only the R signal (or with a second language or separate audio signal) with a deviation of ±2.5kHz. A mode identification signal is provided on a tone modulated 54.6875kHz subcarrier (unmodulated for mono, 17.5Hz AM for stereo, 274.1Hz AM for separate audio).

The Nicam 728 system uses digital quadrature phase shift keying to digitally modulate the second carrier located (for System 1) .552MHz above the vision carrier with a carrier level of –20dB with respect to peak vision. The two audio channels (stereo or bilingual) are combined in time division multiplex as a digital bit stream comprising 728 bit frames each of 1 ms duration, giving a bit rate of 728kbit/s. The audio signals are sampled at 32kHz with an initial resolution of 14 bits/sample and near instantaneous compression to 10 bits/sample in 32 sample blocks. Error protection comprises one parity bit added to each 10 bit sample to check the six most significant bits. The transmission of the conventional mono channel is unaffected.

The characteristics of NICAM-728 for television standards B. G. 1 are shown in Table 57.6.

57.3   Cable distribution systems

Since the early days of television broadcasting, cable distribution systems have been around. They arose because of the difficulty of achieving good quality reception; this often required the aerial to be placed in an advantageous position, probably on high ground. It became natural then to share this facility by cabling to local households.

From the early local enterprises, perhaps initiated by electrical goods shops wishing to increase the sales of receivers, there arose specific cable TV firms. The first heyday of cable distribution systems in the 1950s and 1960s was as an off air TV, and radio, relay system. Though far from universal, it was a significant business in many countries covering areas of poor reception, hotels, appartment blocks, and sometimes towns where external aerials were not allowed for aesthetic reasons.

As over the air broadcast transmissions improved their coverage, the relay systems fell into disuse and cable TV had to look to providing additional services to prove its worth. Systems using

Table 57.6   Main characteristics of NICAM-728

Item	*Characteristic*
Number of sound channels with 15kHz bandwidth	2
Pre-emphasis of sound signals	According to CCIT Recommendation J17
Sampling frequency	32kHz
Initial coding of sound signals	14 bits/sample linear PCM
Companding	Quasi instantaneous with compression to 10 bits/sample in 32 sample blocks
Error protection	Parity check of six most significant bits by adding a parity check to every 10-bit sample
Frame format	Frame length is 728 bits/millisecond (frame sync word 8 bits, control word 5 bits, additional data 11 bits, sound data 704 bits)
Bit rate of sound and data	728kbit/s
Transmission method of digital audio information and data in a composite video signal	Frequency multiplex by introducing an additional sound carrier at 5.85MHz (systems B, G) or 6.552MHz (system 1) from vision carrier
Type of modulation of additional sound carrier	Four positional phase shift keying (DQPSK) i.e. differentially encoded QPSK
Spectrum shaping	100% cosine roll off split equally between transmitter and receiver (overall bandwidth of digital signal approximately 728kHz)
Scale factor signalling	By modification of 9 parity bits per scale factor bit, detected by majority decision logic (3 bits per sound coding block, two blocks per frame)
Bit interleaving (sound data)	44 x 16 (frame alignment word not interleaved)
Energy dispersal scrambling	By modulo two addition of a pseudo-random sequence of length 2^9-1 bits synchronously with the multiplex frame. Frame alignment word not scrambled

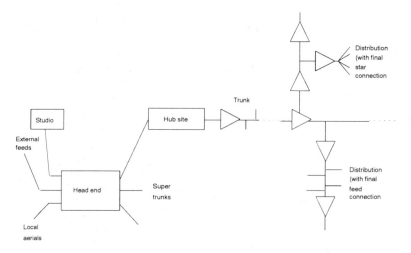

Figure 57.19 Tree and branch cable TV network

coaxial cable were replacing the original multi-line twisted pair systems, and enabling more TV channels to be carried, so 'out of area' broadcasts, satellite receptions and tape based channels could be added. Modern coaxial systems can carry 50 or more channels per cable, and fibre optics is starting to find a foothold.

Cable TV remains very variable in terms of its impact in different countries. From the 1970s it began to increase rapidly in North America and certain European countries, such that by the end of the 1980s some very high penetrations of the service (up to 90%) had been achieved. However in other places it remains in its infancy, or at least confined to certain special areas. Its spread has been influenced by broadcast TV quality, local terrain, prosperity, commercial pressures, and government regulations. The last of these became increasingly important when additional services were introduced, all the more now that carriage of non-TV services like telephony and data is under consideration in some countries.

57.3.1 Terminology

It is useful to establish at the outset some of the general terms used about cable distribution systems. The technical terms will be explained later as they arise.

CATV. Community Antenna TV; although still widely used in a general sense, it has connotations of a limited relay service. The term 'Cable TV' is superseding it for modern systems (those in the industry often just contract this to 'Cable').

MATV. Mast Antenna TV; a local system for a hotel or appartment block. Where a satellite dish supplements the off-air reception the term SMATV is used.

Homes Passed. The number of residences which could be connected to a cable TV system, given the existing extent of its build, i.e. those needing just a final cable drop into the home.

Penetration. The number of homes connected as a percentage of the homes passed.

Churn. The proportion of customers ceasing and taking up the service.

Spin. The changing of customers between levels of services (tiers of channels).

Head end. The source point for service on a cable TV network. This is where the video channels, radio, and any other service are formulated into a multiplex to be launched out on the network. Typically it might be fed itself by links from remote aerial sites and a studio (where the cable operator may generate tape based programming and process other channels).

Hub site. Further site(s) after the head end where sufficient processing occurs to warrant internal housing of equipment.

Super-trunk distribution. Divisions of the external cable network as it gets progressively closer to the customer (with the implication of different equipment and practices being cost effective).

Figures 57.19 and 57.20 illustrate somes of these terms.

57.3.2 Services

Until recently the cable TV service package has been straightforward – multi-channel TV and, probably, FM radio. National regulations may define a 'must carry' set of channels, probably those available locally off air and the radio. The operator would then normally for marketing reasons wish to segment the channels into

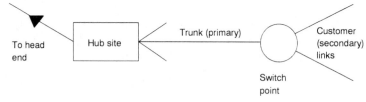

Figure 57.20 Switched star cable TV network

ers, a low cost basic tier incorporating the must carry set, and a umber of premium tiers culminating in the recent film channel. his market need for varying the channel selection delivered to ifferent customers, so called 'conditional access', has important echnical implications; the pursuit of a cost effective and safe (from rogramme theft) means of doing this has been a major preoccupaion of the cable TV industry.

Generally the video format to the customer has conformed to the tandard TV receiver input, namely vestigial sideband amplitude nodulation (VSB-AM) of the national standard format (NTSC, 'AL, SECAM) in a frequency division multiplex (FDM) as illus-ated in Figure 57.21 Because of the large channel capacity of able TV systems there are three major differences from receiving ff air signals. Firstly the frequency range covered is larger, neaning conventional TV set tuners may not cover it fully; secondly hannel spacing may be closer and tuner selectivity may be inade-uate; thirdly the number of presettable tuning buttons may be nadequate to give convenient viewing. In countries with high enetration so called 'cable ready' TV sets are available to which a etwork can directly input. Otherwise set top units may be required o select out the required channel and offer it to the set at an ppropriate frequency.

In recent years further service types have come under consider-tion, the most prominent being pay per view. Whereas the tiers eceived by a customer will be determined by the monthly subscrip-ion paid, pay per view gives the opportunity for access to a specific remium programme at short notice. Technically this implies inter-ction from the customer; though achievable by a telephone call, nore automated techniques are preferable to deal with a potentially arge volume response in a short time window.

The term video on demand can encompass both pay per view and he video library concept. Whereas pay per view remains a broad-ast service, offered to all prepared to pay the premium at the time, video library introduces narrowcasting, whereby a customer (or a imited group of them) accesses a particular item from a centralised source. This concept has had only limited trials to date, but con-inues to excite interest.

Radio relay has been a long term service provided by networks, with it being relatively easy to transmit the FM band at good quality on a coaxial cable. Recently there is interest in providing additional hi-fi audio services, including the possibility of an audio library.

Cable TV networks are starting to look beyond their traditional services into the following types of area:

1. Audience interactive; voting, home shopping, home banking, etc.
2. Information services; data to the home or as text on a screen.
3. Low speed data.
4. Telephony.

57.3.3 Network types

57.3.3.1 *H.f. multipair*

In this old type of system individual channels were modulated at high frequency (h.f. 3MHz to 30MHz region) onto individual twisted pairs. Selection in the home was via a simple switch linking the required pair to the input of a special h.f. TV set. TV sound could be modulated with the video, but was often sent at baseband on its own pair in company with other audio services.

The system was straightforward, there being low loss at h.f., capable of good quality, but of course limited in channel capacity such that it is now obsolete.

57.3.3.2 *Tree and branch coaxial*

The obvious successor to multipair operation was coaxial cable carrying a multiplex of TV channels in the v.h.f. band (30MHz to 300MHz). As this signal spreads out from the originating head end the structure resembles a tree trunk with branches arising as it is both amplified and split (Figure 57.19). Originally systems were truly confined to the v.h.f. region, but have in recent years spread into the u.h.f. region to accommodate greater channel numbers. By the end of the 1980s 550MHz systems were being installed with 860MHz ones in the pipeline. With a 550MHz system channel capacity can be from between 40 and 80 channels, the exact number depending on factors such as channel bandwidth and spacing, for-bidden frequency bands, and compatibility with TV receivers and over the air broadcasts, all of which vary between and perhaps within countries.

The network is of a broadcast nature with all channels reaching all connected customers, unless special measures are taken. Condi-tional access is achieved in two main ways. A frequency trap external to the premises can remove blocks of channels. It is cheap

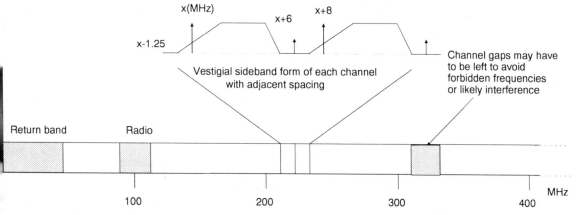

Figure 57.21 Typical spectrum on a tree and branch network. (8MHz spacing for PAL-1 shown; 6MHz and 7MHz spacing also used)

but very inflexible; changes in tiers wanted (spin) means a physical change of trap, and more general re-arrangement of channels into different tiers is awkward for the cable operator.

A more flexible technique is to scramble all but the basic tier of channels, and provide a set top unit to descramble those that the customer has paid extra to watch. A simple unit would have fixed capability, but it then needs changing out if the customer needs a different service. Addressable units change their capability on commands from codes sent in a data stream over the network from the head end. The disadvantages of scrambling are that it involves a relatively expensive unit in the home, that it affects video quality, and that it is liable to programme theft from pirate versions of the set top unit.

There is a strong desire nowadays that at least the basic programme tier should be deliverable without the need for a unit in the home. Hence it should be placed in the spectrum so as to be able to feed directly into the TV set.

The dominant feature of the network design is the amplification need. Loss for a coaxial cable is proportional to the square root of frequency, so it is an increasing problem with modern systems. Amplifiers are required for two reasons however, to allow for splitting as well as cable loss. For the trunk portion larger cross section cable and more sophisticated amplifiers can be affored compared to the distribution area.

57.3.3.3   *Switched star*

From the late 1970s an alternative structure was being considered with a dedicated cable feed to each customer (Figure 57.20). This offered a number of potential advantages, most obviously easier interactivity. Control of the service selection via a video switch gave secure control (no need for scrambling to achieve tiering) and allowed a tailored service package to be delivered to the customer not constrained by the capacity of the final coaxial link (since only the wanted channels have to be transmitted along it). Technology was also a driver, since this network type was seen as an application for fibre.

In Europe a limited number of these systems have been installed, some all coxial, some part fibre, and some all fibre. Matching the low cost of the tree and branch networks for basic TV delivery has proved the expected problem. It was clear that the dedicated link would have to be kept short to reduce per customer cost; how short depended on technical solution, for u.h.f. delivery 200m and for v.h.f. delivery 500m maximum to avoid amplification on a coaxial link; for fibre 1km or more. In nearly all cases the switch was therefore street sited.

57.3.4   Transmission

57.3.4.1   *Modulation techniques*

For video there are the following main techniques employed:

1. Amplitude modulation, the standard method matching the TV receiver input format. To reduce bandwidth (to between 6MHz to 8MHz) vestigial sideband (VSB) is normally used on cable networks, as done over the air. Although simplest and cheapest, it is not a robust technique, being prone to noise as it builds up through amplifier stages and to interfering signals (external or internal from intermodulation). Unitl recently it was not considered appropriate for fibre transmission, because of the intrin-

sic noise and non linearity of optical sources; technology advances have dramatically changed this recently.

2. Frequency modulation. The FM improvement factor gives greatly improved noise and interference immunity at the expense of bandwidth (30MHz per channel typically). It has been used quite extensively on longer super trunk links over both coaxial cable and fibre.

3. Digital modulation. This similarly gives improved noise and interference immunity, but with the additional advantage of no degradation with repeatering. It is more suited to fibre than coaxial cable (the latter having considerable equalisation problems). It has had limited use to date because of cost, but there are signs now of it making a bigger impact.

For audio service the standard FM radio band (88MHz to 108MHz) has been relayed over the cable, perhaps repositioning the carriers and adding channels in on new carriers. However the FM improvement is very low for a stereo broadcast. This then presents almost as severe a problem for fibre as mentioned above for AM transmission of video. Digital audio transmission is now receiving interest because of its impact in the domestic equipment area; it promises very high quality over both coaxial cable and fibre within reasonable bandwidths.

57.3.4.2   *Coaxial*

The essence of designing a coaxial tree and branch system is the balancing of the cable and splitter loss incurred in delivery to the customers by the use of appropriate amplifiers, placed before signal degradation has gone too far. Because street sited amplifiers must be placed regularly at quite short distances (every few hundred metres), and with relatively little tolerance on the distance, design can only proceed with a detailed knowledge of the area to be cabled.

Cable loss varies according to the square root of frequency, and hence equalisation must occur in the amplifiers to boost the higher frequencies compared to the lower. This can be done by both compensation to the received signal, and deliberate tilt to the launched signal. Given that this is done, the basic loss balancing exercise can be done by considering one frequency (usually the highest). Thus a trunk cable might have a loss of 50dB per km at 450MHz. A cable run of 500m therefore needs an amplifier of 25dB gain at this frequency to restore the signal. A splitter in the run would add further loss, around 3.5dB to 4dB for each two way stage in an even split; an asymmetric split can be used to tap off a line at a high loss leaving the through loss relatively low.

As the network spreads out cost and convenience means that cable dimensions get smaller and losses higher. Thus at 450MHz a super trunk cable of diameter 39mm might have a loss of 25dB/km, whereas the final short underground feed might be only 8mm diameter and 170dB/km loss (overhead feeds being smaller and even higher loss).

Amplifiers are imperfect devices and introduce noise and non-linearity. Thus each time one is used the noise performance will deteriorate and cross modulation between the channels will occur; hence the 'run' of amplifiers is limited. The manufacturer's specification will indicate a noise figure and cross modulation performance, which enables the effects to be calculated. Given that the equalisation process is also imperfect, and there are other impairments, the run may be less than this basic calculation indicates.

There are different designs of amplifiers (Slater, 1988), push-pull, feed forward, and power doubling are three main types, each of which has different features in terms of noise, distortion, and of urse cost. They are designed to match different parts of the etwork, there being trunk, distribution and line extender versions the network progresses outwards. Some are also combinations of nplifier(s) and splitter(s), e.g. a mainline bridger combination ving amplification in both the trunk and branch line.

In modern systems impairment has been reduced by having for ich channel incrementally related carriers (IRC, equal spacing etween each channel) or harmonically related carriers (HRC, each irrier an exact multiple of the spacing). This ensures that carrier itermodulation products fall exactly on other carrier frequencies ?nd and 3rd order for HRC, just 3rd order for IRC) rather than ithin the actual video signal, where they would give subjectively innoying interference.

Another important feature to bear in mind is signal level. Ampli-er inputs and outputs are designed for specific levels (though with)me tolerance); differences may affect the gain and certainly could icrease impairments. Additionally coaxial networks, particularly iints, are not perfectly immune from the outside world. Too low a -vel signal could be subject to external interference; too high a -vel could cause radiation beyond national regulations.

It is useful to define a zero reference level in dB terms, rather than)ltage or wattage terms, since cable loss and amplifier gain are in iis form. Thus 0dBmV is defined as the level corresponding to mV across 75 ohms (the characteristic impedance of all coaxial able used in cable TV).

57.3.4.3   *Optical*

xcept for supertrunk links, optical transmission is in its infancy for able TV application, but is rapidly becoming a major issue. In :rms of network design the task is relatively straightforward be-ause the long range of an optical link often means an external :peater can be avoided. The essential features in selecting an ptical system are:

.   Channel capacity per fibre.
.   The video performance requirement, which will obviously in-
    fluence the quality and cost of a link's components, but may
    also limit the channel capacity and the type of modulation
    method that can be used.
.   The input and output interface requirements. For example, are
    the signals baseband or already modulated in a form suitable for
    optical transmission? Also how is TV sound to be carried?
I. The length of link, and hence optical loss to be incurred.
). Optical power output, and whether there are any safety impli-
    cations.

The designer may not need to know optical technicalities in any letail, but some aspects worth being aware of are:

I. Fibre type, only single mode fibre will be relevant nowadays
    for video links. Multi mode is appropriate for shorter, lower
    capacity links. Single mode (core diameter < 10μ) is a little
    more difficult to joint and connectorise than multi mode (core
    diameter > 50μ).
?. Wavelength 1300nm (1.3μ) or 1550nm optical devices could be
    used with single mode fibre. 1550nm offers slightly lower loss,
    but possible bandwidth limitation (caused by 'dispersion')
    which increases with transmission distance.
3. Source output level, measured in milliwatts, or fractions
    thereof, for lasers, or microwatts for lower power LEDs. Alter-

natively dBm is used, which is the power relative to 1mW; thus for example – 3dBm is 0.5mW, and +6dBm is 4mW.

4. Receiver sensitivity, the minimum optical power that can be
    received whilst maintaining the required performance.
5. Relative intensity noise (RIN), the noise within the optical
    source itself, which could degrade the signal prior to launching
    onto the fibre. It is measured as dB/Hz; better than – 120dB/Hz
    might be all right for a digital or FM link, but for AM better than
    – 150dB/Hz is required.
6. Optical budget, the difference in dBs between source output
    level and receiver sensitivity. It shows what is available for
    fibre loss, splice and connector loss, splitter (if used) loss, and
    a margin for temperature, ageing etc.

57.3.5   Switching

Most existing cable TV systems do not apparently incorporate switching. In fact the effective switch is the TV set tuner, selecting a channel by filtering it out from the incoming multiplex, demodu-lating it and routeing it to the set's output stages. A similar function will also be done within a set top unit, ending up with frequency translation of the selected channel to a convenient position in the spectrum (there may be intermediate demodulation to carry out descrambling),

Video switching within the network is of course a central feature of switched star systems. Two basic techniques are used, space switching and frequency agile switching.

57.3.5.1   *Space switching*

This is essentially the familiar crosspoint matrix (Figure 57.22) where an input is physically linked to an output line when a cross-point is made. For a cable TV application a broadcast switch is needed, i.e. one where one input might be connected to several outputs. Thus the loading of an input signal is variable from 1 to n outputs; hence there are buffer amplifiers needed as shown in Figure 57.22.

A number of devices can be used as the crosspoints. Relays make a direct wire connection, and coaxial versions are capable of very high performance and bandwidths; even miniature versions are relatively large and mainly suited to head end or studio uses. Semiconductors, such as the CMOS and DMOS FET devices, can provide analogue switches with a good degree of integration on a chip. Although 'on' resistances are at least a few tens of ohms and capacitive signal leakage occurs in the 'off' state, good quality compact matrices for cable TV use can be constructed able to switch baseband video signals. Higher frequency switching is quite possible, but crosstalk problems will imply very careful board design and probably lower integration.

Digital crosspoints are relatively straight forward; a simple AND gate performs this function with one input as signal and one as control. Both ECL and CMOS technologies are used, the latter in particular being capable of high integration and high speeds (16 in/16 out chips working at 200Mbit/s have been produced). Their use for cable TV has been limited because nearly all transmission has been analogue.

57.3.5.2   *Frequency agile switching*

The second approach used has been frequency agile switching (Figure 57.23), utilising the tuner function described above. This is popular where the incoming feed is a frequency division multiplex

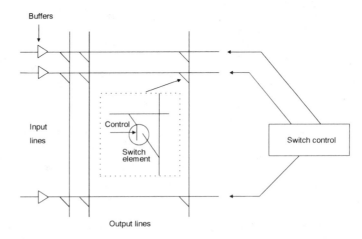

Figure 57.22 Crosspoint matrix with buffered inputs

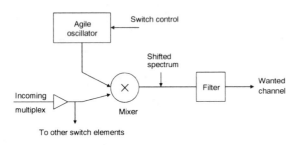

Figure 57.23 Frequency agile switch

of many channels, as on tree and branch systems. A frequency agile oscillator is mixed with the multiplex, such that the desired channel is translated to a specific frequency slot, where it is then filtered out from the rest of the channels. Varying the oscillator frequency will therefore select different channels. The attraction of the technique is that it deals directly with the available signal without demultiplexing; its limitation is the relatively large size of equipment.

Other approaches not yet used in cable TV but of potential interest in the future are:

1. Time switching (i.e. moving from one time slot to another within a digital multiplex).
2. Packet switching, (useful if variable bit rate coding is applied taking account of the fact that changes in picture content vary from time to time).
3. Optical switching, which can itself take the form of space switches, frequency (wavelength) switches, or time switches.

57.3.6 Performance standards

National standards for cable TV are set in many countries, though they may only be guidelines rather than mandatory. Although broadly in agreement on acceptable levels, there are some variations between countries, in particular due to the different TV standards (NTSC, PAL, SECAM). Further it may be possible to trade one parameter off against another, as explained below.

Compared to audio, there is for the uninitiated a bewildering array of video performance parameters, and it is a major topic in its own right. There are in fact two ways that a measured impairment may be quoted, in objective or subjective terms. The objective version is the physical measurement taken (e.g. in dBs, % etc.); sometimes is converted into its subjective equivalent (using standard formulae measured in 'imps'. This latter was derived originally from real viewing assessments made of different levels of each parameter for their annoyance value, and allows one to compare the impairment from different parameters in the same terms.

It is not sensible here to explain each type of parameter, but Table 57.7 does classify them into types and lists the objective value equivalent to 1/8th imp. In this table a weighting filter is used to

Table 57.7 Video performance parameters and their equivalent to an impairment of one-eight imp, measured at baseband for PAL-I signals

	Parameter	*Value*
Linear distortions	K ratings	5%
	Echoes	4.5%
	Chrominance/luminance gain inequality	27%
	Chrominance/luminance delay inequality	150ns
Non-linear distortions	Differential gain	21%
	Differential phase	24 degrees
	Luminance line-time non-linearity	21%
	Chrominance/luminance crosstalk	24%
Noise/ interference	Signal/noise (unified weighting)	45dB
	Single frequency interference	57dB at < 1MHz
	Crosstalk (undistorted)	50dB

allow for the eye's varying sensitivity to noise according to its position in the video signal's spectrum. Also the equivalent carrier/noise figure for VSB-AM signal is 45.6dB. Within reason imps can be added up, and the total for a good network might be no more than 1/2 imp. Most parameters must therefore fall well below the 1/8th imp value, but according to the nature of the network it may be sensible to let some produce more impairment than others e.g. K-rating and single frequency interference might be allowed to be relatively high.

The signal inputting to the network, perhaps received off air, will itself be already impaired, and this will contribute to the ultimate impairment at the end of the network. For concatenated links like this some parameters will add up predictably (e.g. signal/noise ratio), whilst others will not and indeed could even improve if opposite trends occur on the links.

Individual measurement techniques exist for each parameter, but nowadays automatic measurement equipment is available, which, though not cheap, will provide a read out of a large range of these. An associated test signal generator provides the source to input to the network or equipment under test. However most broadcast channels also include the test signals in their vertical blanking period, allowing the total degradation to that channel to be assessed.

The above measurements relate to the baseband video signal, on which a full analysis of impairments can be carried out. However on coaxial tree and branch networks in particular, only signals in their r.f. multiplex are directly accessible; demodulation to baseband must be performed by high quality equipment to avoid this process adding significant impairment itself. Everyday analysis is often better carried out directly at r.f. for those parameters where it is possible; carrier to noise (C/N) is one such measurement (with a target of 43dB upwards for a full cable TV network), and to cover second and third order intermodulation performance composite second order (CSO) and composite triple beat (CTB) are parameters commonly used.

57.3.7 Future trends

This area is well served by papers in journals and conferences, and references are given later to which the reader should turn for detailed information. Service possibilities have been indicated earlier, and how these are taken up will affect the technical evolution significantly. The major areas of activity are likely to be as below.

57.3.7.1 More channels

Proposals for pushing the coaxial network technology to beyond 1GHz means 100+ channels becoming possible. Some of these may be available then for narrowcasting to one or a few individuals.

57.3.7.2 Enhanced TV formats

A number of higher quality formats for the video signal have been proposed round the world, and cable TV is having to start to think about catering for them. One basic point is that a channel may have to be transmitted in both the present standard (NTSC, PAL, SECAM) and the enhanced form. Thus it is another driver towards the need for more channel capacity.

True high definition TV (HDTV) with a base bandwidth of circa 30MHz would present a real problem, except for advanced fibre systems. More modest enhancements, and hence bandwidth requirements, arise from systems like the Japanese MUSE, the Ameri-

can advanced TV (probably now compatible with 6MHz spacing), and the European MAC family (ranging from 7MHz to 16MHz spacing needed according to type and implementation).

The main problem for the cable operator is to know which new format will be widely implemented, and when to plan for the extra capability.

57.3.7.3 Conditional access

Improved techniques will be sought here, particularly with pay per view in mind. Switching is one answer; another is interdiction (spoiling all but the wanted signal) rather than scrambling.

57.3.7.4 Fibre optic enhancement

This made some impact a few years ago with multi channel FM links in the super trunk, and now with significant interest in digital operation there. More recently the practicality of AM multiplexes over fibre has excited enormous interest. The prospect of replacing the large chains of coaxial cable amplifiers allows both improved performance (which in many existing systems has been decidely sub standard) and more channel capacity. This now seems a major trend with perhaps a final feed of just 3 or 4 amplifiers left.

The AM fibre optic links in particular have not to date been cheap; as they reduce in cost this will help their application to become wider. The advent of the optical amplifier may help here, enhancing their modest optical budget and allowing optical splitting.

57.3.7.5 New architectures

The tree and branch structure has remained remarkably resilient and has itself made advances in increased capacity. The fibre optic enhancement above will be a major change, itself creating other openings. It will naturally zone a system into areas of a few hundred or thousands of people depending on its depth of penetration into the network. This may then favour associating with the zone, switches and multiplexers for data and telephony. A hybrid network may grow up mixing switched star and tree and branch concepts.

Instead of the point to point optical links now being installed, splitters will be introduced to share the capacity more economically (but will of course be combiners for any reverse traffic up the network). Whether fibre will ever sensibly be taken through to the home is a matter of fierce debate. Many see coaxial cable surviving for the final feed, both because optical equipment costs will not be low enough on a per customer basis and to avoid powering and housing it in the home. Another alternative to remember is the possibility of radio as that final feed, probably at high microwave frequencies.

57.4 Digital video coding

57.4.1 PCM

Pulse Code Modulation (PCM) encoding of a video signal comprises the steps of sampling, quantisation and allocation of code words. Sampling converts the continuous analogue representation into a series of picture elements though this term and its short forms, pixel and pel, are also used to refer to the digital versions. The Nyquist criterion of the sampling rate being at least twice that of the highest frequency present leads to minimum rates in the region of 10MHz to 12MHz for conventional 525 and 625 line television signals. Though these values are satisfactory for monochrome or colour component signals, it is common practice when sampling composite colour signals to increase the sampling rate to an exact integer multiple of the colour subcarrier frequency f_{sc}. This minimises the visibility of beat frequencies between harmonics of the subcarrier and the sampling clock arising from non-linearities in the digital to analogue and analogue to digital converters. Sampling rates of $3 \times f_{sc}$ have been used in transmission equipments, where the emphasis is on minimising the bit rate and $4 \times f_{sc}$, with its 90 degree subcarrier phase shift between samples, has attractions when subsequent digital signal processing will be employed to modify the input signal in certain ways.

Because of the scanning process, the energy spectrum of video signals tends to be concentrated in the vicinities of harmonics of the line scanning rate. By careful choice of a sub-Nyquist sampling frequency it is possible to arrange for the alias spectrum to interleave with the original and yet be separable at the decoder using comb filter techniques. Some loss of diagonal resolution is introduced but using this technique, composite colour signals have been sampled at $2 \times f_{sc}$ (Ratliff, 1983).

For 525 and 625 colour signals in component form, CCIR Recommendation 601 specifies a family of related sampling frequencies (CCIR, 1990a). The most widely used is the 4:2:2 version in which the luminance component is sampled at 13.5MHz and each of the two colour difference components at 6.75MHz. The latter lower rate reflects the reduced acuity of the human eye to colour detail. Unlike f_{sc} based ones, the CCIR 601 sampling frequencies result in orthogonal arrays of sampling points and they remain stationary from one picture to the next. Conversion of the analogue samples to digital form is normally performed with a uniform quantisation law and 8 bits of resolution. For the highest quality applications where multiple tandem encoding and decoding or subsequent processing will be encountered an extra 1 or 2 bits may be used. Some images,

a notable example being medical scans, have a wide dynamic range and require significantly more bits.

CCIR 601 calls for uniformly spaced quantisation levels and 8 bit code words. The nominal black and white levels are represented by 16 and 235 respectively. The nominal range of the colour differences is from 16 to 240 with 128 representing a zero difference.

The resulting bit rate of the 4:2:2 version of CCIR 601 is 216Mbit/s. CCIR Recommendation 656 covers serial and parallel interface arrangements (CCIR, 1986). Some reduction of the bit rate of PCM encoded video can be obtained by omitting the blanking intervals and synchronising pulses as these can be regenerated at the decoder. CCIR 601 4:2:2 specifies a digital active line as containing 720 luminance samples. Taking into account the vertical blanking period, the net rate representing visible picture information is of the order of 166Mbit/s.

A PCM representation is invariably a prerequisite for video compression coding.

57.4.2 Bit rate reduction

Video signals contain several sources of redundancy which can be used to reduce the bit rate. Some techniques operate on the statistical redundancy and are fully reversible, ie the original can be recovered exactly. Other techniques exploit the characteristics of the human visual system to conceal the distortion they introduce or minimise its visibility. Practical coders often incorporate both techniques.

57.4.3 DPCM

Differential Pulse Code Modulation (DPCM) exploits the facts that adjacent pels are likely to have similar values and that the human eye is more tolerant of distortion in areas containing higher spatial frequencies, i.e. edges and detail. As shown in Figure 57.24, a PCM

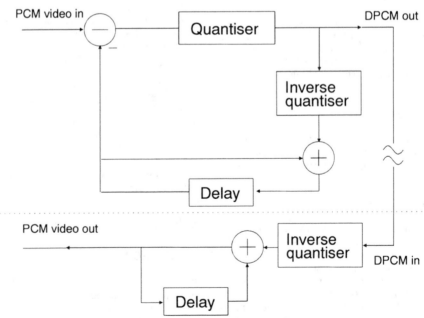

Figure 57.24　DPCM coder (top) and decoder (bottom)

input sample is applied to one input of a subtractor. A prediction value, in this case a previously coded pel, is applied to the other input and the resulting difference, the prediction error, is requantised with fewer bits and with a non-linear law. The non-linearity is such that small differences, which occur in low detail regions, are coded accurately whereas more distortion is allocated to large differences generated in high detail areas.

The DPCM output is thus a sequence of short code words which index the quantiser levels. The decoder converts each index to the relevant representation level and adds it to the prediction to reconstruct each output sample. So that the encoder and decoder remain in track it is essential that the encoder uses only information also available at the decoder. Hence the encoder contains the essential parts of a decoder so that it uses a reconstructed version of the previous pel rather than its original input value.

The prediction can be the pel immediately to the left on the same scan line in which case the delay is one sample period. The delay can be one TV line in which case the pel immediately above is used. The pel in the same spatial position in the previous picture is the result of making the delay equal one picture period. The optimum delay depends on the localised picture content.

Simple DPCM coders utilise a fixed delay or a weighted combination of pels from fixed delays. More sophisticated versions dynamically select the optimum prediction and either explicitly indicate the choice in the coded bit stream or use rules applied to previously coded information. For composite colour signals sampled at $N \times f_{sc}$, setting the delay element to N samples reduces the occurrence of large outputs from the subtractor. Although the subcarrier is a high frequency it must be coded accurately as it is carrying low frequency colour information.

DPCM coding with 5 to 6 bits per pel is considered to offer the subjective quality of 8 bit PCM. The disadvantage is the increased susceptibility to transmission errors which affect all subsequent samples until a reset can be performed, for example at the end of a scan line or bottom of the picture. One way to mitigate against, but not eliminate, this is to introduce a leak factor in the feedback loop by multiplying the prediction by slightly less than unity. The error then diminishes over a number of pels which depends on the leak factor. Leak factors further from unity give faster recovery but at the expense of coding efficiency.

CCIR Recommendation G.721 describes a DPCM codec for use at 140 Mbit/s (CCIR, 1990b). The input video is in 4:2:2 component form according to Recommendation 601. The predictor is two dimensional using the average of the pel immediately above in the same field and the pel immediately to the left on the same line.

57.4.4 Variable length coding

The use of variable length codes (VLCs), also referred to as Huffman coding, or entropy coding, offers compression when the input data does not have a uniform probability distribution (Huffman, 1952). Short code words are allocated to frequently occurring events and longer codes to infrequent ones. The indexes from a DPCM coder typically have a peaked distribution centred on zero magnitude prediction errors and worthwhile compression can be obtained from variable length coding. This coding is completely reversible in that the original input to the VLC coder can be reconstructed exactly in error free conditions. Errors can cause significant problems as the boundaries between code words can only be found from inspection of the received bit stream. A single bit in error can make one transmitted code appear to be two shorter ones at the decoder or vice versa. Not only does this corrupt the corresponding data but the following code words, even if decoded to the correct

values, will have a positional error. To limit this error extension effect it is prudent to include some resynchronisation code words.

57.4.5 Transform Coding

Transform Coding is another method to exploit the similarities of pels which are in the same neighbourhood of space or time. The most commonly used transform is the two dimensional Discrete Cosine Transform (DCT), applied to a rectangular spatial block of m by n pels. The forward transformation is computed according to Equation 57.3 and the inverse (IDCT) by Equation 57.4, where x,y are spatial coordinates in the pel domain and u,v are coordinates in the transform domain. C(u) and C(v) are given by Equations 57.5 and 57.6 respectively.

$$F(u,v) = \frac{1}{4} C(u) C(v) \sum_{x=0}^{m-1} \sum_{y=0}^{n-1} f(x,y)$$

$$\times \cos\left[\frac{(2x+1)u\pi}{2m}\right] \cos\left[\frac{(2y+1)v\pi}{2n}\right] \tag{57.3}$$

$$f(x,y) = \frac{1}{4} \sum_{u=0}^{m-1} \sum_{v=0}^{n-1} C(u) C(v) F(u,v)$$

$$\times \cos\left[\frac{(2x+1)u\pi}{2m}\right] \cos\left[\frac{(2y+1)v\pi}{2n}\right] \tag{57.4}$$

$$C(u) = \frac{1}{\sqrt{2}} \quad \text{for } u = 0, \text{ otherwise } 1 \tag{57.5}$$

$$C(v) = \frac{1}{\sqrt{2}} \quad \text{for } v = 0, \text{ otherwise } 1 \tag{57.6}$$

Blocks are commonly 8 by 8 or 16 by 16 though the horizontal and vertical dimensions are not required to be equal, nor to be a power of 2. Small blocks can fail to take maximum advantage of correlations from low spatial frequencies and may also incur a higher proportion of overhead data to address and describe them. Large transform blocks have a higher implementation difficulty. The transformation does not of itself produce data compression as the number of output values, termed coefficients, is the same as the input. However, the process tends to concentrate the energy into a few coefficients, usually those representing lower spatial frequencies, and the others can be omitted or coarsely quantised. The (0,0) component contains the average level of the block and is called the d.c. component. The others are a.c. components.

The DCT is the basis of the JPEG standard (ISO, 1991) for coding of continuous-tone still images. The basic coder structure is shown in Figure 57.25. After rearranging the input pels into 8 by 8 blocks they are transformed. The resulting coefficients are quantised, each with a different uniform law; the stepsize reflects the visibility of the quantising errors in that coefficient after inverse transformation. The quantised d.c coefficients are DPCM coded from block to block with variable length codes. The quantised a.c. coefficients are rearranged into a zigzag order, F(0,1), F(1,0), F(2,0), F(1,1), F(0,2), ... F(7,6), F(7,7). Each non-zero a.c. coefficient is coded in combination with the run length of the preceding zero value coefficients using variable length codes.

The coefficient weighting matrix and the VLC tables for the d.c. and a.c. coefficients are downloadable to the decoder and so can be optimised for each picture by the coder to obtain maximum bit

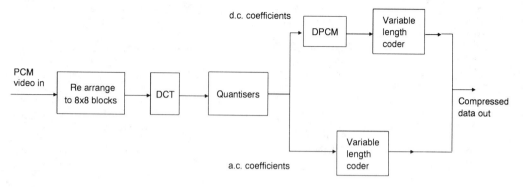

Figure 57.25 JPEG encoder

efficiency. An additional parameter allows scaling of all the quantisers thus providing flexibility of quality and hence compression ratio.

57.4.6 Sub-band Coding

Sub-band coding (SBC) has similarities to transform coding in that the video input is split into frequency bands. Because each sub-band contains a limited range of frequencies it can be reversibly subsampled so that the total number of pels in all the sub-pictures equals the number in the original. The resulting sub-pictures are individually coded, e.g. by DPCM, each with quantisation distortion appropriate to its visibility (Gharavi, 1988). The splitting is performed by filters, usually two dimensional (spatial only) but sometimes three dimensional including the temporal axis. The technique has more flexibility than the DCT in its partitioning of the input energy. In particular, the frequency bands are not constrained to be of equal extent as illustrated in Figure 57.26.

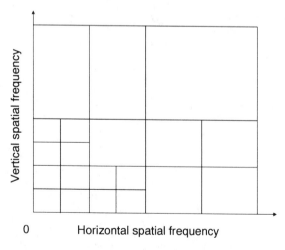

Figure 57.26 Example of sub-band split

57.4.7 Vector Quantisation

Vector quantisation (VQ) is the assignment of one code word to a group of two or more picture elements. Compression is achieved

through the number of available code words being less than the number of permutations of the possible values of the input pels in the group. Thus several input patterns are mapped to one output code. This again exploits the likely similarities between pels in the same neighbourhood of space or time or both and the masking of distortion in highly detailed areas.

Although conceptually simple, the coding process is complex as the number of input permutations increases very rapidly with the number of pels in the group. For example, to implement a VQ encoder operating on a 2 by 2 block of 8 bit pels by means of a direct lookup table would need 32 address bits, which is significantly in excess of current integrated circuit technology. A 64 kbyte ROM has just 16 address lines; 65536 such devices would be required. For this reason it is common to employ a multi-stage approach though this may be sub-optimal. A variation is to extract the mean level and scale the remainder before applying VQ to its shape. The index then consists of three portions.

Because of its complexity, VQ encoding is sometimes performed as an off line process at less than real time speed. By contrast, the decoding is simple as the lookup table required is of modest size.

A form of VQ is the encoding of the three digitised colour components of one pel by a code word having fewer bits than the three together. This technique is used in VGA colour display adapters for personal computers. By means of a colour palette, which is a programmable lookup table containing 256 entries each of 18 bits, a store size of only 8 bits per pel can provide any 256 colours from 262 144. The initial choice of which 256 colours for a particular image is the key step to producing good rendition.

57.4.8 Hybrid Coding

Many of the above techniques can be applied together to yield additional compression. An example for moving pictures is shown in Figure 57.27. Spatial correlation is exploited by the DCT and temporal redundancy is reduced by DPCM coding of the transform coefficients from one frame to the next. Variable length encoding then provides further compression.

57.4.9 Motion compensation

DPCM inter-frame coding can be augmented by motion compensation. The moving areas generate the majority of bits in an inter-frame coder. However, if the motion is of a nature that it can be described by a few parameters then more efficient coding can be obtained by suitably modifying the previous picture before using it as the prediction. For objects undergoing purely translational mo-

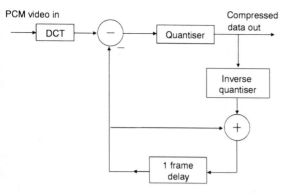

Figure 57.27 Hybrid DCT/DPCM coder

The incorporation of motion compensation in a decoder has only a small effect on its complexity; the main change is that the store in the loop ceases to be a purely serial delay but needs a degree of random access capability. The impact on an encoder is very large, the basic process being one of pattern matching. For the CCITT coder, which is the least demanding of the three in this respect, an exhaustive search for the optimum vector requires over 5×10^9 additions or subtractions of 8 bit numbers per second. Fortunately, because the decoder needs to know only the vector value and not how it was determined, the search method need not be standardised. This permits simplified search methods to be implemented in encoders, though with some loss of performance.

57.4.10 CCITT Recommendation H.261

This Recommendation is for a video codec for audio visual services at multiples of 64 kbit/s up to 2 Mbit/s (CCITT, 1990a). The primary application is videotelephone and videoconference. The first stage of bit rate reduction is achieved by reducing the sampling rates to below those required by CCIR 601. CCITT sought an international standard for world-wide application which would permit users to converse without having to concern themselves over the existence of the two different television scanning standards, namely 625/50 and 525/60.

To meet this goal, the coding kernel operates on a single format known as the Common Intermediate Format (CIF) or its simply related, downsized version called Quarter CIF (QCIF). The luminance component of CIF has 288 lines of 352 coded pels, repeated 29.97 times per second. The two colour components each have half these numbers of pels and lines. QCIF has half the corresponding spatial sampling densities of CIF and is more suitable for the lower bit rates especially when the decoded images are for display on small screens. CIF and QCIF are a technical compromise between 625/50 and 525/60, the number of lines being simply related to the visible portion of the 625 system and the picture repetition rate being exactly half the field rate of the 60Hz format.

tion, a horizontal displacement and a vertical displacement are sufficient. The two components give rise to the term 'motion vector'. The overhead of transmitting a vector for individual pels would more than offset the savings elsewhere so the technique is applied to blocks of pels. In reality, motion is rarely purely translational but includes rotation and deformation and the edges of moving objects rarely coincide exactly with block boundaries. Inter-frame differences also result from uncovered background areas and from illumination variations. Nevertheless motion compensation substantially reduces the energy of inter-frame differences and can yield a halving of bit consumption.

Because the motion compensation is applied to pictures in their pel domain representation, it cannot be inserted directly in the scheme of Figure 57.27. Instead the DCT is positioned inside the loop along with an inverse transform (IDCT) as shown in Figure 57.28 to give a motion compensated hybrid DPCM/DCT codec. This generic structure has attracted a great deal of attention by standardisation bodies and is the basis of the algorithms from CCITT, ISO and CCIR described in the following sections. All three utilise an 8 by 8 DCT.

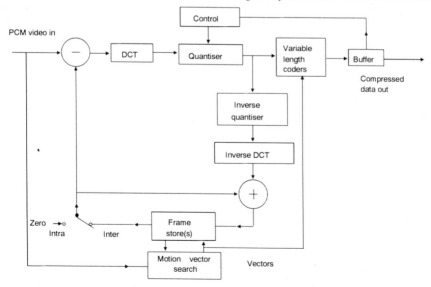

Figure 57.28 Generic diagram of motion compensated hybrid DPCM/DCT coders

At bit rates below about 1Mbit/s it may be subjectively preferable to reduce the coded picture rate and introduce motion jerkiness rather than accept the full amount of spatial quantisation noise.

The motion compensation range is ±15 pels and ±15 lines. Weighting of transform coefficients is not incorporated.

57.4.11 ISO/MPEG Draft International Standard 11172

The mandate of the ISO Working Group is the coding of video and associated audio for storage applications. The first item in the workplan is for bit rates up to about 1.5Mbit/s and is addressed by the Draft International Standard 11172 (ISO, 1992). The algorithm has much in common with CCITT Recommendation H.261 but also some significant differences. A very wide range of picture formats is possible to suit television and computer applications. The full CCIR 601 source quality cannot be maintained at the target bit rates and downsampling is usually employed before the coding kernel. Typical sampling rates are 288 non-interlaced lines of 352 luminance pels repeated 25 times per second and 240/352/29.97, these being simply related to 625 and 525 line television respectively.

To support random access, some pictures are coded entirely in intra mode, i.e. without reference to any information outside that individual picture. These are termed I-pictures. Two forms of motion compensated prediction are employed as shown in Figure 57.29. P-pictures are coded with respect to a previous picture but not necessarily the immediately previous one. The intervening B-pictures use the previous picture or the next picture or an average of the two as a prediction, the selection being possible for each 16 pel by 16 block. The latter mode uses two motion vectors for the block. The motion compensation resolution is half pel and half line, but the permitted range is many times larger than CCITT H.261 or CCIR Rec.723.

The use of prediction from future pictures means that they must be rearranged in time order before entering the coding loop. This modified order is retained in the coded bit stream so that the decoder can process it directly. Restoration to the original time sequencing is carried out after the decoding loop and before display. These processes incur delay, depending on the number of contiguous B-pictures and so the delay through this MPEG algorithm can be significantly more than the CCITT and CCIR ones. For storage applications this is unlikely to be a problem. Although 1 or 2 contiguous B-pictures has been found to work well, the standard permits more or less, including none.

Weighting matrices are applied to the transform coefficients and these are downloaded to the decoder, enabling the encoder to optimise them to the source material. B-pictures are not used as the basis for constructing any others and it has been found possible to quantise them more coarsely than the others. This can yield a small saving in bits.

57.4.12 CCIR Recommendation 723

This Recommendation covers coding of television signals for broadcast contribution quality at bit rates of the order of 30Mbit/s to 45 Mbit/s (CCIR, 1990c). The algorithm handles CCIR 601 4:2:2 input video without any internal subsampling.

In addition to intra coding there are an inter-frame mode and an inter-field mode. The inter-frame one uses the field of the previous frame with the same parity as the field being coded. Motion compensation is performed with half pel resolution within the range 15 pels horizontally and 7.5 lines vertically. The inter-field mode uses the immediately previous field and without motion compensation. Because of interlace, the previous field has a vertical spatial offset. This is compensated for by taking the average of two pels in the previous field, one directly above and one directly below, as the prediction.

Weighting matrices are applied to the transform coefficients in the quantisation process. The matrix for the two colour difference signals is different from the luminance one.

57.4.13 Buffering and coder control

Video coders utilising compression techniques inherently produce coded data at a non-uniform rate because the effectiveness of these methods is dependent upon the spatial and temporal activity of the input pictures and these are not constant. Transmission channels currently operate at fixed bit rates, though variable rate video coding is being studied (Morrison, 1991) for use on future networks which could support this mode (CCITT, 1990b). Buffers in the coder and decoder provide short term smoothing, up to around a few hundred milliseconds. Adjustment of the longer term average rate of bit generation must be accomplished by controlling the coder where, typically, the state of fill of its buffer is fed back to control the quantisation process. The control strategy need not be known to the decoder. Consequently this and other items which do not affect compatibility between coder and decoder may be left open in standards. These then essentially contain only the syntax and se-

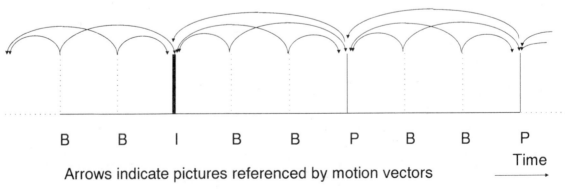

Arrows indicate pictures referenced by motion vectors

Figure 57.29 Example of combination of predictive and interpolative coding in MPEG algorithm

mantics of the coded bit stream such that the decoder can reconstruct the pictures that the encoder intended. Thus, product differentiation between coders is possible and may well result in two coders fed with identical input material giving different coded bit streams and subjectively different decoded qualities. This is more likely with the above CCITT and ISO codecs where the relatively low bit rates mean that coding distortion is larger and more often visible than in the CCIR case.

57.4.14 Inverse DCT Specification

In the above schemes it is important that the loops at coder and decoder track each other. Any divergences manifest themselves as noise and because of the recirculating nature of the loop this noise will steadily increase if there is a continual though small source of error. All the mathematical operations except the IDCT can be precisely specified and implemented. The IDCT, however, contains cosine terms and some of these are transcendental numbers which can never be represented exactly with the finite precision inherent in practical implementations.

Rather than define a unique fixed precision approximation to the IDCT which would have translated to a single architecture with specified accuracy and rounding at every intermediate step, the CCITT chose in Recommendation H.261 to allow some flexibility to manufacturers. The IDCT is specified with an error limit and the accumulation of mismatch between different implementations at coder and decoder is controlled by stipulating the minimum rate at which intra coding must be selected. This action of temporarily breaking the loop clears out any accumulated errors before they become too large. This approach and the same IDCT specification was adopted for the above CCIR and ISO algorithms and supported elsewhere (IEEE, 1990b).

57.4.15 HDTV coding

All the methods outlined above are directly applicable to High Definition Television (HDTV) coding. The higher sampling rates needed, in the region of 70MHz for luminance, currently present some technological challenges in the implementation of the more complex algorithms. The economic balance between the saving in transmission or storage cost gained by more efficient coding and the increased cost of the coding and decoding equipment must be considered. There is some interest in compatible coding schemes for HDTV which simultaneously provide decoded pictures for viewing on conventional displays.

57.4.16 New approaches

Though the techniques mentioned thus far have only recently been incorporated in standards, they have been known for many years, well investigated and further improvements in their compression factors are likely to be small. The attentions of researchers are thus being directed in other directions such as fractal based coding (Jacquin, 1990) and wavelet coding (Rioul, 1991).

An approach which shows promise for some applications such as videophone at very low bit rates is model based or knowledge based coding (Pearson, 1989). From a limited number of still images and knowledge of the generic shape of a human head and shoulders, the encoder and decoder construct a model of the subject. The encoder then transmits parameters to the receiver to move the model in some way, e.g. to nod the head or open the mouth. An extension is to ally this to more conventional methods which are brought into action

when the model fails. Encouraging results have been shown for the synthesis part which is carried out by decoders. The analysis task which must be performed by encoders is more difficult.

57.5 Videophony and videoconferencing

Videophony and videoconferencing are companion audiovisual services which are, at the present time, generally distinguishable by the factors given in Table 57.8.

Table 57.8 Comparison between videophony and videoconferencing

Videophony	Videoconferencing
Primarily person-to-person	Primarily group-to-group
Office environment	Studio or specially equipped room environment
Compact desk top terminals	Large floor standing terminals
On demand service via customer switched digital networks	Bookable service via digital leased lines
Picture quality consistent with low bit rate transmission (e.g. 64kbit/s or 128kbit/s)	Picture quality consistent with high bit rate transmission (e.g. 384kbit/s up to 2Mbit/s)
Telephony quality speech	Wideband speech quality

However, for some applications at least, the boundaries between the two services are becoming less distinct; for example, desktop videoconferencing terminals operating over switched 56kbit/s and 64kbit/s networks are becoming available. The CCITT, which is responsible for the video coding, audio coding and protocol standards for audiovisual services, has appreciated the future need for both types of service to interwork. As a result, the relevant standards ensure that any audiovisual terminal adhering to the standards will automatically interwork with any other standard terminal with the same or lesser capabilities. The standards are discussed further in later sections.

57.5.1 General design considerations

This section deals with the general design considerations for videophone and videoconferencing systems and terminals, but since a number of the considerations are a consequence of the CCITT Rec. H.261 video coding algorithm used (CCITT, 1990a), the reader should be familiar with the earlier section on digital video coding before proceeding further.

57.5.1.1 *Display performance*

The optimum size of the display screen in a videophone terminal is a function of a number of factors including the picture scanning standard, picture resolution (signal bandwidth), viewing distance and, if a data compression scheme is implemented, the visibility of coding artefacts. The 625 line television scanning standard in Europe (525 line in the USA and Japan) was chosen so that the line structure would be imperceptible to the majority of people when viewed at a distance greater than 6 times the picture height (a viewing ratio of 6H).

For videoconferencing terminals in a meeting room equipped with large (65cm diagonal) CRT displays, a viewing distance of at least 2.5m is recommended. Videophone or desk top videoconferencing terminals are usually positioned from 70cm to 1.5m from a single user; for easy reach of controls which are integral with the terminal, 70cm is the more appropriate. At this distance, the display size should be about 20cm diagonal to preserve a viewing ratio of 6H. In practice, designers of wideband terminals may opt for a larger display (25cm to 35cm diagonal), preferring the greater impact of the bigger picture despite some visibility of the line structure. Equally, where low bit rate coding algorithms are used, usually accompanied by a deliberate reduction of the available picture resolution, designers may prefer a smaller size (10cm to 15cm) to mask the loss of picture quality incurred. Larger (30cm to 35cm diagonal) displays are normally used when positioned at the back of the desk, some 1.5m from the user.

The brightness of the displays should be adjustable up to at least 100cd/m^2, measured on a white rectangle occupying 50% of the screen area.

The most important advance in display technology over the past few years has been the development of colour liquid crystal displays (LCD) with the grey scale resolution required for television (White, 1988). At the time of writing, production LCDs for real time television applications are available in sizes up to 15cm diagonal (larger panels up to 35cm exist as development samples) and virtually all employ an active matrix of thin film transistors to control the transmittance of each cell. Colour is provided by having 3 cells per picture element and an overlay colour filter. A light source must be provided behind the LCD, usually by means of a colour matched cold cathode fluorescent tube.

The main attraction of the LCD is that there is much more freedom to design an attractive, compact unit than would be the case with conventional cathode ray tube displays. One limitation of LCDs is that they have a much more limited angle of view than CRTs, being typically ±20 deg. vertically and ±40 deg. horizontally.

Integrated videophone terminals tend to use LCDs up to 15cm diagonal, but a personal computer (PC) is an attractive alternative videophone terminal implementation, particularly where the potential user already has such a unit on his desk. In this case, where low bit rate coding is utilised, a reasonable implementation is to 'window' the small videophone picture into one of the top corners of the PC screen. For wideband videophone terminals, the whole PC screen can be used for the displayed picture if required.

For single viewer use, the normal 4:3 aspect ratio is near optimum for head and shoulders pictures. Although there have been experimental videophone terminals in the past with aspect ratios of 1 and less, to better match the shape of a human face, these were less than satisfactory because the natural sideways movement of a seated user caused difficulty in remaining in the field of view of the camera.

For videoconferences involving groups of people at each location, a 4:3 aspect ratio display is non-optimum, resulting in the pictures of say 6 participants in a central band occupying less than 20% of the picture area. This situation can be significantly improved, at the expense of a second camera, display and some processing, by using the 'split-screen' technique (CCITT, 1988a) illustrated in Figure 57.30. Effectively, the aspect ratio of the display has been changed to 16:3 which is close to the optimum value for 6 participants.

57.5.1.2 Camera performance

For both videophone and 'split-screen' videoconferencing terminals, the camera should have a fixed field of view of about 44 deg. horizontally and 33 deg. vertically, which corresponds to lens focal length of between 7.5mm and 8.5mm when used with an industry standard 0.5 inch format CCD camera sensor (active area about 6.4mm by 4.8mm). The width of the field of view will therefore be about 54cm at a subject distance of 70cm and about 2m at a subject

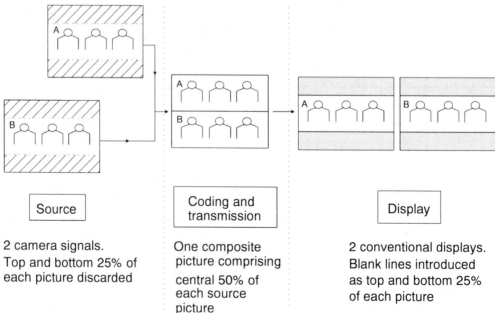

Figure 57.30 Split screen technique

istance of 2.5m. One third inch CCD sensors, already used in consumer video camcorders, are increasingly likely to be used for videophone applications; for the same field of view, the focal length of the lens is reduced to 5mm to 5.5mm.

Fixed focus lenses are to be preferred since, particularly in videophone applications, auto focus lens operation in following small movements will result in picture changes which then have to be coded for transmission, thereby reducing the efficiency of the coding operation. Even for the most critical fixed focus application, e.g. a videophone terminal 70cm from the user and a 0.5 inch CCD camera with 8mm focal length lens and the aperture open at f2.0, the subject will be in focus over the range 40cm to over 3m for a QCIF resolution picture (176 picture elements per line), and over the range 50cm to over 1m for a CIF resolution picture (352 picture elements per line).

Videophone and videoconference terminals in a standard office environment need to operate satisfactorily in lighting conditions which range from bright sunlight to poor artificial lighting. It is the illumination of the user's face that is important, and the camera sensitivity, auto iris lens performance and electronic automatic gain control must be such that satisfactory pictures are obtained over a range of illumination from 200 to 4000 lux. In addition, the colour temperature varies among different types of artificial lights and the colour temperature of daylight also varies with time of day and prevailing weather conditions. Therefore the camera needs an automatic or semi-automatic means of controlling the colour balance in the television pictures so that, for example, white objects always appear white and even more importantly, facial flesh tones are well reproduced. The range of colour temperature over which such colour balance must be maintained is typically from 3000 to 6000 degrees Kelvin. In the more stable environment of a custom designed videoconference room, the need to automatically compensate for the range of lighting conditions described above is drastically reduced.

The signal/weighted noise ratio of the cameras should be at least 45dB, measured in lighting conditions of at least 400 lux (and the appropriate aperture setting) and using the unified noise weighting network specified in Rec. 567 (CCIR, 1990e). For videoconferencing, the face camera should have a limiting resolution of at least 300 lines per picture height in the centre of the sensor area; for videophone applications, this specification can be relaxed but graphics cameras need to be of higher resolution.

Another important aspect of the camera specification is that the field rate of the camera should be the same as the local mains frequency; when cameras are operated in artificial lighting, particularly from fluorescent tubes, the video signal is modulated by the illumination frequency (twice mains frequency). If, for example, a 60 field/s camera is operated in 50Hz lighting, there is 20Hz modulation flicker running through the displayed picture and 20Hz is close to the most visible temporal input frequency for the human eye-brain system.

Another disadvantage of such a system is that the CCITT Rec. H.261 algorithm encodes differences between the current and previous pictures. The modulation flicker is interpreted as a difference signal and valuable transmission capacity will be used unnecessarily to encode the flicker. Means for removing or at least reducing the flicker exist (for example, use of an electronic shutter) but the expense and complexity involved may outweigh the advantage of having a universal camera and display standard.

To provide the most natural conditions for a videophone conversation, good eye contact with the displayed image of the remote user is essential and this implies that the ideal position for the camera is near the centre of the display screen. Systems using a semi-silvered mirror to achieve this apparent position do exist, although there is an inevitable consequential light loss to the camera and from the display. When the camera is mounted in the plane of the display, the options are to position the camera centrally above the display or on one side of the display on the anticipated eyeline of the displayed head and shoulders picture, i.e. slightly above the centre line.

For a fixed viewing distance, the eye contact angle is minimised by positioning the camera above, and as close as possible to, the display, and by using the smallest acceptable display size. However, despite being a less than optimum arrangement, there are a number of videophone terminals (usually the smaller ones) with the camera positioned at the side. One of the reasons the industrial designers concerned give for preferring this arrangement is that a camera at the side is less obtrusive and dominant than one positioned centrally above the display. Further work is required to determine user preference.

A European standard (ETSI, 1991) is in preparation which addresses these and many other design aspects of videophone terminals.

57.5.1.3 Audio performance

For people to be able to converse freely via a telecommunications medium the transmission delay should be less than a few tens of milliseconds. However, with the video coding algorithm specified in CCITT Rec. H.261, the processing delay can vary from 200ms to 500ms depending on the skill of the codec designer and the transmission bit rate available. To ensure acceptable lip synchronisation, the timing of the sound relative to the picture should be in the range −40ms to +20ms (CCIR, 1990f), and although the video delay can vary with the amount of movement to be coded, a fixed compensating audio delay for a given bit rate, if carefully chosen, may be acceptable. With compensating delay in each direction of transmission, the ease of conducting an interactive conversation is adversely affected, rather like telephony via one or two satellite hops, but the presence of a picture may help to avoid the tendency for both parties to speak at the same time as is often experienced by telephone users when the connection is via satellite.

Virtually all videoconferencing terminals use an 'open' audio system in which monophonic sound is transmitted and received on separate channels (4 wire operation). The positioning and relationships between microphones and loudspeakers should be based on the guidelines given in CCITT Supplement No. 25 (CCITT, 1985). The echo return loss between loudspeakers and microphones should be greater than 6dB over the frequency range 0.1kHz to 8kHz to preserve stability. However, even in well designed studios with suitable acoustic treatment, it is difficult to avoid completely the possibility of the received sound being reflected into the microphones and being re-transmitted as a delayed echo (the total delay is room delay plus the processing compensation delay mentioned above) and the use of echo cancellation is advisable. The effect of echo cancellation is to enhance the echo return loss to a value 40dB.

For videophone and desk top videoconferencing terminals having hands free operation, echo cancellation may not at present be a viable economical solution, and voice switched echo suppression, although inferior, may be the preferred solution. Further study is required to confirm satisfactory voice switched echo suppression when the audio signal has been delayed by a few hundred milliseconds. Where a telephone handset is used, the problem of room echo disappears and the only requirement is that the side tone attenuation should be at least 45dB, a figure that is achievable with a well designed handset.

57.5.2 Standards for audiovisual communications

As interest has grown in a whole range of audiovisual services supported by terminals with different capabilities, the CCITT anticipated the need for a framework of interrelated standards to ensure satisfactory interworking at the highest level of compatibilty existing in the different terminals. There are a number of Questions in CCITT Study Groups addressing different aspects requiring standardisation for audiovisual services, and the Rapporteurs for each Question co-operated in the production of a framework (CCITT, 1988b) of target Recommendations, which were designated the AV series. The AV designation is used while the Recommendation is being drafted, but once finalised and formally adopted by the CCITT, the standard is allocated a number in the appropriate series of published CCITT Recommendations.

Only the most significant members of the framework series can be summarised here.

57.5.2.1 *Audio coding*

Telephony quality speech, with a bandwidth of 300Hz to 3.4kHz, can be encoded using PCM into 64kbit/s or 56kbit/s as specified in Rec. G.711 (CCITT, 1984c). The Recommendation specifies different companding laws (A-law for Europe, μ-law for North America and Japan) and different rules as to whether the most significant bit is transmitted first or last. As a result of this incompatiblity, there is a need for A-law/μ-law conversion when international digital telephone traffic is exchanged between incompatible regions.

Better quality speech, with a bandwidth of 7kHz, can be encoded into 64, 56 or 48kbit/s using the ADPCM algorithm of Rec. G.722 (CCITT, 1988c). The systems aspects of wideband audio are covered in Rec. G.725 (CCITT, 1988d). A draft Recommendation, AV 254, for 16kbit/s speech using a codebook excited linear prediction (CELP) algorithm is close to completion and is expected to be formally ratified by the CCITT in 1992 as new Recommendation G.728.

Although other audio coding standards exist, the above are the only ones applicable to audiovisual services at the present time.

57.5.2.2 *Video coding*

Rec. H.261 specifies the video coding algorithm for audiovisual services at rates from 64kbit/s to 1920kbit/s (video bit rate in the range 46.4kbit/s to 1856kbit/s).

57.5.2.3 *Audiovisual systems*

Rec. H.320 (CCITT, 1990c) covers the technical requirements for audiovisual services at channel rates between 64kbit/s and 1920kbit/s. This Recommendation is the 'high level' document that calls all the other relevant Recommendations for audiovisual services. It defines the allowable types of terminal and allowable transmission modes, and where interworking among different terminal types must be supported.

The standards to be adopted for subdividing a transmission channel (again in the range 64kbit/s to 1920kbit/s) into subchannels for the transmission of video, audio and ancillary data are embodied in Rec. H.221 (CCITT, 1990d). The framing structure defined in Rec. H.221 is octet based, with 80 octets per frame; the eighth bit is called

the service channel. Each frame has an 8 bit Frame Alignment Signal (FAS) and an 8 bit Bit Allocation Signal (BAS) occupying the first 16 bits of the service channel and corresponding to a framing overhead of 1.6kbit/s; all the remaining bits of the service channel and the remainder of the frame can be used for a mix of video, audio and ancillary data. Hence, in a 64kbit/s videophone service, the maximum available video rate is 46.4kbit/s with 16kbit/s audio data and 1.6kbit/s framing overhead.

The protocols to be used to establish communications between audiovisual terminals using channels up to 1920kbit/s are embodied in Rec. H.242 (CCITT, 1990e). By defining how the capabilities of different types of terminal are to be exchanged in an unambiguous manner in the BAS codes, each terminal can determine the highest level of common capabilities for interworking.

The BAS codes also provide a number of other controls and indications (C&I) such as audio mute, camera identification and various multipoint controls. These are defined in Rec. H.230 (CCITT, 1990f).

57.5.3 Network aspects

57.5.3.1 *Background*

The early videoconference systems in the 1970s consisted in the main of public studios with analogue transmission of monochrome 525 line or 625 line television signals over dedicated leased circuits.

During the 1980s, the trend was towards private studios or rooms and the digital transmission of colour television signals, encoded according to Rec. H.120 (CCITT, 1988e) at the primary digital hierarchical rates (2048kbit/s in Europe, 1544kbit/s in North America and Japan). Again, digital leased circuits were almost universally used although some network operators introduced a limited switched capability (under their control, not the users) to provide some flexibility in connecting pre-booked calls.

In the 1990s, the trend will be towards user switched (dial up) videophone and videoconferencing services at bit rates in the range 64kbit/s to 384kbit/s using the coding algorithm specified in Rec. H.261, although premium services at rates up to 1920kbit/s will still be a user option.

57.5.3.2 *ISDN*

The new Integrated Services Digital Network (ISDN), the standards for which have been generated and refined by the CCITT over the past decade and more, is the customer switched public digital network most likely to be used for videophone and videoconferencing services. Basic rate access to the ISDN (CCITT, 1984a) provides two full duplex 64bit/s digital connections (the bearer or B-channels) and a full duplex 16kbit/s signalling channel (the data or D-channel), and is commonly referred to by the shortform notation 2B+D. Initially, the marketing of the ISDN will concentrate on business customers as having the most likely need to transmit speech and a mix of data (fax, video, computer files etc.) over the same network.

Videophony and desk top videoconferencing are likely to utilise basic rate access, either 2B (video at 108.8kbit/s, speech at 16kbit/s and framing data at 2 x 1.6kbit/s; if a higher bit rate is used for speech as per Recs. G.711 or G.722, the video bit rate is reduced) or 1B only (video at 46.4kbit/s, speech at 16kbit/s and 1.6kbit/s framing data). It should be noted that in 2B operation, since video data is always present in both channels, the terminal has to synchronise the incoming B-channels to remove any differences in transmission lelay before the video data can be correctly demultiplexed; the network does not guarantee this 'time slot integrity' for 2B operation.

Rec. H.320 stipulates that any 2B terminal must be capable of operating as a 1B terminal and this has the additional advantages that a videophone call can still be established if one of the B-channels is busy and the user can, during a 2B call, free one of the B-channels for other purposes. It is a designer option whether the video codec associated with the terminal supports CIF or QCIF picture resolution. User preferences vary as to the optimum trade off between spatial and temporal resolution, some preferring less sharp pictures with smoother movement to sharper but jerkier pictures. Again however, CIF terminals must be capable of falling back to quarter CIF operation.

For videoconferencing between specially equipped rooms, the preference is likely to be for full CIF pictures with transmission at a rate of 384kbit/s emerging as a popular optimum compromise between picture quality and transmission cost. Switched 384kbit/s access to the ISDN is likely to be provided in the future in one of two ways; either by setting up six independent 64kbit/s connections (with again the need to synchronise all six incoming data streams for satisfactory operation) or by providing an overlay switch to allow direct 384kbit/s access and switching (with guaranteed time slot integrity) within primary rate ISDN access (CCITT, 1984b).

For premium service at rates greater than 384kbit/s, switched access at multiples of 384kbit/s and at the two primary rates of the existing digital transmission hierarchies (2048kbit/s and 1544kbit/s) are likely to be available in the future.

Although the ISDN is considered the most suitable available network to support videophone and videoconferencing services over the next 5 years, it is worth considering the ability of other existing and future networks to support such services, and the consequential effects on the services.

57.5.3.3   Broadband networks

If customer switched digital broadband networks were widely available, and call charges were acceptably low, the main advantages for videophone and videoconferencing services would be that the picture quality would be higher, the processing delay would be small and the video codec would be much simpler. There is currently much activity in the CCITT defining the broadband ISDN (CCITT, 1990b) with a broadband user network interface rate of about 155Mbit/s, of which up to about 130Mbit/s is available for customer data. The optimum rate for videophony and videoconferencing will depend on the tariffing structure adopted for B-ISDN, but in any case, given the long lead time to plan the introduction of such a major change to the access network, it seems unlikely that B-ISDN will become widely available for some years to come.

57.5.3.4   LANs

A Local Area Network, principally used for interconnecting PCs and workstations, is one type of customer premises digital network that may be capable of supporting audiovisual service. The data to be transmitted over a LAN is assembled into packets for transmission, and the ability of a terminal to transmit a particular packet depends on a number of factors, including how many other terminals are trying to do likewise at the same time; the transmission is therefore essentially asynchronous with an unspecified trans-

mission delay. While it does not normally matter whether a computer file is transferred in a few seconds or a few tenths of a second, the quality of real time services such as speech and videophony would be severely affected unless an almost fairly steady throughput and bounded delay could be guaranteed. For this reason, LANs such as Ethernet in common use today are not suitable for real time services; however, the next generation of LANs will be based on the token exchange principle and are likely to be much faster and more intelligent (able to prioritise data), and so could well support videophone services of an acceptable quality.

57.5.3.5   PSTN

It is of interest to consider whether the public switched telephone network (PSTN), the most widespread telecommunications network available, could support a videophone service. Currently available full duplex PSTN modems can operate at a rate of 14.4kbit/s, and designers are confident that 19.2kbit/s will be possible in the near future; 19.2kbit/s modems for use on 4 wire circuits are already available commercially.

For 14.4kbit/s operation, the speech data would need to be encoded to about 4.8 kbit/s and the picture data encoded to about 9.6 kbit/s. To achieve the same picture quality as a 1B ISDN videophone, the video coding algorithm needs to be at least 5 times more powerful, but there is little international activity in standardising such an algorithm at present.

A second option is that PSTN videophone pictures could be designed to have lower spatial and/or temporal resolution while still using the algorithm of Rec. H.261. Yet a third option is that PSTN videophones with lower picture (and speech) quality and proprietary algorithms will be launched by different manufacturers, leaving market forces to determine an eventual 'de facto' standard. However, if incompatible videophones are available at the same time, this can give rise to user uncertainty and dissatisfaction until the de facto standard emerges.

The marketing of PSTN videophones would ideally extend beyond the business community into the residential market, but in the latter case, the terminal costs need to be about 3 to 5 times lower than the ISDN terminal costs. The only hope to reduce the cost significantly is for a manufacturer to be sufficiently convinced of the prospects for large volume sales to enable him to recover the substantial investment in VLSI necessary.

Two different PSTN vidoephone products (one in the USA and the other in the UK) were announced in the first few months of 1992.

57.5.4   Multipoint operation

In general, telecommunications systems have been designed to operate on a point to point basis between two end users. Some form of multipoint operation is necessary when 3 or more users are required to be involved at the same time, and this is usually provided as a network based service via a multipoint control unit (MCU) embedded in the network (Clark, 1990).

The simplest example of an MCU is a telephone conference bridge, located either at a main switching centre or at a private branch exchange. In this instance, the audio signals from all the locations are combined in such a way that each location does not receive its own audio but does receive a mix of all the other signals. Although the speech in a multipoint audiovisual connection is treated in exactly the same way, the video signals have obviously to be treated differently.

In a 'switched' audiovisual MCU, the video signals are voice switched and forwarded from the MCU to each location according to the following rules:

1. The picture of the person currently speaking is forwarded to all the other locations.
2. The person currently speaking is sent the picture of the previous speaker.

Such a system has the advantages of relative simplicity, operates automatically and, apart from some additional control features, uses the same terminals and transmission capacity as point to point connections. The CCITT is drafting a new Recommendation (current document number AV.231) for a multipoint control unit for use with H.261 codecs at rates from 64kbit/s to 2048kbit/s. The multipoint control data is transmitted in the message channel in the H.221 framing structure.

If all the other participants are required to be seen all of the time, so called 'continuous presence' multipoint operation, a more complex solution is required. One way of achieving this would be by increasing the number of receive channels and decoders at each location, and either increasing the number of displays or accepting the fact that all the incoming pictures will be displayed at smaller sizes on the existing display screen. A second solution is to have a single receive channel and decoder but a more complex MCU which could generate a composite picture of all the other incoming pictures, with the picture of the current speaker being of higher resolution than the others and therefore allocated a greater proportion of the channel capacity. Further research and development in this area is continuing.

57.6   References

Bermingham, A. et. al. (1990) *The Video Studio* 2nd edn, Focal Press.

CCIR (1986) Interfaces for digital component video signals in 525-line and 625-line television systems, *Recommendation 656*, Dubrovnik.

CCIR (1990a) Encoding parameters of digital television for studios, *Recommendation 601-2*, Dusseldorf.

CCIR (1990b) Transmission of component-coded digital television signals for contribution-quality applications at bit rates near 140Mbit/s, *Recommendation G.721*, Dusseldorf.

CCIR (1990c) Transmission of component-coded digital television signals for contribution-quality applications at the third hierarchial level of CCITT Recommendation G.702, *Recommendation 723*, Dusseldorf.

CCIR (1990d) Bit-rate reduction for digital television signals, *Report 1089*, Dusseldorf.

CCIR (1990e) Transmission performance of television circuits designed for use in international connections, *Recommendation 567*, Dusseldorf.

CCIR (1990f) Tolerances for transmission time differences between the vision and sound components of a television signal *Recommendation 717*, Dusseldorf.

CCITT (1984a) Basic rate user-network interface, *Recommendation I.420*, Malaga-Torremolinos.

CCITT (1984b) Primary rate user-network interface, *Recommendation I.421*, Malaga-Torremolinos.

CCITT (1984c) Pulse code modulation (PCM) of voice frequencies, *Recommendation G.711*, Malaga-Torremolinos.

CCITT (1985) Guidelines for placement of microphones and loud speakers in telephone conference room, Supplement No.25, p 335, Fascicle III.1, CCITT Red Book, Geneva.

CCITT (1988a) Characteristics of visual telephone systems, *Recommendation H.100*, Melbourne.

CCITT (1988b) Infrastructure for audiovisual services, *Recommendation H.200*, Melbourne.

CCITT (1988c) 7kHz audio coding within 64kbit/s, *Recommendation G.722*, Melbourne.

CCITT (1988d) System aspects for the use of the 7kHz audio codec within 64kbit/s, *Recommendation G.725*, Melbourne.

CCITT (1988e) Codecs for videoconferencing using primary digital group transmission, *Recommendation H.120*, Melbourne.

CCITT (1990a) Video codec for audio-visual services at p x 64kbit/s, *Recommendation H.261*, Geneva.

CCITT (1990b) Broadband aspects of ISDN, *Recommendation I.121*, Matsuyama.

CCITT (1990c) Narrowband visual telephone systems and terminal equipment, *Recommendation H.320*, Geneva.

CCITT (1990d) Frame structure for a 64 to 1920kbit/s channel in audiovisual teleservices, *Recommendation H.221*, Geneva.

CCITT (1990e) System for establishing communication between audiovisual terminals using digital channels up to 2Mbit/s, *Recommendation H.242*, Geneva.

CCITT (1990f) Frame-synchronous control and indication signals for audiovisual systems, *Recommendation H.230*, Geneva.

Clarke, R.J. (1985) *Transform Coding of Images*, Academic Press, London.

Clark, W.J. et. al. (1990) Multipoint audiovisual telecommunications, *Br. Telecom Tech. Jn.*, **8** (3).

ETSI (1991) ISDN and other telecom. networks – Audiovisual services – Narrowband visual telephone system, *European Telecomms. Standards Inst. provisional standard ETS 300 145*.

Gharavi, H. and Tabatabai, A. (1988) Sub-band coding of monochrome and colour images, *IEEE Trans. Circuits and Systems*, **35** (2) pp. 207 – 204.

Griffiths, J.M. (1990) *ISDN Explained*, Wiley, Chichester, UK.

Huffman, D. (1952) A method for the construction of minimum redundancy codes, *Proc. IRE*, September, pp. 1098 – 1101.

IEEE (1990a) *IEEE LCS (Lightwave communication systems) – Special Issue on Optical Fibre Video Delivery Systems of the Future*, **1**, (1), February.

IEEE (1990b) Specification for the implementation of 8 x 8 Inverse Discrete Cosine Transform, *Draft Standard P1180/D2*.

ISO/IEC (1991) Digital compression and coding of continuous-tone still images: Part 1: Requirements and guide-lines, *Draft International Standard 10918-1.*.

ISO/IEC (1992) Coding of moving pictures and associated audio for digital storage media at up to about 1.5Mbit/s, *Draft International Standard 11172-1*.

International Broadcasting Convention, (1980–1990) *IEE Conference Publications*, Nos. 327 (1990), 293 (1988), 268 (1986) 240 (1984), 220 (1982), 191 (1980) etc.

International Journal (1989) *Int. Journal of Digital & Analog Cabled Systems – Special Issue on Cable TV*, **2**, (2), April – June

Jacquin, A. (1990) Fractal image coding based on a theory of iterated contractive image transformations, *SPIE Proc. Visual Communications and Image Processing '90*, **1360** (1), pp. 227 – 239.

Jayant, N.S. and Noll, P. (1984) *Digital Coding of Waveforms – Principles and Applications to Speech and Video*, Prentice-Hall New Jersey.

..uther, A.C. (1988) *Digital Video in the PC Environment*, McGraw-Hill, New York.

Morrison, D.G. and Beaumont, D.O. (1991) Two-layer video coding for ATM networks, *Signal Processing: Image Communication*, (3) pp. 179 – 195.

Mothersole, P. and White, W. (1990) *Broadcast Data Systems : Teletext and RDS*, Butterworths.

NCTA (1990) *1990 NCTA Technical Papers*, Atlanta (May) (see also 1989 papers, Dallas, May) and previous annual conferences.

Pearson, D.E. (1989) Model-based image coding, *Proc. Globecom 1989*, pp. 554 – 558.

Pearson, D. (1991) (ed.) *Image Processing*, McGraw-Hill, Maidenhead, UK.

Ratliff, P.A. and Stott, M.A. (1983) Digital television transmission: 34Mbit/s PAL investigation, *BBC Research Department Report No. RD 1983/9*.

Rioul, O. and Vetterli, M. (1991) Wavelets and signal processing, *IEEE Signal Processing Magazine*, October, pp. 14 – 38.

Roberts, R.S. (ed.) (1985) *Television Engineering — Broadcast, Cable & Satellite*, Part 1 — Fundamentals, Part 2 — Applications, Pentech Press for Royal TV Society.

Sandbank, C.P. (ed.) (1990) *Digital Television*, John Wiley & Sons.

Slater, J.N. (1988) *Cable Television Technology*, Ellis-Horwood, Chichester, UK.

Townsend, B., and Jankson, K.G. (eds.) (1991) *TV & Video Engineer's Reference Book*, Butterworth-Heinemann.

TV (1988) *15th International TV Symposium* Montreux (June) (see also previous symposia held at 2 yearly intervals at Montreux).

Watkinson, J. (1990a) *The D2 Digital Video Recorder*, Focal Press.

Watkinson, J. (1990b) *The Art of Digital Video*, Focal Press.

Weaver, L.E. (1979) *Television Video Transmission Measurements*, Marconi Instruments, St. Albans, UK.

White, J.C. (1988) Colour LCD TV, *Phys. Tech*, **19**.

58

Telephones and headsets

David M Davidson
Northern Telecom
(Sections 58.1–58.10)

Malcolm A Nugent
GN Netcom (UK) Ltd
(Sections 58.11–58.16)

Contents

58.1 Telephones

When we speak our voice sets up sound vibrations which disturb the surrounding air, and travel through the air to be detected by the listener's ear drums. Sound will travel through most media, air, water, wood, plastic, etc. and at different speeds through the different media. For example in air sound travels at approximately 1100 feet per second (335m/s) and approximately 4300 feet per second in water (1311m/s). Electrical signals travel at the speed of light 3×10^8 m/s.

The telephone, patented by Alexander Graham Bell in the USA in 1875-77, was an apparatus named the 'Electrical Speaking Telephone'. It was a means of transmitting sound (especially voice) over a distance, by converting sound vibrations into electrical signals which passed through wires as electrical signals, and were then reconverted to sound at the distant end. This will provide one direction of communication. In a practical telephone bothway communication is necessary, so in a simple telephone system each end is provided with means for transmitting and receiving sound.

In addition some form of mechanism is required to signal to the distant end to attract the distant party's attention to the fact that the caller wishes to talk to the distant end. Numerous forms of signalling schemes have been devised and they vary depending on the type of telephone system to which the telephone is connected. Some form of power supply is required to generate the electrical signals and many forms of circuits exist to provide power to the telephone. These consist of local batteries to power only an individual telephone or central batteries in the telephone exchange (Central Office or CO in the USA) where the power is sent down the individual telephone line to the telephone, where circuits exist to extract the power from the line and feed the telephone circuits. Cost has and is very important in telephone equipment, so the first practical telephones economised on the wiring from one telephone to the other by combining the pair of wires from the transmitter and from the receiver onto one single pair of wires, to connect both telephones together. The basic functional model for a telephone is as shown in Figure 58.1.

58.2 Telephone speech functions

In speech communications we are primarily concerned with intelligibility i.e. the percentage of voice signals transmitted from one telephone and correctly received at the telephone at the distant end. We do not have to transmit every single part of the sound generated, since the listener acts as an error correction mechanism and can fill in any missing elements and still understand completely what has been transmitted. The prime intelligence in the human voice is contained in quite a small segment of the bandwidth of the hearing/voice spectrum. The human ear can detect sounds from 16Hz to 20000Hz and the human voice can generate sounds from 100Hz to 10000Hz.

Most of the energy in an average male voice is contained within the band from 125Hz to 2000Hz and the average female voice from 400Hz to 2000Hz. CCITT recommend a bandwidth of 300Hz to 3400Hz as being adequate for telephony and provide an acceptable level of intelligibility on a speech connection.

58.3 Telephone transmitters

Telephone transmitters have been designed using numerous techniques to convert sound impinging onto the transmitter into electrical energy.

58.3.1 Carbon granule transmitter

Carbon granule transmitters were very common from the earliest days of telephony until comparatively recently. The principle of operation is shown in Figure 58.2.

Sound pressure impinges on the diaphragm causing it to vibrate. The centre of the diaphragm is attached to a carbon electrode which moves, compressing and decompressing the fine carbon granules sealed in the chamber at the rear of the device. A second carbon electrode is fixed to the back wall of the device. The variation in pressure on the fine carbon granules causes the resistance between the two electrodes to vary in unison with movement of the diaphragm. When a d.c. supply is connected between the two carbon electrodes, and the carbon granules are compressed and decompressed, an alternating current is superimposed on the d.c. supply which represents the speech signal.

58.3.2 Rocking armature transmitter

The rocking armature transmitter is shown in Figure 58.3. Sound pressure impinges on the diaphragm causing the armature to pivot,

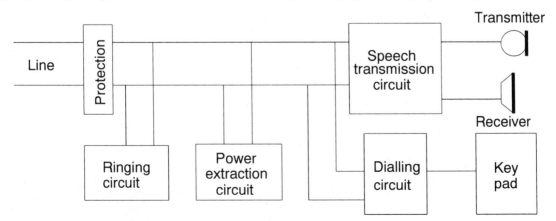

Figure 58.1 Functional diagram of a telephone

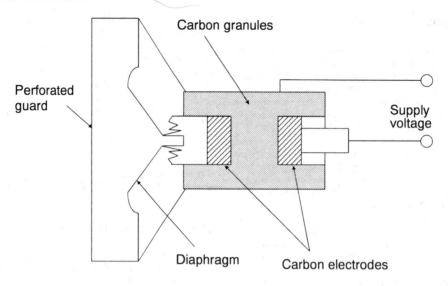

Figure 58.2 Carbon granule transmitter

altering the magnetic field and inducing an alternating current in the coils. This alternating current represents the speech signal.

58.3.3 Piezo-electric transmitter

Piezo-electric transmitters work on the principle that certain types of quartz crystals become electrically polarised when subjected to pressure from sound waves. Sound impinges on the disc of piezo material, causing the disc to be stressed, varying the charge on the capacitor within the disc, which in turn varies the gate voltage of the FET impedance conversion amplifier, shown in Figure 58.4. The disc and the FET are all housed in a pressed aluminium casing. The

apertures at the front of the transmitter have variable hole patterns which are selected to improve the frequency response of the unit.

58.4 Telephone receivers

Like telephone transmitters, telephone receivers have been designed using numerous principles, but the earliest type tended to be electromagnetic as shown in Figure 58.5.

An electromagnet winding terminates the telephone line and picks up the a.c. signals from the line, varying the magnetic field. The thin iron diaphragm, held in close proximity to the ends of the magnetic poles, is moved to and from the poles of the electromagnet. The

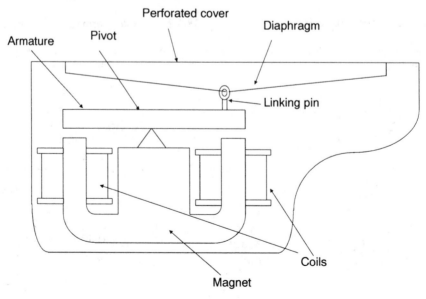

Figure 58.3 Rocking armature transmitter

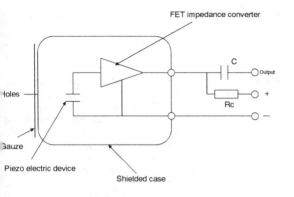

Figure 58.4 Piezo-electric transmitter

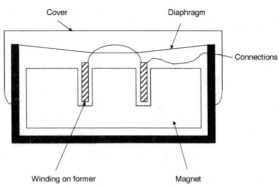

Figure 58.6 Moving coil receiver

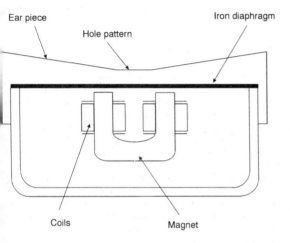

Figure 58.5 Electromagnetic receiver

greater the current detected in the coils the closer the diaphragm is pulled to the poles of the magnet. The diaphragm therefore vibrates in unison with the received speech signal.

58.4.1 Rocking armature receiver

The construction of this type of receiver is the same as the rocking armature transmitter. When this device is used as a receiver it is similar in operation to the electromagnetic type. An a.c. current is detected in the telephone line and this causes the armature to move back and forth in sympathy with the a.c. current on the line. The armature is linked to a diaphragm which vibrates causing sound to be reproduced.

58.4.2 Moving coil receiver

This type of receiver is similar in construction to a loudspeaker, as shown in Figure 58.6. A flexible diaphragm, normally of a plastic material, is formed into a shallow conical shape and a former, wound with very thin wire, is attached to the diaphragm. The assembly is then suspended in the field of a permanent magnet. The coil is connected to the telephone line and detects the a.c. speech

current on the line, inducing a change in the magnet field which causes the diaphragm to vibrate, reproducing sound from the received speech signal.

58.5 Telephone handset design

The telephone handset is designed to provide the optimum ear/mouth geometry for the average human head. Early designs of telephones used a fixed mouthpiece, mainly due to the early forms of carbon microphone, which were subject to the carbon granules generating unwanted noise when the microphone section of the telephone was moved. It was not until manufacture of the carbon microphone improved that it was possible to design a telephone handset that contained both a transmitter and receiver.

The ergonomics of the handset design are equally important as the acoustic design, to provide the user with a telephone of high performance and reliability of operation. The earpiece needs to be designed to sit comfortably on the user's ear. It must form an acoustic seal with the ear to ensure that received sound is directed into the ear and does not leak away into the surrounding air. If the handset has a poor seal to the ear the listener will pick up external noise and will probably complain that the telephone is not loud enough. Furthermore, others in close proximity to the user will hear the telephone conversation.

The positioning of the microphone is also critical. For reliable performance it must be possible to comfortably position the handset such that with the receiver in place on the ear the microphone sits directly in front of the mouth, to ensure that the microphone is in a direct line of any sound being generated. The choice of material for the handset and the size and positioning of any holes, is also critical to the acoustic performance of the handset. Mounting of the transmitter and receiver should also be done with care, with sufficient vibration absorbing material placed between the body of the handset and the transmitter or receiver to ensure that sound vibrations do not travel through the handset body from transmitter to receiver or in the other direction and impair performance.

Sidetone is a unique feature of telephone handset design and is essential for good performance of the telephone. When using a telephone handset the normal acoustic feedback from mouth to ear is partially blocked, therefore to compensate a portion of the talker's own voice is fed back into the receiver. Subjective tests have shown that, at high levels of sidetone, the speech power levels transmitted to the telephone network are significantly reduced, resulting in the distant end experiencing a low volume of received sound. This effect is due to the talker's voice being lowered and moving the handset away as he tries to compensate for the increased sidetone.

High levels of sidetone are also undesirable in environments with high ambient noise since room noise is picked up by the microphone, which is also transmitted to the ear, and this may mask the incoming speech signal, making the telephone unusable.

Acoustic shock is another significant factor in the design of telephone handsets. As the user will have the handset close to the ear during a conversation, it is essential that the telephone circuit has a mechanism to prevent large transients or power surges from the telephone line being transmitted to the receiver, which could produce a sudden surge of sound pressure into the listener's eardrum.

With modern electronic designs of telephone circuits it is necessary to protect the electronics from static discharge from the user into either the transmitter or receiver, or through the body of the handset where the two sections join. No regulatory specifications exist for electrostatic discharge but 10kV is the minimum and for dry low humidity areas 20kV to 30kV is recommended.

The telephone handset must be balanced so that the user feels comfortable holding the handset for lengthy periods of time. Many manufacturers add weight to the handset. This is not always just for balance since it is sometimes necessary to counteract the 'walk on' problem. If a handset is too light, or the telephone is of a poor mechanical design, the switch to seize the line (hookswitch or cradleswitch) is not returned to its normal position at the end of the call by the weight of the handset, and the exchange equipment remains seized preventing incoming calls arriving.

Finally the telephone handset can take considerable abuse during its lifespan, therefore it is required to withstand severe shock tests, dropping on the floor, being hit against a desk, and still continue to function.

This presents the designer with a considerable problem in meeting all the above diverse requirements to ensure reliable efficient telephone service.

58.6 Telephone transmission performance

To assess the transmission performance of an individual telephone, or telephone network, a number of parameters have been established. The voice operation of a telephone can be broken down into the following elements:

1. The path from talker's mouth to the transmitter.
2. The path from the telephone receiver to the listener's ear.
3. The near end path between the transmitter and the receiver.
3. The telephone connection from transmitter and receiver to the distant end.

Different methods exist for comparing the performance of various telephones and for defining the standard to which a particular telephone or system should perform. The four key parameters in determining telephone performance are:

1. Sending sensitivity.
2. Receiving sensitivity
3. Impedance the telephone presents to the line.
4. The line impedance for minimum sidetone.

Each of these parameters can be a function of the frequency range of the telephone and the available line current. Algorithms exist for converting the sensitivity of the transmission path or receive path

into a loudness rating i.e. a single number for a given frequency, sound pressure level, and line length.

A loudness rating is a standardised method of measuring the transmission loss of a speech path. It is a single value related to the loudness with which the listener perceives, speech that has been emitted by the talker. The performance of a telephone is assessed by measuring between the telephone and an impedance representing the telephone termination, at the telephone exchange, over varying line lengths and over the full frequency range in which the telephone operates. Known sound pressure levels are applied to the microphone of the telephone and the resulting voltage changes appearing at the simulated exchange terminations are measured.

In the other direction signals are applied to the simulated exchange termination and the resulting sound pressure levels are measured at the telephone receiver. These measurements are normally carried out with the telephone in a sound absorbing box or in an anechoic chamber, with the telephone clamped into a jig which has an artificial ear and an artificial voice. These are used to detect and measure the received signal and generate the tones to stimulate the transmitter.

58.6.1 Sending sensitivity

The sending sensitivity is defined as the ratio of the voltage measured at the terminating impedance of the exchange feed bridge and the sound pressure level injected into the microphone. This ratio is normally measured over the full frequency range. The sensitivity depends on the frequency response of the microphone, the acoustic path to the microphone, and the transmit gain of the telephone circuit. The sending sensitivity and frequency response are designed to have a rising characteristic within the speech band. The reason for this is that although most of the power in speech is at the lower frequencies, the sharpness of speech is created by the higher frequencies. However, this is the region were losses in the cable are highest, therefore by increasing the sensitivity at the higher frequencies this tends to compensate for the effect of the cable and increases the clarity of the speech. Above 4kHz the sensitivity should fall off rapidly, to prevent unwanted out of band energy to be transmitted to the network, which might interfere with PCM circuits. At low frequencies the sensitivity should roll off to prevent mains hum pickup. The gain introduced into the sending path is chosen to ensure that the telephone send sensitivity is in accordance with the transmission plan for the telephone network. A typical send sensitivity response is shown in Figure 58.7.

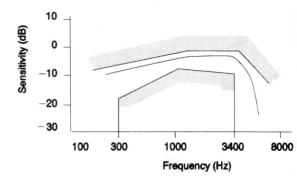

Figure 58.7 Typical send sensitivity response

58.6.2 Receive sensitivity

The receive sensitivity is defined as the ratio of the sound pressure level in the artificial ear, to the voltage applied at the terminating impedance of the exchange feed bridge. This ratio is also measured over the full frequency range and at different line lengths. The receiving sensitivity is nominally flat within the the 300Hz to 3400Hz speech band and tends to roll off at low frequencies. To reduce the effects of picking up mains hum in the telephone, the cut off at low frequencies cannot be too sharp, since the absence of low frequencies increases the difficulty of hearing on quieter calls.

Above 3400Hz the sensitivity drops off sharply to exclude the unwanted high frequency by-products of pulse code modulation systems. This is because PCM systems sample at 8kHz and all codecs put some part of the sampling frequency onto the line, albeit at a very low level. The aim is to reduce the level as much as possible, to prevent it being an annoyance to the user, even if it is heard. A typical receive sensitivity response is shown in Figure 58.8.

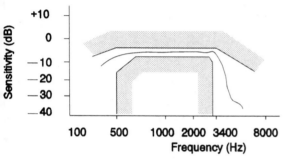

Figure 58.8 Receive sensitivity

58.6.3 Impedance

The impedance that the telephone should present to the line is chosen to suit the transmission plan for the network. As more digital local exchanges are installed in networks, control of the impedance presented to the network becomes more important. Digital exchanges use four wire transmission paths – two for transmitting and two for receiving. However, the cable between the exchange and the telephone is only two wire, therefore a mechanism is necessary to terminate the bi-directional two wire path onto the unidirectional send and receive paths of the four wire circuit.

The four wire circuits are balanced to prevent singing or echo and it is also necessary to include the impedance of the line and the telephone to ensure correct balance. Echo is where the speaker hears his own voice repeated back. Part of the speech signal energy transmitted in one direction is returned in the other direction due to imperfect balance at the 2/4 wire conversion. The length and type of cable connecting the telephone to the exchange will vary and hence its impedance, therefore trying to match the impedance of the telephone line to the balance network would involve individual measurements of each line. In practice a nominal impedance of 600 ohms has been chosen to terminate the line and most telephones have been designed around this value. More recently complex impedances have been specified by the network provider as this is thought to provide a more ideal balance network.

One essential function of any speech circuit of a telephone is to combine the four wire path from the handset (transmitter connections and receiver connections) onto the two wire path to the exchange line, and to do this with minimum coupling from the transmitter into the receiver (sidetone). Sidetone plays an important part in the subjective performance of any telephone but it is desirable to be able to control the amount of sidetone that can occur over the range of exchange line connections, to ensure that transmission difficulties do not arise.

One way to assess the efficiency of the 2/4 wire converter in the telephone circuit is to check for minimum sidetone, or zero sidetone when the telephone is connected into an impedance which completely suppresses the sidetone. Many telephone speech integrated circuits perform the 2/4 wire conversion by means of a Wheatstone bridge principle, as in Figure 58.9, to obtain proper decoupling between the send and receive signals. For balance of the bridge Equation 58.1 must be satisfied.

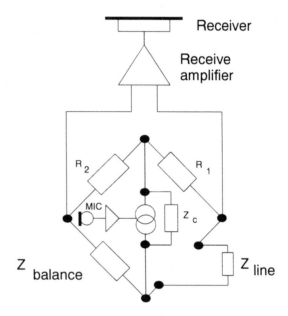

Figure 58.9 Telephone bridge

$$\frac{R_1}{R_2} = \frac{Z_{line}}{Z_{balance}} \tag{58.1}$$

The a.c. signal from the microphone is fed into one diagonal of the bridge and a small amount is fed into the balance impedance, but the majority is fed to line via R_1. The signal coming from the line is detected on the other diagonal of the bridge then amplified and applied to the receiver.

58.6.4 D.c. characteristics

Most telephones which are directly connected to the exchange via a pair of wires derive their power from a central battery in the exchange, which feeds current down the line normally from a –48V or –50V supply. Some earlier telephone systems operated on local batteries, next to the telephone on the customer's premises, but this method of operation is now only reserved for special applications e.g. radio telephones. The exchange battery feed circuit is usually a Stone or a Hayes bridge. The battery feed has balanced windings with respect to earth and presents a relatively low d.c. resistance, but a high impedance to voice frequencies. The d.c. resistance is usually around 200 ohms in the battery feed and the same in the ground return with an inductance of 2 Henrys.

The d.c. characteristics of a telephone are important as they determine the operating parameters for the telephone. It is normal to have a full bridge rectifier at the front end of any telephone circuit, to guard against line reversals which may damage speech and dialling circuits. When the telephone is idle (on-hook) the telephone will extract current from the line. This is normally only insulation resistance leakage and is of the order of a few micro amperes. However, some telephone network providers permit more current to be taken from the line when the telephone is on-hook, to power electronic memory devices in the telephone or LCD displays.

When the telephone is off-hook current is drawn from the network to power the telephone. The telephone network providers set limits to the amount of current that may be drawn and the telephone must operate within the parameters set. The d.c. characteristics are normally specified by a relationship between current and voltage, as in Figure 58.10.

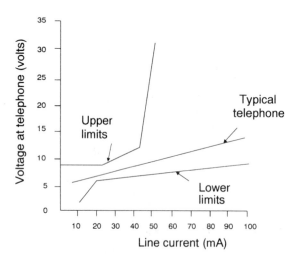

Figure 58.10 D.c. characteristic of a telephone

The upper limits are set to ensure that the telephone will be able to seize and hold the exchange equipment. The off-hook impedance of a telephone should be equal to or greater than the 400 ohms battery feed, to obtain optimum voice signal power transfer in the 200Hz to 3400HZ voice frequency range. Many telecommunication administrations set a lower limit on the voltage that a telephone should operate on, because it is not desirable to subject the feed bridge circuit to a short circuit. However, this is not normally the practical reason since the cable from the exchange must be present. The more practical reason is the need to ensure that sufficient current is available for more than one telephone to operate in parallel.

58.7 Signalling

Signalling in a telephone circuit relates to the ability to seize the exchange in the outgoing state and then pass the address information of the required distant telephone to the exchange. In the incoming state signalling relates to the alerting of the telephone, when it is on-hook, that an incoming call is trying to make contact. A message is then sent to the exchange to inform it that the incoming alerting signal has been successful, as the call has been answered, and the telephone has gone off-hook.

58.7.1 Incoming ringing signals

Ringing is the earliest form of signalling on telephone circuits and has changed little in principle over the years. Even the early manual telephone switchboards used ringing generators that were wound by hand to generate an a.c. signal between 20Hz and 50HZ (70V to 100V). This was superimposed on the exchange battery feed when applied to the line. A.c. signal was then extracted from the line via a capacitor of approximately 2μF to drive a bell. The capacitor also blocked the d.c. battery feed to the telephone, to prevent the d.c. polarising the bell. When the telephone is taken off-hook the bell circuit is short circuited by the telephone receiver and transmitter, resulting in the exchange detecting the change in condition of the line and 'tripping' the ringing circuit.

In today's telephone exchanges the ringing signal is usually a composite of a.c. and d.c. components. The ringing waveform, as shown in Figure 58.11, is typically a sine wave with its axis shifted by the −50V exchange battery. The ringing signal is applied in bursts

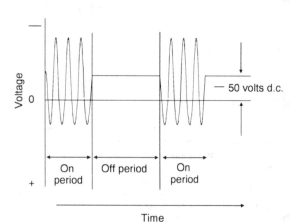

Figure 58.11 Typical ringing waveform

of a few seconds followed by a period of silence and then repeated.

Some exchange systems are able to send additional signals down the line during the ringing phase to provide extra facilities to the user. The most novel is the use of MODEM tones during the silent phase in US exchange equipment to send calling number identity. This has been made possible by the use of electronic exchange equipment, and the growth in CCITT NO.7 signalling between exchanges, to permit the calling number identity to be transmitted across the network.

In the telephone the traditional device to alert the caller has been a bell, consisting of an electromagnet with two coils and an armature which strikes one or two gongs when operated. Modern telephones use a variety of electro-acoustic devices to generate the ringing sound. One of the cheapest forms of device is the ceramic disc resonator. This consists of a brass disc onto which is deposited a ceramic coating. When a potential is applied between the two surfaces the disc resonates at its fundamental frequency. To drive these devices in a telephone circuit the coupling to the line uses the conventional capacitor followed by a full bridge rectifier, to rectify the a.c. ringing signal, then to an IC which amplifies or restricts the signal to a level suitable for the ceramic disc. The ceramic disc is housed inside the plastic moulding of the telephone in an acoustic chamber to ensure good sound reproduction.

58.7.2 Outgoing signalling

Each telephone in the network is assigned a unique number and each country has been assigned a unique number, therefore to obtain a distant telephone it is necessary to pass this number (address) to the telephone exchange, which will then route the request through the network to the distant telephone. There are two basic types of address signalling:

1. Dial pulse or loop disconnect.
2. Multifrequency.

58.7.3 Dial pulse or loop disconnect signalling

Dial pulse or loop disconnect signalling takes its name from the rotary dial method of signalling information to the exchange. The rotary dial is a mechanical device which is connected across the telephone line with a pair of contacts. The user places a finger in the dial and turns the dial round to the finger stop and then releases the dial. The dial then returns to its original position by a spring, which was wound up when the dial was turned. On its return the dial speed is held constant by a mechanical governor and a cam with notches

makes and breaks the telephone line, sending a train of pulses down the line representing the number dialled.

When the dial is first moved by the user off the normal rest position, a further set of contacts are activated (off normal contacts) to short circuit the speech circuit in the telephone, and prevent the user hearing clicks.

Dial pulses are used to signal the address to the exchange by a series of pulses at 10 pulses per second with a tolerance of ±1 pulse as the design objective. The make break ratio is also important for the type of exchange the telephone is signalling into. The ratio is either 60% or 67% nominal break period. The interdigital pause is the period at the end of pulsing as the dial returns to its rest position and on most dials this is approximately 600ms to 800ms. A typical dial pulse train is shown in Figure 58.12.

Modern telephones use integrated circuits to generate the dial pulses. The IC will be connected to a keyboard, and so will have a keyboard scanning circuit and key debouncing circuits, to ensure correct registration of the keys selected. The IC will also provide facilities for muting the speech circuits during dialling, for much the same reason as the off normal contacts in the mechanical dial. In addition to the basic dialling functions the addition of memory cells to the IC provides the user with functions such as last number redial and stores for most frequently dialled numbers.

58.7.4 Dual tone multifrequency signalling

Multifrequency signalling consists of a combination of two tones with frequencies within the speech band, each combination of two frequencies representing a single digit. The tones are presented on the line for approximately 100ms and then an intertone pause of 100ms before the next combination of tones is sent. The speed of dialling is therefore many times faster than loop disconnect dialling. The tones are in two groups, a low band and a high band, and they are geometrically spaced to ensure that any two frequencies of a valid combination are not harmonically related. Table 58.1 details the frequencies and valid combinations.

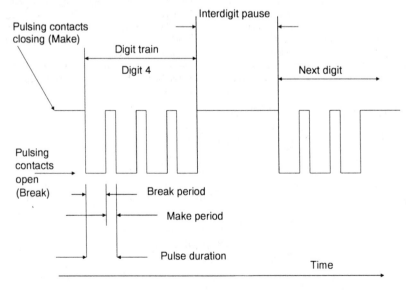

Figure 58.12 Dial pulse train

Table 58.1   DTMF tone assignments

Low	High			
	1209Hz	*1336Hz*	*1447Hz*	*1633Hz*
697Hz	1	2	3	A
770Hz	4	5	6	B
852Hz	7	8	9	C
941Hz	*	0	#	D

The ICs are designed to ensure that frequencies do not deviate more than ±1.5% from the standard and that no unwanted signals are sent to line. In addition the speech transmission is normally muted during signalling, but the receiver normally receives some of the tone to give the user confidence that the tone is being sent to line. The ICs normally have the same facilities for last number redial and digit storage as explained earlier.

DTMF signalling has the added advantage of end to end signalling. Once the connection is set up DTMF signals can be transmitted from the telephone in-band over the link to the distant to control voice mail machines, answering machines and access banking services, etc.

58.8   Loudspeaking telephones

Loudspeaking telephones offer a variety of different functions to the user and in this category of telephone we have the following facilities:

1.   Call progress monitor.
2.   Group listening.
3.   Full handsfree operation.

A telephone with call progress monitoring facilities is equipped with a small loudspeaker and a monitor amplifier. The user presses a button to activate the telephone, seizing the line, and dial tone is applied to the line from the exchange equipment and then fed through the monitor amplifier. The user can dial the distant end, listen to ringing tone and when the distant end answers must then pick up the handset to be able to speak as the only transmitter available is in the handset.

The group listening telephone normally has call progress monitor but in addition has a circuit to enable the user to press a button on the telephone and broadcast the incoming speech signal to others listening in the room. The circuit may also drive the receiver in the handset simultaneously with the loudspeaker in the base of the telephone. Outgoing speech is only possible through the handset transmitter.

The full handsfree telephone is equipped with both a handset and a separate microphone and loudspeaker for handsfree operation. The microphone and speaker are now all provided as part of the telephone, although some older designs consisted of separate units connected in parallel with the standard telephone.

The design of the handsfree telephone creates particular problems. The level of sound being emitted from the loudspeaker is required to be large enough to fill the volume of air in the room where it is being used, so that users can be anywhere in the room and still hear the incoming speech. The microphone in the telephone will also need to pick up this incoming speech signal from the acoustic feedback. Therefore, to prevent the telephone from howling, attenuators need to be switched in to the microphone path. These circuits are often referred to as antilarsen circuits.

Figure 58.13 shows a block diagram of typical handsfree system. When a handsfree telephone connection is established speech signals can be reflected at the two to four wire interface, either in the local exchange or in the digital PBX two to four wire interface, as well as round the local sidetone loop from loudspeaker to microphone. Hence oscillations and speech distorting can occur and in the worst case howling.

To have full duplex working on the loudspeaking telephone requires very fast switching between the transmit and receive circuits and compensation for background noise. This requirement has led to the development of microprocessor controlled handsfree circuits, where the control algorithms are stored in the microprocessor.

Particular attention must be paid to the acoustic design of the telephone body for handsfree operation. The loudspeaker should be housed in a speaker box and acoustically isolated from the microphone as far as possible, to prevent sound travelling through the body of the telephone to the microphone and causing instability. Sound emanating from the back of the speaker can be particularly problematical and many telephones have some sound absorbing material behind the speaker. Microphones for loudspeaking telephones tend to be much more sensitive than telephone transmitters in handsets as they are required to detect speech coming from a few feet away in the room.

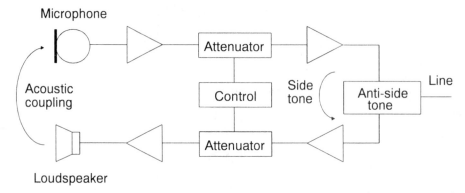

Figure 58.13   Handsfree telephone

58.9   Digital telephones

Digital telephones are characterised by having the codec in the telephone to convert the speech from analogue to digital and vice versa. The PCM encoded speech is then sent to line at a rate of 64kbit/s. In addition a 16kbit/s signalling channel is also present to send address and alerting signals to the exchange. CCITT have now defined standard interfaces for digital operation in the I series of recommendations, but many proprietary interfaces exist.

The I series specifies a 192kbit/s full duplex digital path between the digital telephone (terminal) located in the user's premises and the local exchange. The 192kbit/s is divided into a B1 channel (64kbit/s), a B2 channel (64kbit/s) and a D channel (16kbit/s). The B channels can be used for either voice or data. A digital telephone will consist of a handset and possibly handsfree loudspeaker and microphone connected to an integrated circuit, which will provide the functions of send, receive gain, frequency response, sidetone generation and the codec functions. Additional circuits are necessary to provide the physical drive to the line, extract power from the line and operate the link access procedure on the D channel (LAPD).

The functionality of the telephone can be built into the microprocessor software (functional model) or respond to stimulus signalling from the exchange (stimulus model). In the former all the call processing logic is designed into the telephone, whilst in the latter it is held centrally in the exchange and the telephone responds only to the messages from the exchange.

58.10   Telephone standards

European standards for telephones are country specific and contain many national peculiarities, which prevent the production of a single harmonised telephone suitable for use anywhere in Europe. NET 4 (Norme European de Telecommunication) for basic PSTN access was produced under an EEC directive in 1986 and covers all the essential parameters of signalling, transmission and safety. A new EEC directive in 1991 established the concept of CTRs (Common Technical Regulations) which will supersede the NETs with the aim of establishing the essential requirements to be regulated. The harmonised standards give the specifications and tests to be applied to ensure conformity with the requirements. The CTRs will not duplicate other requirements already in existence, such as the LVD (Low Voltage Directive). The objective is, some time in the future, to be able to test and approve telephones in one country in Europe, apply the EC Mark, and sell that telephone in any other country without further approval testing. At present each country issues its own national standards for telephones, either via the PTT as the controlling authority or via a national standards organisation such as BSI (British Standards Institute) in the UK.

In North America the position on standards for telephones is much simpler. The FCC (Federal Communications Commission) issues the basic standards for all of the USA and in Canada the DOC (Department of Communications) issues similar standards.

58.11   Headsets

Rapid growth in the use of computers and telemarketing means that more and more people in many walks of life are finding themselves before a visual display unit, operating a keyboard accessing data, and using a telephone terminal with a headset. Headsets, once the domain of the telephone switchboard operator, are playing the major role in solving their problem. With the continuing growth in this area it is vital that telephone system designers, manufacturers and suppliers co-operate closely with specialist telecommunication headsets companies early on in the design stage to ensure that the customer gets sufficient choice of quality products.

With the ACD market sector growing at an ever increasing rate, organisations large and small are having to face the fact that more and more of their employees need to have their hands free to operate a computer keyboard when conducting telephone conversations.

Companies involved in the growing business of telemarketing and financial services, and those using direct order entry, such as express delivery services, airline reservations, as well as such public service organisations as police, fire and ambulance are all making use of headsets to overcome the problem, and at the same time increasing their employee's productivity and efficiency.

58.12   Headset aesthetics

Most headsets today are light and efficient and offer excellent sound quality. It is important, however, that operators using these sets, often for most of the day, should look right and feel right when wearing them. When a headset is worn, there is a tendency to regard it as an article of clothing, and if the user doesn't like the headset then he or she will find a reason for not wearing it. So aesthetics as well as comfort are of prime importance.

Headsets are frequently perceived to be expensive but, in comparison with the cost of the telephone systems they are used with, they represent but a fraction of the cost. OEMs need to recognise at the design stage that the headset is the all important man-machine interface, and although an accessory to the system, its performance is a critical aspect of the total system design. The recently introduced range of quality headsets, such as Profile, are of advanced design and construction and offer exceptional performance. They use the latest surface mount technology and because of their microminiature design, and the need for customisation to a wide range of PABX, ACD, Key Systems and other telephone instruments, are generally hand-assembled. The flex cord, too, needs to be of high quality to ensure reliability and, in some cases, is tested to withstand 750000 test flexures.

Compared with a handset, the headset has to be light yet able to withstand hard use. It is constantly picked up and frequently dropped and tends to be under constant flexure.

Developments in modern plastics, and the introduction of the electret microphone have allowed development of headsets weighing ounces and of spider-like proportions, yet which are amazingly strong and flexible. There are even plastics which allow the headset to be formed to fit the head simply by heating with friction from the hand. Headsets come in a variety of forms, over-the-head, under-the-chin, on-the-ear, but the market is tending to standardise on two major types: the over-the-head and the on-the-ear versions as shown in Figures 58.14 and 58.15 respectively. The tip-in-ear variety is in decline, partly due to the fact that it can irritate the inside of the ear, as well as cause aural hygiene problems. Hygiene is also an important consideration in respect of ease of cleaning and maintaining.

58.13   Headset technical considerations

The ergonomics and mechanical design of modern headsets are of paramount importance. Different styles and configurations of headsets, perhaps with a modular concept, are essential. Limited choice

Figure 58.14 Over-the-head headset

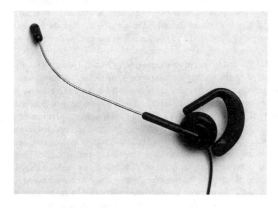

Figure 58.15 On-the-ear headset

of headsets places suppliers and communication managers in an unnecessarily inadequate position.

The acoustic and electrical performance of the headset clearly is also fundamental to its design. In particular, the microphone and earphone transducers must be matched correctly, both to interface with the system being used and to suit user requirements. Ideally, the microphone and earphone transducers in the headset need to operate to the same electrical and acoustic performance as the handset. This is not always easy to achieve mainly due to size and weight considerations, and often sound pressure levels need to be compensated for by automatic gain control and adjustable volume control.

58.13.1 Microphones

Most headsets use either standard electret or electromagnetic microphones. Both types can be boom mounted in miniature form, but the electret type is generally most popular. Acoustic tubes are used on some headsets but these generally provide poorer transmission quality than boom mounted microphones and are subject to considerable crosstalk problems.

Noise cancelling versions of both electret and electromagnetic microphones are also available. However the operation of noise cancelling microphones can often degrade transmission performance if users are not trained properly. There is a tendency to presume that a noise cancelling microphone will automatically provide a superior transmission performance. This is not the case. To explain this it is necessary to know how a noise cancelling microphone works.

The definition of a noise cancelling microphone is a microphone which functions according to the pressure gradient principle. It has two sound ports which give direct access to the front and the back of the microphone diaphragm. The sound ports are symmetrical around the diaphragm.

The noise cancelling microphone reacts to the difference of sound pressure on the diaphragm. It is necessary to distinguish between the sound field originating from a close sound source (called 'near field') and the sound field originating from a distant sound source ('far field'). Noise is a typical distant sound source. The microphone reacts differently to the two types of sound source. The near field frequency response closely resembles a 'normal' pressure microphone characteristic, while the far field frequency response shows a distinct proportional dependence on the frequency.

The directional characteristic of noise cancelling microphones is such that greater attenuation of microphone signals takes place when the sound activates the microphone simultaneously on each side of the diaphragm. In a polar form the characteristic would be shaped as a figure of eight. This means there are two noise reducing effects present in a noise cancelling microphone, partly the effect of direction and partly a strong dampening of low frequencies from the far field sound source.

The near field measurement less the far field measurement is termed noise cancellation. A good noise cancelling microphone has a noise cancellation of not less than 11dB.

Experience with use of noise cancelling microphones is that there is a very minimal real requirement for this type of microphone except in specialised uses such as military, heavy industrial, air traffic control etc. The main objection from other users being the distance dependence of the microphone i.e. the need for careful positioning of the microphone in close proximity to the lips of the user.

58.13.2 Earphones

Handsets normally have a high acoustic impedance and high gain output. Most headsets cannot achieve the same acoustic impedance and gain without amplification. With close coupled earphones, as used on over the head style and under the chin style headsets, this can be achieved easily either with or without an amplifier, according to the system specification with which they are interfacing. However, to overcome the use of unhygienic eartips on single sided headsets, an acoustic low impedance earphone is used which has been specifically designed to work with an acoustic leak between the earphone diaphragm and the ear canal. The first headset to employ this principle is GN Netcom's Profile which has an adjustable earphone to provide users with maximum comfort combined with optimum sound pressure output from the earphone.

58.14 The growing need for headsets

PABX and ACD system designers have always taken care to account for the needs of the headset user. Now more and more key stem and telephone instrument designers are also starting to ognise those needs particularly in view of the increasing telemar- ting activities in the UK.

In the US, every telephone instrument and system normally has a cility to operate with a headset. And since the UK tends to follow osely trend in the USA, we can expect that this will happen here. ith screen based work booming, telephone system designers must sure that all new equipment, including 2-wire sets, have a headset rt as defined in BS 6301.

To facilitate optional handset/headset working a switch arrange- ent can be incorporated simply into many systems. The Dana- itch provided by GN Netcom for this purpose features in many y systems currently on the market.

There is also general feeling among leading headset designers that OEMs worked with them at an early stage in the design of uipment, and there are headset companies perfectly willing and le to do this, then users would benefit considerably from in- eased versatility and a greater choice of headsets.

.15   Headset approval process

terms of approvals, much depends upon the telephone system that e headset is to be used with, and it is frequently the OEM who tains the required approval, under DTI specification 85/013.

The approval process is a lot easier nowadays since the introduc- n of the BABT simple attachment scheme. Previously, testing as carried out under the direct control of BABT and, in the event failure, the modified apparatus had to repeat the entire test ocedure, at considerable expense. Under the new arrangement, sting is carried out directly with one if the accredited test houses ho then submit their report to BABT. Testing, and charging, is rried out until a failure occurs or the test is completed. In the event a failure, the test house informs the designer who can then take e equipment away, rectify it and bring it back to continue testing the point at which failure occurred.

The test is designed to ensure that:

The headset does not electrically damage the public telephone system.

That it meets electrical safety standards.

That no damage to the user can occur through acoustic shock.

58.16   Headset design criteria

First and foremost it must be comfortable. If it is required to be worn for long periods, then weight is vital too. There are few headsets which can be tolerated continuously over an eight hour day. So it is essential to know the shift period that the user will work.

Its design must be attractive to the user.

Does the user have to move around the telephone point in doing the job? If so, a quick-release connector is essential: it also reduces wear and tear on the terminal plug.

Monaural receivers work well when the user needs to listen in two places at once, e.g. a front desk receptionist/telephonist. Binaural receivers help shut out background noise.

Is there a need for split listening? e.g. radio in one ear, telephone in the other, with the ability to switch the microphone from one to the other.

Boom-mounted microphones are better than acoustic tubes and essential in noisy environments.

Under-the-chin headsets don't disturb the hair. Over-the-head style headsets are stable and more robust. Contour 'on-the-ear' style headsets are light, less noticeable. Conversion kits are an important new cost development and allow users to experiment with both over-the-head and on-the-ear styles to decide their preferences. Over-the-ear pads are comfortable, won't cause infection and block out some external sound. In-the-ear tips offer high close acoustic coupling. Some people find the tips uncomfortable, irritating and unhygienic.

The environment is all important. In hot climates, ears sweat. Vinyl ear pads can be wiped clean with a sterilising pad, while foam pads absorb perspiration and need replacing regularly.

Is the office noisy? Does it lack acoustic damping, are the surfaces hard, is there a lot of paper shuffling? In particularly noisy environ- ments, noise cancelling microphones are available but they must be positioned properly for optimum performance. If not, their use can be counter productive.

Automatic Gain Control (AGC) on the microphone circuit cuts the gain when the user is not talking. A manual gain control on the headset allows adjustment to suit line conditions and the speech level of individual callers. A thumbwheel control is usually preferred to a switchable control. Preferably this should provide for −3dB to +12dB gain adjustment.

Modular design eases logistics for maintenance purposes.

After sales service is vitally important. Headsets are fragile and an efficient and speedy after-sales back-up is essential to most users.

59

Telex communications

David M Davidson
Northern Telecom Europe

Contents

9.1 Introduction

Telex has its roots in telegraphy and the first practical telegraph was installed by Wheatstone and Cooke in 1857. The development of telegraphy has been marked by continuous mechanical improvements. Hand sending of Morse code was laborious and so an electric typewriter was developed to a point where it could be connected to a telephone line and operated by a typist (the teleprinter).

The ability to send/receive typed messages from one part of the world to the other became of enormous importance to business and as the machine was able to acknowledge receipt of the transmission of the information in some areas the telex message was accepted as legally binding. The first telex machines were connected to the telephone network alongside a telephone, by setting up a telephone call and then transferring the line to a teleprinter. As the need for the service grew in business the need for a separate telex network became apparent. Initially the telex networks were switched via manual switchboards, but as they were exclusive to business use the networks were quickly converted to automatic working in the late 1950s.

9.2 Characteristics of telex

Telex differs from telephony in that it carries the written rather than spoken communication and is almost exclusively used in the business world. A key element of telex communication is the production of a local record, exactly duplicating the message sent to and received at the distant end. Further, telex can be operated with the distant end completely unattended, which makes it ideal for international working where businesses operate in differing time zones. As telex transmits the written word, then it also makes it ideal for communication between people of different languages, as time can be spent on translating the message and then formulating the reply. Since most countries that adopted telex also had a telephony network, they naturally used the telephony network as the basis for the

design of the telex network, which in turn led to a wide variety of signalling systems to communicate between telex machines and the network.

59.3 Telex signalling

To send the written word, a character set had to be produced and standardised on by all users of the telex system. As the teleprinter grew out of telegraphy and Morse code, then so did the telex character set. The Murray Code, unlike the Morse code, is composed in such a manner that all characters contain the same number of units and each unit takes exactly the same time to transmit. The unequal dot and dash of Morse code is replaced by equal duration 'mark' and 'space'. Each character requires 5 units giving 32 characters in total. The character set is extended by defining two shift characters, figures shift and letters shift.

This code makes up the basis of CCITT International Alphabet Number 2 which is fundamental to the operation of all telex machines (see Figure 59.1). As the telex service grew, the need for a more comprehensive character set was required, particularly when operating over high frequency radio circuits. The CCITT International Alphabet Number 5, with its 7 unit error detecting code and automatic retransmission to correct errors, was adopted for telex working and a translation defined between both character sets. In essence this meant that a TELEX machine sending in CCITT ITA 2 would be translated via a code conversion to CCITT ITA 5.

When a character is sent to line it is preceded with one start element followed by 5 information elements and then one stop element (see Figure 59.2). With the pulse durations shown in Figure 59.1, the telex operates at 50 bits per second.

A variety of line signalling systems exist for telex operation, using voltage and current signalling and mainly designed around the needs of electromagnetic systems, where the transmit and receive elements were contacts and electromagnets respectively. Later single channel voice frequency signalling was added to the telex

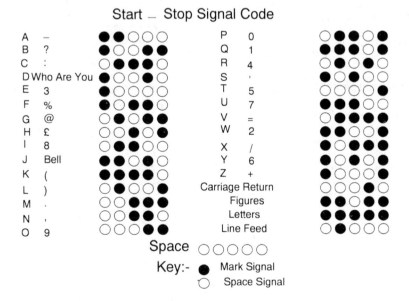

Figure 59.1 CCITT International alphabet number 2

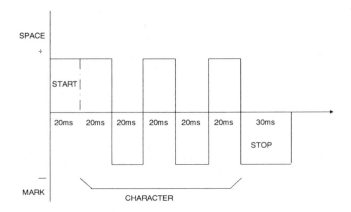

Figure 59.2 Start stop telex signal

system. There are therefore three major signalling systems in use throughout the world all with minor country differences depending on the type of telex exchange operating in the local country. These are double current signalling, single current signalling, single channel voice frequency signalling, as described in the following sections. In addition some telex machines are connected to private networks or point to point private wires using similar signalling systems. The mode of working is also important i.e. full duplex discrete send and receive paths and half duplex common send and receive path. Public telex networks are invariably half duplex in operation.

59.3.1 Single current signalling

This describes a system using the presence or absence of current to indicate a start or stop polarity on the line. Usually the transmitter and receiver are connected in series to obtain the local record. The current source is fed from the telex exchange to the machine, down the telex line. The polarity of the current can change during signalling as well as being at an intermediate level. Single current operation normally works from a 120 volt exchange feed. (Figure 59.3)

59.3.2 Double current signalling

This describes a system using voltage/currents of equal magnitude but opposite polarity, to indicate start or stop information on the line. The system generally has discrete send and receive paths with a common return and is inherently full duplex in operation. However for normal telex use the local record is generated by linking the

transmitter to the receive path in the machine and hence making the system effectively half duplex. Telex machines operate at the following voltages and currents at 20mA, 40mA, and 60mA Line currents for negative mark or positive space: (Figure 59.4)

1. 80-0-80 Volts.
2. 60-0-60 Volts.
3. 48-0-48 Volts.

59.3.3 Single channel voice frequency signalling

Single channel voice frequency signalling (SCVF) was adopted by CCITT R.20 to improve the telex network for the following reasons

1. To reduce the incidence of single or double current high level signals, inducing noise in adjacent cable pairs.
2. To reduce the power consumption of the telex exchange.
3. To enable connections to be made between telex machines over non metallic circuits.
4. To achieve full duplex transmission using relatively inexpensive CCITT V21 modems over 2 wire circuits.

The method of signalling is based on CCITT V21 with the following frequency allocations:

1. Telex exchange to telex machine, Space 0 = 1180 Hz; Mark = 980 Hz.
2. Telex machine to telex exchange, Space 0 = 1850 Hz; Mark = 1650 Hz.

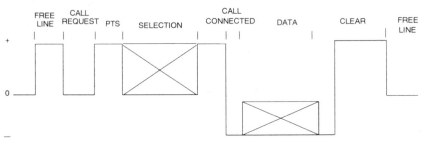

Figure 59.3 Single current call progression

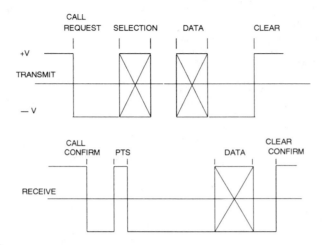

Figure 59.4   Double current call progression

Introduction of this signalling system also gave the opportunity for telex machines to operate at speeds up to 300 baud.

59.3.4   Type A and Type B signalling

Two further subdivisions of the signalling systems have evolved, corresponding to the different types of national network employed. It has been agreed that, where two countries with different types of signalling system are trying to make connection, the country setting up the call will convert its outgoing signals to that of the country receiving the call. Both types of signals convey the same information, the difference is in the detail of implementation. In general Type A signalling has been used where the telex keyboard has been used to send the address signals to the network and Type B signalling where the address signals were sent to the network with dial pulses, much like a telephone. Figure 59.5 shows the sequence of signals in each system.

59.4   Answerback

CCITT recommendation F.60 specifies that every telex machine will have a unique answerback code made up of a one or two letter country code, telex line number and abbreviated subscriber's name. Sending a 'who are you' when connected through to the distant end will trigger the distant telex to transmit the answerback code embedded in the distant telex to the sending telex. This technique enables telex users to confirm that they have reached the correct distant party, before message transmission can begin, so protecting the confidentiality of the message.

59.5   Telex protocol

As telex signalling is machine to machine operation and the distant end may be unattended, then a protocol has been established. Sev-

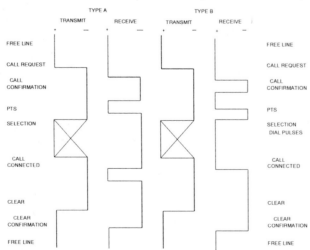

Figure 59.5   Type A and B signalling

eral exist but the ones given in Table 59.1 are generally internationally understood. All telex messages should commence with the sender's answerback so that the distant end can easily find the caller. The sequence of setting up a call on the telex network is seizing the line, receiving call confirmation and proceed to select indication from the telex network. The telex terminal then transmits the address information and if the call set up is successful the distant machine will automatically transmit to the caller the answerback code indicating it is ready to accept the message. If the call is unsuccessful for any reason the failure will be indicated by a service code of up to 3 letters transmitted from the telex network to the originating machine and printed out on the local record of the telex message.

The telex network has facilities for testing the telex lines and can detect if a machine has its power disconnected or the line is out of order, and then send the corresponding service message from the network to the originating machine.

59.6   Telex terminals

Modern telex terminals are highly sophisticated pieces of equipment built around the principles of the personal computer. They comprise a microprocessor, disk drive, keyboard, VDU, and heavy duty printer with paper roll holder. These machines are still required to interwork with the older electromechanical machines, or paper tape transmitters or receivers, that exist on the telex networks. The modern telex terminal has in addition the ability to communicate with the telex network word processing software, to enable the telex operator to prepare messages, edit, store and finally transmit the messages. This makes the telex terminal a very powerful communication tool for business use.

59.7   References

Barton, R.W. (1968) *Telex*, Pitman.
Renton, R. (1974) *The international telex service*, Pitman.

Table 59.1   Telex protocol (* indicates some of the typical service codes)

Code	Meaning
* ABS	Absent subscriber; power switched off the machine
BK	I cut off (break the line)
CFM	Please confirm or I confirm
COL	Collation
CRV	Do you receive / I receive
* DER	Out of order
DF	You are in communication with the called party
GA	You may transmit
* INF	Subscriber temporarily unavailable; call information service
JFE	Office closed because of holiday
MNS	Minutes
* MOM	Wait for reply
MUT	Mutilated
* NA	Number not accessible
* NC	No circuits; trunks busy
* NCH	Number changed
* NP	Called party ceased or spare line
NR	Indicate your called number
* OCC	Subscriber busy
OK	Agree
Tor5	Stop the transmission
PPR	Paper
R	Received
RAP	I will call again
SSSS	Here ready for data transmission
SVP	Please
TAX	What is the charge?
TEST MSG	Please send test message
THRU	You are in communication with a telex position
IPR	Teleprinter
W	Words
WRU	Who are you?
+	Finished
+?	I have finished, do you wish to transmit?

60

Facsimile transmission

L M Davis
NEC (UK) Ltd

Contents

60.1 Introduction

Facsimile, or fax, as it is known for short, is the technique for transmitting a copy of an original page or document to a remote location. It is not taken in the original full sense of an exact copy or reproduction but is a scanned and reproduced copy. The received copy is usually desired as a crisp, clean, good contrast document regardless of the original state, a requirement usually met by modern equipment.

The initial invention was by Alexander Bain in 1843 using a pendulum scanner which made contact with characters of raised metal type. The current flowing was passed, by the pendulum in synchronisation at the receiver, through damp chemically impregnated paper which then discoloured. This invention operated on telegraph wires complementary to Morse and predating the telephone.

One of the early uses of facsimile commercially was for the transmission of photographs for newspapers. In this case it was not just to mark the paper or not, but to mark with a density similar to the original photograph. These were dedicated users with skilled operators, at a time when almost any effort was justified to obtain pictures, not to be compared with today's operation.

Technical problems such as synchronisation, detection of the image at the transmitter and exposure at the recorder, amplification and the transmission by radio and telephone line, were solved step by step.

In parallel with these solutions the search continued for an ideal recording medium with the advantages/disadvantages of photographic, electrolytic, carbon, wax coated, electrostatic, thermal and now plain paper recording, being tested in products and voted on by the users.

Throughout these equipment designs a continuous compromise was necessary concerning resolution and transmission time. The results had to be good but not too good because speed was always of the essence.

Facsimile development, like all communication evolutions, wanted higher bandwidth on existing circuits or faster circuits at the same cost. It may not be too high a claim to make that facsimile developments have pressed network use to its highest efficiency, often exceeding the expectations of the network providers.

The development of weather map transmission equipment from the mid 1940s allowed meteorologists access to International charts, compiled in National Centres, so they could make their own local forecasts. A clear case for the immediate distribution of information in the format preferred by the user. Yesterday's weather forecast is not of much value.

In the mid 1950s page facsimile units for the transmission of whole newspaper pages started to become available. These large format machines, with high resolution to preserve the half tone dot structure, are used to transmit the page layouts for remote printing prior to local distribution. With printing deadlines paramount, high scanning rates and wideband networks encouraged facsimile development and manufacturing teams to keep pressing at the then known limits.

In the years before 1980 (when the CCITT G3 Recommendations were published) there were really only specialist applications for facsimile. Apart from those mentioned there were uses by government, military, police, for telegrams, colour transmissions received as separations and as colour prints, cloud photograph receptions from weather satellites, etc. Many of these applications had different standards and formats, as demanded by the application, and was acceptable since interworking was not necessary.

For document facsimile a different approach was necessary. Interoperation had been the desired aim since 1968 when Group 1 was standardised. No one manufacturer expected to supply the whole requirement and it was expected that business facsimile use, like the telephone, could be to new destinations as yet unknown.

The growth in G3 machines after 1980 was due to the right combination of features:

1. Ease of operation.
2. Adequate quality, convenient size and compatibility with the working environment.
3. Ability to transmit the documents already available in the office.
4. Reasonable operating costs, both line and consumables.
5. Reliable operation.
6. Growing business base.

G3 equipment is stand alone and easy to connect to telephone line and to the power source. Its growth in use has been due to the application of practical CCITT recommendations which reflect the technological and manufacturing possibilities. Coupled with this was the development and availablility of high sensitivity thermal paper, which ensured the realistic equipment purchase price and operating costs.

60.2 Facsimile types

Excluding the document facsimile equipment, all other types perform specialist functions and are exclusively separate transmit and receive units, for transmission in one direction. Document facsimile types are almost exclusively transceivers.

Table 60.1 summarises the characteristics of the different types of facsimile equipment.

60.2.1 Photofax equipment

It is used for the transmission of full tone photographs of size normally less than A4. Often the received picture is printed on photographic paper. The important requirements are not image size but correct aspect ratio, which is preserved by using the same index of co-operation.

Some scanners are designed to transmit colour separations from 35mm colour negatives using sequential transmission. Photofax equipment may be used, one transmitter to one receiver for example for sending news photographs from field locations, or one transmitter broadcasting on a wirephoto distribution network to many receivers. The transmission is simplex; there is no equipment confirmation of reception.

Analogue transmission is used and may be by PSTN, speech band private circuit, high frequency (h.f.) or long wave radio. There are several higher speed proprietary standards for equipment on broadcast distribution networks. Received image may be taken into an editorial workstation for cropping, manipulation and onward processing before printing.

Moves towards a digital standard for compressed images progresses slowly, relying on the CCITT/ISO JPEG work. Interworking may be possible at the application layer, but there seems no agreement on the communication layers at present.

Indications are that compression around 1 bit/picture element (8:1) could be achieved for monochrome images.

Table 60.1 Comparison of facsimile terminal types:
[1]Continuous grey scale response. [2]Analogue in scanning direction. [3]Continuous but limited grey scale. [4]Includes various grey scale and compression options

Type and standard	Page size (mm)	Nominal resolution (lines/mm)	Index of co-operation	Transmission time
Photofax[1] CCITT T.1	210 × 210 to 254 × 270	4 and 8 or 5 and 10 [2]	352 and 704	8 to 30 min
Weatherfax [3] WMO	450 × 560	4 and 2	576 and 288	4 to 36 min
Pagefax proprietary	Up to 450 × 625	15 to 100 [2]	not specified (1600 upwards)	1 to 3 min
Mobilefax[3] proprietary	108 × 150+	4 [2]	132	1 min
Military[4] NATO Stanag 5000	215 × 297	4 and 8	not specified (264/528)	20 sec to 20 min

60.2.2 Weatherfax equipment

These equipments are usually operated on private circuits or radio networks, on a simplex broadcast basis. The analogue transmission involved limits transmission speed and this method of operation is being superseded by point to multipoint computer data transfer. Providing the raw data to the local processor allows action replays of changing conditions, which are not easily appreciated from the printed meteorological charts. The existing network base continues in operation supplementing the data network.

60.2.3 Pagefax equipment

In this area there are no standards, the equipment being tailored to suit individual newspaper requirements. Compression and transmission characteristics, reproduction ratio, and image processing are all selected to suit production requirements in the remote printing of the full newspaper pages.

The savings in transportation costs and time, by using this equipment, funds sophisticated high speed transmission developments, including the transmission of colour separation with sequential receptions on the same receive mechanism.

60.2.4 Mobile equipment

There have been several attempts at mobile facsimile, some using narrow format (100cm) machines. The most popular method was to split the radio speech channel to keep the mobile units in speech contact during facsimile operation, normally transmitting in the direction towards the mobile terminal. These units were costly for their mobile environment and suffered as a result of needing specialised radio equipment.

With the use of the TACS cellular radio system normal G3 equipment can operate when a telephone type interface is available. The Cellular Line Interface connection can be sophisticated and allows automatic answering and call origination by the G3 machine. Calls made between the mobile and normal PSTN connections provide access to the large G3 installed base.

Opinions differ about operations above 4.8kbit/s. Some believe in operating as fast as possible, while the connection is good, whilst others prefer to rely on the improved signal/noise performance at lower modem rates. Most opinions however recommend the use of CCITT ECM.

The question of facsimile use on GSM is another matter because the system codes the voice and there is no synchronous transparent channel available for facsimile. The topic is well studied but no clear proposal has emerged.

60.2.5 Government and military equipment

Similar requirements exist for the transmission of documents, maps, drawings, photographs etc. as in other market segments. One major difference is that for the transmission of documents classified for national security, additional high performance data encryption equipment is required. Further, to avoid plain language signals from the fax equipment itself being intercepted, and to avoid compromising the encryption key generator codes, significant precautions must be taken in equipment design to reduce the relevant radiated and conductive electromagnetic emissions. These security requirements are not normally published.

60.2.5.1 *Strategic requirements*

These machines normally operate in regular office environments and apart from interoperational requirements for secure fax or tactical machines, communication can usually be met by standard CCITT G3 models.

60.2.5.2 *Tactical requirements*

Machines for this use include military battlefield equipment to operate under inhospitable environmental conditions, fast, reliably and securely. Standards are desirable to ensure interoperation between allies of different national forces.

Typical features of the NATO standard are:

1. Up to 16 grey shades for photographs.
2. G3 standard and fine resolution equivalents.
3. Broadcast and duplex network operations.
4. G3 MH compression, also uncompressed and BCH forward error correction.

To be acceptable this equipment should be lightweight, easy to operate in arduous conditions and capable of various communication modes, including high speed burst mode to avoid radio location when necessary.

Table 60.2 Document facsimile types

	Network			
	Public telephone (analogue)		Public data (digital)	
CCITT Group/ recommendation	G1/T.2	G2/T.3	G3/T.4/T.30	G4 Class 1/T.563
Transmission time	6 min (4 min option)	3 min	Around 30 sec (at 9.6kbit/s)	Around 5 sec (at 64kbit/s)
Data rate	Analogue		14.4–2.4kbit/s	64–2.4kbit/s
Modulation	FM	AM/VSB (vestige of upper sideband)	V.17/V.29/V.27 ter	None (line driver and coder to suit network)
White	1300Hz (US 1500Hz)	Maximum carrier reversing phase		
Black	2100Hz (US 2400Hz)	26dB below white		
Synchronisation	±10 parts in 10^6	±5 parts in 10^6	Derived from data rate and sequence	
Index of co-operation	264 (176 option)	264	Not specified (264/528 option)	Not specified (549)
Scan line frequency	3Hz	6Hz	Not specified (around 100Hz)	Not specified (around 600Hz)
Horizontal resolution	Not applicable		1728 pels/215mm (8.04 pels/mm)	200 pels/25.4mm (option 240/300/400)
Scan line length	215mm		215/255/303mm	219/260/308mm
Vertical resolution	3.85 lines/mm (2.57 opt)	3.85 lines/mm	3.85 lines/mm (7.7 lines/mm option)	Square with horizontal
Data compression encoding	None		One dimensional MH 2 dim MR & MMR Uncompressed	2 dimensional MMR Uncompressed

60.3 CCITT document facsimile equipment

This is principally for the transmission of business and commercial papers, letters, drawings and general office documentation around A4 size (210mm x 297mm). The pages are often black or dark coloured text or handwritten characters on white or pastel backgrounds, although machines handle a wide range of original documents.

CCITT has produced and continues to develop recommendations for operation on the public telephone and public data networks, which are summarised in Table 60.2.

60.4 G3 facsimile equipment

World-wide there are approaching 20 million (1991) compatible facsimile transceivers capable of interoperation using the Public Switched Telephone Network. Designs and implementations vary but the most popular scanning method is by CCD (charge coupled device) and printing by thermal head on heat sensitive paper.

Figure 60.1 shows a block diagram of a G3 machine. Discrete LSI is often used for online signal processing, to ensure a manageable load for the main CPU which takes care of the user interface, dialling functions, mechanism control housekeeping and reporting.

The CCITT G3 recommendations include a number of options, for example fine resolution, MR coding, V29 modem, ECM. For these to be used they must be available in both send and receive machines and are usually negotiated automatically.

60.4.1 Scanner

In a typical CCD scanner a section of the original is illuminated by a fluorescent or cold cathode tube. The facsimile line to be scanned is focused onto a 1728 (A4 width) or 2048 (B4) element CCD single line image sensor. The independent elements are discharged by radiated light from the original which is focused on to them. After a suitable time (1ms) the elements are recharged sequentially. By monitoring the current for this recharge the video signal amplitude is obtained. The signal is then processed to allow for background and level variations, and to preserve character size, then converted to binary levels for normal transmission, as a black/white image. It may be converted to amplitude bits for processing for pseudo half tone/grey scale transmission. The original is then advanced 1/3.85mm or 1/7.7mm for the next line to be scanned. If the line transmission buffers are full the scanning may then wait until further data is required.

A second popular method of scanning uses CIS (Contact Image Sensor). This is a single line sensor assembly fitted close to the paper at the document scanning point. It requires an array the full width of the paper, but it saves the space taken up by the CCD optical path. The copy is illuminated by LEDs (Light Emitting Diodes) within the unit and the radiated light from the area being

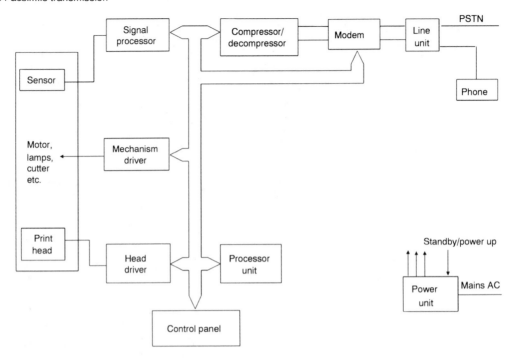

Figure 60.1 Simplified G3 block diagram

scanned is collected by a multiple lens assembly and focused on to the image sensor array. If the sensors are brought almost into contact with the paper, the multiple lens is not required and in this case there are holes in the sensor array to allow the LED illumination from behind.

The detection of black or white at a particular picture element depends on the density and the position of the edge of the image with reference to the sensor element. The resolution in G3 is adequate to preserve character shape but there is almost always a difference between the raster images of identical characters even when adjacent.

To provide facsimile copy with a similar appearance to computer generated printer output, the resolution needs to be greater by about 30%. This has led to resolution incompatibility problems for facsimile and computer interoperation.

60.4.2 Data compression

An A4 scanned page of 297mm at 3.85 lines/mm is 1144 facsimile lines. This together with 1728 elements per line gives 1976832 elements per page, which if sent uncompressed to line at 9.6kbit/s would take 206 seconds, a time which can be significantly reduced by using run length coding.

60.4.2.1   *Modified Huffman*

With data compression a code is transmitted to represent the number of black or white bits to be sent, rather than transmitting the 1 or 0 for the appropriate scanning time. The basic G3 compression is Modified Huffman (MH) where, in a limited code table, the most frequent run lengths are represented by the shortest length codes. Because of the different distributions of black run lengths and white

run lengths in typical documents, different code tables and make up codes for the runs longer than 63 elements are used. This is illustrated in Figure 60.2 and Table 60.3, where the compression is 1728:132 or 13:1 for this particular line.

Tables 60.4 and 60.5 provides extracts from Modified Huffman code tables.

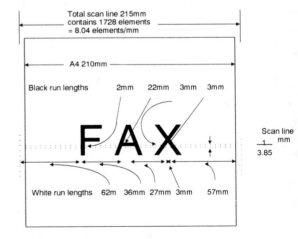

Figure 60.2 G3 resolution and Modified Huffman coding. (See Table 60.2)

Table 60.3 G3 resolution and Modified Huffman Coding. (See Figure 60.2)

Run length mm	No. of pels	Make up code	Terminating code	No. of bits
W62	498	01100100	01010011	16
B2	16	—	0000010111	10
W36	289	0110111	00010010	15
B22	177	000011001000	000001100101	24
W27	217	010111	0101011	13
B3	24	—	00000010111	11
W3	24	—	0101000	7
B3	24	—	00000010111	11
W57	459	01100100	01000	13
215	1728			120
End of line		000000000001		12
			Total bits	132

Table 60.4 Extract from Modified Huffman code table (terminating codes)

White run length	Code word	Black run length	Code word
0	00110101	0	0000110111
1	000111	1	010
2	0111	2	11
3	1000	3	10
4	1011	4	011
5	1100	5	0011
6	1110	6	0010
7	1111	7	00011
8	10011	8	000101
9	10100	9	000100
10	00111	10	0000100
11	01000	11	0000101
12	001000	12	0000111
13	000011	13	00000100
14	110100	14	00000111
15	110101	15	000011000
16	101010	16	0000010111
17	101011	17	0000011000
18	0100111	18	0000001000
19	0001100	19	00001100111
20	0001000	20	00001101000
21	0010111	21	00001101100
22	0000011	22	00000110111
23	0000100	23	00000101000
24	0101000	24	00000010111
25	0101011	25	00000011000
26	0010011	26	000011001010
27	0100100	27	000011001011
.	.	.	.
.	.	.	.
.	.	.	.
60	01001011	60	000000101100
61	00110010	61	000001011010
62	00110011	62	000001100110
63	00110100	63	000001100111

An end of line code is added to provide synchronisation and allow the receiver to check that the decoded line is 1728 elements. Typically a compression of about 7:1 can be obtained.

60.4.2.2 Modified READ

CCITT allows two optional 2 dimensional coding schemes. These are both RElative ADdress or READ techniques where the new line to be coded is based on the previous line. The first CCITT option of the modified version of READ (MR) was standardised before ECM (error correction mode) was available. It had to operate in the presence of network errors and ensure that the remainder of the data on the page could be decoded. To provide for this only one two dimensional line was permitted to follow the one dimensional MH line in standard resolution, and 3 lines were permitted in fine resolution. Inclusion of this redundant data in an MH line allows decoder recovery.

Figure 60.3 and Table 60.6 illustrate the Modified READ coding technique.

A pair of points either between reference and coding lines or on one or other of the lines is recognised and the appropriate code transmitted with the addition of an MH code for longer runs.

MR coding is successful because of the high degree of correlation between facsimile lines in documents and typically a compression of about 10:1 can be obtained.

60.4.2.3 Modified Modified READ

When the G3 ECM option is used the reference lines in MR are redundant and CCITT permit the Modified Modified READ (MMR) option. In this case the line before the first line of the page is assumed white and all subsequent lines are referenced to their previous line. This coding is the same as T.6 used in G4 and can give compressions of the order of 14:1.

MMR is particularly suited to higher resolutions where the correlation between lines increases. For twice the vertical resolution with MH the number of bits to be transmitted doubles but with MMR the increase reduces to around 1.4:1.

Table 60.5 Extract from Modified Huffman code table (make up code)

White run lengths	Code word	Black run lengths	Code word
64	11011	64	0000001111
128	10010	128	000011001000
192	010111	192	000011001001,
256	0110111	256	000001011011
.	.	.	.
.	.	.	.
.	.	.	.
1600	010011010	1600	0000001011011
1664	011000	1664	0000001100100
1728	010011011	1728	0000001100101
EOL	000000000001	EOL	000000000001

Table 60.6 Modified READ coding. (See Figure 60.3)

Mode	Points	Use	Code
Vertical (VO)(V$_L$)(V$_R$)	T$_1$ & T$_2$ T$_{3L}$ & T$_{3R}$	Up to ±3 changing elements offset coded otherwise use horizontal	7 code words allocated (1 to 7 bits)
Pass (P)	T$_4$ & T$_5$	When no accompanying changes on coding line	Single code allocated (0001)
Horizontal (H)	T$_6$ & T$_7$	When no reference for the change on coding line	Single identifying code (001) followed by normal MH black and white run pair

60.4.3 Modulation and demodulation

Digital signals from the data compression encoder are unsuitable for direct transmission to the telephone network. For 9.6kbit/s the necessary transmission frequencies extend from d.c. to 4800Hz, too wide for the telephone networks nominal bandwidth of 300Hz to 3000Hz. For transmission the digital signals are transformed by the modem to analogue voice band signals which can tolerate the frequency shift, noise, amplitude and group delay variation with frequency, and also the echo and phase jitter of the international telephone network. G3 line signals are analogue. They vary in amplitude as a speech signal, but they are generated from digital signals and may be completely and accurately recovered providing line conditions permit.

60.4.3.1 G3 signal transmission

G3 is a half duplex transmission which uses 2 types of modulation/demodulation; the first of 300bit/s for the T.30 protocol and handshaking between terminals. This 300bit/s V.21 modem is a robust FSK transmission. It is easily implemented and does not require training. It is used for the relatively low volume of data establishing machine parameters and providing feedback from receiver to transmitter.

The second is the high speed modem used for the compressed image data transfer. In G3 there is a basic V.27 mode of 4.8kbit/s with 2.4kbit/s fallback where the lines are poor, and optional modes up to 9.6kbit/s and up to 14.4kbit/s for use where terminals and networks permit. It is generally acknowledged that over 80% of transmissions used these higher rates.

Table 60.7 compares the G3 modulation methods, where QAM refers to quadrature amplitude modulation.

60.4.3.2 Modem operation

The data rate modem takes a number of bits of the incoming data (e.g. 4 bits for V.29 9.6kbit/s), and for the symbol time (1/2400 second for V.29 9.6kbit/s) generates the relevant modulation condition for these bits (16 conditions for V.29 9.6kbit/s).

The modulation condition may be generated by a controlled combination of sine and cosine modulated carriers which are then filtered before application to the network to limit damaging out of band signals. The receiving modem tracks the carrier to correct for network frequency shift and recovers the symbol timing. It then studies the signal during this symbol period to decide which of the possible states the received signal most closely matches and decodes that state to provide the digital bit stream.

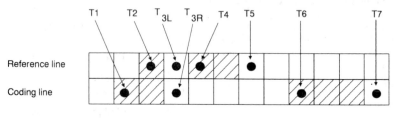

Figure 60.3 Modified READ coding. (See Table 60.6)

Table 60.7 Comparison of G3 modulation methods

	Bit rate (kbit/s)	Carrier (Hz)	Modulation	Baud rate (symbols/s)	Bits/symbol	States in constellation
V.21 channel 2	0.3	1750	FM ±100Hz	300	1	
V.27 ter	2.4	1800	QAM	1200	2	4
	4.8			1600	3	8
V.29	7.2	1700	QAM	2400	3	8
	9.6				4	16
V.17	7.2	1800	QAM (Trellis coded)	2400	4	16
	9.6				5	32
	12				6	64
	14.4				7	128

To establish the symbol timing, and allow the receive modem to set equaliser conditions to compensate for the network impairments, an initial training signal is sent from the transmit modem. In G3 this followed by a 1.5s period all '0' TCF, so that the machine can decide if it can correctly receive at this rate. If not the 300bit/s handshake reply initiates a new training sequence, which the transmitter may choose to send at a lower rate. With ECM it is often found desirable to operate at the higher data rates, accepting that a limited number of errors which can be rapidly corrected may provide an overall increase in transmission efficiency.

60.4.3.3 14.4kbit/s option

The CCITT option at 14.4kbit/s uses V.17 TCM (Trellis Coded Modulation). The symbol rate is the same as V.29 9.6kbit/s which appears optimum for the telephone network, but the bits per symbol increase not to 6 as expected but to 7 to allow FEC (Forward Error Correction) data to be included. The 7th bit, bringing the number of states to be decoded at the receiver to 128, is generated from 2 of the data bits in each symbol interval. This introduced redundancy means that only certain decoded sequences are valid. The receiver knows from the recent signal history when an unlikely condition occurs and can make an educated guess at the correct data. It is this difference in operation which gives a 3dB signal/noise improvement in Gaussian noise tests, and noticeable end to end improvement over QAM in actual use.

60.4.4 Error correction mode

In CCITT ECM the transmitted signal is separated into HDLC frames so that on receive the FCS bytes allow the data accuracy to be checked. G3 transmission is half duplex and when the transmission stops the receiver replies giving the condition for each of the frames. The transmitter then selectively repeats the frames which the receiver advised were in error.

Figure 60.4 shows the ECM transmitted frame structure. Each frame contains 256 octets of image plus its frame number. A block can have up to 256 frames, equivalent to around 0.5Mbits of data, sufficient for most facsimile pages. In this case, if there are no

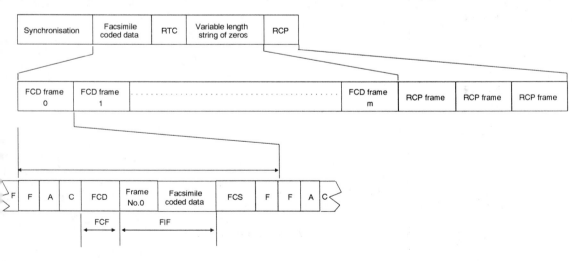

Figure 60.4 ECM transmitted frame structure

errors, there are no additional turn rounds above a standard G3 transmissions.

If the pages are of greater data content than 0.5Mbit (about 50s at 9.6kbit/s) a partial page is generated at 256 frames. This partial page is corrected before proceeding with the next block. Following the image transmission a PPS is sent at 300bit/s to tell the receiver the page and block number and the actual number of frames in that block, for checking and recovery purposes.

60.4.4.1   ECM receiver operation

The receiver knows by the FCS which frames are correctly received. Often, in a thermal paper receiver, the machine will print the copy as received until such time as an error is recognised. It then stops with the data going to memory until corrected data is available. In most practical cases this procedure, and the availability in the receiver of sufficient memory for the next page/partial page, avoids waiting between pages due to printer unavailability.

With the page/partial page correctly received the receiver replies with MCF and the transmitter continues with the next data.

Figure 60.5 shows ECM operation with errors. If errors are detected the receiver sends PPR which has an information field of 256 bits, one for each frame of the transmitted block. The receiver sets each bit of PPR to 'O' for a correctly received frame and waits for the transmitter to selectively repeat the unacceptable frames. Pages/partial pages are often corrected with a single retransmission

but the cycle is repeated for the then outstanding error frames. When the receiver has all frames correct it finishes printing the page and returns MCF for the next block to follow.

60.4.4.2   ECM performance

The overhead for G3 ECM is in the transmit direction and approximately 5% when there are no errors. Normally in non-ECM facsimile transmission a limited number of errors are tolerated due to the image redundancy remaining in the MH and MR coding. The reception at the transmitter of MCF confirms that the document has been satisfactorily received but not necessarily that it is free of errors.

There are 2 main user advantages with ECM:

1.   The sender is 100% confident that acknowledged pages are complete and received free of error.
2.   That as errors are efficiently corrected transmission time (and cost) can be reduced by using higher transmission rates together with MMR coding.

The transmitter has the opportunity from studying the pattern of errors in PPR to reduce the frame size to 64 octets or to change the data rate to maximise throughput. The selective retransmission and large window with minimum turnarounds providing efficient long haul communication even including 3 satellite links.

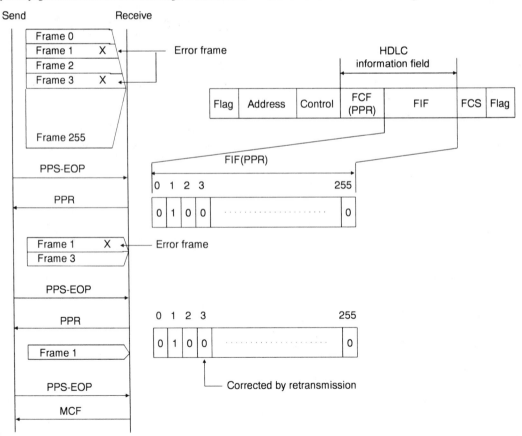

Figure 60.5   ECM operation with errors

0.4.5   Printer

here are several methods of printing the facsimile image including
ectrophotographic (laser or LED), ink jet, thermal transfer and, the
ost popular, recording on thermal paper.

60.4.5.1   *Thermal printers*

eat sensitive paper is passed over a single line thermal head having
heater element for each of the 1728 (A4) picture elements.

A typical method of operation in a thermal printer is at the start of
ception to step the paper back from its normal guillotine or tear
f position, so that the start of the page is under the thermal head.
avoid having a driver for each element the head may be electri-
lly divided into sections for printing in a matrix. The data is
tched into a section and printer in 1 to 2.5ms. When all sections of
e line are printed the paper is either advanced 1/3.85mm for a
andard line or 1/7.7mm for a fineline.

A standard line may be achieved by printing 2 identical fine
solutions lines. The print energy required is about 1/4mJ per black
t, at a temperature on the paper of around 90°C. Print times of
tween 5ms and 20ms per line are typical, with automatic compen-
ation for ambient and head temperature by varying the supply
oltage or the print pulse time.

60.4.5.2   *Plain paper printers*

number of technologies are available to produce the printed image
n plain, office type paper. The advantages of this is that copies feel
ke other office documents and are generally archival.

Thermal Transfer

he paper is usually in roll form to simplify machine handling. It
oves through the machine with, and generally at the same rate, as
thermal transfer film. The thermal head prints in a similar way to
ormal thermal paper printing and the film is a donor, transferring
s image to the plain paper. The thermal transfer film, collected on
take up roll, is used at the same rate as the paper and retains a
egative image which may need careful handling for security rea-
ons.

The facsimile printer is otherwise identical to a thermal paper
rinter.

Electrophotographic

A well established technology in office printers uses either a laser
r an LED array to discharge a photoconductive drum for offset
rinting. The latent image on the drum is developed by the attraction
f charged normally black toner powder. This image is transferred
o a cut sheet and fixed by the combination of heat and pressure at
he output rollers.

The additional hardware required for a facsimile machine is bulky,
xpensive and significantly increases the size and cost. The paper,
ormal copier type paper, is much cheaper than thermal paper but
when allowing for toner, drum replacement and other consumables
this saving is much reduced.

Ink jet

Ink is a simple way to print on plain paper. The problem has been to
keep the ink fluid and flowing until printed and then for it to dry
rapidly. This technique is being used in facsimile equipment with a
replaceable bubble jet ink cartridge. The cartridge is moved across
the paper to print several facsimile lines (typically 16 fine mode
lines) at once and the ink bubbled appropriately through a series of
apertures, one for each facsimile line. The hardware is not complicated or bulky and a range of low cost plain paper machines may
emerge for use at about 30 seconds for an A4 page.

60.4.6   G3 handshake protocol

CCITT G3 uses signals generated in an HDLC frame structure
exchanged in half duplex mode. A preamble of a series of flags,
starting each transmission ensures that valuable data is preserved
when truncation occurs at echo suppressor turnaround. The flag
octet 01111110 is a unique signal that is preserved by a '10' insertion
after a fifth '1' occurring in the data. A 2-byte FCS is used to allow
the receiver to check data validity.

Figure 60.6 gives the T.30 G3 handshake signal format showing
DIS.

60.4.6.1   *G3 handshake basic operation*

This is usually started by a call originated from the transmit machine. However, the significant signal flow is initiated when the
receiver answers the ringing current by sending a DIS to indicate its
capabilities. These includes the paper size, coding schemes and
modem rates it has available.

The transmit machine selects appropriate conditions in conjunction with document size and operator selections, commands the
receiver using DCS and sends the modem training signal and TCF
at the high speed data rate.

The receiver attempts to train, checks the performance on TCF
and replies either CFR or FTT. The transmitter then either starts the
image transmission or sends DCS and training again.

Figure 60.7 shows a typical G3 signal flow chart, and Table 60.8
gives popular G3 handshake signals.

When the transmitter indicates the end of page the receiver replies
with MCF for a correctly received page, or one of the retrain signals
indicating that it requires retraining for any further pages.

If the transmitter signalled MPS, advising more pages to be sent,
it continues with the following pages, finishing with EOP and DCN
in response to MCF before releasing the connection.

60.4.6.2   *G3 machine identification*

Identification of terminals is a useful feature in G3 equipment with
several popular methods implemented.

CCITT CSI/CIG/TSI signals

These are optional T.30 signals completely defined to allow interoperation between different manufacturers' machines. They are
intended by CCITT to contain a '+' sign followed by up to 20
numeric digits giving the subscriber's international telephone number. In most implementations the user can insert/update the number
freely. The way the machine receiving the number uses it varies with
manufacturer; it may be reported on the machine display, listed in
an activity report or printed by the receive machine on the received
copy.

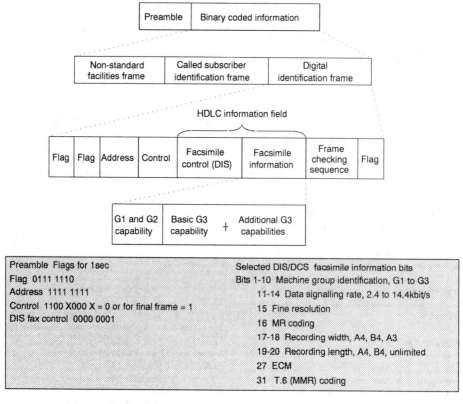

Figure 60.6 T.30 G3 handshake signal format showing DIS

Messages on the transmitted facsimile page

Numeric, alphanumeric or graphical messages held in a transmit memory and sent as part of the facsimile transmission. They are not sent in T.30 format. Because they are facsimile encoded the receive machine remains ignorant of the content and cannot record them in the reports.

The information may contain:

1. Document number, time and date of sending.
2. Sender's name or TSI.
3. Urgent or priority comment.

Although the implementation may be proprietary to the manufacture it is printed on all receivers because it is included in the facsimile message. It is often transmitted outside the regular A4 page increasing the received page length.

CCITT NSF signals

Under the non standard facilities procedure a manufacturer may implement any proprietary identification form desired. When transmitting to another machine of the same manufacturer it may include alpha as well as numeric characters. This can enable the name of the communicating machine to be shown on the display or recorded in the activity report. It is not recognised between machines of different manufacturers.

NSF covers a wide range of proprietary features but in the identification area it also allows the transmission of passwords for confidential operation.

Received copy with typical identification

In addition to the text at the top (date, time and sender identification) transmitted as part of the facsimile image, other information, compiled at the receiver from the transmitted TSI/NSS and from locally available information in the receiver, may be added.

The word 'END' is sometimes inserted at the bottom of the facsimile image to confirm that this is the last page of the document.

60.5   64kbit/s facsimile equipment

The availability of switched digital networks with 64kbit/s channels continues to increase with basic rate and primary rate ISDN. The I Series recommendations developed by CCITT have established international standards for 64kbit/s intercommunication.

The G3 transmissions use the voice speech band which, when converted to PCM digital signals for transmission within the public network, use the complete 64kbit/s channel. This means 9.6kbit/s or 14.4kbit/s maximum rate on a 64kbit/s channel.

Clearly where 64kbit/s digital access is available, as through the ISDN connection, a direct digital input at 64kbit/s machine data rate is desirable giving an improvement of four to six times in speed and

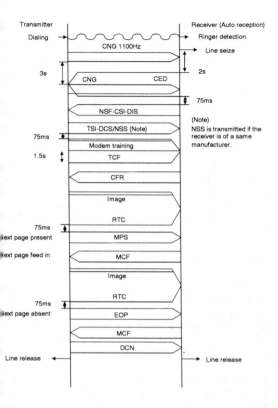

Figure 60.7 Typical G3 signal flow chart

Table 60.8 Popular G3 handshake signals

Abbreviation	Function
CED	Called station identification
CFR	Confirmation to receive
CIG	Calling subscriber identification
CNG	Calling tone
CSI	Called subscriber identification
DCN	Disconnect
DCS	Digital command signal
DIS	Digital identification signal
DTC	Digital transmit command
EOM	End of message
EOP	End of procedure
ERR	Response for end of retransmission
FCD	Facsimile coded date
FCF	Facsimile control field
FCS	Frame checking sequence
FIF	Facsimile information field
FTT	Failure to train
HDLC	High level data link control
MCF	Message confirmation
MPS	Multi-page signal
NSF	Non-standard facilities
NSS	Non-standard set-up
PPS	Partial page signal
PPR	Partial page request
RCP	Return to control for partial page
RNR	Receive not ready
RR	Receive ready
RTC	Return to control
RTN	Retrain negative
RTP	Retrain positive
TCF	Training check
TSI	Transmitting subscriber identification

reduction in transmission cost. To take advantage of this a 64kbit/s data rate facsimile machine is required.

60.5.1 G4 equipment

CCITT has produced recommendations for G4 digital equipment in 3 classes based on the ISO 7 layer model for interoperation with open systems communication standards.

Class 1 is for the transmission of facsimile documents only and is a higher performance equivalent to G3. Class 2 has the transmission capabilities of Class 1 and the receive capabilities of class 3. It is similar in operation to class 1 but can take advantage of the increased efficiency of character transmission where available.

Class 3 provides for the transmission of characters and facsimile data, either separately or combined in a mixed mode format. This is a more complex terminal giving the possibility of keyboard and scanner input with the document architecture to support interoperation with ISO hierarchical models.

The requirements of Classes 2 and 3 will continue to develop as necessary to track the evolution of document architecture standards. Class 1 machines are already being implemented to provide higher performance facsimile with direct digital access to the ISDN network, 3 seconds/page transmission and higher resolutions operation to 400 x 400 pels/inch.

60.5.2 64kbit/s G3 type equipment

With the tremendous growth in G3 an enhancement is being discussed in CCITT to provide a similar operation at the faster digital interface rate of 64kbit/s, to that recommended on the analogue network interface at between 14.4kbit/s and 2.4kbit/s.

This will simplify implementation and provide the user with current G3 facilities at the faster and more efficient digital interface rate. G3-64kbit/s is proposed as an option to the basic G3 mode which is essential for interworking with the existing G3 machine population. In this machine the basic G3 operation is likely to be provided on the I series port by the implementation of the equivalent of a codec converting the G3 modem signals to the ISDN speech equivalent.

60.6 G3 networks, switches, gateways and PC fax.

The success of G3 facsimile has encouraged the provision of additional equipment/facilities to enhance operation and provide cost savings. The communication interfaces are based on T.4 and T.30 recommendations and follow standard facsimile protocols. Where these units are provided by suppliers different from the machine suppliers, the NSF proprietary operation is often precluded. This can result in a loss of facilities and an increase in transmission time. It may also mean that because of simple interfaces used, MR, ECM, 14.4kbit/s CCITT options are not implemented and transmission efficiency is limited.

60.6.1 Managed network use

By the provision of store and forward units with multiline PSTN access, a network operator or value added supplier can relieve the user of major distribution tasks and free the user's machine for other work. With multiline access it is realistic to consider a regular broadcast transmission to 10000 recipients from a single originator transmission to the store. To some extent the network operator can schedule the traffic to suit network loading and therefore offer practical tariffs which could compensate for the delay in delivery and the subsequent confirmation report necessary.

60.6.2 Facsimile switches

The requirements of some major users include facsimile traffic control and costing, archival recording of all transferred facsimile messages and controlled distribution of centrally received incoming messages. By routing the facsimile traffic through an intelligent central switch, possibly associated with the company PBX, the required monitoring and control functions can be provided with cost and traffic reporting developed to suit the individual needs of the user. (Figure 60.8.)

One main area of concern for facsimile users is the onward distribution of documents received at central machines maybe located in the mail room. Onward distribution is often delayed waiting for the next mail round, and onward transmission by facsimile to the department in question is sometimes not felt desirable.

One solution being considered is that the facsimile switch can have a soft copy display of the facsimile message on a VDU. An operator would then display and readdress the document for onward transmission from memory. Clearly, for efficient operations, a suitable compromise must be made between the switch capital cost and the time required by the operator, to re-route the document.

60.6.3 Facsimile gateways

The transmission of facsimile documents and of electronic mail or computer generated text are usually kept separate. However the wide population of G3 machines has encouraged users on electronic mail or local area networks to request interoperation. This is usually achieved by fitting a gateway on the computer network to convert the information to the T.4 and T.30 facsimile format for onward transmission.

The problem is for incoming documents in the facsimile domain. These are virtually impossible to convert to the text environment and require onward transmission in a graphics mode with the high

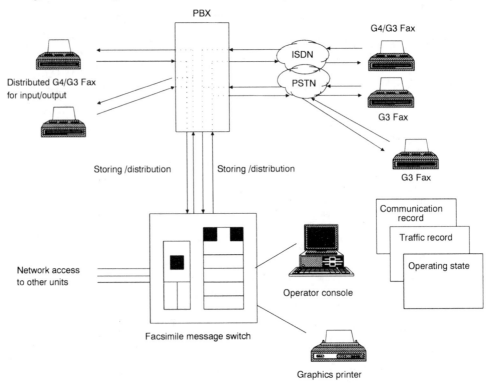

Figure 60.8 G3 fax switch block diagram

bandwidth and large storage capacity associated with raw image data. These facsimile documents are most conveniently printed out on a local facsimile unit and kept separate from the data system.

60.6.4 PC fax cards

The widespread availability of G3 machines and the expansion card provision in desktop personal computers, has encouraged the development of specialised fax cards. With the addition of a dedicated PSTN interface card and support software, it is possible to make facsimile transmissions directly from PC memory without the image being printed. The performance depends on the balance between PC software capability, for example speed of compression, and the processing and memory capability of the card itself.

User expectations that the simple operation of fax machines be available in PC fax are beginning to be met together with background operation of the PC in fax mode. However there are similar incoming document problem as for gateways:

1. Difficult to provide adequate soft copy memory.
2. Slow to print received pages.
3. Limitations of screen resolution or of whole page display.
4. Time to decode/display compressed image limits search mode.

One of the benefits of PC fax cards or fax gateways is their ability to send the equivalent of personalised mailshots by facsimile, a feature not normally available in the broadcast mode of facsimile transceivers which send identical documents to all destinations.

The fax modem fitted to these cards can also be used for PC to PC communication for file transfer over the PSTN. If the growth in this requirement continues, then discussions in CCITT are likely to provide an additional option within the G3 fax recommendations.

The convenience of communicating by facsimile can be extended to operation with the computer in the briefcase. Transmission directly from the keyboard (actually from memory) and soft copy reception without printing are easily possible with existing fax standards over the PSTN.

Customer requirements dominate facsimile developments and the increase in use of the G3 interface in non-fax products is expected to continue although the replacement of documents in the briefcase by facsimile files in the laptop/notebook PC seems remote.

60.7 Facsimile futures

The PSTN remains the major communication network for the foreseeable future with increasing opportunities on the ISDN. Facsimile terminals G3, G3-64kbit/s and G4 will continue to operate on these networks.

Facsimile transmission is particularly appropriate for the future because of the large compatible equipment base and because of the vast and continuing information base on paper and film.

Documents are required on paper for convenience, for availability (even in power failure) and for use when out of communication away from the office.

Development continues in CCITT with higher speed, higher resolution transmission and with high speed character and mixed mode functions.

The potential for communication with this ubiquitous terminal is hardly touched. Interfaces into the facsimile domain to use the proven reliable transmission method are increasing. The terminals provide reliable input/output devices into other applications and systems using the current CCITT recommendations. Continued growth in the number of terminals, including the domestic environment is expected.

60.8 Bibliography

CCITT (1989) *Blue Book Volume VII Fascicle VII.3*, International Telecommunication Union, Geneva, ISBN 92- 61-03611-2

Costigan, D.M. (1971) *The principles and practice of Facsimile Communication*, Philadelphia, Chilton.

Halton, Jones and Treece (1991) Facsimile — the essential image, *Br. Telecom Technol J.* **9**, (1), January.

McConnell, Bodson, Schaphorst (1992) *Fax*, 2nd. ed., Artech House, ISBN 0-89006-310-9.

Payton and Qureshi (1985) Trellis encoding, *Data Communications*, May.

Pugh, A. (1991) Facsimile Today, *Electronics & Communication Engineering Journal*, October.

Reardon, R.(Ed.) (1990) *Facsimile Networks for the 1990s*, Online Publications, ISBN 0-86353-131-8.

61

Telecommunication system measurements

Hugh Walker
BA (Cantab) MSc
Hewlett-Packard Ltd
(Sections 61.1–61.3)

Gary Law
BSc PhD
Andersen Consulting
(Section 61.4)

A C Keene
BSc CEng MIEE
Trend Communications Ltd
(Section 61.5)

J P Russell
Trend Communications Ltd
(Section 61.5)

David Green
Rohde & Schwarz
(Sections 61.6–61-11)

Contents

61.1 Digital circuit testing

The simplified block diagram (Figure 61.1) shows the connection from one end user to another via various network sections. Measurements will be used to characterise the overall end-to-end transmission performance of the system, known as the digital path. Measurements may also be made on individual network sections, and on the electrical parameters at network interfaces, including PCM codec measurements.

The types of measurement and the associated standards are shown in Table 61.1. Measurements, in common with other telecommunications standards, follow either the CCITT recommendations or the North American ANSI T1 standards. Note that many of these standards undergo continuous revision to include new technology and operating conditions. It is important to obtain the latest version of documentation from the appropriate standards organisation.

The following sections cover firstly interface measurements, and secondly transmission measurements, particularly error performance criteria.

61.2 Interface measurements

61.2.1 PCM measurements

PCM measurements characterise the analog to digital and digital to analog conversions that take place at the interface between an analog telephone line and the digital network. In order to provide the best signal to noise ratio and dynamic range within the digitised 64kbit/s channel, companding (compression and expansion) of signals is used.

This involves non-linear conversion between analog amplitude and digital code, which must be exactly matched by the conversion back to analog at the receive end. Measurements of this characterisitic can be made analog to analog (A-A), specified in CCITT recommendations G.712 and G.713, or as a half channel measure-

ment (A-D and D-A) as specified in G.714. Compliance with half channel specifications ensures interworking between PCM codecs.

Either noise or tone stimulus can be used, with levels at the digital interface being interpreted from the digital 8 bit codes present in the selected 64kbit/s timeslot. The companding algorithm is usually checked by a gain versus level plot (Figure 61.2), or quantising

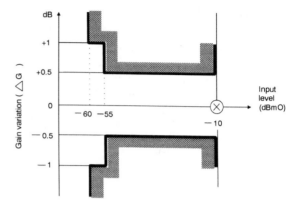

Figure 61.2 CCITT Recommendation G.712: Variation of gain with input level (nise)

distortion versus level (Figure 61.3). A typical set of PCM codec measurements is shown in Table 61.2.

61.2.2 Electrical interface specifications

Electrical interface specifications are usually measured during equipment design and manufacture to ensure compatible interconnection between network elements at a Network Node Interface (NNI) and User Network Interface (UNI). Equipment normally

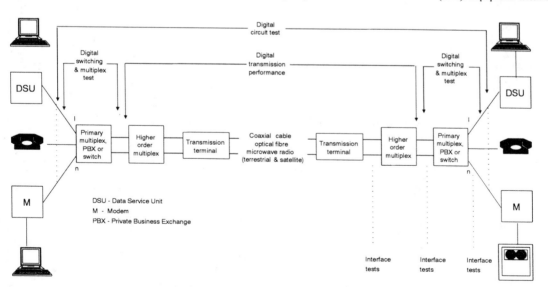

Figure 61.1 A telecommunications network

Table 61.1 Measurement and performance standards for digital transmission tests

Measurement type	International standards (CCITT)	North American standards (ANSI/Bellcore)	
Interface measurements	PCM Codec	G.712/713 (A-A) G.714 (A-D D-A) O.131-133 (measurement)	BSTR 43801 (TR-TSY-000499)
	Pulse shape	G.703, G.975 (SDH)	T1.403
	Clock frequency		T1.102(T1X1.4 revs.) TR-TSY-000499
	Voltage/Impedance		T1.105 (SONET)
	Coding		T1X1.6 (Drafts)
	Framing	G.704, G.706, G.708	TA-NWT-000253 (SONET)
	Jitter/Wander	G.823 (European hierarchy) G.824 (N.A. hierarchy) G.995, G.782, G/783 (SDH)	
O.171 (measurement)	T1.102 T1.403 TR-TSY-000499 TA- NWT-000253 T1X1.4 (Drafts)		

conforms to the electrical characteristics specified in G.703, T1.403, T1.102 or T1.105 (SONET), for the following parameters:

1. Pulse shape, height, equality of negative/positive pulses.
2. Voltage and impedance.
3. Coding (HDB3, CMI, B3ZS, B6ZS, B8ZS).
4. Clock frequency.
5. Framing (G.704, G.706).
6. Timing jitter and wander (G.823, G.824).

61.2.2.1 Pulse shape

The pulse shape of the equipment transmit output is normalised and compared to the mask specified in the standard. This is usually an

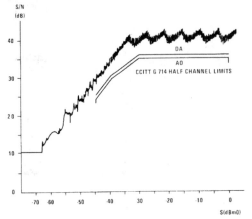

Figure 61.3 S/N characteristic of the A-law for tones

isolated pulse, typically preceded by 3 zeros to minimise inter-symbol interference (ISI). Either an isolated pulse test pattern is used, or the test receiver (e.g. an oscilloscope) must trigger on the right isolated one bit sequence in a random data stream. The measured signal should be terminated in a well matched resistive load. The

Table 61.2 PCM measurements in a typical test set

Standard measurements	A-A	A-D	D-A	D-D
Gain	*	*	*	*
Digital mW gain			*	*
Level (including harmonic distortion)	*	*	*	*
Gain vs level (using tone)	*	*	*	*
Gain vs level (using noise)	*	*	*	*
Gain vs level (using synch 2kHz)			*	*
Gain vs frequency	*	*	*	*
Idle state (choice of filters)	*	*	*	*
Coder offset and peak codes		*		*
Noise with tone	*	*	*	*
Quantising distortion (using tone)	*	*	*	*
Quantising distortion (using noise)	*	*	*	*
Intermodulation (two tone)	*	*	*	*
Intermodulation (four tone)	*	*	*	*

ulse is also sometimes specified at a crossconnect point after
traversing a standard length of coaxial cable.

61.2.2.2 Voltage and impedance

Signal voltage is usually measured as part of the pulse shape test,
though some specifications quote the average signal power for a
particular pattern density.

Impedance is normally 75 ohm unbalanced coaxial, except at the
primary rates of 1.544Mbit/s and 2.048Mbit/s where balanced 110
ohm and 120 ohm connections may be used. The return loss should
be typically 15 to 20dB and ideally be maintained at 6 to 10dB up
to 2 to 3 times the clock frequency, otherwise undesirable overshoot
will appear on the pulse transitions.

61.2.2.3 Coding

Interface codes are intended to ensure satisfactory clock recovery
under varying pattern density. Conformance to the code rules is
usually checked automatically with a digital transmission tester. It
is also useful to inject code errors on a test pattern to check that the
equipment under test recognises this condition.

61.2.2.4 Clock frequency

The clock frequency at a hierarchical interface must lie within the
specified tolerances shown in Table 61.3, otherwise justification
and clock recovery will not operate correctly in terminal equipment.

Table 61.3 Clock tolerance at hierarchical interfaces

Clock rate	Tolerance
PDH	
64kbit/s	±100ppm
1.544Mbit/s (DS-1)	±50ppm
2.048Mbit/s (E1)	±50ppm
8.448Mbit/s	±30ppm
34.368Mbit/s	±20ppm
44.736Mbit/s (DS-3)	±20ppm
139.264Mbit/s	±15ppm
SONET/SDH,	
51.84Mbit/s (STS-1)	< 4.6ppm
155.52Mbit/s (STS-3, STM-1)	< 4.6ppm
622.08Mbit/s (STS-12, STM-3)	< 4.6ppm

61.2.2.5 Framing

As with interface codes, conformance to the specified frame format
is usually checked automatically by a framed digital transmission
tester. Likewise, injecting frame errors in a test pattern checks that
equipment under test recognises the condition.

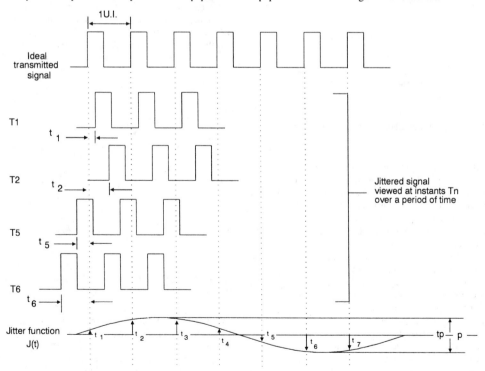

Figure 61.4 Displacement of timing instance of a digital signal due to jitter modulation

Both code errors and frame errors can be used as a simple means of in service error monitoring. Testing may also include a check on the accuracy of these indications.

The standards specify the conditions for loss of frame synchronisation and for regain of synchronisation. These criteria can be tested by injecting a known sequence of frame errors in a test pattern (refer to G.704 and G.706).

61.2.2.6 *Jitter and wander*

Timing jitter is defined as the short term variations of the significant instants of a digital signal from their ideal positions in time. The significant instant might be the rising or falling edge of a pulse. The effect of jitter is shown in Figures 61.4 and 61.5. At certain points in time the pulse is significantly offset from its correct position. If this offset becomes large, then there will be an error when sampling and decoding the digital signal.

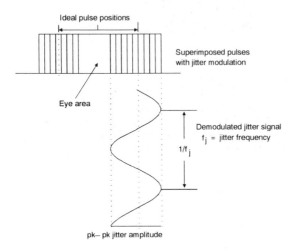

61.5 Effect of jitter modulation on the eye diagram

The disturbance or offset of the timing instant is measured in Unit Intervals peak-to-peak (UI), equivalent to one bit period.

One of the advantages of recovering a timing clock from the data stream is that it will tend to track any timing jitter present in the data. Provided this tracking occurs, then no errors will result when the recovered clock is used to sample the data. In view of the limited bandwidth of clock recovery circuits, this advantage only exists at low jitter modulation frequencies. At higher jitter frequencies, the tracking diminishes and the equipment's tolerance to input jitter is greatly reduced. For this reason, jitter standards are always specified in terms of UI versus jitter frequency for various bit rates.

Timing variations at frequencies below 10Hz are referred to as wander, and are typically caused by changes in phase and propagation delay (e.g. through satellites or long cables subject to temperature changes). Wander is sometimes classified as long term (24 hours, i.e. daily temperature changes) or short term (15 minutes), these definitions being taken from ANSI T1.403.

To fully specify the jitter performance of a piece of equipment, we need to measure the input jitter tolerance, the jitter level at the output and also the jitter transfer function or the degree to which

jitter present at the input is amplified or attenuated by the equipment (Figure 61.6). The input jitter tolerance is checked by increasing the level of jitter on a test pattern at a given modulation frequency and determining the level at which the equipment under test starts to generate errors.

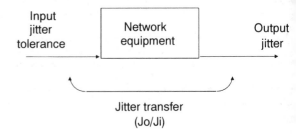

Figure 61.6 Three jitter specifications

The permitted levels for these parameters are specified in CCITT recommendation G.823 for European hierarchy and G.824 for North American hierarchy. A similar set of North American specifications will be found in ANSI T1.102 and in Bellcore TR-TSY-000499. The measuring methods and receiver bandwidths are defined in CCITT recommendation O.171. An example of the jitter tolerance specification and jitter tolerance mask from G.823 is shown in Figure 61.7 and Table 61.4.

Jitter measurements have become important in the new generation of multiplex equipment for SONET and Synchronous Digital Hierarchy (SDH). Synchronisation of payload signals in the SONET/SDH frame is handled by pointer movements. The pointer movements can lead to significant amounts of jitter at the tributary

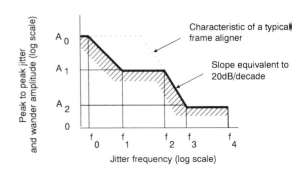

61.7 Lower limit of maximum tolerable input jitter and wander

output of an add/drop multiplexer. Tributary output jitter (e.g. a DS-1 or DS-3) is measured while a SONET/SDH tester forces a specified sequence of pointer movements. These are described in the latest version of Bellcore TA-NWT-000253 and is being discussed further (1991) in ANSI T1X1.6.

When equipment meets the jitter specifications at a hierarchical interface, it should be possible to interconnect network sections without causing bit errors.

able 61.4   Parameter values for input jitter and wander tolerance (G.823)

Digit rate kbit/s	Peak-to-peak amplitude unit interval			Frequency					Pseudo random test signal
	A_0	A_1	A_2	f_0	f_1	f_2	f_3	f_4	
64	1.15 (18μs)	0.25	0.05	1.2 x 10^{-5}Hz	20Hz	600Hz	3kHz	20kHz	$2^{11} - 1$ (Rec. O.152)
2048	36.9 (18μs)	1.5	0.2	1.2 x 10^{-5}Hz	20Hz	2.4kHz	18kHz	100kHz	$2^{15} - 1$ (Rec. O.151)
8448	152 (18μs)	1.5	0.2	1.2 x 10^{-5}Hz	20Hz	400Hz	3kHz	400kHz	$2^{15} - 1$ (Rec. O.151)
34368	618.6 (18μs)	1.5	0.15		100Hz	1kHz	10kHz	800kHz	$2^{23} - 1$ (Rec. O.151)
139264	2506.6 (18μs)	1.5	0.075		200Hz	500Hz	10kHz	3500kHz	$2^{23} - 1$ (Rec. O.151)

1.3   Error performance measurements

1.3.1   Lines, paths and sections

Digital network error performance can be measured over a complete nd-to-end connection called a path, or over parts of the network rmed lines and sections. These network layers are shown in Figure 1.8. Path measurements indicate the overall quality of service to ne customer. Line and section measurements are used for trouble-hooting, installation and maintenance, and for assuring transmission performance objectives are met.

1.3.2   In service and out of service measurements

n service error performance measurements rely on checking known it patterns in an otherwise random data stream of live traffic. As discussed in Section 61.3.6, some in service measurements are more representative than others of the actual error performance of the traffic signal. Furthermore, some are applicable to the path measurement provided the parameters are not reset at an intermediate network interface. Others are only useful at the line or section level.

Out of service measurements involve removing live traffic from the link and replacing it with a known test signal, usually a pseudo-random binary sequence (p.r.b.s.). These tests are disruptive if applied to working networks, but do give very exact performance measurements as every bit is checked for error.

61.3.3   The error performance tester (out of service)

The bit error rate tester (BERT), shown in Figures 61.9 and 61.10, consists of a pattern generator and error detector, often combined in a single instrument though sometimes separate. The p.r.b.s. is gener-

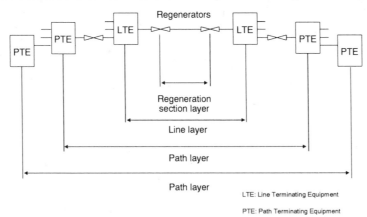

LTE: Line Terminating Equipment

PTE: Path Terminating Equipment

Figure 61.8   Illustration of lines, paths and sections

ated using a feedback shift register which is driven by a very stable clock source, either internally or derived externally from a frequency synthesiser.

The feedback connections on the shift register determine the p.r.b.s. characteristics, and are defined in CCITT Recommendation O.151, O.152, and O.153.

The raw data from the shift register is usually passed through an interface circuit to generate the correct code format and output level (G.703). At the receive side the same type of interface circuit strips off the code and recovers a clock. This clock drives a reference p.r.b.s. generator whose output is compared with the received data.

When the system has synchronised correctly, every bit error in the received data stream will be detected and recorded by the error counter. The error detector can then compute the bit error ratio for a given measurement period as in Equation 61.1 and can also analyse the results statistically to determine how BER varies as a function of time.

$$BER = \frac{Total\ number\ of\ bit\ errors}{Total\ number\ of\ bits\ received} \qquad (61.1)$$

The test patterns used at various bit rates are standardised by CCITT and are summarised in Table 61.5. In addition to p.r.b.s. test patterns, repetitive word patterns with particular "ones" density can be used to explore pattern dependency when trouble-shooting.

61.3.4 CCITT Recommendation G.821

Error performance, or statistical analysis of error occurrence, is usually evaluated in accordance with CCITT Recommendation G.821 (Table 61.6) which specifies the percentage of time that certain thresholds can be exceeded. It gives the error performance of an international digital connection forming part of an ISDN, measured over a period T_L (e.g. one month) on a unidirectional

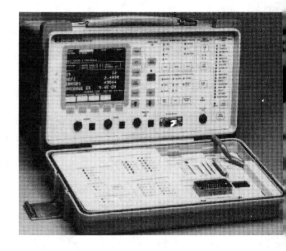

Figure 61.10 A modern error performance analyser

64kbit/s channel of the hypothetical reference connection (HRX) ⟨ 27500km.

G.821 refers to the overall performance for the end-to-er 64kbit/s connection on a very long (27500km) international conne tion. It's the starting point for error performance measurements, b needs interpretation before being applied to a practical transmissi⟨ system.

G.821 defines how error performance parameters are calculate (Figure 61.11). The total measurement time is divided into 1 seco⟨ periods, and unavailable time is subtracted to obtain the availab⟨ time on which the G.821 parameters are calculated.

A period of unavailable time begins when the BER in each seco⟨ is worse than 10^{-3} for a period of ten consecutive seconds. These te⟨ seconds are then considered to be unavailable time. A new period ⟨

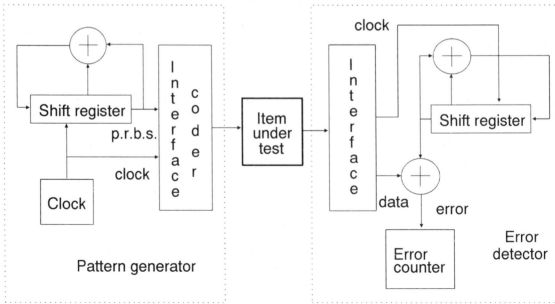

Figure 61.9 Principles of a BER tester

Table 61.5 Test pattern versus bit rate (0.151, 0.152, 0.153)

Bit rate	Test pattern
50bit/s – 168kbit/s (0.153)	$2^9 - 1, 2^{11} - 1, 2^{20} - 1$
64kbit/s (0.152)	$2^{11} - 1$
1.544Mbit/s	$2^{15} - 1, 2^{20} - 1$
2.048Mbit/s	$2^{15} - 1$
8.448Mbit/s	$2^{15} - 1$
34.368Mbit/s	$2^{23} - 1$
44.736Mbit/s	$2^{15} - 1, 2^{20} - 1$
139.264Mbit/s	$2^{23} - 1$

Table 61.6 CCITT Recommendation G.821

Performance classification	Objectives
Degraded Minutes(DM)	Fewer than 10% of one minute intervals to have a Bit Error Ratio (BER) worse than 10^{-6}
Severely Errored Seconds (SES)	Fewer than 0.2% of one second intervals to have a Bit Error Ratio (BER) worse than 10^{-3}
Errored Seconds (ES)	Fewer than 8% of one second intervals to have any errors – equivalent to 92% error free seconds

available time begins with the first second of a period of ten consecutive seconds each of which has a BER better than 10^{-3}.

During available time, any second containing one or more errors is logged as an errored second (ES). Any period of 1 second with a BER exceeding 10^{-3} is classified as a severely errored second (SES) and is subtracted from available time. The remainder is grouped into 60 second periods. Any of these 1 minute periods with a BER exceeding 10^{-6} is classified as a degraded minute (DM).

61.3.4.1 Apportionment

The hypothetical reference connection (HRX) defined in G.821 is shown in Figure 61.12. The connection consists of a local and medium grade section at each end of the link, and a long distance high grade section in the middle. A high capacity transmission system such as microwave or lightwave would be characterised as a high grade section.

Typically a low grade section would be the metallic subscriber loop. Medium grade would be the connection from, say, a local exchange to a trunk switching centre. The three types of section in the network are allocated different portions of the total G.821 specification.

As shown in Tables 61.7 and 61.8, the allocation of degraded minutes and errored seconds is handled slightly differently from severely errored seconds. Low and medium grade sections are allocated a block allowance of 15% of the total G.821 specification at each end (i.e. 1.5% DM and 1.2% ES) irrespective of length. The longer high grade section is apportioned on a distance basis so that 40% allowance is reduced in the ratio L/25000.

Thus for a high grade section of length L km, Equations 61.2 and 61.3 give the values for allowable DM and ES.

$$Allowable\ DM = 10\% \times 0.4 \times \frac{L}{25000}\ or\ 0.00016\%/km \qquad (61.2)$$

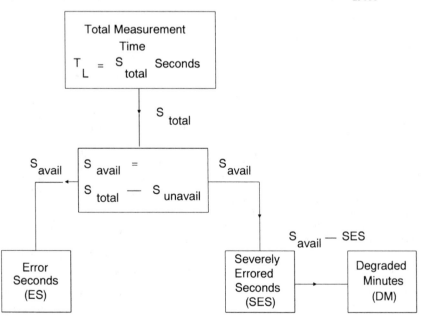

Figure 61.11 G.821 classification

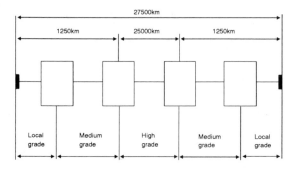

Figure 61.12 Hypothetical reference connection

Table 61.7 Allocation of degraded minutes and errored seconds objectives

Circuit classification	Allocation of degraded minutes and errored seconds objectives
Local grade (two ends)	15% block allowance to each end
Medium grade (two ends)	15% block allowance to each end
High grade	40% (equivalent to conceptual quality of 0.0016%/km.)

Table 61.8 Allocation of severely errored seconds

Circuit classification	Allocation of severely errored seconds objectives
Local grade (two ends)	0.015% block allowance to each end
Medium grade (two ends)	0.015% block allowance to each end
High grade	0.04%

$$Allowable\ ES = 8\% \times 0.4 \times \frac{L}{25000} \quad or \quad 0.000128\%/km \qquad (61.3)$$

Severely errored seconds are allocated on a block basis only. 0.1% (of the total 0.2% G.821 specification) is allocated on a block basis as shown in Table 61.8. The remaining 0.1% SES is allocated to medium and high grade sections to account for adverse operating conditions such as propagation in microwave radio systems. For example, G.821 recommends that an additional 0.05% SES may be allocated to a medium or high grade microwave radio section of 2500km.

61.3.4.2   Conversion of measurements

Error performance standards usually refer to measurements at 64kbit/s, whereas practical measurements on transmission systems are invariably made at a higher multiplex rate. The 1988 (Blue Book) version of G.821 (Annex D) gives provisional guidelines f conversion:

1. Percent DM converted directly.
2. Percent SES converted directly with the addition of perce time with loss of frame alignment.

Error second estimation is given by Equation 61.4 where, n is th number of errors in the *ith* second, N is the higher bit rate divide by 64kbit/s, and j is the total number of seconds.

$$ES_{64kbit/s} = \frac{1}{j} \sum_{i=1}^{i=j} \left(\frac{n}{N} \right)_i \times 100\% \qquad (61.$$

Y% DM measured at the line rate can be compared directly to Y DM at 64kbit/s. Y% SES measured at the line rate can be converte directly to Y% SES at 64kbit/s, but if during the test a loss of fram alignment is detected (or a slip), this time as a percentage should t added.

The conversion for errored seconds is more complicated. Sind the higher multiplexed bit rate contains many 64kbit/s channels, w need to know how many errors are contained in each errored secor at the higher rate in order to estimate how many 64kbit/s channe have been errored. Assuming errors are distributed evenly with the frame (the worst case condition), then Equation 61.4 is repr sentative.

However, the validity of all these conversion algorithms is bein debated in standards committees. Bursts of errors in a high ra transmission stream may cause loss of synchronisation in a sul sequent demultiplexer, creating an extended error burst on a trib tary output. Some practical measurements seem to support thes conclusions. Refer to the latest version of recommendation G.8 for guidance on conversion algorithms.

61.3.5   Related error performance standards

Several other standards exist, however generally these are related G.821 specifications.

61.3.5.1   CCIR Recommendation 594-1

Error performance of digital microwave radio systems is chara terised using CCIR recommendations, notably Recommendati 594-1, for 2500km link (64kbit/s unidirectional channel) as follow

1. BER worse than 1×10^{-6} for less than 0.4% of any month.
2. BER worse than 1×10^{-3} for less than 0.054% of any month
3. Errored seconds should not exceed 0.32% of any month.
4. Residual BER should not exceed 5×10^{-9} (15 minute integr tion).

Recommendation 594-1 is compatible with the high grade porti of G.821.

An additional block allowance of 0.05% SES has been added t adverse propagation conditions and a specification for residual BE has been added.

Both the Residual BER (RBER) threshold and the % for G.8 parameters should be reduced in proportion for systems less th 2500km long.

As these recommendations are compatible with G.821, the san measuring instruments and calculation are used to assess perfc ance. The main consideration is that radio propagation is affected 'weather and so results could be misleading unless measured over 'easonable period (e.g. 1 month)

61.3.5.2 *Recommendation G.921*

CITT Recommendation G.921 defines the performance of a Hy-thetical Reference Digital Section (HRDS) and is based on the quirements of G.821.

G.921 considers digital sections of 280km (or multiples of 0km) and assigns percentage allocation of overall G.821 specifi-tions. Shorter medium grade connections are also defined as own in Table 61.9.

able 61.9 Digital section quality classifications for error erformance

Section quality classification	HRDS length (km)	Allocation	To be used in circuit classification
1	280	0.45%	High grade
2	280	2%	Medium grade
3	50	2%	Medium grade
4	50	5%	Medium grade

61.3.5.3 *Recommendation M.550*

CITT recommendation M.550 is titled 'Performance limits for ringing into service and maintenance of digital paths, sections and ne sections'. This new recommendation is still under development 1991) by CCITT Study Group IV, although a partial version is rinted in the 1988 Blue Books. More recent revisions can be found n Study Group IV documents.

M.550 defines practical performance criteria for digital circuits, neasured over shorter periods than the 1 month defined in G.821. 'eriods of 15 minutes, 24 hours and 3 or 4 days have been sug-ested. It also recommends margins for ageing so that maintenance ntervals can be extended.

Furthermore, M.550 defines Anomaly Events (AE) and Defect vents (DE) for both in service and out of service testing, and ndicates the number of events permissible in a measurement peri-d. For in service testing, it suggests how events should be inter-reted in terms of G.821 parameters. This parallels the North American ANSI T1M1.3 draft recommendation 'In service digital ransmission performance monitoring draft standard' (current ver-ion T1M1.3/91-003R2)

1.3.6 In service measurement parameters and standards

n service measurements have become increasingly important as hey allow long term performance monitoring and preventative naintenance without interrupting customer traffic. In the deregu-ated competitive environment, this is very desirable. In service measurements rely on detecting errors in fixed or allowed bit pat-terns within the data stream, or on computing parity/checksums on blocks of data:

1. BPVs and Line Code Violations are of limited use as they apply to a single transmission section. Equipment will not retransmit code violations to subsequent sections and so this type of parameter cannot be used to indicate overall path performance. (BPV stands for Bipolar Violations in ternary codes such as HDB3, B8ZS, B3ZS, 4B3T etc.)
2. Frame Alignment Signal (FAS) Errors are detected by checking the bits in the repetitive frame alignment word. These form only a small part of the overall frame, and therefore provide only a sample or snapshot of error performance. Good for long term average error ratio (BER).
3. Parity Errors are detected by computing odd or even parity for blocks of data. Has the advantage of checking all payload bits, but can be fooled by even numbers of bit errors in the data block. Effective at low error rates (e.g. less than 10^{-4}). Used in DS-3 (44.736Mbit/s) transmission in the North America, in the SONET/SDH frame standard, and in some line codes.
4. Cyclic Redundancy Checksum (CRC) is computed on blocks of data including payload bits and a CRC remainder sent to the receive end for comparison with the recalculated remainder. A discrepancy indicates one or more errors have occurred in the data block. Provides very reliable detection, giving a good indication of % Errored Seconds as per G.821. Currently used in T1 (1.544Mbit/s) ESF (CRC-6) and E1 (2.048Mbit/s) (CRC-4).

According to CCITT recommendation M.550, system errors are classified as Anomaly Events (AE) such as frame errors, parity errors, code errors, and Defect Events (DE) such as loss of signal, loss of frame synchronisation etc. Table 61.10 shows the anomaly events detection processes available at the various telecommunica-

Table 61.10 In service anomaly events (M.550) and performance primitives (T1M1.3)

BIP= Bit Interleaved Parity; FEBE = Far End Block Error
*Only when operating in these frame formats

Bit rate interface	Section/line	Path
T1, DS-1 1.544Mbit/s	BPVs (B8ZS, AMI) FAS error Line-code errors	CRC-6 errors* G1-G6 bits* (ESF data link)*
E1 2.048Mbit/s	BPVs (HDB3) FAS error Line-code errors	CRC-4 errors* E bits*
DS-3 44.736Mbit/s	BPVs (B3ZS) FAS errors Line-code errors M13 parity errors (P bits)	C-bit parity errors* FEBE bits*
34.368Mbit/s 139.264Mbit/s	BPVs (HDB3) FAS errors Line-code errors	
SONET/SDH	BIP-8 (Byte B1) (section overhead) BIP-8 (Byte B2) (line overhead)	BIP-8 (Byte B3) Path overhead FEBE (Payload path moni-tor e.g. DS-1, DS-3)

tion standard bit rates. (See M.550 and ANSI T1M1.3 draft standards for interpretation of these in service measurements.)

61.4 Data communications network measurement

Network measurement is no longer restricted to the trusty cable tester and a selection of rudimentary software utilities. Along with the wide variety of network installations now in existence, there is an equally diverse range of measurement tools available, with features matched to the needs of the many potential users.

The simplest tool, the cable tester, uses Time Domain Reflectometry (TDR) to check for open or short circuits. Where a problem exists, the tester will indicate the distance from its connection to the fault. More sophisticated devices will passively monitor the traffic on the network, focusing on the electrical characteristics of the transmission.

A more complex tool, the protocol analyser, records conversations between devices on the network, and provides a detailed diagnosis of the protocols used to exchange information.

The most widely used measurement tool is the network monitor. The monitor continuously gathers information about the behaviour of the network, focusing on the data link and network layers. The monitor records the number and size of packets, the source and destination addresses, and uses this data to summarise the nature of traffic on the network.

Information gathered by network measurement devices may be useful to a great many people in an organisation. Each will require differing measurement facilities according to their respective roles.

Network maintenance engineers will concentrate on low level network characteristics, for fault detection and repair. Network managers will be more interested in security and control issues. Board level management will require reports on the usage and performance of the network to enable planning for future needs.

Many of the more common network monitors provide a rich set of functions that go some way towards satisfying the requirements of these groups. The more specialised tools are appropriate for specific tasks, such as installing a new network or development of new communication software.

61.4.1 Physical measurement

Cable testers work by first transmitting a pattern onto the network and then listening for a short period afterwards. The nature of the signal received during the listening period indicates the state of the cable. Analysis of the physical characteristics of the network is best performed by more sophisticated devices.

61.4.1.1 *Electrical characteristics*

Attaching an oscilloscope or logic analyser to a network enables an engineer to see exactly what the signals on the cable look like. A network analyser supplements the view of the electrical signals by comparing the characteristics against a table of technical specifications for that network technology. In particular, the analyser will look at voltage levels, the rise and fall times of signals and the presence of electrical noise. By comparing key parameters against expected values and tolerances, the analyser can perform a health check on the physical network.

The analyser can locate problems such as faulty connectors, improperly terminated cables or network devices operating out of

specification. It can also alert the engineer to potential concerns such as cable degradation.

61.4.1.2 *Multiple attachments*

By attaching a network analyser and a number of subsidiary nodes on a single network segment, it is possible to form an even clearer picture of the physical behaviour of the network. If a network adapter board failed in such a way as to intermittently transmit garbled data onto the network, network measurement equipment operating at a higher level would be swamped with meaningless data. Whilst it would be clear that there was a problem with the network, there may be few clues as to the source of the disruption. However, by analysing the electrical signals at more than one point on the segment, it is possible to quickly and accurately locate the faulty device.

This sort of network trouble shooting is of greatest importance when a network is first installed. Additionally, periodic health checks can aid in pointing the engineer towards areas where corrective action is needed well before network users experience any significant disruption.

61.4.2 Statistical information

Network monitors continuously collect statistics about the traffic on the network, categorise the statistics, form tables, and finally present this information to the user in tabular or graphical form. The user will derive the most benefit from the results of this process if he can apply a significant degree of control over each stage.

61.4.2.1 *Categorisation*

Typically, network monitors will receive all packets transmitted on the network and extract the following details for each packet:

1. The length in bytes.
2. The physical address of the source of the packet.
3. The physical address of the intended destination of the packet.

The monitor may optionally determine the following for each packet:

1. Low level protocol type or identity.
2. Logical network addresses for the source and destination.

Having extracted this information, the monitor may then record it in a form specified by the user. At its simplest, this could involve merely accumulating the total number of bytes transmitted on the network and then taking periodic samples of this total in order to form an indication of how the load on the network varies over time. This would then be displayed as a histogram.

By recording the total number of bytes transmitted in a table, with one entry for each network device, the monitor forms a more complete record of the traffic on the network. Some network monitors record even more information for each station:

1. The number of packets sent or received.
2. The number of bytes sent or received.
3. How many of the packets were in some way erroneous, possibly with a breakdown of errors by type.

Such a detailed table may be displayed without further processing, stored on disc to enable subsequent analysis. Alternatively, by king periodic samples of, say, the total number of bytes transitted by each station, the monitor can display a table or histogram owing how the relative activity of the stations on the network anges over time.

61.4.2.2 *Manipulation*

etwork monitors can perform a limited amount of manipulation on e statistical data before recording it. This manipulation, under the ntrol of the user, means that the monitor can focus on specific eas of concern.

A filter could be applied such that the monitor only records formation for certain types of packets and discards the rest. For :ample, the filter could be programmed such that only packets of particular type are noted. Where there are a number of proto- ls in use on a network, this facility enables the user to focus on ch protocol in turn.

Another way in which the monitor can assist the user is by rouping pieces of information according to a user specified man- er. The most typical instance of this is when monitors are used to ok at communication between certain groups of stations. For xample, this could be a server used by a number of client stations. he user would have to specify that the monitor should only gather atistics on packets in which the server was the source or the estination.

A more complex example requires the monitor to build a matrix show which stations are communicating with which others. This ould help the user to identify where to partition an overloaded etwork.

61.4.2.3 *Presentation*

is common for network monitors to provide both tabular and raphical displays for a variety of statistical information. If the onitor has a windowing interface, it is possible to combine both ets of information on a single screen. The user has control over the cale and sampling period for histograms, and the method of orde- ng entries for tables.

61.4.2.4 *Further processing*

he more powerful network monitors provide sophisticated features or the user to control:

. Which statistics are to be collected.
. What filtering and manipulation is to be performed.
. How the data is to be stored and displayed.

However, it is still important for the user to be able to transfer tatistical records and tables to disc to enable subsequent post rocessing. Most network monitors provide a mechanism to either ecord a snapshot of a table at the user's request, or periodically nake a summary entry to a disc file.

Files of statistics may be processed by the user's own software to perform analysis specific to the user's needs. The files may even be n a form that enables them to be read into a standard software package for more generalised processing, such as report generation. The user is able to produce reports that are tailored to the needs of the target audience. One example would be an annual summary of

the trends in usage of the network for the management team to forecast future purchasing requirements.

61.4.3 Reporting alarm conditions

The experienced user of a network monitor will be able to spot a fault or potential problem on the network merely by studying the various statistical displays. However, more effective use may be made of the monitor by configuring it to watch certain network parameters and raise an alarm if an invalid condition arises.

61.4.3.1 *Thresholds*

Network parameters that may be monitored include the network load and rate at which errors occur. Both of these parameters have a time component, and hence it is important that the user under- stands the sampling period used by the network monitor.

The bursty nature of networks means that the sampling period of the monitor can make it difficult to set a sensible threshold on which to base the alarm. Even a well behaved network can have brief periods of very heavy load. To illustrate the potential difficulty, consider the following example.

A network monitor produces a histogram to show the network usage for a working day, sampling the load every hour. From the resulting display it is clear that the load never exceeds 5%. So, the user specifies a load threshold of 5%, expecting the monitor to sound an alarm if the network suffers from an unusually high load.

However, the monitor takes samples of the network load every 30 seconds when checking for alarm conditions, and frequently during the course of the day the load appears to exceed 15%. Obviously the monitor alarm will be sounding all the time, with little benefit to the user.

61.4.3.2 *Station behaviour*

It is also possible for a network monitor to have alarm thresholds assigned to individual stations. This is useful for monitoring the use of a fileserver or a gateway, for example.

Where a monitor can associate alarm conditions with network stations, it is useful to detect:

1. When a new station appears on the network (sometimes called an intruder alarm).
2. When an important station, such as a server, seems to have stopped transmitting (a dead station).

For the latter, it is necessary to specify the requisite period of silence before the alarm should be generated. For client-server based communication that involves hello or uptime packets, it is quite straightforward to set this time. For less deterministic traffic, the user will probably have to specify quite a long time period.

When an alarm is detected, the network monitor will probably make an audible signal. It might also be possible to use the alarm to trigger some other action, such as packet capture.

61.4.4 Packet capture and decode

Traditionally, it has been the role of the protocol analyser to record conversations between stations on the network and present a chro- nological sequence of packets in an interpreted form. However, many network monitors will also provide a similar function, albeit restricted to the lower protocol layers, or with less detail in the analysis. For most users, the service provided by a network monitor is more than adequate, but for network protocol developers the added sophistication, and expense, of a protocol analyser is justified.

61.4.4.1 *Triggering and filtering*

Sometimes it will be necessary to record all of the traffic on the network for a period of time. However, it is more usual to require just a single conversation, or group of conversations, to be captured. The network monitor will have a number of filters that the user can use to specify patterns that must be matched before a packet is stored.

It is often possible to define a logical relationship between a number of patterns. For example, 2 patterns could be set up such that a server address is specified as the source in one pattern and the destination in the other. The monitor can then be instructed to capture only those packets that match one of the patterns. Hence, the sample of packets will record all packets explicitly sent or received by the identified server. Notice that to capture every packet associated with the server would also require additional patterns specifying appropriate broadcast and multicast, or functional, addresses.

In addition to providing a filtering facility, network monitors also allow the user to specify a condition, or combination of conditions, that must be satisfied before any packet capture commences. These may be dependent on a certain packet sequence occurring, or the raising of an alarm or even a specified time.

The ability to specify a time at which packet capture is to start is useful when the user is interested in the conversations that occur during scheduled events. A typical example of this is filesystem network backups. Backups are performed automatically at times of low activity, such as during the night.

The limit to the size of the capture buffer used to store conversations varies greatly between different monitors. Monitors with lower limits are restricted to storing captured packets in memory, either the network adapter's or that of the system. Devices with larger buffers achieve this in a number of ways:

1. Copying captured packets directly to disc. Since the time to transfer data to the disc is quite long, this method restricts the speed at which packets may be received. Sensible use of the system memory for buffering will help to smooth out bursts of traffic.
2. Using a RAM disc (a virtual disc that actually comprises a dedicated area of system memory). The buffer is not as large as for a real disc, but the limitation on the packet capture rate is eased.
3. Packet slicing, a technique whereby only part of the captured packet is stored, the rest being discarded. This approach extends the limit at little cost, as long as the section of packet stored is sufficient for the user's needs. This may be true for lower protocol layers, but is much harder to achieve for higher layers.

61.4.4.2 *Presentation*

The standard of protocol decode performed on the captured packets varies enormously between network monitors. At its simplest, the display may comprise a sequence of packets with the protocol types identified and the important fields of the lowest network layers interpreted to show mnemonics with associated field values.

Sophisticated packet decode facilities may include a window display, with every packet shown in a variety of layouts, as specified by the user. The full name of every field will be given, along with the corresponding value and a suitable mnemonic. It may be possible to focus on one protocol layer, with higher and lower layers suppressed from the display. The monitor could even summarise each packet on a single line to enable rapid browsing.

With such diversification in the means of decoding packets it is worth considering the true merit of packet decode. The majority of protocol related faults that occur on networks are associated with the lower layers, and are frequently due to the improper configuration of a network device. For such problems, the packet capture and decode facilities provided by most network monitors are more than adequate. The more sophisticated features are only really of use in a development environment.

61.4.4.3 *Protocols*

Just as there is great variety in the display of interpreted packets, there are great differences between the range of protocols supported by network monitors. Most monitors will cope with the commonest low level protocols, such as TCP/IP. For higher protocol layers, or other protocol families, it is often possible to purchase additional software modules to extend the basic decodes provided by the monitor.

Some network monitors support a facility whereby users can write their own protocol decode functions. The user will write programmes using pre-defined library functions, and then link the code with that of the monitor. This will be particularly useful for protocol developers, or users of proprietary protocols.

The way in which most network monitors perform the interpretation of network protocols results in a fundamental limitation to the detail provided in higher protocol layers. This derives from the fact that the recording of conversations, and consequently the decode and display of the detail of those conversations, are all performed on a packet basis. This is different to the operation of the protocol implementation on the interacting stations.

The layering of protocols serves to conceal the packet oriented nature of low level network protocols from the higher levels. The higher protocol layers are concerned with transactions, conversations or sessions. Applications software on one machine will conduct a conversation with peer level software on another machine, oblivious to the way in which the conversation is broken up into packets, transmitted across the network and reassembled at the other end.

However, network monitors interpret protocol information on a packet by packet basis. Consequently, it is difficult to interpret high level protocol information in a packet in the midst of a conversation because the context in which that packet falls is unknown.

Network monitors compromise by either making semi-intelligent guesses, based on 'hints' in the lower level protocols, or just give up and display the data in hexadecimal and ASCII. The only effective means of overcoming this limitation is by copying a sequence of packets to a disc file and then using a specialised analysis package.

61.4.4.4 *Post processing*

Special purpose high level protocol decode software has a limited applicability, and so is not widely used. It overcomes the packet oriented approach to protocol decodes by behaving like the original otocol implementation on the network stations. Hence, every cket's context is meaningful.

The main audience for this type of software is protocol developer- In fact, the software results from a re-engineering of the original otocol implementation. To perform protocol decode, the software ill have been changed to read packets from the disc rather than the twork, and provide output to the screen instead of replying to ceived packets.

The advantage of using this type of software tool is the implicit lidation of the operation of the protocol implementation being onitored. This is of greatest significance when using the packet to lidate a new implementation of the protocol.

1.4.5 Monitors as active stations

though most of the network monitor's functionality is concerned ith passively watching all of the traffic on the network, and rocessing the data in ways already described. There are some atures of a monitor that require it to participate actively in the mmunication on the network.

61.4.5.1 *Testing connections*

he role of a cable tester and the more sophisticated physical twork analyser have already been discussed. Most network moni- rs also provide a limited cable test feature, but with poor accuracy. ome monitors also perform echo tests on stations specified by the ser.

The echo test involves the monitor transmitting a special type of cket to a network station and then waiting for a reply. If a valid ply is received within the timeout period, this shows that the ation is present on the network and that it understands the protocol which the echo packet belongs. Such packets exist for ISO LLC nd Xerox XNS protocols.

61.4.5.2 *Representative loading*

Vhen a network monitor provides a packet transmission capability, ere is usually the means to specify:

. The length of the packet.
. The data content of the packet.
. Whether the packet is to be repeatedly transmitted at a specified interval.

The purpose of re-transmitting the packet, with an interval speci- ed by the user, is to enable the monitor to simulate additional loads n the network. By varying the other parameters, it is possible to enerate a load that is representative of, say, adding another group f workstations and a fileserver. This allows the user to investigate he impact of expanding the use of the network. Particular areas of oncern may be the effect on response times for other workstation sers, or possibly whether a local bridge can cope with the addi- onal load.

61.4.5.3 *Traffic patterns*

f a network monitor is able to transmit packets whose contents are efined entirely by the user, or copied from a packet captured from he network, then the monitor can be used to send out a series of different packets that together form a pattern or signature. By sending a particular series of packets to a single network station, it may be possible to stimulate it into behaving in a desired way. For example, a network server might respond with status information if sent an authentic request, which could be simulated by the monitor.

Alternatively, where the monitor is able to retransmit captured packets, the pattern might be suspected of having caused a network fault. Replaying the packet sequence will give the user the oppor- tunity to monitor the effect more carefully.

61.4.5.4 *Test suites*

The process of using the network monitor to send sequences of packets to particular network devices in order to test their behaviour can be automated. The patterns of packets, together with details of the expected responses, form a suite of tests. Key parameters, such as the destination address, will have to be changed each time the test suite is applied, but this still forms quite a powerful testing facility.

A few network monitors now provide support for the use of test suites. The real benefit for the user comes from the level of analysis that the monitor performs on the results of applying a test suite. It is clear that the maximum benefit would arise from the use of artificial intelligence in the analysis of the results. At least one network analysis tool now attempts to provide a limited form of this.

61.4.6 Effective use

Network monitors are frequently used only in a trouble shooting capacity. So, for example, when users complain of sporadic inter- ruptions in their service from a network server, the network monitor is wheeled out to solve the problem. At that time, the monitor is used to gather whatever information it can from the already faulty net- work.

By leaving the monitor permanently connected to the network, it may be used in a proactive role, gathering information about the operation of the network and providing early warnings of possible problems. Network monitors provide a means of recording the data that they produce. Compiling this data over a period of time enables network managers to observe the changing patterns of usage of the network. This facilitates forward planning of the growth of the network and can pin-point areas of concern.

61.4.7 Larger networks

As the number and size of LANs continues to grow, it is increasingly necessary to partition individual networks and interconnect them to form multi-LANs. The connections between LANs filter out lo- calised traffic, so that a network monitor at one part of the network cannot, by itself, report completely on the status of another part of the network.

61.4.7.1 *Remote monitoring*

Simplified remote monitoring devices may be attached to all seg- ments of the network. These devices lack much of the sophistication of the monitors that have been described here. In particular, they possess no means of providing for direct user interaction.

A central monitoring station can interrogate each of the remote monitors and present the information as if it had been gathered locally. The communication with the remote devices may be in band, using the same network that is being monitored, or out of band, using an alternative route.

The central monitoring station, in addition to being able to act as if it were connected to a single monitor at another point of the network, will be able to summarise data gathered from all of the remote devices. In this way, the user can gain an overall view of how the network is operating.

61.4.7.2   *Network management*

More and more devices are becoming available with support for one of the network management protocols, such as SNMP (Simple Network Management Protocol). An increasing number of networks have a central management station to gather information from these devices. In such networks, the function of network monitors may be unclear.

Certainly, network management stations will be able to perform detailed analysis of how network devices are behaving by directly interrogating tables maintained by the device. By collating such information for all devices on the network, the management station will gain a detailed view of how the devices on the network are interacting.

However, the data supplied to the management station by network devices is only pertinent to each device, and only relates to how that device has interacted with the network. To gain a complete picture of the behaviour of the network requires access to the functionality provided by a network monitor.

A network monitor will continuously record information about all of the traffic that it sees on the network, including erroneous packets. Furthermore, the monitor can independently collect data about how the various network devices interact, forming the network's perspective of the communication patterns.

Remote monitoring devices, connected to all of the network segments, will, provide information to the management station to complement that provided by the other network devices. In this way, the management station will be able to form a complete picture of how the network is operating.

61.5   ISDN test equipment

This section gives an overview to the testing requirements for ISDN, and the test equipment associated with carrying out such testing.

The structure of ISDN, including that of the interfaces of ISDN are examined, determining the types of tests that can be performed. The testing of ISDN interfaces is compared to that of traditional telephony testing and the differences and similarities are summarised.

Testing of ISDN is also examined for the following key areas:

1. Physical testing.
2. Transmission testing.
3. Protocol testing.

61.5.1   Integrated Services Digital Network

The Integrated Services Digital Network is one evolving from a telephony Integrated Digital Network (IDN) that provides end-to-end digital connectivity to support a range of services, including voice and non-voice services, to which users have access by a limited set of standard multi-purpose interfaces. Two interfaces are defined by CCITT for ISDN, the Basic Rate Access (BRA) (see

Figure 61.13) and the Primary Rate Access (PRA) (see Figure 61.14).

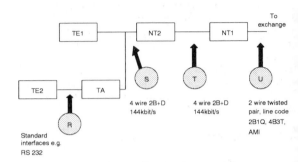

Figure 61.13   ISDN Basic Rate Access

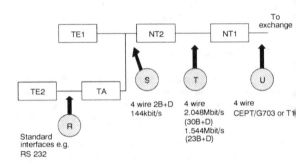

Figure 61.14   ISDN Primary Rate Access

61.5.1.1   *The interfaces*

The structure of ISDN is such that the two ISDN interfaces, the BRA and the PRA are used for customer access, it is therefore apparent that the two interfaces are the most commonly tested component in ISDN (see Figure 61.15).

The two ISDN interfaces BRA and PRA, are well defined by the CCITT a branch of the United Nations, International Telecommunications Union. ISDN as defined by the CCITT however is not just restricted to the interfaces but is defined as being a collection of components and functions: access types, devices, protocols and interfaces. Testing of ISDN is therefore not restricted to the interfaces of ISDN but encompasses the protocols and functions of the devices.

61.5.1.2   *ISDN components*

The channel is the basic unit of service within ISDN, and is a fundamental component in its testing. The Basic and Primary rate interfaces are made up by a number of these channels. Three type of basic channel are defined, Bearer channels (B), Delta channel (D) and High capacity channels (H). A B channel is a 64kbit/s unit of clear digital bandwidth, based on the data rate required to carry one digitised voice conversation. B channels can carry any type of digital information (voice, data or video). A D channel is a signalling channel that carries the information needed to set up and tear

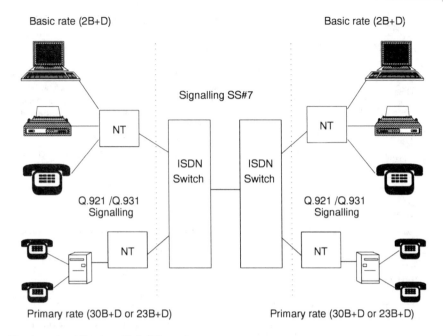

Signalling SS#7

Q.921 /Q.931
Signalling

Q.921 /Q.931
Signalling

Basic rate (2B+D)

Basic rate (2B+D)

NT

NT

ISDN
Switch

ISDN
Switch

NT

NT

Primary rate (30B+D or 23B+D)

Primary rate (30B+D or 23B+D)

Figure 61.15   The Integrated Services Digital Network

down switched connections for the relevant B channels. Connections set up by the D channel are normally B channels that are within the same physical connection as the D channel, although in the case of Signalling System Number 7 this is not always the case.

The Basic Rate Interface is made up of two 64kbit/s B channels and a 16kbit/s D channel and is often referred to as 2B+D and is a world-wide standard. The Primary Rate Interface has two versions one made up of 30 64kbit/s B channels and a 64kbit/s D channel (30B+D) that is found in Europe, Africa and South America and one made up of 23 64kbit/s B channels and a 16kbit/s D channel (23B+D) that is found in the USA, Japan and Canada.

61.5.2   ISDN testing compared

The Basic Rate Access is a new access method defined by CCITT for ISDN and is based on the twisted copper pair used for the existing analogue telephone circuits. The Primary Rate Access is already used for transmission and was initially deployed in inter-local exchange networking for PCM systems.

Testing procedures for Primary Rate circuits already exist, although the testing methods used are normally restricted to physical and transmission and framing tests. Because ISDN makes use of the existing G704 framing structure of the Primary Rate circuits the only extra requirement for ISDN testing is that of the signalling protocol that is carried in the D channel.

The testing of ISDN Basic Rate circuits has no historical precedence but yet can be split into three distinct categories as per the Primary Rate circuits and other non-ISDN circuits, as follows:

1.   Physical testing, the testing of the physical parameters of the media used to carry the signals for the appropriate interface. These tests would normally be impedance, continuity, jitter, signal balance and electrical loading.
2.   Transmission testing, the transmission test being designed to test the transmission capabilities of the physical media as well

as the framing of the signal for the particular service. These tests normally check for errors on a transmitted signal, as well as checking for errors in framing.
3.   Protocol testing, the protocol tests being used to check the logical flow of messages and information according to the rules of the protocols in use on the interface. These tests can operate in a functional and non-functional manner.

61.5.3   Different levels of test equipment

A wide variety test equipment is currently available for ISDN, but the design of ISDN test equipment is still evolving. Most test equipment available for ISDN to date can be categorised by price and functionality. The test products for ISDN have traditionally been split by testing capability such as, protocol testers, physical line testers and transmission testers.

The fragmentation of ISDN testing in this manner suits the R&D laboratories where testing can be easily split into these disciplines. However for those who have to install and commission ISDN this methodology is both cumbersome and expensive. A new generation of ISDN tester is now becoming available that combines elements of all three areas into a simple to use functional tester that can prove to be highly cost effective. Dedicated testers however still have their place to play in ISDN testing, as they can perform far more complex and detailed tests that cannot be achieved with the combinational simple testers.

61.5.4   Testing philosophies

61.5.4.1   *The effect of maturity*

The types of test which are carried out on transmission installations, and the ways in which the test equipment is connected, depend on the maturity of the service transmitted, as illustrated in Figure 61.16. In development, conformance with specification is of prime import-

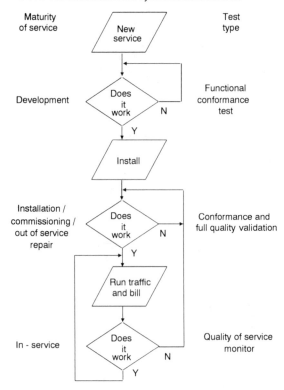

Figure 61.16   Type of test depends on stage of maturity

ance. In installation and commissioning, transmission quality begins to play an important part, and in maintenance work, the specification is assumed, and long term performance is the issue. Therefore, as a particular installation or service matures, the trend is from conformance testing to transmission quality testing. Before the 1990s, ISDN was largely a developing technology, but as more real installations come into service, commissioning and maintenance performance testing is rapidly expanding.

61.5.4.2   *Transmission test connection methods*

A functional test of each transmission component, out of service, can prove the integrity of the component while reducing the risk of damage or impairment to the network due to the connection of faulty equipment. Tests are made in order to establish conformance to specification, in terms of correctly generated signals and the ability to receive, and respond correctly to, error free and errored data. A terminal equipment (TE), for example, may be tested by connecting it to a simulated network, and network terminating units (NTs), by connecting them between a simulated terminal and a simulated network.

A loop test through the network, with loops at strategic points to identify problem areas, or an end to end test through the network, verifies conformance and quality, and can be achieved without taking the equipment out of service. Full quality of service testing to CCITT Recommendation G.821 involves the recording of periods of performance, within specified error ratio bands, for one month. This is normally only practical at the installation and commissioning phase.

61.5.5   ISDN Basic Rate transmission testing

61.5.5.1   *Basic Rate structure*

The ISDN Basic Rate signal is a time division multiplexed composite of two 64kbit/s channels, known as B channels, plus one 16kbit/s control channel, known as the D channel. Basic rate transmission is used to connect subscribers to local exchanges, where ISDN line cards or ISDN multiplexers convert the basic rate for transmission over the network.

The purpose of basic rate testing is to establish the quality of the transmission over the subscriber loop. This is achieved in three phases:

1. Testing of the physical connection.
2. Establishment of a call.
3. Data or speech (voice) transmission testing.

61.5.5.2   *Basic Rate physical line tests*

The first step in Basic Rate testing is to establish the integrity of the physical connection between the subscriber's S interface, via the Network Terminator, to the exchange, or simply the U interface connection between the Network Terminator and the exchange.

The following physical parameters can be measured:

1. Correct wiring polarity of the pairs, presence of out of specification hazardous voltages, and insulation resistance.
2. Presence of phantom power, which is provided by the network as a common mode potential between the two pairs of the S interface. The level and polarity of this voltage can be measured.
3. Presence of, and accuracy of, the clock which is provided by the network.
4. Indication and manipulation of the information states by which the physical communication is set up.
5. Impedance and insertion loss of the line.
6. The relationship of the longitudinal balance of the circuit to the frequency of transmitted signals, for manual or automatic comparison with the limits specified by CCITT I.430.
7. The shape, balance, delay and jitter of transmitted pulses.

61.5.5.3   *Basic Rate test call set up*

In order to carry out transmission tests, a call has first to be established, either to a remote tester or to the other channel of the calling tester. If a speech call transmission test is required, the call has to be to another tester or ISDN telephone, because it is not permissible to have two simultaneous speech calls on one instrument. In the case of data calls, the following logical call connection schemes are possible:

1. One channel (B1 say) of a tester transmits, via the network, to the other channel of the same tester (B2), and B2 transmits, via the network, to B1, performing two full duplex tests using the full bandwidth of one Basic Rate circuit, as shown in Figure 61.17.
2. One channel (e.g. B1) of the tester transmits, via the network, to the other channel (B2) of the same tester, which loops the connection and retransmits, via the network, back to B1, per-

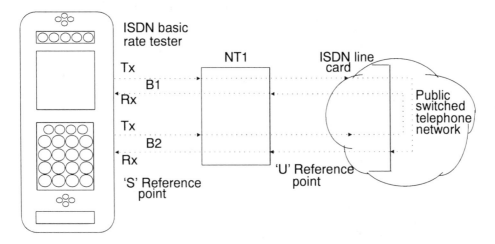

Figure 61.17 Logical connections for ISDN Basic Rate subscriber loop testing

forming one full duplex test using the full bandwidth of one Basic Rate circuit.

3. One channel (e.g. B1) of one tester transmits, via the network, to one channel (B2) of another tester, and B2 transmits to the first tester's B1 channel, performing a full duplex test using half the bandwidth of each of two Basic Rate circuits. The other half of the bandwidth can be simultaneously tested by setting up a similar data call or a voice call, for crosstalk testing or for supervisory communication between the two tester operators.

4. One channel of a tester transmits to the exchange which, by the sending of a special protocol command, is instructed to loop the connection back to the calling channel, performing a full duplex test using half the bandwidth of one Basic Rate circuit. The other half of the bandwidth can be simultaneously tested by setting up a similar data call, a data call to another circuit, or a voice call.

61.5.5.4 *Basic rate transmission tests*

Having achieved a successful call set up as above, the logical path established can be tested for transmission quality. For data calls this normally entails the sending of a pseudo-random binary sequence and the checking of a similar received sequence for errors.

The results measured can range from a simple count of bit errors and bits received, with a calculated Bit Error Ratio Test (BERT), to a full set of G.821 measurements, including errored and severely errored seconds, degraded minutes, and periods of unavailable time.

The duration of the test can range from a few seconds, sufficient to ensure that the call has been successfully established and data can be transferred, to many days for the gathering of G.821 statistics. These relate to the long term quality performance of the connection, and may be displayed in the form of histograms to assist in identifying periods of degraded service.

By setting up two simultaneous test calls, an assessment of crosstalk interference between channels can be made, either by using a voice call in one channel which may be degraded by a data call in the other, or by using two data calls which may mutually interfere.

In the case of voice calls set up, analogue measurements may be made, by sending calibrated tones and measuring received level and frequency, to determine path loss and frequency response, signal to noise ratio etc.

61.5.6 ISDN Primary Rate transmission testing

61.5.6.1 *Primary Rate structure*

The 2Mbit/s framing structure defined by the CCITT recommendation G.704 is the backbone of primary rate ISDN. It is a composite of 64kbit/s basic rate signals, and is itself a building block for the higher order multiplexed rates. The 64kbit/s signals, which can be data or pulse code modulated telephone channels, are each allocated a timeslot within the frame structure. Each frame consists of 32 time division multiplexed timeslots each containing 8 bits of data from one channel, with the data from each channel being identified by its position in the frame.

The first timeslot of each frame (timeslot 0) is used for frame synchronisation and frame supervisory functions, while timeslot 16 can be used for a variety of signalling methods. In ISDN, Common Channel Signalling (CCS) is used, and timeslot 16 carries supervisory signals controlling the status of the calls occupying the remaining timeslots, by the use of special protocols. Error detection can be achieved optionally by the use of a Cyclic Redundancy Check (CRC4), which groups 8 frames into sub-multiframes and 2 sub-multiframes into multiframes.

Clocks for the generation of frames and data are always locked to the master clock of the network. Terminal equipment therefore uses the clock recovered from the received signal to generate the frames and to produce 64kbit/s channel clocks to the tributaries.

Timeslot 0 of each frame is reserved for frame alignment or synchronisation. Alternate frames contain the Frame Alignment Signal (FAS) and the Not Frame Alignment Signal (NFAS). Bits 2 to 8 of the FAS, and bit 2 of the NFAS, are fixed and define frame synchronisation. Bit 3 of the NFAS is used to indicate remote end loss of synchronisation, and bits 4 to 8 are used for application specific signalling functions. Bit 1 of the FAS and NFAS are disregarded for the purposes of frame synchronisation, but can be used for CRC4 operation. Frame synchronisation occurs when 3 consecutive correct FAS (bits 2 to 8), and 3 corresponding correct NFAS (bit 1), are received, and is considered lost when 3 consecutive errored FAS are received.

The integrity of the data contained in the frames can be checked using a CRC4 in bit 1 of the FAS and NFAS. Multiframes are formed of two sub-multiframes, each of 8 frames. Bit 1 of each NFAS in the first sub-multiframe is set to the sequence 0010, and in the second sub-multiframe to 11XX, where X bits are 'don't care' as far as multiframe alignment is concerned, and are used to signal remote CRC errors. The four FAS bit 1's of each sub-multiframe form a four bit word corresponding to the CRC of the data in the preceding sub-multiframe. An error is detected when the received CRC word does not correspond to one locally calculated on the received data.

61.5.6.2 *Out of service Primary Rate tests*

The simplest method of out of service testing is a simple full bandwidth Bit Error Ratio Test (BERT) using, typically, a long pseudo-random pattern at 2.048Mbit/s, with no framing, to qualify the performance of transmission media. G.821 performance statistics can be applied at the primary rate, even though they are intended for use at 64kbit/s, provided that the system can be out of service for long enough to collect valid results. Time related events, or quality degradation periods, can be isolated by using time stamped stored or printed reports, and result histograms.

Alternatively the frames, with or without CRC4, can be generated by the tester for transmission to terminal, multiplexing or network equipment. In this case the tester can be set to corrupt the alignment signals in a pre-defined manner, in order to check the ability of the equipment to detect and recover from sync loss, according to the correct criteria. Testers can be set to replace the normal frame and multiframe alignment signal by programmable words, to exercise the facilities controlled by each word bit, for example distant alarm. At the same time a selection of the data fields (timeslots 1 to 15 and 17 to 31) can be filled with a pseudo-random sequence, performing a BERT test to another similar tester, and CRC4 can be generated and checked to test CRC performance.

By substituting test equipment for network elements, or by using testers connected to individual transmission equipments in isolation, problems of incompatibility or specification interpretation can be resolved. The electrical characteristics of the transmission or terminal equipment, its characteristic impedance, pulse shape and encoding can be measured. When testing into the network, the transmitter of the tester is set to use, and to measure the frequency and jitter of, the clock recovered from the received signal. When testing terminal equipment, the tester has to look like the network, so it uses its own crystal controlled clock to generate the framed signal. The different connection methods are illustrated in Figure 61.18.

61.5.6.3 *In service Primary Rate tests*

In service testing is ideally carried out unobtrusively with minimum disruption to the traffic. Its objective is to assess the quality of the transmission and, where defects are found, to pinpoint the source of the problem.

In service testing can monitor a live network signal for correct frame alignment, condition of the distant alarm signals, CRC4 and signalling protocols. By regular monitoring of an installation, potential trouble can be spotted before it gets too serious. Connection to the network is normally made at a protected high impedance monitoring point, or by a bridge through the tester interface.

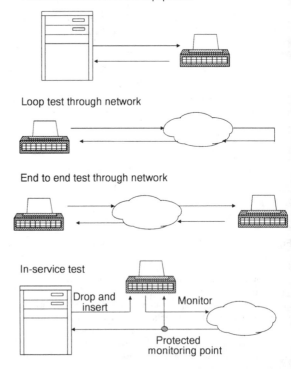

Functional test of terminal equipment

Loop test through network

End to end test through network

In-service test

Drop and insert

Monitor

Protected monitoring point

Figure 61.18   Connections for ISDN Primary Rate testing

Intermittent, or time related, faults can be identified, using a tester with a printer facility to produce time stamped reports in response to error conditions. By comparing physical layer parameters, for example bipolar errors (infringements of the bipolar encoding scheme), with supervisory functions such as long term CRC4 performance, it is possible to differentiate between transmission and terminal equipment faults.   It is also possible to intercept the frames, and either extract single, or multiple, timeslots for analysis, or to drop out timeslots and replace them with data inserted from a tester source. In this way selected channels of a live system can be tested without disturbing the remaining channels, thereby proving the quality of capacity before it is brought into service.

61.5.7   Protocol testing

The level of testing that covers layers 2 and 3 of the OSI stack is commonly known as protocol testing. Protocol testing in ISDN is linked to the testing of the 'D' channel signalling protocol. Protocol testing at layers 2 and 3 as well as the layers above can be split into a number of different areas such as conformance testing, performance testing, inter-operability testing and trouble shooting.

Protocol testing is normally carried out by dedicated protocol analysers with the appropriate ISDN interfaces fitted, although protocol analysers based on cards for use in PCs are becoming more popular. Some ISDN testers such as those that set up a path on Basic Rate connections, and then perform a transmission test, also have protocol support. This support however is only intended to perform a functional test and does not usually include the ability to decode or display protocol events.

61.5.7.1 Inter-operability testing

Inter-operability testing is designed to prove whether two ISDN devices or services can and will work together to specification. Any ISDN product has to be tested for inter-operability with any other ISDN product that it may have to communicate with. A maxim in inter-operability testing is that the commutative law does not apply. In other words, if A interoperates with B and B interoperates with C, A does not necessarily interoperate with C. ISDN products must be tested for interoperability and conformance at every major revision.

61.5.7.2 Conformance testing

Conformance tests are usually run automatically in a long series of short, very specific tests with pass/fail results provided along the way. Many ISDN providers, such as telecommunication ministries, require conformance testing before a given product or service can be operated on their networks, a given product or service is usually only ever tested once for conformance.

In Europe the Conference of European Post and Telecommunications Administrations (CEPT) have produced specifications collectively known as NETs (Norme Europeene de Telecommunications) covering various areas to promote type approval across Europe. NET3 covers the Basic Rate Access and NET5 the Primary Rate Access. Many manufacturers of protocol analysers have application programs available that allow them to carry out conformance tests for the NETs and other conformance specifications.

61.5.7.3 Performance testing

Performance testing requires the gathering and display of statistics on the numbers of protocol units (frames, packets, messages and so on) transmitted and received over a period of time between devices. The goal is to discover deviations from normal operation or from a pre-defined specification, that point to underlying problems in the terminal or switching equipment or in the operation of the protocols themselves.

For ISDN, degrading performance of the D channel protocols, such as longer set up times or a high number of unsuccessful calls, can indicate a number of problems ranging from error at the terminal, to traffic overloading on the ISDN network. Monitoring of the B channels can also indicate problems on the D channel, for example erratic traffic on the B channel may point to problems on the D channel signalling protocol. Performance testing can uncover day to day operating problems that might otherwise pass inter-operability testing.

61.5.7.4 Protocol trouble-shooting

If a problem is discovered protocol trouble-shooting often finds the cause of the problem. ISDN defines new ways of performing routine tasks such as making a phone call. In order to trace the flow of protocol events, for a call being placed, a protocol analyser is often needed. Protocol analysers interpret protocol events by displaying to the user an 'English' breakdown of the protocol events that have occurred on the line (see Figure 61.19). The events displayed on the screen are usually marked with some form of identification indicating which device the message was received from. In addition each message will have a timestamp associated

```
C SAPI=0 (CCP) TEI=66                Time: 12.30:00:1200
I 86 98 24
Q921: 00 85 AC C4
      PD=08 UCC REF=018
      M 05 SETUP
      I 04 Bearer Capability           Len=2
         58 Coding Standard            CCITT
            Transfer Capability        Unrestricted
         90 Transfer Mode              Circuit
            Transfer Rate              64Kbit/s
      I 18 Channel Identification      Len=1
            Interface                  Implicity Identified
         8A Interface Type             Basic
            Indicated Channel Exclusive  Yes
            Channel Indicator          Not D-Channel
            Channel Selection          B2
      I 70 Called Party Number         L=11
         80 Type                       Unknown
            Numbering Plan             Unknown
            Address Digits             0048885030
Q931: 08 01 18 03 04 02 88 90 18 01 8A 70
      0B 80 30 30 34 38 38 38 35 30 33 30
```

Figure 61.19 Typical display of a D Channel protocol from a protocol analyser

with it so that timing measurements or discrepancies can be determined.

ISDN also adds a new layer of complexity to protocol testing in that subtle effects of D channel call set up procedure can affect the protocol events occurring on the B channel. For this reason dual port protocol analysers are very popular in monitoring dual processes simultaneously. In this way the user can simultaneously monitor the protocol events occurring on the same physical line but in different channels, for example the D channel and a B channel.

61.6 Introduction to cellular radio

Mobile telephone systems based on the cellular network concept are in use in most developed countries.

The key to satisfactory operation of these systems is a complex signalling arrangement by means of which a high level of accessibility and good transmission quality are achieved.

Common to all systems is the use of a cellular structure for the optimal re-use of the available frequency channels. There are however significant differences in the signalling techniques and message formats used.

With this approach, each area served by a base station is called a cell, and these cells are arranged to cover the ground in a regular pattern. The service area of each station is roughly circular, but is normally drawn as a hexagon.

All the base stations are linked into a wired network which switches calls to a mobile as it moves about; the cellular arrangement has effectively made the radio link part of the network as short as possible. Figure 61.20 shows a typical 7 cell cluster.

For testing purposes cellular radio systems are divided into two major groups. Those systems which employ digital signalling and analogue speech transmission are generally referred to as analogue cellular systems, and systems which use both digitised signalling and digitised speech transmission are referred to as digital cellular systems.

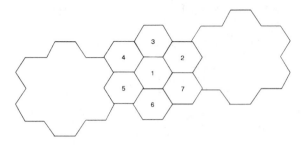

Figure 61.20 A seven cell cliuster

61.6.1 Data signalling

The management of the mobile network calls for information exchange between the mobiles and the base stations in each cell or cluster of cells. Among the procedures to be handled in this way we can identify:

1. Selection of r.f. channels.
2. Transfer of call numbers.
3. Transmitter power level control.
4. Handover of mobile between cells.
5. Registration and call charging.

Depending on the system being considered, data signalling may take place on permanently allocated channels or on voice channels allocated from time to time as required.

For analogue cellular systems the signalling itself takes the form of a data message using typically fast frequency shift keying (FFSK) or phase shift keying (PSK). Digital networks use methods such as gaussian minimum shift keying (GMSK). Various forms o coding including high redundancy error correcting techniques are in use.

61.7 Analogue cellular test equipment

In addition to all the conventional r.f. and a.f. measurements, tes equipment for cellular radio mobiles must also be capable of testing the various signalling procedures.

As a minimum requirement, it must be possible to simulate the base station function to the extent of opening the normal voice channel so that conventional measurements can be performed.

It may also be necessary to analyse the actual bit streams of the messages in order to detect single bit errors in the transmitted data

With a view to simulating the effects of interference in practica systems, the test equipment should also be capable of generating special code sequences, for example, with implanted errors.

In the past this was done using discrete instrumentation controlled via computer. Today it is more commonly performed by integrated Radiotelephone Test Sets.

61.7.1 Analogue cellular test set

The cellular radio test set generates and analyses all data signals required to simulate the cellular base station. It must also provide all the facilities required for r.f. and a.f. measurements on the radio itself. For example, the Rohde and Schwarz CMTA provides these functions. Special signalling firmware is installed for the common cellular systems. These are AMPS, TACS, Radiocom 2000 NMT450/900 and Network C.

A typical hardware configuration is shown in Figure 61.21. The individual instruments are controlled by a central microprocessor Further system components may be integrated with the test set as required. These can be controlled by an external computer via the widely used IEEE bus. For example, users may wish to include a programmable power supply or a second signal generator for inter ference response testing.

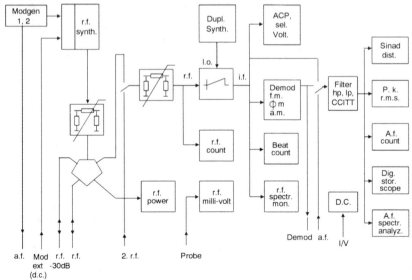

Figure 61.21 Radiotelephone test set block diagram

61.7.2 Operation of the test set

During the test of the mobile radio all signalling functions (generation and analysis of data telegrams) are handled by the test set which must also make the r.f. and a.f. measurements. There are two main testing modes:

1. Many mobile radios feature a service mode which may be accessed via the keyboard of the radio. For radios with special test interfaces, the necessary control signals may be generated by the test set using either the RS232C interface or a general purpose I/O interface. In this mode the functions of the radio (transmit, receive, channel, power) can be controlled directly and all the measurements required such as sensitivity, frequency response, distortion, transmitter power, modulation, signal to noise ratio, power consumption can be performed with the tester.

2. Of much greater interest is the complete system test in which the mobile radio operates as if it were in the cellular network. The test set in this case forms a test system which simulates the base station, permitting calls to be sent from and received at the mobile station in real time via the r.f. connector. Once again the r.f. and a.f. measurements will also be handled by the test set, operated either in the manual mode or under programme control. The test set can also send the telegrams necessary for initiating channel handover or power level switching.

An extensive range of signalling and r.f./a.f. tests must be made as illustrated by the test menus taken from a modern test set, as in Table 61.11.

The table summarises the signalling procedures and measurements required for the three most common analogue cellular standards. A modern cellular radio test set is capable of storing test software for all of these standards plus Radiocom 2000 and C-NET.

61.8 Digital cellular test equipment

With respect to test equipment and methods, the main differences between conventional mobile radio and the new digital radio networks (to which GSM belongs) can be categorised in the following way:

1. The transmitted information is completely digitised and assigned to time slots. Continuous analogue signals that were employed for testing in the past would obviously be out of place in digital environments.
2. Modern digital modulation techniques affect the phase and amplitude of the r.f. carrier continuously over time. Generating digital signals of this kind, or analysing them, is beyond the capabilities of conventional test equipment such as signal generators, modulation analysers and power meters.

In 1992 CEPT established a special working committee called the Groupe Speciale Mobile (GSM) to formulate a new digital cellular standard. This was achieved and in 1992 the GSM (now renamed Global System Mobile) was launched.

61.8.1 Analogue and GSM test methods

The GSM system is one of a range of radio communication systems which use fully digital techniques.

Other examples are:

Table 61.11   Test menus

NMT	AMPS		TACS/ETACS
Call mobile-base	Call mobile-base		Call mobile-base
Call base-mobile	Call base-mobile		Call base-mobile
Channel handover	Channel handover		Channel handover
Roaming	Registration		Registration
Response time	SAT 5.97/6.00/6.03kHz		SAT 5.97/6.00/6.03kHz
Tx power (3 levels)	Tx power (8 levels)		Tx power (8 levels)
Message analysis	Message analysis		Message analysis
Bit error implant	Bit error implant		Bit error implant
	Transmitter	Power	
		Frequency accuracy	
		Modulation sensitivity	
		Modulation frequency response	
		Modulation distortion	
		Adjacent- channel power (option),	
	Receiver	Sensitivity (S/N SINAD quieting)	
		A.F. level	
		A.F. frequency response	
		A.F. distortion	
	General	Power supply voltage	
		Power supply current drain	

1. Cellular networks: D-AMPS, PCN.
2. Paging systems: ERMES.
3. Cordless telephone: CT2, DECT.
4. Trunking networks.

Some of the techniques in GSM have been used in other systems. For example, military radios may use frequency hopping. Digital speech is widely used in telephony.

The techniques that are used for GSM, the European digital mobile radio network, require test functions that cannot be handled by conventional equipment. The following section shows the test standards for GSM with special reference to the radio path or physical layer. The essential characteristics that this new generation of test equipment must have, will then be derived.

Table 61.12 compares conventional and GSM measurements.

61.8.1.1 *Time division multiple access (TDMA)*

In the GSM network the digital information is arranged in blocks and transmitted in precisely defined timeslots. An eight timeslot structure is used. Users are allocated a timeslot by the system during which data transfer takes place. The radio network, and hence the radio test equipment, must be capable of being synchronised together.

In order to measure timing parameters the test equipment must use sampling rates which are much faster than the data rate. The r.f. carrier power may be turned off between timeslots in a controlled manner. The test equipment must, therefore, be able to measure the power output over a wide dynamic range.

61.8.1.2 *Frequency hopping*

Frequency hopping is used within the GSM system. Each timeslot of information may be transmitted at a different radio frequency.

The test equipment must, therefore, be able to generate and measure frequency hopping signals.

GSM employs a complex speech coder in order to reduce the data rate and hence bandwidth required by the system. The traditional 1kHz audio test tone is not considered a meaningful representation of speech. New test methods employing data sequences have, therefore, been developed.

61.9 The OSI Model and GSM

The OSI model is a common method of describing any data transmission system. For GSM applications it is shown in Figure 61.22. A more graphical representation is shown in Figure 61.23

61.10 The radio path or Physical Layer (Layer 1)

As can be seen from the OSI model Layer 1 contains the channel coding, error protection and interleaving. These processes are designed to ensure that data is transmitted correctly. If minor errors occur the decoder may be able to correct them. The interleaving process ensures that, if a signal is degraded for a short period of time, sequential data is not lost.

The following sections describe the testing of the radio link, the lowest part of Layer 1. The fundamental tools for receiver testing are described and the equipment required for transmitter testing is identified.

61.10.1 Receiver measurements

61.10.1.1 *Signal generator requirements*

Signal generators for GSM applications convert a given bit sequence into the corresponding modulated r.f. carrier signal. Con

Table 61.12 Comparison of conventional and digital mobile radio measurements

Conventional mobile-radio measurements	GSM measurements
Measurement modes	
Continuous parameter settings	Time-limited settings
Continuous measurements	Time referenced measurements
Test tones	Data telegrams
Frequency division multiple access	Time division multiple access/frequency division multiple access
Bandwidth	
R.F. 10-25kHz	R.F. 200kHz plus frequency hopping
A.F. 3kHz	A.F. digital
Available test points on radio	
R.F.	R.F.
A.F.	Digital (no a.f.)
Acoustic	Acoustic
Need for co-ordination of test and measurement functions	
For convenience only	Essential for successful measurements
Signalling: limited, typical accuracy 10ms to 1s	Signalling: critical, accuracy 1μs

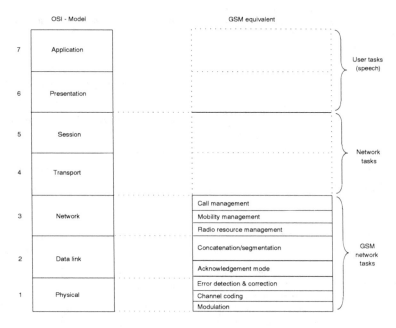

Figure 61.22 The OSI model as applied to GSM

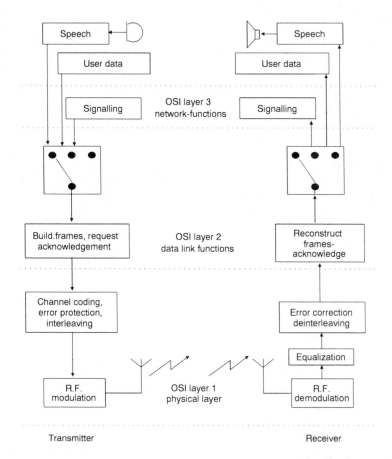

Figure 61.23 Symbolic representation of GSM transmit and receive functions based on the OSI layer model

ventional signal generators are unsuitable for this because there is no direct way of controlling the phase of the carrier. Instead, I/Q modulators will provide this function (Figure 61.24).

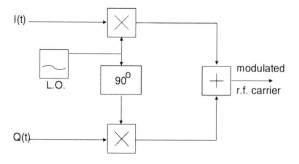

Figure 61.24 I-Q (vector) modulator

As far as the magnitude of the frequency deviation and the stability of the centre frequency (for f.m. d.c. mode) are concerned, signal generators available at present are not completely satisfactory. The few signal generators on the market which have fast enough switching times are unattractive when their price is taken into consideration. Using this analysis as a basis, a short list of required features for a signal generator which would be suitable for GSM applications can be compiled, as in Table 61.13.

The principle of a typical GSM signal generator, such as that used in the Rohde and Schwarz GSM test set CMTA94, is shown in Figure 61.25. Digital signals are modulated by digital signal processing into their in phase (I) and quadrature phase (Q) components. These digital signals are then converted to analogue and modulated into the 900MHz frequency band using a frequency hopping local oscillator. The data is then transmitted in bursts of r.f. power with the amplitude profile of the bursts being shaped as specified by GSM. A fading simulator may be added at the output stage.

Fast digital signal processors are used to condition the (analogue) I and Q modulation signals. These processors replace classic 'analogue' functions such as filtering or integration by equivalent digital processes which increase precision and stability, as a function of time and temperature (Figure 61.26).

Table 61.13 A signal generator for in band GSM measurements

Parameter	Value
R.F. carrier frequency range	890 – 960MHz
Frequency resolution	< 200kHz
Frequency switching speed	< 577µs (1 time slot) to within < 4° of final phase
Frequency uncertainty	$\leq 50 \times 10^{-9}$
Output level range	−115 to 0dBm
Level uncertainty	< 0.5dB
Amplitude response	Pulse modulation with rise and fall times of ≈ 20µs
Modulation	Gaussian minimum shift keying (GMSK)
Modulation data rate	270kbit/s
Spectral purity,	
Phase noise	< 1°rms <4°pk measured in 1 – 100kHz band
Spurious signals	< −50dBc
Fading	Internal or external

As the I/Q modulator itself is still analogue, this circuit largely determines the accuracy of the signal generator. In addition to the usual quality criteria for signal generators, three more must now be considered as in Figure 61.27.

If excessive imbalances are present they can be clearly seen in the generator output spectrum and may be detected as errors in the receiver under test.

61.10.1.2 *Simulation of radio channel*

The simulation of multipath reception (fading simulation) is becoming more and more important for digital radio systems. Fading simulators for GSM tests must be capable of electronically simulating the propagation conditions over various types of terrain. The

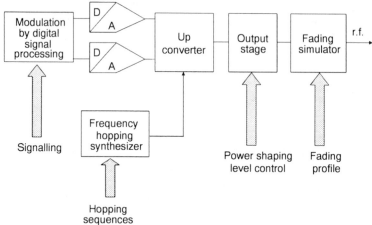

Figure 61.25 Principle of a typical signal generator

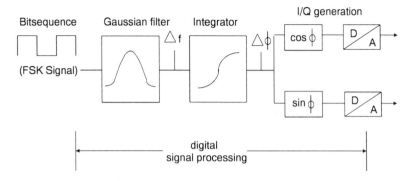

Figure 61.26 Use of digital signal processing

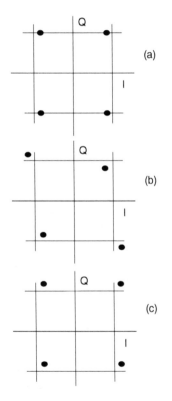

Figure 61.27 Some considerations for signal generators: (a) I/Q imbalance due to unequal gains in the two modulation paths; (b) skew since phase difference between the carriers is not 90°; (c) residual carrier components i.e. residual unmodulated carrier in the output signal

effects of the speed of the vehicle must also be built into the simulation model.

The block diagram of Figure 61.28 shows the principle behind a fading simulator:

1. The signal is split and fed along several paths.
2. Each path contains simulated loss, delay and spurious modulation (Doppler effect).
3. The signal is recombined.

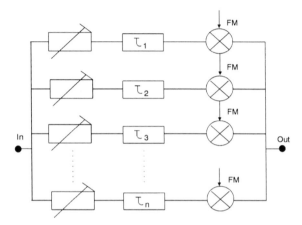

Figure 61.28 Principle of a fading simulator

Table 61.14 Fading simulator test requirements

Designation (km/h)	Speed (km/h)			
	3	50	100	250
Rural area (RA)				*
Hilly terrain (HT)			*	
Typical urban (TU)	*	*		
Equalizer test profile (EQ)				

Typical fading simulator requirements for GSM receiver tests area is given in Table 61.14.

61.10.1.3 *Sensitivity measurements*

The sensitivity of the receiver is a crucial GSM parameter, as it is for other types of radio system. As measurements directly after the demodulator are, in general, not possible and would anyway give different results for different designs, GSM test methods which do not involve opening the radio set have been defined. The loop back method, in effect, makes the radio part of the test set up. If the decoder in the receiver detects an errored telegram (wrong parity), this fact is reported to the test set by the radio's own transmitter. This is indicated by the bad frame indication bit (BFI) in the transmit telegram, bit 58 acting as the BFI flag.

This gives rise to three new test parameters which, depending on application, can be used as a measure of transmission quality (Figure 61.29).

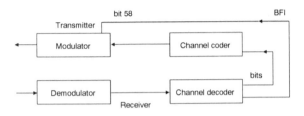

Figure 61.29 Recognising frame errors in the GSM mobile

1. BER; bit error rate, number of bad bits found in the transmission as a whole.
2. FER; frame erasure rate, number of bad frames.
3. RBER; residual bit error rate, BER for 'good' frames.

As these measurements are carried out on the logical GSM channels (e.g. traffic channel, control channel), very long measurement times may result under certain circumstances because of the various data rates and the required BER values.

61.10.1.4 *Additional receiver measurements*

The quality criteria (BER, FER, RBER) described earlier replace the parameters S/N and SINAD in analogue radio systems. With regard to the reception quality, other well known receiver measurements are also carried out, such as co-channel rejection, adjacent channel rejection, blocking and spurious responses to 12.75GHz. In most cases, the interfering signal generator has to meet stringent spectral purity requirements. Depending on the test method, unmodulated or GSM modulated, static or frequency hopping interference generators are required.

With adjacent channel measurements, a special requirement has to be taken into account. Because TDMA is used, there are adjacent channels in both the frequency domain and the time domain. Because of this, the expression 'adjacent time slot rejection' has been introduced. This measurement is carried out implicitly by defining an appropriate level for the adjacent time slots when sensitivity measurements are carried out.

61.10.2 Transmitter measurements

61.10.2.1 *Signal analyser requirements*

Conventional power meters and modulation analysers can only handle settled (static) test signals. This means they cannot be used to analyse signal packets (TDMA time slots). Even the latest display

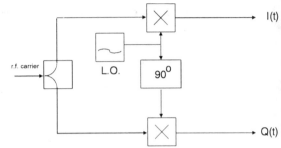

Figure 61.30 I-Q (vector) demodulator

units for analysing digitally modulated signals (constellation analysers) have a limited use.

A precise analysis of dynamic behaviour can only be obtained by fast sampling of the r.f. signal or the corresponding I/Q signals (Figure 61.30). If the samples are stored in a memory of sufficient size, they can be post processed for comprehensive and flexible analysis of the transmitter, as shown in the GSM transmitter measurement flowchart of Figure 61.31.

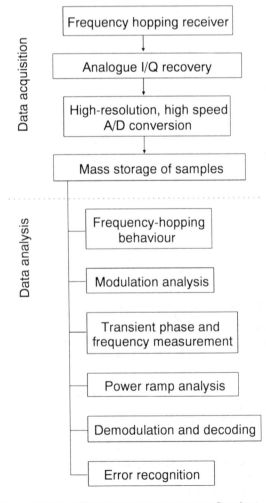

Figure 61.31 GSM transmitter measurement flowchart

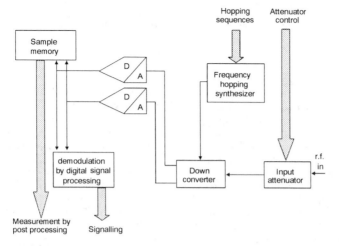

igure 61.32 Principle of the signal analyser

61.10.2.2   *Principle of the signal analyser*

.F. signals at the input of the analyser, shown in Figure 61.32, are ttenuated to the correct level for the down converter. The signals re down converted to an i.f. frequency using a frequency hopping ynthesiser. The signal is then divided into its in phase (I) and uadrature phase (Q) components. These baseband signals are di- itised and stored for post processing.

61.10.2.3   *In channel measurements on transmitters*

ome of the most important measurements on transmitters using ligital modulation are:

.   Power levels, down to 13dBm for the mobile station.
.   Power ramp up for ramp down using stipulated tolerance mask.
.   Phase noise, measured as the deviation from the ideal phase trajectory.
.   Frequency errors, also derived from phase data.

61.10.2.4   *Measuring spectral components*

he spectral components near the carrier are specified by the mask hown in Figure 61.33. The Tx signal is not continuous because of he TDMA used so that the measurement cannot be made by simply connecting up a spectrum analyser. This difficulty can be overcome y triggering the spectrum analyser in synchronism with the TDMA rames and displaying the results in zero-span mode. Further spec- rum analyser settings are given in the specifications, a distinction eing made between:

.   Measurements in the modulated section of the burst (spectrum due to modulation); resolution BW = 30kHz, video BW = 30kHz average mode.
.   Measurements at the edges of the burst (spectrum due to switching); resolution BW = 30kHz, video BW = 100kHz max-hold mode.

Spurious transmissions up to 12.75GHz must also be checked.

61.10.3   Simulation and analysis of Layer 1 coding

As the error free transmission of bits is a prime requirement, the binary data must undergo a certain amount of coding at this, the lowest level of the data transmission chain. In the GSM Specifica- tions, these functions form part of the channel coding. The industry is attempting to implement the coding and decoding functions using VLSI semiconductors. However, great caution must be exercised when ICs of this kind are used in test equipment. If precise informa- tion about the error correction facilities of a mobile phone is re- quired, for type acceptance for example, the test set must have facilities for injecting and detecting errors at different layers. Such facilities, however, cannot be realised, as VLSI circuits do not have the required interfaces.

When precise simulations and analyses are required, e.g. during development or for approval testing, it must be possible to access all levels of signalling. By using the latest fast digital signal processors

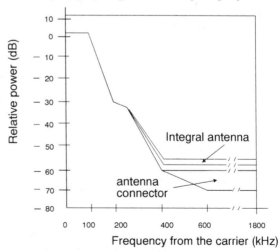

Figure 61.33   Mask used for measurement of spectral components

(DSP), test sets will be able to carry out real time simulations of GSM protocols on the one hand and perform test functions such as error injection, logging etc. on the other.

61.11 Data Link Layer (Layer 2)

The second layer of the OSI model deals with the correct transmission of well defined data blocks or telegrams. The trigger and synchronisation facilities are the most important features of test equipment for dealing at this layer. Special attention must be paid to skew problems which arise when a number of instruments are triggered externally. To solve problems of this kind at an acceptable outlay, it is necessary to design multi function test equipment which is controlled via a common trigger.

Layer 2 of GSM is indeed a highly intelligent processor unit which must make a large number of decisions in real time. Equipment that can test these functions satisfactorily also requires a high degree of built in intelligence and automatic real time behaviour. Here too, modern processors can provide a suitable solution. To simulate situations where errors occur, both layer 2 'error model' which can be modified by the user and an automatic model of correct behaviour are required.

61.12 Network Layer (Layer 3)

The network level of OSI model also specifies an intelligent exchange of datagrams between communicating parties. Each datagram handshake causes the link to go into an appropriate well defined state. These states are the basis for handling the communication service such as speech, video or data transmissions.

In this context, one encounters terminology that is familiar from analogue cellular radio networks:

1. Registration.
2. Call set up by the mobile subscriber.
3. Call set up by the fixed network subscriber.
4. Call clear down.
5. Channel change over within cell or to another cell.
6. Power control levels.
7. Queue mode.

Test sets require an enormous amount of memory to completely handle these processes as it is not just a question of simulation, these processes have to be monitored, and under certain circumstances logged, so that any errors can be analysed at a later date.

61.13 A.F. and speech codec measurements

The test procedures for acceptance testing make a distinction between a.f. measurements and r.f. measurements. The result is a new kind of measurement procedure, requiring acoustic and digital interfaces. It seems very likely that new definitions will emerge for testing the overall function of the transmit and receive path (r.f./acoustics). This kind of measurement will play an important role in the maintenance and repair of telephone handsets, and is illustrated in Figures 61.34 and 61.35.

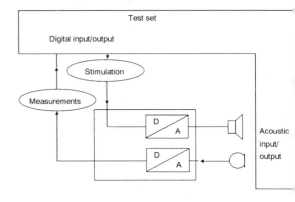

Figure 61.35 A.F./acoustic measurements (GSM)

61.14 Test set up configurations

The set up for GSM will be configured so as to permit both data analysis (protocol checks, error rates etc.) and analogue measurements. As the measurements specified by GSM are nearly always

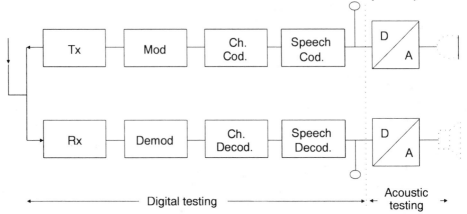

Figure 61.34 Division of measurements into r.f. (digital) and audio (acoustic)

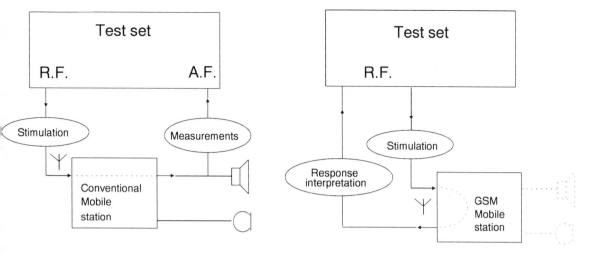

Figure 61.36 Comparison between conventional mobile and GSM measurements set up for receiver

made on closed radio sets, there is a need for test procedures which can supply information about the behaviour of the set using the signals that are available.

61.14.1 Mobile station measurements

The test set up for mobile station type approval measurements is fundamentally different from conventional (analogue) test set up, as shown in Figures 61.36 and 61.37. Because of the loop back technique used, the test set has to rely exclusively on the r.f. port without accessing the a.f. signals. The built in intelligence of the test set largely determines whether only r.f. parameters will be measured or the signalling behaviour of the mobile station will also be checked.

By using the service functions provided by the radio, it is possible to create simple test set up which do not include expensive simulators. A controller sets the radio and remote controls the test set via a suitable interface, usually serial, as illustrated in Figure 61.38. When large batches are being manufactured, the controller also makes it possible to hook up the test system via a computer network

to the factory control by means of standard interfaces such as Ethernet.

61.14.2 Base stations

Because of the widespread use of modular techniques, the distinction between transmitter and receiver measurements is more marked in the base station than in the mobile station. To perform measurements on the modules, further interfaces in addition to the r.f. interface must be defined. After the r.f. interface, the first interface to be explicitly defined by the GSM is the Y/Y level, as in Figure 61.39.

Digital test signals can be fed in or tapped at these interfaces to check the functions of the transmitter and receiver at the physical layer (layer 1). Also, when base stations are being tested, base station functions can usually be controlled automatically by a computer so that the necessary test conditions are established.

If the complete base station is to be tested, the test set has to simulate a mobile station. This places great demands on the test set

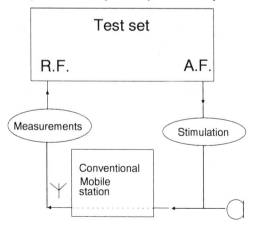
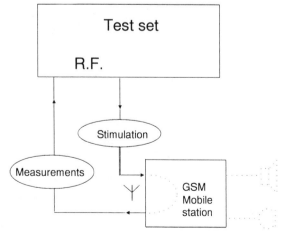

Figure 61.37 Comparison between conventional and GSM measurement set up for transmission

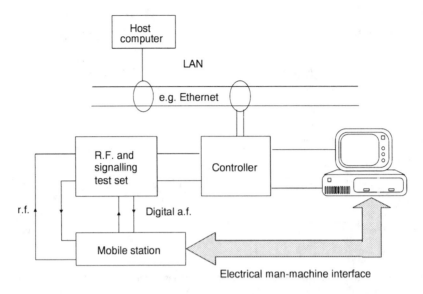

Figure 61.38 Configuration of a text set for r/f/. signalling and digital audio measurements on GSM mobiles

as far as real time characteristics and signalling facilities are concerned.

As part of the network infrastructure, the base station is linked up with other network components via well defined interfaces. When tests are carried out using a simulated mobile station, it is assumed that these network interfaces are functioning correctly, or can be simulated by appropriate test signals. This is because the base stations exhibit transparent behaviour in many cases, for example, are not able to support the protocols of the r.f. interfaces themselves.

61.15 References

HP (1990) High Productivity Measurements in Digital Transmission, *Application Note 387*, Hewlett-Packard Publication No. 5959-7898.

HP (1991a) Standard and CRC-4 Frame Testing, *Application Note 1221-1*, Hewlett-Packard Publication No. 5091-2070E.

HP (1991b) Testing N × 64 kbit/s Services, *Application Note 1211-2*, Hewlett-Packard Publication No. 5091-2069E.

HP (1991c) Testing Sub-rate Data Services (X.50, X.58), *Application Note 1211-3*, Hewlett-Packard Publication No. 1211-3, Hewlett-Packard Publication No. 5091-2072E.

HP (1992a) Introduction to SDH, Hewlett-Packard Publication No. 5091-3935E.

HP (1992b) Introduction to SONET, Hewlett-Packard Publication No. 5091-3936E.

Luttich, F. Klier, J. (1989) Signal generators SMGU and SMHU — nothing but the best, *News from Rohde & Schwarz*, No. 126.

Maucksch, T. (1990) GSM test set CMTA94 for the European digital mobile radio network, *News from Rohde & Schwarz*, No. 129 pp. 4-7.

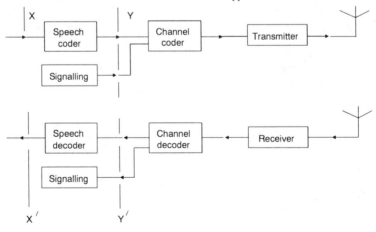

Figure 61.39 Internal interfaces of GSM basic station

62 Glossary

Fraidoon Mazda
MPhil DFH DMS MBIM CEng FIEE
Northern Telecom

Contents

62.1 Introduction

Acronyms and glossary of terms are given in the sections below. Generally the terms are not repeated in the two sections, unless they are equally well known by their acronym and their full description. Where the letters within an acronym can have slightly different interpretations, these are given within the same entry. If the acronym stands for completely different terms then these are listed separately.

62.2 Acronyms

AAN	All Area Networking. (Networking covering local and wide areas. Also used to imply combined use of LAN and WAN.)
ABM	Asynchronous Balanced Mode.
ABSBH	Average Busy Season Busy Hour. (Denotes the three months in the year having the highest average traffic during the busy hour. Special days, such as Christmas, are excluded from the calculations.)
ACK	Acknowledgement. (Control code sent from a receiver to a transmitter to acknowledge the receipt of a transmission.)
ACP	African, Caribbean, Pacific. (Group of Third World countries who have special arrangements with the European Community.)
ACS	Accredited Standards Committee. (ANSI)
ACSE	Association Control Service Element. (OSI application.)
ACTE	Approvals Committee for Terminal Equipment. (Part of European Community.)
ACC	Australian CCITT Committee.
ACD	Automatic Call Distribution. (Facility for allowing incoming calls to be queued and distributed to waiting service operators.)
ADC	Analogue to Digital Conversion.
ADDF	Automatic Digital Distribution Frame. (System used to replace manual distribution frames in plesiochronous transmission networks.)
ADM	Adaptive Delta Modulation. (Digital signal modulation technique.)
ADM	Add-Drop multiplexer. (Term sometimes used to describe a drop and insert multiplexer.)
ADP	Automatic Data Processing.
ADPCM	Addaptive Differential Pulse Code Modulation. (CCITT standard for the conversion and transmission of analogue signals at 32kbit/s.)
AE	Anomaly Events. (E.g. frame errors, parity errors, etc. CCITT M.550 for digital circuit testing.)
AEIA	Australian Electronics Industry Association.
AFC	Automatic Frequency Control.
AFIPS	American Federation of Information Processing Societies.
AFNOR	Association Francaise de Normalisation. (Standardisation body in France.)
AFRTS	American Forces Radio and Television Services.
AGC	Automatic Gain Control.
AIIA	Australian Information Industry Association.
AIN	Advanced Intelligent Network. (Bellcore released specification for provision of wide range of telecommunication capabilities and services.)

AIS	Automatic Intercept System. (System which is programmed to automatically provide information to a telephone caller, who has been intercepted and routed to it.)
ALU	Arithmetic Logic Unit.
AMPS	Advanced Mobile Phone System. (Or American Mobile Phone Standard. Analogue cellular radio standard.)
AM	Amplitude Modulation. (Analogue signal transmission encoding technique.)
AMA	Automatic Message Accounting. (Ability within an office to automatically record call information for accounting purposes. See also CAMA.)
AMI	Alternate Mark Inversion. (Line code system.)
ANBFM	Adaptive Narrow Band Frequency Modulation.
ANBS	American National Bureau of Standards.
ANDF	Architecture Neutral Distribution Format. (Scheme from OSF to enable software to be produced in single code to run on any hardware.)
ANSI	American National Standards Institute.
ANI	Automatic Number Identification. (Feature for automatically determining the identity of the caller.)
AOS	Alternate Operator Services. (Companies, in the US, who provide operator services in competition with existing suppliers such as AT&T and the RBOCs.)
AOTC	Australian and Overseas Telecommunications Corporation. (Australian PTT.)
AOWS	Asian-Oceania OSI Workshop on Standards. (Asian/Pacific area functional standards making group.)
APNSS	Analogue Private Network Signalling System.
AP	Application Processes. (Processes within computer based systems which perform specified tasks.)
APC	Aeronautical Public Correspondence. (CCIR term for airborne communication systems.)
APC	Adaptive Predictive Coding.
APD	Avalanche Photodiode. (A semiconductor device used for fibre optic communications.)
API	Application Programming Interface.
APK	Amplitude Phase Keying. (A digital modulation technique in which the amplitude and phase of the carrier are varied.)
APT	Asia Pacific Telecommunity.
ARPA	Advanced Research Project Agency. (Agency operating within the US Department of Defence.)
ARQ	Automatic Request for repetition. (A feature in transmission systems in which the receiver automatically asks the sender to retransmit a block of information, usually because there is an error in the earlier transmission.)
ARS	Automatic Route Selection. (Facility in an equipment, usually a PABX or multiplexer, to automatically select the best route for transmission through a network.)
ASCII	American Standard Code for Information Interchange. (Popular character code used for data communications and processing. Consists of seven bits, or eight bits with a parity bit added.)
ASIC	Application Specific Integrated Circuit. (Integrated circuit components which can be readily customised for a given application.)
ASN.1	Abstract Syntax Notation One.

ASR	Automatic Send/Receive. (Operation usually carried out by an older type of teleprinter equipment.)
ASTIC	Anti-SideTone Induction Coil. (Hybrid transformer used in voice transmission systems.)
ASTM	American Society for Testing and Materials.
ASE	Application Service Element. (OSI application.)
ASK	Amplitude Shift Keying. (Digital modulation technique.)
ATDM	Asynchronous Time Division Multiplexing.
ATM	Asynchronous Transfer Mode. (CCITT protocol for the transmission of voice, data and video.)
ATUG	Australian Telecommunications Users' Group.
ATV	Advanced Television.
AU	Administrative Unit. (Term used in synchronous transmission. Ref: CCITT C.709. It is the level at which circuit administration is carried out by the operator.)
AUSSAT	Australian national Satellite system operating company.
AUSTEL	Australian Telecommunications authority.
AVDM	Analogue Variable Delta Modulation.
AWG	American Wire Gauge.
B-ISDN	Broadband Integrated Services Digital Network.
BABT	British Approvals Board for Telecommunications.
BASIC	Beginners All Symbolic Instruction Code. (Computer programming language.)
BCC	Block Check Character. (A control character which is added to a block of transmitted data, used in checking for errors.)
BCD	Binary Coded Decimal. (An older character code set, in which numbers are represented by a four bit sequence.)
BCH	Bose Chaudhure Hocquengherm. (Coding technique.)
BDT	Bureau for Development of Telecommunications.
BDF	Building Distribution Frame.
BELLCORE	Bell Communications Research. (Research organisation, incorporating parts of the former Bell Laboratories, established after the divestiture of AT&T. Funded by the BOCs and RBOCs to formulate telecommunication standards.)
BER	Bit Error Ratio. (Also called Bit Error Rate. It is a measure of transmission quality. It is the number of bits received in error during a transmission, divided by the total number of bits transmitted in a specific interval.)
BERT	Bit Error Ratio Tester. (Equipment used for digital transmission testing.)
BETRS	Basic Exchange Telecommunications Radio Service.
BEXR	Basic Exchange Radio.
BHCA	Busy Hour Call Attempts. (Parameter used in the design of telephone exchanges. It is the number of calls placed in the busy hour. Also referred to as Busy Hour Calls or BHC.)
BIP	Bit Interleaved Parity. (A simple method of parity checking.)
BIST	Built In Self Test.
BISYNC	Binary Synchronous communications. (Older protocol used for character oriented transmission on half-duplex links.)

BnZS	Bipolar with n-Zero Substitution. (A channel code Examples are B3ZS which has three-zero substitution; B6ZS with six-zero substitution, etc.)
BOC	Bell Operating Company. (Twenty-two BOCs were formed after the divestiture of AT&T, acting as local telephone companies in the US. They are now organised into seven Regional Bell Operating Companies or RBOCs.)
BORSCHT	Battery, Overload protection, Ringing, Supervision Coding, Hybrid, and Test access. (These are the functions provided in connection with a subscriber line circuit. The functions are usually implemented by an integrated circuit.)
BPON	Broadband over Passive Optical Networks.
BPSK	Binary Phase Shift Keying.
BPV	Bipolar Violation. (Impairment of digital transmission system, using bipolar coding, where two pulses occur consecutively with the same polarity.)
BRA	Basic Rate Access. (ISDN, 2B+D code.)
BRAP	Broadcast Recognition with Alternating Priorities. (Multiple access technique.)
BRITE	Basic Research in Industrial Technology for Europe. (EC programme.)
BRT	British Rail Telecommunications. (Telecommunications arm of British Rail, in the UK.)
BRZ	Bipolar Return to Zero. (A channel coding technique, used for digital transmission.)
BSC	Base Station Controller. (Controllers for Base Transceiver Stations, or BTS, within mobile radio systems.)
BSGL	Branch System General Licence. (Telecommunications licence in the UK.)
BSI	British Standards Institute.
BSS	Broadcast Satellite Service.
BTS	Base Transceiver Station. (Used in mobile radio based systems to provide the air interface to the customer.)
BS	Base Station. (Used in mobile radio systems.)
BT	Formerly British Telecom. (UK.)
CAC	Comite d'Action Commerciale. (Commercial Action Committee. Part of CEPT.)
CAD/CAM	Computer Aided Design/Computer Aided Manufacture.
CAI	Common Air Interface. (Radio communication standard supported by ETSI.)
CAMA	Centralised Automatic Message Acconting. (A centralised version of AMA, used in larger offices serving several smaller ones which may be too small to justify AMA on their own.)
CANTO	Caribbean Association of National Telecommunication Organisations. (Association of state owned or private telecommunications carriers providing domestic and international services in the Caribbean.)
CARS	Community Antenna Radio Service.
CAS	Channel Associated Signalling. (CCITT signalling method.)
CASE	Computer Aided Software Engineering (or Computer Aided System Engineering).
CATA	Community Antenna Television Association.
CATV	Community Antenna Television. (Also refered to as Cable Television.)

CBC — Canadian Broadcasting Corporation.

CBCS — Cordless Business Communication System.

CBDS — Connectionless Broadband Data Service. (ETSI's version of SMDS.)

CBEMA — Computer Business Equipment Manufacturers' Association. (USA.)

CBS — Columbia Broadcasting System.

CBX — Computer Controlled PBX.

CCB — Coin Collection Box. (Pay phone.)

CCC — Clear Channel Capacity.

CCD — Charged Coupled Device. (Semiconductor device used for analogue storage and imaging.)

CCH — Comite de Co-ordination de Harmonisation. (CEPT)

CCI — Co-channel Interference. (Interference between two subscribers, using the same channel but in different cells, of a cellular mobile radio system.)

CCIA — Computer and Communications Industry Association. (USA.)

CCIR — Comite Consultatif Internationale des Radiocommunications. (International Radio Consultative Committee. Standards making body within the ITU.)

CCIS — Common Channel Interoffice Signalling. (North American signalling system which uses a separate signalling network between switches.)

CCITT — Comite Consultatif Internationale de Telephonique et Telegraphique. (Consulative Committee for International Telephone and Telegraphy. Standards making body within the ITU.)

CCR — Commitment, Concurrency and Recovery.

CCS — Cent Call Second. (100 call seconds. It is a measure of the traffic load and is obtained by the product of the number of calls per hour and the average holding time per call, expressed in seconds, and dividing the product by 100.

CCS — Common Channel Signalling. (CCITT standard singalling system. Also called CCSS.)

CCSS — Common Channel Signalling System. (CCITT standard signalling system. Also called CCS or Number 7 signalling.)

CCTA — Central Communications and Telecommunications Agency. (UK Government equipment procurement agency.)

CCTS — Comite de Co-ordination pour les Telecommunications par Satellites. (Co-ordination committee for satellite telecommunications. CEPT.)

CCV — Co-ordination Committee for Vocabulary. (CCITT/CCIR/IEC.)

CCVT — Closed Circuit Vapour Generator. (Thermoelectric power generator.)

CDDI — Copper Distributed Data Interface. (Name given to FDDI running over copper media.)

CDM — Code Delta Modulation. (Or Continuous Delta Modulation.)

CDMA — Code Division Multiple Access.

CDO — Community Dial Office. (Usually refers to an unattended switching centre which serves a small community and is controlled from a larger central office.)

CEC — Commission of the European Communities.

CEE — Central and Eastern Europe.

CEN — Comite Europeen de Normalisation. (Committee for European Standardisation.)

CENELEC — Comite Europeen de Normalisation Electrotechnique. (Committee for European Electrotechnical Standardisation.)

CEPT — Conference des administrations Europeenes des Postes et Telecommunications. (Conference of European Posts and Telecommunications administrations. Body representing European PTTs.)

CFM — Companded Frequency Modulation.

CFM — Composite Fade Margin. (Used in microwave system design.)

CFSK — Coherent Frequency Shift Keying.

CICC — Contactless Integrated Circuit Card. (ISO standard for a smart card in which information is stored and retrieved without use of conductive contacts.)

CIE — Commission Internationale de l'Eclairage.

CIM — Computer Integrated Manufacture. (General term covering the use of computers within the manufacturing processes.)

CIS — Commonwealth of Independent States. (Alliance of states following the collapse of the USSR.)

CISPR — Comite International Special des Perturbations Radioelectriques. (IEC International Special Committee on Radio Interference.)

CLAN — Cableless Local Area Network. (Radio based LAN.)

CLI — Command Line Interface. (Usually refers to an interface which allows remote asynchronous terminal access into a network management system. Also referred to as Command Line Interpreter.)

CLI — Calling Line Identity. (Facility for determining identity of the caller. See also CLID.)

CLID — Calling Line Identification. (Telephone facility which allows the called party to determine the identity of the caller.)

CLIP — Connection-Less Interworking Protocol. (OSI Network Layer.)

CLTA — Comite de liaison pour les telecommunications transatlantiques. (Liaison committee for transatlantic telecommunications. CEPT.)

CLTS — Connection-Less Transport Service.

CMI — Code Mark Inversion. (Line coding technique.)

CMIP — Common Management Information Protocol. (Protocol widely used in network management.)

CMIS — Common Management Information Service.

CMISE — Common Management Information Service Element. (Specific type of ASE.)

CMOL — Common Management information protocol Over Logical link control.

CMOS — Complementary Metal Oxide Semiconductor. (Integrated circuit technology.)

CMOT — CMIP Over TCP/IP.

CMS — Call Management System.

CMT — Character Mode Terminal. (E.g. VT100, which does not provide graphical capability.)

CNLP — Connection-Less Network Protocol. (Same as CLIP.)

CNN — Cable News Network. (USA.)

CO — Central Office. (Usually refers a central switching or control centre belonging to a PTT.)

CoCom — Co-ordinating Committee on Multilateral Export Controls.

COCOT — Consumer Owned Coin Operated Telephone. (Privately owned coin boxes linking to public telephone lines.)

CODEC   COder-DECoder.

COMSAT   Communication Satellite Corporation.

CONUS   Continental United States.

COS   Corporation for Open Systems. (US trade association.)

COSINE   Co-operation for Open Systems Interconnection Networking in Europe.

CPE   Customer Premise Equipment.

CP/M   Control Programme for Microcomputers. (Operating system popularly used for microcomputers.)

CPFSK   Continuous Phase Frequency Shift Keying.

CPODA   Contention Priority-Oriented Demand Assignment protocol. (Multiple access technique with contention for reservations. See PODA and FPODA.)

CPSK   Coherent Phase Shift Keying.

CPU   Central Processing Unit. (Usually part of a computer.)

CR   Carriage Return. (Code used on a teleprinter to start a new line.)

CRA   Call Routing Apparatus.

CRC   Cyclic Redundancy Check. (Bit oriented protocol used for checking for errors in transmitted data.)

CRT   Cathode Ray Tube.

CS   Central Station.

CSDN   Circuit Switched Data Network.

CSMA   Carrier Sense Multiple Access. (LAN Multiple access technique.)

CSMA/CD   Carrier Sense Multiple Access with Collision Detection. (LAN access technique, with improved throughput, under heavy load conditions, compared to pure CSMA.)

CSTA   Computer Supported Telephony Applications. (Or Computer Supported Telecommunication Applications. For example, telemarketing applications.)

CSU   Channel Service Unit. (Subscriber line terminating unit in North America.)

CT   Cordless Telephony. (CT1 is first generation; CT2 is second generation, and CT3 is third generation.)

CTA   Cable Television Association. (UK trade association of cable television suppliers.)

CTCSS   Continuous Tone Controlled Squelch System. (Method for calling in paging systems.)

CTD   Centre for Telecommunications Development. (Part of ITU.)

CTIA   Cellular Telecommunications Industry Association. (USA trade association.)

CTR   Common Technical Regulation. (European Community mandatory standard.)

CTS   Conformance Test Services. (Part of European Commission initiative.)

CTS   Clear To Send. (Control code used for data transmission in modems.)

CVSD   Continuous Variable Slope Delta modulation. (Proprietary method used for speech compression. Also called CVSDM.)

CW   Continuous Wave.

DAMA   Demand Assigned Multiple Access.

DAMPS   Digital Advanced Mobile Phone System. (Digital version of AMPS, which has the same basic architecture and signalling protocol.)

DAR   Dynamic Alternative Routing. (Traffic routing scheme proposed by BT in the UK.)

DARPA   Defence Advanced Research Projects Agency. (USA Government agency.)

DASS   Digital Access Signalling System. (Signalling system introduced in the UK prior to CCITT standards I.440 and I.450.)

DASS   Demand Assignment Signalling and Switching unit.

DATTS   Data Acquisition Telecommand and Tracking Station.

DATV   Digitally Assisted Television.

DBMS   Database Management System.

DBS   Direct Broadcasting by Satellite. (Or Direct Broadcast Satellite. High power satellite suitable for directly beaming television programmes onto small receive-only satellite dishes.)

DBT   Deutsche Bundespost Telekom. (Also written DBP-T. German PTT.)

DCC   Data Communication Channel.

DCDM   Digitally Coded Delta Modulation. (Delta modulation technique in which the step size is controlled by the bit sequence produced by the sampling and quantisation.)

DCE   Data Circuit termination Equipment. (Exchange end of a network, connecting to a DTE. Usually used in packet switched networks.)

DCF   Data Communications Function.

DCN   Data Communications Network.

DCR   Dynamically Controlled Routing. (Traffic routing method proposed by Bell Northern Research, Canada.)

DCS   Digital Cellular System. (For example DCS 1800 operating at 1800MHz.)

DCS   Digital Crossconnect System. (See also DCX and DXC.)

DCS   Dynamic Channel Selection. (For example as used on call set-up in the CEPT 900MHz analogue cordless telephony standard.)

DCT   Discrete Cosine Transform. (Technique used in transform picture coding.)

DCX   Digital Crossconnect. (See also DXC and DSC.)

DDC   Data Country Code. (Part of an international telephone number.)

DDD   Direct Distance Dialling. (Generally refers to conventional dial-up long distance calls placed over a telephone network without operator assistance.)

DDF   Digital Distribution Frame. (Frame for physical connection of transmission lines. See also ADDF and MDDF.)

DDI   Direct Dialling In. (External caller able to dial directly to an extension.)

DDI   Distributed Data Interface. (Proposal to run the FDDI standard over unshielded twisted pair.)

DDN   Digital Data Network.

DDN   Defence Data Network. (US military network derived from the ARPANET.)

DDP   Distributed Data Processing.

DDS   Digital Data Service. (North American data service.)

DE   Defect Events. (E.g. loss of signal, loss of frame synchronisation, etc. CCITT M.550 for digital circuit testing.)

DECT	Digital European Cordless Telephony. (Or Digital European Cordless Telecommunications. ETSI standard, intended to be a replacement for CT2.)
DEDM	Dolby Enhanced Delta Modulation.
DELTA	Developing European Learning through Technological Advance. (European Community information technology and telecommunication programme associated with training.)
DEPSK	Differentially Encoded Phase Shift Keying.
DES	Data Encryption Standard. (Public standard encryption system from the American National Bureau of Standards.)
DFM	Dispersive Fade Margin. (Used in microwave system design.)
DFT	Discrete Fourier Transform.
DG	Directorates-General. (Departments of the European Commission, usually referred to by numerals, e.g. DGIV.)
DID	Direct Inward Dialling. (PABX feature allowing an external caller to connect to an extension without first going through an operator.)
DIL	Dual In Line package. (Integrated circuit packaging. Also known as DIP.)
DIN	Deutsches Institue fur Normung. (Standardisation body in Germany.)
DIP	Dual In line Package. (Integrated circuit packaging. Also known as DIL.)
DIS	Draft International Standard.
DLC	Data Link Control.
DLS	Data Link Service.
DM	Degraded Minutes. (Any one minute period with a BER exceeding 10^{-6}, as per CCITT G.821.)
DM	Delta Modulation. (Digital signal modulation technique.)
DMA	Direct Memory Access.
DME	Distributed Management Environment. (OSF.)
DN	Directory Number. (Of a customer in a switching system.)
DN	Distinguishing Name.
DNHR	Dynamic Non-Hierarchical Routing. (Traffic routing method implemented by AT&T.)
DNIC	Data Network Identification Code. (Part of an international telephone number.)
DOD	Department Of Defence. (US agency.)
DOS	Disk Operating System. (Popular operating system for personal computers.)
DOTAC	Department of Transport And Communications. (Australian.)
DOV	Data Over Voice. (Technique for simultaneous transmission of voice and data over telephone lines. This is a less sophisticated technique than ISDN.)
DPCM	Differential Pulse Code Modulation.
DPNSS	Digital Private Network Signalling System. (Inter-PABX signalling system used in the UK.)
DQDB	Distributed Queue Double Bus. (IEEE standard 802.6 for Metropolitan Area Networks.)
DQPSK	Differential Quaternary Phase Shift Keying.
DRG	Direction a la Reglementation Generale. (Directorate for General Regulation, in France.)
DRIVE	Dedicated Road Infrastructure for Vehicle safety in Europe. (European Community programme in the area of information technology and telecommunications, associated with road transport.)

DS-0	Digital Signal level 0. (Part of the US transmission hierarchy, transmitting at 64kbit/s. DS-1 transmits at 1.544Mbit/s, DS-2 at 6.312Mbit/s, etc.)
DSAP	Destination Service Access Point. (Refers to the address of service at destination.)
DSB	Double Sideband.
DSBEC	Double Sideband Emitted Carrier.
DSBSC	Double Sideband Suppressed Carrier modulation. (A method for amplitude modulation of a signal.)
DSC	District Switching Centre. (Part of the switching hierarchy in BT's network.)
DSE	Data Switching Exchange. (Part of packet switched network.)
DSI	Digital Speech Interpolation. (Method used in digital speech transmission where the channel is activated only when speech is present.)
DSM	Delta Sigma Modulation. (Digital signal modulation technique.)
DSP	Digital Signal Processing.
DSRR	Digital Short-Range Radio.
DSS	Digital Subscriber Signalling. (CCIT term for the N-ISDN access protocol.)
DSSS	Direct Sequence Spread Spectrum.
DSU	Data Service Unit. (Customer premise interface to a digital line provided by a PTT.)
DSX-1	Digital Signal Crossconnect. (Crossconnect used for DS-1 signals.)
DTE	Data Terminal Equipment. (User end of network which connects to a DCE. Usually used in packet switched networks.)
DTI	Department of Trade and Industry.
DTL	Diode Transistor Logic. (An older form of integrated circuit logic family.)
DTMF	Dual Tone Multi-Frequency. (Telephone signalling system used with push button telephones.)
DTP	Distributed Transaction Processing.
DTS	Digital Termination System. (Local radio loop provided by carriers in the US.)
DXC	Digital Crossconnect. (See also DCX and DCS.)
EAU	European Unit of Account. (Earlier monitory unit of the EEC which was created in 1974 and replaced by the ECU in 1981.)
EBCDIC	Extended Binary Coded Decimal Interchange Code. (Eight bit character code set.)
EBIT	European Broadband Interconnect Trial. (Collaborative effort between PTOs to support RACE application pilots into switched broadband. Initial trial was planned at 2Mbit/s switched, progressing to 140Mbit/s.)
EBU	European Broadcasting Union.
EC	European Commission.
ECC	Embedded Communication Channel. (Channel used within SDH to carry communication information rather than data.)
ECC	Error Control Coding. (Coding used to reduce errors in transmission.)
ECITC	European Committee for IT Certification.
ECJ	European Court of Justice.
ECL	Emitter Coupled Logic. (Integrated circuit technology.)
ECMA	European Computer Manufacturers Association.

ECREEA   European Conference of Radio and Electronic Equipment Association.

ECS   European Communication Satellite.

ECSA   Exchange Carriers Standards Association. (USA)

ECTEL   European Conference of Telecommunications managers.

ECTRA   European Committee for Telecommunications Regulatory Affairs. (Part of CEPT.)

ECTUA   European Council of Telecommunications Users' Associations.

ECU   European Currency Unit. (Monetary unit of the EEC, created in 1981.)

EDI   Electronic Data Interchange. (Protocol for interchanging data between computer based systems.)

EDIFACT   EDI For Administration Commerce and Transport. (International rules for trading documents, e.g. purchase orders, payment orders, etc.)

EDP   Electronic Data Processing.

EEA   Electrical Engineering Association.

EEA   Electronic and business Equipment Association.

EEC   European Economic Community.

EEMA   European Electronic Mail Association.

EEPROM   Electrically Erasable Read Only Memory. (Integrated circuit used to store data, which can be erased by electrical methods.)

EET   Equipment Engaged Tone. (Tone customer receives when there is no free line for his call.)

EFS   Error Free Seconds. (In transmitted data it determines the proportion of one second intervals, over a given period, when the data is error free.)

EFT   Electronic Funds Transfer.

EFTA   European Free Trade Association.

EFTPOS   Electronic Funds Transfer at the Point Of Sale.

EHF   Extremely High Frequency. (Usually used to describe the portion of the electromagnetic spectrum in the range 30GHz to 300GHz.)

EIA   Electronic Industries Association. (Trade association in USA)

EIRP   Equivalent Isotropically Radiated Power. (Or Effective Isotropically Radiated Power. Of an antenna.)

EIUF   European ISDN Users Forum.

ELT   Emergency Locator Transmitter.

EM   Element Manager. (First level network manager controlling elements.)

EMA   Electronic Mail Association.

E-MAIL   Electronic Mail.

EMC   Electromagnetic Compatibility.

EMI   Electromagnetic Interference.

EMP   ElectroMagnetic Pulse. (Released by a nuclear explosion.)

EMS   European Monetary System.

EMUG   European MAP Users' Group.

EN   Equipment Number. (Code given to a line circuit, primarily in switches, to indicate its location on equipment racks.)

EN   Europaische Norm. (Norm Europeenne or European standard.)

ENV   European pre-standard.

EOA   End Of Address. (Header code used in a transmitted frame.)

EOB   End Of Block. (Character used at end of a transmitted frame. Also referred to as End of Transmitted Block or ETB.)

EOC   Embedded Operations Channel. (Bits carried in transmission frame which contain auxiliary information such as for maintenance and supervisor. This is also called a Facilities Data Link, FDL.)

EOT   End Of Transmission. (Control code used in transmission to signal the receiver that all the information has been sent.)

EOTC   European Organisation for Testing and Certification.

EOTT   End Office Toll Trunking. (US term for trunks which are located between end offices situated in different toll areas.)

EOW   Engineering Order Wire. (A channel for voice or data communication between two stations on a transmission line.)

EP   European Parliment.

EPHOS   European Procurement Handbook for Open Systems. (Equivalent to GOSIP.)

EPIRB   Emergency Position Indicating Radio Beacon.

ERC   European Radiocommunications Committee. (Part of CEPT.)

ERDF   European Regional Development Fund.

ERL   Echo Return Loss.

ERM   Exchange Rate Mechanism. (Used within the European Community.)

ERMES   European Radio Messaging Service. (pan-European standard for paging.)

ERP   Equipment Radiated Power. (Also referred to as Effective Radiated Power of an antenna.)

ESA   European Space Agency.

ESB   Emergency Service Bureau. (A centralised location to which all emergency calls (e.g. police, ambulance, fire brigade) are routed.)

ESF   Extended Superframe. (North American 24 frame digital transmission format.)

ESN   Electronic Serial Number. (Usually refers to the personal identity number coded into mobile radio handsets.)

ESO   European Standardisation Organisation.

ESPA   European Selective Paging Association.

ESPRIT   European Strategic Programme for Research and Development in Information Technologies.

ESQL   Embedded Structured Query Language.

ESS   Electronic Switching System. (A generic term used to describe stored programme control exchange switching systems.)

ETACS   Extended Total Access Communications System. (Extension of TACS with additional channel allocation below the existing TACS channels.)

ETB   End of Transmission Block. (A control character which denotes the end of a block of Bisync transmitted data.)

ETCO   European Telecommunications Consultancy Organisation.

ETE   Exchange Terminating Equipment.

ETIS   European Telecommunications Information Services. (Part of CEPT.)

ETNO   European Telecommunications Network Operators (Association of European public operators.)

ETS   Electronic Tandem Switch.

ETS   European Telecommunication Standard. (Norme Europeenne de Telecommunications. Standard produced by ETSI.)

TSI	European Telecommunications Standards Institute.
TX	End of Text. (A control character used to denote the end of transmitted text, which was started by a STX character.)
UCATEL	European Conference of Associations of Telecommunication industries.)
URATOM	European Atomic energy community. (Established by the Treaty of Rome in 1957.)
URESCOM	European Institute for Research and Strategic Studies in Communications. (Part of CEPT.)
UTELSAT	European Telecommunications Satellite organisation.
WOS	European Workshop on Open Systems.
AS	Frame Alignment Signal. (Used in the alignment of digital transmission frames.)
AX	Facsimile.
CC	Federal Communications Commission. (US authority, appointed by the President to regulate all interstate and international telecommunications.)
CS	Frame Check Sequence. (Field added to a transmitted frame to check for errors.)
DDI	Fibre Distributed Digital Interface. (Standard for optical fibre transmission.)
DL	Facilities Data Link. (See EOC.)
DM	Frequency Division Multiplexing. (Signal multiplexing technique.)
DMA	Frequency Division Multiple Access. (Multiple access technique based on FDM.)
DX	Full Duplex. (Transmission system in which the two stations connected by a link can transmit and receive simultaneously.)
EC	Feedforward Error Correction. (Also called Forward Error Correction. Technique for correcting errors due to transmission.)
EXT	Far End Crosstalk.
FM	Flat Fade Margin. (Used in microwave system design.)
FSK	Fast Frequency Shift Keying.
HSS	Frequency Hopping Spread Spectrum.
IFO	First In First Out. (Technique for buffering data.)
IPS	Federal Information Processing Standards. (Developed in US by NIST.)
ITL	Fibre In The Loop. (Fibre optic cable access in the local loop to the subscriber.)
M	Facilities Management.
M	Forms Management.
M	Frequency Modulation. (Analogue signal modulation technique.)
MFB	Frequency Modulation Feedback.
PGA	Field Programmable Gate Array.
PLMTS	Future Public Land Mobile Telecommunication System. (CCIR name for third generation land mobile system. See also UMTS.)
PODA	Fixed Priority Oriented Demand Assignment. (Medium multiple access method.)
PS	Fast Packet Switch. (New standard for transmission based on frame relay or cell relay.)
SK	Frequency Shift Keying. (Digital modulation technique.)
SN	Frequency Subset Number. (Number allocated to individual pagers within ERMES.)

FSS	Fixed Satellite Service.
FT	France Telecom. (French PTT.)
FTAM	File Transfer and Access Method. (Or File Transfer Access and Management. International standard.)
FTP	File Transfer Protocol. (Used within TCP/IP.)
FTTC	Fibre To The Curb. (Method for implementing fibre optic access in the local loop, where the fibre is taken to street-side termination points and then dropped off to individual subscribers on copper.)
FTTH	Fibre To The Home. (Method of implementing fibre optic access in the local loop, where the fibre cable is taken all the way to the subscriber's premises.)
GAP	Groupe d'Analyse et de Prevision. (Analysis and Forecasting Group. A sub-committee of SOGT, part of the European Community.)
GATT	General Agreement on Tariffs and Trade.
GDN	Government Data Network. (UK private data network for use by government departments.)
GDP	Gross Domestic Product. (Measure of output from a country.)
GEN	Global European Network. (Joint venture between European PTOs to provide high speed leased line and switched services. Likely to be replaced by METRAN in mid 1990s.)
GEOS	Geodetic Earth Orbiting Satellite.
GHz	GigaHerts. (Measure of frequency. Equal to 1000000000 cycles per second. See Hertz or Hz.)
GMSK	Gaussian Minimum Shift Keying. (Modulation technique, as used in GSM.)
GNMP	Government Network Management Profile. (Government procurement standard for network management, as part of GOSIP.)
GNP	Gross National Product.
GOES	Geostationary Operational Environmental Satellite.
GoS	Grade of Service. (Measure of service performance as perceived by the user.)
GOSIP	Government OSI Profile. (Government procurement standard.)
GPS	Global Positioning System. (Usually refers to satellite based vehicle positioning.)
GSC	Group Switching Centre. (Part of the hierarchy of switching in BT's network. Also called the primary trunk switching centre by CCITT.)
GSLB	Groupe Special Large Bande. (A CEPT broadband working group.)
GSM	Groupe Special Mobile. (pan-European standard for mobile communication.)
GSO	Geostationary Satellite Orbit.
HACBSS	Homestead & Community Broadcasting Satellite Services.
HCI	Human Computer Interface.
HD	Harmonisation Document. (Sometimes used to describe an EN.)
HDB3	High Density Bipolar 3. (Line transmission encoding technique.)
HDLC	Higher level Data Link Control. (CCITT bit oriented protocol for handling data.)

HDSL	High bit rate Digital Subscriber Line. (Bellcore technical advisory for the transmission of high bit rate data over twisted copper lines.)
HDTV	High Definition Television. (New television transmission standard.)
HF	High Frequency. (Radio signal.)
HKTA	Hong Kong Telecommunications Authority.
HLR	Home Location Register. (Database containing subscriber information in mobile communications.)
HOMUX	Higher Order Multiplexer.
HRC	Harmonically Related Carrier. (Carrier system used in cable television.)
HRC	High Rupturing Capacity. (Usually refers to a type of electrical fuse used to break large values of current.)
HRDS	Hypothetical Reference Digital Section. (CCITT G.921 for digital circuit measurements.)
HRP	Horizontal Radiation Pattern. (Of an antenna.)
HSE	Health and Safety Executive. (UK)
Hz	Hertz. (Measure of frequency. One Hertz is equal to a frequency of one cycle per second.)
IA2	International Alphabet 2. (Code used in a teleprinter, also called the Murray code.)
IA5	International Alphabet 5. (International standard alphanumeric code, which has facility for national options. The US version is ASCII.)
IAB	Internet Activities Board.
IBC	Integrated Broadband Communications. (Part of the RACE programme.)
IBCN	Integrated Broadband Communications Network.
IBM	International Business Machines.
IBS	Intelsat Business Services.
IC	Integrated Circuit. (Semiconductor component.)
ICA	International Communications Association. (Telecommunications users' group in the USA.)
ICAO	International Civil Aviation Organisation.
ICMP	Internet Control Message Protocol. (Protocol developed by DARPA as part of Internet for the host to communicate with gateways.)
ICUG	International Closed User Group services.
IDA	Integrated Digital Access. (ISDN pilot service in the UK.)
IDN	Integrated Digital Network. (Usually refers to the digital public network which uses digital transmission and switching.)
IEC	International Electrotechnical Commission.
IEC	Interexchange Carrier. (US term for any telephone operator licensed to carry traffic between LATAs interstate or intrastate.)
IEEE	Institute for Electrical and Electronics Engineers. (USA professional organisation.)
IETF	Internet Engineering Task Force.
I-ETS	Interim European Telecommunicaitons Standard. (ETSI.)
IF	Intermediate Frequency.
IFIPS	International Federation of Information Processing Societies.
IFOS	Integrated Fibre Optic Subscriber. (System used in Japan for fibre cabling to domestic and small businesses.)

IFRB	International Frequency Registration Board.
IFU	Interface Unit. (Module interfacing to a crosscon nect within the SDH.)
IGFET	Insulated Gate Field Effect Transistor. (A semicon ductor unipolar transistor with a high input imped ance.)
IKBS	Intelligent Knowledge Based System.
IM	Intermodulation.
IMO	International Maritime Organisation.
IMSI	International Mobile Subscriber Identity. (Person number associated with a PCN user's handset, an issued on his SIM. It is the number which the ne work uses to identify the mobile.)
IMTS	Improved Mobile Telephone System. (Analogu cellular radio standard, superseded by AMPS. Nor American origin.)
IN	Intelligent Network.
INMARSAT	International Maritime Satellite organisation.
INTELSAT	International Telecommunication Satellite organisa tion.
INTUG	International Telecommunications Users' Group.
IO	International Organisation.
I/O	Input/output. (Usually refers to the input and outp ports of an equipment, such as a computer.)
IOR	Indian Ocean Region.
IP	Internet Protocol.
IPC	Inter-Processor Communications.
IPC	International Private Circuit.
IPM	Inter-Personal Messaging. (Use of Electronic Da Interchange.)
IPR	Intellectual Property Rights.
IPVC	International Private Virtual Circuit.
IR	Infrared.
IRC	Incrementally Related Carrier. (Carrier system use in cable television.)
IRED	Infrared Emitting Diode.
IS	International Standard.
IS	Intermediate System.
ISD	International Subscriber Dialling.
ISDN	Integrated Services Digital Network. (Technique f the simultaneous transmission of a range of service such as voice, data and video, over telephone lines
ISI	Inter-Symbol Interference. (Interference betwee adjacent pulses of a transmitted code.)
ISLAN	Integrated Services Digital Network. (LAN whic can carry an integrated service, such as voice, da and image.)
ISM	Industrial, Scientific and Medical. (Usually refers ISM equipment or applications.)
ISO	International Standardisation Organization.
ISO-DE	ISO Development Environment.
ISP	International Standardised Profile.
ISP	Interface Session Process.
IT	Information Technology. (Generally refers to indu tries using computers e.g. data processing.)
ITA	International Telegraph Alphabet.
ITAC	Information Technology Association of Canada.
ITAEGT	Information Technology Advisory and co-ordinatic Expert Group on private Telecommunication ne work standards.
ITANZ	Information Technology Association of New Ze land.

STC	Information Technology Steering Committee. (Comite de Direction de la Technologie de l'Information. Consists of CEN/CENLEC/ETSI.)
U	International Telecommunication Union.
USA	Information Technology User Standards Association.
A	Integrated Voice Application.
DT	Integrated Voice and Data Terminal. (Equipment with integrated computing and voice capabilities. In its simplest form it consists of a PC with telephone incorporated. Facilities such as storage and recall of telephone numbers is included.)
M	Integrated Voice Mail.
C	Interexchange Carrier. (USA long distance telecommunication carrier.)
I	International X.25 Infrastructure. (Pilot backbone pan-European network used by Europe's academic community.)
IDA	Japan Electronic Industry Development Association.
SI	Joint European Standards Institute. (CEN and CENELEC combined group in the area of information technology.)
PDEC	Japan Information Processing Development Centre.
S	Japanese Industrial Standard. (Product marking used in Japan to denote conformance to a specified standard.)
SC	Japanese Industrial Standards Committee. (Standards making body which is funded by the Japanese government.)
A	Japanese Standards Association.
M	Job Transfer and Manipulation. (Communication protocols used to perform tasks in a network of interconnected open systems.)
BS	Knowledge Based System.
Hz	KiloHertz. (Measure of frequency. Equals to 1000 cycles per second.)
DD	Kokusai Denshin Denwa Co. Ltd. (Japanese international carrier.)
AMA	Localised Automatic Message Accounting. (The ability to use AMA within a local office.)
AN	Local Area Network. (A network shared by communicating devices, usually on a relatively small geographical area. Many techniques are used to allow each device to obtain use of the network.)
AP	Link Access Protocol.
APB	Link Access Protocol Balanced. (X.25 protocol.)
APD	Link Access Protocol Digital. (ISDN standard.)
APM	Link Access Protocol for Modems. (CCITT V.42 standard.)
ASER	Light Amplification by Stimulated Emission of Radiation. (Laser is also used to refer to a component.)
ATA	Local Access and Transport Area. (Area of responsibility of local carrier in USA. When telephone circuits have their start and finish points within a LATA they are the sole responsibility of the local telephone

	company concerned. When they cross a LATA's boundary, i.e. go inter-LATA, they are the responsibility of an interexchange carrier or IEC.)
LBA	Least Busy Alternative. (Traffic routing strategy defined for fully connected networks.)
LBO	Line Build Out. (The extension of the electrical length of a line, for example by adding capacitors.)
LBRV	Low Bit Rate Voice. (Speech encoding technique which allows voice transmission at under 64kbit/s.)
LCD	Liquid Crystal Display.
LCN	Local Communications Network. (CCITT)
LCR	Least Cost Routing. (Usually applies to the use of alternative long distance routes, e.g. by using different carriers, in order to minimise transmission costs.)
LDDC	Long Distance D.C. line signalling. (Method of d.c. signalling.)
LDM	Linear Delta Modulation. (Delta modulation technique in which a series of linear segments of constant slope provides the input time function.)
LEC	Local Exchange Carrier. (USA local telecommunication carrier.)
LED	Light Emitting Diode. (Component which converts electrical energy into light.)
LEO	Low Earth Orbiting.
LEOS	Low Earth Orbit System. (Satellite communication system with satellites not in geostationary orbit.)
LIFO	Last In First Out. (Technique for buffering data.)
LISN	Line Impedance Stabilising Network. (An artificial network used in measurement systems to define the impedance of the mains supply.)
LJU	Line Jack Unit.
LLC	Logical Link Control. (IEEE 802. standard for LANs.)
LLP	Lightweight Presentation Protocol.
LMAE	Layer Management Application Entity. (Specific type of SMAE.)
LME	Layer Managaement Entity.
LMSS	Land Mobile Satellite Services.
LOS	Line Of Sight. (Transmission system, e.g. microwave.)
LPTV	Low Power Television.
LPC	Linear Predictive Coding. (Encoding technique used in pulse code modulation.)
LRC	Longitudinal Redundanc Check. (Error checking procedure for transmitted data.)
LSB	Least Significant Bit. (Referring to bits in a data word.)
LSI	Large Scale Integration. (Describes a complex integrated circuit semiconductor component.)
LSTR	Listener SideTone Rating. (Measure of room noise sidetone effect.)
LTE	Line Terminating Equipment. (Also called Line Terminal Equipment. Equipment which terminates a transmission line.)
MA	Multiple Access.
MAC	Media Access Control. (IEEE standard 802. for access to LANs.)
MAC	Multiplexed Analogue Components. (Television transmission system.)
MACF	Multiple Association Control Function.

MAN	Metropolitan Area Network.
MAP	Manufacturing Automation Protocol.
MASER	Microwave Amplification by Simulated Emission of Radiation.
MAT	Metropolitan Area Trunk. (A cable system which is used to reduce crosstalk effects in regions where there is a large number of circuits between exchanges.)
MATV	Mast Antenna Television. (Or Master Antenna Television. Local cable television system for a hotel or apartment block.)
MCC	Mission Control Centre.
MCM	Multichip module.
MCN	Micro-Cellular Networks. (Small cells used within cellular radio networks to provide PCN-type services.)
MCS	Maritime Communication System.
MD	Mediation Device. (CCITT terminology for a device which carries out a protocol conversion function.)
MDDF	Manual Digital Distribution Frame.
MDF	Main Distribution Frame.
MDNS	Managed Data Network Service. (Earlier proposal by CEPT which has now been discontinued.)
MEP	Member of the European Parliament.
METEOSAT	Meteorological Satellite.
METRAN	Managed European Transmission Network. (CEPT initiative to provide a broadband backbone across Europe.)
MF	Multi Frequency. (A signalling system used with push-button telephones.)
MF	Mediation Function. (CCITT term for a function involving protocol conversion.)
MFJ	Modification of Final Judgement. (Delivered by Judge Harold Greene. 1982 act in the AT&T divestiture case.)
MHS	Message Handling System. (International standard.)
MHz	MegaHertz. (Measure of frequency. Equal to one million cycles per second.)
MIB	Management Information Base. (Refers to the collection of objects made visible to a manager within a network management system.)
MICR	Magnetic Ink Character Recognition.
MIFR	Master International Frequency Register. (Register of allocated international frequencies maintained by the IFRB.)
MIPS	Million Instructions Per Second. (Measure of a computer's processing speed.)
MIT	Management Information Tree.
MITI	Ministry of International Trade and Industry. (Japanese.)
MITT	Minutes of Telecommunication Traffic. (Measure used by telecommunication operators for tariffing purposes.)
MLM	Multi-level Multi-Access protocol. (Multiple access technique.)
MMI	Man Machine Interface. (Another name for the human-computer interface or HCI.)
MMIC	Monolithic Microwave Integrated Circuit.
MO	Managed Object.
MODEM	Modulator/Demodulator. Device for enabling digital data to be send over analogue lines.
MOS	Metal Oxide Semiconductor. (A semiconductor technology.)

MOSFET	Metal Oxide Semiconductor Field Effect Transistor (A transistor made from MOS.)
MOTIS	Message Oriented Text Interchange System. (ISO equivalent of a message handling system.)
MoU	Memorandum of Understanding.
MPG	Microwave Pulse Generator. (A device for generating electrical pulses at microwave frequencies.)
MPT	Ministry of Posts and Telecommunications. (Japan)
MS	Management System.
MSAP	Mini Slotted Alternating Priorities. (Multiple access technique.)
MSC	Main Switching Centre. (Part of the switching hierarchy in BT's network.)
MSC	Mobile Switching Centre. (Switching centre used in mobile radio systems.)
MSDOS	Microsoft Disk Operating System. (Very popular operating system for PCs.)
MSI	Medium Scale Integration. (Usually refers to an integrated circuit with a medium amount of on-chip circuit density.)
MSK	Minimum Shift Keying. (A form of frequency shift keying, or FSK.)
MSME	Management System Management (Application Entity.
MSS	Mobile Satellite Service.
MTA	Message Transfer Agent. (The item which relays stores and delivers messages within a Message Handling System, or MHS.)
MTBF	Mean Time Between Failure. (Measure of equipment reliability. Time for which an equipment is likely to operate before failure.)
MTN	Managed Transmission Network.
MTS	Message Transfer System.
MTS	Message Telephone Service. (US term for a long distance telephone service.)
MTTR	Mean Time To Repair. (A measure of equipment availability. It is the time between an equipment failure and when it is operational again.)
MTX	Mobile Telephone Exchange. (Commonly used to describe a large exchange used within a cellular mobile system and connected to the PSTN.)
MUF	Maximum Usable Frequency.
NA	Numerical Aperture. (Measure of a basic parameter for fibre optic cables.)
NAK	Negative Acknowledgement. (In data transmission this is the message sent by the receiver to the sender to indicate that the previous message contained an error, and requesting a re-send.)
NANP	North American Numbering Plan. (Telephone numbering scheme administered by Bellcore.)
NARS	North Atlantic Radio System.
NASA	National Aeronautics & Space Administration (USA agency.)
NATA	North American Telecommunications Administration.
NBC	National Broadcasting Company. (USA.)
NBS	National Bureau of Standards. (USA.)
NCL	Network Control Layer.
NCP	Network Control Point.
NCTA	National Cable Television Association. (USA trade organisation representing cable television carriers

NCUF	National Computer Users Forum.
NDC	National Destination Code. (Part of numbering system.)
NE	Network Element.
NEF	Network Element Function.
NEP	Noise Equivalent Power.
NET	Nome Europeenne de Telecommunication. (European Telecommunications Standard, which is mandatory.)
NEXT	Near End crosstalk. The unwanted transfer of signal energy from one link to another, often closely located, at the end of the cable where the transmitted is located.
NF	Noise Figure.
NFAS	Not Frame Alignment Signal. (In transmitted code.)
N-ISDN	Narrowband Integrated Services Digital Network.
NIST	National Institute for Standards and Technology. (USA.)
NLC	Network Level Control. (Or Network Layer Control.)
NMC	Network Management Centre.
NMI	Network Management Interface. (Term used within OSI to indicate the interface between the network management system and the network it manages.)
NMT	Nordic Mobile Telephone. (Cellular system designed by the Nordic PTTs. NMT450 operates in the 450MHz band and NMT900 in the 900MHz band.)
NNI	Network Node Interface. (Usually the internal interfaces within a network. See UNI.)
NOAA	National Oceanic Atmospheric Administration.
NOC	Network Operations Centre.
NOI	Notice Of Inquiry. (FCC paper for comment.)
NPA	Numbering Plan Area.
NPI	Null Point Indication.
NPP	Network Performance Parameters.
NPR	Noise Power Ratio.
NRZ	Non Return to Zero. (A binary encoding technique for transmission of data.)
NRZI	Non Return to Zero Inverted. (A binary encoding techniqe for transmission of data.)
NSAP	Network Service Access Point. (Prime address point used within OSI.)
NT	Network Termination. (Termination designed within ISDN e.g. NT1 and NT2.)
NTE	Network Terminating Equipment. (Usually refers to the customer termination for an ISDN line.)
NTIA	National Telecommunications Industry Administration. (USA)
NTN	Network Terminal Number. (Part of an international telephone number.)
NTSC	National Television System Committee. (US.)
NTT	Nippon Telegraph and Telephone. (Japanese carrier.)
NTU	Network Terminating Unit. (Used to terminate subscriber leased line.)
O&M	Operations, Administration and Maintenance. (Also written as OAM.)
OAM&P	Operations, Administration, Maintenance & Provisioning.
O&AM	Object & Attribute Management. (NM Forum.)
O&M	Operations & Maintenance.

OATS	Open Area Test Site. (Used for EMC measurements.)
OC	Optical Carrier. (SONET standard for optical signals, e.g. OC-1 at 51.84Mbit/s.)
OCR	Optical Character Recognition. (System which can read characters by optical scanning and converting these into electrical signals for processing.)
ODA	Open Document Architecture. (Or Office Document Architecture. Standard for transmission of content and layout of a document and of multimedia documents.)
ODIF	Office Document Interchange Format. (Format used to communicate documents within an open system.)
ODP	Open Distributed Processing.
OECD	Organisation for Economic Co-operation and Development.
OEIC	Opto-Electronic Integrated Circuit.
OEM	Original Equipment Manufacturer. Supplier who makes equipment for sale by a third party. The equipment is usually disguised by the third party with his own labels.)
OFTEL	Office of Telecommunications. (UK regulatory body.)
OIW	OSI Implementors Workshop. (USA based.)
OKQPSK	Offset Keyed Quaternary Phase Shift Keying.
OLR	Overall Loudness Rating. (Measurement of end to end connection for transmission planning.)
OLTU	Optical Line Terminating Unit. (Or Optical Line Terminal Unit. Equipment which terminates an optical line, usually converting optical signals to electrical and vice versa.)
ONA	Open Network Architecture.
OND	Open Network Doctrine. (Japanese plan for equal access.)
ONI	Operator Number Identification. (Operator used in a CAMA office to verbally obtain the calling number for calls originating in offices not equipped with ANI.)
ONP	Open Network Provision.
ONT	Optical Network Termination. (Termination point for optical fibre access system.)
OOD	Object Oriented Design. (Software design technique.)
OOK	On-Off Keying. (Digital modulation technique. Also known as ASK or Amplitude Shift Keying.)
OOP	Object Oriented Programming.
OS	Operating System. (Or Operations System. CCITT.)
OS	Outstation.
OSB	One Stop Billing.
OSF	Open Software Foundation
OSF	Operations System Function. (CCITT.)
OSI	Open Systems Interconnection. (Refers to the seven layer reference model.)
OSIE	OSI Environment.
OSITOP	Open Systems Interconnection Technical and Office Protocol.
OSP	Operator Service Provider. (Company in the USA providing competitive toll operator services for billing and call completion.)
OSS	One Stop Shopping.
OTDR	Optical Time Domain Reflectometer.
OTS	Orbital Test Satellite.
OWF	Optimum Working Frequency.

PABX	Private Automatic Branch Exchange. (PBX in which automatic connection is made between extensions.)
PAD	Packet Assembler/Disassembler. (Protocol converter used to provide access into the packet switched network.)
PAL	Pulse Alteration by Line. (Television encoding system.)
PAM	Pulse Amplitude Modulation. (An analogue modulation technique.)
PAMR	Public Access Mobile Radio.
PANS	Peculiar And Novel Services. (Often used in conjunction with POTS.)
PBX	Private Branch Exchange. (This is often used synonymously with PABX.)
PC	Personnel Computer.
PC	Private Circuit.
PCM	Pulse Code Modulation. (Transmission technique for digital signals.)
PCN	Personal Communications Networks.
PCS	Personal Communications Service. (North American term for the service provided over a PCN.)
PDH	Plesiochronous Digital Hierarchy. (Plesiochronous transmission standard.)
PDM	Pulse Duration Modulation. (Signal modulation technique, also known as Pulse Width Modulation or PWM.)
PDU	Protocol Data Unit. (Data and control information passed between layers in the OSI Seven Layer model.)
PEP	Peak Envelope Power.
PF	Presentation Function.
PFD	Power Flux Density. (Measure of spectral emission strength.)
PFM	Pulse Frequency Modulation. (An analogue modulation technique.)
PIN	Personal Identification Number. (Security number used for items such as remote database entry.)
PIN	Positive Intrinsic Negative. (Semiconductor structure used for some types of diodes.)
PLC	Plant Level Controller.
PLL	Phase Locked Loop. (Technique for recovering the clock in transmitted data. Often performed by an integrated circuit.)
PLMN	Public Land Mobile Network.
PLP	Packet Level Protocol.
PM	Payload Manager. (Within an SDH.)
PM	Phase Modulation. (Analogue signal modulation technique.)
PMBX	Private Manual Branch Exchange. (PBX with connections between extensions done by an operator.)
PMR	Public Mobile Radio.
POCSAG	Post Office Code Standardisation Advisory Group. (Name given by study group to U.K. digital paging system. Adopted by CCIR as Radio Paging Code RPC No. 1.)
PODA	Priority-Oriented Demand Assignment protocol. (Multiple access technique. See also FPODA and CPODA.)
POH	Path Overhead. (Information used in SDH transmission structures.)
POL	Problem Oriented Language. (A term sometimes used to describe a high level computer programming language, such as Cobol or Fortran.)
PON	Passive Optical Network. (Technology for implementing fibre optic cable access in the local loop.)
POP	Point Of Presence. (In the US it refers to the point of change over of responsibility from the local telephone company, within a LATA, to the long distance or inter-LATA carrier.)
POPSAT	Precise Orbit Positioning Satellite.
POR	Pacific Ocean Region.
POSI	Promoting conference for OSI. (Japan and Far East users' group active in functional standards and interconnection testing.)
POSP	Private Off-Site Paging.
POTS	Plain Old Telephone Service. (A term loosely applied to an ordinary voice telephone service.)
PPL	Phase Locked Loop. (Component used in frequency stability systems such as demodulators for frequency modulation.)
PPM	Pulse Phase Modulation. (An analogue modulation technique. Sometimes called Pulse Position Modulation.)
PRA	Primary Rate Access. (ISDN, 30B+D or 23B+D code.)
PRBS	Pseudo Random Binary Sequence. (Signal used for telecommunication system testing.)
PRF	Pulse Repetition Frequency. (Of a pulse train.)
PRK	Phase Reversal Keying. (A modification to the PSK modulation technique.)
PROM	Programmable Read Only Memory. (Memory technology, usually semiconductor, where the data is written, or programmed, once by the user and thereafter can only be read and not changed. See also ROM.)
PSDN	Packet Switched Data Network. (Or Public Switched Data Network. X.25 network, which may be private or public.)
PSPDN	Packet Switched Public Data Network.
PSE	Packet Switching Exchange.
PSK	Phase Shift Keying. (Analogue phase modulation technique.)
PSN	Packet Switched Network.
PSN	Public Switched Network.
PSS	Packet Switched Service. (Data service offered by BT.)
PSTN	Public Switched Telephone Network. (Term used to describe the public dial up voice telephone network operated by a PTT.)
PTC	Pacific Telecommunications Council.
PTN	Public Telecommunications Network.
PTO	Public Telecommunication Operator. (A licensed telecommunication operator. Usually used to refer to a PTT.)
PTT	Postal, Telegaph and Telephone. (Usually refers to the telephone authority within a country, often a publicly owned body. The term is also loosely used to describe any large telecomunications carrier.)
PUC	Public Utility Commission. (In USA.)
PVC	Permanent Virtual Circuit. (Method for establishing a virtual circuit link between two nominated points. See also SVC)
PWM	Pulse Width Modulation. (Analogue modulation technique in which the width of pulses is varied. Also called Pulse Duration Modulation, PDM, or Pulse Length Modulation, PLM.)

A	Q interface Adaptor.
AF	Q Adaptor Function.
AM	Quadrature Amplitude Modulation. (A modulation technique which varies the amplitude of the signal. Used in dial up modems. Also known as Quadrature Sideband Amplitude Modulation or QSAM.)
D	Quantising Distortion.
oS	Quality of Service. (Measure of service performance as perceived by the user.)
PRS	Quadrature Partial Response System. (Signal modulation technique.)
PSK	Quadrature Phase Shift Keying. (Signal modulation technique.)
ACE	Research and development in Advanced Communication technologies in Europe.
&D	Research and Development.
ADARSAT	Radar Satellite.
AISE	Rigorous Approach to Industrial Software Engineering. (Esprit project.)
ARC	Regional Administrative Radio Conference.
ARE	Reseaux Associes pour la Recherche Europeene.
BER	Residual Bit Error Ratio. (Measure of transmission quality. CCITT Rec. 594-1.)
BOC	Regional Bell Operating Company. (US local carriers formed after the divestiture of AT&T.)
CU	Remote Concentrator Unit.
DA	Remote Database Access.
DBMS	Relational Database Management System.
DN	Relative Distinguishing Name. (Used within OSI network management.)
DSQL	Relational Database Structured Query Language.
F	Radio Frequency. (Signal.)
FC	Request For Comment.
FI	Radio Frequency Interference.
FNM	Ready For Next Message.
IN	Relative Intensity Noise. (Measure of noise in an optical source.)
ITL	Radio In The Loop. (Radio used for the subscriber's local loop.)
OES	Receive Only Earth Station. (For use with satellites.)
OIV	Remote Operation Invoke.
OM	Read Only Memory. (Memory device, usually semiconductor, in which the contents are defined during manufacture. The stored information can be read but not changed. See also PROM.)
OS	Remote Operation Service.
OSE	Remote Operation Service Element. (OSI application having basic recovery functionality.)
OSI	ROS Interface.
OTL	Remote Office Test Line. (Technique for remotely testing trunk circuits.)
OW	Right Of Way. (Usually refers to costs associated with laying cables.)
PC	Remote Procedure Call.
PE-LTP	Regular Pulse Excitation Long Term Prediction. (Variant of LPC chosen as the speech encoding technique for GSM.)
PFD	Received Power Flux Density.
POA	Recognised Private Operating Agencies.
TL	Resistor Transistor Logic. (An older integrated circuit logic family.)

RTNR	Real Time Network Routing. (Dynamic traffic routing strategy being implemented by AT&T.)
RTS	Request To Send. (Handshaking routine used in anlogue transmission, such as by modems.)
RTSE	Reliable Transfer Service Element.
RTT	Regie des Telegraphes et des Telephones. (Belgian PTT.)
RZ	Return to Zero. (A digital transmission system in which the binary pulse always returns to zero after each bit.)
S×S	Step by Step. (Refers to a Strowger electromechanical switch.)
SA	Standards Australia. (Australian national standards organisation.)
SAC	Special Access Code. (Special telephone numbers e.g. 800 service.)
SANZ	Standards Association of New Zealand.
SAP	Service Access Point. (Port between layers in the OSI seven layer model, one for each of the layers, e.g. LSAP, NSAP, etc.)
SAPI	Service Access Point Identifier. (Used within ISDN Layer 2 frame.)
SAR	Search And Rescue.
SARSAT	Search And Rescue Satellite.
SBS	Satellite Buisness Systems. (USA.)
SCADA	Supervisory Control and Data Acquisition. (Interface for network monitoring.)
SCC	Standards Council of Canada.
SCPC	Single Channel Per Carrier. (A transmission technique used in thin route satellite communication systems. See also SPADE.)
SCVF	Single Channel Voice Frequency. (One of the signalling systems used in telex, i.e. CCITT R.20.)
SDH	Synchronous Digital Hierarchy.
SDL	Specification Description Language. (CCITT recommended language for specification and description of telecommunication systems.)
SDR	Speaker Dependent Recognition. (Speech recognition technique which requires training to individual caller's voice.)
SDU	Service Data Unit. (Data passed between layers in the OSI Seven Layer model.)
SDXC	Synchronous Digital Crossconnect.
SEA	Single European Act. (Amendment to the Treaty of Rome.)
SECAM	Sequence Coleur a Memoire. (Sequential Colour with Memory. French television encoding system.)
SED	Single Error Detecting Code. (Transmission code used for detecting errors by use of single parity checks.)
SELV	Safety Extra Low Voltage circuit. (A circuit which is protected from hazardous voltages.)
SES	Severely Errored Second. (Any second with a BER exceeding 10^{-3}, as per CCITT G.821.)
SES	Ship Earth Station.
SFL	Service Level controller.
SGMP	Simple Gateway Monitoring Protocol.
SHF	Super High Frequency.
SIM	Subscriber Identity Module. (Usually a plug in card used with a mobile radio handset.)
SIO	Scientific and Industrial Organisation.

SIP	Societa Italiana per l'Esercizio delle Telecomunicazion. (Italian PTT.)
SIR	Speaker Independent Recognition. (Speech recognition technique which does not need to be trained to individual caller's voice.)
SITA	Societe Internationale de Telecommunications Aeronautiques. (Refers to the organisation and its telecommunication network which is used by many of the World's airlines and their agents, mainly for flight bookings.)
SLC	Subscriber Line Charge. (USA term for flat charge paid by the end user for line connection.)
SLIC	Subscriber Line Inerface Card. (Circuitry which provides the interface to the network, usually from a central office switch, for digital voice transmission.)
SL-LME	Software Load Layer Managment Entity. (Specific type of LME.)
SM	Service Module.
SMAE	System Management Application Entity.
SMAS	System Management Application Service.
SMASE	System Management Applications Service Element.
SMATV	Satellite Master Television.
SMDS	Switched Multimegabit Data Service. (High speed packet based standard proposed by Bellcore.)
SMF	System Management Function.
SMFA	System Management Functional Area.
SMI	Structure of Management Information.
SMS	Short Messaging Service. (GSM feature which allocates channels for voice or data only when needed.)
SMS	Systeme Multiservice par Satellite. (Multi-service satellite system. A category of service offered by EUTELSAT.)
SMX	Synchronous Multiplexer.
SNAP	Subnetwork Access Protocol. (IEEE protocol which allows non-OSI protocols to be carried within OSI protocols.)
SNI	Subscriber Network Interface.
SNMP	Simple Network Management Protocol. (Network management system within TCP/IP.)
SNR	Signal to Noise Ratio.
SNV	Association Suisse de Normalisation. (Swiss standards making body.)
SOGITS	Senior Officals Group on Information Technology Standards. (Part of the European Community.)
SOGT	Senior Officials Group on Telecommunications. (Part of European Community, composed of Ministers of Telecommunications and Industry from member states.)
SOH	Section Overhead. (Information used in SDH transmission structure.)
SONET	Synchronous Optical Network. (Synchronous optical transmission system developed in North America, and which has been developed by CCITT into SDH.)
SPADE	Single channel per carrier Pulse code modulation multiple Access Demand assignment Equipment. (A SCPC technique.)
SPAG	Standards Promotion and Application Group. (European group involved in preparation of functional standards and inter-operability testing.)
SPC	Stored Program Controller. (Usually referes to a digital exchange.)
SPEC	Speech Predictive Encoding Communications.

SQL	Structured Query Language.
SQNR	Signal Quantisation Noise Ratio.
SSB	Single Sideband.
SSBSC	Single Sideband Suppressed Carrier modulation. (A method for amplitude modulation of a signal.)
SSMA	Spread Spectrum Multiple Access.
SSSO	Specialised Satellite Service Operator.
SSTDMA	Satellite Switched Time Division Multiple Access.
SSTV	Slow Scan Television.
STAR	Special Telecommunications Action for Regional Development. (European programme.)
STD	Subscriber Trunk Dialling.
STDM	Synchronous Time Division Multiplexing.
STDMX	Statistical Time Division Multiplexing.
STE	Signalling Terminal Equipment.
STM	Synchronous Transport Module. (Basic carrier module used within SDH, e.g. STM-1, STM-4 and STM-16.)
STMR	Sidetone Masking Rating. (Measure of talker effects of sidetone.)
STP	Shielded Twisted Pair. (Cable.)
STP	Signal Transfer Point.
STS	Space-Time-Space. (Digital switching method.)
STS	Synchronous Transport Signal. (SONET standard for electrical signals, e.g. STS-1 at 51.84Mbit/s.)
STX	Synchronous Transmission crossconnect. (Crossconnect used within SHD.)
STX	Start of Text. (Control character used to indicate the start of data transmission. It is completed by a End of Text character, or ETX.)
SVC	Switched Virtual Circuit. (Method for establishing any to any virtual circuit link. See also PVC.)
TA	Terminal Adaptor. (Used within ISDN to convert between non-ISDN and ISDN references.)
TA	Telecommunication Authority.
TA 84	Telecommunications Act of 1984. (UK.)
TACS	Total Access Communication Systems. (Adaption of AMPS by the UK to suit European frequency allocations.)
TASI	Time Assignment Speech Interpolation. (Method used in analogue speech transmission where the channel is activated only when speech is present. This allows several users to share a common channel.)
TC	Transport Class. (E.g. TC 0, TC 4, etc.)
TCD	Technical Co-operation Department.
TCM	Time Compression Multiplexing. (Technique which separates the two directions of transmission in time.)
TCM/DPSK	Trellis Coded Modulation/Differential Phase Shift Keying.
TCP/IP	Transmission Control Protocol/ Internet Protocol (Widely used transmission protocol, originating from the US ARPA defence project.)
TDD	Time Division Duplex transmission.
TDM	Time Division Multiplexing. (Technique for combining, by interleaving, several channels of data onto a common channel. The equipment which does this is called a Time Division Multiplexer.)
TDMA	Time Division Multiple Access. (A multiplexing technique where users gain access to a common channel on a time allocation basis. Commonly used

in satellite systems, where several earth stations have total use of the transponder's power and bandwidth for a short period, and transmit in bursts of data.)

TDRS   Tracking and Data Relay Satellite.

TE   Terminal Equipment.

TEDIS   Trade Electronic Data Interchange System. (European Commission programme.)

TEI   Terminal Endpoint Identifier. (Used within ISDN Layer 2 frame.)

TELMEX   Telefonos de Mexico. (Mexican PTT.)

TELR   Talker Echo Loudness Rating. (Overall loudness rating of the talker echo path.)

TEM   Transverse Electromagnetic cell. (Code used for measuring characteristics of receivers such as pagers.)

TEMA   Telecommunication Equipment Manufacturers Association. (UK.)

TETRA   Trans European Trunked Radio. (ETSI standard for PMR.)

TFTS   Terrestrial Flight Telephone Service.

TIA   Telecommunication Industry Association. (US based. Formed from merger of telecommunication sector of the EIA and the USTSA.)

TM   Trade Mark.

TMA   Telecommunication Managers' Association. (UK)

TMN   Telecommunications Management Network.

TMR   Trunked Mobile Radio.

TNV   Telecommunication Network Voltage circuit. (Test circuit for definition of safety in telecommunication systems.)

TOA   Take Off Angle. (Refers to antenna systems.)

TOP   Technical and Office Protocol.

TOT   Telephone Organisation of Thiland. (Thai carrier.)

TPON   Telephony over Passive Optical Networks.

TR   Technical Report. (ISO technical document; not a standard.)

TRAC   Technical Recommendations Application Committee. (Comite Charge de l'Application des Recommendations Techniques. Part of CEPT.)

TSI   Time Slot Interchange. (Switching system technique which switches between circuits by separating the signals in time.)

TST   Time-Space-Time. (Digital switching method.)

TT&C   Tracking, Telemetry & Command. (Satellite antenna.)

TTC   Telecommunications Technology Committee. (Japanese.)

TTE   Telecommunication Terminal Equipment.

TTL   Transistor Transistor Logic. (Integrated circuit logic family.)

TTLS   Transistor Transistor Logic Schottky. (Faster version of TTL.)

TTY   Teletypewriter. (Usually refers to the transmission from a teletypewriter, which is asynchronous ASCII coded.)

TU   Tributary Unit. (Part of SDH. Ref: CCITT G.709.)

TUA   Telecommunications Users' Association. (UK.)

TUF   Telecommunications Users' Foundation. (UK.)

TUG   Tributary Unit Group. (Part of SDH. Ref: CCITT G.709.)

TV   Television.

TVRO   Television Receive Only. (Domestic equipment for the reception of television via satellite.)

TWT   Travelling Wave Tube.

TWTA   Travelling Wave Tube Amplifier.

TWX   Teletypewriter exchange service. (Used in Canada.)

TeraFLOP   (Trillion Floating Point Operations per second. (Measure of a super computer.)

UAP   User Application Process.

UART   Universal Asynchronous Receiver/Transmitter. (The device, usually an integrated cirucit, for transmission of asynchronous data. See also USRT and USART.)

UDF   Unshielded twisted pair Development Forum. (Association of suppliers promoting transmission over UTP.)

UDP   User Datagram Protocol.

UHF   Ultra High Frequency. (Radio frequency, extending from about 300MHz to 3GHz.)

UI   User Interface.

UL   Underwriters Laboratories. (Independent USA organisation involved in standards and certification.)

UMTS   Universal Mobile Telecommunications System. (ETSI terminology for a future public land mobile telecommunications system.)

UN   United Nations.

UNCTAD   United Nations Conference on Trade And Development.

UNI   User Network Interface. (Also called User Node Interface. External interface of a network.)

UPS   Uninterrupted Power Supply. (Used where loss of power, even for a short time, cannot be tolerated.)

UPT   Universal Personal Telecommunications. (CCITT concept of the personal telephone number.)

USART   Universal Synchronous/Asynchronous Receiver/Transmitter. (A device, usually an integrated circuit, used in data communication devices, for conversion of data from parallel to serial form for transmission.)

USB   Upper Sideband.

USITA   US Independent Telephone Association.

USRT   Universal Synchronous Receiver/Transmitter. (A device, usually an integrated circuit, which converts data for transmission over a synchronous channel.)

USTA   US Telephone Association.

USTSA   US Telecommunication Suppliers Association.

UTP   Unshielded Twisted Pair. (Cable.)

VAD   Voice Activity Detection. (Technique used in transmission systems to improve bandwidth utilisation.)

VADS   Value Added Data Service.

VAN   Value Added Network

VANS   Value Added Network Services.

VAS   Value Added Service. (See also VANS.)

VASP   Value Added Service Provider.

VBR   Variable Bit Rate.

VC   Virtual Container. (Transmission mechanism used in SDH, CCITT G.709. Its signals are never presented outside the network.)

VCO	Voltage Controlled Oscillator. (Component used in frequency generating systems.)
VCX	Virtual Container Crossconnect. (Synchronous crossconnect at the VC level. Used within the CCITT SDH hierarchy.)
VDU	Visual Display Unit. (Usually a computer screen.)
VF	Voice Frequency. (Signalling method using frequencies within speech band. Also called in-band signalling. Also refers to the voice frequency band from 300Hz to 3400Hz.)
VFCT	Voice Frequency Carrier Telegraph.
VHF	Very High Frequency. (Radio frequency in the range of about 30MHz and 300MHz.)
VHSIC	Very High Speed Integrated Circuit.
VLF	Very Low Frequency. (Radio frequency in the range of about 3kHz to 30kHz.)
VLR	Visitor Location Register. (Database associated with a MCS in a mobile radio system, containing information of its current users.)
VLSI	Very Large Scale Integration. (A complex integrated circuit.)
VMS	Voice Messaging System.
VNL	Via Net Loss. (The method use to assign minimum loss in telephone lines in order to control echo and singing.)
VOA	Voice Of America.
VPN	Virtual Private Network. (Part of a network operated by a public telephone operator, which is used as a private network.)
VQ	Vector Quantisation. (Encoding method.)
VQL	Variable Quantising Level. (Speech encoding method for transmission of speech at 32kbit/s.)
VRC	Vertical Redundancy Check. (Parity method used on transmitted data for error checking.)
VRP	Vertical Radiation Pattern. (Of an antenna.)
VSAT	Very Small Aperture Terminal. (Satellite receiver.)
VSB	Vestigial Sideband modulation. (A method for amplitude modulation of a signal.)
VSWR	Voltage Standing Wave Ratio.
VT	Virtual Tributary. (SONET terminology for a virtual container.)
VTP	Virtual Terminal Protocol.
WACK	Wait Acknowledgement. (Control signal returned by receiver to indicate to the sender that it is temporarily unable to accept any more data.)
WAN	Wide Area Network.
WARC	World Administrative Radio Conference. (Of ITU.)
WATTC	World Administrative Telephone and Telegraph Conference. (Of ITU.)
WBLLN	Wideband Leased Line Network.
WDM	Wavelength Division Multiplexing. (Multiplexing technique used with optical communications systems.)
WDMA	Wavelength Division Multiple Access. (Multiple access technique.)
WIMP	Windows, Icons, Mouse and Pointer. (Display and manipulation technique for graphical interfaces, e.g. as used for network management.)
WMO	World Meteorological Organisation.
WS	Work Station.
WSF	Workstation Function.
ZVEI	Zurerein der Electronissches Industrie.
ZZF	Zentrasamt fur Zulassungen im Fernmeldewessen.

62.3 Glossary of terms

10BaseFP. Standard for running Ethernet LAN over passive optical fibre.

10BaseT. Standard for running Ethernet LAN over twisted copper wire.

Abbreviated dialling. A feature available in some telephone switches which enable the user to establish a connection by entering fewer digits than would otherwise be required.

Access charge. The same as interconnection charge.

Access line. Usually refers to the line which provides a permanent connection between a subscriber and his local exchange.

Accounting rate. Private bilateral agreement between carriers, which is used to determine the allocation of revenues from international calls.

Acoustic coupler. Device that connects to a telephone handset and converts sounds into electrical data for transmission down a telephone line.

Adaptive equalisation. Technique, commonly used with modems, for compensating for differences in the attenuation characteristics of telephone lines.

Adaptive predictive coding. A coding technique which predicts the present value of the input sample, based on the previous cycle.

Adaptive quantisation. Quantisation in which the step sizes are varied so as to match the changes in the input signal.

Address. Within the context of a telecommunication network, it is a sequence of bits or characters which uniquely identifies a user, element or application. Its most common application is the number which is entered by a caller to identify the called party.

Adjacent channel interference. Interference arising between two transmission channels which are adjacent to each other.

Agent mode. The mode which makes only managed objects visible to other network elements in a network management system.

Agent process. An application which performs operations on managed objects within a network management system and issues events on their behalf.

Alarm category. Grouping of alarms to indicate their severity. Usually these are classified as critical, major, or minor.

Alarms. Events within a network management system which have been designated as having special significance, usually because they indicate a fault.

A-law. Companding technique for PCM, used in Europe.

Alert. Usually refers to the act of indicating to an operator that there is an incoming call. For example by ringing a bell.

ALOHA. An algorithm used for multiple access of a medium, where a station will begin transmission when ready, and will retransmit if a collision occurs.

Alphanumeric display. Display which shows characters as well as numbers.

Alternate routing. A feature of a telecommunication element which enables it to send information via an alternate route if the prime route is unavailable, such as due to congestion. Often used as a route protection measure.

Ameritech. One of the seven regional Bell operating companies covering the mid-Western region of the US.

Amplifier. A device which increaces the level of the signal. Amplification may be of current, voltage or power, of electrical or light signals.

Amplitude modulation. A method of encoding the transmitted information by variations in the level of voltage or current in the signal.

Amplitude distortion. The unwanted change in the amplitude of a signal waveform, usually due to the effect of non-linear components in the communication network.

Analogue. A system in which information is represented by a continuous variation of a parameter, e.g. a voltage level. The sender selects a level to represent his information and the receiver interprets this as an approximation of the encoded value.

Analogue cellular radio. Cellular system which uses digital signalling and analogue speech.

Answerback. Facility in some equipment to respond to a remote control signal. Usually takes the form of handshake sequences between devices, when they set up, before they start to interchange information.

Antenna. A device used to send or collect radio signals from a source or receiver.

Antipodal signalling. Technique for encoding binary signals, which provides good error performance in relation to signal to noise ratio.

Aperture. That area of the antenna which is able to interact with the transmitted radio signal.

Apogee. The peak altitude taken by a satellite in orbit.

Application layer. A logical entity forming the top or seventh layer of the OSI seven layer model. It is largely defined by the user to perform his applications.

Application process. This usually refers to a collection of software modules which carry out all the processing needed to fulfil a certain function.

Assembler. A programme which converts an assembly level computer source code into machine level binary object code.

Asynchronous. It defines the process for communications in which the transmission is not tied to a particular frequency or timing pulse. Some form of start and stop information is added to the transmitted information, to define its content and provide timing for the receiving end.

AT command. Protocol used between modems and terminals to allow for testing, reconfiguration and autodialling of the modem.

Attenuation. A measure of the loss of a signal strength, usually measured in decibels.

Attenuator. A device which reduces the signal strength between two points during transmission.

Attribute. This is a value which defines the property of an object within an object orientated system.

Audiotex. A system used to provide published information (e.g. weather forecast) to callers over a telephone.

Autoanswer. The ability of a terminal, such as a modem, to autonomously answer a call over the switched telephone network, and to set up a route with a remote device.

Autodial. The ability of a terminal, such as a modem, to autonomously place a call over the switched telephone network.

Automatic call distribution. System used to switch incoming calls evenly and automatically to a number of stations on a first come first served basis, so minimising the waiting queue.

Automatic route selection. Capability of a device to automatically select the most optimum route to send information.

Usually this is on the basis of the least cost and is referred to as least cost routing.

Autorate. Facility within a device, such as a modem, which enables it to automatically adjust its transmission rate to suit the requirements of the device located at the other end of the transmission line.

Availability. In telecommunications it usually refers to the percentage of time that a piece of equipment is operational.

Azimuth angle. The angle between the meridian plane and the antenna beam, when measured along the horizontal plane.

Backbone network. A high speed transmission network which is used to interconnect lower speed clusters of devices or lower speed networks.

Backoff. It is the delay, in a multiple access system, which a transmitting station adopts if a collision has occurred in its earlier transmission.

Balanced to ground. A two wire transmission circuit in which the impedance to ground on one wire equals that on the other wire.

Bandwidth. It is the difference between the highest and lowest frequencies of a transmission channel, measured in Hertz. It is therefore often used to define the information carrying capacity of a channel.

Baseband. Usually refers to the frequency band containing the basic information being transmitted, before it is modulated and other characters have been added.

Base station. Usually refers to the radio station in a mobile communication system, containing the transmitters and receivers for communication with a mobile.

Batch processing. Data processing system in which transactions are sent for processing in groups or batches.

Battery feed. The battery supply from the switching centre to the subscriber's telephone.

Baudot code. Data transmission code which uses five bits for character representation. Now rarely used.

Baud rate. It is a measure of the speed of transmission of binary data, and is equal to the maximum number of symbols generated per second.

Beam splitter. A device, used in optical transmission, for splitting an optical beam into several other beams.

Behaviour. This is usually used in the context of managed objects within network management sytems. It is the sequence of attributes and notifications which are exhibited by the managed object due to the occurrence of management operations.

Bell Atlantic. One of the seven regional Bell operating , covering the mid-Atlantic region of the US.

Bias. Usually refers to a voltage which is applied to a circuit or component.

Binary channel. A channel used for transmitting binary digits.

Binary coded. A coding system which uses binary numbers to represent transmitted information.

Binary symmetric channel. A transmission channel in which the probability of error is the same for zeros and ones.

Bipolar. Within telecommunications it refers to a signalling method for digital transmission where the signal carrying the data alternates between a positive and a negative polarity.

Bipolar. A type of semiconductor technology which uses both the positive and negative charged currents. See also unipolar.

Bistable. A component or system which is stable in either one of two modes. See also monostable.

Bit. Smallest form of binary data.

Bit duration. A measure of the time taken by an encoded bit to pass a point in a transmission medium. It is often used as a means for comparing delay times within various transmission media or elements.

Bit error. The instance when the value of an encoded bit is changed during transmission and therefore incorrectly interpreted by the receiver.

Bit error rate. A measure of the proportion of transmission bits which have an error. Usually expressed as a number to the power of 10, e.g. 1 in 10^9 bits.

Bit oriented. A transmission protocol in which the control information is encoded in the form of fields of one or more bits. It is usually more efficient than character mode or byte oriented protocols.

Bits per second. Basic measure of the transmission capability of a medium. High speed channels are specified in kbit/s, Mbit/s and Tbit/s.

Bit stuffing. Process used in transmission for adding additional bits at the receiving end which are removed and discarded at the receiving end. Examples are bit stuffing used for synchronisation in plesiochronous transmission, and the zero bits added to a string of one characters to prevent the receive interpreting it as a flag.

Block. Usually refers to a continuous sequence of information, such as a block of bytes or characters.

Blocked calls cleared. It is a service technique in which unserviceable requests stay in the system, but are not served. A portion of their service time is allowed to elapse before service begins. This feature is also known as lost calls held or LCH.

Blocking. Blocking is said to have occurred if a network, switch or access equipment is unable to provide a user a service due to unavailability of a transmission channel, often caused by overloading or traffic congestion. Blocking is usually measured as the ratio of unsuccessful attempts to use an equipment to the total number of attempts.

Blue box. Refers to any equipment which is used to gain access to the network in order to place unauthorised calls, usually to make calls without charge.

Bounce time. The period over which mechanical contacts, for example those of switches and relays, will bounce before finally remaining closed.

Bridge. A device which is used for connecting two LANs together, where no protocol conversion is needed. It operates at Layers 1 and 2 of the OSI seven layer reference model.

Bridged tap. A pair of wires connected to a main cable and normally left open circuited. It may then be used at a later time to connect to a new customer.

Broadband. Usually refers to any communication channel which has the capability to carry services with bandwidth exceeding that for voice. Broadband services cover high speed data and video transmission. Broadband is often used synonymously with wideband.

Broadcast. The transmission of information to several users simultaneously, such as in television or radio broadcasts.

Buffering. The process in which data is temporarily stored in memory for transmission at a later date. This technique allows communicating devices with different operating speeds to interface to each other.

Burst error. When several symbols in succession, within a transmitted data, are corrupted due to causes such as interference.

Burst mode. A method of modulation in which a four wire circuit is established over two wires by alternately sending bursts of signals first in one direction and then in the other.

Bus. A transmission path, channel or media to which several devices may be connected to receive simultaneous transmission. Example is a local area network bus.

Busy hour. Period when the maximum number of calls are expected through a telephone system. It is the uninterrupted period of sixty minutes during which the traffic is at the maximum.

Bypass carrier. USA based local carrier who provides an alternative to the LEC, connecting large businesses to one or more IXCs, usually using fibre optic and metropolitan area networks.

Byte. This consists of eight bits. It is also referred to as an octet.

Cable vault. Refers to the point where external cables enter a central office building.

Call barring. System which restricts calls to certain numbers.

Call detail recording. Facility within a PABX to allow all calls to be logged, to enable, for example, costs to be charged out to individual departments.

Call forwarding. Feature available on some switches for allowing a user to direct all his incoming calls to another number.

Call waiting indication. A message given to a subscriber, who is on the telephone, that another call is waiting to be connected.

Calling number indication. The facility for displaying to a telephone user the number of the party that is calling him.

Capture effect. When two signals at the same frequency arrive at a receiver the output corresponds to the stronger of the two and not a combination of the two, which would result in interference.

Carrier. In telecommunications refers to a continuous signal which is modulated with a second signal carrying transmitted information.

Carrier. Within electronic component technology it refers to the holes or electrons which cause conduction in semiconductor devices.

Carrier to noise ratio. Measure of the noise within a transmission channel. It is the ratio of the carrier signal level to the noise signal level within a transmission channel.

Caterfone decision. A decision by the FCC, in 1968, to allow telephone subscribers to connect their own equipment to the telephone network, provided it did not harm the network.

C band. Band of frequencies, in the range 4GHz to 6GHz, which is used for satellite and microwave transmission.

Cell. Usually refers to the area covered by a radio base station in cellular transmission, or the packet of information in packet switched transmission.

Central office. Refers to the location where a switching system for a public network is located.

Centre du transit. The CCITT term for international network switching centres.

Centrex. A system in which the PABX function is provided as a virtual group within a public telephone exchange.

Channel. Referes to the path for transmission of information. It may be physical or logical.

Channel associated signalling. System in which signalling is physically and permanently associated with a speech channel even when no signalling information is being transmitted.

Channel bank. Refers to equipment which multiplexes low speed data into high speed data channels. It can also perform other function such as signalling. The equipment is usually sited in a telephone central office.

Characteristic impedance. Usually refers to the impedance which a transmission line would present to a signal entering it, if the line were infinitely long.

Charge retention. The ability of a battery or capacitor to hold its charge under specified conditions.

Chatter. The variation in contact resistance between relay or switch contacts, when they first close. It is measured after the bounce time and before the contact resistance settles to a steady state value.

Checksum. The process of summing a group of data items in order to perform a check, usually on the integrity of the data.

Choke packet. Packet used in data flow control, where the station detecting the congestion sends a control packet to the sending station in order to reduce its data generation rate.

Churning. A generic term refering to frequent changes. For example a customer may churn (change) his key system for a larger PABX. Also refers to the frequent movement of subscribers, which means that many more telephone installations are required than there are new customers.

Ciphertext. A message after it has been encrypted from plaintext in such a way that the recipient can recover the original (plaintext) message.

Circuit. In telecommunications it usually refers to a link connecting two or more nodes.

Circuit switching. The process used to provide a line between two users, in which they have exclusive use of the line for the duration of the call.

Circular polarisation. Radio transmission mode consisting of a circular rotating pattern.

Class of service. The differentiation of different service classes available to a user.

Class X office. US telephone hierarchy, where Class 1 is a regional centre, Class 2 is a sectional centre, Class 3 is a primary centre, Class 4 is a toll centre, and Class 5 is an end office.

Clear channel. A transmission channel in which the full channel bandwidth is available to the user.

Client-server relationship. Usually refers to a service relationship between functional entities, such as managed objects, where the client uses the services provided by the server.

Clock. An electronically generated periodic signal which is used to provide a timing reference to the transmitted data or other circuit functions.

Closed user group. A sub-group of users sharing common facilities and where communication is restricted to other subgroup members.

Cluster controller. A device which handles remote communications processing for several terminals or workstations.

C-message weighting. The characteristics of a filter which approximates the acoustic frequency response of a circuit existing between two telephones.

Co-channel interference. Interference between two subscribers, using the same channel but in different cells of a cellular mobile radio system.

Codec. Refers to a coder/decoder, which is an analogue to digital converter circuit interfacing between an analogue and digital signal. It is usually an integrated circuit.

Code division multiple access. An access method for several devices sharing a common transmission channel, which often uses spread spectrum techniques for modulation.

Coding gain. Parameter used to evaluate the effectiveness of an error correcting code.

Coherent. A beam of light in which the individual waves have the same phase relationship.

Coherent demodulation. A demodulation process using a reference carrier signal which is synchronised in phase and frequency with the carrier used in the modulation process.

Collision. Refers to the interference between packets of data which are transmitted by two stations simultaneously on the same medium.

Comfort noise. Background noise inserted by the receiver to compensate for the fact that no sound is transmitted during speech silence periods in certain transmission systems.

Common air interface. Standard for CT2 to ensure all handsets can operate with all telepoint base stations. (Telepoint allows use of CT2 telephones outside homes and offices.)

Common carrier. Term usually applied to a public or private telecommunication operator, or PTO, who can provide services to private individuals and businesses.

Common channel signalling. Signalling system where one signalling channel is associated with many speech channels and provides a direct data link between control processors within exchanges.

Communications network. A system which carries services by the exchange of information, such as voice and data, between co-operating physical or logical elements.

Community of interest. A community or group of subscribers who generally share the same interests, and are often geographically close to each other. This means that they are more likely to make calls within the community than out of it. See also closed user groups.

Companding. Refers to a compressing/expanding process for reducing the noise transmitted in a signal.

Compiler. A computer programme which converts a programme written in high level language (source code) into lower level machine language (object code). See also assembler.

Compression. Techniques which reduce the number of bits needed to represent the information in a transmitted signal.

Concentrator. A device which enables several sources to share the same communication medium, where the number of channels available on the medium is less than the total number of channels required by all the sources.

Conditioning. Usually refers to the careful balancing of transmission line impedances to improve performance, such as faster transmission rates and higher quality.

Conference call. A telephone call between three or more participants.

Connectionless service. A service in which every block of data interchanged between two communicating elements is totally self contained with control information. No dedicated circuit is set up between the two elements. See also connection oriented service.

Connection oriented service. A service in which a dedicated circuit is set up between the communicating elements and is maintained for as long as the service is being used. The circuit may be real or virtual. See also connectionless service.

Connect time. The time for which a line is being used.

Contact bounce. The bounce of metal contacts, such as on a relay, when they first close, causing the electrical circuit to be made and broken at high frequency.

Contact resistance. The electrical resistance between metal contacts, such as of a switch, relay or connector.

Contention. The situation where multiple sources compete for use of the same resource. For example contention arises when several sources compete for use of a common local area line in the Ethernet system.

Control character. Refers to the extra characters added to a transmitted message, which are not part of the main message but allow auxiliary control functions to be performed, e.g. error checking, synchronisation, framing.

Convolutional code. Code using redundant bits for checking the information in the previous blocks of data.

Corona. The partial discharge in a gas. This can occur in the air spaces contained in a transformer insulation and also in the air in between power distribution lines, leading to interference in electrical circuits.

Cost plus pricing. A pricing method which adds a fixed profit margin onto the cost of manufacturing a component or providing a service, to determine its selling price.

Crossconnect switch. A switch used for connecting one transmission path to another.

Crosspoint. A method for connecting two channels together on a space division basis. It is the method of switching used in the older crosspoint analogue switches.

Crosstalk. The interference between information being transmitted on two different transmission medium, located adjacent to each other.

CT1 Domestic cordless telephone. Uses 4 channels and public radio frequencies in 27MHz band.

CT2 Good quality domestic/business cordless telephony. Digital radio technique. Operates on 40 channels in the 864-868MHz band, using a single frequency time division duplex channel access.

Customer loop. Usually refers to the line connecting the customer's station to the central office. This is the same as an access loop.

Cutover. Usually refers to changing over, within a short time, from one system to another. For example cutting over from an old version of software to a new version.

Cyclic code. Coding system used to detect errors in transmitted data.

Dark current. The current conducted through a photosensitive device, such as a reverse biased photodiode, when there is no light falling on it.

Dark fibre. Optoelectronic fibre cable which has been installed but is not in use (e.g. it is a spare).

Data. A term loosely used to describe any information which is presented in digital form, whether it is text, voice or video.

Data channel. A communication channel used to carry data between two points.

Data communications. The transmission of data between a source and a sink, using appropriate protocols.

Datagram. A message consisting of a short packet which is sent through the network, usually without first setting up the path.

Data link layer. The layer in the ISO OSI model which establishes, maintains and releases the data connection between two elements in a network.

dBm. A measure of power in decibels, referred to a power of one milliwatt.

dBm0. A measure of power in decibels, referred to a point of zero transmission level.

Deadlock. Network congestion which is so severe as to cause the throughput to fall to zero.

Debt capital. US term for money raise by a company by selling bonds. See also Equity capital.

Decibel. Usually written as dB. It is a unit of measure for th strength (or attenuation) of a signal, expressed as the ratio o two values. The dBm is referenced to one milliwatt.

Dedicated line. Usually refers to a private circuit, often non switched.

Delay. The elapsed time between two events, such as between th sending and receipt of a signal.

Delay distortion. The distortion caused in a transmitted signal du to the different frequencies within that signal experiencing different amounts of delay. Also refered to as group delay distortion.

Delta modulation. Digital encoding technique in which the anal ogue signal is continually sampled and only the polarity of th signal slope is transmitted.

Demand assignment. The assignment of a transmission channel t a user on demand. The channel is then available for the time th user takes to complete his transmission. (See also fixed assign ment.)

Demodulation. Translation of the information contained in modulated signal.

Demultiplexer. An device which separates out different signal from a channel, which were originally combined into the chan nel by a multiplexer.

Depletion mode. The operation of a field effect device such that i is conducting with zero bias voltage.

Depth of discharge. A measure of the state of charge of a powe source, such as a battery. It is defined as the percentage of th rated capacity by which the source has been discharged.

Deregulation. Refers to the removal of regulatory controls o telecommunication operations or practices. (Often used in con junction with liberalisation.)

Destination field. The section of a message which contains infor mation about its destination.

Dial pulsing. Method of signalling, used in telephony, where th signal is obtained by interrupting the direct current path.

Dial-up connection. The establishment of a circuit connection using the switched telephone network.

Die. An unencapsulated component, for example a semiconduc tor, before it is put into its package.

Diffusion. A technique for introducing impurities into a semicon ductor, during its production. Under the influence of hig temperatures these impurity atoms gradually work their wa into the crystal lattice of the semiconductor.

Digital cellular radio. Cellular system which uses both digital sig nalling and digitised speech transmission.

Digital system. A system in which information is encoded i discrete binary form, i.e. logical 0 or 1.

Digroup. Term sometimes applied to the USA digital group o 1.544Mbit/s (DS1) signal.

Direct broadcast. Usually refers to satellite systems which broad cast information direct into the home or office.

Direct dialling. Refers to direct inward dialling (DID), where PABX extension may be called by an external user withou going through an operator, and to direct outward dialling (DOD), where the extension on the PABX can make a PSTN call without going through an operator.

Dispersion. The broadening and hence distortion of a pulse withi an optical fibre due to multipath wave propagation.

Distortion. Signal corruption resulting in the received signa being different from the transmitted signal. Distortion may b in various forms, e.g. frequency, time, amplitude.

Distributed data processing. Usually refers to distributed computing system where several nodes share common facilities, such as memory, database, printer.

Distribution frame. Equipment which terminates telephone wires (usually in the telephone central office), where crossconnection can occur.

Diversification. Refers to the act of moving into different areas. For example the RBOCs diversifying from traditional telephony (in USA) to cable television (in Europe).

Diversity. The use of alternative paths, frequencies or polarisation in order to reduce the fading effect of microwave radio relay systems.

Disvestiture. The breakup of AT&T, on 1 January 1984, which created the seven Regional Bell Operating Companies (RBOCs), and also required AT&T to run its manufacturing operations as a separate subsidiary.

Domain. Usually refers to the sphere of responsibility of an agent, such as the management domain of a network manager.

Dopant. An additive to a semiconductor designed to give it certain electrical properties. This is also called an impurity.

Dot matrix display. A display which is made up of an array of individual light sources arranged in a matrix format.

Double sideband modulation. A method for modulating a signal in which a baseband signal, having no d.c. energy, directly modulates a carrier. The output is a signal with no carrier energy but with both upper and lower sidebands.

Down conversion. A device which converts frequency from one value to a lower value.

Down-link. The radio transmission link used to transmit information from a satellite, usually to Earth. (See also up-link.)

Downtime. The period for which a resource is not available to a user due to a fault.

Drop cable. The cable which connects the subscriber's premises to the distribution cable.

Drop out. Termination or break in a call. Usually caused in mobile radio systems, due to a mobile moving out of range of its transmitter.

Dual parenting. Term applied to situations where a local exchange within a network connects to two trunk exchanges.

Duobinary. A coding technique where a two level binary signal is converted to one using three levels.

Duplex. System which is able to carry traffic in both directions simultaneously.

Duty class. Usually used with reference to network management systems, which defines the scope of management facilities available to a user within different duty classes.

Dynamic range. The range available to a signal before it will result in overload. It is measured as the difference between the minimum acceptable signal level and the value at which overload occurs.

E1. Digital trunk used in Europe carrying 32 channels at 64kbit/s each.

E&M signalling. A basic analogue signalling method using two wires designated E and M. (E&M stands for Ear and Mouth.)

Earth station. Refers to the site containing radio equipment, which is used for sending and receiving information from a satellite in orbit.

Echo. In communication terms it refers to some of the transmitted signal being reflected back to the sender, with a delay dependent on the transmission medium and distance.

Echo cancellation. Transmission technique for attenuating or filtering out unwanted echo.

Echo distortion. Distortion caused by a delay in a part of the transmitted signal, which later interferes with the main signal.

Elastic store. A memory unit in which data can be clocked in and out at different rates. It therefore buffers the output from variations of the input signal, such as caused by jitter.

Electroluminescence. A phenomenon based on the emission of light from a semiconductor under the influence of an electrical field.

Electronic mail. A facility which allows text to be sent to one or more remote users via a computer based system. (Also called E-mail.)

Elevation. Usually refers to the angle between an antenna and the horizon.

Emulation. Mimicing of one device by another, such that the second device can perform some or all of the functions of the first device and may be used within the network as its replacement.

Encoding. Processing for formatting information in a form suitable for transmission. Decoding involves converting it back to its original form at the received end.

Encryption. The coding of a signal so that it cannot be read by an unauthorised receiver, without use of a decoder.

End to end signalling. Signalling method in which signals pass right through from end to end without processing within intermediate nodes. See also link by link signalling.

End office. Refers to the US Class 5 telephone central office, used to terminate a subscriber's loop.

Energy dispersal. A process for spreading the power in a signal over the transmission bandwidth, so as to reduce inter-channel interference.

Engineering. Usually refers to the design of a system, such as determining the combination of cards needed in a shelf of equipment to perform a certain function, or the arrangement of the network in terms of links and nodes in order to meet a certain level of performance.

Entity. Usually refers to an element within the OSI seven layer reference model which uses the services of the next lower layer to communicate with another peer entity.

Epitaxial layer. A relatively thin layer of semiconductor with a closely defined chemical structure, which is formed on the surface of a semiconductor substrate.

Equalisation. Process for compensating for transmission distortion using fixed or adaptive circuitry.

Equity capital. US term for money raised by a company by selling its stock. See also debt capital.

Equivalent circuit. An electrical circuit which is used to simulate the behaviour of an electronic component.

Erlang. Unit of measure used to define telecommunications traffic density. It is a measure of the average call traffic on a line for a period of time. One Erlang is equivalent to one circuit being occupied for one hour.

Error burst. A sequence of errors occurring within a transmitted signal. Often taken to represent a single error in error measurement systems.

Ethernet. A popular local area access system, standardised by the IEEE as 802.3.

Event. Usually refers to any occurrence which is reported by a managed element to its manager within a network management system.

Exchange area. The area served by one or more telephone exchanges, grouped together by trunks and tandem offices to form a unit.

Expansion. Usually refers to the arrangement where there are a greater number of links available at the outlet of the equipment, than there are entering the equipment.

Extended addressing. Facility within a protocol which allows it to address a larger range than would normally be the case.

Extinction threshold. The minimum voltage level below which a conducting gas discharge lamp will go off.

Facsimile. The process of scanning a document, containing text or graphics, and transmitting the information over the telephone lines, for printing at the other end.

Fade margin. It is the amount the signal can fade by, measured in decibels, before it goes below the threshold of the receiver.

Fading. Loss of signal strength, due to diversion of a radio signal from its optimum path, usually caused by atmospheric effects.

Fall time. The time needed for a signal pulse to fall from 90% to 10% of its peak value. See also rise time.

False start. Refers to an attempt at dialling which is aborted before it is completed.

Far end crosstalk. Crosstalk which travels in the same direction as the signal being affected. (See also near end crosstalk.)

Fibre loss. Signal loss in a communication fibre cable, due to attenuation of the light in the fibre medium.

Figure of merit. Measure of a quality of a system, such as a satellite earth station.

File server. Refers to a central station, serving several terminals connected to it via a local area network, and containing mass data storage and other filing facilities.

Filter. Refers to a device for removing unwanted signals at specified freqencies, e.g. removing noise from a transmitted signal.

Firmware. A computer programme resident on a microprocessor which is part of the equipment. It implies a state in-between hardware and software. Also called imbedded software i.e. it is imbedded in the hardware module, such as a multiplexer or PABX.

Fixed assignment. A method for allocation of capacity on the medium. This is fixed and cannot be varied by user demand. (See also demand assignment.)

Flag. in a communication system, it refers to a predefined bit pattern used in a transmitted protocol to define some event, such as the beginning of a transmitted frame.

Flooding. Routing technique in which the node receiving the data sends it out again on every outgoing link.

Flow control. A technique used to modulate the information from a device so as to suit line or equipment speeds. Usually done by the use of control signals to enable or disable the information flow from a transmitting device.

Focal length. The distance between an antenna feed point and the centre of the antenna reflector.

Footprint. In communication it refers to the area covered on the earth's surface by a satellite beam. Also commonly used to refer to the physical space occupied on the ground by an equipment.

Foreign exchange circuit. A circuit from a switching exchange to a subscriber who would normally be served by another switching exchange.

Foreign potential. Undesirable voltage which is introduced into the transmission line or trunk, for example due to a power cable falling on to the telephone lines.

Forward channel. Refers to the communication channel carrying data from the calling party to the called party. (Reverse channel flows in the opposite direction.)

Four wire circuit. A transmission system with separate channels for each direction of transmission. Usually this is provided by two different pairs of wires in each direction.

Fractional speech loss. Speech that is clipped in a TASI system due to the fact that all the channels are full when talk begins.

Fractional T1. Full T1 (1.544Mbit/s) delivered to the user but only a proportion (discrete number of channels) used and paid for.

Frame alignment. The situation where the frames of the receiving equipment are correctly phased with respect to the received signal.

Full access network. A network in which any input can access any output.

Frame. A sequence of bits, arranged in a logical pattern, and used for transmitting information over a communication channel. Different protocols have different frame structures, which include such ancillary information as error checking, sychronisation and timing.

Frame alignment. Situation where the frame of the receiving equipment is correctly phased with respect to that of the received signal.

Frame alignment recovery time. Elapsed time between the receipt of a correct frame alignment signal and the establishment of frame alignment in the equipment.

Frequency. Usually specified as the number of cycles of an alternating signal per unit of time, often one second. It is expressed in Hertz.

Frequency diversity. The use of back up equipment and transmission paths within a radio system in order to protect against atmospheric fading effects.

Frequency re-use. Capability of using the same frequency in several locations without interfering with each each, for example due to physical distance or different polarisation.

Fresnel zone. A method for expressing the amount of clearance of a microwave signal over an obstacle.

Functional standards. Standards formed by selecting a limited set of options from international base standards, so as to perform certain functions. There is greater chance of interoperability between implementors of the same functional standard. These standards are also known as profiles.

Gain. The increase in signal power, usually caused by an amplification device. It is measured in decibels, as the ratio of the output to the input signal level.

Gain hit. The surge of signal which causes errors in transmitted data.

Gateway. Usually refers to a device which is used to interface between two other devices or networks, providing protocol conversion between the two sytems.

Geostationary orbit. Refers to the orbit at which a satellite remains over the same Earth location. (Approximately 23300 miles above the earth's surface.) It is the orbit where the velocity of the satellite matches the rotational velocity of the Earth, so the satellite appears to be stationary.

Glare. Situation where both ends of a trunk are seized at the same time.

Gold plating. Adding of non-essential features. Usually occurs in a cost plus situation where the supplier adds 'bells and whistles' in order to increase the price.

Graded index fibre. An optical fibre in which the refractive index varies gradually throughout the cladding and core, and there is no sudden change at the core-cladding interface. (See also step index fibre.)

Grade of service. Measure of the efficiency of a telephone system. Defined as the proportion of call attempts made during the busy hour (or specified overload conditions) which fail.

Ground. Usually an electrical connection which eventually connects to the earth. Often loosely used to define a common point in a circuit.

Ground start. A method used in telephony signalling where the receiver detects the grounding of a circuit at the sender's end.

Ground station. Refers to the equipment located on the Earth and directly associated with a satellite system.

Group delay distortion. See delay distortion.

Groupe Special Mobile. CEPT group which developed the pan-European digital cellular telephone standard. 123 channels, 200kHz separation in frequency band 890–915MHz for mobile to base and 935–960 for base to mobile.

Guard band. A band of frequencies which is kept unused in order to separate the different communicating channels and so prevent interference between adjacent channels.

Half duplex. Transmission system in which communications occurs in both directions but in only one direction at a time.

Half echo suppressor. Echo suppressor in which speech signals on one path control the suppression or loss in the other path, but not vice versa.

Half life. The time to reach half the original value of a parameter. For example the half life of a LED is the time for the luminance level to fall to half its original value.

Half transponder operation. Technique for the transmission of two television signals over a 36MHz transponder, using a lower power and deviation.

Jamming code. A code use for checking and correcting errors in transmitted data.

Jamming distance. It is the number of bit positions in which two code words differ.

Handshake. Refers to exchange of protocol between two communication devices which puts them into a mode for communicating with each other.

Hard wired. A circuit which has a fixed function, which cannot be changed. (Alternative devices may be programmable, their funciton being altered by software changes.)

Harmonisation. Term used (primarily within the EC) for the process of ensuring compatibility between services provided by different operators (in the various member states).

Harmonic distortion. Distortion in the signal caused by harmonics.

Head end. The source point. For example in a cable television network the head end is where the video, radio and other services are formulated before being launched on to the network.

Header. Information contained at the start of a block of user data, which is used for auxiliary functions, such as error checking, synchronisation and timing.

Heat pipe. A component for conducting heat away from a source, to another region where it can be dissipated more easily.

Hermetic sealing. Sealing a package to prevent atmospheric contaminants from entering.

Hertz. A measure of frequency. One Hertz is equal to one cycle per second.

Holding time. The time for which a circuit is held in a busy state.

Hot standby. Situation where identical equipment is kept in a ready state, but is not used, so that it can switch over into active service if the main equipment fails.

Hub polling. A polling technique in which the poll, or permission to transmit data, passes from one station to the next rather than between a central station and other stations. See also roll call polling.

Hub site. Site, usually in a distributed network such as CATV, where processing occurs prior to distribution.

Hub station. Usually refers to the central sation on Earth which is used to control a group of VSATs.

Hybrid. In telephony it usually refers to the ciruit which interfaces between a two wire and a four wire transmission circuit.

Hybrid. A mixture of two technologies or services. For example a hybrid transmission system may consist of private circuits over some routes and public switched circuits over others, using a mixture of microwave for the private lines and copper for public lines.

Idle character. Usually refers to a control character which is inserted into the transmitted frame when there is no information available to be sent.

Impulse hit. Voltage surges which cause errors in data transmission.

Impulse noise. Intermittent noise which consists of short duration pulses of high value.

In-band signalling. Use of frequencies within the speech band (300Hz to 3400HZ for signalling.

Index of refraction. It is a measure of a medium's optical capabilities. It is stated as the ratio of the velocity of light in vacuum to the velocity of light in the medium.

Intercepted calls. Calls which are intercepted and sent to an alternative destination, such as an answering machine, an operator, or a pre-recorded message.

Interconnection charge. Fee paid by one operator to another for use of its network to extend a call to the second area.

Interdigit time. The time between individual digits of transmitted data, which usually consists of address pulses in telephony.

Integrated circuit. A circuit, usually made of semiconductor, which is constructed as an assembly of electronic elements in a single structure.

Intelligent terminal. A terminal which can be programmed to vary its function.

Interactive system. A system which operates in real time, the user entering and receiving information interactively.

Intermodulation. The effect where non-linearity in transmission causes modulation on an adjacent channel.

Interoffice calls. Calls which are made between offices. See also intraoffice calls.

Interoffice trunk. A direct line between telephone central offices.

Interrupt packet. A high priority data packet which interrupts other tasks and is passed through the network.

Intersymbol interference (i.s.i.). Interference resulting from a symbol in one signalling interval, of a digital transmission system, overlapping the sample time of a symbol in another signal interval.

Interworking. The ability for two or more systems or pieces of equipment to work together, usually at the protocol level.

Intraoffice calls. Calls which are made within the same office. See also interoffice calls.

Isarithmic flow control. A method of flow control in which a device can only transmit when it has the permission to do so. This permit circulates throughout the network.

Isochronous signal. A signal in which the time between any two significant instances is equal to one or more multiples of the unit interval. In isochronous transmission the characters are sent in start-stop format, but the ends of the link are both clocked.

Isotropic antenna. An omni-directional antenna which is used as a reference against which the performance of other antennas is measured.

Jamming. Deliberate interference of a signal by generating another signal at greater power and close to the transmitted frequency of the first signal.

Jitter. Small and random variations in time or phase of a transmitted signal which can result in errors or loss of synchronisation.

Junction. Name sometimes applied to the link between two exchanges.

Junctor. Refers to the circuit connecting networks within the same office. It is also sometimes referred to as an intraoffice link.

Justification. The method used to change the rate of a transmitted signal to allow it to match with a system having a different rate.

Ka band. Electromagnetic spectrum in the 12GHz to 30GHz frequency range.

Kelvin. Unit of absolute temperature. Absolute zero is at -273° Celsius.

Ku band. Electromagnetic spectrum in the 10GHz to 12GHz range.

Keys. Symbols used in the encryption of plaintext to ciphertext.

Key phone. A telephone which incorporates a switching function, obtained by pressing keys.

Labelling algorithm. An algorithm in which labels are used on individual nodes, the labels being updated as required. The technique is commonly used for problems such as shortest path routing.

Latency. Waiting time between the request for a transmission channel and the acquisition of a channel.

Layered architecture. Refers to the structure in which the total functionality of the system is broken down into layers of defined functionality, each layer providing a limited service to the layers above and below. The most common layered structure is the ISO OSI seven layer reference model.

L band. Electromagnetic spectrum in the 1GHz region.

Leading edge. The side of a pulse waveform which occurs first in time. The rising amplitude part of a pulse signal. See also trailing edge.

Leased line. A line, generally leased from a PTT, which is used to connect several sites and carry private data.

Liberisation. Usually refers to the licensing of other telecommunications operators to carry traffic or provide services.

Light emitting diode. A semiconductor diode which emits light when conducting current.

Limited access network. A network which restricts access to some of its outlets.

Limit switch. A switch designed to sense the position of an object and to operate a contact when a set position is reached. There is mechanical contact between the switch and the object being sensed. See also proximity switch.

Line code. Defines equivalence between sets of digits generated in a terminal and the corresponding sequence of symbol elements transmitted over a channel.

Line hit. Unwanted signals introduced onto a transmission line due to electrical interference.

Line of sight transmission. Transmission which occurs between two systems having a clear unobstructed view of each other. Example of line of sight transmission is microwave.

Line turnaround. The delay between the sending of data in one direction, and its receipt at the other end, and sending data in the other direction.

Link budget. The process of considering all factors affecting the signal on a transmission line (usually a satellite radio link), in order to determine the signal to noise ratio.

Link by link signalling. Signalling system in which signals are processed in each intermediate point when passing from one end to the other of a system.

Link layer. The layer in the ISO OSI model which is responsible for transmission of data between communicating nodes.

Listener echo. Echo received by listener, where the listener or receiver hears the wanted signal together with a delayed, attenuated version of the original signal.

Load balancing. The process of distributing the traffic over transmission lines so that they carry approximately the same density of traffic.

Loading coil. An inductance added to a transmission line in order to reduce amplitude distortion.

Local area network. A high speed link, usually carrying data, connecting several communicating devices, over a relatively small geographical area.

Local exchange. Exchanges which are local to subscribers and into which their lines terminate.

Local loop. The term for the system (cable or radio) used to connect the subscribers' equipment, such as a telephone or PABX, to a local exchange.

Logarithmic compression. Compression of a signal based on the logarithm of its instantaneous amplitude.

Long haul. Refers to telephone circuits operating over long distances, such as between LATAs.

Longitudinal signal. A signal, usually unwanted, which is impressed across both wires of a two wire transmission line. It may be eliminated by balancing the lines.

Loopback. A system test method in which a signal is sent to the device under test, which is then returned to the transmitter for comparison with the original transmission.

Loop start. Analogue signalling method in which lifting the telephone handset closes a wire loop, which is detected at the other end.

Lost calls cleared. A method of operation in which calls which are blocked are either rejected by the network, or the blocked call leaves voluntarily. These calls may return at a later time.

Lost calls delayed. A method of operation in which calls which are blocked remain in the system until they are served.

Lost calls held. A method of operation in which calls which are blocked are held for a time equal to the average holding time.

oudness rating.   Overall (mouth to ear) performance measure of a telephone connection. This is also known as reference equivalent.

ow pass filter.   A filter which allows all frequencies below a certain value to pass but attenuates all higher frequencies.

Managed object.   An abstract view of a physical or logical resource, which represents its attribute (property) as seen by the network manager. Managed objects are accessed via agent processes.

Management hierarchy.   Usually refers to the different levels within network management systems, where the higher levels obtain a more global view of the managed network than lower levels. Examples are element level management, network level management, and service level management.

Manchester code.   A transmission signal encoding technique.

Mapping.   The logical association of one or more parameters in different networks.

Market capitalisation.   Usually measured by the product of the number of quoted shares in an organisation and the share price at that time.

Master clock.   The clock which acts as the prime source within a network and from which all other clocks derive their synchronisation.

Meridian.   The line passing through the point being considered on the earth's surface, and the earth's axis.

Mesochronous.   The state in which two signals have their corresponding significant instants occurring at the same average rate.

Message switched network.   Network which is primarily carrying text based data, e.g. telex.

Message switching.   Transmission system which uses an intermediate point for the storage and forwarding of messages between two communicating systems.

Microcells.   Small cells used within cellular communication systems, e.g. PCN, so that r.f. propagation is confined to a small local area.

Microcode.   Usually refers to software code which is designed to be unalterable.

Microprocessor.   A powerful and flexible integrated circuit which can be changed by software for different functions.

Mid span meet.   Term usually applied to the capability to interoperate equipment (sourced from different vendors) at the transmission cable interconnection level. This is also referred to as mid fibre meet when the transmission media is optical fibre cable.

Modulation.   The processing of a signal to make it suitable for sending over a transmission line.

Modulo-N counter.   A counter which counts up to N before resetting to zero.

Monochromatic.   A beam of light which has a single frequency or, in practice, a very narrow band of frequencies.

Monomode fibre.   Optical fibre which is designed to carry light of a single wavelength at a time.

Monopulse.   A tracking system which uses multiple feed horns.

Monostable.   A component or system which has only one stable mode, and will return to this mode at the first opportunity. See also bistable.

μ-law.   A companding technique used for PCN systems in North America. (Also written as mu-law.)

Muldex.   A term sometimes used to refer to the combination of a multiplexer and a demultiplexer at a time division multiplexer terminal. Also referred to as a muldem.

Multiframe.   Sequence of frames having the position of each frame identifiable by a multiframe alignment signal, which does not necessarily occur in each multiframe.

Multifrequency signalling.   A signalling system for inter office systems in which two of six possible tones are used to encode ten digits and five special characters.

Multiframe.   A set of consecutive frames. Used in digital transmission, in which the position of each frame can be determined by a multiframe alignment signal covering the group of frames.

Multimode fibre.   An optical fibre which is designed to carry light at two or more different wavelengths at the same time. (See monomode fibre.)

Multiple access.   Techniques by which several users can gain access to a common transmission channel.

Multiplexer.   Equipment for multiplexing several signals onto a common transmission channel.

Multiplexing.   The process of enabling several users to share a common communication channel. Several techniques may be used, such as frequency division and time division multiplexing.

Multiprocessor.   A group of processors which are interconnected and co-operate in performing a task.

Multitasking.   The execution of several simultaneous jobs by a computer.

Mutually synchronised network.   A network in which each clock exerts a degree of control over all other clocks.

Narrowband channel.   A channel which can carry a limited range of frequencies or data rates.

Near end crosstalk.   Crosstalk which occurs on the transmission line at the end where the signal source is located. The energy usually propagates in the opposite direction to the main signal. (See also far end crosstalk.)

Negative acknowledgement.   Error control procedure where the recipient raises a flag when an error is detected in received data. See also positive acknowledgement.

Negative temperature coefficient.   A parameter which decreases as the temperature is increased.

Network layer.   The layer in the ISO OSI model which is responsible for managing data on a network wide basis.

Network topology.   The physical or logical arrangement of nodes located on a network. Examples of topologies are star, tree, ring, bus, etc.

N-key lockout.   A feature of keyboards which prevents an output signal when two or more keys are depressed simultaneously. See also N-key rollover.

N-key rollover.   A feature of keyboards which enables an operator to depress keys in rapid sequence. See also N-key lockout.

Node.   The connection point of a functional unit to the transmission line. Often refers to the physical device used for transmission of data within a network.

Noise.   Generally refers to any unwanted signal in a transmission system. It is usually random in nature and interferes with the wanted signal.

Noise figure.   A measure, in units of decibels, of the noise contained in a system. Usually stated as the ratio of the system's input signal to noise ratio to its output signal to noise ratio.

Noise equivalent power. A measure of the noise generated in a device such as a photodiode. It is the amount of light needed to produce a signal equivalent to the noise level.

Noise suppressor. A filter element which removes or suppresses the unwanted signal from a transmission.

Noise temperature. A measure of the noise in a system. It is defined as the absolute temperature of a resistive source, in degrees Kelvin, which delivers an equal noise power.

Nonblocking. Usually refers to a switch which has a through traffic path for every user attached to it, so that it is able to pass through all calls.

Nonpersistent CSMA. A type of CSMA (Carrier Sense Multiple Access) in which if a station, wishing to transmit, senses that the line is in use it backs off for a random time and then recommences the sensing operation.

Nonvolatile memory. A storage device which does not lose its content when the power source is removed.

Null character. A character which is usually added to a transmitted signal to fill unused space. It may be added or removed without affecting the sense of the transmitted data.

Null modem. Name generally applied to the wired RS-232C cable which allows two DTEs to communicate directly with each other.

Nyquist theorem. Theorem postulated by Nyquist which states that the original analogue signal can be precisely recreated provided a specified minimum number of samples are taken of it.

Nyquist transmission rate. The maximum rate of transmission of pulses over a transmission channel (equal to twice the bandwidth of the channel) without the risk of intersymbol interference.

Object code. Executable machine code. Source code which has been compiled.

Off-hook. A line state which informs the central office that the subscriber requires service. This is the opposite of on-hook.

On-hook. The unused state of a telephone circuit. The opposite of off-hook.

Offset antenna. An antenna which is front fed and in which the feed is not directly on the axis of the reflector. It is offset to a side to reduce signal blocking.

One-stop shopping. Usually refers to the facility provided by a PTT whereby all services (including international) can be obtained from a single source.

One way trunk. A trunk circuit which can only be seized at one end.

Operating system. Software within a computer which controls basic functions, e.g. input/output, file management, etc.

Optical budget. Parameter used in the design of optical transmission system. It is the difference (in dB) between output power level of the source and the receiver sensitivity.

Optical coupler. A component which electrically isolates the input and output signals using light coupling between the two.

OSI Reference Model. A seven layer reference model defined by the International Standardisation Organisation (ISO), in which functions are broken into seven layers, each layer providing cleary defined services to adjacent layers.

Out-band signalling. Use of frequencies outside the speech band (e.g. 3825Hz) for signalling.

Out of frame alignment. The state in which frame alignment has been lost. Out of frame alignment time is the time for which this state lasts and includes the time to detect loss of alignment and to recover from it.

Outsourcing. Term applied to the use of third parties for maintenance and management of a privately owned network.

Overhead. Information added to a user's transmitted message for control purposes, e.g. for error checking, synchronisation, etc.

Overlay network. A telecommunication network which is added over essentially the same route as an existing network, but does not replace it. The overlay network usually carries suplementary services.

Packet switching. Transmission method in which data is formed into discrete segments, usually with its own control information, and is routed through the network in this envelope, referred to as a packet. Packets occupy a communication channel for a short duration, so packets from several users can share a channel.

Pair gain system. Any system in which subscribers can be served by fewer number of wire pairs than otherwise, e.g. by multiplexing, etc. This includes increasing the number of channels over the existing pair of wires, as is done in ISDN. It is measured as a ratio of the number of wires needed without the pair gain system to that required with the pair gain system.

Parallel interface. An interface to equipment where all the bits making up a character are available simultaneously for transmission. See also serial interface.

Parallel processing. A system in which a processor performs two or more simultaneous processes.

Parasitic capacitance. Unwanted capacitance which is unavoidably formed when the system is built. This is also known as stray capacitance or leakage capacitance.

Parity bit. An additional bit which is added to a transmitted data frame to perform a very basic error checking function.

Party line. Telephone line shared by two or more subscribers. This is also known as shared service, whilst one subscriber per line is called exclusive service.

Passivation. A covering on top of a semiconductor die which protects it from contaminants. When this protective layer is made from glassy materials this process is known as glassivation.

Passive component. A component which is not made from semiconductor material.

Peer entity. Usually refers to a layer in the OSI seven layer reference model, located in an end system, which corresponds to an equivalent layer in another end system with which it is communicating.

Peer to peer communication. A communication system in which items performing the same functionality communicate directly with each other. Commonly used in systems based on a layered architecture, where the layers at the same level communicate directly with each other, although they use the services of the layers below them for doing so.

Peg count. Measure or count of the number of traffic attempts made on a circuit during a given period of time.

Personal communication networks. High capacity cellular mobile network for low cost pocket telephones. Radio links in the frequency range 1.7-2.3GHz.

Phase hit. Unwanted and significant shifts in phase of an analogue signal.

Phase jitter. Small, continuous and often random variation in phase of a transmitted signal.

hase modulation. Encoding system used in transmission in which the phase shift in the carrier wave is used to represent different bit values.

hotometric units. Units concerned with measurement of visible light, and with the response of the eye to this radiation. See also radiometric units.

hotopic. Response curve of the human eye at normal illumination levels. See also scotopic.

hysical layer. The lowest layer within the ISO OSI model, which is responsible for the electrical, mechanical and interface aspects of transmitted data.

ixel. Represents the smallest unit of a video display which may be coded to an electrical signal for transmission.

laintext. A message before it is encrypted, after which it is called ciphertext.

latform. Usually refers to the basic hardware and software elements, (e.g. a computer, operating system, relational database) on which an application, such as a network management system, is built.

oint of presence. In the US refers to the point where the local company (LATA) terminates a subscriber's line, for interfacing to the long distance or inter-LATA carrier.

oint to point. A transmission circuit which links two nodes (users) directly, without intermediate nodes or processors.

olar coding. Line code using two balanced levels, positive and negative, to represent binary data. Also called non return to zero or NRZ coding.

olar diagram. A plot for a light source showing how the relative intensity of light emission varies with angular displacement.

olarisation. The rotation of a signal within an electromagnetic wave.

olarised light. Light in which wave motion has been modified. In linearly polarised light the wave motion is in one direction only, in a plane perpendicular to the direction of motion.

olling. System in which a central master node asks each node in turn to transmit data for a specified time.

olling delay. The time interval between two consecutive polls of a node by a master node.

ort. The physical access point into and out of an electrical equipment or a network.

ower spectral density. The case where signal power is distributed as a function of frequency.

ositive acknowledgement. Error control procedure where recipient acknowledges receipt of correct data. (See also negative acknowledgement.)

ositive temperature coefficient. A parameter which increases as the temperature is increased.

ost dialling delay. The delay between the completion of dialling by a subscriber and the receipt by him of a signal indicating success or failure of the operation.

reamble. Usually refers to the pattern of data inserted before the main message in a transmission frame, and used for control functions such as synchronisation, error correction, etc.

resentation layer. The layer in the ISO OSI reference model which enables the application layer to interpret the data being exchanged between two systems.

rice cap. Regulation which fixes the maximum price which can be charged for certain goods or services.

rimary cell. A cell which cannot be recharged and re-used because of irreversible chemical reactions which occur in it when it is producing a current. See also secondary cell.

Primitive. Usually refers to the information passed between adjacent layers within a layered architecture, and not passed outside the architecture.

Private line. Another name for a leased line. (See leased line.)

Private network. Usually refers to a network which is owned and operated by a private organisation. However the term is also used to refer to lines which are leased from a public operator but run by a private organisation for its own use.

Privitisation. Refers to the sale by government of its controlling interests (usually in a PTT) into the private equity market.

Profiles. Within communications usually refers to the selection of a limited set of alternatives from base standards, to suit the requirements of a particular application. Also known as functional standards.

Progress tones. Tones received by a subscriber informing him of the progress of his call. Examples are dialling tone, ringback, busy tone, etc.

Propagation delay. The time taken for a signal to travel over a given distance in a medium.

Protection switching. The facility to recover from a failure by swtiching to another transmission path. For example 1+1 protection switching provides a standby path which can be switched to if the main one fails or deteriorates, e.g. due to signal fading or high errors. In N+M protection switching the N paths are protected by M alternative circuits.

Protocol. Rules, usually defined by a standards making body, for carrying out a specific function, such as exchange of information between two systems, synchronisation, error checking, etc.

Protocol stack. Usually refers to the software layers used for communication between systems. Examples are the seven layer OSI protocol stack and the protocol stack used within TCP/IP.

Proximity switch. A switch which operates when it is within a set distance of an object, but where there is no mechanical contact between the switch and the object being sensed. See also limit switch.

Pseudorandom noise generator. A noise generator obtained by setting the generator to a very long periodic sequence, so that the output stream appears to be random.

Psophometric weighting. A noise weighting filter which is proposed within CCITT recommendations.

Public network. Usually refers to a network owned and operated by a licensed telecommunication authority, providing a PSTN service to the public.

Quantisation. Process of sampling an analogue signal to transform it to digital form.

Quantisation noise. The difference between a discrete sample value represented by a digital code, during the quantisation process, and the original analogue sample value.

Quantum efficiency. Number of electrons released in a photosensitive component for each photon of incident radiation of a given wavelength.

Radiometric units. Units used to measure the radiation of all wavelengths within the optical spectrum. It is therefore concerned with total radiation detection. See also photometric units.

Raised cosine channel. A transmission channel having no intersymbol interference at the sample times of adjacent signalling intervals.

Random noise. A form of noise or interference which is also known as white noise or Gaussian noise.

Real time. A system in which interchange of data takes place interactively. The response to a message is fast enough to affect the subsequent message.

Receive only device. An element which is capable of receiving a transmission but not generating any. Example is a printer connected to a line.

Redundancy checking. A technique used for error control on transmitted signals, in which additional data is appended to the signal, which is subsequently discarded at the receiving terminal.

Redundant equipment. Equipment which is arranged such that if a failure occurs in a working part a standby part can take over the function.

Reframe time. The time between the receipt of a frame alignment signal and the time when alignment occurs.

Refresh rate. The rate at which data is refreshed, for example in a video display, or a dynamic memory.

Regional centre. Refers to a US Class 1 telephone office which connects together several sections of the country.

Repeater. A device used in a transmission link which receives a signal, amplifies and retimes it, and then retransmits it along the line. Also called a regenerative repeater.

Reservation. Usually refers to the process, within a multiple access scheme, where a device wishing to transmit data first reserves part of the capacity of the transmission medium. Example is Reservation Aloha (R-ALOHA).

Return loss. Difference, measured in decibels, between the incident energy and the reflected energy, at a signal reflecting point.

Residual error rate. The error rate remaining after going through error correction systems.

Response time. In a real time system it is the delay between the end of a message and the beginning of the response to that message.

Ringback. The signal which is fed back to a caller to indicate that the called telephone is ringing.

Ringing signal. Signal sent over the line to the called party, to ring his telephone, to indicate that he is being called.

Ring network. A network topology in which each node is connected to two other adjacent nodes, so as to form a ring.

Rise time. The time needed for a signal pulse to rise from 10% to 90% of its maximum value. See also fall time.

Roaming. Ability of a mobile communications device to switch from one transmitter to another.

Robbed bit signalling. Signalling system, used in North America, in which the digit timeslots used for speech transmission are also periodically used for signalling. Also known as speech digit signalling.

Roll call polling. A polling technique where the central station periodically polls each outstation, based on a list which it maintains of their location. See also hub polling.

Routing. Technique for sending a message to a specified address.

Scattering. The loss or diffusion of light in a optical fibre due to defects.

Scotopic. Response curve of the human eye at low levels of illumination. See also photopic.

Scrambler. Usually refers to a device which recodes a signal, so that it does not contain long sequences of zeros, but to set rules so that the signal can be reconstructed at the receiving end.

Secondary cell. A cell which can be recharged and re-used after it has become discharged. See also primary cell.

Self test. A facility for testing the equipment without use of any external test signals. Usually done by connecting its output to its input, i.e. loopback.

Serial interface. An interface to equipment in which the bits making up a character are available serially, i.e. bit by bit.

Session layer. The layer in the ISO OSI model responsible for setting up and breaking links between communicating elements.

Shannon channel capacity theorem. Theorem which specifies the maximum transmission rate for data over a communication channel, with very low probablity of loss of any information.

Shelf life. The time for which an equipment or component can be stored without any of its parameters degrading significantly.

Shielding. Protecting interference to equipment from an external field. Usually refers to protection against electromagnetic radiation.

Shortest path routing. Routing which is performed between two points using the shortest path between them. Usually this is also linked to the lowest cost (called least cost routing).

Shortest path spanning tree. An information tree of all the shortest paths from a transmitting node to all receiving nodes, or from a receiving node to all transmitting nodes. Used in determining shortest path routing.

Short haul. Transmission of signals over relatively short distances. See also long haul.

Short stack. Implementation of only some of the lower layers of the full OSI seven layer model (stack) within an equipment.

Sideband. Signals generated above and below the central carrier frequency, during modulation, the extent of the sideband being determined by the modulating signal used.

Sidelobes. Refers to the response of an antenna off its axis.

Sidetone. Transmission of sound from the microphone to receiver of the same telephone. Two customers may therefore see quite different sidetone conditions at their respective ends.

Signal ground. A common reference potential for all signal carrying circuits within the equipment.

Signalling. The transmission of information relating to switching, such as address, between switching systems or between subscriber and switching system.

Signal skew. Offset between two signals.

Signal to noise ratio. Measure of the strength of a transmitted signal relative to the background noise, measured in decibels.

Simplex. System in which transmission can occur in one direction at a time only.

Singing. Noise in the telephone circuit due to a net amount of gain in a four wire segment of circuit.

Single mode fibre. Optical fibre designed to propagate signals of a single wavelength of light only.

Skin effect. The effect in which current flowing at high frequency in a conductor is confined to a thin surface layer. This causes an increase in resistance at high frequencies.

Smart card. A pocket sized card which has local processing facilities.

Solar outage. The term used to describe the disruption of a satellite's transmission due to radiation from the sun, caused when the sun passes within the field of view of the satellite's antenna.

Source code. A computer programme as it is initially written usually in a higher level language. Once source code is compiled it becomes object code and is in the form a computer operate on.

pace division switching. Telephony switching technique which maintains a separate path through it for each call.

peed dialling. The system in which a shortened address code is used to call often used numbers.

pot beam. Focussed transmission from a satellite system which covers a relatively small area on the Earth's surface, enabling frequency re-use between beams.

pread spectrum. Signal coding technique which spreads the signal energy over a wide bandwidth, so making it hard to detect or jam.

tandby time. Time for which a mobile can be on standby without draining its battery.

tandstill agreement. Agreement amongst ETSI members not to develop conflicting standards, for a defined period, once ETSI has started work on a standard.

tart stop transmission. Asynchronous transmission sytem which uses a bit at the beginning of the message (start) and a second bit at the end (stop) to indicate completion of the message.

tatistical multiplexer. A multiplexer, generally operating with asynchronous data, which enables several channels to utilise the same transmission link. Equipment connected to the link transmit data only when they have information to send.

tep index fibre. An optical fibre construction which has a uniform refractive index throughout the core and cladding, but a sudden change at the core-cladding interface. (See also graded index fibre.)

teradian. A measure of solid angle. It is defined as the solid angle formed at the centre of a sphere by an area, equal to the square of the radius, on the surface of the sphere.

top bit. The last bit used in an asynchronous transmission to indicate completion of the message.

ubrate. Usually refers to transmission rates below 64kbit/s.

upervisory signal. Signal which is used to control equipment on a line or to control and monitor the state of the line.

witched line. Usually refers to a public switched telephone line, in which the path taken can vary for each use.

witching array. Usually refers to a matrix of switching elements forming part of an exchange switch.

witchook. The name given to the hook or button on which a telephone set rests when not in use.

ynchronisation bits. The bits in a data transmission which are used for element or network synchronisation.

ynchronous. Usually refers to the transmission method in which data at the transmitting and receiving stations are sychronised and no stop or start information is used.

yntax. Usually refers to the structure used within a communication message, such as the data format, signal levels, coding, etc.

1. Digital trunk, used in North America, carrying 24 channels at 64kbit/s each (1.544 Mbit/s).

2. Digital trunk, used in North America, and operating at 6.312Mbit/s.

Talker echo. Echo in voice systems which is perceived by the talker or sender. It occurs when the talker's speech is returned with significant delay.

Talking battery. A battery which is isolated from other battery use so that it is electrically quiet and allows good quality voice communication.

Talkoff. Term used to describe the disconnection of a channel due to speech being interpreted as an in-channel disconnect control signal.

Talk time. Maximum time for which a mobile can be used without draining its battery.

Tandem exchange. US name for the exchange which connects together several local exchanges.

Telco. Although the term strictly stands for a telephone central office, it is more commonly used to refer to a telephone company.

Telecommunications watchdog. Regulatory body set up within a country, usually after its telecommunications operations have been opened to competition.

Teleconferencing. Linking together groups of people at different geographical locations, with audio and video.

Telemetry. Control and signalling information which is usually communicated over the transmission line.

Teletex. A data transmission standard, typically operating at 1200bit/s, which is an upgrade on the slower telex standard.

Teletext. Broadcast of graphics or text for reception by low cost terminals, such as television sets.

Telex. Switched message service, for text transmission, using Baudot-coded data.

Temperature coefficient. The rate of change of a parameter with temperature. For example the temperature coefficient of resistance is the change of resistance value with temperature.

Terminated line. A transmission line having a far end resistance equal to the characteristic of the line so that there are no signal reflections.

Ternary coding. A coding system which uses a three level code to send more than one bit of information in a single symbol.

Thermal resistance. A measure of the resistance of a component to the flow of heat. One unit of thermal resistance is that which causes a temperature difference of 1°C when 1W of heat flows through it.

Throughput. The maximum rate of transmitted data, which is received with no errors.

Tie line. A communication line connecting two or more sites, for example through private branch exchanges or multiplexers, and dedicated to their use.

Time congestion. A measure of the proportion of time that all the facilities of a system are busy, or congested.

Time expansion. The process of using more time slots within an equipment, such as a switch, than exist on external links.

Timing diagram. A diagram which shows the change of state of signals over a period of time.

Token passing. Access method used in LANs, where a device has the right to transmit data only when it is holding a 'token'. The token is passed sequentially to all elements on the LAN. The network may be arranged as a bus (known as token bus) or ring (called token ring).

Toll centre. Term used in the US for a Class 4 telephone central office.

Traffic density. A measure of the number of calls which are being made at any instance in time.

Traffic intensity. Usually expressed as the product of the calling rate and the average holding time. It is expressed in Erlangs.

Trailing edge. The side of a signal which occurs after the leading edge. The falling amplitude part of a signal pulse. See also leading edge.

Transceiver. Device which can transmit and receive information.

Transhybrid loss. A measure of the isolation, in decibels, between the go and return paths on the four wire side of a two wire to four wire hybrid.

Transient. Usually refers to an intermittent, unwanted signal, which lasts for a short duration and often causes interference with the wanted signal.

Transmobile. A mobile telephone which can be removed from the vehicle in which it is normally operated, and carried as a hand portable.

Transmultiplexer Equipment used for converting between signals obtained from frequency division multiplexers and time division multiplexers. Also known as transmux.

Transponder. Satellite based equipment which receives an up-link signal at a given frequency, amplifies it and translated it into another frequency, and then retransmits it as a down-link signal.

Transport layer. The layer in the ISO OSI model which is responsible for the optimum use of network resources.

Transverse parity check. A form of parity checking on groups of bits within a transmitted frame.

Transversal equiliser. Equaliser used to remove intersymbol interference.

Treaty of Rome. The treaty, adopted in March 1957, which created the European Community.

Tree. A network topology, often used in CATV, where there is only one route between any two nodes.

Trellis coding. A method of error correction in transmitted data, used with some types of modems.

Truncation. Usually refers to the effect where the signal is filtered to such an extent that too much of the wanted signal is also removed, making the signal unintelligible.

Turnaround time. The time, in a half duplex transmission system, to reverse the direction of transmission (e.g. from receive to transmit of a signal.)

Trunk line. Long distance transmission lines which connect together several primary trunk switching centres. (Also called group switching centres in the UK and a Class 4 office in the USA.)

Twisted pair. Refers to a cable consisting of a pair of wires which are twisted around each other, so as to minimise pick up of unwanted signals from other circuits.

Two wire circuit. A circuit consisting of a single pair of wires and able to carry simultaneous traffic in each direction.

Two way trunk. A trunk circuit which can be seized at either end.

Unattended mode. Any equipment (e.g. answerphone) designed to operate without manual intervention.

Unbalanced to ground. A two wire transmission line in which the impedance to ground on one wire is very different from that on the other wire.

Unipolar. A semiconductor component in which conduction occurs either due to holes or electrons but not both at the same time. See also bipolar.

Up-link. The carrier signal used to transmit information to a satellite from the earth. (See down-link.)

Uptime. The time for which a resource is working and available to users.

Vestigial sideband transmission. A single sideband transmission system which incorporates a vestige of the deleted sideband along with an amount of the carrier energy.

Video text. Usually refers to an interactive communication application in which a user can communicate with a remote database using a low cost video terminal.

Virtual circuit. Network operation which gives the user the impression of having an end to end connection although, as in a packet switched service, this is not the case.

Virtual private circuit. The facility provided by a public telephone operator of using a public line as a private circuit for a private company.

Visible arc. The arc of the geostationary orbit of a satellite during which the satellite can be seen from its earth station.

Vocoder. A component which digitises voice in terms of its amplitude, pitch, and voicing.

Voice grade line. A transmission line designed to handle low speed information (300Hz to 3400Hz) as required for voice applications. This is also known as a voice circuit.

Voice mail. Voice processing application which allows telephone callers to leave messages for other users of the system. Also known as phone mail.

Voice print. Voice recognition technique where the voice print of a caller is taken during an enrolment session and then used to authenticate the caller's identity.

Volatile store. A memory device whose content is lost if the power supply is disconnected.

Voltage coefficient. The rate of change of a parameter with voltage. For example the voltage coefficient of resistance is the change of resistance value with temperature.

Wait on busy. A telephone facility in which a call is held when the called party is busy, and is then put through when the number is free.

White noise. Type of interfering noise caused by movement of electrons.

Wideband. Usually refers to a band of frequencies greater than voice. Transmission speeds often exceed 2Mbit/s.

Window. A flow control system used in packet switching systems. The size of the window indicates the maximum number of packets which can be sent before an acknowledgement is necessary.

Wink. A single pulse sent between switching systems to indicate that they are ready to interchange address data.

Wire centre. Generally used to describe any building which houses one or more large switching system serving several office codes.

INDEX

Compiled by D. C. Tyler